Consumer
Sourcebook

ISSN 0738-0518

Consumer Sourcebook

Twenty-Fourth Edition

A Subject Guide to over 26,400 Federal, State, and Local
Government Agencies and Offices, National, Regional, and Grassroots
Associations and Organizations, Information Centers, Clearinghouses,
Publications, Internet Resources, Multimedia Resources, Media Contacts,
Corporate Contacts and Related Consumer Resources in the Fields of:

- General Consumerism
- Automotive Matters
- Credit and Personal Finance
- Education
- Employment
- Environmental Concerns
- Food and Drugs
- Government Performance
- Health Care and Promotion

- Insurance
- Legal Affairs
- Manufactured Goods
  and Product Safety
- Mass Communications
- Real Estate and Construction
- Retail and Commercial Concerns
- Transportation and Travel
- Utilities

Volume 1

Sections 1-8

Matthew Miskelly
Project Editor

GALE
CENGAGE Learning

Detroit • New York • San Francisco • New Haven, Conn • Waterville, Maine • London

GALE
CENGAGE Learning™

Consumer Sourcebook, 24th Edition

Matthew Miskelly, Project Editor

Editorial Support Specialist: Thomas Potts

Composition and Electronic Prepress: Gary Oudersluys

Manufacturing: Rita Wimberley

Product Management: Jenai Drouillard

For product information and technology assistance, contact us at
Gale Customer Support, 1-800-877-4253.
For permission to use material from this text or product,
submit all requests online at **www.cengage.com/permissions.**
Further permissions questions can be emailed to
permissionrequest@cengage.com

Gale
27500 Drake Rd.
Farmington Hills, MI 48331-3535

LIBRARY OF CONGRESS CATALOG NUMBER 89-190943
ISBN-13: 978-1-4144-4588-5 (3-vol. set)
ISBN-10: 1-4144-4588-1 (3-vol. set)
ISBN-13: 978-1-4144-6653-8 (vol. 1)
ISBN-10: 1-4144-6653-6 (vol. 1)
ISBN-13: 978-1-4144-6654-5 (vol. 2)
ISBN-10: 1-4144-6654-4 (vol. 2)
ISBN-13: 978-1-4144-6655-2 (vol. 3)
ISBN-10: 1-4144-6655-2 (vol. 3)

ISSN 0738-0518

Printed in the United States of America
1 2 3 4 5   14 13 12 11 10
ED103

Contents

- How can I find out about my credit rating and history?
- Where can I find health-related information on the Internet?
- How can I check on infant product recalls?
- Where can I find information on mutual-fund investing?
- I've had a bad experience with a local business. Where do I find the nearest Better Business Bureau so that I can file a complaint?
- Where can I file a complaint of misconduct against my attorney?
- Where do I report my concerns about the landfill adjacent to my property?
- I'm shopping for a used car. What sources of information are available?
- My new car is a lemon. Where can I find out about the "lemon laws" in my state?

The answers to these and thousands of other consumer-related questions can be found using *Consumer Sourcebook (CSB)*. Now in its twenty-fourth edition, *CSB* is a comprehensive guide to over 26,400 free or low-cost programs, web-sites, publications, multimedia sources, and services offered by a variety of public and private groups, including:

- federal, state, and local government agencies and offices
- national, regional, and grassroots associations and organizations
- clearinghouses

New To This Edition

This edition contains over 750 new listings.

Comprehensive Scope

Consumer Sourcebook's seventeen subject chapters cover the full range of consumer interests, from automotive matters to food and drugs...credit and personal finance to environmental concerns...insurance to government performance. Subject indexing allows the user to access information for special categories of consumers, such as the aging, children, the disabled, and veterans, and offers hundreds of terms relevant to all consumers.

If consumers are offered inferior products, if prices are exorbitant, if drugs are unsafe or worthless, if the consumer is unable to choose on an informed basis, then his dollar is wasted, his health and safety may be threatened, and the national interest suffers.

— President John F. Kennedy in the first all-consumer message to Congress, March 15, 1962.

More than four decades ago, consumerism was recognized at the highest national level as being of keen importance to the citizens of the United States and to the country as a whole. Since that time, consumers have become more outspoken in their demands for honest package labeling, fair return policies, a safe work environment, earth-friendly products and practices, safe and effective drugs, and manufacturers and service providers who are responsive to their needs. *Consumer Sourcebook* identifies the resources that can help consumers make informed choices before making a purchase or get results when a product proves faulty or a service unsatisfactory.

Now in its twenty-fourth edition, *CSB* provides a comprehensive directory of resources; in addition, the Consumer Tips section offers immediate guidance on a variety of concerns. *Consumer Sourcebook* describes more than 26,400 organizations, agencies, associations, government offices, corporate and media contacts, publications, and multimedia sources available to help the general public, most at little or no cost.

Organization and Design

This edition contains 17 subject chapters and two appendixes, as well as a combined alphabetical and subject index. Each subject chapter is divided into the following subsections, as applicable:

- Internet Resources
- Federal Government Agencies
- National Associations
- State and Local Organizations and Agencies
- Publications
- Multimedia Resources
- Media Contacts
- Corporate Contacts

See the **User's Guide** following this Introduction for details on these listings.

Scope

Consumer Sourcebook contains listings for government agencies, nonprofit associations, private companies, and other groups that advocate for and protect the consumer. Also included are agencies and organizations willing to share consumer-oriented information with the general public, despite the fact that consumer advocacy is not necessarily part of their overall mission. (For example, the New York Stock Exchange is not a consumer group, but, since it is responsible for the disciplinary oversight of brokers, it is included in the *CSB* chapter on Credit and Personal Finance.) Excluded from coverage are those groups that primarily serve to promote a particular product or industry.

Method of Compilation

Consumer Sourcebook is compiled from a vast array of consumer reference sources. A primary consideration in compiling this directory is that the resources listed serve as valuable sources of information for consumers. Information was carefully selected from other Gale databases, from government sources, and from the websites of organizations listed in *CSB*.

Comments and Suggestions Welcome

Every effort has been made to provide the most accurate, up-to-date information possible in this edition of *CSB*. Comments and suggestions for improvement are welcome, as well as suggestions for areas of additional coverage. Please contact:

Content Project Editor
Consumer Sourcebook
Gale, Cengage Learning
27500 Drake Rd.
Farmington Hills, MI 48331-3535
Phone: (248) 699-4253
Toll-free: 800-877-GALE
E-mail: matthew.miskelly@cengage.com
Web site: http://www.gale.com

Consumer Sourcebook consists of 17 subject chapters dealing with specific aspects of consumerism, two appendixes devoted to hotlines, clearinghouses and testing laboratories, and an **Alphabetical and Subject Index**.

Content of Sections

Descriptive listings of live, electronic and print resources are included in each chapter. Entries are numbered sequentially from the first one of the *General Consumerism* chapter to the last one of the *Utilities* chapter. Within each subject chapter, the listings are arranged in subsections by type of resource. Each of the 17 chapters may include the following types of subsections:

1. Internet Resources sections includes internet databases and online services that are of interest to consumers.

> **Entries include:** Resource name, host organization, address, telephone number, fax and toll-free numbers, e-mail address, organization website address, resource website address, a description the contents, database type, search routines, updating frequency, and usage fees, if applicable.

> **Arrangement:** Alphabetical by resource name.

2. Federal Government Agencies sections comprise federal agencies or their specialized or regional offices that are entirely or partially mandated to protect the interests of consumers. They include regulatory agencies as well as federally sponsored information centers and clearinghouses.

> **Entries include:** Name, address, telephone number, fax number, email address, website, description of purpose, services, members, staff, and publications.

> **Arrangement:** Alphabetical by parent department or agency name.

3. Associations and Other Organizations sections identify and describe nonprofit trade and professional associations, social welfare and public affairs organizations, and other groups that assist and advocate on behalf of American and Canadian consumers. Included are watchdog and citizen action groups, public interest and educational organizations, self-help and victim assistance groups, and information clearinghouses operated by the private sector. While the

majority of information centers and clearinghouses in this edition are publicly available on a no-fee basis, some for-profit facilities that provide services for the general public and whose information services are generally available at nominal cost have also been included.

> **Entries include:** Name, address, telephone number, fax number, contact name, email address, website, date of establishment, membership, staff, number of regional, state, and local groups, description, and publications.

> **Arrangement:** Entries are arranged alphabetically by organization name.

4. State and Local Organizations and Agencies sections provide access to both governmental and nonprofit organizational resources. They include state, local, and regional agencies that function to protect the rights of consumers in their respective jurisdictions on a full- or part-time basis; coalitions of public and private sector agencies; and local nonprofit groups whose activities correspond to those of the national organizations in the preceding subsection.

> **Entries include:** Name, address, telephone number, fax number, contact person, email address, website, and, for some entries, basic description.

> **Arrangement:** States appear in alphabetical order within the subsection. Under each state name, organizations are arranged alphabetically by name.

5. Publications sections identify directories, periodicals, newsletters, books, pamphlets, and other informational materials that cover topics of interest to consumers.

> **Entries include:** Title, publisher, address, email address, website, key personnel, and, for some entries, content description including publication frequency and price.

> **Arrangement:** Entries are arranged alphabetically by publication title.

6. Multimedia Resources sections identify DVDs or videos dealing with consumer issues.

> **Entries include:** Title, producer, address, email address, website, content description, length (in minutes), date of production, and, for some entries, price.

Arrangement: Entries are arranged alphabetically by video title.

7. Media Contacts sections identify newspaper consumer reporters and columnists and radio and television programs that cover consumer issues.

Entries include: Name of program, newspaper, or station, host or reporter name, address of newspaper or station, phone number, fax number, email address, website, and, for some entries, a brief description of the column or program.

Arrangement: Nationally syndicated media listings appear first, arranged alphabetically; local listings are alphabetical within a state list.

8. Corporate Contacts sections encompass consumer affairs offices and customer service departments for businesses offering products or services related to the subject chapter. These offices can be contacted by consumers unsuccessful in resolving their problems with the retailer or franchisee.

Entries include: Name, address, telephone number, fax and toll-free numbers, email address, website, and, for some entries, TDD number.

Arrangement: Alphabetical by company name.

Chapter 1: General Consumerism

Scope: Agencies, groups, publications, internet and multimedia resources, and media contacts that address a number of broad-based consumer issues, or whose consumer interests do not fit within the scope of the *CSB* subject chapters.

Issues include:

- Community development
- Consumer studies and trends
- Farming and agriculture
- General buying guides
- Identity theft

Major chapter resources: One of the most important sources of help for consumers is their local consumer protection office. These offices essentially help resolve complaints and provide consumer-related publications and other information. Many are directly linked to their state Attorney General's office, which has authority to initiate legal action on behalf of the consumer. State consumer protection offices can be found in the State and Local Organizations and Agencies section of this chapter. Consumers should contact the state office in order to find the closest local consumer protection office.

The Federal Citizen Information Center (FCIC) program assists consumers with questions concerning U.S. federal government agencies, programs, and services, and provides toll-free service for key U.S. metropolitan areas.

Consumer reporters; radio, television, and cable consumer programs; and Call-for-Action programs are listed in the "Media Contacts" section of this chapter. Call-for-Action is a nation-wide referral, action, and ombudsman service that gives free and confidential assistance to consumers who call.

Chapter 2: Automotive Matters

Scope: National, state, and local organizations, contacts, and publications that assist consumers with automotive concerns.

Issues include:

- Arbitration programs
- Auto emissions
- Automobile manufacturers
- Car repairs
- Drunk driving
- Dealerships
- Electric vehicles
- "Lemon" laws
- New cars
- Safety belts
- Safety standards
- Used cars
- Warranties

Major chapter resources: Vehicle manufacturers maintain offices to address consumer concerns; they are listed in the Corporate Contacts section of this chapter.

If the car manufacturer's office cannot resolve the problem, consumers may wish to contact an automotive third party dispute resolution program, such as the Better Business Bureau's (BBB) Auto Line Program; the National Automobile Dealers Association's (NADA) Automotive Consumer Action Program (AUTOCAP); or the American Arbitration Association.

The BBB's Auto Line program carries out its functions through central service bureaus and arbitration hearing sites. Local Auto Line arbitration information is available by calling the Auto Line number. Consumers who want information on Auto Line or wish to file a claim should first call toll-free (800) 955-5100. The call will be automatically routed to the appropriate BBB office in the caller's area.

AUTOCAP programs only mediate disputes between dealers and consumers; others mediate new car warranty and product reliability complaints involving certain manufacturers, as well as dealer/consumer disputes. Unless the particular state or local program has obtained appropriate commitments from participating manufacturers and dealers, the decision to accept or reject an AUTOCAP panel recommendation is voluntary and at the sole discretion of the participating manufacturer or dealer. In all cases, panel recommendations are non-binding on consumers.

Selected regional offices of the American Arbitration Association (AAA) also provide automotive arbitration, including administration of the "Lemon" law, for new car buyers who have been unsuccessful in settling disputes with car manufacturers or dealers. AAA offices are listed in the State and Local Organizations and Agencies section of this chapter.

Chapter 3: Credit and Personal Finance

Scope: Agencies, groups, coalitions, and publications that protect the investing public or assist with better money management.

Issues include:

- Bankruptcy
- Credit cards
- Credit counseling
- Credit ratings and reports
- Currency exchange
- Income tax
- Investing
- Money management
- Mutual funds
- Securities
- Stocks and bonds

Major chapter resources: State Banking Authorities regulate and supervise state chartered banks. Many handle consumer complaints involving banks and savings and loan institutions, answer general questions, and make referrals regarding banking and credit. Offices are listed in the State and Local Organizations section of this chapter.

Securities dealers must register with State Securities Offices before selling to the public. These offices, which are charged with regulating the sale of securities within their state, often provide consumers with a first line of defense against abusive securities offerings and sales tactics. They may also offer information about the company's reputation. Offices are listed in the State and Local Organizations and Agencies Section of this chapter.

The National Foundation for Credit Counseling maintains affiliate groups which carry out the Foundation's Consumer Credit Counseling Service (CCCS) program. Local CCCS counselors offer advice to consumers on budgeting and repaying debts, and can design an individual debt repayment plan. To find their local CCCS office, consumers can call toll-free (800) 388-CCCS or visit www.nfcc.org.

Individuals with personal banking problems may contact their nearest Federal Deposit Insurance Corporation (FDIC) Regional Office if the problem cannot be satisfactorily resolved by a senior bank official. Consumers should also submit a written statement of dissatisfaction. FDIC Regional Offices may be found in the Federal Government Agencies section of this chapter.

National Credit Union Administration (NCUA) Regional Offices may investigate complaints initiated by union members against their respective federal credit unions that involve a possible violation of existing statutes. NCUA Regional Offices are listed in the Federal Government Agencies section of this chapter.

Regional and branch offices of the Commodity Futures Trading Commission (CFTC) accept written complaints from consumers who are unsuccessful in resolving futures trading problems with a brokerage firm. CFTC regional and branch offices are listed in the Federal Government Agencies section of this chapter.

Investors who believe they have been defrauded or consumers who have knowledge about violations of federal securities laws are encouraged to contact the U.S. Securities and Exchange Commission (SEC). Complaints and inquiries may be directed to the home office or to any one of the SEC's Regional Offices listed in the Federal Government Agencies section in this chapter.

Chapter 4: Education

Scope: Agencies, groups, and coalitions that promote and protect the rights of individuals to an education, and ensure that students receive the education they, or their guardians, pay for, either through taxes or tuition.

Issues include:

- Adult and continuing education
- Bilingual education
- Day care
- Disabled students
- Discrimination in schools
- Educational reform
- Gifted students
- Home study
- Scholarships and loans
- School safety
- Special education
- Standardized test issues
- Student discipline and corporal punishment
- Student financial aid
- Textbook censorship
- Trade and technical schools
- Tuition
- Vocational schools

Major chapter resources: State Education Departments enforce laws governing public elementary and secondary school systems. In most states they issue and have the power to revoke teaching certificates, although local school boards normally retain the right to suspend and fire teachers. These offices usually offer the last recourse for parents and students dissatisfied with local resolution to problems that may involve pupil progression, student discipline, and professional ethics. They are listed in the State and Local Organizations and Agencies section of this chapter.

Chapter 5: Employment

Scope: Agencies, groups, and coalitions that protect and promote the interests and rights of the employed and unemployed who seek work. Includes publications and videos which serve to inform and assist these individuals.

Issues include:

- Careers
- Employer-employee relations
- Employment agencies
- Employment of people with disabilities
- Equal employment
- Equal pay
- Labor-management relations
- Labor reform
- Occupational safety and health
- Pensions
- Retirement
- Unions
- Vocational rehabilitation
- Workers' compensation

Major chapter resources: The U.S. Department of Labor (DOL) has units involved in all aspects of workers' affairs. DOL Regional Offices can provide information regarding the consumer-oriented services and programs of the Department, or can refer consumers to the DOL agency most equipped to handle a particular inquiry. The Employee Benefits Security Administration and the Pension Benefit Guaranty Corporation—both of which protect pension beneficiaries—are described in this chapter.

Occupational Safety and Health Administration (OSHA) Regional Offices serve as initial contact points for workers to report alleged violations of occupational safety and health codes. These offices should be contacted within 30 days of alleged abuses. These offices are listed in the Federal Government Agencies section of this chapter.

Chapter 6: Environmental Concerns

Scope: Agencies, groups, and coalitions established to promote a healthful environment and to protect consumers

from potential dangers to human health as a result of polluted or hazardous natural environments or indoor air pollution. Also included are groups and publications that help consumers save money on home heating bills through weatherization programs, energy efficiency promotion, energy conservation, and alternative energy methods.

Issues include:

- Acid rain
- Air and water quality
- Asbestos
- Biological contaminants
- Carbon monoxide
- Climate change
- Ecology
- Hazardous waste
- "Green living"
- Indoor air quality
- Industrial waste
- Landfills
- Nuclear energy
- Nuclear waste disposal
- Pesticides
- Pollution
- Radon
- Recycling
- Renewable energy
- Safe drinking water
- Solar energy
- Tobacco smoke
- Toxic cleanup

Major chapter resources: State Environmental Protection Offices are responsible for coordinating the activities and responding to inquiries concerning the control and reduction of air pollution, solid waste, and water pollution within their respective states. Activities are integrated with the national program objectives established by the U.S. Environmental Protection Agency (EPA) whose regional administrators work closely with state and local environmental control offices. State Environmental Protection Offices are listed in the State and Local Organizations and Agencies section of this chapter.

EPA Regional Offices provide the public with both general and technical information about EPA programs and respond to inquiries about specific environmental issues in the states they oversee. The regional offices assist in the development of local programs for pollution abatement and provide information to the public concerning the Agency's mission to control and abate pollution in the areas of air, water, solid waste, pesticides, radiation, and toxic substances. In addition, many regional offices sponsor specialized, issue-specific hotlines. These offices are listed in the Federal Government Agencies section in this chapter.

Chapter 7: Food and Drugs

Scope: Agencies, groups, and coalitions that protect the health of the public against impure and unsafe foods, drugs, cosmetics, and other related potential hazards.

Issues include:

- Alcoholic beverages
- Baby formula and food
- Beverages
- Cosmetics
- Food additives
- Food inspection
- Food irradiation
- Food labeling
- Food safety
- Over-the-counter drugs
- Prescription drugs
- Preservatives
- Tobacco
- Vegetarianism

Major chapter resources: The Food and Drug Administration (FDA) maintains local offices to accept inquiries and complaints concerning misbranded, adulterated, or harmful consumer products in the areas of foods (except meat and poultry), drugs, medical and radiological services (including X-ray machines), animal feeds and medications, biological products (including vaccines and blood plasma), radiological health (including microwave ovens and color TVs), and cosmetics. Written complaints should contain codes and identifying marks that appear on labels or containers. These offices are listed in the Federal Government Agencies section of this chapter.

Chapter 8: Government Performance

Scope: Agencies and organizations which monitor the performance of the federal government in carrying out its mandated services, including benefits and entitlement programs. Also including are groups concerned with the basic consumer right of fair value in return for tax dollars, and with government ethics, waste, and mismanagement of tax revenue.

Issues include:

- Campaign finance and elections
- Children and youth services
- Civil service
- Federal budget and deficit
- Federal domestic assistance programs
- Federal entitlement programs
- Federal programs for the aging
- Freedom of information
- Government employees
- Government reform
- Government regulations
- Government waste
- Head Start
- Internal Revenue Service
- Military benefits
- Public administration
- Public fraud
- Social Security
- Tax reform
- Veterans
- Welfare

Major chapter resources: Regional offices of the Social Security Administration (SSA)—together with a network of 1300 district and branch offices, and teleservice centers—help the public deal with the largest federal entitlements administration. Their activities include assisting consumers with filing claims for retirement, survivors, and disability insurance, and responding to inquiries concerning SSI and Medicare. They also inform people about their rights and responsibilities under SSA programs. These offices are listed in the Federal Government Agencies section of this chapter.

U.S. Department of Veterans Affairs (VA) Regional Offices may be contacted if an inquiry or complaint has not been satisfactorily resolved by the consumer relations officer or patient representative at a local VA medical center, clinic, nursing home or other VA facility. The Regional Office will either respond directly to solve the problem, or will redirect the caller to an appropriate local VA office or veterans' service organization. Regional Offices also serve as resources of information concerning the education, employment, insurance, health care, and pension benefits available to veterans and their families.

A number of active governmental watchdog groups, such as Common Cause and Freedom of Information Clearinghouse, are represented in the National Associations section of this chapter.

Chapter 9: Health Care and Promotion

Scope: Agencies, groups, and coalitions that protect and assist individuals with health-related disorders or help maintain good health. These groups may provide information on and evaluate devices, products, and treatment designed to combat human illness, as well as monitor health care financing programs. Also covers groups concerned with disease prevention and the promotion of optimal health and nutrition status of the public in general.

Issues include:

- Aging
- Birth defects
- Cancer, diabetes, and other diseases
- Dentistry
- Disabilities
- Group homes
- Health care financing
- Health and medical fraud
- Health quality assurance
- Health, safety, and accident prevention
- HMOs (Health Maintenance Organizations)
- Independent living programs for the aging and disabled
- Long-term care
- Maternal and child health
- Medicaid and Medicare
- Mental health
- Nursing homes
- Nutrition
- Physical fitness programs
- Preventative medicine
- Public health
- Rehabilitation services and physical therapy
- Reproductive health and family planning services
- Smoking cessation programs
- Substance abuse
- Surgery
- Weight loss programs

Major chapter resources: State Departments of Public Health seek to prevent in-state health problems, including chronic and infectious diseases, through a variety of activities. In general, they identify potential health hazards within their state and recommend ways to control them; they also license and certify in-state hospitals, nursing homes, health clinics, and home health agencies. Other responsibilities may include the administration of state medical assistance programs and the handling of complaints about health care services and providers. Complaints are usually handled by divisional and district offices that have specific responsibilities. Complaint responsibilities may include quality of medical care in health facilities, dual billing by health care providers, limitations on health care services, adulterated or falsely advertised health and medical products, and misuse of medical products due to incorrect labeling. These offices are listed under the State and Local Organizations and Agencies section of this chapter.

Nonprofit organizations concerned with individual diseases or other specific health concerns can be significant resources. Consult the Associations and Other Organiza-

tions section of this chapter for information on such organizations as the American Diabetes Association and the American Cancer Society.

Chapter 10: Insurance

Scope: Agencies, groups, and coalitions that protect the public from unscrupulous insurance companies and agents and help policy holders with unresolved insurance problems. Also lists groups and publications that assist consumers in making educated choices concerning the purchase of life, health, property, casualty and other forms of insurance.

Issues include:

- Auto insurance
- Disability insurance
- Health insurance
- Homeowners' insurance
- Insurance agents, brokers, and bail bond agents
- Insurance claims
- Insurance rates and premiums
- Insurance reform
- Life insurance
- Long-term care insurance
- Medigap
- National health insurance policy
- Renters' insurance

Major chapter resources: State Commissioners of Insurance are responsible for monitoring and enforcing the insurance laws within their respective states. These offices can help consumers with personal insurance problems left unresolved by their own insurance companies. Many offices also provide information to assist consumers in making educated decisions regarding the purchase of insurance policies. These offices are listed in the State and Local Organizations and Agencies section of this chapter.

Chapter 11: Legal Affairs

Scope: Agencies, groups, and coalitions that advocate legal, constitutional, and civil rights and that protect consumers from unethical lawyers and unfair legal services. Public interest litigation groups are also identified here. As litigation is inherent to many consumer groups and issues, consult the appropriate subject chapter or index subject term to locate additional information on litigation in the special interest. Offices of the State Attorneys General can be found in Chapter 1, General Consumerism. See Chapter 14, Real Estate and Construction, for fair housing concerns.

Issues include:

- Access to information

- Adoption laws
- Advocacy for the rights of the aging and disabled
- Americans with Disabilities Act
- Arbitration and mediation
- Child support enforcement
- Children's rights
- Civil and criminal litigation
- Courts and courtroom assistance
- Discrimination
- Divorce and child custody issues
- Law enforcement
- Lawyer disciplinary problems
- Legal aid
- Legal reform
- Privacy

Major chapter resources: State Bars and Bar Associations act as clearinghouses of information on the availability of legal services in their respective communities. These services include free-of-charge legal aid, with many Legal Aid offices directly supported by their local bar. The State Bar generally handles complaints about lawyers, judges, court clerks, and other court personnel. They also provide lawyer referrals or advice about a particular legal problem and set standards for lawyer-client fee arbitration programs operated by local county bar associations. State Bars and Bar Associations are listed in the State and Local Organizations and Agencies section of this chapter.

Lawyer Disciplinary Agencies have been designated by the American Bar Association's Center for Professional Responsibility. Grievances concerning an attorney's lack of professionalism should be directed to the state Lawyer Disciplinary Agency, each of which is charged with investigating allegations of misconduct under the ethical standards applicable in their jurisdiction. Disciplinary action may take the form of a reprimand, suspension, or even disbarment. These Agencies are listed in the State and Local Organizations and Agencies section of this chapter.

Regional Offices of the American Arbitration Association, as private, non-governmental agencies, serve as a low-cost, timely alternative for dispute resolution. The Regional Offices administer 100 sets of rules, primarily dealing with commercial, medical, construction, and accident claims, as well as automotive arbitration. These offices are listed in the State and Local Organizations and Agencies section of this chapter.

Regional Offices of the U.S. Commission on Civil Rights provide general information about the Commission, coordinate the Commission's operations in their regions, and assist the state advisory committees in their activities. Each office is staffed by a director, equal opportunity specialists, researchers, and attorneys who can answer questions on matters of legal interpretation.

Regional Offices of the U.S. Department of Justice's Community Relations Service provide third party mediation and conciliation programs that primarily seek to alleviate racial tension and conflict at the local level.

Independent affiliates of the American Civil Liberties Union determine which civil liberties issues will be stressed and which cases to take to court in their communities. These decisions generally reflect local conditions and issues. These offices are listed in the State and Local Organizations and Agencies section of this chapter.

Gray Panther local networks provide information about community-level programs that advocate for senior citizens. These networks are listed in the State and Local Organizations and Agencies section of this chapter.

Chapter 12: Manufactured Goods and Product Safety

Scope: Agencies, groups, and coalitions established to protect the public from unreasonable risks of injury from consumer products and to promote programs aimed at preventing product-related injuries, illnesses, and death. These groups may provide mediation services between the consumer and manufacturer; information about competing brands of appliances, household goods and equipment, toys, and other consumer products; statistics on product design, function, efficiency and reliability; they may also handle complaints about products that are potentially hazardous.

Issues include:
- Acceptable product safety standards
- Appliances
- Buying American-made products
- Cost-efficient products
- "Cruelty-free" (non-animal tested) products
- Fair packaging and labeling
- Manufacturer warranties
- Regulations and testing
- Toys

Major chapter resources: U.S. Consumer Product Safety Commission (CPSC) Regional Centers respond to inquiries concerning CPSC actions and programs, provide information about consumer products, and accept complaints regarding potentially hazardous products. These offices are listed in the Federal Government Agencies section of this chapter.

Consumers unsuccessful in resolving a problem with a retailer can contact the manufacturer's corporate headquarters. This chapter contains a listing of selected Corporate Contacts for general products, including those that, if defective, could constitute a violation of consumer product safety codes.

Chapter 13: Mass Communications

Scope: Agencies, groups, and coalitions concerned with regulating, monitoring, and handling consumer complaints concerning radio, television, wire satellite and cable communications, and other forms of mass communication including the media and the music and film industries.

Issues include:

- Accuracy in media
- Audio and video recording rights
- Cable television
- Censorship
- Closed-captioning for the hearing impaired
- Film industry
- Music industry
- Parental discretion advisory labels on recordings
- Radio
- Recording industry

Major chapter resources: District and Field Location offices of the Federal Communications Commission (FCC) can provide information about radio, television, wire cable, and satellite communications services that operate in their jurisdiction. A major function is to ensure that local radio and television stations are responsive to the needs of consumers in the communities they serve. Offices are listed in the Federal Government Agencies section of this chapter.

U.S.-based members of the Organization of News Ombudsmen act upon complaints from the public on issues such as biased or slanted news stories or headlines, inaccuracy or poor quality of news reporting, and deceptive advertising. News ombudsmen investigate complaints and respond to public inquiries concerning the media's policies, attitudes, and operations through direct correspondence, speeches, and newspaper columns. These representatives are listed in the State and Local Organizations and Agencies section of this chapter.

Chapter 14: Real Estate and Construction

Scope: Agencies, groups, and coalitions concerned with housing needs, fair housing opportunities, and tenants' rights; with products and services marketed for home maintenance and repairs; and with the general revitalization of communities and neighborhoods. Also includes groups established to protect consumers from fraudulent practices by land developers, promoters, and sellers and to handle complaints against real estate salespersons and brokers.

Issues include:

- Barrier-free design for the disabled
- Building codes
- Contractors
- Eviction and foreclosure
- Home energy conservation
- Home improvement and repair
- Housing discrimination
- Independent living centers for the aging and disabled
- Landlord-tenant disputes
- Manufactured housing
- Mobile homes
- Mortgages
- Remodeling and rehabilitation
- Rent stabilization and control
- Retirement housing
- Timesharing

Major chapter resources: State Housing Authorities and Agencies generally handle inquiries, make referrals, and assist consumers concerning enforcement of building codes, landlord-tenant disputes, rent stabilization and control, housing discrimination, and state housing laws. These offices are listed in the State and Local Organizations and Agencies section of this chapter.

State Real Estate Commissions license real estate salespersons and brokers and handle related consumer complaints. Allegations of unfair, misleading, or fraudulent treatment by licensees are subject to review and investigation. Complaints against real estate agents operating under the registered trademark "Realtor" can also be made to the appropriate state licensing agency, or to the National Association of Realtors, which operates under its own code of ethics. Commissions are listed in the State and local Organizations and Agencies section of this chapter.

Chapter 15: Retail and Commercial Concerns

Scope: Organizations and publications that deal with issues related to packaging, advertising, pricing, delivery, and retailer policies. Also focuses on services individuals engage directly, such as cleaners, movers, and funeral services.

Issues include:

- Advertising, promotion, and marketing industries
- Anti-trust
- Charitable solicitations
- Counterfeit merchandise
- Fair trade
- Fraud
- Free enterprise
- Funerals and mortuary services
- High-pressure sales
- Mail order companies
- Movers of goods
- 900 numbers
- Pricing policies (over-pricing)
- Return/refund policies
- Telemarketing

- Weights and measures

Major chapter resources: The local branch of the Better Business Bureau (BBB) is by far the most familiar source of help on sales and service complaints, and often the easiest to reach. BBBs are sponsored by local businesses to provide a variety of services collectively targeted at protecting local consumers from disreputable companies. Most Better Business Bureaus have established voluntary consumer arbitration programs to help resolve business/consumer disputes. In addition, they maintain close working relationships with federal government agencies, consumer protection agencies, and state offices of the Attorney General. BBBs are listed in the State and Local Organizations and Agencies section of this chapter.

The Federal Trade Commission (FTC) and several units of the U.S. Department of Commerce are the main regulators for retail and commercial consumer concerns.

State Weights and Measures Offices assure that consumers are not shorted on quantities purchased. Offices are listed in the State and Local Organizations and Agencies section of this chapter.

Chapter 16: Transportation and Travel

Scope: Agencies, groups, and coalitions concerned with safety and standards as they relate to the transportation industry, including mass transportation, railroads, and aviation; with overall improvement of public and private transportation modes; and with travel and vacation options available to consumers. Includes groups that handle unresolved consumer complaints concerning unsafe transportation standards and practices and poor customer service, and that help mediate disputes between consumers and members of the travel industry, including hotels, cruise lines, tour operators, and travel agents. (Note: The automotive industry is covered in Chapter 2: Automotive Matters.)

Issues include:

- Air fares and passenger rights
- Airline safety
- Bicycles
- Boating
- Car rental agencies
- Cruise lines
- Customs service
- Hazardous travel conditions
- Highway and traffic safety
- Marine and water safety
- Mass transit
- Medical advice for travelers
- Package tours
- Passports

- Pedestrian rights
- Railroad grade crossings
- Street and highway conditions
- Tourism boards
- Travel agents
- Visas

Major chapter resources: State Departments of Transportation generally handle public inquiries and complaints concerning state roads, highways, and bridges; public and private airports; and public transit systems, including bus and rail lines. Complaints, which are usually passed on to specific divisional offices, may involve street potholes and highway debris, inadequate road planning, traffic lights, roadway signs, unsafe intersections, public bicycle paths, intrastate air routes, and public bus systems. Departments are listed under the State and Local Organizations and Agencies section of this chapter.

State Offices of Tourism serve as resources of information regarding the travel and vacation options available in their states. They typically provide information about accommodations, attractions, and special events, and usually distribute maps, brochures, and other travel aids to the public free of charge. Offices are listed in the State and Local Organizations and Agencies section of this chapter.

Chapter 17: Utilities

Scope: Includes agencies, groups, and coalitions formed to assure consumers of adequate energy supplies at reasonable rates, and to monitor practices of public utility companies. Many groups represent the consumer interest in utility and energy issues before federal and state governments and regulatory bodies.

Issues include:

- Electric companies
- Gas companies
- Long distance carriers
- Power lines and power plants
- Telephone companies
- Utility billing, payment, and termination of service
- Water/sewer companies

Major chapter resources: State Public Utility Commissions generally regulate rates that consumers pay for public electricity and gas, as well as intrastate telephone service; they may also regulate public water and in-state transportation fees. They typically handle complaints that involve billing, payments, and termination of service by public gas, electric, telephone, and water companies. The Commissions are listed in the State and Local Organizations and Agencies section of this chapter.

State-designated members of the National Association of State Utility Consumer Advocates (NASUCA) represent consumers before state public service commissions on matters involving electricity, gas, and telephone utility rates and service. Some NASUCA members are independently established consumer advocacy agencies, while others function as divisions or branches within larger state government departments (usually offices of the state attorney general). NASUCA members are listed in the State and Local Organizations and Agencies section of this chapter.

Appendixes Provide Handy Contact Lists

This edition features appendixes to help consumers quickly reach two important types of resources: Hotlines and Clearinghouses in Appendix One, Testing Laboratories in Appendix Two. Contact information, including toll-free numbers when known, is provided for each entry. Entries in each of the appendixes are arranged alphabetically by hotline, clearinghouse, or laboratory name.

Index Speeds Access to Information

The *Alphabetical and Subject Index* cites all the organization, agency, company, publication, and video names described in CSB's directory listings. The single alphabetical sequence facilitates searching for desired listings by name. The index also classifies the entries and the consumer tips under all the applicable headings selected from a subject thesaurus of over 500 terms. This feature supports more narrowly focused searches than the chapter arrangement alone and draws together all the entries from multiple chapters that may apply. The term "consumer" has not been used as a subject heading in the index, since, as a general category, it covers all the entries in the book. Similarly, entries have not been assigned subject headings if the subject is essentially synonymous with the chapter name in which the entry appears. For example, an entry appearing in Chapter 6, Environmental Concerns, will not appear under the subject heading "Environment" in the index, as the entire chapter would be duplicated under this subject heading in the index. However, appropriate entries from other chapters may appear under that subject heading.

The following section provides consumer tips for each subject chapter in *Consumer Sourcebook.*

Chapter 1: GENERAL CONSUMERISM

Getting the Most for Your Money While Avoiding Consumer Problems. Today's marketplace offers a variety of products and services. In order to be a smart consumer, consider the following before and after you make a purchase.

Before you buy:

- Think about what you really need and what product or service features are most important to you.

- Compare brands. Ask for word-of-mouth recommendations and consult expert product comparison reports. Check your local library for magazines and other publications that compare products, services, and prices.

- Ask friends and family for recommendations. Avoid companies with which they have had bad experiences.

- Compare stores. Look for a store with a good reputation and plan ahead to take advantage of sales.

- Learn about existing warranties and compare them. To find out about warranties that may be required by law, call your state or local consumer affairs office.

- Check with your local Better Business Bureau (BBB) or consumer affairs office to find out about the company's complaint record. Ask about the nature of any complaints filed. Ask to see the complaint files to determine how the company responded to the complaint. Keep in mind that a number of complaints against a smaller company may be more significant than the same number of complaints against a larger company.

- Check to see if the company is licensed or registered at the local or state level.

- Check for any extra charges, for example, delivery fees, installation charges, and service costs.

- Read warranties to understand what you must do and what the manufacturer must do if you have a problem.

- Read contract terms carefully. Make sure all blank spaces are filled in before you sign a contract. Draw a line through any blank spaces that don't apply or cannot be filled in.

- Bear in mind that extended warranties or service contracts offer a high margin of profit to the business. You need to decide whether the extra peace of mind you gain is worth the price. To find out more about extended warranties and service contracts, contact the Federal Trade Commission or your state or local consumer office. Make sure all documents are in a language you can understand.

- Don't rely on a salesperson's promises. Get everything in writing.

- Consider paying by credit card. If you later have a legitimate dispute with the seller, you do not have to pay a charge made with your credit card.

- Do not give out your credit card number, checking or savings account number, Social Security number, or other personal information to any company you do not know.

- Do not do business with a company whose salespeople hurry you to make a decision, give you any kind of high pressure sales pitch, or ask you to wire money or make payment through a courier.

- Do not do business with an unfamiliar company whose only address is a post office box. The company may be nothing but a mail drop that will give you little or nothing for your money and will be difficult or impossible to locate if you later have a complaint.

- Do not be taken in by lotteries, pyramid schemes, multi-level marketing schemes, or companies that ask for payment in advance, especially for employment referrals, credit repair, or for providing a loan or credit card.

- Use unit pricing in supermarkets to compare costs. Unit pricing allows you to compare prices ounce-for-ounce, pound-for-pound, etc. Bigger packages are not always cheaper than small ones.

- Use coupons carefully. Do not assume they offer the best deal until you've compared them to the prices of competitive products.

- Ask the salesperson to explain the store's return or exchange policy.

- Do not assume an item is a bargain just because it is advertised as one.

- Do not rush into a large purchase because the "price is only good today."

- Walk out or hang up on high-pressure sales tactics. Don't be forced or pressured into buying something.

- Contact your local consumer protection office regarding automatic cancellation periods for the product or service you are considering purchasing. In some states, there are cancellation periods for dating clubs, health clubs, and timeshare and campground memberships. Federal law gives you cancellation rights for certain door-to-door sales.

After you buy:

- Read and follow the instructions on how to use the product or service.

- For safety and to protect your warranties, use the product only for the purposes outlined by the manufacturer's instructions.

- Read and understand the warranty. Keep in mind that you might have additional warranty rights in your state. Check with your state or local consumer protection office for more information.

- Keep all sales receipts, warranties, service contracts, and instructions.

- If trouble develops, report the problem to the company as soon as possible. Trying to fix the product yourself might cancel your rights to service under the warranty.

- Keep a file of your efforts to resolve the problem, including the names of the individuals you speak with and the date, time, and outcome of the conversation. Keep copies of the letters you send to the company and any replies it sends to you.

- Check with your consumer protection office to find out about the warranty rights in your state.

- If you paid for your purchase with a credit card, you have important rights that might help you dispute charges.

- If you take your product in for a repair, be sure the technician understands and writes down the problem you have described.

Handling Your Own Complaint. As a consumer, you have the right to expect quality products and services at fair prices. If something goes wrong, keep in mind the following suggestions for handling your own complaint.

Save records:

- Start a file about your complaint. Include copies of sales receipts, repair orders, warranties, canceled checks, and contracts that back up your complaint and the problem.

Describe the problem:

- When you approach a company with a complaint, first describe the problem, then tell them what (if anything) you have done already to try and resolve it and what you think is a fair solution. Do you want your money back? Would you like the product repaired or exchanged?

Go back to where you made the purchase:

- Contact the business that sold you the item or performed the service. Calmly and accurately explain the problem and what action you would like taken. Avoid displays of anger, which usually don't help. If a salesperson is not helpful, ask for the supervisor or manager and restate your case. Most consumer problems are resolved at this level. Chances are, yours will be too.

- Allow each person you contact time to resolve your problem before contacting someone else for help.

- Keep a record of your efforts and include notes about whom you spoke with and what was done about the problem. Save copies of any letters you send to the company as well as letters sent to you.

Remember:

- First contact the seller if you have a complaint.

- If that does not resolve the problem, contact the company headquarters.

- If your problem is still unresolved, refer to CSB's subject index for the organizations, or local, state, and federal offices that provide help in cases like yours.

- Taking legal action should be the last resort. However, if you decide to exercise this right, be aware that you might have to act within a certain time period. Check with your lawyer about any statutes that apply to your case.

How to Write a Complaint Letter. The complaint letter remains one of the most effective tools for the consumer who refuses to accept unfulfilled promises, substandard quality, or poor service. Historically, it solicits prompt action because businesses are anxious to resolve conflicts that suggest their own failure in adequately serving their customers. In almost all cases, the complaint letter should be the second step in the resolution process, after a dissatisfied customer first tries to resolve the problem at the point of purchase.

Complaint letters should be brief and to the point, one page in length, and businesslike in tone. Avoid writing angry, sarcastic, or threatening remarks. Keep in mind that the person who will read the letter was probably not responsible for the problem, but may be a factor in resolving it. Copies of all relevant receipts, bills, warranties, and canceled checks should accompany the complaint letter. A third party, such as a local consumer protection office, should be mailed a copy of the complaint letter in the event their future assistance is needed. Original records should be kept by the consumer.

Many government agencies and private consumer groups, including the Federal Trade Commission (FTC) and American Association of Retired Persons (AARP), offer guidelines for writing a complaint letter. These organizations suggest that the complaint letter include the following basic elements:

- Name of purchase (description of product, model number, price)
- Date of purchase (month, day, year)
- Place of purchase (store name and location, type of shop-at-home service)
- Statement of the problem (how it failed to perform, what was promised and what was received)
- Recommendation for specific action (refund, repair, replacement)
- Reasonable response deadline (two to three weeks is the norm)
- List of offices or agencies to which copies of the letter are being sent (BBB, FTC, etc.)
- Consumer's name, address, day and evening phone numbers, account number (if any)
- Make your letter brief and to the point
- Be reasonable, not angry or threatening
- Type the letter if possible, or make sure that your handwriting is neat and readable
- Include copies, not originals, of all documents

Cutting Back in the 21st Century. Some reasonable ways to economize in the 21st century:

- Don't buy on impulse. Most grocery and many hardware store buys are spur-of-the-moment purchases.
- Buy the things you need, and only some of the things you want.
- Establish small savings funds for major purchases, and don't buy until you've saved the amount.
- Cut up unnecessary credit cards. Save one for emergencies.
- Try to stay flexible by avoiding getting into debt.
- Buy in bulk.
- Try a meatless meal each week using inexpensive ingredients. This could save over $250 per year.
- Wear it out. Each year, the average American throws away 1,500 pounds of garbage. Using things 20% longer will save 20%. Keep a car five years instead of four.

Consumer Privacy. Follow these tips to reduce unwanted solicitations and guard your privacy:

- Ask manufacturers, catalogue or magazine subscription companies, charities, and others with whom you do business not to sell your name to others for marketing purposes.
- Don't give out personal information to people or companies you don't know.
- Don't give retailers information that isn't required. You don't have to give numbers other than the one you are using for payment.

- Don't release your Social Security number except to an employer, government agency, lender, or credit agency.
- When filling out warranty or other information cards, don't include optional or unnecessary personal information.
- Never give anyone your passwords or PIN numbers.
- Never send credit card information through e-mail.
- Look for privacy policy statements on sales materials, websites, and forms that companies ask you to fill out.
- Federal law gives you the right to ask telemarketers to take your name off their lists and not to call you again. Keep records of their names, addresses, and the dates of your requests. File a complaint with the Federal Communications Commission if the company does not remove your name from their marketing lists once you have made your request.
- Use the free services offered by the Direct Marketing Association (www.the-dma.org) to remove yourself from most national telemarketing lists, mail lists and e-mail lists.
- Register with the National Do Not Call Registry by visiting www.donotcall.gov or calling 1-888-382-1222. Within three months of registering your number, you will receive fewer telemarketing calls
- Personal information is easily obtained by companies promoting sweepstakes, contests, and prize offers. These three types of promotions are in the top ten consumer complaints nationwide. Be careful to check out the companies before deciding to do business with them or releasing personal or financial information.

Advance Fee Scams. Be wary of ads promising guaranteed jobs, guaranteed loans, credit repair, debt consolidation, or similar claims. Many of these offers are only a way to get you to send money in advance in exchange for little or no service.

- Be cautious when responding to advertisements that use 900 telephone numbers. You could be charged substantial and differing amounts for calls to 900 numbers.
- Be careful with your personal information, including Social Security numbers, credit card numbers, and bank account numbers, among others. Fraudulent businesses could use this information to make an unauthorized charge to your credit card or to withdraw money from your bank account.
- Before you make any payment, ask the business to send you a contract and other information stating the terms of the service and whether you can cancel the service and get a refund.
- Ask how long the firm has been in business and if it is licensed properly. Request that the company send you copies of its business or other licenses. Review all contracts carefully.

- Contact your state or local consumer protection agency and the Better Business Bureau to find out a company's complaint record.

- Some states have enacted laws banning or regulating these types of businesses. To find out the law in your state or to report a fraud, contact your state or local consumer protection agency.

- For information on the dangers of these types of scams, call the nonprofit National Fraud Hotline at (800) 876-7060, or visit the National Fraud Information Center at www.fraud.org

Chapter 2: AUTOMOTIVE MATTERS

How to Resolve an Automotive Dispute. Automotive disputes are often the result of a lack of communication between consumers and dealerships or manufacturer or distributor representatives. The National Automobile Dealers Association suggests consumers follow these steps in resolving an automotive dispute:

- Always speak to someone in authority at the dealership. If the problem involves a sales transaction, speak to the sales manager; if service is unsatisfactory or the problem involves a defect in the vehicle, contact the service manager. If a customer is still dissatisfied s/he should ask to see the customer relations manager, general manager, or dealership owner.

- If a satisfactory solution can't be reached and the problem is with the vehicle itself or with service provided by the manufacturer or importer, contact the appropriate national, zone, or distributor customer relations office.

- If the problem is unresolved after following the preceding steps and the manufacturer endorses or sponsors a third-party dispute resolution program (as described above), that program should be contacted directly.

- When a problem arises, the consumer should be prepared to provide the following information:

- Vehicle information (year, make, model, mileage)

- Nature of the problem (sales, service, warranty, advertising)

- Brief description of the problem

- Action or solution desired

Used Cars: Making a Smart Purchase. Consumers who are considering the purchase of a used car should bear in mind these tips:

- Look for and read the buyer's guide which must be displayed in the window of all used cars sold by dealers. The buyer's guide explains who must pay for repairs after purchase. It will tell you if there is a warranty on the car, what the warranty covers, and whether a service contract is available.

- Comparison shop for price, condition, fuel efficiency, warranty, and mileage for the model(s) you are interested in buying. Also compare available interest rates and other terms of financing agreements.

- To estimate total cost of the car, add in any interest rates for financing, the cost of a service contract (if any), and any service or repair expenses you will be likely to pay.

- Before buying the car, consider having a mechanic inspect it.

- To get recall information on a car, call the Hotline at (888) 327-4236. Authorized dealers of vehicles must do recall work on their cars for free no matter how old the car is.

- Check the reliability of the dealer with your state or local consumer protection agency. Also check the local Better Business Bureau to see if there are a large number of complaints against the dealer.

- Ask questions about the previous ownership and mechanical history of the car. Contact the former owner to find out if the car was in an accident or had any other problems.

- Choose a safe car. Look for the current safety inspection sticker required by your state. Call the National Highway Traffic Safety Administration toll free number at (888) 327-4236 to see if the manufacturer has recalled the car for safety defects. If it has been recalled, ask the dealer for proof that the defect has been repaired.

- Check with your state motor vehicle department to research the car's title history. Make sure the car is not a "lemon buy-back," salvaged, or wrecked car. Get the written mileage disclosure statement required by federal law from any seller and make sure it matches the odometer reading on the car. Check the title to the car before you sign on the dotted line.

- Ask the previous owner or the manufacturer for a copy of the original manufacturer's warranty. It might still be in effect and transferable to you.

- When purchasing a used car from someone other than a dealer, get a bill of sale, the proper title and registration, and copies of all financial transactions. Make sure the seller isn't a dealer posing as an individual. That might mean the dealer is trying to evade the law and may indicate problems with the car. Ask to see the registration and make sure the seller is the registered owner of the vehicle.

Choosing a source:

- New and Used Car Dealers: Dealers who also sell new cars are likely to offer good used cars in the same make. They often provide warranties and have repair facilities. However, prices for used cars may be higher than other sellers.

- Independent Used Car Dealers: Prices may be lower than new car dealerships. Selection may include auctioned rejects, old police cars, and taxis. Pre-sale repairs may be merely cosmetic (steam cleaning engine or painting over rust) or minimal. Find out how long the dealer has been in business at that location.

- Private Sellers: Usually the least expensive option. The safest bet is to buy from someone you know. When buying from strangers, ask about the car's mileage, condition, and if the vehicle has ever been in any accidents. Ask to inspect the vehicle and/or take it to a mechanic.

Inspecting used cars:

- Look for fluid or leaks underneath the car, body rust inside and out, dents or dent repair, unmatched paint on exterior, uneven tread wear on tires, spare tire and jack in the trunk, worn shock absorbers, and musty odors inside. Take a road test and check out handling at various speeds and road conditions, test all gauges, lights, signals, windows, etc. Observe engine, brakes, steering, and transmission closely.

- Shop on a sunny day to spot flaws more easily.

- Consult the NADA Official Used Car Guide, published monthly by the National Automobile Dealers Association and available on the web at www.nada.com.

- To order a free publication on buying a used car, consult the Consumer Information Catalog available on the Federal Citizen Information Center's website, www.pueblo.gsa.gov. Publications can also be found on the website for the Federal Trade Commission, www.ftc.gov. Follow the "For Consumers" link.

Used car warranties: Used cars sold at dealerships are required by the Federal Trade Commission to have warranty information on the window of the vehicle. There are three types of used car warranties:

- Warranty: The manufacturer's warranty is still in effect, but the buyer may have to pay a fee for coverage.

- Implied Warranty: An unwritten promise that the car will run. State law typically protects used car buyers with an implied warranty.

- As Is: There is no warranty on the vehicle; the buyer must pay for any and all repairs. Such sales are prohibited in some states.

Car Shopping. Buying a car is a major decision. Don't base your decision on style or performance alone. Do some research before you bring a car home and make the costly discovery that you are unhappy with it. Remember a car depreciates greatly the moment you drive it off the dealer's lot.

Before going to the dealership:

- Decide what features are important to you and find out which models in your price range have them.

- Decide how important fuel efficiency is to you. With today's skyrocketing gas prices, you could be talking about hundreds or even thousands of dollars over the course of a year.

- Read up on available models in magazines or buyers' guides. Several Internet sites can help you compare features and prices. Visit www.where-can-I-buy-a-car-online.com for links to

these sites. Consumer Reports (www.consumerreports.org) and Motor Trend (www.motortrend.com) offer information on vehicle performance, service, and safety.

- Keep the criteria firm.

At the dealership, ask yourself:

- Is there enough room for you to feel comfortable when driving? Adjust seats. How is the leg room? Head room? Are you comfortable with your distance from the steering wheel? (If there will be several drivers, you may want tilt steering.) Are you comfortable with the mirrors? Lights? Signals? Wipers? Gauges? Other gadgets?

- What about passengers? Comfortable seating? Good leg and head room? How many can comfortably fit in the rear seats?

- Do you want a two-door or four-door vehicle? In a two-door model, practice entering and exiting and placing child seats and packages in the rear seats before deciding. Will you have elderly passengers in the rear? A two-door may be difficult for them to get in and out.

- Do you want automatic or manual transmission? Manual transmission is often less expensive than automatic for many models.

- Are safety belts safe and comfortable? Do they fit properly? Does the car come equipped with air bags?

- Check trunk or hatch space. Is there enough room for luggage and parcels and other items you frequently carry?

During the road test:

- Drive at various speeds and road conditions (including the highway). How do the brakes, suspension, and transmission feel?

- Try parking the car different ways. Do you feel comfortable parallel parking, backing out, etc.? Is there any part of the car that would obstruct your view?

- Test drive the car at night, if possible, to check comfort with night driving and lighting.

- Rent, for a few days, a car like the one you're considering, if a test drive isn't long enough.

While negotiating the final price:

- Find out the dealer's invoice price for the car and options. This is what the manufacturer charged the dealer for the car. You can order this information for a small fee from consumer publications available at your local library.

- Get price quotes from several dealers.

- Compare financing from different sources.

- Find out if the manufacturer is offering rebates that will lower the cost.

- Keep your trade-in negotiations separate from the main deal.

Dealer Add-ons. Purchasing optional items at the dealership such as stereos, air-conditioning, custom wheel covers, rust proofing, pin striping, and floor mats can inflate the price of a vehicle, sometimes up to an additional third of the original cost. If you want to save more money at the dealership but still customize your car to your liking, consider these options:

- Refuse a car already equipped with optional items, or have the dealer remove them and subtract the cost.

- Purchase your car stereo at an appliance super store, department, discount, or electronic store for substantial savings compared to a dealer-installed stereo. Some stores provide free installation.

- Shop at discount or department stores for floor mats and other accessories.

- Comparison shop for other items, including pin striping, splash guards, air conditioning, rust proofing, and custom wheel covers.

Leasing a Car. Consumers who are considering leasing a car should heed the following:

- Shop around for the best lease deal. Read lease promotions carefully. The attractive low monthly payment might be available only if you make a large down payment (capitalized cost reduction) or a balloon payment at the end of the lease.

- Beware of open-ended leases. They require the consumer to pay the difference if the vehicle is worth less at the end of the lease than was estimated originally.

- Make sure the manufacturer's warranty covers the entire lease term and the number of miles you are likely to drive. Make sure you get every item of equipment listed on the lease. Otherwise, you could be charged for "missing" equipment at the end of the lease.

- The Consumer Leasing Act requires leasing companies to give you important information in writing before you sign a contract. Read the documents given to you by the leasing company and make sure you understand them before signing anything. Look for up-front costs, terms of the payment plan, termination costs such as excess mileage penalties and excessive wear and tear charges, penalties for early termination or default.

- Before you decide whether to buy or lease your next car, weigh the following factors in your own situation: Advantages of leasing include: No down payment, lower monthly payments than with financing, and able to drive more expensive cars than if buying. Disadvantages include: Higher insurance premiums, and limited mileage (usually 15,000 miles per year maximum).

- Also remember, whether you buy or lease, car maintenance costs come out of your pocket.

Questions to ask. Consumers should ask themselves the following questions when considering leasing a car:

- What fees must be paid up front?

- How many months is the lease term? (Don't lease longer than you want.)

- Do monthly payments include tax and other charges?

- What is the mileage limit? Are there any excess mileage penalties?

- Are there penalties for withdrawing early?

- Are there any extra charges at the end of the lease period?

- Do I have the option to purchase the car at the end of the lease period?

For more information: Refer to the FTC's "Key's to Vehicle Leasing" available on their website at: www.ftc.gov.

Auto Service Contracts. An auto service contract is not a warranty. It costs extra and can be purchased at any time, while a warranty is included in the cost of a new vehicle. Before purchasing such a contract, find out:

- Exactly what the service contract covers and does not cover. If it duplicates coverage on your warranty, there is no point in buying the service contract.

- How much the contract costs, what the deductible will be, and how long the contract is in effect.

- Whether you can transfer the contract if you sell the vehicle.

- If towing or rental is included.

- Who will perform and pay for repairs under the contract terms.

- If you are required to meet certain maintenance procedures.

- The reputation of the party you are buying the contract from.

Car Repair. When taking a car to a garage or dealership for repair, consumers should keep the following suggestions in mind:

- Choose a reliable repair shop recommended to you by family, friends, or an independent consumer rating organization.

- Check your warranty. If the repair is covered, follow the warranty instructions.

- Before having your car repaired, check the shop's complaint record with your state or local consumer protection office or local Better Business Bureau.

- Describe the problems you are having with the car as completely as possible. Don't diagnose the problem.

- Get more than one estimate. Get them in writing.

- Before you leave the car, make sure the work order reflects what you want done. Don't sign a blank repair order.

- Make it clear that work cannot begin until you have authorized it.

- Don't authorize any work without a written estimate. Make sure the work order says that you must approve any additional repair work.

- If additional work is done without your permission, you have the right to have your bill adjusted.

- Ask to inspect and/or keep all replaced parts.

- Keep copies of all work orders and receipts and get all warranties in writing.

- Some car manufacturers may be willing to repair certain problems without charge even though the warranty has expired. Contact the manufacturer's zone representative or the dealer's service department for assistance.

- Many states, cities, and counties have special laws that deal with auto repairs. Contact your local or state consumer protection office for more details.

Shopping for Tires. The correct tire helps assure safe and efficient driving in all types of weather and terrain. The sidewall of a tire indicates the tire's size, maximum recommended air pressure, weight load, tread wear index, traction grade, temperature grade, and the date of manufacture. The following "three threes" of tire buying will help keep consumers from getting "tire'd" out at the auto supply store or repair shop:

Three types of tires:

- Bias or Diagonal Ply: Not very durable, they tend to wear out faster than the other two types; also the least expensive. They are called diagonal ply because the tire fibers are layered diagonally.

- Bias Belted: Belt reinforcement provides better stability and traction than regular bias tires.

- Radial: The newest type of tire and the most durable, radials provide the best stability, traction, and fuel efficiency. They are called radials because the tire fibers run at a 90-degree angle to the edge. Radials also contain a reinforcing belt.

Three types of radial tread design:

- Rib: The straight tread wears evenly on these tires.

- Snow: These contain shoulder lugs that grind into snow and ice; the drawback is that they are very noisy and wear fast on dry pavement.

- All-weather: This type of radial reduces the need for changing to snow tires in the winter and resists hydroplaning.

Three types of tire warranties:

- Standard: Covers tire defect only, not damage from accidents or problems caused by the vehicle.

- Road Hazard: Covers any non-repairable damage to the tire, no matter what the cause.

- Mileage: Requires good tire maintenance (correct alignment and air pressure, etc.) and evidence of even wear. Usually only offered by top quality grades.

Credit and Sublease Brokers. A new and rapidly growing area of consumer fraud involves con artists who prey on people with credit problems. The two most common scams are:

- The "credit broker" offers you to get you a loan in exchange for a high fee. Quite often, the "broker" takes the fee and disappears, or simply refers you to high-interest loan companies.

- The "sublease broker" charges a fee to arrange for you to sublease or take over someone else's car lease or loan. Such deals usually violate the original loan or lease agreement. Your car can be repossessed even if you've made all the payments. You also might have trouble insuring your car.

To avoid becoming involved in these schemes:

- Check with your state or local consumer protection agency to find out if the broker is required to be licensed.

- Do not do business with a company that does not appear to be complying with state law.

- Do not pay for services in advance.

Lemon Laws. Nearly every state has a new car "lemon law" that allows the owner a refund or replacement when a new vehicle has a substantial problem that is not fixed within a reasonable numbers of attempts. Many specify a refund or replacement when a substantial problem is not fixed in four repair attempts, or the car has been out of service for 30 days within the first 12,000 miles/12 months. The U.S. Consumer Protection Agency offers these suggestions if you believe your car is a lemon:

- Contact your state or local consumer protection office for information on the laws in your state.

- Give the dealer a list of symptoms every time your bring your vehicle in for repairs. Keep copies for your records.

- Get copies of the repair orders showing the reported problems, the repairs performed and the dates that the car was in the shop.

- Contact the manufacturer, as well as the dealer, to report the problem. Some state laws require that you do so to give the manufacturer a chance to fix the problem.

- Consumers can obtain information on state or federal lemon laws by visiting the website for the Center for Auto Safety at www.autosafety.org.

Vehicle Repossessions. Before borrowing money to purchase a vehicle you should consider the following facts:

- The lender can repossess if you miss a payment or default (any violation of the contract).

- The lender can repossess without advance notice.

- After repossession the lender may be able to require the borrower to pay off the entire balance of the loan in order to get the vehicle back.

- The lender can sell the vehicle at an auction.

- If the lender sells the car for less than the borrower owes, the lender might be able to sue the borrower for the difference.

- The lender cannot commit a "breach of peace," such as breaking into a home or physically threatening an individual, while repossessing.

- Many times a lender will agree to a delay in a payment or modification to a contract. If you know you are going to be late with a payment, talk to the lender. Be sure to get any agreement reached in writing.

Chapter 3: CREDIT and PERSONAL FINANCE

Selecting a Financial Institution. Finding the right bank, savings and loan, or credit union means figuring out your own needs first. Answering the following questions should help you identify your "banking personality" and make choosing a financial institution a bit easier:

- Does the front door display a government logo indicating that it is federally insured? Generally, if the institution is insured federally, an individual is covered for up to $100,000 in deposits if the institution fails.

- What is your goal in establishing a banking relationship? Answers might include "to save money," "to have a checking account," "to get a loan," or all of the above.

- How much money can you keep on deposit each month and how many checks will you write? Knowing this will help you judge how complex or how simple an account you need.

- Will you be buying a home or car or making another large purchase in the near future? If so, you'll want to find out about the types of loans offered by the institutions you are considering.

- If you hope to save for a big expense or toward your child's (or your own) future education, you'll also want to find out how many different savings programs are offered.

- What time of day do you prefer to do your banking? Do you like the convenience of automated teller machines (ATMs) or do you prefer to deal with live tellers? Answering these two questions will help you determine if you'd be happier at a financial institution with regular, evening, or weekend hours or one with a wide network of ATMs.

- What does the financial institution charge for services like cashier's checks, safe deposit boxes and stop payment orders? Is there a charge for using an automated teller machine? Is there a monthly service charge, or must you maintain a minimum balance in your account to avoid a charge?

- Now you are ready to narrow your options to specific financial institutions. Phone or visit several near your home or office because they are likely to be the most convenient. Take your answers to the above questions with you and find out which accounts and services are most likely to match your needs. Then compare fees and service charges, as well as deposit and loan interest rates.

- Price might not be the most important factor in your "banking personality" so you also should take a minute to think about how comfortable you feel at each institution. For example, are your questions answered quickly and accurately? Do customer service personnel offer helpful suggestions?

- Remember, you can choose more than one financial institution to provide you with different banking services.

- Before making your final choice, make sure the institutions you're considering are federally insured. This means your deposits will be protected up to $150,000 until January 1, 2014. All federally insured financial institutions are required to display a federal deposit insurance sign at each teller's window or teller station.

How to Establish Credit. Few creditors will rely entirely on job and salary information when deciding whether or not to extend credit. Most will want to know about your experience in handling credit in the past—your reliability in repaying past debts. This is particularly frustrating for consumers trying to establish credit for the first time. For these individuals, who have no established credit accounts to prove their fiscal reliability, the Board of Governors of the Federal Reserve System offers the following advice:

- Open a checking account or a savings account, or both. These do not begin your credit file, but may be checked as evidence that you have money and know how to manage it. Canceled checks can be used to show you pay utility or rent bills regularly—a sign of reliability.

- Apply for a department store credit card.

- If you're new in town, write for a summary of any credit record kept by a credit bureau in your former town. (Ask the bank or department store in your old hometown for the name of the agency it reports to.)

- If you don't qualify on the basis of your own credit standing, suggest to the creditor that someone might cosign your application.

- If you're turned down, find out why and try to clear up any misunderstandings.

Protecting Your Credit Rating. Financial institutions, utility companies, and retailers routinely provide information on their accounts with consumers to credit bureaus. These organizations use the data to compile credit histories on individuals. Businesses in turn consult the bureaus' composite files before extending credit to new customers. Chronic late payments, liens, or other negative information can remain on file for up to seven years and up to ten years for bankruptcy. Errors may get into an individual's file either from the institution supplying the data or by mishandling at the credit bureau. Such mistakes could adversely effect a person's credit rating and prevent securing a future loan. To help avoid credit report problems, follow these guidelines:

- Get a copy of your credit report from the three major credit data processing systems: Equifax, TransUnion, and Experian (formerly TRW). For a small fee, you can find out what's in your credit record and the names of the companies that have asked for information about you. Your report is generally free if you have been denied credit in the past 60 days. You are entitled to one free report a year if you can prove that you are unemployed and plan to look for a job within 60 days, if you are on welfare, or if your report is inaccurate because of fraud. Otherwise, the credit reporting agency (CRA) can charge you up to $9 for a copy of your report. For information, contact Equifax toll-free at (800)685-1111 or visit www.equifax.com; TransUnion at (800)888-4213 (www.transunion.com); or Experian at (888)397-3742 (www.experian.com). It takes from two to three weeks to receive the report.

- Get a copy of your credit report at least once a year, or before major credit purchases, to check for inaccuracies. Remember that whenever you apply for credit, insurance, a job, or to rent an apartment, your credit record might be examined.

- If you find a mistake in your credit report, the CRA must check it and correct it for you. Any negative information that cannot be proven must be removed. You also can add to your file a 100-word statement of explanation for a credit problem. When you make a correction in your credit file, make sure the correction is made at all three CRAs. In response to your complaint, the CRA must investigate your dispute and respond to you, usually within 30-35 days; information that is inaccurate or cannot be verified must be corrected or taken off your report. The CRA cannot be required to remove accurate, verifiable information that is less than seven years old (10 years for bankruptcies).

Credit Repair. You might see or hear ads from companies that promise to "clean up" or "erase" your bad credit and give you a fresh start. They charge high fees, usually hundreds of dollars, but do not deliver on their promises. If you are thinking of paying someone to "repair" your credit, remember:

- Credit repair companies are prohibited under the Credit Repair Organizations Act from requiring you to pay until they have completed the promised services.

- Negative credit information can be reported for seven years (10 years for a bankruptcy). No one can require a credit bureau to remove accurate negative information before that period is up.

- There are no "loopholes" or laws that credit repair companies can use to get correct information off your credit report. No credit repair company can do anything you can't do for yourself.

- A "money-back guarantee" does you no good if the company has gone out of business or refuses to make good on its refund promise.

- The only way to "repair" bad credit is by good credit practices over a period of time by handling credit responsibly. You might consider contacting a Consumer Credit Counseling Service office, which are nonprofit organizations that will provide help at little or no cost to you

- Some credit repair companies promise not just to

clean up your existing credit record, but to help you establish a whole new credit identity. Remember, it is illegal to make false statements on a credit application or to misrepresent your Social Security Number. If you use such methods, you could face fines or even prison.

Beware of any company or method that:

- Encourages you to omit or lie about bad credit experience when you apply for new credit

- Tells you to use a new name or address or a new number, for example, and Employer Identification Number (EIN), in place of your Social Security Number in applying for credit

- Says it is legal to establish a new credit identity.

Credit Billing and Disputes. The Fair Credit Billing Act applies to credit card and charge accounts, and to overdraft checking. It can be used for billing errors; unauthorized use of your account; goods or services charged to your account, but not received or not provided as promised; and charges for which you request an explanation or written proof of purchase.

Protect your rights:

- Write to the creditor or card issuer promptly to report any questionable charges. Written inquiries should not be included with your payment. Instead, check the billing statement for the correct address for billing questions. The inquiry must be in writing and must be sent within 60 days to guarantee your rights under the Fair Credit Billing Act.

- The creditor or card issuer must acknowledge your letter in writing within 30 days after it is received, and conduct an investigation within 90 days.

- While the bill is being disputed and investigated, you need not pay the amount in dispute. The creditor or card issuer may not take action to collect the disputed amount, including reporting the amount as delinquent, and may not close or restrict your account.

- If there was an error or you do not owe the amount, the creditor or card issuer must credit your account and remove any finance charges or late fees relating to the amount not owed. For any amount still owed, you have the right to an explanation and copies of documents proving you owe the money.

- If the bill is correct, you must be told in writing what you owe and why. You will owe the amount disputed, plus any finance charges. You may ask for copies of relevant documents.

Debt Collection. The Fair Debt Collection Practices Act applies to those who collect debts owed to creditors for personal, family, and household debts, including car loans, mortgages, charge accounts, and money owed for medical bills. A debt collector is someone hired to collect money owed by you. A debt collector may not:

- Contact you at unreasonable times or places, for example, before 8 a.m. or after 9 p.m., or at work if you tell the debt collector your employer disapproves.

- Contact you after you write a letter to the collection agency telling them to stop, except to notify you if the debt collector or creditor intends to take some specific action.

- Contact your friends, relatives, employer, or others to tell them that you owe money. They may contact such people to find out where you live and work.

- Harass you with, for example, threats of harm to you or your reputation, use of profane language, or repeated telephone calls.

- Make any false statement, including that you will be arrested.

- Threaten to have money deducted from your paycheck or sue you unless it is legal and the collection agency or creditor actually intends to do so.

- If you are contacted by a debt collector, you have a right to a written notice, sent within five days after you are first contacted, telling you the amount owed; the name of the creditor; and what action to take if you believe you don't owe the money.

- If you believe you do not owe the money or don't owe the amount claimed, contact the creditor in writing and send a copy to the debt collection agency with a letter telling them not to contact you. If you do owe the money or part of it, contact the creditor to arrange for payment.

Equal Credit Opportunity Act. The Equal Credit Opportunity Act guarantees you equal rights in dealing with anyone who regularly offers credit, including banks, finance companies, stores, credit card companies, and credit unions. A creditor is someone to whom you owe money.

When you apply for credit, a creditor may not:

- Ask about or consider your sex, race, national origin, or religion.

- Ask about your marital status or your spouse, unless you are applying for a joint account, relying on your spouse's income, or you live in a community property state (Arizona, California, Idaho, Louisiana, Nevada, New Mexico, Texas, Washington, and Wisconsin).

- Ask about your plans to have or raise children.

- Refuse to consider reliable public assistance income or regularly received alimony or child support.

- Discount or refuse to consider income because of your sex or marital status, or because it is from part-time work or retirement benefits.

You have the right to:

- Have credit in your birth name, your first name, and your spouse's last name, or your first name and a combined last name.

- Have a co-signer other than your spouse if one is necessary.

- Keep your own accounts after you change your name or marital status or retire, unless the creditor has evidence you are unable or unwilling to pay.

- Know why a credit application is rejected; the creditor must give you the specific reasons or tell you of your right to find out the reasons if you ask within 60 days.

- Have accounts shared with your spouse reported in both your names.

- Know how much it will cost to borrow money; The Truth in Lending Act requires a lender to inform you of the cost to borrow, so that you can compare the cost and terms of credit offered by various lenders.

Choosing a Credit Card. Credit card issuers offer a wide variety of terms. Consider and compare all the terms, including the following, before you select a card:

- Annual Percentage Rate (APR): the cost of credit as a yearly rate.

- Free or Grace Period: allows you to avoid any finance charge by paying your balance in full before the due date. If there is no free period, you will pay a finance charge from the date of the transaction, even if you pay your entire balance when you receive your bill.

- Fees and Charges: most issuers charge an annual fee; some also might charge a fee for a cash advance, if you fail to make a payment on time, or if you go over your credit limit.

Shop around. Before giving money to a company that promises to help you get a credit card:

- Find out who the card issuer is and get the credit card terms in writing, including all the fees and whether a deposit is required.

- Try to apply to a card issuer directly, rather than giving money to a third party; if you don't get the credit card, you might not be able to get your money back.

- Beware of "credit cards" that allow you to buy only from certain overpriced, restricted goods catalogs.

- Beware of companies that promise "instant credit" or guarantee you a credit card "even if you have bad credit or no credit history;" no one can guarantee you credit in advance.

- Beware of secured credit cards; these cards usually require you to set aside money in a separate bank account in an amount equal to the line of credit on the card to guarantee that you will pay the credit card debt; no matter how well you handle this account, your payment history on past debts still will be taken into consideration when you apply to other lenders for credit or apply for employment or housing.

Tips for Credit Card Users. Credit card users should keep the following in mind:

- Keep a list of your credit card numbers, expiration dates, and the phone number of each card issuer in a safe place.

- Credit card issuers offer a wide variety of terms (annual percentage rate, methods of calculating the balance subject to the finance charge, minimum monthly payments, and actual membership fees). When selecting a card, compare the terms offered by several card issuers to find the card that best suits your needs.

- Know your credit card protections. When you have used your card for a purchase and you don't receive the goods or services as promised, you might be able to withhold payment for the goods or services. Card issuers must investigate billing disputes.

- Protect your credit record. Pay bills promptly to keep finance charges low and to protect your credit rating. Keep track of your charges and don't exceed your credit limit. Report any change of address prior to moving so that you receive bill promptly.

- When you use your credit card, watch your card after giving it to a clerk. Take your card back promptly after the clerk is finished with it and make sure it is yours.

- Never sign a blank receipt; draw a line through any blank spaces above the total when you sign receipts.

- Open credit card bills promptly and compare them with your receipts to check for unauthorized charges and billing errors.

- Never give your credit card number over the telephone unless you made the call and you know the company is reputable. Never put your card number on a postcard or on the outside of an envelope, and never include your card number in an email messages—email messages can be intercepted.

- Before entering your card number into a form on a website, check to see that the site is secure. A secure site encrypts or scrambles personal information so it cannot be easily intercepted. Look for a closed lock or unbroken key in the bottom corner of the screen.

- Sign new cards as soon as they arrive. Cut up and throw away expired cards. Cut up and return unwanted cards to the issuer.

- If any of your credit cards is missing or stolen, report the loss as soon as possible to the card issuer. Check your credit card statement for a telephone number for reporting stolen credit cards. Follow up your phone calls with a letter to each card issuer. The letter should contain your card number, the date the card was missing, and the date you reported the loss. If you report the loss before a credit card is used, the issuer cannot hold you responsible for any subsequent unauthorized charges. If a thief uses your card before you report it missing, the most you will owe for unauthorized charges on each card is $50.

- To file a complaint, contact your state or local consumer protection agency, your state attorney general, or your Better Business Bureau.

Advance-Fee Loan Scams. Advance-fee loans are fraudulent schemes that promise to deliver loans to people with poor or no credit for a fee. These operations advertise on television and radio and in magazines and newspapers to entice individuals into calling for more information; sometimes the caller must use a "900 number" and be charged for the call as well. To prevent becoming a victim of such a scam:

- Look into all credit options and always do research on an institution before doing business. Don't be pressured into a hasty decision.

- Never give your credit card, bank account, or social security number over the telephone.

- Make sure you understand the terms of any offer and get them in writing before agreement.

- If you have any questions about a financial institution or have been a victim of an advance-fee loan scam, contact your local Better Business Bureau (see Chapter 15, Retail and Commercial Concerns.)

Tips on Buying Mutual Funds. Mutual funds pool the resources of small investors to build a securities (stock) portfolio. The investors hold shares in the fund rather than in individual stocks and pay for the services of a fund manager. When planning investing in mutual funds consider these suggestions:

- Establish your financial goals and set aside a reasonable amount for investment.

- Contact your local Better Business Bureau for information on any company you are considering to handle your investment.

- Gather information from all funds you are considering, including the prospectus, the statement of additional information, and the latest shareholder report.

- Make sure you understand and are comfortable with the level of risk associated with the fund's investment strategy. Generally speaking, higher levels of risk are required for higher profit goals as with so-called junk bonds.

- Determine any penalties for early redemption.

- Determine all fees, expenses, and charges.

- Never make a commitment until all your questions are answered satisfactorily; don't give in to high-pressure sales techniques.

Chapter 4: EDUCATION

Choosing a School for Your Child. Education is an investment decision that should be made carefully. Consider the following:

- Parents should be aware that there are many types of schools; magnet schools, public schools, private schools, etc. Every child learns differently. Choose the school that best meets your child's learning style.

- Become involved in your child's education and school.

- Public schools are grouped into local city or county school districts. Check with your local consumer protection office or look in the telephone book to find the address of your local school district office.

Choosing a Job Training Program. If you are looking to improve your own skills, carefully consider the following:

- If you are looking for a job training program, avoid scams by checking with your local consumer protection office or Better Business Bureau before you enroll.

- Before going back to school, check to see if local employers or others offer similar training for free.

- Be sure the skills the school teaches will be useful to you and are currently being used in the workplace.

- If you must learn how to use equipment, does the school have enough equipment so every student can practice using it? Is the equipment up-to-date?

- How many recent students graduated? How many found jobs in their fields? Did the school help them find jobs, and how long did it take? How do current and past students feel about the school's program?

- Will the program improve your math, reading, and thinking skills? Will it teach you how to keep learning after graduation?

- Does the program include on-the-job training? Do teachers work with industry and update their skills regularly?

- Do you have to take out a loan to pay for the program? Who pays back the loan if the school doesn't deliver on its promises?

Private Vocational Schools. There are thousands of private vocational schools throughout the United States that offer courses in a variety of fields, including word processing, auto mechanics, nursing, trucking, cosmetology, travel, and medical technology, to name a few. But no trade school can guarantee employment in the field studied and potential students should remember that these schools are businesses operating to make a profit. Some schools may not be of value to their graduates. For example, employers may not hire graduates of the school's program; the school may not provide a quality education; or it may suddenly go out of business, leaving students without credentials and tuition money lost. If you considering applying to a vocational school, find out as much as possible about the institution, including:

- Accreditation and state licensing. Good schools are both accredited and licensed by the state; this means the school went through a screening process by both a U.S. Department of Education-approved agency and the state. Avoid schools that have not.

- Employment rate. Ask the school how many of their students actually find jobs in the field that they studied. Also be certain to call the personnel office of companies you might be interested in applying to after your training and ask what schools they recommend and typically hire from, or if they even require training from a vocational school.

- Facilities. A good school should welcome prospective applicants to visit the institution. While you are there, you should check out the classroom size (student/teacher ratio); available equipment (are they teaching with up-to-date technology?); and talk with the faculty (what type of experience and how long has s/he been teaching?) and students (would they recommend it to others?).

- Graduation rate. Ask the school what percentage of its students successfully completes its programs. Also ask for a list of graduates you can call and ask for their opinions of the school.

- Student loans. Find out the school's refund policy and student loan obligations. Information on a school's default rate can be obtained from the U.S. Department of Education's Student Financial Aid Information Center by calling (800) 433-3243. Schools with high rates should be avoided.

- Check alternative options. Community colleges or the education departments in some states and communities may provide better training at a lower cost.

- Before you spend money and time training for a particular occupation, talk to someone already in the field. Find out the drawbacks of the job, including the schedule, the pay range, and any difficulties involved with the job.

Finding Financial Aid. Some students or their families who are looking into sources for acquiring scholarships or other financial aid to help pay for the rising costs of higher education turn to scholarship search companies. These businesses charge a fee—some more than $200—to provide listings of scholarships for which the applicant is qualified. Consumers should understand that in many cases they are paying merely for the convenience of someone compiling information they could readily have found on their own. In the worst cases, unscrupulous operators provide few leads or listings clearly unsuitable for the student applicant. None of these services can guarantee that a scholarship will result from the application. Reliable financial aid information can be obtained free through several sources, including:

- Your local public or school library. Libraries carry numerous books and directories on sources of scholarship and other financial aid.

- Your college financial aid or high school guidance counselor. Also try your college admissions office, which probably provides free brochures.

- National databases such as those provided by College Answer (www.collegeanswer.com) are accessible at many colleges and universities to registered students.

Saving for College. Parents should start saving for their child's college education as early as possible. Tuition rates and other costs (room and board, books, etc.), are estimated to increase around an average of seven percent annually. The following are some suggestions for planning such savings:

- Interest earned on U.S. Savings Bonds (Series EE) is income tax-free under certain conditions when used to pay for college expenses.

- Many states offer college savings bonds that are tax-exempt but cannot be redeemed for five to 21 years.

- Many mutual-fund companies offer plans for college investors.

- The same cautions that apply to any securities investment apply to these.

Selecting Child Care. Choosing child care is an important issue for parents. Child care authorities suggest parents consider the following criteria when looking for child care:

- Check the licensing laws for day care providers in your city, county or state. Parents can contact their local consumer protection office. Child Care Aware has a website (www.childcareaware.org) and a toll-free number at (800)424-2246.

- Check caregivers' references. Is special training in child development and education documented? How many children does each adult look after?

- Is the home or center safe and clean? Is there enough space inside and outside for the children to rest and play? Is the playground fenced? Are there enough toys and learning materials? Are the toys safe, clean, and within reach of children?

- If the center is large, do visitors and children sign in and out? What are the safety precautions in case of fire or other emergencies?

- What are the procedures when a child is ill? Does the child stay home? What if the child needs medical help? Are caregivers trained in CPR and first aid?

- How does the staff discipline children? How much of each day is filled with planned activities? Are activities geared to children's ages and development?

- What are the fees for half-days, overtime or sick children?

- Are children's artwork or projects hung up and changed often?

- Do caregivers provide the parents with feedback on what the child does each day? Are parents' visits and ideas welcomed? Are parents invited to drop in at any time?

- After the child is in a program, the parent should note whether the child talks happily about the program.

- Do caregivers enjoy talking and playing with the children?

- Parents should observe new employees. Do they talk to the child?

Chapter 5: Employment

Illegal Employment Interview Questions. The Civil Rights Act of 1964 makes it illegal for a company to discriminate in its hiring on the basis of race, color, religion, sex, or national origin. It also means that any interview questions covering these topics are off-limits. Inquiries about marital status, dependents, or child-bearing plans; questions about relatives, their addresses, or their place of origin. Questions about a job-hunter's arrest record are also forbidden. (If security clearance is required, it can be done after hiring but before work begins.) The following ten questions are illegal in a job interview:

- What is your race?

- What kind of work does your spouse do?

- Are you single, married, or divorced?

- What is your native language?

- Whom should we notify in case of an emergency?

- What clubs, societies, or organizations do you belong to?

- Do you plan to have a family?

- Do you have any disabilities?

- Do you have a good credit record?

- What is your height and weight?

Some of the questions would, however, become legal after the employee is hired. For example, a company would need to know whom to contact in an emergency. If, however, a potential employer does ask one or more of these questions, the job-hunter should politely ask how the question relates to the required job qualifications.

Classified Job Ad Tips for Teens. Classified advertisements can be a good place to begin a job search, provided job-hunters recognize ads that distort the truth. One type of employment ad in particular seeks to exploit teenagers by promising excitement, travel, and good wages. In reality, this may simply mean selling products door-to-door in another state. Often the products sold are of poor quality or overpriced. When seeking employment through the classified ads or online job sites, job-hunters should pay particular attention to the information provided about a position. If benefits sound too good to be true, or the ad leaves out important details such as salary or working hours, job-seekers should be prepared to verify this information with the employer before accepting a position. The following tips can help young job-hunters avoid a negative work experience:

- Beware of "no experience necessary" ads that promise impressive benefits. These ads may signal poor working conditions and straight commission work (pay based on sales alone).

- Clarify all salary information. Find out if a weekly salary is offered, or if wages are based on the amount of materials sold. If the products sold are substandard or overpriced, they may be difficult to sell, making it hard to earn a good commission.

- Ask about applicable requirements. If a job entails door-to-door selling, a license or permit may be necessary to conduct business legally.

- Verify all job duties. Find out how many working hours per day the job requires and if there are sales quotas or other demands employees are expected to meet.

- Find out what products the company sells. A company that profits from low-quality, overpriced products may not stay in business long.

- Clarify all travel arrangements. If an ad promises travel, find out who covers transportation and accommodation expenses.

- Secure a written job description and terms of

employment. Employers should be willing to provide a statement of job duties, working hours, wages, and other specifics related to the job.

Chapter 6: ENVIRONMENTAL CONCERNS

Reduce, Reuse, Recycle. Solid waste disposal is an issue of interest to many consumers, businesses, environmentalists, and government officials. Here are some tips designed to help you understand the garbage issue and to evaluate the related environmental claims some companies are making about their products and packages:

- The EPA suggests that individual consumers can help solve the solid waste problem. They should **reduce** the amount of waste thrown away, **reuse** products whenever possible, and **recycle** as many products and packages as possible.

- Look for specifics when evaluating environmental claims. Two examples of specific claims could be "50% less packaging than an earlier container" or "contains 25-30% recycled content." Claims about a product or package like "environmentally friendly" or "safe for the environment" can be misleading because they are so broad and vague. Environmental issues are complex. If you have questions about a company's environmental claims, call or write the company.

- Reaping the environmental benefits of a "degradable" product depend on proper handling after disposal. A degradable product will break down if exposed to air, water, light and/or microorganisms over time, so it might be appropriate for a composting system that can safely and effectively compost the discarded product into something usable. However, if the degradable product ends up in a landfill, as does more than 70% of waste now, it might not degrade in any usable way because landfills are designed to keep out air, water and light. Additionally, if the product is incinerated or recycled, the degradability of the product is void. Check with your local solid waste management office to find out what waste disposal system is used in your community. If there is a composting facility in your area, be sure to ask what kinds of compostable materials it will accept. For example, some composting programs are limited to yard waste, leaves, etc.

- While it is technically possible to recycle many materials, such as paper, metal, glass, and plastic, practices vary from community to community. Does your city require separation of one or more types of materials for curbside pick-up? Or is there a drop-off recycling center that accepts various types of materials? If a product labeled "recyclable" is not separated from the rest of your trash, it is not likely to be recycled. Check with your local solid waste management office to find out which products and packages are recyclable in your community.

- Many products are being made from recycled materials. This helps "complete the loop" of recycling by using recycled materials to make new products. If you wish to buy a product made primarily from recycled material, check to see if the percentage of recycled material is listed on the product or package.

- For additional information about environmental claims or the garbage disposal programs in your community, contact your state or local consumer protection office. This office will be able to refer you to the local solid waste management authority.

Indoor Air Quality. In the last several years, a growing body of scientific evidence has indicated that the air within homes and other buildings can be more seriously polluted than the outdoor air in even the largest and most industrialized cities. Other research indicates that people spend approximately 90% of their time indoors. Thus, for most people, the risks to health may be greater due to exposure to air pollution indoors than outdoors.

Indoor pollution sources release gases or particles into the air and are the primary cause of indoor air quality problems in homes. Inadequate ventilation can increase indoor pollutant levels by not bringing in sufficient outside air to dilute emissions from indoor sources, and by not carrying indoor air pollutants out of the home. High temperature and humidity can also increase concentrations of some pollutants.

There are many potential sources of indoor air pollution in any home. These sources fall into several general categories:

- oil, gas, kerosene, coal, or wood combustion sources;

- building materials and furnishings such as deteriorated asbestos-containing insulation, wet or damp carpeting, and cabinetry or furniture made of certain pressed wood products;

- products for household cleaning and maintenance, personal care, or hobbies;

- central heating and cooling systems and humidifying devices; and

- outside sources such as radon, pesticides, and outdoor air pollution.

Radon. Radon is a radioactive gas produced from the natural breakdown of uranium. It cannot be seen, smelled, or tasted. Outdoor air dilutes radon to the extent that it is virtually harmless, but once inside an enclosed area, such as a home, radon can accumulate, sometimes to the degree that exposure can increase a person's risk of developing lung cancer. According to the EPA, the risk of developing lung cancer from exposure to radon depends upon the concentration of radon and the length of time the individual is exposed to its radioactive properties. The EPA estimates that 21,000 lung cancer deaths per year in the U.S. may be attributed to radon.

Although radon has always been present in the air, concern about elevated indoor concentrations has escalated in recent years as more cases of high indoor radon levels are reported. Studies by the EPA indicate that as many as one in 15 homes may have high levels of indoor radon. As a result, offices have been set up in every state to provide information to homeowners about radon and to advise homeowners about radon testing services.

To immediately reduce the risk of exposure to radon in the home, the EPA recommends that homeowners take the following actions:

- Spend less time in areas with higher concentrations of radon, such as the basement.
- Whenever practical, open all windows and turn on fans to increase the air flow into and through the house. This is especially important in the basement.
- If your home has a crawl space beneath, keep the crawl space vents on all sides of the house fully open all year.
- Stop smoking and discourage smoking in your home. This not only reduces your chances of developing lung cancer, but also reduces the risk of radon exposure.
- Have your home tested for radon. Long- and short-term radon detection kits can be purchased for about $20 through the mail or from your local grocery or hardware store or other retail outlets. Look for a test kit from a company that is state or EPA approved.
- More information about permanent, cost-effective solutions to the radon problem can be found in two publications produced by the EPA and Centers for Disease Control: Radon Reduction Methods: A Homeowner's Guide and A Citizen's Guide to Radon: What It Is and What to do About It. Both booklets are available from EPA regional offices or on the web at www.epa.gov/radon.
- Before undertaking major home modifications, the EPA also recommends that homeowners consult their state radon office to obtain whatever specific advice or assistance the office may be able to provide.

Carbon Monoxide. Carbon monoxide is a colorless, odorless gas that interferes with the delivery of oxygen throughout the body. At low concentrations, it can cause fatigue in healthy people and episodes of increased chest pain in people with chronic heart disease. The symptoms of carbon monoxide poisoning are sometimes confused with the flu or food poisoning. At higher concentrations, carbon monoxide can cause headaches, dizziness, weakness, nausea, confusion, and disorientation. At very high concentrations carbon monoxide can cause unconsciousness and death. Fetuses, infants, pregnant women, elderly people, and people with anemia or with a history of heart or respiratory disease can be especially sensitive to carbon monoxide exposure.

Sources of carbon monoxide exposure include unvented kerosene and gas heaters; leaking chimneys and furnaces; down-drafting from wood stoves and fireplaces; gas stoves; automobile exhaust from attached garages; and environmental tobacco smoke. Steps to reduce exposure to carbon monoxide in homes:

- Keep gas appliances properly adjusted.
- Consider purchasing vented gas space heaters and furnaces.

- Use proper fuel in kerosene space heaters.
- Install and use exhaust fans vented to outdoors over gas stoves.
- Open flues when gas fireplaces are in use.
- Use properly sized wood stoves that are certified to meet EPA emission standards. Make certain that doors on all wood stoves fit tightly.
- Have a trained professional inspect, clean, and tune-up central heating systems (furnaces, flues, and chimneys) annually. Repair any leaks properly.
- Do not idle car inside garage.

Organic Gases. Organic chemicals are widely used as ingredients in household products because of their many useful characteristics, such as the ability to dissolve substances and evaporate quickly. Paints, paint removers, varnishes, wood preservatives, aerosol sprays, cleansers and disinfectants, moth repellants, air fresheners, stored fuels, automotive products, cosmetics, degreasing, hobby products, and dry cleaned clothing all contain organic solvents. All of these products can release organic gases while you are using them, and, to some degree, when they are stored.

Health effects of organic gases include eye, nose, and throat irritation; headaches; loss of coordination; nausea; and damage to liver, kidney, and central nervous system. Some organics can cause cancer in animals; some are suspected to cause cancer in humans. Steps to reduce exposure to household chemicals in homes:

- Use household products according to manufacturer's directions.
- Use outdoors or in well-ventilated places.
- Throw away unused or little-used containers safely; buy in quantities that you will use up quickly.

Formaldehyde. Formaldehyde is an important chemical used widely by industry to manufacture building materials and numerous household products. It is also a by-product of combustion and certain other natural processes. Thus it may be present in substantial concentrations both indoors and outdoors. Sources of formaldehyde in the home include household products and unvented fuel-burning appliances, like gas stoves or kerosene space heaters; pressed wood products (hardwood, plywood wall paneling, particleboard, fiberboard), and furniture made with these pressed wood products; urea-formaldehyde foam insulation (UFFI); combustion sources; environmental tobacco smoke; durable press drapes; other textiles; and glue.

Health effects of formaldehyde include eye, nose, and throat irritation; wheezing and coughing; fatigue; skin rash; severe allergic reactions and possible headaches; loss of coordination; nausea; damage to liver, kidneys, and central nervous system; or cancer in animals or humans. Steps to reduce exposure to formaldehyde in homes:

- Use "exterior grade" pressed wood products (lower-emitting because they contain phenol resins, not urea resins).

- Use air-conditioning and dehumidifiers to maintain moderate temperature and reduce humidity levels.

- Increase ventilation, particularly after bringing new sources of formaldehyde into the home.

Pesticides. According to an EPA survey, 9 out of 10 U.S. households use pesticides. One study by the EPA suggests that 80-90% of most people's exposure to pesticides in the air occurs indoors and that measurable levels of up to a dozen pesticides have been found in the air inside homes. Pesticides used in and around the home include products to control insects (insecticides), termites (termiticides), rodents (rodenticides), and fungi (fungicides). They are sold as sprays, liquids, sticks, powders, crystals, balls, and foggers, or "bombs." Pesticides are also found in products used on lawns and gardens that drift or are tracked inside the house.

The EPA registers pesticides for use and requires manufacturers to put information on the label about when and how to use the pesticide. It is important to remember that the "-cide" in pesticide means "to kill." These products are dangerous if not used properly. Health effects of pesticides include irritation to the eyes, nose, and throat; damage to central nervous system and kidneys; and cancer. Steps to reduce exposure to pesticides in the home:

- Use strictly according to manufacturer's directions.

- Mix or dilute outdoors.

- Apply only in recommended quantities.

- Take plants or pets outside, where possible. Increase ventilation when using indoors.

- Use non-chemical methods of pest control where possible.

- If you use a pest control company, select it carefully.

- Do not store unneeded pesticides inside a home; dispose of unwanted containers safely.

- Store clothes with moth repellents in separately ventilated areas, if possible.

- Keep indoor spaces clean and well-ventilated in order to eliminate or minimize use of air fresheners.

Asbestos. Asbestos is a mineral fiber that has been used commonly in a variety of building construction materials for insulation and as a fire-retardant. The EPA and the Consumer Product Safety Commission (CPSC) have banned several asbestos products. Manufacturers have also voluntarily limited uses of asbestos. Today asbestos is most commonly found in older homes in pipe and furnace insulation materials, asbestos shingles, millboard, textured paints and other coating materials, and floor tiles.

The most dangerous asbestos fibers are too small to be visible. After they are inhaled, they can remain and accumulate in the lungs. Asbestos can cause lung cancer, mesothelioma (a cancer of the chest and abdominal linings) and asbestosis (irreversible lung scarring that can be fatal). Symptoms of these diseases do not show up until many years after exposure began. Steps to reduce exposure to asbestos in homes:

- Seek professional advice to identify potential asbestos problems. Do not disturb material suspected of containing asbestos.

- Use trained and qualified contractors for control measures that may disturb asbestos and for cleanup.

- Follow proper procedures in replacing wood stove door gaskets that may contain asbestos.

Lead. Lead has long been recognized as a harmful environmental pollutant. There are many ways in which humans are exposed to lead, including air, drinking water, food, and contaminated soil and dust. Airborne lead enters the body when an individual breathes lead particles or swallows lead dust once it has settled. Until recently, the most important airborne source of lead was automobile exhaust.

Lead-based paint is a well-known hazard to children who eat paint chips containing lead. High concentrations of air-borne lead particles in the home can also result from the lead dust from outdoor sources, contaminated soil tracked inside, and use of lead in activities such as soldering, electronics repair, and stained glass art work.

Lead is toxic to many organs within the body at both low and high concentrations and is capable of causing serious damage to the brain, kidneys, peripheral nervous system (the sense organs and nerves controlling the body), and red blood cells. Even low levels of lead may contribute to high blood pressure in adults. Fetuses, infants, and children are more vulnerable to lead exposure than adults since lead is more easily absorbed in growing bodies, and the tissues of small children are more sensitive to the damaging effects of lead. In addition, an equal concentration of lead is more damaging because of a child's smaller body weight. Children may also have higher exposures since they are more likely to get lead dust on their hands and then put their fingers or other lead-contaminated objects into their mouths. The effects of lead exposure on fetuses and young children include delays in physical and mental development, lower IQ levels, shortened attention spans, and increased behavioral problems. Steps to reduce exposure to lead in homes:

- If you suspect that paint you are removing may contain lead, have it tested.

- Leave lead-based paint undisturbed. Do not sand or burn off.

- Cover lead-based paint with wallpaper or other building material. Replace moldings and other woodwork or have them removed and chemically treated offsite.

- Use well-ventilated areas for hobby and house maintenance activities involving lead. Consider using "no-lead" solder.

Does Your Office Suffer from "Sick Building Syndrome?" Indoor air quality problems are not limited to homes. Many office buildings have significant air pollution sources and are inadequately ventilated. In addition, building occupants generally have less control over the indoor environment in their offices than they do in their homes.

In recent years, cases of Legionnaire's disease, asthma,

hypersensitivity pneumonitis, and humidifier fever have been directly traced to specific building problems. These are called "building-related illnesses." Most of these diseases can be treated; nevertheless some can pose serious risks to the health of some individuals.

In some cases, however, a significant number of building occupants may report symptoms that do not fit the pattern of any particular illness and are difficult to trace to any source. This phenomenon has been labeled "sick building syndrome." Building occupants may complain of one or more of the following symptoms: dry or burning mucous membranes in the nose, eyes, and throat; sneezing; stuffy or runny nose; fatigue or lethargy; headache; dizziness; nausea; irritability; and forgetfulness.

There is no single manner in which these health problems appear. In some cases, problems begin as workers enter their offices and diminish as workers leave; other times, symptoms continue until the illness is treated. Sometimes there are outbreaks of illness among many workers in a single building; in other cases, health symptoms show up only in individual workers.

Three major reasons for poor indoor air quality in office buildings are the presence of indoor air contaminant sources; poorly designed, maintained, or operated ventilation systems; and uses of the building that were unanticipated or poorly planned for when the building was designed or renovated. Commonly found office pollutants and their sources include environmental tobacco smoke; asbestos from insulating and fire-retardant building supplies; formaldehyde from pressed wood products; other organics from building materials, carpeting, and other office furnishings, cleaning materials and activities, restroom air fresheners, paints, adhesives, copying machines, and photography and print shops; biological contaminants from dirty ventilation systems or water-damaged walls, ceilings, and carpets; and pesticides from pest management practices. If you or others at your office are experiencing health or comfort problems that you suspect may be caused by indoor air pollution, you may do the following:

- Talk with your own physician and report your problems to the company physician, nurse, or health or biosafety officer so that they can be added to the record of health complaints.

- Talk with your supervisor, other workers, and union representatives to see if the problems are being experienced by others and urge that a record of reported health complaints be kept by management, if one has not already been established.

- Ask the building manager to consider hiring a commercial company that conducts building investigations to diagnose the problem or problems and to suggest solutions. Carefully select such companies on the basis of their experience in identifying and solving indoor air quality problems in non-industrial buildings.

- Call the National Institute for Occupational Safety and

Health (NIOSH) for information on obtaining a health hazard evaluation of your office, (800) CDC-INFO.

- Call your state or local health department or air pollution control agency to talk over the symptoms and possible causes.

- Work with others to establish a smoking policy that minimizes non-smoker exposure to environmental tobacco smoke.

How to Prevent Indoor Air Problems When Building a New Home. Express your concerns about indoor air quality to your architect or builder and enlist his or her cooperation in taking measures to provide good indoor air quality. Talk both about purchasing building materials and furnishings that are low-emitting and about providing an adequate amount of ventilation. The American Society of Heating, Refrigerating, and Air Conditioning Engineers recommends a ventilation rate of 0.35 ach (air changes per hour) for new homes. Here are a few important actions that can make a difference:

- Use radon-resistant construction techniques.

- Choose building materials and furnishings that will keep indoor air pollution to a minimum. Use exterior-grade pressed wood products made with phenol formaldehyde in floors, cabinetry, and wall surfaces. Or, as an alternative, consider using solid wood products. Do not permanently adhere carpets directly to cement floors because cement floors tend to be cold and moisture condenses on the carpet, providing a place for mold and dust mites to grow. Also, carpets laid in this manner do not dry thoroughly if they get wet.

- Provide proper drainage and seal foundations in new construction. Air that enters the home through the foundation can contain more moisture than is generated from all occupant activities.

- Become familiar with how heat recovery ventilators (air-to-heat exchangers) work and consider installing one. A whole-house heat recovery ventilation system permits occupants to enjoy the air quality benefits of drawing more outdoor air into the home while reducing the costs of heating or cooling this air.

- Install exterior-vented air ducts into woodstove fireboxes and near fireplaces. The supplementary air supply from these ducts will provide adequate oxygen for complete combustion, minimize infiltration of cold outside air into the rest of the house, and prevent back drafts from bringing combustion products back down the chimney. Do not close the duct until all embers are extinguished.

Chapter 7: FOOD and DRUGS

Nutrition Labeling. The Food and Drug Administration (FDA) requires that all packaged foods be labeled. The FDA requires a Percent Daily Value column that shows the amount of nutrients an individual is receiving from a product in relation to the value needed daily, based on a 2,000-

calorie diet. (This is an average for all Americans; calorie intake varies by age and gender, so individual needs may be higher or lower.)

Labels must now contain information on a product's total calories, calories from fat, total fat, saturated fat, cholesterol, sodium, total carbohydrates, dietary fiber, sugars, protein, vitamin A, vitamin C, calcium, and iron. Voluntary dietary components that can be listed on the label include calories from saturated fat, polyunsaturated fat, monounsaturated fat, potassium, soluble fiber, insoluble fiber, sugar alcohol, other carbohydrates, and essential vitamins and minerals.

The FDA has set standard serving sizes so that a food product's healthfulness can't be exaggerated by stating nutritional value based on extremely tiny portions. The agency also restricts package claims that tie a product's nutritional content with disease prevention.

In addition, the FDA is standardizing nutritional claims for light or lite and low fat products, etc., so that they mean the same things for all. As of 1992, the FDA set these definitions:

- Cholesterol free: The food contains fewer than two milligrams of cholesterol per serving

- Fat free: The food contains fewer than .5 grams of fat per serving

- High fiber: The food must provide 20% or more of the recommended daily intake of fiber; the label must also state the amount of fat if the product is not low in total fat. (Any nutrient claim of "high in" means the product must provide at least 20% of the recommended daily allowance.)

- Light, lite: Contains one-third fewer calories or 50% less fat than a comparable product.

- Low calorie: Contains fewer than 120 calories per 100 grams

- Low fat: Contains three grams of fat or less per 100 grams and not more than 30% of calories from fat

- Low sodium: The food contains fewer than 140 milligrams per 100 grams

Fountain of Youth Drugs. As the average age of the U.S. consumer increases, the temptation to try so-called anti-aging products may grow stronger. Nevertheless, health experts dismiss all claims of products to improve everything from memory to sex drive, to building muscles and cells for sagging skin and wrinkle prevention. In fact, these drugs often contain animal tissues that could cause allergic reactions, viruses, certain diseases, and even death.

Most of these anti-aging products have not been approved by the federal government. Black marketers have been known to sell these drugs to physicians, health and nutrition stores, or straight to the individual; many can be obtained through direct mail from foreign companies. Congress estimates sales of these miracle youth drugs to be around $2 billion annually, making them the most lucrative portion of the quack-medicine market.

The safest way to increase years, according to legitimate health authorities, is to exercise regularly, follow a well-balanced, low-fat diet regimen, and avoid smoking and excessive alcohol consumption.

Prescription Drug Promotion. Since 1985, pharmaceutical companies have been permitted to promote prescription drugs direct to consumers. They seek to create demand by using television and print ads to suggest to patients that they ask their doctor about a particular drug, and by enlisting physicians and celebrities to make appearances touting the product.

Consider such statements with these points in mind:

- Celebrities are often paid to be spokespersons for a product, and so are physicians. Their testimonials should not be regarded as expert advice.

- Some physicians hesitate to prescribe breakthrough drugs until enough time passes to determine possible side effects.

- All drugs should have gone through extensive study. Don't accept a report of one study as sufficient. Find out how many other studies were performed. What was the length of each study? Who performed them? The government? An unbiased, nonprofit organization? A pharmaceutical company? Was the research reported in respected medical journals such as the New England Journal of Medicine? Were studies based on actual human subjects, tissue, or animals?

- The best advice for consumers who want more information on any drug is to check it out with their physician.

Online Pharmacies. Recently, there has been a large number of online drug stores appearing on the Internet. Consumers should be careful when purchasing prescription drugs online. Some of these sites sell unapproved drugs or provide approved drugs without the traditional safeguards (use of licensed pharmacists or doctors, lack of personal interaction been the patient and the pharmacist). Some online drug sites have gotten criticism for not disclosing profitable commissions and partnerships that they have with hospitals and pharmaceutical companies. Critics say that commissions and partnerships might blur the line between an advertisement and medical advise. Consumers can ensure the quality of an online pharmacy by looking to see if the site has the VIPPS (Verified Internet Pharmacy Practice Sites) seal. They can also contact the National Association of Boards of Pharmacy, (847)391-4406, http://www.nabp.net.

Vitamin Supplements. A well-balanced diet is essential to providing the nutrients needed for good health, yet the majority of Americans do not meet nutritional guidelines in their eating habits. The additional nutrients that vitamin supplements provide may ensure the dosage of vitamins and minerals recommended to promote health. Some researchers believe they may even prevent diseases such as cancer, heart disease, cataracts, and arthritis, but nutrition authorities are not unanimous on taking vitamin supplements. According to Consumer Reports, a growing number of researchers favor certain supplements because:

- Doses higher than the U.S. Recommended Dietary Allowances (RDAs), which vary by age and gender, may be needed to better protect against disease.

- The recommendation of at least three servings of vegetables and two servings of fruits daily may not contain enough vitamins C and E and beta carotene to provide optimal protection against disease.

- It is extremely difficult to obtain the ideal dosage of vitamin E through diet alone.

- A multi-vitamin and mineral supplement with extra supplements of vitamins E, C, and beta-carotene may cost as little as twenty-five cents a day.

- Another viewpoint is held by researchers who think that the nutrients needed to protect against disease may only be found in healthy foods and not in supplements. Moreover, there is no government regulation that ensures that the labels on vitamin supplement bottles accurately reflect the actual supplement pill.

Chapter 8: GOVERNMENT PERFORMANCE

Locating Government Information. Government agencies and departments can be a good source of current information on a wide range of topics. Locating government data, however, is not a well-defined process. Fortunately, the Internet has made this process much easier.

A good starting place for consumers is www.usa.gov, the federal government's official web portal. This website connects the consumer to millions of web pages from the federal government, and also from state, local and tribal governments. The site has topical links, an agency index, and a search engine that makes finding information easy for the consumer.

Government clearinghouses can also be a good source of information. These offices routinely respond to public inquiries and distribute information, often at no cost. Toll-free hotlines, covering everything from drug abuse referrals to tax assistance, are also a good source. If, however, it is not clear where to begin a search for governmental information, the following tips may be helpful:

- Contact the most appropriate department or agency. Most government departments have public information offices that respond to inquiries. (Check the index of this book, or the agency website, which can be accessed through www.usa.gov).

- Explain what type of information you are seeking in a brief, understandable manner.

- Be patient. It may take several calls to reach someone knowledgeable about your particular inquiry.

- Remember to be courteous. The last person you speak with may be the one who can provide the most information.

- Ask about relevant publications or research. In many cases, printed materials on a specific topic are already available to the public.

- Verify subjective information. If you are seeking data such as survey or research results, ask how the information was gathered and, if necessary, present the data to another expert for additional input.

Tips for Taxpayers. Taxpayers are ultimately responsible for the accuracy of their own tax returns, whether they file their own or seek professional assistance. To aid those who choose to prepare their own returns, the IRS offers numerous free publications as well as toll-free assistance numbers. In addition, the federal government offers a number of free tax programs and services, such as tax preparation assistance for older Americans or designating qualified individuals to represent taxpayers in the event of an audit. Taxpayers can request a guide to free tax services from their regional tax office, or call the IRS at (800)829-1040. Information can also be found on the IRS website, www.irs.gov.

Taxpayers who seek professional assistance should choose the type of service that best fits their needs, depending upon the level of complication and fees involved. Tax consultants vary widely, from services that are available only during tax season, to large accounting firms. When considering a tax service, consumers should first find out if they qualify for special tax assistance from the federal government by contacting their regional tax office. If hiring a commercial service, consumers should follow some general guidelines:

- Assess the work necessary. For more complicated tax returns, a certified public accountant or reputable accounting firm may be a better choice than a seasonal tax preparation service.

- Check company history. Find out if the tax service you choose will be available for assistance after tax season in the event of an audit or other complications.

- Research qualifications. Make sure the tax consultant you choose has the professional skills to complete your return.

- Verify the length of time it will take to process your return.

- Secure a letter of agreement confirming what services will be provided, the length of time involved, fees, and other pertinent information.

Chapter 9: HEALTH CARE and PROMOTION

Health and Medical Fraud. Health and medical fraud is typically a by-product of deceptive advertising campaigns that utilize sophisticated sales tactics for marketing bogus products. Most of these products have not been tested by competent medical authorities and, at best, will only delay the consumer from receiving appropriate health care treatment. Health care consumers should, therefore, be aware of the following definitions:

- Quack: "Anyone who promotes medical schemes or

remedies known to be false, or which are unproven, for a profit." U.S. House of Representatives, 1984.

- Quackery: "Promoting health products, services or practices of questionable safety, effectiveness or validity for an intended purpose." National Council Against Health Care Fraud, 1986.

- Health fraud/quacks: "Health fraud is the promotion, for financial gain, of fraudulent or unproven devices, treatments, services, plans or products (including, but not limited to, diets and nutritional supplements) that alter or claim to alter the human condition. Those who promote such medical remedies that do not work are called 'quacks'." The Assembly Republican Task Force on Health Fraud and the Elderly, New York State Assembly, June, 1986.

The U.S. Postal Inspection Service advises consumers to consider the following rules before buying unfamiliar health and medical products:

- Beware of advertisements that offer miracle cures that are unavailable elsewhere.

- Avoid products, devices, or programs that promise unrealistic or easy results.

- Claims that sound too good to be true (such as an instant cure for arthritis or overnight hair growth) usually are.

- Consult your family doctor, local pharmacist, or other reputable health care professional before buying unfamiliar or novel health care products or programs.

Health Hoaxes, Food Fads, and Dangerous Diets. Consumers spend millions of dollars each year on phony medicines and treatments, food fads, and weight loss products and diets that simply do not work and might be dangerous. The information below will help you avoid buying unproven health and diet products and programs:

- If a health claim sounds too good to be true, there's a good chance it is. Be skeptical about claims offering "miracle or secret cures" or "scientific breakthroughs." True cures or breakthroughs are always publicized widely in the media; there are no secret cures.

- Check with a licensed health professional or credible health organization (for example, the American Cancer Society or the American Diabetes Association) before buying "cures" or "miracle diets." For example, science has not yet found a cure for arthritis, as the Arthritis Foundation could tell you, so products that promise to cure you of the disease are phony.

- Be aware that health frauds, food fads, and fake diet products might rob you of more than your money. In extreme cases, they have ruined or even taken lives.

Health Care Information on the Web Thousands of websites are now available to help consumers make health care decisions. Be wary of sites sponsored by companies that are trying to sell you a particular treatment. It is better to visit sites run by government agencies or by recognized organizations such as the American Medical Association. This information should complement, not replace, what you

receive from health care professionals. Here are some sites that are generally recognizes as sources of reliable information.

- **HealthFinder** (www.healthfinder.gov): The federal government's gateway to information on health issues, health care programs, and organizations.

- **Intelihealth** (www.intelihealth.com): Information and practical advice on staying healthy from the Harvard Medical School.

- **Mayo Clinic** (www.mayoclinic.com): An alphabetical index of diseases and Healthy Living Centers. Consult the Health Decisions Guide for information on medical tests and treatments.

- **Medical Library Association** (www.mlanet.org): Websites identified as helpful by librarians

- **Mental Help Net** (www.mentalhelp.net): Links to centers on a broad range of mental health issues and disorders.

- **National Health Council** (www.nationalhealthcouncil .org): Health information links organized by topic.

- **National Library of Medicine** (www.nlm.nih.gov): A government health information center offering answers to questions, links to research, news on clinical trials and more.

Choosing a Health Club. Individuals interested in joining a health club should invest their time before investing their money. Consumers should find out if they are protected under state law in the event the health club closes unexpectedly. In addition, individuals who are interested in a health club membership should consider the following guidelines:

- Carefully check out the health club by visiting the facility during the hours of anticipated use to determine if the club is overcrowded during that time period. Inspect the club's exercise equipment and facilities to make sure they are properly maintained and clean.

- Inquire about the availability of the club. It may be open seven days a week, but limited to men or women on certain days and specific hours.

- Ask about the qualifications and previous training of the club's instructors.

- Read the fine print in all contracts or special offers to avoid making an unwanted commitment to a long-term contract. Make sure that verbal promises or conditions are put in writing.

- Find out if there is a cooling-off period—a time period during which you can change your mind and get your money back. Also ask about the health club's refund policy for cancellations.

- Check with the state or local consumer protection agency or Better Business Bureau to find out if any complaints have been filed against the health club. Beware of clubs offering unreasonably low membership fees. Some clubs close because they fail to charge members enough money necessary to operate the club.

- Ask up front about reciprocal rights. If the club closes or if the member goes on vacation, other clubs may allow the member to use their facilities.

Be cautious of:

- Joining clubs that have not yet opened—they may never open
- Promises that you can cancel anytime and stop paying—check the written contract for the terms of membership and any other promises
- Signing long-term contracts—consumer protection agencies report that many consumers quit using the club within a few months
- Automatic monthly billing to your charge card or debit from a checking account—these are easier to start than to stop
- Unbelievably low one-time fees with no monthly dues. Many clubs will surprise you with monthly "maintenance" fees instead.

Before you sign, be sure to:

- check with your doctor before you begin an exercise program;
- check to see that promised equipment/services are actually available,
- talk to current members regarding their satisfaction with the club;
- check out several clubs before you sign a contract;
- consider your commitment to a long-term program—good intentions seem to fade as the reality of the hard work sets in;
- read the contract carefully before you sign; is interest charged for a payment plan? are all promises in writing?

Chapter 10: INSURANCE

Choosing an Insurance Agent. The local Better Business Bureau (BBB) (see Chapter 15, Retail and Commercial Concerns) is a good starting point for choosing an insurance agent. The BBB records complaints against agents and companies. Information about the company is also available from the State Insurance Commissioner's office. Although commissioners do not generally rate companies, they can tell you if the number of valid complaints against the company is abnormally high, and if the company has ever been barred from any state. In its publication, Inside Underwriting: A Consumer Guide to Buying Insurance, the New Mexico Public Interest Research Group suggests that consumers ask themselves the following questions before selecting an insurance agent.

- Does the agent return your phone calls promptly?
- Can s/he plan for you individually, rather than producing a pre-constructed insurance "package"?
- Does s/he review coverage with you periodically—yearly for fire and casualty, every few years for life insurance?

- Does s/he outline clearly the limitations and exclusions on each policy?
- Does s/he keep abreast of developments in his/her field?
- When renewal time comes, does s/he review your policies with you to see if any changes are necessary or does s/he automatically renew your policy?
- Does s/he allow you to read your entire policy or does s/he simply "explain" it to you?
- How much of a commission is s/he getting from my policy? The answer to this may explain why agents are more anxious to sell you one particular policy over others.

Medigap. Medigap policies are offered by private insurance companies as a supplement to Medicare health coverage for senior citizens. There are ten levels of coverage available, known as Plan A through Plan J, with the latter being the most comprehensive. The cost for each plan rises according to comprehensiveness, but some features are not needed by all seniors. Depending on the plan selected, coverage could include:

- Co-insurance for hospital stays and blood transfusions
- At-home recovery
- Basic drugs
- Foreign travel emergency
- Out-patient charges counted as "excess" under Medicare
- Prescription drugs
- Preventive care
- Co-insurance for limited stays in a nursing facility

Make a full investigation of options before you turn age 65. For the first six months thereafter, you cannot be denied coverage because of pre-existing medical conditions. After purchasing a policy, seniors are entitled to a 30-day review during which they may demand a full refund if unsatisfied.

Disability Insurance. Disability insurance offers income protection to working people who become disabled through illness or accident. The need for disability insurance varies according to a person's circumstances. The more dependents a person has, the greater the need for insurance. If a family has a reserve fund available to pay bills in case someone cannot earn money for an extended period of time, then the need for disability insurance is lessened.

Important policy options to consider:

- Benefit Period: The period of time the insurance will pay benefits, which may range from two years after the onset of disability, up to age 65, or lifetime coverage.
- Waiting Period: The period between the onset of a disability and the start of benefits, usually 30 days to a year.
- Partial Disability: In many cases a worker is not totally disabled, but cannot achieve former income levels because of partial disability. This option pays residual

benefits based on percentage of income loss.

- Cost of Living Adjustments: Disability benefits that follow annual changes in the Consumer Price Index. Can be helpful but expensive.

- Total Disability: Policies may measure this against ability to perform the major duties of one's regular occupation or against the ability to perform any job for which one is "reasonably qualified." The second option is less expensive.

Long-Term Care Insurance. Extended stays in nursing homes or long periods of at-home professional care are not covered by Medicare or Medigap for the elderly, nor by disability insurance for workers. Federal assistance under Medicaid is available only to those who meet poverty guidelines. Long-term care can be very expensive, as can the insurance policies to cover it. No policy covers all expenses completely; consumers should carefully evaluate their own needs and financial situation. Policies may cover care in a nursing facility, at home, or both.

Levels of care are usually described as:

- *Skilled Care:* intensive daily care, usually for a limited time, by a licensed professional under a doctor's supervision.

- *Intermediate Care:* occasional nursing or therapeutic care by professionals that may last for an extended period.

- *Custodial Care:* assistance with daily needs, such as eating, bathing, dressing, etc., which may be provided by non-medical assistants either in nursing facilities or at home (in which case assistants must be from licensed agencies).

In order to keep the cost of premiums down, policies usually exclude some conditions. Limitations may be on any of the following:

- Pre-existing conditions.
- Substance abuse.
- Mental or nervous illnesses. Most long-term policies do, however, cover Alzheimer's disease care.
- Military-service related injuries.
- Self-inflicted injuries.

Before signing a contract:

- Read the policy carefully. Make sure you understand what type of care, in what place, provided by what type of caregiver is covered. Remember that policies pay for care that meets the company's definition of "necessary."

- Consider your income and capital. Look to the future. How long are you likely to pay premiums before drawing benefits? Does the coverage keep pace with inflation? Can premiums also rise?

Cutting Costs on Car Insurance. Car insurance is a basic expense for many consumers. In some urban areas, premiums over the life of a vehicle could total more than its actual purchase price. As a result, the consumer should shop around for car insurance as carefully as shopping

around for a car. In most states, liability is the only type of coverage a motorist must carry. A common rule of thumb for cutting costs on car insurance is to buy at the highest affordable deductible. The following are some other cost-saving measures, as recommended by the New Mexico Public Interest Research Group in its publication, *Inside Underwriting: A Consumer Guide to Buying Insurance:*

- If you don't need it, don't buy it. Every $1 in insurance premiums returns about 60 cents on claims; the remainder is overhead. According to the average driver can save about 40% by "self-insuring" those risks he can afford to assume.

- Choose the right car. Before you buy a car, ask your insurance agent how rates for the car you want compare with rates for similar makes.

- Notify your agent immediately when you move, when you change your marital status, when the use of your car changes from business to non-business, when your insured child leaves home or marries, when you purchase a new car, when a member of your family who was using a car to drive to work stops working.

- Maintain a safe driving record.

- Keep your car in good repair.

- Investigate special discounts. Some companies offer discounts to non-drinkers or non-smokers, and "good student" discounts are also available.

- Install security devices. These can give you a reduction on the comprehensive part of your coverage.

- Again, buy at the highest deductible you can afford.

The Money Management Institute urges consumers to find the right coverage at the best price—but not at the expense of sacrificing good service. In their publication, *Your Automobile Dollar*, the Institute warns that awards in personal injury lawsuits are now so high that anyone with a lot to lose should consider taking the maximum liability coverage available. According to the Institute, the minimum required by most states under financial responsibility laws hardly begins to cover today's medical expenses.

Homeowners' Insurance. There are three main homeowners' insurance policy types for single-family dwellings:

- HO-3: This most popular policy type covers damage or destruction to your home, garage, contents within, and other property from fire, theft, vandalism, windstorms, hail, vehicles, aircraft, falling objects, civil disruption, explosions, weight from snow or ice, and frozen or malfunctioning plumbing, heating, air-conditioning, or fire sprinkler systems. It should also cover hotel expenses if you are forced out of your home due to insured damage. This policy excludes damage from earthquakes, floods, nuclear accident, or war.

- HO-2: Covers damage from household accidents, insects, or vermin. It is not widely available.

- HO-8: Provides specified, limited coverage, usually for older homes. Benefits may only be limited to the actual cash value of the house.

How to lower your rates:

- Raise your deductible.
- Discounts may be available for fire and burglar alarms, fire extinguishers, deadbolts, and fire sprinkler systems.
- Discounts may also be available if you have auto insurance with the company.
- Get your home appraised. This is usually performed at no extra cost when starting a policy. This might also prevent being over-insured and paying higher premiums.
- Ask your carrier about additional discounts.

Temporary Health Insurance. Under the Consolidated Omnibus Budget Reconciliation Act (COBRA), group health coverage must be extended to individuals who would otherwise become ineligible. This applies to the categories of people described below:

- Laid Off Workers: If you were laid off by an organization that employs more than 20 people, but is not a unit of the federal government or a church-related organization, you may keep your group health care coverage for 18 months at your own expense. Your employer has to notify its insurance company within 30 days of the lay-off.
- Divorced Spouse: If you divorce a health-insured employee, you may extend the coverage for 36 months, but you must notify the insurance company within 60 days of your desire to do so.

In either case, you are eligible to keep the same coverage as your former plan or may scale it back to "care coverage." Coverage may be more expensive if the employer formerly paid a percentage of the premiums. Health coverage ends if you obtain insurance under another plan, if the employer discontinues coverage for all employees, or if you become eligible for Medicare.

For additional information, consumers can order the Employee Benefits Security Administration's free booklet, *Health Benefits under COBRA*, by calling 1-866-444-EBSA. The booklet is also available on the web at www.dol.gov/ebsa/publications.

Chapter 11: LEGAL AFFAIRS

Legal Aid. More than 1,000 Legal Aid or Legal Services offices in the U.S. provide free legal assistance to consumers who cannot afford to hire a private attorney and who meet other financial eligibility requirements. These offices are supported by government or private funding, or by local bar associations; they are staffed by lawyers, paralegals and law students.

Legal Aid and Legal Services offices can help individuals resolve legal problems as they relate to such areas as credit, utilities, adoption, divorce, Social Security, Welfare, unemployment, and worker's compensation. Because the board of directors of each office determines its own priorities, some offices are limited in the types of cases they handle. Nevertheless, these offices can usually direct consumers to other sources of legal advice or assistance. For information about the availability of free legal services in their community, consumers can contact their local bar association. Legal Aid offices are also listed in telephone directories under the heading "Legal Services" or "Social Service Organizations" in the yellow pages.

Guarding Your Social Security Number. A Social Security number should be guarded as carefully as a credit card number. Be careful to whom you give it. If it falls into the wrong hands it could be abused to obtain such personal information as credit card and bank account numbers. Here are some tips on how to protect your Social Security number:

- Don't provide your Social Security number over the telephone or in an e-mail message, and don't enter it into a form on an Internet site.
- Don't provide your Social Security number when you cash or write a check or pay with a credit card.
- Don't put your Social Security number on an employment application form until you are hired.
- Don't give out your Social Security number to any government agency unless the agency informs you of their authority to use it and for what it intends to use the number.
- Try to avoid having your Social Security number used as your driver's license number or having it printed on your license.
- Exercise caution when requested by a private business (retail store, credit card company, insurance company, utility company, private college, etc.) for your Social Security number. Suggest offering only the last four digits or ask for a statement that your Social Security number will not be sold to others.
- Provide your Social Security number only to any organization that pays you a salary or wages, interest, or dividends (i.e. an employer or stockbroker); maintains your checking or savings account (i.e. a bank); or charges you interest (lenders). In other words, any institution that has business with you that must be reported to the IRS.
- Tax departments, state motor vehicle departments, and welfare departments are entitled to request your Social Security number.
- Check your Social Security records periodically to make certain that your Social Security number isn't being used by anyone else.
- Call (800)772-1213 to request a Social Security application form, or apply over the Internet at http://www.ssa.gov/onlineservices.

Chapter 12: MANUFACTURED GOODS and PRODUCT SAFETY

Product Safety and Recalls. Every year, in order to prevent injury to consumers, federal agencies recall or issue warnings about hundreds of products, including food, drugs, cars and other vehicles, home and garden products, appliances, recreational boats, and toys. Hazards might occur because of design flaws, product defects, new scientific information about dangers from materials previously thought safe, accidental contamination, tampering, unforeseen misuse of products, or failure to meet safety standards. ConsumerAffairs.com noted that recalls of products such as packaged food, drugs, and medical supplies rose almost 25% from 1999 to 2004.

Consumers are critically important in these product safety efforts because they identify product safety problems and because they respond to warnings and recalls. Product recalls and warnings can protect consumers only if consumers react to them. Yet, only 2% to 5% of all consumers respond to recall notices.

Knowing how to use products correctly, reading instructions, and being alert to hazards will help to ensure a safe environment around you. You also should pay attention to product recalls in the news and consumer magazines. Several federal government agencies provide recall information on a variety of products, including toys, cars, child safety seats, food, and health and beauty aids.

- Read about major appliances, tools, and other items before you buy. There are several consumer magazines that give detailed information on the prices, features, and safety of various products.

- Learn to use power tools and electrical appliances safely. If you don't know what a ground fault circuit interrupter (GFCI) is, find out. Read the instructions carefully before using the equipment.

- Don't use things for purposes the manufacturer never intended. Tools aren't kids' toys.

- Poolside safety demands non-climbable fencing, CPR training, a poolside phone, a GFCI, and constant adult supervision to help ensure the protection of children. Certain building codes require some of these safety features.

- Make sure toys are age appropriate. Your 10-year-old's baseball bat can be a lethal weapon in the hands of your three-year-old slugger.

- Children should always wear bicycle helmets. Some states now require it. When shopping for helmets, look for the ANSI and/or SNELL sticker to ensure the safest helmet.

- Small parts can present choking hazards to children who put things in their mouths. Beware of balloons, balls, marbles, and older children's toys.

- Baby items demand special attention. Cribs, baby walkers, and baby gates have changed dramatically as the result of new safety requirements. Don't buy used items that don't comply with current standards.

- Garage and tag sales are places where small appliances, power tools, baby furniture, and toys with safety defects, lead paints, or other hazards get passed along to new owners. Make sure these types of items meet current safety requirements.

- If you spot a product defect, design flaw, allergic reaction, or hidden hazard, contact the U.S. Consumer Product Safety Commission or your state or local consumer protection agency.

- Read product labels. Some products can turn into deadly poisons when mixed with other products, stored improperly, or used in poorly vented areas.

- Keep all medicines, cleaning products, wood finishes, toxic art supplies, and paints out of the sight and reach of young children. Keep leftover products in their original containers. Have the poison control emergency number near your phone. Get rid of old and dated products.

- Look for tamper-resistant packaging on foods and medicine.

- Watch out for dinnerware decorated with lead paint or glaze, and for lead crystal decanters.

- Report safety problems by contacting the Auto Safety Hotline at (888)327-4236 or on the web at www.odi.nhsta.dot.gov/hotline/. Through this site consumers can also obtain recall and safety information on new and used cars, trucks, motorcycles, motor homes, child seats, and other motor vehicle equipment.

Consumers can visit www.Recalls.gov to find out which federal agencies issue consumer product safety warnings and recalls, the kinds of products each of them covers, what products are on their current recall lists, and how to let them know about product safety problems. Contact the U.S. Food and Drug Administration for consumer education material or to file a complaint on food, drugs, medical devices, and radiological products such as microwave ovens, televisions, and sunlamps.

Every issue of *Consumer Reports* (as well as its website, www.ConsumerReports.org) provides recall information. You can also visit the recall link at www.ConsumerAffair.com.

Warranties and Guarantees. Before making a purchase, use these guidelines to review the warranty/guarantee:

- Do not wait until the product fails or needs repair to find out what is covered in the warranty.

- If the product costs $15 or more, the law says that the seller must provide any warranty before you buy, if you ask to see it. Use your rights to compare the terms and conditions of warranties (or guarantees) on products or services before you buy. Look for the warranty that best meets your needs.

- When purchasing a product or service, ask the following questions: How long is the warranty, and when does it start and end? What is covered? Which parts? What kinds of problems? Will the warranty pay for 100% of repair costs, or will it pay for parts, but not the labor to do the repairs? Will it pay for testing the product before it is repaired? Will it pay for shipping and/or a loaner? What do you have to do and when? Are regular inspections or maintenance required? Do you have to ship the product out of state for repairs? Who offers the warranty, manufacturer or retailer? How reliable are they?

- Keep sales receipts and warranties in a safe place.

- Some states have additional warranty rights for consumers. Check with your state or local consumer protection office to find information about the laws in your state.

Smoke Detectors. When fire occurs in your home, your chances for survival are twice as good when smoke detectors are installed and functioning. Properly maintained smoke detectors provide early warning when fires occur. Early warning increases your chances for survival and allows the fire department to save more of your property. For this reason, many cities and states have laws requiring smoke detectors in homes. Check with your local fire department or state fire marshal for additional information about what might be required in your community. The tips below will help you use your smoke detector to the best advantage:

- For minimum protection, install a smoke detector outside each sleeping area in your home and keep your bedroom doors closed while you are asleep. For greater protection, install smoke detectors on every floor of your home. Be sure to install the detectors away from air vents.

- Keep your smoke detectors properly maintained. Test them at least once a month to ensure that they are working properly. At least once a year, clean them by dusting with a vacuum cleaner. Batteries in battery-operated detectors should be changed annually. Use only the type of batteries recommended on the detector.

- If your smoke detector sounds an alarm when no smoke is present, consult with the manufacturer or with your local fire department. If smoke from cooking causes the detector to sound an alarm, do not remove the batteries or disconnect the power source. Simply fan the smoke away from the detector until the alarm stops. If this happens frequently, it might be necessary to relocate the detector or install a different type.

- Develop a fire escape plan and review the plan with all members of the household. The plan should include: helping children and elderly people who might need special assistance; getting out of the house when fire occurs and using a neighbor's telephone, rather than your own, to notify the fire department; picking a place outside the house where all members of the family will meet to ensure that everyone is out safely.

- Parents should also teach children: how to open locks and remove screens or storm windows; to avoid hiding in a place such as a closet or under a bed, where firefighters will have difficulty finding them; to report fire or smoke immediately and get out of the house quickly in the case of a fire.

- For additional information on smoke detectors, contact the U.S. Fire Administration, 16825 S. Seton Ave., Emmitsburg, MD 21727, or on the web at www.usfa.dhs.gov.

Chapter 13: MASS COMMUNICATIONS

Wireless Cable TV Scams. Wireless cable television permits cable access via a rooftop antenna as opposed to the traditional cable wire. Licenses to offer the service in a given area are awarded by the Federal Communications Commission under a lottery system. Services that prepare applications for the lottery solicit investors to put up the necessary fees in the hope of quick rewards. Unfortunately, some such application services are fraudulent, creating one of the fastest growing telemarketing problems in the U.S., according to state securities regulators.

These solicitors abuse the system and convince individuals to invest thousands of dollars to own a wireless cable market; they do this by understating the complications and risks while exaggerating the quick and easy profits. These application services solicit investors through telemarketing, direct mail and newspaper advertisements, and radio and television "infomercials."

If you have been approached by an application preparation service and are considering investment, you should be aware of some of the risks involving investing in wireless cable.

- The wireless cable industry faces competition from broadcast TV, traditional cable, home satellite dishes, video rental stores, and new high-tech services, making its success less than a sure thing. Wireless cable technology is also limited in transmission and is unsuited for areas with obstructions such as buildings, hills, and trees.

- Investors may lose all of their capital.

- Wireless cable companies truly interested in the business prefer rich investors who can afford to take a chance on tens or hundreds of thousands of dollars—not the mere $5,000 or so that small investors victimized by this scam usually speculate.

- Being granted an FCC license does not guarantee profit. Individual licenses are awarded only for channels in each market. It could take more than five years for any profits to materialize.

- Fraudulent lottery application services attempt to file as many applications as possible; therefore, your application may be one of many applying for the same market.

- It can take several months to learn whether or not your application "won the lottery" for the market you wanted. It can also take several months to learn if you were misled by a fraudulent application firm.

If you think you have already been a victim of fraud by a wireless cable lottery application service, you can contact any of the following organizations:

- The Federal Trade Commission (FTC) by writing to Investment Fraud, Federal Trade Commission, 600 Pennsylvania Ave., NW, Rm. 200, Washington, DC 20580. A complaint form is also available on the FTC website, www.ftc.gov.

- The securities commission in your state or territory. (Addresses for these can be found in Chapter 3: Credit and Personal Finance, State and Local Organizations and Agencies section).

- The Better Business Bureau in the city in which the application preparation service is located (BBBs are listed in Chapter 15, Retail and Commercial Concerns).

Chapter 14: REAL ESTATE and CONSTRUCTION

Home Improvements. Hiring a contractor to renovate your home, add a room, or make some other improvement can be a confusing maze of contracts, licenses, permits, and payment schedules. The suggestions below can help guide you through the maze:

- Compare costs by getting more than one estimate or bid. Each estimate should be based on the same building specifications, materials, and time frame.

- Before choosing a contractor, check with state, county, or local consumer protection agencies and the Better Business Bureau to see if any complaints have been filed against the contractor. Ask about information on unresolved cases and how long a contracting company has been in business under its current name.

- Ask a potential contractor for a list of previous customers whom you could call to find out about work quality and to see if they would hire that contractor for future work.

- Check with your local building inspections department to see if licensing and/or bonding are required of contractors in your area. If so, ask to see the contractor's license and bonding papers.

- Before signing a written contract, be sure it includes the contractor's full name, address, phone number, and professional license number (where required), a thorough description of the work to be done, grade and quality of materials to be used, agreed upon starting and completion dates, total cost, payment schedule, warranty, how debris will be removed, and any other agreement information. Never sign a partially blank contract. Fill in or draw a line through any blank spaces.

- Call your insurance company to find out if you are covered for any injury or damage that might occur. Most contractors have liability and compensation insurance to protect the customer from a lawsuit in the event of an accident. Ask to see a copy of the insurance certificate.

- If the work requires a building permit, let the contractor apply for it in his name. That way, if the work does not pass inspection, you are not financially responsible for any corrections that must be made.

- When you sign a non-emergency home improvement contract in your home and in the presence of a contractor (or contractor's representative), you usually have three business days in which to cancel the contract. You must be told about your cancellation rights and be provided with cancellation forms. If you decide to cancel, it is recommended that you send a notice of cancellation by telegram or certified mail, return receipt requested.

- For a remodeling job involving many subcontractors and a substantial amount of money, it is wise to protect yourself from liens against your home in case the contractor does not pay subcontractors or suppliers. If state law permits, add a release-of-lien clause to the contract or place your payments in an escrow account until the work is completed.

- If you cannot pay for a project without a loan, add a clause to your contract stating it is valid only if financing is obtained.

- When signing a contract, limit your first payment to not more than 30% of the contract price. The remaining payments should depend on the progress of the work. Ten percent of the contract amount should be held back until the job is complete, and all problems, if any, are corrected. Some states have home improvement laws that specify the amount of deposit and payment schedule. Check with your state and local consumer protection offices to see if there is such a law in your community.

- Thoroughly inspect the contractor's work before making final payment or signing a completion certificate.

Home Improvement Fraud. Part of the mission at the U.S. Department of Housing and Urban Development (HUD) is to educate consumers about home improvement rackets. Although most dealers and contractors conscientiously try to give their clients service equal to the price they charge, HUD urges homeowners to follow these common sense rules when contracting for home improvements:

- Plan ahead. Know what you want or need to have done before contacting a contractor.

- Read and understand every word of all contracts and papers before signing them.

- Never sign a contract with anyone who makes fantastic promises. Reputable dealers are not running give-away businesses.

- Avoid wild bargains. The best bargain is a good job.

- If possible, talk to the workers or suppliers. If they are having trouble getting paid, chances are the contracting business is not doing well.

- Never consolidate existing loans through a home improvement contractor.

- Don't let salespeople pressure you into signing up to buy their materials or services.

- Avoid salespeople who tell you they have material left over from a recent job, offer you discounts for finding him/her other customers, can be reached only through an answering service, or drive an unmarked van.

- Be cautious of salespeople who arrive door-to-door or seek you out.

- Be wary of salespeople who try to scare you into signing for repairs that they say are urgent. Seek the advice of an expert as to how urgent such repairs are. High-pressure and scare tactics are often the mark of a phony deal.

- Avoid salespeople who offer you trial purchases or some form of bonus, such as cash, for allowing them to use your house as a model for any purpose. Such offers are well-known gimmicks of swindlers.

- Never sign a completion certificate until all the work called for in the contract has been completed to your satisfaction. Be careful not to sign a completion certificate along with a sales order. Proceed cautiously when the lender or contractor demands a lien on your property. Contact HUD for information about applicable laws.

Home Settlement Costs. Settlement costs, also known as closing costs, are extra fees charged to a home buyer for various services associated with the transfer of home ownership from seller to buyer. Many of these services are required by state or federal law—others are not. The U.S. Department of Housing and Urban Development (HUD) urges consumers to shop for services, negotiate fees, and ask questions before closing on a house. To help homebuyers reduce their settlement costs, HUD offers the following guidelines:

- Before signing a sales contract, negotiate with the seller to share with you the costs of such items as the settlement or escrow fee, points, title insurance, survey, and transfer taxes.

- If a survey is required, ask the seller to give you the old survey plus an affidavit that no changes have been made in the structures on the property which would overlap the boundaries. Many lenders will accept this in lieu of a new survey.

- Insist on the right to choose your own lawyer, title company, surveyor, or other necessary suppliers of settlement services. Avoid delegating this right to a real estate salesperson or to the seller, except in newly constructed housing where the builder has arranged an unusually favorable rate.

- Don't hesitate to shop around and to bargain with suppliers of settlement services. These include the lawyer, title company, escrow or settlement company, lender, and surveyor. Make sure that fees they quote are totals, with no extra or miscellaneous charges to be added.

- If you retain a lawyer, make it clear that you are the exclusive client. Ask whether the attorney is receiving a rebate or commission from the title company or any other party, and, if so, that it be refunded to you.

- Read the Special Information Booklet you receive when you apply for a loan, then carefully study the Good Faith Estimate. Request an explanation of any items you don't understand or think are excessive.

Tenants' Rights: Information for Renters. Although tenants' rights vary according to state law, certain basic precepts are consistent in spirit in all states. First among these is the right to safe living conditions. A tenant has the right to demand that the landlord repair any condition that may substantially affect the tenant's health and safety. Such a request should be made in writing, with reasonable time allowed for repairs to be made. If the landlord consistently fails to properly maintain the dwelling, the tenant can register a complaint with a local tenant organization, housing official, or health inspector. Details about specific landlord-tenant laws can be obtained from state housing authorities or from the state attorney general's office. The following is a list of basic tenants' rights, based on information furnished by offices of the attorney general in the states of New York, Minnesota, and Idaho:

- The tenant may form, join, and participate in tenant associations in order to protect his or her rights. A tenant who exercises the right to complain to a government agency about health or safety law violations, or who joins a tenant organization, is protected by law from harassment, penalty, and retaliation on the part of the landlord.

- The landlord may be held liable for personal injury and property damage to the tenant caused by the landlord's negligence—even if provisions in the lease exempt the landlord from such liability.

- The tenant is protected against lockouts and seizure of personal property by the landlord and may only be evicted by due process of law.

- The tenant has the right to privacy. The landlord may enter the rental unit only at a reasonable hour—given prior consent—for purposes of making repairs in accordance with the lease, showing the apartment to prospective tenants, or during emergencies.

- Upon termination of the rental agreement, the security deposit should be returned to the tenant, usually within 30 days. (In some states, the tenant is also entitled to the interest accrued on the deposit.) It is illegal for the landlord to withhold the deposit or deduct any portion of it for normal wear and tear to the property.

Home Buying Considerations. The first steps in buying a house may be difficult for first-time homebuyers. Here's some advice:

- Call a real estate office, ask for the owner, then ask which salesperson is good with first-time buyers. The highest-volume salesperson may not have the patience to do the extra work.

- Start shopping casually to get a feel for the market.

See what's available in your price range so your expectations will be realistic.

- Work with a bank or other mortgage institution to pre-qualify for your mortgage. Look for programs that have lower payments or small closing costs. This will give you a realistic price range and, with a pre-approved mortgage, any offer you make will become more attractive to the seller.

Chapter 15: Retail and Commercial Concerns

A Consumer's Prerogative. The Federal Trade Commission (FTC) has a three-day cooling-off rule that lets consumers cancel (in person or by mail) many different contracts until midnight of the third business day after the contract was signed. Prior to signing the contract, the seller should have informed you of this right. If the seller failed to do so, you may have longer than three days to cancel the contract. Once the contract is canceled, your money must be refunded within ten days.

These contracts include:

- Home improvement loans
- Second mortgages
- Door-to-door sales (for more than $25)
- Health club memberships
- Discount buying club memberships
- Contracts made at sales presentations, trade shows, private homes, etc.

Canceling the contract:

- Call the seller as soon as possible to give notice that you no longer want the product or service.
- Sign and date a copy of the cancellation form you were given. (If you were not given a cancellation form, either request one immediately or write your own letter or telegram.)
- Return the copy either by certified mail (for proof you mailed it on time) or by fax.

Some states have their own contract cancellation rules that may include cancellation of items like furniture, major appliances, dating services, dance lessons, and weight loss programs.

Tips for Shopping by Mail, Telephone, Television, and the Internet. Many consumers buy items through mail order, the Internet, telephone, or from television shopping programs. Consumers should these tips in mind when shopping by mail, phone, TV, or the Internet:

- Be suspicious of exaggerated product claims or very low prices, and read product descriptions very carefully—sometimes pictures of products are misleading.
- If you have any doubts about the company, check with the U.S. Postal Service, your state or local consumer protection agency, or Better Business Bureau before ordering.
- Ask about the firm's return policy. If it is not stated,

ask before you order. For example, does the company pay charges for shipping and return? Is a warranty or guarantee available? Does the company sometimes substitute comparable goods for the product you want to order?

- Ask for further information in writing or from the customer service representative. If your questions aren't answered, don't order.
- Keep a complete record of your order; include the company's name, address, phone number, web site and e-mail addresses, the price of the items ordered, any handling or other charges, the date you mailed (or telephoned) in the order, and your method of payment. Keep copies of canceled checks and/or statements.
- If you order by mail, phone, computer, or fax, your order should be shipped within 30 days after the company receives your complete order, unless another period is agreed upon when placing the order or is stated in an advertisement. If your order is delayed, a notice of delay should be sent to you within the promised shipping period along with an option to cancel the order.
- If you buy a product through a television shopping program, check the cost of the same item sold by other sources, including local stores, catalogs, etc.
- If you want to buy a product based on a telephone call from the company, ask for the name, address, and phone number where you can reach the caller after considering the offer.
- Never agree to immediate payment to a courier.
- Never give your credit card or social security number over the telephone as proof of your identity.
- Don't be pressured into placing an order until you feel comfortable about the decision.
- If you are buying perishable goods, make sure that the company offers a replacement or full refund if the goods arrive spoiled.
- Postal regulations allow you to write a check payable to the sender, rather than the delivery company, for cash on delivery (C.O.D.) orders. If, after examining the merchandise, you feel there has been misrepresentation or fraud, you can stop payment on the check and file a complaint with the U.S. Postal Inspector's Office.
- You can have a charge removed from your bill if you did not receive the goods or services or if your order was obtained through misrepresentation or fraud. You must notify the credit card company in writing, at the billing inquires/disputes address, within 60 days after the charge first appeared on your bill.

Specific Tips for Shopping Online

- Research the seller. Company websites often provide information in a section called "About Us". Some online sellers participate in programs such as BBOnline that help resolve problems. Look for a logo or endorsement seal on the company website. This is an indication, but not a guarantee, of the seller's reliability

- Check www.bizrate.com to see how other consumers rated online stores. Some auction sites post ratings of sellers based on comments by buyers.
- Comparison shop at a variety of online stores. Shopping "bots" like www.mysimon.com may help. Other feature and price comparisons can be found using the shopping page of www.consumerworld.org.
- Make sure you are clear on the condition of the product.
- Never send your credit card number by e-mail because e-mails are not secure.
- Save all transaction details. Print and save copies of your order confirmation screen and all e-mail communications.
- Look for security prompts when shopping on the Internet. Don't send sensitive information if you are unsure that it is being transmitted securely.
- Pay attention to online shipping and handling charges. Online order forms may default to the more expensive two-day air option. Sometimes the customer has to manually change it to a less expensive delivery option.

For more information about shopping online, visit www.safeshopping.org and "A Consumer's Guide to E-Payments" at www.ftc.gov/bcp/conline/pubs/online/payments.htm.

Mail Fraud. More and more consumers are receiving misleading or downright fraudulent mail promotions. These promotions take several forms. Some examples are:

- Sweepstakes that require you to pay an entry fee or order a product.
- Notices of prizes that require you to call a 900 number or buy a product.
- Mailings that look like they are from government agencies, but they are not.
- Classified "employment" or "business opportunity" advertisements promising easy money for little work.
- Prize awards that ask for your credit card or bank account number.

Contact your state or local consumer office or Better Business Bureau if you have any doubts about promotions you have received through the mail.

For more information about the dangers of these types of mail solicitations, contact the Alliance Against Fraud in Telemarketing and Electronic Commerce, administered by the National Consumers League, 1701 K St. NW, Ste. 1200, Washington, DC 20006; phone (202) 835-3323.

900 Number Rip-offs. The Federal Trade Commission (FTC) offers these tips to protect yourself from 900 number (long distance) or 976 (local) telephone number scams:

- Don't confuse 900 numbers with toll-free 800

numbers. The caller pays for the 900-number call; the company called pays for the 800-number call.

- Find out up front how a 900-number call will be priced and beware of services that aren't forthright about charges, or those that force you to listen to many expensive minutes before delivering the message.
- Make calls only to companies you know.
- Educate your children about 900 numbers; have them get permission for any calls. Some local phone companies offer a service to block these numbers from being dialed from your phone.
- Notify your phone company immediately if you dispute any 900-number charges on your bill. Your local and long distance telephone service cannot be disconnected for disputed pay-per-call charges.
- Write the Federal Trade Commission, 600 Pennsylvania Ave., NW, Washington, DC 20580 for a free single copy of its 900 numbers fact sheet. (Also available on the FTC website, www.ftc.gov.) Complaints about 900-number scams help the FTC in its law enforcement efforts.

Getting Off Promotional Lists and Blocking Telemarketing Calls. Consumers are protected in several ways from direct mail and telephone promotions they aren't interested in receiving. You have the following rights under federal law:

- You may tell a company not to call you by phone or not to contact you in writing. Each company must keep a list of these consumers and not contact them. Keep a record for your files.
- You should not get calls before 8 a.m. or after 9 p.m.
- You should not receive unsolicited ads by fax.
- You should be disconnected from a prerecorded machine-delivered message within five seconds of hanging up.
- Some states do not allow telemarketers to call people who do not want to receive calls. Contact your state or local consumer protection agency to check your state's rights. To report violations of the telephone order rule, contact the Federal Trade Commission.
- To reduce unwanted telemarketing calls, contact the Telephone Preference Service (TPS), sponsored by the Direct Marketing Association (DMA). They will delete an individual's name from the lists of DMA members who participate in the service. Write: DMA Telephone Preference Service, 1120 Ave. of the Americas, New York, NY 10036-6700. DMA offers a companion Mail Preference Service (MPS), which gets you off of mailing lists too. DMS also offers an E-mail Preference Service which allows you to "opt-out" of national email lists. Consumers can register for this service, as well as the mail and telephone services, by visiting the DMA consumer website at dmachoice.org/index.php.
- To stop promotions from firms that are not DMA

members, consumers must write the individual companies to request that their names be dropped.

- Consumers can also reduce unwanted telemarketing calls by registering with the National Do Not Call Registry. To register, visit www.donotcall.gov, or call 1-888-382-1222.

Dealing with Spam. Spam has become one of the most serious inconveniences of e-mail usage. Spam is not only unwanted but oftentimes offensive, as in the pornographic spam that fills many consumers' in-boxes. There are ways to decrease the number of spam emails you receive.

Six ways to block spam:

- Do not buy anything promoted through spam. If you do, you are helping to finance spam.

- If your email has a "preview pane," disable it to prevent the spam from reporting to its sender that you've received it.

- Use one email address for friends and family, and another for everyone else. You can pick up a free email account from services like Hotmail. When one address attracts too much spam, abandon it for a new one.

- Use a provider that filters email, such as AOL, Earthlink, or MSN. If you get lots of spam, your provider may not be filtering effectively.

- Report spam to your ISP. To help the Federal Trade Commission (FTC) control spam, forward it to spam@uce.gov

- If you receive spam that promotes a brand, complain to the company behind the brand by postal mail, which makes more of a statement than email.

Six mistakes to avoid:

- Posting your email address on a public website. If you do post it, you can thwart spammers' harvesting software by using "janedoe at isp.com" and not the "at sign," as in "janedoe@isp.com".

- Using your regular email address in a chat room. Instead, use a different, disposable screen name.

- Using an easy to guess e-mail like "JimSmith@isp.com". Use a harder-to-guess one with embedded digits, such as "Jim8mith2@isp.com".

- Clicking on an e-mail's "unsubscribe" link. That can inform the sender you're there. Don't do it unless you trust the sender.

- Disclosing your address to a site without checking its privacy policy. Also, make sure to uncheck any check boxes that grant the site permission to send you e-mail that you don't want.

- Forwarding chain letters, petitions, or virus warnings. All could be spammers ploy to collect addresses

Business Opportunity Fraud. For people considering paying a substantial sum of money for a business opportunity, the Direct Selling Education Foundation offers this piece of advice: if it's worth your money, it's worth your time to investigate. Although many legitimate companies assist people in starting their own businesses, law enforcement agencies report that many consumers turn over large sums of money to companies which have neither the ability nor the intention of keeping their promises. Before investing in a business opportunity, the Foundation recommends that would-be entrepreneurs take the following precautions:

- Ask about the company, where it is incorporated, and whether it has an in-state office. Ask about its owners and officers, their backgrounds, and prior business experience.

- If the business opportunity is a sales position, ask about the product(s) you will be selling, cost to you, selling price of similar products in your area, your source of supply, any performance claims and guarantees, and the company's replacement and repair policies and procedures for handling complaints from you or your customers.

- Ask about the initial fee that you will have to pay, what it is to be used for, whether it will be held in escrow, and if so, where, by whom, until when, and under what restrictions.

- Ask about other individuals who have already invested (get their addresses and phone numbers).

- Get copies of the company's business and financial statements and other important documents.

- Investigate and verify all information received from the salesperson and check the references and background information of the company and its principals. Do not assume that official-looking documents are either authentic or complete.

- Consult with people who know the particular product and business area which you may be entering. Review with them the selling company's claims concerning marketability of the product, pricing, and projected profits.

- You may want to review the contract and other documents with an attorney.

- If you decide to participate, get all promises in writing in a contract signed by an authorized agent of the company.

In addition, the Direct Selling Education Foundation recommends that people be aware of the warning signs of fraud. They include:

- Pressure to sign a contract quickly and to pay a large sum of money before sales claims can be investigated or legal advice obtained.

- Promises of extraordinarily high or guaranteed profits.

- Claims that profits can be achieved easily.

- A required initial fee which greatly exceeds the fair market value of any products, kits, or training.

- A large fee payable before you receive anything in return.

- Evasive answers by the salesperson or unwillingness to provide disclosure documents required by law.

Packaging and Price Increases. Manufacturers sometimes disguise price increases of their products by making changes in packaging, contents, and servings. Many well-known manufacturers accomplish this by:

- Decreasing the amount of a product while maintaining the original package size and price.
- Downsizing the content of a product and decreasing the price, but doing so disproportionately (i.e. 2.5 oz. of deodorant originally for $1.79 changed to 1.8 oz. and selling for $1.69).
- Increasing the size of the package or container but not the content, to make it appear as if there is more product along with the increased price.
- Enhancing the package or container, not the product itself, and raising the price.
- Diluting product mixtures and maintaining the same price.
- When you buy a product, read the label; mentally note the size, price, net weight, ingredients, and directions. When you need to replace it, check if there are any changes. Compare other brands, and compare unit costs per brand.

Tips for Smart Giving. The decision to contribute to a charitable cause is personal and often based on an emotional reaction. Donors should give with their heads as well as their hearts. Costs associated with fund raising are only one of many factors involved in the decision to give. Donors should also find out what the charity will do with the money it receives. Donors should ask how the charity will actually accomplish its charitable purpose. In the publication, *Professional Fund Raising: Whose Pockets Prosper?*, the Minnesota Office of the Attorney General and the Charities Review Council of Minnesota offer the following suggestions when donating to charities:

- Don't judge a charity solely on its impressive sounding name.
- Ask how the charitable purpose will be accomplished.
- Ask how much of your contribution will pay fund raising and overhead costs.
- Ask whether your contribution is tax deductible; ask for a receipt for your donation.
- Don't be unduly swayed by emotional appeals.
- Don't be pressured. Ask for written information. If convinced, send a check later.
- Contribute by check. Cash donations are impossible to trace and difficult for the charity to protect.
- Check with the Attorney General to determine if the organization is registered. Registration documents reveal facts and information on the organization.

The Pre-Arranged Funeral. Purchasing a pre-need funeral package allows the consumer self-determination in choosing the specific type and cost of his/her own funeral, sparing the family the difficulty of making such decisions at a stressful time. Pre-need can also be more economical in the long run,

since prices will probably be higher in the future—and may allow for less-costly installment payments.

It is generally the role of each state to regulate the transaction of pre-need funeral services and merchandise, including cemetery lots and the subsequent care of burial sites. Accordingly, the consumer should become familiar with state statutes before entering into a pre-need agreement. In most states, funeral directors are required to place 100 percent of pre-need funeral service money into a trust fund account. Many consumer protection agencies urge consumers to ask where the trust fund will be located and to check with the bank to ensure that the deposit was made. This money should remain in the trust fund account and draw interest until the contracted funeral service is provided. Also, in many states, the consumer has the right at any time to request a complete refund of funeral pre-purchase money, plus any interest it has earned. It is largely the responsibility of State Funeral Service Examining Boards to ensure that funeral directors properly hold money deposited for pre-need funeral arrangements. Rules governing cemetery lots may differ. In some states, for example, the cemetery owner is required to deposit a percentage of the purchase money into the trust fund account. And in some states, the consumer who chooses to break a pre-need arrangement bears the burden of reselling the cemetery property. If a time limitation is involved, the consumer may end up selling the gravesite for considerably less than the original purchase price.

Consumers are also protected under the Federal Trade Commission's Funeral Rule, enacted in 1984, which cannot be restricted by state law. It allows consumers to obtain comparative information about prices and services over the phone or in writing before selecting a funeral director. In addition, it gives consumers the right to demand from the funeral director a general price list containing the cost of each item and service offered, plus the legal rights and requirements of funeral arrangements, including pre-need.

Rent-To-Own. Although buying in a rent-to-own transaction sounds like a simple solution when you are short of cash, rent-to-own can be expensive. The rental charge can be three or four times what it would cost if you paid cash or financed the purchase at the highest interest rate typically charged in installment sales. Before signing a rent-to-own contract, ask yourself the following questions:

- Is the item something I absolutely have to have right now?
- Can I delay the purchase until I have saved enough money to pay cash or at least make a down payment on an installment plan?
- Does a retail store offer a layaway plan for the item?
- Have I considered all my credit options, including applying for retail credit from the merchant or borrowing money from a credit union, bank, or small loan company?
- Would a used item purchased from a garage sale, classified ad, or secondhand store serve the purpose?

If you decide that rent-to-own is the best choice for you, here are some questions you should ask before you sign on the dotted line:

- What is the total cost of the item? The total cost can be determined by multiplying the amount of each payment by the number of payments require to purchase the item. Make sure to add in any additional charges, for example, finance, handling, or balloon payments at the end of the contract.

- Am I getting a new or used item?

- Can I purchase the item before then end of the rental term? If so, how is the price calculated?

- Will I get credit for all of my payments if I decide to purchase the item?

- Is there a charge for repairs during the rental period? Will I get a replacement while the rented item is not in my possession?

- What happens if I am late on a payment? Will the item be repossessed? Will I pay a penalty if I return the item before the end of the contract period?

Comparison shop among various rent-to-own merchants. Contact your local or state consumer protection agency to find out if there are any complaints on record against the business. Check for any specific state laws. Read the contract carefully and make sure you understand all the terms, and get all promises in writing.

Remember, know what you are paying. Compare the cash price plus finance charges in an installment plan with the total cost of rent-to-own transaction.

Long-term rent-to-own contracts cost so much more than installment plans that you could rent an item, make a number of payments, return the item, buy it on installment plan, and still come out ahead.

Door-to-Door Sales. Keep the following tips in mind for successfully dealing with door-to-door sales tactics:

- Ask to see the salesperson's personal identification and/or license, registration etc. Make note of his/her name, the name and address of the company, and whether the salesperson carries proper identification.

- Ask for sales literature. Call local stores selling similar merchandise and compare prices. Some door-to-door products might be overpriced.

- Don't be pressured into buying something. Be wary of free gifts, offers that are good only for one day, and stories of neighbors who have just made a purchase.

- If you feel threatened or intimidated, ask the person to leave. Don't leave the person unattended in any room of your home. If you are suspicious, report the incident to the police immediately.

- Many purchases are subject to the "Door-to-Door Sales Rule" (or "Cooling Off Rule") which gives customers the right to cancel orders of $25 or more. Notify the company in writing by midnight of the third business day following the sale. Saturdays are

considered business days; Sundays and holidays are not.

- The seller must give you two dated copies of a cancellation form showing the seller's name and address and explaining your rights to cancel. If you are not given a cancellation form at the time of purchase, your right to cancel continues until three days after the seller finally gives it to you.

- Once you cancel, you have the right to a refund within 10 days.

- Some states may have additional cancellation laws that protect consumers. Contact your state or local consumer protection agency for details.

Chapter 16: TRANSPORTATION and TRAVEL

Travel Scams. Consider the following to avoid being taken in by this type of scam:

- Don't be taken by solicitations by postcard, letter, or phone calls claiming you've won a free trip or can get discounts on hotels and airfares. These offers usually don't disclose the hidden fees involved, for example, deposits, surcharges, excessive handling fees, or taxes.

- Some travel scams require you to purchase a product to get a trip that's "free" or "two-for-one." You'll end up paying more for the "free" trip than the trip is worth, and the two-for-one deal might be more expensive than if you had arranged a trip yourself by watching for airfare deals.

- Be wary of travel offers that ask you to redeem vouchers or certificates from out-of-state companies. Their offers are usually valid only for a limited time and on a space-available basis. The hotels are often budget rooms that are small and uncomfortable. The company charges you in advance, but will the company still be in business when you are ready to take the trip?

- Check the reputation of any travel service you use, especially travel clubs offering discounts on their services in exchange for an annual fee. Contact your state or local consumer protection agency or the Better Business Bureau for information.

- Request copies of a travel club's or agent's brochures and contracts before purchasing your ticket. Don't rely on oral promises. Find out about cancellation policies and never sign contracts that have blank or incomplete spaces.

- Never give out your credit card number to a club or company with which you're unfamiliar or one that requires you to call a 900 number for information.

- Don't feel pressured by requests for an immediate decision or a statement that the offer is good only "if you act now." Don't deal with companies that request payment in advance or that don't have escrow accounts where your deposit is held.

- Research cut-rate offers, especially when dealing with

travel consolidators who might not be able to provide your tickets until close to your departure date.

- You can protect yourself by using a credit card to purchase travel services. If you don't get what you paid for, contact the credit card issuer and you might be able to get the charges reversed. Be aware that you have 60 days to dispute a charge. (See the Consumer Tips for Chapter 3.)

Selecting a Travel Agent. The travel agent can be the consumer's best source for personalized travel services, but the consumer should be cautious in choosing one. Few states require either the licensing or registration of travel agents. As part of the selection process, The Travel Institute recommends that the consumer visit the agency to see how efficiently the office is staffed, stocked, and organized. The potential client should find out if the agent is a Certified Travel Counselor (CTC)—a designation of The Travel Institute that indicates expertise in the field.

Services of a travel agent are usually free to the consumer since the agent typically receives commissions paid by hotels, airlines, cruise lines, and other travel suppliers. Be sure to ask in advance if any service fees will be charged. A good travel agent will answer questions, listen to requests, and try to meet the client's needs—no matter how inexpensive the trip might be. Moreover, the agent should be able to provide the client with breaking industry news, such as new packages, reduced airfares, recent mergers, terrorist activity, and the strength of the U.S. dollar in the foreign market. To ensure that consumers fully understand their travel arrangements, the American Society of Travel Agents (ASTA) suggests that clients get answers to the following questions from their travel agents:

- What hotel accommodations are available? Are meals included? What are the local customs for tipping?
- What do sight-seeing tours include?
- Do I need a passport, visa, inoculations, or special travel documents? What is the rate of foreign currency exchange?
- What weather conditions can I expect? What is the average temperature? What types of clothing are appropriate?
- What are the local customs?
- How convenient is the hotel to restaurants, the beach, the golf course, etc.?
- In case of a group tour, who is the tour operator? What is the size of the group? Is there an itinerary?
- Is travel insurance available? If so, does it cover cancellation, lost luggage, accidents, etc.?
- What are the cancellation provisions of the trip? Are there any cancellation fees?

Airline Travel Tips. Airline travelers should keep the following suggestions in mind:

- When making an airline reservation, always ask about fees or penalties for changing or canceling a reservation or a paid ticket. There may be a variety of

ticket prices with varying penalties and conditions. Choose the one that best fits your needs.

- Read the disclosure statement on the back of your ticket. It explains your rights and responsibilities as a passenger, in addition to the airline's liability for overbooking seats and for losing or damaging luggage.
- When flights are overbooked, airline representatives are required to ask for volunteers to give up their reservations in exchange for a payment of the airline's choosing. If you volunteer, be sure to get any compensation arrangements in writing.
- If you are "bumped" or involuntarily reassigned to a later flight, the airline must provide a written statement of your rights and entitled compensation. The complete rules for compensation are available at all airport ticket counters and boarding locations.

Tickets on Bankrupt Airlines. An airline can declare bankruptcy and go out of business while you're still holding on to an expensive, unused ticket. Before you're left on the ground and in the red, consider these tips on how to insure ticket reimbursement or exchange:

- Purchase your ticket with a major credit card, rather than cash or check. Credit card companies are required by law to remove charges for products and services not rendered; however, the problem must be reported within 60 days of receiving your credit card bill.
- If you must pay cash, purchase trip-cancellation insurance. The cost is about $5.50 per $100 of ticket price.
- A ticket might be accepted by another airline, if your original carrier has made the proper arrangements.
- Persons who have frequent flyer credit with a financially unstable airline should use it as soon as possible, or try to obtain a voucher from another airline in the same frequent flyer program.

Budget Travel Tips. In order to save money while traveling, consider the following:

Flying on the lowest fares:
- Fly during the off-peak season of your destination.
- Look into eligibility for status group discounts such as family, group (two or more), military, senior citizen, or student discounts.
- If your plans are flexible, try waiting for last-minute, unsold seats.
- Look for an intermediate city between your departure and destination points that may offer cheaper fares for each leg of the trip than a single direct flight would.
- Purchase tickets more than two weeks before departure if your plans are fixed.
- Use coupons.
- Join a travel club.
- Accumulate frequent flyer credit.

Cruises for less:

- Travel in the off-peak season of your destination. (Christmas and the winter months are usually the most popular season for traveling to warm climates, so try to avoid these times.)

- Wait as close to departure time as possible to book a cruise, if your plans are flexible. Cruise lines sometimes offer up to 50 percent off to fill unbooked cabins.

- Share a cabin with at least one other person. The more people in a cabin, the cheaper the price.

- Get a cabin in a lower level part of the ship and/or without a window; these cabins are less expensive.

- Planning your honeymoon? Some cruise lines offer discounts to newlyweds.

Timeshares/Campgrounds.

- Prizes and awards might be used in promoting timeshares and campgrounds. They are sometimes overvalued or misrepresented. Free awards might "bait" you into driving a long distance to the property, only to attend a long high-pressure sales pitch to obtain your prize.

- Be realistic. Make your decision based on how much you will use it and if it suits your recreational and vacation purposes. Don't decide to purchase based on an investment possibility. It might be difficult or almost impossible to resell.

- Ask about additional costs such as finance charges, annual fees, and maintenance fees. Maintenance fees can go up yearly.

- Compare your total annual cost with that of hotels or your normal vacation expenses.

- Ask about availability during your vacation periods. Ask what other timeshares or campgrounds you may use with your membership.

- Talk to individuals who already purchased from the company, about the services, availability, upkeep, and reciprocal rights to use other facilities.

- Get everything in writing and make sure verbal promises are in the written contract. Have an attorney review any contracts/documents and make sure there are no blanks on papers you sign.

- Do you have cancellation rights?

- State laws vary. Check with your local or state consumer agency.

- Check for any complaints against the company, seller, developer, and management company with your consumer agency or the Better Business Bureau.

Renting a Car.
Federal law does not cover short-term car and truck rentals. However, there are state laws that do. Contact your state or local consumer protection office for more information on laws in your area. The Consumer Protection Agency offers the following tips for hassle-free car rentals:

- Shop around for the best rates.

- Compare all fees, in addition to the daily/weekly rate, before renting.

- Most car rental contracts make the consumer liable for all damage to the vehicle, regardless of who caused it. Before buying a rental company's collision or loss damage waiver, check with your own car insurance company and credit card company to see if they cover car rentals. Avoid paying additional charges ($3 to $15 per day) to the rental company for coverage you may already have.

- If you pay by credit card, some rental companies will place a hold or freeze on your account during the rental period. Others might start to charge your account before the rental period is over. Ask about the company's policy in advance.

- Carefully inspect the vehicle and its tires before renting. Write down all the dents and scratches you see.

- Check refueling policies. You can refill at the local gas station. This is usually less expensive than letting the car rental company refuel the car at its price. Paying in advance for a refill will cost you needlessly if there is any gas remaining in the tank upon returning the vehicle.

- To order a free publication on car rentals, contact: Consumer Response Center Federal Trade Commission, 600 Pennsylvania Avenue NW, H-130, Washington, DC 20580, (877) 382-4357. The publications can also be viewed on the FTC website at www.ftc.gov.

Chapter 17: UTILITIES

Choosing a Long Distance Telephone Service.
Tips on choosing a long distance telephone service:

- To compare long distance telephone carriers, think about when, how often, and where you use long distance service. Then compare the charges, restrictions, and procedures for making calls.

- Not all carriers provide service to all areas. Make sure the one you choose provides service to the areas you call most often.

- Each long distance carrier may have a different billing system. Some give credit for uncompleted calls, wrong numbers, or calls that are unanswered.

- Ask about one-time only and regular charges. Inquire about subscription fees, monthly service fees, and monthly minimum charges.

- Judge the quality of a carrier's performance (transmission capability, service, billing, and crediting). Allow a trial period to decide whether the quality of phone service is adequate. Before signing up, be sure you understand the terms of the carrier's cancellation policy, and the costs involved in switching to another carrier.

- Many companies now provide operator services, including directory assistance and collect calls for telephones in hotels, airports, and other public places. When you dial the operator, ask which carrier is providing the service and how much you will be billed. If you prefer a different service, you may have to dial a separate access number. Check with your long distance company to see if it provides operator services and how to use them.

900 Numbers and Your Telephone Bill. Consumers can take advantage of a variety of helpful information services by using 900 numbers. Generally, four different types of companies work together to provide 900 number services. They are:

- Information providers: the business or person who created the 900 number program and is responsible for its content.

- Service bureaus: a business providing a message storage system to help the information provider answer the calls to the 900 number (not all information providers hire outside service bureaus; some have their own message storage equipment).

- Long distance carriers: the long distance company hired by the information provider to carry the 900 number programs (this is not necessarily the long distance company that provides your regular long distance service).

- Local phone companies: the business responsible for billing the 900 number services.

The tips listed below will help you use these numbers wisely and cost effectively:

- There is a fee for every 900 number call, and the cost varies from call to call, so be sure you know what the fee is before you dial. Usually, there are two charges: 1) a connection fee to make the call; and 2) an additional fee based on the length of your call.

- If you have a billing problem and cannot resolve it through your local phone company, complain directly to the long distance carrier involved.

- If you have a billing or other problem, you should also complain to the information provider and the service bureau. The long distance carrier can provide you with the name and address of the information provider and service bureau.

- If your problem is not resolved by contacting your local phone company, long distance carrier, service bureau, or information provider, you should contact the Federal Trade Commission, 600 Pennsylvania Ave. NW, Washington, D.C. 20580 (A complaint form is also available on the FTC website, www.ftc.gov). If you received the solicitation for the 900 number in the mail, you can file a mail fraud complaint through the USPS website at www.usps.com/postalinspectors/fraud/MailFraudComplaint.htm. You can also contact the state attorney general's office, local Better Business Bureau, or Consumer Credit Counseling Service.

- Arrangements can be made with the local phone company so that 900 numbers cannot be dialed from your phone. There might be a fee for this service. Call your local phone company for more information.

Geographic Abbreviations

U.S. States and Territories

AK	Alaska
AL	Alabama
AR	Arkansas
AZ	Arizona
CA	California
CO	Colorado
CT	Connecticut
DC	District of Columbia
DE	Delaware
FL	Florida
GA	Georgia
GU	Guam
HI	Hawaii
IA	Iowa
ID	Idaho
IL	Illinois
IN	Indiana
KS	Kansas
KY	Kentucky
LA	Louisiana
MA	Massachusetts
MD	Maryland
ME	Maine
MI	Michigan
MN	Minnesota
MO	Missouri
MS	Mississippi
MT	Montana
NC	North Carolina
ND	North Dakota
NE	Nebraska
NH	New Hampshire
NJ	New Jersey
NM	New Mexico
NV	Nevada
NY	New York
OH	Ohio
OK	Oklahoma
OR	Oregon
PA	Pennsylvania
PR	Puerto Rico
RI	Rhode Island
SC	South Carolina
SD	South Dakota
TN	Tennessee
TX	Texas
UT	Utah
VA	Virginia
VI	Virgin Islands
VT	Vermont
WA	Washington
WI	Wisconsin
WV	West Virginia
WY	Wyoming

Canadian Provinces and Territories

AB	Alberta
BC	British Columbia
MB	Manitoba
NB	New Brunswick
NL	Newfoundland and Labrador
NS	Nova Scotia
NT	Northwest Territories
NU	Nunavut
ON	Ontario
PE	Prince Edward Island
QC	Quebec
SK	Saskatchewan
YT	Yukon Territory

Internet Resources

1 ■ AdoptUSKids
The Adoption Exchange
8015 Corporate Dr., Ste. C
Baltimore, MD 21236
Contact: Kathy Ledesma, Project Dir.
Free: 888-200-4005
E-mail: info@adoptuskids.org
URL: http://www.adoptuskids.org
URL(s): www.adoptuskids.org/ **Descr:** Contains detailed information on children seeking adoption in the United States. Provides information on U.S. families approved to adopt. Includes information on children of varying ages and race groups. Allows users to search for children with or without physical, emotional, learning, and mental disabilities. Includes information on children in all 50 U.S. states. Provides comprehensive general information on adoption, the adoption process, its effects on families and children, and more. **Type:** Directory. **Fees:** Free. **Searching routines or searchable elements:** Provides keyword search functions.

2 ■ American Veterinary Medical Association
1931 N Meacham Rd., Ste. 100
Schaumburg, IL 60173-4360
Contact: James Cook, Pres.
Ph: (847)925-8070
Free: 800-248-2862
Fax: (847)925-1329
E-mail: avmainfo@avma.org
URL(s): www.avma.org/ **Descr:** Provides information about pet food recalls in its "News" section. Shares animal health information as well as selection tips with consumers interested in buying a pet cat, dog, bird, horse, or rodent.

3 ■ Angie's List
1030 E. Washington St.
Indianapolis, IN 46202
Free: 888-944-5478
Fax: (866)249-1336
URL(s): www.angieslist.com/ **Descr:** Provides a forum for users to profile and rate home repair service companies they've had experiences with, following other users to access their feedback. Available to members only.

4 ■ At-Home Dads
At-Home Dad
61 Drightwood Ave.
North Andover, MA 01845-1702
Ph: (978)685-7931
E-mail: athomedad@aol.com
URL(s): www.athomedad.com/ **Descr:** At-Home Dad is devoted to providing connections and resources for the more than two million fathers who stay home with their children. The homepage links you to tips, stories, and sample articles from back issues and to other information, including how to subscribe. **Type:** Full-text; Directory. **Updating freq.:** Quarterly. **Fees:**

Free. **Searching routines or searchable elements:** Searching is not available.

5 ■ Beckett Collectibles Online
Beckett Media LLC
4635 McEwen Rd.
Dallas, TX 75244
Contact: Todd Barker, Dir. Business Development
Ph: (972)991-6657
Fax: (972)991-8930
E-mail: customerservice@beckett.com
URL(s): www.beckett.com/ **Descr:** This is a sports card collecting and sports memorabilia publication-- providing convention information, pricing guides, news, auctions and current events, and much, much, more. The online site is a powerhouse of information which gives much of the printed offerings and provides additions, including sports collecting tips and many interactive resources. Links to other subscriptions available. **Type:** Full-text; Image; Directory; Video; Bulletin board. **Updating freq.:** Monthly. **Fees:** Pricing varies. **Searching routines or searchable elements:** Searching is available

6 ■ Breeder's Directory
American Cat Fanciers Association
PO Box 1949
Nixa, MO 65714-1949
Contact: Connie Vandre, Exec.Dir.
Ph: (417)725-1530
Fax: (417)725-1533
E-mail: acfa@aol.com
URL(s): www.acfacats.com/breeders_directory.htm **Descr:** Whether it's Balinese or Siamese, Turkish Van or Highland Fold, this database is a showcase for breeder's displaying their felines. Categorized by breed, entries contain a brief description of the breed, location of breeder, and when available, email address. Also includes articles on purebred cats, training, finding a reputable breeder, and more. **Type:** Full-text; Directory; Image. **Updating freq.:** As needed. **Fees:** Free. **Searching routines or searchable elements:** Searchable by breed.

7 ■ Bridal Guide
RFP, LLC
330 Seventh Ave., 10th Fl.
New York, NY 10001
Contact: Lisa Dickens, V.P., Dir. of Marketing
Ph: (212)838-7733
Free: 800-472-7744
Fax: (212)308-7165
E-mail: ldickens@bridalguide.com
URL: http://www.bridalguide.com
URL(s): www.bridalguide.com **Descr:** The online website for *Bridal Guide* magazine. Offers information on traditions and etiquette, planning and budgeting, fashion and beauty, home and registry, honeymoons, and featured weddings. **Searching routines**

or searchable elements: Keyword searching is available.

8 ■ BtoBonline.com
BtoB Magazine, Inc.
711 Third Ave.
New York, NY 10017
Contact: Bob Felsenthal, VP
Ph: (212)210-0100
E-mail: bfelsenthal@crain.com
URL(s): www.btobonline.com/ **Descr:** This site offers extensive coverage of various business topics, such as marketing, money matters, environmental issues, the Internet, and technology. Contains links to relevant sites, and articles may be submitted for consideration. **Type:** Full-text; Directory; Numeric. **Updating freq.:** Ten times per year. **Fees:** Free. **Searching routines or searchable elements:** Searching is available.

9 ■ Care for Animals
American Veterinary Medical Association
1931 N. Meacham Rd., Ste. 100
Schaumburg, IL 60173-4360
Contact: James Cook DVM, Pres.
Ph: (847)925-8070
Free: 800-248-2862
Fax: (847)925-1329
E-mail: avmainfo@avma.org
URL(s): www.avma.org/careforanimals/default.asp **Descr:** This page, sponsored by the AVMA, promotes responsible pet ownership and provides details on a variety of topics, ranging from animal health and safety to choosing or losing a pet. Features also include Paws for Pets (tips for selecting a puppy, housebreaking, meals, health, training, and grooming), Kids Corner (a collection of games, puzzles, and playsheets), Animated Journeys, links to other AVMA sites with more information for pet owners and veterinarians, and others. An excellent resource for all pet owners. **Type:** Full-text; Image; Statistical. **Fees:** Free. **Searching routines or searchable elements:** The site is not searchable.

10 ■ Consumer Protection
Federal Trade Commission
600 Pennsylvannia Ave. NW
Washington, DC 20580
Contact: David Vladeck, Dir.
Ph: (202)326-2222
Free: 877-382-4357
URL(s): www.ftc.gov/bcp/index.shtml **Descr:** This database maintained by the Federal Trade Commission covers topics of consumer fraud, misleading advertising, credit card information and scams, other consumer protection matters, and antitrust or competition issues in many different areas. Also covered are proposed rules and regulations and recall notices. An online form is available to log a complaint against a particular company or organization with the FTC. A complete index of the entire website is available, along with indices to specific collections. A spare-looking site, but easy to navigate and a comprehensive site for anyone looking for consumer

protection information. Links go to new sites, text articles, or downloadable PDF files. **Type:** Full-text; Dictionary. **Updating freq.:** Daily. **Fees:** Free. **Searching routines or searchable elements:** Keyword searching is available.

11 ■ ConsumerAffairs.com
11400 W Olympic Blvd., Ste. 200
Los Angeles, CA 90064
Ph: (213)291-8086
Fax: 800-779-0816
URL(s): www.consumeraffairs.com/ **Descr:** Informs users about product recalls, consumer scams, lemon laws, and other information intended to protect consumers. Serves as a forum for consumers to post favorable and unfavorable company reviews.

12 ■ Consumer.gov
URL(s): www.consumer.gov/ **Descr:** Site is a one-stop link to a wide range of federal information resources available online. Designed so that users can locate information by category, including Food, Health, Product Safety, Your Money, and Transportation. *ScamAlert!* link provides the latest information on fraudulent and deceptive practices in the marketplace. *In the Spotlight* highlights new education and consumer awareness campaigns.

13 ■ ConsumerHelpWeb
Consumer Help Web, Inc.
4094 Majestic Lane, PMB 279
Fairfax, VA 22033
URL: http://www.consumerhelpweb.com/
Descr: Online site of the organization that "helps consumers resolve complaints they have about a company or organization and to inform consumers about safety, finance, recall, and similar issues." Also offers a blog touching on consumer issues in the news, such as recalls and product safety.

14 ■ ConsumerSearch.com
ConsumerSearch, Inc.
249 W. 17th St.
New York, NY 10011
Contact: Christine Frietchen, Managing Editor
Ph: (212)204-1701
E-mail: cfrietch@consumersearch.com
URL(s): www.consumersearch.com **Descr:** This website looks for the best reviews of products, both on and off the Internet, and then ranks them according to how well they identify a certain category's best products. Next they develop their Full Story report, analyzing whether experts agree or disagree. Finally, they distill the results about which products are top-rated and best in their class in Fast Answers. Dozens and dozens of products and services are ranked, including mattresses, ISPs, home gyms, MP3 players, laptops, digital cameras, tax preparation software, hiking boots, SUVs, hybrid cars, and baby monitors.

15 ■ DoItYourself.com
909 N. Sepulveda Blvd., 11th Fl.
El Segundo, CA 90245
Contact: Robert N. Brisco, CEO
Free: 800-692-2200
E-mail: webmaster@doityourself.com
URL(s): www.doityourself.com/ **Descr:** If there's something that needs to be done around the house, a leaky faucet or squeaky door or perhaps something even more complex, and you have no idea how to get started on the job, this site will help. Billed as "the original Internet community for do-it-yourselfers," there's a wealth of information and advice here on a huge variety of do-it-yourself project areas, including plumbing, heating, appliance care and repair, electrical and lighting, remodeling of kitchens and baths, and painting and decorating. You can also discuss your do-it-yourself projects or questions in the more than one hundred forums, buy videos and DVDs on do-it-yourself projects, or, when you just don't have the time or patience to do it yourself, you can even find a contractor at this site to do it for you. **Type:** Image; Directory; Full-text. **Updating freq.:**

Regularly. **Fees:** Free. **Searching routines or searchable elements:** A search engine is available.

16 ■ Epinions
800 Marina Blvd., 5th Fl.
Brisbane, CA 94005
Ph: (650)616-6500
URL: http://www.epinions.com/
URL(s): www.epinions.com/ **Descr:** Website that helps consumers make informed buying decisions. Offers valuable insight, unbiased advice, in-depth product evaluations, and personalized recommendations. Just some of the areas covered by ordinary Internet users worldwide include cars, movies, music, computers, electronics, home and garden, office supply, and travel. **Type:** Full-text.

17 ■ Expo TV
Expo Communications Inc.
E. 11th St., 11th Floor
New York, NY 10003
URL: http://www.expotv.com
URL(s): www.expotv.com **Descr:** Expo TV is a new social shopping destination with thousands of consumer-generated reviews and product demonstrations all available in full-motion video. Features thousands of Videopinions reviews--short, unbiased consumer-generated videos reviewing products that members love or hate. Also provides consumers with informative "how-to-buy" videos. **Type:** Video; text.

18 ■ Fight Identity Theft
E-mail: info@fightidentitytheft.com
URL(s): www.fightidentitytheft.com/ **Descr:** According to the U.S. Federal Trade Commission, it takes a year, on average, for a victim of identity theft to notice the crime. This site provides information on how to find out if you're a victim of identity theft, how to stop identity theft and start repairing the damage, how to report a scam, ways to put a fraud alert on your credit, methods to stop junk mail and telemarketers, and how to keep informed about identity theft and fraud legislation. Also features blog posts on identity theft, scams, privacy, and technology.

19 ■ GrocerySavingTips.com
BlueRidgePublishing.com
PO Box 795
Powder Springs, GA 30127
Contact: Michelle Jones, Founder
E-mail: contact@grocerysavingtips.com
URL(s): www.grocerysavingtips.com/ **Descr:** Offers users help with saving money on groceries, with links including Free Grocery Tips By-The-Aisle; What's On Sale This Week; How to Save More With Coupons; Print Grocery Coupons; Expired Coupons; Print Free Price Log; Frugal Cookbooks; Frugal Recipes; Grocery Saving Books; and Discount Shopping Links. **Type:** Full-text.

20 ■ How to Avoid Phishing Scams
Anti-Phishing Working Group
E-mail: info@antiphishing.org
URL(s): www.antiphishing.org/consumer_recs.html **Descr:** The number and sophistication of phishing scams sent out to consumers continues to increase dramatically. While online banking and e-commerce are very safe, as a general rule you should be careful about giving out your personal financial information over the Internet. This website offers a list of recommendations that you can use to avoid becoming a victim of these scams.

21 ■ Identity Theft
California Office of Privacy Protection
1325 J St., Ste. 1650
Sacramento, CA 95814
Contact: Teri Takai, State Chief Info.Officer
Ph: (916)323-7300
Free: 866-785-9663
Fax: (916)323-7299
E-mail: privacy@oispp.ca.gov
URL: http://www.privacyprotection.ca.gov/
URL(s): www.privacyprotection.ca.gov/ **Descr:** Offers information on preventing identity theft. Includes online documents such as Top 10 Tips for Identity

Theft Protection, Identity Theft Victim Check List, and Your Social Security Number: Controlling the Key to Identity Theft.

22 ■ Identity Theft Prevention and Survival
Porpoise Press
28202 Cabot Rd., Ste. 300
Laguna Niguel, CA 92677
Free: 800-725-0807
Fax: (949)363-7561
URL(s): www.identitytheft.org/ **Descr:** Offers tips on how to prevent identity theft, as well as resources you can use if you have become a victim. **Type:** Full-text.

23 ■ Identity Theft and Your Social Security Number
Social Security Administration
Office of Public Inquiries
Windsor Park Bldg.
6401 Security Blvd.
Baltimore, MD 21235
Free: 800-772-1213
URL: http://www.socialsecurity.gov
URL(s): www.ssa.gov/pubs/10064.html **Descr:** Small but helpful government page that offers information on identity theft and your social security number, including how someone might steal your number and what to do if you think your number has been stolen. **Type:** Full-text.

24 ■ The Psychology of Consumers: Consumer Behavior and Marketing
Marshall School of Business
University of Southern California
Los Angeles, CA 90089-0443
Contact: Lars Perner PhD, Asst.Prof.
Ph: (213)740-7127
URL(s): www.consumerpsychologist.com/ **Descr:** Provides extensive information on consumer psychology and marketing strategy, including the areas of research methods, demographics, social influences, motivation, pricing, learning and memory, and consumer decision-making. **Type:** Full-text.

25 ■ The Resource Directory for Older People
National Institute on Aging
Bldg. 31, Rm. 5C27
31 Center Dr., MSC 2292
Bethesda, MD 20892
Contact: Richard J. Hodes MD, Dir.
Ph: (301)496-1752
Fax: (301)496-1072
E-mail: bapquery@nia.nih.gov
URL: http://www.nia.nih.gov
URL(s): www.nia.nih.gov/HealthInformation/ResourceDirectory.htm **Descr:** Contains data about organizations which provide information and services to older persons. Includes names, addresses, phone and fax numbers, email and website addresses. Covers Administration on Aging supported resource centers, federal agencies, private groups, professional societies, and volunteer programs. **Type:** Directory. **Fees:** Free. **Telecom. Svcs:** TTY toll free number is (800)222-4225.

26 ■ Scripps News Consumer Issues
Contact: Peter Copeland, Editor/General Mgr.
Ph: (202)408-2756
URL(s): www.scrippsnews.com/taxonomy/term/182 **Descr:** Scripps Newspaper Group online site that offers the latest news and advice on consumer issues. Recent topics include resume tips, monthly best buys, new car reviews, options to consider when foreclosure looms, and the jumbo-mortgage market. **Type:** Full-text. **Searching routines or searchable elements:** Searching options available.

27 ■ superpages.com
Idearc
2200 W. Airfield Dr.
PO Box 619810
DFW Airport, TX 75261-9810
Free: 800-555-4833
URL: http://www.idearc.com/contact.jsp
URL(s): www.bigyellow.com **Descr:** Provides all

Business listings for the U.S., including current advertising information. Ability to search by Business name, location, heading, zip code, person, email and more. Also provides categories and hierarchies of listings for browsing. Allows creation of customized directory for personal usage. **Type:** Directory. **Updating freq.:** Continuous. **Fees:** Free.

Federal Government Agencies

28 ■ Consumer Advisory Committee (CAC)
Consumer and Governmental Affairs Bureau
Federal Communications Commission
445 12th St. SW
Washington, DC 20554
Contact: Scott Marshall, Designated Fed.Off.
Ph: (202)418-2809
Fax: (202)418-1797
URL: http://www.fcc.gov/cgb/cac/
Descr: Committee provides general guidance to the Federal Communications Commission and makes specific recommendations on issues (within the jurisdiction of the Commission.) Its recommendations are on issues including telecommunications relay services, video description, captioning, access billing, lifeline/linkup programs, outreach to underserved populations, and the impact of new and emerging technologies on consumers and persons with disabilities. **Mem:** Committee comprises 29 members who are recognized experts in their fields, including consumer advocacy organizations, organizations representing persons with disabilities, representatives of underserved populations, equipment manufacturers, telecommunications providers, and state/local regulators.

29 ■ Consumer Advisory Council (1976)
Consumer and Community Affairs Div.
Federal Reserve System
20th & C Streets, NW, Rm. 8042
Washington, DC 20551-0001
Contact: Jennifer Kerslake, Secretary
Ph: (202)452-6470
Fax: (202)872-4995
URL: http://www.federalreserve.gov/aboutthefed/cac.htm
Staff: Jennifer Kerslake, Consumer Advisory Council Section, Consumer and Community Affairs Division, serves as staff contact. **Descr:** Council advises the Board of Governors of the Federal Reserve System on its duties under the Consumer Credit Protection Act and on other consumer-related matters. Council represents the interests of the consumer and the financial community. **Mem:** Council consists of 30 members representing interests of consumers, communities, and the finance services industry. Members serve three-year terms. Edna R. Sawady, New York, NY, chairs the Council.

30 ■ President's Council on Physical Fitness and Sports (PCPFS)
200 Independence Ave. SW, Rm. 738-H
Washington, DC 20201-0004
Contact: Melissa A. Johnson, Exec.Dir.
Ph: (202)690-9000
Fax: (202)690-5211
URL: http://www.fitness.gov/
Descr: Council advises the President through the Secretary of Health and Human Services on the enlisting of support of individual citizens and private enterprise to promote physical fitness; the initiation of programs to inform the general public of the importance of physical activity; the strengthening of federal services and programs relating to fitness and sports; encouraging state and local governments to emphasize the importance of physical activity and fitness for overall good health; the development of cooperative programs between medical and other professional societies to encourage sound physical fitness practices encouraging research in sports medicine; and assisting educational agencies, national sports bodies and recreation agencies, and business and industry in developing physical fitness programs. The Council advises the President through the Secretary of Health and Human Services about

the progress made in carrying out recommended programs and about ways and means of enhancing opportunities for participation in physical fitness and sports activities through state, local, and private actions in order to extend and improve physical activity programs and services for Americans of all ages, backgrounds and abilities. **Mem:** Council consists of 20 members appointed by the President. Council membership is active in the following fields: medicine and health, professional and amateur sports, physical education, business, non-profit organizations, and advocacy for the physically disabled. Members serve two-year terms.

Associations and Other Organizations

31 ■ 100 Women in Hedge Funds Association
331 W 57th St., No. 239
New York, NY 10019
Contact: Amanda Pullinger, Exec. Dir.
E-mail: webmaster@100womenhedgefunds.org
URL: http://www.100womeninhedgefunds.org
Descr: Represents individuals who are professional women. Conducts educational programming, professional leverage initiatives and philanthropy. Provides fundraising and volunteer oppotunities for members. **Fnd:** 2001.

32 ■ Access Point
2015 9th St.
Los Osos, CA 93402
Contact: Jill Denton LMFT
Ph: (805)534-1101
Fax: (805)534-1718
E-mail: info@accesspt.com
URL: http://www.accesspt.com
Descr: Provides supportive coaching and counseling to individuals, couples, groups, and businesses both locally and throughout North America. **Fnd:** 1981. **Pub:** Newsletter.

33 ■ AccountAbility
1250 24th St. NW, Ste. 300
Washington, DC 20037
Contact: Nina Inamahoro
Ph: (202)835-1692
Fax: (202)835-1693
E-mail: secretariat@accountability21.net
URL: http://www.accountability21.net
Descr: Brings together businesses, academics, and practitioners to measure and report on the social and ethical performance of organizations. Advises and mentors businesses, nonprofits, and governments in the development of their approach to accountability, learning, and performance. Promotes tools and systems that enable individuals, institutions, and alliances to respond to global challenges. **Fnd:** 1996. **Pub:** Newsletter (monthly).

34 ■ Adventure Cycling Association
PO Box 8308
Missoula, MT 59802
Contact: Mr. Jim Sayer, Exec. Dir.
Ph: (406)721-1776
Free: 800-755-2453
Fax: (406)721-8754
E-mail: info@adventurecycling.org
URL: http://www.adventurecycling.org
Staff: 24. **Descr:** Originally founded to develop the TransAmerica Coast-to-Coast Bicycle Trail (4450 miles) that was inaugurated in 1976 during the 200th birthday celebration of the U.S. Focuses on the research, maintenance, and mapping of over 20,000 miles of bicycle touring and mountain biking routes. Efforts are aimed at promoting bicycle adventure travel and educating the public in bicycle usage and safety. **Fnd:** 1973. **Mem:** 40000. **Pub:** Adventure Cyclist: The Periodical of Bicycle Adventure (9/year); Cyclists' Yellow Pages (annual).

35 ■ Advertising Standards Canada (ASC)
S Tower
175 Bloor St. E, Ste. 1801

Toronto, ON, Canada M4W 3R8
Contact: Linda J. Nagel, Pres./CEO
Ph: (416)961-6311
Fax: (416)961-7904
E-mail: info@adstandards.com
URL: http://www.adstandards.com/en
Staff: 15. **Descr:** Committed to ensuring the integrity and viability of advertising through industry self-regulation. Administers the Canada Code of Advertising Standards, accepts and reviews complaints about advertising, and provides advertising pre-clearance services. **Fnd:** 1957. **Mem:** 200. **Pub:** Ad Complaints Report (annual).

36 ■ Alliance of Faith and Feminism
PO Box 7246
York, PA 17404
Contact:Rev.Dr. Della Fahnestock, Pres.
E-mail: alliance@faithfeminism.org
URL: http://www.faithfeminism.org
Descr: Promotes the feminist ideals of mutuality and equality among all people. Advances the religious and spiritual practice conducted within and protected by secular government. Supports the prudent use of and conscientious protection of nature and natural resources.

37 ■ Alliance for Smiles (AFS)
2565 3rd St., Ste. 237
San Francisco, CA 94107
Contact: Anita Stangl, Pres./CEO
Ph: (415)647-4481
Fax: (415)647-7041
E-mail: info@allianceforsmiles.org
URL: http://allianceforsmiles.org
Descr: Provides support for underserved children who are born with a cleft lip or palate. Contributes to the economic well being of underserved communities by enabling children to receive treatment. Empowers medical professionals through education and exchange of ideas concerning procedures and treatment protocol. **Fnd:** 2004.

38 ■ Alliance of Supplier Diversity Professionals (ASDP)
PO Box 782049
Orlando, FL 32878-2049
Contact: Debbie Melvin, Pres.
Ph: (407)306-6904
Fax: (407)306-2839
E-mail: president@asdp.us
URL: http://www.asdp.us
Descr: Represents supplier diversity professionals throughout the United States. Offers education and professional development opportunities, certification for professionals within management, supplier diversity, procurement and similar career paths. Provides a forum for members to exchange information on all aspects of the supplier diversity profession.

39 ■ American Association of Family and Consumer Sciences (AAFCS)
400 N Columbus St., Ste. 202
Alexandria, VA 22314
Contact: Marilyn Swierk CFCS, Pres.
Ph: (703)706-4600
Free: 800-424-8080
Fax: (703)706-4663
E-mail: staff@aafcs.org
URL: http://www.aafcs.org
Descr: Elementary, secondary, post-secondary and extension educators and administrators; other professionals in government, business and nonprofit sectors; and students preparing for the field. Works to improve the quality of individual and family life through programs that "educate, influence public policy, disseminate information and publish research findings". **Fnd:** 1909. **Mem:** 7000. **Reg. Groups:** 4. **State Groups:** 54. **Pub:** Family and Consumer Sciences Research Journal (5/year); Journal of Family

and Consumer Sciences (quarterly); *Products and Publications Catalog* (annual).

40 ■ American Association of Professional Technical Analysts (AAPTA)

209 W Jackson Blvd., 6th Fl.
Chicago, IL 60606
Contact: Peter Mauthe, Pres.
Ph: (972)213-8516
E-mail: membership@aapta.com
URL: http://www.aapta.com
Descr: Aims to promote the use of technical analysis. Provides a forum for members to share ideas, information, research and analytical techniques. Encourages the highest professional ethics and competence among technical analysts.

41 ■ American Camp Association (ACA)

5000 State Rd., 67 N
Martinsville, IN 46151-7902
Contact: Peg Smith, CEO
Ph: (765)342-8456
Free: 800-428-CAMP
Fax: (765)342-2065
E-mail: psmith@acacamps.org
URL: http://www.acacamps.org
Staff: 30. **Descr:** Camp owners, directors, program directors, businesses, and students interested in resident and day camp programming for youth and adults. Conducts camp standards. Offers educational programs in areas of administration, staffing, child development, promotion, and programming. **Fnd:** 1910. **Mem:** 7000. **Local Groups:** 24. **Pub:** *Camping Magazine* (bimonthly); *Guide to Accredited Camps* (annual); Books.

42 ■ American Canoe Association (ACA)

1340 Central Park Blvd., Ste. 210
Fredericksburg, VA 22401
Contact: Mr. Marty Bartels, Exec. Dir.
Ph: (540)907-4460
Fax: (703)636-0296
E-mail: aca@americancanoe.org
URL: http://www.acanet.org
Staff: 20. **Descr:** Promotes the sport of canoeing and kayaking and to the preservation of streams and rivers. Sponsors races, cruises, encampments, and training classes. Provides publications information and offers computerized services on canoe clubs, manufacturers, liveries, and outfitters; promotes safety and skill on the water. Conducts instructor certification and methods workshops. **Fnd:** 1880. **Mem:** 45000. **Reg. Groups:** 13. **Local Groups:** 250. **Pub:** *American Canoeist* (quarterly); *Canoeing and Kayaking*; *Canoeing and Kayaking for Persons with Physical Disabilities*; *Paddler Magazine* (bimonthly).

43 ■ American Council on Consumer Interests (ACCI)

555 E Wells St., Ste. 1100
Milwaukee, WI 53202
Contact: Terri Haffner, Exec. Dir.
Ph: (414)918-3189
Fax: (414)276-3349
E-mail: info@consumerinterests.org
URL: http://www.consumerinterests.org
Staff: 3. **Descr:** Teachers, researchers, counselors, and others working in information media and for the government who are concerned with problems of the economy from the point of view of the consumer. Works to: stimulate an exchange of ideas among consumer groups and between them and other groups in the economy; contribute to a better understanding of the role of the consumer in the economy as well as of the producer and distributor; contribute to more effective research and fact finding; disseminate information on consumer problems; promote better consumer education. **Fnd:** 1953. **Mem:** 750. **Pub:** *Consumer Interests Annual* (annual); *Journal of Consumer Affairs* (semiannual).

44 ■ American Family Association (AFA)

PO Drawer 2440
Tupelo, MS 38803
Contact: Donald E. Wildmon, Founder/Chm.
Ph: (662)844-5036
Fax: (662)842-7798
E-mail: afa@afa.net
URL: http://www.afa.net
Staff: 25. **Descr:** Fosters "the biblical ethic of decency in American society with a primary emphasis on television and other media". Urges viewers to write letters to networks and sponsors, protesting shows that promote "violence, immorality, profanity and vulgarity" and encouraging the airing of programs that are "clean, constructive, wholesome and family oriented". Compiles statistics on television broadcasts of scenes involving sex, profanity, and violence. Maintains speakers' bureau. **Fnd:** 1977. **Local Groups:** 560. **Pub:** *AFA Journal* (monthly).

45 ■ American National CattleWomen (ANCW)

PO Box 3881
Englewood, CO 80155
Contact: Jackie Buehner
Ph: (303)694-0313
Fax: (303)694-2390
E-mail: ancw@beef.org
URL: http://www.ancw.org
Staff: 1. **Descr:** Individuals who are employed or interested in the cattle industry. Promotes versatility and healthfulness of beef. Conducts promotional and educational programs including National Beef Cook-Off and Beef Ambassador Competition. **Fnd:** 1952. **Mem:** 2300. **Reg. Groups:** 7. **State Groups:** 31. **Pub:** *American CattleWoman* (quarterly).

46 ■ American Recreation Coalition (ARC)

1225 New York Ave. NW, Ste. 450
Washington, DC 20005-6405
Contact: Derrick A. Crandall, Pres.
Ph: (202)682-9530
Fax: (202)682-9529
E-mail: arc@funoutdoors.com
URL: http://www.funoutdoors.com
Descr: Businesses, recreation associations, and corporations interested in promoting a wide variety of recreational activities and providing information to government and the public about the value of recreation to American society and the economy. Objectives are to serve as an authoritative source of information about recreation and to act as the advocate for all types of recreation. Sponsors research studies on the effects of federal policy on recreation and public and private planning for resources designed to meet future recreational needs. Compiles statistics. Conducts recreation exchanges featuring key federal officials. **Fnd:** 1979. **Pub:** *Outdoor Recreation in America* (annual).

47 ■ American Running Association (ARA)

4405 East-West Hwy., Ste. 405
Bethesda, MD 20814
Contact: David Watt, Exec. Dir.
Ph: (301)913-9517
Free: 800-776-2732
E-mail: run@americanrunning.org
URL: http://www.americanrunning.org
Staff: 2. **Descr:** Represents individual runners, exercise enthusiasts, and sports medicine professionals. Promotes running and other aerobic activities; fosters the preventive maintenance concept in health preservation. Serves as a repository for data on running and fitness. Reports on research in exercise physiology and in techniques of increasing total human performance and maintaining physical fitness. Maintains speakers' bureau. Conducts educational programs and charitable activities. **Fnd:** 1968. **Mem:** 15000. **Pub:** *Running and FitNews* (bimonthly); Brochures.

48 ■ American Sports Institute (ASI)

PO Box 1837
Mill Valley, CA 94942
Contact: Joel Kirsch, Pres.
Ph: (415)383-5750
Fax: (415)383-5785
E-mail: info@amersports.org
URL: http://www.amersports.org
Staff: 4. **Descr:** Represents educators, administrators, coaches, and other individuals with an interest in education. Promotes improved educational performance through the study and practice of sports; seeks to transfer sports coaching techniques to the classroom. Conducts training programs for teachers. Operates Promoting Achievement in School Through Sports program, through which middle and high school students study fundamentals of athletic excellence and apply these to academics. **Fnd:** 1985. **Pub:** *Athlete's View* (quarterly); *PASS*.

49 ■ Antiquarian Booksellers Association of America (ABAA)

20 W 44th St.
New York, NY 10036-6604
Contact: Susan Benne, Exec. Dir.
Ph: (212)944-8291
Fax: (212)944-8293
E-mail: sbenne@abaa.org
URL: http://www.abaa.org
Staff: 2. **Descr:** Dealers and appraisers of fine, rare and out-of-print books, manuscripts, and related materials. Sponsors two annual regional international book fairs and four biennial regional international book fairs. Promotes ethical standards in the industry. Sponsors educational programs for members, librarians, archivists, and the public. Administers the Antiquarian Booksellers' Benevolent Fund. **Fnd:** 1949. **Mem:** 475. **Reg. Groups:** 8. **Pub:** Membership Directory (annual); Directories; Newsletter (quarterly).

50 ■ Armenian International Women's Association (AIWA)

65 Main St., No. 3A
Watertown, MA 02472
Contact: Suzanne Moranian, Pres.
Ph: (617)926-0171
Fax: (617)926-0171
E-mail: aiwainc@aol.com
URL: http://www.aiwa-net.org
Descr: Aims to establish contacts with women's organizations, both Armenian and non-Armenian, in the United States, in Armenia and around the world. Works to provide a forum for dialogue and discussion on issues of interest to Armenian women in the fields of education, social welfare, culture and business. Seeks to gather information on the changing role of women in the world. **Fnd:** 1990. **Mem:** 350. **Pub:** Newsletter (quarterly).

51 ■ Artfully AWARE (AfA)

PO Box 281
Buffalo, NY 14201
Contact: Hilary Wallis, Exec. Dir.
E-mail: create@artfullyaware.org
URL: http://www.artfullyaware.org
Descr: Promotes international arts education and community development. Encourages the use of arts to enrich, educate and empower individuals and communities. Supports the development of psychological well-being and increases the self-esteem of individuals in depressed communities. **Pub:** Newsletter.

52 ■ Association of Brethren Caregivers (ABC)

1451 Dundee Ave.
Elgin, IL 60120-1949
Contact: Kathryn G. Reid, Exec. Dir.
Ph: (847)742-5100
Free: 800-323-8039
Fax: (847)742-6103
E-mail: abc@brethren.org
URL: http://www.brethren.org/abc
Descr: Develops resources, leadership, and programs within the caring ministries of the Church of the Brethren and the wider community. **Fnd:** 1968. **Reg. Groups:** 15. **Pub:** *Caregiving* (quarterly).

53 ■ Association for Consumer Research (ACR)

University of Minnesota Duluth
Labovitz School of Business and Economics
11 E Superior St., Ste. 210
Duluth, MN 55802
Contact: Rajiv Vaidyanathan, Exec. Dir.
Ph: (218)726-7853

Fax: (218)726-6338
E-mail: acr@acrwebsite.org
URL: http://www.acrwebsite.org

Descr: Individuals in academia, government, and business interested in consumer research. Facilitates the exchange of scholarly information among members of academia, industry, and government worldwide. **Fnd:** 1969. **Mem:** 1800. **Pub:** *Advances in Consumer Research* (annual).

54 ■ Association for Research on Nonprofit Organizations and Voluntary Action (AR-NOVA)
340 W Michigan St., Canal Level Ste. A
Indianapolis, IN 46202
Contact: Thomas Jeavons, Exec. Dir.
Ph: (317)684-2120
Fax: (317)684-2128
E-mail: tjeavons@arnova.org
URL: http://www.arnova.org

Staff: 4. **Descr:** Scholars and professionals interested and/or engaged in research, scholarship, or programs related to non-profit organizations, voluntary action, philanthropy, or citizen participation. This includes social movements, interest groups, consumer groups, political participation, community development, and religious organizations. Stimulates, coordinates, and aids the efforts of those engaged in voluntary action research, scholarship, and professional activity; makes the results of that research, scholarship, and action more readily available both to fellow professionals and scholars and to leaders of participants in voluntary associations and voluntary action agencies; fosters the dissemination and application of knowledge about voluntary action in order to enhance the quality of life and the general welfare of citizens and communities. **Fnd:** 1971. **Mem:** 1341. **Pub:** *ARNOVA Abstracts* (quarterly); *ARNOVA News* (quarterly); *Nonprofit and Voluntary Sector Quarterly* (quarterly); *Occasional Paper Series* (periodic).

55 ■ Association of Social Work Boards (ASWB)
400 S Ridge Pkwy., Ste. B
Culpeper, VA 22701
Contact: Donna DeAngelis ACSW, Exec. Dir.
Ph: (540)829-6880
Free: 800-225-6880
Fax: (540)829-0142
E-mail: info@aswb.org
URL: http://www.aswb.org

Staff: 20. **Descr:** State boards and authorities empowered to regulate the practice of social work within their own jurisdictions. Seeks to protect the recipient of social work service and promote confidence in and accountability of the social work profession by establishing national regulatory standards for the practice of professional social work. Works to facilitate communication and the exchange of information concerning the regulation of social workers; promote the standardization of credential assessment by encouraging collaborative efforts by states to develop compatible standards and procedures for regulation; provide guidance and education on regulation of the practice of social work to legal bodies, regulatory agencies, and other groups concerned with the protection of the public; offer assistance in fulfilling statutory, public, and ethical obligations in legal regulation and enforcement. Provides uniform examinations to state boards and agencies to enable them to evaluate qualifications for social work credentials. Promotes research on matters regarding legal regulations; has established the American Foundation for Research and Consumer Education in Social Work Regulation to research the ramifications of licensing, explore ethical issues raised by professional regulation, and educate the public in what constitutes good social work practice. **Fnd:** 1979. **Mem:** 52. **Pub:** *Association News* (bimonthly);

Reciprocity and Endorsement in Social Work Licensure.

56 ■ Association for Wedding Professionals International (AFWPI)
6700 Freeport Blvd., Ste. 202
Sacramento, CA 95822
Contact: Richard Markel, Dir.
Ph: (916)392-5000
Free: 800-242-4461
Fax: (916)392-5222
E-mail: richard@afwpi.com
URL: http://www.afwpi.com

Staff: 5. **Descr:** Professionals working in the wedding industry. Promotes adherence to high standards of ethics and practice by members; seeks to advance members' professional standing. Serves as a network linking members; offers member discounts on business services, insurance, and advertising; sponsors educational programs. **Fnd:** 1995. **Mem:** 826. **Reg. Groups:** 7. **State Groups:** 4. **Local Groups:** 8. **Pub:** *Professional Connection* (quarterly); Membership Directory.

57 ■ Beauty 4 Ashes International
PO Box 1904
Greensboro, NC 27402
Contact: Jacquelyn Clark Johnson, Exec. Dir.
Ph: (336)544-0699
Fax: (336)869-0760
E-mail: info@beauty4ashesintl.org
URL: http://www.beauty4ashesintl.org

Descr: Represents and promotes the role of women at home, in the workplace and in the community. Creates opportunities for women to develop self-sufficiency, financial independence and community empowerment. Provides grooming services, education and career training programs for women.

58 ■ Bicycle Network (BN)
PO Box 8194
Philadelphia, PA 19101
Contact: John Dowlin, Ed.
Ph: (215)222-1253
Fax: (215)222-1253
E-mail: cyclerecycle@hotmail.com

Descr: Advocates the bicycle as a healthful, low-cost, and energy efficient means of transportation. Seeks to demonstrate the practical importance of bicycle transit and pedal technology worldwide. Works for the "veloration" on a global basis. (According to the network, "veloration" is the French-Canadian word for "bicycle revolution.") Disseminates information. Addresses issues such as: safe and practical cycling facilities (parking, commuting, and transport); cyclist education; bicycle integration with public transportation; the role of the bicycle in developing countries. **Fnd:** 1976. **Mem:** 500. **Pub:** *Cycle and Recycle* (annual); *Network News: The Bicycle Network's Clipping Service* (quarterly).

59 ■ Birambye International
6948 Howell St.
Arvada, CO 80004
Contact: Mark Reiner, Pres.
Ph: (303)596-1401
Fax: (303)417-6385
E-mail: reiner@birambye.org
URL: http://www.birambye.org

Descr: Works with business agencies, business people and local economic developers and educators in pursuing economic growth and expansion. Aims to develop integrated sustainable business projects. Seeks to provide sustainable development/architecture workshops at any location that serves a community in need.

60 ■ Black Women of Essence (BWOE)
PO Box 471001
Lake Monroe, FL 32747-1001
Contact: Renee G. Ellis, Pres.
Ph: (321)279-8784
E-mail: info@bwoe.org
URL: http://www.bwoe.org

Descr: Aims to enhance the quality of life by providing resources, services, education, and networking

opportunities along with advocacy and promoting self-awareness within communities. Helps in improving the quality of life related to children's advocacy, HIV/AIDS awareness, domestic violence prevention/awareness and breast cancer awareness. **Fnd:** 2003.

61 ■ Blessings International (BI)
5881 S Garnett
Tulsa, OK 74146
Contact: Harold C. Harder PhD, Pres.
Ph: (918)250-8101
Fax: (918)250-1281
E-mail: info@blessing.org
URL: http://www.blessing.org

Staff: 4. **Descr:** Serves as a source of pharmaceuticals, vitamins, and medical supplies for churches and non-profit groups planning medical mission outreaches to developing nations; have helped in situations such as Hurricane Mitch in Central America, cyclone in Orissa, India, and flooding in Mozambique. Ongoing projects include partnering with clinics and hospitals in Liberia, Sierra Leone, Nigeria, Ghana, and Myanmar. **Fnd:** 1981. **Pub:** *Blessings Report*; *Pharmaceutical Bulletin for Medical Personnel Planning Medical Mission Trip*; *Prayer Letter* (monthly).

62 ■ Bonus Families
PO Box 1926
Discovery Bay, CA 94514
Contact: Jann Blackstone-Ford MA, Dir./Co-Founder
Ph: (925)516-2681
Fax: (925)634-3300
E-mail: jann@bonusfamilies.com
URL: http://www.bonusfamilies.com

Descr: Works to improve the quality of life for stepfamilies. Promotes peaceful coexistence between divorced or separated parents and their new families. Provides information, advice and support services to parents. Offers mediation, conflict management, and education to people attempting to combine families after a divorce or separation. Acts as a support network for stepparents, remarried parents, and their children. **Fnd:** 1999. **Pub:** *Bonus Families Support* (monthly).

63 ■ BPA Worldwide (BPA)
Two Corporate Dr., 9th Fl.
Shelton, CT 06484
Contact: Glenn J. Hansen, Pres./CEO
Ph: (203)447-2800
Fax: (203)447-2900
E-mail: info@bpaww.com
URL: http://www.bpaww.com

Staff: 37. **Descr:** Provides global audited data to the marketing, media, and information industries. **Fnd:** 1931. **Mem:** 4300. **Pub:** *Comparability Update* (bimonthly); *Directory to BPA Membership and Marketing Compatibility Programs* (annual); *Forum* (quarterly); Annual Report (annual).

64 ■ British Canadian Chamber of Trade and Commerce (BCCTC)
PO Box 26732
Beaconsfield, QC, Canada H9W 6G7
Contact: Philip Gorick, Exec. Dir.
Ph: (514)841-6664
Fax: (514)630-0280
E-mail: east@bcctc.ca
URL: http://www.bcctc.ca

Descr: Canadian corporations doing business in the United Kingdom. Promotes increased trade between Britain and Canada. Represents members' interests; lobbies for removal of statutory impediments to trade. **Pub:** *Connections* (quarterly).

65 ■ Canadian Amputee Sports Association
304-85 Skymark Dr.
Toronto, ON, Canada M2H 3P2
Contact: Archie M. Watts, Treas.
Ph: (416)494-5000
Fax: (416)490-6333
E-mail: ampsport@interlog.com
URL: http://www.canadianamputeesports.ca

Descr: Amputees and other individuals with an interest in sports for people with disabilities. Seeks to increase the availability of sports programs for amputees. Conducts athletic and other recreational programs. **Fnd:** 1977. **Mem:** 160. **State Groups:** 5.

66 ■ Canadian Association for Community Living (CACL)
York University
Kinsmen Bldg.
4700 Keele St.
Toronto, ON, Canada M3J 1P3
Contact: Bendina Miller, Pres.
Ph: (416)661-9611
Fax: (416)661-5701
E-mail: inform@cacl.ca
URL: http://www.cacl.ca

Staff: 34. **Descr:** People with disabilities and their families; professionals; volunteers. Works to ensure people with an intellectual disability are integrated into their communities as participating members. Provides support and encouragement for parents and family members. Works with provincial governments and service providers to establish legislation and policies. Offers public awareness and education campaigns on issues affecting the mentally handicapped. Operates the Roeher Institute, which conducts and sponsors research, initiates policy development, and provides training and information services. **Fnd:** 1958. **Mem:** 40000. **Reg. Groups:** 2. **State Groups:** 10. **Local Groups:** 420. **Pub:** *Entourage* (quarterly); *Newsbreak* (quarterly).

67 ■ Canadian Association of Gift Planners (CAGP)
325 Dalhousie St., Ste. 201
Ottawa, ON, Canada K1N 7G2
Contact: Anne Williams, Membership Coor.
Ph: (613)232-7991
Free: 888-430-9494
Fax: (613)232-7286
E-mail: membership@cagp-acpdp.org
URL: http://www.cagp-acpdp.org/en/default.aspx

Staff: 4. **Descr:** Specializing in charitable gift planning. Promotes charitable giving; works to raise awareness of the financial advantages gained through charitable donations. Makes available gift planning services. **Fnd:** 1982. **Mem:** 1300. **Reg. Groups:** 20. **Pub:** *Planner* (monthly).

68 ■ Canadian German Chamber of Industry and Commerce (CGCIC)
480 University Ave., Ste. 1500
Toronto, ON, Canada M5G 1V2
Contact: Thomas Beck, Pres./CEO
Ph: (416)598-3355
Fax: (416)598-1840
E-mail: info.toronto@germanchamber.ca
URL: http://www.germanchamber.ca

Descr: Canadian and German corporations and trade and industrial organizations. Promotes increased trade between Canada and Germany. Lobbies for removal of barriers to trade; represents the interests of business before government agencies, international trade organizations, and the public. **Fnd:** 1968. **Mem:** 600. **Pub:** *Canadian German Headlines* (monthly).

69 ■ Care USA
151 Ellis St. NE
Atlanta, GA 30303-2420
Contact: Helene Gayle, Pres./CEO
Ph: (404)681-2552
Free: 800-422-7385
Fax: (404)577-5977
E-mail: managemyaccount@care.org
URL: http://www.care.org

Descr: Focuses on designing and furnishing benefit programs for affiliated consumer associations. **Fnd:** 1985. **Pub:** Bulletin (periodic).

70 ■ Catholic Golden Age (CGA)
PO Box 249
Olyphant, PA 18447
Contact:Rev. Gerald N. Dino, Pres.
Free: 800-836-5699

E-mail: cgaemail@aol.com
URL: http://www.catholicgoldenage.org

Staff: 8. **Descr:** Catholics 50 years of age and over. Studies and discusses the meaning of a longer life and gerontology, emphasizing religion and spirituality. Provides older persons with motivation to lead self-fulfilling lives. Emphasizes the role of religious faith in the endeavors and activities of older people. Assists the aged in their social, physical, economic, intellectual, and spiritual needs. Sponsors apostolic and charitable work and member-oriented religious worship, stressing participation; also sponsors annual Million Candles celebration by encouraging lighting of candles in homes, offices, and parishes, and uniting in prayer for world peace. Maintains Catholic Golden Age Foundation to sponsor and provide financial assistance to charitable, religious, benevolent, and educational programs designed to enrich the lives of older adults. Offers masses for members, living and deceased; discounts on hotels, motels, rental cars, eyeglasses, merchandise, and prescriptions; group travel rates to places of religious significance; and supplemental insurance at group rates. Participates in local, state, and national forums. Gives discounts on nursing homes and home healthcare. **Fnd:** 1974. **Mem:** 1400000. **Local Groups:** 132. **Pub:** *CGA World* (bimonthly).

71 ■ Cemetery Consumer Service Council (CCSC)
PO Box 2028
Reston, VA 20195-8407
Contact: Robert M. Fells, External COO/Gen. Counsel
Ph: (703)391-8400
Free: 800-645-7700
Fax: (703)391-8416
E-mail: gen4@icfa.org
URL: http://www.icfa.org

Staff: 6. **Descr:** Council members are: the International Cemetery and Funeral Association, Cremation Association of North America,, Southern Cemetery Association, and Central States Cemetery Association. Acts as a central clearinghouse for consumer inquiries and complaints concerning the cemetery industry, including cremation. Establishes uniform standards and guidelines for the handling of these inquiries and complaints on a national, state, and local basis. Publicizes the availability and mechanics of the council's services to consumer groups, governmental agencies, and other interested parties; seeks, through cooperative efforts within the various segments of the cemetery industry, the correction of unfair and unbusinesslike procedures. **Fnd:** 1979. **Mem:** 7.

72 ■ Center for Consumer Affairs, University of Wisconsin-Milwaukee (CCA-UWM)
161 W Wisconsin Ave., Ste. 6000
Milwaukee, WI 53203-2602
Contact: Prof. James L. Brown, Dir.
Ph: (414)227-3200
Free: 800-222-3623
Fax: (414)227-3146
E-mail: jbrown@uwm.edu
URL: http://cfprod.imt.uwm.edu/sce/dci_long.cfm?id=1

Staff: 4. **Descr:** Develops consumer leadership skills through adult education programs. Provides referral service to appropriate agencies for the handling of consumer complaints. Makes available lecturers and resource persons for community group meetings and programs. Holds conferences, seminars, institutes, and meetings. Conducts extensive research on consumer issues. **Fnd:** 1964. **Pub:** *Wisconsin Funeral Service: A Consumer's Guide*; Booklets; Manuals; Pamphlets.

73 ■ Center on Human Policy (CHP)
Syracuse University
805 S Crouse Ave.
Syracuse, NY 13244-2280
Contact: Steven Taylor PhD, Co-Dir.
Ph: (315)443-3851
Free: 800-894-0826

Fax: (315)443-4338
E-mail: thechp@syr.edu
URL: http://thechp.syr.edu

Descr: Consumers and students; parents of persons with disabilities; human services administrators and staff members; professionals in psychology, special education, rehabilitation, sociology, law, social work, and planning. Promotes the inclusion of persons with severe disabilities into the mainstream of society. Disseminates information to families, human services professionals, and others on laws, regulations, and programs affecting children and adults with disabilities, focusing on those with developmental disabilities. Provides speakers to professional gatherings and parents' groups. Documents outstanding community living and educational programs and assists in creating exemplary services. Evaluates public policies to determine their impact on people with disabilities. Participates in public forums, legislative hearings, national conventions, and other community events involving issues relating to people with disabilities. Operates National Resource Center on Supported Living and Choice for people with developmental disabilities. Offers technical assistance, consultation, and training on service system issues to local, regional, state, and national organizations and agencies. Conducts research related to community inclusion. **Fnd:** 1971.

74 ■ CEOs Without Borders (CWB)
35 Claremont Ave., 3S
New York, NY 10027
Contact: Xavier Sala-i-Martin, Pres.
E-mail: info@ceoswb.org
URL: http://www.ceoswb.org

Descr: Encourages businessmen and businesswomen to use their leadership positions to foster the growth of business in developing countries. Provides humanitarian aid to alleviate the effects of natural and economic disasters. Promotes cooperation and works with research institutions to find sustainable business solutions. **Fnd:** 2006. **Pub:** Newsletter.

75 ■ Choices
4701 N Keystone Ave., Ste. 150
Indianapolis, IN 46205
Contact: Knute Rotto, CEO
Ph: (317)726-2121
Free: 888-543-9727
Fax: (317)726-2130
E-mail: choices@choicesteam.org
URL: http://www.choicesteam.org

Staff: 250. **Descr:** Aims to advance systems of care. Strengthens individuals and families by developing natural support systems and community resources. Provides communities with a spectrum of human services and business management solutions. **Fnd:** 1997. **Pub:** *Collaborative Adventures* (quarterly).

76 ■ Common Ground Alliance (CGA)
1421 Prince St., Ste. 410
Alexandria, VA 22314
Contact: Bob Kipp, Pres.
Ph: (703)836-1709
Fax: (309)407-2244
E-mail: bobk@commongroundalliance.com
URL: http://www.commongroundalliance.com

Descr: Works to ensure public safety, environmental protection and the integrity of services. Promotes effective damage prevention practices. Seeks to reduce damages to all underground facilities in North America. Supports research and develops public awareness and education programs concerning underground facilities protection. **Fnd:** 2000. **Pub:** *CGA in Action*; Brochure.

77 ■ Community Development Society (CDS)
17 S High St., Ste. 200
Columbus, OH 43215
Contact: Linda Sunde, Pres.
Ph: (614)221-1900
Fax: (614)221-1989
E-mail: cds@assnoffices.com
URL: http://www.comm-dev.org

Descr: Professionals and practitioners in community development; international, national, state, and local groups interested in community development efforts. Provides a forum for exchange of ideas and experiences; disseminates information to the public; advocates excellence in community programs, scholarship, and research; promotes citizen participation as essential to effective community development. Sponsors educational programs. **Fnd:** 1969. **Mem:** 1100. **State Groups:** 21. **Pub:** *CDS Membership Directory* (annual); *Journal of the Community Development Society* (semiannual); *Vanguard* (quarterly); Books; Brochures.

78 ■ Community Managers International Association (CMIA)
PO Box 848
Dana Point, CA 92629
Contact: David E. Johnston, Pres.
Ph: (619)225-8156
Free: 888-900-2642
Fax: (619)225-8151
E-mail: cmiamanager@sbcglobal.net
URL: http://www.cmiamanager.org

Descr: Aims to promote the community management profession. Provides an environment for the exchange of ideas among members. Collaborates with other national and state organizations. Sponsors seminars and workshops.

79 ■ Concern Worldwide (CW)
104 E 40th St., Ste. 903
New York, NY 10016
Contact: Thomas J. Moran, Chm.
Ph: (212)557-8000
Free: 800-59-CONCERN
Fax: (212)557-8004
E-mail: info.usa@concern.net
URL: http://www.concernusa.org

Descr: Individuals in the United States who provide volunteer support to relief and development organizations worldwide. Promotes more effective provision of relief to victims of disaster; seeks to ensure appropriate and sustainable economic development. Conducts programs in areas including water supply and sanitation, women's empowerment, health and nutrition, and education and training. **Fnd:** 1968.

80 ■ Consumer Action (CA)
221 Main St., Ste. 480
San Francisco, CA 94105
Contact: Ken McEldowney, Exec. Dir.
Ph: (415)777-9648
Fax: (415)777-5267
E-mail: info@consumer-action.org
URL: http://www.consumer-action.org

Descr: Consumer advocacy organization. Provides free, non-legal advice and referrals on a wide range of issues, in Chinese, English and Spanish. **Fnd:** 1971.

81 ■ Consumer Alert (CA)
3050 K St. NW, Ste. 400
Washington, DC 20007
Contact: Mr. William MacLeod, Chm.
Ph: (202)467-5809
E-mail: consumer@consumeralert.org
URL: http://www.consumeralert.org

Descr: Public interest group opposing excessive regulations and supporting free enterprise, consumer rights, and freedom of choice for individual consumers. Examines current and proposed regulations in terms of demonstrated need and ultimate cost in areas where CA believes consumer interests are being abused; if the regulation is deemed excessive, CA develops proposals to change or abolish it or inform the public about its cause and effects. Works with other public interest groups to take legal action to remedy consumer abuse. Current activities include: lowering taxes; preventing public interest organizations from using tax revenues from students to further their own legislative objectives and goals; disseminating risk data. Conducts lectures nationwide; maintains Speaker's Bureau.; provides educa-

tional programs. **Fnd:** 1977. **Pub:** *Consumer Alert Consumer Comments* (quarterly).

82 ■ Consumer Federation of America (CFA)
1620 I St. NW, Ste. 200
Washington, DC 20006
Contact: Mel Hall Crawford
Ph: (202)387-6121
Fax: (202)265-7989
E-mail: cfa@consumerfed.org
URL: http://www.consumerfed.org
Staff: 30. **Descr:** National, regional, state, and local consumer groups; consumer cooperatives; public utilities and labor organizations; state and local protection agencies. Supports activities of members. Gathers and disseminates information on consumer issues. Serves as an advocate of pro-consumer policies before Congress, regulatory agencies, and the courts. **Fnd:** 1968. **Mem:** 300. **Pub:** *Annual Voting Record of U.S. Congress*; *CFA News* (bimonthly).

83 ■ Consumer Federation of America Foundation (CFAF)
1620 I St. NW, Ste. 200
Washington, DC 20006
Contact: Mel Hall Crawford
Ph: (202)387-6121
Fax: (202)265-7989
E-mail: cfa@consumerfed.org
URL: http://www.consumerfed.org
Descr: Consumer advocates. Strives to complement the work of the Consumer Federation of America by assisting state and local organizations, providing consumer information through projects, and conducting consumer research. **Fnd:** 1972. **Pub:** *CFAnews* (annual); Brochures.

84 ■ Consumer Trends Forum International (CTFI)
7076 Drinkard Way
Mechanicsville, VA 23111
Contact: Ms. Kimberly Thies, Exec. Dir.
Ph: (804)559-6519
Fax: (804)559-4087
E-mail: info@consumerexpert.org
URL: http://www.consumerexpert.org
Staff: 1. **Descr:** Provides global trend information and networking resources to assist members to identify and integrate trends into the design and marketing of consumer goods and services; educates businesses to interpret impact of trends on consumer needs and expectations. Hosts an annual Consumer Trends Forum with speakers addressing consumer trends. **Fnd:** 1998. **Mem:** 250. **Pub:** *Trendline* (biweekly).

85 ■ Consumers' Association of Canada (CAC)
PO Box 9300
Ottawa, ON, Canada K1G 3T9
Contact: Bruce Cran, Pres.
Ph: (613)238-2533
Fax: (613)238-2538
E-mail: info@consumer.ca
URL: http://www.consumer.ca
Descr: Represents and informs consumers on marketplace issues. **Fnd:** 1947. **Pub:** *Consumer Connections*.

86 ■ Consumers Union of United States (CU)
101 Truman Ave.
Yonkers, NY 10703-1057
Contact: Sharon L. Nelson, Chair
Ph: (914)378-2000
URL: http://www.consumersunion.org
Descr: Testing, rating, and reporting organization providing information on competing brands of appliances, automobiles, food products, and household equipment. Aims to provide consumers with information and advice on consumer goods and services; to give information and assistance on all financial matters affecting consumers; to initiate and to cooperate with individual and group efforts seeking to create, maintain, and enhance the quality of life for consumers. Regional offices represent consumer interests in the legislature, courts, and administrative

agencies. Derives income from sale of its publication, *Consumer Reports*, and other publications. All subscribers may become members. Produces a syndicated radio program, Report to Consumers; a syndicated newspaper column, From Consumer Reports; and television series for cable television, Consumer Reports Presents. **Fnd:** 1936. **Pub:** *Consumer Reports* (monthly); *On Health* (monthly); *Travel Letter* (monthly); *Zillions* (bimonthly).

87 ■ Consumers for World Trade (CWT)
1707 L St. NW, Ste. 570
Washington, DC 20036
Contact: Maureen Smith, Pres.
Ph: (202)293-2944
Fax: (202)293-0495
URL: http://www.cwt.org
Staff: 3. **Descr:** Economists, educators, students, trade experts, consumer specialists, civic and political leaders, legal consultants, and concerned citizens. Represents the consumer interest in U.S. trade policy. Lobbies against protectionism and for expanded overseas markets for U.S. goods and services in order to give consumers more choices, to counter inflationary prices, and to promote healthy and stable economic growth. Has established an education fund to conduct seminars and forums in various cities, and to carry out other research projects designed to educate consumers on trade issues and maintain communication with the federal government. Maintains speakers' bureau. **Fnd:** 1978. **Pub:** *World Trade Connections* (semimonthly); Pamphlets.

88 ■ Customer Relationship Management Association (CRMA)
12460 Crabapple Rd., Ste. 202-417
Alpharetta, GA 30004
Contact: Michael Thomas, Pres.
Ph: (404)735-2950
E-mail: mwthomas@crmassociation.org
URL: http://www.crmassociation.org
Descr: Represents the Customer Relationship Management (CRM) industry and all its constituents. Protects and promotes the interests of Customer Relationship Management and its institutions. Provides members with the tools needed to enrich and improve their customer experience, be it the member's direct customers or the customers of their customers.

89 ■ DataCenter
1904 Franklin St., Ste. 900
Oakland, CA 94612-2923
Contact: Alex Vazquez, Chm.
Ph: (510)835-4692
Free: 800-735-3741
Fax: (510)835-3017
E-mail: datacenter@datacenter.org
URL: http://www.datacenter.org
Staff: 12. **Descr:** Provides the social justice community with strategic information. Develops original sources and adds value to existing information sources by conducting targeted research and analysis, publishing, accessing progressive publications, and training community-based organizations in the use of information technology. **Fnd:** 1977.

90 ■ Disabled Drummers Association (DDA)
18901 NW 19th Ave.
Miami Gardens, FL 33056-2808
Contact: Debbie Rice
Ph: (305)621-9022
E-mail: ddafathertime@comcast.net
URL: http://www.disableddrummers.org
Descr: Works to give support to people with disabilities. Provides opportunities for disabled drummers by conducting campaigns to lessen and eliminate the stereotype of the disabled musician. Raises public awareness and funds for the benefits of those disabled. **Fnd:** 1996.

91 ■ DROKPA
1032 Irving St.
San Francisco, CA 94122
Contact: Ken Bauer, Admin.

E-mail: nomad@drokpa.org
URL: http://www.drokpa.org
Descr: Works with pastoral communities in the Himalaya and Central Asia regions to implement grassroots development and catalyze social entrepreneurship. Facilitates the introduction and use of appropriate and renewable technologies across the Himalaya, Tibetan Plateau, and Central Asia regions. Provides seed money, technical know-how and ongoing support for local entrepreneurs and community organizations. **Pub:** Annual Report.

92 ■ Ebenezer Society (ES)
2722 Park Ave. S
Minneapolis, MN 55407
Contact: Sandy Hopkins, Dev. Off.
Ph: (612)874-3460
URL: http://www.fairviewebenezer.org
Descr: Lutheran congregations and their delegates. Works to provide quality services and facilities for older people with varying needs; to make their lives more healthful, meaningful, and secure. Services are not limited to Lutheran clients. Offers nursing home care for low-income elderly; provides home services, including medical treatment, to help persons remain in their own homes as long as possible. Sponsors Ebenezer Center for Aging and Human Development which provides consultative services, conducts educational events and applied research, and issues publications. Maintains Ebenezer Foundation as the support arm of the society. Compiles research statistics; offers placement service. Ebenezer means "stone of help". **Fnd:** 1917. **Mem:** 45.

93 ■ Edutechnia
4849 S Darrow Dr., No. L138
Tempe, AZ 85282
Contact: Jorge Madrid, CEO/Chm.
E-mail: info@edutechnia.org
URL: http://edutechnia.org
Descr: Focuses on integrating communities into the information society by taking steps to extend the benefits of technology and innovation to all citizens and reversing current trends toward economic inequality. Promotes global development through education and technology. Empowers people, communities and organizations to increase performance capability to become productive citizens of society. Reaches out to poor communities around the world and connects families to the tools, knowledge and resources needed to overcome poverty.

94 ■ EMDR - Humanitarian Assistance Programs (EMDR HAP)
PO Box 6505
Hamden, CT 06517
Contact: Robert A. Gelbach PhD, Exec. Dir.
Ph: (203)288-4450
Fax: (203)288-4060
E-mail: emdrhap@emdrhap.org
URL: http://www.emdrhap.org
Descr: Represents individuals committed to relieving human suffering and preventing the after-effects of trauma and violence. Promotes recovery from traumatic stress through direct service and community-based training in EMDR for mental health workers all over the world. Provides training to mental health professionals serving traumatized communities worldwide. Promotes further research on trauma risk and recovery factors and treatment outcomes. **Fnd:** 1995. **Pub:** What's Happening Now.

95 ■ Entertainment Consumers Association (ECA)
64 Danbury Rd., Ste. 700
Wilton, CT 06897-4406
Contact: Hal Halpin, Founder/Pres.
Ph: (203)761-6180
Fax: (203)761-6184
E-mail: feedback@theeca.com
URL: http://www.theeca.com
Descr: Represents and promotes consumers of interactive entertainment. Serves the needs of individuals who play computer and video games. Advocates for consumer rights and anti-games legislation. **Fnd:** 2006. **Pub:** ECA Today.

96 ■ Entertainment Industries Council (EIC)
1760 Reston Pkwy., Ste. 415
Reston, VA 20190
Contact: Brian L. Dyak, Pres./CEO/Co-Founder
Ph: (703)481-1414
Fax: (703)481-1418
E-mail: eiceast@eiconline.org
URL: http://eiconline.org
Staff: 14. **Descr:** Aims to utilize the power and influence of the entertainment industry in a national campaign to combat and deglamorize substance abuse, especially among young people. Seeks to identify, provide celebrity role models for young people, and increase youth awareness of drug abuse through television, radio, music, and motion pictures. Develops projects to aid in eliminating substance abuse problems within the entertainment industry. Conducts seminars, training sessions on drug abuse prevention, radio interview series, television specials, outreach programs, and employee assistance and fundraising programs. Collects and disseminates information on progress made by the entertainment industry in drug abuse prevention. **Fnd:** 1983. **Mem:** 130. **Pub:** Profile (monthly); Spotlight on Depiction (annual); Annual Report (annual).

97 ■ Family Campers and RVers (FCRV)
4804 Transit Rd., Bldg. 2
Depew, NY 14043
Contact: Jack Smye, Natl. Pres.
Ph: (716)668-6242
Free: 800-245-9755
Fax: (716)668-6242
E-mail: fcrvnat@verizon.net
URL: http://www.fcrv.org
Staff: 3. **Descr:** Family campers and hikers; others interested in outdoor activities. Promotes and enhances the experience of "family" style camping/RVing. **Fnd:** 1949. **Mem:** 7000. **Reg. Groups:** 7. **State Groups:** 40. **Local Groups:** 1000. **Pub:** Camping Today (monthly).

98 ■ Federal Consumer Information Center Program
1800 F St. NW, Rm. G-142
Washington, DC 20405
Ph: (202)501-1794
Free: 800-FED-INFO
E-mail: catalog.pueblo@gsa.gov
URL: http://www.pueblo.gsa.gov
Staff: 24. **Descr:** Serves as a nationwide federal consumer information service providing printed publications. Topics covered include: getting Federal benefits; dealing with consumer complaints; buying cars and houses; making investments and handling credit problems; researching health questions; and finding the best sources of Federal information and assistance. **Fnd:** 1966. **Pub:** Consumer Information Catalog (quarterly); Brochures (periodic).

99 ■ Federation of American Consumers and Travelers (FACT)
PO Box 104
Edwardsville, IL 62025
Contact: Vicki Rolens, Managing Dir.
Free: 800-872-3228
Fax: (618)656-5369
E-mail: cservice@usafact.org
URL: http://usafact.org
Descr: Individuals organized to obtain lower prices for merchandise, consumer services, and travel. Disseminates consumer information to members; monitors legislation affecting consumers; conducts educational programs. Provides assistance to members affected by federally-declared disasters. **Fnd:** 1984. **Mem:** 1000000. **Pub:** FACTFINDER (quarterly).

100 ■ Friends Women's Association (FWA)
1001 Park Ave.
St. Louis, MO 63104
Contact: Dr. Alexia Nibona, Dir.
E-mail: nibalex@yahoo.fr
URL: http://www.fwaburundi.com
Descr: Represents women who are working together for self improvement. Aims to create awareness of violence against women in the community. Works to address the problem of HIV/AIDS. **Fnd:** 2002.

101 ■ Gerda Lissner Foundation
135 E 55th St., 8th Fl.
New York, NY 10022
Contact: Mrs. Dolores Anne Fraide, Pres./CEO
Ph: (212)826-6100
Fax: (212)826-0366
E-mail: gerdalissner@aol.com
URL: http://gerdalissner.org
Descr: Works to help gifted singers develop their talent into an international career in opera, including coaches; teachers for opera languages, acting, dance, etc.; guidance in makeup and etiquette grants for stage clothing, domestic and foreign travel, etc. **Fnd:** 1994. **Mem:** 5.

102 ■ Giving Institute (GI)
4700 W Lake Ave.
Glenview, IL 60025
Contact: Ms. Nancy L. Raybin CME, Chair
Ph: (847)375-4709
Free: 800-462-2372
Fax: 888-374-7258
E-mail: info@givinginstitute.org
URL: http://www.givinginstitute.org
Staff: 3. **Descr:** Represents fund-raising counseling firms engaged in consulting on the management and planning of campaigns for hospitals, universities, religious groups, community funds, arts organizations, social service groups and other nonprofit institutions. Conducts research in philanthropy. **Fnd:** 1935. **Mem:** 38. **Pub:** AAFRC Book on Fund-Raising Consulting 1999 (periodic); Giving USA (annual); Giving USA Update (quarterly); Legislative Monitor (periodic).

103 ■ Global Grassroots
45 Lyme Rd., Ste. 206
Hanover, NH 03755-1222
Contact: Gretchen Wallace, Chair
Ph: (603)643-0400
Fax: (603)619-0076
URL: http://www.globalgrassroots.org/index.htm
Descr: Works to empower, unite, and and support relief of poor, distressed and underprivileged women worldwide. Benefits women by establishing a global network of leading entrepreneurs. Raises awareness of critical issues facing women worldwide, especially sexual and gender-based violence during conflict. **Fnd:** 2004.

104 ■ Interfaith Center on Corporate Responsibility (ICCR)
475 Riverside Dr., Ste. 1842
New York, NY 10115
Contact: Ms. Laura Berry, Exec. Dir.
Ph: (212)870-2295
Fax: (212)870-2023
E-mail: info@iccr.org
URL: http://www.iccr.org
Staff: 10. **Descr:** Religious agencies and their representatives, including 25 Protestant denominations and Jewish agencies and over 250 Roman Catholic orders, pension funds, healthcare corporations and dioceses. Assists members in coordinating their corporate responsibility programs and expressing social responsibility with their investments by facilitating exchange of views, sharing research and information, and developing strategies. Conducts research in the areas of sweat shops, equal employment opportunity, nuclear weapons production, infant formula, tobacco marketing, board diversity, land mines, energy, environment and alternative investments among others. Provides channel for cooperating with other institutions and coalitions; encourages education and interpretation efforts in the field of socially responsible investment. Sponsors research on specific corporations; maintains contact with other corporate responsibility action groups; conducts discussions with representatives of government,

business and industry, foundations, and universities; develops information related to the concern for social criteria in investment policy. Maintains subscriber service of topical materials on corporate responsibility. **Fnd:** 1971. **Pub:** *Corporate Examiner* (10/year).

105 ■ International Association of Women in Family Enterprises (IAWIFE)
1906 Vista Del Lago Dr., No. L-119
Valley Springs, CA 95252
Contact: Sandy Reed, Founder/Pres.
Ph: (209)772-9200
Fax: (209)772-2810
E-mail: info@iawife.com
URL: http://www.iawife.com
Descr: Aims to support women who are building and growing family businesses. Offers opportunities to help members become successful in family enterprises. Provides support, education and networking among members. **Fnd:** 2008.

106 ■ International Family Recreation Association (IFRA)
PO Box 520
Gonzalez, FL 32560-0520
Contact: K.W. Stephens, Exec. Off.
Ph: (850)937-8354
Free: 800-281-9186
E-mail: rltresource@spydee.net
Staff: 3. **Descr:** Individual and commercial advocates of family recreation, leisure and travel. Supports recommendations and legislation advantageous to recreation, leisure, and travel. Promotes safety policies and public participation in family recreational, leisure, and travel activities. Encourages the conservation of natural resources. Reviews and evaluates products. Supports the Recreation Vehicle Industry Association. Sponsors workshops, leadership training, and volunteer instruction programs. Conducts rallies, caravans, tours, cruises, tournaments, and charitable and youth programs. Maintains speakers' bureau; compiles statistics. Provides consulting services to recreation, leisure and travel-type businesses (including manufacturers, dealers, campgrounds, resorts, parks international). **Fnd:** 1982. **Mem:** 6840. **Reg. Groups:** 7. **State Groups:** 2. **Local Groups:** 15. **Pub:** *On the Line*; *Recreation Advisor* (10/year); *Update* (monthly).

107 ■ International Feminist Approaches to Bioethics (FAB)
5 Riverpoint Rd.
Hastings-on-Hudson, NY 10706
Contact: Rachel Ankeny, Treas.
Ph: (914)674-0122
Fax: (914)478-2885
E-mail: adonchin@iupui.edu
URL: http://www.fabnet.org
Descr: Membership automatically includes a subscription to its journal, IJFAB. Is committed to a non-hierarchical model of organizations and seeks to include all who share the goals and will strive to advance them. Exchanges information with many organizations. Aims to develop a more inclusive theory of bioethics encompassing the standpoints and experiences of women and other marginalized social groups; to examine presuppositions embedded in the dominant bioethical discourse that privilege those already empowered; and to create new methodologies and strategies responsive to the disparate conditions of women's lives across the globe. Bioethics is a discipline dealing with the ethical implications of matters related to health care practice, systems, institutions, and decisions. Conducts exchange of information about research initiatives; organizes presentations at national and international bioethics conferences; and develops collaborative research projects. **Fnd:** 1992. **Mem:** 380. **Pub:** *The International Network on Feminist Approaches to Bioethics* (semiannual).

108 ■ International Life Sciences Institute - North America (ILSINA)
1156 15th St. NW, Ste. 200
Washington, DC 20005

Contact: Sharon Weiss, Deputy Exec. Dir.
Ph: (202)659-0074
Fax: (202)659-3859
E-mail: sweiss@ilsi.org
URL: http://www.ilsina.org
Staff: 11. **Descr:** Advances the understanding of scientific issues related to the nutritional quality and safety of the food supply, as well as health issues related to consumer self-care products. Sponsors relevant research programs, professional education programs and workshops, seminars, and publications, as well as providing a neutral forum for government, academic, and industry scientists to discuss and resolve scientific issues of common concern for the well-being of the general public. Fosters career development of outstanding new scientists. Programs are supported primarily by its industry membership. **Fnd:** 1985. **Mem:** 44. **Pub:** Newsletter.

109 ■ International Ombudsman Association (IOA)
390 Amwell Rd., Ste. 403
Hillsborough, NJ 08844
Contact: Gary Yamashita, Pres.
Ph: (908)359-0246
Fax: (908)842-0376
E-mail: info@ombudsassociation.org
URL: http://www.ombudsassociation.org
Staff: 1. **Descr:** Individuals actively engaged in the practice of organizational ombudsmanry, as designated neutrals. Works to enhance the quality and value of the ombudsman function by: establishing and communicating appropriate standards of excellence for the profession; developing and disseminating ethical guidelines for organizational ombudspeople; training new and experienced ombuds practitioners in complaint handling skills and principles of effective practice; communicating the latest developments of the profession; and fostering appropriate forums to share common interests and strengthen skills. **Fnd:** 1982. **Mem:** 600. **Pub:** *Neutrality*; *The Ombuds Confidentiality Privilege*; *Ombudsman Handbook* (periodic); *Ombudsman News* (quarterly); *Options Functions and Skills*; *Reprisal, Retaliation and Redress*; *Why an Organizational Ombudsman*.

110 ■ International Parrotlet Society (IPS)
PO Box 2428
Santa Cruz, CA 95063-2428
Contact: Leslie Huegerich, Pres.
Ph: (831)688-5560
E-mail: ips@internationalparrotletsociety.org
URL: http://www.internationalparrotletsociety.org
Descr: Owners, breeders, and admirers of parrotlets. Promotes interest in parrotlets and seeks to insure breeding conducive to species improvement. Sponsors parrotlet breeding cooperatives. Conducts research and educational programs like Parrotlet Placement Program; sponsors competitions; maintains speakers' bureau; compiles statistics. **Fnd:** 1992. **Mem:** 500. **Pub:** Journal (bimonthly).

111 ■ Light Millennium
87-82 115th St.
Richmond Hill, NY 11418
Contact: Bircan Unver, Founding Pres.
Ph: (718)846-5776
Fax: (718)441-8881
E-mail: contact@lightmillennium.org
URL: http://lightmillennium.org
Descr: Aims to provide an international platform for the free expression of ideas and experiences in order to foster understanding and connections between people of different cultures and beliefs. Promotes social welfare for the people of Turkey, Greece and the United States. Conducts research and compiles and publishes information concerning art, literature and ideas about the future. Promotes the theory and practice of the principles of good government and good citizenship. Provides a forum for discussion of

all matters of public interest, partisan politics and sectarian religion. **Fnd:** 2001.

112 ■ Living Waters Organization
PO Box 640
Union, NJ 07083
Contact: Terrill H. McGill, Pres./Founder
Ph: (908)967-8578
E-mail: livingwatersorganization@yahoo.com
URL: http://www.livingwatersorganization.org
Descr: Aims to serve the community through housing, education, job training, employment, crime prevention, mentoring and counseling people of all ages, and leadership development. Helps young individuals to become men and women of good values and to fulfill their dreams and visions.

113 ■ Music Industries Association of Canada (MIAC)
505 Consumers Rd., Ste. 807
Toronto, ON, Canada M2J 4V8
Contact: Al Kowalenko CAE, Exec. Dir.
Ph: (416)490-1871
Free: 877-490-6422
Fax: (416)490-0369
E-mail: al@miac.net
URL: http://www.miac.net
Descr: Manufacturers, distributors, and retailers of musical instruments, accessories, sound reinforcement products, and published music. Promotes and represents members' interests. **Fnd:** 1972. **Mem:** 160. **Pub:** *MIAC E-News* (monthly).

114 ■ National Alliance of Community Economic Development Associations (NACEDA)
2101 Wilson Blvd., Ste. 610
Arlington, VA 22201-3040
Contact: Jane DeMarines, Exec. Dir.
Ph: (703)741-0144
E-mail: info@naceda.org
URL: http://www.naceda.org
Descr: Serves as a vehicle and a national voice for developing and pursuing a national community agenda. Supports the work of Community Economic Development (CED) associations, local Community Development Corporations (CDCs) and practitioners nationwide. Works to strengthen and expand the role of state CEDs in promoting the efforts of local CDCs and building the capacity and reach of the CDC field. Convenes a national policy committee to gather input from the field, craft positions on public policy issues and develop strategies for their implementation. Coordinates with other like-minded national and regional organizations working on community development issues to leverage resources and maximize impact. **Fnd:** 2006. **Mem:** 41.

115 ■ National Antique and Art Dealers Association of America (NAADAA)
220 E 57th St.
New York, NY 10022
Contact: James McConnaughy, Pres.
Ph: (212)826-9707
Fax: (212)832-9493
E-mail: inquiries@naadaa.org
URL: http://www.naadaa.org
Descr: Art and antique dealers who handle antiques and works of art of the highest quality. Safeguards the interests of those who buy, sell, and collect antiques and works of art. Sponsors periodic exhibitions; maintains speakers' bureau. **Fnd:** 1954. **Mem:** 40. **Pub:** Membership Directory (annual).

116 ■ National Association of Consumer Advocates (NACA)
1730 Rhode Island Ave. NW, Ste. 710
Washington, DC 20036
Contact: Ian Lyngklip, Co-Chm.
Ph: (202)452-1989
Fax: (202)452-0099
E-mail: info@naca.net
URL: http://www.naca.net
Staff: 2. **Descr:** Consumer advocates and attorneys. Works to promote justice for all consumers and combat unfair, fraudulent, and abusive business practices. Provides information and resources, litiga-

tion support, consulting services, and educational programs. **Fnd:** 1994. **Mem:** 600. **Pub:** *Consumer Advocate* (bimonthly).

117 ■ National Association of Consumer Agency Administrators (NACAA)
2 Brentwood Commons, Ste. 150
750 Old Hickory Blvd.
Brentwood, TN 37027
Contact: Elizabeth Owen, Exec. Dir.
Ph: (615)498-1563
Fax: (615)369-6225
E-mail: eowen@nacaa.net
URL: http://www.nacaa.net
Staff: 2. **Descr:** Administrators of state, county, provincial, and local governmental consumer protection agencies; federal agencies and universities in the U.S. and several other countries. Seeks to enhance consumer services available to the public. Sponsors public policy forums. Acts as a clearinghouse for consumer education and legislation information. Works jointly with corporations, trade groups, non-profit organizations, and others to produce consumer education materials. **Fnd:** 1976. **Mem:** 162. **Pub:** *NACAA Forum*; *NACAA News* (bimonthly).

118 ■ National Association of Consumer Credit Administrators (NACCA)
PO Box 20871
Columbus, OH 43220-0871
Contact: Susan E. Hancock, Pres.
Ph: (614)326-1165
Fax: (614)326-1162
E-mail: nacca2007@sbcglobal.net
URL: http://www.naccaonline.org
Staff: 1. **Descr:** Represents state government officials who administer consumer finance laws in the U.S., Guam, Puerto Rico, and Canada. Holds roundtable discussions to exchange views on consumer credit and administration of applicable laws. **Fnd:** 1935. **Mem:** 46. **Pub:** *Minutes of Annual Meeting* (annual).

119 ■ National Association of Neighborhoods (NAN)
1300 Pennsylvania Ave. NW, Ste. 700
Washington, DC 20004
Contact: Ricardo C. Byrd, Exec. Dir.
Ph: (202)332-7766
URL: http://www.nanworld.org
Descr: Neighborhood organizations and city-wide coalitions in 120 cities. Promotes better neighborhoods through self-help, welfare reforms, and crime and safety programs. Seeks to help neighborhood leaders secure a political voice and facilitates the exchange of information about programs, issues, structures, and ethics. Has formulated National Neighborhood Platform and Neighborhood Bill of Responsibilities and Rights. Plans to establish a neighborhood leadership training institute. **Fnd:** 1975. **Mem:** 2500. **Pub:** *NAN Bulletin* (quarterly).

120 ■ National Association of State Administrators for Family Consumer Sciences (NASAFACS)
State Department of Education
120 SE 10th Ave.
Topeka, KS 66612-1182
Contact: Robin Harris, Treas.
Ph: (785)296-4912
Fax: (785)296-2214
E-mail: rharris@ksde.org
Descr: Represents state administrators of family and consumer sciences in each state and members of state family and consumer sciences education staffs whose major responsibilities are to: provide for group expression and group action on problems of national importance to family and consumer sciences education; provide an avenue for disseminating information for strengthening and improving family and consumer sciences education in public schools; serve in an advisory capacity in the interest of family and consumer sciences when requested by organizations and agencies working for common goals; provide supervision and administration for family and

consumer sciences education programs. **Mem:** 70. **Pub:** Membership Directory (annual).

121 ■ National Center for Bicycling and Walking (NCBW)
26 DeHart Rd.
Maplewood, NJ 07040
Contact: Sharon Z. Roerty AICP, Exec. Dir.
Ph: (973)378-3137
E-mail: info@bikewalk.org
URL: http://www.bikewalk.org
Staff: 5. **Descr:** Promotes bicycling for transportation and recreation; encourages increased quality and number of local bicycling programs; facilitates communication within the bicycle community. Disseminates information and provides technical assistance to community bicycle activists and city officials involved in bicycle programs. Designs and manages national bicycle promotion campaigns. Studies liability issues; develops guidelines for community bicycle programs; sponsors training seminars and programs for safety and planning professionals; conducts workshops on bicycle safety. Plans to offer advocacy and promotion services to government, industry, consumers, and organizations. **Fnd:** 1977. **Pub:** *CenterLines* (biweekly); *NCBW Forum* (quarterly); *Pro Bike Directory* (periodic); *Pro Bike News* (monthly); *Pro Bike Proceedings* (biennial).

122 ■ National Committee for Responsive Philanthropy (NCRP)
2001 S St. NW, Ste. 620
Washington, DC 20009
Contact: Aaron Dorfman, Exec. Dir.
Ph: (202)387-9177
Fax: (202)332-5084
E-mail: info@ncrp.org
URL: http://www.ncrp.org
Descr: Represents low income, minorities, women, consumers, environmentalists, older Americans, youth, and others working for social change and the public interest who are concerned about the lack of philanthropic giving to organizations working for social change or progressive issues. Works with leaders in the philanthropic community and the recipients of philanthropic giving to increase public accountability by philanthropies. Works to increase access to philanthropy's monies for those groups representing "critical public needs." Initiates efforts to facilitate access to charity drives in the workplace. Is concerned with the giving patterns of private foundations, United Way, and corporations with philanthropic programs. Conducts research; compiles statistics; publicizes reports; organizes local alternatives to United Way. **Fnd:** 1976.

123 ■ National Community Development Association (NCDA)
522 21st St. NW, No. 120
Washington, DC 20006-5059
Contact: Emory Counts, Pres.
Ph: (202)293-7587
Fax: (202)887-5546
E-mail: ncda@ncdaonline.org
URL: http://www.ncdaonline.org
Staff: 4. **Descr:** Represents community development program directors. Supports the interests of Community Development Block Grant Programs as well as other community and economic development issues; disseminates information; operates workshops on various aspects of housing, economic, and community development. **Fnd:** 1973. **Mem:** 500. **Reg. Groups:** 10. **Pub:** *Washington Report*.

124 ■ National Community Reinvestment Coalition (NCRC)
727 15th St. NW, Ste. 900
Washington, DC 20005
Contact: John Taylor, Pres./CEO
Ph: (202)628-8866
Fax: (202)628-9800
E-mail: jtaylor@ncrc.org
URL: http://www.ncrc.org
Staff: 7. **Descr:** Works with national and local nonprofit organizations and banks to increase the level of money going into low income, minority, and

disadvantaged communities through the Community Reinvestment Act (CRA). Monitors legislation related to the CRA. Provides information to organizations seeking to establish CRA agreements with local lending institutions. Disseminates legislative and regulatory updates. Offers many member services. **Fnd:** 1990. **Mem:** 500. **Pub:** *Compendium*; *Reinvest Works* (quarterly); Brochures.

125 ■ National Consumers League (NCL)
1701 K St. NW, Ste. 1200
Washington, DC 20006
Contact: Erma Angevine, Honorary Pres.
Ph: (202)835-3323
Fax: (202)835-0747
E-mail: info@nclnet.org
URL: http://www.nclnet.org
Staff: 19. **Descr:** Identifies, protects, represents, and advances the economic and social interests of consumers and workers. Addresses issues including healthcare, food and drug safety, and consumer fraud. Promotes fairness and safety at the marketplace and in the workplace. Coordinates the Alliance Against Fraud in Telemarketing and the Child Labor Coalition. Administers the National Fraud Information Center and Internet Fraud Watch. **Fnd:** 1899. **State Groups:** 2. **Pub:** *Focus on Fraud* (quarterly); *NCL Bulletin* (bimonthly); *Online Child Labor Monitor* (weekly); Bulletin.

126 ■ National Odd Shoe Exchange (NOSE)
PO Box 1120
Chandler, AZ 85244-1120
Ph: (480)892-3484
URL: http://www.oddshoe.org
Descr: Provides new single shoes to amputees and pairs of different sizes to people with feet of significantly different sizes due to disease, injury, and genetic disorders. **Fnd:** 1943.

127 ■ National Partnership for Women and Families
1875 Connecticut Ave. NW, Ste. 650
Washington, DC 20009
Contact: Debra L. Ness, Pres.
Ph: (202)986-2600
Fax: (202)986-2539
E-mail: info@nationalpartnership.org
URL: http://www.nationalpartnership.org
Staff: 30. **Descr:** Represents attorneys, administrators, publicists, and secretaries. Aims to secure equal rights for women through advocacy and monitoring, and public education. Works to promote women's rights in family law, employment, women's health, and other areas. Maintains speakers' bureau. **Fnd:** 1971. **Mem:** 2500. **Pub:** *Expecting Better: A State-by-State Analysis of Parental Leave Programs*; *Guide to HIPAA: What the Health Insurance Reform Law Means for Women and Families*; *Guide to the Family & Medical Leave Act: Questions & Answers*; *National Partnership News* (quarterly); Manuals.

128 ■ National Ski Areas Association (NSAA)
133 S Van Gordon St., Ste. 300
Lakewood, CO 80228
Contact: Michael Berry, Pres.
Ph: (303)987-1111
Fax: (303)986-2345
E-mail: nsaa@nsaa.org
URL: http://www.nsaa.org
Staff: 12. **Descr:** Ski area owners and operators; suppliers to the mountain resort industry. Seeks to foster, stimulate, and promote the skiing and mountain resort industries. Conducts marketing activities benefiting the sports of skiing and snowboarding; compiles industry statistics. Produces educational and training materials for ski area owners and personnel covering areas including pertinent federal safety and environmental regulations, resort operations, and guest services. **Fnd:** 1962. **Mem:** 752. **Pub:** *NSAA Journal* (bimonthly); *Source Book*; *Sus-*

tainable Slopes: Annual Report; Newsletter (bimonthly).

129 ■ New Brunswick Women's Institute (NBWI)
Victoria Health Centre, Rm. 279
65 Brunswick St.
Fredericton, NB, Canada E3B 1G5
Contact: Pat Boone, Pres.
Ph: (506)454-0798
Fax: (506)451-8949
E-mail: nbwi@nb.aibn.com
URL: http://www.nbfarm.com/nbwi/index.htm
Descr: Dedicated to informing and educating women about issues and events of concern to them and their communities; fosters the development of leadership and involvement of women in building stronger communities, families and life in Canada. **Fnd:** 1911. **Mem:** 9000000. **Reg. Groups:** 16.

130 ■ NonProfit Necessity (NPN)
8301 Elm Ave., Ste. 450
Rancho Cucamonga, CA 91730
Contact: Jenna Van Son, Pres.
Ph: (909)581-3160
Fax: (909)581-3170
E-mail: info@npnemail.com
URL: http://www.nonprofitnecessity.com
Descr: Promotes and supports nonprofit entities. Educates the public about the need for nonprofit organizations. Provides resources and offers services that are needed to establish viable nonprofit organizations.

131 ■ NuBian Exchange News
PO Box 422
Vienna, VA 22183
Contact: Claudette Brown, Owner
Ph: (703)698-7150
Free: 888-840-1481
Fax: (703)698-1416
E-mail: nubian5@iname.com
URL: http://nubian_exchange.tripod.com/newsltr.html
Staff: 1. **Descr:** Seeks to assist consumers in locating African-American businesses, products, services, and organizations nationally. **Fnd:** 1994. **Mem:** 200.

132 ■ One Hundred Days
PO Box 29715
Atlanta, GA 30359
Contact: Simon Nziramakenga
Ph: (404)461-9596
E-mail: info@onehundreddays.org
URL: http://www.onehundreddays.org
Descr: Seeks to assist the Good Shepherd Community Church in Rwanda to fulfill its vision of meeting the spiritual, emotional, and physical needs of the people through the provision of pediatric care, community and physician education and public health services. **Fnd:** 2005.

133 ■ Open Applications Group (OAGi)
PO Box 4897
Marietta, GA 30061
Contact: David Connelly, Pres./CEO
Ph: (678)715-7588
Fax: (770)234-6036
E-mail: dconnelly@openapplications.org
URL: http://www.openapplications.org
Staff: 3. **Descr:** Software vendors. Focuses on best practices and process-based XML content for eBusiness and Application Integration; strives for a unified standard for eBusiness and application software interoperability. **Fnd:** 1994.

134 ■ Paddlesports Industry Association (PIA)
PO Box 5204
Frankfort, KY 40602
Contact: Ed Councill, Pres.
Ph: (502)395-1513
Fax: (502)227-8086
E-mail: canoeky@aol.com
URL: http://www.paddlesportsindustry.org
Staff: 2. **Descr:** Renters and outfitters of canoes, kayaks, and rafts; manufacturers and distributors of equipment and products. Promotes safety in non-

power watercraft; seeks to protect the nation's waterways and the rights of the public to use them. Provides members with legislative representation; on-water liability insurance; member service programs; certification courses; and professional development. **Fnd:** 1978. **Mem:** 500. **Reg. Groups:** 5. **State Groups:** 12.

135 ■ Papillon Incorporated
PO Box 981
Hillside, NJ 07205
Contact: LoGina Davis, Pres.
Ph: (973)243-0085
E-mail: papillon@papilloninc.org
URL: http://papilloninc.org
Descr: Aims to design and implement programs which provide enrichment and encouragement to those affected by social issues surrounding urban youth, women's health and economic development. Gives solutions to social challenges by providing programs and services that enhance and enable individuals in need. **Fnd:** 2003.

136 ■ Parenting Publications of America (PPA)
1970 E Grand Ave., Ste. 330
El Segundo, CA 90245
Contact: C. James Dowden, Exec. Dir.
Ph: (310)364-0193
Fax: (310)364-0196
E-mail: jdowden@prodigy.net
URL: http://www.parentingpublications.org
Staff: 3. **Descr:** Publishers of parenting publications. Promotes publications for and about parents. Sponsors competitions; compiles statistics. **Fnd:** 1988. **Mem:** 120. **Pub:** Newsletter (quarterly); Directory (annual).

137 ■ Pet Care Services Association
1702 E Pikes Peak Ave.
Colorado Springs, CO 80909-5717
Contact: Joseph Lyman, CEO
Ph: (719)667-1600
Free: 877-570-7788
Fax: (719)667-0116
E-mail: membership@petcareservices.org
URL: http://www.petcareservices.org
Staff: 13. **Descr:** Persons or firms that board pets; kennel suppliers; others interested in the facility boarding kennel industry. Seeks to upgrade the industry through accreditation educational programs, seminars and conventions. Provides insurance resources for members and supplies pet care information to the public. Promotes code of ethics and accreditation program for recognition and training of superior kennel operators. Compiles boarding facility statistics. **Fnd:** 1977. **Mem:** 3000. **Reg. Groups:** 11. **Pub:** *A Collection of Kennel Floor Plans*; *All About Dog Daycare*; *Building, Buying and Operating a Boarding Kennel*; *Guidelines for Creating a Business Plan*; *Pet Age* (bimonthly); *Pet First Aid and Disaster Response Guide*.

138 ■ PlaNet Finance US
195 Broadway, 12th Fl.
New York, NY 10007
Contact: Elisa Sitbon, Exec. Dir.
Ph: (646)587-5018
E-mail: contactus@planetfinance.org
URL: http://us.planetfinance.org
Descr: Works to alleviate poverty through the development of microfinance. Seeks to support and strengthen the capacity of the microfinance sector. Raises public awareness of microfinancing.

139 ■ Professional Climbing Instructors Association (PCIA)
PO Box 784
Bishop, CA 93515
Contact: Jon Tierney
Ph: (207)461-3472
URL: http://pcia.us
Descr: Provides quality education and instruction for new and existing climbing instructors who primarily teach basic skills and/or facilitate climbing experiences. Seeks to improve the safety, quality

and delivery of technical climbing instruction. Offers training and continuing education programs through national and regional professional conferences.

140 ■ Rebuilding Together
1536 Sixteenth St. NW
Washington, DC 20036-1402
Contact: Mary Herche, Chair
Free: 800-473-4229
Fax: (202)483-9081
E-mail: info@rebuildingtogether.org
URL: http://www.rebuildingtogether.org
Staff: 17. **Descr:** Works in partnership with the community. Preserves and revitalizes houses and communities to ensure that low-income homeowners, particularly the elderly, disabled, and families with children, live in safety, warmth and independence. **Fnd:** 1988. **Mem:** 251. **Pub:** *Community Warehouses*; *Home Modifications*; *Homeowner Information*; *Homeowner Maintenance Workshops*; *Involving Youth*; Newsletter (semiannual); Annual Report (annual).

141 ■ Red Hat Society (RHS)
431 S Acacia Ave.
Fullerton, CA 92831
Contact: Sue Ellen Cooper, Exalted Queen Mother
Ph: (714)738-0001
Free: 866-FUN-AT50
E-mail: info@redhatsociety.com
URL: http://www.redhatsociety.com
Descr: Offers nurturing network for women over age 50 with agenda of humor and laughter; promotes visibility of women in that age group. **Pub:** *LifeStyle* (bimonthly); *News and Notes* (quarterly).

142 ■ Rwanda Knits
5 Emmons St., No. 2
Montpelier, VT 05602
Contact: Cari Clement, Founder/Dir.
Ph: (518)791-0212
E-mail: cari@rwandaknits.org
URL: http://www.rwandaknits.org
Descr: Represents knitters in Rwanda, Africa area. Promotes interest in knitting and knitting programs.

143 ■ September's Mission
548 Broadway, 3rd Fl.
New York, NY 10012
Contact: Monika Iken, Founder/Chair
Free: 888-424-4685
Fax: (212)575-7669
E-mail: info@septembersmission.org
URL: http://www.septembersmission.org
Descr: Supports the development of a memorial park and an overall redevelopment of Lower Manhattan. Works to ensure that the future of the WTC site not only honors the lives that were lost on September 11, but serves generations to come. Hosts and supports events throughout the year for families and children, to strengthen personal connections and create a positive, nurturing forum that contributes to healing.

144 ■ Society of American Florists (SAF)
1601 Duke St.
Alexandria, VA 22314-3406
Contact: Peter J. Moran, Exec. VP/CEO
Ph: (703)836-8700
Free: 800-336-4743
Fax: (703)836-8705
E-mail: info@safnow.org
URL: http://www.safnow.org
Staff: 30. **Descr:** Growers, wholesalers, retailers, and allied tradesmen in the floral industry. Lobbies Congress on behalf of the industry; sponsors educational programs; promotes the floral industry; prepares materials for consumers and for high school and college students; provides business resources. Sponsors Floricultural Hall of Fame, American Academy of Floriculture, and Professional Floral Commentators International. Compiles statistics; sponsors competitions. **Fnd:** 1884. **Mem:** 15000.

Pub: *Dateline: Washington*; *Floral Management* (monthly).

145 ■ Society of Sensory Professionals (SSP)
10860 Kenwood Rd.
Cincinnati, OH 45242
Contact: Gail Vance Civille, Chm.
Ph: (513)891-9100
URL: http://www.sensorysociety.org
Descr: Advances the science and education of sensory evaluation including consumer research and the role/work of sensory professionals. Provides a forum for sharing knowledge, exchanging ideas, mentoring and educating its members. Promotes and maintains professional conduct and ethical standards among members. **Pub:** *Journal of Sensory Studies* (bimonthly).

146 ■ Society for Social Work and Research (SSWR)
11240 Waples Mill Rd., Ste. 200
Fairfax, VA 22030
Contact: Jennifer Lewis, Admin. Dir.
Ph: (703)352-7797
Fax: (703)359-7562
E-mail: info@sswr.org
URL: http://www.sswr.org
Descr: Promotes the development and dissemination of high quality research to improve the social welfare of all people. Encourages the design, implementation and dissemination of high quality research that addresses critical social practice and social policy issues. Fosters a support network among researchers conducting research on social work practice and social policy in the United States and around the world. Promotes increased research funding and training programs for social workers. **Fnd:** 1994. **Mem:** 1300. **Pub:** *Research on Social Work Practice* (bimonthly); *SSWR News*.

147 ■ SouthernChristian Leadership Conference (SCLC)
PO Box 89128
Atlanta, GA 30312
Contact: Mr. Charles Steele Jr., Pres./CEO
Ph: (404)522-1420
Fax: (404)527-4333
E-mail: president@sclcnational.org
URL: http://www.sclcnational.org
Staff: 12. **Descr:** Nonsectarian coordinating and service agency for local organizations seeking full citizenship rights, equality, and the integration of African-Americans in all aspects of life in the U.S. and subscribing to the Ghandian philosophy of nonviolence. Works primarily in 16 southern and border states to improve civic, religious, economic, and cultural conditions. Fosters nonviolent resistance to all forms of racial injustice, including state and local laws and practices. Conducts leadership training program embracing such subjects as registration and voting, social protest, use of the boycott, picketing, nature of prejudice, and understanding politics. Sponsors citizenship education schools to teach reading and writing, help persons pass literacy tests for voting, and provide information about income tax forms, tax-supported resources, aid to handicapped children, public health facilities, how government is run, and social security. Conducts Crusade for the Ballot, which aims to double the black vote in the South through increased voter registrations. Sponsors lectures; disseminates literature. **Fnd:** 1957. **Pub:** Newsletter (monthly); Magazine (5/year).

148 ■ Support Dogs, Inc. (SDI)
11645 Lilburn Park Rd.
St. Louis, MO 63146
Contact: Scot Seabaugh, Pres.
Ph: (314)997-2325
Fax: (314)997-7202
E-mail: rkjames@supportdogs.org
URL: http://www.supportdogs.org
Staff: 6. **Descr:** Helps people with special needs achieve greater independence and improve the quality of their lives by providing them with professionally trained dogs. Dogs are prematched and custom trained for each individual and assist their owners with tasks such as: opening mall and house doors; pulling wheelchairs long distances and up ramps; loading wheelchairs into vehicles; retrieving a dropped or distant object; bringing the phone and operating an emergency assistance switch; rising to high counters to assist with business transactions. **Fnd:** 1981. **Mem:** 15000. **Pub:** *Paw Prints* (quarterly).

149 ■ Survivor Corps
2100 M St. NW, Ste. 302
Washington, DC 20037
Contact: Jerry White, Exec. Dir./Co-Founder
Ph: (202)464-0007
Fax: (202)464-0011
E-mail: info@survivorcorps.org
URL: http://www.survivorcorps.org
Descr: Survivors of landmines. Aims to empower individuals, families and communities affected by landmines to recover from trauma, reclaim their lives, and fulfill their rights. **Fnd:** 1997.

150 ■ TeamPact
2897 N Druid Hills Rd. NE, Ste. 163
Atlanta, GA 30329-3924
Contact: Horace D. Allen, Founder/CEO
Ph: (404)683-1044
Fax: (404)745-0668
E-mail: horacedallen@teampact.org
URL: http://www.teampact.org
Descr: Provides support and utilizes the social enterprise model to transform men of color. Assists residents in underserved communities of color transition from welfare to work through technology education and certification. Develops programs on improving the retention, graduation and employment rate for men of color. **Fnd:** 2003.

151 ■ Total Family Care Coalition (TFCC)
1214 I St. SE, Ste. 11
Washington, DC 20003-4103
Contact: Gail Avent, Founder
Ph: (202)758-3281
Fax: (202)248-5713
E-mail: totalfamilycarecoalition@gmail.com
URL: http://totalfamilycarecoalition.org
Descr: Seeks to empower families by providing educational resources and support. **Fnd:** 2005.

152 ■ United States Canoe Association (USCA)
487 Wylie School Rd.
Voluntown, CT 06384
Contact: John Edwards, Exec. Dir.
E-mail: canoechamp@aol.com
URL: http://www.uscanoe.com
Descr: Represents individuals interested in canoeing. Encourages the growth of recreational and competitional paddling; preserves scenic and wild waters; promotes and disseminates safety standards; develops design criteria for cruising canoes, kayaks, and related gear; teaches paddling skills and water safety; and sponsors recreational canoe trips and races. Serves as the marathon sanctioning body in the United States that has jurisdiction over competitions in cruising or pleasure-type canoes and kayaks. Establishes club affiliates to support the association's Five-Star Program: Competition-Cruising-Conservation-Camping-Camaraderie. Offers insurance program to race participants and spectators. **Fnd:** 1968. **Mem:** 4000. **Reg. Groups:** 4. **State Groups:** 60. **Pub:** *Canoe News* (bimonthly); *Canoe Plans and Manual*; *Safety Canoeing*; Membership Directory (annual).

153 ■ United States Conference of City Human Services Officials (USCCHSO)
1620 Eye St. NW, 4th Fl.
Washington, DC 20006
Contact: Greg Nickels, Pres.
Ph: (202)293-7330
Fax: (202)293-2352
E-mail: info@usmayors.org
URL: http://www.usmayors.org/humanservices
Staff: 2. **Descr:** Promotes improved coordination and management of human services in cities throughout the U.S. and provides useful information and assistance to city human services officials. Facilitates exchange of ideas and experiences among city human services officials; provides information on city human services activities to federal officials; promotes cooperation among federal, state, and local governments and between the public and private sectors in human services. Defines human services as assistance provided directly to the people such as social services, child day-care, income assistance, and employment and training and services to specific populations such as children and disabled persons. Offers technical assistance and referral services. **Fnd:** 1981. **Pub:** *Impact of Unfunded Federal Mandates and Cost on U.S. Cities*; Brochures.

154 ■ U.S. Metric Association (USMA)
10245 Andasol Ave.
Northridge, CA 91325-1504
Contact: Valerie Antoine, Exec. Dir.
Ph: (818)363-5606
Fax: (818)363-5606
E-mail: valerie.antoine@verizon.net
URL: http://lamar.colostate.edu/~hillger
Staff: 2. **Descr:** Scientists, engineers, teachers, government and industry personnel, students, and laymen interested in promoting greater use of the metric system of measurement; appointed by the U.S. Department of Commerce to represent the private sector on government metric committees. Aids teachers, consumers, government, and industry in implementing the metric system. Maintains a Certified Metrication Specialist Board which is responsible for screening qualified applicants to work with metric system units. Distributes educational fliers on the metric system. Compiles statistics. **Fnd:** 1916. **Mem:** 1000. **Reg. Groups:** 3. **Pub:** *Metric Today* (bimonthly); *SI Metric System Guide*.

155 ■ United Way of Canada - Centraide Canada (UWC-CC)
404-56 Sparks St.
Ottawa, ON, Canada K1P 5A9
Contact: Al Hatton, Pres./CEO
Ph: (613)236-7041
Free: 800-267-8221
Fax: (613)236-3087
E-mail: info@unitedway.ca
URL: http://www2.unitedway.ca/uwcanada/default.aspx
Staff: 30. **Descr:** Provides leadership, support and technical assistance to local United Ways and Centraides in their efforts to improve social conditions in communities across Canada. **Fnd:** 1939. **Mem:** 120.

156 ■ VSA arts
818 Connecticut Ave. NW, Ste. 600
Washington, DC 20006
Contact: Soula Antoniou, Pres.
Ph: (202)628-2800
Free: 800-933-8721
Fax: (202)429-0868
E-mail: info@vsarts.org
URL: http://www.vsarts.org
Descr: Promotes educational and lifelong learning opportunities through the arts for people of all abilities. The Organization's educational programs use alternative curricula and teaching strategies designed to promote optimal learning experiences in a fully inclusive environment, providing youth and adults with an artistic means of self-expression, creating self-confidence and teaching marketable skills while fostering communication and independence. Offers comprehensive programs in literary, performing, and visual arts, in collaboration with local educational agencies, cultural institutions, institutions of higher education, arts agencies, disability associations, and health and rehabilitation organizations in 49 states and DC, and in more than 60 countries worldwide. **Fnd:** 1974. **State Groups:** 49. **Pub:** *Disability Awareness Guide* (periodic).

157 ■ WeTip
PO Box 1296
Rancho Cucamonga, CA 91729-1296

Free: 800-78C-RIME
E-mail: info@wetip.com
URL: http://www.wetip.com

Staff: 60. **Descr:** Business, industry, service clubs, private citizens, foundations, insurance companies, chambers of commerce, and veterans' and fraternal groups. Serves as a citizens' self-help program designed to eliminate drug trafficking and major crimes. Aids in murder arrests and successful apprehensions of criminals who have committed robbery, burglary, fraud, rape, drug trafficking, auto theft, or assault. Anonymous tips are conveyed to law officers and arrests are made only after verified law enforcement investigations. Rewards of up to 1000 are given upon verified factual reports from law enforcement agencies that WeTIP information was received prior to arrest and that the information was helpful in the arrest and conviction. Conducts Witness Anonymous Program, which includes corporations, insurance companies, and institutions. Program is dedicated to reducing crime and fear of crime in business communities by providing crime information directly to the concerned corporation, as well as the appropriate law enforcement agency. Maintains speakers' bureau; compiles statistics; conducts educational programs. **Fnd:** 1972. **Mem:** 19000. **Reg. Groups:** 180. **State Groups:** 6. **Local Groups:** 40. **Pub:** *Personal Student Identification Handbook*; *War on Arson Yearbook* (annual); *We Tip Crimeline* (quarterly); *WeTIP's National Crimefighter* (periodic); *WeTIP's War on Arson* (periodic).

158 ■ Wings and Dreams for Kids
3210 E Fur Hollow Dr.
Sandy, UT 84092-4268
Contact: Aaron Mangone
E-mail: amangone@wingsanddreams.org
URL: http://www.wingsanddreams.org

Descr: Aims to raise awareness and support throughout the aviation industry for the network of hospitals within the Children's Miracle Network. Works to educate families and gives help to children in need. Raises funds and initiates programs for the kids' benefit. **Fnd:** 2008.

159 ■ Women of Hope Project (WOHP)
4876-118 Princess Anne Rd., No. 203
Virginia Beach, VA 23462
Contact: Betsy Beamon, Founder
E-mail: info@womenofhopeproject.org
URL: http://www.womenofhopeproject.org

Descr: Aims to restore hope and dignity to women who have been oppressed and denied personal freedom, health, opportunity and respect. Provides resources and encourages opportunities for self-sufficiency to Afghan women and their families. Provides training programs that give emphasis to daily food and food security needs, economic development opportunities and vocational and business training. **Fnd:** 2001.

160 ■ Women in Photography International (WIPI)
569 N Rossmore Ave., No. 604
Los Angeles, CA 90004
Contact: Jean Ferro, Pres./Interim Exec. Dir.
Ph: (303)462-1444
E-mail: info@womeninphotography.org
URL: http://www.womeninphotography.org

Descr: Promotes the visibility of women photographers and their work through a variety of programs, exhibitions, juried competitions and publications. **Fnd:** 1981. **Pub:** *F2 eZine* (quarterly).

161 ■ Women in Progress (WIP)
PO Box 18323
Minneapolis, MN 55418
Contact: Renae Adam, Exec. Dir.
Free: 800-338-3032
Fax: (612)781-0450
E-mail: info@womeninprogress.org
URL: http://www.womeninprogress.org

Staff: 2. **Descr:** Strives to alleviate poverty by

increasing opportunity for African American women entrepreneurs. **Fnd:** 2002.

162 ■ Women Watch Afrika (WWA)
4151 Memorial Dr., Ste. 205-A
Decatur, GA 30032
Contact: Glory Kilanko, Founder/Pres.
Ph: (404)759-6419
E-mail: gloryk_99@yahoo.com
URL: http://www.womenwatchafrika.org

Descr: Works to promote social and economic development and the rights of women and girls. Seeks to eliminate discrimination. **Fnd:** 1997. **Pub:** Newsletter.

163 ■ Women of Yemen Association
PO Box 16176
San Francisco, CA 94116
Contact: Ali Kassim, Pres.
Ph: (415)753-0973
E-mail: contactus@womenofyemenassociation.org
URL: http://www.womenofyemenassociation.org

Descr: Represents Yemeni women who are giving help to those in need. Provides information on women's issues. Raises awareness on the needs of the community.

164 ■ Women's Sports Foundation (WSF)
1899 Hempstead Tpke., Ste. 400
East Meadow, NY 11554
Contact: Karen Durkin, CEO
Ph: (516)542-4700
Free: 800-227-3988
Fax: (516)542-4716
E-mail: info@womenssportsfoundation.org
URL: http://www.womenssportsfoundation.org

Staff: 25. **Descr:** Encourages and supports the participation of women in sports activities for their health, enjoyment, and mental development; educates the public about athletic opportunities and the value of sports for women. Develops educational guides, provides travel and training grants, scholarships and internship program, and supports the enforcement of the Title IX Amendments of the 1972 Equal Education Act and the Amateur Sports Act. Sponsors an information and resource clearinghouse on women's sports and fitness. Maintains International Women's Sports Hall of Fame. Compiles statistics on women's sports and fitness. **Fnd:** 1974. **Mem:** 6000. **Pub:** *GoGirl News* (quarterly); *Parents Guide to Girls Sports*; *Playing Fair*; *SportsTalk* (quarterly); *The Women's Sports Experience* (quarterly); Newsletter (weekly).

165 ■ Work for Progress
1536 Wynkoop St., Ste. B100
Denver, CO 80202
Contact: Yana Kucher, Operations Dir.
Ph: (303)623-4900
Fax: (720)306-3699
E-mail: info@workforprogress.org
URL: http://www.workforprogress.org

Descr: Focuses on strengthening organizations that work for social change. Recruits job-seekers to work with the nation's nonprofit organizations and progressive campaigns for social justice, consumer protection and the environment. Helps activist-minded job-seekers to connect with progressive campaigns and organizations that are working across the country on progressive issues. **Fnd:** 2008.

State and Local Organizations and Agencies

Alabama

166 ■ Alabama Office of the Attorney General Consumer Affairs Section
500 Dexter Ave.
Montgomery, AL 36130
Contact: W.Rushing Payne, Asst. Attorney Gen.
Ph: (334)242-7300
Free: 800-392-5658
URL: http://www.ago.state.al.us

Descr: Provides three primary services for the State of Alabama and its residents: serves as a mediator of consumers' complaints that relate to retail transaction; investigates allegations of fraud or illegal practices by a business which may violate state or certain federal laws; and offers information and consumer education to the public and how to avoid becoming a victim of fraud.

Alaska

167 ■ Alaska Office of the Attorney General Consumer Protection Unit
1031 W. 4th Ave., Ste. 200
Anchorage, AK 99501-5903
Contact: Daniel S. Sulliva, Attorney Gen.
Ph: (907)269-5100
Fax: (907)276-8554
URL: http://www.law.state.ak.us

Descr: Has the authority to investigate business and trade practices and takes legal action on behalf of the State of Alaska, in order to stop unfair, false, misleading, or deceptive acts and practices.

168 ■ Sail Outdoor Recreation and Community Access
3225 Hospital Dr., Ste. 300
Juneau, AK 99801
Contact: Sierra Kaden
Ph: (907)586-0104
Fax: (907)586-4980
E-mail: info@sailinc.org
URL: http://www.sailinc.org

Arizona

169 ■ Arizona Association of Activity Professionals (AAAP)
PO Box 2206
Scottsdale, AZ 85252
Contact: Carolyn Elliott, Pres.
Ph: (602)339-0645
E-mail: actdirctr@yahoo.com
URL: http://www.theaaap.org

Descr: Provides assistance at the state level to promote certification of activity professionals, working toward uniform professional standards for activity practice.

170 ■ Arizona Office of the Attorney General Consumer Protection
400 W. Congress
South Bldg., Ste. 315
Tucson, AZ 85701-1367
Contact: Terry Goddard, Attorney Gen.
Ph: (520)628-6504
Free: 800-352-8431
Fax: (520)628-6530
URL: http://www.azag.gov

Rmks: The Arizona Attorney General has the authority to bring actions alleging violations of the Consumer Fraud Act.

171 ■ Arizona Office of the Attorney General Consumer Protection and Advocacy Section
1275 W. Washington St.
Phoenix, AZ 85007
Contact: Terry Goddard, Attorney Gen.
Ph: (602)542-5763
Free: 800-352-8431
Fax: (602)542-4579
E-mail: consumerinfo@azag.gov
URL: http://www.azag.gov

Descr: Has the authority to bring actions alleging violations of the Consumer Fraud Act. A private citizen can also bring an action for a violation of the Consumer Fraud Act within one year from the date the claim arises.

Arkansas

172 ■ Arkansas Office of the Attorney General Consumer Protection Division
323 Center St., Ste. 200
Little Rock, AR 72201

Ph: (501)682-2007
Free: 800-482-8982
Fax: (501)682-8118
E-mail: consumer@arkansasag.gov
URL: http://www.ag.state.ar.us
Descr: Represents and protects the State, its subdivisions, the legitimate business community, and the general public as consumers.

California

173 ■ California Department of Consumer Affairs
1625 N. Market Blvd., Ste. N112
Sacramento, CA 95834
Ph: (916)445-1254
Free: 800-952-5210
E-mail: dca@dca.ca.gov
URL: http://www.dca.ca.gov
Descr: Protects and serves California consumers while ensuring a competent and fair marketplace. DCA helps consumers learn how to protect themselves from unscrupulous and unqualified individuals. **Pub:** List of DCA publications online (www.dca.ca/gov/r_r/conspub1.htm).

174 ■ California Office of the Attorney General Public Inquiry Unit
PO Box 944255
Sacramento, CA 94244-2550
Contact: Edmund G. Brown Jr., Attorney Gen.
Ph: (916)322-3360
Free: 800-952-5225
Fax: (916)323-5341
URL: http://www.caag.state.ca.us
Descr: Works to protect Californians and legitimate businesses in the state through enforcement of consumer protection and fair competition laws.

175 ■ Marin Canoe and Kayak Club (MC&KC)
810 Idylberry Rd.
San Rafael, CA 94903
Ph: (415)472-5837
E-mail: paddlemarin@gmail.com
URL: http://marincanoeclub.org
Descr: Dedicated to the sport of canoeing and kayaking and to the preservation of streams and rivers. **Fnd:** 1965.

176 ■ Northern California Council of Activity Coordinators
1630 E Lassen Ave.
Chico, CA 95973
Contact: Lois Sciligo
Ph: (530)894-5429
Descr: Provides assistance at the state level to promote certification of activity professionals, working toward uniform professional standards for activity practice.

177 ■ Southern California Council of Activity Professionals
1501 E 16th St.
Newport Beach, CA 92663
Contact: Joan Flannigan, Pres.
Ph: (760)473-5754
Descr: Provides assistance at the state level to promote certification of activity professionals, working toward uniform professional standards for activity practice.

Colorado

178 ■ Arkansas Valley CattleWomen
38821 County Rd. 810
La Junta, CO 81050
Contact: Cody Koontz
Ph: (719)853-6526
URL: http://www.yampavalley.info/coloradocattlewo.asp

179 ■ Black Mesa CattleWomen
3906 B Rd.
Crawford, CO 81415
Contact: Chandra Carr

Ph: (970)921-3267
URL: http://www.yampavalley.info/coloradocattlewo.asp

180 ■ Cheyenne County CattleWomen
8535 County Rd. B
Eads, CO 81036
Contact: Judy Jacobs
Ph: (719)438-5649
URL: http://www.yampavalley.info/coloradocattlewo.asp

181 ■ Colorado Activity Professionals Association (CAPA)
PO Box 573
Englewood, CO 80151
Contact: John McIlvennan, Pres.
E-mail: bjscott1@comcast.net
URL: http://www.thecapa.org
Descr: Provides assistance at the state level to promote certification of activity professionals, working toward uniform professional standards for activity practice. **Pub:** *Connection* (bimonthly).

182 ■ Colorado Attorney General's Office Consumer Protection Division
1525 Sherman St.
Denver, CO 80203
Ph: (303)866-4500
Free: 800-222-4444
Fax: (303)866-5691
E-mail: stop.fraud@state.co.us
URL: http://www.ago.state.co.us/index.cfm

183 ■ Colorado CattleWomen - Northeast Quarter
165 Mike Lounge Dr.
Burlington, CO 80807
Contact: Heather Hays, Quarter Rep.
E-mail: cuckhays@yahoo.com
URL: http://www.yampavalley.info/coloradocattlewo.asp

184 ■ Colorado CattleWomen - Southwest Quarter
15121 Rd. 22
Dolores, CO 81323
Contact: Sammi Coulon, Quarter Rep.
Ph: (970)882-7359
E-mail: r_coulon@msn.com
URL: http://www.yampavalley.info/coloradocattlewo.asp

185 ■ Custer County CattleWomen
PO Box 448
Westcliffe, CO 81252
Contact: Claricy Rusk
Ph: (719)783-0505
URL: http://www.yampavalley.info/coloradocattlewo.asp

186 ■ Delta CattleWomen
445 Hwy. 348
Delta, CO 81416
Contact: Jo Gore
Ph: (970)874-4672
URL: http://www.yampavalley.info/coloradocattlewo.asp

187 ■ Elbert County CattleWomen
PO Box 68
Matheson, CO 80830
Contact: Jody Davis
Ph: (719)541-2763
URL: http://www.yampavalley.info/coloradocattlewo.asp

188 ■ Fremont County CattleWomen
1625 Sherman Ave.
Canon City, CO 81212
Contact: Geraldine Colette
Ph: (719)275-5552
URL: http://www.yampavalley.info/coloradocattlewo.asp

189 ■ Huerfano County CowBelles
5239 County Rd. 230
Walsenburg, CO 81089

Contact: Francis Davis
Ph: (719)738-2896
URL: http://www.yampavalley.info/coloradocattlewo.asp

190 ■ Larimer County CattleWomen
5215 E County Rd. 16
Loveland, CO 80539
Contact: Patti Ludwick
Ph: (970)669-2003
URL: http://www.yampavalley.info/coloradocattlewo.asp

191 ■ Las Animas County CowBelles
42031 R 36
Trinidad, CO 81082
Contact: Troy Abuokal
Ph: (719)845-1443
URL: http://www.yampavalley.info/coloradocattlewo.asp

192 ■ Lincoln County CattleWomen
6245 State Rd. 71
Ordway, CO 81063
Contact: Janell Reid
Ph: (719)446-5210
URL: http://www.yampavalley.info/coloradocattlewo.asp

193 ■ Mesa County CattleWomen
1098 Q Rd.
Mack, CO 81525
Contact: Verla Rossi
Ph: (970)858-3212
E-mail: rranch@mail2.gj.net
URL: http://www.yampavalley.info/coloradocattlewo.asp

194 ■ Mile Hi CattleWomen
PO Box 16142
Denver, CO 80216-0142
Contact: Stephanie Schara
Ph: (303)294-0146
E-mail: stephanies@maverickranch.com
URL: http://www.yampavalley.info/coloradocattlewo.asp

195 ■ Moffat County CowBelles
1358 County Rd. 178
Craig, CO 81625
Contact: BettyAnn Duzik
Ph: (970)824-4268
URL: http://www.yampavalley.info/coloradocattlewo.asp

196 ■ Montrose CattleWomen
6805 Hwy. 62
Ridgway, CO 81432
Contact: Mary June Wolf
Ph: (970)626-5916
URL: http://www.yampavalley.info/coloradocattlewo.asp

197 ■ Morgan County CattleWomen
10476 Hwy. 52
Wiggins, CO 80654
Contact: Wendy Collier
Ph: (970)483-6353
E-mail: collierplumbing@aol.com
URL: http://www.yampavalley.info/coloradocattlewo.asp

198 ■ National Sports Center for the Disabled (NSCD)
PO Box 1290
Winter Park, CO 80482
Contact: Craig Pollitt, Pres./CEO
Ph: (970)726-1540
Fax: (970)726-4112
E-mail: info@nscd.org
URL: http://www.nscd.org
Staff: 30. **Descr:** Works to serve people with disabilities. Provides outdoor recreation for disabled people in 20 different sports/activities. Offers skiing, snowboarding, snowshoeing, horseback riding, raft-

ing, canoeing, golf, fishing, hiking, camping, sport camps, and many others. **Fnd:** 1972.

199 ■ North Park CattleWomen
13244 Hwy. 14
Walden, CO 80480
Contact: Gina Hackett
E-mail: dghackett54@yahoo.com
URL: http://www.yampavalley.info/coloradocattlewo.
asp

200 ■ Northeast Colorado CattleWomen
61284 County Rd. 14
Holyoke, CO 80734
Contact: Cynthia Hayes
E-mail: cowsru@kci.net
URL: http://www.yampavalley.info/coloradocattlewo.
asp

201 ■ Northeastern Junior College Cattle-Women
147 College Ave.
205 Herbie Hall
Sterling, CO 80751
Contact: Emma Vaughn
Ph: (970)521-7043
E-mail: proffesionalcowgirl@yahoo.com
URL: http://www.yampavalley.info/coloradocattlewo.
asp

202 ■ Pikes Peak CattleWomen
1679 Crystola Rd.
Woodland Park, CO 80863
Contact: Jane Lass
Ph: (719)687-6975
E-mail: richardhl@msn.com
URL: http://www.yampavalley.info/coloradocattlewo.
asp

203 ■ Plateau Valley CattleWomen
PO Box 68
Mesa, CO 81643-0068
Contact: April Nichols
Ph: (970)268-5488
URL: http://www.yampavalley.info/coloradocattlewo.
asp

204 ■ Rio Blanco County CattleWomen
1966 County Rd. 26
Rifle, CO 81650
Contact: Barb Vaughn
Ph: (970)878-5107
E-mail: diamondv@starband.net
URL: http://www.yampavalley.info/coloradocattlewo.
asp

205 ■ Routt County CattleWomen
41505 County Rd. 44
Steamboat Springs, CO 80487
Contact: Marsha Daughenbaugh
Ph: (970)879-1820
E-mail: rockingc@springsips.com
URL: http://www.yampavalley.info/coloradocattlewo.
asp

206 ■ San Luis Valley CattleWomen
23234 W Hwy. 160
Del Norte, CO 81132
Contact: Becky Jo Mayo
Ph: (719)657-3380
URL: http://www.yampavalley.info/coloradocattlewo.
asp

207 ■ Southeast Colorado CattleWomen
33983 E US Hwy. 50
La Junta, CO 81050
Contact: Jennie Adrain
Ph: (719)384-5833
E-mail: whitegateranch@wmconnect.com
URL: http://www.yampavalley.info/coloradocattlewo.
asp

208 ■ Southwestern CowBelles
PO Box 114
Mancos, CO 81328
Contact: Beverly Humiston

Ph: (970)533-1110
URL: http://www.yampavalley.info/coloradocattlewo.
asp

209 ■ Washington County CowBelles
376 County Rd. Y
Lindon, CO 80740
Contact: Pat Hill
Ph: (719)768-3223
URL: http://www.yampavalley.info/coloradocattlewo.
asp

210 ■ Weld County CattleWomen
PO Box 2
Hereford, CO 80732
Contact: Ursula Dill
Ph: (970)895-2452
E-mail: ranchdill@msn.com
URL: http://www.yampavalley.info/coloradocattlewo.
asp

211 ■ Yuma County CattleWomen
306 E Wilson St.
Eckley, CO 80727
Contact: Shelli Smith
Ph: (970)359-2232
URL: http://www.yampavalley.info/coloradocattlewo.
asp

Connecticut

212 ■ Camp Sloane YMCA
124 Indiana Mountain Rd.
Lakeville, CT 06039
Contact: Paul Bryant, Exec. Dir.
Free: 800-545-9367
Fax: (860)435-2599
E-mail: info@camp-sloane.org
URL: http://www.camp-sloane.org

Staff: 170. **Descr:** Provides experiences that promote growth, leadership, and character development based on traditional values in a multi-cultural, outdoor environment through summer camping and year-round education and training programs. **Fnd:** 1928. **Pub:** *The Birch Bark* (quarterly).

213 ■ Connecticut Department of Consumer Protection
165 Capitol Ave.
Hartford, CT 06106-1630
Contact: Jerry Farrell Jr., Commnr.
Ph: (860)713-6050
Free: 800-842-2649
Fax: (860)713-7239
URL: http://www.ct.gov/dcp/site/default.asp

Descr: Mission is to ensure a fair and equitable marketplace, safe products, and services for consumers in the industries that the DCP licenses, regulates, and enforces. **Telecom. Svcs:** TDD phone number is (860)713-7240.

Delaware

214 ■ Delaware Council of Activity Professionals
525 S Spinnaker Ln.
Milton, DE 19968
Contact: Sandy Dole
Ph: (302)645-4664

Descr: Provides assistance at the state level to promote certification of activity professionals, working toward uniform professional standards for activity practice.

215 ■ Delaware Office of the Attorney General Consumer Protection Unit
820 N. French St., 5th Fl.
Wilmington, DE 19801
Ph: (302)577-8600
Free: 800-220-5424

Fax: (302)577-2496
URL: http://attorneygeneral.delaware.gov/

216 ■ Delaware Office of the Attorney General Fraud and Consumer Protection Division
820 N. French St., 5th Fl.
Wilmington, DE 19801
Contact: Beau Biden, Attorney Gen.
Ph: (302)577-8600
Free: 800-220-5424
Fax: (302)577-2496
E-mail: Attorney.General@State.DE.US
URL: http://attorneygeneral.delaware.gov/

Descr: Fraud and Consumer Protection Division protects the public from Securities fraud, Medicaid provider fraud, Patient Abuse, Neglect and Mistreatment, public corruption, white collar crime, organized crime, and misleading or deceptive business practices. TTY phone number is (302)577-5783.

District of Columbia

217 ■ District of Columbia Office of the Attorney General
Office of Consumer Protection
941 N. Capitol St., NE, Ste. 9700
Washington, DC 20004
Ph: (202)442-4615
Fax: (202)727-6546
URL: http://occ.dc.gov/

Enforces the District's consumer protection and antitrust laws.

Florida

218 ■ Florida Office of the Attorney General Economic Crimes Division
1515 N. Flagler Ave., Ste. 900
West Palm Beach, FL 33401
Ph: (561)837-5000
Free: 866-966-7226
Fax: (561)837-5109
URL: http://myfloridalegal.com

Descr: The Economics Crimes Unit is the enforcement authority for all multi-circuit violations of the Florida Deceptive and Unfair Trade Practices Act.

219 ■ Florida Office of the Attorney General Economic Crimes Division
The Capitol
Tallahassee, FL 32399-1050
Ph: (850)414-3300
Free: 866-966-7226
Fax: (850)488-4483
URL: http://myfloridalegal.com

Descr: The Economics Crimes Unit is the enforcement authority for all multi-circuit violations of the Florida Deceptive and Unfair Trade Practices Act.

220 ■ Florida Office of the Attorney General Economic Crimes Division
Concourse Center 4
3507 E. Frontage Rd., Ste. 325
Tampa, FL 33607-1795
Ph: (813)287-7950
Free: 866-966-7226
Fax: (813)281-5515
URL: http://myfloridalegal.com

Descr: The Economics Crimes Unit is the enforcement authority for all multi-circuit violations of the Florida Deceptive and Unfair Trade Practices Act.

221 ■ Florida Office of the Attorney General Economic Crimes Division
110 SE 6th St., 9th Fl.
Fort LAuderdale, FL 33301-5000
Ph: (954)712-4600
Free: 866-966-7226
Fax: (954)712-4706
URL: http://myfloridalegal.com

Descr: The Economics Crimes Unit is the enforcement authority for all multi-circuit violations of the Florida Deceptive and Unfair Trade Practices Act.

222 ■ Florida Office of the Attorney General Economic Crimes Division
135 W. Central Blvd., Ste. 1000
Orlando, FL 32801
Ph: (407)999-5588
Free: 866-966-7226
Fax: (407)245-0365
URL: http://myfloridalegal.com

Descr: The Economics Crimes Unit is the enforcement authority for all multi-circuit violations of the Florida Deceptive and Unfair Trade Practices Act.

223 ■ Florida Office of the Attorney General Multi-State Litigation and Intergovernmental Affairs
The Capitol
Tallahassee, FL 32399
Ph: (850)414-3300
Free: 866-966-7226
Fax: (850)410-2672
URL: http://myfloridalegal.com

224 ■ SER - Jobs for Progress, Florida
PO Box 661597
Miami Springs, FL 33266-1597
Contact: Jose L. Cela, Pres.
Ph: (305)871-2820
Fax: (305)871-5643
E-mail: jlcela@serflorida.org
URL: http://www.serflorida.org

Georgia

225 ■ Georgia Association of Activity Professionals
10016 Pin Point Ave.
Savannah, GA 31406
Contact: Susan Harris
Ph: (912)598-5030

Descr: Provides assistance at the state level to promote certification of activity professionals, working toward uniform professional standards for activity practice.

226 ■ Georgia CattleWomen's Association
PO Box 24570
Macon, GA 31212
Contact: Carla Payne, Pres.
Ph: (478)474-6500
Free: 877-444-BEEF
Fax: (478)474-5732
URL: http://www.gabeef.org/gacattlewomen

227 ■ Georgia CattleWomen's Association - Barrow Chapter
1343 Hog Mountain Rd.
Winder, GA 30680
Contact: Linda Crumley
Ph: (770)725-7804
E-mail: whalinda23@hotmail.com
URL: http://www.gabeef.org/gacattlewomen

228 ■ Georgia CattleWomen's Association - Mid-Georgia Chapter
5500 Barnesville Hwy.
The Rock, GA 30285
Contact: Cynthia Douglas
Ph: (706)647-9414
Fax: (706)647-9234
URL: http://www.gabeef.org/gacattlewomen

229 ■ Georgia Governor's Office of Consumer Affairs
2 Martin Luther King, Jr. Dr., Ste. 356
Atlanta, GA 30334-4600
Ph: (404)651-8600
Free: 800-869-1123
Fax: (404)651-9018
URL: http://consumer.georgia.gov/

Descr: Protects Georgia consumers from unfair, deceptive, and unlawful practices in the marketplace.

Hawaii

230 ■ Hawaii Office of Consumer Protection Department of Commerce and Consumer Affairs
235 S. Beretania St., Rm. 801
Honolulu, HI 96813-2419
Ph: (808)586-2630
Fax: (808)586-2640
E-mail: dcca@dcca.hawaii.gov
URL: http://www.hawaii.gov/dcca

Descr: Investigates consumer complaints alleging unfair or deceptive trade practices in a broad range of areas, including advertising, refunds, motor vehicle rentals, door-to-door sales, and credit practices.

231 ■ Hawaii Office of Consumer Protection Department of Commerce and Consumer Affairs
1063 Lower Main St., Ste. C-216
Wailuku, HI 96793
Ph: (808)984-8244
Fax: (808)243-5807
URL: http://www.hawaii.gov/dcca/ocp

Descr: Investigates consumer complaints alleging unfair or deceptive trade practices in a broad range of areas, including advertising, refunds, motor vehicle rentals, door-to-door sales, and credit practices.

232 ■ Hawaii Office of Consumer Protection Department of Commerce and Consumer Affairs
345 Kekuanaoa. Ste. 12
Hilo, HI 96720
Ph: (808)933-0910
Fax: (808)933-8845
E-mail: dcca@dcca.hawaii.gov
URL: http://www.hawaii.gov/dcca

Descr: Investigates consumer complaints alleging unfair or deceptive trade practices in a broad range of areas, including advertising, refunds, motor vehicle rentals, door-to-door sales, and credit practices.

Idaho

233 ■ Idaho Attorney General's Office Consumer Protection Unit
700 W. State St.
PO Box 83720
Boise, ID 83720-0010
Ph: (208)334-2424
Free: 800-432-3545
Fax: (208)334-2830
URL: http://www2.state.id.us/ag/

Descr: Enforces various consumer laws, including Idaho's Consumer Protection Act, Competition Act, Telephone Solicitation Act, Pay-Per-Telephone Call Act, and Charitable Solicitation Act.

Illinois

234 ■ Bethel New Life (BNL)
4950 W Thomas
Chicago, IL 60651
Contact: Steven McCullough, Pres./CEO
Ph: (773)473-7870
Fax: (773)473-7871
E-mail: smccullough@bethelnewlife.org
URL: http://www.bethelnewlife.org

Descr: Aims to empower individuals, strengthen families, and build neighborhoods through community-driven, solution-oriented, and value-centered approaches. **Fnd:** 1979.

235 ■ Chicago Whitewater Association (CWA)
1701 Genualdi Ave.
Streamwood, IL 60107
Contact: Steve Paolini, Pres.
E-mail: cwa@chicagowhitewater.org
URL: http://www.chicagowhitewater.org

Descr: Works to promote fun, safety, and awareness on the river. Members include individuals

interested in kayaking and canoeing. **Fnd:** 1970. **Mem:** 300. **Pub:** *The Gradient* (10/year).

236 ■ Illinois Activity Professionals Association (IAPA)
1711 W Oakton St.
Arlington Heights, IL 60004
Contact: Mary Rillie, Pres.
Ph: (847)342-1814
E-mail: iapa@illinoisactivities.org
URL: http://www.illinoisactivities.org

Descr: Provides assistance at the state level to promote certification of activity professionals, working toward uniform professional standards for activity practice. **Pub:** *Illinois Activities in ...ACTION* (quarterly).

237 ■ Illinois Consumer Fraud Bureau
100 W. Randolph, 12th Fl.
Chicago, IL 60601
Ph: (312)814-3000
Free: 800-386-5438
Fax: (312)814-2549
E-mail: ag_consumer@atg.state.il.us
URL: http://www.illinoisattorneygeneral.gov

Descr: Protects Illinois consumers and businesses victimized by fraud, deception, and unfair business practices. **Telecom. Svcs:** The TTY toll free number is (800)964-3013.

238 ■ Illinois Governor's Office of Citizens Assistance
500 S. Second St.
Springfield, IL 62706
Ph: (217)782-1090
Free: 800-642-3112
Fax: (217)524-4049
E-mail: governor@state.il.us

Telecom. Svcs: The TTY toll free number is (877)844-5461.

239 ■ Illinois Office of the Attorney General Consumer Fraud Bureau
1001 E. Main St.
Carbondale, IL 62901
Ph: (618)529-6400
Free: 800-243-0607
Fax: (618)529-6416
E-mail: ag.consumer@atg.state.il.us
URL: http://www.illinoisattorneygeneral.gov

Descr: Protects Illinois consumers and businesses victimized by fraud, deception, and unfair business practices. **Telecom. Svcs:** TTY toll free phone number is (877)675-9339.

Indiana

240 ■ Indiana Activity Directors Association
PO Box 215
Mooresville, IN 46158
Contact: Glenda Dearth, Pres.
Ph: (765)763-6438
E-mail: info@indianaactivitydirectors.org
URL: http://members.aol.com/iadassoc

Descr: Provides assistance at the state level to promote certification of activity professionals, working toward uniform professional standards for activity practice. **Pub:** Newsletter (quarterly).

Iowa

241 ■ American Camping Association, Great Rivers Section
2335 300th St.
Ventura, IA 50482-8502
Contact: James Cherry, Section Exec.
Free: 888-748-3783
E-mail: executive@acagreatrivers.org
URL: http://www.acagreatrivers.org

Descr: Enriches the lives of children, youth and

adults through the camp experience. **Pub:** Newsletters.

242 ▪ Iowa Association of Activity Coordinators
1116 Hazel St.
Pella, IA 50219
Contact: Chris Thomas
Ph: (641)628-6660
Descr: Provides assistance at the state level to promote certification of activity professionals, working toward uniform professional standards for activity practice.

243 ▪ Iowa Office of the Attorney General Consumer Protection Division
1305 E. Walnut St., 2nd Fl.
Des Moines, IA 50319
Ph: (515)281-5926
Free: 888-777-4590
Fax: (515)281-6771
E-mail: consumer@ag.state.ia.us
URL: http://www.IowaAttorneyGeneral.org
Descr: Protects consumers from fraud and ensures fair competition in the marketplace.

Kansas

244 ▪ Kansas Activity Directors Association
4 Ridgeway Rd.
Rose Hill, KS 67133
Contact: Susan Hatcher
Ph: (316)733-1340
Descr: Provides assistance at the state level to promote certification of activity professionals, working toward uniform professional standards for activity practice.

245 ▪ Kansas CattleWomen (KCW)
2016 Hayes Dr.
Manhattan, KS 66502
Contact: Carrie Edmonds, Co-Chair
Ph: (785)776-0578
E-mail: carrie_edmonds@hotmail.com
URL: http://users.pld.com/millerfy

246 ▪ Kansas Office of the Attorney General Consumer Protection Division
Memorial Hall, 2nd Fl.
120 SW 10th St.
Topeka, KS 66612-1597
Ph: (785)296-3751
Free: 800-432-2310
Fax: (785)291-3699
E-mail: cprotect@ksag.org
URL: http://www.ksag.org/content/page/id/39
Descr: Investigates scams, mediates, and prosecutes violations of the Consumer Protection Act, Kansas Charitable Organizations and Solicitations Act, the Funeral and Cemetery Merchandise Agreements Act, and the Kansas Cemetery Corporation Act.

247 ▪ Southwest Kansas CattleWomen (SWKCW)
605 Sage Hill Trail
Garden City, KS 67846
Contact: Angie Price, Pres.
Ph: (620)275-2679
E-mail: abprice@odsgc.net
URL: http://users.pld.com/millerfy/SWKCW.htm

Kentucky

248 ▪ Kentucky Office of the Attorney General Consumer Protection Division
700 Capitol Ave., Ste. 118
Frankfort, KY 40601
Ph: (502)696-5389
Free: 888-432-9257
Fax: (502)573-8317

E-mail: consumerprotection@ag.ky.gov
URL: http://ag.ky.gov/consumer/

249 ▪ Kentucky Office of the Attorney General Office of Consumer Protection
310 Whittington Pkwy., Ste. 101
Louisville, KY 40222
Ph: (502)429-7134
Fax: (502)429-7129
URL: http://ag.ky.gov/consumer/

Louisiana

250 ▪ Louisiana Office of the Attorney General Consumer Protection Section
PO Box 94005
Baton Rouge, LA 70804-9005
Ph: (225)326-6465
Free: 800-351-4889
Fax: (225)342-6499
E-mail: ConsumerInfo@ag.state.la.us
URL: http://www.ag.state.la.us
Descr: Has authority to conduct investigations as necessary when the Attorney Generals Office has reason to believe an unfair or deceptive trade practice has taken place, is taking place, or is about to take place. Also conducts consumer awareness seminars throughout Louisiana on subjects such as shoplifting, fraud, theft, and other deceptive trade practices.

251 ▪ VSA Arts of Louisiana
2758-D Brightside Ln.
Baton Rouge, LA 70820
Contact: Ms. Mazie Malveaux, Exec. Dir.
Ph: (225)761-4243
Fax: (225)761-4243
E-mail: vsalouisiana@bellsouth.net
URL: http://www.vsalouisiana.org
Descr: Conducts extensive public awareness programs. Provides additional artists-in-schools and professional development, in the area of arts and arts-technology, to teachers and exceptional and disabled students.

Maine

252 ▪ Maine Office of the Attorney General Consumer Protection Division
6 State House Station
Augusta, ME 04333
Ph: (207)626-8800
Fax: (204)626-8812
E-mail: consumer.mediation@maine.gov
URL: http://www.maine.gov/ag/consumer/index.shtml
Pub: Consumer Law Guide (online at www.maine.gov/ag/consumer/consumer_law_guide.shtml).
Telecom. Svcs: TTY phone number is (207)626-8865.

253 ▪ Maine Office of Consumer Credit Regulation
35 State House Station
Augusta, ME 04333
Ph: (207)624-8527
Free: 800-332-8529
Fax: (207)582-7699
E-mail: william.n.lund@maine.gov
URL: http://www.maine.gov/pfr/consumercredit/contact_us.htm
Descr: Serves the citizens of Maine by administering laws relating to non-bank mortgage lending, consumer credit, and collection. **Telecom. Svcs:** TTY toll free number is (888)577-6690.

Maryland

254 ▪ DC Recreational Activities Coordinators Society
9532 Hale Dr.
Clinton, MD 20735
Contact: Barrington Scott
Ph: (202)895-0104
Descr: Provides assistance at the state level to promote certification of activity professionals, work-

ing toward uniform professional standards for activity practice.

255 ▪ Maryland Activity Coordinators Society
17118 Spataro Ln. NW
Frostburg, MD 21532
Contact: Melanie Whitman
Ph: (301)777-5941
Descr: Provides assistance at the state level to promote certification of activity professionals, working toward uniform professional standards for activity practice.

256 ▪ Maryland Office of the Attorney General Consumer Protection Division
200 St. Paul Pl., 16th Fl.
Baltimore, MD 21202-2021
Ph: (410)528-8662
Free: 888-734-0023
E-mail: consumer@oag.state.md.us
URL: http://www.oag.state.md.us/consumer
Descr: Provides mediation services to consumers to help resolve complaints against businesses and health insurance carriers.

Massachusetts

257 ▪ American Camp Association of New England (ACANE)
80 Westview St.
Lexington, MA 02421
Contact: Bette S. Bussel, Exec. Dir.
Ph: (781)541-6080
Fax: (781)541-6084
E-mail: acane@acane-camps.org
URL: http://acane-camps.org
Staff: 6. **Descr:** Summer camp professionals in Connecticut, Maine, Massachusetts, New Hampshire, Rhode Island, and Vermont. Provides training, management, and programming education. Also provides educational service for parents seeking summer camp for their children. Assists potential staff in locating a job in a camp environment. **Fnd:** 1949. **Mem:** 900. **Pub:** *Communicate* (bimonthly).

258 ▪ Massachusetts Council of Activity Professionals
350 Market St.
Swansea, MA 02777
Contact: Sandy Sarza
Ph: (401)725-8888
Descr: Provides assistance at the state level to promote certification of activity professionals, working toward uniform professional standards for activity practice.

259 ▪ Massachusetts Executive Office of Consumer Affairs and Business Regulation
Ten Park Plaza, Ste. 5170
Boston, MA 02116
Ph: (617)973-8700
Free: 888-283-3757
Fax: (617)973-8799
E-mail: consumer@state.ma.us
URL: http://www.mass.gov/consumer

260 ▪ Massachusetts Office of the Attorney General Consumer Protection and Antitrust Division
1 Ashburton Place
Boston, MA 02108
Ph: (617)727-8400
Fax: (617)727-3265
URL: http://www.mass.gov/ago
Pub: List of consumer forms and publications online.

261 ▪ Massachusetts Office of the Attorney General - Springfield Consumer Protection and Antitrust Division
436 Dwight St.
Springfield, MA 01103
Ph: (413)784-1240
Fax: (413)784-1244

Michigan

262 ■ League of Michigan Bicyclists (LMB)
416 S Cedar St., Ste. A
Lansing, MI 48912
Contact: Mr. Rich Moeller, Exec. Dir.
Ph: (517)334-9100
Free: 888-642-4537
Fax: (517)334-9111
E-mail: office@lmb.org
URL: http://www.lmb.org
Staff: 2. **Descr:** Strives to promote biking for transportation and recreation. Educates motorists and bicyclists on safe sharing of the roadways by partnering with public and private agencies. Promotes bicycle tours and events and conducts charitable activities. Sponsors educational programs on bicycle safety and enjoyment. **Fnd:** 1981. **Mem:** 1500. **Pub:** *Michigan Bicyclist* (quarterly).

263 ■ Michigan Association of Activity Professionals
PO Box 1265
Grand Rapids, MI 49501
Contact: Pam Campau, Pres.
E-mail: cornelle@scmcf.org
URL: http://www.maaponline.org
Descr: Provides assistance at the state level to promote certification of activity professionals, working toward uniform professional standards for activity practice.

264 ■ Michigan Office of the Attorney General
Consumer Protection Division
PO Box 30213
Lansing, MI 48909
Ph: (517)373-1140
Free: 877-765-8388
Fax: (517)241-3771
URL: http://www.michigan.gov/

265 ■ SER - Jobs for Progress, Metro Detroit
9301 Michigan Ave.
Detroit, MI 48210
Contact: Eva Garza Dewaelsche, Pres./CEO
Ph: (313)846-2240
Fax: (313)846-2247
E-mail: info@sermetro.org
URL: http://www.sermetro.org
Fnd: 1971.

Minnesota

266 ■ Minnesota Attorney General's Office
Consumer Services Division
1400 Bremer Tower
445 Minnesota St.
St. Paul, MN 55101
Contact: Lori Swanson, Attorney Gen.
Ph: (612)296-3353
Free: 800-657-3787
Fax: (612)282-2155
E-mail: attorney.general@state.mn.us
URL: http://www.ag.state.mn.us/consumer

267 ■ Minnesota Statewide Association of Activity Professionals
Ridgewater Colorado
2 Century Ave.
Hutchinson, MN 55350
Contact: Julie Reginek
Ph: (320)234-8588
E-mail: julie.reginek@ridgewater.edu
URL: http://www.mnswap.org
Descr: Provides assistance at the state level to promote certification of activity professionals, working toward uniform professional standards for activity practice. **Pub:** *SWAP Line* (3/year).

Mississippi

268 ■ Mississippi Association of Activity Professionals
139 Richardson Rd.
Louisville, MS 39339
Contact: Brandi Krajewski
Ph: (662)779-5121
Descr: Provides assistance at the state level to promote certification of activity professionals, working toward uniform professional standards for activity practice.

269 ■ Mississippi Attorney General's Office
Consumer Protection Division
PO Box 22947
Jackson, MS 39225-2947
Contact: Jim Hood, Attorney Gen.
Ph: (601)359-4230
Free: 800-281-4418
Fax: (601)359-4231
URL: http://www.ago.state.ms.us
Descr: Mission is to shield Mississippi consumers against unfair, false, deceptive, misleading, or unconscionable business practices.

270 ■ Mississippi Department of Agriculture and Commerce
Bureau of Regulatory Services
PO Box 1609
Jackson, MS 39215
Contact: Richard A. Benton, Dir.
Ph: (601)359-1111
Fax: (601)359-1175
URL: http://www.mdac.state.ms.us
Descr: Goal is to effectively and efficiently administer and enforce the laws and regulations charged to the Bureau, to afford a measure of economic protection which citizens cannot provide for themselves, and to strive for equity in the marketplace.

Missouri

271 ■ Activity Directors' Association of Missouri
ABSV
4005 Ripa Ave.
St. Louis, MO 63125
Contact: Linda Amoroso, Pres.
Ph: (314)544-1111
E-mail: gdxgal@yahoo.com
URL: http://www.activitydirectorsofmo.org
Descr: Provides assistance at the state level to promote certification of activity professionals, working toward uniform professional standards for activity practice.

272 ■ Associated Rental Stores of Kansas City
Beagle's Rental Center
5029 NE Vivion Rd.
Kansas City, MO 64119
Contact: Bert Dowell, Pres.
Ph: (816)454-2484
Descr: Promotes the success of members and advances the growth of the rental industry. Fosters better business methods and studies the economic trends in the rental industry.

273 ■ Missouri Consumer Protection Division
Old Post Office Bldg.
815 Olive St., Ste. 200
St. Louis, MO 63101
Contact: Chris Koster, Attorney Gen.
Ph: (314)340-6816
Free: 800-392-8222
Fax: (314)340-7957
E-mail: attgenmail@moago.org
URL: http://ago.mo.gov

Montana

274 ■ Montana Department of Administration
Consumer Protection Office
2225 11th Ave.
PO Box 200151
Helena, MT 59620-0151
Ph: (406)444-4500
Free: 800-481-6896
Fax: (406)444-9680
E-mail: contactocp@mt.gov
URL: http://doj.mt.gov/consumer/

Nebraska

275 ■ Call to Action Nebraska (CTAN)
PO Box 6773
Lincoln, NE 68506
E-mail: ctan@windstream.net
URL: http://www.calltoactionnebraska.org

276 ■ Nebraska CattleWomen
204 E 3rd St.
Alliance, NE 69301-0040
Contact: Carol Young, Admin. Asst.
Ph: (308)762-3005
Fax: (308)762-3016
URL: http://www.nebraskacattlewomen.org

277 ■ Nebraska Department of Justice
2115 State Capitol
PO Box 98920
Lincoln, NE 68509
Contact: Jon Bruning, Attorney Gen.
Ph: (402)471-2682
Free: 800-727-6432
Fax: (402)471-0006
URL: http://www.ago.ne.gov

Nevada

278 ■ Desert Activity Professionals Association
1950 Abarth St.
Las Vegas, NV 89142
Contact: Alisa Wilde
Ph: (702)938-8333
Descr: Provides assistance at the state level to promote certification of activity professionals, working toward uniform professional standards for activity practice.

279 ■ Nevada Bureau of Consumer Protection
555 E. Washington Ave., Ste. 3900
Las Vegas, NV 89101
Contact: Catherine Cortez Masto, Attorney Gen.
Ph: (702)486-3420
Fax: (702)486-3768
URL: http://ag.state.nv.us/org/bcp/bcp.htm
Descr: Enforces various consumer protection by filing lawsuits on behalf of the state of Nevada and the public good.

280 ■ Nevada Consumer Affairs Division
1850 E. Sahara Ave., Ste. 101
Las Vegas, NV 89104
Contact: Dianne Cornwall, Dir.
Ph: (702)486-7355
Free: 800-326-5202
Fax: (702)486-7371
E-mail: ncad@fyiconsumer.org
URL: http://www.fyiconsumer.org
Descr: Regulates deceptive trade practices in the marketplace through investigations and protects consumers by registering and bonding businesses, clubs, telemarketers, organizations, and sports betting information services.

281 ■ Nevada Department of Business and Industry
Consumer Affairs Division
4600 Kietzke Ln., Bldg. B, Ste. 113
Reno, NV 89502
Contact: Dianne Cornwall, Dir.
Ph: (775)688-1800
Free: 800-326-5202
Fax: (702)688-1803
E-mail: renocad@fyiconsumer.org
URL: http://www.fyiconsumer.org
Descr: Regulates deceptive trade practices in the marketplace through investigations and protects consumers by registering and bonding businesses,

clubs, telemarketers, organizations, and sports betting information services.

282 ■ Northern Nevada Activity Professionals Association
PO Box 940
Yerington, NV 89447
Contact: Vanessa Hicks
Ph: (775)463-2301
Descr: Provides assistance at the state level to promote certification of activity professionals, working toward uniform professional standards for activity practice.

283 ■ Southern Nevada Activity Professionals Association
601 Adams Blvd.
Boulder City, NV 89005
Contact: Donna Bird
Ph: (702)293-5151
Descr: Provides assistance at the state level to promote certification of activity professionals, working toward uniform professional standards for activity practice.

New Hampshire

284 ■ Call to Action New England
84 Bunker Hill Rd.
Stratham, NH 03885
Ph: (860)688-5186
E-mail: cta-ne@comcast.net
URL: http://www.ctanewengland.org

285 ■ Granite State Wheelmen
215 S Broadway
PMB 216
Salem, NH 03079-3309
Contact: Bill Kennedy, Pres.
Ph: (603)898-5479
E-mail: gsw-office@bigfoot.com
URL: http://www.granitestatewheelmen.org
Descr: Recreational bicycling. Promotes bicycling safety and education. **Fnd:** 1971. **Mem:** 900. **State Groups:** 1. **Pub:** *Pedal Talk* (bimonthly).

286 ■ Ledyard Canoe Club
PO Box 9
Hanover, NH 03755
Ph: (603)643-6709
E-mail: lcc@dartmouth.edu
URL: http://www.dartmouth.edu/~lcc
Descr: Persons interested in kayaking and canoeing. Provides canoe and kayak rental for the general public. **Fnd:** 1920. **Mem:** 500. **Pub:** *The River Rat* (semiannual).

287 ■ New Hampshire Attorney General's Office
Consumer Protection and Antitrust Bureau
33 Capitol St.
Concord, NH 03301
Ph: (603)271-3641
Fax: (603)271-2110
URL: http://www.doj.nh.gov/consumer/index.html
Descr: Protects consumers from unfair and deceptive business practices in New Hampshire.

New Jersey

288 ■ Consumers League of New Jersey
60 S Fullerton Ave.
Montclair, NJ 07043
Contact: Patricia Royer, Pres.
Ph: (973)744-6449
E-mail: staff@consumersleague.org
URL: http://www.clnj.org
Descr: Represents the interests of Businesses, individuals, lawyers, and libraries. Works to protect consumers in the marketplace and promote consumer responsibility for the condition under which goods and services are produced and distributed. Educates the public on legislation affecting

consumers. Holds quarterly board meeting. **Fnd:** 1900. **Mem:** 300. **Pub:** Newsletter (periodic).

289 ■ New Jersey Activity Professionals Association
13 Aspen Ct.
Paramus, NJ 07652
Contact: Guylaine Mazure
Ph: (201)599-3748
Descr: Provides assistance at the state level to promote certification of activity professionals, working toward uniform professional standards for activity practice.

290 ■ New Jersey Department of Law and Public Safety
Division of Consumer Affairs
124 Halsey St.
PO Box 45025
Newark, NJ 07102
Ph: (973)504-6200
Free: 800-242-5846
Fax: (973)273-8035
E-mail: askconsumeraffairs@lps.state.nj.us
URL: http://www.state.nj.us/lps/ca/home.htm
Descr: Mission is to protect citizens from consumer fraud, blanket the state with consumer education, and make our operation consumer-friendly to the public when they contact us.

New Mexico

291 ■ Association of New Mexico Activity Professionals (ANMAP)
905 N Jefferson
Hobbs, NM 88240
Contact: Inez Crawley, Pres.
Ph: (505)291-2342
E-mail: president@anmap.com
URL: http://www.anmap.com
Descr: Provides assistance at the state level to promote certification of activity professionals, working toward uniform professional standards for activity practice.

292 ■ New Mexico Office of the Attorney General
Consumer Protection Division
PO Drawer 1508
408 Galisteo St.
Santa Fe, NM 87504-1508
Contact: Gary King, Attorney Gen.
Ph: (505)827-6000
Free: 800-678-1508
Fax: (505)827-5826
URL: http://www.nmag.gov/office/Divisions/CP/Default.aspx
Descr: Enforces consumer laws in the state of New Mexico that are intended to shield the public from fraudulent and unfair business practices.

New York

293 ■ American Camp Association - New York
1375 Broadway, 4th Fl.
New York, NY 10018
Contact: Adam Weinstein, Exec. Dir.
Ph: (212)391-5208
Free: 800-777-CAMP
Fax: (212)391-5207
E-mail: camp@aca-ny.org
URL: http://www.aca-ny.org
Descr: Promotes better camp experiences by providing guidance in matching a child's specific interests with appropriate camp programs. **Mem:** 500.

294 ■ Highbridge Community Life
979 Ogden Ave.
Bronx, NY 10452
Contact: Michael Potack, Chm.
Ph: (718)681-2222
Fax: (718)681-4137

E-mail: information@highbridgelife.org
URL: http://www.highbridgelife.org

295 ■ New York Office of the Attorney General
Bureau of Consumer Frauds and Protection
State Capitol
Albany, NY 12224-0341
Ph: (518)474-5481
Free: 800-771-7755
Fax: (518)474-3618
URL: http://www.oag.state.ny.us
Descr: Prosecutes businesses and individuals engaged in fraudulent, misleading, deceptive, or illegal trade practices.

296 ■ New York State Consumer Protection Board
5 Empire State Plaza, Ste. 2101
Albany, NY 12223
Ph: (518)474-8583
Free: 800-697-1220
Fax: (518)486-3936
E-mail: webmaster@consumer.state.ny.us
URL: http://www.nysconsumer.gov
Descr: Mission is to protect New Yorkers by publicizing unscrupulous and questionable business practices and product recalls; conducting investigations and hearings; enforcing the "Do Not Call Law"; researching issues; developing legislation; creating consumer education programs and materials; responding to individual marketplace complaints by securing voluntary agreements; and representing the interests of consumers before the Public Service Commission and other State and federal agencies.

297 ■ North Country Access Cycling
119 Washington St.
Watertown, NY 13601
Contact: Susan Zabriskie, Chair
Ph: (315)782-2838
Fax: (315)782-0802
E-mail: ncaccess@hotmail.com
URL: http://www.ncaccess.org
Fnd: 2002.

298 ■ SER - Jobs for Progress, Westchester
171 E Post Rd., Ste. 201
White Plains, NY 10601
Contact: Ms. Jennifer Aponte, Exec. Dir.
Ph: (914)681-0996
Fax: (914)681-1978
E-mail: serofwestchester@verizon.net

299 ■ Society of Consumer Affairs Professionals in Business, New York Metropolitan Chapter (SOCAP)
PO Box 349
Slate Hill, NY 10973
Contact: Dawn Kirspel, Pres.
Ph: (845)355-7966
E-mail: ljrhorner@nymetrochapter.org
URL: http://www.nymetrochapter.org
Staff: 6. **Descr:** Represents individuals engaged in the management of consumer affairs/customer service divisions of businesses. Aims to provide the tools needed to reach maximum customer loyalty, excellent customer service and value-added innovations.

North Carolina

300 ■ Carolina Canoe Club (CCC)
PO Box 12932
Raleigh, NC 27605
Contact: Greg Short, Business Mgr.
E-mail: info@carolinacanoeclub.org
URL: http://www.carolinacanoeclub.com
Staff: 7. **Descr:** Persons interested in paddlesports. **Fnd:** 1969. **Mem:** 700. **Pub:** *The Paddler* (bimonthly).

301 ■ North Carolina Empowerment
109 N Graham St., Ste. 200
Chapel Hill, NC 27516
Contact: Delores Bailey, Exec. Dir.
Ph: (919)967-8779

Fax: (919)967-0710
E-mail: info@empowerment-inc.org
URL: http://www.empowerment-inc.org

Staff: 4. **Descr:** Promotes a new model of community development that is focused on making real impacts in people's lives while helping neighborhoods organize for greater self-determination.

302 ■ North Carolina Office of the Attorney General
Consumer Protection Division
9001 Mail Service Center
Raleigh, NC 27699-9001
Contact: Roy Cooper, Attorney Gen.
Ph: (919)716-6000
Free: 877-566-7226
Fax: (919)716-6050
URL: http://www.ncdoj.com/

Descr: Works to protect the public from unfair and deceptive business practices.

North Dakota

303 ■ North Dakota Office of the Attorney General
Consumer Protection and Antitrust Division
4205 State St.
PO Box 1054
Bismarck, ND 58502-1054
Contact: Wayne Stenehjem, Attorney Gen.
Ph: (701)328-3404
Free: 800-472-2600
Fax: (701)328-5568
E-mail: cpat@state.nd.us
URL: http://www.ag.state.nd.us/CPAT/CPAT.htm

Descr: Enforces the state's consumer fraud laws in connection with the sale or advertisement of merchandise. Also investigates and prosecutes consumer fraud cases, mediates individual consumer complaints, and educates the public on how to avoid becoming victims of fraud.

Ohio

304 ■ The Adaptive Adventure Sports Coalition (TAASC)
6000 Harriot Rd.
Powell, OH 43065
Contact: Steve Ricker, Pres.
Ph: (614)293-4963
E-mail: info@taasc.org
URL: http://www.taasc.org

Descr: Enhance the quality of life for people with disabilities by providing sports and recreational activities. **Fnd:** 1997.

305 ■ East Side Organizing Project (ESOP)
3631 Perkins Ave., Ste. 4 C-S
Cleveland, OH 44114
Contact: Mark Seifert, Exec. Dir.
Ph: (216)361-0718
Fax: (216)361-0920
E-mail: mseifert@esop-cleveland.org
URL: http://www.esop-cleveland.org

Descr: Creates organized leadership around issues that impact neighborhood life in Cleveland. **Fnd:** 1993.

306 ■ Ohio Attorney General's Office
Consumer Protection Section
30 E. Broad St.
Columbus, OH 43215-3428
Contact: Richard Cordray, Attorney Gen.
Ph: (614)466-8831
Free: 800-282-0515
Fax: (614)728-7583
E-mail: consumer@ag.state.oh.us
URL: http://www.ag.state.oh.us

Descr: Enforces the statutes that regulate consumer transactions, investigates consumer complaints, mediates settlements, and in some cases initiates

litigation against companies accused of unfair, deceptive, or unconscionable sales practices.

307 ■ Ohio CattleWomen (OCW)
16657 Lock-Two Rd.
Botkins, OH 45306
Contact: Joyce Russell, Pres.
Ph: (937)693-3293
E-mail: ksautter@cros.net
URL: http://www.ohiocattlewomen.com

308 ■ Ohio Consumers' Counsel
10 W. Broad St., Ste. 1800
Columbus, OH 43215-3485
Ph: (614)466-8574
Free: 877-742-5622
E-mail: occ@occ.state.oh.us
URL: http://www.pickocc.org

309 ■ Resident Activity Personnel In Ohio
491 N St., Rte. 741
Lebanon, OH 45036
Contact: Tammy Point
Ph: (513)932-5963
Fax: (513)932-7369
E-mail: rapohio@embarqmail.com

Descr: Provides assistance at the state level to promote certification of activity professionals, working toward uniform professional standards for activity practice. **Fnd:** 1975.

Oklahoma

310 ■ Oklahoma Department of Consumer Credit
4545 N. Lincoln Blvd., Ste. 164
Oklahoma City, OK 73105
Contact: Scott Lesher, Admin.
Ph: (405)521-3653
Free: 800-448-4904
Fax: (405)521-6740
E-mail: dhardin@okdocc.state.ok.us
URL: http://www.okdocc.state.ok.us

Descr: Mission is to further understanding of the terms of credit transactions; protect consumer buyers, lessees, and borrowers against unfair practices; and permit and encourage the development of fair and economically sound consumer credit practices in the state of Oklahoma.

311 ■ Oklahoma Office of the Attorney General
Consumer Protection Unit
313 NE 21st St.
Oklahoma City, OK 73105
Contact: W.A.Drew Edmondson, Attorney Gen.
Ph: (405)521-3921
Fax: (405)581-2885
URL: http://www.oag.state.ok.us

Descr: Mission is to protect vulnerable consumers from fraudulent, unfair, or undeceptive business practices.

Oregon

312 ■ Oregon Activity Professional Groups
1447 Holly St.
West Linn, OR 97068
Contact: Mike Watters
Ph: (503)557-7529

Descr: Provides assistance at the state level to promote certification of activity professionals, working toward uniform professional standards for activity practice.

313 ■ Oregon CattleWomen
50887 Happy Valley Rd.
Princeton, OR 97721-9518
Contact: Ruth Moody, Pres.
Ph: (541)259-1654

E-mail: rmoodylym@peoplepc.com
URL: http://orbeef.org/OCW/index.htm

314 ■ Oregon Department of Justice
Financial Fraud/Consumer Protection Section
1162 Court St., NE
Salem, OR 97301-4096
Contact: John Kroger, Attorney Gen.
Ph: (503)378-4400
Free: 877-877-9392
Fax: (503)378-5017
E-mail: consumer.hotline@doj.state.or.us
URL: http://www.doj.state.or.us/finfraud/index.shtml

Descr: Protects consumers in the marketplace, primarily by enforcing Oregon's Unlawful Trade Practices Act. Duties also include educating consumers and businesses about their rights and obligations under the law; representing the interests of the State in multi-state, consumer-related enforcement actions; operating a hotline for consumers with questions or complaints about business practices; and assisting local and state law enforcement agencies with consumer-related matters.

Pennsylvania

315 ■ Pennsylvania Office of the Attorney General
Bureau of Consumer Protection
Strawberry Sq., 14th Fl.
Harrisburg, PA 17120
Ph: (717)787-9707
Free: 800-441-2555
Fax: (717)787-1190
URL: http://www.attorneygeneral.gov/consumers.aspx?id=255

Descr: Investigates commercial and trade practices in the distribution, financing, and furnishing of goods and services to the use of consumers; investigates fraud and deception in the sale, servicing, and furnishing of goods and products, and strives to eliminate such illegal actions; and promotes consumer education and publicize matters relating to consumer fraud, deception, and misrepresentation.

316 ■ Pennsylvania Office of the Attorney General
Bureau of Consumer Protection
Health Care Section
15th Fl. Strawberry Sq.
Harrisburg, PA 17120
Contact: Tom Corbett, Attorney Gen.
Ph: (717)787-9707
Free: 800-441-2555
Fax: (717)787-1190
URL: http://www.attorneygeneral.gov

Descr: Aims to protect the public from unfair healthcare practices and help shape Pennsylvania's policies in favor of the consumer.

Puerto Rico

317 ■ Puerto Rico Department of Consumer Affairs
Minilas Station
PO Box 41059
Santurce, PR 00940
Contact: Fernando J. Bonilla, Sec. of State
Ph: (787)721-0940
Fax: (787)726-0077
E-mail: agarcia2@daco.gobierno.pr

318 ■ Puerto Rico Department of Justice
PO Box 902192
San Juan, PR 00902-0192
Ph: (787)721-2900
Fax: (787)725-2475
URL: http://www.justicia.gobierno.pr/

Rhode Island

319 ■ Rhode Island Department of Attorney General
Consumer Protection Unit
150 S. Main St.
Providence, RI 02903
Contact: Patrick C. Lynch, Attorney Gen.
Ph: (401)274-4400
Free: 888-621-1112
Fax: (401)222-5110
URL: http://www.riag.state.ri.us
Descr: Investigates and mediates consumer complaints concerning unfair and unlawful business practices and misleading advertising arising out of alleged violations of the Deceptive Trade Practices Act.

320 ■ SER - Jobs for Progress, Rhode Island
101 Main St., Ste. 302
Pawtucket, RI 02860
Contact: Lissa Dreyer, Exec. Dir.
Ph: (401)724-1820
Fax: (401)724-8490
E-mail: ldreyer@verizon.net

South Carolina

321 ■ South Carolina Activity Professionals Association (SCAPA)
1530 Pkwy.
Greenwood, SC 29646
Contact: Rita Dixon, Pres.
E-mail: dixon@nctv.com
URL: http://www.scapasc.org
Descr: Provides assistance at the state level to promote certification of activity professionals, working toward uniform professional standards for activity practice.

322 ■ South Carolina Department of Consumer Affairs
3600 Forest Dr., 3rd Fl.
PO Box 5757
Columbia, SC 29250
Contact: Brandolyn Thomas Pinkston, Admin.
Ph: (803)734-4200
Free: 800-922-1594
Fax: (803)734-4286
E-mail: scdca@dca.state.sc.us
URL: http://www.state.sc.us/consumer
Descr: Protects consumers in South Carolina through education, mediation, enforcement, and advocacy.

South Dakota

323 ■ Crook County CattleWomen
295 Jensen Rd.
Belle Fourche, SD 57717
Contact: Janet Jensen, Pres.
Ph: (307)896-2261
E-mail: tjensen@starband.net
URL: http://www.wyocattlewomen.org

324 ■ South Dakota Office of the Attorney General
Consumer Protection Division
1302 E. Hwy. 14, Ste. 3
Pierre, SD 57501-8503
Ph: (605)773-4400
Free: 800-300-1986
Fax: (605)773-7163
E-mail: consumerhelp@state.sd.us
URL: http://www.state.sd.us/attorney/
Descr: The Division investigates false, misleading, or deceptive trade practices; enforces consumer laws designed to protect the public and legitimate business community; advises consumers of their basic rights under consumer laws; assists in the preparation of legislation designed to protect consumer; and advises consumers of complaints on file against specific companies.

Tennessee

325 ■ American Camp Association, Heart of the South
4132 Rocky Branch Rd.
Walland, TN 37886
Contact: Wanda DeWaard
Ph: (865)379-5187
Free: 888-829-2267
E-mail: acaheartofthesouth@acacamps.org

326 ■ Tennessee Attorney General's Office Consumer Advocate and Protection Division of Consumer Protection
PO Box 20207
Nashville, TN 37202-0207
Contact: Cynthia E. Kinser, Deputy
Ph: (615)741-1671
Fax: (615)532-2910
URL: http://attorneygeneral.state.tn.us/cpro/cpro

327 ■ Tennessee Division of Consumer Affairs
500 James Robertson Pkwy.
Nashville, TN 37243-0600
Contact: Mary Clement, Dir.
Ph: (615)741-4737
Free: 800-342-8385
Fax: (615)532-4994
E-mail: consumer.affairs@state.tn.us
URL: http://www.tennessee.gov/consumer/
Descr: Works to protect consumers and businesses from unfair business practices.

Texas

328 ■ Austin Cycling Association (ACA)
PO Box 5993
Austin, TX 78763
Contact: Mr. Stanton Truxillo, Pres.
Ph: (512)282-1987
Fax: (512)282-7413
E-mail: stgetr@worldnet.att.net
URL: http://www.austincycling.org
Staff: 1. **Descr:** Bicycle advocates that promotes bicycle access, safety, education, and enjoyment. Members receive a monthly newspaper and may participate in activities such as weekly bike rides in Central TX. Host fundraising ride each spring. **Fnd:** 1975. **Mem:** 1500. **State Groups:** 1. **Local Groups:** 3. **Pub:** *Southwest Cycling News* (monthly).

329 ■ Girl Scouts of the Permian Basin (GSPB)
5217 N Dixie
Odessa, TX 79762
Contact: Cindy Shelton, CEO
Ph: (432)550-2688
Free: 800-594-5677
Fax: (432)550-9754
E-mail: info@gspb.org
URL: http://www.gspb.org
Staff: 21. **Descr:** Unites to enable girls to develop their potential and become contributors to their communities. Members include girls and adult volunteers in 15-county jurisdiction. Maintains Camp Mitre Peak near Alpine. **Fnd:** 1947. **Mem:** 3800. **Pub:** *Pipeline* (quarterly).

330 ■ Houston Canoe Club (HCC)
PO Box 925516
Houston, TX 77292-5516
Contact: William Grimes, Commodore
E-mail: william.grimes@centerpointenergy.com
URL: http://www.houstoncanoeclub.org
Descr: Persons interested in kayaking and canoeing. **Fnd:** 1964. **Mem:** 350. **Pub:** *The Waterline* (monthly).

331 ■ SER - Jobs for Progress, Fort Worth
Northside Job Ctr.
303 W Central Ave.
Fort Worth, TX 76106
Contact: Andrew Mantecon, Exec. Dir.
Ph: (817)624-3260
Fax: (817)624-3765

E-mail: andrewmantecon@yahoo.com
URL: http://www.fwser.com

332 ■ SER - Jobs for Progress, Texas Gulf Coast
7211 Regency Sq. Blvd., Ste. 150
Houston, TX 77036
Contact: Jesse Castaneda, Exec. Dir.
Ph: (713)773-6000
Fax: (713)773-6010
E-mail: webmaster@serhouston.org
URL: http://www.serhouston.org

333 ■ Texas Association of Family and Consumer Sciences (TAFCS)
PO Box 6731
Lubbock, TX 79493
Contact: Sandra Marquez-Hall PhD, Exec. Dir.
E-mail: sandramarquezhall@sbcglobal.net
URL: http://www.tafcs.org
Descr: Family and consumer science professionals. Works to optimize well-being of families and individuals. **Fnd:** 1918. **Mem:** 650. **Pub:** *TAFCS Action* (3/year); *TAFCS Research Journal* (annual).

334 ■ Texas CattleWomen
PO Box 235
Pattison, TX 77466
Contact: Rosemary Gambino, Pres.
Fax: (281)375-8836
E-mail: rgambino@consolidated.net
URL: http://www.texascattlewomen.org

335 ■ Texas Consumer Protection/Austin Regional Office
PO Box 12548
Austin, TX 78711-2548
Ph: (512)463-2100
Fax: (512)494-8017
E-mail: public.information@oag.state.tx.us
URL: http://www.oag.state.tx.us
Descr: Protects consumers and the legitimate business community by filing civil lawsuits under the Deceptive Trades Practices Act and other consumer protection statutes.

336 ■ Texas Office of the Attorney General Consumer Protection Division
300 W. 15th St., 9th Fl.
PO Box 12548
Austin, TX 78711
Ph: (512)463-2185
Free: 800-621-0508
Fax: (512)473-8301
E-mail: publication.information@oag.state.tx.us
URL: http://www.oag.state.tx.us/consumer/consumer.shtml
Descr: Protects consumers and the legitimate business community by filing civil lawsuits under the Deceptive Trades Practices Act and other consumer protection statutes.

337 ■ Texas Office of the Attorney General Consumer Protection/Houston Regional Office
808 Travis, Ste. 1520
Houston, TX 77002-1702
Ph: (713)223-5886
Fax: (713)223-5821
E-mail: john.owens@oag.state.tx.us
Descr: Protects consumers and the legitimate business community by filing civil lawsuits under the Deceptive Trades Practices Act and other consumer protection statutes.

United States Virgin Islands

338 ■ Virgin Islands Department of Licensing and Consumer Affairs
Rock Shopping Center
Christiansted
St. Croix, VI 00820
Contact: Wayne Biggs, Commnr.
Ph: (340)773-2226
Fax: (340)778-8250
URL: http://http://dlca.vi.gov/links

Descr: Responsible for developing and implementing community-wide activities to inform the public of their rights as consumers, for investigating and settling consumer complaints against businesses, and for promoting activities that protect and guide consumers in the best use of their income.

339 ■ Virgin Islands Department of Licensing and Consumer Affairs
Property and Procurement
Property and Procurement Bldg.
No. 1 Sub Base, Rm. 205
St. Thomas, VI 00802
Ph: (340)774-3130
Fax: (340)776-0675
URL: http://http://dlca.vi.gov

Utah

340 ■ Utah Department of Commerce
Division of Consumer Protection
160 E. 300 S.
Salt Lake City, UT 84111
Ph: (801)530-6601
Free: 800-721-SAFE
Fax: (801)530-6001
E-mail: consumerprotection@utah.gov
URL: http://www.consumerprotection.utah.gov

Vermont

341 ■ Vermont Office of the Attorney General
Consumer Assistance Program
103B Morrill Hall-UVM
Burlington, VT 05405
Ph: (802)656-3183
Free: 800-649-2424
Fax: (802)656-1423
URL: http://www.atg.state.vt.us/

Serves as the contact for consumers who have a problem with good or services they purchased. Also provides information about a consumer's rights, options, and responsibilities.

Virginia

342 ■ American Canoe Association (ACA)
1340 Central Park Blvd., Ste. 210
Fredericksburg, VA 22401
Contact: Martin A. Bartels, Exec. Dir.
Ph: (540)907-4460
Fax: 888-229-3792
E-mail: aca@americancanoe.org
URL: http://www.americancanoe.org

Staff: 11. **Descr:** Provides education on paddling, and supports stewardship in environment, and paddlesport recreation. **Fnd:** 1880. **Mem:** 47000. **Local Groups:** 200. **Pub:** *American Paddler* (quarterly).

343 ■ Virginia Association of Activity Professionals
750 Greencastle Rd.
Richmond, VA 23236
Contact: Patricia Geary
Ph: (540)776-7513

Descr: Provides assistance at the state level to promote certification of activity professionals, working toward uniform professional standards for activity practice.

344 ■ Virginia Department of Agriculture and Consumer Services
Office of Consumer Affairs
102 Governor St.
Richmond, VA 23219
Ph: (804)786-2042
Free: 800-552-9963
Fax: (804)225-2666
E-mail: webmaster.vdacs@vdacs.virginia.gov
URL: http://www.vdacs.virginia.gov/consumers/index.shtml

Descr: Provides protection to consumers against

fraudulent, deceptive, and illegal practices in the marketplace.

345 ■ Virginia Office of the Attorney General
Antitrust and Consumer Litigation Section
900 E. Main St.
Richmond, VA 23219
Ph: (804)786-2116
Free: 800-451-1525
Fax: (804)786-0122
E-mail: mail@oag.state.va.us
URL: http://www.oag.state.va.us

Washington

346 ■ Cascade Bicycle Club
PO Box 15165
Seattle, WA 98115
Contact: Mr. Chuck Ayers, Exec. Dir.
Ph: (206)522-3222
Fax: (206)522-2407
E-mail: info@cascadebicycleclub.org
URL: http://cascade.org

Staff: 15. **Descr:** Aims to create a better community through bicycling. Provides bicycle activities to promote health and recreation. Serves as a voice for the cycling community to improve facilities and the environment for cyclists. Promotes cycling as a transportation alternative. **Fnd:** 1970. **Mem:** 6700. **Pub:** *Cascade Courier* (monthly).

347 ■ SER - Jobs for Progress, Centro Latino
1208 S 10th St.
Tacoma, WA 98405
Contact: David Artis, Chm.
Ph: (253)572-7717
Fax: (253)572-7837
E-mail: reception@clatino.org
URL: http://www.clatino.org

348 ■ Washington Office of the Attorney General
Consumer Resource Center
PO Box 2317
Tacoma, WA 98401
Ph: (253)593-2904
Free: 800-551-9883
Fax: (253)593-2449
E-mail: cynthial@atg.wa.gov
URL: http://www.wa.gov/ago

349 ■ Washington Office of the Attorney General
Consumer Resource Center
1220 Main St., Ste. 549
Vancouver, WA 98660-2964
Ph: (360)759-2150
Fax: (360)759-2159
URL: http://www.atg.wa.gov/consumer

350 ■ Washington Office of the Attorney General
Consumer Resource Center
800 5th Ave., Ste. 2000
Seattle, WA 98104-3188
Ph: (206)464-6684
Free: 800-551-4636
Fax: (206)389-2801
URL: http://www.wa.gov/ago

351 ■ Washington Office of the Attorney General
Consumer Resource Center
1116 W. Riverside
Spokane, WA 99201-1194
Ph: (509)456-3123
Fax: (509)458-3548

352 ■ Washington Office of the Attorney General
Consumer Resource Center
1125 Washington St. SE
PO Box 40118
Olympia, WA 98504-0100

Free: 800-551-4636
URL: http://www.atg.wa.gov

353 ■ Washington Office of the Attorney General
Consumer Resource Center
103 E. Holly St., Ste. 308
Bellingham, WA 98225
Ph: (360)738-6185
Free: 800-551-4636
Fax: (360)738-6190
URL: http://www.atg.wa.gov/FileAComplaint/ByMail.aspx

354 ■ Washington Office of the Attorney General
Consumer Resource Center
500 N. Morain St., Ste. 1250
Kennewick, WA 99336-2607
Ph: (509)734-7140
Free: 800-551-4636
Fax: (509)734-7285
URL: http://www.atg.wa.gov/FileAComplaint/ByMail.aspx

355 ■ Washington State Association of Activity Professionals
614 Sheridan Rd., No. 8
Bremerton, WA 98310
Contact: Rae Anne Randall
Ph: (360)479-1515

Descr: Provides assistance at the state level to promote certification of activity professionals, working toward uniform professional standards for activity practice.

West Virginia

356 ■ West Virginia Office of the Attorney General
Consumer Protection Division
812 Quarrier St., 6th Fl.
PO Box 1789
Charleston, WV 25326
Ph: (304)558-8986
Free: 800-368-8808
Fax: (304)558-0184
E-mail: consumer@wvago.gov
URL: http://www.wvago.us/

Wisconsin

357 ■ American Camp Association, Wisconsin (ACA-WI)
N9659 Hopfensperger Rd.
Appleton, WI 54915
Contact: Kim Rathsack, Section Exec.
Ph: (920)716-4133
E-mail: acawisconsin@sbcglobal.net
URL: http://www.acawisconsin.org

Staff: 2. **Descr:** Represents camp owners, directors, and counselors; businesses and students interested in organized camping. **Fnd:** 1938. **Mem:** 225. **State Groups:** 1. **Pub:** *Badger Tracks* (5/year).

358 ■ Wisconsin Department of Agriculture, Trade and Consumer Protection
Division of Trade and Consumer Protection
200 N. Jefferson St., Ste. 146A
Green Bay, WI 54301
Ph: (608)224-4949
E-mail: datcphotline@datcp.state.wi.us
URL: http://datcp.state.wi.us

359 ■ Wisconsin Department of Agriculture, Trade and Consumer Protection
Division of Trade and Consumer Protection
2811 Agriculture Dr.
PO Box 8911
Madison, WI 53708-8911
Ph: (608)224-4949
Free: 800-422-7128
Fax: (608)224-4939
E-mail: hotline@datcp.state.wi.us
URL: http://www.datcp.state.wi.us

Telecom. Svcs: TDD phone number is (608)224-5058.

360 ■ Wisconsin Representatives of Activity Professionals (WRAP)
Portage County Health Care Center
825 Whiting Ave.
Stevens Point, WI 54481
Contact: Debbie Bera, Pres.
Ph: (715)346-1613
E-mail: berad@co.portage.wi.us
URL: http://www.wrap-wi.org
Descr: Provides assistance at the state level to promote certification of activity professionals, working toward uniform professional standards for activity practice. **Fnd:** 1977.

Wyoming

361 ■ Albany County CowBelles
979 Snowy Range Rd.
Laramie, WY 82070
Contact: Connie Lindemier, Pres.
Ph: (307)745-5186
E-mail: connie@hughes.net
URL: http://www.wyocattlewomen.org

362 ■ Campbell County CattleWomen
128 Clarkelen Rd.
Gillette, WY 82718
Contact: Gwen Geis, Pres.
Ph: (307)686-7456
E-mail: hiewe@wbaccess.net
URL: http://www.wyocattlewomen.org

363 ■ Carbon - Snowy Range CattleWomen
PO Box 63 18C
Saratoga, WY 82331
Contact: Laurie Wood, Pres.
Ph: (307)327-5389
E-mail: laurie@union-tel.com
URL: http://www.wyocattlewomen.org

364 ■ Converse County CowBelles
1390 Twenty Mile Rd.
Lost Springs, WY 82224
Contact: Ammie Murray, Pres.
Ph: (307)358-3867
URL: http://www.wyocattlewomen.org

365 ■ Crowheart CattleWomen
PO Box 606
Crowheart, WY 82512
Contact: Kaye Stoll, Pres.
Ph: (307)486-2241
E-mail: kastoll@wyoming.com
URL: http://www.wyocattlewomen.org

366 ■ Green River Valley CowBelles
Box 184
Big Piney, WY 83113
Contact: Rita Thomas, Pres.
Ph: (307)276-3472
E-mail: rita_thomas@eogresources.com
URL: http://www.wyocattlewomen.org

367 ■ Hot Springs CowBelles
2884 Owl Creek Rd.
Thermopolis, WY 82443
Contact: Barbara Campbell, Pres.
Ph: (307)856-2352
E-mail: jocampbe@wyoming.com
URL: http://www.wyocattlewomen.org

368 ■ Jackson Hole CowBelles
PO Box 3157
Jackson, WY 83001
Contact: Elizabeth Lockhart, Pres.
Ph: (307)733-8038
URL: http://www.wyocattlewomen.org

369 ■ Johnson County CattleWomen
PO Box 137
Kaycee, WY 82639
Contact: Joyce Black, Pres.

Ph: (307)738-2659
URL: http://www.wyocattlewomen.org

370 ■ Lander Valley CattleWomen
381 Lyons Valley Rd.
Lander, WY 82520
Contact: Diane Frank, Pres.
Ph: (307)332-4062
URL: http://www.wyocattlewomen.org

371 ■ Laramie County CowBelles
PO Box 14
Chugwater, WY 82210
Contact: Roxanne Vossler, Pres.
Ph: (307)422-3449
URL: http://www.wyocattlewomen.org

372 ■ Meeteetse CowBelles
16 Rd. 5RU
Meeteetse, WY 82433
Contact: Lili Turnell, Pres.
Ph: (307)868-2407
URL: http://www.wyocattlewomen.org

373 ■ Natrona County CowBelles
PO Box 429
Evansville, WY 82636
Contact: May Stewart, Pres.
Ph: (307)266-5818
URL: http://www.wyocattlewomen.org

374 ■ Niobrara County CattleWomen
18323 US Hwy. 85
Lusk, WY 82225
Contact: Sena Pearson, Pres.
Ph: (307)334-3571
URL: http://www.wyocattlewomen.org

375 ■ Park-Cody Country CattleWomen
60 Rd. 6JM
Cody, WY 82414
Contact: Darlene McCarty, Pres.
Ph: (307)587-3710
E-mail: darmick@wavecom.net
URL: http://www.wyocattlewomen.org

376 ■ Platte-Laramie Peak CattleWomen
195 Bordeaux Rd.
Wheatland, WY 82201
Contact: Donita Graves, Pres.
Ph: (307)322-3344
E-mail: gravesranch@starbank.net
URL: http://www.wyocattlewomen.org

377 ■ Riverton CowBelles
1534 17 Mile Rd.
Riverton, WY 82501
Contact: Darla Griffin, Pres.
Ph: (307)856-1921
URL: http://www.wyocattlewomen.org

378 ■ Sheridan County CattleWomen
62 Hwy. 343
Parkman, WY 82838
Contact: Riki Davidson, Pres.
Ph: (307)655-9400
E-mail: riki@wavecom.net
URL: http://www.wyocattlewomen.org

379 ■ Shoshoni Lysite CowBelles/Goshen CattleWomen
4905 State Hwy. 161, No. A
Torrington, WY 82240
Contact: Dawn Coxbill, Pres.
Ph: (307)532-2871
URL: http://www.wyocattlewomen.org

380 ■ Sweetwater County CowBelles
Fontenelle Rte., Hwy. 372
Kemmerer, WY 83101
Contact: Mickey Thoman, Pres.
Ph: (307)877-9336
URL: http://www.wyocattlewomen.org

381 ■ Uinta County CattleWomen
PO Box 314
Fort Bridger, WY 82933
Contact: Patty Micheli, Pres.

Ph: (307)782-3897
E-mail: pmicheli7@yahoo.com
URL: http://www.wyocattlewomen.org

382 ■ Washakie County CowBelles
222946 C Hwy. 16
Ten Sleep, WY 82442
Contact: Dani Rice, Pres.
Ph: (307)366-2571
URL: http://www.wyocattlewomen.org

383 ■ Weston County CowBelles
1331 Morrisey Rd.
Newcastle, WY 82701
Contact: Nancy Darnell, Pres.
Ph: (307)746-4044
E-mail: mdarnel@vcn.com
URL: http://www.wyocattlewomen.org

384 ■ Wyoming Activity Coordinators Association
1601 E F St.
Torrington, WY 82240
Contact: Sarah DeBolt
Ph: (307)532-4038
Descr: Provides assistance at the state level to promote certification of activity professionals, working toward uniform professional standards for activity practice.

385 ■ Wyoming CattleWomen
1106 Decker Rd.
Sheridan, WY 82801
Contact: Bobi Lentz, Pres.
Ph: (307)750-2465
E-mail: milironf@rangeweb.net
URL: http://www.wyocattlewomen.org
Fnd: 1940.

386 ■ Wyoming Office of the Attorney General Consumer Protection Unit
123 State Capitol Bldg.
Cheyenne, WY 82002
Ph: (307)777-7874
Free: 800-438-5799
Fax: (307)777-7956
E-mail: baylwa@state.wy.us
URL: http://attorneygeneral.state.wy.us/consumer.htm
Descr: Primary duty is the enforcement of the Wyoming Consumer Protection Act, which prohibits unfair and deceptive acts and practices in consumer transactions.

Publications

387 ■ *AAFRC Book on Fund-Raising Consulting*
Giving Institute
4700 W Lake Ave.
Glenview, IL 60025
Ph: (847)375-4709
Fax: 888-374-7258
E-mail: info@givinginstitute.org
URL: http://www.givinginstitute.org
Freq: periodic.

388 ■ *Advances in Consumer Research*
Association for Consumer Research
University of Minnesota Duluth
Labovitz School of Business and Economics
11 E Superior St., Ste. 210
Duluth, MN 55802
Ph: (218)726-7853
Fax: (218)726-6338
E-mail: acr@acrwebsite.org
URL: http://www.acrwebsite.org
Descr: Contains papers presented at the October conference. **Freq:** annual. **Price:** $59.

389 ■ *Adventure Cyclist: The Periodical of Bicycle Adventure*
Adventure Cycling Association
PO Box 8308
Missoula, MT 59802
Ph: (406)721-1776

Fax: (406)721-8754
E-mail: info@adventurecycling.org
URL: http://www.adventurecycling.org
Descr: Contains information on bicycle travel. **Freq:** 9/year. **Price:** included in membership dues.

390 ■ All About Dog Daycare
Pet Care Services Association
1702 E Pikes Peak Ave.
Colorado Springs, CO 80909-5717
Ph: (719)667-1600
Fax: (719)667-0116
E-mail: membership@petcareservices.org
URL: http://www.petcareservices.org
Descr: Provides valuable information for seasoned industry veteran and newcomer. **Price:** $25.95 for nonmembers.

391 ■ Alternatives to Marriage Update
Alternatives to Marriage Project
PO Box 320151
Brooklyn, NY 11232-0151
Ph: (718)788-1911
Fax: (718)832-7098
URL: http://www.unmarried.org
Descr: Features short reviews of books relating to marriage and its alternatives. **Freq:** quarterly.

392 ■ American Canoeist
American Canoe Association
1340 Central Park Blvd., Ste. 210
Fredericksburg, VA 22401
Ph: (540)907-4460
Fax: (703)636-0296
E-mail: aca@americancanoe.org
URL: http://www.acanet.org
Descr: Contains editorials, upcoming events, and articles on conservation, recreation, and safety. **Freq:** quarterly. **ISSN:** 0739-8344.

393 ■ American Guidance for Seniors
Uniformed Services Almanac Inc.
PO Box 4144
Falls Church, VA 22044
Ph: (703)532-1631
E-mail: militaryalmanac@erois.com
URL: http://www.militaryalmanac.com
Descr: Consumer magazine covering benefits and entitlements for seniors and caregivers.

394 ■ ARNOVA Abstracts
Association for Research on Nonprofit Organizations and Voluntary Action
340 W Michigan St., Canal Level Ste. A
Indianapolis, IN 46202
Ph: (317)684-2120
Fax: (317)684-2128
E-mail: tjeavons@arnova.org
URL: http://www.arnova.org
Descr: Lists latest journal and magazine publications on philanthropy, voluntary action and non-profit studies. **Freq:** quarterly. **Price:** $1 for nonmembers, free for members.

395 ■ ARNOVA News
Association for Research on Nonprofit Organizations and Voluntary Action
340 W Michigan St., Canal Level Ste. A
Indianapolis, IN 46202
Ph: (317)684-2120
Fax: (317)684-2128
E-mail: tjeavons@arnova.org
URL: http://www.arnova.org
Descr: Includes articles, research summaries, general information, book reviews and calendar of events. **Freq:** quarterly. **Price:** included in membership dues.

396 ■ Bay Area Consumers' CHECKBOOK
Consumers' Checkbook
1625 K St. NW, 8th Fl.
Washington, DC 20006
Ph: (202)347-9612
Free: 800-213-7283
Fax: (202)347-4000

E-mail: subscriptions@checkbook.org
URL: http://www.checkbook.org
Key Personnel: Caroline Phillips, Contact, info@caroline-phillips.co.uk; Robert Krughoff, Pres.
URL(s): http://www.checkbook.org **Covers:** Evaluations of various types of consumer-oriented services in each issue, such as health services, auto repair services, TV repair shops, etc. Coverage limited to San Francisco Bay metropolitan area. **Entries include:** Generally, each entry contains firm name, address, and details on their policies, prices, and competence derived from the firms and from customer reports. **Freq:** Semiannual. **Price:** $34, individuals.

397 ■ BCA Journal
Black Coaches and Administrators
Pan American Plaza
201 S Capitol Ave., Ste. 495
Indianapolis, IN 46225
Ph: (317)829-5600
Fax: (317)829-5601
E-mail: fkeith@bcasports.org
URL: http://bcasports.cstv.com
Descr: Includes activities and awards updates. **Freq:** quarterly. **Price:** included in membership dues.

398 ■ BCG Application Guide
Board for Certification of Genealogists
PO Box 14291
Washington, DC 20044
E-mail: office@bcgcertification.org
URL: http://www.bcgcertification.org
Descr: Provides requirements and procedures for certification. **Price:** $13 plus shipping and handling.

399 ■ BCG Genealogical Standards Manual
Board for Certification of Genealogists
PO Box 14291
Washington, DC 20044
E-mail: office@bcgcertification.org
URL: http://www.bcgcertification.org
Descr: Clarifies, codifies and organizes standards generally accepted in the field. **Price:** $19.25 plus shipping and handling.

400 ■ BikeLeague News
League of American Bicyclists
1612 K St. NW, Ste. 800
Washington, DC 20006-2850
Ph: (202)822-1333
Fax: (202)822-1334
E-mail: bikeleague@bikeleague.org
URL: http://www.bikeleague.org
Freq: bimonthly.

401 ■ The Birch Bark
Camp Sloane YMCA
124 Indiana Mountain Rd.
Lakeville, CT 06039
Fax: (860)435-2599
E-mail: info@camp-sloane.org
URL: http://www.camp-sloane.org
Descr: Presents news from and about Camp Sloane YMCA. **Freq:** quarterly. **Price:** free.

402 ■ The Black Woman
Black Women in Sisterhood for Action
PO Box 1592
Washington, DC 20013
Ph: (202)543-6013
Fax: (202)543-5719
E-mail: info@bisa-hq.org
URL: http://www.bisa-hq.org
Freq: quarterly.

403 ■ Blessings Report
Blessings International
5881 S Garnett
Tulsa, OK 74146
Ph: (918)250-8101
Fax: (918)250-1281
E-mail: info@blessing.org
URL: http://www.blessing.org

Price: available upon request.

404 ■ Bonus Families Support
Bonus Families
PO Box 1926
Discovery Bay, CA 94514
Ph: (925)516-2681
Fax: (925)634-3300
E-mail: jann@bonusfamilies.com
URL: http://www.bonusfamilies.com
Freq: monthly. **Price:** included in membership dues.

405 ■ Camping/Outdoor Recreation, National Institute on Camping for DisABLED
Special Recreation for disABLED International
701 Oaknoll Dr.
Iowa City, IA 52246-5168
Ph: (319)466-3192
Fax: (319)351-6772
E-mail: john-nesbitt@uiowa.edu
URL: http://www.globalvisionproject.org

406 ■ Camping Today
Family Campers and RVers
4804 Transit Rd., Bldg. 2
Depew, NY 14043
Ph: (716)668-6242
Fax: (716)668-6242
E-mail: fcrvnat@verizon.net
URL: http://www.fcrv.org
Descr: Includes calendar of events, discount information, and convention report. **Freq:** monthly. **Price:** included in membership dues. **ISSN:** 8750-1465.

407 ■ Canadian Almanac and Directory
Micromedia ProQuest
20 Victoria St.
Toronto, ON, Canada M5C 2N8
Ph: (416)362-5211
Free: 800-387-2689
Fax: (416)362-6161
E-mail: info@micromedia.ca
URL: http://il.proquest.com/brand/micromedia.shtml
Key Personnel: Alyson Henry, Contact; Peter Asselstine, Contact. **URL(s):** http://www.micromedia.ca/Directories/Cdn_Almanac.htm **Covers:** 60,000 Canadian agencies and institutions in education, government, and law at all levels (including list of lawyers); other lists of cultural institutions and associations, trade associations, publishers, trade unions, foundations, zoological and botanical gardens, transportation firms, libraries, museums, stock brokerage firms, stock exchange member firms, mutual funds, federal government lobbyists, major Canadian companies exhibition and show planners, electronic communications, astronomical calculations, postal information, liquor regulations, and awards. **Entries include:** Comprehensive lists may include agency or institution name, address, names and titles of key personnel, phone, organization profiles; other lists contain less information. **Freq:** Annual, December.

408 ■ Canoe News
United States Canoe Association
487 Wylie School Rd.
Voluntown, CT 06384
E-mail: canoechamp@aol.com
URL: http://www.uscanoe.com
Descr: Contains paddlesports information. **Freq:** bimonthly. **Price:** available to members only.

409 ■ Canoe Plans and Manual
United States Canoe Association
487 Wylie School Rd.
Voluntown, CT 06384
E-mail: canoechamp@aol.com
URL: http://www.uscanoe.com

410 ■ Canoeing and Kayaking
American Canoe Association
1340 Central Park Blvd., Ste. 210
Fredericksburg, VA 22401
Ph: (540)907-4460
Fax: (703)636-0296

E-mail: aca@americancanoe.org
URL: http://www.acanet.org

411 ■ *Caregiving*
Association of Brethren Caregivers
1451 Dundee Ave.
Elgin, IL 60120-1949
Ph: (847)742-5100
Fax: (847)742-6103
E-mail: abc@brethren.org
URL: http://www.brethren.org/abc
Freq: quarterly. **Price:** $12/year for individuals, $6/year congregation.

412 ■ *Cascade Courier*
Cascade Bicycle Club
PO Box 15165
Seattle, WA 98115
Ph: (206)522-3222
Fax: (206)522-2407
E-mail: info@cascadebicycleclub.org
URL: http://cascade.org
Descr: Contains information on membership. **Freq:** monthly. **Price:** free to members.

413 ■ *CDS Membership Directory*
Community Development Society
17 S High St., Ste. 200
Columbus, OH 43215
Ph: (614)221-1900
Fax: (614)221-1989
E-mail: cds@assnoffices.com
URL: http://www.comm-dev.org
Freq: annual.

414 ■ *CFAnews*
Consumer Federation of America Foundation
1620 I St. NW, Ste. 200
Washington, DC 20006
Ph: (202)387-6121
Fax: (202)265-7989
E-mail: cfa@consumerfed.org
URL: http://www.consumerfed.org
Freq: annual.

415 ■ *Christian Record*
Christian Record Services
PO Box 6097
Lincoln, NE 68506-0097
Ph: (402)488-0981
Fax: (402)488-7582
E-mail: info@christianrecord.org
URL: http://www.christianrecord.org
Descr: Contains contemporary interest stories presented from a Christian viewpoint. **Freq:** quarterly.

416 ■ *Christian Record Talking Magazine*
Christian Record Services
PO Box 6097
Lincoln, NE 68506-0097
Ph: (402)488-0981
Fax: (402)488-7582
E-mail: info@christianrecord.org
URL: http://www.christianrecord.org
Descr: Contains inspirational stories, articles and interviews of contemporary interest presented from a Christian viewpoint. **Freq:** quarterly.

417 ■ *Collaborative Adventures*
Choices
4701 N Keystone Ave., Ste. 150
Indianapolis, IN 46205
Ph: (317)726-2121
Fax: (317)726-2130
E-mail: choices@choicesteam.org
URL: http://www.choicesteam.org
Freq: quarterly.

418 ■ *A Collection of Kennel Floor Plans*
Pet Care Services Association
1702 E Pikes Peak Ave.
Colorado Springs, CO 80909-5717
Ph: (719)667-1600
Fax: (719)667-0116
E-mail: membership@petcareservices.org
URL: http://www.petcareservices.org

Price: $11 for nonmembers.

419 ■ *Community-Based Special Recreation, National Institute on New Models of Community-Based Special Recreation for Dis-ABLED*
Special Recreation for disABLED International
701 Oaknoll Dr.
Iowa City, IA 52246-5168
Ph: (319)466-3192
Fax: (319)351-6772
E-mail: john-nesbitt@uiowa.edu
URL: http://www.globalvisionproject.org

420 ■ *Connection*
Colorado Activity Professionals Association
PO Box 573
Englewood, CO 80151
E-mail: bjscott1@comcast.net
URL: http://www.thecapa.org
Freq: bimonthly.

421 ■ *Conscious Choice*
Conscious Choice Subscriptions
920 N Franklin St., Ste. 202
Chicago, IL 60610
Ph: (312)440-4373
Fax: (312)751-3973
E-mail: info@consciouschoice.com
URL: http://www.dragonflymedia.com
Key Personnel: Christopher Miglino, Publisher/CEO. **URL(s):** http://consciouschoice.com/index.html **Descr:** Consumer magazine covering health, nutrition and environmental issues. **Freq:** Monthly. **Price:** $24, individuals, 3rd class; $36, individuals, first class.

422 ■ *Consumer Action Handbook*
Federal Citizen Information Center
1800 F St. NW, Rm. G-142
Washington, DC 20405
Ph: (202)501-1794
Free: 888-878-3256
Fax: (202)501-4281
E-mail: action.handbook@gsa.gov
URL: http://www.pueblo.gsa.gov
URL(s): http://www.consumeraction.gov **Covers:** More than 2,700 corporate consumer contacts, automobile manufacturers corporate contacts, Better Business Bureau offices, industry third-party dispute resolution programs, trade associations, state and local consumer protection offices, and other federal and state agencies commissioned to handle consumer complaints. **Entries include:** Generally each entry contains company or agency name, name and title of contact, address, phone, including toll-free numbers and numbers for telecommunication devices for the deaf, website, and email address. **Freq:** Biennial, Latest edition 2009. **Price:** Free.

423 ■ *Consumer Advocate*
National Association of Consumer Advocates
1730 Rhode Island Ave. NW, Ste. 710
Washington, DC 20036
Ph: (202)452-1989
Fax: (202)452-0099
E-mail: info@naca.net
URL: http://www.naca.net
Freq: bimonthly. **Price:** included in membership dues.

424 ■ *Consumer Alert Consumer Comments*
Consumer Alert
3050 K St. NW, Ste. 400
Washington, DC 20007
Ph: (202)467-5809
E-mail: consumer@consumeralert.org
URL: http://www.consumeralert.org
Descr: Covers activities and issues of CA. **Freq:** quarterly. **Price:** $35/year, $35 included in membership dues.

425 ■ *Consumer Confidence Survey*
The Conference Board
845 3rd Ave.
New York, NY 10022

Ph: (212)759-0900
Fax: (212)980-7014
E-mail: nick.sutcliffe@conference-board.org
URL: http://www.conference-board.org
Freq: monthly. **Price:** $200/year, $165/year for associates.

426 ■ *Consumer Connections*
Consumers' Association of Canada
PO Box 9300
Ottawa, ON, Canada K1G 3T9
Ph: (613)238-2533
Fax: (613)238-2538
E-mail: info@consumer.ca
URL: http://www.consumer.ca

427 ■ *Consumer Fraud*
ABC-CLIO
130 Cremona Dr.
PO Box 1911
Santa Barbara, CA 93117-5599
Ph: (805)968-1911
Free: 800-368-6868
Fax: (805)685-9685
E-mail: customerservice@abc-clio.com
URL: http://www.abc-clio.com
Key Personnel: Lee E. Norrgard, Author; Julia M. Norrgard, Author. **URL(s):** http://www.abc-clio.com **Entries include:** For individuals--Biographical data. For agencies--Contact information. Principal content of publication is a discussion of tactics used to defraud consumers and a background and history of the topic. **Publication includes:** Individuals notable in the field of consumer advocacy and fraud; federal, national, state, and local agencies that provide information and assistance to consumers.

428 ■ *Consumer Guide*
Publications International Ltd.
7373 N Cicero Ave.
Lincolnwood, IL 60712
Ph: (847)676-3470
Free: 800-595-8484
Fax: (847)676-3671
URL: http://www.pilbooks.com/
Key Personnel: Becky Bell, Exec. Editorial Dir.; Louis Weber, CEO; Frank Peiler, Publisher. **Descr:** Consumer magazine featuring articles on products, sports, entertainment, and health and fitness. **Freq:** 34/year.

429 ■ *Consumer Info News*
EWA Publications
2122 P St. NW, Ste. 201
Washington, DC 20037
Ph: (202)452-9830
Fax: (202)452-9837
E-mail: ewa@ewa.org
URL: http://www.ewa.org/desktopdefault.aspx?page_id=10
Key Personnel: Kevin Browne, Editor; Justin Baron, Publisher; Bill Tarrington, Advertising Mgr. **Descr:** Magazine on consumer interests. **Freq:** Weekly (Mon.). **Price:** $24.

430 ■ *Consumer Information Catalog*
Federal Consumer Information Center Program
1800 F St. NW, Rm. G-142
Washington, DC 20405
Ph: (202)501-1794
E-mail: catalog.pueblo@gsa.gov
URL: http://www.pueblo.gsa.gov
Freq: quarterly. **Price:** free.

431 ■ *Consumer Interests Annual*
American Council on Consumer Interests
555 E Wells St., Ste. 1100
Milwaukee, WI 53202
Ph: (414)918-3189
Fax: (414)276-3349
E-mail: info@consumerinterests.org
URL: http://www.consumerinterests.org

Freq: annual.

432 ■ Consumer Reports
Consumers Union of U.S. Inc.
Consumer Reports for Kids Online
101 Truman Ave.
Yonkers, NY 10703-1057
Ph: (914)378-2455
Fax: (914)378-2928
URL: http://www.consumersunion.org/aboutcu/
publications.html
Descr: Magazine featuring analyses and investigative reporting of products. **Freq:** Monthly. **Price:** $26, individuals, per year.

433 ■ Consumer Resource and Referral Guide
California Department of Consumer Affairs
1625 N Market Blvd., Ste. N 112
Sacramento, CA 95834
Ph: (916)445-1254
Free: 800-952-5210
E-mail: dca@dca.ca.gov
URL: http://www.dca.ca.gov
Key Personnel: Nancy Hardaker, Contact. **URL(s):** http://www.dca.ca.gov/publications/guide/index.shtml **Covers:** Federal, state, local, and legal agencies and trade associations that are involved in resolving consumer complaints in the state of California. **Entries include:** Organization name, address, phone, description of function, examples of complaints within and outside of the organization's jurisdiction, method of registering complaint. **Freq:** Continuous. **Price:** Free.

434 ■ Consumer Services Companies Contact Lists
Sheila Greco Associates L.L.C.
174 County Hwy. 67
Amsterdam, NY 12010
Ph: (518)843-4611
Free: 888-400-8049
Fax: (518)843-5498
E-mail: info@sheilagreco.com
URL: http://www.sheilagreco.com
Descr: Consists of 5 individually-priced lists covering consumer services companies in the U.S. Each list features details for one company and includes global headquarter name, address, phone, fax, U.S. headquarter phone number, URL, company description, ticker symbol, revenues reported, industry type, key executive names and titles. All lists downloadable via PDF format. **Freq:** updated quarterly. **Price:** $21.99, to 49.99.

435 ■ Consumers Digest
Consumers Digest Inc.
8001 N Lincoln Ave.
Skokie, IL 60077
Ph: (847)763-9200
E-mail: postmaster@consumersdigest.com
URL: http://www.consumersdigest.com
Key Personnel: John Manos, Editor; Randy Weber, Publisher. **URL(s):** http://www.consumersdigest.com **Descr:** Magazine featuring product and service evaluation, information, and advice. **Freq:** Bimonthly. **Price:** $15.97, individuals.

436 ■ Consumers' Research
Consumers' Research
800 Maryland Ave. NE
Washington, DC 20002
Ph: (202)546-1713
Fax: (202)546-1638
E-mail: crmag@aol.com
Key Personnel: Alex Adrianson, Editor; M. Stanton Evans, Publisher; Erin Condon, Managing Editor. **Descr:** Magazine that investigates issues of consumer concern, including health, finance, automobiles, nutrition, and government regulation. **Freq:** Monthly. **Price:** $30, individuals.

437 ■ Cornerstone
Stewards of the Range
PO Box 1190
Taylor, TX 76574
Ph: (512)365-8038

Fax: (512)365-7931
E-mail: stewards@stewards.us
URL: http://www.stewards.us
Freq: periodic.

438 ■ Cyclists' Yellow Pages
Adventure Cycling Association
PO Box 8308
Missoula, MT 59802
Ph: (406)721-1776
Fax: (406)721-8754
E-mail: info@adventurecycling.org
URL: http://www.adventurecycling.org
Descr: Includes government agencies, private organizations, and publications useful to bicyclists for planning bike trips. **Freq:** annual. **Price:** included in membership dues.

439 ■ Dialogue
Blindskills Inc.
PO Box 5181
Salem, OR 97304-0181
Ph: (503)581-4224
Free: 800-860-4224
Fax: (503)581-0178
E-mail: info@blindskills.com
URL: http://www.blindskills.com
Key Personnel: Carol M. McCarl, Publisher; Karen Lynn Thomas, Editor. **URL(s):** http://www.blindskills.com/dialogue.html **Descr:** Consumer magazine publishing articles, reviews, fiction, interviews, technology, sports, and information of special interest to visually impaired persons. **Freq:** Quarterly. **Price:** $35, individuals; $7, single issue.

440 ■ Diet & Fitness
Lifetime Periodicals Inc.
2131 Hollywood Blvd.
Hollywood, FL 33020
Ph: (954)925-5242
Fax: (954)925-5244
E-mail: lifetime@shadow.net
Key Personnel: Donald Lessne, President. **Descr:** Consumer magazine covering health, diet, and fitness. **Freq:** Quarterly.

441 ■ The Director
National Funeral Directors Association
13625 Bishop's Dr.
Brookfield, WI 53005-6607
Ph: (262)789-1880
Free: 800-228-6332
Fax: (262)789-6977
E-mail: nfda@nfda.org
URL: http://www.nfda.org
Key Personnel: Chris Raymond, Editor-in-Chief; Benjamin Lund, Asst. Ed.; Kellie Schilling, Dir. of Business Development. **Descr:** Magazine for the funeral service profession. Includes medical updates, business trends, federal regulations, and bereavement issues. **Freq:** Monthly. **Price:** $50, individuals; $65, other countries, including Canada.

442 ■ Directory of Funding Sources in Health, Physical Education, Recreation, and Dance
Fitness Information Technology
275G Coliseum, WVU-PE
PO Box 6116
Morgantown, WV 26506-6116
Ph: (304)293-6888
Free: 800-477-4348
Fax: (304)293-6658
E-mail: fitcustomerservice@mail.wvu.edu
URL: http://www.fitinfotech.com
Key Personnel: Dana D. Brooks, Author; Kim Cameon, Author; Damien Clement, Author. **URL(s):** http://www.fitinfotech.com **Covers:** 140 funding sources from private and corporate foundations, organizations, and other funding agencies. **Entries include:** Organization's contact information. **Price:** $49, individuals.

443 ■ Directory of Kansas Foundation
Kansas Nonprofit Association
PO Box 47054
Topeka, KS

Ph: (785)266-6422
Fax: (785)266-2113
E-mail: knpa@mainstreaminc.net
URL: http://www.mainstreaminc.net/knpa
URL(s): http://www.mainstreaminc.net/knpa/directory.html **Covers:** Independent foundations and non-profit organizations in Kansas. **Freq:** Latest edition 2008-2009. **Price:** $70, members; $90, nonmembers.

444 ■ The Discussion Club 1955-1995
Discussion Club
2206 Rose Garden Dr.
St. Louis, MO 63125
Ph: (314)416-7722
Fax: (314)416-7760
E-mail: discussionclub@sbcglobal.net
URL: http://discussionclub.org

445 ■ Distinguished Black Women
Black Women in Sisterhood for Action
PO Box 1592
Washington, DC 20013
Ph: (202)543-6013
Fax: (202)543-5719
E-mail: info@bisa-hq.org
URL: http://www.bisa-hq.org
Freq: quinquennial.

446 ■ ECA Today
Entertainment Consumers Association
64 Danbury Rd., Ste. 700
Wilton, CT 06897-4406
Ph: (203)761-6180
Fax: (203)761-6184
E-mail: feedback@theeca.com
URL: http://www.theeca.com
Descr: Contains news summaries from leading partner websites, original content about legislation and initiatives and job opportunities.

447 ■ En La Brega
Puerto Rican Studies Association
Cornell University
434 Rockefeller Hall
Ithaca, NY 14853-2502
E-mail: prsa@cornell.edu
URL: http://www.puertorican-studies.org
Freq: semiannual.

448 ■ Encounter
Christian Record Services
PO Box 6097
Lincoln, NE 68506-0097
Ph: (402)488-0981
Fax: (402)488-7582
E-mail: info@christianrecord.org
URL: http://www.christianrecord.org
Descr: Features a regular sermon-of-the-month, Bible-oriented discussions, questions and answers from the Bible and in-depth studies of Bible prophecy. **Freq:** bimonthly.

449 ■ Entourage
Canadian Association for Community Living
York University
Kinsmen Bldg.
4700 Keele St.
Toronto, ON, Canada M3J 1P3
Ph: (416)661-9611
Fax: (416)661-5701
E-mail: inform@cacl.ca
URL: http://www.cacl.ca
Freq: quarterly. **Price:** $18.

450 ■ The Eternalist
International Association for Spiritual Consciousness
401 W International Airport Rd., No. 17
Anchorage, AK 99518-1168
Ph: (907)344-5533
E-mail: spiritma@iasc-ak.org

Descr: Contains schedules for classes, meetings and retreats. **Price:** free for members.

451 ■ Eureka!
Canadian Innovation Centre
Waterloo Research and Technology Park
Accelerator Centre
295 Hagey Blvd., Ste. 15
Waterloo, ON, Canada N2L 6R5
Ph: (519)885-5870
Fax: (519)513-2421
E-mail: info@innovationcentre.ca
URL: http://www.innovationcentre.ca
Freq: quarterly.

452 ■ F2 eZine
Women in Photography International
569 N Rossmore Ave., No. 604
Los Angeles, CA 90004
Ph: (303)462-1444
E-mail: info@womeninphotography.org
URL: http://www.womeninphotography.org
Descr: Contains member profiles and portfolios, interviews, book reviews, product information and gallery listings. **Freq:** quarterly.

453 ■ Family and Consumer Sciences Research Journal
American Association of Family and Consumer Sciences
400 N Columbus St., Ste. 202
Alexandria, VA 22314
Ph: (703)706-4600
Fax: (703)706-4663
E-mail: staff@aafcs.org
URL: http://www.aafcs.org
Descr: Features scholarly, refereed journal reports and records scientific methods and applications of family and consumer sciences research. **Freq:** 5/year. **Price:** $30 for members, $129 for nonmembers individuals, $469 for nonmembers institutions.

454 ■ Farm Folk/City Folk
FarmFolk/CityFolk Society
1937 W 2nd Ave.
Vancouver, BC, Canada V6J 1J2
Ph: (604)730-0450
Fax: (604)730-0451
E-mail: info@ffcf.bc.ca
URL: http://www.ffcf.bc.ca
Descr: Contains project updates, events, news, book reviews and more. **Freq:** quarterly. **Price:** included in membership dues.

455 ■ FDA Consumer
U.S. Government Printing Office and Superintendent of Documents
Mail Stop: IDCC
732 N Capitol St. NW
Washington, DC 20401
Ph: (202)512-1800
Free: 866-512-1800
Fax: (202)512-2104
E-mail: contactcenter@gpo.gov
URL: http://www.gpoaccess.gov
URL(s): http://www.fda.gov/fdac/default.htm **Descr:** Magazine containing in-depth information on how to get healthy and stay healthy, current FDA activities to ensure that the products the agency regulates food, human and animal drugs, medical devices, cosmetics, radiation-emitting products, biologics--are fit to use. **Freq:** Bimonthly, 6/yr. **Price:** $14, individuals; $20, other countries; $5, single issue; $6, single issue, other countries.

456 ■ Forum
BPA Worldwide
Two Corporate Dr., 9th Fl.
Shelton, CT 06484
Ph: (203)447-2800
Fax: (203)447-2900
E-mail: info@bpaww.com
URL: http://www.bpaww.com

Descr: For membership. **Freq:** quarterly.

457 ■ Funeral Consumers Alliance
Funeral Consumers Alliance
33 Patchen Rd.
South Burlington, VT 05403
Ph: (802)865-8300
Free: 800-765-0107
Fax: (802)865-2626
E-mail: fca@funerals.org
URL: http://www.funerals.org
Key Personnel: Joshua Slocum, Exec. Dir., joshua@funerals.org. **URL(s):** http://www.funerals.org **Covers:** over 120 nonprofit funeral consumer groups that educate the public about affordable funeral options. Monitors funeral industry practices for consumers. **Entries include:** Name, address, phone, email address. **Freq:** Quarterly. **Price:** Free.

458 ■ G.ADVOCACY
Genetic Alliance
4301 Connecticut Ave. NW, Ste. 404
Washington, DC 20008
Ph: (202)966-5557
Fax: (202)966-8553
E-mail: info@geneticalliance.org
URL: http://www.geneticalliance.org
Descr: Includes announcements, calendar of events, and membership information. **Freq:** quarterly. **Price:** free, for members only.

459 ■ Gale Journal
Just One Break
570 Seventh Ave.
New York, NY 10018
Ph: (212)785-7300
Fax: (212)785-4513
E-mail: jobs@justonebreak.com
URL: http://www.justonebreak.com
Freq: annual.

460 ■ GAMA International Journal
GAMA International
2901 Telestar Ct., Ste. 140
Falls Church, VA 22042-1205
Ph: (703)770-8184
Fax: (703)770-8182
E-mail: gamamail@gamaweb.com
URL: http://www.gamaweb.com
Descr: Provides solutions for the leaders in the insurance and financial services industry. **Freq:** bimonthly. **Price:** $30 for members (in addition to annual dues), $150 for nonmembers, $175 for international subscriptions. **ISSN:** 1095-7367.

461 ■ Giving
Goodwill Industries Volunteer Services
15810 Indianola Dr.
Rockville, MD 20855
E-mail: contactus@goodwill.org
URL: http://www.goodwill.org
Freq: quarterly.

462 ■ Giving USA
Giving Institute
4700 W Lake Ave.
Glenview, IL 60025
Ph: (847)375-4709
Fax: 888-374-7258
E-mail: info@givinginstitute.org
URL: http://www.givinginstitute.org
Descr: Reports on philanthropy in the United States. **Freq:** annual. **Price:** $49.95. **ISSN:** 0436-0257.

463 ■ Giving USA Update
Giving Institute
4700 W Lake Ave.
Glenview, IL 60025
Ph: (847)375-4709
Fax: 888-374-7258
E-mail: info@givinginstitute.org
URL: http://www.givinginstitute.org

Freq: quarterly.

464 ■ GoGirl News
Women's Sports Foundation
1899 Hempstead Tpke., Ste. 400
East Meadow, NY 11554
Ph: (516)542-4700
Fax: (516)542-4716
E-mail: info@womenssportsfoundation.org
URL: http://www.womenssportsfoundation.org
Descr: Contains information for junior athletes. **Freq:** quarterly.

465 ■ Goodwill Volunteer Services Directory
Goodwill Industries Volunteer Services
15810 Indianola Dr.
Rockville, MD 20855
E-mail: contactus@goodwill.org
URL: http://www.goodwill.org
Freq: annual.

466 ■ Goodwill Volunteer Services Handbook
Goodwill Industries Volunteer Services
15810 Indianola Dr.
Rockville, MD 20855
E-mail: contactus@goodwill.org
URL: http://www.goodwill.org
Freq: annual.

467 ■ The Gradient
Chicago Whitewater Association
1701 Genualdi Ave.
Streamwood, IL 60107
E-mail: cwa@chicagowhitewater.org
URL: http://www.chicagowhitewater.org
Descr: Includes trip reports, event schedules. **Freq:** 10/year.

468 ■ Harvest
Compatible Technology International
800 Transfer Rd., Ste. 6
St. Paul, MN 55114
Ph: (651)632-3912
Fax: (651)204-9033
E-mail: cti@compatibletechnology.org
URL: http://www.compatibletechnology.org
Freq: annual. **Price:** free.

469 ■ House Handbill
Michigan Women's Studies Association
213 W Main St.
Lansing, MI 48933
Ph: (517)484-1880
Fax: (517)372-0170
E-mail: michiganwomen@sbcglobal.net
URL: http://www.michiganwomenshalloffame.org
Freq: quarterly.

470 ■ How Can I Help
RID - U.S.A.
PO Box 520
Schenectady, NY 12301
Ph: (518)372-0034
Fax: (518)370-4917
E-mail: dwi@rid-usa.org
URL: http://www.rid-usa.org
Price: $5.

471 ■ Illinois Activities in ...ACTION
Illinois Activity Professionals Association
1711 W Oakton St.
Arlington Heights, IL 60004
Ph: (847)342-1814
E-mail: iapa@illinoisactivities.org
URL: http://www.illinoisactivities.org
Descr: Features articles about activity programming and resources. **Freq:** quarterly.

472 ■ INFORM Reports
INFORM
5 Hanover Sq., Fl. 19
New York, NY 10004
Ph: (212)361-2400
Fax: (212)361-2412
E-mail: ramsey@informinc.org
URL: http://www.informinc.org

Descr: Provides updates on research projects and outreach activities. **Freq:** quarterly. **Price:** $25. **ISSN:** 0275-522X.

473 ■ The International Network on Feminist Approaches to Bioethics
International Feminist Approaches to Bioethics
5 Riverpoint Rd.
Hastings-on-Hudson, NY 10706
Ph: (914)674-0122
Fax: (914)478-2885
E-mail: adonchin@iupui.edu
URL: http://www.fabnet.org
Freq: semiannual. **Price:** free for members.

474 ■ Internet Shopper
Jupitermedia Corporation
23 Old Kings Hwy. S
Darien, CT 06820
Ph: (203)662-2800
Fax: (203)655-4686
URL: http://www.webmediabrands.com/
URL(s): http://www.internetshopper.com/ **Descr:** Consumer magazine covering Internet shopping. **Freq:** Quarterly.

475 ■ ISWM Membership Directory and Product Guide
International Society of Weighing and Measurement
9707 Key West Ave., Ste. 100
Rockville, MD 20850
Ph: (301)258-1115
Fax: (301)990-9771
E-mail: staff@iswm.org
URL: http://www.iswm.org
Descr: Lists of members alphabetically and by ISWM division; also includes alphabetical product guide and listing product categories. **Freq:** annual. **Price:** $25 for members, $50 for nonmembers.

476 ■ ISWM News
International Society of Weighing and Measurement
9707 Key West Ave., Ste. 100
Rockville, MD 20850
Ph: (301)258-1115
Fax: (301)990-9771
E-mail: staff@iswm.org
URL: http://www.iswm.org
Descr: Contains calendar of events, new product information, industry updates, technical articles, and association news. **Freq:** 3/year. **Price:** available to members only.

477 ■ Journal of the Community Development Society
Community Development Society
17 S High St., Ste. 200
Columbus, OH 43215
Ph: (614)221-1900
Fax: (614)221-1989
E-mail: cds@assnoffices.com
URL: http://www.comm-dev.org
Freq: semiannual. **Price:** $12/issue, $65/year outside U.S. **ISSN:** 0010-3829.

478 ■ Journal of Consumer Affairs
American Council on Consumer Interests
555 E Wells St., Ste. 1100
Milwaukee, WI 53202
Ph: (414)918-3189
Fax: (414)276-3349
E-mail: info@consumerinterests.org
URL: http://www.consumerinterests.org
Freq: semiannual.

479 ■ Journal of Family and Consumer Sciences
American Association of Family and Consumer Sciences
400 N Columbus St., Ste. 202
Alexandria, VA 22314
Ph: (703)706-4600
Fax: (703)706-4663
E-mail: staff@aafcs.org
URL: http://www.aafcs.org
Descr: Carries articles by AACS members and other

professionals. **Freq:** quarterly. **Price:** $175/year for individuals in U.S., $350/year for institutions in U.S., $375/year for institutions outside U.S., $200/year for individuals outside U.S.

480 ■ Just One Breaking News
Just One Break
570 Seventh Ave.
New York, NY 10018
Ph: (212)785-7300
Fax: (212)785-4513
E-mail: jobs@justonebreak.com
URL: http://www.justonebreak.com
Freq: periodic.

481 ■ Know Your Custom Roll Former
Custom Roll Forming Institute
6363 Oak Tree Blvd.
Independence, OH 44131-2500
Ph: (216)901-8800
Fax: (216)901-9190
URL: http://www.pma.org/division

482 ■ Kosher Directory
Union of Orthodox Jewish Congregations of America
11 Broadway
New York, NY 10004
Ph: (212)613-8123
Fax: (212)564-9058
E-mail: kosherq@ou.org
URL: http://www.ou.org
URL(s): http://www.ou.org **Covers:** Over 10,000 consumer, institutional, and industrial products and services produced under the rabbinical supervision of the Orthodox Union. **Entries include:** Product name, name and location of manufacturer, caloric information. Publication contains no listings for Passover products, which are covered separately in the Union's "Passover Products Directory," published annually in February and available without charge. **Freq:** Irregular. **Price:** $12, individuals, 4 issues; $20, individuals, 8 issues; $30, elsewhere, 4 issues; $55, elsewhere, 8 issues.

483 ■ Library Catalog
Christian Overcomers
PO Box 2007
Garfield, NJ 07026
Ph: (973)253-2343
E-mail: overcomers2007@optonline.net
URL: http://www.christian-overcomers.org
Freq: annual.

484 ■ Lifeglow
Christian Record Services
PO Box 6097
Lincoln, NE 68506-0097
Ph: (402)488-0981
Fax: (402)488-7582
E-mail: info@christianrecord.org
URL: http://www.christianrecord.org
Descr: Contains articles and stories from a Christian perspective. **Freq:** quarterly.

485 ■ LifeStyle
Red Hat Society
431 S Acacia Ave.
Fullerton, CA 92831
Ph: (714)738-0001
E-mail: info@redhatsociety.com
URL: http://www.redhatsociety.com
Descr: Contains how-to-crafts, travel excursions, party theme ideas, inspiration on fun and friendship, and much more. **Freq:** bimonthly.

486 ■ Little Tradeswomen Coloring Book
Tradeswomen
1433 Webster St.
Oakland, CA 94612
Ph: (510)891-8773
Fax: (510)891-8775
E-mail: bonnie@tradeswomen.org
URL: http://tradeswomen.org

Price: $4.

487 ■ Local Meeting Directory
Huron Valley Area Intergroup
31 S Huron St.
Ypsilanti, MI 48197
Ph: (734)482-0707
E-mail: office@hvai.org
URL: http://www.hvai.org

488 ■ MABCS Resource Update
MAB Community Services
200 Ivy St.
Brookline, MA 02446
Ph: (617)738-5110
Fax: (617)738-1247
E-mail: webmaster@mabcommunity.org
URL: http://www.mabcommunity.org
Freq: quarterly.

489 ■ Marriage
Resource Pathways Inc.
22525 SE 64th Pl., Ste. 253
Issaquah, WA 98027-9939
Ph: (425)557-4370
Free: 888-702-8882
Fax: (425)557-4366
Key Personnel: Rich Wemhoff, Author. **Descr:** Covers more than 160 print and media resources focusing on marriage for people contemplating marriage, researching marriage, or dealing with marital problems, with bibliographic details, subject, author information, description, and evaluation of source. **Publication includes:** A directory of organizations, including organization address, costs, and area of expertise; and a section of resources that focus on specific marital issues. **Freq:** Published 1999. **Price:** $3.85, individuals, trade paper.

490 ■ Membership List
PUSH Commercial Division
930 E 50th St.
Chicago, IL 60615-2702
Ph: (773)373-3366
Fax: (773)373-3571
E-mail: info@rainbowpush.org
URL: http://www.rainbowpush.org
Freq: quarterly.

491 ■ Metric Today
U.S. Metric Association
10245 Andasol Ave.
Northridge, CA 91325-1504
Ph: (818)363-5606
Fax: (818)363-5606
E-mail: valerie.antoine@verizon.net
URL: http://lamar.colostate.edu/~hillger
Descr: Covers metric developments in the U.S. and abroad. Provides data on new metric literature and metric activities. Includes book reviews and obituaries. **Freq:** bimonthly. **Price:** included in membership dues, $30/year for nonmembers. **ISSN:** 1050-5628.

492 ■ Michigan Bicyclist
League of Michigan Bicyclists
416 S Cedar St., Ste. A
Lansing, MI 48912
Ph: (517)334-9100
Fax: (517)334-9111
E-mail: office@lmb.org
URL: http://www.lmb.org
Descr: Features international bicycling topics. **Freq:** quarterly. **Price:** included in membership dues.

493 ■ Michigan Women: Firsts and Founders, Vol. I & Vol. II
Michigan Women's Studies Association
213 W Main St.
Lansing, MI 48933
Ph: (517)484-1880
Fax: (517)372-0170

E-mail: michiganwomen@sbcglobal.net
URL: http://www.michiganwomenshalloffame.org

494 ■ *Milestones*
Bethany Care Society
1001 17th St. NW
Calgary, AB, Canada T2N 2E5
Ph: (403)210-4663
Fax: (403)284-1992
E-mail: info@bethanycare.com
URL: http://www.bethanycare.com
Freq: 3/year.

495 ■ *Moccasin Print*
Native American Business Alliance
290 Town Center Dr., Ste. 624
Dearborn, MI 48126
Ph: (248)988-9344
Fax: (248)988-9348
E-mail: naba@n-a-b-a.org
URL: http://www.native-american-bus.org
Freq: monthly.

496 ■ *Motorboating*
Times Mirror Magazines Inc.
Two Park Ave.
New York, NY 10016
Ph: (212)779-5000
Descr: Consumer magazine covering boating. **Freq:** Monthly.

497 ■ *National Trade and Professional Associations of the U.S.*
Columbia Books & Information Services
8120 Woodmont Ave., Ste. 110
Bethesda, MD 20814
Ph: (202)464-1662
Free: 888-265-0600
Fax: (202)464-1775
E-mail: info@columbiabooks.com
URL: http://www.columbiabooks.com
Key Personnel: Buck Downs, Contact. **URL(s):** http://www.columbiabooks.com **Covers:** Approximately 7,400 trade associations, professional societies and labor unions. **Entries include:** Name, year established, name of chief executive and other senior staff, address, phone, toll free, fax, e-mail & internet addresses; number of staff members, budget, size of membership; date, expected attendance, and location of annual meeting; publications; historical and descriptive data. Title formerly included '. and Canada and Labor Unions'; Canadian coverage was dropped beginning with 1982 edition, but American labor unions are still included. **Freq:** Annual, Latest edition 44th, Published January 2009. **Price:** $199, individuals, shipping is free to U.S. locations; $299, individuals, mailing list; per thousand; minimum order $269.

498 ■ *Network News: The Bicycle Network's Clipping Service*
Bicycle Network
PO Box 8194
Philadelphia, PA 19101
Ph: (215)222-1253
Fax: (215)222-1253
E-mail: cyclerecycle@hotmail.com
Descr: Includes monitoring world bicycle news between 1979-99 and complete set of back issues 1-80. Back issues available to libraries and collectors. **Freq:** quarterly. **Price:** $6 for 10 or more copies, $10 for 10 or more copies in Canada, $95 plus shipping and handling.

499 ■ *Neutrality*
International Ombudsman Association
390 Amwell Rd., Ste. 403
Hillsborough, NJ 08844
Ph: (908)359-0246
Fax: (908)842-0376
E-mail: info@ombudsassociation.org
URL: http://www.ombudsassociation.org
Descr: Discusses the aspects and value of neutrality

by the ombuds. **Price:** included in membership dues, $13 for nonmembers.

500 ■ *News and Notes*
Red Hat Society
431 S Acacia Ave.
Fullerton, CA 92831
Ph: (714)738-0001
E-mail: info@redhatsociety.com
URL: http://www.redhatsociety.com
Freq: quarterly.

501 ■ *Newsbreak*
Canadian Association for Community Living
York University
Kinsmen Bldg.
4700 Keele St.
Toronto, ON, Canada M3J 1P3
Ph: (416)661-9611
Fax: (416)661-5701
E-mail: inform@cacl.ca
URL: http://www.cacl.ca
Freq: quarterly.

502 ■ *Nonprofit and Voluntary Sector Quarterly*
Association for Research on Nonprofit Organizations and Voluntary Action
340 W Michigan St., Canal Level Ste. A
Indianapolis, IN 46202
Ph: (317)684-2120
Fax: (317)684-2128
E-mail: tjeavons@arnova.org
URL: http://www.arnova.org
Descr: Contains timely articles from a variety of disciplinary perspectives. **Freq:** quarterly. **Price:** included in membership dues. **ISSN:** 0094-0607.

503 ■ *The Northwest NEWS*
Northwest Passage Outing Club
1130 Greenleaf Ave.
Wilmette, IL 60091
Ph: (847)256-4409
Fax: (847)256-4476
E-mail: info@nwpassage.com
URL: http://www.nwpassage.com
Freq: bimonthly. **Price:** $5/year.

504 ■ *Occasional Paper Series*
Association for Research on Nonprofit Organizations and Voluntary Action
340 W Michigan St., Canal Level Ste. A
Indianapolis, IN 46202
Ph: (317)684-2120
Fax: (317)684-2128
E-mail: tjeavons@arnova.org
URL: http://www.arnova.org
Descr: Contains issues about nonprofit management, volunteerism and philanthropy. **Freq:** periodic. **Price:** $25.

505 ■ *The Ombuds Confidentiality Privilege*
International Ombudsman Association
390 Amwell Rd., Ste. 403
Hillsborough, NJ 08844
Ph: (908)359-0246
Fax: (908)842-0376
E-mail: info@ombudsassociation.org
URL: http://www.ombudsassociation.org
Descr: Written for practicing ombuds and/or organizations considering an ombuds function. Deals with the aspect of ombuds confidentiality. **Price:** included in membership dues, $13 for nonmembers.

506 ■ *Ombudsman Handbook*
International Ombudsman Association
390 Amwell Rd., Ste. 403
Hillsborough, NJ 08844
Ph: (908)359-0246
Fax: (908)842-0376
E-mail: info@ombudsassociation.org
URL: http://www.ombudsassociation.org
Descr: Includes information for newly appointed organizational Ombuds or people considering an

Ombuds function in their organization. **Freq:** periodic. **Price:** $35 for members, $125 for nonmembers.

507 ■ *Ombudsman News*
International Ombudsman Association
390 Amwell Rd., Ste. 403
Hillsborough, NJ 08844
Ph: (908)359-0246
Fax: (908)842-0376
E-mail: info@ombudsassociation.org
URL: http://www.ombudsassociation.org
Descr: Includes legal issues, profiles of practicing organizational ombuds, training information, etc. **Freq:** quarterly. **Price:** included in membership dues.

508 ■ *On the Line*
International Family Recreation Association
PO Box 520
Gonzalez, FL 32560-0520
Ph: (850)937-5354
E-mail: rltresource@spydee.net
Price: for commercial members only.

509 ■ *Onboard*
Board for Certification of Genealogists
PO Box 14291
Washington, DC 20044
E-mail: office@bcgcertification.org
URL: http://www.bcgcertification.org
Descr: Includes information about board activities and certification procedures. **Freq:** 3/year. **Price:** $15.

510 ■ *Options Functions and Skills*
International Ombudsman Association
390 Amwell Rd., Ste. 403
Hillsborough, NJ 08844
Ph: (908)359-0246
Fax: (908)842-0376
E-mail: info@ombudsassociation.org
URL: http://www.ombudsassociation.org
Descr: Discusses the role of the ombuds in organizations. **Price:** included in membership dues, $13 for nonmembers.

511 ■ *Ordinary People Doing the Extraordinary (The Story of Ed & Joyce Koupal & the Initiative Process)*
People's Lobby
359 Jean St.
Mill Valley, CA 94941
Ph: (415)383-7880
E-mail: attila@myexcel.com
URL: http://peopleslobby.hypermart.net

512 ■ *Outdoor Recreation in America*
American Recreation Coalition
1225 New York Ave. NW, Ste. 450
Washington, DC 20005-6405
Ph: (202)682-9530
Fax: (202)682-9529
E-mail: arc@funoutdoors.com
URL: http://www.funoutdoors.com
Descr: Features surveys monitoring recreation participation and analysis of societal concerns. **Freq:** annual.

513 ■ *The Overcomer*
Christian Overcomers
PO Box 2007
Garfield, NJ 07026
Ph: (973)253-2343
E-mail: overcomers2007@optonline.net
URL: http://www.christian-overcomers.org
Freq: quarterly.

514 ■ *The Paddler*
Carolina Canoe Club
PO Box 12932
Raleigh, NC 27605
E-mail: info@carolinacanoeclub.org
URL: http://www.carolinacanoeclub.com
Descr: Contains information about trips, activities, and advertisement for paddling gear. **Freq:**

bimonthly. **Price:** included in membership dues, $15 3rd class mail, $20 1st class mail.

515 ■ *Paddler Magazine*
American Canoe Association
1340 Central Park Blvd., Ste. 210
Fredericksburg, VA 22401
Ph: (540)907-4460
Fax: (703)636-0296
E-mail: aca@americancanoe.org
URL: http://www.acanet.org
Descr: Contains information on places to paddle, skill enhancement, gear reviews, industry updates and profiles of leading paddlers. **Freq:** bimonthly. **Price:** $18/year.

516 ■ *Parents Guide to Girls Sports*
Women's Sports Foundation
1899 Hempstead Tpke., Ste. 400
East Meadow, NY 11554
Ph: (516)542-4700
Fax: (516)542-4716
E-mail: info@womenssportsfoundation.org
URL: http://www.womenssportsfoundation.org

517 ■ *Paw Prints*
Support Dogs, Inc.
11645 Lilburn Park Rd.
St. Louis, MO 63146
Ph: (314)997-2325
Fax: (314)997-7202
E-mail: rkjames@supportdogs.org
URL: http://www.supportdogs.org
Descr: Contains education about service dogs. **Freq:** quarterly. **Price:** free.

518 ■ *Pet Age*
Pet Care Services Association
1702 E Pikes Peak Ave.
Colorado Springs, CO 80909-5717
Ph: (719)667-1600
Fax: (719)667-0116
E-mail: membership@petcareservices.org
URL: http://www.petcareservices.org
Freq: bimonthly.

519 ■ *PGHS News*
Protestant Guild for Human Services
411 Waverley Oaks Rd., Ste. 104
Waltham, MA 02452
Ph: (781)893-6000
Fax: (781)893-1171
E-mail: admin@protestantguild.org
URL: http://www.protestantguild.org
Freq: semiannual.

520 ■ *Physical Activity Monitor*
Canadian Fitness and Lifestyle Research Institute
201-185 Somerset St. W
Ottawa, ON, Canada K2P 0J2
Ph: (613)233-5528
Fax: (613)233-5536
E-mail: info@cflri.ca
URL: http://www.cflri.ca
Freq: annual. **Price:** $50 each.

521 ■ *Pipeline*
Girl Scouts of the Permian Basin
5217 N Dixie
Odessa, TX 79762
Ph: (432)550-2688
Fax: (432)550-9754
E-mail: info@gspb.org
URL: http://www.gspb.org
Descr: Contains information about agency. **Freq:** quarterly. **Price:** free.

522 ■ *Planner*
Canadian Association of Gift Planners
325 Dalhousie St., Ste. 201
Ottawa, ON, Canada K1N 7G2
Ph: (613)232-7991
Fax: (613)232-7286
E-mail: membership@cagp-acpdp.org
URL: http://www.cagp-acpdp.org/en/default.aspx

523 ■ *Playing Fair*
Women's Sports Foundation
1899 Hempstead Tpke., Ste. 400
East Meadow, NY 11554
Ph: (516)542-4700
Fax: (516)542-4716
E-mail: info@womenssportsfoundation.org
URL: http://www.womenssportsfoundation.org

524 ■ *Post Harvest*
Compatible Technology International
800 Transfer Rd., Ste. 6
St. Paul, MN 55114
Ph: (651)632-3912
Fax: (651)204-9033
E-mail: cti@compatibletechnology.org
URL: http://www.compatibletechnology.org
Descr: Features activities of CTI and upcoming events. **Freq:** bimonthly. **Price:** free.

525 ■ *Prayer Letter*
Blessings International
5881 S Garnett
Tulsa, OK 74146
Ph: (918)250-8101
Fax: (918)250-1281
E-mail: info@blessing.org
URL: http://www.blessing.org
Freq: monthly.

526 ■ *Pro Bike Directory*
National Center for Bicycling and Walking
26 DeHart Rd.
Maplewood, NJ 07040
Ph: (973)378-3137
E-mail: info@bikewalk.org
URL: http://www.bikewalk.org
Freq: periodic.

527 ■ *Pro Bike News*
National Center for Bicycling and Walking
26 DeHart Rd.
Maplewood, NJ 07040
Ph: (973)378-3137
E-mail: info@bikewalk.org
URL: http://www.bikewalk.org
Freq: monthly.

528 ■ *Pro Bike Proceedings*
National Center for Bicycling and Walking
26 DeHart Rd.
Maplewood, NJ 07040
Ph: (973)378-3137
E-mail: info@bikewalk.org
URL: http://www.bikewalk.org
Freq: biennial.

529 ■ *Professional Connection*
Association for Wedding Professionals International
6700 Freeport Blvd., Ste. 202
Sacramento, CA 95822
Ph: (916)392-5000
Fax: (916)392-5222
E-mail: richard@afwpi.com
URL: http://www.afwpi.com
Descr: Contains articles, member news, and association's announcements. **Freq:** quarterly.

530 ■ *Profile*
Entertainment Industries Council
1760 Reston Pkwy., Ste. 415
Reston, VA 20190
Ph: (703)481-1414
Fax: (703)481-1418
E-mail: eiceast@eiconline.org
URL: http://www.eiconline.org
Freq: monthly.

531 ■ *Profile Directory*
Heavy Duty Representatives Association
160 Symphony Way
Elgin, IL 60120
Ph: (847)760-0067

E-mail: kholliday@wade-partners.com
URL: http://hdra.org
Freq: annual.

532 ■ *Program Guide*
InTouch Networks
15 W 65th St.
New York, NY 10023
Ph: (212)769-6270
Fax: (917)386-9811
E-mail: intouchinfo@jgb.org
URL: http://www.jgb.org/InTouch/default.asp
Freq: annual.

533 ■ *Progressive Rentals Magazine*
Association of Progressive Rental Organizations
1504 Robin Hood Trail
Austin, TX 78703
Fax: (512)794-0097
E-mail: tigercleek@cleeksrto.com
URL: http://www.rtohq.org
Freq: bimonthly. **Price:** included in membership dues, $30/year for nonmembers.

534 ■ *Proxy Season Preview*
As You Sow Foundation
311 California St., Ste. 510
San Francisco, CA 94104
Ph: (415)391-3212
Fax: (415)391-3245
E-mail: asyousow@asyousow.org
URL: http://www.asyousow.org
Freq: quarterly. **Price:** free.

535 ■ *Purple Directory*
Shugar's Publishing
The Purple Directory
15873 Hartwell St.
PO Box 38665
Detroit, MI 48238-0665
Ph: (313)836-8600
Free: 800-377-9129
Fax: (313)836-8600
E-mail: purfuneral@aol.com
URL: http://www.purpledirectory.com
Key Personnel: Miriam E. Pipes, Publisher/Ed. in Ch. **URL(s):** http://www.purpledirectory.com **Covers:** Approximately 2,700 African-American funeral firms in the U.S. **Entries include:** Firm name, address, phone; some listings include fax and name and title of contact. **Freq:** Annual, Latest edition 9th, 2008-2009. **Price:** $40, individuals, inclusive of shipping and handling.

536 ■ *Recreation Advisor*
International Family Recreation Association
PO Box 520
Gonzalez, FL 32560-0520
Ph: (850)937-8354
E-mail: rltresource@spydee.net
Descr: Tabloid covering the recreation, leisure, and travel industry. Includes association and legislative news, calendar of events, and membership profiles. **Freq:** 10/year. **Price:** included in membership dues.

537 ■ *Rental-To-Own Almanac*
Association of Progressive Rental Organizations
1504 Robin Hood Trail
Austin, TX 78703
Fax: (512)794-0097
E-mail: tigercleek@cleeksrto.com
URL: http://www.rtohq.org
Freq: annual.

538 ■ *Rental Viewpoint Online*
Association of Progressive Rental Organizations
1504 Robin Hood Trail
Austin, TX 78703
Fax: (512)794-0097
E-mail: tigercleek@cleeksrto.com
URL: http://www.rtohq.org
Freq: biweekly. **Price:** free.

539 ■ *Representative Locator Services*
Heavy Duty Representatives Association
160 Symphony Way

Elgin, IL 60120
Ph: (847)760-0067
E-mail: kholliday@wade-partners.com
URL: http://hdra.org

540 ■ Reprisal, Retaliation and Redress
International Ombudsman Association
390 Amwell Rd., Ste. 403
Hillsborough, NJ 08844
Ph: (908)359-0246
Fax: (908)842-0376
E-mail: info@ombudsassociation.org
URL: http://www.ombudsassociation.org
Descr: Written for practicing ombuds dealing with potential retaliation problems within the work area. **Price:** included in membership dues, $10 for nonmembers.

541 ■ Research on Social Work Practice
Society for Social Work and Research
11240 Waples Mill Rd., Ste. 200
Fairfax, VA 22030
Ph: (703)352-7797
Fax: (703)359-7562
E-mail: info@sswr.org
URL: http://www.sswr.org
Freq: bimonthly. **Price:** included in membership dues.

542 ■ Riben Nehrah Quarterly
Allied Beauty Association
145 Traders Blvd. E, Units 26 and 27
Mississauga, ON, Canada L4Z 3L3
Ph: (905)568-0158
Fax: (905)568-1581
E-mail: abacan@idirect.com
URL: http://www.abacanada.com
Freq: quarterly.

543 ■ RTO Today
Association of Progressive Rental Organizations
1504 Robin Hood Trail
Austin, TX 78703
Fax: (512)794-0097
E-mail: tigercleek@cleeksrto.com
URL: http://www.rtohq.org
Descr: Contains news, upcoming events, association news and more. **Freq:** weekly.

544 ■ Scaleman's Handbook of Metrology
International Society of Weighing and Measurement
9707 Key West Ave., Ste. 100
Rockville, MD 20850
Ph: (301)258-1115
Fax: (301)990-9771
E-mail: staff@iswm.org
URL: http://www.iswm.org
Price: $20 for members, $40 for nonmembers.

545 ■ SFL Bulletin
Ski for Light
1455 W Lake St.
Minneapolis, MN 55408
Ph: (612)827-3232
E-mail: info@sfl.org
URL: http://www.sfl.org
Descr: Contains organizational news. **Freq:** quarterly. **Price:** free.

546 ■ Shop America
Shop America Alliance
1308 Westhampton Woods Ct.
Chesterfield, MO 63005
Ph: (707)224-3795
E-mail: shopamericanews@aol.com
URL: http://www.shopamericavip.com

547 ■ Showcase
GAMA International
2901 Telestar Ct., Ste. 140
Falls Church, VA 22042-1205
Ph: (703)770-8184
Fax: (703)770-8182

E-mail: gamamail@gamaweb.com
URL: http://www.gamaweb.com

548 ■ SI Metric System Guide
U.S. Metric Association
10245 Andasol Ave.
Northridge, CA 91325-1504
Ph: (818)363-5606
Fax: (818)363-5606
E-mail: valerie.antoine@verizon.net
URL: http://lamar.colostate.edu/~hillger

549 ■ Significant Living Today
Significant Living
2880 Vision Ct.
Aurora, IL 60506
Ph: (630)801-3838
Fax: (630)801-3839
E-mail: info@significantliving.org
URL: http://significantliving.org
Descr: Provides updates on new benefits, travel opportunities, and CAP activities. **Freq:** bimonthly.

550 ■ Sister to Sister/S2S
Women of Color Resource Center
1611 Telegraph Ave., No. 303
Oakland, CA 94612
Ph: (510)444-2700
Fax: (510)444-2711
E-mail: info@coloredgirls.org
URL: http://www.coloredgirls.org
Descr: Provides highlights of women-of-color organizing across the U.S. and updates on events and issues. **Freq:** quarterly. **Price:** $35/three issues, $55/year for organizations. **ISSN:** 1090-3887.

551 ■ Ski for Light Event Journal
Ski for Light
1455 W Lake St.
Minneapolis, MN 55408
Ph: (612)827-3232
E-mail: info@sfl.org
URL: http://www.sfl.org
Descr: Contains schedule of the international week and background information about the program. **Freq:** annual.

552 ■ SLA Manual
Surplus Line Association of California
50 California St., 18th Fl.
San Francisco, CA 94111
Ph: (415)434-4900
Fax: (415)434-3716
E-mail: tpierce@slacal.org
URL: http://www.sla-cal.org
Descr: Provides members of SLA key information about surplus line business.

553 ■ SLA Quarterly
Surplus Line Association of California
50 California St., 18th Fl.
San Francisco, CA 94111
Ph: (415)434-4900
Fax: (415)434-3716
E-mail: tpierce@slacal.org
URL: http://www.sla-cal.org
Freq: quarterly.

554 ■ South Truth Magazine
Clearer Vision Ministries
PO Box 297
St. Augustine, FL 32085-0297
Ph: (904)797-8384
E-mail: cvminc@clearervisionministries.org
URL: http://www.clearervisionministries.org
Descr: Features a collection of interviews, music, stories, and Bible studies. **Freq:** bimonthly.

555 ■ Southern Actions
Southern Regional Council
1201 W Peachtree St. NE, Ste. 2000
Atlanta, GA 30309-3453
Ph: (404)522-8764
Fax: (404)522-8791

E-mail: info@southerncouncil.org
URL: http://www.southerncouncil.org

556 ■ Southern Changes
Southern Regional Council
1201 W Peachtree St. NE, Ste. 2000
Atlanta, GA 30309-3453
Ph: (404)522-8764
Fax: (404)522-8791
E-mail: info@southerncouncil.org
URL: http://www.southerncouncil.org
Descr: Covers the politics, history, literature, racial, social, and economic conditions of the south; includes book reviews. **Freq:** quarterly. **Price:** included in membership dues, $75/year for institutions, $30/year for individuals. **ISSN:** 0193-2446.

557 ■ Southwest Cycling News
Austin Cycling Association
PO Box 5993
Austin, TX 78763
Ph: (512)282-1987
Fax: (512)282-7413
E-mail: stgetr@worldnet.att.net
URL: http://www.austincycling.org
Descr: Contains cycling related articles and events. **Freq:** monthly. **Price:** $20/year for members.

558 ■ Sports-n-Spokes
Paralyzed Veterans of America
801 18th St. NW
Washington, DC 20006-3517
E-mail: info@pva.org
URL: http://www.pva.org
Descr: Features articles on wheelchair sporting activities. Includes calendar of events and new product reviews. **Freq:** bimonthly. **Price:** $21/year in U.S., $38/2 years in U.S., $27/year outside U.S., $50/2 years outside U.S. **ISSN:** 0161-6706.

559 ■ Sports and Spokes
Wisconsin Paralyzed Veterans of America
2311 S 108th St.
West Allis, WI 53227-1901
Ph: (414)328-8910
Fax: (414)328-8948
E-mail: info@wisconsinpva.org
URL: http://www.wisconsinpva.org
Freq: monthly.

560 ■ SportsTalk
Women's Sports Foundation
1899 Hempstead Tpke., Ste. 400
East Meadow, NY 11554
Ph: (516)542-4700
Fax: (516)542-4716
E-mail: info@womenssportsfoundation.org
URL: http://www.womenssportsfoundation.org
Freq: quarterly.

561 ■ Spotlight on Depiction
Entertainment Industries Council
1760 Reston Pkwy., Ste. 415
Reston, VA 20190
Ph: (703)481-1414
Fax: (703)481-1418
E-mail: eiceast@eiconline.org
URL: http://eiconline.org
Freq: annual.

562 ■ SSW News
Society for Social Work and Research
11240 Waples Mill Rd., Ste. 200
Fairfax, VA 22030
Ph: (703)352-7797
Fax: (703)359-7562
E-mail: info@sswr.org
URL: http://www.sswr.org
Price: included in membership dues.

563 ■ Standing Tall
Association des Aides Familiales du Quebec
2348, Jean talon est, Local 407
Montreal, QC, Canada H2E 1V7
Ph: (514)272-2670

Fax: (514)272-8338
E-mail: aafq@aafq.ca
URL: http://www.aafq.ca
Freq: bimonthly. **Price:** included in membership dues.

564 ■ *SWAP Line*
Minnesota Statewide Association of Activity Professionals
Ridgewater Colorado
2 Century Ave.
Hutchinson, MN 55350
Ph: (320)234-8588
E-mail: julie.reginek@ridgewater.edu
URL: http://www.mnswap.org
Descr: Features local, state and national issues and news that affect the activity professional in Minnesota. **Freq:** 3/year.

565 ■ *TAFCS Action*
Texas Association of Family and Consumer Sciences
PO Box 6731
Lubbock, TX 79493
E-mail: sandramarquezhall@sbcglobal.net
URL: http://www.tafcs.org
Freq: 3/year. **Price:** included in membership dues.

566 ■ *TAFCS Research Journal*
Texas Association of Family and Consumer Sciences
PO Box 6731
Lubbock, TX 79493
E-mail: sandramarquezhall@sbcglobal.net
URL: http://www.tafcs.org
Freq: annual.

567 ■ *Technical Publications Packet*
International Society of Weighing and Measurement
9707 Key West Ave., Ste. 100
Rockville, MD 20850
Ph: (301)258-1115
Fax: (301)990-9771
E-mail: staff@iswm.org
URL: http://www.iswm.org

568 ■ *Teen Talk*
Family Career and Community Leaders of Nebraska
State Dept. of Education
301 Centennial Mall S
PO Box 94987
Lincoln, NE 68509-4987
Ph: (402)471-4815
E-mail: janis.brandt@nebraska.gov
URL: http://www.nebraskafccla.org
Freq: periodic.

569 ■ *Teen Times*
Family, Career and Community Leaders of America, Missouri
Dept. of Elementary and Secondary Education
PO Box 480
Jefferson City, MO 65102-0480
Ph: (573)751-7964
Fax: (573)526-4261
E-mail: christine.hollingsworth@dese.mo.gov
URL: http://dese.mo.gov/divcareered/fccla.htm
Freq: quarterly. **Price:** included in membership dues.

570 ■ *Teen Times*
Family, Career and Community Leaders of America
1910 Association Dr.
Reston, VA 20191-1584
Ph: (703)476-4900
Fax: (703)860-2713
E-mail: mbenjamin@fcclainc.org
URL: http://www.fcclainc.org
Freq: quarterly. **Price:** $8/year for nonmembers, included in membership dues.

571 ■ *Tradeswomen Magazine*
Tradeswomen
1433 Webster St.
Oakland, CA 94612
Ph: (510)891-8773
Fax: (510)891-8775
E-mail: bonnie@tradeswomen.org
URL: http://tradeswomen.org

Price: $5 plus shipping and handling.

572 ■ *Trendline*
Consumer Trends Forum International
7076 Drinkard Way
Mechanicsville, VA 23111
Ph: (804)559-6519
Fax: (804)559-4087
E-mail: info@consumerexpert.org
URL: http://www.consumerexpert.org
Descr: Contains email report. **Freq:** biweekly.

573 ■ *Unlocking the Power of the Proxy*
As You Sow Foundation
311 California St., Ste. 510
San Francisco, CA 94104
Ph: (415)391-3212
Fax: (415)391-3245
E-mail: asyousow@asyousow.org
URL: http://www.asyousow.org

574 ■ *Unmarried To Each Other: The Essential Guide to Living Together as an Unmarried Couple*
Alternatives to Marriage Project
PO Box 320151
Brooklyn, NY 11232-0151
Ph: (718)788-1911
Fax: (718)832-7098
URL: http://www.unmarried.org

575 ■ *Update*
International Family Recreation Association
PO Box 520
Gonzalez, FL 32560-0520
Ph: (850)937-8354
E-mail: rltresource@spydee.net
Freq: monthly.

576 ■ *Vanguard*
Community Development Society
17 S High St., Ste. 200
Columbus, OH 43215
Ph: (614)221-1900
Fax: (614)221-1989
E-mail: cds@assnoffices.com
URL: http://www.comm-dev.org
Descr: Contains current activities, topical issues and ideas. **Freq:** quarterly.

577 ■ *VANTAGE*
The Signature Group
200 N Martingale Rd.
Schaumburg, IL 60173
Ph: (847)605-5522
Fax: (847)605-4595
Key Personnel: Paul Misniak, Publisher; Joanie Davies, Associate Publisher. **Descr:** Magazine for active consumers over 55 years of age. **Freq:** Bimonthly. **Price:** $17.50; $3, single issue.

578 ■ *Washington Consumers' CHECKBOOK*
Consumers' Checkbook
1625 K St. NW, 8th Fl.
Washington, DC 20006
Ph: (202)347-9612
Free: 800-213-7283
Fax: (202)347-4000
E-mail: subscriptions@checkbook.org
URL: http://www.checkbook.org
Key Personnel: Robert Krughoff, Pres. **URL(s):** http://www.checkbook.org **Covers:** Evaluation of consumer-oriented businesses or service industries in each issue, such as health services, auto repair services, TV repair shops, etc. Coverage limited to Washington, DC metropolitan area. **Entries include:** In the directory sections, large numbers of firms are mentioned by name and address, and details on their policies, prices, and competence derived from the firms and from customer reports are given. In general information sections, suggestions are given on evaluating common situations, on choosing a shop, etc. **Freq:** Semiannual. **Price:** $34, individuals.

579 ■ *The Waterline*
Houston Canoe Club
PO Box 925516

Houston, TX 77292-5516
E-mail: william.grimes@centerpointenergy.com
URL: http://www.houstoncanoeclub.org
Freq: monthly. **Price:** included in membership dues.

580 ■ *Week in Review*
Women's Leadership Forum
430 S Capitol St. SE
Washington, DC 20003-4024
Ph: (202)479-5103
Fax: (202)479-5149
E-mail: wlf@dnc.org
URL: http://www.democrats.org/a/communities/women/womens_leadership_forum
Freq: weekly.

581 ■ *WEST News*
Women Entrepreneurs in Science and Technology
155 Seaport Blvd., 11th Fl.
Boston, MA 02210
Ph: (617)988-6120
Fax: (641)453-3086
E-mail: info@westorg.org
URL: http://www.westorg.org
Descr: Contains news and other updates on the organization's activities. **Freq:** monthly.

582 ■ *What's Happening Now*
EMDR - Humanitarian Assistance Programs
PO Box 6505
Hamden, CT 06517
Ph: (203)288-4450
Fax: (203)288-4060
E-mail: emdrhap@emdrhap.org
URL: http://www.emdrhap.org

583 ■ *Why an Organizational Ombudsman*
International Ombudsman Association
390 Amwell Rd., Ste. 403
Hillsborough, NJ 08844
Ph: (908)359-0246
Fax: (908)842-0376
E-mail: info@ombudsassociation.org
URL: http://www.ombudsassociation.org
Descr: Discusses the reasons organizations might consider having an ombuds function. **Price:** included in membership dues, $13 for nonmembers.

584 ■ *The Wildcatter*
Wildcat Service Corporation
2 Washington St., 3rd Fl.
New York, NY 10004
Ph: (212)209-6000
URL: http://www.wildcatnyc.org

585 ■ *Will the Circle Be Unbroken?*
Southern Regional Council
1201 W Peachtree St. NE, Ste. 2000
Atlanta, GA 30309-3453
Ph: (404)522-8764
Fax: (404)522-8791
E-mail: info@southerncouncil.org
URL: http://www.southerncouncil.org
Price: $145 cassette tape set, $160 CD set.

586 ■ *Wisconsin Funeral Service: A Consumer's Guide*
Center for Consumer Affairs, University of Wisconsin-Milwaukee
161 W Wisconsin Ave., Ste. 6000
Milwaukee, WI 53203-2602
Ph: (414)227-3200
Fax: (414)227-3146
E-mail: jbrown@uwm.edu
URL: http://cfprod.imt.uwm.edu/sce/dci_long.cfm?id=7

587 ■ *The Women's Sports Experience*
Women's Sports Foundation
1899 Hempstead Tpke., Ste. 400
East Meadow, NY 11554
Ph: (516)542-4700
Fax: (516)542-4716
E-mail: info@womenssportsfoundation.org
URL: http://www.womenssportsfoundation.org

Freq: quarterly.

588 ■ World Research News
World Research Foundation
41 Bell Rock Plz.
Sedona, AZ 86351
Ph: (928)284-3300
Fax: (928)284-3530
E-mail: info@wrf.org
URL: http://www.wrf.org
Freq: quarterly.

589 ■ WSUSA Newsletter
Wheelchair Sports, USA
1236 Jungermann Rd., Ste. A
St. Peters, MO 63376
Ph: (636)614-6784
Fax: (636)246-0110
E-mail: office@wsusa.org
URL: http://www.wsusa.org
Freq: quarterly. **Price:** $10/year.

590 ■ Zillions
Consumers Union of United States
101 Truman Ave.
Yonkers, NY 10703-1057
Ph: (914)378-2000
URL: http://www.consumersunion.org
Descr: For young consumers. **Freq:** bimonthly.

Multimedia Resources

591 ■ Advanced Shooting
Stagestep
2000 Hamilton St., Ste. C200
Philadelphia, PA 19130
Ph: (215)636-9000
Free: 800-523-0961
Fax: 800-877-3342
E-mail: stagestep@juno.com
URL: http://www.stagestep.com
Format(s): Videocassette. **Descr:** Covers how to use shot sheets, storyboards, logs and slates to map shots and boost production quality; use of filters; Charge Coupled Devices; use of dollys, trucks, arcs and cranes; handheld techniques; converging lines, depth of frame, and much much more. **Length:** 30. **Price:** $19.95.

592 ■ Con Games and Swindles
Bullfrog Films, Inc.
PO Box 149
Oley, PA 19547
Ph: (610)779-8226
Free: 800-543-3764
Fax: (610)370-1978
E-mail: video@bullfrogfilms.com
URL: http://bullfrogfilms.com
Format(s): Videocassette. **Descr:** This program illustrates how to recognize the high pressured phoney offers of the con artist. **Prod. Date:** 1982. **Length:** 25.

593 ■ Consumer Buying: Let's Go Shopping
Cambridge Educational
c/o Films Media Group
PO Box 2053
Princeton, NJ 08843-2053
Free: 800-257-5126
Fax: (609)671-0266
E-mail: custserve@filmsmediagroup.com
URL: http://www.cambridgeol.com
Format(s): Videocassette. **Descr:** Chock-full of consumer buying information, this presentation visits the grocery store to illustrate how to shop wisely. Covers coupons, understanding price per unit and per serving, comparing bulk and smaller items, and reading food labels. **Prod. Date:** 1991. **Length:** 16. **Price:** $89.

594 ■ Consumer Reports Series
Warner Home Video, Inc.
5775 Linder Canyon Rd
Westlake Village, CA 91362
URL: http://whv.warnerbros.com
Format(s): Videocassette. **Descr:** A series for careful consumers sponsored by the award-winning magazine. **Prod. Date:** 1987. **Length:** 50. **Price:** $14.98.

595 ■ Consumer Squad Series
PBS Home Video
Catalog Fulfillment Center
PO Box 751089
Charlotte, NC 28275-1089
Ph: 800-531-4727
Free: 800-645-4PBS
E-mail: info@pbs.org
URL: http://www.pbs.org
Format(s): Videocassette. **Descr:** This series describes a group of four young people who counsel the public on a full range of consumer-related problems. **Prod. Date:** 1982. **Length:** 20.

596 ■ Creating Wellness: Taking Time Making Time
Aquarius Productions
Olde Medfield Sq
18 N Main St
Sherborn, MA 01770
Ph: (508)650-1616
Free: 888-440-2963
Fax: (508)650-1665
E-mail: tm@aquariusproductions.com
URL: http://www.aquariusproductions.com
Format(s): Videocassette. **Descr:** Explains how to be happier and healthier using effective time management. **Prod. Date:** 2000. **Length:** 27. **Price:** $99.

597 ■ Desktop Video
Stagestep
2000 Hamilton St., Ste. C200
Philadelphia, PA 19130
Ph: (215)636-9000
Free: 800-523-0961
Fax: 800-877-3342
E-mail: stagestep@juno.com
URL: http://www.stagestep.com
Format(s): Videocassette. **Descr:** Discusses tools and techniques for producing professional quality video. Covers editing systems, computer settings and configurations, the process of rendering nonlinear projects for tape, CD, DVD and more. **Length:** 27. **Price:** $19.95.

598 ■ The Etiquette Survival Guide for Adults
Tapeworm Video Distributors
27833 Hopkins Ave., Unit 6
Valencia, CA 91355
Ph: (661)257-4904
Fax: (661)257-4820
E-mail: sales@tapeworm.com
URL: http://www.tapeworm.com
Format(s): Videocassette. **Descr:** Explains basic dining and social skills presented in a concise and entertaining series of workshops with host Lyndy Janes. **Prod. Date:** 1997. **Price:** $14.95.

599 ■ Every Dog's Guide to the Playground
National Film Board of Canada
1123 Broadway, Ste 307
New York, NY 10010
Ph: (212)629-8890
Free: 800-542-2164
Fax: (866)299-9928
URL: http://www.nfb.ca
Format(s): Videocassette. **Descr:** Zany continuation of the adventures of Wally the safety dog who helps teach kids about playground safety. Animated. **Prod. Date:** 1992. **Length:** 11. **Price:** $40.00.

600 ■ Good Savings—Good Service
Bullfrog Films, Inc.
PO Box 149
Oley, PA 19547
Ph: (610)779-8226
Free: 800-543-3764
Fax: (610)370-1978
E-mail: video@bullfrogfilms.com
URL: http://bullfrogfilms.com
Format(s): Videocassette. **Descr:** A humorous dramatization in which a careless customer becomes a responsible consumer at a self-service gas station. **Prod. Date:** 1982. **Length:** 21.

601 ■ How to Buy a Vintage Guitar
Homespun Tapes
PO Box 340
Woodstock, NY 12498
Ph: (845)246-2550
Free: 800-338-2737
Fax: (845)246-5282
E-mail: info@homspuntapes.com
URL: http://www.homespuntapes.com
Format(s): Videocassette. **Descr:** A guide to appraising vintage guitars, discovering their true value and spotting counterfeits. Hosted by George Gruhn, a leading authority on fretted instruments. **Prod. Date:** 1991. **Length:** 116. **Price:** $49.95.

602 ■ How to Protect Your Bike
AIMS Multimedia
20765 Superior St
Chatsworth, CA 91311-4409
Ph: (818)773-4300
Free: 800-367-2467
Fax: (818)341-6700
E-mail: info@aims.multimedia.com
URL: http://www.aimsmultimedia.com
Format(s): Videocassette. **Descr:** An outline of five ways kids can use to protect their bikes from the likes of Creepo, the consummate bike thief. **Prod. Date:** 1980. **Length:** 12.

603 ■ Lab Housekeeping and Personal Hygiene
Williams Learning Network
15400 Calhoun Dr
Rockville, MD 20855-2762
Ph: (301)315-6700
Free: 800-848-1717
Fax: (301)315-6880
E-mail: mait@willearn.com
URL: http://www.willearn.com
Format(s): Videocassette. **Descr:** Demonstrates the importance of hygiene and cleanliness in the lab, giving 11 rules for good housekeeping and seven rules for personal hygiene. Includes Leader's Guide and 25 Program Guides.

604 ■ Let the Current Do the Work
Visual Horizons
180 Metro Park
Rochester, NY 14623-2666
Ph: (585)424-5300
Free: 800-424-1011
Fax: (585)424-5313
E-mail: CS@visualhorizons.com
URL: http://www.visualhorizons.com
Format(s): Videocassette. **Descr:** The techniques for waterproof packing and loading a raft are described. **Prod. Date:** 1988. **Length:** 30. **Price:** $44.95.

605 ■ The Old Lady's Camping Trip
National Film Board of Canada
1123 Broadway, Ste 307
New York, NY 10010
Ph: (212)629-8890
Free: 800-542-2164
Fax: (866)299-9928
URL: http://www.nfb.ca
Format(s): Videocassette. **Descr:** The do's and don'ts of fire and outdoor safety are discussed. **Prod. Date:** 1987. **Length:** 10.

606 ■ Peace Is Every Step
Mystic Fire Video
PO Box 422
New York, NY 10012
Ph: (212)941-0999
Free: 800-292-9001
Fax: (212)941-1443
E-mail: mysticfire@echonyc.com
URL: http://www.mysticfire.com
Format(s): Videocassette. **Descr:** Presents the

teachings of Zen Buddhist Thich Nhat Hanh. Narrated by Ben Kingsley. **Prod. Date:** 1998. **Length:** 60. **Price:** $29.95.

607 ■ *Piano for Quitters*
Leslie T. McClure
PO Box 1223
Pebble Beach, CA 93953
Ph: (831)656-0553
Fax: (831)656-0555
URL: http://www.411videoinfo.com

Format(s): Videocassette. **Descr:** Mark Almond provides instruction for those who have previously tried to learn piano-playing. **Prod. Date:** 1998. **Length:** 80. **Price:** $29.95.

608 ■ *Planning Your Wedding, Vol. 1: Selecting Your Formal Wear*
Leslie T. McClure
PO Box 1223
Pebble Beach, CA 93953
Ph: (831)656-0553
Fax: (831)656-0555
URL: http://www.411videoinfo.com

Format(s): Videocassette. **Descr:** Part of a ten-volume series for brides- and grooms-to-be that follows the steps taken by a typical couple, Jeff and Lisa, in their preparation for the big event. **Prod. Date:** 1998. **Length:** 38. **Price:** $29.95.

609 ■ *Planning Your Wedding, Vol. 2: A Visit to Your Caterer*
Leslie T. McClure
PO Box 1223
Pebble Beach, CA 93953
Ph: (831)656-0553
Fax: (831)656-0555
URL: http://www.411videoinfo.com

Format(s): Videocassette. **Descr:** Part of a ten-volume series for brides- and grooms-to-be that follows the steps taken by a typical couple, Jeff and Lisa, in their preparation for the big event. **Prod. Date:** 1998. **Length:** 25. **Price:** $29.95.

610 ■ *Planning Your Wedding, Vol. 3: Selecting Your Wedding Cake*
Leslie T. McClure
PO Box 1223
Pebble Beach, CA 93953
Ph: (831)656-0553
Fax: (831)656-0555
URL: http://www.411videoinfo.com

Format(s): Videocassette. **Descr:** Part of a ten-volume series for brides- and grooms-to-be that follows the steps taken by a typical couple, Jeff and Lisa, in their preparation for the big event. **Prod. Date:** 1998. **Length:** 17. **Price:** $29.95.

611 ■ *Planning Your Wedding, Vol. 4: Selecting Your Photographer*
Leslie T. McClure
PO Box 1223
Pebble Beach, CA 93953
Ph: (831)656-0553
Fax: (831)656-0555
URL: http://www.411videoinfo.com

Format(s): Videocassette. **Descr:** Part of a ten-volume series for brides- and grooms-to-be that follows the steps taken by a typical couple, Jeff and Lisa, in their preparation for the big event. **Prod. Date:** 1998. **Length:** 41. **Price:** $29.95.

612 ■ *Planning Your Wedding, Vol. 5: Visiting Your Travel Agent*
Leslie T. McClure
PO Box 1223
Pebble Beach, CA 93953
Ph: (831)656-0553
Fax: (831)656-0555
URL: http://www.411videoinfo.com

Format(s): Videocassette. **Descr:** Part of a ten-volume series for brides- and grooms-to-be that follows the steps taken by a typical couple, Jeff and

Lisa, in their preparation for the big event. **Prod. Date:** 1998. **Length:** 32. **Price:** $29.95.

613 ■ *Planning Your Wedding, Vol. 8: Meeting with Your Minister*
Leslie T. McClure
PO Box 1223
Pebble Beach, CA 93953
Ph: (831)656-0553
Fax: (831)656-0555
URL: http://www.411videoinfo.com

Format(s): Videocassette. **Descr:** Part of a ten-volume series for brides- and grooms-to-be that follows the steps taken by a typical couple, Jeff and Lisa, in their preparation for the big event. **Prod. Date:** 1998. **Length:** 28. **Price:** $29.95.

614 ■ *Planning Your Wedding, Vol. 9: Selecting Your Flowers*
Leslie T. McClure
PO Box 1223
Pebble Beach, CA 93953
Ph: (831)656-0553
Fax: (831)656-0555
URL: http://www.411videoinfo.com

Format(s): Videocassette. **Descr:** Part of a ten-volume series for brides- and grooms-to-be that follows the steps taken by a typical couple, Jeff and Lisa, in their preparation for the big event. **Prod. Date:** 1998. **Length:** 30. **Price:** $29.95.

615 ■ *Planning Your Wedding, Vol. 10: Meeting with Your Bridal Consultant*
Leslie T. McClure
PO Box 1223
Pebble Beach, CA 93953
Ph: (831)656-0553
Fax: (831)656-0555
URL: http://www.411videoinfo.com

Format(s): Videocassette. **Descr:** Part of a ten-volume series for brides- and grooms-to-be that follows the steps taken by a typical couple, Jeff and Lisa, in their preparation for the big event. **Prod. Date:** 1998. **Length:** 28. **Price:** $29.95.

616 ■ *Practical Living Series*
Phoenix Learning Group
2349 Chaffee Dr
St. Louis, MO 63146
Ph: (314)569-0211
Free: 800-221-1274
Fax: (314)569-2834
URL: http://www.phoenixlearninggroup.com

Format(s): Videocassette. **Descr:** This series serves to enlighten consumers in several areas of daily living. Programs are available individually. Discounts available on the purchase of four or more programs. **Length:** 14.

617 ■ *Problems for Young Consumers*
Video Knowledge, Inc.
29 Bramble Ln
Melville, NY 11747
Ph: (631)367-3694
Fax: (631)367-1006
E-mail: REDBRAMBLE@aol.com
URL: http://www.redbrambleirishsetters.com

Format(s): Videocassette. **Descr:** This progrma presents real consumer problems for children to face and solve, problems they are likely to meet in their everyday lives. **Prod. Date:** 1980. **Length:** 25.

618 ■ *Raising Your Dog with the Monks of New Skete*
PBS Home Video
Catalog Fulfillment Center
PO Box 751089
Charlotte, NC 28275-1089
Ph: 800-531-4727
Free: 800-645-4PBS
E-mail: info@pbs.org
URL: http://www.pbs.org

Format(s): Videocassette. **Descr:** The Monks of New Skete present a unique view of the bond between dogs and humans and how this relationship can be used in the successful training of a puppy to

bring out the best sides of both dog and human. Two hours and 53 minutes on three videocassettes. **Prod. Date:** 1998. **Length:** 58. **Price:** $64.95.

619 ■ *Searching for Roots*
PBS Home Video
Catalog Fulfillment Center
PO Box 751089
Charlotte, NC 28275-1089
Ph: 800-531-4727
Free: 800-645-4PBS
E-mail: info@pbs.org
URL: http://www.pbs.org

Format(s): Videocassette. **Descr:** Uses stories and techniques used by those who have traced their family trees to show the viewer why they should and how they can locate records of their ancestors. Available with softcover book for an additional price. Five hours on four videocassettes. **Prod. Date:** 1998. **Length:** 75. **Price:** $59.98.

620 ■ *Shopping Wisely*
Bullfrog Films, Inc.
PO Box 149
Oley, PA 19547
Ph: (610)779-8226
Free: 800-543-3764
Fax: (610)370-1978
E-mail: video@bullfrogfilms.com
URL: http://bullfrogfilms.com

Format(s): Videocassette. **Descr:** Lots of practical suggestions for getting the best buy for the money spent when doing crisis shopping, planned shopping, gift shopping, and clothes shopping. **Prod. Date:** 1982. **Length:** 24.

621 ■ *Smart Shopping*
New Orleans Video Access Center
4040 Tulane Ave
New Orleans, LA 70119-6888
Ph: (504)339-4350
E-mail: info@novacvideo.org
URL: http://www.novacvideo.org/

Format(s): Videocassette. **Descr:** A program which suggests money-saving shopping habits to consumers. **Length:** 10.

622 ■ *Still Killing Us Softly: Advertising's Images of Women*
Cambridge Documentary Films, Inc.
PO Box 390385
Cambridge, MA 02139-0004
Ph: (617)484-3993
Fax: (617)484-0754
E-mail: cdf@shore.net
URL: http://www.cambridgedocumentaryfilms.org

Format(s): Videocassette. **Descr:** Based on the lectures of Dr. Jean Kilbourne, this documentary examines ads from magazines, newspapers, album covers, and billboards to analyze an industry which preys on the fears and insecurities of consumers. A companion work to "Killing Us Softly." **Prod. Date:** 1987. **Length:** 30. **Price:** $299.

623 ■ *Successful Camera Work for Video*
Stagestep
2000 Hamilton St., Ste. C200
Philadelphia, PA 19130
Ph: (215)636-9000
Free: 800-523-0961
Fax: 800-877-3342
E-mail: stagestep@juno.com
URL: http://www.stagestep.com

Format(s): Videocassette. **Descr:** Camcorder basics including focus, aperture, shutter speed, depth of field, zoom, framing aspects, image composition, and the relationship between the subject and camera movement. **Length:** 30. **Price:** $129.

624 ■ *Successful Editing for Video*
Stagestep
2000 Hamilton St., Ste. C200
Philadelphia, PA 19130
Ph: (215)636-9000
Free: 800-523-0961
Fax: 800-877-3342

E-mail: stagestep@juno.com
URL: http://www.stagestep.com

Format(s): Videocassette. **Descr:** Explains linear videotape and nonlinear digital techniques of editing. Covers jumps in time and space, cutting interview material, crossing the line of action, jump cuts, controlling pace, association of ideas and audio editing techniques. **Length:** 32. **Price:** $129.

625 ■ *Successful Lighting for Video*
Stagestep
2000 Hamilton St., Ste. C200
Philadelphia, PA 19130
Ph: (215)636-9000
Free: 800-523-0961
Fax: 800-877-3342
E-mail: stagestep@juno.com
URL: http://www.stagestep.com

Format(s): Videocassette. **Descr:** Discusses how to control sunlight, artificial light, and use professional lighting. Explains contrast, quality, direction, intensity and color plus details three-point lighting methods. **Length:** 32. **Price:** $129.

626 ■ *Successful Sound for Video*
Stagestep
2000 Hamilton St., Ste. C200
Philadelphia, PA 19130
Ph: (215)636-9000
Free: 800-523-0961
Fax: 800-877-3342
E-mail: stagestep@juno.com
URL: http://www.stagestep.com

Format(s): Videocassette. **Descr:** Explains sound recording techniques during production and postproduction including type of microphones, appropriate use of sound, audio mixers, recording levels, distortion, multitracking, sound effects and more. **Length:** 33. **Price:** $129.

627 ■ *The Team Approach*
Kantola Productions, LLC
55 Sunnyside Ave
Mill Valley, CA 94941-1935
Ph: (415)381-9363
Free: 800-989-8273
Fax: (415)381-9801
E-mail: info@kantola.com
URL: http://kantola.com

Format(s): Videocassette. **Descr:** Teaches the viewer how to assemble an effective team in a business environment and how to define roles within the group. Includes study guide. **Prod. Date:** 2000. **Length:** 24. **Price:** $89.95.

628 ■ *Till Death Do Us Part*
Aquarius Productions
Olde Medfield Sq
18 N Main St
Sherborn, MA 01770
Ph: (508)650-1616
Free: 888-440-2963
Fax: (508)650-1665
E-mail: tm@aquariusproductions.com
URL: http://www.aquariusproductions.com

Format(s): Videocassette. **Descr:** Explores the challenges of being widowed in your eighties. Discusses an independent living community in Florida and how it allows elderly who live on their own to keep their independence and still feel safe. **Prod. Date:** 2000. **Length:** 15. **Price:** $195.

629 ■ *Understanding Cats*
PBS Home Video
Catalog Fulfillment Center
PO Box 751089
Charlotte, NC 28275-1089
Ph: 800-531-4727
Free: 800-645-4PBS
E-mail: info@pbs.org
URL: http://www.pbs.org

Format(s): Videocassette. **Descr:** Cat expert Roger Tabor examines why cats behave the way they do.

Covers both understanding and caring for cats. **Prod. Date:** 1998. **Length:** 80. **Price:** $19.98.

630 ■ *Why Ads Work: The Power of Self-Deception*
The Learning Seed
330 Telser Rd
Lake Zurich, IL 60047
Free: 800-634-4941
Fax: (847)540-0854
E-mail: info@learningseed.com
URL: http://www.learningseed.com

Format(s): Videocassette. **Descr:** Examines how ads are carefully crafted so viewers can deceive themselves. **Length:** 21. **Price:** $89.

Media Contacts

631 ■ "Antiques and Collecting Column"
King Features
300 W. 57th St., 15th Fl.
New York, NY 10019
Contact: Terry Kovel, Columnist
Ph: (212)969-7550
URL: http://www.kingfeatures.com

632 ■ Bloomberg News
Bloomberg L.P.
731 Lexington Ave.
New York, NY 10022
Contact: Mike Nol, Consumer Team Leader
Ph: (212)617-2384
E-mail: mnol@bloomberg.net
URL: http://www.bloomberg.com

633 ■ Bloomberg News
Bloomberg L.P.
731 Lexington Ave.
New York, NY 10022
Contact: Josh Fineman, Consumer Reporter
Ph: (212)617-8953
E-mail: jfineman@bloomberg.net
URL: http://www.bloomberg.com

634 ■ Bloomberg News
Atlanta Bureau
Bloomberg L.P.
235 Peachtree St. NE, Ste. 2210
Atlanta, GA 30303
Contact: Mark Clothier, U.S. Consumer Reporter
Ph: (404)507-1333
Fax: (404)524-3668
E-mail: mclothier@bloomberg.net
URL: http://www.bloomberg.com

635 ■ Bloomberg News
Washington Bureau
Bloomberg L.P.
1399 New York Ave., 11th Fl.
Washington, DC 20005
Contact: Andrea Snyder, Consumer Reporter
Ph: (202)654-1831
Fax: (202)624-1800
E-mail: asnyder@bloomberg.net
URL: http://www.bloomberg.com

636 ■ Bloomberg News
Washington Bureau
Bloomberg L.P.
1399 New York Ave., 11th Fl.
Washington, DC 20005
Contact: Cotten Timberlake, Consumer Reporter
Ph: (202)654-1286
Fax: (202)624-1800
E-mail: ctimberlake@bloomberg.net
URL: http://www.bloomberg.com

637 ■ Bloomberg News
Washington Bureau
Bloomberg L.P.
1399 New York Ave., 11th Fl.
Washington, DC 20005
Contact: Carol Wolf, Consumer Reporter
Ph: (202)624-1868
Fax: (202)624-1300

E-mail: cwolf@bloomberg.net
URL: http://www.bloomberg.com

638 ■ *Investor's Business Daily*
12655 Beatrice St.
Los Angeles, CA 90066
Contact: Pete Barlas, Internet Reporter
Ph: (408)720-2101
E-mail: pete.barlas@investors.com
URL: http://www.investors.com

639 ■ MarketWatch.com
Chicago Bureau
Dow Jones & Company, Inc.
One S. Wacker Dr., Ste. 2250
Chicago, IL 60606
Contact: William Spain, Consumer Reporter
Ph: (321)750-4212
E-mail: wspain@marketwatch.com
URL: http://www.marketwatch.com

640 ■ Thomson Reuters
Reuters Bldg.
3 Times Sq.
New York, NY 10036
Contact: Franklin Paul, Consumer Electronics Reporter
Ph: (646)223-6193
E-mail: franklin.paul@thomsonreuters.com
URL: http://www.thomsonreuters.com

641 ■ *The Wall Street Journal*
Dow Jones & Company
1211 Ave. of the Americas
New York, NY 10036
Contact: Kara Swisher, Home Economics Columnist
Ph: (415)765-6103
URL: http://www.wsj.com

642 ■ *The Wall Street Journal*
Dow Jones & Company
1211 Ave. of the Americas
New York, NY 10036
Contact: Anjali Athavaley, Computer Interest Reporter
Ph: (212)416-2000
E-mail: anjali.athavaley@wsj.com
URL: http://www.wsj.com

643 ■ *The Wall Street Journal*
Dow Jones & Company
1211 Ave. of the Americas
New York, NY 10036
Contact: Rachel Dodes, Women's Apparel Reporter
Ph: (212)416-2000
URL: http://www.wsj.com

644 ■ *The Wall Street Journal*
Dow Jones & Company
1025 Connecticut Ave. NW, Ste. 800
Washington, DC 20036
Contact: Walter S. Mossberg, Personal Tech. Columnist
Ph: (202)862-9287
E-mail: mossberg@wsj.com
URL: http://www.wsj.com

645 ■ *Willamette Week*
2220 NW Quimby St.
Portland, OR 97210
Contact: Kelly Clarke, Arts and Culture Editor
Ph: (503)243-2122
E-mail: kclarke@wsjournal.com
URL: http://www.wweek.com

Arizona

646 ■ *Arizona Daily Star*
Lee Enterprises, Inc.
PO Box 26807
Tucson, AZ 85726-6807
Contact: Kimberly Matas, Pets Reporter
Ph: (520)573-4191

E-mail: kmatas@azstarnet.com
URL: http://www.azstarnet.com

647 ■ The Arizona Republic
Gannet Co., Inc.
PO Box 1950
Phoenix, AZ 85001
Contact: Karina Bland, Busy Mom Reporter
Ph: (602)444-8814
URL: http://www.azcentral.com

California

648 ■ Los Angeles Times
Tribune Company
388 Market St.
San Francisco, CA 94111
Contact: Jessica Guynn, Technology Writer
Ph: (213)237-7163
E-mail: jessica.guynn@latimes.com
URL: http://www.latimes.com

649 ■ Orange County Register
625 N. Grand Ave.
Santa Ana, CA 92701-4347
Contact: Tamara Chuang, Technology Columnist
Ph: (714)796-4952
E-mail: tchuang@ocregister.com
URL: http://www.ocregister.com

650 ■ San Diego Union-Tribune
Copley Press, Inc.
PO Box 120191
San Diego, CA 92112-0191
Contact: Penni Crabtree, Consumer Affairs Reporter
Ph: (619)293-1237
E-mail: penni.crabtree@uniontrib.com
URL: http://www.uniontrib.com

Connecticut

651 ■ Hartford Courant
Tribune Company
285 Broad St.
Hartford, CT 06115
Contact: George Gombossy, "Watchdog" Column
Ph: (860)241-6736
Fax: (860)241-3865
E-mail: ggombossy@courant.com
URL: http://www.courant.com

District of Columbia

652 ■ The Washington Post
1150 15th St., NW
Washington, DC 20071-0070
Contact: Steve Mufson, Energy Reporter
Ph: (202)334-6414
E-mail: mufsons@washpost.com
URL: http://www.washingtonpost.com

653 ■ The Washington Post
1150 15th St., NW
Washington, DC 20071-0070
Contact: Mike Musgrove, Consumer Tech. Reporter
Ph: (202)334-7320
E-mail: business@washpost.com
URL: http://www.washingtonpost.com

654 ■ The Washington Post
1150 15th St., NW
Washington, DC 20071-0070
Contact: Annys Shin, Consumer Affairs Reporter
Ph: (202)334-5456
E-mail: shina@washpost.com
URL: http://www.washingtonpost.com

Florida

655 ■ The Florida Times-Union
PO Box 1949
Jacksonville, FL 32231
Contact: Jim Schoettler, Investigative Reporter
Ph: (904)359-4385

E-mail: jim.schoettler@jacksonville.com
URL: http://www.jacksonville.com

656 ■ The Miami Herald
The McClatchy Company
One Herald Plaza
Miami, FL 33132-1693
Contact: Monica Hatcher, Consumer Issues Reporter
Ph: (305)376-2001
E-mail: mhatcher@miamiherald.com
URL: http://www.herald.com

657 ■ Orlando Sentinel
Tribune Company
633 N. Orange Ave.
Orlando, FL 32801-1349
Contact: Mark Skoneki, Consumer/Transportation
Editor
Ph: (407)420-5000
E-mail: mskoneki@orlandosentinel.com
URL: http://www.orlandosentinel.com

658 ■ Orlando Sentinel
Tribune Company
633 N. Orange Ave.
Orlando, FL 32801-1349
Contact: Mary Ann Horne, Consumer Editor
Ph: (407)420-5047
E-mail: mahorne@orlandosentinel.com
URL: http://www.orlandosentinel.com

659 ■ The Palm Beach Post
Palm Beach Newspapers, Inc.
2751 S. Dixie Hwy.
West Palm Beach, FL 33405
Contact: Susan Salisbury, Consumer Affairs Reporter
Ph: (561)820-4577
E-mail: ssalisbury@pbpost.com
URL: http://www.pbpost.com

Georgia

660 ■ Atlanta Journal-Constitution
Cox Newspapers, Inc.
72 Marietta St., NW
Atlanta, GA 30303
Contact: Leon Stafford, ITP Economy Reporter
Ph: (404)526-5366
E-mail: lstafford@ajc.com
URL: http://www.ajc.com

661 ■ Atlanta Journal-Constitution
Cox Newspapers, Inc.
72 Marietta St., NW
Atlanta, GA 30303
Contact: Nedra Rhone, Shopping/Fashion Reporter
Ph: (404)526-5465
E-mail: nrhone@ajc.com
URL: http://www.ajc.com

Hawaii

662 ■ The Honolulu Advertiser
605 Kapiolani Blvd.
Honolulu, HI 96813
Contact: Robbie Dingeman, Consumer Affairs Reporter
Ph: (808)535-2429
Fax: (808)525-8037
E-mail: rdingeman@honoluluadvertiser.com

Maryland

663 ■ The Baltimore Sun
Tribune Company
501 N. Calvert St.
Baltimore, MD 21278
Contact: Liz Kay, Consumer Issues Editor
Ph: (410)332-6100
E-mail: liz.kay@baltsun.com
URL: http://www.baltimoresun.com

664 ■ The Capital
Capital Gazette Newspapers
PO Box 911

Annapolis, MD 21404
Contact: Elisha Sauers, Watchdog Reporter
Ph: (410)280-5932
E-mail: esauers@capitalgazette.com
URL: http://HometownAnnapolis.com

Massachusetts

665 ■ Boston Globe
The New York Times Company
135 Morrissey Blvd.
Boston, MA 02125
Contact: Hiawatha Bray, Tech/Internet Reporter
Ph: (617)929-3115
E-mail: h_bray@globe.com
URL: http://www.boston.com

Minnesota

666 ■ St. Paul Pioneer Press
MediaNews Group, Inc.
345 Cedar St.
St. Paul, MN 55101-1057
Contact: Debra O'Connor, Watchdog Reporter
Ph: (651)228-5419
E-mail: watchdog@pioneerpress.com
URL: http://www.pioneerpress.com

667 ■ Star Tribune
McClatchy Newspapers, Inc.
425 Portland Ave., S.
Minneapolis, MN 55415
Contact: H.J. Cummins, Consumer Affairs Reporter
Ph: (612)673-4671
E-mail: hcummins@startribune.com
URL: http://www.startribune.com

Missouri

668 ■ St. Louis Post-Dispatch
Lee Enterprises, Inc.
900 N. Tucker Blvd.
St. Louis, MO 63101
Contact: Michael D. Sorkin, Consumer Affairs Reporter
Ph: (314)340-8347
E-mail: msorkin@post-dispatch.com
URL: http://www.stltoday.com

Nevada

669 ■ Las Vegas Review Journal
PO Box 70
Las Vegas, NV 89125
Contact: Lynnette Curtis, Minority Affairs Reporter
Ph: (702)383-0285
E-mail: lcurtis@reviewjournal.com
URL: http://www.reviewjournal.com

New Mexico

670 ■ Albuquerque Journal
Journal Publishing Company
PO Drawer J
Albuquerque, NM 87103
Contact: Harry Moskos, Speak Up! Editor
Ph: (505)823-3911
E-mail: hmoskos@abqjournal.com
URL: http://www.abqjournal.com

New York

671 ■ The Buffalo News
Berkshire Hathaway Inc.
PO Box 100
Buffalo, NY 14240
Contact: Rod Watson, Urban Affairs Editor
Ph: (716)849-3434
Free: 800-777-8680
Fax: (716)856-5150

E-mail: rwatson@buffnews.com
URL: http://www.buffalo.com

672 ■ New York 1 News
Time Warner Entertainment Company, LP
75 9th Ave., 6th Fl.
New York, NY 10011
Contact: Jill Scott, Home Reporter
Ph: (212)379-3434
E-mail: jill.scott@ny1news.com
URL: http://www.ny1.com

673 ■ The Pet Show
WOR-AM, 710
111 Broadway, 3rd Floor
New York, NY 10006
Contact: Warren Eckstein, Host
Ph: (212)642-4500
Free: 800-321-8828
E-mail: warreneckstein@wor710.com
URL: http://www.wor710.com
Descr: Radio program offering pet behavior and psychology advice.

Ohio

674 ■ Akron Beacon Journal
Sound Publishing Holdings, Inc.
PO Box 640
Akron, OH 44309-0640
Contact: Betty Lin-Fisher, Consumer Reporter
Ph: (330)996-3724
Fax: (330)376-9235
E-mail: blinfisher@thebeaconjournal.com
URL: http://www.ohio.com

675 ■ The Columbus Dispatch
34 S. Third St.
Columbus, OH 43215-4241
Contact: Tracy Turner, Consumer/Youth Reporter
Ph: (614)461-5268
E-mail: tturner@dispatch.com
URL: http://www.dispatch.com

Pennsylvania

676 ■ The Philadelphia Inquirer
Philadelphia Media Holdings LLC
400 N. Broad St.
Philadelphia, PA 19103
Contact: Kellie Patrick Gates, Weddings Columnist
Ph: (215)854-2000
URL: http://www.philly.com

Texas

677 ■ San Antonio Express-News
Hearst Newspapers
PO Box 2171
San Antonio, TX 78297-2171
Contact: David Uhler, Consumer Reporter
Ph: (210)250-3412
E-mail: duhler@express-news.net
URL: http://www.mysa.com

678 ■ San Antonio Express-News
Hearst Newspapers
PO Box 2171
San Antonio, TX 78297-2171
Contact: William Pack, Agriculture/Energy Reporter
Ph: (210)250-3327
E-mail: wpack@express-news.net
URL: http://www.mysa.com

Virginia

679 ■ Richmond Times-Dispatch
Media General, Inc.
PO Box 85333
Richmond, VA 23293
Contact: Iris Taylor, Consumer Columnist
Ph: (804)649-6349
Fax: (804)775-8059
URL: http://www.timesdispatch.com

Washington

680 ■ Seattle Post-Intelligencer
Hearst Newspapers
PO Box 1909
Seattle, WA 98111
Contact: Cecelia Goodnow, Consumer Reporter
Ph: (206)448-8322
E-mail: ceceliagoodnow@seattlepi.com
URL: http://www.seattlepi.com

681 ■ Seattle Post-Intelligencer
Hearst Newspapers
PO Box 1909
Seattle, WA 98111
Contact: Phuong Le, Consumer Reporter
Ph: (206)448-8390
URL: http://www.seattlepi.com

Corporate Contacts

682 ■ Bear Creek Corp.
2500 S. Pacific Hwy.
Medford, OR 97501-2675
Free: 877-322-1200
Fax: 800-648-6640
URL: http://www.harryanddavid.com

683 ■ Blockbuster Entertainment Corp.
Customer Care
1201 Elm St.
Dallas, TX 75270
Ph: (214)258-1017
Free: 866-692-2789
URL: http://www.blockbuster.com

684 ■ Brunswick Corporation
Service Department
1 N. Field Ct.
Lake Forest, IL 60045-4811
Contact: Dustan E. McCoy, CEO
Ph: (847)735-4700
Fax: (847)735-4765
E-mail: services@brunswick.com
URL: http://www.brunswick.com

685 ■ Citizen America
Customer Service
363 Van Ness Way, Ste. 404
Torrance, CA 90501
Ph: (310)781-1460
Free: 800-421-6516
Fax: (310)781-9152
E-mail: customerservice@citizen-america.com
URL: http://www.citizen-america.com

686 ■ ConocoPhillips
600 N. Dairy Ashford Rd.
PO Box 2197
Houston, TX 77079
Contact: James J. Mulva, CEO
Ph: (281)293-1000
URL: http://www.conocophillips.com

687 ■ DWS Scudder
Customer Service
PO Box 219151
Kansas City, MO 64121-9151
Free: 800-728-3337
E-mail: service@dws.com
URL: http://www.dws-scudder.com

688 ■ Ethan Allen, Inc.
PO Box 1966
Danbury, CT 06813-1966
Ph: (203)743-8668
Free: 888-EAHELP1
Fax: (203)743-8298
E-mail: orders@ethanallen.com
URL: http://www.ethanallen.com

689 ■ Fasco Industries Inc.
402 E. Haven St.
Eaton Rapids, MI 48827
Ph: (517)663-2161
Fax: (517)663-1315

E-mail: fascohelp@RegalBeloit.com
URL: http://www.fasco.com

690 ■ Florsheim, Inc.
333 W. Estabrook Blvd.
Glendale, WI 53212
Ph: (312)458-2710
Free: 866-454-0449
E-mail: us.consumers@florsheim.com
URL: http://www.florsheim.com

691 ■ Fortune Brands
Consumer Affairs Dept.
520 Lake Cool Rd.
Deerfield, IL 60015
Contact: C. Clarkson Hines, VP, Corp.Comm.
Ph: (847)484-4400
Free: 800-989-4923
Fax: 800-247-1317
E-mail: mail@fortunebrands.com
URL: http://www.fortunebrands.com

692 ■ Gold's Gym International
Customer Care Dept.
125 E. John Carpenter, Ste. 1300
Irving, TX 75062
Ph: (214)574-4653
Free: 866-465-3775
URL: http://www.goldsgym.com

693 ■ JanSport, Inc.
Customer Service Department
2011 Farallon Drive
San Leandro, CA 94577
Ph: (510)614-4000
Free: 800-558-3600
E-mail: consumer_relations@vfc.com
URL: http://www.jansport.com

694 ■ Jarden Communications Solutions, Inc.
Sunbeam Products Consumer Affairs
2381 Executive Center Dr.
Boca Raton, FL 34331
Ph: (516)912-4100
Free: 800-458-8407
URL: http://www.sunbeam.com

695 ■ Konica Minolta Holdings, Inc.
Business Division
101 Williams Dr.
Ramsey, NJ 07446
Contact: Masatoshi Matsuzaki, Pres./CEO
Ph: (201)825-4000
Free: 800-523-2696
URL: http://www.konicaminolta.com

696 ■ Lowe's Companies, Inc.
Customer Care
PO Box 1111
North Wilkesboro, NC 28656
Free: 800-445-6937
Fax: (336)658-2607
URL: http://www.lowes.com

697 ■ Marshall Field's
685 Market St.
San Francisco, CA 94105
Free: 800-289-6229
URL: http://www.macys.com

698 ■ Merillat Industries
5353 West U.S. 223
Adrian, MI 49221
Free: 866-850-8557
URL: http://www.merillat.com

699 ■ Merisant Worldwide, Inc.
33 N. Dearborn St., Ste. 200
Chicago, IL 60602
Ph: (312)840-6000
Free: 800-323-5316
URL: http://www.merisant.com

700 ■ National Presto Industries, Inc.
3925 N. Hastings Way
Eau Claire, WI 54703-3703
Ph: (715)839-2121

Fax: (715)839-2122
URL: http://www.gopresto.com

701 ■ Nestle Purina PetCare Company
Office of Consumer Affairs
Checkerboard Sq.
St. Louis, MO 63164
Ph: (314)982-2261
Free: 800-778-7462
URL: http://www.purina.com

702 ■ The North Face, Inc.
Customer Service
2013 Farallon Dr.
San Leandro, CA 94577
Ph: (510)618-3500
Free: 800-447-2333
Fax: (510)618-3541
E-mail: tnf_consumerservices@vfc.com
URL: http://www.thenorthface.com

703 ■ Oneida, Ltd.
Customer Service
PO Box 1

Oneida, NY 13421-2899
Ph: (315)361-3000
Free: 888-263-7195
URL: http://www.oneida.com

704 ■ Proview Technology, Inc.
7373 Hunt Ave.
Garden Grove, CA 92841
Ph: (714)799-3899
Free: 800-776-8439
Fax: (714)379-6290
E-mail: customersupport@proview.net
URL: http://www.proview.net

705 ■ Rayovac Corporation
PO Box 44960
Madison, WI 53744
Free: 800-323-1993
Fax: 888-677-4770
E-mail: consumers@rayovac.com
URL: http://www.rayovac.com

706 ■ Sanofi-Aventis
300 Somerset Corporate Blvd.
Bridgewater, NJ 08807-2854

Free: 800-981-2491
URL: http://www.sanofi-aventis.us

707 ■ Top-Flite Professional Golf Company
Consumer Department
425 Meadow St.
PO Box 901
Chicopee, MA 01021-0901
Ph: (413)536-1200
Free: 866-834-6532
URL: http://www.topflite.com

708 ■ True Value Company
8600 W. Bryn Mawr
Chicago, IL 60631-3505
Ph: (773)695-5000
URL: http://www.truevalue.com

709 ■ United Online Inc.
LNR Warner Center
2301 Burbank Blvd.
Woodland Hills, CA 91367
Ph: (805)418-2000
Fax: (805)413-2001
URL: http://www.unitedonline.com

Internet Resources

710 ■ AAA Fuel Cost Calculator
American Automobile Association
2040 Market St.
Philadelphia, PA 19103
Ph: (407)444-8000
Free: 800-763-9900
Fax: (407)444-8030
URL: http://www.aaa.com
URL(s): www.fuelcostcalculator.com/ **Descr:** Allows users to calculate the estimated gasoline costs from any two major cities in the continental U.S.

711 ■ Alternative Fuel Vehicle Businesses in the World
Momentum Technologies LLC
PO Box 460813
Glendale, CO 80246
Ph: (303)229-4841
Fax: (408)705-2031
E-mail: info@mtt.com
URL: http://www.mtt.com
URL(s): energy.sourceguides.com/businesses/byP/altfuel/altfuel.shtml **Descr:** Contains detailed directory listings and contact information for dozens of businesses involved with alternative fuel vehicles in operation throughout the world. Includes business name, address, phone number, fax number, e-mail address, and web site address. Includes brief descriptions of product lines, services offered, and business type. Covers manufacturers, wholesale and retail suppliers, system design businesses, system installers, nonprofit organizations, trade organizations, and more. **Type:** Directory. **Updating freq.:** Monthly. **Fees:** Free. **Searching routines or searchable elements:** Provides keyword search functions.

712 ■ Arizona Gas Prices
GasBuddy.com
7964 Brooklyn Blvd., No. 318
Brooklyn Park, MN 55445
Ph: (612)875-2766
URL: http://gasbuddy.com/gb_index.aspx
URL(s): www.arizonagasprices.com/ **Descr:** Helps drivers find the lowest gas prices in Arizona. Also offers a message forum, tips on saving gas, and the latest media coverage on rising fuel costs.

713 ■ The Auto Channel
332 W. Broadway, Ste. 1604
Louisville, KY 40202
Contact: Robert Jay Gordon, Pres.
Ph: (502)992-0200
Fax: (502)992-0201
E-mail: bgordon@theautochannel.com
URL(s): www.theautochannel.com/ **Descr:** Using all the latest technology, this site offers a variety of searchable databases chock full of car stuff. The main page links car aficionados to recent automotive news and racing news articles. Also provides new car reviews, a message board where users can buy or sell cars and parts, and a Media link where you'll

find videos of press conferences, full line factory tours, or clips from the 2009 North America International Auto Show. **Type:** Full-text; Directory; Image; Audio. **Fees:** Free. **Searching routines or searchable elements:** The site is keyword searchable.

714 ■ Autofind
Dealer Specialties
Ph: (513)705-2000
Free: 800-438-2886
E-mail: sales@getauto.com
URL(s): www.autofind.com/ **Descr:** This site has a search engine that puts you in contact with the pre-owned or new auto of your dreams, or at least one that fits your budget from thousands of dealers and owners across the nation. Try out the various links, fill out some forms, let the computer do the legwork. **Type:** Full-text; Directory. **Fees:** Free. **Searching routines or searchable elements:** Searching is available by state, model, model year, body type, state and county, zip code, and price range.

715 ■ AutoSite
Autobytel Inc.
18872 MacArthur Blvd., Ste. 200
Irvine, CA 92612
Contact: Jim Riesenbach, Pres. & CEO
Ph: (949)225-4500
Fax: (949)757-8920
E-mail: consumercare@autobytel.com
URL: http://www.autosite.com
URL(s): www.autosite.com/ **Descr:** Contains more than 30,000 records on new and used cars, trucks, and vans. Provides suggested retail price, dealer invoice price, car specifications, car name and make, location built, and warranty information. Also includes lists of standard equipment and optional equipment. Allows searches by make, model, and personalized criteria. **Type:** Directory; Numeric; Image. **Updating freq.:** Weekly (September-November); biweekly for the rest of the year. **Fees:** Free.

716 ■ Autosite Recalls
Autobytel Inc.
18872 MacArthur Blvd., Ste. 200
Irvine, CA 92612
Ph: (949)225-4500
E-mail: consumercare@autobytel.com
URL(s): www.autosite.com/ **Descr:** Assists users with the buying and selling of automobiles by providing reviews, safety recalls, and price quotes on both new and used vehicles. Unites dealers with potential customers via its website.

717 ■ AutoWeek
Crain Communications Inc.
1155 Gratiot Ave.
Detroit, MI 48207-2997
Contact: Keith E. Crain, Chairman
Ph: (313)446-6000
E-mail: info@crain.com
URL: http://www.crain.com
URL(s): www.autoweek.com **Descr:** Contains the complete text of *AutoWeek*, a weekly magazine for

automotive enthusiasts and consumers. Covers product news, reviews of domestic and imported products, major motor sports, new technology, profiles of automotive personalities, book reviews, and travel planners. **Type:** Full-text. **Updating freq.:** Weekly, within 14 days of publication. **Fees:** $39.95 FAN

718 ■ Buick Club of America
PO Box 360775
Columbus, OH 43236
Contact: Mike Book, Office Mgr.
Ph: (614)472-3939
Fax: (614)472-3222
E-mail: buickcluboffice@aol.com
URL(s): www.buickclub.org/ **Descr:** Here's a fun site that provides information on the Buick Club of America (BCA), a nonprofit organization dedicated to the restoration of automobiles built by the Buick Motor Division of General Motors. It features a photo gallery of historical Buicks, a history of the Buick, links to individual BCA chapters and other Buick clubs, a classified section for people who want to buy or sell Buick cars or parts, discussion forums, a BCA store, a calendar of events, and membership information. **Type:** Full-text; Image. **Updating freq.:** As needed. **Fees:** Free. **Searching routines or searchable elements:** Searching is not available.

719 ■ Cadillac
Cadillac-General Motors
Customer Assistance Center
PO Box 33169
Detroit, MI 48232-5169
Free: 800-333-4CAD
URL(s): www.cadillac.com/index.jsp?noredirect=true **Descr:** Interactive and attractively designed, Cadillac's Web home offers information on all the cars manufactured in that line. Includes information on every aspect of buying a Cadillac from pricing to dealers to options. Includes calendars of Cadillac sponsors and a section on related merchandise. **Type:** Full-text; Directory; Image. **Updating freq.:** As needed. **Fees:** Free. **Searching routines or searchable elements:** Searching is not available, although a site map is provided.

720 ■ Car Collector Magazine Online
Car Collector Magazine, Inc.
425 Cheney Hwy.
Titusville, FL 32780
Contact: Jeffrey Broadus, Publisher
Ph: (321)267-8011
Free: 800-523-6322
Fax: (321)269-7004
E-mail: info@carcollector.com
URL(s): www.carcollector.com/ **Descr:** A magazine for vintage auto collectors, restorers, and enthusiasts, Car Collector offers listings of classic auto events, clubs, and merchandise. Select full-text articles from the current issue and tables of contents of back issues are available online. Also features advice, letters, and Q&A sections, plus links to related Web Sites. **Type:** Image; Full-text. **Updating**

freq.: Monthly. **Fees:** Online offerings are free. Printed edition costs $29.95/year in the U.S. **Searching routines or searchable elements:** Searching is not available.

721 ■ Car and Driver

Hachette Filipacchi Magazines
1585 Eisenhower Place
Ann Arbor, MI 48108
Contact: Mike Dushane, Exec.Ed.
Ph: (734)971-3600
E-mail: editors@caranddriver.com
URL(s): www.caranddriver.com/ **Descr:** This publication covers all aspects of automobiles. It includes industry news, reviews, auto show information, and a buyers guide. The site includes the table of contents and selected articles from the current newsstand issue, and up to date news. Visitors can also interact in forums, check vehicle price quotes and read reviews. The interactive buyers guide is also a great feature. Multiple images complement the extremely informative (and entertaining) articles to be found here. Contains links to sister publications. **Type:** Full-text; Image; Directory; Transactional; Audio; Video. **Updating freq.:** Monthly. **Fees:** Free. **Searching routines or searchable elements:** Keyword search is available.

722 ■ Chilton Auto Library

Cengage Learning
5 Maxwell Dr.
Clifton Park, NY 12065-2919
Free: 800-648-7450
Fax: (518)881-1247
E-mail: chiltonFAQs@thomson.com
URL: http://www.chiltononline.com
URL(s): www.chiltononline.com/totalcare.aspx **Descr:** Contains Total Car Care CDs and DVDs featuring a variety of repair manuals. Provides users with all levels of total maintenance, service and repair information. All information is available online at ChiltonDIY.com. **Type:** Image; Full-text; Numeric. **Updating freq.:** Annual. **Fees:** Contact vendor for pricing information.

723 ■ Colorado Gas Prices

7964 Brooklyn Blvd., No. 318
Brooklyn Park, MN 55445
Contact: Dustin Coupal
Ph: (612)875-2766
URL: http://gasbuddy.com/gb_index.aspx
URL(s): www.coloradogasprices.com/ **Descr:** Helps drivers find the lowest gas prices in Colorado. Also provides a message forum, tips on saving gas, and the latest news on rising fuel costs.

724 ■ Consumer Guide Automotive

HowStuffWorks.com
One Capital City Plaza
3350 Peachtree Rd., Ste. 1500
Atlanta, GA 30326
Ph: (404)760-4729
E-mail: cservice@consumerguide.com
URL: http://auto.consumerguide.com
Descr: Offers information on new and used cars, including prices, ratings, reviews, local dealers, and vehicle history reports. **Type:** Full-text; Statistical. **Searching routines or searchable elements:** Searching options are available.

725 ■ Detroit Auto Dealers Association

1900 W. Big Beaver Rd.
Troy, MI 48084
Contact: Barron Meade, Pres.
Ph: (248)643-0250
Fax: (248)643-8788
E-mail: Info@dada.org
URL(s): www.dada.org **Descr:** The Detroit Auto Dealers Association offers a short history of the Association and several pages devoted to The North American International Auto Show with events, exhibition and travel information. There is also a list of dealers for every make of auto, including foreign vehicles in the Detroit area; and several articles on car care and the automobile's colorful past as well as links to other auto sites. **Type:** Full-text; Directory.

Updating freq.: As needed. **Fees:** Free. **Searching routines or searchable elements:** Keyword searching is not available.

726 ■ Edmunds.com
URL: http://www.edmunds.com/

Descr: Site where prospective car buyers can go to get regional prices on certain makes, buying tips and advice, reviews, and insurance tips.

727 ■ Florida State Gas Prices

GasBuddy.com
7964 Brooklyn Blvd., No. 318
Brooklyn Park, MN 55445
Contact: Dustin Coupal
Ph: (612)875-2766
URL: http://gasbuddy.com/gb_index.aspx
URL(s): www.floridastategasprices.com/ **Descr:** With gas prices in the U.S. climbing again in early 2010, it's important for consumers to find the best deals on gasoline. This website lists the lowest regular gas prices in the last 24 hours, from tips sent by drivers all over Florida. Also includes a message forum and pointers for saving gas.

728 ■ Gas Price Data

U.S. Department of Energy
Energy Efficiency and Renewable Energy
EERE Information Center
656 Quince Orchard Rd., Ste. 500
Gaithersburg, MD 20878
Contact: Alexander Karsner, Asst.Sec.
Free: 877-337-3463
E-mail: fueleconomy@ornl.gov
URL: http://www.eere.energy.gov/
URL(s): www.fueleconomy.gov **Descr:** Provides links to gasoline prices for U.S. cities in all fifty states, as well as gas mileage tips.

729 ■ GasBuddy.com

GasBuddy Organization, Inc.
7964 Brooklyn Blvd., No. 318
Brooklyn Park, MN 55445
Contact: Dustin Coupal
Ph: (612)875-2766
URL(s): www.gasbuddy.com **Descr:** Gasoline prices change frequently and may vary by as much as 20 percent within only a few blocks. GasBuddy websites allow motorists to share information about low-priced fuel with others as well as target the lowest-priced stations to save money when filling up at the pump. Users can search by state, county, and zip code, as well as by Canadian province. Also includes helpful tips on curbing your gas spending. **Searching routines or searchable elements:** Searching is available.

730 ■ GasPriceWatch.com

GasPriceWatch.com
707 Miamisburg-Centerville Rd.
Centerville, OH 45451
Ph: (937)252-4111
E-mail: info@gaspricewatch.com
URL(s): www.gaspricewatch.com **Descr:** GasPrice-Watch's goal is to encourage low-priced leaders in your community by increasing their sales while punishing the high-priced stations by decreasing theirs. You can search U.S. gas prices by using the zip code search or the more advanced search by specifying street, city, state, and so on. There are also sections for spotters, news, and fuel tax information. Site allows users to become one of the over 170,000 "member spotters" and add to the more than 129,000 gas stations listed over the years. **Searching routines or searchable elements:** Advanced search options are available.

731 ■ Georgia Gas Prices

GasBuddy.com
7964 Brooklyn Blvd., No. 318
Brooklyn Park, MN 55445
Ph: (612)875-2766
URL: http://gasbuddy.com/gb/index.aspx
URL(s): www.georgiagasprices.com/ **Descr:** With gas prices in the U.S. climbing again in early 2010, it's important for consumers to find the best deals on

gasoline. This website lists the lowest regular gas prices in the last 36 hours in Georgia. It also has a message forum, price charts, and tips on saving gas.

732 ■ GreenerCars.org

American Council for an Energy-Efficient Economy
529 14th St., NW, Ste. 600
Washington, DC 20045
Ph: (202)507-4000
Fax: (202)429-2248
E-mail: greenercars@aceee.org
URL: http://www.aceee.org
URL(s): http://greenercars.org **Descr:** Offers green driving tips, a guide on how to "buy green" when auto shopping, the latest in news and technology, a list of the best and worst "green" cars.

733 ■ Illinois Gas Prices

GasBuddy.com
7964 Brooklyn Blvd., No. 318
Brooklyn Park, MN 55445
Ph: (612)875-2766
URL: http://gasbuddy.com/gb_index.aspx
URL(s): www.illinoisgasprices.com/ **Descr:** Website allows users to find the best gas prices at stations in Illinois. Also offers a message board, tips on saving gas, and the latest news on rising fuel costs.

734 ■ LeaseGuide.com

The Lease Guide
555 W. Broadway
New York, NY 10036
Ph: (212)776-2554
E-mail: contact@leaseguide.com
URL: http://www.leaseguide.com
URL(s): leaseguide.com/index2.htm **Descr:** Provides information to help consumers make sound decisions when leasing a car. The goal is to protect the consumer during transactions with dealers and financial institutions. The site contains tips on dealer secrets, getting out of a lease, protecting your credit, prices, and more. Handy FAQs, a lease calculator, a lease "kit" with tools, and many articles explaining all facets of auto leasing make this an extensive site. Covers everything from preparing the deal to the end of lease. **Type:** Full-text. **Fees:** Free. **Searching routines or searchable elements:** Searching is by keyword.

735 ■ Los Angeles Gas Prices

GasBuddy.com
7964 Brooklyn Blvd., No. 318
Brooklyn Park, MN 55445
Ph: (612)875-2766
URL: http://gasbuddy.com/gb_index.aspx
URL(s): www.losangelesgasprices.com/ **Descr:** With gas prices in California climbing again in early 2010, it's important for consumers to find the best deals on gasoline. This website lists the lowest regular gas prices in the last 36 hours in the metro Los Angeles area. It also includes a message forum, tips on saving gas, and the latest news on fuel costs.

736 ■ Maryland Gas Prices

GasBuddy.com
7964 Brooklyn Blvd., No. 318
Brooklyn Park, MN 55445
Ph: (612)875-2766
URL: http://gasbuddy.com/gb_index.aspx
URL(s): www.marylandgasprices.com/ **Descr:** With gas prices in the U.S. climbing again in early 2010, it's important for consumers to find the best deals on gasoline. This website lists the lowest regular gas prices in the last 24 hours, from tips sent by users all across Maryland. Also includes gas saving tips and the latest news on fuel costs.

737 ■ Massachusetts Gas Prices

GasBuddy.com
7964 Brooklyn Blvd., No. 318
Brooklyn Park, MN 55445
Ph: (612)875-2766
URL: http://gasbuddy.com/gb_index.aspx
URL(s): www.massachusettsgasprices.com **Descr:** With gas prices in the U.S. back on the rise in 2009, it's important for consumers to find the best deals on

gasoline. This website lists the lowest regular gas prices in the last 24 hours, from tips sent by drivers all across Massachusetts. Also includes links to a message forum and gas saving tips.

738 ■ Michigan Gas Prices
GasBuddy.com
7964 Brooklyn Blvd., No. 318
Brooklyn Park, MN 55445
Ph: (612)875-2766
URL: http://gasbuddy.com/gb-index.aspx

URL(s): www.michigangasprices.com/ **Descr:** With gas prices back on the rise in 2009, it's essential for drivers to find the best deals on fuel. This website allows consumers to post both low and high prices of any gas station in Michigan. Also provides a message forum and tips for saving gas.

739 ■ Missouri Gas Prices
GasBuddy.com
7964 Brooklyn Blvd., No. 318
Brooklyn Park, MN 55445
Ph: (612)875-2766
URL: http://gasbuddy.com/gb_index.aspx

URL(s): www.missourigasprices.com/ **Descr:** Helps consumers find the best gas prices (provided by drivers who post on the site) in all areas of Missouri. Also includes a message board, price charts, and tips on saving gas.

740 ■ MSN Autos
Microsoft Corporation
One Microsoft Way
Redmond, WA 98052-6399
Contact: Perry Stern, Ed.
E-mail: perrys@microsoft.com

URL(s): autos.msn.com/ **Descr:** Aspiring to be the complete one-stop web site for car and truck buying information, MSN Autos offers browsers the chance to do their homework before buying a vehicle, with free quotes online, classified ads, blue book values, even insurance leads. It also gives you information on new and used vehicles of all makes and models complete with pictures, reviews, prices, etc. Plus a free personal page where you can track scheduled maintenance, oil changes, parts and labor costs, even safety recalls, after you buy. But the real fun of the site is in its special features. The Virtual Auto Show that takes you through auto shows around the country and spotlights new concept vehicles; or the Surround Video Gallery that lets you actually rotate the image of a vehicle to get a panoramic view of the exterior. If you would like to inspect the interior, all you have to do is point and drag your cursor inside the picture of the interior. You can then stop at any point and zoom in for a closer look. It's a totally interactive experience. **Type:** Directory; Full-text; Video; Bulletin board; Image. **Updating freq.:** Regularly. **Fees:** Free. **Searching routines or searchable elements:** Website is searchable by make/model and automobile category.

741 ■ New York Gas Prices
GasBuddy.com
7964 Brooklyn Blvd., No. 318
Brooklyn Park, MN 55445
Ph: (612)875-2766
URL: http://gasbuddy.com/gb_index.aspx

URL(s): www.newyorkgasprices.com/ **Descr:** Helps drivers find the best prices on gasoline in New York. Also has a message board, tips on saving gas, and the latest media coverage on fuel prices.

742 ■ Ohio Gas Prices
GasBuddy.com
7964 Brooklyn Blvd., No. 318
Brooklyn Park, MN 55445
Ph: (612)875-2766
URL: http://gasbuddy.com/gb_index.aspx

URL(s): www.ohiogasprices.com/ **Descr:** This website helps Ohio motorists find the best gas prices in

their area. Also includes a message forum, fuel logbook, and fuel saving tips.

743 ■ Ontario Gas Prices
GasBuddy.com
7964 Brooklyn Blvd., No. 318
Brooklyn Park, MN 55445
Ph: (612)875-2766
URL: http://gasbuddy.com/gb_index.aspx

URL(s): www.ontariogasprices.com/ **Descr:** Helps drivers find the lowest gas prices in Ontario. Also offers a message board, tips on saving gas, and the latest media coverage on rising fuel costs.

744 ■ Oregon Gas Prices
GasBuddy.com
7964 Brooklyn Blvd., No. 318
Brooklyn Park, MN 55445
Ph: (612)875-2766
URL: http://gasbuddy.com/gb_index.aspx

URL(s): www.oregongasprices.com/ **Descr:** Helps drivers find the best gas prices in Oregon. Also offers a message board, tips for saving gas, and the latest news on rising fuel costs.

745 ■ Pennsylvania Gas Prices
GasBuddy.com
7964 Brooklyn Blvd., No. 318
Brooklyn Park, MN 55445
Ph: (612)875-2766
URL: http://gasbuddy.com/gb_index.aspx

URL(s): www.pennsylvaniagasprices.com/ **Descr:** Helps drivers find the lowest gas prices in any area of Pennsylvania. Also includes tips on saving gas, the latest media coverage of fuel costs, and a message board where consumers can touch base with one another on a variety of topics.

746 ■ Recall Campaigns Database
U.S. Department of Transportation
1200 New Jersey Ave. SE
Washington, DC 20590
Contact: Nicole Nason, Admin.
Ph: (202)366-4198
Free: 888-327-4236
Fax: (202)366-1767
E-mail: NCSAweb@nhtsa.dot.gov
URL: http://www.nhtsa.dot.gov

URL(s): www-odi.nhtsa.dot.gov/cars/problems/recalls/ **Descr:** Contains information on safety recall campaigns on child safety seats, tires, equipment and vehicles, including school buses. Enables searches by type of recall, year, vehicle make and model. **Type:** Full-text. **Fees:** Free. **Telecom. Svcs:** TTY toll free phone number is (800)424-9153.

747 ■ Tailpipe Tally
Environmental Defense
257 Park Ave. S
New York, NY 10010
Contact: Fred Krupp, Pres.
Ph: (212)505-2100
Free: 800-684-3322
Fax: (212)505-2375
E-mail: members@environmentaldefense.org
URL: http://www.environmentaldefense.org

Descr: Contains detailed comparative information on fuel cost, fuel consumption, and fuel emissions of thousands of vehicles manufactured from 1978 to date. Includes information on how much each model pollutes. Provides information on the emission of carbon dioxide, carbon monoxide, nitrogen oxides, and hydrocarbons. Covers both domestic and imported vehicles. **Type:** Numeric. **Fees:** Free. **Searching routines or searchable elements:** Provides keyword search functions.

748 ■ Texas Gas Prices
GasBuddy.com
7964 Brooklyn Blvd., No. 318
Brooklyn Park, MN 55445
Ph: (612)875-2766
URL: http://gasbuddy.com/gb_index.aspx

URL(s): www.texasgasprices.com/ **Descr:** With gas prices in the U.S. climbing again in early 2010, it's important for consumers to find the best deals on

gasoline. This website lists the lowest regular gas prices in the last 36 hours in Texas. It also includes a message board, tips on saving gas, and the latest news on rising fuel costs.

749 ■ Virginia Gas Prices
GasBuddy.com
7964 Brooklyn Blvd., No. 318
Brooklyn Park, MN 55445
Ph: (612)875-2766
URL: http://gasbuddy.com/gb_index.aspx

URL(s): www.virginiagasprices.com/ **Descr:** With gas prices in the U.S. climbing again in early 2010, it's important for consumers to find the best deals on gasoline. This website lists the lowest regular gas prices in the last 24 hours, from tips sent by drivers all over Virginia. Also includes a message forum, tips on saving fuel, and the latest news on gasoline prices across the country.

750 ■ Washington Gas Prices
GasBuddy.com
7964 Brooklyn Blvd., No. 318
Brooklyn Park, MN 55445
Ph: (612)875-2766
URL: http://gasbuddy.com/gb_index.aspx

URL(s): www.washingtongasprices.com **Descr:** With gas prices in the U.S. climbing again, it's important for consumers to find the best deal for their money. This website allows you to find the best gas prices in Washington state. Also provides a message board, tips on saving gas, and the latest media coverage on fuel costs.

Federal Government Agencies

751 ■ Commercial Drivers License Task Force
Enforcement and Program Delivery
Federal Motor Carrier Safety Administration
Department of Transportation
1200 New Jersey Ave. SE
Washington, DC 20590
Contact: William A. Quade, Designated Fed.Off.
Ph: (202)366-4553
Fax: (202)366-7908
URL: http://www.fmcsa.dot.gov/registration-licensing/cdl/cdl.htm

Staff: Support services were provided by the Federal Motor Carrier Safety Administration. William A. Quade, Associate Administrator, Enforcement and Program Delivery, served as designated federal official. **Descr:** Task Force studied and addressed current impediments and foreseeable challenges to the Commercial Driver's License (CDL) program effectiveness, and measures needed to realize the full safety potential of the CDL program. Task Force provided advice and recommendations to the Secretary of Transportation on issues such as: state enforcement practices, operational procedures to detect and deter fraud, needed improvements for seamless information sharing between states, effective methods for accurately sharing electronic data between states, adequate proof of citizenship, updated technology, and timely notification from judicial bodies concerning traffic and criminal convictions of CDL holders. **Mem:** Task Force consisted of 15 members, including state motor vehicle administrators, organizations representing government agencies or officials, members of the Judicial Conferences, representatives of the trucking industry, labor organizations, safety advocates, and other significant stakeholders. Members were appointed for up to one-year terms by the Secretary of Transportation with the advice and recommendation of the Administrator of the Federal Motor Carrier Safety Administration. **Pub:** Commercial Driver's License Program Review: Recommended Measures for Achieving the Program's Full Safety Potential (December 2008).

Associations and Other Organizations

752 ■ 4 R Kids Sake
PO Box 77693
Corona, CA 92877
Contact: Tammy Russell, Founder
Ph: (951)278-1820
Fax: (951)737-2539
E-mail: information@4rkidssake.org
URL: http://www.4rkidssake.org
Descr: Aims to protect children from preventable injuries and death in and around cars. Provides awareness, education, legislation and product redesign. Creates and maintains database of injuries resulting from children being left unattended in and around vehicles. **Fnd:** 2000. **Pub:** *Save A Child*.

753 ■ 1953-54 Buick Skylark Club
51 Statesville Quarry Rd.
Lafayette, NJ 07848
Contact: Joanne DePeppo, Corresponding Sec.
Ph: (973)383-6035
Fax: (973)383-6035
E-mail: buick5354@aol.com
URL: http://www.skylarkclub.org
Descr: Owners and admirers of Buick Skylark automobiles built in 1953 and 1954. Promotes preservation and maintenance of classic Buicks. Serves as a clearinghouse on 1953 and 1954 Buick Skylarks; facilitates communication and good fellowship among members. **Fnd:** 1978. **Mem:** 200. **Pub:** Newsletter (quarterly).

754 ■ 1956 Studebaker Golden Hawk Owners Register (56SGHOR)
31654 Wekiva River Rd.
Sorrento, FL 32776-9233
Contact: Frank Ambrogio
E-mail: fja56gh@gmail.com
URL: http://www.1956goldenhawk.com
Staff: 1. **Descr:** Owners of 1956 Studebaker Golden Hawks. **Fnd:** 1989. **Mem:** 260. **Pub:** *56J Only* (3/year).

755 ■ Alberta Motor Association (AMA)
4700 17 Ave. SW
Calgary, AB, Canada T3E 0E3
Ph: (403)240-5300
URL: http://www.ama.ab.ca/cps/rde/xchg/ama
Descr: Provides products and services promoting quality service, safety and protection for members; advocates for motoring and related consumer issues; offers automotive and other travel services. **Fnd:** 1926. **Mem:** 800000. **Pub:** *Westworld Alberta* (5/year).

756 ■ American Association of Motor Vehicle Administrators (AAMVA)
4301 Wilson Blvd., Ste. 400
Arlington, VA 22203
Contact: Neil D. Schuster, Pres./CEO
Ph: (703)522-4200
Fax: (703)522-1905
E-mail: info@aamva.org
URL: http://www.aamva.org
Staff: 75. **Descr:** Officials representing 68 states, provinces, and territories who administer motor vehicle laws and regulations. Promotes reasonable and uniform laws and regulations governing registration, certification of ownership, equipment and operation of motor vehicles, and issuance of motor vehicle driver's licenses. **Fnd:** 1933. **Mem:** 1500. **Reg. Groups:** 4. **State Groups:** 50. **Pub:** *MOVE Magazine* (3/year); Membership Directory.

757 ■ American Automobile Association (AAA)
One River Pl.
Wilmington, DE 19801
Contact: Robert Darbelnet, Pres./CEO
Free: 800-763-9900
URL: http://www.aaa.com
Descr: Federation of automobile clubs (1,000 offices) providing domestic and foreign travel services, emergency road services, and insurance. Sponsors public services for traffic safety, better highways, more efficient and safer cars, energy conservation, and improvement of motoring and travel conditions. **Fnd:** 1902. **Mem:** 40000000. **Pub:** *Digest of Motor Laws* (annual); *Maps and Tour Books* (annual); *Sportsmanlike Driving* (periodic).

758 ■ American Highway Users Alliance (Hwy-Users)
1101 14th St. NW, Ste. 750
Washington, DC 20005
Contact: Greg Cohen PE, Pres./CEO
Ph: (202)857-1200
Fax: (202)857-1220
E-mail: info@highways.org
URL: http://www.highways.org
Descr: Broad-based consumers group for American motorists, truckers and businesses. Employs lobbying, media, communications and grassroots advocacy, promotes public policy that devotes highway use taxes to investments in safe and uncongested national highway systems. **Fnd:** 1932. **Pub:** *Driving Ahead* (bimonthly).

759 ■ America's Corvette Club (ACC)
PO Box 250754
West Bloomfield, MI 48325
Contact: Connie Harper
Ph: (248)788-6119
E-mail: accsocial@aol.com
URL: http://www.americascorvetteclub.org
Descr: Brings together Corvette enthusiasts of varied backgrounds and interests. Promotes appreciation of Corvette automobiles. Conducts competitive driving, cruises, car shows and social gatherings. **Fnd:** 2000. **Pub:** Newsletter.

760 ■ Automobile Protection Association (APA)
292 St. Joseph Blvd. W
Montreal, QC, Canada H2V 2N7
Contact: George Iny, Pres.
Ph: (514)272-5555
Fax: (514)273-0797
E-mail: apamontreal@apa.ca
URL: http://www.apa.ca
Descr: Seeks to protect purchasers of automobiles from unfair sales practices; promotes ethical practice among automotive services providers; seeks to insure adherence to high standards of engineering and manufacturing among automotive manufacturers. Monitors the automotive industries and publicizes product defects and instances of unfair practice in the automotive services industries. **Fnd:** 1969. **Mem:** 17000. **Pub:** *Lemon-Aid Magazine* (annual).

761 ■ Automotive Body Parts Association (ABPA)
1510 Eldridge Pkwy. S, Ste. 110-168
Houston, TX 77077
Contact: Stanley A. Rodman, Exec. Dir.
Ph: (281)531-0809
Free: 800-323-5832
Fax: (281)531-9411
E-mail: srodman1@sbcglobal.net
URL: http://www.autobpa.com
Staff: 3. **Descr:** Represents the industry interests of distributors, suppliers and manufacturers of independently produced collision replacement parts such as bumpers, fenders, hoods, doors, lights, radiators, etc., and is also involved with the recycling of both steel bumpers and urethane and rubber bumper fascias. **Fnd:** 1980. **Mem:** 170. **Pub:** *Body Language*; *Collision Parts Journal* (semiannual); *International Collision Parts Industry Suppliers Guide and Membership Roster*.

762 ■ Automotive Consumer Action Program (AUTOCAP)
5301 Wisconsin Ave. NW, Ste. 210
Washington, DC 20015
Ph: (202)237-7200
Fax: (202)237-9090
E-mail: autocap@wanada.org
URL: http://www.wanada.org/autocap.html
Descr: Participating new car dealers' associations and automobile manufacturers complying with standards administered through the National Automobile Dealers Association. Acts as a public service program providing dealers and their customers with consumer dispute resolution assistance. Act as "mini-juries" through panels of volunteers (usually 3 dealers and 3 consumer representatives) in cases of customer dissatisfaction with dealers, when direct contact fails to resolve the problem. **Fnd:** 1973. **Mem:** 31. **State Groups:** 19. **Local Groups:** 12. **Pub:** *Automotive Customer Relations Directory*.

763 ■ Automotive Industries Association of Canada (AIAC)
1272 Wellington St. W
Ottawa, ON, Canada K1Y 3A7
Contact: Marc Brazeau, Pres.
Ph: (613)728-5821
Free: 800-808-2920
Fax: (613)728-6021
E-mail: info.aia@aiacanada.com
URL: http://www.aiacanada.com
Staff: 10. **Descr:** Represents automotive aftermarket industry, including suppliers, distributors, wholesalers and retailers, in all areas that impact the growth and prosperity of the industry. **Fnd:** 1942. **Mem:** 1400. **Reg. Groups:** 13. **Pub:** *Outlook Study* (biennial).

764 ■ Automotive Occupant Restraints Council (AORC)
1081 Dove Run Rd., Ste. 403
Lexington, KY 40502
Ph: (859)269-4240
Fax: (859)269-4241
URL: http://www.aorc.org
Staff: 2. **Descr:** Manufacturers of motor vehicle occupant restraint systems and of primary and secondary component materials and supplies. Undertakes research; cooperates with other organizations in promulgating performance standards; and promotes the installation and use of safety belts and air bags. Conducts public education program on air bags and seat belts. **Fnd:** 1965. **Mem:** 54.

765 ■ Automotive Women's Alliance (AWA)
PO Box 4305
Troy, MI 48099-4305
Contact: Susan West, Pres.
Ph: (248)643-6590
Free: 877-393-AWAF
Fax: (248)239-0291
URL: http://www.automotivewomensalliance.com
Descr: Represents and supports women in automotive and affiliated industries. **Fnd:** 2001. **Mem:** 300. **Pub:** *Member Roster*; *Up To Speed* (quarterly); Brochure.

766 ■ Canadian Auto Workers (CAW)
205 Placer Ct.
Toronto, ON, Canada M2H 3H9
Contact: Ken Lewenza, Pres.
Ph: (416)497-4110
Free: 800-268-5763
Fax: (416)495-6552
E-mail: caw@caw.ca
URL: http://www.caw.ca
Staff: 200. **Descr:** Represents the economic and workplace safety interests of Canadian automobile workers. Conducts economic and social action activities; maintains educational, charitable and research programs. Operates speakers' bureau. **Fnd:** 1985. **Mem:** 250000. **Pub:** *Contact* (weekly).

767 ■ Canadian Automobile Dealers Association (CADA)
85 Renfrew Dr.
Markham, ON, Canada L3R 0N9
Contact: Richard C. Gauthier, Pres./CEO
Ph: (905)940-4959
Free: 800-463-5289
Fax: (905)940-6870

E-mail: mail@cada.ca
URL: http://www.cada.ca
Staff: 10. **Descr:** Automobile dealers. Seeks to advance the automotive and automotive services industries. Facilitates communication and cooperation among members; represents members' interests before industrial organizations and government agencies. **Fnd:** 1941. **Reg. Groups:** 3. **State Groups:** 10. **Pub:** *Newsline* (monthly).

768 ■ Canadian Automotive Repair and Service Council (CARS)
57 Auriga Dr., Ste. 203
Ottawa, ON, Canada K2E 8B2
Contact: Jennifer Steeves, Exec. Dir.
Ph: (613)798-0500
Free: 888-224-3834
Fax: (613)798-9963
E-mail: askus@cars-council.ca
URL: http://www.carcare.ca
Descr: Seeks to advance the automotive service industry. Facilitates communication and cooperation among members; represents members' interests before industrial organizations, government agencies, organizations, and the public. **Fnd:** 1988.

769 ■ Canadian Carwash Association (CCA)
346-4195 Dundas St. W
Toronto, ON, Canada M8X 1Y4
Contact: Richard McKinnon, Pres.
Ph: (416)239-0339
Fax: (416)239-1076
E-mail: office@canadiancarwash.ca
URL: http://www.canadiancarwash.ca
Descr: Owners of car wash facilities. Promotes growth and development of the industry. Facilitates exchange of information among members; monitors legislation of interest to members and conducts lobbying activities; makes available continuing professional education programs; conducts public relations campaigns. Provides benefits to members including discount insurance programs and customer handouts. **Mem:** 200. **Pub:** *Wash-Word* (quarterly).

770 ■ Car Care Council (CCC)
7101 Wisconsin Ave., Ste. 1300
Bethesda, MD 20814
Contact: Rich White, Sr. VP
Ph: (240)333-1088
E-mail: marcella.tilli@aftermarket.org
URL: http://www.carcare.org
Staff: 2. **Descr:** Works as the source of information for the "Be Car Care Aware" consumer education campaign promoting the benefits of regular vehicle care, maintenance and repair to consumers. **Fnd:** 1969. **Pub:** *Car Care Chronicles* (quarterly).

771 ■ Cyclone Montego Torino Registry (CMTR)
19 Glyn Dr.
Newark, DE 19713-4016
Contact: Robert Day
Ph: (302)737-4252
E-mail: robscyclone@aol.com
URL: http://clubs.hemmings.com/frameset.cfm?club=cyclonemontegotorinoregistry
Staff: 5. **Descr:** Owners and admirers of Cyclone, Torino, and Montego automobiles manufactured between 1964-76, and 1968-79 Rancheros, 1970-71 Torino Cobras, 1970 1/2 Falcons, and 77-79 LTD II's and Cougars. Promotes collection, preservation, and restoration of classic Ford and Mercury cars. **Fnd:** 1992. **Mem:** 150. **Pub:** *Registry Update* (3/year).

772 ■ Driving School Association of the Americas (DSAA)
3090 E Gause Blvd., Ste. 425
Slidell, LA 70461
Contact: Ms. Sheila Varnado, Controller
Free: 800-270-DSAA
Fax: (985)649-9877
E-mail: info@thedsaa.org
URL: http://www.thedsaa.org
Descr: Owners of licensed professional driving schools in the U.S. and Canada. Conducts safe driver training for high schools and the public;

achieves legislation beneficial to driving schools; promotes high ethical standards within the training program. Conducts trade exhibitions of products and services that best service the driving school owner and its consumer. **Fnd:** 1972. **Mem:** 400. **State Groups:** 35. **Pub:** *Dual News Magazine* (3/year).

773 ■ Electrical Rebuilder's Association (ERA)
PO Box 906
Union, MO 63084
Contact: Jim Thomas, Pres.
Ph: (636)584-7400
Fax: (636)584-7401
E-mail: eraoffice@charterinternet.com
URL: http://www.electricalrebuilders.org
Descr: Represents rebuilders, suppliers, and individuals involved in the automotive electrical parts rebuilding industry. Promotes the well being and professionalism of the electrical rebuilding industry in North America through education and training. Serves as a forum for members to exchange information on all aspects of the industry. **Fnd:** 2001.

774 ■ Faith Alliance Against Slavery and Trafficking (FAAST)
625 Slaters Ln., Ste. 200
Alexandria, VA 22314
Free: 888-466-4673
E-mail: faast@worldhope.net
URL: http://www.faastinternational.org
Descr: Represents faith-based, community-oriented and non-profit organizations that deeply value the "physical, emotional and spiritual dignity of the whole person." Aims to eliminate human trafficking through prevention, victim protection and sustainable restoration. Mobilizes communities to generate a united and active response to the injustices of slavery and human trafficking. **Fnd:** 2003.

775 ■ Future Corvette Owners Association (FCOA)
S68 W17323 Rossmar Ct.
Muskego, WI 53150-8575
Contact: Pat Kelly, Dir.
Ph: (414)422-0874
E-mail: fcoakids@aol.com
URL: http://www.corvettesnccc.org/fcoa1.html
Descr: Aims to interest the younger generation in the Corvette hobby. Promotes restoration, reconstruction and education about Chevrolet Corvette automobiles. Encourages and increases the enjoyment and popularity of Corvette automobiles. **Fnd:** 1991.

776 ■ Gold Wing Road Riders Association (GWRRA)
21423 N 11th Ave.
Phoenix, AZ 85027
Contact: Mike Wright, Pres.
Ph: (623)581-2500
Free: 800-843-9460
Fax: (623)581-3844
E-mail: customerservice@gwrra.org
URL: http://www.gwrra.org
Staff: 21. **Descr:** Owners of Honda Gold Wing motorcycles; spouses and dependents of owners. Promotes the pleasure and recreational aspects of Gold Wing motorcycle riding. Coordinates common motorcycle efforts and provides for exchange of information. Strives to improve public acceptance of motorcyclists and motorcycling, educate noncyclists to motorcycling problems, promote safe and skillful riding, and assist in local civic improvement, and police, government, and charity activities. Supports similarly motivated organizations, local Honda dealerships, American Honda, and the Motorcycle Safety Foundation. Informs members of trips, tours, and rallies; offers insurance discounts; compiles statistics. Develops plans for increased member benefits, motorcycle skills course, and a store carrying approved accessories and wearables. Maintains speakers' bureau. **Fnd:** 1977. **Mem:** 82000. **Reg. Groups:**

11. **State Groups:** 57. **Local Groups:** 950. **Pub:** *Gold Book* (annual); *Wing World Magazine* (monthly).

777 ■ Japan Automobile Manufacturers Association, Washington Office (JAMA)
1050 17th St. NW, Ste. 410
Washington, DC 20036
Contact: Charley Powers
Ph: (202)296-8537
Fax: (202)872-1212
E-mail: cpowers@porternovelli.com
URL: http://www.jama.org
Descr: Trade association representing Japanese automobile manufacturers. Promotes the development of the automobile industry. Conducts research programs involving vehicle production, trade policy, overseas investment, and parts procurement; exchanges information with other sectors of the industry. **Fnd:** 1967. **Mem:** 13. **Pub:** *Japan Auto Trends* (quarterly); *The Motor Industry of Japan* (annual); *Motor Vehicle Statistics* (annual); *Press Releases* (monthly); Brochures (periodic).

778 ■ Mothers Against Drunk Driving (MADD)
511 E John Carpenter Fwy., Ste. 700
Irving, TX 75062
Contact: Laura Dean-Mooney, Natl. Pres.
Ph: (214)744-6233
Free: 800-GET-MADD
Fax: (972)869-2206
E-mail: info@madd.org
URL: http://www.madd.org
Staff: 317. **Descr:** Represents victims of drunk driving crashes; concerned citizens. Encourages citizen participation in working towards reform of the drunk driving problem and the prevention of underage drinking acts and providing materials for use in medical facilities, and health and driver education programs. Conducts a variety of programs for youth and in the schools. Supports Law Enforcement Programs and state and federal legislation for reform of laws on drunk driving; provides public education programs for encouraging more stringent laws requiring mandatory minimum punishment. Conducts research programs; maintains biographical archives and extensive library; sponsors competitions; compiles statistics; maintains speakers' bureau. Holds regional workshops. **Fnd:** 1980. **Mem:** 3200000. **State Groups:** 37. **Local Groups:** 300. **Pub:** *Closed Head Injury*; *Don't Call Me Lucky*; *Driven* (biennial); *Drunk Driving: An Unacknowledged Form of Child Endangerment*; *Financial Recovery After A Drunk Driving Crash*; *Helping Children Cope With Death*; *How You Can Help*; *MADDvocate* (semiannual); *Men and Mourning*; *Selecting a Civil Attorney*; *Someone You Know Drinks and Drives*; *Straight Talk About Death for Teenagers*; *Track*; *Victim Information*; *We Hurt Too: Guide for Adult Siblings*; *Will It Always Feel This Way?*; *Your Grief: You're Not Going Crazy*; *You're Not Alone: MADD Can Help!*.

779 ■ Mothers Against Drunk Driving - Canada (MADD)
2010 Winston Park Dr., Ste. 500
Oakville, ON, Canada L6H 5R7
Contact: Ms. Wanda Kristensen, Dir. of Programs
Ph: (905)829-8805
Free: 800-665-6233
Fax: (905)829-8860
E-mail: info@madd.ca
URL: http://www.madd.ca
Staff: 25. **Descr:** Eliminates impaired driving. Increases awareness on dangers of drinking and driving. Offers support services to victims of violent crime. Works to save lives and prevent injuries on roads. **Fnd:** 1990. **Mem:** 7500. **Reg. Groups:** 4. **Local Groups:** 104. **Pub:** Newsletter (quarterly).

780 ■ National Bus Traffic Association (NBTA)
700 13th St. NW, Ste. 575
Washington, DC 20005-5923
Ph: (202)898-2700
Fax: (202)842-0850
URL: http://www.bustraffic.org
Staff: 3. **Descr:** Establishes by the intercity regular route bus carriers. Serves as tariff publisher for its

industry. **Fnd:** 1933. **Mem:** 270. **Pub:** *Bus Passenger Tariffs* (periodic); *National Mileage Guides* (periodic).

781 ■ National Commission Against Drunk Driving (NCADD)
8403 Colesville Rd., Ste. 370
Silver Spring, MD 20910
Contact: Mr. Robert C. Stempel, Chm.
Ph: (240)247-6004
Fax: (240)247-7012
E-mail: info@ncadd.com
Staff: 3. **Descr:** Individuals and organizations concerned with increasing highway safety. Seeks to reduce the incidence of drunk driving and resulting accidents. Holds public hearings; coordinates implementation of recommendations by the Presidential Commission on Drunk Driving. Operates speakers' bureau; conducts educational programs; compiles statistics. **Fnd:** 1984. **Pub:** *Intersections* (quarterly).

782 ■ National Institute for Automotive Service Excellence (ASE)
101 Blue Seal Dr. SE, Ste. 101
Leesburg, VA 20175
Contact: Tim Zilke, Pres./CEO
Ph: (703)669-6600
Free: 888-273-8378
Fax: (703)669-6123
E-mail: webmaster@ase.com
URL: http://www.asecert.org
Staff: 50. **Descr:** Governed by a 40-member board of directors selected from all sectors of the automotive service industry and from education, government, and consumer groups. Encourages and promotes the highest standards of automotive service in the public interest. Conducts continuing research to determine the best methods for training automotive technicians; encourages the development of effective training programs. Tests and certifies the competence of automobile, medium/heavy truck, collision repair, school bus and engine machinist technicians as well as parts specialists. **Fnd:** 1972. **Mem:** 400000. **Pub:** *ASE Blue Seal Tech News* (quarterly); *ASE Catalogs of Tests* (annual); *ASE Certification Test Registration Booklet* (semiannual).

783 ■ National Traffic Incident Management Coalition (NTIMC)
4802 Sheboygan Ave.
Madison, WI 53705-2927
Contact: John Corbin, Chm.
Ph: (608)266-0459
E-mail: john.corbin@dot.state.wi.us
URL: http://timcoalition.org
Descr: Aims to promote the safe and efficient management of traffic incidents. Provides a partnership forum that enables the public safety and transportation communities to coordinate experiences, knowledge, practices, and ideas toward the end of safer and more efficient management of incidents affecting the public. Works to enhance the safety of on-scene responders and of motorists passing or approaching a roadway incident. Collaborates with the transportation, public safety, towing and recovery, technology, academic and research, and motorist communities to lead a national effort to improve traffic incident management policies, practices and programs. **Fnd:** 2004.

784 ■ Native American Business Alliance (NABA)
290 Town Center Dr., Ste. 624
Dearborn, MI 48126
Contact: Lee Pepion, Pres.
Ph: (248)988-9344
Fax: (248)988-9348
E-mail: naba@n-a-b-a.org
URL: http://www.native-american-bus.org
Descr: Represents Native Americans to the private sector; facilitates business and cultural educational

programs. **Fnd:** 1995. **Pub:** *Moccasin Print* (monthly).

785 ■ Partnership for Safe Driving
1312 18th St. NW, Rm. 501
Washington, DC 20036
Contact: Lisa Lewis, Founder
E-mail: info2@crashprevention.org
URL: http://crashprevention.org
Descr: Aims to reduce the total number of crashes, injuries and fatalities on U.S. roads. Works to change the driving culture in America through education, research and grassroots activism. Educates Americans about all forms of dangerous driving and halting the epidemic of motor vehicle crashes. **Fnd:** 1997. **Pub:** *Crash Prevention News* (monthly).

786 ■ RID - U.S.A. (RID)
PO Box 520
Schenectady, NY 12301
Contact: Doris Aiken, Pres./Founder
Ph: (518)372-0034
Free: 888-283-5144
Fax: (518)370-4917
E-mail: dwi@rid-usa.org
URL: http://www.rid-usa.org
Staff: 5. **Descr:** Businesses, organizations, churches, educational agencies, victims, citizen activists, and others dedicated to removing intoxicated drivers from the road. Goals include: heightening public awareness of the effects drunken drivers have on society; encouraging the development of and public demand for passage of more effective laws dealing with drunk drivers; increasing public involvement; supporting victims of drunk drivers. Provides background information on court procedures; acts as liaison between victims and agencies, courts, coroners, district attorneys, and police. Holds victim witness panels for convicted drunk drivers. Conducts educational programs to discourage underage binge drinking and prevent alcohol poisoning. Compiles statistics; maintains speakers' bureau. Sponsors competitions, charitable programs, and youth services. **Fnd:** 1978. **Reg. Groups:** 4. **State Groups:** 41. **Local Groups:** 153. **Pub:** *Arive Alive*; *Citizen Activist Register* (semiannual); *History of RID*; *How Can I Help*; *How to Hire a Lawyer*; *Media Game & How to Play It*; *My Life as a Pit Bull*; *RID Action Newsletter* (semiannual); *RID Directory* (annual); *RID In Action Bulletin* (bimonthly); *RID Media Manual*; *Victims Aid Network: How Can I Help* (annual); *Victims Memorial*; *Victims' Rights*; *Without Warning*.

787 ■ SAE International - Society of Automotive Engineers (SAE)
400 Commonwealth Dr.
Warrendale, PA 15096-0001
Contact: Thomas W. Ryan III, Pres.
Ph: (724)776-4841
Free: 877-606-7323
Fax: (724)776-0790
E-mail: customerservice@sae.org
URL: http://www.sae.org
Staff: 380. **Descr:** Collects and disseminates information on mobility technology. Fosters information exchange among the worldwide automotive and aerospace communities. Conducts educational programs. **Fnd:** 1905. **Mem:** 80000. **State Groups:** 66. **Pub:** *Aerospace Engineering* (monthly); *Aerospace Standards*; *Automotive Consultant's Directory* (annual); *Automotive Engineering* (monthly); *Bosch Handbook* (annual); *Off Highway Engineering* (bimonthly); *Progress in Technology*; *SAE Aerospace Material Specifications*; *SAE Technical Papers*; *SAE Transactions* (annual); *SAE Update* (monthly).

788 ■ SFI Foundation (SFI)
15708 Pomerado Rd., Ste. N208
Poway, CA 92064-2066
Ph: (858)451-8868
Fax: (858)451-9268
E-mail: sfi@sfifoundation.com
URL: http://www.sfifoundation.com
Staff: 9. **Descr:** Develops and administrates minimum performance specifications for the automobile industry, including consumer automotive, automotive

aftermarket, and high performance racing products. Encourages suggestions on specifications as they are developed through committee meetings and public hearings. **Fnd:** 1978. **Pub:** Articles.

789 ■ Standing Up for SUV, Pickup and Van Owners of America (SUVOA)
PO Box 34076
Washington, DC 20043
Contact: Larry Innis, Chm.
Ph: (202)289-4370
Free: 877-447-8862
E-mail: info@suvoa.com
URL: http://www.suvoa.com
Descr: Supports the rights and serves the interests of SUV, Pickup and Van Owners. Acts as a voice of and advocates for SUV owners from unfounded attacks by special interest groups and unwarranted government regulation. Serves the public with information about SUV ownership. **Fnd:** 1999.

790 ■ Swiss-American Business Council (SABC)
PO Box 641724
Chicago, IL 60601
Contact: David Kouidri, Exec. Dir.
Ph: (312)624-7697
E-mail: info2008@sabcnow.com
URL: http://www.sabcnow.com
Descr: Focuses on strengthening transatlantic business and technology partnerships. Assists companies, trade groups, entrepreneurs and professionals to expand opportunities in regional, national and transatlantic commerce. Provides information resources and networking opportunities designed to enhance business partnerships, trade and research collaboration. **Fnd:** 1999. **Pub:** *SABC Business & Technology Directory*; Newsletter (quarterly).

791 ■ Tire Industry Association (TIA)
1532 Pointer Ridge Pl., Ste. G
Bowie, MD 20716-1883
Contact: Peggy Fisher, Pres.
Ph: (301)430-7280
Free: 800-876-8372
Fax: (301)430-7283
E-mail: info@tireindustry.org
URL: http://www.tireindustry.org
Staff: 6. **Descr:** Corporations engaged in all sectors of the replacement tire industry. Seeks to advance members' interests. Serves as a clearinghouse on economic and regulatory issues affecting the replacement tire industry; conducts educational programs; sponsors lobbying activities. **Fnd:** 1921. **Mem:** 4500. **State Groups:** 25. **Pub:** *TANA--Who's Who Membership Directory* (annual); *Video Training Network Directory*; Magazine (quarterly); Newsletter (monthly).

792 ■ Transmission Rebuilders Network International (TRNi)
3851 E Thunderbird Rd., Ste. 111-235
Phoenix, AZ 85032
Contact: Bill Fuller, Founder
Free: 888-582-8764
Fax: (602)404-7650
E-mail: info@trannybuilder.com
URL: http://www.trannybuilder.com
Descr: Advances the science of rebuilding automatic transmissions and the art of managing a transmission shop. Serves as a forum for the members to share and exchange ideas on automatic transmissions. Provides training, support and technical information based on the needs, trends and opportunities of the transmission/powertrain industry. **Fnd:** 1996.

793 ■ United States Council for Automotive Research (USCAR)
1000 Town Center Dr., Ste. 300
Southfield, MI 48075
Contact: Larry Burns
Ph: (248)223-9000
URL: http://www.uscar.org
Descr: Works to create and support U.S. cooperative research and development to advance automotive technologies. Provides a common voice to the

supply base. Aims to improve quality and reduce the cost for noncompetitive technologies and activities. **Fnd:** 1992.

794 ■ Women On Wheels Motorcycle Association
PO Box 83076
Lincoln, NE 68501
Ph: (402)477-1280
Free: 800-322-1969
E-mail: general@womenonwheels.org
URL: http://www.womenonwheels.org
Staff: 1. **Descr:** Women motorcyclists. Aims to unite women motorcyclists and to gain recognition from the motorcycle industry concerning the needs of female consumers. Promotes camaraderie of women motorcyclists and participation in motorcycle events. Organizes rallies, interchapter social affairs, fashion activities, and fundraising for public service projects. **Fnd:** 1982. **Mem:** 3500. **Local Groups:** 90. **Pub:** *Women On Wheels* (bimonthly); Brochure; Membership Directory (annual).

State and Local Organizations and Agencies

Alabama

795 ■ Alabama Department of Public Safety Driver License Division
PO Box 1471
Montgomery, AL 36102-1471
Contact: Major Charles Andrews, Division Chf.
Ph: (334)353-1470
E-mail: driverlicenseinfo@dps.alabama.gov
URL: http://www.dps.alabama.gov/Default.aspx

796 ■ Alabama Tire Dealers Association (ATDA)
6096 County Rd. 434
Trinity, AL 35673
Contact: Cheryl Lentz, Co-Exec. Dir.
Ph: (256)616-3587
Fax: (256)974-1480
E-mail: alatiredealers@cs.com
URL: http://www.alatiredealers.com
Descr: Represents corporations engaged in all sectors of the replacement tire industry. Seeks to advance and protect the interests of members and to promote goodwill within the industry. Serves as a clearinghouse on economic and regulatory issues affecting the replacement tire industry.

797 ■ Mothers Against Drunk Driving, Alabama
2101 Eastern Blvd., Ste. 210
Montgomery, AL 36117
Contact: James Rogers, Development Off.
Ph: (334)277-7722
Free: 800-635-0722
Fax: (334)277-8228
E-mail: al.state@madd.org
URL: http://www.madd.org/chapter/0100_3143
Descr: Seeks to prevent drunk driving, support victims of this violent crime, and prevent underage drinking. Provides strong victim support and assistance, speakers bureau, coalition work, public awareness, and education to prevent underage drinking. **Pub:** *Driven Magazine*; *Maddvocate Magazine*; Brochure.

798 ■ Mothers Against Drunk Driving, Dekalb County Chapter
600 Hammonds Rd.
Fyffe, AL 35971
Free: 800-635-0722

799 ■ Mothers Against Drunk Driving, Greater Montgomery
2101 Eastern Blvd., Ste. 210
Montgomery, AL 36117
Ph: (334)277-7722
Fax: (334)277-8228
E-mail: al.state@madd.org

Descr: Victims of drunk driving crashes; concerned citizens. Encourages citizen participation in working towards reform of the drunk driving problem and the prevention of underage drinking. Acts as the voice of victims of drunk driving crashes by speaking on their behalf to communities, businesses, and educational groups.

800 ■ Mothers Against Drunk Driving, Jefferson County
PO Box 632
Montevallo, AL 35115
Ph: (205)744-6001
Free: 800-635-0722
Descr: Victims of drunk driving crashes; concerned citizens. Encourages citizen participation in working towards reform of the drunk driving problem and the prevention of underage drinking. Acts as the voice of victims of drunk driving crashes by speaking on their behalf to communities, businesses, and educational groups.

801 ■ Society of Automotive Engineers, University of Alabama-Birmingham
University of Alabama Birmingham
Mechanical Engineering Department
BEC 257
1150 10th Ave. S
Birmingham, AL 35294-0001
Contact: Tina Oliver
Ph: (205)934-1824
Fax: (205)975-7217
E-mail: toliver@uab.edu
URL: http://www.main.uab.edu
Descr: Collects and disseminates information on mobility technology. Fosters information exchange among the worldwide automotive and aerospace communities.

802 ■ Society of Automotive Engineers, University of Alabama-Huntsville
Mechanical and Aerospace Engineering
N274 Technology Hall
Huntsville, AL 35899
Contact: Dr. Donald B. Wallace, Advisor
Ph: (256)824-6154
E-mail: wallace@mae.uah.edu
URL: http://www.eng.uah.edu/org/sae
Descr: Collects and disseminates information on mobility technology. Fosters information exchange among the worldwide automotive and aerospace communities.

803 ■ Society of Automotive Engineers, University of South Alabama
Dept. of Mechanical Engineering
Engineering Classroom Bldg., EGCB 212
307 University Blvd. N
Mobile, AL 36688-0002
Contact: Frank Lansdon, Pres.
Ph: (251)460-6168
Fax: (251)460-6549
E-mail: fll401@jaguar1.usouthal.edu
URL: http://www.southalabama.edu/engineering/mechanical/sae/sae2005/index.htm
Descr: Collects and disseminates information on mobility technology. Fosters information exchange among the worldwide automotive and aerospace communities.

Alaska

804 ■ Alaska Division of Motor Vehicles
1300 W. Benson Blvd., Ste. 900
Anchorage, AK 99503
Contact: Whitney Brewster, Dir.
Ph: (907)269-5559
Fax: (907)465-5509
E-mail: DOA.DMV.JDL@Alaska.gov
URL: http://www.state.ak.us/dmv/
Descr: Responsible for the administration of the safety responsibility law, driver improvement point

system, and the collection of motor vehicle registration taxes.

805 ■ Mothers Against Drunk Driving, Anchorage
4105 Turnagain Blvd., Ste. A
Anchorage, AK 99517
Contact: Mrs. Marti Greeson, Exec. Dir.
Ph: (907)562-6890
Fax: (907)562-6896
E-mail: info@madd.org
Descr: Strives to stop drunk driving, supports the victims of drunk driving and prevents underage drinking. **Fnd:** 1980. **Mem:** 400. **State Groups:** 6. **Local Groups:** 1.

806 ■ Mothers Against Drunk Driving, Fairbanks Chapter
PO Box 84679
Fairbanks, AK 99708
Ph: (907)374-3088

Arizona

807 ■ Arizona Department of Transportation Motor Vehicle Division
PO Box 2100
Phoenix, AZ 85001-2100
Contact: Victor Mendez, Dir.
Ph: (602)255-0072
Free: 800-251-5866
E-mail: mvdinfo@azdot.gov
URL: http://www.dot.state.az.us/mvd/

808 ■ Mothers Against Drunk Driving, Arizona Chapter
4020 N 20th St., No. 300
Phoenix, AZ 85016
Contact: Ericka Espino, Exec. Dir.
Ph: (602)240-6500
Free: 800-553-6233
Fax: (602)287-0545
E-mail: az.state@madd.org
URL: http://www.madd.org/az

809 ■ Mothers Against Drunk Driving, Phoenix Metro
4020 N 20th St., Ste. 300
Phoenix, AZ 85016
Contact: Marcia Harmon, State Exec. Dir.
Ph: (602)240-6500
Free: 800-553-6233
Fax: (602)287-0545
E-mail: az.state@madd.org
URL: http://www.madd.org
Descr: Victims of drunk driving crashes; concerned citizens. Encourages citizen participation in working towards reform of the drunk driving problem and the prevention of underage drinking. Acts as the voice of victims of drunk driving crashes by speaking on their behalf to communities, businesses, and educational groups.

810 ■ Mothers Against Drunk Driving, Pima County Chapter (MADD AZ)
2221 E Broadway Blvd., No. 200
Tucson, AZ 85705
Contact: Ms. Kelly Larkin, Affiliate Exec. Dir.
Ph: (520)322-5253
Fax: (520)322-6245
E-mail: pima.az@madd.org
URL: http://www.madd.org/az/pima
Staff: 3. **Descr:** Works to stop drunk driving, support the victims of this crime and prevent underage drinking. Offers free victim assistance, court accompaniment and referrals for civil restitution, victim compensation and mental health counseling. Speaks at schools and businesses and works to bring community awareness to the most frequently committed violent crime in America: drunk driving. **Fnd:** 1982.

Mem: 630. **State Groups:** 2. **Local Groups:** 1. **Pub:** *MADD News* (quarterly).

811 ■ Mothers Against Drunk Driving Support Groups (MADD)
4020 N 20th St., No. 300
Phoenix, AZ 85016
Contact: Ericka Espino, Exec. Dir.
Ph: (602)240-6500
Free: 800-553-6233
Fax: (602)287-0545
E-mail: az.state@madd.org
URL: http://www.maddaz.org

Descr: Works to stop drunk driving, support the victims of such activity, and prevent underage drinking.

Arkansas

812 ■ Arkansas Department of Finance and Administration
Office of Motor Vehicles
PO Box 3153
Little Rock, AR 72203-3153
Contact: Richard Weiss, Dir.
Ph: (501)682-4692
Free: 888-389-8336
Fax: (501)682-4756
E-mail: marsha.ellis@rev.state.ar.us
URL: http://www.arkansas.gov/dfa/motor_vehicle/mv_tagrenew.html

Descr: Chief responsibilities are to administer the State of Arkansas vehicle registration, title, and lien perfection laws.

813 ■ Arkansas Independent Tire Dealers Association (AITDA)
PO Box 4078
Horseshoe Bend, AR 72512
Free: 888-670-5915
URL: http://www.driveusa.net/aitda.htm

Descr: Represents corporations engaged in all sectors of the replacement tire industry. Seeks to advance and protect the interests of members and to promote goodwill within the industry. Serves as a clearinghouse on economic and regulatory issues affecting the replacement tire industry.

814 ■ Mothers Against Drunk Driving, Arkansas State
10515 W Markham St., No. 121
Little Rock, AR 72205
Contact: Teresa Belew, Exec. Dir.
Ph: (501)376-6100

Descr: Supports victims of drunk driving by offering emotional support, help with the justice system and other areas as needed. Works to stop drunk driving and prevent underage drinking through public awareness and educational programs at community events, educational institutions and businesses.

815 ■ Mothers Against Drunk Driving, Cleburne County Chapter
44 Windwood Dr.
Heber Springs, AR 72543
Ph: (501)362-5633

California

816 ■ California Department of Consumer Affairs
Bureau of Automotive Repair
PO Box 989001
West Sacramento, CA 95798-9001
Ph: (916)255-3145
Free: 800-952-5210
E-mail: BAREditor@dca.ca.gov
URL: http://www.autorepair.ca.gov

Descr: The mission of the Bureau of Automotive Repair is to protect and serve consumers while ensuring a fair and competitive marketplace and

implementing a model motor vehicle emissions reduction program.

817 ■ California Department of Motor Vehicles
Vehicle Registration Operations
PO Box 942869
Sacramento, CA 94269-0001
Contact: George Valverde, Dir.
Ph: (916)229-0370
Free: 800-777-0133
URL: http://www.dmv.ca.gov/dmv.htm
Pub: List of publications available online (www.dmv.ca.gov/pubs/pubs.htm). **Telecom. Svcs:** TTY toll free number is (800)368-4327.

818 ■ California Tire Dealers Association - North
780 Sea Spray Ln., Apt. 309
Foster City, CA 94404
Contact: Ejnar Fink-Jenson, Exec. Dir.
Ph: (650)357-0600
E-mail: ejnar@catiredealers.com
URL: http://www.catiredealers.com

Descr: Represents corporations engaged in all sectors of the replacement tire industry. Seeks to advance and protect the interests of members and to promote goodwill within the industry. Serves as a clearinghouse on economic and regulatory issues affecting the replacement tire industry.

819 ■ Mothers Against Drunk Driving, Alameda County Chapter
PO Box 11748
Pleasanton, CA 94588
Free: 800-426-6233

820 ■ Mothers Against Drunk Driving, California State Organization
2222 Watt Ave., Ste. C1
Sacramento, CA 95825
Ph: (916)481-6233

Descr: Supports victims of drunk driving by offering emotional support, help with the justice system and other areas as needed. Works to stop drunk driving and prevent under age drinking through public awareness and educational programs at community events, educational institutions and businesses.

821 ■ Mothers Against Drunk Driving, Central Valley California Chapter
1901 E Hedges Ave.
Fresno, CA 93703
Ph: (559)485-6233

822 ■ Mothers Against Drunk Driving, San Diego County
938 S Andreasen Dr., Ste. M
Escondido, CA 92029-1920
Contact: Pamela Naiman
Ph: (760)746-6233
URL: http://www.maddsandiego.org

Descr: Victims of drunk driving crashes; concerned citizens. Encourages citizen participation in working towards reform of the drunk driving problem and the prevention of underage drinking. Acts as the voice of victims of drunk driving crashes by speaking on their behalf to communities, businesses, and educational groups. **Fnd:** 1982.

823 ■ Mothers Against Drunk Driving, San Joaquin County
PO Box 691237
Stockton, CA 95269-1237
Ph: (209)466-6600

Descr: Victims of drunk driving crashes; concerned citizens. Encourages citizen participation in working towards reform of the drunk driving problem and the prevention of underage drinking. Acts as the voice of victims of drunk driving crashes by speaking on their behalf to communities, businesses, and educational groups.

824 ■ Orange County Chapter of Mothers Against Drunk Driving
17772 Irvine Blvd., No. 103
PO Box 975
Tustin, CA 92780

Contact: Reidel Post, Exec.Dir.
Ph: (714)838-6199
Fax: (714)838-6045
E-mail: info@maddorangecounty.org
URL: http://www.maddorangecounty.org

Descr: Strives to stop drunk driving, to support the victims of this violent crime and to prevent underage drinking. Services include Speakers Bureau, literature, High School Outreach Program, Video Library, Health Fair Days, educational programs and more. Attends court proceedings and acts as liaison between the court system and the victims. **Fnd:** 1981.

825 ■ Society of Automotive Engineers, California State University-Chico
400 W 1st St.
Chico, CA 95926
Contact: Prof. Leonard W. Fallscheer, Advisor
E-mail: lfallscheer@csuchico.edu

Descr: Collects and disseminates information on mobility technology. Fosters information exchange among the worldwide automotive and aerospace communities.

826 ■ Society of Automotive Engineers, California State University-Fresno
Madden Lib Periodicals Dept.
5200 N Barton Ave.
Fresno, CA 93740-0001
Contact: Clift C. Cullen, Advisor
E-mail: cliftc@csufresno.edu

Descr: Collects and disseminates information on mobility technology. Fosters information exchange among the worldwide automotive and aerospace communities.

827 ■ Society of Automotive Engineers, Loyola Marymount University
Mechanical Engineering
1 LMU Dr.
Los Angeles, CA 90045-2623
Contact: Dr. Matthew Thomas Siniawski, Advisor
E-mail: msiniawski@lmu.edu

Descr: Collects and disseminates information on mobility technology. Fosters information exchange among the worldwide automotive and aerospace communities.

828 ■ Society of Automotive Engineers, San Francisco State University
Mechanical Engineering
1600 Holloway Ave., No. SCI112A
San Francisco, CA 94132-1740
Contact: Adelbert Cheng, Advisor
E-mail: ascheng@sfsu.edu

Descr: Collects and disseminates information on mobility technology. Fosters information exchange among the worldwide automotive and aerospace communities.

829 ■ Southern California Tire, Automotive and Retread Services Association (SCTARSA)
10240 Petit Ave.
North Hills, CA 91343
Contact: Ed Cohn, Exec. VP
Ph: (818)363-8028
E-mail: duffered@aol.com
URL: http://www.driveusa.net/sctarsa.htm

Descr: Represents corporations engaged in all sectors of the replacement tire industry. Seeks to advance and protect the interests of members and to promote goodwill within the industry. Serves as a clearinghouse on economic and regulatory issues affecting the replacement tire industry.

Colorado

830 ■ Colorado Motor Vehicle Business Group
1881 Pierce St.
Lakewood, CO 80214
Contact: Roxy Huber, Exce.Dir.
Ph: (303)205-5600

E-mail: mvadmin@spike.dor.state.co.us
URL: http://www.revenue.state.co.us/mv_dir/home.asp

831 ■ Mothers Against Drunk Driving, Colorado State
444 Lincoln St.
Denver, CO 80203
Contact: Emily Tompkins, Exec. Dir.
Ph: (303)425-5905
Free: 800-621-6233
Fax: (303)425-5674
E-mail: co.state@madd.org
URL: http://www.madd.org/co
Descr: Victims of drunk driving crashes; concerned citizens. Encourages citizen participation in working towards reform of the drunk driving problem and the prevention of underage drinking. Acts as the voice of victims of drunk driving crashes by speaking on their behalf to communities, businesses, and educational groups.

832 ■ Mothers Against Drunk Driving, Pikes Peak
2220 E Bijou St., Ste. 154
Colorado Springs, CO 80909
Contact: Cassie Kemp, Office Mgr.
Ph: (719)380-8673
Fax: (719)380-8682
E-mail: katherine.kemp@madd.org
URL: http://www.madd.org/co
Descr: Victims of drunk driving crashes; concerned citizens. Encourages citizen participation in working towards reform of the drunk driving problem and the prevention of underage drinking. Acts as the voice of victims of drunk driving crashes by speaking on their behalf to communities, businesses, and educational groups.

833 ■ Mothers Against Drunk Driving, Southwest Colorado
484 Turner Dr., Ste. E104
Durango, CO 81303
Ph: (970)385-4211
Descr: Victims of drunk driving crashes; concerned citizens. Encourages citizen participation in working towards reform of the drunk driving problem and the prevention of underage drinking. Acts as the voice of victims of drunk driving crashes by speaking on their behalf to communities, businesses, and educational groups.

Connecticut

834 ■ Connecticut Department of Motor Vehicles
60 State St.
Wethersfield, CT 06161
Contact: Robert M. Ward, Commnr.
Ph: (860)263-5700
Free: 800-842-8222
E-mail: mail@dmvct.org
URL: http://www.ct.gov/dmv/site/default.asp

835 ■ Connecticut Tire Dealers and Retreaders Association
160 Colony St.
Meriden, CT 06451
Contact: Bob Malerba, Pres.
Ph: (203)237-5595
Fax: (203)235-5506
E-mail: bob@malerbas.com
Descr: Represents corporations engaged in all sectors of the replacement tire industry. Seeks to advance and protect the interests of members and to promote goodwill within the industry. Serves as a clearinghouse on economic and regulatory issues affecting the replacement tire industry.

836 ■ Mothers Against Drunk Driving, Connecticut State
565 Washington Ave.
North Haven, CT 06473
Contact: Janice Heggie Margolis, Exec. Dir.
Ph: (203)234-6521
Fax: (203)234-6523

E-mail: ct.state@madd.org
URL: http://www.madd.org/ct
Descr: Victims of drunk driving crashes; concerned citizens. Encourages citizen participation in working towards reform of the drunk driving problem and the prevention of underage drinking. Acts as the voice of victims of drunk driving crashes by speaking on their behalf to communities, businesses, and educational groups.

Delaware

837 ■ Delaware Division of Motor Vehicles
303 Transportation Cir.
PO Box 698
Dover, DE 19903
Contact: Jennifer L. Cohan, Dir.
Ph: (302)744-2500
E-mail: dot-public-relations@state.de.us
URL: http://www.dmv.de.gov/
Descr: Responsible for the licensing of Delaware residents and the registration of motor vehicles.

838 ■ Mothers Against Drunk Driving, Delaware Chapter
17 E Market St.
Georgetown, DE 19947
Contact: Caroline Cash, Exec. Dir.
Ph: (302)853-6233
Fax: (302)854-9175
E-mail: delaware.de@madd.org
URL: http://www.madd.org/DE
Descr: Victims of drunk driving crashes; concerned citizens. Encourages citizen participation in working towards reform of the drunk driving problem and the prevention of underage drinking. Acts as the voice of victims of drunk driving crashes by speaking on their behalf to communities, businesses, and educational groups. **Fnd:** 1998.

District of Columbia

839 ■ District of Columbia Department of Motor Vehicles
Government of the District of Columbia
PO Box 90120
Washington, DC 20090
Contact: Lucinda M. Babers, Dir.
Ph: (202)737-4404
E-mail: dmv@dc.gov
URL: http://dmv.dc.gov

Florida

840 ■ Florida Department of Highway Safety and Motor Vehicles (DHSMV)
Neil Kirkman Bldg.
2900 Apalachee Pkwy.
Tallahassee, FL 32399-0500
Contact: Julie L. Jones, Exec.Dir.
Ph: (850)922-9000
E-mail: publicrecords@flhsmv.gov
URL: http://www.flhsmv.gov/

841 ■ Mothers Against Drunk Driving, Brevard County
1209 Helias St. NW
Palm Bay, FL 32907
Ph: (407)455-1485
Descr: Victims of drunk driving crashes; concerned citizens. Encourages citizen participation in working towards reform of the drunk driving problem and the prevention of underage drinking. Acts as the voice of victims of drunk driving crashes by speaking on their behalf to communities, businesses, and educational groups.

842 ■ Mothers Against Drunk Driving, Broward County
2425 E Commercial Blvd., No. 404
Fort Lauderdale, FL 33308
Contact: Hugo Reiner, Pres.
Ph: (954)229-0884
E-mail: maddbroward@bellsouth.net

Descr: Victims of drunk driving crashes; concerned citizens. Encourages citizen participation in working towards reform of the drunk driving problem and the prevention of underage drinking. Acts as the voice of victims of drunk driving crashes by speaking on their behalf to communities, businesses, and educational groups.

843 ■ Mothers Against Drunk Driving, Emerald Coast Chapter
PO Box 907
Milton, FL 32572
Contact: Jerry Fifer, Leader
Ph: (850)983-6775
Fax: (850)983-6775
E-mail: maddemeraldcoast@bellsouth.net
URL: http://www.madd.org/fl/emerald
Descr: Victims of drunk driving crashes; concerned citizens. Encourages citizen participation in working towards reform of the drunk driving problem and the prevention of underage drinking. Acts as the voice of victims of drunk driving crashes by speaking on their behalf to communities, businesses, and educational groups.

844 ■ Mothers Against Drunk Driving, Marion/ Alachua Counties Chapter
821 NE 36th Terr., Ste. 14
Ocala, FL 34470
Ph: (352)369-9328
Fax: (352)369-9358
E-mail: maddocala@earthlink.net
URL: http://www.madd.org/fl/marion

845 ■ Mothers Against Drunk Driving, Miami - Dade County
7700 N Kendall Dr., Ste. 803
Miami, FL 33156
Contact: Janet Mondshein, Exec. Dir.
Ph: (305)273-3744
Fax: (305)273-3745
E-mail: maddmiami@bellsouth.com
URL: http://www.madd.org/fl/dade
Descr: Victims of drunk driving crashes; concerned citizens. Encourages citizen participation in working towards reform of the drunk driving problem and the prevention of underage drinking. Acts as the voice of victims of drunk driving crashes by speaking on their behalf to communities, businesses, and educational groups. **Fnd:** 1983. **Mem:** 5000. **Pub:** *Driven* (quarterly); *Maddvocate* (quarterly).

846 ■ Mothers Against Drunk Driving, Northeast Florida
1717 Blanding Blvd., Ste. 102
Jacksonville, FL 32210
Ph: (904)388-2455
Free: 866-444-6233
Fax: (904)743-6506
E-mail: maddnefl1@bellsouth.net
Descr: Victims of drunk driving crashes; concerned citizens. Encourages citizen participation in working towards reform of the drunk driving problem and the prevention of underage drinking. Acts as the voice of victims of drunk driving crashes by speaking on their behalf to communities, businesses, and educational groups. **Mem:** 220.

847 ■ Mothers Against Drunk Driving, Pinellas County
2847 Executive Dr., Ste. 120
Clearwater, FL 33762
Ph: (727)556-0633
E-mail: rsschumaker@msn.com
Descr: Victims of drunk driving crashes; concerned citizens. Encourages citizen participation in working towards reform of the drunk driving problem and the prevention of underage drinking. Acts as the voice of victims of drunk driving crashes by speaking on their behalf to communities, businesses, and educational groups.

848 ■ Mothers Against Drunk Driving, Southwest Florida
PO Box 151418
Cape Coral, FL 33915-1418
Contact: Brenda Gellinger

Ph: (239)936-2902
E-mail: swflmadd@yahoo.com
URL: http://www.madd.org/fl
Descr: Supports victims of drunk driving by offering emotional support, help with the justice system and other areas as needed. Works to stop drunk driving and prevent under age drinking through public awareness and educational programs at community events, educational institutions and businesses.

Georgia

849 ■ Georgia Department of Driver Services
PO Box 80447
Conyers, GA 30013
Contact: Greg Dozier, Commnr.
Ph: (678)413-8400
Free: 877-835-5337
E-mail: motorvehicleinquiry@dor.ga.gov
URL: http://www.dds.ga.gov/

850 ■ Metropolitan Atlanta Tire Dealers Association
PO Box 162532
Atlanta, GA 30321
Contact: Becky St. Clair, Exec. Sec.
Ph: (404)762-8433
Fax: (678)244-8894
Descr: Represents corporations engaged in all sectors of the replacement tire industry. Seeks to advance and protect the interests of members and to promote goodwill within the industry. Serves as a clearinghouse on economic and regulatory issues affecting the replacement tire industry.

851 ■ Mothers Against Drunk Driving, Georgia State
1000 Cir. 75 Pkwy., Ste. 45
Atlanta, GA 30339
Contact: Mia Clemons, Office Mgr.
Ph: (770)615-3737
Free: 888-833-6033
Fax: (770)615-3738
E-mail: stateoffice@maddga.org
URL: http://www.maddga.org
Descr: Victims of drunk driving crashes; concerned citizens. Encourages citizen participation in working towards reform of the drunk driving problem and the prevention of underage drinking. Acts as the voice of victims of drunk driving crashes by speaking on their behalf to communities, businesses, and educational groups via the regional chapters. **Fnd:** 1982. **Mem:** 3000.

Hawaii

852 ■ Hawaii Department of Transportation Motor Vehicle Safety Office
Aliiaimoku Bldg.
869 Punchbowl St.
Honolulu, HI 96813
Contact: Brennon Morioka, Dir.
Ph: (808)587-2150
Fax: (808)587-2167
URL: http://www.hawaii.gov/dot/

853 ■ Hawaii Highway Users Alliance (HHUA)
680 Ala Moana Blvd., Ste. 303
Honolulu, HI 96813
Contact: Panos Prevedouros PhD, Pres.
Ph: (808)524-6424
Fax: (808)524-6044
E-mail: info@hhua.org
URL: http://www.hhua.org

Idaho

854 ■ Idaho Transportation Department
3311 W. State St.
PO Box 7129
Boise, ID 83707-1129
Contact: Scott Stokes, Actg.Dir.

Ph: (208)334-8000
Fax: (208)334-3858
E-mail: DMV-info@itd.idaho.gov
URL: http://www.itd.idaho.gov/
Descr: Mission is to provide cost-effective transportation systems that are safe, reliable, and responsive to the economical and efficient movement of people and products. **Telecom. Svcs:** TDD phone number is (208)334-4458.

855 ■ Mothers Against Drunk Driving, Ada County
PO Box 44333
Boise, ID 83711-0333
Contact: Loretta Stadler, Office Admin.
Ph: (208)853-3700
Free: 800-680-6233
Fax: (208)853-4120
E-mail: maddidaho@qwest.net
Descr: Victims of drunk driving crashes; concerned citizens. Encourages citizen participation in working towards reform of the drunk driving problem and the prevention of underage drinking. Acts as the voice of victims of drunk driving crashes by speaking on their behalf to communities, businesses, and educational groups.

856 ■ Mothers Against Drunk Driving, Idaho State Office
PO Box 44333
Boise, ID 83711
Ph: (208)853-3700
Descr: Assist victims and families of victims of drunk driving crashes. Encourages citizen participation in working towards reform of the drunk driving problem and the prevention of underage drinking. Acts as the voice of victims of drunk driving crashes by speaking on their behalf to communities, businesses, and educational groups.

Illinois

857 ■ Illinois Driver Services Department
2701 S. Dirksen Pkwy.
Springfield, IL 62723
Contact: Michael J. Mayer, Dir.
Ph: (217)782-6212
Free: 800-252-8980
URL: http://www.sos.state.il.us/departments/drivers/home.html
Telecom. Svcs: TDD/TTY toll free number is (888)261-5238.

858 ■ Mothers Against Drunk Driving, Dewitt County Chapter
PO Box 306
Clinton, IL 61727
Ph: (217)935-6079

859 ■ Mothers Against Drunk Driving, McLean County
PO Box 794
Bloomington, IL 61702-0794
Fax: (309)747-3490
Descr: Victims of drunk driving crashes; concerned citizens. Encourages citizen participation in working towards reform of the drunk driving problem and the prevention of underage drinking. Acts as the voice of victims of drunk driving crashes by speaking on their behalf to communities, businesses, and educational groups.

860 ■ Mothers Against Drunk Driving, Mercer County
PO Box 635
Matherville, IL 61263
Ph: (309)754-8748
Descr: Victims of drunk driving crashes; concerned citizens. Encourages citizen participation in working towards reform of the drunk driving problem and the prevention of underage drinking. Acts as the voice of victims of drunk driving crashes by speaking on their

behalf to communities, businesses, and educational groups.

861 ■ Mothers Against Drunk Driving, Northeast Illinois Region
2900 Ogden Ave.., No. 106
Lisle, IL 60532
Ph: (630)428-2442
Fax: (630)428-2442
E-mail: northeastregion.il@madd.org
URL: http://www.madd.org/il/northeast

862 ■ Mothers Against Drunk Driving, Shelby County
PO Box 14
Shelbyville, IL 62565
Ph: (217)774-2030
Descr: Victims of drunk driving crashes; concerned citizens. Encourages citizen participation in working towards reform of the drunk driving problem and the prevention of underage drinking. Acts as the voice of victims of drunk driving crashes by speaking on their behalf to communities, businesses, and educational groups.

863 ■ Mothers Against Drunk Driving, Vermilion County Chapter
1120 Glenwood Dr.
Danville, IL 61832
Ph: (217)709-0387

864 ■ Society of Automotive Engineers - University of Illinois-Chicago
MIE Department
842 W Taylor St.
Chicago, IL 60607-7021
Contact: Mohammad Ghaffarpour PhD
E-mail: mghaffar@uic.edu
Descr: Advances the engineering mobility systems. Provides technical information and expertise used in designing, building, maintaining and operating self-propelled vehicles, whether land, sea, air or space based. Collects and disseminates information on cars, trucks, aircraft, space vehicles, off-highway vehicles, marine equipment and engine of all types. Fosters information exchange among the worldwide automotive and aerospace communities.

Indiana

865 ■ Indiana Bureau of Motor Vehicles
100 N. Senate Ave.
Indianapolis, IN 46204
Contact: Ronald L. Stiver, Commissioner
Ph: (317)233-6000
URL: http://www.state.in.us/bmv
Descr: Dedicated to providing professional and efficient service in the licensing of drivers, the registration and titling of vehicles, the collection and distribution of taxes and the management of records related to these functions.

866 ■ Indiana/Illinois Tire Dealers Association (IITDA)
1227 Southbrook Dr.
Indianapolis, IN 46240
Contact: Ken McCune, Exec. Dir.
Ph: (317)431-7070
E-mail: iitda@comcast.net
URL: http://www.iitda.org
Descr: Represents corporations engaged in all sectors of the replacement tire industry. Seeks to advance and protect the interests of members and to promote goodwill within the industry. Serves as a clearinghouse on economic and regulatory issues affecting the replacement tire industry.

867 ■ Mothers Against Drunk Driving, Wabash Valley Chapter (MADD)
PO Box 3265
Terre Haute, IN 47803
Free: 800-247-6233
Descr: Victims of drunk driving and other concerned citizens in Clay, Parke, Putnam, Sullivan, Vermillion,

and Vigo counties, IN. Mobilizes victims and their allies to establish that impaired driving is unacceptable and a criminal offense. Works to increase public awareness of the problem and to educate the public about the drinking and driving problem. Seeks to improve the laws and the judicial system and promote corresponding policies, programs, and personal accountability. Works with first time offenders. **Fnd:** 1983. **Mem:** 100. **State Groups:** 1. **Local Groups:** 1. **Pub:** Newsletter (quarterly).

868 ■ Mothers Against Drunk Driving, West Central Indiana Chapter
PO Box 2147
West Lafayette, IN 47996
Free: 800-247-6233
E-mail: dan@ddreform.org
URL: http://www.madd.org/in

Iowa

869 ■ Iowa Department of Transportation Motor Vehicle Division
PO Box 9204
Des Moines, IA 50306-9204
Ph: (515)244-9124
Free: 800-532-1121
Fax: (515)237-3152
URL: http://www.dot.state.ia.us/mvd/index.htm

870 ■ Mothers Against Drunk Driving, Dubuque/Jackson Counties
30805 216th St.
Bellevue, IA 52031
Ph: (563)872-4474
Descr: Victims of drunk driving crashes; concerned citizens. Encourages citizen participation in working towards reform of the drunk driving problem and the prevention of underage drinking. Acts as the voice of victims of drunk driving crashes by speaking on their behalf to communities, businesses, and educational groups.

871 ■ Mothers Against Drunk Driving, Polk County
PO Box 65130
West Des Moines, IA 50265-0130
Ph: (515)223-8144
Descr: Victims of drunk driving crashes; concerned citizens. Encourages citizen participation in working towards reform of the drunk driving problem and the prevention of underage drinking. Acts as the voice of victims of drunk driving crashes by speaking on their behalf to communities, businesses, and educational groups.

Kansas

872 ■ Kansas Department of Revenue Division of Motor Vehicles
Docking State Office Bldg.
915 SW Harrison St., 1st Fl.
Topeka, KS 66625
Ph: (785)296-3963
Fax: (785)296-0691
E-mail: driver_license@kdor.state.ks.us
URL: http://www.ksrevenue.org/dmv.htm

Telecom. Svcs: TTY phone number is (785) 296-3601.

873 ■ Mothers Against Drunk Driving, Washburn University Chapter
3601 SW 29th St., Ste. 211
Topeka, KS 66614
Free: 800-443-6233
E-mail: ks.state@madd.org
URL: http://www.madd.org/ks

Kentucky

874 ■ Kentucky Transportation Cabinet Division of Driver Licensing
200 Mero St.
Frankfort, KY 40622
Contact: Bill Heise, Dir.
Ph: (502)564-6800
E-mail: kytc.ddlwebservices@ky.gov
URL: http://transportation.ky.gov/drlic

875 ■ Mothers Against Drunk Driving, Barren County Chapter
649 Charity Ct.
Frankfort, KY 40601
Contact: Angela Criswell, Exec. Dir.
Ph: (502)223-4930
Fax: (502)223-4932
E-mail: ky.state@madd.org
URL: http://www.madd.org/ky

876 ■ Mothers Against Drunk Driving, Daviess/Mclean Counties
4533 Bridle Ridge Ct.
Owensboro, KY 42303
Ph: (270)926-9408

877 ■ Mothers Against Drunk Driving, Kentucky State (MADD)
649 Charity Ct.
Frankfort, KY 40601
Contact: Ms. Angela Criswell, Exec. Dir.
Ph: (502)223-4930
Free: 800-944-6233
Fax: (502)223-4932
E-mail: maddky@fewpb.net
URL: http://www.madd.org/ky
Descr: Represents victims and survivors of drunk driving crashes and members of the general public who are concerned about drunk driving. Stops drunk driving, support the victims of this violent crime, and prevent underage drinking. Works with law enforcement, government officials, and community leaders to make Kentucky's roads safer. Educates Kentucky youth about the consequences of underage drinking and empower youth to change community norms that view underage drinking as a "rite of passage". **Fnd:** 1981. **Pub:** *Driven* (semiannual); *MADDvocate* (semiannual).

878 ■ Mothers Against Drunk Driving, Nelson County Chapter
2912 Pin Oak Dr.
Bardstown, KY 40004
Ph: (502)349-1143

879 ■ Mothers Against Drunk Driving, Taylor County Chapter
PO Box 355
Campbellsville, KY 42719
Ph: (270)469-6160

Louisiana

880 ■ Louisiana Independent Tire Dealers Association (LITDA)
PO Box 60903
Lafayette, LA 70596
Contact: Ron Pratt, Exec. Dir.
Ph: (337)981-7021
Fax: (337)981-7021
Descr: Represents corporations engaged in all sectors of the replacement tire industry. Seeks to advance and protect the interests of members and to promote goodwill within the industry. Serves as a clearinghouse on economic and regulatory issues affecting the replacement tire industry.

881 ■ Louisiana Office of Motor Vehicles
PO Box 64886
Baton Rouge, LA 70896
Free: 877-368-5463
URL: http://omv.dps.state.la.us
Descr: Mission in the Office of Motor Vehicles is to serve people through the administration of motor vehicle registration and driver licensing laws in a professional, compassionate and responsive man-

ner, while maintaining a high standard of quality through our innovative approach to customer service today and in the future.

882 ■ Mothers Against Drunk Driving, Louisiana State
2644 S Sherwood Forest Plz., No. 123
Baton Rouge, LA 70816-2248
Contact: Donna Tate, Exec. Dir.
Ph: (225)926-0807
Free: 877-MADD-HELP
Fax: (225)926-3842
E-mail: la.state@madd.org
URL: http://www.madd.org/la
Staff: 9. **Descr:** Victims of drunk driving crashes; concerned citizens. Encourages citizen participation in working towards reform of the drunk driving problem and the prevention of underage drinking. Acts as the voice of victims of drunk driving crashes by speaking on their behalf to communities, businesses, and educational groups. **Fnd:** 1980. **Mem:** 23000.

883 ■ Mothers Against Drunk Driving, Rapides Parish Chapter
1105 Texas Ave.
Alexandria, LA 71301
Ph: (318)445-7373

Maine

884 ■ Maine Bureau of Motor Vehicles
29 State House Station
Augusta, ME 04333-0029
Contact: Catherine Curtis, Deputy Sec. of State
Ph: (207)624-9000
Fax: (207)624-9013
URL: http://www.state.me.us/sos/bmv
Telecom. Svcs: TTY phone number is (877) 456-8195.

885 ■ New England Tire and Service Association (NETSA)
PO Box 1012
Yarmouth, ME 04096
Contact: Dick Cole, Exec. Dir.
Ph: (207)846-0986
E-mail: netsapros@aol.com
URL: http://www.netsa.org
Descr: Represents corporations engaged in all sectors of the replacement tire industry. Seeks to advance and protect the interests of members and to promote goodwill within the industry. Serves as a clearinghouse on economic and regulatory issues affecting the replacement tire industry.

Maryland

886 ■ Maryland Motor Vehicle Administration
6601 Ritchie Highway, NE
Glen Burnie, MD 21062
Contact: John T. Kuo, Admin.
Ph: (301)729-4550
Free: 800-950-1682
Fax: (410)424-3050
E-mail: MVACS@mdot.state.md.us
URL: http://www.mva.state.md.us/

887 ■ Mothers Against Drunk Driving, Chesapeake Region
11820 Parklawn Dr., No. 250
Rockville, MD 20852-2505
Ph: (301)230-2990
Fax: (301)230-2991
E-mail: chesapeake.region@madd.org
URL: http://www.madd.org/md

888 ■ Mothers Against Drunk Driving, Eastern Shore
10440 Shaker Dr., No. 207
Columbia, MD 21046
Free: 800-446-6233
Fax: (410)964-0959

E-mail: chesapeake.region@madd.org
URL: http://www.madd.org/md

Descr: Supports victims of drunk driving by offering emotional support, help with the justice system and other areas as needed. Works to stop drunk driving and prevent under age drinking through public awareness and educational programs at community events, educational institutions and businesses.

889 ■ Mothers Against Drunk Driving, Howard County

3277 Pine Orchard Ln., Ste. 1
Ellicott City, MD 21042
Ph: (410)465-5757
Fax: (410)465-5757
E-mail: admin@maddhowardcounty.org
URL: http://mywebpages.comcast.net/maddhowardcounty

Descr: Supports victims of drunk driving by offering emotional support, help with the justice system and other areas as needed. Works to stop drunk driving and prevent under age drinking through public awareness and educational programs at community events, educational institutions and businesses.

Massachusetts

890 ■ Massachusetts Registry of Motor Vehicles

PO Box 55889
Boston, MA 02205-5889
Contact: Rachel Kaprielian, Registrar
Ph: (617)351-4500
Free: 800-858-3926
URL: http://www.mass.gov/rmv/

891 ■ Mothers Against Drunk Driving, Greater Boston

18 Tremont St., Ste. 703
Boston, MA 02108
Ph: (617)227-2701
Free: 800-438-6233
Fax: (617)227-2704
E-mail: info@maddmass.org
URL: http://www.madd.org

Descr: Victims of drunk driving crashes; concerned citizens. Encourages citizen participation in working towards reform of the drunk driving problem and the prevention of underage drinking. Acts as the voice of victims of drunk driving crashes by speaking on their behalf to communities, businesses, and educational groups. **Fnd:** 1980.

892 ■ Mothers Against Drunk Driving, Massachusetts State

18 Tremont St., Ste. 703
Boston, MA 02108
Ph: (617)227-2701

Descr: Victims of drunk driving crashes; concerned citizens. Encourages citizen participation in working towards reform of the drunk driving problem and the prevention of underage drinking. Acts as the voice of victims of drunk driving crashes by speaking on their behalf to communities, businesses, and educational groups. **Pub:** *MADDVocate, Driven* (quarterly).

Michigan

893 ■ Michigan Department of State

Lansing, MI 48918
Contact: Terri Lynn Land, Sec. of State
Ph: (517)322-1460
Free: 888-767-6424
E-mail: secretary@michigan.gov
URL: http://www.michigan.gov/sos

Descr: One of twenty state departments in Michigan and is responsible for licensing motor vehicles and drivers, monitoring state elections, and consumer protection for motorists. The Department is also very involved in promoting safety.

894 ■ Mothers Against Drunk Driving, Grand Traverse County Chapter

PO Box 86
Traverse City, MI 49685
Ph: (231)947-6233

895 ■ Mothers Against Drunk Driving, Kent County Chapter

PO Box 21157
Lansing, MI 48909
Ph: (616)456-6233

Staff: 1. **Descr:** Men and women dedicated to supporting victims of drunk driving. Advocates for tougher legislation and penalties for drunk driving. Promotes community awareness. **Fnd:** 1982. **Mem:** 150. **State Groups:** 1. **Local Groups:** 23. **Pub:** *Local Newsletter* (semiannual).

896 ■ Mothers Against Drunk Driving, Macomb County

59 N Walnut St., No. 206
Mount Clemens, MI 48043
Contact: Alice Stacy, Exec. Dir.
Ph: (586)463-3611
Fax: (586)463-5048
E-mail: maddmacomb@aol.com

Descr: Supports victims of drunk driving by offering emotional support, help with the justice system and other areas as needed. Works to stop drunk driving and prevent under age drinking through public awareness and educational programs at community events, educational institutions and businesses. **Fnd:** 1993.

897 ■ Mothers Against Drunk Driving, Michigan State Organization

PO Box 21157
Lansing, MI 48909
Ph: (517)487-6233
Free: 800-323-6233
Fax: (517)702-0185
E-mail: mi.state@madd.org
URL: http://www.madd.org/mi

Descr: Seeks to stop drunk driving, supports the victims of this violent crime, and prevents underage drinking. Offers services to individuals and families who have been affected by a drunk driving crash. Conducts programs and training for individuals and groups working with young people in order to prevent underage drinking. Conducts annual community awareness and advocates for public policy initiatives that affect its mission. **Fnd:** 1981.

898 ■ Mothers Against Drunk Driving, St. Clair/Sanilac Counties

108 Huron Blvd.
Marysville, MI 48040
Ph: (810)364-9919

Descr: Victims of drunk driving crashes; concerned citizens. Encourages citizen participation in working towards reform of the drunk driving problem and the prevention of underage drinking. Acts as the voice of victims of drunk driving crashes by speaking on their behalf to communities, businesses, and educational groups.

899 ■ Mothers Against Drunk Driving, Wayne County

19650 Harper Ave., Ste. 2B
Grosse Pointe Woods, MI 48236
Contact: Marty Johnson, Office Admin.
Ph: (313)881-8181
Fax: (313)881-3735
E-mail: maddwaynecounty@yahoo.com
URL: http://www.madd.org/mi/wayne

Descr: Victims of drunk driving crashes; concerned citizens. Encourages citizen participation in working towards reform of the drunk driving problem and the prevention of underage drinking. Acts as the voice of victims of drunk driving crashes by speaking on their behalf to communities, businesses, and educational groups.

Minnesota

900 ■ Minnesota Department of Public Safety Driver and Vehicle Services

444 Cedar St.
St. Paul, MN 55101
Contact: Pat McCormack, Dir.
Ph: (651)297-2126
E-mail: motor.vehicles@state.mn.us
URL: http://www.dps.state.mn.us/dvs/index.html

Descr: Responsibilities include driver's license testing and issuance, driver safety compliance, motor vehicle title and registration, commercial vehicle registration, and auto dealer licensing and regulation. **Telecom. Svcs:** TDD/TTY phone number is (651)282-6555.

901 ■ Mothers Against Drunk Driving, Chisago/Isanti Counties (MADD)

35497 Falcon Ave.
North Branch, MN 55056
Ph: (651)209-3251

Descr: Victims of drunk driving crashes; concerned citizens. Encourages citizen participation in working towards reform of the drunk driving problem and the prevention of underage drinking. Acts as the voice of victims of drunk driving crashes by speaking on their behalf to communities, businesses, and educational groups. **Fnd:** 1997. **Mem:** 40.

902 ■ Mothers Against Drunk Driving, Minnesota Chapter

155 S Wabasha St., Ste.104
St. Paul, MN 55107
Contact: Jean Mulvey, Exec. Dir.
Ph: (651)523-0802
Fax: (651)523-0817
E-mail: mn.state@madd.org
URL: http://www.maddmn.org

903 ■ North Central Tire Dealers and Suppliers Association (NCTDSA)

13304 Stone Rd.
Minnetonka, MN 55305
Contact: Bonnie McCleary, Exec. Dir.
Ph: (952)544-6805
Fax: (952)545-5126
E-mail: bonniemccleary@northcentraltiredealers.com
URL: http://www.northcentraltiredealers.com

Descr: Represents corporations engaged in all sectors of the replacement tire industry. Seeks to advance and protect the interests of members and to promote goodwill within the industry. Serves as a clearinghouse on economic and regulatory issues affecting the replacement tire industry.

Mississippi

904 ■ Mississippi Department of Public Safety Driver Services

PO Box 958
Jackson, MS 39205
Contact: Stephen B. Simpson, Commissioner
Ph: (601)987-1212
URL: http://www.dps.state.ms.us/dps/dps.nsf/main?OpenForm

905 ■ Mothers Against Drunk Driving, Mississippi State

PO Box 97845
Pearl, MS 39288-7845
Contact: Ms. Fran Harvey, State Exec. Dir.
Ph: (601)939-0233
Free: 800-368-6233
Fax: (601)939-1986
E-mail: ms.state@madd.org
URL: http://www.madd.org/MS

Descr: Victims of drunk driving crashes; concerned citizens. Encourages citizen participation in working towards reform of the drunk driving problem and the prevention of underage drinking. Acts as the voice of victims of drunk driving crashes by speaking on their behalf to communities, businesses, and educational groups.

906 ■ Mothers Against Drunk Driving - Northwest Mississippi
2810 Forest Bend Dr.
Southaven, MS 38671
Ph: (662)781-2926

Missouri

907 ■ Missouri Department of Revenue Division of Motor Vehicle and Drivers Licensing
Harry S. Truman State Office Bldg.
301 W. High St., Rm. 370
Jefferson City, MO 65101
Contact: Karen King Mitchell, Dir.
Ph: (573)751-4509
E-mail: mvbmail@dor.mo.gov
URL: http://www.dor.mo.gov/mvdl/

Descr: Issues drivers' licenses and Missouri state ID cards, and titles and registers motor vehicles, boats/vessels and outboard motors.

908 ■ Missouri Tire Dealers and Retreaders Association - Eastern
7510 N Palmer Ave.
Kansas City, MO 64158
Contact: Sheri Hamilton, Exec. Dir.
Ph: (816)415-4400
Fax: (816)415-0272

Descr: Represents corporations engaged in all sectors of the replacement tire industry. Seeks to advance and protect the interests of members and to promote goodwill within the industry. Serves as a clearinghouse on economic and regulatory issues affecting the replacement tire industry.

909 ■ Missouri Tire Dealers and Retreaders Association - Southern
7511 N Palmer Ave.
Kansas City, MO 64158
Contact: Sheri Hamilton, Exec. Dir.
Ph: (816)415-4400
Fax: (816)415-0272

Descr: Represents corporations engaged in all sectors of the replacement tire industry. Seeks to advance and protect the interests of members and to promote goodwill within the industry. Serves as a clearinghouse on economic and regulatory issues affecting the replacement tire industry.

910 ■ Missouri Tire Dealers and Retreaders Association - Western
7512 N Palmer Ave.
Kansas City, MO 64158
Contact: Sheri Hamilton, Exec. Dir.
Ph: (816)415-4400
Fax: (816)415-0272

Descr: Represents corporations engaged in all sectors of the replacement tire industry. Seeks to advance and protect the interests of members and to promote goodwill within the industry. Serves as a clearinghouse on economic and regulatory issues affecting the replacement tire industry.

911 ■ Missouri Tire Industry Association (MTIA)
7513 N Palmer Ave.
Kansas City, MO 64158
Contact: Bob Hamilton, Exec. Dir.
Ph: (816)415-4400
Fax: (816)415-0272
E-mail: bhamilton@4mtia.org
URL: http://www.4mtia.org

Descr: Represents corporations engaged in all sectors of the replacement tire industry. Seeks to advance and protect the interests of members and to promote goodwill within the industry. Serves as a

clearinghouse on economic and regulatory issues affecting the replacement tire industry.

912 ■ Mothers Against Drunk Driving, Cass/Heartland County
14815 S 71 Hwy., No. 4
Grandview, MO 64030
Ph: (816)318-4515

Descr: Victims of drunk driving crashes; concerned citizens. Encourages citizen participation in working towards reform of the drunk driving problem and the prevention of underage drinking. Acts as the voice of victims of drunk driving crashes by speaking on their behalf to communities, businesses, and educational groups.

913 ■ Mothers Against Drunk Driving, Gateway
2538 Woodson Rd.
Overland, MO 63114
Ph: (314)426-1595

Descr: Victims of drunk driving crashes; concerned citizens. Encourages citizen participation in working towards reform of the drunk driving problem and the prevention of underage drinking. Acts as the voice of victims of drunk driving crashes by speaking on their behalf to communities, businesses, and educational groups.

914 ■ Mothers Against Drunk Driving, Heartland Region
14815 S 71 Hwy., No. 4
Grandview, MO 64030
Ph: (816)318-4515

Montana

915 ■ Montana Department of Justice Motor Vehicle Division
Scott Hart Bldg., Second Fl.
303 N. Roberts
PO Box 201430
Helena, MT 59620-1430
Contact: Brenda Nordlund, Admin.
Ph: (406)444-3933
E-mail: mvd@mt.gov
URL: http://www.doj.mt.gov/driving/default.asp

Descr: Mission is to pursue and promote efficient, cost-effective programs that benefit the interests, safety, and well-being of Montana citizens through licensing, registering, and regulating the monitoring activities of the public.

916 ■ Mothers Against Drunk Driving, Gallatin County
PO Box 11002
Bozeman, MT 59719
Ph: (406)585-4225
Fax: (406)585-3009
E-mail: gallatin.mt@madd.org
URL: http://www.madd.org/mt/gallatin

Descr: Victims of drunk driving crashes; concerned citizens. Encourages citizen participation in working towards reform of the drunk driving problem and the prevention of underage drinking. Acts as the voice of victims of drunk driving crashes by speaking on their behalf to communities, businesses, and educational groups.

Nebraska

917 ■ Mothers Against Drunk Driving, Nebraska State
800 S 13th St.
Lincoln, NE 68508
Ph: (402)434-5330

Descr: Supports victims of drunk driving by offering emotional support, help with the justice system and other areas as needed. Works to stop drunk driving and prevent under age drinking through public

awareness and educational programs at community events, educational institutions and businesses.

918 ■ Nebraska Department of Motor Vehicles
301 Centennial Mall S.
PO Box 94729
Lincoln, NE 68509-4726
Contact: Betty Johnson, Admin.
Ph: (402)471-3861
Free: 888-622-1222
Fax: (402)471-4020
URL: http://www.dmv.state.ne.us/

Nevada

919 ■ Nevada Department of Motor Vehicles
555 Wright Way
Carson City, NV 89711
Contact: Ginny Lewis, Dir.
E-mail: glewis@dmv.state.nv.us
Ph: (775)684-4368
Free: 877-368-7828
Fax: (775)684-4992
E-mail: info@dmv.nv.gov
URL: http://www.dmvnv.com

New Hampshire

920 ■ Mothers Against Drunk Driving - Cheshire County
481 Hackett Swamp Rd.
Charlestown, NH 03603
Ph: (603)499-5487

921 ■ New Hampshire Department of Safety Division of Motor Vehicles
Stephen E. Merrill Bldg.
23 Hazen Dr.
Concord, NH 03305
Contact: Virginia C. Beecher, Dir.
Ph: (603)271-2371
E-mail: webcoordinator@safety.state.nh.us
URL: http://www.nh.gov/safety/dmv/

New Jersey

922 ■ Mothers Against Drunk Driving, New Jersey State
PO Box 5085
Trenton, NJ 08638
Contact: Steven Benvenisti
Ph: (609)434-7233
Free: 800-448-6233
Fax: (609)585-1890
E-mail: nj.state@madd.org
URL: http://www.madd.org/nj

Staff: 2. **Descr:** Acts to stop drunk driving; supports the victims of this violent crime and works to prevent underage drinking. **Fnd:** 1984. **Mem:** 8000. **Local Groups:** 10.

923 ■ New Jersey Motor Vehicle Commission
Customer Advocacy Office
PO Box 160
Trenton, NJ 08666
Contact: Shawn B. Sheekey, Ch.Admin.
Ph: (609)292-6500
Free: 888-486-3339
URL: http://www.state.nj.us/mvc/

Telecom. Svcs: TTY phone number is (609)292-5120.

924 ■ New Jersey State Tire Dealers Association
PO Box 794
Matawan, NJ 07747
Contact: Bill Ruete, Pres.
Ph: (201)935-3444
Fax: (201)935-4042

Descr: Represents corporations engaged in all sectors of the replacement tire industry. Seeks to advance and protect the interests of members and to promote goodwill within the industry. Serves as a clearinghouse on economic and regulatory issues affecting the replacement tire industry.

New Mexico

925 ■ Mothers Against Drunk Driving, Curry County

PO Box 367
Clovis, NM 88102
Ph: (505)762-9272
Descr: Aims to stop drunk driving, support the victims of this violent crime and prevent underage drinking.

926 ■ Mothers Against Drunk Driving, New Mexico State

1100 4th St. NW
Albuquerque, NM 87102
Contact: Terry Huertaz, Exec. Dir.
Ph: (505)255-2955
Free: 800-522-0352
Fax: (505)255-0352
E-mail: nm.state@madd.org
URL: http://www.madd.org/nm
Descr: Victims of drunk driving crashes; concerned citizens. Encourages citizen participation in working towards reform of the drunk driving problem and the prevention of underage drinking. Acts as the voice of victims of drunk driving crashes by speaking on their behalf to communities, businesses, and educational groups.

927 ■ Mothers Against Drunk Driving - San Juan County

825 W Broadway
Farmington, NM 87401
Ph: (505)632-0749

928 ■ New Mexico Taxation and Revenue Department

Motor Vehicle Division
Joseph Montoya Bldg.
1100 S. St. Frances Dr.
PO Box 630
Santa Fe, NM 87504-0630
Contact: Rick Homans, Sec.
Ph: (505)827-0369
Free: 888-683-4636
Fax: (505)827-0469
E-mail: GGarcia@state.nm.us
URL: http://www.state.nm.us/tax/mvd/mvd_home.htm

New York

929 ■ Mothers Against Drunk Driving, Long Island Chapter

33 Walt Whitman Rd., Ste. LL7
Huntington Station, NY 11746
Ph: (631)547-6233
Descr: Supports innocent drunk driving victims, victims' families and concerned citizens. Prevents drunk driving and underage drinking. Provides victim support and education programs. Advocates for anti-DWI legislation. Monitors law enforcement and judicial procedures in DWI cases.

930 ■ Mothers Against Drunk Driving - Western New York

2125 Buffalo Rd., No. 115
Rochester, NY 14624
Ph: (585)426-3130

931 ■ New York State Department of Motor Vehicles

6 Empire State Plaza
Albany, NY 12228
Contact: David J. Swarts, Commnr.
Ph: (212)645-5550
Free: 800-342-5368
URL: http://www.nydmv.state.ny.us/

932 ■ New York Tire Dealers Association

258 N Broadway
Amityville, NY 11701
Contact: Chris Pickrell, Exec. Dir.
Ph: (631)345-2600
E-mail: chris782@aol.com
URL: http://www.nytda.com

Descr: Represents corporations engaged in all sectors of the replacement tire industry. Seeks to advance and protect the interests of members and to promote goodwill within the industry. Serves as a clearinghouse on economic and regulatory issues affecting the replacement tire industry.

North Carolina

933 ■ Mothers Against Drunk Driving, Cabarrus County

PO Box 207
Concord, NC 28026-0207
Contact: Becky Blackwell, Pres.
Ph: (704)782-3300
Fax: (704)547-8098
E-mail: cabarrus.nc@madd.org
URL: http://www.madd.org/nc/cabarrus

Descr: Victims of drunk driving crashes; concerned citizens. Encourages citizen participation in working towards reform of the drunk driving problem and the prevention of underage drinking. Acts as the voice of victims of drunk driving crashes by speaking on their behalf to communities, businesses, and educational groups. **Fnd:** 1992.

934 ■ Mothers Against Drunk Driving, Cumberland County

PO Box 1223
Fayetteville, NC 28302
Contact: Anita Byrd Gunther Hepner, VP
Ph: (910)630-1942
E-mail: neato@mail.apcnet.com

Descr: Victims of drunk driving crashes; concerned citizens. Encourages citizen participation in working towards reform of the drunk driving problem and the prevention of underage drinking. Acts as the voice of victims of drunk driving crashes by speaking on their behalf to communities, businesses, and educational groups.

935 ■ Mothers Against Drunk Driving - Foothills

188 Whitney Ave.
Tryon, NC 28782
Ph: (828)859-5110

936 ■ Mothers Against Drunk Driving, Guilford County

PO Box 13205
Greensboro, NC 27415
Ph: (336)333-1556
Fax: (336)378-0677
E-mail: guilfordmadd@att.net

Descr: Victims of drunk driving crashes; concerned citizens. Encourages citizen participation in working towards reform of the drunk driving problem and the prevention of underage drinking. Acts as the voice of victims of drunk driving crashes by speaking on their behalf to communities, businesses, and educational groups.

937 ■ Mothers Against Drunk Driving - Metrolina

5104 Western Blvd., Ste. B
Raleigh, NC 27606
Free: 800-248-6233

938 ■ Mothers Against Drunk Driving, North Carolina State

5104 Western Blvd., Ste. B
Raleigh, NC 27606
Ph: (919)787-6599
Free: 800-248-6233
Fax: (919)787-6330
E-mail: nc.state@madd.org
URL: http://www.madd.org/chapter/3700_3327

Descr: Victims of drunk driving crashes; concerned citizens. Encourages citizen participation in working towards reform of the drunk driving problem and the prevention of underage drinking. Acts as the voice of victims of drunk driving crashes by speaking on their

behalf to communities, businesses, and educational groups.

939 ■ Mothers Against Drunk Driving - Sandhills

5419 Laramie Ct.
Fayetteville, NC 28303
Ph: (919)787-6533

940 ■ Mothers Against Drunk Driving - Triad

1501 S Main St.
Graham, NC 27253
Ph: (919)787-6533

941 ■ North Carolina Department of Transportation

Division of Motor Vehicles
3148 Mail Service Center
Raleigh, NC 27699-3148
Contact: William C. Gore Jr., Commnr.
Ph: (919)715-7000
Fax: (919)733-0126
E-mail: gtatum@dot.state.nc.us
URL: http://www.dmv.dot.state.nc.us

North Dakota

942 ■ Mothers Against Drunk Driving, Cass County

PO Box 236
West Fargo, ND 58078
Ph: (701)492-0901
Descr: Victims of drunk driving crashes; concerned citizens. Encourages citizen participation in working towards reform of the drunk driving problem and the prevention of underage drinking. Acts as the voice of victims of drunk driving crashes by speaking on their behalf to communities, businesses, and educational groups. **Fnd:** 1998. **Mem:** 60. **Local Groups:** 1.

943 ■ North Dakota Department of Transportation

Drivers License and Traffic Safety
608 E. Blvd. Ave.
Bismarck, ND 58505-0700
Contact: Francis G. Ziegler P.E., Dir.
Ph: (701)328-2500
E-mail: dot@nd.gov
URL: http://www.dot.nd.gov/
Telecom. Svcs: TTY number is (701)328-4156.

Ohio

944 ■ AAA Barberton Automobile Club

139 E Tuscarawas Ave.
Barberton, OH 44203

945 ■ AAA Columbiana County

516 Broadway St.
East Liverpool, OH 43920
Ph: (330)385-2020

946 ■ AAA Massillon Automobile Club

1972 Whales Rd. NE
Massillon, OH 44646
Ph: (330)833-1084
E-mail: info@aaamassillon.com

947 ■ Greater Cleveland Tire Dealers Association

21651 S Lakeshore Blvd.
Euclid, OH 44123
Contact: Ray Adamowicz, Exec. Dir.
Ph: (216)261-0268
Descr: Represents corporations engaged in all sectors of the replacement tire industry. Seeks to advance and protect the interests of members and to promote goodwill within the industry. Serves as a clearinghouse on economic and regulatory issues affecting the replacement tire industry.

948 ■ Mothers Against Drunk Driving, Allen/Putnam Counties

PO Box 1491
Lima, OH 45802
Ph: (419)224-6233

Descr: Victims of drunk driving crashes; concerned citizens. Encourages citizen participation in working towards reform of the drunk driving problem and the prevention of underage drinking. Acts as the voice of victims of drunk driving crashes by speaking on their behalf to communities, businesses, and educational groups.

949 ■ Mothers Against Drunk Driving - Coshocton County
46340 TWP Rd. 1209
Coshocton, OH 43812
Contact: Jill Hammersly, Leader
Ph: (740)622-4104
E-mail: forcodycoshmadd@yahoo.com
URL: http://www.ohiomadd.org/index_files/Page481.
htm

950 ■ Mothers Against Drunk Driving, Fayette/Pickaway Counties
141 Eastview Dr.
Washington Court House, OH 43160
Ph: (740)636-9960
Descr: Victims of drunk driving crashes; concerned citizens. Encourages citizen participation in working towards reform of the drunk driving problem and the prevention of underage drinking. Acts as the voice of victims of drunk driving crashes by speaking on their behalf to communities, businesses, and educational groups.

951 ■ Mothers Against Drunk Driving, Greater Toledo Area
PO Box 218
Sylvania, OH 43560
Ph: (419)885-6233
Descr: Victims of drunk driving crashes; concerned citizens. Encourages citizen participation in working towards reform of the drunk driving problem and the prevention of underage drinking. Acts as the voice of victims of drunk driving crashes by speaking on their behalf to communities, businesses, and educational groups.

952 ■ Mothers Against Drunk Driving, Greene County
203 Garland Ave.
Fairborn, OH 45324
Ph: (937)372-1220
Descr: Victims of drunk driving crashes; concerned citizens. Encourages citizen participation in working towards reform of the drunk driving problem and the prevention of underage drinking. Acts as the voice of victims of drunk driving crashes by speaking on their behalf to communities, businesses, and educational groups.

953 ■ Mothers Against Drunk Driving - Mid-Ohio Valley
5900 Roche Dr., Ste. 250
Columbus, OH 43229-3722
Ph: (614)885-6233
Free: 800-552-8641
Fax: (614)885-0105
E-mail: doug.scoles@madd.org
URL: http://www.ohiomadd.org

954 ■ Mothers Against Drunk Driving - North Central
PO Box 763
Shelby, OH 44875
Ph: (419)342-6333

955 ■ Mothers Against Drunk Driving, Northeastern Ohio
15666 Snow Rd., Ste. 201
Cleveland, OH 44142
Contact: Julie Leggett, Exec. Dir.
Ph: (216)265-9229
Free: 800-691-MADD
Fax: (216)265-9243
E-mail: northeastern.oh@madd.org
URL: http://www.maddnortheastern.org
Descr: Victims of drunk driving crashes; concerned citizens. Encourages citizen participation in working

towards reform of the drunk driving problem and the prevention of underage drinking. Acts as the voice of victims of drunk driving crashes by speaking on their behalf to communities, businesses, and educational groups.

956 ■ Mothers Against Drunk Driving, Portage County
PO Box 226
Ravenna, OH 44266
Ph: (330)677-6200
Descr: Victims of drunk driving crashes; concerned citizens. Encourages citizen participation in working towards reform of the drunk driving problem and the prevention of underage drinking. Acts as the voice of victims of drunk driving crashes by speaking on their behalf to communities, businesses, and educational groups.

957 ■ Mothers Against Drunk Driving, Southwestern Ohio
4015 Executive Park Dr., No. 215
Cincinnati, OH 45241
Contact: Andrea Rehkamp, Exec. Dir.
Ph: (513)769-6800
Free: 877-721-6233
Fax: (513)769-6801
E-mail: southwestern.oh@madd.org
URL: http://www.madd.org/oh/southwestern
Descr: Victims of drunk driving crashes; concerned citizens. Encourages citizen participation in working towards reform of the drunk driving problem and the prevention of underage drinking. Acts as the voice of victims of drunk driving crashes by speaking on their behalf to communities, businesses, and educational groups. **Fnd:** 1981.

958 ■ Mothers Against Drunk Driving, Tuscarawas County
PO Box 993
New Philadelphia, OH 44663
Contact: Mary Mears
Ph: (330)602-6233
E-mail: maddtuscarawasco@tusco.org
URL: http://www.ohiomadd.org

959 ■ Northeast Ohio Regional Tire Dealers Association
1020 Northview Ave.
Barberton, OH 44203
Contact: Joan Floyd, Exec. Sec.
Ph: (330)825-6556
Fax: (330)825-9125
Descr: Represents corporations engaged in all sectors of the replacement tire industry. Seeks to advance and protect the interests of members and to promote goodwill within the industry. Serves as a clearinghouse on economic and regulatory issues affecting the replacement tire industry.

960 ■ Ohio Bureau of Motor Vehicles
PO Box 16520
Columbus, OH 43216-6520
Contact: Henry Guzman, Dir.
Ph: (614)752-7500
URL: http://ohiobmv.com/
Telecom. Svcs: TDD phone number is (614)752-4559.

Oklahoma

961 ■ Mothers Against Drunk Driving, Oklahoma State
5500 N Western Ave., Ste. 284
Oklahoma City, OK 73118
Contact: Virgil L. Green Sr., Exec. Dir.
Ph: (405)748-3122
Free: 866-706-4646
Fax: (405)748-3132
E-mail: ok.state@madd.org
URL: http://www.madd.org/ok
Descr: Victims of drunk driving crashes; concerned citizens. Encourages citizen participation in working towards reform of the drunk driving problem and the prevention of underage drinking. Acts as the voice of victims of drunk driving crashes by speaking on their

behalf to communities, businesses, and educational groups.

962 ■ Mothers Against Drunk Driving - Ottawa County
PO Box 173
Picher, OK 74360
Ph: (918)673-1003

963 ■ Oklahoma Department of Public Safety Drivers License Service
PO Box 11415
Oklahoma City, OK 73136
Ph: (405)425-2424
E-mail: comment@dps.state.ok.us
URL: http://www.dps.state.ok.us/dls/

Oregon

964 ■ Mothers Against Drunk Driving - Eugene
PO Box 11396
Eugene, OR 97440
Ph: (541)343-8115
Free: 888-855-6233
Fax: (541)343-2068
E-mail: eugene@maddpnw.org
URL: http://www.maddeugene.org

965 ■ Mothers Against Drunk Driving - Portland
97375 SW Wilsonville Rd. Ste. B
Wilsonville, OR 97070
Ph: (503)783-1597

966 ■ Oregon Department of Transportation Driver and Motor Vehicle Services
1905 Lana Ave. NE
Salem, OR 97314
Ph: (503)945-5000
URL: http://www.oregon.gov/ODOT/DMV/index.shtml
Descr: Mission is to promote driver safety, protect financial and ownership interests in vehicles, and collect revenue for Oregon's roads. **Telecom. Svcs:** TTY phone number is (503)945-5001.

Pennsylvania

967 ■ Greater Delaware Valley Tire Dealers Association
PO Box 1205
West Chester, PA 19380
Contact: Larry L. Samples, Exec. Sec.
Ph: (610)692-5556
Fax: (610)692-5557
Descr: Represents corporations engaged in all sectors of the replacement tire industry. Seeks to advance and protect the interests of members and to promote goodwill within the industry. Serves as a clearinghouse on economic and regulatory issues affecting the replacement tire industry.

968 ■ Mothers Against Drunk Driving, Pennsylvania State
2323 Patton Rd.
Harrisburg, PA 17112
Contact: Rebecca Shaver, State Exec. Dir.
Ph: (717)657-3911
Fax: (717)540-4824
E-mail: maddpa@verizon.net
URL: http://www.maddpa.org
Descr: Victims of drunk driving crashes; concerned citizens. Encourages citizen participation in working towards reform of the drunk driving problem and the prevention of underage drinking. Acts as the voice of victims of drunk driving crashes by speaking on their behalf to communities, businesses, and educational groups.

969 ■ Mothers Against Drunk Driving, Southeastern PA (MADD)
1100 E Hector St., No. 440
Conshohocken, PA 19428
Ph: (610)825-4902
URL: http://www.madd.org/Local-Chapters/Chapters.
aspx?state=PA
Descr: Victims of drunk driving crashes; concerned

citizens. Encourages citizen participation in working towards reform of the drunk driving problem and the prevention of underage drinking. Acts as the voice of victims of drunk driving crashes by speaking on their behalf to communities, businesses, and educational groups.

970 ■ Mothers Against Drunk Driving - Western Pennsylvania
222 W Cunningham St.
Butler, PA 16001
Contact: Traci Vetovich
Ph: (724)256-5600
Fax: (724)256-5602
URL: http://www.maddpa.org

971 ■ Pennsylvania Department of Transportation
Driver and Vehicle Services
1101 S. Front St.
Harrisburg, PA 17104
Contact: Allen D. Biehler P.E., Sec.
Ph: (717)412-5300
Free: 800-932-4600
URL: http://www.dmv.state.pa.us/
Pub: List of publications online (www.dmv.state.pa.us/forms/pennDotPublications.shtml).

972 ■ Society of Automotive Engineers - Grove City College
100 Campus Dr.
Grove City, PA 16127
Contact: Richard G. Jewell, Pres.
Ph: (724)458-2500
Fax: (724)458-2190
E-mail: rgjewell@gcc.edu
URL: http://www.gcc.edu
Descr: Advances the engineering mobility systems. Provides technical information and expertise used in designing, building, maintaining and operating self-propelled vehicles, whether land, sea, air or space based. Collects and disseminates information on cars, trucks, aircraft, space vehicles, off-highway vehicles, marine equipment and engine of all types. Fosters information exchange among the worldwide automotive and aerospace communities.

973 ■ Society of Automotive Engineers - Temple University (TSAE)
Mechanical Engineering Dept.
1947 N 12th St.
Philadelphia, PA 19122
Contact: Richard S. Cohen
Ph: (215)204-7808
E-mail: rscohen@temple.edu
URL: http://www.temple.edu/sae
Descr: Advances the engineering mobility systems. Provides technical information and expertise used in designing, building, maintaining and operating self-propelled vehicles, whether land, sea, air or space based. Collects and disseminates information on cars, trucks, aircraft, space vehicles, off-highway vehicles, marine equipment and engine of all types. Fosters information exchange among the worldwide automotive and aerospace communities. **Fnd:** 1984.

974 ■ Tire Dealers Association of Western Pennsylvania
PO Box 1524
Greensburg, PA 15601
Contact: Jack Greiner, Exec. Dir.
Ph: (724)836-0309
Fax: (724)836-0309
E-mail: jack@tdaofwpa.org
URL: http://www.tdaofwpa.org
Descr: Represents corporations engaged in all sectors of the replacement tire industry. Seeks to advance and protect the interests of members and to promote goodwill within the industry. Serves as a clearinghouse on economic and regulatory issues affecting the replacement tire industry.

Rhode Island

975 ■ Rhode Island Division of Motor Vehicles
100 Main St.
Pawtucket, RI 02860
Ph: (401)462-4368
URL: http://www.dmv.state.ri.us/

South Carolina

976 ■ Mothers Against Drunk Driving, Darlington County
2711 Middleburg Dr., No. 307
Columbia, SC 29204
Contact: Juliet Nader Smith, Admin. Asst.
Ph: (803)748-7333
Free: 800-543-8692
Fax: (803)748-8600
E-mail: sc.state@madd.org
URL: http://www.madd.org/sc
Descr: Victims of drunk driving crashes; concerned citizens. Encourages citizen participation in working towards reform of the drunk driving problem and the prevention of underage drinking. Acts as the voice of victims of drunk driving crashes by speaking on their behalf to communities, businesses, and educational groups.

977 ■ Mothers Against Drunk Driving - Florence County
PO Box 6111
Florence, SC 29501
Ph: (843)662-6867

978 ■ Mothers Against Drunk Driving, South Carolina
810 Dutch Square Blvd., No. 211
Columbia, SC 29210
Contact: Ms. Traci D. Thompson
Ph: (803)748-7333
Free: 800-543-8692
Fax: (803)748-8600
E-mail: sc.state@madd.org
URL: http://www.madd.org/sc
Staff: 3. **Descr:** Works to stop drunk driving, supports the victim of this violent crime, and prevent underage drinking. Encourage members and volunteers to get involved and work in the accomplishment of this mission throughout the state of South Carolina. **Fnd:** 1985. **Mem:** 1500. **Local Groups:** 11. **Pub:** *Driven* (biennial); *MADDvocate* (biennial).

979 ■ South Carolina Department of Motor Vehicles
PO Box 1498
Blythewood, SC 29016
Contact: Marcia S. Adams, Dir.
Ph: (803)896-5000
Free: 800-442-1368
E-mail: help@scdmvonline.com
URL: http://www.scdmvonline.com/

South Dakota

980 ■ Mothers Against Drunk Driving - Codington County
212 N Maple
Watertown, SD 57201
Ph: (605)698-3966
E-mail: codington.sd@madd.org
URL: http://www.madd.org/sd/codington

981 ■ South Dakota Department of Public Safety
Office of Driver Licensing
118 W. Capitol Ave.
Pierre, SD 57501
Contact: Jane Schrank, Prog.Dir.
Ph: (605)773-6883
Free: 800-952-3696
URL: http://www.state.sd.us/dps/dl/
Descr: Mission is to make South Dakota roadways safe by issuing driver licenses to applicants who have met the minimum qualifications for safely operating a motor vehicle and to protect South Dakota's citizens by issuing a secure document by issuing driver licenses to applicants who have met the minimum qualifications.

Tennessee

982 ■ Mothers Against Drunk Driving - Northeast Tennessee
188 Henley St.
Tazewell, TN 37879
Ph: (865)909-9154

983 ■ Mothers Against Drunk Driving, Shelby County
3340 Poplar Ave., Ste. 227
Memphis, TN 38111
Ph: (901)458-4800
Fax: (901)458-9432
Descr: Victims of drunk driving crashes; concerned citizens. Encourages citizen participation in working towards reform of the drunk driving problem and the prevention of underage drinking. Acts as the voice of victims of drunk driving crashes by speaking on their behalf to communities, businesses, and educational groups.

984 ■ Mothers Against Drunk Driving, Tennessee State
1100 Kermit Dr., Ste. 022
Nashville, TN 37217
Contact: Laura Dial, Exec. Dir.
Ph: (615)360-8055
Free: 800-544-6233
Fax: (615)360-9022
E-mail: info@maddtn.org
URL: http://www.maddtn.org
Descr: Victims of drunk driving crashes; concerned citizens. Encourages citizen participation in working towards reform of the drunk driving problem and the prevention of underage drinking. Acts as the voice of victims of drunk driving crashes by speaking on their behalf to communities, businesses, and educational groups.

985 ■ Mothers Against Drunk Driving - Tri-cities Area
359 Easley Dr.
Kingsport, TN 37664
Ph: (423)246-1802

986 ■ Mothers Against Drunk Driving - Upper Cumberland
PO Box 2663
Cookeville, TN 38502
Ph: (931)520-6233

987 ■ Mothers Against Drunk Driving - West Tennessee
3340 Poplar Ave., Ste. 227
Memphis, TN 38111
Ph: (901)458-4800

988 ■ Remove Intoxicated Drivers, Oak Ridge/Anderson County Chapter
110 Newton Ln.
Oak Ridge, TN 37830
Contact: W. Kelly Dagenhart, Pres.
Ph: (865)483-8801
Fax: (775)417-7954
E-mail: dagenhartwk@bellsouth.net
URL: http://www.discoveret.org/ridorac
Descr: Individuals and organizations interested in removing intoxicated drivers from the road and thus lessening the amount of number of deaths and injuries resulting from drunk driving accidents. **Fnd:** 1981. **Mem:** 150. **Pub:** Newsletter (quarterly).

989 ■ Society of Automotive Engineers - University of Memphis
312 Engineering Science
Department of Mechanical Engineering
Memphis, TN 38152-3180
Contact: Teong Eng Tan, Advisor
E-mail: ttan@memphis.edu
URL: http://www.me.memphis.edu/Orgs/stu/SAE/SAE/Team 20SAE.htm

Descr: Dedicated to all interested students of University of Memphis to learn about automotive engineering.

990 ■ Tennessee Department of Safety Motor Vehicle Services
PO Box 945
Nashville, TN 37202
Contact: Dave Mitchell, Commnr.
Ph: (615)251-5166
Fax: (615)253-2092
E-mail: email.safety@tn.gov
URL: http://www.state.tn.us/safety/

991 ■ Tennessee/Kentucky Tire Dealers Association
PO Box 6146
Manchester, TN 37355
Contact: Shaw Jared, Exec. Dir.
Free: 888-256-5660
Fax: (931)723-7946
E-mail: sjared32@yahoo.com
Descr: Represents corporations engaged in all sectors of the replacement tire industry. Seeks to advance and protect the interests of members and to promote goodwill within the industry. Serves as a clearinghouse on economic and regulatory issues affecting the replacement tire industry.

Texas

992 ■ Mothers Against Drunk Driving, Brazos Valley
207 N Main St., Ste. E
Bryan, TX 77803
Ph: (979)823-7008
Free: 888-665-6233
Fax: (979)823-7008
E-mail: beverly.weeks@madd.org
URL: http://www.maddbv.org
Descr: Victims of drunk driving crashes; concerned citizens. Encourages citizen participation in working towards reform of the drunk driving problem and the prevention of underage drinking. Acts as the voice of victims of drunk driving crashes by speaking on their behalf to communities, businesses, and educational groups. **Fnd:** 1982.

993 ■ Mothers Against Drunk Driving, East Texas
215 Winchester Dr., Ste. 100
Tyler, TX 75701
Contact: Rita A. Fyer, Exec. Dir.
Ph: (903)534-6000
Free: 888-665-6233
Fax: (903)534-6085
E-mail: east.tx@madd.org
URL: http://www.madd.org/tx/east
Descr: Victims of drunk driving crashes; concerned citizens. Encourages citizen participation in working towards reform of the drunk driving problem and the prevention of underage drinking. Acts as the voice of victims of drunk driving crashes by speaking on their behalf to communities, businesses, and educational groups. Provides courtroom advocacy and assistance with crime victims' compensation. Provides free service.

994 ■ Mothers Against Drunk Driving - Southeast Texas
15355 W Vantage Pkwy., No. 220
Houston, TX 77032
Ph: (281)590-2222
Fax: (281)987-2274
E-mail: southeast.tx@madd.org

995 ■ Mothers Against Drunk Driving, Texas State
611 S Congress Ave., Ste. 505
Austin, TX 78704-1733
Contact: Chris Johnson, Chm.
Ph: (512)445-4976
Fax: (512)445-4979
E-mail: tx.state@madd.org
URL: http://www.madd.org/tx
Descr: Victims of drunk driving crashes; concerned

citizens. Encourages citizen participation in working towards reform of the drunk driving problem and the prevention of underage drinking. Acts as the voice of victims of drunk driving crashes by speaking on their behalf to communities, businesses, and educational groups.

996 ■ Mothers Against Drunk Driving - West Texas
6070 Gateway Blvd. E, Ste. 217
El Paso, TX 79905
Ph: (915)779-1987
Free: 888-779-2185
Fax: (915)779-2084
E-mail: west.tx@madd.org
URL: http://www.madd.org/tx

997 ■ Texas Department of Public Safety Driver License Division
PO Box 4087
Austin, TX 78773-0001
Contact: Steve McCraw, Dir.
Ph: (512)424-2000
E-mail: license.issuance@txdps.state.tx.us
URL: http://www.txdps.state.tx.us/
Descr: Promotes public safety and enhances safe driving on all Texas roadways.

998 ■ University of Texas at Austin Society of Automotive Engineers (UTSAE)
1 University Sta. C2200
Austin, TX 78712-0292
Contact: Prof. Ronald D. Matthews
Ph: (512)471-5399
E-mail: sae-officers@utlists.utexas.edu
URL: http://www.me.utexas.edu/~sae/index.html
Descr: Advances the engineering mobility systems. Provides technical information and expertise used in designing, building, maintaining and operating self-propelled vehicles, whether land, sea, air or space based. Collects and disseminates information on cars, trucks, aircraft, space vehicles, off-highway vehicles, marine equipment and engine of all types. Fosters information exchange among the worldwide automotive and aerospace communities.

Utah

999 ■ Mothers Against Drunk Driving, Salt Lake County
PO Box 18769
Kearns, UT 84118
Ph: (801)269-8645
Fax: (801)424-9261
E-mail: saltlake.ut@madd.org
URL: http://www.madd.org/ut/saltlake
Descr: Victims of drunk driving crashes; concerned citizens. Encourages citizen participation in working towards reform of the drunk driving problem and the prevention of underage drinking. Acts as the voice of victims of drunk driving crashes by speaking on their behalf to communities, businesses, and educational groups.

1000 ■ Utah State Tax Commission Division of Motor Vehicles
210 N. 1950 W.
Salt Lake City, UT 84134
Ph: (801)297-7780
Free: 800-368-8824
E-mail: dmv@utah.gov
URL: http://dmv.utah.gov/

Vermont

1001 ■ Vermont Association of Independent Tire Dealers
PO Box 278
Rutland, VT 05701
Contact: Don Westebbe, Pres.
Ph: (802)773-2741
Fax: (802)747-3241
Descr: Represents corporations engaged in all sec-

tors of the replacement tire industry. Seeks to advance and protect the interests of members and to promote goodwill within the industry. Serves as a clearinghouse on economic and regulatory issues affecting the replacement tire industry.

1002 ■ Vermont Department of Motor Vehicles
120 State St.
Montpelier, VT 05603-0001
Contact: Robert Ide, Commnr.
Ph: (802)828-2011
Free: 866-259-5368
Fax: (802)828-2170
E-mail: commissionersoffice@state.vt.us
URL: http://www.aot.state.vt.us/dmv/dmvhp.htm
Telecom. Svcs: TTY/TDD toll free number is (800)253-0191.

Virginia

1003 ■ Association of Certified Fraud Examiners, Hampton Roads Chapter No. 35
105 Marina Reach
Chesapeake, VA 23320
Contact: Mr. Edwin Wayne Bostain CFE, Pres.
Ph: (757)410-5215
E-mail: cpa@bostaincpa.com
Descr: Works to reduce the incidence of fraud and white-collar crime and to assist the members in its detection and deterrence. Sponsors training seminars on fraud and loss prevention. Administers credentialing programs for Certified Fraud Examiners.

1004 ■ Better Business Bureau of Greater Hampton Roads
586 Virginian Dr.
Norfolk, VA 23505
Contact: C.C. Shelton, Pres./CEO
Ph: (757)531-1300
Fax: (757)531-1388
E-mail: info@hamptonroadsbbb.org
URL: http://norfolk.bbb.org
Staff: 6. **Descr:** Seeks to promote and foster ethical relationship between businesses and the public through voluntary self-regulation, consumer and business education, and service excellence. Provides information to help consumers and businesses make informed purchasing decisions and avoid costly scams and frauds; settles consumer complaints through arbitration and other means.

1005 ■ Financial Planning Association of Hampton Roads
PO Box 6191
Norfolk, VA 23508-0191
Contact: Mark O. Flaherty CFP, Pres.
Ph: (757)277-6150
Free: 866-360-6845
E-mail: info@fpahamptonroads.com
URL: http://www.fpahamptonroads.com
Descr: Promotes advancement of knowledge in financial planning by supporting programs and projects that enable members to increase their professional knowledge and better serve their clients.

1006 ■ Hampton Roads Realtors Association (HRRA)
638 Independence Pkwy., Ste. 100
Chesapeake, VA 23320
Contact: J. Michael Reitelbach, Exec. Off.
Ph: (757)473-9700
Fax: (757)473-9897
E-mail: info@hrra.com
URL: http://www.centerforrealestate.com
Descr: Represents residential and commercial real estate brokers, salespeople, property managers, appraisers, counselors and others engaged in all aspects of the real estate industry. Seeks to advocate for the right to own, use, and transfer real property. Provides a facility for professional development and

exchange of information among its members, to the public, and government.

1007 ■ Hampton Roads Taxpayer Coalition
804 Riverside Dr.
Newport News, VA 23606
Ph: (757)599-4190
E-mail: mtstall4@cox.net

1008 ■ Mothers Against Drunk Driving - Blue Ridge
PO Box 15036
Lynchburg, VA 24502
Ph: (434)832-1113

1009 ■ Mothers Against Drunk Driving, Loudoun County
PO Box 4252
Leesburg, VA 20177
Contact: Ms. Susan Cleveland, Pres./Victim Advocate
Ph: (703)771-8127
Fax: (703)430-5744
E-mail: maddloudoun@aol.com
URL: http://www.maddloudounva.org
Descr: Victims of drunk driving crashes; concerned citizens. Encourages citizen participation in working towards reform of the drunk driving problem and laws and the prevention of underage drinking. Acts as the voice of victims of drunk driving crashes by speaking on their behalf to communities, businesses, and educational groups. Programs include Tie One On for Safety, poster essay contest, Great American Picnic, court monitoring, victim advocacy, sobriety checkpoints, public awareness, car poker run, legislative action day, court accompaniment for victims, free literature to help victims cope emotionally and to guide through justice system. **Fnd:** 1991. **Mem:** 600.

1010 ■ Mothers Against Drunk Driving, Northern Virginia (MADD NoVA)
PO Box 4248
Falls Church, VA 22044
Contact: Jennifer Cipolla Hamilton, Exec. Dir.
Ph: (703)379-1135
Fax: (703)379-1930
E-mail: office@maddnova.org
URL: http://maddnova.org
Staff: 3. **Descr:** Victims of drunk driving crashes; concerned citizens. Encourages citizen participation in working towards reform of the drunk driving problem and the prevention of underage drinking. Acts as the voice of victims of drunk driving crashes by speaking on their behalf to communities, businesses, and educational groups. **Fnd:** 1982. **Pub:** *MADDNOVA Newsletter* (quarterly).

1011 ■ Mothers Against Drunk Driving, Peninsula
PO Box 2496
Newport News, VA 23609
Ph: (757)595-4101
Fax: (757)595-4619
E-mail: rampage@bellatlantic.net
Descr: Victims of drunk driving crashes; concerned citizens. Encourages citizen participation in working towards reform of the drunk driving problem and the prevention of underage drinking. Acts as the voice of victims of drunk driving crashes by speaking on their behalf to communities, businesses, and educational groups.

1012 ■ Mothers Against Drunk Driving - Richmond Area
5414 Nine Mile Rd.
Richmond, VA 23223
Ph: (804)814-0976

1013 ■ Mothers Against Drunk Driving, Virginia State
5310 Markel Rd., Ste. 101
Richmond, VA 23230
Contact: Christopher R. Konschak, Exec. Dir.
Ph: (804)353-7121
Free: 800-533-6233
Fax: (804)353-7122

E-mail: office@maddva.org
URL: http://www.maddva.org
Descr: Victims of drunk driving crashes; concerned citizens. Encourages citizen participation in working towards reform of the drunk driving problem and the prevention of underage drinking. Acts as the voice of victims of drunk driving crashes by speaking on their behalf to communities, businesses, and educational groups.

1014 ■ Mothers Against Drunk Driving - Wakefield
PO Box 853
Waverly, VA 23890
Ph: (804)834-3025

1015 ■ Small Business Development Center of Hampton Roads
400 Volvo Pkwy.
Chesapeake, VA 23320
Contact: James Carroll, Dir.
Ph: (757)664-2592
Fax: (757)548-1835
E-mail: jcarroll@hrccva.com
URL: http://www.hrsbdc.org
Descr: Represents and promotes the small business sector. Provides management assistance to current and prospective small business owners. Helps to improve management skills and expand the products and services of members.

1016 ■ Small Business Development Center of Hampton Roads - Eastern Shore
PO Box 133
Melfa, VA 23410
Contact: Nial Finnegan, Dir.
Ph: (757)789-3418
Fax: (757)787-7579
E-mail: sbdc@esva.net
URL: http://www.hrsbdc.org
Descr: Represents and promotes the small business sector. Provides management assistance to current and prospective small business owners. Helps to improve management skills and expand the products and services of members.

1017 ■ Small Business Development Center of Hampton Roads - Franklin
108 3rd St.
Franklin, VA 23851
Contact: Teresa Beal, Counselor
Ph: (757)562-4900
E-mail: join@fsachamber.com
URL: http://www.hrsbdc.org
Descr: Represents and promotes the small business sector. Provides management assistance to current and prospective small business owners. Helps to improve management skills and expand the products and services of members.

1018 ■ Small Business Development Center of Hampton Roads - Smithfield
100 Main St.
Smithfield, VA 23431
Contact: Debbie Stohlman, Business Counselor
Ph: (757)357-3502
Fax: (757)357-3502
E-mail: dstohlman@theisle.org
URL: http://www.hrsbdc.org
Descr: Represents and promotes the small business sector. Provides management assistance to current and prospective small business owners. Helps to improve management skills and expand the products and services of members.

1019 ■ Small Business Development Center of Hampton Roads - Suffolk
127 E Washington St.
Suffolk, VA 23434
Contact: Jack Leach, Counselor
Ph: (757)664-2613
E-mail: jleach@hrccva.com
URL: http://www.hrsbdc.org
Descr: Represents and promotes the small business sector. Provides management assistance to current and prospective small business owners. Helps to

improve management skills and expand the products and services of members.

1020 ■ Small Business Development Center of Hampton Roads - Thomas Nelson
Thomas Nelson Community College
600 Butler Farm Rd., Ste. A, Rm. 1105
Hampton, VA 23666
Contact: Debra Farley, Dir.
Ph: (757)865-3127
Fax: (757)865-5885
E-mail: dfarley@tncc.edu
URL: http://www.hrsbdc.org
Descr: Represents and promotes the small business sector. Provides management assistance to current and prospective small business owners. Helps to improve management skills and expand the products and services of members.

1021 ■ Small Business Development Center of Hampton Roads - Williamsburg
PO Box 3495
Williamsburg, VA 23185
Contact: Debbie Wright, Business Analyst
Ph: (757)229-6511
Fax: (757)253-1397
E-mail: dwright@hrccva.com
URL: http://www.hrsbdc.org
Descr: Represents and promotes the small business sector. Provides management assistance to current and prospective small business owners. Helps to improve management skills and expand the products and services of members.

1022 ■ Urban League of Hampton Roads (ULHR)
830 Goff St.
Norfolk, VA 23504
Contact: Edith G. White, Pres./CEO
Ph: (757)226-7589
Fax: (757)226-9039
E-mail: giving@ulhr.org
URL: http://www.ulhr.org

1023 ■ Virginia Counselors Association, Hampton Roads
4236 Valencia Rd.
Chesapeake, VA 23321
Contact: Deborah Finlay, Pres.
Ph: (757)638-7920
E-mail: finladbe@cps.k12.va.us
URL: http://www.vcacounselors.org

1024 ■ Virginia Department of Motor Vehicles
PO Box 27412
Richmond, VA 23269
Contact: D.B. Smit, Commnr.
Ph: (804)497-7100
Free: 866-368-5463
Fax: (804)367-6631
URL: http://www.dmv.state.va.us/
Descr: Mission is to promote security, safety, and service through the administration of motor vehicle and tax-related laws. **Telecom. Svcs:** TTY toll free number is (800)272-9268.

Washington

1025 ■ Mothers Against Drunk Driving, Kitsap County
PO Box 3936
Silverdale, WA 98383
Ph: (360)551-6233
E-mail: maddmasters@msn.com
URL: http://www.maddpnw.org
Descr: Victims of drunk driving crashes; concerned citizens. Encourages citizen participation in working towards reform of the drunk driving problem and the prevention of underage drinking. Acts as the voice of victims of drunk driving crashes by speaking on their

behalf to communities, businesses, and educational groups. **Fnd:** 1982.

1026 ■ Mothers Against Drunk Driving - Pacific Northwest Region
18000 72nd Ave. S, Ste. 180
Kent, WA 98032
Ph: (425)251-5252
Fax: (425)251-5253
E-mail: pacificnw.region@madd.org
URL: http://www.madd.org/nw

1027 ■ Washington Department of Licensing
PO Box 9020
Olympia, WA 98507-9020
Contact: Liz Luce, Dir.
Ph: (360)902-3600
Fax: (360)902-4042
E-mail: doldirector@dol.wa.gov
URL: http://www.dol.wa.gov/
Telecom. Svcs: TTY phone number is (360) 664-8885.

West Virginia

1028 ■ Mothers Against Drunk Driving, Mercer County
PO Box 1343
Princeton, WV 24740
Ph: (304)425-1010
Descr: Victims of drunk driving crashes; concerned citizens. Encourages citizen participation in working towards reform of the drunk driving problem and the prevention of underage drinking. Acts as the voice of victims of drunk driving crashes by speaking on their behalf to communities, businesses, and educational groups.

1029 ■ Mothers Against Drunk Driving - Monongalia County
502 Old Goff Mountain Rd.
Cross Lanes, WV 25313
Ph: (304)776-0222

1030 ■ West Virginia Department of Transportation
Division of Motor Vehicles
Bldg. 3, Capitol Complex, Rm. 113
1900 Kanawha Blvd. E.
Charleston, WV 25305
Contact: Paul A. Mattox Jr., Cabinet Sec.
Ph: (304)558-0444
Free: 800-642-9066
Fax: (304)558-1004
E-mail: dot.dmvcommissioner@wv.gov
URL: http://www.wvdot.com/6_motorists/dmv/6G_DMV.HTM
Descr: Mission is to create and maintain for the people of West Virginia, the U.S., and the world a multi-modal and inter-modal transportation system that supports the safe, effective, and efficient movement of people, information, and goods that enhances the opportunity for people and communities to enjoy environmentally sensitive and economically sound development.

Wisconsin

1031 ■ Wisconsin Automotive Aftermarket Association
5330 Wall St., No. 100
Madison, WI 53718
Contact: Richard Blatter, Pres.
Ph: (608)240-2065
Fax: (608)240-2069
E-mail: rblatter@gdinet.com
URL: http://www.waaa.info
Descr: Represents corporations engaged in all sectors of the replacement tire industry. Seeks to advance and protect the interests of members and to promote goodwill within the industry. Serves as a

clearinghouse on economic and regulatory issues affecting the replacement tire industry.

1032 ■ Wisconsin Department of Transportation
Bureau of Vehicle Services
Hill Farms State Transportation Bldg.
4802 Sheboygan Ave.
PO Box 7999
Madison, WI 53707-7999
Contact: Frank Busalacchi, Sec.
Ph: (608)261-2583
E-mail: vehiclequestions@dot.wi.us
URL: http://www.dot.state.wi.us/drivers/index.htm

Wyoming

1033 ■ Wyoming Department of Transportation
Driver Services
5300 Bishop Blvd.
Cheyenne, WY 82009-3340
Contact: John Cox, Dir.
Ph: (307)777-4375
Fax: (307)777-4803
URL: http://www.dot.state.wy.us/wydot/

Publications

1034 ■ *56J Only*
1956 Studebaker Golden Hawk Owners Register
31654 Wekiva River Rd.
Sorrento, FL 32776-9233
E-mail: fja56gh@gmail.com
URL: http://www.1956goldenhawk.com
Freq: 3/year. **Price:** free.

1035 ■ *AAA Southern Traveler*
AAA Southern Traveler
12901 N 40th Dr.
Saint Louis, MO 63141
Free: 800-451-4006
URL: http://www.ouraaa.com/
URL(s): http://www.aaasouth.com/home.aspx?zip=38583 **Descr:** Magazine for AAA members in Arkansas, Louisiana, and Mississippi. **Freq:** Bimonthly.

1036 ■ *AAA World—Delaware*
AAA World Publishing
2040 Market St.
Philadelphia, PA 19103
Free: 888-222-4252
E-mail: letters@aaaworld.com
URL: http://www.aaaworld.com
Key Personnel: Brian Case, Editor-in-Chief. **URL(s):** http://www.aaaworld.com **Descr:** Auto club publication featuring automotive, travel, and insurance stories. **Freq:** Bimonthly. **Price:** Included in membership.

1037 ■ *AAA World—Potomac*
AAA World Publishing
2040 Market St.
Philadelphia, PA 19103
Free: 888-222-4252
E-mail: letters@aaaworld.com
URL: http://www.aaaworld.com
Key Personnel: Brian Case, Editor-in-Chief. **URL(s):** http://www.aaaworld.com **Descr:** Auto club publication featuring auto, travel, and insurance stories. **Freq:** Bimonthly. **Price:** Free to qualified subscribers.

1038 ■ *AAA World—Valley*
AAA World Publishing
2040 Market St.
Philadelphia, PA 19103
Free: 888-222-4252
E-mail: letters@aaaworld.com
URL: http://www.aaaworld.com
Key Personnel: Brian Case, Editor-in-Chief. **URL(s):** http://www.aaaworld.com **Descr:** Auto club publica-

tion featuring auto, travel, and insurance stories. **Freq:** Bimonthly. **Price:** Free to qualified subscribers.

1039 ■ *AAA World—Virginia*
AAA World Publishing
2040 Market St.
Philadelphia, PA 19103
Free: 888-222-4252
E-mail: letters@aaaworld.com
URL: http://www.aaaworld.com
Key Personnel: Brian Case, Editor-in-Chief. **URL(s):** http://www.aaaworld.com **Descr:** Auto club publication featuring auto, travel, and insurance stories. **Freq:** Bimonthly. **Price:** Free to qualified subscribers.

1040 ■ *Aerospace Engineering*
SAE International - Society of Automotive Engineers
400 Commonwealth Dr.
Warrendale, PA 15096-0001
Ph: (724)776-4841
Fax: (724)776-0790
E-mail: customerservice@sae.org
URL: http://www.sae.org
Freq: monthly. **Price:** $66/year in North America, $118/year outside North America. **ISSN:** 0736-2536.

1041 ■ *Aerospace Standards*
SAE International - Society of Automotive Engineers
400 Commonwealth Dr.
Warrendale, PA 15096-0001
Ph: (724)776-4841
Fax: (724)776-0790
E-mail: customerservice@sae.org
URL: http://www.sae.org

1042 ■ *Annual Business Survey*
National Association of Fleet Resale Dealers
2521 Brown Blvd.
Arlington, TX 76006
Ph: (817)649-5858
Fax: (817)649-5866
E-mail: jd@niada.com
URL: http://www.nafrd.com
Descr: Includes comprehensive view of used fleet marketing. **Freq:** annual.

1043 ■ *Annual Supplement to Automobile Design Liability*
Center for Auto Safety
1825 Connecticut Ave. NW, Ste. 330
Washington, DC 20009-5708
Ph: (202)328-7700
E-mail: accounts@autosafety.org
URL: http://www.autosafety.org
Descr: Supplements a reference book on automobile liability laws and consumer protection. **Freq:** annual.

1044 ■ *Arrive Alive*
RID - U.S.A.
PO Box 520
Schenectady, NY 12301
Ph: (518)372-0034
Fax: (518)370-4917
E-mail: dwi@rid-usa.org
URL: http://www.rid-usa.org

1045 ■ *ASE Blue Seal Tech News*
National Institute for Automotive Service Excellence
101 Blue Seal Dr. SE, Ste. 101
Leesburg, VA 20175
Ph: (703)669-6600
Fax: (703)669-6123
E-mail: webmaster@ase.com
URL: http://www.asecert.org
Descr: Contains news of ASE technicians and their employers. **Freq:** quarterly. **Price:** free.

1046 ■ *ASE Catalogs of Tests*
National Institute for Automotive Service Excellence
101 Blue Seal Dr. SE, Ste. 101
Leesburg, VA 20175
Ph: (703)669-6600
Fax: (703)669-6123
E-mail: webmaster@ase.com
URL: http://www.asecert.org
Descr: Includes bibliographic listing of training materials for upgrading technicians' skills in automo-

tive repair; sample test questions; and task lists. **Freq:** annual. **Price:** free individual copies.

1047 ■ *ASE Certification Test Registration Booklet*
National Institute for Automotive Service Excellence
101 Blue Seal Dr. SE, Ste. 101
Leesburg, VA 20175
Ph: (703)669-6600
Fax: (703)669-6123
E-mail: webmaster@ase.com
URL: http://www.asecert.org
Descr: Includes registration for technicians who wish to become ASE certified. Provides registration information and sample questions. **Freq:** semiannual. **Price:** free.

1048 ■ *Automotive Consultant's Directory*
SAE International - Society of Automotive Engineers
400 Commonwealth Dr.
Warrendale, PA 15096-0001
Ph: (724)776-4841
Fax: (724)776-0790
E-mail: customerservice@sae.org
URL: http://www.sae.org
Freq: annual.

1049 ■ *Automotive Customer Relations Directory*
Automotive Consumer Action Program
5301 Wisconsin Ave. NW, Ste. 210
Washington, DC 20015
Ph: (202)237-7200
Fax: (202)237-9090
E-mail: autocap@wanada.org
URL: http://www.wanada.org/autocap.html

1050 ■ *Automotive Engineering*
SAE International - Society of Automotive Engineers
400 Commonwealth Dr.
Warrendale, PA 15096-0001
Ph: (724)776-4841
Fax: (724)776-0790
E-mail: customerservice@sae.org
URL: http://www.sae.org
Freq: monthly. **Price:** $96 in U.S., $150 outside U.S. **ISSN:** 0098-2571.

1051 ■ *Body Language*
Automotive Body Parts Association
1510 Eldridge Pkwy. S, Ste. 110-168
Houston, TX 77077
Ph: (281)531-0809
Fax: (281)531-9411
E-mail: srodman1@sbcglobal.net
URL: http://www.autobpa.com
Descr: Provides information on aftermarket auto parts, new association policies, and industry and members' news. **ISSN:** 1526-8918.

1052 ■ *Bosch Handbook*
SAE International - Society of Automotive Engineers
400 Commonwealth Dr.
Warrendale, PA 15096-0001
Ph: (724)776-4841
Fax: (724)776-0790
E-mail: customerservice@sae.org
URL: http://www.sae.org
Descr: Contains book of ground vehicle standards. **Freq:** annual.

1053 ■ *Bus Passenger Tariffs*
National Bus Traffic Association
700 13th St. NW, Ste. 575
Washington, DC 20005-5923
Ph: (202)898-2700
Fax: (202)842-0850
URL: http://www.bustraffic.org
Freq: periodic.

1054 ■ *The Car Book*
Center for Auto Safety
1825 Connecticut Ave. NW, Ste. 330
Washington, DC 20009-5708
Ph: (202)328-7700

E-mail: accounts@autosafety.org
URL: http://www.autosafety.org
Descr: Features a guide to buying new and used cars. Covers crash safety, fuel economy, maintenance, insurance, child seat ratings, and state lemon laws. **Freq:** annual. **Price:** $20/copy, $30 in Canada and outside U.S.

1055 ■ *Car Care Chronicles*
Car Care Council
7101 Wisconsin Ave., Ste. 1300
Bethesda, MD 20814
Ph: (240)333-1088
E-mail: marcella.tilli@aftermarket.org
URL: http://www.carcare.org
Freq: quarterly. **Price:** free.

1056 ■ *Center for Auto Safety—Impact: A Journal of Safety News*
Center for Auto Safety
1825 Connecticut Ave. NW, Ste. 330
Washington, DC 20009-5708
Ph: (202)328-7700
E-mail: accounts@autosafety.org
URL: http://www.autosafety.org
Descr: Provides information on automobile defects, product liability, recalls, secret warranties, federal investigations, and center automobile safety work. **Freq:** bimonthly. **Price:** $100/year in U.S., $100/year outside U.S. **ISSN:** 0162-4989.

1057 ■ *Collision Parts Journal*
Automotive Body Parts Association
1510 Eldridge Pkwy. S, Ste. 110-168
Houston, TX 77077
Ph: (281)531-0809
Fax: (281)531-9411
E-mail: srodman1@sbcglobal.net
URL: http://www.autobpa.com
Descr: Provides information for industry and insurance companies on collision parts, their availability, and suppliers. Includes reports on new products. **Freq:** semiannual.

1058 ■ *Contact*
Canadian Auto Workers
205 Placer Ct.
Toronto, ON, Canada M2H 3H9
Ph: (416)497-4110
Fax: (416)495-6552
E-mail: caw@caw.ca
URL: http://www.caw.ca
Freq: weekly.

1059 ■ *Crash Prevention News*
Partnership for Safe Driving
1312 18th St. NW, Rm. 501
Washington, DC 20036
E-mail: info2@crashprevention.org
URL: http://www.crashprevention.org
Freq: monthly.

1060 ■ *Digest of Motor Laws*
American Automobile Association
One River Pl.
Wilmington, DE 19801
URL: http://www.aaa.com
Freq: annual.

1061 ■ *Directory of Accessible Van Rentals*
Twin Peaks Press
PO Box 8
Vancouver, WA 98666-0008
Ph: (360)694-2462
Free: 800-637-2256
Fax: (360)696-3210
E-mail: info@twinpeakspress.com
URL: http://www.twinpeakspress.com
Covers: rental companies in the U.S. and Canada that provide vans that are accessible to disabled travelers. **Entries include:** Company name, address, phone, location, name and title of contact, geographical area served, description of services.

Freq: Every three to six months. **Price:** $12.95, individuals, plus 5 for shipping and handling.

1062 ■ *Don't Call Me Lucky*
Mothers Against Drunk Driving
511 E John Carpenter Fwy., Ste. 700
Irving, TX 75062
Ph: (214)744-6233
Fax: (972)869-2206
E-mail: info@madd.org
URL: http://www.madd.org

1063 ■ *Driven*
Mothers Against Drunk Driving
511 E John Carpenter Fwy., Ste. 700
Irving, TX 75062
Ph: (214)744-6233
Fax: (972)869-2206
E-mail: info@madd.org
URL: http://www.madd.org
Descr: Includes national activities, public policy initiatives, calendars and chapter events. **Freq:** biennial.

1064 ■ *Driven*
Mothers Against Drunk Driving, South Carolina
810 Dutch Square Blvd., No. 211
Columbia, SC 29210
Ph: (803)748-7333
Fax: (803)748-8600
E-mail: sc.state@madd.org
URL: http://www.madd.org/sc
Descr: Includes stories about victims of drunk driving, public policy issues, MADD programs and youth initiatives, personal and corporate profiles. **Freq:** biennial.

1065 ■ *Driven*
Mothers Against Drunk Driving, Kentucky State
649 Charity Ct.
Frankfort, KY 40601
Ph: (502)223-4930
Fax: (502)223-4932
E-mail: maddky@fewpb.net
URL: http://www.madd.org/ky
Descr: Contains information on activities, articles on public policy, youth and victim issues, and profiles of MADD volunteers. **Freq:** semiannual. **Price:** free for members.

1066 ■ *Driven*
Mothers Against Drunk Driving, Miami - Dade County
7700 N Kendall Dr., Ste. 803
Miami, FL 33156
Ph: (305)273-3744
Fax: (305)273-3745
E-mail: maddmiami@bellsouth.com
URL: http://www.madd.org/fl/dade
Freq: quarterly.

1067 ■ *Driven Magazine*
Mothers Against Drunk Driving, Alabama
2101 Eastern Blvd., Ste. 210
Montgomery, AL 36117
Ph: (334)277-7722
Fax: (334)277-8228
E-mail: al.state@madd.org
URL: http://www.madd.org/chapter/0100_3143
Price: based on available funds.

1068 ■ *Driving Ahead*
American Highway Users Alliance
1101 14th St. NW, Ste. 750
Washington, DC 20005
Ph: (202)857-1200
Fax: (202)857-1220
E-mail: info@highways.org
URL: http://www.highways.org
Freq: bimonthly.

1069 ■ *Dual News Magazine*
Driving School Association of the Americas
3090 E Gause Blvd., Ste. 425
Slidell, LA 70461
Fax: (985)649-9877

E-mail: info@thedsaa.org
URL: http://www.thedsaa.org
Descr: Contains articles that discuss educational changes and methods. **Freq:** 3/year.

1070 ■ *Ethics Policies and Programs in American Business*
Ethics Resource Center
2345 Crystal Dr., Ste. 201
Arlington, VA 22202
Ph: (703)647-2185
Fax: (703)647-2180
E-mail: ethics@ethics.org
URL: http://www.ethics.org

1071 ■ *Financial Recovery After A Drunk Driving Crash*
Mothers Against Drunk Driving
511 E John Carpenter Fwy., Ste. 700
Irving, TX 75062
Ph: (214)744-6233
Fax: (972)869-2206
E-mail: info@madd.org
URL: http://www.madd.org

1072 ■ *Gold Book*
Gold Wing Road Riders Association
21423 N 11th Ave.
Phoenix, AZ 85027
Ph: (623)581-2500
Fax: (623)581-3844
E-mail: customerservice@gwrra.org
URL: http://www.gwrra.org
Freq: annual. **Price:** $40.

1073 ■ *Guide to Sources of Information on Auto Defects*
Center for Auto Safety
1825 Connecticut Ave. NW, Ste. 330
Washington, DC 20009-5708
Ph: (202)328-7700
E-mail: accounts@autosafety.org
URL: http://www.autosafety.org

1074 ■ *Helping Children Cope With Death*
Mothers Against Drunk Driving
511 E John Carpenter Fwy., Ste. 700
Irving, TX 75062
Ph: (214)744-6233
Fax: (972)869-2206
E-mail: info@madd.org
URL: http://www.madd.org

1075 ■ *History of RID*
RID - U.S.A.
PO Box 520
Schenectady, NY 12301
Ph: (518)372-0034
Fax: (518)370-4917
E-mail: dwi@rid-usa.org
URL: http://www.rid-usa.org
Descr: Preface to Arrive Alive. **Price:** free.

1076 ■ *How You Can Help*
Mothers Against Drunk Driving
511 E John Carpenter Fwy., Ste. 700
Irving, TX 75062
Ph: (214)744-6233
Fax: (972)869-2206
E-mail: info@madd.org
URL: http://www.madd.org

1077 ■ *Human Rights Report on Trafficking in Persons, Especially Women and Children*
Protection Project
The Johns Hopkins University
1717 Massachusetts Ave. NW
Washington, DC 20036
Ph: (202)663-5894
Fax: (202)663-5899
E-mail: protection_project@jhu.edu
URL: http://www.protectionproject.org
Freq: annual.

1078 ■ *Inside Tracks*
National Association of Fleet Resale Dealers
2521 Brown Blvd.

Arlington, TX 76006
Ph: (817)649-5858
Fax: (817)649-5866
E-mail: jd@niada.com
URL: http://www.nafrd.com

Freq: quarterly. **Price:** free for members.

1079 ■ *International Collision Parts Industry Suppliers Guide and Membership Roster*
Automotive Body Parts Association
1510 Eldridge Pkwy. S, Ste. 110-168
Houston, TX 77077
Ph: (281)531-0809
Fax: (281)531-9411
E-mail: srodman1@sbcglobal.net
URL: http://www.autobpa.com

1080 ■ *Intersections*
National Commission Against Drunk Driving
8403 Colesville Rd., Ste. 370
Silver Spring, MD 20910
Ph: (240)247-6004
Fax: (240)247-7012
E-mail: info@ncadd.com
Freq: quarterly. **Price:** included in membership dues.

1081 ■ *Japan Auto Trends*
Japan Automobile Manufacturers Association, Washington Office
1050 17th St. NW, Ste. 410
Washington, DC 20036
Ph: (202)296-8537
Fax: (202)872-1212
E-mail: cpowers@porternovelli.com
URL: http://www.jama.org
Descr: Provides in-depth coverage of the industry.
Freq: quarterly.

1082 ■ *Journey*
AAA Washington/Inland
1745 114th Ave. SE
Bellevue, WA 98004
Ph: (509)358-6950
Fax: (509)358-6902
E-mail: info@aaawin.com
URL: http://www.aaawa.com/index.asp?zip=98004
Freq: bimonthly. **Price:** included in membership dues.

1083 ■ *Lemon-Aid*
Consumer Publications Inc.
292 St. Joseph Blvd. W
Montreal, QC, Canada H2V 2N7
Ph: (514)272-5555
Fax: (514)273-0797
E-mail: apal@cam.org
Key Personnel: George Iny, Editor. **Descr:** Magazine rating new and used automobiles and informing Canadian motorists about safety issues, vehicle recalls, service tips, and extended warranties (English and French). **Freq:** 2/yr. **Price:** $5, single issue plus taxes.

1084 ■ *Lemon-Aid Magazine*
Automobile Protection Association
292 St. Joseph Blvd. W
Montreal, QC, Canada H2V 2N7
Ph: (514)272-5555
Fax: (514)273-0797
E-mail: apamontreal@apa.ca
URL: http://www.apa.ca
Descr: Includes new and used vehicle buyers' guide, consumer news. **Freq:** annual. **Price:** $15 plus $2 tax and shipping. **ISSN:** 0834-2423.

1085 ■ *The Lemon Book*
Center for Auto Safety
1825 Connecticut Ave. NW, Ste. 330
Washington, DC 20009-5708
Ph: (202)328-7700
E-mail: accounts@autosafety.org
URL: http://www.autosafety.org

Price: $17.50.

1086 ■ *Lemon Times*
Center for Auto Safety
1825 Connecticut Ave. NW, Ste. 330
Washington, DC 20009-5708
Ph: (202)328-7700
E-mail: accounts@autosafety.org
URL: http://www.autosafety.org
Descr: Covers center's actions and findings. Includes consumer success stories and annual report.
Freq: quarterly. **Price:** $20/year in U.S., $25/year outside U.S.

1087 ■ *Little Secrets of the Auto Industry*
Center for Auto Safety
1825 Connecticut Ave. NW, Ste. 330
Washington, DC 20009-5708
Ph: (202)328-7700
E-mail: accounts@autosafety.org
URL: http://www.autosafety.org
Descr: Features a guide to finding and using secret warranties. **Price:** $17.50.

1088 ■ *Local Newsletter*
Mothers Against Drunk Driving, Kent County Chapter
PO Box 21157
Lansing, MI 48909
Ph: (616)456-6233
Freq: semiannual. **Price:** included in membership dues.

1089 ■ *MADD News*
Mothers Against Drunk Driving, Pima County Chapter
2221 E Broadway Blvd., No. 200
Tucson, AZ 85705
Ph: (520)322-5253
Fax: (520)322-6245
E-mail: pima.az@madd.org
URL: http://www.madd.org/az/pima
Freq: quarterly.

1090 ■ *MADDNOVA Newsletter*
Mothers Against Drunk Driving, Northern Virginia
PO Box 4248
Falls Church, VA 22044
Ph: (703)379-1135
Fax: (703)379-1930
E-mail: office@maddnova.org
URL: http://maddnova.org
Freq: quarterly.

1091 ■ *MADDvocate*
Mothers Against Drunk Driving, Kentucky State
649 Charity Ct.
Frankfort, KY 40601
Ph: (502)223-4930
Fax: (502)223-4932
E-mail: maddky@fewpb.net
URL: http://www.madd.org/ky
Descr: Features victims and survivors of drunk driving crashes and those who work with crash victims.
Freq: semiannual. **Price:** free for members.

1092 ■ *Maddvocate*
Mothers Against Drunk Driving, Miami - Dade County
7700 N Kendall Dr., Ste. 803
Miami, FL 33156
Ph: (305)273-3744
Fax: (305)273-3745
E-mail: maddmiami@bellsouth.net
URL: http://www.madd.org/fl/dade
Freq: quarterly.

1093 ■ *MADDvocate*
Mothers Against Drunk Driving, South Carolina
810 Dutch Square Blvd., No. 211
Columbia, SC 29210
Ph: (803)748-7333
Fax: (803)748-8600
E-mail: sc.state@madd.org
URL: http://www.madd.org/sc
Descr: Contains informative news, helpful resources

and tips, and legal updates that will arm readers with knowledge and power. **Freq:** biennial.

1094 ■ *MADDvocate*
Mothers Against Drunk Driving
511 E John Carpenter Fwy., Ste. 700
Irving, TX 75062
Ph: (214)744-6233
Fax: (972)869-2206
E-mail: info@madd.org
URL: http://www.madd.org
Descr: Includes victims' stories, legislative updates, feature editions. **Freq:** semiannual.

1095 ■ *MADDVocate, Driven*
Mothers Against Drunk Driving, Massachusetts State
18 Tremont St., Ste. 703
Boston, MA 02108
Ph: (617)227-2701
Freq: quarterly. **Price:** free, for members.

1096 ■ *Maddvocate Magazine*
Mothers Against Drunk Driving, Alabama
2101 Eastern Blvd., Ste. 210
Montgomery, AL 36117
Ph: (334)277-7722
Fax: (334)277-8228
E-mail: al.state@madd.org
URL: http://www.madd.org/chapter/0100_3143
Price: based on available funds.

1097 ■ *Maps and Tour Books*
American Automobile Association
One River Pl.
Wilmington, DE 19801
URL: http://www.aaa.com
Freq: annual.

1098 ■ *Member Roster*
Automotive Women's Alliance
PO Box 4305
Troy, MI 48099-4305
Ph: (248)643-6590
Fax: (248)239-0291
URL: http://www.automotivewomensalliance.com

1099 ■ *Men and Mourning*
Mothers Against Drunk Driving
511 E John Carpenter Fwy., Ste. 700
Irving, TX 75062
Ph: (214)744-6233
Fax: (972)869-2206
E-mail: info@madd.org
URL: http://www.madd.org

1100 ■ *Microprocessor Manual for Traffic Signals*
International Municipal Signal Association
PO Box 539
Newark, NY 14513-0539
Ph: (315)331-2182
Fax: (315)331-8205
E-mail: info@imsasafety.org
URL: http://www.imsasafety.org

1101 ■ *MOVE Magazine*
American Association of Motor Vehicle Administrators
4301 Wilson Blvd., Ste. 400
Arlington, VA 22203
Ph: (703)522-4200
Fax: (703)522-1905
E-mail: info@aamva.org
URL: http://www.aamva.org
Freq: 3/year. **Price:** included in membership dues, $26 for nonmembers.

1102 ■ *NAFRD Resource Guide*
National Association of Fleet Resale Dealers
2521 Brown Blvd.
Arlington, TX 76006
Ph: (817)649-5858
Fax: (817)649-5866
E-mail: jd@niada.com
URL: http://www.nafrd.com

Freq: annual.

1103 ■ *National Mileage Guides*
National Bus Traffic Association
700 13th St. NW, Ste. 575
Washington, DC 20005-5923
Ph: (202)898-2700
Fax: (202)842-0850
URL: http://www.bustraffic.org
Freq: periodic.

1104 ■ *Newsline*
Canadian Automobile Dealers Association
85 Renfrew Dr.
Markham, ON, Canada L3R 0N9
Ph: (905)940-4959
Fax: (905)940-6870
E-mail: mail@cada.ca
URL: http://www.cada.ca
Freq: monthly. **Price:** free for members.

1105 ■ *Off Highway Engineering*
SAE International - Society of Automotive Engineers
400 Commonwealth Dr.
Warrendale, PA 15096-0001
Ph: (724)776-4841
Fax: (724)776-0790
E-mail: customerservice@sae.org
URL: http://www.sae.org
Freq: bimonthly. **Price:** $54/year in North America, $78/year outside North America. **ISSN:** 1074-6919.

1106 ■ *Outlook Study*
Automotive Industries Association of Canada
1272 Wellington St. W
Ottawa, ON, Canada K1Y 3A7
Ph: (613)728-5821
Fax: (613)728-6021
E-mail: info.aia@aiacanada.com
URL: http://www.aiacanada.com
Descr: Features statistical overview of trends and forecasts. **Freq:** biennial. **Price:** $750.

1107 ■ *Preventive Maintenance of Traffic Signals*
International Municipal Signal Association
PO Box 539
Newark, NY 14513-0539
Ph: (315)331-2182
Fax: (315)331-8205
E-mail: info@imsasafety.org
URL: http://www.imsasafety.org

1108 ■ *Privacy and American Business*
Center for Social and Legal Research
2 University Plz., Ste. 414
Hackensack, NJ 07601
Ph: (201)996-1154
Fax: (201)996-1883
E-mail: ctrslr@aol.com
URL: http://www.privacyexchange.org
Descr: Contains information concerning current privacy issues. **Freq:** monthly. **Price:** $195. **ISSN:** 1070-0536.

1109 ■ *Progress in Technology*
SAE International - Society of Automotive Engineers
400 Commonwealth Dr.
Warrendale, PA 15096-0001
Ph: (724)776-4841
Fax: (724)776-0790
E-mail: customerservice@sae.org
URL: http://www.sae.org

1110 ■ *The Protection Project Report: A Periodical on the Current Status of Anti-Trafficking Legislation*
Protection Project
The Johns Hopkins University
1717 Massachusetts Ave. NW
Washington, DC 20036
Ph: (202)663-5894
Fax: (202)663-5899

E-mail: protection_project@jhu.edu
URL: http://www.protectionproject.org

1111 ■ *Registry Update*
Cyclone Montego Torino Registry
19 Glyn Dr.
Newark, DE 19713-4016
Ph: (302)737-4252
E-mail: robscyclone@aol.com
URL: http://clubs.hemmings.com/frameset.cfm?club=cyclonemontegotorinoregistry
Freq: 3/year. **Price:** $6 in U.S., $7 in Canada, $8 outside U.S. and Canada.

1112 ■ *RID In Action Bulletin*
RID - U.S.A.
PO Box 520
Schenectady, NY 12301
Ph: (518)372-0034
Fax: (518)370-4917
E-mail: dwi@rid-usa.org
URL: http://www.rid-usa.org
Freq: bimonthly. **Price:** available to chapters only.

1113 ■ *SAE Aerospace Material Specifications*
SAE International - Society of Automotive Engineers
400 Commonwealth Dr.
Warrendale, PA 15096-0001
Ph: (724)776-4841
Fax: (724)776-0790
E-mail: customerservice@sae.org
URL: http://www.sae.org

1114 ■ *SAE Technical Papers*
SAE International - Society of Automotive Engineers
400 Commonwealth Dr.
Warrendale, PA 15096-0001
Ph: (724)776-4841
Fax: (724)776-0790
E-mail: customerservice@sae.org
URL: http://www.sae.org

1115 ■ *SAE Transactions*
SAE International - Society of Automotive Engineers
400 Commonwealth Dr.
Warrendale, PA 15096-0001
Ph: (724)776-4841
Fax: (724)776-0790
E-mail: customerservice@sae.org
URL: http://www.sae.org
Freq: annual.

1116 ■ *SAE Update*
SAE International - Society of Automotive Engineers
400 Commonwealth Dr.
Warrendale, PA 15096-0001
Ph: (724)776-4841
Fax: (724)776-0790
E-mail: customerservice@sae.org
URL: http://www.sae.org
Freq: monthly.

1117 ■ *Safe Driver*
National Safety Council
1121 Spring Lake Dr.
Itasca, IL 60143-3201
Ph: (630)285-1121
Fax: (630)285-1315
E-mail: info@nsc.org
URL: http://www.nsc.org
Freq: monthly.

1118 ■ *SafetyBeltSafe News*
SafetyBeltSafe U.S.A.
PO Box 553
Altadena, CA 91003
Ph: (310)222-6860
Fax: (310)222-6862
E-mail: stombrello@carseat.org
URL: http://www.carseat.org
Freq: bimonthly. **Price:** included in membership dues.

1119 ■ *Selecting a Civil Attorney*
Mothers Against Drunk Driving
511 E John Carpenter Fwy., Ste. 700
Irving, TX 75062

Ph: (214)744-6233
Fax: (972)869-2206
E-mail: info@madd.org
URL: http://www.madd.org

1120 ■ Someone You Know Drinks and Drives
Mothers Against Drunk Driving
511 E John Carpenter Fwy., Ste. 700
Irving, TX 75062
Ph: (214)744-6233
Fax: (972)869-2206
E-mail: info@madd.org
URL: http://www.madd.org

1121 ■ Sportsmanlike Driving
American Automobile Association
One River Pl.
Wilmington, DE 19801
URL: http://www.aaa.com
Freq: periodic.

1122 ■ Straight Talk About Death for Teenagers
Mothers Against Drunk Driving
511 E John Carpenter Fwy., Ste. 700
Irving, TX 75062
Ph: (214)744-6233
Fax: (972)869-2206
E-mail: info@madd.org
URL: http://www.madd.org

1123 ■ Sudden Acceleration
Center for Auto Safety
1825 Connecticut Ave. NW, Ste. 330
Washington, DC 20009-5708
Ph: (202)328-7700
E-mail: accounts@autosafety.org
URL: http://www.autosafety.org
Descr: Tells about the serious defect of sudden acceleration. **Price:** $25.

1124 ■ Tailgate
Paisano Publications L.L.C.
28210 Dorothy Dr.
Agoura Hills, CA 91301
Ph: (818)889-8740
Free: 800-247-6246
Fax: (818)735-6518
E-mail: bulkmagazines@paisanopub.com
URL: http://www.easyriders.com
URL(s): http://www.easyriders.com **Descr:** Consumer magazine covering custom trucks, truck events, and custom truck lifestyle information. **Freq:** Quarterly. **Price:** $16.95, individuals; $27.95, two years.

1125 ■ TANA—Who's Who Membership Directory
Tire Industry Association
1532 Pointer Ridge Pl., Ste. G
Bowie, MD 20716-1883
Ph: (301)430-7280
Fax: (301)430-7283
URL: http://www.tireindustry.org
Freq: annual. **Price:** included in membership dues, $50 for nonmembers.

1126 ■ Track
Mothers Against Drunk Driving
511 E John Carpenter Fwy., Ste. 700
Irving, TX 75062
Ph: (214)744-6233
Fax: (972)869-2206
E-mail: info@madd.org
URL: http://www.madd.org

1127 ■ Traffic Law and Procedure
Michigan Sheriffs' Association
515 N Capitol Ave.
Lansing, MI 48933-1209
Ph: (517)485-3135
Fax: (517)485-1013

E-mail: dcarmichael@michigansheriff.com
URL: http://www.michigansheriff.com

1128 ■ Traffic Safety
NSC Press
1121 Spring Lake Dr.
Itasca, IL 60143-3201
Ph: (630)285-1121
Free: 800-621-7615
Fax: (630)285-1315
E-mail: info@nsc.org
URL: http://www.nsc.org
Key Personnel: Suzanne Powills, Publisher, powillss@nsc.org. **URL(s):** http://secure.nsc.org **Descr:** Vehicle collision prevention magazine includes information on driver training, traffic and road engineering, and law enforcement. **Freq:** Monthly. **Price:** $24, members; $31, nonmembers; $20, single issue; $13, members, quantity 10 - 24.

1129 ■ Truck Trend
PRIMEDIA Los Angeles
6420 Wilshire Blvd.
Los Angeles, CA 90048-5515
Ph: (323)782-2084
Fax: (323)782-2920
E-mail: information@primedia.com
URL: http://www.primedia.com
Key Personnel: Alan Reed, Contact, alan.reed@sourceinterlink.com. **URL(s):** http://www.trucktrend.com **Descr:** Consumer magazine covering light trucks. **Freq:** Bimonthly. **Price:** $18, individuals, 12 issues; $10, individuals, 6 issues; $44, Canada, 12 issues; $23, Canada, 6 issues.

1130 ■ U.S. Auto Scene
Springer Publications
31201 Chicago Rd. S
Warren, MI 48093
Ph: (586)939-6800
E-mail: info@detroitautoscene.com
URL: http://www.detroitautoscene.com/
URL(s): http://www.usautoscene.com; http://www.detroitautoscene.com/detas.html **Descr:** Automotive newspaper. **Freq:** Weekly. **Price:** Free.

1131 ■ Up To Speed
Automotive Women's Alliance
PO Box 4305
Troy, MI 48099-4305
Ph: (248)643-6590
Fax: (248)239-0291
URL: http://www.automotivewomensalliance.com
Freq: quarterly.

1132 ■ Vehicle Leasing Today
National Vehicle Leasing Association
1199 N Fairfax St., Ste. 400
Alexandria, VA 22314
Free: 800-225-6852
Fax: (703)548-8536
E-mail: nvla@fernley.com
URL: http://www.nvla.org/
Key Personnel: Chris Brown, Editor, chris.brown@bobit.com. **URL(s):** http://www.datakey.org; http://www.leasemobilecalifornia.com/dk_profile.htm **Descr:** Trade magazine covering the consumer and commercial automobile leasing markets. **Freq:** Quarterly: Winter, Spring, Summer and Fall. **Price:** $39, individuals, per year.

1133 ■ VIA
California State Automobile Association
160 Sutter St.
At Kearny St.
San Francisco, CA 94104
Ph: (415)773-1900
URL: http://www.csaa.com
Key Personnel: Anne McSilver, Managing Editor, anne_mcsilver@csaa.com; John Poppy, Exec. Ed., john_poppy@csaa.com. **URL(s):** http://viamagazine.com **Descr:** Magazine covering worldwide and regional travel and recreation, restaurants, cars and

car care, motorists issues, and traffic safety. **Freq:** Bimonthly.

1134 ■ Victim Information
Mothers Against Drunk Driving
511 E John Carpenter Fwy., Ste. 700
Irving, TX 75062
Ph: (214)744-6233
Fax: (972)869-2206
E-mail: info@madd.org
URL: http://www.madd.org

1135 ■ Wash-Word
Canadian Carwash Association
346-4195 Dundas St. W
Toronto, ON, Canada M8X 1Y4
Ph: (416)239-0339
Fax: (416)239-1076
E-mail: office@canadiancarwash.ca
URL: http://www.canadiancarwash.ca
Freq: quarterly.

1136 ■ We Hurt Too: Guide for Adult Siblings
Mothers Against Drunk Driving
511 E John Carpenter Fwy., Ste. 700
Irving, TX 75062
Ph: (214)744-6233
Fax: (972)869-2206
E-mail: info@madd.org
URL: http://www.madd.org

1137 ■ Westworld Alberta
Alberta Motor Association
4700 17 Ave. SW
Calgary, AB, Canada T3E 0E3
Ph: (403)240-5300
URL: http://www.ama.ab.ca/cps/rde/xchg/ama
Freq: 5/year.

1138 ■ Will It Always Feel This Way?
Mothers Against Drunk Driving
511 E John Carpenter Fwy., Ste. 700
Irving, TX 75062
Ph: (214)744-6233
Fax: (972)869-2206
E-mail: info@madd.org
URL: http://www.madd.org

1139 ■ Wing World Magazine
Gold Wing Road Riders Association
21423 N 11th Ave.
Phoenix, AZ 85027
Ph: (623)581-2500
Fax: (623)581-3844
E-mail: customerservice@gwrra.org
URL: http://www.gwrra.org
Descr: Includes information on new products, listing of officers, calendar of tours and rallies, and regional news. **Freq:** monthly. **Price:** included in membership dues. **ISSN:** 0745-273X.

1140 ■ Women On Wheels
Women On Wheels Motorcycle Association
PO Box 83076
Lincoln, NE 68501
Ph: (402)477-1280
E-mail: general@womenonwheels.org
URL: http://www.womenonwheels.org
Descr: Contains stories and articles written by and for membership, and reports on new products and industry events. **Freq:** bimonthly. **Price:** included in membership dues.

1141 ■ Your Grief: You're Not Going Crazy
Mothers Against Drunk Driving
511 E John Carpenter Fwy., Ste. 700
Irving, TX 75062
Ph: (214)744-6233
Fax: (972)869-2206
E-mail: info@madd.org
URL: http://www.madd.org

1142 ■ You're Not Alone: MADD Can Help!
Mothers Against Drunk Driving
511 E John Carpenter Fwy., Ste. 700
Irving, TX 75062
Ph: (214)744-6233

Fax: (972)869-2206
E-mail: info@madd.org
URL: http://www.madd.org

Multimedia Resources

1143 ■ Auto Mechanics
RMI Media
1365 N. Winchester
Olathe, KS 66061
Ph: (913)768-1696
Fax: (913)768-0184
E-mail: actmedia@act.org
URL: http://www.rmimedia.com
Format(s): Videocassette. **Descr:** Provides step-by-step instruction in auto mechanics, including set-up procedures, alignment techniques, and brake repair and installation. **Prod. Date:** 1988. **Length:** 10. **Price:** $75.

1144 ■ Automobile Safety
Handel Film Corp.
8787 Shoreham Dr., Ste. 609
West Hollywood, CA 90069
Ph: (310)652-3887
Free: 800-395-8990
Fax: (310)657-2746
Format(s): Videocassette. **Descr:** Correct ways to work on cars while they are standing still are explained. **Prod. Date:** 1981. **Length:** 17.

1145 ■ Avoid Repair Ripoffs: How to Find an Honest Mechanic
Cambridge Educational
c/o Films Media Group
PO Box 2053
Princeton, NJ 08843-2053
Free: 800-257-5126
Fax: (609)671-0266
E-mail: custserve@filmsmediagroup.com
URL: http://www.cambridgeol.com
Format(s): Videocassette. **Descr:** People who watch this tape will know if they are being cheated when they get their car fixed. **Prod. Date:** 1988. **Length:** 30. **Price:** $29.95.

1146 ■ Avoiding Collisions: How to Survive the Teenage Driving Years
E-mail: books@amerinursery.com
URL: http://www.amerinursery.com
Format(s): Videocassette. **Descr:** Real life dialogue between parents and teens discussing safe driving issues. **Prod. Date:** 19??. **Length:** 15.

1147 ■ Basic Motorcycle Maintenance Series
International Film Bureau, Inc.
332 S. Michigan Ave
Chicago, IL 60604-4382
Ph: (312)427-4545
Fax: (312)427-4550
Format(s): Videocassette. **Descr:** Basic maintenance checks that should be made on the motorcycle periodically are outlined to help insure the safety of both the bike and the rider. Programs are available individually. **Prod. Date:** 1980. **Length:** 5.

1148 ■ Be Your Own Traffic Policeman
AIMS Multimedia
20765 Superior St
Chatsworth, CA 91311-4409
Ph: (818)773-4300
Free: 800-367-2467
Fax: (818)341-6700
E-mail: info@aims.multimedia.com
URL: http://www.aimsmultimedia.com
Format(s): Videocassette. **Descr:** An animated/live action film detailing traffic safety for kids. **Prod. Date:** 1979. **Length:** 10. **Price:** $125.00.

1149 ■ Before You Buy: How to Inspect a Used Car
Tapeworm Video Distributors
27833 Hopkins Ave., Unit 6
Valencia, CA 91355
Ph: (661)257-4904

Fax: (661)257-4820
E-mail: sales@tapeworm.com
URL: http://www.tapeworm.com
Format(s): Videocassette. **Descr:** Helps the viewer to determine whether the car that they are about to buy is a dependable vehicle or a lemon. Produced by an ASE certified mechanic who has owned a used automobile inspection service since 1993. Also included is a checklist for reviewing used cars before purchase. **Prod. Date:** 1996. **Price:** $14.95.

1150 ■ Buckle Up
BCI Eclipse
810 Lawrence Dr., Ste. 100
Newbury Park, CA 91320
Ph: (805)375-9998
Fax: (805)375-9908
E-mail: info@bcieclipse.com
URL: http://www.navarre.com/bci.aspx
Format(s): Videocassette. **Descr:** Crash test dummies Vince and Larry get help from over 100 celebrities as they promote the use of seat belts. Includes a performance by The Fifth Dimension. **Prod. Date:** 1988. **Length:** 22. **Price:** $19.99.

1151 ■ Burglar-Proofing Your Home and Car
Cambridge Educational
c/o Films Media Group
PO Box 2053
Princeton, NJ 08843-2053
Free: 800-257-5126
Fax: (609)671-0266
E-mail: custserve@filmsmediagroup.com
URL: http://www.cambridgeol.com
Format(s): Videocassette. **Descr:** With the ever-increasing rates of car and house vandalism, this tape shows Joe Average how to fight back and protect what is his. **Prod. Date:** 1988. **Length:** 55. **Price:** $19.95.

1152 ■ Buying a Used Car
RMI Media
1365 N. Winchester
Olathe, KS 66061
Ph: (913)768-1696
Fax: (913)768-0184
E-mail: actmedia@act.org
URL: http://www.rmimedia.com
Format(s): Videocassette. **Descr:** A program designed to prepare teenagers and others interested in purchasing a used car and familiarizes viewer with a car's main systems: engine, brakes, steering, power train, cooling, electrical, and auto body condition, and provides tips on routine maintenance, insurance budgeting, licensing, taxes, and operation. **Prod. Date:** 1988. **Length:** 17.

1153 ■ The Cambridge Car Buying System
Cambridge Educational
c/o Films Media Group
PO Box 2053
Princeton, NJ 08843-2053
Free: 800-257-5126
Fax: (609)671-0266
E-mail: custserve@filmsmediagroup.com
URL: http://www.cambridgeol.com
Format(s): Videocassette. **Descr:** Presents an overview of the steps a smart buyer takes when buying a car: research, ask advice, investigate, negotiate. Includes a book (which can be purchased separately for $8.95). **Prod. Date:** 1992. **Length:** 30. **Price:** $79.95.

1154 ■ The Car That's Right For You
Cambridge Educational
c/o Films Media Group
PO Box 2053
Princeton, NJ 08843-2053
Free: 800-257-5126
Fax: (609)671-0266
E-mail: custserve@filmsmediagroup.com
URL: http://www.cambridgeol.com
Format(s): Videocassette. **Descr:** Outlines important information for car shoppers, such as the value of checklists, price negotiation, and finance. Also identi-

fies the responsibilities involved with car ownership. **Prod. Date:** 1991. **Length:** 15. **Price:** $89.

1155 ■ The Car of Your Dreams
Pyramid Media
PO Box 1048/WEB
Santa Monica, CA 90406
Ph: (310)828-7577
Free: 800-421-2304
Fax: (310)453-9083
E-mail: info@pyramedia.com
URL: http://www.pyramidmedia.com
Format(s): Videocassette. **Descr:** A look at the history of automobile marketing in America, and how it manipulates the customer. **Prod. Date:** 1985. **Length:** 18. **Price:** $375.

1156 ■ The Carr Buying System
Cambridge Educational
c/o Films Media Group
PO Box 2053
Princeton, NJ 08843-2053
Free: 800-257-5126
Fax: (609)671-0266
E-mail: custserve@filmsmediagroup.com
URL: http://www.cambridgeol.com
Format(s): Videocassette. **Descr:** Former car sales manager Gary Carr explains to people how to avoid getting stuck with a high-priced lemon. Comes with an audio tape and a book. **Prod. Date:** 1988. **Length:** 90. **Price:** $79.95.

1157 ■ Coaching the Emergency Vehicle Operator: Ambulance
National Safety Council
1121 Spring Lake Dr
Itasca, IL 60143-3201
Ph: (630)285-1121
Free: 800-621-7619
Fax: (630)285-1315
E-mail: info@nsc.org
URL: http://www.nsc.org
Format(s): Videocassette. **Descr:** Ambulance drivers are frequently also accident victims themselves. Program is part of a comprehensive course determined to put ambulance vehicle operators back in the driver's seat, and keep them out of harm's way. Comes with discussion slides illustrating actual crash situations and leader's guide. **Price:** $325.00.

1158 ■ Coaching the Emergency Vehicle Operator: Ambulance: Maneuvering Skills
National Safety Council
1121 Spring Lake Dr
Itasca, IL 60143-3201
Ph: (630)285-1121
Free: 800-621-7619
Fax: (630)285-1315
E-mail: info@nsc.org
URL: http://www.nsc.org
Format(s): Videocassette. **Descr:** Learn how to drive through riots, earthquakes, and other upheavals. Instructs in how to set up a test site and figure your way around the inspection, the drop test, safety procedures and course set-up. **Price:** $215.00.

1159 ■ Coaching the Emergency Vehicle Operator: Ambulance: Supplement—Driving Under Lights and Sirens
National Safety Council
1121 Spring Lake Dr
Itasca, IL 60143-3201
Ph: (630)285-1121
Free: 800-621-7619
Fax: (630)285-1315
E-mail: info@nsc.org
URL: http://www.nsc.org
Format(s): Videocassette. **Descr:** Displays techniques for driving under special conditions frequently encountered. Shows how to deal with tailgaters, pedestrians, intersections, passing, and more.

Comes with case study slides and instructor's guide. **Prod. Date:** 19??. **Length:** 60. **Price:** $160.00.

1160 ■ *Coaching the Emergency Vehicle Operator: Fire*
National Safety Council
1121 Spring Lake Dr
Itasca, IL 60143-3201
Ph: (630)285-1121
Free: 800-621-7619
Fax: (630)285-1315
E-mail: info@nsc.org
URL: http://www.nsc.org
Format(s): Videocassette. **Descr:** Vehicle collisions are even more of a threat to firetruck drivers than the rest of us. Takes a close look at this oft-overlooked aspect of an already dangerous profession. Comes with discussion slides and leader's guide. **Prod. Date:** 19??. **Length:** ?. **Price:** $336.00.

1161 ■ *Coaching the Emergency Vehicle Operator: Fire—Maneuvering Skills*
National Safety Council
1121 Spring Lake Dr
Itasca, IL 60143-3201
Ph: (630)285-1121
Free: 800-621-7619
Fax: (630)285-1315
E-mail: info@nsc.org
URL: http://www.nsc.org
Format(s): Videocassette. **Descr:** Instructs driving of firetrucks, executing a thorough vehicle inspection, and more. Comes with detailed administrator's guide. **Prod. Date:** 19??. **Length:** ?. **Price:** $215.00.

1162 ■ *Coaching the Emergency Vehicle Operator: Fire—Supplement*
National Safety Council
1121 Spring Lake Dr
Itasca, IL 60143-3201
Ph: (630)285-1121
Free: 800-621-7619
Fax: (630)285-1315
E-mail: info@nsc.org
URL: http://www.nsc.org
Format(s): Videocassette. **Descr:** Features fire vehicles and interviews with firefighters. Shows how lights and sirens can affect firefighter's driving behavior. Studies actual cases of collisions that resulted in litigation. Comes with detailed instructor's guide. **Prod. Date:** 19??. **Length:** 60. **Price:** $160.00.

1163 ■ *Coaching the Emergency Vehicle Operator: Police*
National Safety Council
1121 Spring Lake Dr
Itasca, IL 60143-3201
Ph: (630)285-1121
Free: 800-621-7619
Fax: (630)285-1315
E-mail: info@nsc.org
URL: http://www.nsc.org
Format(s): Videocassette. **Descr:** Part of a comprehensive course teaching police vehicle drivers how to recognize and respond to driving hazards in emergency and non-emergency situations. Gives special driving techniques for a variety of circumstances. Comes with discussion slides illustrating actual crash situations, and leader's guide. **Prod. Date:** 19??. **Length:** ?. **Price:** $350.00.

1164 ■ *Coaching the Emergency Vehicle Operator: Police: Supplement—Driving Under Lights and Sirens*
National Safety Council
1121 Spring Lake Dr
Itasca, IL 60143-3201
Ph: (630)285-1121
Free: 800-621-7619
Fax: (630)285-1315
E-mail: info@nsc.org
URL: http://www.nsc.org
Format(s): Videocassette. **Descr:** Police vehicle operators are increasingly being injured in emergency situations, raising the need for heightened awareness of the hazards of responding to the call of duty. Studies concepts of speed and environment. Comes with slides illustrating actual emergency situations, and instructor's guide. **Prod. Date:** 19??. **Length:** 60. **Price:** $160.00.

1165 ■ *Coaching the Maintenance Vehicle Operator*
National Safety Council
1121 Spring Lake Dr
Itasca, IL 60143-3201
Ph: (630)285-1121
Free: 800-621-7619
Fax: (630)285-1315
E-mail: info@nsc.org
URL: http://www.nsc.org
Format(s): Videocassette. **Descr:** Shows front loaders, dumptrucks, and other maintenance vehicles being driven in a safe and effective manner. Intended as part of driving course for municipal workers. Written materials available separately. **Prod. Date:** 19??. **Length:** ?. **Price:** $365.00.

1166 ■ *The Company Car*
URL: http://www.lasafety.org
Format(s): Videocassette. **Descr:** A safety program for drivers of company owned cars which are prime causes of injuries, property damage and fatalities. **Length:** 15. **Price:** $445.

1167 ■ *Defensive Driving Techniques*
Gun Video
4585 Murphy Canyon Rd
San Diego, CA 92123
Ph: (858)569-4000
Free: 800-942-8273
Fax: (858)569-0505
E-mail: info2@gunvideo.com
URL: http://www.gunvideo.com
Format(s): Videocassette. **Descr:** Advice on high-speed driving from expert instructors. **Prod. Date:** 19??. **Length:** 60. **Price:** $49.95.

1168 ■ *Drinking and Driving: What Teens Should Know*
Cambridge Educational
c/o Films Media Group
PO Box 2053
Princeton, NJ 08843-2053
Free: 800-257-5126
Fax: (609)671-0266
E-mail: custserve@filmsmediagroup.com
URL: http://www.cambridgeol.com
Format(s): Videocassette. **Descr:** A program aimed at students, detailing the hazards of driving while under the influence. **Prod. Date:** 1985. **Length:** 60.

1169 ■ *Drive to Be the Best*
Excellence in Training Corp.
c/o ICON Training
804 Roosevelt St
Polk City, IA 50226
Free: 800-609-0479
URL: http://www.icontraining.com
Format(s): Videocassette. **Descr:** A driver safety training program for those who have to drive for a living. Includes a training leader's guide. **Prod. Date:** 1991. **Length:** 20. **Price:** $495.

1170 ■ *Drive Home a Better Deal: Insider Secrets*
Instructional Video
2219 C St
Lincoln, NE 68502
Ph: (402)475-6570
Free: 800-228-0164
Fax: (402)475-6500
E-mail: feedback@insvideo.com
URL: http://www.insvideo.com
Format(s): Videocassette. **Descr:** Explains various techniques to help the consumer get a better deal when shopping for an automobile. Includes tips on shopping with confidence, negotiating skills, and get-ting the most for your money. Includes a pocket book. **Length:** 55. **Price:** $19.95.

1171 ■ *Driven by Design's Porsche Video Series*
Instructional Video
2219 C St
Lincoln, NE 68502
Ph: (402)475-6570
Free: 800-228-0164
Fax: (402)475-6500
E-mail: feedback@insvideo.com
URL: http://www.insvideo.com
Format(s): Videocassette. **Descr:** Two-part series that teaches the average consumer how to inspect Porsche automobiles so that they can reduce the risks associated with buying a used Porsche. **Prod. Date:** 19??. **Length:** 120.

1172 ■ *Driving Safety*
Gulf Publishing Co.
PO Box 2608
Houston, TX 77252-2608
Ph: (713)520-4448
Free: 800-231-6275
Fax: (713)204-4433
E-mail: csv@gulfpub.com
URL: http://www.gulfpub.com
Format(s): Videocassette. **Descr:** This series is designed for on-site training and is ideal for safety meeting use. **Prod. Date:** 1984. **Length:** 25. **Price:** $195.00.

1173 ■ *Driving to Survive Series*
URL: http://www.lasafety.org
Format(s): Videocassette. **Descr:** A driving safety series for employers that covers all aspects of safe driving. **Prod. Date:** 19??. **Length:** 16. **Price:** $420.00.

1174 ■ *Driving Tips to Avoid Accidents*
Phoenix Learning Group
2349 Chaffee Dr
St. Louis, MO 63146
Ph: (314)569-0211
Free: 800-221-1274
Fax: (314)569-2834
URL: http://www.phoenixlearninggroup.com
Format(s): Videocassette. **Descr:** Shows viewers easily remembered tips for avoiding the most common car accidents. **Prod. Date:** 1979. **Length:** 19.

1175 ■ *Drugs, Drinking, and Driving (2nd edition)*
AIMS Multimedia
20765 Superior St
Chatsworth, CA 91311-4409
Ph: (818)773-4300
Free: 800-367-2467
Fax: (818)341-6700
E-mail: info@aims.multimedia.com
URL: http://www.aimsmultimedia.com
Format(s): Videocassette. **Descr:** This updated film shows driving reaction tests of people subjected to doses of marijuana and alcohol, and demonstrates how dangerous it is to combine the two before driving. **Prod. Date:** 1983. **Length:** 15. **Price:** $195.00.

1176 ■ *Drunk Driving: What Are You Going to Do About It?*
SouthWestern Publishing Co.
5101 Madison Rd
Cincinnati, OH 45227
Ph: (513)271-8811
Free: 800-543-0487
Format(s): Videocassette. **Descr:** A program about drunk driving that sets up a group discussion on the subject. **Prod. Date:** 1984. **Length:** 19.

1177 ■ *The Ford Automobiles*
The Video Collection
PO Box 2284
South Burlington, VT 05407-2284
Format(s): Videocassette. **Descr:** Two-video set chronicles the "golden age of Ford cars." Titles

include: "Ford Motor's Cars of the '50s" and "Ford Mustang." Includes vintage TV commercials and rare footage of early prototypes. One hour and 40 minutes on two videocassettes. **Prod. Date:** 1998. **Length:** 50. **Price:** $34.95.

1178 ■ *Freewayphobia*
Phoenix Learning Group
2349 Chaffee Dr
St. Louis, MO 63146
Ph: (314)569-0211
Free: 800-221-1274
Fax: (314)569-2834
URL: http://www.phoenixlearninggroup.com
Format(s): Videocassette. **Descr:** A view of the evolution of the modern expressway from primitive trails and paths; beginning drivers also learn about problems on the road that begin off the freeway. **Prod. Date:** 1987. **Length:** 15. **Price:** $295.

1179 ■ *Hassle-Free New Car Buying*
United Learning
1560 Sherman Ave., Ste. 100
PO Box 48718
Evanston, IL 60201
Ph: 888-892-3484
Fax: (847)328-6706
E-mail: info@interaccess.com
URL: http://www.unitedlearning.com
Format(s): Videocassette. **Descr:** This lesson in consumer education tells how to avoid shady car dealers and their notorious shenanigans. Caveat Emptor! **Prod. Date:** 1989. **Length:** 28.

1180 ■ *How to Buy a Better Used Car*
Driven by Design
8440 Carmel Valley Rd
Carmel, CA 93923-9538
Ph: (831)625-1393
Fax: (831)625-9342
E-mail: DrByDesign@aol.com
Format(s): Videocassette. **Descr:** Save time and money and eliminate frustration with these helpful tips from experts on the fine art of getting the most car for your money. **Prod. Date:** 1991. **Length:** 45. **Price:** $29.95.

1181 ■ *How to Buy or Lease a New Car*
Karol Media
Hanover Industrial Estates
375 Stewart Rd
PO Box 7600
Wilkes Barre, PA 18773-7600
Ph: (570)822-8899
Free: 800-526-4773
Fax: (570)822-8226
E-mail: sales@karolmedia.com
URL: http://www.karolmedia.com
Format(s): Videocassette. **Descr:** An explanation of buying or leasing a new car, presented in seven simple steps. **Prod. Date:** 1989. **Length:** 30. **Price:** $14.95.

1182 ■ *How to Buy a New Car*
Cambridge Educational
c/o Films Media Group
PO Box 2053
Princeton, NJ 08843-2053
Free: 800-257-5126
Fax: (609)671-0266
E-mail: custserve@filmsmediagroup.com
URL: http://www.cambridgeol.com
Format(s): Videocassette. **Descr:** Everything concerning the purchase of a new car from evaluating the car to finding a bank to checking the car's mileage record is covered. **Prod. Date:** 1989. **Length:** 30. **Price:** $89.00.

1183 ■ *How to Buy the Right New Car at the Right Price*
Instructional Video
2219 C St
Lincoln, NE 68502
Ph: (402)475-6570
Free: 800-228-0164
Fax: (402)475-6500

E-mail: feedback@insvideo.com
URL: http://www.insvideo.com
Format(s): Videocassette. **Descr:** Outlines techniques to help the consumer shop for new cars, including choosing the right car for you, financing, and when to buy. Also discusses the games that salespeople play and offers countermeasures to overcome these tricks of the trade. **Length:** 45. **Price:** $29.95.

1184 ■ *How to Buy a Used Car*
Meridian Education Corp.
2572 Brunswick Ave
Lawrenceville, NJ 08648-4128
Ph: (609)671-1000
Free: 800-727-5507
Fax: 888-340-5507
E-mail: custmserv@meridianeducation.com
URL: http://www.meridianeducation.com
Format(s): Videocassette. **Descr:** A video guide to inspecting a used car before purchase. **Prod. Date:** 1988. **Price:** $89.00.

1185 ■ *How to Buy a Used Car*
Cambridge Educational
c/o Films Media Group
PO Box 2053
Princeton, NJ 08843-2053
Free: 800-257-5126
Fax: (609)671-0266
E-mail: custserve@filmsmediagroup.com
URL: http://www.cambridgeol.com
Format(s): Videocassette. **Descr:** Step-by-step plan for used car shoppers, identifying where to look and what to look for in a car. Demonstrates a body and mechanical inspection and encourages checklists. **Prod. Date:** 1990. **Length:** 45. **Price:** $29.95.

1186 ■ *How to Buy a Used Car without Getting Burned*
Video 11
PO Box 401
Durango, CO 81302
Format(s): Videocassette. **Descr:** Video gives instruction on how to avoid being taken by car salesman. Topics include negotiation skills, uncovering scams, easy car inspections, revealing false advertisements, and more. **Prod. Date:** 1990. **Length:** 30. **Price:** $29.95.

1187 ■ *Internet Roadside Cafe: Episode 6-Electronic Commerce and the Internet*
Library Video Network (LVN)
320 York Rd
Baltimore, MD 21204-5179
Ph: (410)887-2090
Free: 800-441-8273
Fax: (410)887-2091
E-mail: lvn@bcpl.net
URL: http://www.lvn.org
Format(s): Videocassette. **Descr:** Takes an in-depth look at Web business transactions, potential risks, client privacy and security issues by asking businesses and consumers how they do business on the internet. Also contains advice about choosing a secure password, the use of credit cards and a list of interactive sites. **Prod. Date:** 199?. **Length:** 30. **Price:** $39.00.

1188 ■ *Kick the Tires: Finding and Financing a Used Car*
Zenger Media
10200 Jefferson Blvd
Box 802
Culver City, CA 90232
Ph: (310)839-2436
Free: 800-421-4246
Fax: (310)839-2249
E-mail: service@zengermedia.com
URL: http://zengermedia.com
Format(s): Videocassette. **Descr:** Gives advice on how to inspect a car and describes six types of sell-

ers from an individual owner to franchised dealers. **Prod. Date:** 1998. **Length:** 20. **Price:** $95.00.

1189 ■ *Low Riders*
Image Associates
3617 E. Thousand Oaks Blvd., Ste 123
Westlake Village, CA 91362
Ph: (805)777-1106
Fax: (805)777-1136
E-mail: sales@imageassoc.com
URL: http://www.imageassoc.com
Format(s): Videocassette. **Descr:** Designed for a teenage audience, this program deals with suitable alternatives to drinking and driving by dramatizing the story of two teenagers who work hard to customize a car, only to have one of them wreck it during a drunk driving spree. **Prod. Date:** 1984. **Length:** 22.

1190 ■ *Night Driving Tactics*
AIMS Multimedia
20765 Superior St
Chatsworth, CA 91311-4409
Ph: (818)773-4300
Free: 800-367-2467
Fax: (818)341-6700
E-mail: info@aims.multimedia.com
URL: http://www.aimsmultimedia.com
Format(s): Videocassette. **Descr:** This updated program demonstrates how light, mass and motion combine with the physiology of vision and reaction time to drastically alter a night driver's perception. **Prod. Date:** 1984. **Length:** 13.

1191 ■ *One More for the Road?*
Karol Media
Hanover Industrial Estates
375 Stewart Rd
PO Box 7600
Wilkes Barre, PA 18773-7600
Ph: (570)822-8899
Free: 800-526-4773
Fax: (570)822-8226
E-mail: sales@karolmedia.com
URL: http://www.karolmedia.com
Format(s): Videocassette. **Descr:** The number one killer in the United States is drinking and driving. Dave Roever tells parents and teens how this tragedy can be prevented. **Prod. Date:** 19??. **Length:** 45. **Price:** $49.95.

1192 ■ *Open Secrets*
Phoenix Learning Group
2349 Chaffee Dr
St. Louis, MO 63146
Ph: (314)569-0211
Free: 800-221-1274
Fax: (314)569-2834
URL: http://www.phoenixlearninggroup.com
Format(s): Videocassette. **Descr:** A dramatization of three family members waiting in a hospital lounge upon the occasion of an alcohol-related accident involving a fourth. **Prod. Date:** 1985. **Length:** 25.

1193 ■ *Our Own Road*
Aquarius Productions
Olde Medfield Sq
18 N Main St
Sherborn, MA 01770
Ph: (508)650-1616
Free: 888-440-2963
Fax: (508)650-1665
E-mail: tm@aquariusproductions.com
URL: http://www.aquariusproductions.com
Format(s): Videocassette. **Descr:** Discusses the importance of helping disabled people be independent and productive in their daily life. **Prod. Date:** 2000. **Length:** 28. **Price:** $99.00.

1194 ■ *Please God, I'm Only 17*
SVE & Churchill Media
6465 N. Avondale Ave
Chicago, IL 60631
Ph: (773)775-9433
Free: 800-253-2788
Fax: 800-444-9855

E-mail: custserv@clearvue.com
URL: http://www.clearvue.com

Format(s): Videocassette. **Descr:** Carefree 17-year-old boy who believes that nothing will come of driving recklessly ends up at the hospital in critical condition. Emphasizes that age is not an indicator of invincibility and that everyone is vulnerable to harm, no matter what their age. Includes teacher's guide. **Prod. Date:** 1992. **Length:** 37. **Price:** $275.

1195 ■ Porsche 356 Close-up
Driven by Design
8440 Carmel Valley Rd
Carmel, CA 93923-9538
Ph: (831)625-1393
Fax: (831)625-9342
E-mail: DrByDesign@aol.com

Format(s): Videocassette. **Descr:** Over two dozen body inspections and nearly 50 mechanical ones are featured here. Don't buy a Porsche without knowing the ABCs about them. That is where this informative and money saving video inspection guide comes in. **Prod. Date:** 1990. **Length:** 45. **Price:** $39.95.

1196 ■ Porsche 911 & 930 Close-up
Driven by Design
8440 Carmel Valley Rd
Carmel, CA 93923-9538
Ph: (831)625-1393
Fax: (831)625-9342
E-mail: DrByDesign@aol.com

Format(s): Videocassette. **Descr:** A quality inspection video for the first time used Porsche buyer. Includes a step by step worksheet and method of examining a Porsche before taking the big step of purchasing. **Prod. Date:** 1990. **Length:** 75. **Price:** $39.95.

1197 ■ Proud Owners of Mustangs
Tapeworm Video Distributors
27833 Hopkins Ave., Unit 6
Valencia, CA 91355
Ph: (661)257-4904
Fax: (661)257-4820
E-mail: sales@tapeworm.com
URL: http://www.tapeworm.com

Format(s): Videocassette. **Descr:** Five privately owned Ford Mustangs are examined, including modifications that have been made to the cars. Features an upbeat soundtrack and beautiful models. **Prod. Date:** 1996. **Length:** 28. **Price:** $14.95.

1198 ■ Ride of Your Life
E-mail: books@amerinursery.com
URL: http://www.amerinursery.com
Format(s): Videocassette. **Descr:** Outlines the need for automobile safety as presented by Roger Penske, Rick Mears, Danny Sullivan, Lyn St. James, and Al Unser Sr. **Length:** 24.

1199 ■ Risks and Rewards of Purchasing a Grey Market Car
SmartPros LTD
12 Skyline Dr
Hawthorne, NY 10532
Ph: (914)345-2620
Free: 800-621-0043
URL: http://www.smartpros.com

Format(s): Videocassette. **Descr:** A comprehensive view of the ins and outs of grey market cars, and their viability for the individual consumer. **Prod. Date:** 1985. **Length:** 50.

1200 ■ The Roadbuilders
International Film Bureau, Inc.
332 S. Michigan Ave
Chicago, IL 60604-4382
Ph: (312)427-4545
Fax: (312)427-4550

Format(s): Videocassette. **Descr:** As a highway superintendent hears a song by his favorite group, little does he know that the group is about to have

an accident in this program about safety. **Prod. Date:** 198?. **Length:** 20.

1201 ■ Safety in the Auto Shop
Bergwall Productions, Inc.
1224 Baltimore Pike, Ste. 203
Kennett Square, PA 19317
Ph: (610)361-0334
Free: 800-934-8696
Fax: (610)361-0092
E-mail: bergwall@bergwall.com
URL: http://www.bergwall.com

Format(s): Videocassette. **Descr:** This safety program shows how to be accident free in a body shop. **Prod. Date:** 1985. **Length:** 8. **Price:** $299.00.

1202 ■ Safety Belts
International Film Bureau, Inc.
332 S. Michigan Ave
Chicago, IL 60604-4382
Ph: (312)427-4545
Fax: (312)427-4550

Format(s): Videocassette. **Descr:** This program demonstrates the importance of wearing a safety belt in construction work and how the belts are made. **Prod. Date:** 198?. **Length:** 24.

1203 ■ The SMART Buyer's Guide to Purchasing a New Car
Silver Mine Video Inc.
31316 Via Colinas, Ste. 104
Westlake Village, CA 91362-3905
Ph: (818)707-0300
URL: http://www.quicksilverrecords.zoomshare.com

Format(s): Videocassette. **Descr:** Protect yourself from dishonest car salesmen with this easy to understand video. Describes car dealership scams and gives advice for purchasing your new car at the lowest possible price. **Prod. Date:** 1990. **Length:** 51. **Price:** $29.95.

1204 ■ Survival Driving
Williams Learning Network
15400 Calhoun Dr
Rockville, MD 20855-2762
Ph: (301)315-6700
Free: 800-848-1717
Fax: (301)315-6880
E-mail: mait@willearn.com
URL: http://www.willearn.com

Format(s): Videocassette. **Descr:** Eleven-section series that centers on defensive driving techniques for large trucks, both on- and off-road. Covers weather and terrain, roads, traffic, accidents, and losing control. Includes Instructor's Manual and 10 Student Workbooks. **Prod. Date:** 19??. **Length:** 86.

1205 ■ Surviving Winter Driving
National Safety Council
1121 Spring Lake Dr
Itasca, IL 60143-3201
Ph: (630)285-1121
Free: 800-621-7619
Fax: (630)285-1315
E-mail: info@nsc.org
URL: http://www.nsc.org

Format(s): Videocassette. **Descr:** Covers loading for winter conditions, vehicle condition, starting, curves, turns, braking, jackknifing, skids, and emergency equipment. **Prod. Date:** 1988. **Length:** 10.

1206 ■ Targets
Phoenix Learning Group
2349 Chaffee Dr
St. Louis, MO 63146
Ph: (314)569-0211
Free: 800-221-1274
Fax: (314)569-2834
URL: http://www.phoenixlearninggroup.com

Format(s): Videocassette. **Descr:** Five teenagers emerge from an auto wreck into Victim School, where an angel will decide their fate, in this caution-

ary dramatization for young people grades 7 to 12. **Prod. Date:** 1986. **Length:** 19.

1207 ■ Think Safety Driving System (TSDS)
Williams Learning Network
15400 Calhoun Dr
Rockville, MD 20855-2762
Ph: (301)315-6700
Free: 800-848-1717
Fax: (301)315-6880
E-mail: mait@willearn.com
URL: http://www.willearn.com

Format(s): Videocassette. **Descr:** Seven-part program that provides all the information needed for a company to conduct a 2-, 4-, or 8-hour driver training course for their employees. Includes pre-test, three proficiency quizzes, Instructor's Guide, and ten Student Handout Kits. **Prod. Date:** 19??. **Length:** 83.

1208 ■ Those Incredible Alcos, Vol. 1: Diesel Dinosaur Delights - The Early Years
Pentrex Media Group
PO Box 94911
Pasadena, CA 91109-4911
Ph: (626)793-3400
Free: 800-950-9333
Fax: (626)793-3797
E-mail: pentrex@pentrex.com
URL: http://www.pentrex.com

Format(s): Videocassette. **Descr:** Covers the early history of Alco diesel locomotives. **Prod. Date:** 1998. **Length:** 117. **Price:** $29.95.

1209 ■ Three for the Road Series
International Film Bureau, Inc.
332 S. Michigan Ave
Chicago, IL 60604-4382
Ph: (312)427-4545
Fax: (312)427-4550

Format(s): Videocassette. **Descr:** This series examines the "safe driving" techniques and teaches the viewer about the effects of alcohol. **Prod. Date:** 1983. **Length:** 20.

1210 ■ Tofino: The Road Stops Here
Moving Images Distribution
402 W. Pender St., Ste. 606
Vancouver, BC, Canada V6B 1T6
Ph: (604)684-3014
Fax: (604)684-7165
E-mail: mailbox@movingimages.ca
URL: http://www.movingimages.bc.ca

Format(s): Videocassette. **Descr:** Tofino, a small logging village situated on Canada's West Coast, has been the scene of some of the country's oldest and most famous environmental standoffs. The town also plays host to an increasing tourist industry. This portrait of a community in transition features interviews with long-term residents, environmentalists and loggers who are forced to live with each other as neighbors and the changing future of Tofino. **Prod. Date:** 1996. **Length:** 30.

1211 ■ Traffic Watcher
Encyclopedia Britannica
331 N. LaSalle St
Chicago, IL 60610
Ph: (312)347-7159
Free: 800-323-1229
Fax: (312)294-2104
URL: http://www.britannica.com

Format(s): Videocassette. **Descr:** Captain Dan, a traffic reporter for a radio station, teaches young kids how to avoid accidents when near streets. **Prod. Date:** 1988. **Length:** 15. **Price:** $240.00.

1212 ■ 20 Keys to Buying a Used Car
Tapeworm Video Distributors
27833 Hopkins Ave., Unit 6
Valencia, CA 91355
Ph: (661)257-4904
Fax: (661)257-4820
E-mail: sales@tapeworm.com
URL: http://www.tapeworm.com

Format(s): Videocassette. **Descr:** Provides all the

structural, mechanical and legal information you will need to save money and time when purchasing a used vehicle. **Prod. Date:** 1994. **Length:** 45. **Price:** $19.95.

1213 ■ *Until I Get Caught*
Kinetic Film Enterprises Ltd.
255 Delaware Ave
Buffalo, NY 14202
Ph: (716)856-7631
E-mail: info@kineticinc.com
URL: http://www.kineticinc.com
Format(s): Videocassette. **Descr:** This program provides a realistic view of issues related to drinking and driving. **Prod. Date:** 1984. **Length:** 28. **Price:** $425.

1214 ■ *Winter Driving Tactics*
AIMS Multimedia
20765 Superior St
Chatsworth, CA 91311-4409
Ph: (818)773-4300
Free: 800-367-2467
Fax: (818)341-6700
E-mail: info@aims.multimedia.com
URL: http://www.aimsmultimedia.com
Format(s): Videocassette. **Descr:** Demonstrates precautions necessary when driving on icy and snowy roads. **Prod. Date:** 198?. **Length:** 16. **Price:** $295.00.

Media Contacts

1215 ■ "Click and Clack Talk Cars Column"
King Features
300 W. 57th St., 15th Fl.
New York, NY 10019
Contact: Tom Magliozzi, Columnist
Ph: (212)969-7550
URL: http://www.kingfeatures.com

1216 ■ "Click and Clack Talk Cars Column"
King Features
300 W. 57th St., 15th Fl.
New York, NY 10019
Contact: Ray Magliozzi, Columnist
Ph: (212)969-7550
URL: http://www.kingfeatures.com

1217 ■ *USA Today*
Gannett Co., Inc.
10960 Wilshire Blvd., Ste. 1000
Los Angeles, CA 90024
Contact: Chris Woodyard, Automotive Reporter
Ph: (310)882-2403
E-mail: cwoodyard@usatoday.com
URL: http://www.usatoday.com

California

1218 ■ *Los Angeles Times*
Tribune Company
202 W. First St.
Los Angeles, CA 90012
Contact: Ken Bensinger, Automobiles Writer
Ph: (213)237-7163
E-mail: ken.bensinger@latimes.com
URL: http://www.latimes.com

Illinois

1219 ■ *The Chicago Sun-Times*
Hollinger International, Inc.
350 N. Orleans
Chicago, IL 60654
Contact: Dan Jedlicka, Automotive Editor
Ph: (312)321-2638
E-mail: djedlicka@suntimes.com
URL: http://www.suntimes.com

Michigan

1220 ■ *Detroit News*
MediaNews Group
615 W. Lafayette Blvd.
Detroit, MI 48226
Contact: Christine Tierney, Foreign Auto Editor
Ph: (313)222-1463
E-mail: ctierney@detnews.com
URL: http://www.detnews.com

1221 ■ *Detroit News*
MediaNews Group
615 W. Lafayette Blvd.
Detroit, MI 48226
Contact: Alisa Priddle, Auto Reporter (Chrysler)
Ph: (313)222-2504
E-mail: apriddle@detnews.com
URL: http://www.detnews.com

1222 ■ *Detroit News*
MediaNews Group
615 W. Lafayette Blvd.
Detroit, MI 48226
Contact: Scott Burgess, Automotive Critic
Ph: (313)223-3217
E-mail: sburgess@detnews.com
URL: http://www.detnews.com

Ohio

1223 ■ *The Cincinnati Enquirer*
Gannett Co., Inc.
312 Elm St.
Cincinnati, OH 45202-2739
Contact: Mike Boyer, Automotive Reporter
Ph: (513)755-4143
E-mail: mboyer@enquirer.com
URL: http://www.enquirer.com

1224 ■ *Dayton Daily News*
Cox Newspapers, Inc.
45 S. Ludlow St.
Dayton, OH 45402
Contact: Thomas Gnau, Automotive/Labor Reporter
Ph: (937)225-2390
E-mail: tgnau@daytondailynews.com
URL: http://www.daytondailynews.com

Rhode Island

1225 ■ *The Providence Journal*
A.H. Belo Corporation
75 Fountain St.
Providence, RI 02902
Contact: Peter CT Elsworth, Automotive Reporter
Ph: (401)277-7179
Fax: (401)277-7346
E-mail: pelsworth@projo.com
URL: http://www.projo.com

Texas

1226 ■ *Wheels with Ed Wallace*
KLIF-AM
Susquehanna Radio Corporation
3500 Maple Ave., Ste. 1600
Dallas, TX 75219
Contact: Ed Wallace, Host
Ph: (214)526-2400
Free: 800-823-8255
URL: http://www.klif.com
Descr: Radio program offering expertise in cars and auto repair.

Corporate Contacts

1227 ■ AAMCO Transmissions, Inc.
Consumer Affairs
201 Gilbraltar Rd.
Horsham, PA 19044
Contact: Anna Wright
Ph: (610)668-2900
Free: 800-292-8500

Fax: (610)664-5897
E-mail: awright@AAMCO.com
URL: http://www.aamco.com

1228 ■ Acura
Customer Relations Dept.
1919 Torrance Blvd. 500-2N-7E
Torrance, CA 90501-2746
Free: 800-382-2238
Fax: (310)783-3535
URL: http://www.acura.com
Telecom. Svcs: For roadside assistance, call toll-free (800)594-8500.

1229 ■ Alfa Romeo Distributors of North America, Inc.
7453 Brokerage Dr.
Orlando, FL 32809
Ph: (407)856-5000

1230 ■ American Automobile Association
Member Relations
1000 AAA Dr., Mailspace 61
Heathrow, FL 32746
Ph: (407)444-8391
Free: 800-222-6424
Fax: (407)444-8416
URL: http://www.aaa.com

1231 ■ American Suzuki Motor Corp.
Customer Relations Dept.
PO Box 1100
3251 E. Imperial Hwy.
Brea, CA 92822-1100
Ph: (714)572-1490
Free: 800-934-0934
Fax: (714)524-8499
URL: http://www.suzuki.com
Telecom. Svcs: For motorcycles, call (714)996-7040, ext. 380; for automotive only, call toll-free (800)934-0934.

1232 ■ Aston Martin
Customer Relations Department
U.S. National Headquarters
1 Premier Pl.
Irvine, CA 92618
Ph: (949)341-5800
Free: 800-452-4827
Fax: (949)341-6152
URL: http://www.astonmartin.com

1233 ■ Atlantic Richfield Co.
ARCO Products Co.
Manager
4 Center Point Dr.
La Palma, CA 90623
Ph: (213)486-3511
Free: 800-322-2726
URL: http://www.arco.com

1234 ■ Audi of America, Inc.
Customer Care
2200 Ferdinand Porsche Dr.
Herndon, VA 20171
Free: 800-367-2834
URL: http://www.audiusa.com

1235 ■ BMW of North America, Inc.
Corporate Office
Customer Relations
300 Chestnut Ridge Rd.
Woodcliff Lake, NJ 07677-7731
Ph: (201)307-4000
Free: 800-831-1117
Fax: (201)930-8362
URL: http://www.bmwusa.com

1236 ■ BP Corporation
Consumer Relations
501 West Lake Park Blvd.
Houston, TX 77079-2604
Ph: (281)366-2000
Free: 800-333-3991
Fax: (630)300-5254
E-mail: bpconsum@bp.com
URL: http://www.bp.com

Telecom. Svcs: For credit card use, call toll-free (800)227-3329; for club emergency services, call (800)782-7787.

1237 ■ Bridgestone Firestone Retail & Commercial Operations, LLC
Consumer Affairs
PO Box 7988
Chicago, IL 60680-9534
Free: 800-367-3872
Fax: 800-760-7859
E-mail: firestone_consumer_affairs@faneuil.com
URL: http://www.firestonecompleteautocare.com

1238 ■ Buick Division, General Motors Corp.
Customer Assistance Ctr.
PO Box 33136
Detroit, MI 48232-5136
Ph: (313)556-5000
Free: 800-521-7300
URL: http://www.buick.com
Telecom. Svcs: TDD toll-free: 800-832-8425; for roadside assistance, call toll-free (800)252-1112.

1239 ■ Cadillac Motor Car Division
Customer Assistance Ctr.
PO Box 33169
Detroit, MI 48232-5169
Free: 800-458-8006
URL: http://www.cadillac.com
Telecom. Svcs: TDD toll free: (800)833-2622; for roadside assistance, call toll-free (800)882-1112.

1240 ■ CARFAX, Inc.
Consumer Affairs
10304 Eaton Pl., Ste. 500
Fairfax, VA 22030
Ph: (703)218-0340
Fax: (866)728-6455
E-mail: carfaxwebsupport@carfax.com
URL: http://www.carfax.com/help

1241 ■ Chevrolet Motor Division, General Motors Corp.
Customer Assistance Ctr.
PO Box 33170
Detroit, MI 48232-5170
Free: 800-222-1020
Fax: (313)556-5108
URL: http://www.chevrolet.com
Telecom. Svcs: TDD toll-free: (800)833-2438

1242 ■ Chevron Corp.
Consumer Connection Center
6001 Bollinger Canyon Rd.
San Ramon, CA 94583
Contact: Melanie Leach
Ph: (925)842-1000
Free: 800-962-1223
E-mail: comment@chevron.com
URL: http://www.chevron.com

1243 ■ Columbia Gas of Ohio
PO Box 117
200 Civic Center Dr.
Columbus, OH 43216-0117
Free: 800-344-4077
Fax: (614)450-5502
URL: http://www.columbiagasohio.com
Telecom. Svcs: TDD/TTY: 977-460-2443.

1244 ■ Continental Tire North America, Inc.
Consumer Relations
1800 Continental Blvd.
Charlotte, NC 28273
Contact: Ron Forsyth
Free: 800-847-3349
Fax: 888-847-3329
URL: http://www.continentaltire.com

1245 ■ Daihatsu America, Inc.
Consumer Affairs Dept.
28 Centerpointe Dr., Ste. 120
La Palma, CA 90623
Ph: (714)690-4700
Free: 800-777-7070

Fax: (714)952-4720
URL: http://www.daihatsu.com/

1246 ■ Daimler Chrysler
Daimler Chrysler Customer Ctr.
PO Box 21-8004
Auburn Hills, MI 48321-8004
Free: 800-992-1997
Fax: (248)512-8084
URL: http://www.chrysler.com

1247 ■ Exxon Mobil
Customer Relations
Fuels Marketing Company
PO Box 1049
Buffalo, NY 14240-1049
Free: 800-243-9966
URL: http://www.exxonmobil.com

1248 ■ Ferrari North America, Inc.
Corporate Office
250 Sylvan Ave.
Englewood Cliffs, NJ 07632
Ph: (201)816-2600
Fax: (201)816-2626
E-mail: administrative@ferrariworld.com
URL: http://www.ferrariworld.com

1249 ■ Ford Motor Co.
Customer Relationship Center
16800 Executive Plaza Dr.
PO Box 6248
Dearborn, MI 48121
Free: 800-392-3673
URL: http://www.ford.com

1250 ■ General Motors Acceptance Corp. (GMAC)
PO Box 380901
Bloomington, MN 55438
Free: 800-200-4622
Fax: (248)879-4134
URL: http://www.gmacfs.com

1251 ■ General Motors Corp.
Corporate Affairs/Community Relations
100 Renaissance Ctr.
Detroit, MI 48265
Ph: (313)667-3800
Free: 800-462-8782
URL: http://www.gmc.com

1252 ■ GMC Division General Motors Corp.
Customer Assistance
PO Box 33172
Detroit, MI 48232-5172
Free: 800-462-8782
URL: http://www.gmc.com

1253 ■ Goodrich Corporation
Consumer Care Department
PO Box 19001
Greenville, SC 29602-9001
Free: 877-788-8899
URL: http://www.bfgoodrichtires.com

1254 ■ The Goodyear Tire & Rubber Co.
Department 728
1144 E. Market St.
Akron, OH 44316-0001
Ph: (330)796-2121
Free: 800-321-2136
Fax: (330)796-2222
URL: http://www.goodyear.com

1255 ■ Hyundai Motor America
Consumer Affairs
10550 Talbert Ave.
PO Box 20850
Fountain Valley, CA 92708-0850
Ph: (714)965-3000
Free: 800-633-5151
Fax: (714)965-3861

E-mail: cmd@hma.service.com
URL: http://cmd@hma.service.com

1256 ■ Isuzu Motors America, Inc.
Owner Relations Dept.
13340 183rd St.
Cerritos, CA 90702
Ph: (562)229-5000
Free: 800-255-6727
Fax: (562)921-9523
URL: http://www.isuzu.com

1257 ■ Jeep/Eagle Division of Chrysler Corp.
Customer Relations
PO Box 21-8004
Auburn Hills, MI 48321
Free: 800-992-1997
Fax: (248)512-8084
URL: http://www-5.jeep.com/webselfservice/jeep/index.jsp

1258 ■ Jiffy Lube International, Inc.
Customer Service
PO Box 4458
Houston, TX 77210-4458
Ph: (713)546-4100
Free: 800-344-6933
URL: http://www.jiffylube.com

1259 ■ Kawasaki Motor Corp., USA
Consumer Services
PO Box 25252
Santa Ana, CA 92799-5252
Ph: (949)460-5688
Free: 800-661-RIDE
URL: http://www.kawasaki.com

1260 ■ Lexus
PO Box 2991
Mail Drop L201
Torrance, CA 90509-2991
Free: 800-255-3987
Fax: (310)468-2992
URL: http://www.lexus.com

1261 ■ MAACO Enterprises, Inc.
381 Brooks Rd.
King of Prussia, PA 19406
Ph: (610)265-6606
Free: 800-523-1180
URL: http://www.maaco.com

1262 ■ Mazda North American Operations
Customer Assistance Center
PO Box 19734
Irvine, CA 92623-9734
Free: 800-222-5500
Fax: (949)727-6703
URL: http://www.mazdausa.com

1263 ■ Meinecke Car Care Centers, Inc.
Customer Relations Dept.
128 S. Tryon St., Ste. 900
Charlotte, NC 28202-2401
Ph: (704)377-3070
Free: 800-447-3070
URL: http://www.meineke.com

1264 ■ Mercedes Benz USA, Inc.
Customer Assistance Ctr.
3 Mercedes Dr.
Montvale, NJ 07645
Free: 800-367-6372
Fax: (201)476-6213
URL: http://www.mbusa.com
Telecom. Svcs: Additional toll-free: (800)367-6372.

1265 ■ Michelin North America, Inc.
Consumer Relations Dept.
PO Box 19001
Greenville, SC 29602-9001
Free: 800-847-3435
URL: http://www.michelin-us.com

1266 ■ Midas Inc.
Consumer Relations
1300 Arlington Heights Blvd.
Itasca, IL 60143

Free: 800-621-8545
URL: http://www.midas.com

1267 ■ Mitsubishi Motor North America, Inc.
Customer Relations
6400 Katella Ave.
Cypress, CA 90630-0064
Free: 888-648-7820
URL: http://www.mitsubishimotors.com

1268 ■ Mobil
ExxonMobil Customer Relations
436 Creamery Way, Ste. 300
Exton, PA 19341
Free: 800-243-9966
URL: http://www.mobil.com

1269 ■ Nissan Motor Corp. in U.S.A.
Consumer Affairs Group
PO Box 685003
Franklin, TN 37068-5003
Ph: (310)532-3111
Free: 800-647-7261
Fax: (310)771-2025
URL: http://www.nissanusa.com

1270 ■ Oldsmobile Division, General Motors Corp.
Customer Assistance Network
PO Box 33171
Detroit, MI 48232-5171
Free: 800-442-6537
URL: http://www.oldsmobile.com
Telecom. Svcs: TDD toll-free: (800)833-6537; for roadside assistance, call (800)535-6537.

1271 ■ Pennzoil
Pennzoil Place
PO Box 2967
Houston, TX 77252-2967
Ph: (713)546-4000
Free: 800-990-9811
URL: http://www.pennzoil.com

1272 ■ Pep Boys Auto
311 W. Allegheny Ave.
Philadelphia, PA 06851
Free: 800-737-2697
Fax: (205)430-4622
E-mail: custserv@pepboys.com
URL: http://www.pepboys.com

1273 ■ Peugeot Motors of America, Inc.
Consumer Relations
Overlook at Great Notch
150 Clove Rd.
Little Falls, NJ 07424
Ph: (973)812-4444
Free: 800-345-5549
Fax: (973)812-2148
E-mail: customerservice@peugeotusa.net
URL: http://www.peugeot.com

1274 ■ Phillips Petroleum Co.
PO Box 1267
Ponca City, OK 74602

Ph: (918)661-1215
Free: 800-527-5476
Fax: (918)662-2075
URL: http://p66conoco76.conocophillips.com/index.htm

1275 ■ Pirelli Tire Corp.
100 Pirelli Dr.
Rome, GA 30161
Ph: (706)368-5800
Free: 800-747-3554
Fax: (706)368-5832
E-mail: consumer.affairs@us.pirelli.com
URL: http://www.us.pirelli.com

1276 ■ Pontiac Division, General Motors Corp.
Customer Assistance Ctr.
PO Box 33172
Detroit, MI 48232-5172
Free: 800-762-2737
URL: http://www.pontiac.com
Telecom. Svcs: TDD toll-free: (800)833-7668; for roadside assistance (800)762-3743.

1277 ■ Porsche Cars North America, Inc.
Customer Commitment
Owner Relations
980 Hammond Dr., Ste. 1000
Atlanta, GA 30328
Ph: (770)290-3500
Free: 800-545-8039
Fax: (770)360-3711
URL: http://www.porsche.com

1278 ■ Saab Cars USA, Inc.
Customer Assistance Center
PO Box 33166
Detroit, MI 48232-5166
Ph: (770)279-0100
Free: 800-955-9007
Fax: (770)279-6499
URL: http://www.saabusa.com

1279 ■ Saturn Corp
Saturn Customer Assistance Ctr.
PO Box 33173
Detroit, MI 48232-5173
Free: 800-522-5000
URL: http://www.saturn.com

1280 ■ Shell Oil Co.
ATTN: TellShell US
PO Box 2463
Houston, TX 77252
Ph: (713)241-6161
Free: 888-467-4355
E-mail: ShellCustomerCare@Shell.com
URL: http://www.shellus.com

1281 ■ Subaru of America, Inc.
National Customer Service Ctr.
Subaru Plaza
PO Box 6000
Cherry Hill, NJ 08034
Ph: (856)488-8500
Free: 800-782-2783

Fax: (856)488-0485
URL: http://www.subaru.com

1282 ■ Tenneco, Inc.
500 N. Field Dr.
Lake Forest, IL 60045
Ph: (847)482-5000
Fax: (847)482-5940
URL: http://www.tenneco.com

1283 ■ Toyota Motor Sales, USA, Inc.
Customer Experience Ctr.
Dept. WC11
19001 S. Western Ave.
Torrance, CA 90501
Ph: (310)468-4000
Free: 800-331-4331
Fax: (310)468-7814
URL: http://www.toyota.com
Telecom. Svcs: TDD toll-free: (800)443-4999.

1284 ■ Uniroyal Tires
Consumer Relations
PO Box 19001
Greenville, SC 29602-9001
Free: 877-458-5878
URL: http://www.uniroyal.com

1285 ■ The Valvoline Co.
Customer Service
PO Box 14000
Lexington, KY 40512
Free: 800-TEAM-VAL
URL: http://www.valvoline.com
Telecom. Svcs: Additional toll-free fax: (800)682-6994.

1286 ■ Volkswagen of America
Customer Relations
3800 W. Hamlin Rd.
Auburn Hills, MI 48326-2856
Free: 800-822-8987
Fax: (248)340-4660
URL: http://www.vw.com
Telecom. Svcs: Additional toll-free: (800)822-8987.

1287 ■ Volvo Cars of North America
Customer Care Ctr.
1 Volvo Dr.
Rockleigh, NJ 07647
Free: 800-458-1552
Fax: 800-992-3970
URL: http://www.volvocars.com

1288 ■ Yamaha Motor Corp.
Customer Relations
6555 Katella Ave.
Cypress, CA 90630
Ph: (714)761-7435
Free: 800-962-7926
Fax: (714)761-7730
URL: http://www.yamaha-motor.com

Internet Resources

1289 ■ ABI World
American Bankruptcy Institute
44 Canal Center Plaza, Ste. 400
Alexandria, VA 22314
Contact: Samuel J. Gerdano, Exec.Dir.
Ph: (703)739-0800
Fax: (703)739-1060
E-mail: support@abiworld.org
URL: http://www.abiworld.org

URL(s): www.abiworld.org/ **Descr:** This site provides a valuable resource for those facing the difficult decision to file for bankruptcy. Legislative news, court opinions, and recent headlines are provided, as well as a special section devoted to individuals facing bankruptcy. Listings of certified bankruptcy professionals, including attorneys and valuation experts, are also available. Other resources include an online library, product and service information, an online weekly newsletter, and an online bookstore. **Type:** Full-text; Audio; Video. **Updating freq.:** Daily. **Fees:** Free. **Searching routines or searchable elements:** Search options are available.

1290 ■ AnnualCreditReport.com
Annual Credit Report Request Service
PO Box 105283
Atlanta, GA 30348-5283
URL: http://www.annualcreditreport.com/

Descr: Offers consumers a place to request their free credit report, either online, by phone, or through the mail. Monitoring and reviewing your credit report is an important way to fight identity theft. Service was created by the three nationwide consumer credit reporting companies: Equifax, Experian, and TransUnion.

1291 ■ Bankrate.com
Bankrate.com
11760 U.S. Hwy. 1, Ste. 200
North Palm Beach, FL 33408
Contact: Thomas R. Evans, Pres. & CEO
Ph: (561)630-2400
Fax: (561)625-4540
E-mail: tevans@bankrate.com

URL(s): www.bankrate.com/brm/default.asp **Descr:** Updated constantly, Bankrate.com offers the very latest in rate information, including the current rates being paid by financial institutions on savings accounts and certificates of deposit. You'll also find links to tons of useful articles and Q&A's on saving, budgeting, mortgaging, debt, credit cards, and much more. An online calculator further enhances the value of this site if you're shopping for the most attractive rates available today. **Type:** Full-text; Directory; Image; Statistical. **Updating freq.:** Continuous. **Fees:** Free. **Searching routines or searchable elements:** Keyword searching is available.

1292 ■ Black Enterprise Online
Earl G. Graves, Ltd.
130 Fifth Ave., 10th Fl.

New York, NY 10011-4399
Contact: Earl G. Graves Jr., Pres./CEO
Ph: (212)242-8000
E-mail: customerservice@blackenterprise.com

URL(s): www.blackenterprise.com/ **Descr:** The Black Enterprise (BE) is "the authority on business news, strategies, information and resources for African-American entrepreneurs, corporate executives, managers and professionals." Launched in 1968 by Earl G. Graves, one of America's most successful entrepreneurs, BE's print version now boasts more than 3.1 million readers. BE provides "monthly access to a news analyst, business consultant, consumer advocate, technology specialist, career counselor and financial advisor. BE empowers its readers with award-winning coverage of the following areas key to their economic advancement: Technology; Business News And Trends; Small Business Management; Personal Finance; Career Opportunities And Development; Consumer Affairs." You'll find lots of "top 100" lists and reports, BE events and conference dates and descriptions, books to buy, and even a section to invest in BE online. "Channels" cover the topics of Investing, Small Business, Personal Finance, Career, and the Magazine, with articles, tips, tools, resources and links. Most areas allow reader response through e-mail. **Type:** Full-text; Directory. **Updating freq.:** Monthly. **Fees:** Free online (limited); print subscription is $17.95 per year, or $15.95 when you subscribe online (billing is handled offline). **Searching routines or searchable elements:** Keyword search is available for back issues of BE and a stock quote search by name or symbol is also available.

1293 ■ Credit Union Times
Credit Union Times, Inc.
33-41 Newark St., 2nd Fl.
Hoboken, NJ 07030
Contact: Sarah Snell Cooke, Editor-in-Chief
E-mail: scooke@cutimes.com
Ph: (201)526-1230
Fax: (201)526-1260
E-mail: editor@cutimes.com

URL(s): www.cutimes.com/ **Descr:** An independent credit union industry trade publication. Seeks to provide timely, unbiased news coverage of credit unions and the related financial services industry. A typical article might profile the role credit unions have in community and individual life. **Type:** Full-text. **Updating freq.:** Weekly. **Fees:** Online offerings are free; an annual subscription to the printed edition is $120. **Searching routines or searchable elements:** Searching is not available.

1294 ■ Identity Theft Resource Center Online
Identity Theft Resource Center
PO Box 26833
San Diego, CA 92196
Contact: Rex Davis, Dir. of Operations
Ph: (858)693-7935
E-mail: itrc@idtheftcenter.org

URL(s): www.idtheftcenter.org/ **Descr:** Online site of the firm that is dedicated to the development and

implementation of a comprehensive program against identity theft. Links include Victim Resources, where users can learn the laws and resources available to them; Consumer Resources, which offers prevention tips and an ID theft test; Scam and Consumer Alerts; In the Workplace; and Reference Library. Available in English or Spanish.

1295 ■ InvestmentNews
Crain Communications Inc.
711 Third Ave.
New York, NY 10017
Ph: (212)210-0100
Fax: (212)210-0117
E-mail: info@crain.com
URL: http://www.crain.com

URL(s): www.investmentnews.com/ **Descr:** Contains investment news, articles, and features from the print version of *InvestmentNews*. Includes material for investors, financial planners, investment advisors, and other players in the stock market. Includes interviews, company profiles, investment analysis, calendars of upcoming events, and the latest investment news from around the world. Includes classified advertisements for jobs, services, products, and other resources. Includes news archives search, company reports, and a financial services stock index. **Type:** Full-text; Numeric. **Updating freq.:** Weekly. **Fees:** $29 for an annual subscription U.S.; $103 for an annual subscription Canada/Mexico; $183 for an annual subscription other countries.

1296 ■ Living a Better Life: The Free Money Saving Tips Ezine
BlueRidgePublishing.com
PO Box 795
Powder Springs, GA 30127
Contact: Michelle Jones, Publishing Ed.
Ph: (770)439-8740
E-mail: editor@betterbudgeting.com

URL(s): www.betterbudgeting.com/ **Descr:** Online magazine that offers expertise on saving money on gas, insurance, grocery items, cars, homes, and more. Also has links where users can learn much more about credit reports, dealing with debt, grocery coupons, lowering bills, frugal traveling, and decorating on a budget. In addition, provides a budget calculator and editor's blog. **Type:** Full-text. **Updating freq.:** As needed.

1297 ■ Ripoff Report
PO Box 310
Tempe, AZ 85280
Contact: Ed Magedson, Founder
Ph: (602)359-4357
Fax: (305)832-2949
E-mail: editor@RipOffReport.com

URL(s): www.ripoffreport.com/ **Descr:** Provides a forum for users to post complaints of consumer dealings in which they believe they have been treated unfairly or inadequately. Allows companies that believe they have been branded unfairly to file "rebuttal" reports and to reconnect with the unsatisfied customer. Provides tips on how to avoid consumer scams and protects one's identity.

1298 ■ Wise Bread: Living Large on a Small Budget
URL(s): www.wisebread.com/ **Descr:** Online community where users can share tips on personal finance, frugal living, careers, and money-saving deals. **Type:** Full-text.

Federal Government Agencies

1299 ■ Board of Actuaries of the Civil Service Retirement System
Off. of the Actuaries
Retirement & Insurance Services
Off. of Personnel Management
1900 E St. NW, Rm. 4307
Washington, DC 20415
Ph: (202)606-0722
Fax: (202)606-2711
URL: http://www.opm.gov
Staff: Administrative support is provided by the Office of Actuaries. **Descr:** Board annually reviews the actuarial status of the Civil Service Retirement System and makes recommendations on changes that are necessary to protect the public interest and maintain the System on a sound financial basis. **Mem:** Board is composed of three members, all of whom are actuaries. **Pub:** Board issues actuarial valuations every five years.

1300 ■ Board of Directors, Securities Investor Protection Corporation
805 15th St. NW, Ste. 800
Washington, DC 20005-2215
Contact: Stephen P. Harbeck, Pres. & CEO
Ph: (202)371-8300
Fax: (202)371-6728
E-mail: asksipc@sipc.org
URL: http://www.sipc.org
Staff: Stephen P. Harbeck, President and CEO, Securities Investor Protection Corp., serves as staff contact. **Descr:** Board governs the operations of the Securities Investor Protection Corporation, an independent nonprofit membership corporation, which administers a fund for limited investor protection against financial failures of brokerage firms. **Mem:** Board consists of seven members who serve three-year terms; five are appointed by the President of the United States with the consent of the U.S. Senate and one each by the Secretary of the Treasury and the Federal Reserve Board. Armando J. Bucelo Jr., The Timken Company, chairs the Board.

1301 ■ Commodity Futures Trading Commission
Central Region
525 W. Monroe St., Ste. 1100
Chicago, IL 60661
Ph: (312)596-0700
Fax: (312)596-0716
Descr: Mission is to protect market users and the public from fraud, manipulation, and abusive practices related to the sale of commodity and financial futures and options, and to foster open, competitive, and financially sound futures and option markets. **Telecom. Svcs:** TTY phone number is (312)596-0565.

1302 ■ Commodity Futures Trading Commission
Eastern Region
140 Broadway
New York, NY 10005
Ph: (646)746-9700
Fax: (646)746-9938
Descr: Mission is to protect market users and the public from fraud, manipulation, and abusive practices related to the sale of commodity and financial futures and options, and to foster open, competitive, and financially sound futures and option markets.

Telecom. Svcs: TTY phone number is (646)746-9820.

1303 ■ Commodity Futures Trading Commission
Southwestern Region
510 Grain Exchange Bldg.
Minneapolis, MN 55415
Ph: (612)370-3255
Fax: (612)370-3257
Descr: Mission is to protect market users and the public from fraud, manipulation, and abusive practices related to the sale of commodity and financial futures and options, and to foster open, competitive, and financially sound futures and option markets.

1304 ■ Commodity Futures Trading Commission
Southwestern Region
Two Emanuel Cleaver II Blvd., Ste. 300
Kansas City, MO 64112
Ph: (816)960-7700
Fax: (816)960-7750
Descr: Mission is to protect market users and the public from fraud, manipulation, and abusive practices related to the sale of commodity and financial futures and options, and to foster open, competitive, and financially sound futures and option markets. **Telecom. Svcs:** TTY phone number is (816)960-7704.

1305 ■ Federal Deposit Insurance Corporation
Community Affairs Program
Atlanta Regional Office
10 Tenth St. NE, Ste. 800
Atlanta, GA 30309-3906
Contact: Thomas E. Stokes, Community Affairs Officer
Ph: (678)916-2249
Free: 800-765-3342
E-mail: tstokes@fdic.gov

1306 ■ Federal Deposit Insurance Corporation
Community Affairs Program
Boston Area Office
15 Braintree Hill Office Pk.
Braintree, MA 02184-8701
Contact: Timothy W. DeLessio, Community Affairs Officer
Ph: (781)794-5632
Free: 866-728-9953
E-mail: tdelessio@fdic.gov

1307 ■ Federal Deposit Insurance Corporation
Community Affairs Program
Chicago Regional Office
300 S. Riverside Plaza
Chicago, IL 60606-3447
Contact: Glenn E. Brewer, Acting Community Affairs Officer
Ph: (312)382-7505
Free: 800-944-5343
E-mail: gbrewer@fdic.gov

1308 ■ Federal Deposit Insurance Corporation
Community Affairs Program
Dallas Regional Office
1601 Bryan St., 37th Fl.
Dallas, TX 75201-4586
Contact: Eloy Villafranca, Community Affairs Officer
Ph: (972)761-8010
Free: 800-568-9161
E-mail: evillafranc@fdic.gov

1309 ■ Federal Deposit Insurance Corporation
Community Affairs Program
Kansas City Regional Office
2345 Grand Blvd., Ste. 1200
Kansas City, MO 64108-2638
Contact: Teresa Perez, Community Affairs Officer

Ph: (816)234-8151
Free: 800-209-7459
E-mail: tperez@fdic.gov

1310 ■ Federal Deposit Insurance Corporation
Community Affairs Program
Memphis Area Office
5100 Poplar Ave., Ste. 1900
Memphis, TN 38137-5900
Contact: Clinton Vaughn, Community Affairs Officer
Ph: (901)818-5706
Free: 800-210-6354
E-mail: clvaughn@fdic.gov

1311 ■ Federal Deposit Insurance Corporation
Community Affairs Program
New York Regional Office
20 Exchange Pl., 4th Fl.
New York, NY 10005-3270
Contact: Valerie J. Williams, Community Affairs Officer
Ph: (917)320-2621
Free: 800-334-9593
E-mail: vwilliams@fdic.gov

1312 ■ Federal Deposit Insurance Corporation
Community Affairs Program
San Francisco Regional Office
25 Jessie St. at Ecker Sq., Ste. 902
San Francisco, CA 94105-2780
Contact: Linda D. Ortega, Community Affairs Officer
Ph: (415)808-8115
Free: 800-756-3558
E-mail: lortega@fdic.gov

1313 ■ Federal Financial Institutions Examination Council (FFIEC)
L. William Seidman Center
Mail Stop D 8073a
3501 Fairfax Dr.
Fairfax, VA 22226-3550
Contact: Paul T. Sanford, Exec.Sec.
Ph: (703)516-5590
URL: http://www.ffiec.gov
Staff: Administrative and support services are provided by Council staff and by the agencies represented on the Council. **Descr:** Council was established to prescribe uniform principles, standards, and report forms for the federal examination of financial institutions (commercial banks, savings and loan associations, building and loan associations, homestead associations, cooperative banks, and credit unions). It makes recommendations on matters such as uniformity in classifying loans subject to country risk, identifying financial institutions in need of special supervisory attention, and evaluating the soundness of large loans shared by two or more financial institutions. Council also conducts schools for examiners employed by the agencies represented on the Council and makes available such schools to employees of state financial institutions supervisory agencies. Council was given additional responsibilities under the Housing and Community Development Act of 1980, Section 340 of P.L. 96-399, which include the implementation of a public access system to data that depository institutions are required to disclose under the Home Mortgage Disclosure Act of 1975, and the aggregation of annual Home Mortgage Disclosures Act data. **Mem:** Council is composed of the Comptroller of the Currency, Department of the Treasury; the Chairperson of the Board of Directors, Federal Deposit Insurance Corporation; a member of the Board of Governors, Federal Reserve System, appointed by the Chairperson of the Board; the Director, Office of Thrift Supervision; and the Chairperson of the National Credit Union Administration Board. Randall S. Kroszner, Governor, Board of Governors of the Federal Reserve System, chairs the Council. **Pub:** Uniform Bank Performance Report (UBPR) (quarterly); Bank Holding Company Performance Report; Reports of Condition and Income (Call) and Thrift Financial Reports (TFR); E.16 Country Exposure Lending Survey and Country Exposure Information

Report; Aggregates Reports; Disclosure Statements; National Aggregate Reports.

1314 ■ Interagency Committee on Women's Business Enterprise (IACWBE)
Off. of Women's Business Ownership
Small Business Admin.
409 3rd St. SW, Rm. 6250
Washington, DC 20416
Contact: Marilyn Carlson Nelson, Chair
Ph: (202)205-6673
Fax: (202)205-7287
E-mail: owbo@sba.gov
URL: http://www.sba.gov/test/wbc/docs/procure/p2_gov_progs.htm
Descr: Committee promotes, coordinates, and monitors the plans, programs, and operations of the departments and agencies of the executive branch which may contribute to the establishment, preservation, and strengthening of women's business enterprise. It develops comprehensive interagency plans and specific program goals for women's business enterprise with the cooperation of the departments and agencies. It also promotes the mobilization of activities and resources of state and local governments, business and trade associations, foundations, private industry, colleges and universities, and volunteer and other groups toward the growth of women's business enterprise and facilitates the coordination of the efforts of these groups with those of the departments and agencies. **Mem:** Committee is composed of representatives of the following agencies: Departments of Commerce, Defense, Labor, Transportation, the Treasury, and Health and Human Services; General Services Administration; the Federal Reserve; Small Business Administration; and the Executive Office of the President. Wilma Goldstein, Assistant Administrator, Office of Women's Business Ownership, Small Business Administration, serves as vice chair. **Pub:** Committee's annual report to the President is available from the Government Printing Office. Regular publications and data on women owners produced by the Office of Women's Business Ownership are available; call or write for listing of topics.

1315 ■ IRS Taxpayer Advocacy Panel
Office of the Assistant Secretary for Management
Department of the Treasury
1500 Pennsylvania Ave. NW, Rm. 2421
Washington, DC 20220
Contact: Shawn F. Collins, Dir.
Ph: (202)622-1245
Free: 888-912-1227
Fax: (202)622-0000
URL: http://www.improveirs.org
Staff: Support services are provided by the IRS. Shawn F. Collins, Director, Taxpayer Advocacy Panel, serves as designated federal official. **Descr:** Panel advises the Secretary of the Treasury, the Commissioner of Internal Revenue, and the National Taxpayer Advocate on ways to improve IRS service and responsiveness to its customers. Panel members pilot new customer service initiatives by serving as customer focus groups and evaluating/validating IRS materials. Panel provides vital feedback on issues relative to overhauling or implementing new processes and procedures including dual notices, earned income tax credit forms and publications, the installment agreement annual notice, oral agreements, and Offers in Compromise. **Mem:** Panel comprises members from each state and the District of Columbia and Puerto Rico. Efforts were made to balance the panel by gender, ethnicity, socioeconomic status and occupations ensuring representation from both wage earners and those who are self-employed. Using the analysis of the Wage and Investment and Small Business/Self Employed taxpayer base, a ratio of one panelist to each 1.9 million taxpayers was employed (with a maximum of six per state except for California, which has 10 members). This analysis applies to the geographic areas only. Members serve three-year terms. Approximately 119 members currently serve on the

Panel. **Pub:** See Panel's website: http://www.improveirs.org for publications.

1316 ■ Joint Board for the Enrollment of Actuaries
Internal Revenue Service
SE:OPR
1111 Constitution Ave. NW
Washington, DC 20224
Contact: Patrick W. McDonough, Exec.Dir.
Ph: (202)622-8229
Fax: (202)622-8300
E-mail: nhqjbea@irs.gov
URL: http://www.irs.gov/taxpros/actuaries
Descr: Board establishes reasonable standards and qualifications for persons performing actuarial services with respect to employee retirement benefits and, upon application by any individual, enrolls the individual if it deems that he or she satisfies the standards and qualifications. Board also, after notice and an opportunity for a hearing, suspends or terminates the enrollment of an individual if the individual has failed to discharge his or her duties. **Mem:** Board consists of three members appointed by the Secretary of the Treasury, two members appointed by the Secretary of Labor, and one nonvoting member appointed by the Executive Director of the Pension Benefit Guaranty Corporation. The bylaws also provide for the appointment of an alternate to serve in the absence of a board member. Michael Roach chairs the Board.

1317 ■ Municipal Securities Rulemaking Board (MSRB)
1900 Duke St., Ste. 600
Alexandria, VA 22314
Contact: Lynnette Kelly Hotchkiss, Exec.Dir.
Ph: (703)797-6600
Fax: (703)797-6700
URL: http://ww1.msrb.org/msrb1
Descr: Board proposes and adopts rules with respect to transactions in municipal securities affected by brokers, dealers, and municipal securities dealers for the purpose of establishing standards and ethical practices for the municipal securities dealer community. Board is designed to prevent fraudulent and manipulative acts and practices and provide for the arbitration of claims, disputes, and controversies relating to transactions in municipal securities. **Mem:** Board consists of fifteen members who serve staggered three-year terms. Five members are individuals who are not associated with any broker, dealer, or municipal securities dealer, at least one of whom is representative of investors in municipal securities and at least one of whom is representative of issuers of municipal securities; five members are individuals who are associated with and representative of municipal securities brokers and municipal securities dealers that are not banks or subsidiaries or departments or divisions of banks; and five members are individuals who are associated with and representative of municipal securities dealers that are banks or subsidiaries or departments or divisions of banks. A chair is elected from the members of the Board each year. Ronald A. Stack, Managing Director, Head of Public Finance, Barclays Capital, New York, NY, chairs the Board. **Pub:** *MSRB Reports* (semi-annual); MSRB Rule Book (semi-annual); Form G-36 Manual; Glossary of Municipal Securities Terms; Professional Qualification Handbook; Manual on Close-Out Procedure. Publications are available on the MSRB website at http://ww1.msrb.org/msrb1/PUBLIST.asp

1318 ■ National Credit Union Administration Region I - Albany
9 Washington Sq.
Washington Ave. Extension
Albany, NY 12205
Contact: Mark Treichel, Dir.
Ph: (518)862-7400

Fax: (518)862-7420
E-mail: region1@ncua.gov

1319 ■ National Credit Union Administration Region II - Capital
1775 Duke St.
Alexandria, VA 22314-3437
Contact: Jane Walters, Dir.
Ph: (703)519-4600
Fax: (703)519-4620
E-mail: region2@ncua.gov

1320 ■ National Credit Union Administration Region III - Atlanta
7000 Central Pkwy., Ste. 1600
Atlanta, GA 30328
Contact: Alonzo Swann, Dir.
Ph: (678)443-3000
Fax: (678)443-3020
E-mail: region3@ncua.gov

1321 ■ National Credit Union Administration Region IV - Austin
4807 Spicewood Springs Rd., Ste. 5200
Austin, TX 78759-8490
Contact: C. Keith Morton, Dir.
Ph: (512)342-5600
Fax: (512)342-5620
E-mail: region4@ncua.gov

1322 ■ National Credit Union Administration Region V - Tempe
1230 W. Washington St., Ste. 301
Tempe, AZ 85281
Contact: Jane Walters, Dir.
Ph: (602)302-6000
Fax: (602)302-6024
E-mail: region5@ncua.gov

1323 ■ SEC Government-Business Forum on Small Business Capital Formation
Off. of Small Business Policy
Div. of Corporation Finance
Securities & Exchange Commission
100 F St. NE, Rm. 3650
Washington, DC 20549-3628
Contact: Gerald J. Laporte, Chief
Ph: (202)551-3460
E-mail: smallbusiness@sec.gov
URL: http://www.sec.gov/info/smallbus/sbforum.shtml
Staff: Support services are provided by the Securities and Exchange Commission. Gerald J. Laporte, Chief, Office of Small Business Policy, Division of Corporation Finance, serves as Committee chair and director. **Descr:** Forum has been held annually since 1982 to address issues relating to small business capital formation, including ways of removing governmental impediments to the capital-raising ability of small business. Forum is attended by small business representatives and officials of both federal and state governments. **Mem:** Committee is comprised of representatives of government agencies and small business and professional organizations concerned with small business capital formation. **Pub:** Final Reports of the SEC Government-Business Forum on Small Business Capital Formation (annual reports).

1324 ■ Small Business Administration District Advisory Councils (7)
Small Business Admin.
409 Third St. SW
Mail Code 2111
Washington, DC 20416
Ph: (202)205-6882
Fax: (202)481-0906
URL: http://www.sba.gov/dc/AdvisoryCouncil.pdf; http://www.sba.gov/sops/9054/sop90545.pdf
Staff: District Directors serve as designated federal officials. **Descr:** Councils work closely with their respective district offices to keep them informed of local, state, and national issues affecting small business. They also play a key role in channeling information to local commercial enterprises regarding SBA programs and assist in evaluating program usefulness in specific geographical areas. **Mem:** Councils consist of members representative of small businesses, banking, accounting, law, small busi-

ness organizations, trade associations, and chambers of commerce, within the individual regions. Council members select the chair for their council with the approval of their District Director.

1325 ■ U.S. Securities and Exchange Commission
Atlanta Regional Office
3475 Lenox Rd., NE, Ste. 1000
Atlanta, GA 30326-1232
Contact: Katherine Addleman, Reg.Dir.
Ph: (404)842-7600
E-mail: atlanta@sec.gov

1326 ■ U.S. Securities and Exchange Commission
Boston Regional Office
33 Arch St., 23rd Fl.
Boston, MA 02110-1424
Contact: David Bergers, Reg.Dir.
Ph: (617)573-8900
E-mail: boston@sec.gov

1327 ■ U.S. Securities and Exchange Commission
Chicago Regional Office
175 W. Jackson Blvd., Ste. 900
Chicago, IL 60604
Contact: Merri Jo Gillette, Reg.Dir.
Ph: (312)353-7390
E-mail: chicago@sec.gov

1328 ■ U.S. Securities and Exchange Commission
Denver Regional Office
1801 California St., Ste. 1500
Denver, CO 80202-2656
Contact: Donald Hoerl, Reg.Dir.
Ph: (303)844-1000
E-mail: denver@sec.gov

1329 ■ U.S. Securities and Exchange Commission
Fort Worth Regional Office
Burnett Plaza, Ste. 1900
801 Cherry St., Unit 18
Fort Worth, TX 76102
Contact: Rose L. Romero, Reg.Dir.
Ph: (817)978-3821
E-mail: dfw@sec.gov

1330 ■ U.S. Securities and Exchange Commission
Los Angeles Regional Office
5670 Wilshire Blvd., 11th Fl.
Los Angeles, CA 90036-3648
Contact: Rosalind Tyson, Reg.Dir.
Ph: (323)965-3998
E-mail: losangeles@sec.gov

1331 ■ U.S. Securities and Exchange Commission
Miami Regional Office
801 Brickell Ave., Ste. 1800
Miami, FL 33131
Contact: David Nelson, Reg.Dir.
Ph: (305)982-6300
E-mail: miami@sec.gov

1332 ■ U.S. Securities and Exchange Commission
New York Regional Office
3 World Financial Ctr., Ste. 400
New York, NY 10281-1022
Contact: George S. Canellos, Reg.Dir.
Ph: (212)336-1100
E-mail: newyork@sec.gov

1333 ■ U.S. Securities and Exchange Commission
Philadelphia Regional Office
The Mellon Independence Center
701 Market St.
Philadelphia, PA 19106-1532
Contact: Daniel M. Hawke, Reg.Dir.

Ph: (215)597-3100
E-mail: philadelphia@sec.gov

1334 ■ U.S. Securities and Exchange Commission
Salt Lake Regional Office
15 W. South Temple St., Ste. 1800
Salt Lake City, UT 84101
Contact: Kenneth D. Israel Jr., Reg.Dir.
Ph: (801)524-5796
E-mail: saltlake@sec.gov

1335 ■ U.S. Securities and Exchange Commission
San Francisco Regional Office
44 Montgomery St., Ste. 2600
San Francisco, CA 94104
Contact: Marc J. Fagel, Reg.Dir.
Ph: (415)705-2500
E-mail: sanfrancisco@sec.gov

1336 ■ Walla Walla Sweet Onion Marketing Committee
PO Box 644
Walla Walla, WA 99362
Ph: (509)525-1031
Fax: (509)522-2038
E-mail: info@sweetonions.org
URL: http://www.sweetonions.org
Descr: Committee administers Marketing Order 956, which authorizes the production research, marketing research, and marketing development and promotion programs, including paid advertising, of Walla Walla sweet onions. It also regulates container markings. **Mem:** Committee consists of ten members including six producers, three handlers and one public member. Members serve staggered three-year terms. Michael F. Locati, Walla Walla, WA, chairs the Committee.

Associations and Other Organizations

1337 ■ American Accounts Payable Association (AAPA)
660 N Main Ave., Ste. 200
San Antonio, TX 78205-1217
Contact: Mark Coindreau, Public Relations Mgr.
Ph: (210)630-4373
Fax: (210)630-4410
E-mail: info@americanap.org
URL: http://www.americanap.org
Descr: Seeks to uphold the standards of practice in the accounts payable profession. Fosters the professional development of members. Offers comprehensive educational programs for accounts payable professionals. **Fnd:** 2008. **Pub:** AP Journal Online (biweekly).

1338 ■ American Bankers Association (ABA)
1120 Connecticut Ave. NW
Washington, DC 20036
Contact: Edward L. Yingling, Pres./CEO
Ph: (202)663-5564
Free: 800-226-5377
Fax: (202)663-7543
E-mail: custserv@aba.com
URL: http://www.aba.com
Staff: 410. **Descr:** Members are principally commercial banks and trust companies; combined assets of members represent approximately 90 of the U.S. banking industry; approximately 94 of members are community banks with less than $500 million in assets. Seeks to enhance the role of commercial bankers as preeminent providers of financial services through communications, research, legal action, lobbying of federal legislative and regulatory bodies, and education and training programs. Serves as spokesperson for the banking industry; facilitates exchange of information among members. Maintains the American Institute of Banking, an industry-sponsored adult education program. Conducts educational and training programs for bank employees and officers through a wide range of banking schools and national conferences. Maintains

liaison with federal bank regulators; lobbies Congress on issues affecting commercial banks; testifies before congressional committees; represents members in U.S. postal rate proceedings. Serves as secretariat of the International Monetary Conference and the Financial Institutions Committee for the American National Standards Institute. Files briefs and lawsuits in major court cases affecting the industry. Conducts teleconferences with state banking associations on such issues as regulatory compliance; works to build consensus and coordinate activities of leading bank and financial service trade groups. Provides services to members including: public advocacy; news media contact; insurance program providing directors and officers with liability coverage, financial institution bond, and trust errors and omissions coverage; research service operated through ABA Center for Banking Information; fingerprint set processing in conjunction with the Federal Bureau of Investigation; discounts on operational and income-producing projects through the Corporation for American Banking. Conducts conferences, forums, and workshops covering subjects such as small business, consumer credit, agricultural and community banking, trust management, bank operations, and automation. Sponsors ABA Educational Foundation and the Personal Economics Program, which educates schoolchildren and the community on banking, economics, and personal finance. **Fnd:** 1875. **Mem:** 8000. **Pub:** ABA Bank Compliance (bimonthly); ABA Banking Journal (monthly); Bank Operations Bulletin (monthly); Bankers News (biweekly); Commercial Lending Review (quarterly); Consumer Credit Delinquency Bulletin (quarterly); Journal of Agricultural Lending (quarterly); Network News (3/year); Securities Processing Digest (quarterly); Trust and Financial Advisor (quarterly); Trust Letter (monthly).

1339 ■ American Bankruptcy Institute (ABI)
44 Canal Center Plz., Ste. 400
Alexandria, VA 22314
Contact: Robert J. Keach, Pres.
Ph: (703)739-0800
Fax: (703)739-1060
E-mail: support@abiworld.org
URL: http://www.abiworld.org
Staff: 26. **Descr:** Attorneys, accountants, and other providers of financial services, lending institutions, credit organizations, consumer groups, federal and state governments, and other interested individuals. Provides a multidisciplinary forum for the exchange of information on bankruptcy and insolvency issues. Fosters dialogue among lawyers, businesspersons, and legislators on current and potential bankruptcy problems. Reviews existing and proposed legislation as it affects bankruptcy and insolvency. Conducts nationally televised panel discussions and research projects; provides information to the public and legislators. Maintains speakers bureau; compiles statistics. Conducts research and educational programs. **Fnd:** 1982. **Mem:** 10600. **Pub:** ABI Annual Membership Directory (annual); ABI Journal (10/year); ABI Law Review (semiannual); ABI Update Newsletter; Legislative Updates.

1340 ■ American Financial Services Association (AFSA)
919 18th St. NW, Ste. 300
Washington, DC 20006-5517
Contact: Chris Stinebert, Pres./CEO
Ph: (202)296-5544
Fax: (202)223-0321
E-mail: cstinebert@afsamail.org
URL: http://www.afsaonline.org
Staff: 26. **Descr:** Represents companies whose business is primarily direct credit lending to consumers and/or the purchase of sales finance paper on consumer goods. Has members that have insurance and retail subsidiaries; some are themselves subsidiaries of highly diversified parent corporations. Encourages the business of financing individuals and families for necessary and useful purposes at reasonable charges, including interest; promotes consumer understanding of basic money management principles as well as constructive uses of

consumer credit. Includes educational services such as films, textbooks, and study units for the classroom and budgeting guides for individuals and families. Compiles statistical reports; offers seminars. **Fnd:** 1916. **Mem:** 325. **State Groups:** 48. **Pub:** *Credit* (bimonthly); *Independent Credit Operations* (quarterly); *Spotlight* (monthly).

1341 ■ American Risk Retention Coalition (ARRC)
1250 H St. NW, Ste. 901
Washington, DC 20005
Contact: Larry L. Smith, Chm.
Free: 877-963-8050
Fax: (202)463-8155
E-mail: emassey@arrcoalition.org
URL: http://www.arrcoalition.org
Descr: Represents risk retention owners and their service providers as well as excess insurers and reinsurers. Aims to revise the Federal Liability Risk Retention Act (LRRA). Works with members of Congress to enhance and strengthen the LRRA. **Fnd:** 2006.

1342 ■ American Small Business Coalition (ASBC)
PO Box 2786
Columbia, MD 21045-1786
Contact: Margaret H. Timberlake, COO/Pres.
Ph: (410)381-7378
Fax: (410)630-1221
E-mail: mhtimberlake@theasbc.org
URL: http://www.theasbc.org
Descr: Focuses on supporting the development of relationships, best practices and market intelligence for companies doing business in the government sector. Seeks to augment industry education and outreach efforts as a resource partner to agencies of the U.S. Government. Assists in the ongoing development and growth of member companies who support agency mission requirements through their direct and indirect provisioning of goods and services. Provides industry education, relationship development and strategy alignment assistance to member companies new to government contracting. Supports the success of government contractors designated "other than small business" who seek assistance with identifying viable small business partners in multiple industry domains. **Fnd:** 2004.

1343 ■ American Society of Appraisers (ASA)
555 Herndon Pkwy., Ste. 125
Herndon, VA 20170
Contact: Laurie M. Saunders, Exec. VP
Ph: (703)478-2228
Free: 800-ASA-VALU
Fax: (703)742-8471
E-mail: asainfo@appraisers.org
URL: http://www.appraisers.org/ASAHome.aspx
Staff: 30. **Descr:** Professional appraisal educator, testing, and accrediting society. Sponsors mandatory recertification program for all members. Offers a consumer information service to the public. **Fnd:** 1952. **Mem:** 6000. **Local Groups:** 83. **Pub:** *ASA Professional Magazine* (quarterly); *Business Valuation Review* (quarterly); *Directory of Professional Appraisal Services* (annual); *The MTS Journal* (quarterly); *Personal Property Journal* (quarterly); *Real Property Journal* (3/year); Audiotapes; Monographs.

1344 ■ American Society of Tax Problem Solvers (ASTPS)
2250 Wehrle Dr., Ste. 3
Williamsville, NY 14221
Contact: Lawrence M. Lawler CPA, Natl. Dir.
Ph: (716)630-1650
Fax: (716)630-1651
E-mail: ron@astps.org
URL: http://www.astps.org
Descr: Represents professionals who specialize in representing taxpayers before the IRS. Promotes education and professionalism in the area of Tax Problem Resolution. Advocates for taxpayer rights and responsiveness in taxing entities. Assists its members in maintaining a high level of skills, knowledge and professionalism in the area of tax

representation. **Pub:** *The TAPeR Practitioner Times* (quarterly).

1345 ■ American Stock Exchange (AMEX)
86 Trinity Pl.
New York, NY 10006
Contact: Neal L. Wolkoff, Chm./CEO
Ph: (212)306-1000
Free: 866-422-2639
E-mail: amexfeedback@amex.com
URL: http://www.amex.com
Staff: 777. **Descr:** Represents domestic and international equities and derivative securities market. Provides an auction marketplace that integrates service and information programs for its listed companies. **Mem:** 864. **Pub:** *American Stock Exchange--Annual Report* (annual); *AMEX Fact Book* (annual).

1346 ■ Antique Appraisal Association of America (AAAA)
386 Park Ave. S, No. 2000
New York, NY 10016
Contact: Margaret Swenson, Sec.
Ph: (212)889-5404
Fax: (212)889-5503
E-mail: appraisers@appraiserassoc.org
URL: http://www.appraisersassoc.org/
Descr: Antique appraisers. Purposes are to: initiate, sponsor, and promote plans and activities that will upgrade and maintain high ethical standards for antique appraising; provide for a cooperative working environment among antique appraisers; assure the public of ethical practices in antique appraising. Plans to conduct training program. **Fnd:** 1972. **Mem:** 200. **Pub:** *Membership Roster* (biennial); Newsletter (monthly).

1347 ■ Appraisal Institute (AI)
550 W Van Buren St., Ste. 1000
Chicago, IL 60607
Contact: Fred Grubbe, CEO
Ph: (312)335-4100
Free: 888-756-4684
Fax: (312)335-4400
E-mail: aiceo@appraisalinstitute.org
URL: http://www.appraisalinstitute.org
Staff: 100. **Descr:** General appraisers who hold the MAI designation, and residential members who hold the SRA designation. Enforces Code of Professional Ethics and Standards of Professional Appraisal Practice. Confers one general designation, the MAI, and one residential designation, the SRA. Provides training in valuation of residential and income properties, market analysis, and standards of professional appraisal practice. Sponsors courses in preparation for state certification and licensing; offers continuing education programs for designated members. **Fnd:** 1991. **Mem:** 21000. **Reg. Groups:** 10. **State Groups:** 102. **Pub:** *Appraisal Institute Directory of Designated Members* (annual); *The Appraisal Journal* (quarterly); *The Appraisal of Real Estate, 12th Edition* (quarterly); *Appraiser News in Brief* (8/year); *Appraising Residential Property, 3rd Edition* (8/year); *The Dictionary of Real Estate Appraisal, 4th Edition*; *MarketSource* (quarterly); *Products and Services Catalog* (annual); *Real Estate Valuation in Litigation, 2nd Edition* (annual); *Valuation Insights and Perspectives* (quarterly).

1348 ■ Association of Appraiser Regulatory Officials (AARO)
13200 Strickland Rd., Ste. 114-264
Raleigh, NC 27613
Contact: Neva Conway, Pres.
Ph: (919)235-4544
Fax: (919)870-5392
E-mail: brent.jayes@meetingsoncue.com
URL: http://www.aaro.net
Descr: Represents real estate appraiser licensing agencies in the United States and its territories. Seeks to improve the administration and enforcement of real estate appraisal laws. Provides education, research, communication and cooperation

among appraiser regulatory officials. **Pub:** Newsletter.

1349 ■ Association of Divorce Financial Planners (ADFP)
514 Fourth St.
East Northport, NY 11731
Contact: Lili A. Vasileff CFP, Pres.
Ph: (631)754-6125
Free: 888-838-7773
Fax: (631)754-6125
E-mail: adfp@optonline.net
URL: http://www.divorceandfinance.org
Descr: Aims to create awareness of the benefits of divorce financial planning. Provides members with continuing education. Promotes communication, networking and peer review. **Pub:** *ADFP News* (quarterly).

1350 ■ Association of Sales Administration Managers (ASAM)
Box 1356
Laurence Harbor, NJ 08879
Contact: Bill Martin, Sec.-Treas.
Ph: (732)264-7722
E-mail: asamnet@aol.com
Descr: Independent consultants providing sales and marketing services, including establishing broker and rep sales networks, field sales management, and marketing and branch office administrative services. Primary expertise is in the consumer packaged goods field, both private label and branded. Offers consulting services. **Fnd:** 1981. **Mem:** 100.

1351 ■ Black Business and Professional Association (BBPA)
675 King St. W, Ste. 210
Toronto, ON, Canada M5V 1M9
Contact: Howard Wright, Interim Pres.
Ph: (416)504-4097
Fax: (416)504-7343
E-mail: bbpa@bellnet.ca
URL: http://www.bbpa.org
Descr: Canadian businesspeople and professionals of African descent. Seeks to "address discrimination in business, employment, education, housing, policing, political representation, and immigration." Provides assistance to young adults attempting to enter business or the professions. Serves as a unified voice speaking for members on business and economic issues. Facilitates networking among members; conducts community outreach programs; sponsors social activities. Makes available continuing professional education programs for members. **Fnd:** 1982.

1352 ■ Business Alliance for Commerce in Hemp (BACH)
PO Box 1716
El Cerrito, CA 94530
Contact: Chris Conrad, Dir.
Ph: (510)215-8326
Fax: (510)234-4460
E-mail: chris@chrisconrad.com
URL: http://www.equalrights4all.org/bach/BACHcore.html
Descr: Businesses, consumers, and other individuals and organizations with an interest in hemp and hemp products. Promotes "full and unrestricted restoration of hemp as a sustainable farm crop and industrial resource"; seeks to legalize therapeutic use of marijuana and regulate adult consumption. Conducts lobbying, community organization, and outreach activities supporting hemp producers and consumers; consulting services; disseminates information on the commercial and industrial uses of hemp and the therapeutic benefits of marijuana. **Fnd:** 1989. **Pub:** *Cannabis Yields and Dosage*; *Hemp for Health*; *Hemp, Lifeline to the Future*.

1353 ■ Business Alliance for Local Living Economies (BALLE)
165 11th St.
San Francisco, CA 94103
Contact: Don Shaffer, Natl. Coor.
Ph: (415)255-1108

Fax: (415)863-1356
E-mail: info@livingeconomies.org
URL: http://www.livingeconomies.org
Descr: Represents individuals dedicated to building local living economies. Seeks to build long-term economic empowerment and prosperity through local business ownership, economic justice, cultural diversity, and environmental stewardship. Advocates public policies that strengthen independent local businesses and farms, promote economic equity, and protect the environment. Supports the growth and development of community-based business. **Fnd:** 2001. **Mem:** 12000. **Pub:** *Living Economy Newsletter* (monthly).

1354 ■ Business and Professional Women/ USA (BPW/USA)
1620 Eye St. NW, Ste. 210
Washington, DC 20006
Contact: Deborah L. Frett, CEO
Ph: (202)293-1100
Fax: (202)861-0298
E-mail: memberservices@bpwusa.org
URL: http://www.bpwusa.org
Staff: 13. **Descr:** Represents men and women of every age, religion, political party, and socioeconomic background. Works to achieve equity for all women in the workplace through advocacy, education, and information. Provides professional development, networking, and career advancement opportunities for working women. Sponsors a grass roots action team to influence elected officials on issues concerning women. Sponsors National Business Women's Week during the third week of October. **Fnd:** 1919. **Mem:** 35000. **Reg. Groups:** 53. **Local Groups:** 2000. **Pub:** *BusinessWoman* (quarterly); *Making Workplaces Work: Quality Work Policies for Small Business* (annual); *Work and Family Policies: Options for the 90's and Beyond.*

1355 ■ Business Women's Network (BWN)
1990 M St. NW, Ste. 700
Washington, DC 20036
Contact: Edie Fraser, Pres./Founder
Ph: (202)466-8209
Free: 800-48W-OMEN
Fax: (202)833-1808
E-mail: inquire@tpag.com
URL: http://www.bwni.com
Descr: Supports women in business; provides ongoing programs on mentoring, networking and managing skills. **Fnd:** 1993. **Pub:** *Directory of Women's Association; Women and Diversity WOW! Facts 2002;* Newsletter (monthly).

1356 ■ Canada's Venture Capital and Private Equity Association (CVCA)
MaRS Centre
Heritage Bldg.
101 College St., Ste. 120 J
Toronto, ON, Canada M5G 1L7
Contact: Ms. Lauren Linton, Dir. of Marketing
Ph: (416)487-0519
Fax: (416)487-5899
E-mail: cvca@cvca.ca
URL: http://www.cvca.ca
Descr: Ventures and risks capital companies. Promotes economic growth through provision of capital to emerging businesses. Conducts research; facilitates exchange of information among members; represents the venture capital industry before government agencies, industrial and financial organizations, and the public. **Fnd:** 1974. **Mem:** 1100. **Pub:** *Enterprise* (quarterly).

1357 ■ Canadian Bankers Association (CBA)
PO Box 348
Toronto, ON, Canada M5L 1G2
Contact: Nancy Hughes Anthony, Pres./CEO
Ph: (416)362-6092
Free: 800-263-0231
Fax: (416)362-7705
E-mail: inform@cba.ca
URL: http://www.cba.ca/lang.php
Descr: Banks and bank employees. Promotes growth and development of the banking industry.

Conducts educational, promotional, public relations, and advocacy programs.

1358 ■ Canadian Innovation Centre
Waterloo Research and Technology Park
Accelerator Centre
295 Hagey Blvd., Ste. 15
Waterloo, ON, Canada N2L 6R5
Contact: Ted Cross, Chm./CEO
Ph: (519)885-5870
Fax: (519)513-2421
E-mail: info@innovationcentre.ca
URL: http://www.innovationcentre.ca
Staff: 2. **Descr:** Investors, entrepreneurs, and innovative companies. Promotes innovation in economic activity; seeks to ensure that developers of inventions or innovations receive full credit for their discoveries. Provides support and assistance to members. Conducts research and educational programs. **Fnd:** 1981. **Pub:** *Eureka!* (quarterly).

1359 ■ Canadian Institute of Financial Planning (CIFP)
3660 Hurontario St., Ste. 600
Mississauga, ON, Canada L5B 3C4
Contact: Keith Costello, Pres./CEO
Free: 866-635-5526
E-mail: cifp@cifps.ca
URL: http://www.cifp.ca/Desktop/English/Index.asp
Descr: Works to promote excellence in the field of financial planning. Facilitates communication and cooperation among members, which includes financial planning professionals. Sponsors continuing professional education courses.

1360 ■ Canadian Payments Association (CPA)
180 Elgin St., 12th Fl.
Ottawa, ON, Canada K2P 2K3
Contact: Janet Cosier, Chair
Ph: (613)238-4173
Fax: (613)233-3385
E-mail: info@cdnpay.ca
URL: http://www.cdnpay.ca
Staff: 70. **Descr:** Represents banks, trust and loan companies, and credit unions, charged with the establishment and operation of the Canadian national clearings and settlement systems. Promotes effective operation of the national payments systems. Serves as a forum for the exchange of information among members; gathers and disseminates information on settlements and clearings. **Fnd:** 1980. **Mem:** 120. **Pub:** *Forum* (quarterly).

1361 ■ Canadian ShareOwners Association (CSA)
4 King St. W, Ste. 806
Toronto, ON, Canada M5H 1B6
Contact: John T. Bart, Founder/Pres.
Ph: (416)595-9600
Free: 800-268-6881
Fax: (416)595-0400
E-mail: customercare@shareowner.com
URL: http://www.shareowner.com/index.html
Staff: 10. **Descr:** Investors in securities. Promotes successful investment by independent investors. Conducts educational programs; sponsors research. **Fnd:** 1987. **Mem:** 20000. **Pub:** *Share Owner* (bimonthly).

1362 ■ Canadian Tax Foundation (CTF)
595 Bay St., Ste. 1200
Toronto, ON, Canada M5G 2N5
Contact:FCA Larry Chapman, Dir./CEO
Ph: (416)599-0283
Free: 877-733-0283
Fax: (416)599-9283
E-mail: lchapman@ctf.ca
URL: http://www.ctf.ca
Staff: 27. **Descr:** Individuals and organizations with an interest in taxation. Promotes increased awareness of the Canadian Tax Code and the social ramifications of taxation. Serves as a clearinghouse on taxation; sponsors research and educational

programs. **Fnd:** 1945. **Mem:** 9000. **Pub:** *Canadian Tax Journal* (quarterly).

1363 ■ Canadian Taxpayers' Federation (CTF)
130 Albert St., Ste. 512
Ottawa, ON, Canada K1P 5G4
Contact: Kevin Gaudet, Federal Dir.
Ph: (613)234-6554
Free: 800-265-0442
Fax: (613)234-7748
E-mail: on.director@taxpayer.com
URL: http://www.taxpayer.com/taxpayer/home1
Descr: Individuals and organizations. Promotes appropriate and efficient taxation and responsible use by government of tax revenues. Serves as a clearinghouse on taxation and the disbursement of tax revenues; conducts lobbying and advocacy programs.

1364 ■ Catalog and Multichannel Marketing Council
1120 Ave. of the Americas
New York, NY 10036-6700
Contact: Donn Rappaport, Chm.
Ph: (212)768-7277
Fax: (212)302-6714
E-mail: customerservice@the-dma.org
URL: http://www.the-dma.org
Descr: Catalog houses, catalog printers, and list brokers; members of Direct Marketing Association. Objectives are to: keep members abreast of legislative and legal matters concerning the industry; exchange up-to-date ideas on graphics, production, and lists; share the benefits of consumer-oriented publicity projects about catalogs in newspapers and magazines. Provides representation in Congress on legislative and postal matters. Conducts workshops. **Mem:** 378. **Pub:** *Current and Crossroads* (monthly); *DMA Insider* (quarterly); Newsletter (bimonthly).

1365 ■ Chicago Stock Exchange (CHX)
One Financial Pl.
440 S LaSalle St.
Chicago, IL 60605
Contact: David A. Herron, CEO
Ph: (312)663-2222
E-mail: info@chx.com
URL: http://www.chx.com
Descr: Brokers and dealers in local and national securities. Wholly-owned subsidiaries: Midwest Securities Trust Company; Midwest Clearing Corp.; Mortgage Backed Securities Clearing Corporation. Provides an auction market for purchase and sale of equity securities. **Fnd:** 1882. **Mem:** 446. **Pub:** Report (annual).

1366 ■ Coalition for Economic Survival (CES)
514 Shatto Pl., Ste. 270
Los Angeles, CA 90020
Contact: Larry Gross, Exec. Dir.
Ph: (213)252-4411
Fax: (213)252-4422
E-mail: contactces@earthlink.net
URL: http://www.cesinaction.org
Staff: 7. **Descr:** Addresses the economic concerns of senior citizens and low-income families, especially issues dealing with rent control, tenants' rights, and affordable housing. Conducts tenants' rights clinic and organizes tenant unions to empower tenants to fight against increases, displacement, and obtain needed repairs; disseminates information. **Fnd:** 1973. **Mem:** 5000. **Pub:** *Gone, But Not Forgotten; Mark to Market Tenant Outreach Brochure; Organizing Times* (quarterly); Bulletin (periodic).

1367 ■ Coalition for Tax Fairness (CTF)
PO Box 9205
Arlington, VA 22219-1205
Contact: Tim Carlson
Ph: (301)515-6584
E-mail: tcarlson@ti.com
URL: http://www.fair-iso.org
Descr: Strives to make the public aware of the full advantage of the ISO AMT legislation, a legislative initiative that remedied the Incentive Stock Option Alternative Minimum (ISO AMT) crisis. Disseminates

information about the key points that the public needs to know in order to benefit from the ISO AMR legislation. Ensures that ISO AMT relief is extended to all families at all income levels.

1368 ■ Consumer Bankers Association (CBA)
1000 Wilson Blvd., Ste. 2500
Arlington, VA 22209-3912
Contact: Brendan McDonagh, Chm./CEO
Ph: (703)276-1750
Fax: (703)528-1290
E-mail: membership@cbanet.org
URL: http://www.cbanet.org
Staff: 20. **Descr:** Federally insured deposit-taking institutions. Sponsors Graduate School of Retail Bank Management at the university of Virginia. **Fnd:** 1919. **Pub:** *CBA Report* (monthly).

1369 ■ Consumer Credit Industry Association (CCIA)
542 S Dearborn, Ste. 400
Chicago, IL 60605
Contact: Rebecca Smart, Chair
Fax: (312)939-2242
E-mail: webmaster@cciaonline.com
URL: http://www.cciaonline.com
Staff: 5. **Descr:** Insurance companies underwriting consumer credit insurance in areas of life insurance, accident and health insurance, and property insurance. **Fnd:** 1951. **Mem:** 140. **Pub:** *Consumer Credit Insurance Association--Annual Meeting Proceedings* (annual); *Consumer Credit Insurance Association--Digest Bulletin* (periodic); *Consumer Credit Insurance Association--Information Bulletin* (periodic); *Consumer Credit Insurance Association--Legislative Bulletin* (periodic); *Newsletter* (monthly).

1370 ■ Consumers United for Rail Equity (CURE)
1050 Thomas Jefferson St. NW, 7th Fl.
Washington, DC 20007
Contact: Robert S. Szabo, Exec. Dir.
Ph: (202)298-1959
Fax: (202)338-2416
E-mail: sch@vnf.com
URL: http://www.railcure.org
Descr: Coalition of railroad shippers that are captive to a single railroad for their transportation needs. **Fnd:** 1983. **Pub:** *Rail Report* (monthly).

1371 ■ Credit Institute of Canada (CIC)
219 Dufferin St., Ste. 216C
Toronto, ON, Canada M6K 3J1
Contact: Rodger D. Noel ACI, Chm./Pres./Dean
Ph: (416)572-2615
Free: 888-447-3324
Fax: (416)572-2619
E-mail: geninfo@creditedu.org
URL: http://www.creditedu.org
Staff: 4. **Descr:** Professionals dedicated to excellence in credit management and education. Conducts educational programs. Represents members' interests. Grants professional designations in credit management. **Fnd:** 1928. **Mem:** 3000. **Pub:** *To Your Credit* (3/year).

1372 ■ Credit Union National Association (CUNA)
PO Box 431
Madison, WI 53701-0431
Contact: Daniel A. Mica, Pres./CEO
Free: 800-356-9655
Fax: (608)231-4263
URL: http://www.cuna.org
Staff: 185. **Descr:** Serves as trade association serving more than 90

of credit unions in the U.S. through their respective state leagues with a total membership of more than 77 million persons. (A credit union is a member-owned, nonprofit institution formed to encourage saving and to offer low interest loans to members, usually people working for the same employer, belonging to the same association, or living in the same community.) Promotes credit union membership, use of services, and organization of new credit unions. Seeks to perfect credit union laws; aids in the

development of new credit union services, including new payment systems techniques; assists in the training of credit union officials and employees; compiles statistics, annually, by state. Offers charitable program. **Fnd:** 1934. **Mem:** 9000. **State Groups:** 52. **Pub:** *Credit Union Directors Newsletter* (monthly); *Credit Union Executive Newsletter* (bi-weekly); *Credit Union Magazine* (monthly); *Credit Union Newswatch* (weekly); *Everybody's Money* (quarterly).

1373 ■ Data Interchange Standards Association (DISA)
7600 Leesburg Pike, Ste. 430
Falls Church, VA 22043
Contact: Jerry C. Connors, Pres.
Ph: (703)970-4480
Fax: (703)970-4488
E-mail: info@disa.org
URL: http://www.disa.org
Staff: 9. **Descr:** Serves as a home for the development of cross-industry electronic business interchange standards. Provides technical and administrative support to e-business, standards and XML specification development organizations through its affiliate division. **Fnd:** 1987. **Mem:** 350.

1374 ■ Debtors Anonymous (DA)
PO Box 920888
Needham, MA 02492-0009
Ph: (781)453-2743
Free: 800-421-2383
Fax: (781)453-2745
E-mail: office@debtorsanonymous.org
URL: http://www.debtorsanonymous.org
Staff: 2. **Descr:** Fellowship of men and women who share their experience, strength, and hope with each other that they may solve their common problem of compulsive debiting. Adapts the Twelve Steps and Twelve Traditions of Alcoholics Anonymous World Services for compulsive debtors. Establishes and coordinates self help support groups for people seeking to live without incurring unsecured debt. Helps members develop workable plans for long-term financial and lifestyle goals. **Fnd:** 1968. **State Groups:** 26. **Local Groups:** 420. **Pub:** *Communicating with Creditors*; *Debt Payment*; *The P.I Manual*; *Pressure Groups and Pressure Meetings*; *Ways and Means* (quarterly); Books; Pamphlets; Brochures; Handbooks.

1375 ■ Direct Marketing Association (DMA)
1120 Ave. of the Americas
New York, NY 10036-6700
Contact: John A. Greco Jr., Pres./CEO
Ph: (212)768-7277
Fax: (212)302-6714
E-mail: presiden@the-dma.org
URL: http://www.the-dma.org
Staff: 136. **Descr:** Manufacturers, wholesalers, public utilities, retailers, mail order firms, publishers, schools, clubs, insurance companies, financial organizations, business equipment manufacturers, paper and envelope manufacturers, list brokers, compilers, managers, owners, computer service bureaus, advertising agencies, letter shops, research organizations, printers, lithographers, creators, and producers of direct mail and direct response advertising. Studies consumer and business attitudes toward direct mail and related direct marketing statistics. Offers Mail Preference Service for consumers who wish to receive less mail advertising, Mail Order Action Line to help resolve difficulties with mail order purchases, and Telephone Preference Service for people who wish to receive fewer telephone sales calls. Maintains hall of fame; offers placement service; compiles statistics. Sponsors several three-day Basic Direct Marketing Institutes, Advanced Direct Marketing Institutes, and special interest seminars and workshops. Maintains Government Affairs office in Washington, DC. Operates Direct Marketing Educational Foundation. **Fnd:** 1917. **Mem:** 5200. **Pub:** *Business Review* (quarterly); *Council Newsletter* (quarterly); *Dateline: DMA* (quarterly); *Direct Line: The DMA Newsletter Serving the Direct Marketing Industry* (monthly); *The DMA*

Insider (quarterly); *DMA Washington Report: Federal and State Regulatory Issues of Concern* (monthly); *Fact Book on Direct Marketing* (annual); *Membership Roster* (annual); *MyDMA*; *Washington Alert*; Annual Report (annual).

1376 ■ Direct Selling Association (DSA)
1667 K St. NW, Ste. 1100
Washington, DC 20006
Contact: Mr. Neil H. Offen, Pres.
Ph: (202)452-8866
Fax: (202)452-9010
E-mail: info@dsa.org
URL: http://www.dsa.org
Staff: 22. **Descr:** Manufacturers and distributors selling consumer products through person-to-person sales, by appointment, and through home-party plans. Products include food, gifts, house wares, dietary supplements, cosmetics, apparel, jewelry, decorative accessories, reference books, and telecommunications products and services. Offers specialized education; conducts research programs; compiles statistics. Maintains hall of fame. Sponsors Direct Selling Education Foundation. **Fnd:** 1910. **Mem:** 200. **Pub:** *Data Tracker* (quarterly); *News from Neil* (monthly); *State Status Sheet* (weekly); Annual Report (annual).

1377 ■ Disabled Businesspersons Association (DBA)
3590 Camino del Rio N
San Diego, CA 92108-1716
Contact: Mr. Urban Miyares, Pres.
Ph: (619)594-8805
Fax: (619)594-4208
E-mail: ahoy@challengedamerica.org
URL: http://www.ChallengedAmerica.org
Staff: 5. **Descr:** Assists active and enterprising individuals with disabilities maximize their rehabilitation and potential in the workplace and business, and work with vocational rehabilitation, government, education and business. Encourages the participation and enhances the performance of the disabled in the work force. Membership is not a prerequisite for services or assistance. **Fnd:** 1985. **Mem:** 12000. **Pub:** *Challenged America Newsletter* (quarterly); *DBA Advisor* (quarterly).

1378 ■ eBusiness Association (eBA)
PO Box 500
Penfield, NY 14526
Contact: Ralph Dandrea, Pres.
E-mail: eba_rochester@yahoo.com
URL: http://www.ebusinessassociation.org
Staff: 2. **Descr:** Corporations advertising on the Internet; professionals engaged in developing Internet marketing and advertising strategies and campaigns. Seeks to advance the practice of online advertising, marketing and business; promotes professional development of members. Represents members' interests before government agencies, industry associations, and the public. Conducts research and educational programs; sponsors advocacy campaigns; maintains speakers' bureau. **Fnd:** 1996. **Mem:** 300. **Reg. Groups:** 1. **Pub:** *IMAA News Group* (quarterly).

1379 ■ Fifty Plus Financial Network
5755 N Point Pkwy., Ste. 57
Alpharetta, GA 30022-1145
Contact: Richard A. Alford, Pres.
Ph: (678)297-9500
Free: 877-974-9800
Fax: (678)297-9514
E-mail: info@ammg.us
URL: http://www.ammg.us
Descr: Provides money management and financial planning services for persons age 50 plus.

1380 ■ Financial Planning Association (FPA)
4100 E Mississippi Ave., Ste. 400
Denver, CO 80246-3053
Contact: Marvin W. Tuttle Jr., Exec. Dir.
Ph: (303)759-4900
Free: 800-322-4237
Fax: (303)759-0749

E-mail: webfeedback@fpanet.org
URL: http://www.fpanet.org
Staff: 80. **Descr:** Works to support the financial planning process in order to help people achieve their goals and dreams. Believes that everyone needs objective advice to make smart financial decisions and that when seeking the advice of a financial planner, the planner should be a CFP professional. **Fnd:** 2000. **Mem:** 30000. **Local Groups:** 100. **Pub:** *FPA This Week* (weekly); *Journal of Financial Planning* (monthly).

1381 ■ Fixed Income Analysts Society (FIASI)
244 Fifth Ave., Ste. L230
New York, NY 10001
Contact: Lauren Nauser, Exec. Dir.
Ph: (212)726-8100
E-mail: fiasi@fiasi.org
URL: http://www.fiasi.org
Staff: 1. **Descr:** Corporate research analysts and portfolio managers involved in high yield, asset, mortgage backed, and municipal research. **Fnd:** 1975. **Mem:** 300. **Pub:** *Membership Brochure.*

1382 ■ Food Marketing Institute (FMI)
2345 Crystal Dr., Ste. 800
Arlington, VA 22202-4801
Contact: Leslie G. Sarasin, Pres./CEO
Ph: (202)452-8444
Fax: (202)429-4519
URL: http://www.fmi.org
Staff: 130. **Descr:** Grocery retailers and wholesalers. Maintains liaison with government and consumers. Conducts 30 educational conferences and seminars per year. Conducts research programs; compiles statistics. **Fnd:** 1977. **Mem:** 1500. **Pub:** *Advantage* (monthly); *Facts About Supermarket Development* (annual); *Food Marketing Industry Speaks* (annual).

1383 ■ Forum for Investor Advice
PO Box 3216
Mercerville, NJ 08619
Contact: Barbara Levin, Exec. Dir.
Fax: (609)890-8037
E-mail: investoradvice@optonline.net
URL: http://www.investoradvice.org
Descr: Financial services organizations including mutual fund companies, securities firms, and banks and insurance companies. Promotes increased public awareness of the availability and effectiveness of financial and investment services provided by members. Gathers and disseminates information; conducts public relations and promotional activities; sponsors continuing professional development courses for financial services providers. **Fnd:** 1994. **Mem:** 70. **Pub:** *Do You Really Need a Financial Advisor?*; *Getting Help Made All the Difference*; *Managing Investment Risk*; *Media Directory* (periodic).

1384 ■ Futures Industry Association (FIA)
2001 Pennsylvania Ave. NW, Ste. 600
Washington, DC 20006
Contact: Michael C. Dawley, Chm.
Ph: (202)466-5460
Fax: (202)296-3184
E-mail: info@futuresindustry.org
URL: http://www.futuresindustry.org
Staff: 24. **Descr:** Acts as a principal spokesman for the futures and options industry. Represents all facets of the futures industry, including many international exchanges. Works to preserve the system of free and competitive markets by representing the interests of the industry in connection with legislative and regulatory issues. **Fnd:** 1955. **Mem:** 250. **Pub:** *eMarketBeat* (weekly); *FIA Membership Directory* (annual); *FIA Membership Guide*; *Futures Industry* (bimonthly); *Volume Reports* (monthly); *Weekly Bulletin.*

1385 ■ Herocare
10491 Six Mile Cypress Pkwy., Ste. 204
Fort Myers, FL 33966-6406
Contact: Lane Houk, Program Dir.
Free: 877-437-6411
E-mail: concierge@herocare.org
URL: http://www.herocare.org

Descr: Works to address the housing and financial needs of essential service workers across United States. Offers programs for the easy navigation of home ownership and financial security. Aims to become a non profit advocate for public servants in the nation.

1386 ■ Identity Theft Resource Center (ITRC)
PO Box 26833
San Diego, CA 92196
Contact: Rex Davis, Dir. of Operations
Ph: (858)693-7935
E-mail: itrc@idtheftcenter.org
URL: http://www.idtheftcenter.org
Descr: Dedicated to the development and implementation of a comprehensive program against identity theft. **Fnd:** 1999. **Pub:** *Identity Theft: The Aftermath* (periodic).

1387 ■ Information Technology Services Marketing Association (ITSMA)
Lexington Office Park
420 Bedford St., Ste. 110
Lexington, MA 02420
Contact: David C. Munn, Pres./CEO
Ph: (781)862-8500
Fax: (781)674-1366
E-mail: info@itsma.com
URL: http://www.itsma.com
Descr: Supports marketing executives who market and sell technology-related services and solutions. Provides research, consulting and training to the world's leading technology, communications, and professional services providers. Facilitates peer sharing and networking opportunities among members.

1388 ■ Institute of Business Appraisers (IBA)
PO Box 17410
Plantation, FL 33318
Contact: Michelle G. Miles Esq., Exec. Dir.
Ph: (954)584-1144
Fax: (954)584-1184
E-mail: hqiba@go-iba.org
URL: http://www.go-iba.org
Staff: 9. **Descr:** Individuals involved or with interested in the practice of business valuation and appraisal. Seeks to educate the public in matters relating to business valuation and appraisal; to support legislation establishing minimum standards of competence for persons offering these services; to promulgate a code of ethics for all members to observe. Conducts advancement programs that include the awards of the professional designation's Certified Business Appraiser (CBA) and Business Valuator Accredited in Litigation to qualifying members. Maintains referral program and speakers' bureau; compiles statistics. Offers educational programs. **Fnd:** 1978. **Mem:** 3000. **Reg. Groups:** 7. **Local Groups:** 3. **Pub:** *Basic Business Appraisal*; *Business Appraisal Practice* (semiannual); *IBA Applicants Handbook*; *Institute of Business Appraisers-- Newsletter* (quarterly); Monographs; Audiotapes.

1389 ■ Institute for Professionals in Taxation (IPT)
600 Northpark Town Center
1200 Abernathy Rd., Ste. L-2
Atlanta, GA 30328-1040
Contact: Billy D. Cook, Exec. Dir.
Ph: (404)240-2300
Fax: (404)240-2315
E-mail: ipt@ipt.org
URL: http://www.ipt.org
Staff: 13. **Descr:** Corporate property and sales tax representatives; attorneys, appraisers, consultants, and accountants who represent corporate taxpayers. Seeks to foster the education of members; promotes study in property and sales taxation; encourages the interchange of ideas and assistance among members; facilitates cooperation with governmental authorities in solving problems of ad valorem (imposed at a rate percent of value) and sales tax administration. Strives for high standards of competence and efficiency in corporate property and sales tax management. Offers professional certification for

property and sales tax professionals. Presents views of members to other taxpayer organizations, governmental bodies, and interested persons. Analyzes existing and proposed legislation, regulations, administrative actions, and to her relevant matters; keeps members informed of findings. **Fnd:** 1976. **Mem:** 4400. **Pub:** *Property Tax Report* (monthly); *Property Taxation*; *Sales and Use Taxation*; *Sales Tax Report* (monthly); *Third-Party Drop Shipment Survey* (semiannual); Proceedings; Brochures; Papers.

1390 ■ International Association of Assessing Officers (IAAO)
314 W 10th St.
Kansas City, MO 64105-1616
Contact: Lisa Daniels MPA, Exec. Dir.
Ph: (816)701-8100
Free: 800-616-4226
Fax: (816)701-8149
E-mail: daniels@iaao.org
URL: http://www.iaao.org
Staff: 20. **Descr:** State and local officials concerned with valuation of property for ad valorem property tax purposes. Works to improve standards and conduct research on tax assessment. Offers educational programs and seminars; awards professional designations; makes available research and consulting services. Organizes task forces on special topics. **Fnd:** 1934. **Mem:** 7600. **Reg. Groups:** 4. **State Groups:** 35. **Pub:** *Fair and Equitable* (monthly); *Journal of Property Tax Assessment and Administration* (quarterly).

1391 ■ International Association of Financial Crimes Investigators (IAFCI)
1020 Suncast Ln., Ste. 102
El Dorado Hills, CA 95762
Contact: Jan Moffett
Ph: (916)939-5000
Fax: (916)939-0395
E-mail: admin@iafci.org
URL: http://www.iafci.org
Staff: 4. **Descr:** Special agents, investigators, and investigation supervisors who investigate criminal violations of credit card laws and prosecute offenders; law enforcement officers, prosecutors, or related officials who investigate, apprehend, and prosecute credit card offenders; employees of card issuing institutions who are responsible for credit card security and investigations; management personnel of companies performing services for the credit card industry. Aids in the establishment of effective credit card security programs; suppresses fraudulent use of credit cards; and detects and proceeds with the apprehension of credit card thieves. Emphasizes a professional approach to the investigative function, a free exchange of criminal intelligence, and a vigorous prosecution policy. Encourages members to use existing federal and local criminal statutes and to seek more effective legislation in areas where it is lacking. Provides workshops and training conferences to acquaint law enforcement bodies and the membership with technological advances in the industry. **Fnd:** 1968. **Mem:** 3500. **Local Groups:** 42. **Pub:** *IAFCI News* (quarterly); Newsletter (quarterly).

1392 ■ International Association of Financial Engineers (IAFE)
347 5th Ave., Ste. 703
New York, NY 10016
Contact: David Jaffe, Exec. Dir.
Ph: (646)736-0705
Fax: (646)417-6378
E-mail: main@iafe.org
URL: http://www.iafe.org
Descr: Seeks to develop and advance financial engineering as a formal discipline and profession. Provides a forum for the exchange of ideas on topics of relevance and interest to the financial engineering community. Facilitates interaction and communication between the practitioners of quantitative finance and the academic financial community. Raises awareness of the value of the field to industry. **Fnd:**

1992. **Pub:** *The Journal of Derivatives* (quarterly); Newsletter (quarterly); Papers.

1393 ■ International Economic Alliance (IEA)
1 Mifflin Pl., Ste. 400
Cambridge, MA 02138
Contact: Alexandre Gourevitch, Exec. Dir.
Ph: (617)359-5711
Fax: (617)812-0499
E-mail: van.mccormick@iealliance.org
URL: http://www.iealliance.org
Descr: Aims to further global trade, economic development and advance business relations. Brings together the world's key players and decision-makers (business and government leaders, investors and leading intellectuals) for practical, open, bi-partisan and solution-oriented exchange of ideas. Serves as a source of knowledge, facilitator of relationships, and catalyst for new business opportunities. **Fnd:** 2003.

1394 ■ International Franchise Association (IFA)
1501 K St. NW, Ste. 350
Washington, DC 20005
Contact: Cecelia Bond, Exec. Asst.
Ph: (202)628-8000
Fax: (202)628-0812
E-mail: ifa@franchise.org
URL: http://www.franchise.org
Staff: 30. **Descr:** Firms in 100 countries utilizing the franchise method of distribution for goods and services in all industries. **Fnd:** 1960. **Mem:** 30000. **Pub:** *Franchise Opportunities Guide* (semiannual); *Franchising World Magazine* (bimonthly).

1395 ■ International Reciprocal Trade Association (IRTA)
524 Middle St.
Portsmouth, VA 23704
Contact: Ron D. Whitney, Exec. Dir.
Ph: (757)393-2292
Fax: (757)257-4014
E-mail: ron@irta.com
URL: http://www.irta.com
Staff: 2. **Descr:** Individuals, partnerships, corporations, and firms that engage in the commercial barter industry worldwide, including local trade exchanges which act as clearinghouses, and corporate trade companies which arrange domestic and international barter transactions. Works to foster and promote the interests of the commercial barter industry through the establishment of ethical standards and self-regulation; to represent members before government agencies in matters affecting the industry; to introduce firms engaged in bartering activities; to resolve disputes between members; influence public laws and regulations affecting the industry; disseminate information and conduct public relations programs. Serves as a clearinghouse for industry and public inquiries. Compiles statistics on the segment of commercial barter accounted for by organized trade exchanges and corporate trade companies. Conducts consumer protection, educational, and training programs. Operates Corporate Barter Council as a self-governing body for the corporate trade sector. Awards professional accreditation; operates referral and placement services; maintains speakers' bureau; supports charitable programs. **Fnd:** 1979. **Mem:** 200. **Pub:** *IRTA Dialogue* (quarterly).

1396 ■ International Society of Appraisers (ISA)
737 N Michigan Ave., Ste. 2100
Chicago, IL 60611
Contact: Fred J. Winer, Pres.
Ph: (312)981-6778
Fax: (312)981-6787
E-mail: isa@isa-appraisers.org
URL: http://www.isa-appraisers.org
Staff: 8. **Descr:** Represents personal property appraisers. Seeks to provide the public with a network of appraisal specialists who have been pre-screened by ISA. Conducts educational opportunities for members, the consumer public, and other affinity groups. Offers Certified Appraiser of Personal Property Program, education, testing, and certification program. Compiles statistics; maintains speakers' bureau. Offers free appraisal referral service in the U.S. and Canada. **Fnd:** 1979. **Mem:** 1400. **State Groups:** 17. **Pub:** *ISA Professional Appraisers Information Exchange*; Membership Directory (annual).

1397 ■ Howard Jarvis Taxpayers Association (HJTA)
621 S Westmoreland Ave., Ste. 202
Los Angeles, CA 90005
Contact: Kris Vosburgh, Exec. Dir.
Ph: (213)384-9656
E-mail: info@hjta.org
URL: http://www.hjta.org
Staff: 5. **Descr:** Dedicated to tax relief for Californians. **Fnd:** 1978. **Mem:** 200000. **Pub:** *Taxing Times* (quarterly).

1398 ■ JumpStart Coalition for Personal Financial Literacy
919 18th St. NW, Ste. 300
Washington, DC 20006
Contact: Laura Levine, Exec. Dir.
Ph: (202)466-8610
Free: 888-45-EDUCATE
E-mail: info@jumpstart.org
URL: http://www.jumpstartcoalition.org
Descr: Aims to improve the financial literacy of kindergarten through college-age youth. Seeks to prepare youth for life-long, successful financial decision-making. Provides advocacy, research, standards, and educational resources. **Fnd:** 1997. **Pub:** *JumpStart Update* (quarterly).

1399 ■ Marketing Ethnic Faculty Association (MEFA)
1705 College St.
Columbia, SC 29208
Contact: Dr. David Crockett, Exec. Sec./Treas.
E-mail: info@mefa-web.org
URL: http://mefa-web.org
Descr: Aims to promote the professional development of underrepresented ethnic faculty in the fields of marketing and related business disciplines. Provides supportive networks of individuals interested in advancing the field of marketing through scholarship, teaching, and other professional interests. Fosters awareness and appreciation for cultural diversity in business schools and other higher education institutions. **Fnd:** 2008.

1400 ■ Money Management International (MMI)
9009 W Loop S, 7th Fl.
Houston, TX 77096-1719
Contact: Cate Williams, VP of Financial Literacy
Free: 866-889-9347
E-mail: cate.williams@moneymanagement.org
URL: http://www.moneymanagement.org
Descr: Serves as a full service credit-counseling agency. Provides professional financial guidance, counseling, community-wide educational programs and debt management assistance to consumers. **Pub:** Newsletter; Annual Report (annual); Articles (monthly).

1401 ■ Multi-Level Marketing International Association (MLMIA)
11956 Bernardo Plaza Dr., No. 313
San Diego, CA 92128
Contact: Doris Wood, Chair
Ph: (949)854-0484
Fax: (949)854-7687
E-mail: info@mlmia.com
URL: http://www.mlmia.com
Staff: 2. **Descr:** Companies, support groups, and distributors. Seeks to strengthen and improve the Multi-Level Marketing (also known as Network Marketing) industry in the U.S. and abroad. (Multi-Level Marketing is a method of selling products directly, independently, and usually out of the home, without the medium of a retail outlet.) Provides educational services to consumers and law enforcement agencies. Serves as an information source for the industry. Offers recommendations for start-up companies; maintains speakers' bureau; conducts training programs. **Fnd:** 1985. **Mem:** 5000. **Pub:** *Connecting Point*; *Corporate Directory - Support Directory* (quarterly); Articles.

1402 ■ MultiState Tax Commission (MTC)
444 N Capitol St. NW, Ste. 425
Washington, DC 20001-1512
Contact: Joe Huddleston, Exec. Dir.
Ph: (202)624-8699
Fax: (202)624-8819
E-mail: mtc@mtc.gov
URL: http://www.mtc.gov
Staff: 40. **Descr:** States that have enacted the Multistate Tax Compact into law; states whose governors have requested associate membership or which have enacted the Compact legislation conditional upon congressional approval. Purposes are to: facilitate proper determination of state and local tax liability of multistate taxpayers, including the equitable apportionment of tax bases and settlement of apportionment disputes; promote uniformity or compatibility in significant components of tax systems; facilitate taxpayer convenience and compliance in the filing of tax returns and in other phases of tax administration; to avoid duplicative taxation. Performs corporate income tax audits, sales and use tax audits, and property tax audits in the form of a joint audit. (A joint audit is the audit of a corporate business on behalf of several states at one time.) Maintains National Nexus Program that encourages multistate businesses to comply with state tax laws. Represents states before Congress and the Executive Branch with respect to federal laws and policies having an impact on state tax authority. **Fnd:** 1967. **Mem:** 21. **Pub:** *MTC Review* (periodic); *Multistate Tax Commission Review*; Annual Report.

1403 ■ My Own Business, Inc. (MOBI)
13181 Crossroads Pkwy. N, Ste. 190
City of Industry, CA 91746
Contact: Phil Holland, Founder
Ph: (562)463-1800
Fax: (562)463-1802
E-mail: support@myownbusiness.org
URL: http://www.myownbusiness.org
Descr: Educates entrepreneurs by providing free coursework. Develops, produces, implements, updates and markets educational offerings through multiple delivery channels. Seeks to expand collaborations with schools, the community and other institutions. **Fnd:** 1992. **Pub:** *FYI Newsletter* (quarterly).

1404 ■ Myvesta
701 E Gudie Dr.
Rockville, MD 20850
Contact: Steve Rhode, Pres./Co-Founder
Ph: (301)762-5270
Free: 800-MY-VESTA
URL: http://myvesta.org
Descr: Works to assist people overcome money troubles through education and assistance. **Pub:** *Get Out of Debt*; *Path to Happiness & Wealth*; Newsletter.

1405 ■ National Association of Credit Union Services Organizations (NACUSO)
PMB 3419 Via Lido, No. 135
Newport Beach, CA 92663
Contact: Thomas C. Davis, Pres./CEO
Ph: (949)645-5296
Free: 888-462-2870
Fax: (949)645-5297
E-mail: info@nacuso.org
URL: http://www.nacuso.org
Staff: 3. **Descr:** Credit union service organizations and their employees. Promotes professional advancement of credit union service organization staff; seeks to insure adherence to high standards of ethics and practice among members. Conducts research and educational programs; formulates and enforces standards of conduct and practice; maintains speakers' bureau; compiles statistics. **Fnd:** 1985. **Mem:** 400. **Pub:** *Higher Ground: Thoughts on taking it to*

the next level; National CUSO Directory (annual); *Now and in the Future: NACUSO is Here to Stay; Ten Keys to Transitioning Investment Services from the CUSO;* Brochure.

1406 ■ National Association of Enrolled Agents (NAEA)
1120 Connecticut Ave. NW, Ste. 460
Washington, DC 20036-3953
Contact: Sandra Martin EA, Pres.
Ph: (202)822-6232
Fax: (202)822-6270
E-mail: info@naea.org
URL: http://www.naea.org
Staff: 14. **Descr:** Individuals who have gained Enrolled Agent status and are thus qualified to represent all classes of taxpayers at any administrative level of the Internal Revenue Service. Promotes ethical representation of the financial position of taxpayers before government agencies. Conducts seminars and conferences to keep members informed of legislation and regulations affecting the profession and taxpayers. Makes presentations to civic, community, educational, and employee groups to inform the public of its rights, privileges, and obligations under tax laws and regulations. Operates seminars in taxation and taxpayer representation including the National Tax Practice Institute, a 3-year, tri-level program in taxpayer representation and audit procedures. **Fnd:** 1972. **Mem:** 11000. **State Groups:** 39. **Local Groups:** 42. **Pub:** *E@lert* (weekly); *EA Journal* (bimonthly); Membership Directory (annual).

1407 ■ National Association of Small Business Contractors (NASBC)
1200 G St. NW, Ste. 800
Washington, DC 20005
Contact: Cris Young, Pres.
Free: 888-861-9290
URL: http://www.nasbc.org
Descr: Serves and advances the interests of small business contractors. Seeks to establish opportunities for small business owners to meet with state and federal agencies, prime contractors, potential teaming partners and procurement experts. Strives to create a strong and respected voice for advocacy in support of small business' interests.

1408 ■ National Coalition for Capital (NCC)
3128 M St. NW, Ste. 300
Washington, DC 20007
Contact: Ben Dupuy
Ph: (202)337-1661
E-mail: ben@nationalcoalitionforcapital.org
URL: http://www.nationalcoalitionforcapital.org
Descr: Represents leaders who support economic development and job creation through long-term access to capital for entrepreneurs and emerging companies. Serves as a resource for promising small and emerging companies, entrepreneurs, investors, economic developers and other stakeholders within the nation's emerging investment infrastructure.

1409 ■ National Committee on Pay Equity (NCPE)
555 New Jersey Ave. NW
Washington, DC 20001-2029
Contact: Michele Leber, Chair
Ph: (703)920-2010
Fax: (703)979-6372
E-mail: fairpay@pay-equity.org
URL: http://www.pay-equity.org
Descr: Individuals and organizations such as women's groups, labor unions, professional associations, minority and civil rights groups, and governmental and educational groups. Educates the public about the historical, legal, and economic basis for pay inequities between men and women and white people and people of color. Promotes grassroots activism. **Fnd:** 1979. **Mem:** 85. **Pub:** *Bargaining for Pay Equity: A Strategy Manual; Briefing Paper: The Wage Gap; Erase the Bias: A Pay Equity Guide to Eliminating Race and Sex Bias from Wage Setting Systems; The Intersection Between Pay Equity and Workplace Representation; Pay Equity Activity in the Public Sector, 1979-1989; Pay Equity: An Issue of Race, Ethnicity, and Sex; Pay Equity Bibliography and Resource Listing; Pay Equity Makes Good Business Sense.*

1410 ■ National Credit Reporting Association (NCRA)
125 E Lake St., Ste. 200
Bloomingdale, IL 60108
Contact: Terry Clemans, Exec. Dir.
Ph: (630)539-1525
Fax: (630)539-1526
E-mail: tclemans@ncrainc.org
URL: http://www.ncrainc.org
Descr: Represents consumer reporting agencies and associated professionals that provide products and services to credit grantors, employers, landlords, and all types of general businesses. Aims to further and promote the general welfare of its members, credit grantors, and consumers. Fosters sound business practices within the consumer credit and credit reporting industries. **Fnd:** 1992. **Pub:** *The Advocate* (bimonthly); *The Credit Reporter* (bimonthly).

1411 ■ National Futures Association (NFA)
300 S Riverside Plz., No. 1800
Chicago, IL 60606-6615
Contact: Daniel J. Roth, Pres.
Ph: (312)781-1300
Free: 800-621-3570
Fax: (312)781-1467
E-mail: information@nfa.futures.org
URL: http://www.nfa.futures.org
Staff: 246. **Descr:** Futures commission merchants; commodity trading advisors; commodity pool operators; brokers and their associated persons. Works to: strengthen and expand industry self-regulation to include all segments of the futures industry; provide uniform standards to eliminate duplication of effort and conflict; remove unnecessary regulatory constraints to aid effective regulation. Conducts member qualification screening, financial surveillance, and registration. Monitors and enforces customer protection rules and uniform business standards. Maintains information center. Arbitrates customer disputes; audits non-exchange member FCM's. **Fnd:** 1982. **Mem:** 3772. **Pub:** *Annual Review* (annual); *National Futures Association--News Release* (periodic); *News, Facts, Actions* (quarterly); *NFA Manual;* Pamphlets.

1412 ■ National Investment Banking Association (NIBA)
PO Box 6625
Athens, GA 30604
Contact: Emily Foshee, Exec. Dir.
Ph: (706)208-9620
Fax: (706)208-1033
E-mail: emily@nibanet.org
URL: http://www.nibanet.org
Descr: Represents regional and independent brokerages, investment banking firms, and related capital market service providers. Provides a forum for small companies seeking access and exposure to underwriters and brokers/dealers in connection with their capital formation. Supports an enhanced capital formation environment for small companies. **Pub:** Newsletter.

1413 ■ National Taxpayers Union (NTU)
108 N Alfred St.
Alexandria, VA 22314
Contact: Duane Parde, Pres.
Ph: (703)683-5700
Fax: (703)683-5722
E-mail: ntu@ntu.org
URL: http://www.ntu.org
Staff: 20. **Descr:** Seeks to: reduce government spending; cut taxes; protect the rights of taxpayers. Claims to have helped generate federal budget cuts of over 120 billion dollars. Activities include research programs and an intense lobbying campaign in Washington, DC; has been a leader in the fights against government ventures such as: social security tax; guaranteed income; congressional and bureaucratic pay raises; federal subsidies; foreign aid; national health insurance. Works for a balanced federal budget/tax limitation constitutional amendment; federal pension reform; reduction of capital gains and personal income tax; social security reform. Has worked for airline deregulation; indexing of federal income tax, California's Proposition 13, Massachusetts Proposition 2 1/2, and other state tax cutting initiatives. Conducts annual voting study of congressmen and senators, rating their votes on spending and tax issues and presenting awards for best and worst records. **Fnd:** 1969. **Mem:** 335000. **Pub:** *Dollars and Sense* (bimonthly); *How to Fight Property Taxes; Tax Savings Report* (10/year); *Taxpayer's Action Guide; Taxpayers Resource Book.*

1414 ■ New York Stock Exchange (NYSE)
11 Wall St.
New York, NY 10005
Contact: John A. Thain, CEO/Dir.
Ph: (212)656-3000
E-mail: boardofdirectors@nyse.com
URL: http://www.nyse.com
Descr: Aims to add value to the capital raising and asset management process by providing a cost effective, self regulated marketplace for the trading of financial instruments. Promotes confidence in, and understanding of, industry processes and serves as a forum for discussion of relevant national and international policy issues. **Fnd:** 1792. **Pub:** *The Exchange* (monthly); *New York Stock Exchange: Another Century; The New York Stock Exchange: The First 200 Years; Weekly Bulletin* (weekly); Magazine (bimonthly).

1415 ■ North American Securities Administrators Association (NASAA)
750 1st St. NE, Ste. 1140
Washington, DC 20002-8034
Contact: Russ Iuculano, Exec. Dir.
Ph: (202)737-0900
Fax: (202)783-3571
E-mail: info@nasaa.org
URL: http://www.nasaa.org
Staff: 16. **Descr:** Represents the interests of the state, provincial and territorial securities administrators in the U.S., Canada, Mexico and Puerto Rico. Provides support to its members in government relations and with federal regulators, industry SROs and other groups. **Fnd:** 1919. **Mem:** 67. **Pub:** *NASAA Reports in CCH* (monthly).

1416 ■ Pacific Stock Exchange (PSE)
115 Sansome St.
San Francisco, CA 94104
Contact: Philip D. Defeo, Chm./CEO
Ph: (415)393-4000
Fax: (415)954-5507
E-mail: info@pacificex.com
Staff: 376. **Descr:** Maintains markets in nearly 1800 equity issues and 300 options in San Francisco and Los Angeles, CA. **Fnd:** 1957. **Mem:** 551. **Pub:** *Directory of Securities* (quarterly); Annual Report (annual); Newsletter (quarterly).

1417 ■ Professional Women of Color Network (PWOCN)
PO Box 22367
Seattle, WA 98122
Contact: Meko L. Lawson, Founder
Ph: (206)568-3044
Fax: (206)568-3476
E-mail: info@pwocn.org
URL: http://www.pwocn.org
Descr: Seeks to create a business resource for all professional women of color. Facilitates and encourages strategic business relationships amongst all women of color. Fosters the professional advancement of all women of color. **Fnd:** 2002.

1418 ■ Small Business Legislative Council (SBLC)
1100 H St. NW, Ste. 540
Washington, DC 20005
Contact: John Satagaj, Pres./Gen. Counsel
Ph: (202)639-8500
Fax: (202)296-5333
E-mail: email@sblc.org
URL: http://www.sblc.org

Staff: 2. **Descr:** Serves as an independent coalition of trade and professional associations that share a common commitment to the future of small business. Represents the interests of small businesses in such diverse economic sectors as manufacturing, retailing, distribution, professional and technical services, construction, transportation, and agriculture. **Fnd:** 1976. **Mem:** 106. **Pub:** Brochure; Newsletter (monthly).

1419 ■ Smart Card Alliance
191 Clarksville Rd.
Princeton Junction, NJ 08550
Contact: Randy Vanderhoof, Exec. Dir.
Free: 800-556-6828
Fax: (609)587-4248
E-mail: info@smartcardalliance.org
URL: http://www.smartcardalliance.org
Descr: Promotes acceptance of multiple application smart cards for banking, financial services, telecommunications, technology, healthcare, retail, and entertainment industries. **Fnd:** 2001. **Mem:** 185. **Pub:** Smart Card Talk (monthly); Reports.

1420 ■ Society of Consumer Affairs Professionals in Business (SOCAP)
675 N Washington St., Ste. 200
Alexandria, VA 22314
Contact: Matthew R. D'Uva, Pres.
Ph: (703)519-3700
Fax: (703)549-4886
E-mail: socap@socap.org
URL: http://www.socap.org
Staff: 8. **Descr:** Individuals engaged in the management of consumer affairs/customer service divisions of businesses. Fosters the integrity of business in its dealings with consumers. Promotes harmonious relationships among business, government, and consumers. Advances the consumer affairs profession. Seeks to provide a means for businesses to compare their successes and failures in consumer affairs. Conducts research and educational programs; maintains speakers' bureau; operates placement service. **Fnd:** 1973. **Mem:** 2000. **Reg. Groups:** 21. **Pub:** Customer Relationship Management (quarterly); Society of Consumer Affairs Professionals in Business--Membership Directory (annual); Update (monthly).

1421 ■ Society of Cost Estimating and Analysis (SCEA)
527 Maple Ave. E, Ste. 301
Vienna, VA 22180
Contact: Robyn Kane, Sec.
Ph: (703)938-5090
Fax: (703)938-5091
E-mail: scea@sceaonline.org
URL: http://www.sceaonline.net
Staff: 3. **Descr:** Works to improve cost estimating and analysis in government and industry and to enhance the professional competence and achievements of its members. Administers a professional certification program leading to the designation of Certified Cost Estimator/Analyst; offers extensive literature in the field through its Professional Development Program. Goals of the Society include enhancing the profession of cost estimating and analysis, fostering the professional growth of its members, enhancing the understanding and application of cost estimating, analysis and related disciplines throughout government and industry and providing forums and media through which current issues of interest to the profession can be addressed and advances in the state-of-the-art can be shared. **Fnd:** 1990. **Mem:** 2000. **Local Groups:** 12. **Pub:** Journal of Cost Analysis & Parametrics (annual); National Estimator (semiannual).

1422 ■ Society of Management Accountants of Canada (SMAC)
1 Robert Speck Pkwy., Ste. 1400
Mississauga, ON, Canada L4Z 3M3
Contact: Mr. Steve F. Vieweg, Pres./CEO
Ph: (905)949-4200
Free: 800-263-7622
Fax: (905)949-0888

E-mail: svieweg@cma-canada.org
URL: http://www.cma-canada.org
Staff: 26. **Descr:** Certified Management Accountants (CMAs). Provides business advice and direction to improve organizational decisions. Offers educational and research programs. **Fnd:** 1920. **Mem:** 47000. **State Groups:** 12. **Pub:** CMA Management Magazine (9/year).

1423 ■ Society of Professional Accountants of Canada (SPAC)
250 Consumers Rd., Ste. 1007
Toronto, ON, Canada M2J 4V6
Contact: Henry J. Balazs, Exec. Sec.
Ph: (416)350-8145
Free: 877-515-4447
Fax: (416)350-8146
E-mail: ceo@professionalaccountant.org
Descr: Professional accountants and individuals working to pass qualifying accountancy examinations. Promotes ongoing professional education among accountants; encourages students to enter the accounting field; works to advance the profession of accounting. Gathers and disseminates information on accounting; sponsors educational programs; conducts professional accountancy qualifying examinations. **Fnd:** 1978. **Mem:** 348. **Pub:** Professional Accountant (quarterly).

1424 ■ Society of Risk Management Consultants (SRMC)
330 S Executive Dr., Ste. 301
Brookfield, WI 53005-4275
Contact: Thomas J. Krzys CPCU
Free: 800-765-SRMC
E-mail: webmaster@srmcsociety.org
URL: http://www.srmcsociety.org
Descr: Independent risk management and insurance consultants who do not sell insurance. Aims to ensure high ethical standards, professional competence, and independence among risk management and insurance consultants. Maintains speakers' bureau. **Fnd:** 1984. **Mem:** 150. **Pub:** SRMC Journal; Membership Directory (periodic).

1425 ■ SOHO America
130 E John Carpenter Fwy.
Irving, TX 75062
Free: 800-495-SOHO
E-mail: soho@1sas.com
URL: http://www.soho.org
Descr: Provides virtual community for small business and home office professionals with information pertaining to small and home-based businesses.

1426 ■ Taxpayers for Common Sense (TCS)
651 Pennsylvania Ave. SE
Washington, DC 20003
Contact: Ryan Alexander, Pres.
Ph: (202)546-8500
Free: 800-829-7293
Fax: (202)546-8511
E-mail: info@taxpayer.net
URL: http://www.taxpayer.net
Descr: Independent advocate for the American taxpayer dedicated to cutting wasteful government spending and subsidies in order to achieve a responsible, efficient government. Assists grassroots partners, works with congress, and communicates through the media. **Fnd:** 1995. **Pub:** Annual Report (annual).

1427 ■ United for a Fair Economy (UFE)
29 Winter St.
Boston, MA 02108
Contact: Ann C. Manning, Interim Exec. Dir.
Ph: (617)423-2148
Fax: (617)423-0191
E-mail: info@faireconomy.org
URL: http://www.faireconomy.org
Staff: 17. **Descr:** Individuals concerned about "the excessive inequality of income and wealth in the United States." Promotes a more equitable distribution of wealth; seeks to empower the economically disenfranchised. Conducts grassroots economic education courses; maintains theater troupe and arts

programs; sponsors public education programs to raise awareness of economic inequality. **Fnd:** 1995. **Mem:** 5000. **Pub:** Fair Play (semiannual); Annual Report (annual); Reports.

1428 ■ U.S. Asian Business Council (USABC)
6348 N Milwaukee Ave., No. 337
Chicago, IL 60646
Contact: Jimmy D. Lee, Managing Dir.
Ph: (202)255-5301
URL: http://www.usasianbusiness.org
Descr: Seeks to develop mutually beneficial relationships amongst the Asian business community, government institutions, and corporations in the United States and abroad. Works to advocate policies and programs that grow and support Asian businesses in the global marketplace. Supports the development of small businesses and entrepreneurship in the Asian Pacific American community. **Pub:** Newsletter (quarterly).

1429 ■ Women Business Owners (WBO)
12123 Quail Creek Dr.
Houston, TX 77070-2214
Contact: Anna Campbell, Pres.
Free: 877-209-9461
E-mail: info@womenbizowners.org
URL: http://www.womenbizowners.org
Descr: Aims to empower, educate and enhance the lives of children and women business owners throughout the world. Provides programs and workshops on educating future entrepreneurs. Works to develop and encourage entrepreneurship, achievement and success in business. **Fnd:** 2004.

1430 ■ Women Entrepreneurs in Science and Technology (WEST)
155 Seaport Blvd., 11th Fl.
Boston, MA 02210
Contact: Gwen Acton PhD, Pres.
Ph: (617)988-6120
Fax: (641)453-3086
E-mail: info@westorg.org
URL: http://www.westorg.org
Descr: Seeks to advance women in science and technology to achieve success and recognition as contributors and leaders. Develops and offers programs that cover issues that are relevant to the career and business issues in the diverse environments of life sciences, biotech, engineering, technology and research. Serves as a forum for men and women, educational institutions, service organizations and corporations. **Pub:** WEST News (monthly).

1431 ■ Women's International Shipping and Trading Association (WISTA)
Blank Rome, LLP
600 New Hampshire Ave. NW
Washington, DC 20037
Contact: Jeanne M. Grasso, Pres.
E-mail: grasso@blankrome.com
URL: http://www.wista.net
Descr: Seeks to advance the interests of women engaged in shipping and trading-related business throughout the world. **Fnd:** 1974. **Mem:** 500.

1432 ■ Women's World Banking - USA (WWB)
8 W 40th St., 9th Fl.
New York, NY 10018
Contact: Ms. Mary Ellen Iskenderian, Pres./CEO
Ph: (212)768-8513
Fax: (212)768-8519
E-mail: communications@swwb.org
URL: http://www.swwb.org
Staff: 30. **Descr:** Aims to expand low-income women's economic assets, participation and power by opening access to finance, information and markets. Provides and organizes support to affiliates who in turn offer direct services to low-income women. Builds learning and change networks comprised of leading microfinance institutions and banks. Works with policy makers to build financial systems that work for the "poor majority". Seeks to create an environment that will help a low income woman build her business, improve her living conditions, keep her family well-fed and healthy, educate her children,

develop respect at home and in her community, and secure a political voice. **Fnd:** 1979. **Mem:** 49. **Pub:** *Global Network for Banking Innovation*; *What Works* (periodic); Manuals.

1433 ■ World Federation of Direct Selling Associations (WFDSA)
1667 K St. NW, Ste. 1100
Washington, DC 20006
Contact: Neil H. Offen, Chm.
Ph: (202)452-8866
Fax: (202)452-9010
E-mail: info@wfdsa.org
URL: http://www.wfdsa.org
Staff: 6. **Descr:** Organized for the purpose of promoting the common business interests of its members. Exchanges information among members. Fosters highest standards of direct selling practices, consumer protection and ethics in the marketplace, by adoption and promotion of the Codes of Conduct for Direct Selling. Improves communications through sponsorship of World Congress of direct selling. Encourages personal relationships and cooperation among people in direct selling. Promotes education internationally through programs and funding, relying on the United States Direct Selling Education Foundation (USDSEF) to help it towards this objective. **Fnd:** 1978. **Mem:** 59. **Reg. Groups:** 10. **Pub:** *WFDSA Directory of Members* (annual); *World Federation News* (bimonthly).

State and Local Organizations and Agencies

Alabama

1434 ■ Alabama A & M University Small Business Development Center
PO Box 429
Normal, AL 35762
Contact: Eric O'hene, Dir.
Ph: (256)372-5608
URL: http://www.asbdc.org
Descr: Represents and promotes the small business sector. Provides management assistance to current and prospective small business owners. Helps to improve management skills and expand the products and services of members.

1435 ■ Alabama Credit Union League (ACUL)
PO Box 380428
Birmingham, AL 35238-0428
Contact: Ms. Adena Whitman Zamora, Dir., Public and Political Affairs
Ph: (205)991-9710
Free: 800-846-8374
Fax: (205)991-2576
E-mail: awhitman@acul.com
URL: http://www.acul.com
Descr: Promotes credit union membership, use of services, and organization of new credit unions. Seeks to perfect credit union laws; aids in the development of credit union services; assists in the training of credit union officials and employees. **Fnd:** 1934. **Pub:** *ACULetter* (quarterly); *Alabama Credit Union League Annual Report* (annual).

1436 ■ Alabama Small Business Development Consortium (ASBDC)
1500 1st Ave. N, Ste. R118
Birmingham, AL 35203
Contact: William Campbell, Dir.
Ph: (205)307-6510
Fax: (205)307-6511
URL: http://www.asbdc.org
Descr: Represents and promotes the small business sector. Provides management assistance to current and prospective small business owners. Helps to

improve management skills and expand the products and services of members.

1437 ■ Alabama Society of Enrolled Agents (ALSEA)
PO Box 8184
Dothan, AL 36304
Contact: Brenda Maupin, Treas.
Ph: (334)794-4087
E-mail: brenje@aol.com
URL: http://www.alsea.org
Descr: Aims to improve the knowledge, skills and professionalism of members in all areas of taxation. Enhances the role of enrolled agents among government agencies, other professions and the public at large. Advocates for taxpayer rights and protects members' interests.

1438 ■ Alabama State University Small Business Development Center
915 S Jackson St.
Montgomery, AL 36104
Contact: Lorenza Patrick, Dir.
Ph: (334)229-4138
Fax: (334)269-1102
E-mail: lpatrick@alasu.edu
URL: http://www.cobanetwork.com/sbdc
Descr: Represents and promotes the small business sector. Provides management assistance to current and prospective small business owners. Helps to improve management skills and expand the products and services of members.

1439 ■ Alabama Taxpayers Association
3712 Everest Dr.
Montgomery, AL 36106
Ph: (334)409-3119

1440 ■ American Society of Appraisers, Alabama Chapter
Corporate Art Source
2960 F Zelda Rd.
Montgomery, AL 36106
Contact: Jean Rainer Belt, Sec.
Fax: (334)271-2562
E-mail: casjb@mindspring.com
Descr: Serves as a professional appraisal educator, testing and accrediting society. Sponsors mandatory recertification program for all members. Offers consumer information service to the public.

1441 ■ Auburn-Opelika AIFA
2320 Moore's Mill Rd.
Auburn, AL 36830
Contact: Jenny Perry
Ph: (334)821-5433
Fax: (334)466-9168
URL: http://www.naifa-alabama.com
Descr: Represents the interests of insurance and financial advisors. Advocates for a positive legislative and regulatory environment. Enhances business and professional skills of members.

1442 ■ Auburn University Small Business Development Center
108 Lowder Business Bldg.
Auburn, AL 36849
Contact: Jackie Alexander Di Pofi, Dir.
Ph: (334)844-4220
E-mail: dipofja@auburn.edu
URL: http://www.sbdc.auburn.edu
Descr: Represents and promotes the small business sector. Provides management assistance to current and prospective small business owners. Helps to improve management skills and expand the products and services of members.

1443 ■ Central AIFA
301 1st St.
Clanton, AL 35046
Contact: Linda Foshee
Ph: (205)755-3375
Fax: (205)755-3798
URL: http://www.naifa-alabama.com
Descr: Represents the interests of insurance and financial advisors. Advocates for a positive legisla-

tive and regulatory environment. Enhances business and professional skills of members.

1444 ■ Demopolis AIFA
PO Box 320
Demopolis, AL 36732-0320
Contact: Nelson Beech
Ph: (334)289-3500
Fax: (334)289-3501
Descr: Represents the interests of insurance and financial advisors. Advocates for a positive legislative and regulatory environment. Enhances business and professional skills of members.

1445 ■ Desoto AIFA
903 Grand Ave. SW
Fort Payne, AL 35967
Ph: (256)845-2206
Fax: (256)845-3571
URL: http://www.naifa-alabama.com
Descr: Represents the interests of insurance and financial advisors. Advocates for a positive legislative and regulatory environment. Enhances business and professional skills of members.

1446 ■ Financial Planning Association of North Alabama
PO Box 1812
Birmingham, AL 35201-1812
Contact: Pete McCarn CFP, Pres.
Ph: (205)212-5353
E-mail: fpana@charter.net
URL: http://www.fpana.org
Descr: Supports the financial planning process in order to help people achieve their goals and dreams. Promotes the legislative, regulatory and professional interests of the financial services industry. **Fnd:** 2000.

1447 ■ Gadsden AIFA
400 Duncan St.
Gadsden, AL 35901
Contact: Kerry L. Wilson, Exec. Sec.
Ph: (256)546-4626
Fax: (256)546-9052
E-mail: tlewis@terrylewisinsurance.com
URL: http://www.gadsdenalu.com
Descr: Represents the interests of insurance and financial advisors. Advocates for a positive legislative and regulatory environment. Enhances business and professional skills of members.

1448 ■ Jacksonville State University Small Business Development Center
College of Commerce and Business Administration
Merrill Hall, Rm. 114
700 Pelham Rd. N
Jacksonville, AL 36265
Contact: Pat Shaddix, Dir.
Ph: (256)782-5271
E-mail: sbdc@jsu.edu
URL: http://www.jsu.edu/depart/sbdc
Descr: Represents and promotes the small business sector. Provides management assistance to current and prospective small business owners. Helps to improve management skills and expand the products and services of members.

1449 ■ Metro Multiline AIFA
4851 Cahaba River Rd., Ste. 117
Birmingham, AL 35243
Contact: Danny G. Wakefield, Pres.
Ph: (205)967-6886
Fax: (205)969-3656
E-mail: rene@reneburke.com
Descr: Represents the interest of insurance and financial advisors. Advocates for a positive legislative and regulatory environment. Enhances business and professional skills of members.

1450 ■ Morgan-Lawrence AIFA
PO Box 2405
Decatur, AL 35602
Contact: Michael E. Bates, Chm.
Ph: (256)355-2555
Fax: (256)355-2555
E-mail: armourgaa@aol.com

Descr: Represents the interests of insurance and financial advisors. Advocates for a positive legislative and regulatory environment. Enhances business and professional skills of members.

1451 ■ Phenix City AIFA
3544 Hwy. 431 N, No. B
Phenix City, AL 36867-2340
Ph: (334)297-2902
Fax: (334)297-3439
E-mail: emann@alfains.com
Descr: Represents the interests of insurance and financial advisors. Advocates for a positive legislative and regulatory environment. Enhances business and professional skills of members.

1452 ■ Sylacauga AIFA
PO Box 147
Sylacauga, AL 35150-0147
Ph: (256)362-2274
Fax: (256)632-2276
E-mail: dholland@alfains.com
Descr: Represents the interests of insurance and financial advisors. Advocates for a positive legislative and regulatory environment. Enhances business and professional skills of members.

1453 ■ Tombigbee AIFA
PO Box 198
Gilbertown, AL 36908-0198
Contact: Debbie Rentz
Ph: (251)843-5594
Fax: (251)246-5752
Descr: Represents the interest of insurance and financial advisors. Advocates for a positive legislative and regulatory environment. Enhances business and professional skills of members.

1454 ■ Troy University Small Business Development Center
Troy Campus
100 Industrial Blvd.
Troy, AL 36081
Contact: Sandra Lucas, Dir.
Ph: (334)674-2425
E-mail: slucas@troy.edu
URL: http://cibed.troy.edu/sbdc
Descr: Represents and promotes the small business sector. Provides management assistance to current and prospective small business owners. Helps to improve management skills and expand the products and services of members.

1455 ■ University of Alabama in Huntsville Small Business Development Center
301 Sparkman Dr.
Huntsville, AL 35899
Contact: Kannan Grant, Dir.
Ph: (256)824-6422
Fax: (256)824-4339
E-mail: sbdc@uah.edu
URL: http://sbdc.uah.edu
Descr: Represents and promotes the small business sector. Provides management assistance to current and prospective small business owners. Helps to improve management skills and expand the products and services of members.

1456 ■ University of Alabama Small Business Development Center
214 AIME Bldg.
720 2nd St.
Tuscaloosa, AL 35401
Contact: Paavo Hanninen, Dir.
Ph: (205)348-7011
URL: http://www.asbdc.org
Descr: Represents and promotes the small business sector. Provides management assistance to current and prospective small business owners. Helps to improve management skills and expand the products and services of members.

1457 ■ University of North Alabama - Small Business Development Center (UNA-SBDC)
Keller Hall 135
1 Harrison Plz.

Florence, AL 35632
Contact: Rick A. Lester, Dir.
Ph: (256)765-4599
Fax: (256)765-4813
URL: http://business.una.edu/sbdc
Descr: Represents and promotes the small business sector. Provides management assistance to current and prospective small business owners. Helps to improve management skills and expand the products and services of members.

1458 ■ University of South Alabama Small Business Development Center
MCOB, Rm. 118
307 University Blvd.
Mobile, AL 36688
Contact: Thomas Tucker, Dir.
Ph: (251)460-6004
Fax: (251)460-6246
E-mail: sbdc@usouthal.edu
URL: http://www.southalabama.edu/sbdc
Descr: Represents and promotes the small business sector. Provides management assistance to current and prospective small business owners. Helps to improve management skills and expand the products and services of members.

1459 ■ University of West Alabama Small Business Development Center
Guy Hunt Technical Complex, R122, Sta. 35
Livingston, AL 35470
Contact: Donald Mills, Dir.
Ph: (205)652-3665
URL: http://www.asbdc.org
Descr: Represents and promotes the small business sector. Provides management assistance to current and prospective small business owners. Helps to improve management skills and expand the products and services of members.

1460 ■ West Alabama AIFA
PO Box 336
Demopolis, AL 36732-2124
Ph: (334)289-0797
Fax: (334)289-1332
Descr: Represents the interest of insurance and financial advisors. Advocates for a positive legislative and regulatory environment. Enhances business and professional skills of members.

Alaska

1461 ■ Alaska Small Business Development Center - Central Region
201 N Lucille St., Ste. 2A
Wasilla, AK 99654
Contact: Jason Dinneen, Dir.
Ph: (907)373-7232
Free: 877-373-7232
Fax: (907)373-7234
E-mail: anjad2@uaa.alaska.edu
URL: http://www.aksbdc.org
Descr: Represents and promotes the small business sector. Provides management assistance to current and prospective small business owners. Helps to improve management skills and expand the products and services of members.

1462 ■ Alaska Small Business Development Center - Great North Region
UAF Tanana Valley Campus
604 Barnette St., Ste. 220
Fairbanks, AK 99701
Contact: Matt Tullar, Dir.
Ph: (907)456-7232
Free: 800-478-1701
Fax: (907)456-7233
E-mail: anmkt@uaa.alaska.edu
URL: http://www.tvc.uaf.edu/sbdc.html
Descr: Represents and promotes the small business sector. Provides management assistance to current and prospective small business owners. Helps to

improve management skills and expand the products and services of members.

1463 ■ Alaska Small Business Development Center - South Central Region
430 W 7th Ave., Ste. 110
Anchorage, AK 99501
Contact: Isaac Vanderburg, Dir.
Ph: (907)274-7232
Free: 800-478-7232
Fax: (907)274-9524
E-mail: anibv@uaa.alaska.edu
URL: http://www.aksbdc.org
Descr: Represents and promotes the small business sector. Provides management assistance to current and prospective small business owners. Helps to improve management skills and expand the products and services of members.

1464 ■ Alaska Small Business Development Center - South West Region
43335 Kalifornsky Beach Rd., Ste. 12
Soldotna, AK 99669
Contact: Mark Gregory, Dir.
Ph: (907)260-5629
Fax: (907)260-1695
E-mail: inmeg@uaa.alaska.edu
URL: http://www.aksbdc.org
Descr: Represents and promotes the small business sector. Provides management assistance to current and prospective small business owners. Helps to improve management skills and expand the products and services of members.

1465 ■ Alaska Small Business Development Center - Southeast Region
3100 Channel Dr., Ste. 306
Juneau, AK 99801
Contact: Amy Daugherty, Dir.
Ph: (907)463-3789
Fax: (907)463-3430
E-mail: anamd1@uaa.alaska.edu
URL: http://www.aksbdc.org
Descr: Represents and promotes the small business sector. Provides management assistance to current and prospective small business owners. Helps to improve management skills and expand the products and services of members.

1466 ■ Business and Professional Women, Alaska
PO Box 202406
Anchorage, AK 99520
Contact: Michelle Martin, Pres.
E-mail: mikkirm@yahoo.com
URL: http://www.bpwalaska.org
Descr: Represents the interests of business and professional women. Elevates the standards for women in business and professional settings. Promotes equity for all women in the workplace through advocacy, education and information. Provides professional development, networking and career advancement opportunities for working women.

1467 ■ International Association of Assessing Officers, Alaska
PO Box 196650
Anchorage, AK 99519
Contact: John W. Woodke, Rep.
Ph: (907)344-1345
Fax: (907)343-6599
E-mail: woodkejw@ci.anchorage.ak.us
Descr: Represents state and local officials concerned with valuation of property for ad valorem property tax purposes. Works to improve standards and conduct research on tax assessment. Promotes innovation and excellence in property appraisal, assessment administration, and property tax policy through professional development, education, research, and technical assistance.

1468 ■ North American Securities Administrators Association, Alaska
PO Box 110807
Juneau, AK 99811

Contact: Lorie Hovanec, Dir.
Ph: (907)465-2521
Descr: Represents the interests of the state, provincial and territorial securities administrators in the U.S.

Arizona

1469 ■ American Society of Appraisers, Phoenix Metro Chapter
PO Box 32662
Phoenix, AZ 85016-2662
Contact: Sandy St. Arnauld, Pres.
Ph: (602)265-5001
E-mail: allison@artappraisalsbyallison.com
URL: http://www.asaphoenix.org
Descr: Serves as a professional appraisal educator, testing and accrediting society. Sponsors mandatory recertification program for all members. Offers consumer information service to the public. **Fnd:** 1952.

1470 ■ American Society of Appraisers, Tucson Chapter
Artabella Jewelry Appraisals
760 E River Rd., Ste. 119
Tucson, AZ 85718
Contact: Tracy Lee Aros, Pres.
Ph: (520)751-7435
Fax: (520)546-5641
E-mail: tracyaros@aol.com
URL: http://www.appraisers.org/tucson
Descr: Serves as a professional appraisal educator, testing and accrediting society. Sponsors mandatory recertification program for all members. Offers consumer information service to the public.

1471 ■ Appraisal Institute, Phoenix Chapter
2525 E Camelback Rd., Ste. 1000
Phoenix, AZ 85016
Contact: Kathleen Holmes MAI, Pres.
Ph: (602)229-5837
Fax: (602)229-5996
E-mail: kathleen.holmes@cushwake.com
URL: http://www.aiphoenix.org
Descr: General appraisers who hold the MAI or SRPA designations, and residential members who hold the SRA designation.

1472 ■ Arizona Federation of Taxpayers (AFT)
1 E Camelback Rd., Ste. 550
Phoenix, AZ 85016
Contact: Tom Jenney, Exec. Dir.
Ph: (602)478-0146
E-mail: vc@aztaxpayers.org
URL: http://aztaxpayers.org/index.htm

1473 ■ Arizona Food Marketing Alliance (AFMA)
120 E Pierce St.
Phoenix, AZ 85004
Contact: Ms. George Seitts, Pres.
Ph: (602)252-9761
Fax: (602)252-9021
E-mail: droth@afmaaz.org
URL: http://www.afmaaz.org
Staff: 3. **Descr:** Strives to serve, represent, and advocate the interests of the Arizona food industry through legislation, regulation, and education. **Fnd:** 1943. **Mem:** 400. **Pub:** *Arizona Food Industry* (monthly); *Arizona Food Industry Directory* (annual); *Arizona Food Industry Journal* (monthly).

1474 ■ Arizona Society of Enrolled Agents (AzSEA)
118 E Carleton St., Ste. B
Prescott, AZ 86303
Contact: John G. Wood, Pres.
Ph: (928)771-1120
Fax: (928)771-1099
E-mail: jackwood@cableone.net
URL: http://www.aztaxpros.org
Descr: Aims to improve the knowledge, skills and professionalism of members in all areas of taxation. Enhances the role of enrolled agents among government agencies, other professions and the public at

large. Advocates for taxpayer rights and protects members' interests.

1475 ■ Arizona Western College Small Business Development Center
1351 S Redondo Center Dr., Ste. 101
Yuma, AZ 85365
Contact: Randy Nelson, Dir.
Ph: (928)317-6151
E-mail: randy.nelson@azwestern.edu
URL: http://www.azsbdc.net
Descr: Represents and promotes the small business sector. Provides management assistance to current and prospective small business owners. Helps to improve management skills and expand the products and services of members.

1476 ■ Business and Professional Women, Arizona
PO Box 1079
Safford, AZ 85548
Contact: Barbara Haralson
Ph: (928)348-0548
E-mail: ccbpw@aol.com
URL: http://www.bpwaz.org
Descr: Represents the interests of business and professional women. Elevates the standards for women in business and professional settings. Promotes equity for all women in the workplace through advocacy, education and information. Provides professional development, networking and career advancement opportunities for working women.

1477 ■ Business and Professional Women, Phoenix
PO Box 55208
Phoenix, AZ 85078-5208
Contact: Katherine Peterson, Co-Pres.
Ph: (602)996-4066
Fax: (602)996-5422
E-mail: prpc5@earthlink.net
URL: http://www.bpwphoenix.org
Descr: Represents the interests of business and professional women. Elevates the standards for women in business and professional settings. Promotes equity for all women in the workplace through advocacy, education and information. Provides professional development, networking and career advancement opportunities for working women.

1478 ■ Central Arizona Chapter of Enrolled Agents
Aquarian Tax Service
1310 W Palo Verde Dr.
Chandler, AZ 85224
Contact: James Henry, Treas.
Ph: (480)786-8585
Fax: (480)786-8515
E-mail: taxpro@cox.net
URL: http://cacea.com
Descr: Aims to improve the knowledge, skills and professionalism of members in all areas of taxation. Enhances the role of enrolled agents among government agencies, other professions and the public at large. Advocates for taxpayer rights and protects members' interests.

1479 ■ Central Arizona College Small Business Development Center
540 N Camino Mercado, No. 1
Casa Grande, AZ 85222
Contact: Jim Rhodes, Dir.
Ph: (520)494-6610
Fax: (520)494-6612
E-mail: sbdc@centralaz.edu
URL: http://www.centralaz.edu/biz
Descr: Represents and promotes the small business sector. Provides management assistance to current and prospective small business owners. Helps to

improve management skills and expand the products and services of members.

1480 ■ Cochise College Small Business Development Center
901 N Colombo Ave., Rm. 308
Sierra Vista, AZ 85635
Contact: Mignonne Hollis, Dir.
Ph: (520)515-5478
Free: 800-966-7943
E-mail: hollism@cochise.edu
URL: http://www.cochise.edu/conteducation/sbdc
Descr: Represents and promotes the small business sector. Provides management assistance to current and prospective small business owners. Helps to improve management skills and expand the products and services of members.

1481 ■ Coconino Community College Small Business Development Center
3000 N 4th St.
Flagstaff, AZ 86004
Contact: Annette Zinky, Dir.
Ph: (928)526-7653
Fax: (928)526-8693
E-mail: sbdc@coconino.edu
URL: http://www.coconino.edu/sbdc
Descr: Represents and promotes the small business sector. Provides management assistance to current and prospective small business owners. Helps to improve management skills and expand the products and services of members.

1482 ■ Eastern Arizona College Small Business Development Center (EAC SBDC)
Student Services Bldg., Rm. 113
615 N Stadium Ave.
Thatcher, AZ 85552
Contact: Mike Fox, Dir.
Ph: (928)428-8590
Free: 888-322-5780
Fax: (928)428-8591
E-mail: sbdc@eac.edu
URL: http://www.eac.edu/sbdc
Descr: Represents and promotes the small business sector. Provides management assistance to current and prospective small business owners. Helps to improve management skills and expand the products and services of members.

1483 ■ Financial Planning Association of Greater Phoenix Chapter
4718 E Cactus Rd., No. 815
Phoenix, AZ 85032-7710
Contact: Denise Reed CFP, Pres.
Ph: (480)483-9035
Fax: (480)483-9035
E-mail: jolynne@cgecentral.net
URL: http://www.fpaofphoenix.org
Descr: Promotes the advancement of knowledge in financial planning, supporting programs and projects that enable members to better serve their clients. Fosters the value of financial planning and advances the financial planning profession.

1484 ■ International Association of Assessing Officers, Arizona
Arizona Department of Revenue
1600 W Monroe St., 8th Fl.
Phoenix, AZ 85007
Contact: Anthony Hagenstein CAE, Rep.
Ph: (602)716-6865
Fax: (602)716-7994
E-mail: thagenstein@azdor.gov
Descr: Represents state and local officials concerned with valuation of property for ad valorem property tax purposes. Works to improve standards and conduct research on tax assessment. Promotes innovation and excellence in property appraisal, assessment administration, and property tax policy through professional development, education, research, and technical assistance.

1485 ■ Maricopa Community Colleges at Phoenix Small Business Development Center
2400 N Central Ave., Ste. 104
Phoenix, AZ 85004

Contact: Richard Senopole, Dir.
Ph: (480)784-0590
Fax: (602)230-7989
E-mail: rich.senopole@maricopasbdc.com
URL: http://www.maricopasbdc.com

Descr: Represents and promotes the small business sector. Provides management assistance to current and prospective small business owners. Helps to improve management skills and expand the products and services of members.

1486 ■ Mesa Minority/Micro Small Business Development Center (M3SBDC)
165 N Centennial Way, No. 209-213
Mesa, AZ 85201
Contact: Luis Reynoso, Dir.
Ph: (480)784-0590
E-mail: luis.reynoso@domail.maricopa.edu
URL: http://www.maricopasbdc.com

Descr: Represents and promotes the small business sector. Provides management assistance to current and prospective small business owners. Helps to improve management skills and expand the products and services of members.

1487 ■ Mohave Community College Small Business Development Center (MCC SBDC)
1971 E Jagerson Ave.
Kingman, AZ 86409
Contact: Kelley Marsh, Dir.
Ph: (928)757-0895
E-mail: kmarsh@mohave.edu
URL: http://www.mohave.edu/pages/195.asp

Descr: Represents and promotes the small business sector. Provides management assistance to current and prospective small business owners. Helps to improve management skills and expand the products and services of members.

1488 ■ NAIFA-Tucson
3305 N Swan Rd., No. 109
PMB No. 139
Tucson, AZ 85718
Contact: Jeanie Meredith, Exec. Dir.
Ph: (520)299-6787
Fax: (520)299-6431
E-mail: jgmerideth@aol.com
URL: http://209.61.156.20/main-pub.cfm?usr=030332

Descr: Represents the interests of insurance and financial advisors. Advocates for a positive legislative and regulatory environment. Enhances business and professional skills of members.

1489 ■ North American Securities Administrators Association, Arizona
1300 W Washington St., 3rd Fl.
Phoenix, AZ 85007
Contact: Matthew J. Neubert, Dir.
Ph: (602)542-4242
Fax: (602)594-7470

Descr: Represents the interests of the state, provincial and territorial securities administrators in the U.S.

1490 ■ Northland Pioneer College's Small Business Development Center
PO Box 610
Holbrook, AZ 86025
Contact: Mark Engle, Dir.
Ph: (928)532-6170
Fax: (928)532-6171
E-mail: mengle98@yahoo.com
URL: http://www.npcsbdc.com

Descr: Represents and promotes the small business sector. Provides management assistance to current and prospective small business owners. Helps to improve management skills and expand the products and services of members.

1491 ■ Pima College's Small Business Development Center
PCC Community Campus
401 N Bonita Ave.
Tucson, AZ 85709
Contact: Susan Kifer, Dir.

Ph: (520)206-6404
Fax: (520)206-6550
E-mail: sbdc@pima.edu
URL: http://www.pima.edu/smallbusiness

Descr: Represents and promotes the small business sector. Provides management assistance to current and prospective small business owners. Helps to improve management skills and expand the products and services of members.

1492 ■ Sun City Taxpayers Association (SCTA)
12630 N 103rd Ave., Ste. 144
Sun City, AZ 85351
Contact: Raymond E. Dare, Pres.
Ph: (623)933-7530
Fax: (623)933-0394
E-mail: president@suncitytaxpayers.org
URL: http://suncitytaxpayers.org

1493 ■ Superstition Business and Professional Women
8O W Ranch Rd.
Tempe, AZ 85284
Contact: Nancy Muir, Pres.
Ph: (480)345-7124
E-mail: njmaz@cox.net
URL: http://www.bpwsuperstition.org

Descr: Represents the interests of business and professional women. Elevates the standards for women in business and professional settings. Promotes equity for all women in the workplace through advocacy, education and information. Provides professional development, networking and career advancement opportunities for working women.

Arkansas

1494 ■ Arkansas Business and Professional Women
PO Box 1019
Mountain Home, AR 72654
Contact: Donna Hopkins, Pres.
Ph: (870)425-6061
Fax: (870)424-2922
E-mail: donna_hopkins@hotmail.com
URL: http://www.arkansasbpw.org

Descr: Represents the interests of business and professional women. Elevates the standards for women in business and professional settings. Promotes equity for all women in the workplace through advocacy, education and information. Provides professional development, networking and career advancement opportunities for working women.

1495 ■ Arkansas Credit Union League (ACUL)
PO Box 3446
Little Rock, AR 72203
Contact: Ms. Reta Kahley, Pres./CEO
Ph: (501)376-6508
Free: 800-880-2285
Fax: (501)376-3206
E-mail: acul@sbcglobal.net
URL: http://www.acul.org

Staff: 4. **Descr:** Credit unions. Promotes cooperation among credit unions and spreads understanding of international credit union principles. Provides information regarding guidance and training in the development of leadership. Represents members' interests in legislative and regulatory matters. **Fnd:** 1934. **Mem:** 72. **Pub:** *CU Connection* (bimonthly).

1496 ■ Arkansas Small Business and Technology Development Center - Fayetteville
University of Arkansas - Fayetteville
Sam M. Walton College of Business
Donald W. Reynolds Center for Enterprise Development, Ste. 2
145 N Buchanan Ave.
Fayetteville, AR 72701
Contact: Larry Brian, Dir.
Ph: (479)575-5148
Fax: (479)575-4013

E-mail: lbrian@walton.uark.edu
URL: http://sbdc.waltoncollege.uark.edu

Descr: Represents and promotes the small business sector. Provides management assistance to current and prospective small business owners. Helps to improve management skills and expand the products and services of members.

1497 ■ Arkansas Small Business and Technology Development Center - Fort Smith
PO Box 3649
Fort Smith, AR 72913
Contact: Vonelle Vanzant, Dir.
Ph: (479)788-7758
Free: 888-512-5466
Fax: (479)788-7757
E-mail: vvanzant@uafortsmith.edu
URL: http://www.uafortsmith.edu/SBDC

Descr: Represents and promotes the small business sector. Provides management assistance to current and prospective small business owners. Helps to improve management skills and expand the products and services of members.

1498 ■ Arkansas Small Business and Technology Development Center - McGehee
PO Box 747
McGehee, AR 71654
Contact: Kathryn Peacock, Dir.
Ph: (870)222-4900
Fax: (870)222-4900
E-mail: peacockk@uamont.edu
URL: http://www.uamont.edu/McGehee/sbdc

Descr: Represents and promotes the small business sector. Provides management assistance to current and prospective small business owners. Helps to improve management skills and expand the products and services of members.

1499 ■ Arkansas Society of Enrolled Agents (ARKSEA)
PO Box 94239
North Little Rock, AR 72190
Contact: Joyce Anderson
Ph: (501)753-2724
Fax: (501)753-7829
E-mail: abc@nwark.net
URL: http://www.arksea.org

Descr: Aims to improve the knowledge, skills and professionalism of members in all areas of taxation. Enhances the role of enrolled agents among government agencies, other professions and the public at large. Advocates for taxpayer rights and protects members' interests.

1500 ■ Arkansas State University Small Business Development Center (ASU SBDC)
PO Box 2650
State University, AR 72467
Contact: Herb Lawrence, Dir.
Ph: (870)972-3517
E-mail: hlawrenc@astate.edu
URL: http://www.deltaced.astate.edu/asbdc.htm

Descr: Represents and promotes the small business sector. Provides management assistance to current and prospective small business owners. Helps to improve management skills and expand the products and services of members.

1501 ■ Business and Professional Women, Augusta
1379 Hwy. 33
Newport, AR 72112
Contact: Jeannie Whitehead
Ph: (870)347-3352
Fax: (870)347-5556
E-mail: jeannie.whitehead@wrrhc-ar.org
URL: http://www.arkansasbpw.org

Descr: Represents the interests of business and professional women. Elevates the standards for women in business and professional settings. Promotes equity for all women in the workplace through advocacy, education and information. Provides professional development, networking and

career advancement opportunities for working women.

1502 ■ Business and Professional Women, Batesville
243 Harmontown Rd.
Batesville, AR 72501
Contact: Gwenda Dobbs, Co-Pres.
Ph: (870)793-0090
Fax: (870)793-3027
E-mail: cmerrymcspadden@aol.com
URL: http://www.arkansasbpw.org
Descr: Represents the interests of business and professional women. Elevates the standards for women in business and professional settings. Promotes equity for all women in the workplace through advocacy, education and information. Provides professional development, networking and career advancement opportunities for working women.

1503 ■ Business and Professional Women, Benton
605 Martin Ln.
Bryant, AR 72022
Contact: Phyllis Rogers, Chm.
Ph: (501)228-9797
E-mail: phyllis@tcmgi.com
URL: http://www.arkansasbpw.org
Descr: Represents the interests of business and professional women. Elevates the standards for women in business and professional settings. Promotes equity for all women in the workplace through advocacy, education and information. Provides professional development, networking and career advancement opportunities for working women.

1504 ■ Business and Professional Women, Berryville
201 S Main St.
Berryville, AR 72616
Contact: Pam Yarberry
Ph: (870)423-2848
URL: http://www.arkansasbpw.org
Descr: Represents the interests of business and professional women. Elevates the standards for women in business and professional settings. Promotes equity for all women in the workplace through advocacy, education and information. Provides professional development, networking and career advancement opportunities for working women.

1505 ■ Business and Professional Women, Camden
305 Red Hill Rd.
Chidester, AR 71726
Contact: Jannette Mosley
Ph: (870)685-2906
Fax: (870)685-2876
E-mail: treasurercity@cei.net
URL: http://www.arkansasbpw.org
Descr: Represents the interests of business and professional women. Elevates the standards for women in business and professional settings. Promotes equity for all women in the workplace through advocacy, education and information. Provides professional development, networking and career advancement opportunities for working women.

1506 ■ Business and Professional Women, Conway
PO Box 84
Conway, AR 72033
Contact: Lois Lee
Ph: (501)470-1811
E-mail: donlo187@arkansas.net
URL: http://www.arkansasbpw.org
Descr: Represents the interests of business and professional women. Elevates the standards for women in business and professional settings. Promotes equity for all women in the workplace through advocacy, education and information. Provides professional development, networking and

career advancement opportunities for working women.

1507 ■ Business and Professional Women, Crawford County
1110 Main St.
Van Buren, AR 72956
Contact: Teresa Nelson
Ph: (479)474-4300
E-mail: tnelson@summitbrokerage.com
URL: http://www.arkansasbpw.org
Descr: Represents the interests of business and professional women. Elevates the standards for women in business and professional settings. Promotes equity for all women in the workplace through advocacy, education and information. Provides professional development, networking and career advancement opportunities for working women.

1508 ■ Business and Professional Women, Downtown Little Rock
1123 S University Ave., Ste. 919
Little Rock, AR 72204
Contact: DJ Lynch
Ph: (501)907-1414
Free: 866-977-1414
Fax: (501)661-1212
E-mail: djlynch@arhypnosis.com
URL: http://www.arkansasbpw.org
Descr: Represents the interests of business and professional women. Elevates the standards for women in business and professional settings. Promotes equity for all women in the workplace through advocacy, education and information. Provides professional development, networking and career advancement opportunities for working women.

1509 ■ Business and Professional Women, Fayetteville
4288 E Hwy. 264
Lowell, AR 72745
Contact: Becky Morehouse
Ph: (479)601-1443
E-mail: becky_morehouse@hotmail.com
URL: http://www.arkansasbpw.org
Descr: Represents the interests of business and professional women. Elevates the standards for women in business and professional settings. Promotes equity for all women in the workplace through advocacy, education and information. Provides professional development, networking and career advancement opportunities for working women.

1510 ■ Business and Professional Women, Fordyce
402 Estes Rd.
Fordyce, AR 71742
Contact: Carolyn Jenkins
Ph: (870)352-2822
E-mail: bavrogers@yahoo.com
URL: http://www.arkansasbpw.org
Descr: Represents the interests of business and professional women. Elevates the standards for women in business and professional settings. Promotes equity for all women in the workplace through advocacy, education and information. Provides professional development, networking and career advancement opportunities for working women.

1511 ■ Business and Professional Women, Fort Smith
423 N 18th St.
Fort Smith, AR 72901
Contact: Lori L. Smith
Ph: (479)784-9114
Fax: (479)784-9116
E-mail: lorial1958@aol.com
URL: http://www.arkansasbpw.org
Descr: Represents the interests of business and professional women. Elevates the standards for women in business and professional settings. Promotes equity for all women in the workplace

through advocacy, education and information. Provides professional development, networking and career advancement opportunities for working women.

1512 ■ Business and Professional Women, Heber Springs
1910 W Maple St.
Heber Springs, AR 72543-3607
Contact: Jan Awalt
Ph: (501)362-5229
Fax: (501)250-4426
E-mail: j.janawalt@suddenlink.net
URL: http://www.arkansasbpw.org
Descr: Represents the interests of business and professional women. Elevates the standards for women in business and professional settings. Promotes equity for all women in the workplace through advocacy, education and information. Provides professional development, networking and career advancement opportunities for working women.

1513 ■ Business and Professional Women, Jonesboro
1805 Starling Dr.
Jonesboro, AR 72401
Contact: Emily Devereux
Ph: (870)919-2586
Fax: (870)336-5676
E-mail: edevereux@sbrmc.org
URL: http://www.arkansasbpw.org
Descr: Represents the interests of business and professional women. Elevates the standards for women in business and professional settings. Promotes equity for all women in the workplace through advocacy, education and information. Provides professional development, networking and career advancement opportunities for working women.

1514 ■ Business and Professional Women, Little Rock
33 Flag Rd.
Little Rock, AR 72205
Contact: Sarah Ware
Ph: (501)280-3100
Fax: (501)280-3155
E-mail: sayra@sbcglobal.net
URL: http://www.arkansasbpw.org
Descr: Represents the interests of business and professional women. Elevates the standards for women in business and professional settings. Promotes equity for all women in the workplace through advocacy, education and information. Provides professional development, networking and career advancement opportunities for working women.

1515 ■ Business and Professional Women, Mountain Home
7 Lakeview Dr.
Mountain Home, AR 72653
Contact: Carol Abel
Ph: (870)424-2155
E-mail: cabe4@suddenlink.net
URL: http://www.arkansasbpw.org
Descr: Represents the interests of business and professional women. Elevates the standards for women in business and professional settings. Promotes equity for all women in the workplace through advocacy, education and information. Provides professional development, networking and career advancement opportunities for working women.

1516 ■ Business and Professional Women, Newport
5 Mickey Cir.
Newport, AR 72112
Contact: Karen Hunt
Ph: (870)523-5822
Fax: (870)523-4640
E-mail: kahunt@yahoo.com
URL: http://www.arkansasbpw.org
Descr: Represents the interests of business and

professional women. Elevates the standards for women in business and professional settings. Promotes equity for all women in the workplace through advocacy, education and information. Provides professional development, networking and career advancement opportunities for working women.

1517 ■ Business and Professional Women, Paragould
3407 Dayton Ave.
Jonesboro, AR 72401
Contact: Nellie Murphy
Ph: (870)931-4880
Free: 800-759-4218
Fax: (870)931-5082
E-mail: nmurp@mynewroads.com
URL: http://www.arkansasbpw.org
Descr: Represents the interests of business and professional women. Elevates the standards for women in business and professional settings. Promotes equity for all women in the workplace through advocacy, education and information. Provides professional development, networking and career advancement opportunities for working women.

1518 ■ Business and Professional Women, Paris
PO Box 129
Paris, AR 72855
Contact: Geneva Morton
Ph: (479)963-2287
URL: http://www.arkansasbpw.org
Descr: Represents the interests of business and professional women. Elevates the standards for women in business and professional settings. Promotes equity for all women in the workplace through advocacy, education and information. Provides professional development, networking and career advancement opportunities for working women.

1519 ■ Business and Professional Women, Waldron
823 Poteau Mountain Rd.
Waldron, AR 72958
Contact: Jean Starr
Ph: (479)637-4975
Fax: (479)637-0540
E-mail: jstarr@valuelinx.net
URL: http://www.arkansasbpw.org
Descr: Represents the interests of business and professional women. Elevates the standards for women in business and professional settings. Promotes equity for all women in the workplace through advocacy, education and information. Provides professional development, networking and career advancement opportunities for working women.

1520 ■ Business and Professional Women, Walnut Ridge
501 Liberty Dr.
Walnut Ridge, AR 72476
Contact: Diana Shelton
Ph: (870)886-2292
Fax: (870)886-6186
E-mail: diana.shelton@pulaskibank.com
URL: http://www.arkansasbpw.org
Descr: Represents the interests of business and professional women. Elevates the standards for women in business and professional settings. Promotes equity for all women in the workplace through advocacy, education and information. Provides professional development, networking and career advancement opportunities for working women.

1521 ■ Business and Professional Women, Wynne
PO Box 1230
Wynne, AR 72396
Contact: Debbie Hedge
Ph: (870)208-8152
E-mail: debbiehedge@crosscountybank.com

URL: http://www.arkansasbpw.org
Descr: Represents the interests of business and professional women. Elevates the standards for women in business and professional settings. Promotes equity for all women in the workplace through advocacy, education and information. Provides professional development, networking and career advancement opportunities for working women.

1522 ■ Financial Planning Association of Arkansas
PO Box 2341
Little Rock, AR 72203-2341
Contact: Lori Payne, Exec. Dir.
Ph: (501)626-9226
Fax: (501)377-8417
E-mail: fpaarkansas@sbcglobal.net
URL: http://www.fpaarkansas.org
Descr: Supports the financial planning process in order to help people achieve their goals and dreams. Promotes the legislative, regulatory and professional interests of the financial service industry. Fosters the value of financial planning and advances the financial planning profession.

1523 ■ International Association of Assessing Officers, Arkansas
Arkansas Mass Appraisal Group
406 Manson Rd., Ste. 240
Sherwood, AR 72120
Contact: Page Kutait RES, Rep.
Ph: (501)823-2624
Fax: (501)823-2628
E-mail: pagek@armass.net
Descr: Represents state and local officials concerned with valuation of property for ad valorem property tax purposes. Works to improve standards and conduct research on tax assessment. Promotes innovation and excellence in property appraisal, assessment administration, and property tax policy through professional development, education, research, and technical assistance.

1524 ■ NAIFA-Northwest Arkansas
2367-2 Green Acres Rd.
Fayetteville, AR 72703
Contact: John Ogden, Pres.
Ph: (479)444-3344
E-mail: jogden@farmersagent.com
URL: http://www.naifa-nwa.org
Descr: Represents the interests of insurance and financial advisors. Advocates for a positive legislative and regulatory environment. Enhances business and professional skills of members.

1525 ■ NAIFA-South Arkansas
1123 S Univ., No. 230
Little Rock, AR 72204
Contact: Jake Hillard
Ph: (501)614-7301
Fax: (501)614-7199
Descr: Represents the interests of insurance and financial advisors. Advocates for a positive legislative and regulatory environment. Enhances business and professional skills of members.

1526 ■ North American Securities Administrators Association, Arkansas
Heritage West Bldg.
201 E Markham St., Rm. 300
Little Rock, AR 72201
Contact: Michael Johnson
Ph: (501)324-9260
Fax: (501)324-9268
Descr: Represents the interests of the state, provincial and territorial securities administrators in the U.S.

1527 ■ Southern Arkansas University Small Business Development Center (SAU SBDC)
PO Box 9192
Magnolia, AR 71754
Contact: Felicia Bozeman
Ph: (870)235-5033

E-mail: tpconsidine@saumag.edu
URL: http://www.saumag.edu/sbdc
Descr: Represents and promotes the small business sector. Provides management assistance to current and prospective small business owners. Helps to improve management skills and expand the products and services of members.

California

1528 ■ Alameda Small Business Development Center
475 14th St., Ste. 150
Oakland, CA 94612
Contact: Rick Ohlrich, Lead Business Advisor
Ph: (510)208-0412
E-mail: rohlrich@eastbaysbdc.org
URL: http://www.eastbaysbdc.org
Descr: Represents and promotes the small business sector. Provides management assistance to current and prospective small business owners. Helps to improve management skills and expand the products and services of members.

1529 ■ Alliance Small Business Development Center
1010 Eleventh St., Ste. 1013
Modesto, CA 95354
Ph: (209)567-4910
Fax: (209)567-4955
URL: http://www.alliancesbdc.com
Descr: Represents and promotes the small business sector. Provides management assistance to current and prospective small business owners. Helps to improve management skills and expand the products and services of members.

1530 ■ Alliance Small Business Development Center - Mariposa
5078 Bullion St.
Mariposa, CA 95338
Ph: (209)381-6557
URL: http://www.alliancesbdc.com
Descr: Represents and promotes the small business sector. Provides management assistance to current and prospective small business owners. Helps to improve management skills and expand the products and services of members.

1531 ■ Alliance Small Business Development Center - Merced
PO Box 1029
Merced, CA 95341
Contact: William Anderson, Mgr.
Ph: (209)381-6557
Fax: (209)381-6552
URL: http://www.alliancesbdc.com
Descr: Represents and promotes the small business sector. Provides management assistance to current and prospective small business owners. Helps to improve management skills and expand the products and services of members.

1532 ■ Alpine County Small Business Development Center
PO Box 265
Markleeville, CA 96120
Ph: (530)694-2475
Fax: (530)694-2478
E-mail: alpcntv@powernet.net
URL: http://www.sbdc.deltacollege.edu
Descr: Represents and promotes the small business sector. Provides management assistance to current and prospective small business owners. Helps to improve management skills and expand the products and services of members.

1533 ■ Amador County Small Business Development Center
PO Box 1077
Jackson, CA 95642
Ph: (530)223-0351
Fax: (530)223-2261
E-mail: aedc@cdepot.net
URL: http://www.sbdc.deltacollege.edu
Descr: Represents and promotes the small business

sector. Provides management assistance to current and prospective small business owners. Helps to improve management skills and expand the products and services of members.

1534 ■ American Society of Appraisers, Central Valley Chapter
Noell Agnew & Morse, LLP
8365 N Fresno St., Ste. 110
Fresno, CA 93720
Contact: Kenneth T. Wittwer, Sec.
Ph: (559)438-6590
Fax: (559)438-6593
E-mail: kwittwer@namcpa.com
Descr: Serves as a professional appraisal educator, testing and accrediting society. Sponsors mandatory re-certification program for all members. Offers consumer information service to the public.

1535 ■ American Society of Appraisers, Los Angeles Chapter
Wells Fargo Bank
RETECHS Department
707 Wilshire Blvd., 11th Fl.
Los Angeles, CA 90017
Contact: Douglas A. Nason, VP
Ph: (213)614-4902
Fax: (213)683-8568
E-mail: nasond@wellsfargo.com
Descr: Serves as a professional appraisal educator, testing and accrediting society. Sponsors mandatory re-certification program for all members. Offers consumer information service to the public.

1536 ■ American Society of Appraisers, San Diego Chapter
Greg Rogers Historic House
616 2nd Ave.
Chula Vista, CA 91910
Contact: Pamela Bensoussan, Pres.
Ph: (619)420-7782
Fax: (619)420-7788
E-mail: asainfo@appraisers.org
URL: http://www.sandiegoappraisers.org
Descr: Serves as a professional appraisal educator, testing and accrediting society. Sponsors mandatory recertification program for all members. Offers consumer information service to the public. **Pub:** Newsletter (monthly).

1537 ■ American Society of Appraisers, San Francisco Chapter
IRS-LMSB-1856
450 Golden Gate Ave., Stop 6-0107
San Francisco, CA 94102-3661
Contact: James E. McCann, Membership Chm.
Ph: (415)847-7496
E-mail: jmc1492@yahoo.com
Descr: Serves as a professional appraisal educator, testing and accrediting society. Sponsors mandatory re-certification program for all members. Offers consumer information service to the public.

1538 ■ Appraisal Institute, Northern California Chapter
1243 Alpine Rd., Ste. 102
Walnut Creek, CA 94596
Contact: Lisa M. Estes, Exec. Dir.
Ph: (925)932-7753
Fax: (925)932-7754
E-mail: lisa@norcal-ai.org
URL: http://www.norcal-ai.org
Descr: Represents the interests of real estate appraisers. Sustain and advance its members as the choice of real estate solutions and advocate professional credentials, standards of professional practice and ethics reliable with the public good.

1539 ■ Appraisal Institute, San Diego Chapter
4849 Ronson Ct., Ste. 216
San Diego, CA 92111-1805
Contact: Bob Backer MAI, Pres.
Ph: (858)292-7324
Fax: (858)292-7333
E-mail: bob@rbackerappraisal.com
URL: http://www.sdcai.org

Descr: Represents professional real estate appraisers and valuation consultants.

1540 ■ Bay Capital District Business and Professional Women
1174 Orangewood Dr.
Lodi, CA 95240
Contact: Jacqueline Zupo, Pres.
Ph: (209)368-6765
E-mail: jackiezupo@juno.com
URL: http://www.baycapitalbpw.org
Descr: Represents the interests of business and professional women. Elevates the standards for women in business and professional settings. Promotes equity for all women in the workplace through advocacy, education and information. Provides professional development, networking and career advancement opportunities for working women.

1541 ■ Business and Professional Women, Valley Sunset District
13790 Oro Grande St.
Sylmar, CA 91342-2208
Contact: Marjory Hopper, Pres.
Ph: (818)367-0010
E-mail: info@bpwvsd.org
URL: http://www.bpwvsd.org
Descr: Represents the interests of business and professional women. Elevates the standards for women in business and professional settings. Promotes equity for all women in the workplace through advocacy, education and information. Provides professional development, networking and career advancement opportunities for working women.

1542 ■ Butte College Small Business Development Center
19 Williamsburg Ln.
Chico, CA 95928
Contact: Sophie Konuwa, Dir.
Ph: (530)895-9017
Fax: (530)566-9851
E-mail: konuwaso@butte.edu
URL: http://www.bcsbdc.org
Descr: Represents and promotes the small business sector. Provides management assistance to current and prospective small business owners. Helps to improve management skills and expand the products and services of members.

1543 ■ Calaveras County Small Business Development Center
700 Mountain Ranch Rd., Ste. A
San Andreas, CA 95249
Ph: (209)754-9791
Fax: (209)754-9792
URL: http://www.sbdc.deltacollege.edu
Descr: Represents and promotes the small business sector. Provides management assistance to current and prospective small business owners. Helps to improve management skills and expand the products and services of members.

1544 ■ California Society of Enrolled Agents (CSEA)
3200 Ramos Cir.
Sacramento, CA 95827-2513
Contact: Catherine A. Apker CAE, Exec. VP
Ph: (916)366-6646
Free: 800-777-2732
Fax: (916)366-6674
E-mail: info@csea.org
URL: http://www.csea.org
Staff: 9. **Descr:** Individuals licensed by the Department of Treasury to prepare taxes and represent taxpayers before the Internal Revenue Service. Provides professional continuing education. Supplies public information and promotes public awareness of the profession. Conducts free seminars for taxpayers in FEMA-declared disaster areas to instruct on the loss provisions of the tax laws for disaster victims. **Fnd:** 1977. **Mem:** 4100. **State Groups:** 1.

Local Groups: 20. **Pub:** *California Enrolled Agent* (9/year).

1545 ■ California Society of Enrolled Agents - North Bay Chapter
818 5th Ave., Ste. 100
San Rafael, CA 94901
Contact: Sandra L. Danioth-Jones, Pres.
Ph: (415)453-6235
Fax: (415)258-0957
E-mail: info@northbayea.org
URL: http://www.northbayea.org
Descr: Aims to improve the knowledge, skills and professionalism of members in all areas of taxation. Enhances the role of enrolled agents among government agencies, other professions and the public at large. Advocates for taxpayer rights and protects members' interests.

1546 ■ California Society of Enrolled Agents - Orange County Chapter (OCEA)
17632 Irvin Blvd., Ste. 150
Tustin, CA 92780
Contact: Joni Terens EA
Ph: (714)899-2221
Free: 800-797-1410
E-mail: info@eaoc.org
URL: http://www.eaoc.org

1547 ■ California Society of Enrolled Agents - Solano-Napa Chapter
2437 Springs Rd.
Vallejo, CA 94591
Contact: Matthew J. Jones, Newsletter Ed.
Ph: (707)557-6838
Fax: (707)557-7702
E-mail: info@solanonapa.org
URL: http://solanonapa-ea.org
Descr: Aims to improve the knowledge, skills and professionalism of members in all areas of taxation. Enhances the role of enrolled agents among government agencies, other professions and the public at large. Advocates for taxpayer rights and protects members' interests.

1548 ■ Central California Small Business Development Center - Fresno
Manchester Center
3302 N Blackstone Ave., Ste. 225
Fresno, CA 93726
Contact: Bryan Moe, Dir.
Ph: (559)230-4056
URL: http://www.ccsbdc.org
Descr: Represents and promotes the small business sector. Provides management assistance to current and prospective small business owners. Helps to improve management skills and expand the products and services of members.

1549 ■ Central California Small Business Development Center - Visalia
PO Box 787
Visalia, CA 93279
Contact: Gil Jaramillo, Mgr.
Ph: (559)625-3051
URL: http://www.ccsbdc.org
Descr: Represents and promotes the small business sector. Provides management assistance to current and prospective small business owners. Helps to improve management skills and expand the products and services of members.

1550 ■ Central Coast Chapter of the California Enrolled Agents Society
PO Box 397
Santa Ynez, CA 93460
Contact: Jeanne Watkins, Pres.
Ph: (805)688-6317
URL: http://www.ccccsea.org
Descr: Aims to improve the knowledge, skills and professionalism of members in all areas of taxation. Enhances the role of enrolled agents among government agencies, other professions and the public at

large. Advocates for taxpayer rights and protects members' interests.

1551 ■ Central Coast Small Business Development Center
Cabrillo College
6500 Soquel Dr.
Aptos, CA 95003
Ph: (831)479-6136
Fax: (831)479-6166
E-mail: sbdc@cabrillo.edu
URL: http://www.cabrillo.edu/services/sbdc
Descr: Represents and promotes the small business sector. Provides management assistance to current and prospective small business owners. Helps to improve management skills and expand the products and services of members.

1552 ■ Central Solano Citizen/Taxpayer Group (CSCTG)
PO Box 3532
Fairfield, CA 94533
Ph: (707)422-4491
E-mail: info@taxwatchers.org
URL: http://thetaxwatchers.org/Contact_Us.htm

1553 ■ CHARO Small Business Development Center
4301 E Valley Blvd.
Los Angeles, CA 90032
Ph: (323)269-0751
Fax: (323)343-9483
URL: http://www.charosbdc.com
Descr: Represents and promotes the small business sector. Provides management assistance to current and prospective small business owners. Helps to improve management skills and expand the products and services of members.

1554 ■ Coachella Valley Small Business Development Center
500 S Palm Canyon Dr., Ste. 222
Palm Springs, CA 92264
Ph: (760)864-1311
Fax: (760)864-1319
E-mail: cvsbdc@dc.rr.com
URL: http://www.leadsbdc.org
Descr: Represents and promotes the small business sector. Provides management assistance to current and prospective small business owners. Helps to improve management skills and expand the products and services of members.

1555 ■ College of the Canyons Small Business Development Center
28460 Stanford Ave., Ste. 100
Santa Clarita, CA 91355
Contact: Donna Plummer, Interim Assistant Dir.
Ph: (661)294-9375
Fax: (661)294-5203
E-mail: donna.plummer@canyons.edu
URL: http://www.canyonsecondev.org/content/small-business-dev.-center.html
Descr: Represents and promotes the small business sector. Provides management assistance to current and prospective small business owners. Helps to improve management skills and expand the products and services of members.

1556 ■ Contra Costa Small Business Development Center (CCSBDC)
2425 Bisso Ln., No. 200
Concord, CA 94520
Contact: Beverly Hamile, Dir.
Ph: (925)646-5377
Fax: (925)646-5299
E-mail: info@contracostasbdc.com
URL: http://www.contracostasbdc.com
Descr: Represents and promotes the small business sector. Provides management assistance to current and prospective small business owners. Helps to improve management skills and expand the products and services of members.

1557 ■ Contra Costa Taxpayers Association
PO Box 27
Martinez, CA 94553

Contact: Kris Hunt, Exec. Dir.
Ph: (925)228-5610
E-mail: krishunt@cocotax.org
URL: http://www.cocotax.org
Fnd: 1937.

1558 ■ Cuesta College Small Business Development Center
3211 Broad St., Ste. 109
San Luis Obispo, CA 93401
Ph: (805)549-0401
E-mail: sccsbdc@smallbusinessinfo.org
URL: http://www.smallbusinessinfo.org
Descr: Represents and promotes the small business sector. Provides management assistance to current and prospective small business owners. Helps to improve management skills and expand the products and services of members.

1559 ■ East Bay Association of Enrolled Agents
30100 Mission Blvd., Ste. 6
Hayward, CA 94544
Contact: Thomas Johnston, Pres.
Ph: (925)828-4500
Free: 800-617-1040
Fax: (510)487-1501
E-mail: ebaea@ebaea.org
URL: http://www.eastbayea.org
Descr: Aims to improve the knowledge, skills and professionalism of members in all areas of taxation. Enhances the role of enrolled agents among government agencies, other professions and the public at large. Advocates for taxpayer rights and protects members' interests.

1560 ■ East Bay Small Business Development Center
475 14th St., Ste. 150
Oakland, CA 94612
Contact: Steve Roth, Dir.
Ph: (510)208-0410
Fax: (510)208-0413
E-mail: sroth@eastbaysbdc.org
URL: http://www.eastbaysbdc.org
Descr: Represents and promotes the small business sector. Provides management assistance to current and prospective small business owners. Helps to improve management skills and expand the products and services of members.

1561 ■ El Camino College Small Business Development Center
13430 Hawthorne Blvd.
Hawthorne, CA 90250
Contact: A. Alex Vaughan, Dir.
Ph: (310)973-3177
Fax: (310)973-3132
E-mail: avaughan@elcamino.edu
URL: http://www.elcamino.edu/commadv/sbdc
Descr: Represents and promotes the small business sector. Provides management assistance to current and prospective small business owners. Helps to improve management skills and expand the products and services of members.

1562 ■ Financial Planning Association of Central California
802 W Pinedale Ave.
Fresno, CA 93711
Contact: John Longstaff CFP, Membership Dir.
Ph: (559)325-8200
Fax: (559)325-8278
E-mail: info@fpacentralcal.org
URL: http://www.fpacentralcal.org
Descr: Supports the financial planning process in order to help people achieve their goals and dreams. Promotes the legislative, regulatory and professional interests of the financial service industry. Fosters the value of financial planning and advances the financial planning profession.

1563 ■ Financial Planning Association of the East Bay
781 McKean Pl.
Concord, CA 94518-2835

Contact: Gary Gardner CFP, Chm.
Ph: (925)686-4819
Fax: (925)686-4819
E-mail: association_office@worldnet.att.net
URL: http://www.fpaeastbay.org
Descr: Supports the financial planning process in order to help people achieve their goals and dreams. Promotes the legislative, regulatory and professional interests of the financial service industry. Fosters the value of financial planning and advances the financial planning profession. **Mem:** 400.

1564 ■ Financial Planning Association of the Inland Empire
PO Box 3740
Apple Valley, CA 92307
Contact: Tom Curtis, Exec. Dir.
Ph: (760)780-7702
E-mail: tlcurtis@verizon.net
URL: http://www.fpanet.org/chapters/inlandempire
Descr: Promotes the value of the financial planning process to the public. Provides professional education and networking opportunities for the financial planning community.

1565 ■ Financial Planning Association Los Angeles Chapter
PO Box 11376
Burbank, CA 91510
Contact: Mark S. Rothstein, Chm.
Ph: (818)558-3908
Free: 800-722-7173
Fax: (818)843-7423
E-mail: fpa@emaoffice.com
URL: http://www.fpala.org
Descr: Supports the financial planning process in order to help people achieve their goals and dreams. Promotes the legislative, regulatory and professional interests of the financial service industry. Fosters the value of financial planning and advances the financial planning profession.

1566 ■ Financial Planning Association Monterey Bay Chapter
PO Box 574
Monterey, CA 93942-0574
Contact: Denise Robertson, Chair
Ph: (831)747-7471
E-mail: denise@mbay.net
Descr: Supports the financial planning process in order to help people achieve their goals and dreams. Promotes the legislative, regulatory and professional interests of the financial service industry. Fosters the value of financial planning and advances the financial planning profession.

1567 ■ Financial Planning Association of Northern California
PO Box 188293
Sacramento, CA 95818
Contact: Holly Wilkerson, Exec. Dir.
Ph: (916)443-4237
Fax: (916)714-4977
E-mail: info@fpanc.org
URL: http://www.fpanc.org
Descr: Supports the financial planning process in order to help people achieve their goals and dreams. Promotes the legislative, regulatory and professional interests of the financial service industry. Fosters the value of financial planning and advances the financial planning profession.

1568 ■ Financial Planning Association, San Francisco Chapter
1326 Ross St., Ste. A
Petaluma, CA 94954
Contact: Davina Hansen, Exec. Dir.
Ph: (707)878-2874
Fax: (707)238-1405
E-mail: info@fpasf.org
URL: http://www.fpasf.org
Descr: Promotes the value of the financial planning process to the public. Provides professional educa-

tion and networking opportunities for the financial planning community.

1569 ■ Financial Planning Association of San Joaquin Valley
Olsen and Associates
431 S Ham Ln., Ste. A
Lodi, CA 95242
Contact: Christopher J. Olsen CFP, Pres.
Ph: (209)367-8700
Fax: (209)334-2896
E-mail: christopher.j.olsen@ampf.com
URL: http://www.fpasjv.org
Descr: Promotes the value of the financial planning process to the public. Provides professional education and networking opportunities for the financial planning community.

1570 ■ Financial Planning Association of Silicon Valley
987 University Ave., Ste. 8
Los Gatos, CA 95032
Contact: Marion S. Briggs, Exec. Dir.
Ph: (650)851-4414
Free: 877-808-2699
E-mail: execdirector@fpasv.org
URL: http://www.fpasv.org
Descr: Financial planning professionals united to maintain high standards of practice in the field. Conducts educational programs. **Fnd:** 1970. **Mem:** 400. **Pub:** Newsletter (monthly).

1571 ■ Financial Planning Association of Ventura County
PO Box 188
Camarillo, CA 93011
Contact: Alan Ungar, Pres.
Ph: (818)222-4773
Free: 877-281-0675
E-mail: info@fpaventura.org
URL: http://www.fpaventura.org
Descr: Promotes the value of the financial planning process to the public. Provides professional education and networking opportunities for the financial planning community.

1572 ■ Gavilan Small Business Development Center
8351 Church St., Bldg. E
Gilroy, CA 95020
Ph: (408)847-0373
Free: 800-847-0373
URL: http://www.gavilan.edu/catalog/2005_2007/community.html#98
Descr: Represents and promotes the small business sector. Provides management assistance to current and prospective small business owners. Helps to improve management skills and expand the products and services of members.

1573 ■ Golden Gate Chapter of the California Society Enrolled Agents (GGCEA)
129 Laurel St.
San Carlos, CA 94070
Contact: Emerice Stettiner EA, Pres.
Fax: (650)591-5637
E-mail: ggcea@goldengate-ea.org
URL: http://www.goldengate-ea.org

1574 ■ Humboldt Taxpayers League
PO Box 1432
Eureka, CA 95502
Contact: Phil Nyberg, Pres.
Ph: (707)442-8299
E-mail: pjnyberg@aol.com
URL: http://www.fredtyg.freeservers.com/HTL.html

1575 ■ Imperial Valley Small Business Development Center at Imperial Valley College
301 N Imperial Ave., Ste. B
El Centro, CA 92243
Ph: (760)312-9800
Fax: (760)312-9838
E-mail: info@ivsbdc.org
URL: http://www.ivsbdc.org
Descr: Represents and promotes the small business sector. Provides management assistance to current

and prospective small business owners. Helps to improve management skills and expand the products and services of members.

1576 ■ Inland Empire North Small Business Development Center
15490 Civic Dr., Ste. 102
Victorville, CA 92392
Ph: (760)951-1592
Fax: (760)951-8929
E-mail: jthomas@iesbdc.org
URL: http://www.leadsbdc.org
Descr: Represents and promotes the small business sector. Provides management assistance to current and prospective small business owners. Helps to improve management skills and expand the products and services of members.

1577 ■ International Association of Assessing Officers, California
Los Angeles County Appraiser's Office
500 W Temple St., Rm. 180
Los Angeles, CA 90012
Contact: John Noguez, Rep.
Ph: (213)974-1573
Fax: (213)626-0850
E-mail: jnoguez@assessor.lacounty.gov
Descr: Represents state and local officials concerned with valuation of property for ad valorem property tax purposes. Works to improve standards and conduct research on tax assessment. Promotes innovation and excellence in property appraisal, assessment administration, and property tax policy through professional development, education, research, and technical assistance.

1578 ■ International Association of Assessing Officers, Los Angeles County Chapter (IAA-OLA)
Kenneth Hahn Hall of Administration
500 W Temple St., Rm. 226
Los Angeles, CA 90012
Contact: Tammy Yue, Pres.
E-mail: admin@iaaola.org
URL: http://www.iaaola.org
Descr: Represents state and local officials concerned with valuation of property for ad valorem property tax purposes. Works to improve standards and conduct research on tax assessment. Promotes innovation and excellence in property appraisal, assessment administration, and property tax policy through professional development, education, research, and technical assistance.

1579 ■ Kern County Taxpayers Association
331 Truxtun Ave.
Bakersfield, CA 93301
Ph: (661)322-2973
Fax: (661)321-9550
URL: http://www.kerntaxpayers.org/kerntax

1580 ■ Lake County Small Business Development Center
55 First St.
Lakeport, CA 95453
Contact: Jim Magliulo
Ph: (707)263-0330
URL: http://www.yubasbdc.org/Lake-County-SBDC.asp
Descr: Represents and promotes the small business sector. Provides management assistance to current and prospective small business owners. Helps to improve management skills and expand the products and services of members.

1581 ■ League of Placer County Tax Payers
PO Box 4899
Auburn, CA 95604
Contact: Wally Reemelin, Pres.
Ph: (916)763-1015
E-mail: info@placertaxpayers.org
URL: http://www.placertaxpayers.org

1582 ■ Long Beach City College Small Business Development Center
3447 Atlantic Ave., Ste. 205
Long Beach, CA 90807

Ph: (562)570-4574
Fax: (562)570-4575
URL: http://lbsbdc.lbcc.edu
Descr: Represents and promotes the small business sector. Provides management assistance to current and prospective small business owners. Helps to improve management skills and expand the products and services of members.

1583 ■ Los Angeles Small Business Development Center Network
4040 Paramount Blvd., Ste. 107
Lakewood, CA 90712
Contact: Sheneui Sloan, Regional Dir.
Ph: (562)938-5020
Fax: (562)938-5030
E-mail: sbdc@lbcc.edu
URL: http://lasbdcnet.lbcc.edu
Descr: Represents and promotes the small business sector. Provides management assistance to current and prospective small business owners. Helps to improve management skills and expand the products and services of members.

1584 ■ Loyola Marymount University Small Business Development Center
1 LMU Dr.
Los Angeles, CA 90045
Ph: (310)338-5171
Fax: (310)338-5187
URL: http://www.lmu.edu/Page27514.aspx
Descr: Represents and promotes the small business sector. Provides management assistance to current and prospective small business owners. Helps to improve management skills and expand the products and services of members.

1585 ■ Marin United Taxpayers Association (MUTA)
PO Box 2214
Mill Valley, CA 94942
Contact: Basia Crane, Pres.
Ph: (415)456-7910
E-mail: info@marintaxpayers.org
URL: http://marintaxpayers.org
Pub: *Tax News* (quarterly).

1586 ■ Mendocino Small Business Development Center
760B Stewart St.
Fort Bragg, CA 95437
Contact: Pamela Patterson, CEO
Ph: (707)964-7571
Fax: (707)964-7576
URL: http://www.westcompany.org
Descr: Represents and promotes the small business sector. Provides management assistance to current and prospective small business owners. Helps to improve management skills and expand the products and services of members.

1587 ■ Mission Society of Enrolled Agents (MSEA)
1475 S Bascom Ave., No. 206
Campbell, CA 95008
Contact: Randy Warshawsky, Pres.
Free: 800-832-6732
Fax: (408)371-8677
E-mail: office@missioneas.org
URL: http://www.missioneas.org
Descr: Aims to improve the knowledge, skills and professionalism of members in all areas of taxation. Enhances the role of enrolled agents among government agencies, other professions and the public at large. Advocates for taxpayer rights and protects members' interests.

1588 ■ Monterey Peninsula Taxpayers
PO Box 15
Monterey, CA 93942
Ph: (408)373-1906

1589 ■ NAIFA-Fresno
PO Box 1071
Fresno, CA 93714-1071
Contact: Clay Blanton, Pres.

Ph: (559)228-3597
Fax: (559)227-1463
E-mail: contact@naifafresno.org
URL: http://www.naifafresno.org
Descr: Represents the interests of insurance and financial advisors. Advocates for a positive legislative and regulatory environment. Enhances business and professional skills of members.

1590 ■ NAIFA-Mount Diablo
1043 Stuart St., No. 175
Lafayette, CA 94549
Ph: (925)283-2520
Fax: (925)283-2521
E-mail: myassociation@sbcglobal.net
URL: http://naifanet.com/mountdiablo
Descr: Represents the interest of insurance and financial advisors. Advocates for a positive legislative and regulatory environment. Enhances business and professional skills of members.

1591 ■ NAIFA-Pasadena
PO Box 94116
Pasadena, CA 91109
Contact: Piera Y. Pickett, Co-Exec. Dir.
Ph: (626)524-6949
Fax: (714)893-1313
E-mail: naifapasadena@aol.com
URL: http://naifanet.com/page.cfm?usr=050460&pageid=2035
Descr: Represents the interests of insurance and financial advisors. Advocates for a positive legislative and regulatory environment. Enhances business and professional skills of members.

1592 ■ NAIFA-San Fernando Valley
PO Box 1088
Palos Verdes Estates, CA 90274
Contact: Marlowe Clemens, Exec. Dir.
Ph: (310)375-6300
Fax: (310)943-2737
E-mail: sfv@naifa-sfv.org
URL: http://209.61.156.20/main-pub.cfm?usr=050624
Descr: Represents the interest of insurance and financial advisors. Advocates for a positive legislative and regulatory environment. Enhances business and professional skills of members.

1593 ■ NAIFA-Silicon Valley
PO Box 26130
San Jose, CA 95159-6130
Contact: James L. Heitzig, Exec. Dir.
Ph: (408)275-1530
Fax: (831)687-0210
E-mail: jimbocando@sbcglobal.net
URL: http://www.naifasiliconvalley.org
Descr: Represents the interest of insurance and financial advisors. Advocates for a positive legislative and regulatory environment. Enhances business and professional skills of members.

1594 ■ NAIFA-Stockton
15 S Rose St.
Lodi, CA 95240
Contact: Kim Metz, Exec. Sec.
Ph: (209)339-4651
Fax: (209)339-8273
E-mail: kimmetz@naifacentralvalley.org
Descr: Represents the interests of insurance and financial advisors. Advocates for a positive legislative and regulatory environment. Enhances business and professional skills of members.

1595 ■ Napa City/County Taxpayers Association
2040 Stockton St.
Napa, CA 94559

1596 ■ Napa Valley College Small Business Development Center
1556 First St., Ste. 103
Napa, CA 94559
Ph: (707)253-3210
Fax: (707)253-3068

E-mail: nvcsbdc@napasbdc.org
URL: http://www.napasbdc.org
Descr: Represents and promotes the small business sector. Provides management assistance to current and prospective small business owners. Helps to improve management skills and expand the products and services of members.

1597 ■ North American Securities Administrators Association, California
1515 K St., Ste. 200
Sacramento, CA 95814
Contact: Preston DuFauchard
Ph: (916)445-7205
Fax: (916)445-7975
Descr: Represents the interests of the state, provincial and territorial securities administrators in the U.S.

1598 ■ North San Diego Small Business Development Center
Mira Costa College
1823 Mission Ave.
Oceanside, CA 92054
Ph: (760)795-8740
E-mail: centerinfo@miracosta.edu
URL: http://www.sandiegosmallbiz.com
Descr: Represents and promotes the small business sector. Provides management assistance to current and prospective small business owners. Helps to improve management skills and expand the products and services of members.

1599 ■ Northcoast Small Business Development Center - Del Norte
225 H St.
Crescent City, CA 95531
Contact: Barbara Burke
Ph: (707)464-2168
Fax: (707)464-1349
E-mail: burke@northcoastsbdc.org
URL: http://www.northcoastsbdc.org
Descr: Represents and promotes the small business sector. Provides management assistance to current and prospective small business owners. Helps to improve management skills and expand the products and services of members.

1600 ■ Northcoast Small Business Development Center - Humboldt
Prosperity Center
520 E St.
Eureka, CA 95501
Contact: Sandy Neal
Ph: (707)445-9720
Fax: (707)445-9652
E-mail: neal@northcoastsbdc.org
URL: http://www.northcoastsbdc.org
Descr: Represents and promotes the small business sector. Provides management assistance to current and prospective small business owners. Helps to improve management skills and expand the products and services of members.

1601 ■ Northern California Small Business Development Center
Humboldt State University
209 Siemens Hall
Arcata, CA 95521
Contact: Kristin Johnson, Dir.
Ph: (707)826-3919
Fax: (707)826-3912
E-mail: kristin.johnson@humboldt.edu
URL: http://www.norcalsbdc.org
Descr: Represents and promotes the small business sector. Provides management assistance to current and prospective small business owners. Helps to improve management skills and expand the products and services of members.

1602 ■ Pacific Coast Regional Small Business Development Corporation
3255 Wilshire Blvd., Ste. 1501
Los Angeles, CA 90010
Contact: Mark Robertson Sr., Pres./CEO
Ph: (213)739-2999

Fax: (213)739-0639
E-mail: mark.robertson@pcrcorp.org
URL: http://www.pcrcorp.org
Descr: Represents and promotes the small business sector. Provides management assistance to current and prospective small business owners. Helps to improve management skills and expand the products and services of members.

1603 ■ Redwood Empire Small Business Development Center
Santa Rosa Junior College
606 Healdsburg Ave.
Santa Rosa, CA 95401
Contact: Lorraine DuVernay, Dir.
Ph: (707)524-1770
Free: 888-346-SBDC
Fax: (707)524-1772
E-mail: lduvernay@santarosa.edu
URL: http://www.santarosa.edu/sbdc
Descr: Represents and promotes the small business sector. Provides management assistance to current and prospective small business owners. Helps to improve management skills and expand the products and services of members.

1604 ■ Sacramento County Taxpayers League
1620 35th Ave., Ste. K
Sacramento, CA 95822
Contact: Ken Payne, Pres.
Ph: (916)399-5600
Fax: (916)921-5991
E-mail: info@sactax.org
URL: http://www.sactax.org

1605 ■ Sacramento Valley Chapter California Society of Enrolled Agents
PO Box 661353
Sacramento, CA 95866
Contact: Susan P. Growney, Pres.
Ph: (530)674-1156
Fax: (530)674-7242
E-mail: president@sacvalleyeas.com
URL: http://www.sacvalleyeas.com
Descr: Aims to improve the knowledge, skills and professionalism of members in all areas of taxation. Enhances the role of enrolled agents among government agencies, other professions and the public at large. Advocates for taxpayer rights and protects members' interests.

1606 ■ San Diego/Imperial Counties Small Business Lead Development Center
Southwestern Community College
900 Otay Lakes Rd., Bldg. 1600
Chula Vista, CA 91910
Ph: (619)482-6375
URL: http://www.ccsbdc.org/AboutUs/SBDCCenters
Descr: Represents and promotes the small business sector. Provides management assistance to current and prospective small business owners. Helps to improve management skills and expand the products and services of members.

1607 ■ San Francisco Small Business Development Center
City College of San Francisco
300 Montgomery St., Ste. 789
San Francisco, CA 94104
Contact: Susie Biehler, Consultant
Ph: (415)841-4050
URL: http://www.sfsbdc.org
Descr: Represents and promotes the small business sector. Provides management assistance to current and prospective small business owners. Helps to improve management skills and expand the products and services of members.

1608 ■ San Francisco Taxpayers Union
601 Van Ness Ave.
San Francisco, CA 94102
Ph: (415)267-4805

E-mail: sftaxpayersunion@sftaxpayersunion.org
URL: http://sftaxpayersunion.com/index.html

1609 ■ San Gabriel Valley Small Business Development Center
Mt. San Antonio College
5200 Irwindale Ave., Ste.140
Irwindale, CA 91706
Contact: Daniel Morales, Dir.
Ph: (626)337-2101
Fax: (626)337-2104
E-mail: info@mtsacsbdc.com
URL: http://www.sangabrielvalleysbdc.com
Descr: Represents and promotes the small business sector. Provides management assistance to current and prospective small business owners. Helps to improve management skills and expand the products and services of members.

1610 ■ San Joaquin Delta College Small Business Development Center
56 S Lincoln St.
Stockton, CA 95203
Contact: Gillia Murphy, Dir.
Ph: (209)954-5089
Fax: (209)939-0385
E-mail: gmurphy@sjdccd.cc.ca.us
URL: http://www.sbdc.deltacollege.edu
Descr: Represents and promotes the small business sector. Provides management assistance to current and prospective small business owners. Helps to improve management skills and expand the products and services of members.

1611 ■ Santa Ana Regional Lead Small Business Development Center
California State University, Fullerton
Langsdorf Hall, Rm. 640
800 N State College Blvd.
Fullerton, CA 92834
Contact: Vi Pham, Dir.
Ph: (714)278-2719
Fax: (714)278-7858
E-mail: vpham@fullerton.edu
URL: http://www.leadsbdc.org
Descr: Represents and promotes the small business sector. Provides management assistance to current and prospective small business owners. Helps to improve management skills and expand the products and services of members.

1612 ■ Santa Barbara County Taxpayers Association (SBTCA)
PO Box 21621
Santa Barbara, CA 93121
Contact: Joe Armendariz, Exec. Dir.
Ph: (805)684-0678
Fax: (805)684-8260
E-mail: sbcta@cox.net
URL: http://www.sbcta.org

1613 ■ Santa Monica College Small Business Development Center
3400 Airport Ave., Ste. 76
Santa Monica, CA 90405
Contact: Patricia Ramos, Dir.
Ph: (310)434-3566
Fax: (310)434-3891
URL: http://www.smc.edu/sbdc
Descr: Represents and promotes the small business sector. Provides management assistance to current and prospective small business owners. Helps to improve management skills and expand the products and services of members.

1614 ■ Shasta County Taxpayers Association
PO Box 298
Redding, CA 96099
Ph: (530)243-0441

1615 ■ Silicon Valley Small Business Development Center at West Valley/Mission College
84 W Santa Clara St., Ste. 100
San Jose, CA 95113
Ph: (408)494-0240
URL: http://www.siliconvalley-sbdc.org
Descr: Represents and promotes the small business

sector. Provides management assistance to current and prospective small business owners. Helps to improve management skills and expand the products and services of members.

1616 ■ Silicon Valley Taxpayers Association
1584 Branham Ln., Ste. 266
San Jose, CA 95118
Ph: (408)279-5000
URL: http://www.svtaxpayers.org

1617 ■ Small Business Development Center - Greater Sacramento
1410 Ethan Way
Sacramento, CA 95825-2205
Contact: Panda Morgan, Dir.
Ph: (916)563-3210
Fax: (916)563-3266
E-mail: info@sbdc.net
URL: http://www.sbdc.net
Descr: Represents and promotes the small business sector. Provides management assistance to current and prospective small business owners. Helps to improve management skills and expand the products and services of members.

1618 ■ Small Business Development Center at Shasta College
1420 Butte St.
Redding, CA 96001
Contact: Keli Anthis, Dir.
Ph: (530)225-2770
E-mail: kanthis@sbdcsc.org
URL: http://www.sbdcsc.org
Descr: Represents and promotes the small business sector. Provides management assistance to current and prospective small business owners. Helps to improve management skills and expand the products and services of members.

1619 ■ Small Business Development and International Trade Center
Southwestern College
Higher Education Ctr.
880 National City Blvd., Ste. 103
National City, CA 91950
Contact: Victor M. Castillo, Dir.
Ph: (619)482-6391
Fax: (619)216-6703
E-mail: support@sbditc.org
URL: http://www.sbditc.org
Descr: Represents and promotes the small business sector. Provides management assistance to current and prospective small business owners. Helps to improve management skills and expand the products and services of members.

1620 ■ SOCAP International - Northwest Regional Chapter
1541 Cummins Dr.
Modesto, CA 95358
Contact: Marie Shubin, Pres.
Ph: (209)341-3117
URL: http://www.nwsocap.org
Descr: Promotes customer care and customer management as a competitive advantage in business. Provides educational tools and professional resources to help members drive business transformation within their companies.

1621 ■ SOCAP International - Southwest Regional Chapter
4275 Executive Sq., Ste. 500
La Jolla, CA 92037
Contact: Pat Harrison, Pres.
Ph: (858)274-8870
E-mail: pharrison@kashi.com
URL: http://www.socapsrcchapter.org
Descr: Promotes customer care and customer management as a competitive advantage in business. Provides educational tools and profes-

sional resources to help members drive business transformation within their companies.

1622 ■ Solano College Small Business Development Center
360 Campus Ln., Ste. 102
Fairfield, CA 94534
Contact: Charles Eason, Dir.
Ph: (707)864-3382
E-mail: charles.eason@solano.edu
URL: http://www.solanosbdc.org
Descr: Represents and promotes the small business sector. Provides management assistance to current and prospective small business owners. Helps to improve management skills and expand the products and services of members.

1623 ■ Sonoma County Taxpayers' Association
PO Box 14241
Santa Rosa, CA 95402
Ph: (707)481-1089
Fax: (707)576-1460
E-mail: taxpayer@sonic.net

1624 ■ Stanislaus Taxpayers Association
PO Box 1070
Modesto, CA 95353
Ph: (209)544-8914
Fax: (209)544-0375

1625 ■ TriTech Small Business Development Center
2 Park Plz., Ste. 100
Irvine, CA 92614
Ph: (949)794-7226
URL: http://www.leadsbdc.org
Descr: Represents and promotes the small business sector. Provides management assistance to current and prospective small business owners. Helps to improve management skills and expand the products and services of members.

1626 ■ UC Merced Small Business Development Center Regional Network
550 E Shaw Ave., Ste. 100
Fresno, CA 93710
Contact: Diane R. Howerton, Dir.
Ph: (559)241-7406
Free: 877-826-7232
Fax: (559)241-7422
E-mail: casbdc@ucmerced.edu
URL: http://sbdc.ucmerced.edu
Descr: Represents and promotes the small business sector. Provides management assistance to current and prospective small business owners. Helps to improve management skills and expand the products and services of members.

1627 ■ Ventura College Small Business Development Center
71 Day Rd.
Ventura, CA 93003
Ph: (805)648-8925
Fax: (805)648-8965
E-mail: info@vcsbdc.com
URL: http://www.vcsbdc.com
Descr: Represents and promotes the small business sector. Provides management assistance to current and prospective small business owners. Helps to improve management skills and expand the products and services of members.

1628 ■ Ventura County Taxpayers Association
5156 McGrath St.
Ventura, CA 93003
Contact: Don Facciano, Pres.
Ph: (805)644-3291
Fax: (805)644-9208
E-mail: vcta@att.net
URL: http://www.vcta.org

1629 ■ Weill Institute Small Business Development Center at Bakersfield College
2100 Chester Ave.
Bakersfield, CA 93301

Contact: Cope Norcross
Ph: (661)336-5010
Fax: (661)395-4134
E-mail: contact@weill-sbdc.com
URL: http://www.weill-sbdc.com
Descr: Represents and promotes the small business sector. Provides management assistance to current and prospective small business owners. Helps to improve management skills and expand the products and services of members.

1630 ■ Woodland Small Business Development Center
307 First St.
Woodland, CA 95695
Contact: David Flory Sr.
Ph: (530)822-0140
URL: http://www.yubasbdc.org/Woodland-SBDC.asp
Descr: Represents and promotes the small business sector. Provides management assistance to current and prospective small business owners. Helps to improve management skills and expand the products and services of members.

1631 ■ Yolo County Taxpayers Association
PO Box 1411
Woodland, CA 95776
Contact: Bert H. Brooks DVM, Communication Facilitator/Bulletin Ed.
Ph: (530)666-7322
E-mail: holisticvet@direcway.com
URL: http://www.yolotaxpayers.com

1632 ■ Yuba Community College District Small Business Development Center
1227 Bridge St., Ste. C
Yuba City, CA 95991
Contact: Ken Freeman, Dir.
Ph: (530)822-0140
Fax: (530)822-0163
URL: http://www.yubasbdc.org
Descr: Represents and promotes the small business sector. Provides management assistance to current and prospective small business owners. Helps to improve management skills and expand the products and services of members.

Colorado

1633 ■ American Society of Appraisers, Denver Chapter
2655 W 39th Ave.
Denver, CO 80211
Contact: Joseph M. Cornell, Pres.
Ph: (303)455-1717
Fax: (303)455-7171
E-mail: asappraiser@aol.com
URL: http://www.appraisers.org/denver
Descr: Serves as a professional appraisal educator, testing and accrediting society. Sponsors mandatory recertification program for all members. Offers consumer information service to the public.

1634 ■ Appraisal Institute, Colorado Chapter
1540 S Holly St., Ste. 5
Denver, CO 80222
Contact: J. Virginia Messick, Pres.
Ph: (303)691-0487
Fax: (303)757-0158
E-mail: jvmenb@msn.com
URL: http://www.colo-ai.org
Staff: 1. **Descr:** Represents professional real estate appraisers. Advances the real estate solutions and upholds the standards of practice and credentials of real estate appraisers. **Fnd:** 1931. **Mem:** 630. **State Groups:** 1.

1635 ■ Boulder Business and Professional Women
PO Box 17398
Boulder, CO 80308-0398
Contact: Jennifer Olson, Pres.
Ph: (303)415-3780
E-mail: president@boulderbpw.org
URL: http://www.boulderbpw.org
Descr: Represents the interests of business and

professional women. Elevates the standards for women in business and professional settings. Promotes equity for all women in the workplace through advocacy, education and information. Provides professional development, networking and career advancement opportunities for working women.

1636 ■ Boulder Small Business Development Center
2440 Pearl St.
Boulder, CO 80302
Contact: Sharon King
Ph: (303)442-1475
URL: http://www.bouldersbdc.com
Descr: Represents and promotes the small business sector. Provides management assistance to current and prospective small business owners. Helps to improve management skills and expand the products and services of members.

1637 ■ Boulder Small Business Development Center - Longmont
528 Main St.
Longmont, CO 80501
Contact: Sharon King
Ph: (303)442-1475
E-mail: sharon.king@boulderchamber.com
URL: http://www.bouldersbdc.com
Descr: Represents and promotes the small business sector. Provides management assistance to current and prospective small business owners. Helps to improve management skills and expand the products and services of members.

1638 ■ Cherry Creek Business and Professional Women
PO Box 1178
Conifer, CO 80433
Contact: Karen Kilde, Pres.
Ph: (303)300-5523
E-mail: info@cherrycreekbpw.org
URL: http://www.cherrycreekbpw.org
Descr: Represents the interests of business and professional women. Elevates the standards for women in business and professional settings. Promotes equity for all women in the workplace through advocacy, education and information. Provides professional development, networking and career advancement opportunities for working women.

1639 ■ Colorado Credit Union System
4905 W 60th Ave.
Arvada, CO 80003
Contact: John Dill, Pres.
Ph: (303)427-4222
Free: 800-477-1697
Fax: (720)479-3423
E-mail: info@colocu.com
URL: http://www.colocu.com
Descr: Serves credit unions in the areas of legislation, education, operations, research, member services and training. Provides a variety of resources to assist credit unions in their daily operations. **Fnd:** 1934. **Mem:** 1500000.

1640 ■ Colorado Society of Enrolled Agents
4740 Table Mesa Dr.
Boulder, CO 80305
Contact: Mark E. Sehnert, Pres.
Ph: (303)449-4413
E-mail: mark@taxworks.biz
URL: http://www.taxproco.org
Descr: Aims to improve the knowledge, skills and professionalism of members in all areas of taxation. Enhances the role of enrolled agents among government agencies, other professions and the public at large. Advocates for taxpayer rights and protects members' interests.

1641 ■ Colorado Springs Small Business Development Center
Citti Bldg.
1420 Austin Bluffs Pkwy.
Colorado Springs, CO 80933

Contact: Michelle Bracewell, Counselor
Ph: (719)262-3844
URL: http://cssbdc.org
Descr: Represents and promotes the small business sector. Provides management assistance to current and prospective small business owners. Helps to improve management skills and expand the products and services of members.

1642 ■ Colorado Union of Taxpayers (CUT)
1685 S Colorado Blvd., Unit S
PMB 162
Denver, CO 80222
Ph: (303)494-2400
URL: http://www.coloradotaxpayer.org

1643 ■ Credit Union Association of Colorado
4905 W 60th Ave.
Arvada, CO 80003
Contact: Melia D. Heimback, Exec. Dir.
Free: 800-477-1697
Fax: (720)479-3423
URL: http://www.colocu.com
Descr: Seeks to perfect credit union laws; aids in the development of new credit union services, including new payment systems techniques; assists in the training of credit union officials and employees.

1644 ■ Denver Metro Small Business Development Center
1445 Market St.
Denver, CO 80202
Contact: Tameka Montgomery, Exec. Dir.
Ph: (303)620-8076
Fax: (303)534-2145
E-mail: denver.sbdc@den-chamber.org
URL: http://www.denversbdc.org
Descr: Represents and promotes the small business sector. Provides management assistance to current and prospective small business owners. Helps to improve management skills and expand the products and services of members.

1645 ■ Denver Tech Center Business and Professional Women
PO Box 370507
Denver, CO 80237-0507
Contact: Carol Naff, Pres.
Ph: (303)277-8292
E-mail: dtcbpwpres@comcast.net
URL: http://www.dtcbpw.org
Descr: Represents the interests of business and professional women. Elevates the standards for women in business and professional settings. Promotes equity for all women in the workplace through advocacy, education and information. Provides professional development, networking and career advancement opportunities for working women.

1646 ■ Financial Planning Association of Southern Colorado
Capstone Investments
5045 Sapphire Dr.
Colorado Springs, CO 80918
Contact: William Sigrist, Pres.
Ph: (719)477-9883
E-mail: wsigrist@att.net
URL: http://www.scfpa.org
Descr: Promotes the value of the financial planning process to the public. Provides professional education and networking opportunities for the financial planning community. **Mem:** 92.

1647 ■ Fort Morgan Small Business Development Center
300 Main St.
Fort Morgan, CO 80701
Ph: (970)542-3263
E-mail: tim.edgar@morgancc.edu
URL: http://www.coloradosbdc.org
Descr: Represents and promotes the small business sector. Provides management assistance to current and prospective small business owners. Helps to

improve management skills and expand the products and services of members.

1648 ■ Grand Junction Small Business Development Center
2591 B 3/4 Rd.
Grand Junction, CO 81503
Ph: (970)243-5242
E-mail: jmorey@gjincubator.org
URL: http://www.coloradosbdc.org
Descr: Represents and promotes the small business sector. Provides management assistance to current and prospective small business owners. Helps to improve management skills and expand the products and services of members.

1649 ■ Greeley/Weld Small Business Development Center
902 7th Ave.
Greeley, CO 80631
Contact: Valeen Thomas
Ph: (970)352-3661
E-mail: valeen.thomas@unco.edu
URL: http://mcb.unco.edu/Programs/sbdc
Descr: Represents and promotes the small business sector. Provides management assistance to current and prospective small business owners. Helps to improve management skills and expand the products and services of members.

1650 ■ Institute of Business Appraisers, Northwest Region
Gibraltar Business Appraisals, Inc.
1325 Dry Creek Dr., Ste. No. 201
Longmont, CO 80503
Contact: Chris D. Treharne
Ph: (303)532-2545
Free: 888-428-2583
Fax: (303)532-2546
E-mail: ctreharne@4avalue.com
URL: http://www.4avalue.com
Descr: Provides business appraisal education and professional accreditation. Disseminates information about the profession of business valuation, appraising, and the industry. **Fnd:** 1978. **Mem:** 3000.

1651 ■ International Association of Assessing Officers, Colorado
Douglas County Assessor's Office
301 Wilcox St., Ste. 201
Castle Rock, CO 80104
Contact: Theresa Cox, Rep.
Ph: (303)660-7470
Fax: (303)660-1429
E-mail: tcox@douglas.co.us
Descr: Represents state and local officials concerned with valuation of property for ad valorem property tax purposes. Works to improve standards and conduct research on tax assessment. Promotes innovation and excellence in property appraisal, assessment administration, and property tax policy through professional development, education, research, and technical assistance.

1652 ■ La Junta Small Business Development Center
Otero Junior College
1802 Colorado Ave.
La Junta, CO 81050
Ph: (719)384-6959
E-mail: bryan.bryant@ojc.edu
URL: http://www.coloradosbdc.org
Descr: Represents and promotes the small business sector. Provides management assistance to current and prospective small business owners. Helps to improve management skills and expand the products and services of members.

1653 ■ Lakewood Small Business Development Center
Bldg. 19, Ste. 400
1667 Cole Blvd.
Golden, CO 80401
Ph: (303)233-5555
E-mail: jayne.reiter@denverchamber.org
URL: http://www.coloradosbdc.org

Descr: Represents and promotes the small business sector. Provides management assistance to current and prospective small business owners. Helps to improve management skills and expand the products and services of members.

1654 ■ Larimer County Small Business Development Center
125 S Howes St., Ste. 150
Fort Collins, CO 80521
Ph: (970)498-9295
Fax: (970)498-8924
E-mail: sbdc@frii.com
URL: http://www.sbdc-larimer.com
Descr: Represents and promotes the small business sector. Provides management assistance to current and prospective small business owners. Helps to improve management skills and expand the products and services of members.

1655 ■ Loveland Small Business Development Center
5400 Stone Creek Cir.
Loveland, CO 80538
Ph: (970)667-4106
E-mail: sbdcloveland@frii.com
URL: http://www.coloradosbdc.org
Descr: Represents and promotes the small business sector. Provides management assistance to current and prospective small business owners. Helps to improve management skills and expand the products and services of members.

1656 ■ Mile-Hi AIFA
8184 W Iliff Ln.
Lakewood, CO 80227
Contact: Doug Whitten, Pres.
Ph: (303)570-0203
Fax: (303)989-7819
E-mail: dwhitten@comcast.net
URL: http://www.naifanet.com/mile-hi
Descr: Represents the interests of insurance and financial advisors. Advocates for a positive legislative and regulatory environment. Enhances business and professional skills of members.

1657 ■ NAIFA-Denver
2170 S Parker Rd., Ste. 255
Denver, CO 80231
Contact: Bob Lundy, Exec. Dir.
Ph: (303)283-6001
Fax: (303)750-0085
E-mail: naifa-denver@kareams.com
URL: http://209.61.156.20/main-pub.cfm?usr=070736
Descr: Represents the interests of insurance and financial advisors. Advocates for a positive legislative and regulatory environment. Enhances business and professional skills of members.

1658 ■ NAIFA-Greeley/Weld
710 11th Ave., Ste. 215
Greeley, CO 80631
Contact: Barry R. Bode, Pres.
Ph: (970)356-4990
Fax: (970)356-4991
E-mail: brb@bodeagency.com
URL: http://www.naifanet.com/greeley
Descr: Represents the interests of insurance and financial advisors. Advocates for a positive legislative and regulatory environment. Enhances business and professional skills of members.

1659 ■ NAIFA-Western Colorado
743 Horizon Ct., Ste. 334
Grand Junction, CO 81506
Contact: Cindy Atwood, Pres.
Ph: (970)263-9000
Fax: (970)263-9001
E-mail: cindy@gjinsbenefitsbydesign.com
URL: http://naifanet.com/westerncolorado
Descr: Represents the interests of insurance and financial advisors. Advocates for a positive legisla-

tive and regulatory environment. Enhances business and professional skills of members.

1660 ■ North American Securities Administrators Association, Colorado
1560 Broadway St., Ste. 900
Denver, CO 80202
Contact: Fred Joseph
Ph: (303)894-2320
Fax: (303)861-2126
Descr: Represents the interests of the state, provincial and territorial securities administrators in the U.S.

1661 ■ North Metro Small Business Development Center
Front Range Community College
3645 W 112th Ave., Rm. No. 2014
Westminster, CO 80031
Contact: Chris Luchs, Dir.
Ph: (303)460-1032
Fax: (303)469-7143
E-mail: wcicpd@frontrange.edu
URL: http://www.frontrange.edu/FRCCTemplates/FRCC7.aspx?id=132
Descr: Represents and promotes the small business sector. Provides management assistance to current and prospective small business owners. Helps to improve management skills and expand the products and services of members.

1662 ■ Pueblo Small Business Development Center
Pueblo Community College
900 W Orman Ave.
Pueblo, CO 81004
Ph: (719)549-3224
E-mail: caroline.parra@pueblocc.edu
URL: http://www.coloradosbdc.org
Descr: Represents and promotes the small business sector. Provides management assistance to current and prospective small business owners. Helps to improve management skills and expand the products and services of members.

1663 ■ San Luis Valley Small Business Development Center
609 Main St., Ste. 108
Alamosa, CO 81102
E-mail: donna@slv-sbdc.com
URL: http://www.coloradosbdc.org
Descr: Represents and promotes the small business sector. Provides management assistance to current and prospective small business owners. Helps to improve management skills and expand the products and services of members.

1664 ■ South Metro Denver Small Business Development Center - Aurora
5430 S Biscay Cir.
Aurora, CO 80015
E-mail: lhajek@bestchamber.com
URL: http://www.coloradosbdc.org
Descr: Represents and promotes the small business sector. Provides management assistance to current and prospective small business owners. Helps to improve management skills and expand the products and services of members.

1665 ■ South Metro Denver Small Business Development Center - Centennial
6840 S University Blvd.
Centennial, CO 80122
Contact: Marcia Pessemier, Dir.
Ph: (303)795-0142
E-mail: lhajek@bestchamber.com
URL: http://www.smallbusinessdenver.com
Descr: Represents and promotes the small business sector. Provides management assistance to current and prospective small business owners. Helps to improve management skills and expand the products and services of members.

1666 ■ Southwest Colorado Small Business Development Center - Durango
2700 Main Ave.
Durango, CO 81301

Ph: (970)247-7009
URL: http://www.coloradosbdc.org
Descr: Represents and promotes the small business sector. Provides management assistance to current and prospective small business owners. Helps to improve management skills and expand the products and services of members.

1667 ■ Southwest Colorado Small Business Development Center - Pagosa
402 San Juan Dr.
Pagosa Springs, CO 81147
Ph: (970)247-7009
E-mail: beckelhymer_r@fortlewis.edu
URL: http://www.coloradosbdc.org
Descr: Represents and promotes the small business sector. Provides management assistance to current and prospective small business owners. Helps to improve management skills and expand the products and services of members.

1668 ■ Southwestern Colorado Small Business Development Center
1000 Rim Dr., EBH 140
Durango, CO 81301
Ph: (970)247-7009
E-mail: sbdc@fortlewis.edu
URL: http://www.coloradosbdc.org
Descr: Represents and promotes the small business sector. Provides management assistance to current and prospective small business owners. Helps to improve management skills and expand the products and services of members.

1669 ■ West Central Small Business Development Center
600 N Adams St.
Gunnison, CO 81231
Ph: (970)943-3157
E-mail: sbdc@western.edu
URL: http://www.coloradosbdc.org
Descr: Represents and promotes the small business sector. Provides management assistance to current and prospective small business owners. Helps to improve management skills and expand the products and services of members.

1670 ■ West Central Small Business Development Center - Chaffee and Lake County
104 Crestone Ave.
Salida, CO 81201
Ph: (719)530-5613
E-mail: eolson@chaffeecounty.org
URL: http://www.coloradosbdc.org
Descr: Represents and promotes the small business sector. Provides management assistance to current and prospective small business owners. Helps to improve management skills and expand the products and services of members.

1671 ■ Wyoming Credit Union League
4905 W 60th Ave.
Arvada, CO 80003
Ph: (303)427-4222
Free: 800-477-1697
Fax: (720)479-3423
E-mail: ga@colocu.com
Descr: Promotes credit union membership, use of services, and organization of new credit unions. Seeks to perfect credit union laws; aids in the development of new credit union services; assists in the training of credit union officials and employees. **Fnd:** 1958. **Mem:** 175000. **Local Groups:** 30.

Connecticut

1672 ■ American Society of Appraisers, Connecticut Chapter
111 Godfrey W Rd.
Weston, CT 06883-1325
Contact: Carolyn A. Armbrust, Pres.
Ph: (203)483-2222
Fax: (203)488-4577
E-mail: c.armbrust@axcessvalue.com
URL: http://www.appraisers.org/connecticut

Descr: Serves as a professional appraisal educator, testing and accrediting society. Sponsors mandatory recertification program for all members. Offers consumer information service to the public. **Pub:** Newsletter (monthly).

1673 ■ Appraisal Institute, Connecticut Chapter (CCAI)
PO Box 509
Torrington, CT 06790-0509
Contact: Jacqueline B. Cswerko, Exec. Dir.
Ph: (860)482-9992
Fax: (860)482-8342
E-mail: aict@earthlink.net
URL: http://www.ai-ct.org
Descr: Serves as the leader in residential and commercial appraisal education. **Fnd:** 1991.

1674 ■ Avon Taxpayers Association
PO Box 934
Avon, CT 06001
Contact: Florence Stahl
Ph: (860)673-2725
E-mail: flostahl@snet.net
URL: http://www.ctact.org

1675 ■ Brookfield Taxpayers Association
5 S Mountain Rd.
Brookfield, CT 06804
Contact: Fred Standt
Ph: (203)775-9364
E-mail: fstndt@aol.com
URL: http://www.ctact.org

1676 ■ Connecticut Federation of Business and Professional Women
297 Fishtown Rd.
Mystic, CT 06355
Contact: Marguerita S. Rollinson, Pres.
E-mail: webmaster@bpwct.org
URL: http://www.bpwct.org
Descr: Represents the interests of business and professional women. Elevates the standards for women in business and professional settings. Promotes equity for all women in the workplace through advocacy, education and information. Provides professional development, networking and career advancement opportunities for working women.

1677 ■ Connecticut Small Business Development Center - Eastern Connecticut State University
Beckert Hall
83 Windham St.
Willimantic, CT 06226
Contact: Milena Stankova Erwin, Business Development Advisor
Ph: (860)832-0650
Fax: (860)832-0656
E-mail: twissdec@ccsu.edu
URL: http://www.ccsu.edu/sbdc
Descr: Represents and promotes the small business sector. Provides management assistance to current and prospective small business owners. Helps to improve management skills and expand the products and services of members.

1678 ■ Connecticut Small Business Development Center - Southern Connecticut State University
Old Student Ctr., Rm. 104
501 Crescent St.
New Haven, CT 06515
Contact: Maryann Cruz, Counselor
Ph: (860)832-0650
Fax: (860)832-0656
E-mail: cruz_ma@ccsu.edu
URL: http://www.ccsu.edu/sbdc
Descr: Represents and promotes the small business sector. Provides management assistance to current and prospective small business owners. Helps to

improve management skills and expand the products and services of members.

1679 ■ Connecticut Small Business Development Center - Western Connecticut State University
Ancell School of Business
181 White St.
Danbury, CT 06810
Contact: Charlotte Cilley, Business Development Advisor
Ph: (860)832-0650
Fax: (860)832-0656
E-mail: cilleychj@ccsu.edu
URL: http://www.ccsu.edu/sbdc
Descr: Represents and promotes the small business sector. Provides management assistance to current and prospective small business owners. Helps to improve management skills and expand the products and services of members.

1680 ■ Connecticut Society of Enrolled Agents
554 Boston Post Rd., Ste. 15
Milford, CT 06460
Contact: Raymond J. LaLuna
Ph: (203)878-1568
Fax: (203)877-4171
E-mail: ray@lalunatax.com
Descr: Aims to improve the knowledge, skills and professionalism of members in all areas of taxation. Enhances the role of enrolled agents among government agencies, other professions and the public at large. Advocates for taxpayer rights and protects members' interests.

1681 ■ Fairfield Taxpayers' Association
1275 Post Rd., A13
Fairfield, CT 06824
Ph: (203)259-0051

1682 ■ Federation of Connecticut Taxpayer Organizations (FCTO)
5 S Mountain Rd.
Brookfield, CT 06804
Ph: (203)775-9364
Fax: (203)775-6618
E-mail: fctopresident@ctact.org
URL: http://ctact.org

1683 ■ Financial Planning Association of Connecticut, Greater New Haven Chapter
2415 Boston Post Rd., Unit 14
Guilford, CT 06437
Contact: Mrs. Kelly Acquarulo, Chapter Admin.
Ph: (203)453-3458
Fax: (203)453-1557
E-mail: newhaven@fpact.org
URL: http://www.fpact.org
Staff: 1. **Descr:** Supports the financial planning process in order to help people achieve their goals and dreams. Promotes the legislative, regulatory and professional interests of the financial service industry. Fosters the value of financial planning and advances the financial planning profession. **Mem:** 95. **State Groups:** 3.

1684 ■ NAIFA-Eastern Fairfield
56 Partridge Dr.
Waterbury, CT 06708
Contact: Kevin J. Delaney, Pres.
Ph: (203)756-9890
Fax: (203)757-4010
E-mail: dusar@aol.com
Descr: Represents the interests of insurance and financial advisors. Advocates for a positive legislative and regulatory environment. Enhances business and professional skills of members.

1685 ■ NAIFA - Greater New Haven
PO Box 3377
New Haven, CT 06515
Contact: Harriet Haggerty RHU, Pres.
E-mail: exec@naifanewhaven.org
URL: http://www.naifanet.com/main-pub.cfm?usr=080816
Descr: Represents the interests of insurance and

financial advisors. Advocates for a positive legislative and regulatory environment. Enhances business and professional skills of members.

1686 ■ NAIFA-Greater Waterbury
56 Partridge Dr.
Waterbury, CT 06708-3327
Contact: Garret W. Post, Pres.
Ph: (203)756-9890
Fax: (203)757-4010
E-mail: dusar@aol.com
Descr: Represents the interests of insurance and financial advisors. Advocates for a positive legislative and regulatory environment. Enhances business and professional skills of members.

1687 ■ NAIFA-New London County
1751 Ellington Rd.
South Windsor, CT 06074-2707
Contact: Mitchell A. Bright, Pres.
Ph: (860)644-4751
Fax: (860)644-9640
E-mail: mitchell.bright@prudential.com
Descr: Represents the interests of insurance and financial advisors. Advocates for a positive legislative and regulatory environment. Enhances business and professional skills of members.

1688 ■ NAIFA - Southwestern Connecticut
PO Box 3125
Milford, CT 06460
Contact: Kimberly Crandley, Association Exec.
Ph: (203)549-0435
Fax: (203)549-0435
E-mail: kcrandley@sbcglobal.net
URL: http://naifanet.com/southwesternconn
Descr: Represents the interests of insurance and financial advisors. Advocates for a positive legislative and regulatory environment. Enhances business and professional skills of members.

1689 ■ New Haven Taxpayers Union
PO Box 8381
New Haven, CT 06530
Ph: (203)773-1571

1690 ■ North American Securities Administrators Association, Connecticut
260 Constitution Plz.
Hartford, CT 06103
Contact: Ralph Lambiase, Dir.
Ph: (860)240-8230
Fax: (860)240-8295
Descr: Represents the interests of the state, provincial and territorial securities administrators in the U.S.

1691 ■ Putnam Taxpayers Association
51 Arthur St.
Putnam, CT 06260
Ph: (860)928-4382
E-mail: csp371@hotmail.com

1692 ■ Stafford Taxpayers Association
42 Hampden Rd.
Stafford Springs, CT 06076
Ph: (860)684-3287

1693 ■ Watertown/Oakville Taxpayers Association
39 Phillips Dr.
Oakville, CT 06779
Ph: (860)274-4413
Fax: (860)274-4413
E-mail: jacc45@hotmail.com

1694 ■ West Hartford Taxpayers Association
PO Box 270201
West Hartford, CT 06127
E-mail: president@whta.org
URL: http://whta.org
Fnd: 1933.

1695 ■ West Shore Taxpayers Association (WSTA)
119 Cooper Rd.
West Haven, CT 06516

Contact: Lynn M. Fiorillo, Sec.
E-mail: membership@westshoretaxpayers.org
URL: http://www.westshoretaxpayers.org

1696 ■ Westport Taxpayers Association
5 Turtleback Ln.
Westport, CT 06880
Ph: (203)227-6147
E-mail: beardavis@prodigy.net

1697 ■ Wethersfield Taxpayers Association
850 Cloverdale Cir.
Wethersfield, CT 06109
Ph: (860)563-4549
E-mail: ekardas@sbcglobal.net

1698 ■ Windham Taxpayers Association
6 South St., Ext. RR1
Willimantic, CT 06226
Ph: (860)423-5280
E-mail: squaret@mindspring.com

Delaware

1699 ■ Business and Professional Women, Harrington
93 Clark St.
Harrington, DE 19952
Contact: Dawn Elliott, Pres.
Ph: (302)398-8505
Fax: (302)398-8591
E-mail: holidaymart@bpwharrington.org
URL: http://www.bpwharrington.org
Descr: Represents the interests of business and professional women. Elevates the standards for women in business and professional settings. Promotes equity for all women in the workplace through advocacy, education and information. Provides professional development, networking and career advancement opportunities for working women.

1700 ■ Delaware Federation of Business and Professional Women
PO Box 58
Dover, DE 19903
Contact: Maribeth Dockety, Pres.
Free: 800-PBW-DELA
E-mail: info@bpwdelaware.org
URL: http://www.bpwdelaware.org
Descr: Represents the interests of business and professional women. Elevates the standards for women in business and professional settings. Promotes equity for all women in the workplace through advocacy, education and information. Provides professional development, networking and career advancement opportunities for working women.

1701 ■ DeVries Chapter of Business and Professional Women
18864 Cool Spring Rd.
Milton, DE 19968
Contact: Laura Ritter, Acting Pres.
E-mail: lritter@capegazette.com
URL: http://www.bpwdelaware.org/devries.htm
Descr: Represents the interests of business and professional women. Elevates the standards for women in business and professional settings. Promotes equity for all women in the workplace through advocacy, education and information. Provides professional development, networking and career advancement opportunities for working women.

1702 ■ Dover Small Business Development Center
1200 N DuPont Hwy., Ste. 108
Dover, DE 19901
Ph: (302)678-1555
E-mail: apaoli@udel.edu
URL: http://www.delawaresbdc.org
Descr: Represents and promotes the small business sector. Provides management assistance to current and prospective small business owners. Helps to

improve management skills and expand the products and services of members.

1703 ■ Georgetown Small Business Development Center
103 W Pine St.
Georgetown, DE 19947
Ph: (302)856-1555
E-mail: wpfaff@udel.edu
URL: http://www.delawaresbdc.org
Descr: Represents and promotes the small business sector. Provides management assistance to current and prospective small business owners. Helps to improve management skills and expand the products and services of members.

1704 ■ Newark Small Business Development Center
1 Innovation Way, Ste. 301
Newark, DE 19711
Ph: (302)831-0770
E-mail: mdd@udel.edu
URL: http://www.delawaresbdc.org
Descr: Represents and promotes the small business sector. Provides management assistance to current and prospective small business owners. Helps to improve management skills and expand the products and services of members.

1705 ■ Wilmington Small Business Development Center
100 W 10th St., Ste. 812
Wilmington, DE 19801
Ph: (302)831-2770
E-mail: mdd@udel.edu
URL: http://www.delawaresbdc.org
Descr: Represents and promotes the small business sector. Provides management assistance to current and prospective small business owners. Helps to improve management skills and expand the products and services of members.

Florida

1706 ■ American Society of Appraisers, Greater Miami Chapter
Kaufman Rossin and Co.
2699 S Bayshore Dr., Ste. 300
Miami, FL 33133
Contact: Edward V. Gannon, Pres.
Ph: (305)858-5600
E-mail: egannon@kaufmanrossin.com
URL: http://old.appraisers.org/miami
Descr: Serves as a professional appraisal educator, testing and accrediting society. Sponsors mandatory recertification program for all members. Offers consumer information service to the public.

1707 ■ American Society of Appraisers, North Florida Chapter
PO Box 23817
Gainesville, FL 32602-3817
Contact: Linda Colleen Power, Pres.
Ph: (352)338-3264
Fax: (352)374-5278
E-mail: cpower@acpafl.org
URL: http://old.appraisers.org/north_florida
Descr: Serves as a professional appraisal educator, testing and accrediting society. Sponsors mandatory recertification program for all members. Offers consumer information service to the public.

1708 ■ American Society of Appraisers, Orland-Central Florida Chapter
R.E. Pender Inc.
1133 Louisiana Ave., Ste. 106
Winter Park, FL 32789
Contact: Robert E. Pender, Pres.
Ph: (407)644-9795
Fax: (407)645-4070
E-mail: bob@repender.com
URL: http://old.appraisers.org/orlando
Descr: Serves as a professional appraisal educator, testing and accrediting society. Sponsors mandatory recertification program for all members. Offers

consumer information service to the public. **Mem:** 60.

1709 ■ American Society of Appraisers, Roanoke Chapter
1403 S Riverside Dr.
New Smyrna Beach, FL 32168
Contact: Harris J. Samuels, Region Governor
Ph: (386)409-3618
Fax: (775)244-2133
E-mail: harrisam@aol.com
URL: http://www.appraisers.org/roanoke
Descr: Serves as a professional appraisal educator, testing and accrediting society. Sponsors mandatory recertification program for all members. Offers consumer information service to the public.

1710 ■ American Society of Appraisers, Tampa Bay Chapter
Equipment Valuation Management Inc.
9009 Quail Creek Dr.
Tampa, FL 33647-2226
Contact: Daniel L. Lagace, Treas.
Ph: (813)929-6605
Fax: (813)929-3173
E-mail: dlagace@evm-corp.com
URL: http://www.appraisers.org/tampabay
Descr: Serves as a professional appraisal educator, testing and accrediting society. Sponsors mandatory recertification program for all members. Offers consumer information service to the public. **Pub:** Newsletter (monthly).

1711 ■ American Society of Appraisers, Titusville Chapter
1961 Adale Ct.
Titusville, FL 32796
Contact: Bob G. Bates, Pres.
Ph: (321)264-6973
Fax: (321)264-6776
E-mail: bob.bates@brevardpropertyappraiser.com
URL: http://www.appraisers.org/titusville
Descr: Serves as a professional appraisal educator, testing and accrediting society. Sponsors mandatory recertification program for all members. Offers consumer information service to the public.

1712 ■ Broward AIFA (BAIFA)
PO Box 491208
Fort Lauderdale, FL 33349-1208
Contact: Joan Roberts-Gould, Pres.-Elect
Ph: (954)753-2262
Fax: (954)796-0618
E-mail: info@baifa.net
URL: http://www.baifa.net
Descr: Represents the interests of insurance and financial advisors. Advocates for a positive legislative and regulatory environment. Enhances business and professional skills of members.

1713 ■ Business and Professional Women, Athens
PO Box 3056
DeLand, FL 32721
Contact: Marcie Kirkland, Pres.
E-mail: gscotland@cfl.rr.com
URL: http://www.bpwathens.org
Descr: Represents the interests of business and professional women. Elevates the standards for women in business and professional settings. Promotes equity for all women in the workplace through advocacy, education and information. Provides professional development, networking and career advancement opportunities for working women.

1714 ■ Business and Professional Women of Charlotte County
PO Box 510180
Punta Gorda, FL 33951-0180
Contact: Joan Ehrman, Pres.-Elect
Ph: (941)637-1608
E-mail: rehrman2@comcast.net
URL: http://www.bpwcharlottecounty.org
Descr: Represents the interests of business and professional women. Elevates the standards for

women in business and professional settings. Promotes equity for all women in the workplace through advocacy, education and information. Provides professional development, networking and career advancement opportunities for working women.

1715 ■ Business and Professional Women, District II
PO Box 10794
Tallahassee, FL 32302
Contact: Yolanda Miranda-Hill
Ph: (850)245-0870
E-mail: yolyhill@comcast.net
URL: http://www.bpwfl.org
Descr: Represents the interests of business and professional women. Elevates the standards for women in business and professional settings. Promotes equity for all women in the workplace through advocacy, education and information. Provides professional development, networking and career advancement opportunities for working women.

1716 ■ Business and Professional Women, District IV
406 E Kentucky Ave.
DeLand, FL 32724
Contact: Pat Poore
Ph: (386)734-8472
Fax: (386)738-6911
E-mail: gscotland@cfl.rr.com
URL: http://www.bpwfl.org
Descr: Represents the interests of business and professional women. Elevates the standards for women in business and professional settings. Promotes equity for all women in the workplace through advocacy, education and information. Provides professional development, networking and career advancement opportunities for working women.

1717 ■ Business and Professional Women, District V
312 Golfview Ave.
Chuluota, FL 32766
Contact: Ginnie Aires
Ph: (407)740-0770
Fax: (407)740-0862
E-mail: ginnyaries@earthlink.net
URL: http://www.bpwfl.org
Descr: Represents the interests of business and professional women. Elevates the standards for women in business and professional settings. Promotes equity for all women in the workplace through advocacy, education and information. Provides professional development, networking and career advancement opportunities for working women.

1718 ■ Business and Professional Women, District VIII
8668 Wendy Ln.
West Palm Beach, FL 33411
Contact: Mary Sue Patchett
Ph: (561)753-5684
Fax: (561)753-9619
E-mail: marysuepatchett@aol.com
URL: http://www.bpwfl.org
Descr: Represents the interests of business and professional women. Elevates the standards for women in business and professional settings. Promotes equity for all women in the workplace through advocacy, education and information. Provides professional development, networking and career advancement opportunities for working women.

1719 ■ Business and Professional Women, Englewood and Venice
PO Box 611
Englewood, FL 34295-0611
Contact: Katie Malloy, Pres.
E-mail: katieactress@comcast.net
URL: http://www.bpwengven.org
Descr: Represents the interests of business and

professional women. Elevates the standards for women in business and professional settings. Promotes equity for all women in the workplace through advocacy, education and information. Provides professional development, networking and career advancement opportunities for working women.

1720 ■ Business and Professional Women, Flagler County
PO Box 353502
Palm Coast, FL 32135
Contact: Rebecca DeLorenzo, Pres.
E-mail: info@bpwflagler.com
URL: http://www.bpwflagler.com
Descr: Represents the interests of business and professional women. Elevates the standards for women in business and professional settings. Promotes equity for all women in the workplace through advocacy, education and information. Provides professional development, networking and career advancement opportunities for working women.

1721 ■ Business and Professional Women Four Townes
1731 Langley Ave.
DeLand, FL 32724
Contact: Rachel Sieg, 1st VP
Ph: (386)734-8295
E-mail: rsieg@cfl.rr.com
URL: http://www.bpwfourtownes.org
Descr: Represents the interests of business and professional women. Elevates the standards for women in business and professional settings. Promotes equity for all women in the workplace through advocacy, education and information. Provides professional development, networking and career advancement opportunities for working women.

1722 ■ Business and Professional Women, Jupiter
10103 Oakbark Ln.
Palm Beach Gardens, FL 33410
Contact: Nancy Robinson, Treas.
Ph: (561)743-9646
E-mail: nancyr@lkdcpa.com
URL: http://www.bpwjupiter.org
Descr: Represents the interests of business and professional women. Elevates the standards for women in business and professional settings. Promotes equity for all women in the workplace through advocacy, education and information. Provides professional development, networking and career advancement opportunities for working women.

1723 ■ Business and Professional Women, St. Petersburg Evening
PO Box 10934
St. Petersburg, FL 33733
Contact: Tracy Riordan, Membership Chair
Ph: (727)823-9629
URL: http://www.bpwstpeteevening.org
Descr: Represents the interests of business and professional women. Elevates the standards for women in business and professional settings. Promotes equity for all women in the workplace through advocacy, education and information. Provides professional development, networking and career advancement opportunities for working women.

1724 ■ Business and Professional Women, Tallahassee
PO Box 10794
Tallahassee, FL 32302
Contact: Jennifer Harrison, Pres.
E-mail: president@bpwtallahassee.com
URL: http://www.bpwtallahassee.com
Descr: Represents the interests of business and professional women. Elevates the standards for women in business and professional settings. Promotes equity for all women in the workplace through advocacy, education and information.

Provides professional development, networking and career advancement opportunities for working women.

1725 ■ Calusa Business and Professional Women
PO Box 447
Port Richey, FL 34673-0447
Contact: Cindy Ewald, Pres.
Ph: (727)853-0842
URL: http://www.bpwcalusa.org
Descr: Represents the interests of business and professional women. Elevates the standards for women in business and professional settings. Promotes equity for all women in the workplace through advocacy, education and information. Provides professional development, networking and career advancement opportunities for working women.

1726 ■ Center for Financial Training, Southeast Regional (SER-CFT)
126 W Adams St., Ste. 501
Jacksonville, FL 32202
Contact: Lisa Phillips, Exec. Dir.
Ph: (904)354-4830
Fax: (904)354-1834
E-mail: lisaphillipscft@bellsouth.net
URL: http://www.cft-flsc.org
Staff: 2. **Descr:** Employees of financial institutions in Alachua, Baker, Bay, Brevard, Bradford, Calhoun, Citrus, Clay, Columbia, Dixie, Duval, Escambia, Flagler, Gilchrist, Hamilton, Lafayette, Nassau, Putnam, St. Johns, Suwanee, Union, Brevard, Desoto, Hardee, Highlands, Hillsborough, Manatee, Orange, Osceola, Pasco, Pinellas, Polk, Sarasota, Seminole, and Volusia counties, Florida, as well as in South Carolina. Provides professional education, seminars, and training in the theory and practice of banking. Conducts annual community project in conjunction with Salvation Army. Holds annual awards ceremony. Also services the state of South Carolina. Holds spring, summer, and fall term classes. **Fnd:** 1910. **Pub:** *Schedule of Classes* (periodic); Annual Report (annual); Newsletter (periodic).

1727 ■ Financial Planning Association of Central Florida
PO Box 520310
Longwood, FL 32752
Contact: Paul Auslander, Chm.
Ph: (407)814-9905
Fax: (407)699-4892
E-mail: fpafl@barqmail.com
URL: http://www.fpafla.com
Descr: Supports the financial planning process in order to help people achieve their goals and dreams. Promotes the legislative, regulatory and professional interests of the financial service industry. Fosters the value of financial planning and advances the financial planning profession.

1728 ■ Financial Planning Association of Gold Coast Chapter
12157 W Linebaugh Ave.
PMB 312
Tampa, FL 33626-1732
Contact: Deborah A. Rathbun CFP, Pres.
Ph: (561)575-6724
Free: 866-730-4530
Fax: (561)744-3975
E-mail: info@fpagoldcoast.org
URL: http://www.fpagoldcoast.org
Descr: Offers educational and professional enhancement programs and forums for all Financial Planning Professionals.

1729 ■ Financial Planning Association, Gulf States
12157 W Linebaugh Ave.
PMB 312
Tampa, FL 33626-1732
Contact: Christine Brown, Exec.
Ph: (813)854-3759
Fax: (813)830-6113
E-mail: fpa@gulfstatesfpa.org

URL: http://www.gulfstatesfpa.org
Descr: Promotes the value of the financial planning process to the public. Provides professional education and networking opportunities for the financial planning community. **Mem:** 27500.

1730 ■ Financial Planning Association of Miami-Dade
PO Box 560982
Miami, FL 33256-0982
Contact: Amy Miller, Exec. Dir.
Ph: (786)390-7655
Fax: (305)470-7487
E-mail: info@fpamiamidade.org
URL: http://www.fpamiamidade.org
Descr: Supports the financial planning process in order to help people achieve their goals and dreams. Promotes the legislative, regulatory and professional interests of the financial service industry. Fosters the value of financial planning and advances the financial planning profession.

1731 ■ Financial Planning Association of Northeast Florida
SunTrust Bank
76 S Laura St., 1st Fl.
Jacksonville, FL 32202
Contact: Nassim H. Elias AEP, Pres.
Ph: (904)632-2593
Fax: (904)632-2860
E-mail: nassim.elias@suntrust.com
URL: http://www.northeastfloridafpa.org
Descr: Promotes the value of the financial planning process to the public. Provides professional education and networking opportunities for the financial planning community.

1732 ■ Financial Planning Association, Southwest Florida
Carole Peck Financial Advisors, Inc.
3301 Bonita Beach Rd., Ste. 208
Bonita Springs, FL 34134
Contact: Susan P. Steiner CFP, Pres.
Ph: (941)637-7526
Fax: (941)637-7526
E-mail: info@fpa-swlf.org
URL: http://www.fpa-swfl.org
Descr: Promotes the value of the financial planning process to the public. Provides professional education and networking opportunities for the financial planning community.

1733 ■ Florida Chapter of the International Association of Assessing Officers (FCIAAO)
Government Center, 5th Fl.
301 N Olive Ave.
West Palm Beach, FL 33401
Contact: Dorothy Jacks AAS, Pres.
Ph: (561)355-3233
Fax: (561)355-3963
E-mail: djacks@co.palm-beach.fl.us
URL: http://www.fciaao.org
Descr: Represents state and local officials concerned with valuation of property for ad valorem property tax purposes. Works to improve standards and conduct research on tax assessment. Promotes innovation and excellence in property appraisal, assessment administration, and property tax policy through professional development, education, research, and technical assistance.

1734 ■ Florida Federation of Business and Professional Women's Clubs
3150 Holiday Springs Blvd., Bldg. 8, No. 111
Margate, FL 33063
Contact: Venita Garvin Valdez, Pres.
Ph: (305)743-5452
Fax: (305)289-1589
E-mail: info@bpwfl.org
URL: http://www.bpwfl.org
Descr: Represents the interests of business and professional women. Elevates the standards for women in business and professional settings. Promotes equity for all women in the workplace

through advocacy, education and information. Provides professional development, networking and career advancement opportunities for working women.

1735 ■ Florida Small Business Development Center at Daytona State College
Daytona State College
Bldg. 110, Rm. 222
1200 W International Speedway Blvd.
Daytona Beach, FL 32114
Contact: Ned Harper, Dir.
Ph: (386)506-4723
Fax: (386)506-4602
E-mail: sbdc@daytonastate.edu
URL: http://www.sbdcdaytona.com
Descr: Represents and promotes the small business sector. Provides management assistance to current and prospective small business owners. Helps to improve management skills and expand the products and services of members.

1736 ■ Florida Small Business Development Center at Seminole Community College
1445 Dolgner Pl.
Sanford, FL 32771
Contact: Renee D. Templeton, Admin. Asst.
Ph: (407)321-3495
Fax: (407)321-4184
E-mail: goetzr@scc-fl.edu
URL: http://sbdc.scc-fl.edu
Descr: Represents and promotes the small business sector. Provides management assistance to current and prospective small business owners. Helps to improve management skills and expand the products and services of members.

1737 ■ Florida Society of Enrolled Agents (FSEA)
PO Box 3877
Clearwater, FL 33767
Contact: Diana Molina EA, Pres.
Free: 800-422-3732
Fax: (727)466-0830
E-mail: info@fseaonline.org
URL: http://www.fseaonline.org

1738 ■ Florida Society of Enrolled Agents - Capital City Chapter
PO Box 487
Tallahassee, FL 32302
Contact: William Weidenbach Jr.
Ph: (850)576-1118
Fax: (850)575-6749
E-mail: william@makinglifealittlelesstaxing.com
URL: http://www.fseaonline.org/capitolcity.htm
Descr: Aims to improve the knowledge, skills and professionalism of members in all areas of taxation. Enhances the role of enrolled agents among government agencies, other professions and the public at large. Advocates for taxpayer rights and protects members' interests.

1739 ■ Florida Society of Enrolled Agents - Manasota Chapter
333 Tamiami Trail S, Ste. 257
Venice, FL 34285
Contact: Sandi Raasch EA, Pres.
Ph: (941)484-0968
E-mail: sandr@comcast.net
URL: http://floridaenrolledagents.com
Mem: 60.

1740 ■ Florida Society of Enrolled Agents - Miami-Dade Chapter
250 Catalonia Ave., No. 400
Coral Gables, FL 33134
Contact: Anna-Magda Guillen EA, Pres.
Ph: (305)444-2423

Fax: (305)444-8077
E-mail: amguillen@aol.com

1741 ■ Florida Taxpayers Coalition
PO Box 773609
Ocala, FL 34473
E-mail: sma@floridapropertytaxappeals.com

1742 ■ Jacksonville AIFA
PO Box 37028
Jacksonville, FL 32236
Contact: Chris Harclerode, Pres.
Ph: (904)695-2300
Fax: (904)783-6857
E-mail: jaifa@bellsouth.net
URL: http://www.jaifainfo.org
Descr: Represents the interests of insurance and financial advisors. Advocates for a positive legislative and regulatory environment. Enhances business and professional skills of members. **Fnd:** 1926. **Mem:** 400.

1743 ■ Lake Sumter County AIFA
1836 Heritage Blvd., No. 200
Tallahassee, FL 32308-7704
Contact: Charles Cangialosi, Pres.
Ph: (850)422-1701
Fax: (850)422-2762
E-mail: heierman@faifa.org
Descr: Represents the interests of insurance and financial advisors. Advocates for a positive legislative and regulatory environment. Enhances business and professional skills of members.

1744 ■ Martin County Taxpayers Association (MCTA)
PO Box 741
Stuart, FL 34995
Contact: Donald S. Pickard, Pres.
Ph: (772)288-0474
E-mail: admin@mctaxpayers.org
URL: http://www.mctaxpayers.org
Fnd: 1950.

1745 ■ Miami-Dade AIFA
9241 SW 54th Pl.
Cooper City, FL 33328
Contact: Maud Marie Santucci, Exec. Dir.
Ph: (954)680-0448
Free: 888-918-6505
Fax: (954)434-4564
E-mail: naifa-miamidade@bellsouth.net
URL: http://www.naifanet.com/miamidade
Descr: Represents the interests of insurance and financial advisors. Advocates for a positive legislative and regulatory environment. Enhances business and professional skills of members.

1746 ■ Palm Beaches AIFA
PO Box 151
Lake Worth, FL 33460-0151
Contact: Charles Edris, Pres.
Ph: (561)588-5444
Fax: (561)588-1444
E-mail: info@pbaifa.org
URL: http://www.pbaifa.org
Descr: Represents the interest of insurance and financial advisors. Advocates for a positive legislative and regulatory environment. Enhances business and professional skills of members.

1747 ■ St. Lucie AIFA
1836 Hermitage Blvd., No. 200
Tallahassee, FL 32308-7704
Ph: (850)422-1701
Fax: (850)422-2762
E-mail: heierman@faifa.org
Descr: Represents the interests of insurance and financial advisors. Advocates for a positive legislative and regulatory environment. Enhances business and professional skills of members.

1748 ■ Sawgrass AIFA
National Medical Resources/EMSI
2700 W Cypress Creek Rd., Ste. D-128
Fort Lauderdale, FL 33309

Contact: Lynn Goldblatt, Sec.
Ph: (954)370-0041
Fax: (954)382-1893
E-mail: info@sawgrassaifa.com
URL: http://www.sawgrassaifa.com
Descr: Represents the interest of insurance and financial advisors. Advocates for a positive legislative and regulatory environment. Enhances business and professional skills of members.

1749 ■ Small Business Development Center at Central Florida Development Council of Polk County
3433 Winter Lake Rd.
Modular-LMC
Lakeland, FL 33803-9807
Contact: Doretha Brooks, Dir.
Ph: (863)667-7913
Fax: (863)667-7911
E-mail: info@polksbdc.org
URL: http://www.polksbdc.org
Descr: Represents and promotes the small business sector. Provides management assistance to current and prospective small business owners. Helps to improve management skills and expand the products and services of members.

1750 ■ Small Business Development Center at Florida A & M University - Perry
Taylor County Chamber of Commerce
428 N Jefferson St.
Perry, FL 32347-2510
Contact: Dawn Taylor
Ph: (850)584-5366
URL: http://floridasbdc.org
Descr: Represents and promotes the small business sector. Provides management assistance to current and prospective small business owners. Helps to improve management skills and expand the products and services of members.

1751 ■ Small Business Development Center at Florida A & M University Tallahassee
Innovation Park
The Morgan Bldg., Ste. 130
2035 E Paul Dirac Dr.
Tallahassee, FL 32310-3700
Contact: Robert Nixon, Exec. Dir.
Ph: (850)599-3407
E-mail: robert.nixon@famu.edu
URL: http://www.sbdcatfamu.org
Descr: Represents and promotes the small business sector. Provides management assistance to current and prospective small business owners. Helps to improve management skills and expand the products and services of members.

1752 ■ Small Business Development Center at Florida Atlantic University - Boca Raton
777 Glades Rd., Bldg. T-11
Boca Raton, FL 33431-0991
Contact: Nancy Young, Dir.
Ph: (561)297-1140
Fax: (561)297-1141
E-mail: sbdc@fau.edu
URL: http://www.fausbdc.com
Descr: Represents and promotes the small business sector. Provides management assistance to current and prospective small business owners. Helps to improve management skills and expand the products and services of members.

1753 ■ Small Business Development Center at Florida Atlantic University Downtown Campus
Downtown Ft. Lauderdale Campus
Reubin O'D Askew Tower, Rm. 530
111 E Las Olas Blvd.
Fort Lauderdale, FL 33301
Contact: Rafael Cruz, Associate Dir.
Ph: (954)762-5201
URL: http://www.fausbdc.com
Descr: Represents and promotes the small business sector. Provides management assistance to current and prospective small business owners. Helps to

improve management skills and expand the products and services of members.

1754 ■ Small Business Development Center at Florida Atlantic University Florida Keys Community College
5901 College Rd., Ste. No. C-226
Key West, FL 33040
Contact: Greg Baumann
Ph: (305)809-3156
Fax: (305)292-2397
E-mail: gbaumann@fau.edu
URL: http://www.fausbdc.com
Descr: Represents and promotes the small business sector. Provides management assistance to current and prospective small business owners. Helps to improve management skills and expand the products and services of members.

1755 ■ Small Business Development Center at Florida Atlantic University Miami-Dade County
Festival Plaza-Miami
8500 SW 8th St., No. 224
Miami, FL 33144
Contact: Carlos Cardenas, Associate Dir.
Ph: (786)388-9040
Fax: (786)388-9060
E-mail: cardenas@fau.edu
URL: http://www.fausbdc.com
Descr: Represents and promotes the small business sector. Provides management assistance to current and prospective small business owners. Helps to improve management skills and expand the products and services of members.

1756 ■ Small Business Development Center at Florida Atlantic University Okeechobee
Okeechobee One-Stop Career Center
209 SW Park St.
Okeechobee, FL 34972-4160
Contact: Jim Lilly
Ph: (863)462-5350
Fax: (863)462-5355
E-mail: jlilly2@fau.edu
URL: http://www.fausbdc.com
Descr: Represents and promotes the small business sector. Provides management assistance to current and prospective small business owners. Helps to improve management skills and expand the products and services of members.

1757 ■ Small Business Development Center at Florida Atlantic University - Port St. Lucie
Bldg. SL, Rm. 125A
500 NW California Blvd.
Port St. Lucie, FL 34986-2601
Contact: Ken R. Stephanz
Ph: (772)873-3428
E-mail: kstepha2@fau.edu
URL: http://www.fausbdc.com
Descr: Represents and promotes the small business sector. Provides management assistance to current and prospective small business owners. Helps to improve management skills and expand the products and services of members.

1758 ■ Small Business Development Center at Florida Atlantic University Treasure Coast
SR Bldg., Rm. 221
5353 Parkside Dr.
Jupiter, FL 33458
Contact: Ted Kramer, Asst. Dir.
Ph: (561)799-8101
E-mail: ekramer@fau.edu
URL: http://www.fausbdc.com
Descr: Represents and promotes the small business sector. Provides management assistance to current and prospective small business owners. Helps to improve management skills and expand the products and services of members.

1759 ■ Small Business Development Center at Florida Gulf Coast University - Cape Coral
1020 Cultural Park Blvd.
Cape Coral, FL 33990-1229
Contact: Judith Pultro

Ph: (239)573-2737
Fax: (239)573-2797
E-mail: jpultro@fgcu.edu
URL: http://cli.fgcu.edu/sbdc
Descr: Represents and promotes the small business sector. Provides management assistance to current and prospective small business owners. Helps to improve management skills and expand the products and services of members.

1760 ■ Small Business Development Center at Florida Gulf Coast University Clewiston
College of Business, Career and Service Center
215 S Franscisco St.
Clewiston, FL 33440-4002
Contact: Sean Moore
Ph: (863)517-0097
URL: http://www.floridasbdc.com

Descr: Represents and promotes the small business sector. Provides management assistance to current and prospective small business owners. Helps to improve management skills and expand the products and services of members.

1761 ■ Small Business Development Center at Florida Gulf Coast University - Fort Myers
Florida Gulf Coast University
Lutgert Hall, Rm. 2320
Fort Myers, FL 33965-6565
Contact: Dan Regelski, Dir.
Ph: (239)745-3705
E-mail: dregelsk@fgcu.edu
URL: http://cli.fgcu.edu/sbdc

Descr: Represents and promotes the small business sector. Provides management assistance to current and prospective small business owners. Helps to improve management skills and expand the products and services of members.

1762 ■ Small Business Development Center at Florida Gulf Coast University Immokalee
Florida Gulf Coast University
Lutgert Hall, Rm. 2317
Fort Myers, FL 33965-6565
Contact: Julio Estremera, Program Facilitator
Ph: (239)745-3707
E-mail: jestreme@fgcu.edu
URL: http://cli.fgcu.edu/sbdc

Descr: Represents and promotes the small business sector. Provides management assistance to current and prospective small business owners. Helps to improve management skills and expand the products and services of members.

1763 ■ Small Business Development Center at Florida Gulf Coast University - Port Charlotte
2702 Tamiami Trail
Port Charlotte, FL 33952-5129
Contact: Peter Keating
Ph: (941)627-2222
URL: http://www.floridasbdc.com

Descr: Represents and promotes the small business sector. Provides management assistance to current and prospective small business owners. Helps to improve management skills and expand the products and services of members.

1764 ■ Small Business Development Center at Gulf Coast Community College
2500 Minnesota Ave.
Lynn Haven, FL 32444-4815
Contact: Joe Chavarria, Dir.
Ph: (850)271-1108
Free: 800-542-7232
Fax: (850)271-1109
E-mail: info@northfloridabiz.com
URL: http://www.northfloridabiz.com

Descr: Represents and promotes the small business sector. Provides management assistance to current and prospective small business owners. Helps to

improve management skills and expand the products and services of members.

1765 ■ Small Business Development Center of the Heartland at South Florida Community College
600 W College Dr.
Avon Park, FL 33825
Contact: Bill McKown
Ph: (863)784-7379
Fax: (863)784-7355
E-mail: bmckown@coba.usf.edu
URL: http://www.southflorida.edu/sbdc

Descr: Represents and promotes the small business sector. Provides management assistance to current and prospective small business owners. Helps to improve management skills and expand the products and services of members.

1766 ■ Small Business Development Center at Manatee Community College - Venice
8000 S Tamiami Trail, Rm. 809
Venice, FL 34293
Contact: Art Mahoney
Ph: (941)408-1412
E-mail: baxterl@mccfl.edu
URL: http://www.mccfl.edu/pages/324.asp

Descr: Represents and promotes the small business sector. Provides management assistance to current and prospective small business owners. Helps to improve management skills and expand the products and services of members.

1767 ■ Small Business Development Center at North Florida Community College
Business Education Bldg. No.7, Rm. 107
325 NW Turner Davis Dr.
Madison, FL 32340-1602
Contact: Devona Sewell
Ph: (850)973-9409
URL: http://www.nfcc.edu/community-programs/sbdc

Descr: Represents and promotes the small business sector. Provides management assistance to current and prospective small business owners. Helps to improve management skills and expand the products and services of members.

1768 ■ Small Business Development Center at University of Central Florida Clermont
Lake-Sumter Community College
Bldg. 1, Rm. 106
1250 N Hancock Rd.
Clermont, FL 34711
Contact: Gene Romagna, Area Mgr.
Ph: (352)536-2224
E-mail: gromagna@bus.ucf.edu
URL: http://www.bus.ucf.edu/sbdc

Descr: Represents and promotes the small business sector. Provides management assistance to current and prospective small business owners. Helps to improve management skills and expand the products and services of members.

1769 ■ Small Business Development Center at University of Central Florida Kissimmee
1425 E Vine St.
Kissimmee, FL 34744
Contact: Janice Lopez, Area Mgr.
Ph: (407)847-2452
E-mail: nperez@bus.ucf.edu
URL: http://www.bus.ucf.edu/sbdc

Descr: Represents and promotes the small business sector. Provides management assistance to current and prospective small business owners. Helps to improve management skills and expand the products and services of members.

1770 ■ Small Business Development Center at University of Central Florida Melbourne
Brevard Community College
3865 N Wickam Rd.
Melbourne, FL 32935
Contact: Vicky Peake, Dir.
Ph: (321)433-5570
E-mail: pfrimmers@brevardcc.edu
URL: http://www.bus.ucf.edu/sbdc

Descr: Represents and promotes the small business

sector. Provides management assistance to current and prospective small business owners. Helps to improve management skills and expand the products and services of members.

1771 ■ Small Business Development Center at University of Central Florida Orlando
315 E Robinson St., Ste. 100
Orlando, FL 32801
Contact: Eunice Choi, Dir.
Ph: (407)420-4850
Fax: (407)420-4862
E-mail: sbdc@bus.ucf.edu
URL: http://www.bus.ucf.edu/sbdc

Descr: Represents and promotes the small business sector. Provides management assistance to current and prospective small business owners. Helps to improve management skills and expand the products and services of members.

1772 ■ Small Business Development Center at University of North Florida Gainesville
Gainesville Technology Enterprise Center
2153 SE Hawthorne Rd., Ste. 126
Gainesville, FL 32641
Contact: Dominic Orsini
Ph: (352)334-7230
E-mail: sbdcgnv@atlantic.net
URL: http://www.sbdc.unf.edu

Descr: Represents and promotes the small business sector. Provides management assistance to current and prospective small business owners. Helps to improve management skills and expand the products and services of members.

1773 ■ Small Business Development Center at University of North Florida Jacksonville
UNF University Center
1 2000 Alumni Dr.
Jacksonville, FL 32224
Contact: Janice William Donaldson, Dir.
Ph: (904)620-2476
Free: 800-450-4624
Fax: (904)620-2567
E-mail: smallbiz@unf.edu
URL: http://www.sbdc.unf.edu

Descr: Represents and promotes the small business sector. Provides management assistance to current and prospective small business owners. Helps to improve management skills and expand the products and services of members.

1774 ■ Small Business Development Center at University of North Florida Ocala/Marion County
110 E Silver Springs Blvd.
Ocala, FL 34470
Contact: Dr. Philip Geist, Area Dir.
Ph: (352)622-8763
E-mail: sbdcoca@atlantic.net
URL: http://www.sbdc.unf.edu

Descr: Represents and promotes the small business sector. Provides management assistance to current and prospective small business owners. Helps to improve management skills and expand the products and services of members.

1775 ■ Small Business Development Center at University of South Florida Hillsborough County
Bldg. 400, Ste. 425
7402 N 56th St.
Temple Terrace, FL 33617-7743
Contact: Vandita Trivedi, Gen. Business Asst.
Ph: (813)914-4028
Fax: (813)914-4027
URL: http://sbdc.usf.edu

Descr: Represents and promotes the small business sector. Provides management assistance to current and prospective small business owners. Helps to improve management skills and expand the products and services of members.

1776 ■ Small Business Development Center at University of South Florida - St. Petersburg
College of Business
263 13th Ave. S

St. Petersburg, FL 33701-5511
Contact: Wayne Brass, Area Mgr.
Ph: (727)873-4753
URL: http://sbdc.usf.edu
Descr: Represents and promotes the small business sector. Provides management assistance to current and prospective small business owners. Helps to improve management skills and expand the products and services of members.

1777 ■ Small Business Development Center at University of South Florida - Tampa
1101 Channelside Dr., Ste. 210
Tampa, FL 33602
Contact: Eileen Rodriguez, Interim Dir.
Ph: (813)905-5800
Fax: (813)905-5801
E-mail: sbdc@coba.usf.edu
URL: http://sbdc.usf.edu
Descr: Represents and promotes the small business sector. Provides management assistance to current and prospective small business owners. Helps to improve management skills and expand the products and services of members.

1778 ■ Small Business Development Center at University of West Florida - Fort Walton Beach
922 Mar Walt Dr., Ste. 203
Fort Walton Beach, FL 32547-6703
Contact: Jane Briere, Mgr.
Ph: (850)833-9400
E-mail: fwbsbdc@uwf.edu
URL: http://www.sbdc.uwf.edu
Descr: Represents and promotes the small business sector. Provides management assistance to current and prospective small business owners. Helps to improve management skills and expand the products and services of members.

1779 ■ Small Business Development Center at University of West Florida Pensacola
401 E Chase St., Ste. 100
Pensacola, FL 32502-6160
Contact: Larry Strain, Exec. Dir.
Ph: (850)473-7830
E-mail: sbdc@uwf.edu
URL: http://www.sbdc.uwf.edu
Descr: Represents and promotes the small business sector. Provides management assistance to current and prospective small business owners. Helps to improve management skills and expand the products and services of members.

1780 ■ SOCAP International - Florida Chapter
7226 Burnway Dr.
Orlando, FL 32819
Contact: Nate Battle, Pres.
Ph: (407)370-9090
Descr: Promotes customer care and customer management as a competitive advantage in business. Provides educational tools and professional resources to help members drive business transformation within their companies.

1781 ■ Walton County Taxpayers Association (WCTA)
PO Box 1085
Santa Rosa Beach, FL 32459
Contact: Bonnie McQuiston, Pres.
Fax: (850)231-5609
E-mail: info@waltontaxpayers.org
URL: http://www.waltontaxpayers.org

1782 ■ Westshore Business and Professional Women
5219 E Seneca Ave.
Temple Terrace, FL 33617
Contact: Anna Allen, Pres.
E-mail: dawnsvariety@yahoo.com
URL: http://bpwwestshore.org
Descr: Represents the interests of business and professional women. Elevates the standards for women in business and professional settings. Promotes equity for all women in the workplace through advocacy, education and information. Provides professional development, networking and

career advancement opportunities for working women.

Georgia

1783 ■ American Society of Appraisers, Atlanta Chapter
American Appraisal Associates
2839 Paces Ferry Rd., Ste. 400
Atlanta, GA 30339
Contact: Cynthia Nicole White, Pres.
Ph: (404)233-0503
Fax: (404)233-2336
E-mail: cwhite@american-appraisal.com
URL: http://www.asa-atlanta.com
Descr: Serves as a professional appraisal educator, testing and accrediting society. Sponsors mandatory recertification program for all members. Offers consumer information service to the public. **Fnd:** 1952.

1784 ■ Financial Planning Association of Georgia
248 Creekstone Ridge
Woodstock, GA 30188
Contact: Tom Hebrank CFP, Pres.
Ph: (770)516-8322
Fax: (770)516-0236
E-mail: admin@fpaga.org
URL: http://www.fpaga.org
Descr: Supports the financial planning process in order to help people achieve their goals and dreams. Promotes the legislative, regulatory and professional interests of the financial service industry. Fosters the value of financial planning and advances the financial planning profession.

1785 ■ Georgia Association of Enrolled Agents (GAEA)
100-C N Houston Lake Blvd.
Centerville, GA 31028-1713
Contact: Audrey L. Griffin EA, Exec. Dir.
Ph: (478)953-5016
Fax: (478)953-6092
E-mail: griftax@grifsolu.com
URL: http://www.4gaea.org

1786 ■ Georgia Society of Enrolled Agents - Savannah Chapter
37 W Fairmont Ave., Ste. 321
Savannah, GA 31406
Contact: Kathleen Collins EA, Pres.
Ph: (912)355-1040
Fax: (912)961-9590
E-mail: kathleencollins9049@msn.com
URL: http://www.4gaea.org

1787 ■ Greater Augusta AIFA
PO Box 211153
Augusta, GA 30917-1153
Ph: (803)480-1487
Fax: (803)275-4813
E-mail: bjclark5@bellsouth.net
Descr: Represents the interests of insurance and financial advisors. Advocates for a positive legislative and regulatory environment. Enhances business and professional skills of members.

1788 ■ International Association of Assessing Officers, Georgia
PO Box 562
Conyers, GA 30012
Contact: Lynn Cumbie CAE, Rep.
Ph: (770)929-4124
Fax: (770)918-6433
E-mail: lynn.cumbie@rockdalecounty.org
Descr: Represents state and local officials concerned with valuation of property for ad valorem property tax purposes. Works to improve standards and conduct research on tax assessment. Promotes innovation and excellence in property appraisal, assessment administration, and property tax policy

through professional development, education, research, and technical assistance.

1789 ■ NAIFA-Albany
1810 Peachtree Industrial Blvd., Ste. 225
Duluth, GA 30097
Ph: (770)455-4459
Fax: (770)455-4469
E-mail: christina@naifageorgia.org
Descr: Represents the interest of insurance and financial advisors. Advocates for a positive legislative and regulatory environment. Enhances business and professional skills of members.

1790 ■ NAIFA-Atlanta
1016 Rosser St., NW
Conyers, GA 30012
Contact: Sheldon Berch, Pres.
Ph: (770)483-2950
Fax: (770)388-7772
E-mail: info@naifa-atlanta.org
URL: http://www.naifa-atlanta.org
Descr: Represents the interests of insurance and financial advisors. Advocates for a positive legislative and regulatory environment. Enhances business and professional skills of members. **Mem:** 500.

1791 ■ SOCAP International - Georgia Chapter
1031 Knotts Pointe Dr.
Woodstock, GA 30188
Contact: Wade T. Hauser, Pres.
Free: 877-520-3072
Descr: Promotes customer care and customer management as a competitive advantage in business. Provides educational tools and professional resources to help members drive business transformation within their companies.

Hawaii

1792 ■ American Society of Appraisers, Hawaii Chapter
Dole Capital LLC
1188 Bishop St., Ste. 1712
Honolulu, HI 96813
Contact: Richard B. Dole, Sec.
Ph: (808)537-6007
Fax: (808)536-5318
E-mail: rsdole@aol.com
Descr: Serves as a professional appraisal educator, testing and accrediting society. Sponsors mandatory re-certification program for all members. Offers consumer information service to the public.

1793 ■ Financial Planning Association of Hawaii
516 Kawaihae St., Ste. E
Honolulu, HI 96825
Contact: Cynthia Hayakawa, Exec. Dir.
Ph: (808)394-3451
Fax: (808)395-4417
E-mail: hayacyn@hawaii.rr.com
URL: http://www.fpahawaii.org
Descr: Certified financial planners, certified public accountants, attorneys, bank officials, insurance agents, and other professionals with an interest in financial planning. Works to strengthen the community by building an organization of financial professionals dedicated to helping clients achieve their financial objectives through the financial planning process. Seeks to enhance the growth and success of members by providing educational and networking opportunities while upholding the highest standards of ethics and integrity. **Fnd:** 2000. **Mem:** 100. **Pub:** *FPA Hawaii Newsletter* (monthly).

1794 ■ Hawaii Credit Union League (HCUL)
1654 S King St.
Honolulu, HI 96826-2097
Contact: Dennis K. Tanimoto, Pres.
Ph: (808)941-0556
Fax: (808)945-0019
E-mail: info@hcul.org
URL: http://www.hcul.org
Staff: 18. **Fnd:** 1937. **Mem:** 97. **State Groups:** 1.

Local Groups: 4. **Pub:** *Hawaii Credit Union Directory* (annual); *HCUL Journal* (semiweekly); *League News* (monthly).

1795 ■ Hawaii Small Business Development Center
308 Kamehameha Ave., Ste. 201
Hilo, HI 96720
Contact: Bill Carter, Dir.
Ph: (808)974-7515
Fax: (808)974-7683
URL: http://www.hawaii-sbdc.org
Descr: Represents and promotes the small business sector. Provides management assistance to current and prospective small business owners. Helps to improve management skills and expand the products and services of members.

1796 ■ Hawaii Society of Enrolled Agents
801 S King St.
Honolulu, HI 96813
Contact: Terie Nakayama
Ph: (808)524-0417
Fax: (808)524-0417
E-mail: terie4464@yahoo.com
Descr: Aims to improve the knowledge, skills and professionalism of members in all areas of taxation. Enhances the role of enrolled agents among government agencies, other professions and the public at large. Advocates for taxpayer rights and protects members' interests.

1797 ■ Honolulu Small Business Development Center
1833 Kalakaua Ave., Ste. 400
Honolulu, HI 96815
Contact: Caroline Kim, Dir.
Ph: (808)945-1430
Fax: (808)945-1432
URL: http://www.hawaii-sbdc.org/honolulucenter.htm
Descr: Represents and promotes the small business sector. Provides management assistance to current and prospective small business owners. Helps to improve management skills and expand the products and services of members.

1798 ■ Kaua'i Small Business Development Center
Kaua'i Community College
3-1901 Kaumuali'i Hwy.
Lihue, HI 96766
Contact: Diana Shaw, Dir.
Ph: (808)241-3148
Fax: (808)241-3229
URL: http://www.hawaii-sbdc.org/kauaicenter.htm
Descr: Represents and promotes the small business sector. Provides management assistance to current and prospective small business owners. Helps to improve management skills and expand the products and services of members.

1799 ■ Maui Small Business Development Center
590 Lipoa Pkwy., Ste. 130
Kihei, HI 96753
Contact: David Fisher, Dir.
Ph: (808)875-2402
Fax: (808)875-2406
URL: http://www.hawaii-sbdc.org/mauicenter.htm
Descr: Represents and promotes the small business sector. Provides management assistance to current and prospective small business owners. Helps to improve management skills and expand the products and services of members.

1800 ■ North American Securities Administrators Association, Hawaii
335 Merchant St., Rm. 203
Honolulu, HI 96813
Contact: Tung Chan
Ph: (808)586-2744
Fax: (808)586-2733
Descr: Represents the interests of the state, provincial and territorial securities administrators in the U.S.

Idaho

1801 ■ Boise State University Small Business Development Center, Region III
1910 University Dr.
Boise, ID 83725-1655
Contact: Rick Vycital, Dir.
Ph: (208)426-3875
Fax: (208)426-3877
E-mail: klabrum@boisestate.edu
URL: http://www.idahosbdc.org/index.cfm?fuseaction=content.region&id=4
Descr: Represents and promotes the small business sector. Provides management assistance to current and prospective small business owners. Helps to improve management skills and expand the products and services of members.

1802 ■ College of Southern Idaho Small Business Development Center
PO Box 1238
Twin Falls, ID 83303-1238
Contact: Bryan J. Matsuoka, Dir.
Ph: (208)732-6450
Fax: (208)445-1492
E-mail: isbdc@csi.edu
URL: http://www.csi.edu/support/isbdc/SBDC.html
Descr: Represents and promotes the small business sector. Provides management assistance to current and prospective small business owners. Helps to improve management skills and expand the products and services of members.

1803 ■ Idaho Federation of Business and Professional Women
2627 Grandee St.
Boise, ID 83704
Contact: Carma Maxey, Pres.-Elect
Ph: (208)376-2345
E-mail: carma.maxey@rupert.id.us
URL: http://www.bpwidaho.org
Descr: Represents the interests of business and professional women. Elevates the standards for women in business and professional settings. Promotes equity for all women in the workplace through advocacy, education and information. Provides professional development, networking and career advancement opportunities for working women.

1804 ■ Idaho State University Small Business Development Center, Region V
1651 Alvin Ricken Dr.
Pocatello, ID 83201
Contact: Matthew Creamer, Dir.
Ph: (208)232-4921
Fax: (208)282-4813
E-mail: dittmike@isu.edu
URL: http://www.idahosbdc.org/index.cfm?fuseaction=content.region&id=6
Descr: Represents and promotes the small business sector. Provides management assistance to current and prospective small business owners. Helps to improve management skills and expand the products and services of members.

1805 ■ Idaho State University Small Business Development Center, Region VI
2300 N Yellowstone Hwy.
Idaho Falls, ID 83401
Contact: David Noack, Dir.
Ph: (208)523-1087
Fax: (208)528-7127
E-mail: wilsfros@isu.edu
URL: http://www.idahosbdc.org/index.cfm?fuseaction=content.region&id=7
Descr: Represents and promotes the small business sector. Provides management assistance to current and prospective small business owners. Helps to improve management skills and expand the products and services of members.

1806 ■ International Association of Assessing Officers, Idaho
2384 Roanoke Dr.
Boise, ID 83712

Contact: Marilee Fuller CAE, Rep.
Ph: (208)344-7874
E-mail: marileefuller@cableone.net
Descr: Represents state and local officials concerned with valuation of property for ad valorem property tax purposes. Works to improve standards and conduct research on tax assessment. Promotes innovation and excellence in property appraisal, assessment administration, and property tax policy through professional development, education, research, and technical assistance.

1807 ■ Lewis-Clark State College Small Business Development Center, Region II
500 8th Ave.
Lewiston, ID 83501
Contact: Jill Thomas-Jorgenson, Dir.
Ph: (208)792-2465
Fax: (208)792-2878
E-mail: adanttila@lcsc.edu
Descr: Represents and promotes the small business sector. Provides management assistance to current and prospective small business owners. Helps to improve management skills and expand the products and services of members.

1808 ■ North American Securities Administrators Association, Idaho
800 E Park Blvd., Ste. 200
Boise, ID 83712
Contact: Marilyn T. Chastain, Chief
Ph: (208)332-8004
Fax: (208)332-8099
Descr: Represents the interests of the state, provincial and territorial securities administrators in the U.S.

1809 ■ North Idaho College Small Business Development Center, Region I
525 W Clearwater Loop
Post Falls, ID 83854-9400
Contact: William Jhung, Dir.
Ph: (208)666-8009
Fax: (208)769-3223
E-mail: idaho_sbdc@nic.edu
URL: http://www.idahosbdc.org/index.cfm?fuseaction=content.region&id=2
Descr: Represents and promotes the small business sector. Provides management assistance to current and prospective small business owners. Helps to improve management skills and expand the products and services of members.

Illinois

1810 ■ Alton Area Business and Professional Women's Organization
PO Box 314
Godfrey, IL 62035
Contact: Ann Bromaghim, Pres.
Ph: (618)465-9491
URL: http://www.altonareabpw.org
Descr: Represents the interests of business and professional women. Elevates the standards for women in business and professional settings. Promotes equity for all women in the workplace through advocacy, education and information. Provides professional development, networking and career advancement opportunities for working women.

1811 ■ American Society of Appraisers, Chicago Chapter
8600 W Bryn Mawr Ave., Ste. 950N
Chicago, IL 60631-3505
Contact: Timothy J. Meinhart, Pres.
Ph: (773)399-4331
Fax: (773)399-4310
E-mail: tjmeinhart@willamette.com
URL: http://www.appraisers.org/chicago
Descr: Serves as a professional appraisal educator, testing and accrediting society. Sponsors mandatory

recertification program for all members. Offers consumer information service to the public.

1812 ■ Barrington Enlightened Taxpayers Association (BETA)

PO Box 1522
Barrington, IL 60010
Contact: Carol A. Schubert, Pres.
E-mail: beta@betaonline.us
URL: http://www.betaonline.us

1813 ■ Business and Professional Women, Edwardsville

PO Box 831
Edwardsville, IL 62025
Contact: Jeanne Reeves Hortica, Pres.
E-mail: jreeves@hortica-brokerage.com
URL: http://www.bpwedwardsville.org

Descr: Represents the interests of business and professional women. Elevates the standards for women in business and professional settings. Promotes equity for all women in the workplace through advocacy, education and information. Provides professional development, networking and career advancement opportunities for working women.

1814 ■ Chicago Chapter of the Appraisal Institute (CCAI)

205 W Wacker Dr., Ste. 202
Chicago, IL 60606
Contact: L.A. Anderson, Exec. Off.
Ph: (312)616-9400
Fax: (312)616-9404
E-mail: laanderson@ccai.org
URL: http://www.ccai.org

Descr: Appraises real property, commercial and residential. Offers courses to become a real estate appraiser, as well as continuing education seminars for its members. Seeks to be the global authority providing real estate solutions. **Fnd:** 1991. **Mem:** 1200. **Pub:** *Appraisal Institute Directory of Members*; *Appraisal Journal*; *MarketSource* (quarterly).

1815 ■ East Side NAIFA

Country Insurance
925 E Harris
Greenville, IL 62246
Contact: Darnall Jones CLU, Pres.
Ph: (618)664-1341
Fax: (618)624-4355
E-mail: naifaeastside@yahoo.com
URL: http://www.naifanet.com/eastside

Descr: Represents the interests of insurance and financial advisors. Advocates for a positive legislative and regulatory environment. Enhances business and professional skills of members.

1816 ■ Eastern Illinois AIFA

733 Windsor Rd.
Charleston, IL 61920
Contact: William E. Myers CSA, Pres.
Ph: (217)345-3832
Fax: (217)756-3210
E-mail: williamm@dimondbros.com

Descr: Represents the interests of insurance and financial advisors. Advocates for a positive legislative and regulatory environment. Enhances business and professional skills of members.

1817 ■ Financial Planning Association of Illinois

PO Box 205
Gurnee, IL 60031
Contact: Edward W. Gjertsen CFP, Chm.
Ph: (847)244-3691
Free: 800-430-4237
Fax: (847)244-9813
E-mail: ed@macktracks.com
URL: http://www.fpaillinois.org

Descr: Supports the financial planning process in order to help people achieve their goals and dreams. Promotes the legislative, regulatory and professional interests of the financial service industry. Fosters the value of financial planning and advances the financial planning profession.

1818 ■ Granite City Business and Professional Women (GCBPW)

3156 Yale Dr.
Granite City, IL 62040
Contact: Donna Stephens, Pres.
Ph: (618)452-2914
URL: http://www.gcbpw.org

Descr: Represents the interests of business and professional women. Elevates the standards for women in business and professional settings. Promotes equity for all women in the workplace through advocacy, education and information. Provides professional development, networking and career advancement opportunities for working women.

1819 ■ Illinois Small Business Development Center at Black Hawk College

4703 16th St., Ste. G
Moline, IL 61265-7066
Contact: Donna Scalf
Ph: (309)764-2213
Fax: (309)797-9344
E-mail: scalfd@bhc.edu
URL: http://www.ilsbdc.biz

Descr: Represents and promotes the small business sector. Provides management assistance to current and prospective small business owners. Helps to improve management skills and expand the products and services of members.

1820 ■ Illinois Small Business Development Center at Bradley University

141 Jobst Hall
1501 W Bradley Ave.
Peoria, IL 61606-1048
Contact: Ken Klotz
Ph: (309)677-2992
Fax: (309)677-3386
E-mail: sbdc@bradley.edu
URL: http://www.ilsbdc.biz

Descr: Represents and promotes the small business sector. Provides management assistance to current and prospective small business owners. Helps to improve management skills and expand the products and services of members.

1821 ■ Illinois Small Business Development Center at Chicago Community Ventures

700 N Sacramento Blvd., Ste. 130
Chicago, IL 60612
Contact: Tom Cassell
Ph: (773)822-0320
E-mail: sbdc@chiventures.org
URL: http://www.ilsbdc.biz

Descr: Represents and promotes the small business sector. Provides management assistance to current and prospective small business owners. Helps to improve management skills and expand the products and services of members.

1822 ■ Illinois Small Business Development Center at Chicago State University/Greater Southside

9501 S King Dr.
BHS 601
Chicago, IL 60628-1598
Contact: Isabelle Conda
Ph: (773)995-3938
Fax: (773)821-2841
E-mail: i-conda@csu.edu
URL: http://www.ilsbdc.biz

Descr: Represents and promotes the small business sector. Provides management assistance to current and prospective small business owners. Helps to improve management skills and expand the products and services of members.

1823 ■ Illinois Small Business Development Center at College of DuPage

2525 Cabot Dr.
Lisle, IL 60532
Contact: David Gay
Ph: (630)942-2771
Fax: (630)942-3789
E-mail: gaydav@cod.edu
URL: http://www.ilsbdc.biz

Descr: Represents and promotes the small business sector. Provides management assistance to current and prospective small business owners. Helps to improve management skills and expand the products and services of members.

1824 ■ Illinois Small Business Development Center at College of Lake County

19351 W Washington St., Rm. T-302
Grayslake, IL 60030-1198
Contact: Jan Bauer
Ph: (847)543-2033
Fax: (847)223-9371
E-mail: clcsbdc@clcillinois.edu
URL: http://www.ilsbdc.biz

Descr: Represents and promotes the small business sector. Provides management assistance to current and prospective small business owners. Helps to improve management skills and expand the products and services of members.

1825 ■ Illinois Small Business Development Center at Danville Area Community College

2917 N Vermillion St.
Danville, IL 61832
Contact: Michael O'Brian
Ph: (217)442-7232
Fax: (217)442-1897
E-mail: sbdc@dacc.edu
URL: http://www.ilsbdc.biz

Descr: Represents and promotes the small business sector. Provides management assistance to current and prospective small business owners. Helps to improve management skills and expand the products and services of members.

1826 ■ Illinois Small Business Development Center at Elgin Community College

1700 Spartan Dr.
Elgin, IL 60123-7193
Contact: Kriss Knowles
Ph: (847)214-7488
Fax: (847)931-3911
E-mail: kknowles@elgin.edu
URL: http://www.ilsbdc.biz

Descr: Represents and promotes the small business sector. Provides management assistance to current and prospective small business owners. Helps to improve management skills and expand the products and services of members.

1827 ■ Illinois Small Business Development Center at Evanston Technology Innovation Center

820 Davis St., Ste. 137
Evanston, IL 60201
Contact: TJ Weber
Ph: (847)866-1817
Fax: (847)866-1808
E-mail: tjw@evanstonsbdc.com
URL: http://www.ilsbdc.biz

Descr: Represents and promotes the small business sector. Provides management assistance to current and prospective small business owners. Helps to improve management skills and expand the products and services of members.

1828 ■ Illinois Small Business Development Center at Greater Northwest Chicago Development Corporation

6600 W Armitage Ave.
Chicago, IL 60707-3908
Contact: Reid Mackin
Ph: (773)637-2768
Fax: (773)637-2698
E-mail: sbdc@gncdc.org
URL: http://www.ilsbdc.biz

Descr: Represents and promotes the small business sector. Provides management assistance to current and prospective small business owners. Helps to

improve management skills and expand the products and services of members.

1829 ■ Illinois Small Business Development Center at Harper College

Harper Professional Bldg., Ste. 106
650 E Higgins Rd.
Schaumburg, IL 60173
Contact: Bonita Richter
Ph: (847)925-6520
Fax: (847)925-6109
E-mail: brichter@harper.edu
URL: http://www.ilsbdc.biz

Descr: Represents and promotes the small business sector. Provides management assistance to current and prospective small business owners. Helps to improve management skills and expand the products and services of members.

1830 ■ Illinois Small Business Development Center at Hull House

Jane Addams Hull House - Parkway Community House
500 E 67th St.
Chicago, IL 60637-4097
Contact: Kathleen Robbins
Ph: (773)955-8027
Fax: (773)955-8028
E-mail: krobbins@hullhouse.org
URL: http://www.ilsbdc.biz

Descr: Represents and promotes the small business sector. Provides management assistance to current and prospective small business owners. Helps to improve management skills and expand the products and services of members.

1831 ■ Illinois Small Business Development Center at Illinois State University

214 College of Business Bldg.
Mail Code 5580
Normal, IL 61761-5580
Contact: Elizabeth Binning
Ph: (309)438-3610
Fax: (309)438-2114
E-mail: ejbinni@ilstu.edu
URL: http://www.ilsbdc.biz

Descr: Represents and promotes the small business sector. Provides management assistance to current and prospective small business owners. Helps to improve management skills and expand the products and services of members.

1832 ■ Illinois Small Business Development Center at Illinois Valley Community College

815 N Orlando Smith Ave., Bldg. 11
Oglesby, IL 61348-9692
Contact: Bev Malooley
Ph: (815)224-0212
Fax: (815)223-1780
E-mail: bev_malooley@ivcc.edu
URL: http://www.ilsbdc.biz

Descr: Represents and promotes the small business sector. Provides management assistance to current and prospective small business owners. Helps to improve management skills and expand the products and services of members.

1833 ■ Illinois Small Business Development Center at Industrial Council of Nearwest Chicago

2010 W Fulton St., Ste. 280
Chicago, IL 60612
Contact: Andrew Fogarty
Ph: (312)433-2373
Fax: (312)421-1871
E-mail: sbdc@industrialcouncil.com
URL: http://www.ilsbdc.biz

Descr: Represents and promotes the small business sector. Provides management assistance to current and prospective small business owners. Helps to improve management skills and expand the products and services of members.

1834 ■ Illinois Small Business Development Center at Joliet Jr. College

City Center Campus, Rm. 400
Joliet, IL 60432-4077

Contact: Bob Hansen
Ph: (815)280-1400
Fax: (708)488-2290
E-mail: bhansen@jjc.edu
URL: http://www.ilsbdc.biz

Descr: Represents and promotes the small business sector. Provides management assistance to current and prospective small business owners. Helps to improve management skills and expand the products and services of members.

1835 ■ Illinois Small Business Development Center at Joseph Center

7600 W Roosevelt Rd.
Forest Park, IL 60130
Contact: Edna Chapman
Ph: (708)697-6200
Fax: (708)488-2290
E-mail: sbdc@josephcenter.com
URL: http://www.ilsbdc.biz

Descr: Represents and promotes the small business sector. Provides management assistance to current and prospective small business owners. Helps to improve management skills and expand the products and services of members.

1836 ■ Illinois Small Business Development Center at Kankakee Community College

100 College Dr.
Kankakee, IL 60901
Contact: Ken Crite
Ph: (815)802-8222
Fax: (815)802-8101
E-mail: kcrite@kcc.edu
URL: http://www.ilsbdc.biz

Descr: Represents and promotes the small business sector. Provides management assistance to current and prospective small business owners. Helps to improve management skills and expand the products and services of members.

1837 ■ Illinois Small Business Development Center at Kaskaskia College

Institute for Entrepreneurial Success
325 S Poplar St.
Centralia, IL 62801
Contact: Todd Tracy
Ph: (618)545-3260
Fax: (618)545-3258
E-mail: ttracy@kaskaskia.edu
URL: http://www.ilsbdc.biz

Descr: Represents and promotes the small business sector. Provides management assistance to current and prospective small business owners. Helps to improve management skills and expand the products and services of members.

1838 ■ Illinois Small Business Development Center at Lincoln Land Community College

3 S Old State Capitol Plz.
Springfield, IL 62701
Contact: Kevin Lust
Ph: (217)544-7232
Fax: (217)522-3512
E-mail: sbdc@llcc.edu
URL: http://www.ilsbdc.biz

Descr: Represents and promotes the small business sector. Provides management assistance to current and prospective small business owners. Helps to improve management skills and expand the products and services of members.

1839 ■ Illinois Small Business Development Center at McHenry County College

4100 W Shamrock Ln.
McHenry, IL 60050
Contact: Mary Margaret Maule
Ph: (815)455-6098
Fax: (815)578-9684
E-mail: sbdc@mchenry.edu
URL: http://www.ilsbdc.biz

Descr: Represents and promotes the small business sector. Provides management assistance to current and prospective small business owners. Helps to

improve management skills and expand the products and services of members.

1840 ■ Illinois Small Business Development Center at Rend Lake College

327 Potomac Blvd., Ste. A
Mount Vernon, IL 62864
Contact: Curt Mowrer
Ph: (618)242-5813
Fax: (618)242-8220
E-mail: mowrer@rlc.edu
URL: http://www.ilsbdc.biz

Descr: Represents and promotes the small business sector. Provides management assistance to current and prospective small business owners. Helps to improve management skills and expand the products and services of members.

1841 ■ Illinois Small Business Development Center at Rock Valley College

EIGER Lab
605 Fulton Ave., Rm. E109
Rockford, IL 61103
Contact: Pam Schallhorn
Ph: (815)921-2082
Fax: (815)921-2089
E-mail: sbdc-rvc@rockvalleycollege.edu
URL: http://www.ilsbdc.biz

Descr: Represents and promotes the small business sector. Provides management assistance to current and prospective small business owners. Helps to improve management skills and expand the products and services of members.

1842 ■ Illinois Small Business Development Center at Sauk Valley Community College

173 Illinois Rte. No. 2
Dixon, IL 61021-9188
Contact: Michelle Miller
Ph: (815)288-5511
Fax: (815)288-5958
E-mail: millerm@svcc.edu
URL: http://www.ilsbdc.biz

Descr: Represents and promotes the small business sector. Provides management assistance to current and prospective small business owners. Helps to improve management skills and expand the products and services of members.

1843 ■ Illinois Small Business Development Center at Shawnee Community College

8364 Shawnee College Rd.
Ullin, IL 62992-2206
Contact: Candy Eastwood
Ph: (618)634-3371
Fax: (618)634-2347
E-mail: sccsbdc@shawneecc.edu
URL: http://www.ilsbdc.biz

Descr: Represents and promotes the small business sector. Provides management assistance to current and prospective small business owners. Helps to improve management skills and expand the products and services of members.

1844 ■ Illinois Small Business Development Center at Southeastern Illinois College

2 E Locust St., Ste. 200
Harrisburg, IL 62946
Contact: Lori Cox
Ph: (618)252-5001
Fax: (618)252-0210
E-mail: lori.cox@sic.edu
URL: http://www.ilsbdc.biz

Descr: Represents and promotes the small business sector. Provides management assistance to current and prospective small business owners. Helps to improve management skills and expand the products and services of members.

1845 ■ Illinois Small Business Development Center at Southern Illinois University - Edwardsville

Campus Box 1107
Alumni Hall 2126
Edwardsville, IL 62026
Contact: Kwa Mister
Ph: (618)650-2929

Fax: (618)650-2647
E-mail: kmister@siue.edu
URL: http://www.ilsbdc.biz

Descr: Represents and promotes the small business sector. Provides management assistance to current and prospective small business owners. Helps to improve management skills and expand the products and services of members.

1846 ■ Illinois Small Business Development Center at Waubonsee Community College
Aurora Campus
5 E Galena Blvd.
Aurora, IL 60506-4178
Contact: Harriet Parker
Ph: (630)906-4143
Fax: (630)892-4668
E-mail: hparker@waubonsee.edu
URL: http://www.ilsbdc.biz

Descr: Represents and promotes the small business sector. Provides management assistance to current and prospective small business owners. Helps to improve management skills and expand the products and services of members.

1847 ■ Illinois Small Business Development Center at Western Illinois University
510 N Pearl St., Ste. 1400
Macomb, IL 61455
Contact: Dan Voorhis
Ph: (309)836-2640
E-mail: sb-center@wiu.edu
URL: http://www.ilsbdc.biz

Descr: Represents and promotes the small business sector. Provides management assistance to current and prospective small business owners. Helps to improve management skills and expand the products and services of members.

1848 ■ Illinois Society of Enrolled Agents
1415 Matanuska Trail
McHenry, IL 60050
Contact: Jacqueline D. Meyer EA
Ph: (815)385-6889
Fax: (815)363-1623
E-mail: meyer.jd@comcast.net
URL: http://www.naea.org/MemberPortal/StateAffiliates/Listing

1849 ■ Illinois Society of Enrolled Agents - Northwest Chapter
13726 Fieldstone Dr.
Huntley, IL 60142
Contact: Barbara Helzing
Ph: (847)669-7000
Fax: (847)669-7272
E-mail: bhelzing@comcast.net
URL: http://www.ilsea.org

Descr: Aims to improve the knowledge, skills and professionalism of members in all areas of taxation. Enhances the role of enrolled agents among government agencies, other professions and the public at large. Advocates for taxpayer rights and protects members' interests.

1850 ■ International Association of Assessing Officers, Illinois
1019 27th Ave.
Rock Island, IL 61201
Contact: Susan Carpentier, Rep.
Ph: (309)788-4513
Fax: (309)788-9343
E-mail: scarpentier@sritownship.com

Descr: Represents state and local officials concerned with valuation of property for ad valorem property tax purposes. Works to improve standards and conduct research on tax assessment. Promotes innovation and excellence in property appraisal, assessment administration, and property tax policy

through professional development, education, research, and technical assistance.

1851 ■ McHenry Taxpayers United
6411 Coachlight Rd.
Crystal Lake, IL 60012
Ph: (815)455-5438

1852 ■ National Taxpayers United of Illinois
407 S Dearborn St., Ste. 1170
Chicago, IL 60605
Contact: Jim Tobin, Pres.
Ph: (312)427-5128
Fax: (312)427-5139
E-mail: ntui@ntui.org
URL: http://ntui.org

1853 ■ North American Securities Administrators Association, Illinois
69 W Washington St., Ste. 1220
Chicago, IL 60602
Contact: Tanya Solov, Dir. of Securities
Ph: (217)782-2256
Free: 800-628-7937
Fax: (217)524-2172

Descr: Represents the interests of the state, provincial and territorial securities administrators in the U.S.

1854 ■ Peoria AIFA
PO Box 3505
Peoria, IL 61612-3505
Contact: Laurie A. Adams, Pres.
Ph: (309)685-2470
E-mail: laurie.adams@countryfinancial.com
URL: http://www.naifanet.com/peoria

Descr: Represents the interests of insurance and financial advisors. Advocates for a positive legislative and regulatory environment. Enhances business and professional skills of members.

1855 ■ Rockford AIFA
7445 Newburg
Rockford, IL 61108
Contact: Ned M. Burns, Pres.
Ph: (815)332-6700
Fax: (815)332-6701
E-mail: nedburns@nfpsi.com
URL: http://www.raifa.org

Descr: Represents the interests of insurance and financial advisors. Advocates for a positive legislative and regulatory environment. Enhances business and professional skills of members.

1856 ■ SOCAP International - Chicago Chapter
2001 Ruppman Plz.
Peoria, IL 61614
Contact: Mark Hamilton, Pres.
Ph: (309)679-4401

Descr: Promotes customer care and customer management as a competitive advantage in business. Provides educational tools and professional resources to help members drive business transformation within their companies.

1857 ■ Southeastern Illinois AIFA
PO Box 367
Olney, IL 62450
Contact: Frank S. Ladner CLU, Pres.
Ph: (618)395-8484
Fax: (217)342-2757
E-mail: fladner@yahoo.com

Staff: 3. **Descr:** Represents the interests of insurance and financial advisors. Advocates for a positive legislative and regulatory environment. Enhances business and professional skills of members.

1858 ■ Winnebago County Taxpayers
2041 Wedgewood Way
Rockford, IL 61107
Ph: (815)218-8784
E-mail: t.emert@insightbb.com

Indiana

1859 ■ Association of Monroe County Taxpayers
PO Box 3066
Bloomington, IN 47402
Contact: Gregory Travis, Exec. Dir.
E-mail: info@assmotax.org
URL: http://www.assmotax.org

1860 ■ Hoosier Heartland Small Business Development Center
Burton D. Morgan Center for Entrepreneurship
1201 W State St.
West Lafayette, IN 47907
Contact: Jenna Wargo
Ph: (765)496-6491
Free: 877-882-7273
Fax: (765)496-9676
E-mail: hoosierheartland@isbdc.org
URL: http://www.hhsbdc.org

Descr: Represents and promotes the small business sector. Provides management assistance to current and prospective small business owners. Helps to improve management skills and expand the products and services of members.

1861 ■ South Bend Small Business Development Center
Commerce Center Bldg.
401 E Colfax Ave., Ste. 120
South Bend, IN 46617
Contact: Janet A. Fye, Dir.
Ph: (574)282-4350
URL: http://www.southbendbcg.com

Descr: Represents and promotes the small business sector. Provides management assistance to current and prospective small business owners. Helps to improve management skills and expand the products and services of members.

Iowa

1862 ■ American Society of Appraisers, Iowa Chapter
Corporate Continuity Group LLC
1601 22nd St., Ste. 400
West Des Moines, IA 50266-1408
Contact: Ronald L. Andersen, Pres.
Ph: (515)453-1603
E-mail: gpatterson@ccgltd.com
URL: http://www.appraisers.org/iowa

Descr: Serves as a professional appraisal educator, testing and accrediting society. Sponsors mandatory recertification program for all members. Offers consumer information service to the public.

1863 ■ Eastern Iowa Small Business Development Center - Davenport
331 W 3rd St., Ste. 100
Davenport, IA 52801
Contact: Ann Hutchinson, Dir.
Ph: (563)336-3401
Free: 800-462-3255
Fax: (563)336-3479
E-mail: ahutchinson@eicc.edu
URL: http://www.iowasbdc.org/Categories/Davenport/tabid/1752/Default.aspx

Descr: Represents and promotes the small business sector. Provides management assistance to current and prospective small business owners. Helps to improve management skills and expand the products and services of members.

1864 ■ Financial Planning Association of Eastern Iowa
Principal Financial Group
200 Second Ave. SE
Cedar Rapids, IA 52401
Contact: Steve Odegaard, Pres.
Ph: (319)362-2149
E-mail: odegaard.steven@principal.com
URL: http://www.fpaofeasterniowa.org

Descr: Provides a forum for education and career development for its members while adhering to the highest ethical and professional standards. Promotes financial planning profession through education, networking, and mentoring. Enhances public awareness of the value of the financial planning process.

1865 ■ Financial Planning Association of Iowa
15130 New York Cir.
Clive, IA 50325
Contact: Kristin Rinderknecht, Exec. Dir.
Ph: (515)987-8344
Fax: (515)987-2301
E-mail: office@fpaiowa.org
URL: http://www.fpaiowa.org
Descr: Promotes financial planning profession through education, networking, and mentoring. Enhances public awareness of the value of the financial planning process. Provides forum for education and career development for its members.

1866 ■ Indian Hills Small Business Development Center - Ottumwa
651 Indian Hills Dr., Bldg. 17
Ottumwa, IA 52501
Contact: Brian Ziegler, Dir.
Ph: (641)683-5127
Free: 800-726-2585
Fax: (641)683-5296
E-mail: bziegler@indianhills.edu
URL: http://www.iowasbdc.org/Categories/Ottumwa/tabid/1766/Default.aspx
Descr: Represents and promotes the small business sector. Provides management assistance to current and prospective small business owners. Helps to improve management skills and expand the products and services of members.

1867 ■ International Association of Assessing Officers, Iowa
PO Box 2957
Clinton, IA 52733
Contact: John S. Moreland RES, Rep.
Ph: (563)244-0571
Fax: (563)243-9731
E-mail: jmoreland@clintoncountyiowa.com
Descr: Represents state and local officials concerned with valuation of property for ad valorem property tax purposes. Works to improve standards and conduct research on tax assessment. Promotes innovation and excellence in property appraisal, assessment administration, and property tax policy through professional development, education, research, and technical assistance.

1868 ■ Iowa AIFA
409 Washington St., Ste. A
Cedar Falls, IA 50613
Contact: Jay A. Ochanpaugh, Pres.
Free: 866-632-1491
Fax: (515)233-8788
E-mail: naifaiowa@grassleygroup.com
URL: http://www.naifanet.com/main-pub.cfm?usr=180000
Descr: Represents the interests of insurance and financial advisors. Advocates for a positive legislative and regulatory environment. Enhances business and professional skills of members.

1869 ■ Iowa Small Business Development Center
Iowa State University
340 Gerdin Business Bldg.
Ames, IA 50011
Contact: Jim Heckmann, Dir.
Ph: (515)294-2030
Fax: (515)294-6522
E-mail: iowasbdc@iastate.edu
URL: http://www.iowasbdc.org
Descr: Represents and promotes the small business sector. Provides management assistance to current and prospective small business owners. Helps to improve management skills and expand the products and services of members.

1870 ■ Iowa State University Small Business Development Center - Ames
2501 N Loop Dr., Ste. 1615
Ames, IA 50010-8283

Contact: Mike Upah, Dir.
Ph: (515)296-7828
Fax: (515)296-6714
E-mail: mjupah@iastate.edu
URL: http://www.iowasbdc.org/Categories/Ames/tabid/1108/Default.aspx
Descr: Represents and promotes the small business sector. Provides management assistance to current and prospective small business owners. Helps to improve management skills and expand the products and services of members.

1871 ■ Iowa Taxpayers Association (ITA)
East Grand Office Park
100 E Grand Ave.
Des Moines, IA 50309
Contact: Edward T. Wallace, Pres.
Ph: (515)243-0300
Fax: (515)243-2049
E-mail: staff@iowataxpayers.org
URL: http://www.iowataxpayers.org
Staff: 5. **Fnd:** 1935.

1872 ■ Iowa Western Small Business Development Center - Council Bluffs
21915 Cessna Ave.
Council Bluffs, IA 51503
Contact: Sue Pitts, Dir.
Ph: (712)256-6552
Fax: (712)256-6555
E-mail: spitts@iwcc.edu
URL: http://www.iowasbdc.org/Categories/CouncilBluffs/tabid/1750/Default.aspx
Descr: Represents and promotes the small business sector. Provides management assistance to current and prospective small business owners. Helps to improve management skills and expand the products and services of members.

1873 ■ Kirkwood Small Business Development Center - Marion
Kirkwood Community College
3375 Armar Dr.
Marion, IA 52302
Contact: Al Beach, Dir.
Ph: (319)377-8256
Fax: (319)398-5698
E-mail: al.beach@kirkwood.edu
URL: http://www.iowasbdc.org/Categories/MarionCedarRapids/tabid/1765/Default.aspx
Descr: Represents and promotes the small business sector. Provides management assistance to current and prospective small business owners. Helps to improve management skills and expand the products and services of members.

1874 ■ NAIFA-Western Iowa Chapter
PO Box 419
Elk Horn, IA 51531-0419
Contact: Larry L. Haas, Pres.
Ph: (712)764-7512
Fax: (712)764-3557
Descr: Represents the interests of insurance and financial advisors. Advocates for a positive legislative and regulatory environment. Enhances business and professional skills of members.

1875 ■ North American Securities Administrators Association, Iowa
340 E Maple St.
Des Moines, IA 50319
Contact: Jim Mumford
Ph: (515)281-4441
Fax: (515)281-3059
Descr: Represents the interests of the state, provincial and territorial securities administrators in the U.S.

1876 ■ North Central Iowa Small Business Development Center - Fort Dodge
217 S 25th St., Ste. C12
Fort Dodge, IA 50501
Contact: Lisa Shimkat, Dir.
Ph: (515)576-6242
Fax: (515)576-6447
E-mail: ncibusinesscenter@gmail.com

URL: http://www.iowasbdc.org/Categories/FortDodge/tabid/1764/Default.aspx
Descr: Represents and promotes the small business sector. Provides management assistance to current and prospective small business owners. Helps to improve management skills and expand the products and services of members.

1877 ■ North Iowa Area Small Business Development Center - Mason City
500 College Dr.
Mason City, IA 50401
Contact: Ted Bair, Dir.
Ph: (641)422-4342
Free: 888-466-4222
Fax: (641)422-4129
E-mail: bairted@niacc.edu
URL: http://www.iowasbdc.org/Categories/MasonCity/tabid/1768/Default.aspx
Descr: Represents and promotes the small business sector. Provides management assistance to current and prospective small business owners. Helps to improve management skills and expand the products and services of members.

1878 ■ Northeast Iowa Small Business Development Center - Dubuque
680 Main St.
Dubuque, IA 52001
Contact: Terry Sullivan, Dir.
Ph: (563)588-3350
Fax: (563)557-0319
E-mail: sullivan@nicc.edu
URL: http://www.iowasbdc.org/Categories/Dubuque/tabid/1762/Default.aspx
Descr: Represents and promotes the small business sector. Provides management assistance to current and prospective small business owners. Helps to improve management skills and expand the products and services of members.

1879 ■ Northwest Iowa Small Business Development Center - Spencer
Iowa Lakes Community College
1900 N Grand Ave., Ste. 8
Spencer, IA 51301
Contact: Kelly McCarty, Dir.
Ph: (712)262-4213
Fax: (712)262-4047
URL: http://www.iowasbdc.org/tabid/1770/Default.aspx
Descr: Represents and promotes the small business sector. Provides management assistance to current and prospective small business owners. Helps to improve management skills and expand the products and services of members.

1880 ■ Polk-Des Moines Taxpayers Association
525 SW 5th Ave., Ste. A
Des Moines, IA 50309
Contact: Jeff Riese, Pres.
Ph: (515)282-8192
E-mail: jriese@assoc-mgmt.com
URL: http://www.polkdesmoinestaxpayers.org

1881 ■ South Central Iowa Small Business Development Center - Creston
1501 W Townline St.
Creston, IA 50801
Contact: Dave McLaren, Dir.
Ph: (641)782-1483
Fax: (641)782-1334
E-mail: mclaren@swcciowa.edu
URL: http://www.iowasbdc.org/Categories/Creston/tabid/1751/Default.aspx
Descr: Represents and promotes the small business sector. Provides management assistance to current and prospective small business owners. Helps to improve management skills and expand the products and services of members.

1882 ■ Southeastern Iowa Small Business Development Center - Burlington
River Park Pl.
610 N 4th St., Ste. 201
Burlington, IA 52601

Contact: Janine Clover, Dir.
Ph: (319)752-2731
Fax: (319)752-3407
E-mail: jclover@scciowa.edu
URL: http://www.iowasbdc.org/Categories/Burlington/tabid/1749/Default.aspx
Descr: Represents and promotes the small business sector. Provides management assistance to current and prospective small business owners. Helps to improve management skills and expand the products and services of members.

1883 ■ University of Iowa Small Business Development Center - Iowa City
2663 University Capitol Ctr.
Iowa City, IA 52242
Contact: Paul Heath, Dir.
Ph: (319)335-3742
E-mail: paul-heath@uiowa.edu
URL: http://www.iowasbdc.org/Categories/IowaCity/tabid/1763/Default.aspx
Descr: Represents and promotes the small business sector. Provides management assistance to current and prospective small business owners. Helps to improve management skills and expand the products and services of members.

1884 ■ University of Northern Iowa Small Business Development Center - Waterloo
212 E 4th St.
Waterloo, IA 50703
Contact: Maureen Collins-Williams, Dir.
Ph: (319)236-8123
Fax: (319)236-8240
E-mail: maureen.collins-williams@uni.edu
URL: http://www.iowasbdc.org/Categories/Waterloo/tabid/1772/Default.aspx
Descr: Represents and promotes the small business sector. Provides management assistance to current and prospective small business owners. Helps to improve management skills and expand the products and services of members.

1885 ■ Western Iowa Tech Small Business Development Center - Sioux City
Box 5199
Sioux City, IA 51102-5199
Contact: Dan Wubbena, Dir.
Ph: (712)274-6454
E-mail: wubbend@witcc.edu
URL: http://www.iowasbdc.org/Categories/SiouxCity/tabid/1769/Default.aspx
Descr: Represents and promotes the small business sector. Provides management assistance to current and prospective small business owners. Helps to improve management skills and expand the products and services of members.

Kansas

1886 ■ American Society of Appraisers, Kansas City/Metropolitan Chapter
7701 College Blvd., Ste. 150
Overland Park, KS 66210-1866
Contact: Laurie Anne Poe, Pres.
Ph: (913)529-7633
Fax: (913)498-9020
E-mail: lpoe@marksnelsoncpa.com
URL: http://old.appraisers.org/kansas_city
Descr: Serves as a professional appraisal educator, testing and accrediting society. Sponsors mandatory recertification program for all members. Offers consumer information service to the public.

1887 ■ Appraisal Institute, Greater Kansas State Chapter
Courtley Jackson Co.
262 N Waco, Ste. 100
Wichita, KS 67202
Contact: Bob Robertson SRA, Pres.
Ph: (316)265-7880
Fax: (316)265-7660
E-mail: info@kansasappraisers.org
URL: http://www.kansasappraisers.org
Descr: General appraisers who hold the MAI or

SRPA designations, and residential members who hold the SRA designation.

1888 ■ Financial Planning Association of Greater Kansas City
8826 Santa Fe Dr., Ste. 208
Overland Park, KS 66212
Contact: Randall Gerard CFP, Pres.
Ph: (913)381-4458
Fax: (913)381-9308
E-mail: fpagkc@sbcglobal.net
URL: http://www.fpakc.org
Descr: Promotes financial planning profession through education, networking, and mentoring. Enhances public awareness of the value of the financial planning process. Provides forum for education and career development for its members.

1889 ■ International Association of Assessing Officers, Kansas
1100 Massachusetts St.
Lawrence, KS 66044
Contact: Steven W. Miles CAE, Rep.
Ph: (785)832-5188
Fax: (785)841-0021
E-mail: smiles@douglas-county.com
Descr: Represents state and local officials concerned with valuation of property for ad valorem property tax purposes. Works to improve standards and conduct research on tax assessment. Promotes innovation and excellence in property appraisal, assessment administration, and property tax policy through professional development, education, research, and technical assistance.

1890 ■ Kansas Taxpayer Network (KTN)
PO Box 20050
Wichita, KS 67208
Contact: Karl Peterjohn, Exec. Dir.
Ph: (316)684-0082
Fax: (316)684-7527
E-mail: info@kansastaxpayers.com
URL: http://www.kansastaxpayers.com

1891 ■ North American Securities Administrators Association, Kansas
618 S Kansas Ave.
Topeka, KS 66603
Contact: Chris Biggs
Ph: (785)296-3307
Fax: (785)296-6872
Descr: Represents the interests of the state, provincial and territorial securities administrators in the U.S.

1892 ■ Northeast Kansas AIFA
619 S 4th St.
Leavenworth, KS 66048
Contact: Max Valdez
Ph: (913)682-7311
Fax: (913)682-7288
E-mail: mark.begley@axa-advisors.com
Descr: Represents the interests of insurance and financial advisors. Advocates for a positive legislative and regulatory environment. Enhances business and professional skills of members.

1893 ■ Northwest Kansas AIFA
PO Box 761
111 W 8th St.
Hays, KS 67601
Contact: Randy Mader, Sec.
Ph: (785)628-6134
Fax: (785)628-7989
E-mail: jkaempfe@comlinkusa.net
Descr: Represents the interests of insurance and financial advisors. Advocates for a positive legislative and regulatory environment. Enhances business and professional skills of members.

1894 ■ South Central Kansas Regional Chapter of the International Association of Assessing Officers
525 N Main St., Ste. 227
Wichita, KS 67203
Contact: Ronnie Tidwell III, Pres.
Ph: (316)660-5464

Fax: (316)660-5479
E-mail: rtidwell@sedgwick.gov
URL: http://www.sckiaao.org
Descr: Represents state and local officials concerned with valuation of property for ad valorem property tax purposes. Works to improve standards and conduct research on tax assessment. Promotes innovation and excellence in property appraisal, assessment administration, and property tax policy through professional development, education, research, and technical assistance.

1895 ■ Southwest Kansas AIFA
825 S Kansas Ave., No. 500
Topeka, KS 66612
Contact: Christina Driggs, Accounting Mgr.
Ph: (785)354-7770
Fax: (785)233-2206
E-mail: christi@naifakansas.org
URL: http://www.naifakansas.org
Descr: Represents the interests of insurance and financial advisors. Advocates for a positive legislative and regulatory environment. Enhances business and professional skills of members.

1896 ■ Sunflower Community Action (SCA)
1528 N Broadway, No. 103
Wichita, KS 67214
Contact: Ms. Laura Dungan, Exec. Dir.
Ph: (316)264-9972
Fax: (316)267-3580
E-mail: laura@sunfloweract.com
URL: http://www.sunfloweract.com
Staff: 8. **Descr:** Aims to develop the power in each individual to create social and economic change in people's lives and communities. **Fnd:** 1991. **Mem:** 245.

Kentucky

1897 ■ American Society of Appraisers, Dayton - Cincinnati Chapter
ComStock Valuation Advisors, Inc.
1 Levee Way, Ste. 3109
Newport, KY 41071-1660
Contact: Nickolas N. Sypniewski, Pres.
Ph: (859)957-2300
Fax: (859)957-2305
E-mail: nsypniewski@comstockvaluation.com
URL: http://old.appraisers.org/dayton_cincinnati
Descr: Serves as a professional appraisal educator, testing and accrediting society. Sponsors mandatory recertification program for all members. Offers consumer information service to the public.

1898 ■ Ashland AIFA
PO Box 870
Ashland, KY 41105-0870
Contact: Sandra F. Woodward, Pres.
Ph: (606)325-8865
Fax: (606)325-1285
E-mail: sandy@marcuswoodward.com
URL: http://www.naifanet.com/ashland
Descr: Represents the interests of insurance and financial advisors. Advocates for a positive legislative and regulatory environment. Enhances business and professional skills of members.

1899 ■ Ashland Small Business Development Center - Kentucky
1645 Winchester Ave., 2nd Fl.
Ashland, KY 41101
Contact: Kimberly Jenkins, Dir.
Ph: (606)329-8011
Fax: (606)324-4570
E-mail: k.jenkins@moreheadstate.edu
URL: http://www.ksbdc.org/locations/ashland
Descr: Represents and promotes the small business sector. Provides management assistance to current and prospective small business owners. Helps to

improve management skills and expand the products and services of members.

1900 ■ Bluegrass AIFA
PO Box 12346
Lexington, KY 40582
Contact: Trish Vanaman, Pres.
Ph: (859)263-3936
E-mail: bluegrassaifa@aol.com
URL: http://www.baifa.org
Descr: Represents the interests of insurance and financial advisors. Advocates for a positive legislative and regulatory environment. Enhances business and professional skills of members.

1901 ■ Bluegrass Small Business Development Center
330 E Main St., Ste. 210
Lexington, KY 40507
Contact: Shirie Mack, Dir./Management Consultant
Ph: (859)257-7666
Free: 888-475-SBDC
Fax: (859)257-1751
E-mail: smack3@uky.edu
URL: http://www.ksbdc.org/locations/lexington
Descr: Represents and promotes the small business sector. Provides management assistance to current and prospective small business owners. Helps to improve management skills and expand the products and services of members.

1902 ■ Business and Professional Women, Louisville
3620 Fern Valley Rd.
Louisville, KY 40219
Contact: Anita Ellison, Pres.
E-mail: webmaster@bpwlouisville.org
URL: http://www.bpwlouisville.org
Descr: Represents the interests of business and professional women. Elevates the standards for women in business and professional settings. Promotes equity for all women in the workplace through advocacy, education and information. Provides professional development, networking and career advancement opportunities for working women.

1903 ■ Business and Professional Women, Oldham County
PO Box 1272
Crestwood, KY 40014
Contact: Kay Webb, Pres.-Elect
E-mail: general@bpwoldhamco.org
URL: http://bpwoldhamco.org
Descr: Represents the interests of business and professional women. Elevates the standards for women in business and professional settings. Promotes equity for all women in the workplace through advocacy, education and information. Provides professional development, networking and career advancement opportunities for working women.

1904 ■ Financial Planning Association, Kentuckiana Chapter
PO Box 22014
Louisville, KY 40252
Contact: Kim Weddington, Admin.
Ph: (502)893-3649
E-mail: fpaky@aol.com
URL: http://www.fpanet.net
Descr: Promotes the value of the financial planning process to the public. Provides professional education and networking opportunities for the financial planning community.

1905 ■ Greater Louisville Small Business Development Center
614 W Main St.
Louisville, KY 40202
Contact: Toni Cardell, Asst. Dir.
Ph: (502)625-0123
Fax: (502)625-1181
E-mail: tcardell@louisvillesmallbiz.org
URL: http://www.ksbdc.org/locations/louisville
Descr: Represents and promotes the small business

sector. Provides management assistance to current and prospective small business owners. Helps to improve management skills and expand the products and services of members.

1906 ■ Hopkinsville Small Business Development Center
2800 Ft. Campbell Blvd.
Hopkinsville, KY 42240
Contact: Roy Keller, Dir./Management Consultant
Ph: (270)886-8666
Fax: (270)881-9366
E-mail: roy.keller@murraystate.edu
URL: http://www.ksbdc.org/locations/hopkinsville
Descr: Represents and promotes the small business sector. Provides management assistance to current and prospective small business owners. Helps to improve management skills and expand the products and services of members.

1907 ■ Kentucky Chapter of the International Association of Assessing Officers (KYIAAO)
PO Box 1547
Frankfort, KY 40602
Contact: Brad Bailey, Pres.
URL: http://www.kyiaao.com
Descr: Represents state and local officials concerned with valuation of property for ad valorem property tax purposes. Works to improve standards and conduct research on tax assessment. Promotes innovation and excellence in property appraisal, assessment administration, and property tax policy through professional development, education, research, and technical assistance.

1908 ■ Kentucky Small Business Development Center
University of Kentucky
225 Gatton College of Business and Economics
Lexington, KY 40506-0034
Contact: Becky Naugle, Dir.
Ph: (859)257-7668
Fax: (859)323-1907
URL: http://www.ksbdc.org
Descr: Represents and promotes the small business sector. Provides management assistance to current and prospective small business owners. Helps to improve management skills and expand the products and services of members.

1909 ■ Kentucky Small Business Development Center at Eastern Kentucky University - Richmond
Eastern Kentucky University
College of Business & Technology
Hall Dr., Rm. 145
Richmond, KY 40475
Contact: Kevin Norvell, Dir.
Ph: (859)622-1384
Free: 877-358-7232
Fax: (859)622-1413
E-mail: kevin.norvell@eku.edu
URL: http://ekubiz.com
Descr: Represents and promotes the small business sector. Provides management assistance to current and prospective small business owners. Helps to improve management skills and expand the products and services of members.

1910 ■ Kentucky Small Business Development Center at Eastern Kentucky University - Somerset
675 Monticello St., Ste. A
Somerset, KY 42501
Contact: John Preston, Business Coor.
Ph: (606)678-3042
Free: 877-EKU-SBDC
Fax: (606)678-3065
E-mail: johnpreston@alltel.net
URL: http://ekubiz.com
Descr: Represents and promotes the small business sector. Provides management assistance to current and prospective small business owners. Helps to

improve management skills and expand the products and services of members.

1911 ■ Kentucky Society of Enrolled Agents
8333 Alexandria Pike, Ste. 204
Alexandria, KY 41001
Contact: John C. razier
Ph: (859)694-3000
Fax: (859)448-2762
E-mail: jctaxpro@aol.com
Descr: Promotes ethical representation of the financial position of taxpayers before government agencies.

1912 ■ Kentucky Taxpayers United
9878 Camp Ernst Rd.
Union, KY 41091
Ph: (859)835-3688
E-mail: brettg@fuse.net

1913 ■ Lake Cumberland AIFA
895 N Hwy. 27
Somerset, KY 42503
Contact: Lisa Phelps, Exec.
Ph: (606)678-5124
Fax: (606)679-1971
E-mail: ml-oa-8d@msnlife.com
Descr: Represents the interests of insurance and financial advisors. Advocates for a positive legislative and regulatory environment. Enhances business and professional skills of members.

1914 ■ Maysville Small Business Development Center
201 E Third St.
Maysville, KY 41056
Contact: Mike Jackson, Management Consultant
Ph: (606)564-2707
E-mail: m.jackson@moreheadstate.edu
URL: http://www.ksbdc.org/locations/maysville
Descr: Represents and promotes the small business sector. Provides management assistance to current and prospective small business owners. Helps to improve management skills and expand the products and services of members.

1915 ■ Morehead Small Business Development Center
150 E First St.
Morehead, KY 40351
Contact: David Barber, Dir./Management Consultant
Ph: (606)783-2895
Fax: (606)783-5020
E-mail: d.barber@moreheadstate.edu
URL: http://www.ksbdc.org/locations/morehead
Descr: Represents and promotes the small business sector. Provides management assistance to current and prospective small business owners. Helps to improve management skills and expand the products and services of members.

1916 ■ Murray Small Business Development Center
Murray State University
Business Bldg. S, Rm. 253
Murray, KY 42071
Contact: Chris Wooldridge, Dir.
Ph: (270)809-2856
Fax: (270)809-3049
E-mail: chris.wooldridge@murraystate.edu
URL: http://www.ksbdc.org/locations/murray
Descr: Represents and promotes the small business sector. Provides management assistance to current and prospective small business owners. Helps to improve management skills and expand the products and services of members.

1917 ■ Northern Kentucky University Small Business Development Center
305 Johns Hill Rd.
Highland Heights, KY 41076-1412
Contact: Carol Cornell, Dir.
Ph: (859)442-4281
Fax: (859)442-4285
E-mail: cornellc1@nku.edu
URL: http://www.ksbdc.org/locations/highland-heights

Descr: Represents and promotes the small business sector. Provides management assistance to current and prospective small business owners. Helps to improve management skills and expand the products and services of members.

1918 ■ Owensboro Small Business Development Center
200 E 3rd St., Ste. 302
Owensboro, KY 42303
Contact: Mickey Johnson, Dir./Management Consultant
Ph: (270)926-8085
Fax: (270)684-0714
E-mail: mickey.johnson@murraystate.edu
URL: http://www.ksbdc.org/locations/owensboro

Descr: Represents and promotes the small business sector. Provides management assistance to current and prospective small business owners. Helps to improve management skills and expand the products and services of members.

1919 ■ Paducah Small Business Development Center
401 Kentucky Ave.
Paducah, KY 42003-1551
Contact: Kirby Halsell, Admin. Asst.
Ph: (270)443-2783
Fax: (270)442-9152
E-mail: khalsell@kyinnovation.com
URL: http://www.ksbdc.org/locations/paducah

Descr: Represents and promotes the small business sector. Provides management assistance to current and prospective small business owners. Helps to improve management skills and expand the products and services of members.

1920 ■ Paintsville Small Business Development Center
120 Scott Perry Dr.
Teays Branch Rd.
Paintsville, KY 41240-9000
Contact: Sabrina Jude, Data Entry Specialist
Ph: (606)788-6008
Fax: (606)789-5623
E-mail: sk.jude@moreheadstate.edu
URL: http://www.ksbdc.org/locations/paintsville

Descr: Represents and promotes the small business sector. Provides management assistance to current and prospective small business owners. Helps to improve management skills and expand the products and services of members.

1921 ■ Pikeville Small Business Development Center
3455 N Mayo Trail, No. 4
Pikeville, KY 41501-3298
Contact: Mike Morley, Dir./Management Consultant
Ph: (606)432-5848
Fax: (606)432-8924
E-mail: m.morley@moreheadstate.edu
URL: http://www.ksbdc.org/locations/pikeville

Descr: Represents and promotes the small business sector. Provides management assistance to current and prospective small business owners. Helps to improve management skills and expand the products and services of members.

1922 ■ Small Business Development Center at Western Kentucky University
Garrett Conference Ctr.
1906 College Heights Blvd., No. 61086
Bowling Green, KY 42101
Contact: Adam Brownlee, Dir.
Ph: (270)745-1905
Fax: (270)745-1931
E-mail: adam.brownlee@wku.edu
URL: http://wkusbdc.com

Descr: Represents and promotes the small business sector. Provides management assistance to current and prospective small business owners. Helps to

improve management skills and expand the products and services of members.

1923 ■ Southeast Small Business Development Center
Bell County Campus
1300 Chichester Ave.
Middlesboro, KY 40965-2265
Contact: Sam Coleman, Dir./Management Consultant
Ph: (606)248-0563
Fax: (606)248-3267
E-mail: samuel.coleman@kctcs.edu
URL: http://www.ksbdc.org/locations/middlesboro

Descr: Represents and promotes the small business sector. Provides management assistance to current and prospective small business owners. Helps to improve management skills and expand the products and services of members.

1924 ■ University of Kentucky Small Business Development Center - Elizabethtown
1105 Juliana Ct., No. 6
Elizabethtown, KY 42701-7937
Contact: Patricia Krausman, Dir./Management Consultant
Ph: (270)765-6737
Fax: (270)769-5095
E-mail: patricia.krausman@uky.edu
URL: http://www.ksbdc.org/locations/elizabethtown

Descr: Represents and promotes the small business sector. Provides management assistance to current and prospective small business owners. Helps to improve management skills and expand the products and services of members.

1925 ■ West Liberty Small Business Development Center
Morehead State University Regional Enterprise Ctr.
151 University Dr.
West Liberty, KY 41472
Contact: Michael Rodriguez, Management Consultant
Ph: (606)743-4005
Fax: (606)743-4002
E-mail: m.rodriguez@moreheadstate.edu
URL: http://www.ksbdc.org/locations/west-liberty

Descr: Represents and promotes the small business sector. Provides management assistance to current and prospective small business owners. Helps to improve management skills and expand the products and services of members.

Louisiana

1926 ■ American Society of Appraisers, Baton Rouge Chapter
1637 Stoneleigh Dr.
Baton Rouge, LA 70808
Contact: David L. Pourciau, Membership Chm.
Ph: (225)237-1247
Fax: (225)237-1201
E-mail: dlpourciau@cox.net
URL: http://www.appraisers.org/batonrouge

Descr: Serves as a professional appraisal educator, testing and accrediting society. Sponsors mandatory recertification program for all members. Offers consumer information service to the public.

1927 ■ American Society of Appraisers, Harold S. Clark Sr./New Orleans Chapter
PO Box 609
Destrehan, LA 70047-0609
Contact: Chris G. LaBure, Pres.
Ph: (985)764-8321
Fax: (985)764-3087
E-mail: untmar@cox.net
URL: http://old.appraisers.org/neworleans

Descr: Serves as a professional appraisal educator, testing and accrediting society. Sponsors mandatory recertification program for all members. Offers consumer information service to the public.

1928 ■ Appraisal Institute, Louisiana Chapter
101 Vincent Ave.
Metairie, LA 70005

Contact: Bill Kipf SRA, Pres.
Ph: (504)833-4949
Fax: (504)833-4984
E-mail: lcai@lcai.org
URL: http://www.lcai.org

Descr: Works to support and advance its members as the choice for real estate solutions and uphold professional credentials, standards of professional practice and ethics consistent with the public good. Members include General appraisers who hold the MAI or SRPA designations, and residential members who hold the SRA designation.

1929 ■ Arklatex Chapter Financial Planning Association
9417 Garfield Dr.
Shreveport, LA 71118-3908
Contact: Hal Bundrick CFP, Pres.
Ph: (318)828-2876
Fax: (318)828-2871
E-mail: msbutt@comcast.net
URL: http://www.fpa-arklatex.org

Descr: Supports the financial planning process in order to help people achieve their goals and dreams. Promotes the legislative, regulatory and professional interests of the financial service industry. Fosters the value of financial planning and advances the financial planning profession.

1930 ■ Business and Professional Women, West St. Tammany
PO Box 831
Mandeville, LA 70470
Contact: Pam Eiffert, Pres.
Ph: (504)569-3499
E-mail: info@bpw-wst.org
URL: http://www.bpw-wst.org

Descr: Represents the interests of business and professional women. Elevates the standards for women in business and professional settings. Promotes equity for all women in the workplace through advocacy, education and information. Provides professional development, networking and career advancement opportunities for working women.

1931 ■ Financial Planning Association of Baton Rouge
1 Oak Sq.
8280 YMCA Plaza Dr., No. 4
Baton Rouge, LA 70810
Contact: Brent R. Graham, Chm.
Ph: (225)291-0343
Fax: (225)291-0419
E-mail: fpabatonrouge@gmail.com
URL: http://www.batonrougefpa.com

Descr: Provides education, networking, and professional growth for its members. Enhances public awareness of the financial planning process.

1932 ■ Financial Planning Association of Greater New Orleans
PO Box 9202
Metairie, LA 70055-9202
Contact: Allen M. Kuhn, Pres.
Free: 866-730-4530
E-mail: fpa@financialplanningnola.com
URL: http://www.financialplanningnola.org

Descr: Promotes financial planning profession through education, networking, and mentoring. Enhances public awareness of the value of the financial planning process. Provides forum for education and career development for its members.

1933 ■ Louisiana Federation Business and Professional Women
321 Iris Park Dr.
Pineville, LA 71360
Contact: Delia Flynn, Pres.
Ph: (318)484-7522
Fax: (318)487-7193
E-mail: deliaflynn@msn.com
URL: http://www.bpwlouisiana.org

Descr: Represents the interests of business and professional women. Elevates the standards for women in business and professional settings.

Promotes equity for all women in the workplace through advocacy, education and information. Provides professional development, networking and career advancement opportunities for working women.

1934 ■ Louisiana Small Business Development Center - Greater New Orleans Region
UNO Jefferson Center
3330 N Causeway Blvd., Ste. 422
Metairie, LA 70002
Ph: (504)831-3730
E-mail: lsbdc.gnor@lsbdc.org
URL: http://www.lsbdc.org
Descr: Represents and promotes the small business sector. Provides management assistance to current and prospective small business owners. Helps to improve management skills and expand the products and services of members.

1935 ■ Louisiana Small Business Development Center at Louisiana State University in Shreveport
LSUS Technology Ctr., Rm. 209
One University Pl.
Shreveport, LA 71115
Ph: (318)797-5144
E-mail: lsbdc.lsus@lsbdc.org
URL: http://www.lsbdc.org
Descr: Represents and promotes the small business sector. Provides management assistance to current and prospective small business owners. Helps to improve management skills and expand the products and services of members.

1936 ■ Louisiana Small Business Development Center - LSU South Campus
LBTC Bldg. 3000
8000 GSRI Ave.
Baton Rouge, LA 70820
Ph: (225)578-7555
Fax: (225)578-3975
E-mail: lbtc@lsu.edu
URL: http://www.bus.lsu.edu/sbdc
Descr: Represents and promotes the small business sector. Provides management assistance to current and prospective small business owners. Helps to improve management skills and expand the products and services of members.

1937 ■ Louisiana Small Business Development Center at McNeese State University
Burton Business Center
4450 Ryan St.
Lake Charles, LA 70605
Ph: (337)475-5529
E-mail: lsbdc.msu@lsbdc.org
URL: http://www.lsbdc.org
Descr: Represents and promotes the small business sector. Provides management assistance to current and prospective small business owners. Helps to improve management skills and expand the products and services of members.

1938 ■ Louisiana Small Business Development Center - New Orleans and the Bayou Region
Nicholls State University
310 Ardoyne Ave.
Thibodaux, LA 70301
Ph: (985)448-4485
E-mail: lsbdc.slec@lsbdc.org
URL: http://www.lsbdc.org
Descr: Represents and promotes the small business sector. Provides management assistance to current and prospective small business owners. Helps to improve management skills and expand the products and services of members.

1939 ■ Louisiana Small Business Development Center at Northwestern State University
Dunbar Plz., Ste. 114C
3600 Jackson St.
Alexandria, LA 71303-3064
Ph: (318)484-2123
E-mail: lsbdc.nsu@lsbdc.org
URL: http://www.lsbdc.org

Descr: Represents and promotes the small business sector. Provides management assistance to current and prospective small business owners. Helps to improve management skills and expand the products and services of members.

1940 ■ Louisiana Small Business Development Center at Southeastern Louisiana University
Southeast Louisiana Business Center
1514 Martens Dr.
Hammond, LA 70402-0001
Ph: (985)549-3831
E-mail: lsbdc.slu@lsbdc.org
URL: http://www.lsbdc.org
Descr: Represents and promotes the small business sector. Provides management assistance to current and prospective small business owners. Helps to improve management skills and expand the products and services of members.

1941 ■ Louisiana Small Business Development Center at Southern University
4826 Jamestown Ave., Ste. 1
Baton Rouge, LA 70808-3224
Ph: (225)922-0998
E-mail: lsbdc.subr@lsbdc.org
URL: http://www.lsbdc.org
Descr: Represents and promotes the small business sector. Provides management assistance to current and prospective small business owners. Helps to improve management skills and expand the products and services of members.

1942 ■ Louisiana Small Business Development Center at University of Louisiana at Lafayette
220 E St. Mary Blvd.
Lafayette, LA 70503-2036
Ph: (337)262-5344
E-mail: lsbdc.ull@lsbdc.org
URL: http://www.lsbdc.org
Descr: Represents and promotes the small business sector. Provides management assistance to current and prospective small business owners. Helps to improve management skills and expand the products and services of members.

1943 ■ Louisiana Small Business Development Center at University of Louisiana Monroe
Administration Bldg.
700 University Ave., Bldg. 2-123
Monroe, LA 71209
Ph: (318)342-1224
E-mail: lsbdc.ulm@lsbdc.org
URL: http://www.lsbdc.org
Descr: Represents and promotes the small business sector. Provides management assistance to current and prospective small business owners. Helps to improve management skills and expand the products and services of members.

1944 ■ Monroe-West Monroe Business and Professional Women
PO Box 15046
Monroe, LA 71207
Contact: Peggy Wells, Pres.
E-mail: mmwells@dow.com
URL: http://www.bpwmonroe-westmonroe.org
Descr: Represents the interests of business and professional women. Elevates the standards for women in business and professional settings. Promotes equity for all women in the workplace through advocacy, education and information. Provides professional development, networking and career advancement opportunities for working women.

1945 ■ NAIFA-Greater New Orleans
639 Loyola Ave., Ste. 1900
New Orleans, LA 70113
Contact: Michael J. Mire Jr., Pres.
Ph: (504)569-0774
Fax: (504)569-0508
E-mail: mmire@ft.newyorklife.com
URL: http://naifa-gno.org

Descr: Represents the interests of insurance and financial advisors. Advocates for a positive legislative and regulatory environment. Enhances business and professional skills of members.

1946 ■ New Orleans Business and Professional Women
PO Box 50215
New Orleans, LA 70150
Contact: Cynthia Edwards, Webmaster/Treas.
Ph: (504)261-6930
Fax: (504)368-8956
E-mail: neworleansbpw@mail.com
URL: http://www.bpwneworleans.org
Descr: Represents the interests of business and professional women. Elevates the standards for women in business and professional settings. Promotes equity for all women in the workplace through advocacy, education and information. Provides professional development, networking and career advancement opportunities for working women.

1947 ■ North American Securities Administrators Association, Louisiana
8660 United Plaza Blvd., 2nd Fl.
Baton Rouge, LA 70809
Contact: Rhonda Reeves
Ph: (225)925-4512
Fax: (225)925-4548
Descr: Represents the interests of the state, provincial and territorial securities administrators in the U.S.

1948 ■ Slidell Business and Professional Women
PO Box 1299
Slidell, LA 70459
Contact: Kaki DiCarlo, Pres.
Ph: (985)882-2295
Fax: (985)882-2297
E-mail: thekak@charter.net
URL: http://www.slidellbpw.org
Descr: Represents the interests of business and professional women. Elevates the standards for women in business and professional settings. Promotes equity for all women in the workplace through advocacy, education and information. Provides professional development, networking and career advancement opportunities for working women.

Maine

1949 ■ Caribou Business and Professional Women
356 Parsons Rd.
Presque Isle, ME 04769
Contact: Denise Dumais, Pres.
Ph: (207)764-1738
E-mail: denisecustomtouch@myctmh.com
URL: http://www.bpwmaine.org
Descr: Represents the interests of business and professional women. Elevates the standards for women in business and professional settings. Promotes equity for all women in the workplace through advocacy, education and information. Provides professional development, networking and career advancement opportunities for working women.

1950 ■ DownEast Business and Professional Women
343 Shore Rd.
Ellsworth, ME 04605
Contact: Jeri White, Pres.
Ph: (207)667-5429
E-mail: berpha@roadrunner.com
URL: http://www.bpwmaine.org
Descr: Represents the interests of business and professional women. Elevates the standards for women in business and professional settings. Promotes equity for all women in the workplace through advocacy, education and information. Provides professional development, networking and

career advancement opportunities for working women.

1951 ■ Fort Kent Business and Professional Women
PO Box 1259
Caribou, ME 04736
Contact: Geri Martin, Pres.
Ph: (207)496-3130
E-mail: impacauto@ainop.com
URL: http://www.bpwmaine.org

Descr: Represents the interests of business and professional women. Elevates the standards for women in business and professional settings. Promotes equity for all women in the workplace through advocacy, education and information. Provides professional development, networking and career advancement opportunities for working women.

1952 ■ Maine Association of Assessing Officers (MAAO)
271 Falmouth Rd.
Falmouth, ME 04105
Contact: Anne Gregory, Pres.
Ph: (207)781-5253
Fax: (207)781-8677
E-mail: agregory@town.falmouth.me.us
URL: http://www.maineassessors.org

Descr: Represents state and local officials concerned with valuation of property for ad valorem property tax purposes. Works to improve standards and conduct research on tax assessment. Promotes innovation and excellence in property appraisal, assessment administration, and property tax policy through professional development, education, research, and technical assistance.

1953 ■ Maine Chapter of the Appraisal Institute
18 Vannah Ave.
Portland, ME 04103
Contact: Robert E. Lynch, Pres.
Ph: (207)772-8989
Fax: (207)772-8989
E-mail: info@maineai.com
URL: http://www.maineai.com

Descr: Represents the interests of real estate appraisers. **Fnd:** 1971.

1954 ■ NAIFA-Androscoggin Valley
1220 Lisbon St., No. 102
Lewiston, ME 04240-5938
Contact: Patricia J. Gagne, Pres.
Ph: (207)783-4529
Fax: (207)783-4612
E-mail: pattigagne@allstate.com

Descr: Represents the interests of insurance and financial advisors. Advocates for a positive legislative and regulatory environment. Enhances business and professional skills of members.

1955 ■ NAIFA-Eastern Maine
PO Box 1172
Bangor, ME 04402
Contact: Maureen Hedges, Sec.
Ph: (207)992-4412
Free: 866-363-0816
E-mail: healthbenefits@nudmaine.com

Descr: Represents the interests of insurance and financial advisors. Advocates for a positive legislative and regulatory environment. Enhances business and professional skills of members.

1956 ■ NAIFA-Kennebec Valley
PO Box 306
Litchfield, ME 04350-0306
Contact: Candace J. Snow, Pres.
Ph: (207)737-7587
Fax: (207)622-4616
E-mail: lmquirion@maineinsure.com

Descr: Represents the interests of insurance and financial advisors. Advocates for a positive legisla-

tive and regulatory environment. Enhances business and professional skills of members.

1957 ■ NAIFA - Maine
PO Box 2695
Bangor, ME 04402-2695
Contact: Susan Willey McKay, Association Exec.
Ph: (207)945-4766
Fax: (207)941-0241
E-mail: exec@naifa-me.org
URL: http://www.naifa-me.org

Descr: Represents the interests of insurance and financial advisors. Advocates for a positive legislative and regulatory environment. Enhances business and professional skills of members. **Local Groups:** 5.

1958 ■ NAIFA-Southern Maine
PO Box 11515
Portland, ME 04104
Contact: Warren G. Berger III, Pres.
Ph: (207)283-8903
Fax: (207)283-8903
E-mail: dneault54@yahoo.com

Descr: Represents the interests of insurance and financial advisors. Advocates for a positive legislative and regulatory environment. Enhances business and professional skills of members.

1959 ■ North American Securities Administrators Association, Maine
Office of Securities
State House Sta. 121
Augusta, ME 04333
Contact: Bonnie Russell
Ph: (207)624-8551
Fax: (207)624-8590
URL: http://www.maine.gov/pfr/securities/index.shtml

Descr: Represents the interests of the state, provincial and territorial securities administrators in the U.S.

1960 ■ Waterville Business and Professional Women
35 S Gage Rd.
Oakland, ME 04963
Contact: Myra Chaloult, Pres.
Ph: (207)465-2162
E-mail: michal23@yahoo.com
URL: http://www.bpwmaine.org

Descr: Represents the interests of business and professional women. Elevates the standards for women in business and professional settings. Promotes equity for all women in the workplace through advocacy, education and information. Provides professional development, networking and career advancement opportunities for working women.

Maryland

1961 ■ American Society of Appraisers, Maryland Chapter
6416 Autumn Gold Ct.
Columbia, MD 21045
Contact: Kimberly A. Esposito, Pres.
Ph: (410)487-3193
E-mail: kimesposito@verizon.net
URL: http://www.appraisers.org/maryland

Descr: Serves as a professional appraisal educator, testing and accrediting society. Sponsors mandatory recertification program for all members. Offers consumer information service to the public. **Pub:** Newsletter (monthly).

1962 ■ American Society of Appraisers, Washington D.C. Chapter
Sloans and Kenyon Auctioneers and Appraisers
7034 Wisconsin Ave.
Chevy Chase, MD 20815
Contact: Stephanie A. Kenyon, Pres.
Ph: (301)320-2270
Fax: (301)320-5089
E-mail: kenyons@sloansandkenyon.com
URL: http://asadc.homestead.com

Descr: Serves as a professional appraisal educator,

testing and accrediting society. Sponsors mandatory recertification program for all members. Offers consumer information service to the public. **Pub:** Newsletter (monthly).

1963 ■ Anne Arundel County Taxpayers Association
1188 Bacon Ridge Rd.
Crownsville, MD 21032
Ph: (410)923-3331
E-mail: spearlib@comcast.net

1964 ■ Anne Arundel Small Business Development Center
Anne Arundel Economic Development Corporation
2660 Riva Rd., Ste. 200
Annapolis, MD 21401
Contact: Thomas Francovitch
Ph: (410)222-4476
Fax: (410)222-7415
E-mail: tfrancovitch@aaedc.org
URL: http://www.centralmdsbdc.org/counseling/annearundelcounty.php

Descr: Represents and promotes the small business sector. Provides management assistance to current and prospective small business owners. Helps to improve management skills and expand the products and services of members.

1965 ■ Baltimore City Small Business Resource Center
ETC at Johns Hopkins Eastern
1101 E 33rd St., Ste. C308
Baltimore, MD 21218
Contact: Terry Trusty
Ph: (443)451-7162
Fax: (443)451-7169
E-mail: ttrusty@towson.edu
URL: http://www.centralmdsbdc.org/counseling/baltimorecity.php

Descr: Represents and promotes the small business sector. Provides management assistance to current and prospective small business owners. Helps to improve management skills and expand the products and services of members.

1966 ■ Baltimore County Small Business Development Center
Towson University
7400 York Rd.
Towson, MD 21204
Contact: Craig Panos
Ph: (410)296-6142
Fax: (410)296-6142
E-mail: cpanos@towson.edu
URL: http://www.centralmdsbdc.org/counseling/baltimorecounty.php

Descr: Represents and promotes the small business sector. Provides management assistance to current and prospective small business owners. Helps to improve management skills and expand the products and services of members.

1967 ■ Baltimore County Taxpayers Association
21053 Millers Mill Rd.
Freeland, MD 21053
Ph: (410)357-5555

1968 ■ Business and Professional Women, Frederick
PO Box 1045
Frederick, MD 21702
Contact: Mary Ellen Poole
Ph: (301)371-8575
URL: http://www.bpwfrederick.org

Descr: Represents the interests of business and professional women. Elevates the standards for women in business and professional settings. Promotes equity for all women in the workplace through advocacy, education and information. Provides professional development, networking and

career advancement opportunities for working women.

1969 ■ Dorchester County Taxpayers Association of Maryland
5122 Williamsburg Rd.
Hurlock, MD 21643
Ph: (410)754-5834

1970 ■ Financial Planning Association of Maryland
PO Box 799
Reisterstown, MD 21136
Contact: F. Michael Curley, Exec. Dir.
Ph: (410)833-9200
Fax: (443)381-0078
E-mail: director@fpamd.org
URL: http://www.fpamd.org
Descr: Builds a community for financial planning professionals. Facilitates the exchange of knowledge and experience, furthers the professional development and stimulates career advancement and opportunities for members. Expands awareness and enhances the perception of the financial planning profession. Advocates on behalf of the financial planning profession. **Fnd:** 2000.

1971 ■ Harford County Maryland Small Business Development Center
Harford Community College
Edgewood Hall
401 Thomas Run Rd.
Bel Air, MD 21015
Contact: Russell Teter, Dir.
Ph: (410)836-4237
Fax: (410)836-4353
E-mail: sbdc@harford.edu
URL: http://www.harford.edu/sbdc/Index.asp
Descr: Represents and promotes the small business sector. Provides management assistance to current and prospective small business owners. Helps to improve management skills and expand the products and services of members.

1972 ■ Howard County Small Business Development Center
Howard County Center for Business and Technology Development
9250 Bendix Rd.
Columbia, MD 21045
Contact: Mary Redmond
Ph: (410)313-6190
Fax: (410)313-7515
E-mail: mredmond@towson.edu
URL: http://www.centralmdsbdc.org/counseling/howardcounty.php
Descr: Represents and promotes the small business sector. Provides management assistance to current and prospective small business owners. Helps to improve management skills and expand the products and services of members.

1973 ■ Howard County Taxpayers Association
5809 Timberview Dr.
Elkridge, MD 21075
Ph: (410)796-1022

1974 ■ International Association of Assessing Officers, Maryland
59 Richardson Ave.
Crisfield, MD 21817
Contact: Leslie Pruitt, Rep.
Ph: (410)651-0868
Fax: (410)651-1995
E-mail: lpruitt@dat.state.md.us
Descr: Represents state and local officials concerned with valuation of property for ad valorem property tax purposes. Works to improve standards and conduct research on tax assessment. Promotes innovation and excellence in property appraisal, assessment administration, and property tax policy

through professional development, education, research, and technical assistance.

1975 ■ Maryland/DC Society of Enrolled Agents
550M Ritchie Hwy., No. 145
Severna Park, MD 21146
Contact: Robert S. Jacobs
Ph: (410)544-4680
Fax: (410)544-9057
E-mail: ataxguru@prodigy.net
Descr: Promotes ethical representation of the financial position of taxpayers before government agencies.

1976 ■ Maryland Federation of Business and Professional Women
143 Othoridge Rd.
Lutherville, MD 21093
Contact: Alicia Newman, Pres.
Ph: (410)828-7895
E-mail: teddybear8@outdrs.net
URL: http://www.bpwmaryland.org
Descr: Represents the interests of business and professional women. Elevates the standards for women in business and professional settings. Promotes equity for all women in the workplace through advocacy, education and information. Provides professional development, networking and career advancement opportunities for working women.

1977 ■ Maryland Small Business Development Center - Central Region
8000 York Rd.
Towson, MD 21252
Contact: Sonia Stockton, Dir.
Ph: (410)296-5613
Free: 877-421-0830
Fax: (410)296-6142
E-mail: sstockton@towson.edu
URL: http://www.centralmdsbdc.org
Descr: Represents and promotes the small business sector. Provides management assistance to current and prospective small business owners. Helps to improve management skills and expand the products and services of members.

1978 ■ Maryland Small Business Development Center - Eastern Region
Perdue School of Business - Salisbury University
215 E Campus Complex
Salisbury, MD 21801
Contact: John Hickman, Dir.
Ph: (410)548-4419
Free: 800-999-7232
Fax: (410)548-5389
E-mail: sbdctraining@salisbury.edu
URL: http://www.salisbury.edu/sbdc
Descr: Represents and promotes the small business sector. Provides management assistance to current and prospective small business owners. Helps to improve management skills and expand the products and services of members.

1979 ■ Maryland Small Business Development Center - Southern Region
PO Box 910
La Plata, MD 20646
Contact: Brian DuBoff, Dir.
Ph: (301)934-7583
E-mail: bduboff@csmd.edu
URL: http://www.sbdchelp.com
Descr: Represents and promotes the small business sector. Provides management assistance to current and prospective small business owners. Helps to improve management skills and expand the products and services of members.

1980 ■ Maryland Taxpayers Association (MTA)
9613-C Harford Rd., No. 527
Baltimore, MD 21234
Contact: Dee Hodges, Pres.
Ph: (410)665-4769

E-mail: mdtaxes@comcast.net
URL: http://www.mdtaxes.org

1981 ■ Montgomery County Taxpayers League
PO Box 826
Rockville, MD 20848
Ph: (301)946-3799
E-mail: mctaxpayersleague@msn.com

1982 ■ NAIFA-Maryland
9 State Cir., Ste. 303
Annapolis, MD 21401
Contact: Nanci Richards, Exec. Dir.
Free: 877-304-9934
E-mail: nrichards@papalaw.com
URL: http://www.naifa-maryland.org
Descr: Represents the interests of insurance and financial advisors. Advocates for a positive legislative and regulatory environment. Enhances business and professional skills of members.

1983 ■ Queen Anne County Taxpayers Association
306 Cove Rd.
Queenstown, MD 21658
Ph: (410)827-7671

1984 ■ Washington County Taxpayers Association
19503 Spring Valley Rd.
Hagerstown, MD 21742
Ph: (410)820-4704

Massachusetts

1985 ■ American Society of Appraisers, Boston Chapter
272 County St.
Attleboro, MA 02703
Contact: Richard Conti, Pres.
Ph: (508)223-3333
Descr: Serves as a professional appraisal educator, testing and accrediting society. Sponsors mandatory recertification program for all members. Offers consumer information service to the public. **Pub:** Newsletter (monthly).

1986 ■ Appraisal Institute, Massachusetts Chapter
51 Pleasant St., Ste. 164
Malden, MA 02148
Contact: David L. Cary Jr., Pres.
Ph: (781)397-8922
Fax: (781)388-9052
E-mail: office@ma-appraisalinstitute.org
URL: http://www.ma-appraisalinstitute.org
Staff: 1. **Descr:** Real estate appraisers organized to advance interests of the profession. Lobbies and monitors legislation. Conducts educational programs. **Fnd:** 1932. **Mem:** 580. **Pub:** Newsletter (quarterly).

1987 ■ Berkshire Business and Professional Women
PO Box 3152
Pittsfield, MA 01202-3152
Contact: Judy Sayers, Membership Chair
Ph: (413)442-5300
E-mail: jsayers@arrowpressonline.com
URL: http://www.berkshirebpw.org
Descr: Represents the interests of business and professional women. Elevates the standards for women in business and professional settings. Promotes equity for all women in the workplace through advocacy, education and information. Provides professional development, networking and career advancement opportunities for working women.

1988 ■ Central Massachusetts Small Business Development Center
950 Main St.
Worcester, MA 01610
Contact: Larry Marsh, Dir
Ph: (508)793-7615
E-mail: sbdc@clarku.edu
URL: http://www.clarku.edu/offices/sbdc

Descr: Represents and promotes the small business sector. Provides management assistance to current and prospective small business owners. Helps to improve management skills and expand the products and services of members.

1989 ■ Downtown Boston Business and Professional Women
PO Box 174
Boston, MA 02133
Contact: Deborah Bouras, Pres.
Ph: (617)462-7480
E-mail: dbbbour8@aol.com
URL: http://www.downtownbostonbpw.org

Descr: Represents the interests of business and professional women. Elevates the standards for women in business and professional settings. Promotes equity for all women in the workplace through advocacy, education and information. Provides professional development, networking and career advancement opportunities for working women.

1990 ■ Easton Taxpayers Association
PO Box 711
South Easton, MA 02375
E-mail: eta02375@lycos.com

1991 ■ Financial Planning Association of Massachusetts
Chapter Office
411 Waverley Oaks Rd., Ste. 331B
Waltham, MA 02452
Contact: Diana Webster, Pres.
Ph: (781)899-3530
Free: 866-804-0484
Fax: (781)647-7222
E-mail: admin@fpama.org
URL: http://www.fpama.org

Descr: Promotes financial planning profession through education, networking, and mentoring. Focuses on professional development and education of financial planning professionals. Educates the public on the financial planning profession.

1992 ■ Framingham Taxpayers Association (FTPA)
PO Box 2223
Framingham, MA 01703
Contact: William McCarthy
Ph: (508)875-1556
E-mail: info@framinghamtpa.org
URL: http://www.framinghamtpa.org

1993 ■ Massachusetts Association of Assessing Officers (MAAO)
Assessors Office, City Hall
1305 Hancock St.
Quincy, MA 02169
Contact: Marion A. Fantucchio MAA, Sec.-Treas.
Ph: (617)376-1171
Fax: (617)376-1185
E-mail: mfantucchio@ci.quincy.ma.us
URL: http://www.maao.org
Staff: 1. **Descr:** Professional organization of assessors and associated companies. Promotes continuing development and education within the field; conducts educational programs, workshops, and seminars. **Fnd:** 1890. **Mem:** 1775. **Pub:** *MAAO Newsletter* (semimonthly); Membership Directory (annual).

1994 ■ Massachusetts Small Business Development Center - Berkshire
75 North St., Ste. 360
Pittsfield, MA 01201
Contact: Keith Girouard
Ph: (413)499-0933
Fax: (413)499-3005
E-mail: kgirouard@msbdc.umass.edu
URL: http://www.msbdc.org/berkshire

Descr: Represents and promotes the small business sector. Provides management assistance to current and prospective small business owners. Helps to improve management skills and expand the products and services of members.

1995 ■ Massachusetts Small Business Development Center Network - Western
Scibelli Enterprise Center
1 Federal St.
Springfield, MA 01105
Contact: Dianne Fuller Doherty, Dir.
Ph: (413)737-6712
Fax: (413)737-2312
E-mail: ddoherty@msbdc.umass.edu
URL: http://www.msbdc.org/wmass

Descr: Represents and promotes the small business sector. Provides management assistance to current and prospective small business owners. Helps to improve management skills and expand the products and services of members.

1996 ■ Massachusetts Small Business Development Center - Northeast
Enterprise Center
121 Loring Ave., Ste. 310
Salem, MA 01970
Contact: Margaret Somer, Dir.
Ph: (978)542-6343
Fax: (978)542-6345
E-mail: msomer@salemstate.edu
URL: http://www.salemstate.edu/sbdc

Descr: Represents and promotes the small business sector. Provides management assistance to current and prospective small business owners. Helps to improve management skills and expand the products and services of members.

1997 ■ NAIFA - Massachusetts
PO Box 500
Hingham, MA 02043
Contact: Linda M. Surovick, Exec. Dir.
Ph: (617)266-1919
Fax: (617)266-6849
E-mail: naifamass@mindspring.com
URL: http://www.naifamass.org

Descr: Represents the interests of insurance and financial advisors. Advocates for a positive legislative and regulatory environment. Enhances business and professional skills of members.

1998 ■ NAIFA-New Hampshire
PO Box 500
Hingham, MA 02043
Contact: Linda Surovick, Exec. Dir.
Ph: (617)266-1919
Free: 800-480-8719
Fax: (617)266-6849
E-mail: naifanh@mindspring.com
URL: http://www.naifanh.org

Descr: Represents the interests of insurance and financial advisors. Advocates for a positive legislative and regulatory environment. Enhances business and professional skills of members.

1999 ■ NAIFA-Southeast Massachusetts
PO Box 500
Hingham, MA 02043
Contact: John C. Cameron, Pres.
Ph: (617)266-1919
Fax: (617)266-6849
E-mail: ahqboston@mindspring.com

Descr: Represents the interests of insurance and financial advisors. Advocates for a positive legislative and regulatory environment. Enhances business and professional skills of members.

2000 ■ Newton Taxpayers Association
PO Box 451
Newton, MA 02460
Contact: Jeff Seideman
Ph: (617)965-9290
E-mail: main@newtontaxpayers.org
Fnd: 1936.

2001 ■ North American Securities Administrators Association, Massachusetts
One Ashburton Pl., Rm. 1701
Boston, MA 02108

Contact: Bryan Lantagne, Dir.
Ph: (617)727-3548
Fax: (617)248-0177
E-mail: securities@sec.state.ma.us
URL: http://www.sec.state.ma.us/sct/sctidx.htm

Descr: Represents the interests of the state, provincial and territorial securities administrators in the U.S.

2002 ■ North Andover Taxpayers Association (NATA)
262 Boston St.
North Andover, MA 01845
Ph: (978)725-6509
E-mail: tripp@gis.net
URL: http://www.nataxpayers.com

2003 ■ Northern Berkshire Business and Professional Women
Box 622
North Adams, MA 01247
Contact: Paulette Remillard, Pres.
E-mail: premillard@roadrunner.com
URL: http://www.northernberkshirebpw.org

Descr: Represents the interests of business and professional women. Elevates the standards for women in business and professional settings. Promotes equity for all women in the workplace through advocacy, education and information. Provides professional development, networking and career advancement opportunities for working women.

2004 ■ Northern Massachusetts Commercial-Investment Board of Realtors (NM-CIBOR)
3 Courthouse Ln., Unit 9
Chelmsford, MA 01824
Contact: Anne Rendle, CEO
Ph: (978)458-2901
Fax: (978)970-0443
E-mail: rendle@massnear.com
URL: http://www.nmcibor.com

Descr: Strives to develop real estate business practices. Advocates the right to own, use and transfer real property. Provides a facility for professional development, research and exchange of information among members.

2005 ■ SOCAP International - New England Chapter
PO Box 1087
Lynnfield, MA 01940
Contact: Ronna Caras, Pres.
Ph: (978)531-2022
E-mail: inquire@socapnewengland.org
URL: http://www.socapnewengland.org

Descr: Promotes customer care and customer management as a competitive advantage in business. Provides educational tools and professional resources to help members drive business transformation within their companies.

2006 ■ Southeastern Massachusetts Regional Small Business Development Center
200 Pocasset St.
Fall River, MA 02721
Contact: Melinda Ailes
Ph: (508)673-9783
Fax: (508)674-1929
E-mail: mlailes@msbdc.umass.edu
URL: http://www.msbdc.org/semass

Descr: Represents and promotes the small business sector. Provides management assistance to current and prospective small business owners. Helps to improve management skills and expand the products and services of members.

2007 ■ Spencer Taxpayers Association
10 Irving St., No. 2
Spencer, MA 01562
Ph: (508)885-1241

Fax: (508)885-1241
E-mail: spencertaxpayers@aol.com

2008 ■ Taxpayers Association of Wakefield (TAW)
PO Box 87
Wakefield, MA 01880
E-mail: mick1@pipeline.com
URL: http://www.pipeline.com/~mick1/index.html

Michigan

2009 ■ American Society of Appraisers, Detroit Chapter
Kres Inc.
113 E University Dr., Ste. 5
Rochester, MI 48307
Contact: Brian Stephen Kirksey, Pres.
Ph: (248)336-2086
Fax: (248)928-0969
E-mail: bkirksey@kresinc.com
URL: http://www.appraisers.org/detroit
Descr: Works to enhance professional deportment of valuation expertise. Provides immediate and long lasting value-added amenities.

2010 ■ American Society of Appraisers, Greater Michigan Chapter
Plante and Moran, PLLC
333 Bridge St. NW, Ste. 600
Grand Rapids, MI 49504
Contact: Paul H. Taylor, VP
Ph: (616)643-4083
Fax: (616)774-0702
E-mail: paul.taylor@plantemoran.com
URL: http://old.appraisers.org/michigan
Descr: Serves as a professional appraisal educator, testing and accrediting society. Sponsors mandatory recertification program for all members. Offers consumer information service to the public.

2011 ■ Direct Marketing Association of Detroit (DMAD)
32621 Grand River Ave.
Farmington, MI 48336
Contact: Dan Chester, Pres.
Ph: (248)478-4888
Fax: (248)478-6437
E-mail: dmad@ameritech.net
URL: http://www.stayinvolved.com/frontdoor/main.asp?omID=94
Staff: 1. **Descr:** Promotes excellence in the direct marketing industry in Michigan. Facilitates networking; provides referrals. **Fnd:** 1959. **Mem:** 675. **Pub:** *Response* (monthly); Membership Directory (annual).

2012 ■ Financial Planning Association of Michigan (FPAMI)
PO Box 476
South Lyon, MI 48178-0476
Contact: Jennifer Bacarella, Pres.
Ph: (248)446-8909
Fax: (248)446-8939
E-mail: admin@fpami.com
URL: http://www.fpami.com
Descr: Supports the financial planning process in order to help people achieve their goals and dreams. Promotes the value of the financial planning process and advances the financial planning profession. Promotes its members in reaching their highest potential for serving the needs of their clients.

2013 ■ International Association of Assessing Officers, Michigan
241 W South St.
Kalamazoo, MI 49007
Contact: Andrew Falkenberg, Rep.
Ph: (616)337-8656
Fax: (616)337-8448
E-mail: falkenberga@kalamazoocity.org
Descr: Represents state and local officials concerned with valuation of property for ad valorem property tax purposes. Works to improve standards and conduct research on tax assessment. Promotes innovation and excellence in property appraisal, assessment administration, and property tax policy

through professional development, education, research, and technical assistance.

2014 ■ Kalamazoo County Taxpayers Association
PO Box 50122
Kalamazoo, MI 49005
Contact: Don Schultz, Treas.
E-mail: stoptaxes@yahoo.com
URL: http://www.kaltax.org

2015 ■ Macomb County Taxpayers' Association
PO Box 112
Mount Clemens, MI 48046
Ph: (586)463-1950
Fax: (586)463-4032

2016 ■ Michigan Small Business and Technology Development Center - Region 1
2950 College Ave.
Escanaba, MI 49829
Contact: Joel Schultz, Dir.
Ph: (906)789-0558
Fax: (906)789-9952
E-mail: jschultz@jobforce.org
URL: http://www.gvsu.edu/misbtdc
Descr: Represents and promotes the small business sector. Provides management assistance to current and prospective small business owners. Helps to improve management skills and expand the products and services of members.

2017 ■ Michigan Small Business and Technology Development Center - Region 2
PO Box 506
Traverse City, MI 49685
Contact: Chris Wendel, Dir.
Ph: (231)922-3782
Fax: (231)922-3737
E-mail: cwendel@nwm.cog.mi.us
URL: http://www.gvsu.edu/misbtdc
Descr: Represents and promotes the small business sector. Provides management assistance to current and prospective small business owners. Helps to improve management skills and expand the products and services of members.

2018 ■ Michigan Small Business and Technology Development Center - Region 3
Alpena Community College
Newport Center, Rm. 108
665 Johnson St.
Alpena, MI 49707
Contact: Carl Bourdelais, Dir.
Ph: (989)358-7383
Free: 888-468-6222
Fax: (989)358-7554
E-mail: bourdelc@alpenacc.edu
URL: http://www.gvsu.edu/misbtdc
Descr: Represents and promotes the small business sector. Provides management assistance to current and prospective small business owners. Helps to improve management skills and expand the products and services of members.

2019 ■ Michigan Small Business and Technology Development Center - Region 4
Mid Michigan Community College
M-TEC Bldg.
1375 S Clare Ave.
Harrison, MI 48625
Contact: Anthony Fox, Dir.
Ph: (989)386-6630
Fax: (989)802-0971
E-mail: aefox@midmich.edu
URL: http://www.gvsu.edu/misbtdc
Descr: Represents and promotes the small business sector. Provides management assistance to current and prospective small business owners. Helps to improve management skills and expand the products and services of members.

2020 ■ Michigan Small Business and Technology Development Center - Region 5
Delta College, H Wing
1961 Delta Rd.

University Center, MI 48710
Contact: Christine Greve, Dir.
Ph: (989)686-9597
Fax: (989)667-2222
E-mail: christinegreve@delta.edu
URL: http://www.gvsu.edu/misbtdc
Descr: Represents and promotes the small business sector. Provides management assistance to current and prospective small business owners. Helps to improve management skills and expand the products and services of members.

2021 ■ Michigan Small Business and Technology Development Center - Region 6
Kettering University
1700 W 3rd Ave.
Flint, MI 48504
Contact: Marsha Lyttle, Dir.
Ph: (810)762-9660
Fax: (810)762-9678
E-mail: mlyttle@kettering.edu
URL: http://www.gvsu.edu/misbtdc
Descr: Represents and promotes the small business sector. Provides management assistance to current and prospective small business owners. Helps to improve management skills and expand the products and services of members.

2022 ■ Michigan Small Business and Technology Development Center - Region 7
GVSU DeVos Center, No. 414C
401 Fulton St. W
Grand Rapids, MI 49504
Contact: Dante Villarreal, Dir.
Ph: (616)331-7486
Fax: (616)331-7195
E-mail: villarda@gvsu.edu
URL: http://www.gvsu.edu/misbtdc
Descr: Represents and promotes the small business sector. Provides management assistance to current and prospective small business owners. Helps to improve management skills and expand the products and services of members.

2023 ■ Michigan Small Business and Technology Development Center - Region 8
PO Box 40010
Lansing, MI 48901
Contact: Tom Donaldson, Dir.
Ph: (517)483-1921
Fax: (517)483-1675
E-mail: donaldt2@lcc.edu
URL: http://www.gvsu.edu/misbtdc
Descr: Represents and promotes the small business sector. Provides management assistance to current and prospective small business owners. Helps to improve management skills and expand the products and services of members.

2024 ■ Michigan Small Business and Technology Development Center - Region 9
Eastern Michigan University
300 W Michigan Ave., Ste. 306
Ypsilanti, MI 48197
Contact: Richard King, Dir.
Ph: (734)487-0490
Fax: (734)481-3354
E-mail: rking@emich.edu
URL: http://www.gvsu.edu/misbtdc
Descr: Represents and promotes the small business sector. Provides management assistance to current and prospective small business owners. Helps to improve management skills and expand the products and services of members.

2025 ■ Michigan Small Business and Technology Development Center - Region 10
1 S Main St., 7th Fl.
Mount Clemens, MI 48043
Contact: Don Morandini, Dir.
Ph: (586)469-5118
Fax: (586)469-6787
E-mail: don.morandini@macombcountymi.gov
URL: http://www.gvsu.edu/misbtdc
Descr: Represents and promotes the small business sector. Provides management assistance to current

and prospective small business owners. Helps to improve management skills and expand the products and services of members.

2026 ■ Michigan Small Business and Technology Development Center - Region 11
Western Michigan University
Haworth College of Business
3110 Schneider Hall
Kalamazoo, MI 49008
Contact: Steven Dobbs, Dir.
Ph: (269)387-6004
Fax: (269)387-5710
E-mail: steve.dobbs@wmich.edu
URL: http://www.gvsu.edu/misbtdc
Descr: Represents and promotes the small business sector. Provides management assistance to current and prospective small business owners. Helps to improve management skills and expand the products and services of members.

2027 ■ Michigan Small Business and Technology Development Center - Region 12
301 W Michigan Ave., Ste. 101
Ypsilanti, MI 48197
Contact: Charles Penner, Dir.
Ph: (734)961-0501
Fax: (734)547-9178
E-mail: cpenner@wccnet.org
URL: http://www.gvsu.edu/misbtdc
Descr: Represents and promotes the small business sector. Provides management assistance to current and prospective small business owners. Helps to improve management skills and expand the products and services of members.

2028 ■ Michigan Society of Enrolled Agents (MISEA)
7688 N Adrian Hwy.
Tecumseh, MI 49286
Contact: Nadine Smith EA
Ph: (517)423-0800
Fax: (517)423-8941
E-mail: tax@cass.net
URL: http://www.naea.org/MemberPortal/StateAffiliates/Listing

2029 ■ North American Securities Administrators Association, Michigan
611 W Ottawa St., 3rd Fl.
Lansing, MI 48933
Contact: Ken Ross, Acting Commissioner
Free: 877-999-6442
Fax: (517)241-3953
Descr: Represents the interests of the state, provincial and territorial securities administrators in the U.S.

2030 ■ SOCAP International - Great Lakes Chapter
230 Glenmoor Dr.
Rochester, MI 48307
Contact: Craig Zurcher, Pres.
Ph: (248)656-8625
URL: http://www.socapgreatlakes.org
Descr: Promotes customer care and customer management as a competitive advantage in business. Provides educational tools and professional resources to help members drive business transformation within their companies.

2031 ■ Wayne County Taxpayers Association (WCTA)
PO Box 181
Dearborn Heights, MI 48127
Contact: Rose Bogaert, Chair
Ph: (313)278-8383
E-mail: wctaxpayers@comcast.net
URL: http://mywebpages.comcast.net/bogaert

Minnesota

2032 ■ Aitkin County Tax-Payers Union
26258 Paddy Ave.
Aitkin, MN 56431
Ph: (218)927-2778

Fax: (218)927-2778
E-mail: dmerrell@mlecmn.net

2033 ■ Albert Lea-Austin AIFA
2110 SW 7th Ave.
Austin, MN 55912
Contact: Robert C. Hoeg, Pres.
Ph: (507)433-7890
Fax: (507)433-7998
E-mail: pswahlstrom@charter.net
Descr: Represents the interests of insurance and financial advisors. Advocates for a positive legislative and regulatory environment. Enhances business and professional skills of members.

2034 ■ American Society of Appraisers, Twin Cities Chapter
Appraisal Advisors, Inc.
3110 W 90th St.
Bloomington, MN 55431
Contact: James P. Roff ASA, Pres.
Ph: (952)881-6572
Fax: (952)881-1301
E-mail: jimroff@earthlink.net
URL: http://www.twincitiesappraisers.org
Descr: Serves as a professional appraisal educator, testing and accrediting society. Sponsors mandatory recertification program for all members. Offers consumer information service to the public.

2035 ■ Business and Professional Women, Fergus Falls
PO Box 384
Fergus Falls, MN 56538-0384
Contact: Katy J. Olson, Pres.
E-mail: webmaster@bpwfergusfalls.org
URL: http://bpwfergusfalls.org
Descr: Represents the interests of business and professional women. Elevates the standards for women in business and professional settings. Promotes equity for all women in the workplace through advocacy, education and information. Provides professional development, networking and career advancement opportunities for working women.

2036 ■ Business and Professional Women, Minnesota
11090 Wild Life Ct.
Holdingford, MN 56340
Contact: Jaci Olson, Pres.
E-mail: jaci.olson@nahan.com
URL: http://www.bpwmn.org
Descr: Represents the interests of business and professional women. Elevates the standards for women in business and professional settings. Promotes equity for all women in the workplace through advocacy, education and information. Provides professional development, networking and career advancement opportunities for working women.

2037 ■ Business and Professional Women, St. Cloud
PO Box 891
St. Cloud, MN 56302
Contact: Sharon Wilson, Pres.
E-mail: webmaster@bpwstcloud.org
URL: http://www.bpwstcloud.org
Descr: Represents the interests of business and professional women. Elevates the standards for women in business and professional settings. Promotes equity for all women in the workplace through advocacy, education and information. Provides professional development, networking and career advancement opportunities for working women.

2038 ■ Central Lakes College Small Business Development Center
501 W College Dr.
Brainerd, MN 56401
Contact: Greg Bergman, Dir.
Ph: (218)855-8142
Fax: (218)855-8141
E-mail: gbergman@clcmn.edu

URL: http://www.clcmn.edu/smallbusiness
Descr: Represents and promotes the small business sector. Provides management assistance to current and prospective small business owners. Helps to improve management skills and expand the products and services of members.

2039 ■ Central Minnesota Small Business Development Center
St. Cloud State University
616 Roosevelt Rd.
St. Cloud, MN 56301
Contact: LaRae Ross
Ph: (320)308-4842
Fax: (320)255-4957
E-mail: klross@stcloudstate.edu
URL: http://www.stcloudstate.edu/sbdc
Descr: Represents and promotes the small business sector. Provides management assistance to current and prospective small business owners. Helps to improve management skills and expand the products and services of members.

2040 ■ Dakota County Taxpayers Association
14539 Florissant Path
Apple Valley, MN 55124
Ph: (952)431-3616
E-mail: takruse@att.net

2041 ■ Financial Planning Association of Greater Hudson Valley
3900 Main St. NE
Minneapolis, MN 55421
Contact: Julie Doetsch CFP, Chair
Free: 877-817-8400
Fax: (763)226-2393
E-mail: office@fpaghv.org
URL: http://www.fpaghv.org
Descr: Supports the financial planning process in order to help people achieve their goals and dreams. Promotes the legislative, regulatory and professional interests of the financial service industry. Fosters the value of financial planning and advances the financial planning profession.

2042 ■ Financial Planning Association of Minnesota (FPA MN)
3900 Main St. NE
Minneapolis, MN 55421
Contact: Joan Rossi CFP, Pres.
Ph: (763)781-1212
Fax: (763)226-2393
E-mail: office@fpamn.org
URL: http://www.fpamn.org
Descr: Supports the financial planning process in order to help people achieve their goals and dreams. Promotes the value of the financial planning process and advances the financial planning profession. Fosters stewardship the development of recognized knowledge and competence.

2043 ■ International Association of Assessing Officers, Minnesota
Olmsted County Assessor's Office
151 4th St. SE
Rochester, MN 55904
Contact: William Krupski CAE, Rep.
Ph: (507)281-6293
Fax: (507)287-7186
E-mail: krupski.mark@co.olmstead.mn.us
Descr: Represents state and local officials concerned with valuation of property for ad valorem property tax purposes. Works to improve standards and conduct research on tax assessment. Promotes innovation and excellence in property appraisal, assessment administration, and property tax policy through professional development, education, research, and technical assistance.

2044 ■ Midwest Direct Marketing Association (MDMA)
1821 University Ave. West, Ste. S256
St. Paul, MN 55104
Contact: Joan M. Forde, Pres.
Ph: (651)999-5351
Fax: (651)917-1835

E-mail: mdma@mdma.org
URL: http://www.mdma.org
Descr: Dedicated to the advancement of professional and ethical practice of direct response marketing by members throughout the Upper Midwest. **Fnd:** 1960. **Pub:** *Direct Hit* (bimonthly).

2045 ■ Minneapolis AIFA
1405 Lilac Dr. N, No. 121
Minneapolis, MN 55422
Contact: Todd Johnson, Exec. Dir.
Ph: (763)544-8087
Free: 800-896-5143
Fax: (763)544-1631
E-mail: naifa@naifa-mn.org
URL: http://209.61.156.20/page.
cfm?usr=260000&pageid=2628
Staff: 5. **Descr:** Represents the interests of insurance and financial advisors. Advocates for a positive legislative and regulatory environment. Enhances business and professional skills of members. **Fnd:** 1934. **Mem:** 2000. **State Groups:** 1. **Local Groups:** 19. **Pub:** *NAIFAmn LifeNotes* (monthly).

2046 ■ Minnesota Small Business Development Center - Northeast
University of Minnesota Duluth
Center for Economic Development
Duluth Technology Village
11 E Superior St., Ste. 210
Duluth, MN 55802
Contact: Elaine Hansen, Dir.
Ph: (218)726-7298
Fax: (218)726-6338
E-mail: ehansen@umdced.com
URL: http://www.mnsbdc.com
Descr: Represents and promotes the small business sector. Provides management assistance to current and prospective small business owners. Helps to improve management skills and expand the products and services of members.

2047 ■ Minnesota Small Business Development Center - Northwest
Bemidji State University
Center for Research and Innovation
3801 Bemidji Ave. N
Bemidji, MN 56601
Contact: Shari Augustine, Coor.
Ph: (218)755-4255
Fax: (218)755-4903
E-mail: saugustine@bemidjistate.edu
URL: http://www.mnsbdc.com
Descr: Represents and promotes the small business sector. Provides management assistance to current and prospective small business owners. Helps to improve management skills and expand the products and services of members.

2048 ■ Minnesota Small Business Development Center - South Central
Region Nine Development Commission
1961 Premier Dr., Ste. 268
Mankato, MN 56001
Contact: Bob Klanderud, Dir.
Ph: (507)389-8875
Fax: (507)389-8868
E-mail: robertk@rndc.mankato.mn.us
URL: http://www.mnsbdc.com
Descr: Represents and promotes the small business sector. Provides management assistance to current and prospective small business owners. Helps to improve management skills and expand the products and services of members.

2049 ■ Minnesota Small Business Development Center - Southeast
Rochester Community and Technical College
Heintz Center
1926 Collegeview Rd. E
Rochester, MN 55904
Contact: Kay Wiegert, Coor.
Ph: (507)285-7536
Fax: (507)280-5502
E-mail: kay.wiegert@roch.edu
URL: http://www.mnsbdc.com

Descr: Represents and promotes the small business sector. Provides management assistance to current and prospective small business owners. Helps to improve management skills and expand the products and services of members.

2050 ■ Minnesota Small Business Development Center - West Central
Minnesota State University - Moorhead
1104 7th Ave. S
Moorhead, MN 56563
Contact: Leonard Sliwoski, Dir.
Ph: (218)477-2289
Fax: (218)477-2280
E-mail: sliwoski@mnstate.edu
URL: http://www.mnsbdc.com
Descr: Represents and promotes the small business sector. Provides management assistance to current and prospective small business owners. Helps to improve management skills and expand the products and services of members.

2051 ■ NAIFA-Minnesota
1405 Lilac Dr. N, Ste. 121
Golden Valley, MN 55422
Contact: Todd Johnson, Exec. Dir.
Ph: (763)544-8087
Free: 800-896-5143
Fax: (763)544-1631
E-mail: naifa@naifa-mn.org
URL: http://www.naifa-mn.org
Descr: Represents the interests of insurance and financial advisors. Advocates for a positive legislative and regulatory environment. Enhances business and professional skills of members. **Mem:** 2000.

2052 ■ North Hennepin Business and Professional Women
6936 Halifax Ave. N
Minneapolis, MN 55429
Contact: Gina Smith, Pres.
Ph: (763)488-3601
E-mail: ginas@firstmnbank.com
URL: http://www.northhennepinbpw.org
Descr: Represents the interests of business and professional women. Elevates the standards for women in business and professional settings. Promotes equity for all women in the workplace through advocacy, education and information. Provides professional development, networking and career advancement opportunities for working women.

2053 ■ North Star Chapter of the Appraisal Institute
1265 Josephine Rd.
Roseville, MN 55113
Contact: William Ruff MAI, Pres.
Ph: (651)633-0676
Fax: (651)633-5956
E-mail: maribelle@northstarai.org
URL: http://www.northstarai.org

2054 ■ SOCAP International - Minnesota Chapter
610 Opperman Dr.
Eagan, MN 55123
Contact: Kathryn Bracke, Pres.
Ph: (651)687-6850
Descr: Promotes customer care and customer management as a competitive advantage in business. Provides educational tools and professional resources to help members drive business transformation within their companies.

2055 ■ Southwest Small Business Development Center - Minnesota
Southwest Minnesota State University
1501 State St., Ste. 105
Marshall, MN 56258
Contact: Liz Struve, Dir.
Ph: (507)537-7386
Free: 800-642-0684
Fax: (507)537-6094
E-mail: sbdc@southwestmsu.edu
URL: http://www.southwestmsu.edu/sbdc

Descr: Represents and promotes the small business sector. Provides management assistance to current and prospective small business owners. Helps to improve management skills and expand the products and services of members.

2056 ■ Stillwater Business and Professional Women
PO Box 893
Stillwater, MN 55082-0893
Contact: Lorraine Weber, Treas.
Ph: (651)439-4354
E-mail: stillwaterbpw@yahoo.com
URL: http://www.pressenter.com/~stillbpw
Descr: Represents the interests of business and professional women. Elevates the standards for women in business and professional settings. Promotes equity for all women in the workplace through advocacy, education and information. Provides professional development, networking and career advancement opportunities for working women.

2057 ■ Three Rivers Business and Professional Women
PO Box 117
Champlin, MN 55316
Contact: Shari Pikkaraine, Pres.
Ph: (612)747-0150
E-mail: sharipikk@hotmail.com
URL: http://www.threeriversbpw.org
Descr: Represents the interests of business and professional women. Elevates the standards for women in business and professional settings. Promotes equity for all women in the workplace through advocacy, education and information. Provides professional development, networking and career advancement opportunities for working women.

2058 ■ Twin Cities Small Business Development Center
University of St. Thomas
Opus College of Business
Schulze Hall 103
46 S 11th St.
Minneapolis, MN 55403
Contact: Michael Ryan, Dir.
Ph: (651)962-4500
Fax: (651)962-4508
E-mail: mpryan@stthomas.edu
URL: http://www.stthomas.edu/business/centers/sbdc
Descr: Represents and promotes the small business sector. Provides management assistance to current and prospective small business owners. Helps to improve management skills and expand the products and services of members.

Mississippi

2059 ■ American Society of Appraisers, Mississippi Chapter
PO Box 12814
Jackson, MS 39236-2814
Contact: Guy Blankinship, Pres.
Ph: (601)829-3949
Fax: (601)829-3949
E-mail: n9863e@aol.com
URL: http://www.appraisers.org/mississippi
Descr: Serves as a professional appraisal educator, testing and accrediting society. Sponsors mandatory recertification program for all members. Offers consumer information service to the public.

2060 ■ Business and Professional Women, Mississippi
848 Viney Ridge Rd.
Clarksdale, MS 38614
Contact: Linda Humber, Pres.
Ph: (662)624-3028
Fax: (662)624-3029
E-mail: ccboard@gmi.net
URL: http://www.bpwms.biz
Descr: Represents the interests of business and professional women. Elevates the standards for

women in business and professional settings. Promotes equity for all women in the workplace through advocacy, education and information. Provides professional development, networking and career advancement opportunities for working women.

2061 ■ Concerned Taxpayers of Mississippi
PO Box 700
Magee, MS 39111
Ph: (601)849-2210

2062 ■ East Central Community College Small Business Development Center
52 E 9th St.
Decatur, MS 39327
Contact: Ronald B. Westbrook, Dir.
Ph: (601)635-6297
Fax: (601)635-4031
E-mail: rwestbrook@eccc.edu
URL: http://www.mssbdc.org/center.aspx?center=47026&subloc=0
Descr: Represents and promotes the small business sector. Provides management assistance to current and prospective small business owners. Helps to improve management skills and expand the products and services of members.

2063 ■ Jackson State University Small Business Development Center
Box 500
Jackson, MS 39204
Contact: Mr. Henry Thomas, Dir.
Ph: (601)979-2795
Fax: (601)914-0833
E-mail: henry.thomas@jsums.edu
URL: http://www.jsums.edu/business/sbdc
Descr: Represents and promotes the small business sector. Provides management assistance to current and prospective small business owners. Helps to improve management skills and expand the products and services of members.

2064 ■ Jones County Junior College Small Business Development Center
900 S Court St.
Ellisville, MS 39437
Contact: Greg Butler, Dir.
Ph: (601)477-4165
Fax: (601)477-4166
E-mail: sbdc@jcjc.edu
URL: http://www.jcjc.edu/depts/sbdc/index.htm
Descr: Represents and promotes the small business sector. Provides management assistance to current and prospective small business owners. Helps to improve management skills and expand the products and services of members.

2065 ■ Mississippi Chapter of the Financial Planning Association
205 E Main St.
Clinton, MS 39056
Contact: Danny Chancellor, Pres.
Ph: (601)925-8099
E-mail: dannyc@air2lan.net
URL: http://www.fpanet.org/chapters/centralms
Descr: Offers educational and professional enhancement programs and forums for all Financial Planning Professionals. Fosters stimulating and cooperative environment for its diverse membership of financial planning professionals.

2066 ■ Mississippi Chapter of the International Association of Assessing Officers
PO Box 1488
Grenada, MS 38902
Contact: Sherrie Greeer, Pres.
Ph: (662)226-1741
URL: http://www.mstax.org/msiaao
Descr: Represents state and local officials concerned with valuation of property for ad valorem property tax purposes. Works to improve standards and conduct research on tax assessment. Promotes innovation and excellence in property appraisal, assessment administration, and property tax policy

through professional development, education, research, and technical assistance.

2067 ■ Mississippi Credit Union Association
PO Box 9575
Jackson, MS 39286-9575
Contact: Charles Elliott, Pres.
Ph: (601)981-4552
Free: 800-748-8627
Fax: (601)981-4564
URL: http://www.mcus.com
Descr: Seeks to perfect credit union laws; aids in the development of new credit union services, including new payment systems techniques; assists in the training of credit union officials and employees. **Pub:** *Systems Resource Center Bulletins.*

2068 ■ Mississippi Small Business Development Center at Delta State University
PO Box 3235
Cleveland, MS 38733
Contact: Christie D. Sledge, Dir.
Ph: (662)846-4236
E-mail: csledge@deltastate.edu
URL: http://www.deltastate.edu/pages/294.asp
Descr: Represents and promotes the small business sector. Provides management assistance to current and prospective small business owners. Helps to improve management skills and expand the products and services of members.

2069 ■ Mississippi Society of Enrolled Agents
PO Box 63
Pontotoc, MS 38863
Contact: Michael T. Scott
Ph: (662)489-4828
Fax: (601)489-4829
E-mail: mscott@hrblock.com
Descr: Aims to improve the knowledge, skills and professionalism of members in all areas of taxation. Enhances the role of enrolled agents among government agencies, other professions and the public at large. Advocates for taxpayer rights and protects members' interests.

2070 ■ Mississippi State University Small Business Development Center (MSU SBDC)
PO Box 5288
Mississippi State, MS 39762
Contact: Sonny Fisher, Dir.
Ph: (662)325-8684
Fax: (662)325-4016
E-mail: sfisher@cobilan.msstate.edu
URL: http://www.cbi.msstate.edu/sbdc
Descr: Represents and promotes the small business sector. Provides management assistance to current and prospective small business owners. Helps to improve management skills and expand the products and services of members.

2071 ■ NAIFA-Corinth
PO Box 807
Corinth, MS 38835
Ph: (662)286-6329
Fax: (662)287-6358
E-mail: joe.garrett@sfbcic.com
Descr: Represents the interest of insurance and financial advisors. Advocates for a positive legislative and regulatory environment. Enhances business and professional skills of members.

2072 ■ NAIFA-North Mississippi
PO Box 803
Southaven, MS 38671
Ph: (662)342-6566
Fax: (662)342-0279
E-mail: bmedcalf@bellsouth.net
Descr: Represents the interests of insurance and financial advisors. Advocates for a positive legislative and regulatory environment. Enhances business and professional skills of members.

2073 ■ University of Mississippi Small Business Development Center (UMSBDC)
PO Box 1848
University, MS 38677

Contact: Don Fischer, Dir.
Ph: (662)915-1291
Free: 800-725-7232
Fax: (662)915-5650
E-mail: umsbdc@olemiss.edu
URL: http://www.olemiss.edu/depts/umsbdc
Descr: Represents and promotes the small business sector. Provides management assistance to current and prospective small business owners. Helps to improve management skills and expand the products and services of members.

Missouri

2074 ■ American Society of Appraisers, St. Louis Chapter
Health Capital Consultants, LLC
9666 Olive Blvd., Ste. 375
St. Louis, MO 63132-3025
Contact: Robert James Cimasi, Pres.
Ph: (314)994-7641
Fax: (314)991-3435
E-mail: rcimasi@healthcapital.com
URL: http://old.appraisers.org/st_louis
Descr: Serves as a professional appraisal educator, testing and accrediting society. Sponsors mandatory recertification program for all members. Offers consumer information service to the public.

2075 ■ International Association of Assessing Officers, Missouri
St. Louis City Assessor's Office
4 Willmore Rd.
St. Louis, MO 63109
Contact: Waynetta Alderson PPS, Rep.
Ph: (314)622-4696
Fax: (314)622-4695
E-mail: aldersonwm@stlouiscity.com
Descr: Represents state and local officials concerned with valuation of property for ad valorem property tax purposes. Works to improve standards and conduct research on tax assessment. Promotes innovation and excellence in property appraisal, assessment administration, and property tax policy through professional development, education, research, and technical assistance.

2076 ■ Kansas City Regional Chapter of the International Association of Assessing Officers (KCIAAO)
Johnson County Appraiser's Office
415 E 12th St., No. 1M
Kansas City, MO 64106
Contact: Curtis Koons, Pres.
Ph: (816)881-3239
E-mail: ckoons@jacksongov.org
URL: http://www.kciaao.org
Descr: Represents state and local officials concerned with valuation of property for ad valorem property tax purposes. Works to improve standards and conduct research on tax assessment. Promotes innovation and excellence in property appraisal, assessment administration, and property tax policy through professional development, education, research, and technical assistance. **Pub:** *The Journal* (quarterly).

2077 ■ Maryville Business and Professional Women
PO Box 453
Maryville, MO 64468
Contact: Mary E. Theodore, Dir.
E-mail: maryvillebpw@maryvillebpw.org
URL: http://www.maryvillebpw.org
Descr: Represents the interests of business and professional women. Elevates the standards for women in business and professional settings. Promotes equity for all women in the workplace through advocacy, education and information. Provides professional development, networking and career advancement opportunities for working women.

2078 ■ Missouri AIFA (MAIFA)
PO Box 1729
Jefferson City, MO 65102

Contact: Harry S. Truman, Pres.
Ph: (573)634-5202
Free: 888-634-5202
Fax: (573)634-5954
E-mail: lsmith@maifa.com
URL: http://www.maifa.com
Descr: Represents the interests of insurance and financial advisors. Advocates for a positive legislative and regulatory environment. Enhances business and professional skills of members.

2079 ■ Missouri Business and Professional Women
PO Box 1517
Lebanon, MO 65536
Contact: Sharon Lee Mangan, Pres.
E-mail: bpwmo@yahoo.com
URL: http://bpwmo.org
Descr: Represents the interests of business and professional women. Elevates the standards for women in business and professional settings. Promotes equity for all women in the workplace through advocacy, education and information. Provides professional development, networking and career advancement opportunities for working women.

2080 ■ Missouri Credit Union Association (MCUA)
2055 Craigshire Dr.
St. Louis, MO 63146-4009
Contact: Ms. Amy McLard, VP, Public/Legislative Affairs
Ph: (314)542-0555
Free: 800-392-3074
Fax: (314)542-1312
E-mail: contact@mcua.org
URL: http://www.mcua.org
Descr: Represents member credit unions and credit union members in Missouri. **Fnd:** 1929. **Mem:** 174. **Pub:** *CourierNet* (weekly); *Missouri Courier* (quarterly); Annual Report (annual).

2081 ■ Missouri Small Business Development Centers - Chillicothe
715 Washington St.
Chillicothe, MO 64601
Contact: Steve Holt, Dir.
Ph: (660)646-6920
Fax: (660)646-6811
E-mail: sbdchill@greenhills.net
URL: http://www.nwmissouri.edu/sbdc
Descr: Represents and promotes the small business sector. Provides management assistance to current and prospective small business owners. Helps to improve management skills and expand the products and services of members.

2082 ■ Missouri Small Business Development Centers - Northwest Region
423 N Market St.
Maryville, MO 64468
Contact: Frank Veeman, Dir.
Ph: (660)562-1701
Fax: (660)582-3071
E-mail: fveeman@nwmissouri.edu
URL: http://www.nwmissouri.edu/sbdc
Descr: Represents and promotes the small business sector. Provides management assistance to current and prospective small business owners. Helps to improve management skills and expand the products and services of members.

2083 ■ Missouri Small Business Development Centers - St. Joseph
3003 Frederick Ave.
St. Joseph, MO 64506
Contact: Rebecca Evans, Dir.
Ph: (816)232-4461
Fax: (816)364-4873
E-mail: evanssbdc@saintjoseph.com
URL: http://www.nwmissouri.edu/sbdc
Descr: Represents and promotes the small business sector. Provides management assistance to current and prospective small business owners. Helps to

improve management skills and expand the products and services of members.

2084 ■ Missouri Society of Enrolled Agents (MoSEA)
4243 NE Lakewood Way, Ste. 101
Lee's Summit, MO 64064
Contact: William A. Sunderland, Pres.
Ph: (816)350-9800
Fax: (816)795-8805
E-mail: bill@wmsunderlandcpa.com
URL: http://www.mosea.org
Descr: Aims to improve the knowledge, skills and professionalism of members in all areas of taxation. Enhances the role of enrolled agents among government agencies, other professions and the public at large. Advocates for taxpayer rights and protects members' interests.

2085 ■ Missouri State University Small Business and Technology Development Center
901 S National Ave.
Springfield, MO 65897
Contact: Rayanna Anderson, Dir.
Ph: (417)836-5685
Fax: (417)836-7666
URL: http://sbtdc.missouristate.edu
Descr: Represents and promotes the small business sector. Provides management assistance to current and prospective small business owners. Helps to improve management skills and expand the products and services of members.

2086 ■ North American Securities Administrators Association, Missouri
600 W Main St.
Jefferson City, MO 65102
Contact: Matt Kitzi
Ph: (573)751-4136
Fax: (573)526-3124
Descr: Represents the interests of the state, provincial and territorial securities administrators in the U.S.

2087 ■ North Central Business and Professional Women's Organization
PO Box 409
Grain Valley, MO 64029
Contact: CJ Johnson, Pres.
E-mail: cjadair@sbcglobal.net
URL: http://www.ncbpw.org
Descr: Represents the interests of business and professional women. Elevates the standards for women in business and professional settings. Promotes equity for all women in the workplace through advocacy, education and information. Provides professional development, networking and career advancement opportunities for working women.

2088 ■ Small Business Development Center - Southeast Missouri State University
1 University Plz.
MS 0110
Cape Girardeau, MO 63701
Contact: Bill Vickery
Ph: (573)986-6084
E-mail: wrvickery@semo.edu
URL: http://www2.semo.edu/sesbdc/homepage.html
Descr: Represents and promotes the small business sector. Provides management assistance to current and prospective small business owners. Helps to improve management skills and expand the products and services of members.

2089 ■ Small Business and Technology Development Center at Missouri Southern State University
Plaster Hall
3950 Newman Rd.
Joplin, MO 64801
Contact: Jim Krudwig, Dir.
Ph: (417)625-3128
Fax: (417)625-9782
E-mail: sbdc@mssu.edu
URL: http://www.mssutraining.com

Descr: Represents and promotes the small business sector. Provides management assistance to current and prospective small business owners. Helps to improve management skills and expand the products and services of members.

2090 ■ SOCAP International - St. Louis Gateway Chapter
1700 Gilsinn Ln.
Fenton, MO 63026
Contact: Paul Langhorst, Pres.
Ph: (636)660-8026
Descr: Promotes customer care and customer management as a competitive advantage in business. Provides educational tools and professional resources to help members drive business transformation within their companies.

2091 ■ Springfield AIFA
4721 S Stewart
Springfield, MO 65804
Contact: Brian Dixon, Pres.
Ph: (417)886-8606
Fax: (417)886-3685
E-mail: jean@clubmanagementservices.com
URL: http://www.naifanet.com/springfield
Descr: Represents the interests of insurance and financial advisors. Advocates for a positive legislative and regulatory environment. Enhances business and professional skills of members.

2092 ■ Truman State University's Small Business Development Center
100 E Normal Ave.
Kirksville, MO 63501
Contact: Glen Giboney, Dir.
Ph: (660)785-4307
Fax: (660)785-4357
E-mail: sbdc@truman.edu
URL: http://sbdc.truman.edu
Descr: Represents and promotes the small business sector. Provides management assistance to current and prospective small business owners. Helps to improve management skills and expand the products and services of members.

2093 ■ University of Central Missouri Small Business and Technology Development Center
Dockery Ste. 102
Warrensburg, MO 64093
Contact: Don Davis
Ph: (660)543-4402
Fax: (660)543-8159
E-mail: sbtdc@ucmo.edu
URL: http://www.ucmo.edu/sbtdc
Descr: Represents and promotes the small business sector. Provides management assistance to current and prospective small business owners. Helps to improve management skills and expand the products and services of members.

2094 ■ University of Missouri - Kansas City Small Business and Technology Development Center
4747 Troost Ave., Ste. 104A
Kansas City, MO 64110
Contact: Carmen DeHart, Dir.
Ph: (816)235-6063
Fax: (816)235-2947
E-mail: umkcsbtdc@umkc.edu
URL: http://www.entrepreneurship.bloch.umkc.edu/sbtdc
Descr: Represents and promotes the small business sector. Provides management assistance to current and prospective small business owners. Helps to improve management skills and expand the products and services of members.

Montana

2095 ■ Billings Small Business Development Center
Big Sky Economic Development Authority
222 N 32nd St.
Billings, MT 59101

Contact: Rebecca Helvik, Business Advisor
Ph: (406)254-6014
Fax: (406)256-6877
E-mail: helvik@bigskyeda.org
URL: http://bigskyeda-edc.org/small-business-development.php
Descr: Represents and promotes the small business sector. Provides management assistance to current and prospective small business owners. Helps to improve management skills and expand the products and services of members.

2096 ■ Bozeman Business and Professional Women
PO Box 644
Bozeman, MT 59771
Contact: Lindsey Van Hemelryck, Pres.
Ph: (406)351-1174
E-mail: lindsey@altc.biz
URL: http://www.bozemanbpw.org
Descr: Represents the interests of business and professional women. Elevates the standards for women in business and professional settings. Promotes equity for all women in the workplace through advocacy, education and information. Provides professional development, networking and career advancement opportunities for working women.

2097 ■ Bozeman Small Business Development Center
Northern Rocky Mountain RC&D
502 S 19th Ave., Ste. 105
Bozeman, MT 59718
Contact: Gary Slane, Business Advisor
Ph: (406)582-5700
Fax: (406)582-5855
E-mail: sbdc@nrmrcd.org
URL: http://www.nrmrcd.org/business_assistance.htm
Descr: Represents and promotes the small business sector. Provides management assistance to current and prospective small business owners. Helps to improve management skills and expand the products and services of members.

2098 ■ Business and Professional Women, Flathead Valley
PO Box 2973
Bigfork, MT 59911
Contact: Irene Paine, Pres.
Ph: (406)837-2437
Fax: (406)837-2426
E-mail: irenepaine@gmail.com
URL: http://www.bpwflatheadvalley.com
Descr: Represents the interests of business and professional women. Elevates the standards for women in business and professional settings. Promotes equity for all women in the workplace through advocacy, education and information. Provides professional development, networking and career advancement opportunities for working women.

2099 ■ Butte Small Business Development Center
Headwaters RC&D Area, Inc.
305 W Mercury, Ste. 211
Butte, MT 59701
Contact: Deanna Johnson, Business Advisor
Ph: (406)782-7333
Fax: (406)782-2990
E-mail: djohnson@bigskyhsd.com
URL: http://www.headwatersrcd.org/sbdc.html
Descr: Represents and promotes the small business sector. Provides management assistance to current and prospective small business owners. Helps to improve management skills and expand the products and services of members.

2100 ■ Cascade County Business and Professional Women (CCBPW)
1111 14th St. S, Ste. B
Great Falls, MT 59405
Contact: Tracy Houck, Pres.
Ph: (406)454-0222

Fax: (406)454-0388
E-mail: cascadebpw@yahoo.com
URL: http://www.cascadebpw.org
Descr: Represents the interests of business and professional women. Elevates the standards for women in business and professional settings. Promotes equity for all women in the workplace through advocacy, education and information. Provides professional development, networking and career advancement opportunities for working women.

2101 ■ Great Falls Small Business Development Center
PO Box 949
Great Falls, MT 59403
Contact: Rebecca Engum, Business Advisor
Ph: (406)453-8834
Fax: (406)454-2995
E-mail: rengum@gfdevelopment.org
URL: http://sbdc.mt.gov
Descr: Represents and promotes the small business sector. Provides management assistance to current and prospective small business owners. Helps to improve management skills and expand the products and services of members.

2102 ■ Havre Small Business Development Center
PO Box 170
Havre, MT 59501
Contact: Joe LaPlante
Ph: (406)265-4945
Fax: (406)265-5602
E-mail: jlaplante@bearpaw.org
URL: http://www.bearpaw.org/services.html#sbdc
Descr: Represents and promotes the small business sector. Provides management assistance to current and prospective small business owners. Helps to improve management skills and expand the products and services of members.

2103 ■ Helena Small Business Development Center
Montana Business Assistance Connections, Inc.
225 Cruise Ave.
Helena, MT 59601
Contact: Dan Anderson, Business Advisor
Ph: (406)447-1510
Fax: (406)447-1514
E-mail: danderson@mbac.biz
URL: http://www.mbac.biz/index.php?pr=Small_Business_Development_Center
Descr: Represents and promotes the small business sector. Provides management assistance to current and prospective small business owners. Helps to improve management skills and expand the products and services of members.

2104 ■ Kalispell Small Business Development Center
Kalispell Area Chamber of Commerce
15 Depot Park
Kalispell, MT 59901
Ph: (406)758-2802
Fax: (406)758-2805
URL: http://sbdc.mt.gov
Descr: Represents and promotes the small business sector. Provides management assistance to current and prospective small business owners. Helps to improve management skills and expand the products and services of members.

2105 ■ Missoula Business and Professional Women
3819 Stephens Ave.
Missoula, MT 59806
Contact: Caryl Wickes-Connick, Corresponding Sec.
Ph: (406)542-1307
E-mail: carylwc@blackfoot.net
URL: http://missoulabpw.org
Descr: Represents the interests of business and professional women. Elevates the standards for women in business and professional settings. Promotes equity for all women in the workplace through advocacy, education and information.

Provides professional development, networking and career advancement opportunities for working women.

2106 ■ Missoula Small Business Development Center
Montana Community Development Corporation
110 E Broadway, 2nd Fl.
Missoula, MT 59802
Contact: Lynn Dankowski, Co-Business Advisor
Ph: (406)728-9234
Fax: (406)542-6671
E-mail: lynnd@mtcdc.org
URL: http://sbdc.mt.gov/offices.asp
Descr: Represents and promotes the small business sector. Provides management assistance to current and prospective small business owners. Helps to improve management skills and expand the products and services of members.

2107 ■ Montana AIFA (MtAIFA)
824 Holter St.
Helena, MT 59601
Contact: Anita A. Newlin, Exec. Dir.
Ph: (406)443-6300
Fax: (406)443-2090
E-mail: peterdan@sullivanfinancialgroup.com
URL: http://209.61.156.20/main-pub.cfm?usr=290000
Descr: Represents the interests of insurance and financial advisors. Advocates for a positive legislative and regulatory environment. Enhances business and professional skills of members.

2108 ■ Montana Business and Professional Women
1123 Woodland Dr.
Bozeman, MT 59718
Contact: Pat Simmons, Pres.
Ph: (406)585-0101
E-mail: psimmons@imt.net
URL: http://www.montanabpw.org
Descr: Represents the interests of business and professional women. Elevates the standards for women in business and professional settings. Promotes equity for all women in the workplace through advocacy, education and information. Provides professional development, networking and career advancement opportunities for working women.

2109 ■ Montana Taxpayers Association
PO Box 4909
Helena, MT 59604
Contact: Pam Hyatt, Office Mgr.
Ph: (406)442-2130
Fax: (406)422-1230
E-mail: phyatt@montax.org
URL: http://www.montax.org

2110 ■ North American Securities Administrators Association, Montana
840 Helena Ave.
Helena, MT 59604
Contact: Lynne Egan
Ph: (406)444-2040
Fax: (406)444-5558
Descr: Represents the interests of the state, provincial and territorial securities administrators in the U.S.

2111 ■ Southeastern Montana Small Business Development Center
PO Box 1935
Colstrip, MT 59323
Contact: Blayr Barnard, Business Advisor
Ph: (406)748-2990
Fax: (406)748-2900
E-mail: sbdc@bhwi.net
URL: http://www.semdc.org/sbdc.htm
Descr: Represents and promotes the small business sector. Provides management assistance to current and prospective small business owners. Helps to

improve management skills and expand the products and services of members.

2112 ■ Southwestern Montana AIFA
PO Box 3982
Butte, MT 59702
Contact: Lori L. Renz, Sec.
Ph: (406)782-4253
Fax: (406)782-4254
E-mail: steve@danielfinancial.com
Descr: Represents the interests of insurance and financial advisors. Advocates for a positive legislative and regulatory environment. Enhances business and professional skills of members.

2113 ■ Wolf Point Small Business Development Center
233 Cascade St.
Wolf Point, MT 59201
Contact: Lorene Hintz, Business Advisor
Ph: (406)653-2590
Fax: (406)653-1840
E-mail: sbdc@gndc.org
URL: http://www.gndc.org/sbdc.htm
Descr: Represents and promotes the small business sector. Provides management assistance to current and prospective small business owners. Helps to improve management skills and expand the products and services of members.

Nebraska

2114 ■ American Society of Appraisers, Nebraska Chapter
Best Business Appraisals LLC
14344 Y St., Ste. 102
Omaha, NE 68137-2805
Contact: Chris E. Best
Ph: (402)895-6222
Fax: (402)896-0845
E-mail: chrisbest@bestbusinessappraisals.com
URL: http://old.appraisers.org/nebraska
Descr: Serves as a professional appraisal educator, testing and accrediting society. Sponsors mandatory recertification program for all members. Offers consumer information service to the public.

2115 ■ International Association of Assessing Officers, Nebraska
PO Box 1270
Kearney, NE 68848
Contact: Josiah Woodward, Rep.
Ph: (308)236-1205
Fax: (308)233-3713
E-mail: assessor@kearney.net
Descr: Represents state and local officials concerned with valuation of property for ad valorem property tax purposes. Works to improve standards and conduct research on tax assessment. Promotes innovation and excellence in property appraisal, assessment administration, and property tax policy through professional development, education, research, and technical assistance.

2116 ■ NAIFA-Blue Valley
PO Box 216
Beatrice, NE 68310-0216
Contact: Steve Spilker, Pres.
Ph: (402)228-4232
Fax: (402)228-4233
E-mail: steve03@nefb.com
URL: http://naifanet.com/bluevalley
Descr: Represents the interests of insurance and financial advisors. Advocates for a positive legislative and regulatory environment. Enhances business and professional skills of members.

2117 ■ NAIFA-Grand Island
PO Box 315
Grand Island, NE 68802
Contact: Greg Sanchez, VP
Ph: (308)382-8032
E-mail: greg.sanchez.ggvv@statefarm.com
URL: http://www.naifanet.com/grandisland
Descr: Represents the interests of insurance and financial advisors. Advocates for a positive legisla-

tive and regulatory environment. Enhances business and professional skills of members.

2118 ■ NAIFA-Hastings
2727 W 2nd St., Ste. 217
Hastings, NE 68901
Contact: Kenneth R. Pittz, Pres.
Ph: (402)463-2851
Fax: (402)463-2863
E-mail: jyost@isimail.com
Descr: Represents the interests of insurance and financial advisors. Advocates for a positive legislative and regulatory environment. Enhances business and professional skills of members.

2119 ■ NAIFA-Lincoln
PO Box 23085
Lincoln, NE 68542
Contact: Gregory Berstler, Pres.
Ph: (402)483-6848
Fax: (402)483-6848
E-mail: marge@naifa-lincoln.org
URL: http://209.61.156.20/main-pub.cfm?usr=303480
Descr: Represents the interests of insurance and financial advisors. Advocates for a positive legislative and regulatory environment. Enhances business and professional skills of members.

2120 ■ NAIFA-Northeast Nebraska
PO Box 544
Norfolk, NE 68702-0544
Contact: Casey Knake, Membership Chair
Ph: (402)379-1811
E-mail: cknake@heritagefin.net
URL: http://www.naifanet.com/northeastnebraska
Descr: Represents the interests of insurance and financial advisors. Advocates for a positive legislative and regulatory environment. Enhances business and professional skills of members.

2121 ■ NAIFA-Omaha
PO Box 24133
Omaha, NE 68124
Contact: Preston Speece, Pres.
Ph: (402)397-0280
Fax: (402)397-0283
E-mail: naifa@cam-omaha.com
URL: http://www.naifanet.com/omaha
Descr: Represents the interests of insurance and financial advisors. Advocates for a positive legislative and regulatory environment. Enhances business and professional skills of members.

2122 ■ Nebraska Bankers Association (NBA)
PO Box 80008
Lincoln, NE 68501
Contact: George Beattie, Pres.
Ph: (402)474-1555
Fax: (402)474-2946
E-mail: nba@nebankers.org
URL: http://www.nebankers.org
Descr: Works constantly to monitor the banking scene, watchful for new ideas and approaches to help financial institutions respond to an ever-changing environment. Strives to anticipate and respond quickly to events that impact its members more than 16,000 men and women who work in financial institutions. Priorities include legislative representation, education, industry promotion and public relations, cost-saving products and services, and an array of other services designed to meet the needs of banks and savings and loan institutions.
Fnd: 1890. **Mem:** 369. **Pub:** *Update* (weekly).

2123 ■ Nebraska Business and Professional Women
14115 Hartman Ave.
Omaha, NE 68164
Contact: Mary Fraser Meints, Pres.
Ph: (402)496-4683
E-mail: president@nebpw.com
URL: http://nebpw.com
Descr: Represents the interests of business and professional women. Elevates the standards for women in business and professional settings.

Promotes equity for all women in the workplace through advocacy, education and information. Provides professional development, networking and career advancement opportunities for working women.

2124 ■ Nebraska Chapter of the Financial Planning Association
PO Box 24133
Omaha, NE 68124
Contact: Joe Pittman, Exec. Dir.
Ph: (402)397-0280
E-mail: fpa@cam-omaha.com
URL: http://www.fpanebraska.com
Descr: Promotes the value of the financial planning process to the public. Provides professional education and networking opportunities for the financial planning community.

2125 ■ Nebraska Individual Taxpayers Association
1111 Lincoln Mall, Ste. 308
Lincoln, NE 68508
Ph: (402)476-1258
Fax: (402)476-1259

2126 ■ Nebraska Small Business Development Center
University of Nebraska at Omaha
College of Business Administration
Roskens Hall, Rm. 415
Omaha, NE 68182-0248
Contact: Robert E. Bernier, Dir.
Ph: (402)554-2521
URL: http://nbdc.unomaha.edu
Descr: Represents and promotes the small business sector. Provides management assistance to current and prospective small business owners. Helps to improve management skills and expand the products and services of members.

2127 ■ Nebraska Small Business Development Center - Chadron State College
1000 Main St.
Chadron, NE 69337
Contact: James Koehn, Dir.
Ph: (308)432-6282
E-mail: jkoehn@csc.edu
URL: http://nbdc.unomaha.edu
Descr: Represents and promotes the small business sector. Provides management assistance to current and prospective small business owners. Helps to improve management skills and expand the products and services of members.

2128 ■ Nebraska Small Business Development Center - Kearney
University of Nebraska at Kearney
West Center Bldg., Rm. 127E
1917 W 24th St.
Kearney, NE 68849-4440
Contact: Odee Ingersoll, Dir.
Ph: (308)865-8344
Fax: (308)865-8153
E-mail: ingersollo@unk.edu
URL: http://nbdc.unomaha.edu
Descr: Represents and promotes the small business sector. Provides management assistance to current and prospective small business owners. Helps to improve management skills and expand the products and services of members.

2129 ■ Nebraska Small Business Development Center - Lincoln
UNL Office of Technology Development
1320 Q St., Office 109
Lincoln, NE 68588-0467
Contact: Marisol U. Rodriguez, Dir.
Ph: (402)472-5222
Fax: (402)472-0398
E-mail: mrodriguez2@unl.edu
URL: http://nbdc.unomaha.edu
Descr: Represents and promotes the small business sector. Provides management assistance to current and prospective small business owners. Helps to

improve management skills and expand the products and services of members.

2130 ■ Nebraska Small Business Development Center - Norfolk
Lifelong Learning Center
801 E Benjamin Ave.
Norfolk, NE 68702-0469
Contact: Renee Held, Consultant
Ph: (402)564-0105
E-mail: rheld@mail.unomaha.edu
URL: http://nbdc.unomaha.edu
Descr: Represents and promotes the small business sector. Provides management assistance to current and prospective small business owners. Helps to improve management skills and expand the products and services of members.

2131 ■ Nebraska Small Business Development Center - North Platte
300 E 3rd St., Rm. 275
North Platte, NE 69101
Contact: Jason Tuller, Dir.
Ph: (308)534-5115
Fax: (308)534-5117
E-mail: jtuller@mail.unomaha.edu
URL: http://nbdc.unomaha.edu
Descr: Represents and promotes the small business sector. Provides management assistance to current and prospective small business owners. Helps to improve management skills and expand the products and services of members.

2132 ■ Nebraska Small Business Development Center - Scottsbluff
Panhandle Research and Extension Center
4502 Ave. I
Scottsbluff, NE 69361
Contact: Ingrid Battershell, Dir.
Ph: (308)635-7513
E-mail: ibattershell@mail.unomaha.edu
URL: http://nbdc.unomaha.edu
Descr: Represents and promotes the small business sector. Provides management assistance to current and prospective small business owners. Helps to improve management skills and expand the products and services of members.

2133 ■ Nebraska Small Business Development Center - Wayne
Wayne State College
Gardner Hall
1111 Main St.
Wayne, NE 68787
Contact: Loren Kucera, Dir.
Ph: (402)375-7575
E-mail: lokucer1@wsc.edu
URL: http://nbdc.unomaha.edu
Descr: Represents and promotes the small business sector. Provides management assistance to current and prospective small business owners. Helps to improve management skills and expand the products and services of members.

2134 ■ Nebraska Taxpayers Association
PO Box 22042
Lincoln, NE 68542
Ph: (402)393-7840
Fax: (402)390-0465
E-mail: netaxman@radiks.net

2135 ■ North American Securities Administrators Association, Nebraska
PO Box 95006
Lincoln, NE 68509
Contact: Jack Herstein, Asst. Dir.
Ph: (402)471-3445
Descr: Represents the interests of the state, provincial and territorial securities administrators in the U.S.

2136 ■ Nova Business and Professional Women Organization
US Bank
233 S 13th St.
Lincoln, NE 68508
Contact: Elizabeth Wood

Ph: (402)423-4343
E-mail: ewood@hbecpa.com
URL: http://www.geocities.com/nova_bpw
Descr: Represents the interests of business and professional women. Elevates the standards for women in business and professional settings. Promotes equity for all women in the workplace through advocacy, education and information. Provides professional development, networking and career advancement opportunities for working women.

2137 ■ SOCAP International - Heartland Chapter
5 ConAgra Dr., No. 5-105
Omaha, NE 68102
Contact: Cindy Fritton, Pres.
Ph: (402)595-7171
Descr: Promotes customer care and customer management as a competitive advantage in business. Provides educational tools and professional resources to help members drive business transformation within their companies.

Nevada

2138 ■ Carson City Nevada Small Business Development Center
1900 S Carson St., No. 100
Carson City, NV 89701-4514
Ph: (775)882-1565
Fax: (775)882-4179
URL: http://www.nsbdc.org
Descr: Represents and promotes the small business sector. Provides management assistance to current and prospective small business owners. Helps to improve management skills and expand the products and services of members.

2139 ■ Carson Valley Nevada Small Business Development Center
1477 Hwy. 395
Gardnerville, NV 89410
Ph: (775)782-8144
Fax: (775)782-1025
URL: http://www.nsbdc.org
Descr: Represents and promotes the small business sector. Provides management assistance to current and prospective small business owners. Helps to improve management skills and expand the products and services of members.

2140 ■ Churchill County Nevada Small Business Development Center
PO Box 1236
Fallon, NV 89407
Ph: (775)623-1064
Fax: (775)623-1664
E-mail: sbdc@ceda-nv.org
URL: http://www.nsbdc.org
Descr: Represents and promotes the small business sector. Provides management assistance to current and prospective small business owners. Helps to improve management skills and expand the products and services of members.

2141 ■ Elko Nevada Small Business Development Center
Great Basin College
723 Railroad St.
Elko, NV 89801
Contact: Judy Emerson, Management Consultant
Ph: (775)753-2245
Fax: (775)753-2242
E-mail: judye@gwmail.gbcnv.edu
URL: http://www.nsbdc.org
Descr: Represents and promotes the small business sector. Provides management assistance to current and prospective small business owners. Helps to improve management skills and expand the products and services of members.

2142 ■ Ely Nevada Small Business Development Center
1320 E Alultman St.
Ely, NV 89301

Contact: Clint Koble, Business Advisor
Ph: (775)289-8519
Free: 866-404-5204
Fax: (775)289-8214
E-mail: clint@rndcnv.org
URL: http://www.nsbdc.org
Descr: Represents and promotes the small business sector. Provides management assistance to current and prospective small business owners. Helps to improve management skills and expand the products and services of members.

2143 ■ Financial Planning Association of Southern Nevada Chapter
Wallstreet Financial Services
3431 E Sunset Rd., C-302
Las Vegas, NV 89120
Contact: Staci Scharadin CFP, Pres.
Ph: (702)451-8099
Fax: (702)451-8109
E-mail: sscharadin@rr.firstallied.com
URL: http://www.fpanv.org
Descr: Promotes the value of the financial planning process to the public. Provides professional education and networking opportunities for the financial planning community.

2144 ■ Henderson Nevada Small Business Development Center
112 Water St., Ste. 108
Henderson, NV 89015
Ph: (702)992-7208
Fax: (702)992-7245
URL: http://www.nsbdc.org
Descr: Represents and promotes the small business sector. Provides management assistance to current and prospective small business owners. Helps to improve management skills and expand the products and services of members.

2145 ■ International Association of Assessing Officers, Nevada
PO Box 551401
Las Vegas, NV 89155
Contact: Carol Burgeson, Rep.
Ph: (702)455-3891
E-mail: cls@co.clark.nv.us
Descr: Represents state and local officials concerned with valuation of property for ad valorem property tax purposes. Works to improve standards and conduct research on tax assessment. Promotes innovation and excellence in property appraisal, assessment administration, and property tax policy through professional development, education, research, and technical assistance.

2146 ■ Laughlin Nevada Small Business Development Center
1585 S Casino Dr.
Laughlin, NV 89029
Ph: (702)298-2214
Fax: (702)298-5708
URL: http://www.nsbdc.org
Descr: Represents and promotes the small business sector. Provides management assistance to current and prospective small business owners. Helps to improve management skills and expand the products and services of members.

2147 ■ Nevada Society of Enrolled Agents
2300 S Jones Blvd.
Las Vegas, NV 89146
Contact: Juanita Roper EA
Ph: (702)733-8438
Fax: (702)733-9366
E-mail: jwwvm@aol.com
Descr: Promotes ethical representation of the financial position of taxpayers before government agencies.

2148 ■ North American Securities Administrators Association, Nevada
555 E Washington Ave., 5th Fl., Ste. 5200
Las Vegas, NV 89101
Contact: Gary Abraham, Admin.

Ph: (702)486-2440
Fax: (702)486-2452
Descr: Represents the interests of the state, provincial and territorial securities administrators in the U.S.

2149 ■ Pahrump Nevada Small Business Development Center
Rural Nevada Development Corporation
NSB Bldg., 2nd Fl.
1301 S Hwy. 160
Pahrump, NV 89048
Contact: Allan Parker, Business Consultant
Ph: (775)751-1947
Fax: (775)751-1933
E-mail: alparker@rndcnv.org
URL: http://www.nsbdc.org
Descr: Represents and promotes the small business sector. Provides management assistance to current and prospective small business owners. Helps to improve management skills and expand the products and services of members.

2150 ■ Winnemucca Nevada Small Business Development Center
90 W Fourth St.
Winnemucca, NV 89445
Contact: Bill Sims
Ph: (775)623-1064
Fax: (775)623-1664
E-mail: bills@unr.edu
URL: http://www.nsbdc.org
Descr: Represents and promotes the small business sector. Provides management assistance to current and prospective small business owners. Helps to improve management skills and expand the products and services of members.

New Hampshire

2151 ■ Alliance of Derry Taxpayers
PO Box 1323
Derry, NH 03038
Contact: Sandy Shapiro, Chair
E-mail: info@derrytax.org
URL: http://www.derrytax.org

2152 ■ American Society of Appraisers, Vermont/New Hampshire Chapter
1 Wardbobe Rd.
Hanover, NH 03755-4919
Contact: Raymond G. Hogue, Pres.
Ph: (603)643-8990
Fax: (603)643-8931
E-mail: rhogue@hoguebusinessvaluations.com
URL: http://www.appraisers.org/vermont
Descr: Serves as a professional appraisal educator, testing and accrediting society. Sponsors mandatory recertification program for all members. Offers consumer information service to the public.

2153 ■ Business and Professional Women, Concord
PO Box 4171
Concord, NH 03302-4171
Contact: Lori J. Mader, Pres.
E-mail: concordbpw@comcast.net
URL: http://www.bpwconcordnh.org
Descr: Represents the interests of business and professional women. Elevates the standards for women in business and professional settings. Promotes equity for all women in the workplace through advocacy, education and information. Provides professional development, networking and career advancement opportunities for working women.

2154 ■ Business and Professional Women, Greater Londonderry
PO Box 336
Londonderry, NH 03053
Contact: Bonnie Roberts, Pres.
E-mail: broberts@amconstructionco.com
URL: http://www.bpwgreaterlondonderry.org
Descr: Represents the interests of business and professional women. Elevates the standards for

women in business and professional settings. Promotes equity for all women in the workplace through advocacy, education and information. Provides professional development, networking and career advancement opportunities for working women.

2155 ■ Coalition of New Hampshire Taxpayers
8 N Main St., Ste. 2
Concord, NH 03301
URL: http://www.cnht.org

2156 ■ Granite State Taxpayers
PO Box 10473
Bedford, NH 03110
Ph: (603)472-3421
Fax: (603)471-0435
E-mail: mail@granitestatetaxpayers.org
URL: http://www.granitestatetaxpayers.org

2157 ■ New Hampshire Association of Assessing Officials (NHAAO)
PO Box 617
Concord, NH 03302-0617
Contact: Wiliam Ingalls, Pres.
Ph: (603)472-8104
E-mail: info@nhaao.org
URL: http://www.nhaao.org
Descr: Represents state and local officials concerned with valuation of property for ad valorem property tax purposes. Works to improve standards and conduct research on tax assessment. Promotes innovation and excellence in property appraisal, assessment administration, and property tax policy through professional development, education, research, and technical assistance.

2158 ■ North American Securities Administrators Association, New Hampshire
Bureau of Securities Regulation
State House Annex, Ste. 317A, 3rd Fl.
Concord, NH 03301
Contact: Mark Connolly, Dir.
Ph: (603)271-1463
Fax: (603)271-7933
Descr: Represents the interests of the state, provincial and territorial securities administrators in the U.S.

2159 ■ Northern New England, Society of Enrolled Agents
32 Webster St.
Manchester, NH 03104
Contact: Thomas J. Wisniewski EA
Ph: (603)669-3006
Fax: (603)669-0018
E-mail: wisniewskitax@comcast.net
URL: http://www.naea.org/MemberPortal/StateAffiliates/Listing
Descr: Seeks to: foster professionalism and growth among members; be an advocate of taxpayer rights; protect the interests of members; and enhance the role of the enrolled agent among government agencies, other professions and the public at large, with an emphasis at the state and local levels.

2160 ■ Small Business Development Center - Keene
Keene State College
Mailstop 2101
Keene, NH 03435-2101
Contact: Christina Flanagan, Program Asst.
Ph: (603)358-2602
Fax: (603)358-2612
E-mail: cflanagan@keene.edu
URL: http://www.nhsbdc.org
Descr: Represents and promotes the small business sector. Provides management assistance to current and prospective small business owners. Helps to improve management skills and expand the products and services of members.

2161 ■ Small Business Development Center - Littleton
120 Main St.
Littleton, NH 03561

Ph: (603)444-1053
Fax: (603)444-5463
E-mail: nh.sbdc@unh.edu
URL: http://www.nhsbdc.org
Descr: Represents and promotes the small business sector. Provides management assistance to current and prospective small business owners. Helps to improve management skills and expand the products and services of members.

2162 ■ Small Business Development Center - Manchester
33 S Commercial St.
Manchester, NH 03101-1796
Ph: (603)624-2000
Fax: (603)647-4410
E-mail: jason.cannon@unh.edu
URL: http://www.nhsbdc.org
Descr: Represents and promotes the small business sector. Provides management assistance to current and prospective small business owners. Helps to improve management skills and expand the products and services of members.

2163 ■ Small Business Development Center - Nashua
Daniel Webster College
20 University Dr.
Nashua, NH 03060-5086
Contact: Rosemary McMillan, Program Asst.
Ph: (603)546-1551
E-mail: mcmillan_rosemary@dwc.edu
URL: http://www.nhsbdc.org
Descr: Represents and promotes the small business sector. Provides management assistance to current and prospective small business owners. Helps to improve management skills and expand the products and services of members.

2164 ■ Small Business Development Center - Seacoast
18 S Main St., Ste. 2A
Rochester, NH 03867
Contact: Krysteen Hopkins, Program Asst.
Ph: (603)330-1929
Fax: (603)330-1948
E-mail: krysteen.hopkins@unh.edu
URL: http://www.nhsbdc.org
Descr: Represents and promotes the small business sector. Provides management assistance to current and prospective small business owners. Helps to improve management skills and expand the products and services of members.

New Jersey

2165 ■ American Society of Appraisers, Northern New Jersey Chapter
Aronson & Fernandez PA
354 Eisenhower Pkwy.
Livingston, NJ 07039
Contact: Rufino Fernandez Jr., Pres.
Ph: (973)533-0080
Fax: (973)533-0920
E-mail: aronsonfernandez@verizon.net
URL: http://www.asanj.com
Descr: Serves as a professional appraisal educator, testing and accrediting society. Sponsors mandatory recertification program for all members. Offers consumer information service to the public.

2166 ■ American Society of Appraisers, Princeton Chapter
CBIZ Valuation Group
1009 Lenex Dr., Ste. 105
Lawrenceville, NJ 08648-2315
Contact: Thomas J. Amendolari, Pres.
Ph: (609)895-5318
Fax: (609)896-1849
E-mail: tamendolari@cbiz.com
Descr: Serves as a professional appraisal educator, testing and accrediting society. Sponsors mandatory

re-certification program for all members. Offers consumer information service to the public.

2167 ■ American Society of Appraisers, Southern New Jersey Chapter
101 Poor Farm Rd.
Princeton, NJ 08540
Contact: Rose R. Moroz, Pres.
Ph: (609)924-4200
Fax: (609)924-4573
E-mail: gizmo4100@aol.com
Descr: Serves as a professional appraisal educator, testing and accrediting society. Sponsors mandatory recertification program for all members. Offers consumer information service to the public.

2168 ■ Bergen Small Business Development Center
Ciarco Learning Center
355 Main St.
Hackensack, NJ 07601
Contact: Vincent A. D'Elia, Dir.
Ph: (201)489-8670
Fax: (201)489-8673
E-mail: sbdc@bergen.edu
URL: http://www.bergen.edu/pages/675.asp
Descr: Represents and promotes the small business sector. Provides management assistance to current and prospective small business owners. Helps to improve management skills and expand the products and services of members.

2169 ■ Berkeley Heights Taxpayers Association
PO Box 214
Berkeley Heights, NJ 07922
Ph: (908)464-1104

2170 ■ Business and Professional Women, East Bergen
15-12 Elmary Pl.
Fair Lawn, NJ 07410-2403
Contact: Violet Etler
Ph: (201)797-6610
E-mail: vietler@juno.com
URL: http://www.bpwnj.org
Descr: Represents the interests of business and professional women. Elevates the standards for women in business and professional settings. Promotes equity for all women in the workplace through advocacy, education and information. Provides professional development, networking and career advancement opportunities for working women.

2171 ■ Business and Professional Women, Gloucester County
1038 Walnut Ave.
Woodbury Heights, NJ 08097
Contact: Linda Worman
Ph: (856)931-5000
Fax: (856)931-6400
E-mail: linda1954@verizon.net
URL: http://www.bpwnj.org
Descr: Represents the interests of business and professional women. Elevates the standards for women in business and professional settings. Promotes equity for all women in the workplace through advocacy, education and information. Provides professional development, networking and career advancement opportunities for working women.

2172 ■ Business and Professional Women, Greater Trenton
89 Fairfield Ave., 2nd Fl.
Lawrenceville, NJ 08648
Contact: Debbi Lasky
Ph: (215)826-2904
E-mail: dlask@stonemor.com
URL: http://www.bpwnj.org
Descr: Represents the interests of business and professional women. Elevates the standards for women in business and professional settings. Promotes equity for all women in the workplace through advocacy, education and information. Provides professional development, networking and

career advancement opportunities for working women.

2173 ■ Business and Professional Women, Lincroft
114 Kingsley Way
Freehold, NJ 07728
Contact: Gwendolyn Evans
Ph: (732)224-2395
E-mail: gshrimp@aol.com
URL: http://www.bpwnj.org
Descr: Represents the interests of business and professional women. Elevates the standards for women in business and professional settings. Promotes equity for all women in the workplace through advocacy, education and information. Provides professional development, networking and career advancement opportunities for working women.

2174 ■ Business and Professional Women, Middlebrook
50 Poplar Rd.
Piscataway, NJ 08854
Contact: Shirley Myers, Pres.
Ph: (732)562-2382
URL: http://www.bpwnj.org
Descr: Represents the interests of business and professional women. Elevates the standards for women in business and professional settings. Promotes equity for all women in the workplace through advocacy, education and information. Provides professional development, networking and career advancement opportunities for working women.

2175 ■ Business and Professional Women, New Brunswick
322 Hillcrest Ave.
Somerset, NJ 08873
Contact: Marie Thompson
Ph: (732)828-4830
E-mail: mariethompson2@aol.com
URL: http://www.bpwnj.org
Descr: Represents the interests of business and professional women. Elevates the standards for women in business and professional settings. Promotes equity for all women in the workplace through advocacy, education and information. Provides professional development, networking and career advancement opportunities for working women.

2176 ■ Business and Professional Women, Southern Ocean County
259 Serpent Ln.
Manahawkin, NJ 08050
Contact: Carol Lieber, Pres.
Ph: (609)489-0564
E-mail: mopmopl@aol.com
URL: http://www.bpwnj.org
Descr: Represents the interests of business and professional women. Elevates the standards for women in business and professional settings. Promotes equity for all women in the workplace through advocacy, education and information. Provides professional development, networking and career advancement opportunities for working women.

2177 ■ Business and Professional Women, Suburban Essex
33 Rosewood Terr.
Bloomfield, NJ 07003
Contact: Lucy M. Tarangelo
Ph: (973)473-4589
E-mail: lucylopest@aol.com
URL: http://www.bpwnj.org
Descr: Represents the interests of business and professional women. Elevates the standards for women in business and professional settings. Promotes equity for all women in the workplace through advocacy, education and information. Provides professional development, networking and

career advancement opportunities for working women.

2178 ■ Centenary College Small Business Development Center
400 Jefferson St.
Hackettstown, NJ 07840
Contact: Dolores J. Stammer, Dir.
Ph: (908)852-1400
E-mail: sbdc@centenarycollege.edu
URL: http://www.centenarycollege.edu/cms/index.php?id=sbdc
Descr: Represents and promotes the small business sector. Provides management assistance to current and prospective small business owners. Helps to improve management skills and expand the products and services of members.

2179 ■ Financial Planning Association of New Jersey (FPANJ)
551 Valley Rd., No. 365
Upper Montclair, NJ 07043
Contact: Patrick J. Gilmore CFP, Pres.
Free: 877-773-7265
Fax: (973)556-1211
E-mail: info@fpanj.org
URL: http://www.fpanj.org
Descr: Promotes the value of financial planning, advances the financial planning profession, and enhances the professional development of its members.

2180 ■ Fort Lee Taxpayers Association
PO Box 167
Fort Lee, NJ 07024
Ph: (201)944-3177

2181 ■ Greater Essex AIFA
PO Box 9358
Elizabeth, NJ 07202
Contact: Frank J. Petrulla, Pres.
Ph: (908)289-5259
Fax: (908)289-5259
E-mail: nalu1@voicenet.com
Descr: Represents the interests of insurance and financial advisors. Advocates for a positive legislative and regulatory environment. Enhances business and professional skills of members.

2182 ■ International Association of Assessing Officers, New Jersey
820 Mercer St.
Cherry Hill, NJ 08002
Contact: Thomas G. Glock, Rep.
Ph: (856)488-7899
Fax: (856)424-6278
E-mail: tglock@chtownship.com
Descr: Represents state and local officials concerned with valuation of property for ad valorem property tax purposes. Works to improve standards and conduct research on tax assessment. Promotes innovation and excellence in property appraisal, assessment administration, and property tax policy through professional development, education, research, and technical assistance.

2183 ■ Lyndhurst Taxpayers Association
PO Box 224
Lyndhurst, NJ 07071
Ph: (201)438-1654

2184 ■ Middlesex-Somerset AIFA
New York Life
399 Thornall St.
Edison, NJ 08837
Contact: Irene Stolte, Pres.-Elect
Ph: (732)642-1313
Fax: (732)744-0644
E-mail: istolte@ft.newyorklife.com
URL: http://www.naifanet.com/middlesexsomerset
Descr: Represents the interests of insurance and financial advisors. Advocates for a positive legisla-

tive and regulatory environment. Enhances business and professional skills of members.

2185 ■ Monmouth/Ocean Small Business Development Center
765 Newman Springs Rd.
Lincroft, NJ 07738
Contact: Bill Nunnally, Dir.
Ph: (732)842-8685
URL: http://ux.brookdalecc.edu/staff/sbdc/Default/Default.htm
Descr: Represents and promotes the small business sector. Provides management assistance to current and prospective small business owners. Helps to improve management skills and expand the products and services of members.

2186 ■ NAIFA-Monmouth/Ocean
200 White Rd., No. 204
Little Silver, NJ 07739-1162
Contact: Kevin A. O'Grady, Pres.
Ph: (732)741-2887
Fax: (732)741-4831
E-mail: mholevinski@ft.newyorklife.com
Descr: Represents the interests of insurance and financial advisors. Advocates for a positive legislative and regulatory environment. Enhances business and professional skills of members.

2187 ■ New Jersey Business and Professional Women
128 Springfield Ave.
Summit, NJ 07901
Contact: Julia Domingue, Pres.
E-mail: pres.bpwnj@gmail.com
URL: http://www.bpwnj.org
Descr: Represents the interests of business and professional women. Elevates the standards for women in business and professional settings. Promotes equity for all women in the workplace through advocacy, education and information. Provides professional development, networking and career advancement opportunities for working women.

2188 ■ New Jersey City University Small Business Development Center
20 College St.
Jersey City, NJ 07305-1520
Contact: Barbara O'Neal, Dir.
Ph: (201)200-2156
Fax: (201)200-3404
E-mail: boneal@njcu.edu
URL: http://www.njsbdc.com/contact/njcu.php
Descr: Represents and promotes the small business sector. Provides management assistance to current and prospective small business owners. Helps to improve management skills and expand the products and services of members.

2189 ■ New Jersey Small Business Development Center, Rutgers University - Camden
Waterfront Technology Center
200 Federal St., Ste. 435
Camden, NJ 08103
Contact: Gary Rago, Dir.
Ph: (856)225-6221
Fax: (856)225-6621
E-mail: rsbdc@camden.rutgers.edu
URL: http://crab.rutgers.edu/~rsbdc/index.htm
Descr: Represents and promotes the small business sector. Provides management assistance to current and prospective small business owners. Helps to improve management skills and expand the products and services of members.

2190 ■ New Jersey Society of Enrolled Agents
119 Tunicflower Ln.
West Windsor, NJ 08550
Contact: Leonard Steinberg, Pres.
Ph: (609)443-0469
Free: 877-652-6232
Fax: (609)443-0499
E-mail: lsteinberg@leonardsteinberg.com
URL: http://www.njsea.org
Descr: Aims to improve the knowledge, skills and

professionalism of members in all areas of taxation. Enhances the role of enrolled agents among government agencies, other professions and the public at large. Advocates for taxpayer rights and protects members' interests.

2191 ■ New Jersey Taxpayers Association
2 Berry Ln.
Randolph, NJ 07869
Contact: Jerry Cantrell
Ph: (973)252-9274
E-mail: jcantrell@njtaxes.org
URL: http://www.njtaxes.org

2192 ■ North American Securities Administrators Association, New Jersey
PO Box 47029
Newark, NJ 07101
Ph: (973)504-3600
URL: http://www.njsecurities.gov
Descr: Represents the interests of the state, provincial and territorial securities administrators in the U.S.

2193 ■ Northwest Jersey AIFA
CLU
121 McGregor Ave.
Mount Arlington, NJ 07856
Contact: Jacquelyn S. Coy, Assoc. Exec.
Ph: (973)879-9070
Fax: (973)663-2410
E-mail: jsc164@aol.com
URL: http://www.naifanet.com/nwjersey
Descr: Represents the interests of insurance and financial advisors. Advocates for a positive legislative and regulatory environment. Enhances business and professional skills of members.

2194 ■ Passaic-Bergen AIFA
445 Godwin Ave.
Midland Park, NJ 07432
Contact: Louis Minichini, Pres.
Ph: (973)573-6011
Fax: (201)445-8392
E-mail: lminichini@insurance-nj.com
URL: http://www.naifanet.com/passaicbergen
Descr: Represents the interests of insurance and financial advisors. Advocates for a positive legislative and regulatory environment. Enhances business and professional skills of members.

2195 ■ Rutgers-Newark Small Business Development Center (RNSBDC)
43 Bleeker St.
Newark, NJ 07102
Contact: Tendai Ndoro, Dir.
Ph: (973)353-5950
Fax: (973)353-1030
E-mail: rnsbdc@newark.rutgers.edu
URL: http://www.rnsbdc.newark.rutgers.edu
Descr: Represents and promotes the small business sector. Provides management assistance to current and prospective small business owners. Helps to improve management skills and expand the products and services of members.

2196 ■ Rutherford Taxpayers Association
PO Box 361
Rutherford, NJ 07070
E-mail: webmaster@rutherfordtaxpayer.com
URL: http://www.rutherfordtaxpayers.com

2197 ■ Small Business Development Center at Raritan Valley Community College
PO Box 3300
Somerville, NJ 08876
Contact: Larry Jenkins, Dir.
Ph: (908)526-1200
E-mail: sbdc@raritanval.edu
URL: http://www.sbdcrvcc.com/about.html
Descr: Represents and promotes the small business sector. Provides management assistance to current and prospective small business owners. Helps to

improve management skills and expand the products and services of members.

2198 ■ Small Business Development Center - The College of New Jersey
Forcina Hall 447
2000 Pennington Ave.
Ewing, NJ 08628
Ph: (609)771-2947
Fax: (609)637-5217
E-mail: sbdc@tcnj.edu
URL: http://www.tcnj.edu/~sbdc
Descr: Represents and promotes the small business sector. Provides management assistance to current and prospective small business owners. Helps to improve management skills and expand the products and services of members.

2199 ■ Summit Business and Professional Women
PO Box 831
Summit, NJ 07901
Contact: Celeste Cafiero, Pres.
E-mail: membership@summitbpw.org
URL: http://www.summitbpw.org
Descr: Represents the interests of business and professional women. Elevates the standards for women in business and professional settings. Promotes equity for all women in the workplace through advocacy, education and information. Provides professional development, networking and career advancement opportunities for working women.

2200 ■ Summit Taxpayers Association (STA)
PO Box 474
Summit, NJ 07902
Ph: (908)273-1660
E-mail: info@summittaxpayers.org
URL: http://www.summittaxpayers.org

2201 ■ Sussex Wantage Taxpayers' Association
152 Mt. Salem Rd.
Sussex, NJ 07461
URL: http://www.sussexwantagetaxpayers.com

2202 ■ William Paterson University Small Business Development Center
131 Ellison St.
Paterson, NJ 07505
Contact: Kate Muldoon, Dir.
Ph: (973)754-8695
E-mail: sbdc@wpunj.edu
URL: http://www.wpunj.edu/sbdc
Descr: Represents and promotes the small business sector. Provides management assistance to current and prospective small business owners. Helps to improve management skills and expand the products and services of members.

New Mexico

2203 ■ Alamogordo Small Business Development Center
2230 Lawrence Blvd.
Alamogordo, NM 88310
Contact: G. Dwight Harp, Dir.
Ph: (575)434-5272
Fax: (575)434-1432
E-mail: kat@nmsua.nmsu.edu
URL: http://www.nmsbdc.org/alamogordo
Descr: Represents and promotes the small business sector. Provides management assistance to current and prospective small business owners. Helps to improve management skills and expand the products and services of members.

2204 ■ Albuquerque Small Business Development Center
2501 Yale Blvd. SE, Ste. 302
Albuquerque, NM 87106
Contact: Ray Garcia, Dir.
Ph: (505)224-5250
Fax: (505)224-5256

E-mail: sbdc@cnm.edu
URL: http://www.nmsbdc.org/albuquerque

Descr: Represents and promotes the small business sector. Provides management assistance to current and prospective small business owners. Helps to improve management skills and expand the products and services of members.

2205 ■ American Society of Appraisers, New Mexico Chapter
7408 Gila Rd. NE
Albuquerque, NM 87109
Contact: Martin J. Molloy, Pres.
Ph: (505)265-8818
Fax: (505)265-8810
E-mail: asainfo@appraisers.org
URL: http://old.appraisers.org/new_mexico

Descr: Serves as a professional appraisal educator, testing and accrediting society. Sponsors mandatory recertification program for all members. Offers consumer information service to the public.

2206 ■ Business and Professional Women, New Mexico
HCR 63, Box 605
Raton, NM 87740
Contact: Paula Cacciatore, Pres.
Ph: (505)445-0445
E-mail: pcjc69@yahoo.com
URL: http://www.bpwnm.com

Descr: Represents the interests of business and professional women. Elevates the standards for women in business and professional settings. Promotes equity for all women in the workplace through advocacy, education and information. Provides professional development, networking and career advancement opportunities for working women.

2207 ■ Capital City Business and Professional Women
PO Box 22417
Santa Fe, NM 87502
Contact: Mary Stramel, Pres.
Ph: (505)474-4990
E-mail: mary_stramel@generalmailingnm.com
URL: http://www.capitalcitybpw.org

Descr: Represents the interests of business and professional women. Elevates the standards for women in business and professional settings. Promotes equity for all women in the workplace through advocacy, education and information. Provides professional development, networking and career advancement opportunities for working women.

2208 ■ Carlsbad Small Business Development Center
221 S Canyon St.
Carlsbad, NM 88220
Contact: Larry Coalson, Dir.
Ph: (505)885-9531
Fax: (505)885-1515
E-mail: lcoalson@cavern.nmsu.edu
URL: http://www.nmsbdc.org/carlsbad

Descr: Represents and promotes the small business sector. Provides management assistance to current and prospective small business owners. Helps to improve management skills and expand the products and services of members.

2209 ■ Clovis Small Business Development Center
Clovis Community College
417 Schepps Blvd.
Clovis, NM 88101-8381
Contact: Dr. Sandra Taylor-Sawyer, Dir.
Ph: (575)769-4136
Fax: (575)769-4135
E-mail: sbdc@clovis.cc.nm.us
URL: http://www.nmsbdc.org/clovis

Descr: Represents and promotes the small business sector. Provides management assistance to current and prospective small business owners. Helps to

improve management skills and expand the products and services of members.

2210 ■ Credit Union Association of New Mexico (CUANM)
4200 Wolcott Ave. NE
Albuquerque, NM 87109-4502
Contact: Ann Adrian
Ph: (505)298-9899
Free: 800-366-6628
Fax: (505)298-0162
E-mail: info@cuanm.org
URL: http://www.cuanm.org/index.php

2211 ■ Las Cruces Small Business Development Center
2345 E Nevada Ave., Ste. 101
Las Cruces, NM 88001-3902
Contact: Fred K. Owensby, Dir.
Ph: (575)527-7676
Fax: (575)528-7432
E-mail: fowensby@nmsu.edu
URL: http://www.nmsbdc.org/lascruces/index.html

Descr: Represents and promotes the small business sector. Provides management assistance to current and prospective small business owners. Helps to improve management skills and expand the products and services of members.

2212 ■ Los Alamos Small Business Development Center
190 Central Park Sq.
Los Alamos, NM 87544
Contact: Patrick Sullivan, Dir.
Ph: (505)662-0004
Fax: (505)662-0099
URL: http://www.nmsbdc.org/losalamos

Descr: Represents and promotes the small business sector. Provides management assistance to current and prospective small business owners. Helps to improve management skills and expand the products and services of members.

2213 ■ Los Lunas Small Business Development Center
University of New Mexico-Valencia
280 La Entrada Rd.
Los Lunas, NM 87031
Contact: Roberta Scott, Dir.
Ph: (505)925-8980
Fax: (505)925-8981
E-mail: robscott@unm.edu
URL: http://www.nmsbdc.org/loslunas

Descr: Represents and promotes the small business sector. Provides management assistance to current and prospective small business owners. Helps to improve management skills and expand the products and services of members.

2214 ■ Mesalands Community College Small Business Development Center
911 S 10th St.
Tucumcari, NM 88401
Contact: Carl Kallansrud, Dir.
Ph: (575)461-4413
Fax: (575)461-1901
E-mail: sbdc@mesalands.edu
URL: http://www.nmsbdc.org/tucumcari

Descr: Represents and promotes the small business sector. Provides management assistance to current and prospective small business owners. Helps to improve management skills and expand the products and services of members.

2215 ■ NAIFA-New Mexico
46 Ramblewood
Tijeras, NM 87059
Contact: Carol A. Ames IFA, Dir.
Ph: (505)286-2216
Fax: (505)286-2215
E-mail: carolame@naifa.com
URL: http://www.naifa.com/local/directors.cfm

Descr: Represents the interests of insurance and financial advisors. Advocates for a positive legisla-

tive and regulatory environment. Enhances business and professional skills of members.

2216 ■ New Mexico Society of Enrolled Agents (NMSEA)
PO Box 30974
Albuquerque, NM 87190-0974
Contact: Linda A. Ruckel, Pres.
Ph: (505)988-9572
Fax: (505)988-9574
E-mail: nmsea@hotmail.com
URL: http://www.nmsea.net

Descr: Promotes ethical representation of the financial position of taxpayers before government agencies.

2217 ■ New Mexico State University-Grants Small Business Development Center
701 E Roosevelt Ave.
Grants, NM 87020-2113
Contact: Clemente Sanchez, Dir.
Ph: (505)287-8221
Fax: (505)287-2125
E-mail: clemente@nmsu.edu
URL: http://www.nmsbdc.org/grants

Descr: Represents and promotes the small business sector. Provides management assistance to current and prospective small business owners. Helps to improve management skills and expand the products and services of members.

2218 ■ North American Securities Administrators Association, New Mexico
2550 Cerrillos Rd.
Santa Fe, NM 87505
Contact: Bruce R. Kohl, Dir.
Ph: (505)476-4580
Fax: (505)984-0617

Descr: Represents the interests of the state, provincial and territorial securities administrators in the U.S.

2219 ■ Roswell Small Business Development Center
PO Box 6000
Roswell, NM 88202-6000
Contact: Eugene Simmons, Dir.
Ph: (505)624-7133
Fax: (505)624-7132
E-mail: eugene.simmons@roswell.enmu.edu
URL: http://www.nmsbdc.org/roswell

Descr: Represents and promotes the small business sector. Provides management assistance to current and prospective small business owners. Helps to improve management skills and expand the products and services of members.

2220 ■ Sandoval County's Small Business Development Center
282 Camino del Pueblo, Ste. 2-A
Bernalillo, NM 87004
Contact: Ted Trujillo, Dir.
Ph: (505)867-5066
Fax: (505)867-3746
E-mail: sandovalsbdc@la.unm.edu
URL: http://www.nmsbdc.org/sandoval

Descr: Represents and promotes the small business sector. Provides management assistance to current and prospective small business owners. Helps to improve management skills and expand the products and services of members.

2221 ■ Santa Fe Small Business Development Center
Santa Fe Community College
6401 Richards Ave.
Santa Fe, NM 87508-4887
Contact: Michael Mykris, Dir.
Ph: (505)428-1343
Fax: (505)428-1469
E-mail: sfccsbdc@sfccnm.edu
URL: http://www.nmsbdc.org/santafe

Descr: Represents and promotes the small business sector. Provides management assistance to current and prospective small business owners. Helps to

improve management skills and expand the products and services of members.

2222 ■ Small Business Development Center at Northern New Mexico College
1027 N Railroad Ave.
Espanola, NM 87532
Ph: (505)747-2236
Fax: (505)747-2234
E-mail: jbarbee@nnmc.edu
URL: http://www.nmsbdc.org/espanola

Descr: Represents and promotes the small business sector. Provides management assistance to current and prospective small business owners. Helps to improve management skills and expand the products and services of members.

2223 ■ South Valley Small Business Development Center
1309 4th St., Ste. A SW
Albuquerque, NM 87102
Ph: (505)248-0132
Fax: (505)248-0127
E-mail: svsbdc@abq.com
URL: http://www.nmsbdc.org/southvalley

Descr: Represents and promotes the small business sector. Provides management assistance to current and prospective small business owners. Helps to improve management skills and expand the products and services of members.

2224 ■ Southwest Small Business Development Center - New Mexico
PO Box 680
Silver City, NM 88062
Contact: Mary Vigil-Tarazoff, Dir.
Ph: (575)538-6320
Fax: (575)538-6341
E-mail: sbdc@wnmu.edu
URL: http://www.nmsbdc.org/silvercity

Descr: Represents and promotes the small business sector. Provides management assistance to current and prospective small business owners. Helps to improve management skills and expand the products and services of members.

2225 ■ University of New Mexico-Gallup Small Business Development Center
103 W Hwy. 66
Gallup, NM 87301
Contact: Elsie Sanchez, Dir./Business Counselor
Ph: (505)722-2220
Fax: (505)863-6006
E-mail: esanchez@cia-g.com
URL: http://www.nmsbdc.org/gallup

Descr: Represents and promotes the small business sector. Provides management assistance to current and prospective small business owners. Helps to improve management skills and expand the products and services of members.

New York

2226 ■ Albany Small Business Development Center
7A Harriman Campus Rd.
Albany, NY 12206
Contact: William Brigham, Dir.
Ph: (518)485-7647
Fax: (518)485-8223
E-mail: wbrigham@uamail.albany.edu
URL: http://www.nyssbdc.org

Descr: Represents and promotes the small business sector. Provides management assistance to current and prospective small business owners. Helps to improve management skills and expand the products and services of members.

2227 ■ All-County Taxpayers Association (ACTA)
2458 Ridge Rd.
Queensbury, NY 12804

Ph: (518)656-3578
E-mail: info@givemeliberty.org

2228 ■ American Society of Appraisers, Hudson Valley, New York Chapter
Fog Hill and Co. Inc.
173 Fog Hill Rd.
Hoosick Falls, NY 12090
Contact: Barbara J. Sussman, Pres.
Ph: (518)686-4809
Fax: (518)686-4809
E-mail: barbara@sussmanart.com
URL: http://www.appraisers.org/hudson_valley

Descr: Serves as a professional appraisal educator, testing and accrediting society. Sponsors mandatory recertification program for all members. Offers consumer information service to the public.

2229 ■ American Society of Appraisers, Long Island Chapter
5 Lake Wood Dr.
Katonah, NY 10536
Contact: Ellen J. Epstein, Pres.
Ph: (914)232-0102
Fax: (914)301-5243
E-mail: ee@theartappraiser.com
URL: http://www.longislandappraisers.com

Descr: Serves as a professional appraisal educator, testing and accrediting society. Sponsors mandatory recertification program for all members. Offers consumer information service to the public.

2230 ■ American Society of Appraisers, New York Chapter
PO Box 122
Bedford, NY 10506
Contact: Mark E. Atkinson, Pres.
Ph: (914)391-9071
Fax: (646)390-8170
E-mail: mark.atkinson@navigantcapitaladvisors.com
URL: http://www.asany.com

Descr: Serves as a professional appraisal educator, testing and accrediting society. Sponsors mandatory recertification program for all members. Offers consumer information service to the public.

2231 ■ American Society of Appraisers, Western New York Chapter
Empire Valuation Consultants LLC
777 Canal View Blvd., Ste. 200
Rochester, NY 14623-2825
Contact: Hugh Herman Woodside, Pres.
Ph: (585)475-9260
Fax: (585)475-9380
E-mail: hwoodside@empireval.com
URL: http://old.appraisers.org/western_newyork

Descr: Serves as a professional appraisal educator, testing and accrediting society. Sponsors mandatory recertification program for all members. Offers consumer information service to the public.

2232 ■ Appraisal Institute, Metropolitan New York Chapter
60 E 42nd St., Ste. 1166
New York, NY 10165
Contact: Connie Puccio, Admin.
Free: 866-966-3710
Fax: (866)966-7139
E-mail: secretary@aimetrony.com
URL: http://www.aimetrony.com

Descr: General appraisers who hold the MAI or SRPA designations, and residential members who hold the SRA designation. **Pub:** Newsletter (quarterly).

2233 ■ Binghamton Small Business Development Center
Binghamton University
The Artco Bldg., 3rd Fl.
Binghamton, NY 13901-2705
Contact: Douglas Boyce, Dir.
Ph: (607)777-4024
Fax: (607)777-4029
E-mail: sbdc@binghamton.edu
URL: http://www.nyssbdc.org

Descr: Represents and promotes the small business sector. Provides management assistance to current

and prospective small business owners. Helps to improve management skills and expand the products and services of members.

2234 ■ Blasdell Taxpayers Association
PO Box 1923
Blasdell, NY 14219
Contact: Rolf Rehbein
Ph: (518)622-8938
E-mail: cttapres@aol.com
URL: http://nyspropertytaxreform.org

2235 ■ Brockport Small Business Development Center
350 New Campus Dr.
Brockport, NY 14420
Contact: Jan Pisanczyn, Dir.
Ph: (585)395-8410
Fax: (585)395-2467
E-mail: sbdc@brockport.edu
URL: http://www.nyssbdc.org

Descr: Represents and promotes the small business sector. Provides management assistance to current and prospective small business owners. Helps to improve management skills and expand the products and services of members.

2236 ■ Bronx Small Business Development Center
250 Bedford Park Blvd. W
Bronx, NY 10468-1589
Contact: Clarence Stanley, Dir.
Ph: (718)960-8806
Fax: (718)960-7340
E-mail: clarence.stanley@lehman.cuny.edu
URL: http://www.nyssbdc.org

Descr: Represents and promotes the small business sector. Provides management assistance to current and prospective small business owners. Helps to improve management skills and expand the products and services of members.

2237 ■ Buffalo AIFA (BAIFA)
989 Ave. of the Americas, 6th Fl.
New York, NY 10018
Contact: John C. Moshides, Pres.
Ph: (716)204-0304
Fax: (212)764-8693
URL: http://www.buffaloaifa.org

Descr: Represents the interest of insurance and financial advisors. Advocates for a positive legislative and regulatory environment. Enhances business and professional skills of members.

2238 ■ Buffalo State College Small Business Development Center
Buffalo State College
Cleveland Hall 206
1300 Elmwood Ave.
Buffalo, NY 14222
Contact: Susan A. McCartney, Dir.
Ph: (716)878-4030
Fax: (716)878-4067
E-mail: smallbus@buffalostate.edu
URL: http://www.buffalostate.edu/sbdc

Descr: Represents and promotes the small business sector. Provides management assistance to current and prospective small business owners. Helps to improve management skills and expand the products and services of members.

2239 ■ Business and Professional Women, Brookhaven
PO Box 141
Patchogue, NY 11772
Contact: Roseann Bunshaft, Pres.
Ph: (631)878-3464
Fax: (631)726-8066
E-mail: strum222@optonline.net
URL: http://bpwbrookhaven.org

Descr: Represents the interests of business and professional women. Elevates the standards for women in business and professional settings. Promotes equity for all women in the workplace through advocacy, education and information. Provides professional development, networking and

career advancement opportunities for working women.

2240 ■ Business and Professional Women of Buffalo, Amherst
31 Autumn Ln.
Depew, NY 14043
Contact: Lucy Mysiak, Pres.
Ph: (716)683-5822
E-mail: info@buffaloamherstbpw.com
URL: http://buffaloamherstbpw.com

Descr: Represents the interests of business and professional women. Elevates the standards for women in business and professional settings. Promotes equity for all women in the workplace through advocacy, education and information. Provides professional development, networking and career advancement opportunities for working women.

2241 ■ Business and Professional Women, Deer Park
PO Box 192
Deer Park, NY 11729
Contact: Patricia Becker, VP
E-mail: pkqbdesign@optonline.net
URL: http://www.bpwdeerpark.org

Descr: Represents the interests of business and professional women. Elevates the standards for women in business and professional settings. Promotes equity for all women in the workplace through advocacy, education and information. Provides professional development, networking and career advancement opportunities for working women.

2242 ■ Business and Professional Women, Gloria Hutchings
2838 County Rd. 7
Montour Falls, NY 14865
Contact: Annette Martin, Co-Pres.
E-mail: gloriaj7@aol.com
URL: http://www.watkinsglenbpw.org

Descr: Represents the interests of business and professional women. Elevates the standards for women in business and professional settings. Promotes equity for all women in the workplace through advocacy, education and information. Provides professional development, networking and career advancement opportunities for working women.

2243 ■ Business and Professional Women, Tech Valley
PO Box 528
Clifton Park, NY 12065
Contact: Colleen Ostiguy, Pres.
E-mail: bpwtv@bpwtechvalley.com
URL: http://www.bpwtechvalley.com

Descr: Represents the interests of business and professional women. Elevates the standards for women in business and professional settings. Promotes equity for all women in the workplace through advocacy, education and information. Provides professional development, networking and career advancement opportunities for working women.

2244 ■ Business and Professional Women's Clubs of New York State
4940 Merrick Rd., No. 144
Massapequa Park, NY 11762
Contact: Neale Steiniger, Pres.
Ph: (718)816-0093
E-mail: info@bpwnys.org
URL: http://www.bpwnys.org

Descr: Represents the interests of business and professional women. Elevates the standards for women in business and professional settings. Promotes equity for all women in the workplace through advocacy, education and information. Provides professional development, networking and

career advancement opportunities for working women.

2245 ■ Canton Small Business Development Center
PO Box 6069
Massena, NY 13662
Contact: Dale Rice, Dir.
Ph: (315)764-0683
Fax: (315)764-0854
E-mail: sbdc@canton.edu
URL: http://www.nyssbdc.org

Descr: Represents and promotes the small business sector. Provides management assistance to current and prospective small business owners. Helps to improve management skills and expand the products and services of members.

2246 ■ Capital District AIFA
PO Box 14773
Albany, NY 12212-4773
Contact: Kimberly Harris ACS
Ph: (518)608-8939
E-mail: membersupport@naifa.org
URL: http://www.cdaifa.org

Descr: Represents the interests of insurance and financial advisors. Advocates for a positive legislative and regulatory environment. Enhances business and professional skills of members.

2247 ■ Catskill Mountain Business and Professional Women
PO Box 1043
Monticello, NY 12701
Contact: Shirley Felder-Morton, Pres.
Ph: (845)434-7221
E-mail: admin@catskillmountainbpw.org
URL: http://www.catskillmountainbpw.org

Descr: Represents the interests of business and professional women. Elevates the standards for women in business and professional settings. Promotes equity for all women in the workplace through advocacy, education and information. Provides professional development, networking and career advancement opportunities for working women.

2248 ■ Central McKinley Taxpayers Association
PO Box 447
Hamburg, NY 14075
Ph: (716)863-6404
E-mail: philbest@adelphia.net
URL: http://www.ntu.org/main/groups_details.php?GroupsID=531&state=ny

2249 ■ Central New York Business and Professional Women
500 Plum St.
Syracuse, NY 13204
Contact: Karen Clark, Pres.
Ph: (315)474-9233
Free: 800-448-5773
E-mail: webmaster@bpwcny.org
URL: http://www.bpwcny.org

Descr: Represents the interests of business and professional women. Elevates the standards for women in business and professional settings. Promotes equity for all women in the workplace through advocacy, education and information. Provides professional development, networking and career advancement opportunities for working women.

2250 ■ Chautauqua Region AIFA
Alliance Advisory Group
513 W 3rd St.
Jamestown, NY 14701-4803
Contact: Mark R. Nelson, Sec.
Ph: (716)483-1531
Fax: (716)483-2048
E-mail: mark_r_nelson@glic.com

Descr: Represents the interests of insurance and financial advisors. Advocates for a positive legisla-

tive and regulatory environment. Enhances business and professional skills of members.

2251 ■ Coalition of New York Taxpayers
31 Union Ave.
Center Moriches, NY 11934
Ph: (631)878-3109
URL: http://nyspropertytaxreform.org

2252 ■ College of Staten Island Small Business Development Center
College of Staten Island
2800 Victory Blvd., Bldg. 2A
Staten Island, NY 10314-9806
Contact: Dean Balsamini, Dir.
Ph: (718)982-2560
Fax: (718)982-2323
E-mail: sullivane@mail.csi.cuny.edu
URL: http://www.nyssbdc.org

Descr: Represents and promotes the small business sector. Provides management assistance to current and prospective small business owners. Helps to improve management skills and expand the products and services of members.

2253 ■ Corning Area United Taxpayers Association
214 Seneca St.
Corning, NY 14830
Ph: (607)962-6205
Fax: (607)962-6205
E-mail: phuber@stny.rr.com

2254 ■ Dutchess County AIFA
PO Box 427
Lagrangeville, NY 12540-0427
Ph: (845)471-0591
E-mail: sadlerhayes@gmail.com

Descr: Represents the interests of insurance and financial advisors. Advocates for a positive legislative and regulatory environment. Enhances business and professional skills of members.

2255 ■ Farmingdale Small Business Development Center
Farmingdale State College
Campus Commons
2350 Rte. 110
Farmingdale, NY 11735
Contact: Lucille Wesnofske, Dir.
Ph: (631)420-2765
Fax: (631)370-8895
E-mail: sbdc@farmingdale.edu
URL: http://www.farmingdale.edu/campuspages/CAMPUSAFFILIATES/SBDC/homepage.htm

Descr: Represents and promotes the small business sector. Provides management assistance to current and prospective small business owners. Helps to improve management skills and expand the products and services of members.

2256 ■ Financial Planning Association of Long Island
1895 Lincoln Ave.
East Meadow, NY 11554
Contact: Janet N. Cino, Admin.
Ph: (516)542-2004
Fax: (516)542-2005
E-mail: fpali@optonline.net
URL: http://www.fpanet.org/chapters/longisland

Descr: Promotes financial planning profession through education, networking, and mentoring. Enhances public awareness of the value of the financial planning process. Promotes the CFP marks as the cornerstone of the financial planning profession. Provides forum for education and career development for its members. **Fnd:** 2000.

2257 ■ Financial Planning Association of Northeastern New York (FPA NENY)
PO Box 11565
Loudonville, NY 12211-0565
Contact: Mrs. Stephanie Cogan, Chapter Exec.
Ph: (518)458-7774
E-mail: chapexec@fpa-neny.org
URL: http://www.fpa-neny.org

Descr: Promotes financial planning profession

through education, networking, and mentoring. Enhances public awareness of the value of the financial planning process. Provides forum for education and career development for its members.

2258 ■ Financial Planning Association of Western New York
PO Box 54
East Amherst, NY 14051
Contact: Karen Pomicter, Exec. Dir.
Ph: (716)688-3096
Fax: (716)688-4671
E-mail: info@fpawny.org
URL: http://www.fpawny.org
Descr: Promotes the value of the financial planning process to the public. Provides professional education and networking opportunities for the financial planning community.

2259 ■ Finger Lakes AIFA
354 Clinton St.
Penn Yan, NY 14527
Contact: Mike Snyder, Sec.
Ph: (315)536-6407
Fax: (315)536-6451
E-mail: mike_snyder@farmfamily.com
Descr: Represents the interests of insurance and financial advisors. Advocates for a positive legislative and regulatory environment. Enhances business and professional skills of members.

2260 ■ Hamburg, Orchard Park Business and Professional Women
S-3466 Alsace Pl.
Blasdell, NY 14219
Contact: Jackie Wazny
Ph: (716)824-5411
Fax: (716)821-1618
E-mail: jackiewaz@verizon.net
URL: http://www.bpwhamburgorchardpark.org
Descr: Represents the interests of business and professional women. Elevates the standards for women in business and professional settings. Promotes equity for all women in the workplace through advocacy, education and information. Provides professional development, networking and career advancement opportunities for working women.

2261 ■ International Association of Assessing Officers, New York
10 Maple Ave.
New City, NY 10956
Contact: Cathy Conklin, Rep.
Ph: (845)639-2031
Fax: (845)639-2800
E-mail: c_conklin@towns.clarkstown.ny.us
Descr: Represents state and local officials concerned with valuation of property for ad valorem property tax purposes. Works to improve standards and conduct research on tax assessment. Promotes innovation and excellence in property appraisal, assessment administration, and property tax policy through professional development, education, research, and technical assistance.

2262 ■ Jamestown Small Business Development Center
Jamestown Community College
525 Falconer St.
Jamestown, NY 14702-0020
Contact: Irene Dobies, Dir.
Ph: (716)338-1024
Fax: (716)338-1476
E-mail: irenedobies@mail.sunyjcc.edu
URL: http://www.nyssbdc.org
Descr: Represents and promotes the small business sector. Provides management assistance to current and prospective small business owners. Helps to improve management skills and expand the products and services of members.

2263 ■ Manhattan Small Business Development Center at Pace University
163 William St., 16th Fl.
New York, NY 10038

Contact: Ira Davidson, Dir.
Ph: (212)618-6655
Fax: (212)618-6669
E-mail: sbdc@pace.edu
URL: http://www.nyssbdc.org
Descr: Represents and promotes the small business sector. Provides management assistance to current and prospective small business owners. Helps to improve management skills and expand the products and services of members.

2264 ■ Mid-Hudson Small Business Development Center
Business Resource Center
One Development Ct.
Kingston, NY 12401
Contact: Arnaldo Sehwerert, Dir.
Ph: (845)339-0025
Fax: (845)339-1631
E-mail: sbdc@sunyulster.edu
URL: http://www.nyssbdc.org
Descr: Represents and promotes the small business sector. Provides management assistance to current and prospective small business owners. Helps to improve management skills and expand the products and services of members.

2265 ■ Midtown Manhattan Small Business Development Center at Baruch College
Baruch College, Field Ctr.
55 Lexington Ave.
New York, NY 10010-0010
Contact: Monica Dean, Dir.
Ph: (646)312-4790
Fax: (646)312-4781
E-mail: sbdc@baruch.cuny.edu
URL: http://www.nyssbdc.org
Descr: Represents and promotes the small business sector. Provides management assistance to current and prospective small business owners. Helps to improve management skills and expand the products and services of members.

2266 ■ Mohawk Valley AIFA
PO Box 49
Marcy, NY 13403
Contact: Mark D. Daviau, Pres.
Ph: (315)424-4061
Fax: (315)424-4570
E-mail: jhobika@mtb.com
Descr: Represents the interests of insurance and financial advisors. Advocates for a positive legislative and regulatory environment. Enhances business and professional skills of members.

2267 ■ Mohawk Valley Small Business Development Center
PO Box 3050
Utica, NY 13504-3050
Ph: (315)792-7547
Fax: (315)792-7554
E-mail: sbdc@sunyit.edu
URL: http://www.sunyit.edu/sbdc
Descr: Represents and promotes the small business sector. Provides management assistance to current and prospective small business owners. Helps to improve management skills and expand the products and services of members.

2268 ■ NAIFA-Broome County
11 Devon Blvd.
Binghamton, NY 13903
Contact: Debora Russell
Ph: (607)723-1606
Fax: (607)722-8320
E-mail: rusdbr@aol.com
Descr: Represents the interests of insurance and financial advisors. Advocates for a positive legislative and regulatory environment. Enhances business and professional skills of members.

2269 ■ NAIFA - New York State (NAIFA-NYS)
38 Sheridan Ave.
Albany, NY 12210-2714
Contact: Mark L. Yavornitzki CAE, Exec. VP/CEO
Ph: (518)462-5567

Fax: (518)462-5569
E-mail: markyav@aol.com
URL: http://www.naifanys.org
Descr: Represents the interests of insurance and financial advisors. Advocates for a positive legislative and regulatory environment. Enhances business and professional skills of members.

2270 ■ Nassau AIFA
337 Merrick Rd., Ste. 7
Lynbrook, NY 11563
Contact: Pamela Mollet
Ph: (516)561-8050
Fax: (516)561-8020
E-mail: contact@nassauaifa.com
Descr: Represents the interests of insurance and financial advisors. Advocates for a positive legislative and regulatory environment. Enhances business and professional skills of members.

2271 ■ New York City AIFA
989 Ave. of the Americas, 6th Fl.
New York, NY 10018-0873
Contact: David A. Dreifuss JD, Exec. Dir.
Ph: (212)221-3500
Fax: (212)764-8693
E-mail: ddreifuss@taifp.com
URL: http://www.taifp.com
Descr: Represents the interests of insurance and financial advisors. Advocates for a positive legislative and regulatory environment. Enhances business and professional skills of members.

2272 ■ New York State Society of Enrolled Agents (NYSSEA)
38 Vautrin Ave.
Holtsville, NY 11742
Contact: Victoria A. McGinn EA, Pres.
Ph: (631)730-8803
Fax: (631)758-4983
E-mail: vicki1219@aol.com
URL: http://nyssea.org
Descr: Enables Enrolled Agents to increase their value to clients. Accomplish this by providing Education courses, advocacy and increasing recognition of Enrolled Agents. **Fnd:** 1981. **Mem:** 600.

2273 ■ New York State Society of Enrolled Agents - Capital District Chapter
PO Box 639
Cobleskill, NY 12043
Contact: Judy M. Strauss EA, Treas.
Ph: (518)234-4066
Fax: (518)234-0250
E-mail: jstrauss@jstraussassociates.com
URL: http://www.nyssea.org
Descr: Seeks to: foster professionalism and growth among members; be an advocate of taxpayer rights; protect the interests of members; and enhance the role of the enrolled agent among government agencies, other professions and the public at large, with an emphasis at the state and local levels.

2274 ■ New York State Society of Enrolled Agents - Central Chapter
115 Dewberry Ln.
Syracuse, NY 13219
Contact: Michael R. Hayes EA, VP
Ph: (315)468-0182
Fax: (315)455-9667
E-mail: m.hayes@ieee.org
URL: http://www.nyssea.org
Descr: Seeks to: foster professionalism and growth among members; be an advocate of taxpayer rights; protect the interests of members; and enhance the role of the enrolled agent among government agencies, other professions and the public at large, with an emphasis at the state and local levels.

2275 ■ New York State Society of Enrolled Agents - Lower Hudson Chapter
16 Stubbe Dr.
Stony Point, NY 10980
Contact: Elizabeth Simeone EA, Pres.
Ph: (845)942-4194
Fax: (845)942-0190

E-mail: thetaxpert@earthlink.net
URL: http://www.nyssea.org

2276 ■ New York State Society of Enrolled Agents - Metro Chapter
555 Madison Ave., Fl. 17
New York, NY 10022
Contact: David S. Locker, Pres.
Ph: (212)371-3950
Fax: (212)758-4967
E-mail: dlocker@heroldinc.com
URL: http://www.nyssea.org
Descr: Aims to improve the knowledge, skills and professionalism of members in all areas of taxation. Enhances the role of enrolled agents among government agencies, other professions and the public at large. Advocates for taxpayer rights and protects members' interests.

2277 ■ New York State Society of Enrolled Agents - Nassau/Suffolk Chapter
38 Vautrin Ave.
Holtsville, NY 11742
Contact: Victoria McGinn, Pres.
Ph: (631)642-3406
Fax: (631)758-4983
E-mail: vicki1219@aol.com
URL: http://www.nyssea.org
Descr: Aims to improve the knowledge, skills and professionalism of members in all areas of taxation. Enhances the role of enrolled agents among government agencies, other professions and the public at large. Advocates for taxpayer rights and protects members' interests.

2278 ■ New York State Taxpayers Union (NYSTU)
PO Box 7294
Albany, NY 12224
Contact: Matthew F. Guilbault, Exec. Dir.
Ph: (518)605-8100

2279 ■ Niagara Small Business Development Center
3111 Saunders Settlement Rd.
Sanborn, NY 14132
Contact: Richard Gorko, Dir.
Ph: (716)434-3815
Fax: (716)433-5155
E-mail: sbdc@niagaracc.suny.edu
URL: http://www.nyssbdc.org
Descr: Represents and promotes the small business sector. Provides management assistance to current and prospective small business owners. Helps to improve management skills and expand the products and services of members.

2280 ■ North American Securities Administrators Association, New York
120 Broadway, 23rd Fl.
New York, NY 10271
Contact: Jennifer Koh
Ph: (212)416-8165
URL: http://www.nasaa.org
Descr: Represents the interests of the state, provincial and territorial securities administrators in the U.S.

2281 ■ North Country Small Business Development Center
State University of New York College at Plattsburgh
194 US Oval
Plattsburgh, NY 12903-3900
Contact: Rick Leibowitz, Dir.
Ph: (518)564-2042
Fax: (518)564-2043
E-mail: sbdc@plattsburgh.edu
URL: http://www.nyssbdc.org
Descr: Represents and promotes the small business sector. Provides management assistance to current and prospective small business owners. Helps to improve management skills and expand the products and services of members.

2282 ■ Northern New York AIFA
23313 County Rte. 144
Black River, NY 13612

Contact: William P. Griffith, Pres.
Ph: (315)493-2110
Fax: (315)493-2728
E-mail: wgriffith@twcny.rr.com
Descr: Represents the interests of insurance and financial advisors. Advocates for a positive legislative and regulatory environment. Enhances business and professional skills of members.

2283 ■ Onondaga Small Business Development Center
Onondaga Community College
Whitney ATC , Ste. 206
Syracuse, NY 13215-4585
Contact: Patricia Higgins, Dir.
Ph: (315)498-6070
Fax: (315)492-3704
E-mail: sbdc@sunyocc.edu
URL: http://www.nyssbdc.org
Descr: Represents and promotes the small business sector. Provides management assistance to current and prospective small business owners. Helps to improve management skills and expand the products and services of members.

2284 ■ Rochester AIFA
40 Brougham Dr.
Penfield, NY 14526
Contact: Jennifer Sauter, Exec. Dir.
Ph: (585)388-8182
Fax: (585)388-9717
E-mail: raifa@rochester.rr.com
URL: http://www.naifanet.com/rochester
Descr: Represents the interests of insurance and financial advisors. Advocates for a positive legislative and regulatory environment. Enhances business and professional skills of members.

2285 ■ Rome Business and Professional Women
7980 River Rd.
Rome, NY 13440
Contact: Lucille Argenzia, Pres.
E-mail: info@bpwrome.org
URL: http://www.bpwrome.org
Descr: Represents the interests of business and professional women. Elevates the standards for women in business and professional settings. Promotes equity for all women in the workplace through advocacy, education and information. Provides professional development, networking and career advancement opportunities for working women.

2286 ■ Schenectady Business and Professional Women
7120 Pinewood Trail
Galway, NY 12074
Contact: Elena Alvarez, Pres.
E-mail: ealv111@aol.com
URL: http://www.bpwschenectady.org
Descr: Represents the interests of business and professional women. Elevates the standards for women in business and professional settings. Promotes equity for all women in the workplace through advocacy, education and information. Provides professional development, networking and career advancement opportunities for working women.

2287 ■ Stony Brook Small Business Development Center
Stony Brook University
Harriman Hall, Rm. 109
Stony Brook, NY 11794-3777
Contact: Jeff Saelens, Dir.
Ph: (631)632-9070
Fax: (631)632-7176
E-mail: lynne.schmidt@sunysb.edu
URL: http://www.nyssbdc.org
Descr: Represents and promotes the small business sector. Provides management assistance to current and prospective small business owners. Helps to

improve management skills and expand the products and services of members.

2288 ■ Syracuse AIFA (SAIFA)
606 State Tower Bldg.
Syracuse, NY 13202
Contact: Evan H. Walker, Pres.
Ph: (315)474-6775
Fax: (315)474-6775
E-mail: cgcrandall@usadatanet.net
URL: http://www.naifa-syracuse.org
Descr: Represents the interests of insurance and financial advisors. Advocates for a positive legislative and regulatory environment. Enhances business and professional skills of members.

2289 ■ Triple Cities Business and Professional Women
146 Riverside Dr.
Binghamton, NY 13905
Contact: Robin Allen
Ph: (607)724-6941
Fax: (607)217-0719
E-mail: info@triplecitiesbpw.org
URL: http://www.triplecitiesbpw.org
Descr: Represents the interests of business and professional women. Elevates the standards for women in business and professional settings. Promotes equity for all women in the workplace through advocacy, education and information. Provides professional development, networking and career advancement opportunities for working women.

2290 ■ Ulster County AIFA
PO Box 2426
Kingston, NY 12402
Contact: Steven J. DeSalvo, Pres.
Ph: (845)331-4500
Fax: (845)331-0525
E-mail: stevendesalvo@allstate.com
Descr: Represents the interests of insurance and financial advisors. Advocates for a positive legislative and regulatory environment. Enhances business and professional skills of members.

2291 ■ Westchester AIFA
PO Box 1295
Wappingers Falls, NY 12590
Contact: Luis Guerra, Pres.
Ph: (845)297-2992
Fax: (845)297-2993
E-mail: info@waifa.com
URL: http://waifa.com
Descr: Represents the interests of insurance and financial advisors. Advocates for a positive legislative and regulatory environment. Enhances business and professional skills of members.

2292 ■ Westchester Small Business Development Center
Rockland Community College
Brucker Hall, No. 6101
Suffern, NY 10901-3699
Contact: Thomas Morley, Dir.
Ph: (845)356-6065
Fax: (845)356-6117
E-mail: tmorley@sunyrockland.edu
URL: http://www.nyssbdc.org
Descr: Represents and promotes the small business sector. Provides management assistance to current and prospective small business owners. Helps to improve management skills and expand the products and services of members.

2293 ■ Western Catskill AIFA
297 River St., Service Rd., Ste. 100
Oneonta, NY 13820
Contact: Stanley R. Holmes, Pres.
Ph: (607)432-4180
Fax: (607)433-1868
E-mail: chip.holmes@manginsurance.com
Descr: Represents the interests of insurance and financial advisors. Advocates for a positive legisla-

tive and regulatory environment. Enhances business and professional skills of members.

2294 ■ York Small Business Development Center
City University of New York, York College
9450 159th St.
Jamaica, NY 11451
Ph: (718)262-2880
Fax: (718)262-2881
E-mail: sbdc@york.cuny.edu
URL: http://www.nyssbdc.org
Descr: Represents and promotes the small business sector. Provides management assistance to current and prospective small business owners. Helps to improve management skills and expand the products and services of members.

North Carolina

2295 ■ American Society of Appraisers, North Carolina Chapter
310 Hillsboro Dr.
Winston-Salem, NC 27104-2406
Contact: John G. Potter, Pres.
Ph: (336)760-3468
E-mail: potterjg@co.forsyth.nc.us
URL: http://www.asanc.net
Descr: Serves as a professional appraisal educator, testing and accrediting society. Sponsors mandatory recertification program for all members. Offers consumer information service to the public. **Pub:** Newsletter (monthly).

2296 ■ American Society of Appraisers, North Carolina-Western Chapter
BB&T Leasing Corp.
5130 Parkway Plaza Blvd.
Charlotte, NC 28217
Contact: Nicholas A. Mermigas, Pres.
Ph: (704)685-3852
E-mail: nmermigas@bbandt.com
URL: http://old.appraisers.org/nc_western
Descr: Serves as a professional appraisal educator, testing and accrediting society. Sponsors mandatory recertification program for all members. Offers consumer information service to the public.

2297 ■ Appraisal Institute, North Carolina Chapter (NCAI)
3717 W Market St., Ste. C
Greensboro, NC 27407
Contact: Nancy L. Toombs, Exec. Dir.
Ph: (336)297-9511
Fax: (336)297-9055
E-mail: ncai@bellsouth.net
URL: http://www.ncappraisalinstitute.org
Staff: 1. **Descr:** Real estate appraisers organized to protect and advance industry interests. Strives to support and advance its members as the choice for real estate solutions. Works to uphold professional credentials, standards of professional practice and ethics consistent with the public good. Conducts seminars and workshops. **Fnd:** 1993. **Mem:** 543. **State Groups:** 11. **Local Groups:** 2. **Pub:** *North Carolina Appraiser* (quarterly).

2298 ■ Association of County Taxpayers - Polk County
PO Box 1537
Tryon, NC 28782
Ph: (704)859-5920

2299 ■ Brevard Business and Professional Women
PO Box 897
Pisgah Forest, NC 28768
Contact: Pam Bishop, Pres.
E-mail: pjbishop@citcom.net
URL: http://www.brevardbpw.org
Descr: Represents the interests of business and professional women. Elevates the standards for women in business and professional settings. Promotes equity for all women in the workplace through advocacy, education and information. Provides professional development, networking and

career advancement opportunities for working women.

2300 ■ Business and Professional Women, Granite Falls
83 N Highland Ave.
Granite Falls, NC 28630
Contact: Linda R. Crowder, Pres./Corresponding Sec.
Ph: (828)396-1066
E-mail: webmaster@bpwgranitefalls.org
URL: http://www.bpwgranitefalls.org
Descr: Represents the interests of business and professional women. Elevates the standards for women in business and professional settings. Promotes equity for all women in the workplace through advocacy, education and information. Provides professional development, networking and career advancement opportunities for working women.

2301 ■ Business and Professional Women of Raleigh
PO Box 1851
Cary, NC 27512-1851
Contact: Christy New, Pres.
E-mail: mail@bpwraleigh.org
URL: http://www.bpwraleigh.org
Descr: Represents the interests of business and professional women. Elevates the standards for women in business and professional settings. Promotes equity for all women in the workplace through advocacy, education and information. Provides professional development, networking and career advancement opportunities for working women.

2302 ■ Catawba Valley AIFA
PO Box 3232
Hickory, NC 28603
Contact: Warren Ross, Pres.
Ph: (828)612-6887
E-mail: wross@graniteinsurance.com
URL: http://naifanet.com/catawba
Descr: Represents the interests of insurance and financial advisors. Advocates for a positive legislative and regulatory environment. Enhances business and professional skills of members.

2303 ■ Financial Planning Association of Charlotte
8019 Regent Park Ln.
Charlotte, NC 28210
Contact: Eugene C. Curtis, Chapter Exec.
Ph: (704)556-7919
Fax: (704)553-0797
E-mail: fpacharlotte@aol.com
URL: http://www.fpanet.org/chapters/charlotte
Descr: Advances financial planning profession by providing education, interaction and leadership for the Financial Planning Community and the Public it serves, in accordance with the Certified Financial Planner Board's Code of Professional Standards. Offers educational and professional enhancement programs and forums for all Financial Planning Professionals.

2304 ■ Financial Planning Association of Triangle
PO Box 1144
Cary, NC 27512-1144
Contact: Augustus R. Thompson, Pres.
Ph: (919)326-0732
E-mail: administrator@fpatriangle.org
URL: http://www.fpatriangle.org/index.html
Descr: Promotes the advancement of knowledge in financial planning, supporting programs and projects that enable its members to better serve their clients.

2305 ■ Financial Planning Association of Western North Carolina
900 Hendersonville Rd., Ste. 306
Asheville, NC 28803
Contact: Joel Kelley CFP, Pres.
Ph: (828)274-4944
Fax: (828)274-5568

E-mail: info@fpa-wnc.org
URL: http://www.fpa-wnc.org
Descr: Promotes the value of the financial planning process to the public. Provides professional education and networking opportunities for the financial planning community. **Fnd:** 2003.

2306 ■ Greensboro AIFA
PO Box 518
Greensboro, NC 27402
Contact: John Nee, Pres.
Ph: (336)274-3132
E-mail: john.nee@axa-advisors.com
URL: http://naifanet.com/greensboro
Descr: Represents the interests of insurance and financial advisors. Advocates for a positive legislative and regulatory environment. Enhances business and professional skills of members.

2307 ■ International Association of Assessing Officers, North Carolina
200 E Main St., 1st Fl.
Durham, NC 27701
Contact: Kenneth L. Joyner RES, Rep.
Ph: (919)560-0425
Fax: (919)560-0385
E-mail: kjoyner@co.durham.nc.us
Descr: Represents state and local officials concerned with valuation of property for ad valorem property tax purposes. Works to improve standards and conduct research on tax assessment. Promotes innovation and excellence in property appraisal, assessment administration, and property tax policy through professional development, education, research, and technical assistance.

2308 ■ Lincolnton Business and Professional Women
PO Box 533
Lincolnton, NC 28093-0533
Contact: Rhonda Hunter, Pres.
Ph: (704)735-9053
Fax: (704)735-5166
E-mail: rhonda@lincolneda.org
URL: http://www.bpwlincolnton.org
Descr: Represents the interests of business and professional women. Elevates the standards for women in business and professional settings. Promotes equity for all women in the workplace through advocacy, education and information. Provides professional development, networking and career advancement opportunities for working women.

2309 ■ Metropolitan Business and Professional Women
PO Box 36663
Charlotte, NC 28236
Contact: Elizabeth Kennedy, Pres.
Free: 866-851-9446
E-mail: info@mbpw.org
URL: http://www.mbpw.org
Descr: Represents the interests of business and professional women. Elevates the standards for women in business and professional settings. Promotes equity for all women in the workplace through advocacy, education and information. Provides professional development, networking and career advancement opportunities for working women.

2310 ■ North Carolina Credit Union League
PO Box 49379
Greensboro, NC 27419-1379
Contact: John Radebaugh, Pres.
Ph: (336)299-6286
Free: 800-822-8859
Fax: (336)299-7842
URL: http://www.ncleague.org
Descr: Seeks to perfect credit union laws; aids in the development of new credit union services, includ-

ing new payment systems techniques; assists in the training of credit union officials and employees.

2311 ■ North Carolina Credit Union Network
PO Box 49379
Greensboro, NC 27419
Contact: Lisa Brothers
Ph: (336)299-6286
Free: 800-822-8859
Fax: (336)299-7845
E-mail: lbrothers@ncleague.org
URL: http://www.ncleague.org

2312 ■ North Carolina Federation of Business and Professional Women
175 BPW Club Rd.
Carrboro, NC 27510
Contact: Caryl Sinfield, Pres.
E-mail: csinfield@citcom.net
URL: http://www.bpwnc.org
Descr: Represents the interests of business and professional women. Elevates the standards for women in business and professional settings. Promotes equity for all women in the workplace through advocacy, education and information. Provides professional development, networking and career advancement opportunities for working women.

2313 ■ Rocky Mount AIFA
PO Box 8385
Rocky Mount, NC 27804-1445
Contact: Jeffrey L. Collins
Ph: (252)937-6391
Fax: (252)937-0591
E-mail: jeffrey.collins@axa-advisors.com
URL: http://naifanet.com/rockymount
Descr: Represents the interests of insurance and financial advisors. Advocates for a positive legislative and regulatory environment. Enhances business and professional skills of members.

2314 ■ Small Business and Technology Development Center Appalachian-Foothills
905 Hwy. 321 NW, Ste. 120
Hickory, NC 28601
Contact: Bill Parrish, Regional Dir.
Ph: (828)345-1110
E-mail: info@sbtdc.org
URL: http://www.sbtdc.org
Descr: Represents and promotes the small business sector. Provides management assistance to current and prospective small business owners. Helps to improve management skills and expand the products and services of members.

2315 ■ Small Business and Technology Development Center Cape Fear
PO Box 1334
Fayetteville, NC 28302-1334
Contact: Greg Taylor, Regional Dir.
Ph: (910)672-1727
E-mail: info@sbtdc.org
URL: http://www.sbtdc.org
Descr: Represents and promotes the small business sector. Provides management assistance to current and prospective small business owners. Helps to improve management skills and expand the products and services of members.

2316 ■ Small Business and Technology Development Center Capital Region
920 Main Campus Dr., Ste. 101
Raleigh, NC 27606
Contact: Mike Seibert, Regional Dir.
Ph: (919)424-4450
E-mail: info@sbtdc.org
URL: http://www.sbtdc.org
Descr: Represents and promotes the small business sector. Provides management assistance to current and prospective small business owners. Helps to

improve management skills and expand the products and services of members.

2317 ■ Small Business and Technology Development Center Central Carolina Region
Campus Box No. 1823
Chapel Hill, NC 27599-1823
Contact: Ron Ilinitch, Regional Dir.
Ph: (919)962-0389
E-mail: info@sbtdc.org
URL: http://www.sbtdc.org
Descr: Represents and promotes the small business sector. Provides management assistance to current and prospective small business owners. Helps to improve management skills and expand the products and services of members.

2318 ■ Small Business and Technology Development Center Eastern Region
ECU Willis Bldg.
300 E First St.
Greenville, NC 27858-4353
Contact: Carolyn Wilburn, Regional Dir.
Ph: (252)737-1385
E-mail: info@sbtdc.org
URL: http://www.sbtdc.org
Descr: Represents and promotes the small business sector. Provides management assistance to current and prospective small business owners. Helps to improve management skills and expand the products and services of members.

2319 ■ Small Business and Technology Development Center Northeastern Region
K.E. White Graduate Center
1704 Weeksville Rd.
Elizabeth City, NC 27909-7806
Contact: George Brown, Regional Dir.
Ph: (252)335-3247
E-mail: info@sbtdc.org
URL: http://www.sbtdc.org
Descr: Represents and promotes the small business sector. Provides management assistance to current and prospective small business owners. Helps to improve management skills and expand the products and services of members.

2320 ■ Small Business and Technology Development Center Southeastern Region
5051 New Centre Dr.
Wilmington, NC 28403-3297
Contact: Leslie Langer, Regional Dir.
Ph: (910)962-3744
E-mail: info@sbtdc.org
URL: http://www.sbtdc.org
Descr: Represents and promotes the small business sector. Provides management assistance to current and prospective small business owners. Helps to improve management skills and expand the products and services of members.

2321 ■ Small Business and Technology Development Center Southern Piedmont
Ben Craig Center
8701 Mallard Creek Rd.
Charlotte, NC 28262-9705
Contact: George McAllister, Regional Dir.
Ph: (704)548-1090
E-mail: info@sbtdc.org
URL: http://www.sbtdc.org
Descr: Represents and promotes the small business sector. Provides management assistance to current and prospective small business owners. Helps to improve management skills and expand the products and services of members.

2322 ■ Small Business and Technology Development Center Triad Region
2007 Yanceyville St., Ste. 303
Greensboro, NC 27405
Contact: Blair Abee, Regional Dir.
Ph: (336)334-7005
E-mail: info@sbtdc.org
URL: http://www.sbtdc.org
Descr: Represents and promotes the small business sector. Provides management assistance to current and prospective small business owners. Helps to

improve management skills and expand the products and services of members.

2323 ■ Small Business and Technology Development Center Western Region
WCU College of Business
182 Belk Bldg.
Centennial Dr.
Cullowhee, NC 28723-9646
Contact: Wendy Cagle, Regional Dir.
Ph: (828)227-3459
E-mail: info@sbtdc.org
URL: http://www.sbtdc.org
Descr: Represents and promotes the small business sector. Provides management assistance to current and prospective small business owners. Helps to improve management skills and expand the products and services of members.

2324 ■ Triangle AIFA
2125 Guess Rd.
Durham, NC 27705-3338
Contact: Sybil Hill, Exec.
Ph: (919)286-4635
Fax: (919)286-4748
E-mail: sybil.hill@att.net
URL: http://www.naifanet.com/triangle
Descr: Represents the interests of insurance and financial advisors. Advocates for a positive legislative and regulatory environment. Enhances business and professional skills of members.

2325 ■ Virginia Dare Business and Professional Women
PO Box 3222
Kitty Hawk, NC 27949
Contact: Shirley Mozingo, Co-Pres.
E-mail: oceanwriter@earthlink.net
URL: http://www.bpwouterbanks.org
Descr: Represents the interests of business and professional women. Elevates the standards for women in business and professional settings. Promotes equity for all women in the workplace through advocacy, education and information. Provides professional development, networking and career advancement opportunities for working women.

2326 ■ Wake County Taxpayers Association (WCTA)
1821 Falls Church Rd.
Raleigh, NC 27609-3544
Ph: (919)790-8918
URL: http://www.wcta.org

North Dakota

2327 ■ International Association of Assessing Officers, North Dakota
200 N 3rd St.
Fargo, ND 58102
Contact: Dana Pulfrey, Rep.
Ph: (701)241-1331
Fax: (701)241-1339
E-mail: dlpulfrey@ci.fargo.nd.us
Descr: Represents state and local officials concerned with valuation of property for ad valorem property tax purposes. Works to improve standards and conduct research on tax assessment. Promotes innovation and excellence in property appraisal, assessment administration, and property tax policy through professional development, education, research, and technical assistance.

2328 ■ Mid-America Credit Union Association
PO Box 7250
Bismarck, ND 58507-7250
Contact: Tony Richards, Pres.
Ph: (701)258-5760
Free: 800-279-6328
Fax: (701)258-7794
E-mail: info@midamericacua.coop
URL: http://www.midamericacua.coop
Descr: Seeks to perfect credit union laws; aids in the development of new credit union services, includ-

ing new payment systems techniques; assists in the training of credit union officials and employees.

2329 ■ North American Securities Administrators Association, North Dakota
State Capitol, 5th Fl.
600 East Blvd.
Bismarck, ND 58505
Contact: Karen Tyler
Ph: (701)328-2910
Fax: (701)255-3113

Descr: Represents the interests of the state, provincial and territorial securities administrators in the U.S.

2330 ■ North Dakota AIFA (NDAIFA)
PO Box 5010
Bismarck, ND 58502-5010
Contact: Ted Haugan, Pres.
Ph: (701)258-9525
Fax: (701)222-0103
E-mail: info@naifa-nd.org
URL: http://www.naifa-nd.org

Descr: Represents the interests of insurance and financial advisors. Advocates for a positive legislative and regulatory environment. Enhances business and professional skills of members.

2331 ■ North Dakota Small Business Development Center - Belcourt
Box 900
Belcourt, ND 58316
Contact: Betty Hamley, Consultant
Ph: (701)477-2606
E-mail: hamleyb@utma.com
URL: http://www.ndsbdc.org

Descr: Represents and promotes the small business sector. Provides management assistance to current and prospective small business owners. Helps to improve management skills and expand the products and services of members.

2332 ■ North Dakota Small Business Development Center - Bismarck
Bank of North Dakota Bldg.
1200 Memorial Hwy.
Bismarck, ND 58504
Contact: Nancy Krogen-Abel, Regional Dir.
Ph: (701)328-5865
E-mail: nancy@dakotamep.com
URL: http://www.ndsbdc.org

Descr: Represents and promotes the small business sector. Provides management assistance to current and prospective small business owners. Helps to improve management skills and expand the products and services of members.

2333 ■ North Dakota Small Business Development Center - Devils Lake
PO Box 651
Devils Lake, ND 58301
Contact: Barbara Britsch, Consultant
Ph: (701)662-8131
Fax: (701)662-8132
E-mail: barbncpc@gondtc.com
URL: http://www.ndsbdc.org

Descr: Represents and promotes the small business sector. Provides management assistance to current and prospective small business owners. Helps to improve management skills and expand the products and services of members.

2334 ■ North Dakota Small Business Development Center - Dickinson
Strom Center for Entrepreneurship & Innovation
1679 6th Ave. W
Dickinson, ND 58601
Contact: Ray Ann Kilen, Regional Dir.
Ph: (701)483-2470
E-mail: rayann@goinnovative.us
URL: http://www.ndsbdc.org

Descr: Represents and promotes the small business sector. Provides management assistance to current and prospective small business owners. Helps to

improve management skills and expand the products and services of members.

2335 ■ North Dakota Small Business Development Center - Fargo
51 N Broadway, Ste. 505
Fargo, ND 58102
Contact: Donovan Wadholm, Regional Dir.
Ph: (701)235-1495
E-mail: djwadholm@dakotamep.com
URL: http://www.ndsbdc.org

Descr: Represents and promotes the small business sector. Provides management assistance to current and prospective small business owners. Helps to improve management skills and expand the products and services of members.

2336 ■ North Dakota Small Business Development Center - Fort Yates
1341 92nd St.
Fort Yates, ND 58538
Contact: Jonathan Anderson, Mgr.
Ph: (701)854-8122
E-mail: jonathana@sbci.edu
URL: http://www.ndsbdc.org

Descr: Represents and promotes the small business sector. Provides management assistance to current and prospective small business owners. Helps to improve management skills and expand the products and services of members.

2337 ■ North Dakota Small Business Development Center - Grand Forks
600 Demers Ave., Ste. 501
Grand Forks, ND 58201
Contact: Josh Klug, Consultant
Ph: (701)746-8516
E-mail: joklug@nd.gov
URL: http://www.ndsbdc.org

Descr: Represents and promotes the small business sector. Provides management assistance to current and prospective small business owners. Helps to improve management skills and expand the products and services of members.

2338 ■ North Dakota Small Business Development Center - Jamestown
120 2nd St. SE
Jamestown, ND 58402
Contact: Deb Kantrud, Regional Dir.
Ph: (701)952-8060
E-mail: scdrc@daktel.com
URL: http://www.ndsbdc.org

Descr: Represents and promotes the small business sector. Provides management assistance to current and prospective small business owners. Helps to improve management skills and expand the products and services of members.

2339 ■ North Dakota Small Business Development Center - Minot
1925 S Broadway, Ste. 2
Minot, ND 58703
Contact: Mary Beth Votava, Regional Dir.
Ph: (701)857-8211
E-mail: marybethv@dakotamep.com
URL: http://www.ndsbdc.org

Descr: Represents and promotes the small business sector. Provides management assistance to current and prospective small business owners. Helps to improve management skills and expand the products and services of members.

Ohio

2340 ■ Akron Small Business Development Center
526 S Main St., Ste. 813
Akron, OH 44311-4403
Contact: Mary Ann Jasionowski, Business Advisor
Ph: (330)375-2111
E-mail: info@akronsbdc.org
URL: http://www.akronsbdc.org

Descr: Represents and promotes the small business sector. Provides management assistance to current and prospective small business owners. Helps to

improve management skills and expand the products and services of members.

2341 ■ American Society of Appraisers, Akron - Cleveland Chapter
1111 E Superior Ave., No. 310
Cleveland, OH 44114
Contact: Rose M. Lysobey, Sec.
Ph: (330)204-4660
Fax: (216)736-3546
E-mail: roseoh@roadrunner.com
URL: http://old.appraisers.org/akron_cleveland

Descr: Serves as a professional appraisal educator, testing and accrediting society. Sponsors mandatory recertification program for all members. Offers consumer information service to the public.

2342 ■ American Society of Appraisers, Columbus Chapter
1111 Polaris Pkwy., Ste. A3
Columbus, OH 43240-2050
Contact: Thomas K. Walsh, Pres.
Ph: (614)213-7602
Fax: (614)213-1041
E-mail: thomas.k.walsh@chase.com
URL: http://www.appraisers.org/columbus

Descr: Serves as a professional appraisal educator, testing and accrediting society. Sponsors mandatory recertification program for all members. Offers consumer information service to the public.

2343 ■ American Society of Appraisers, Pittsburgh Chapter
8700 E Market St., Ste. 3
Warren, OH 44484
Contact: Kelly Lynn Bianco, Pres.
Ph: (330)373-1620
Fax: (330)373-1640
E-mail: kcarrier@strategicvaluationgroup.net
URL: http://www.appraisers.org/pittsburgh

Descr: Serves as a professional appraisal educator, testing and accrediting society. Sponsors mandatory recertification program for all members. Offers consumer information service to the public.

2344 ■ American Society of Appraisers, Toledo Chapter
Toledo Bldg., Ste. 620
316 N Michigan St.
Toledo, OH 43624
Contact: Michael J. Binkowski AM, Chm.
Ph: (419)243-6108
Fax: (419)824-0487
E-mail: mbink@buckeye-express.com
URL: http://www.appraisers.org/toledo

Descr: Serves as a professional appraisal educator, testing and accrediting society. Sponsors mandatory recertification program for all members. Offers consumer information service to the public.

2345 ■ Ashland Business and Professional Women
PO Box 854
Ashland, OH 44805
Contact: Traci Bartley, Pres.
Ph: (419)368-6942
URL: http://www.bpwohio.org/ashland

Descr: Represents the interests of business and professional women. Elevates the standards for women in business and professional settings. Promotes equity for all women in the workplace through advocacy, education and information. Provides professional development, networking and career advancement opportunities for working women.

2346 ■ Ashland Small Business Development Center - Ohio
Ashland University
401 College Ave.
Ashland, OH 44805
Contact: Timothy Moore, Dir.
Ph: (419)289-5316
Free: 877-289-1468
Fax: (419)289-5910
E-mail: tmoore3@ashland.edu

URL: http://www.ashland.edu/academics/business/sbdc

Descr: Represents and promotes the small business sector. Provides management assistance to current and prospective small business owners. Helps to improve management skills and expand the products and services of members.

2347 ■ Business and Professional Women, Berea
PO Box 95
Berea, OH 44017
Contact: Virginia Collings, Pres.
E-mail: akreigerf@aol.com
URL: http://www.bpwohio.org/berea

Descr: Represents the interests of business and professional women. Elevates the standards for women in business and professional settings. Promotes equity for all women in the workplace through advocacy, education and information. Provides professional development, networking and career advancement opportunities for working women.

2348 ■ Business and Professional Women Ohio, District 6
10395 US Rte. 127
Versailles, OH 45380
Contact: Merri Niekamp, Pres.
Ph: (937)337-4825
E-mail: markandmerrin24@earthlink.net
URL: http://www.bpwohio.org/region6

Descr: Represents the interests of business and professional women. Elevates the standards for women in business and professional settings. Promotes equity for all women in the workplace through advocacy, education and information. Provides professional development, networking and career advancement opportunities for working women.

2349 ■ Coshocton Business and Professional Women
PO Box 656
Coshocton, OH 43812
Contact: Karen Fry, Membership Chair
Ph: (740)622-3113
Fax: (740)622-5286
E-mail: karenf@noveltyadv.com
URL: http://www.bpwohio.org/coshocton.html

Descr: Represents the interests of business and professional women. Elevates the standards for women in business and professional settings. Promotes equity for all women in the workplace through advocacy, education and information. Provides professional development, networking and career advancement opportunities for working women.

2350 ■ Financial Planning Association of Central Ohio
5481 Haverhill Dr.
Dublin, OH 43017
Contact: Matthew J. Stewart CFP, Pres.
Ph: (614)336-9333
Fax: (614)793-1946
E-mail: admin@fpacentralohio.org
URL: http://www.fpacentralohio.org

Descr: Orchestrates the promotion and education of the financial planning profession to its members and the Central Ohio community.

2351 ■ Financial Planning Association, Dayton Ohio Chapter
629 Kenbrook Dr.
Vandalia, OH 45377
Contact: Hope Barker, Admin.
Ph: (937)520-7032
E-mail: admin@fpa-dayton.org
URL: http://www.fpanet.org/chapters/dayton

Descr: Promotes the value of the financial planning process to the public. Provides professional educa-

tion and networking opportunities for the financial planning community.

2352 ■ Financial Planning Association of Greater Cincinnati
4100 Executive Park Dr., Ste. 16
Cincinnati, OH 45241
Contact: Erik Christman CFP, Pres.
Ph: (513)554-3063
Fax: (513)563-9743
E-mail: admin@fpacinti.org
URL: http://www.fpacinti.org

Descr: Promotes the value of the financial planning process to the public. Provides professional education and networking opportunities for the financial planning community.

2353 ■ Financial Planning Association of Northeast Ohio Chapter
28022 Osborn Rd.
Bay Village, OH 44140
Contact: Amy Saban CFP, Pres.
Ph: (440)899-5055
Fax: (440)899-1010
E-mail: fpaneo@aol.com
URL: http://www.fpaneo.com

Descr: Promotes the value of the financial planning process and advances the financial planning profession. Provides forum for education and career development for its members.

2354 ■ Financial Planning Association, Northwest Ohio Chapter
Three Seagate
PO Box 10099
Toledo, OH 43699
Contact: Angela Granata, Pres.
Ph: (419)250-8066
Fax: (419)259-8450
E-mail: angela_granata@keybank.com
URL: http://www.fpanet.org/chapters/fpanwo/index.cfm

Descr: Promotes the value of the financial planning process to the public. Provides professional education and networking opportunities for the financial planning community.

2355 ■ International Association of Assessing Officers, Ohio
Fairfield County Auditor's Office
210 E Main St.
Lancaster, OH 43130
Contact: Barbara Curtiss AAS, Rep.
Ph: (740)687-7027
Fax: (740)684-6781
E-mail: bcurtiss@co.fairfield.oh.us

Descr: Represents state and local officials concerned with valuation of property for ad valorem property tax purposes. Works to improve standards and conduct research on tax assessment. Promotes innovation and excellence in property appraisal, assessment administration, and property tax policy through professional development, education, research, and technical assistance.

2356 ■ Kent/Portage Small Business Development Center
Kent State University
College of Business Administration, Rm. 300
Kent, OH 44242-0001
Ph: (330)672-1275
Fax: (330)672-9338
URL: http://www.krba.biz/sbdc

Descr: Represents and promotes the small business sector. Provides management assistance to current and prospective small business owners. Helps to improve management skills and expand the products and services of members.

2357 ■ NAIFA - Akron/Canton Area Association
1205 Sellman Dr.
Akron, OH 44333
Contact: Daniel James Leslie CLU, Pres.
Ph: (330)670-8103
E-mail: kathysidaway@hotmail.com

Descr: Represents the interests of insurance and financial advisors. Advocates for a positive legislative and regulatory environment. Enhances business and professional skills of members.

2358 ■ NAIFA-Columbus
8457 Invergordon Ct.
Dublin, OH 43017
Contact: Karen Shepherd, Association Exec.
Ph: (614)766-8472
Fax: (614)766-8474
E-mail: exec@naifa-columbus.org
URL: http://www.naifa-columbus.org

Descr: Represents the interests of insurance and financial advisors. Advocates for a positive legislative and regulatory environment. Enhances business and professional skills of members.

2359 ■ NAIFA-Lima
PO Box 256
Middle Point, OH 45863
Contact: Doris Dickman, Sec.
Ph: (419)233-3078
E-mail: limaaifa@hotmail.com
URL: http://www.naifa.org

Descr: Represents the interest of insurance and financial advisors. Advocates for a positive legislative and regulatory environment. Enhances business and professional skills of members.

2360 ■ North American Securities Administrators Association, Ohio
77 S High St., 22nd Fl.
Columbus, OH 43215
Contact: Brian Misencik, Commissioner
Ph: (614)644-7381
Fax: (614)466-3316

Descr: Represents the interests of the state, provincial and territorial securities administrators in the U.S.

2361 ■ Ohio Butler County Small Development Center
Biztech Center
20 High St.
Hamilton, OH 45011
Contact: Matt Eisenbraun, Dir./Business Advisor
Ph: (513)737-6543
URL: http://www.biztechcenter.com/OHIOSBDC.html

Descr: Represents and promotes the small business sector. Provides management assistance to current and prospective small business owners. Helps to improve management skills and expand the products and services of members.

2362 ■ Ohio Coalition of Taxpayers
3289 Rochfort Bridge Dr. E
Columbus, OH 43221
Ph: (614)777-4071

2363 ■ Ohio Small Business Development Center at Terra Community College
2830 Napoleon Rd.
Fremont, OH 43420-9670
Ph: (419)559-2210
Free: 800-826-2431
URL: http://www.terra.edu/learning/kerndirectory/sbdc.asp

Descr: Represents and promotes the small business sector. Provides management assistance to current and prospective small business owners. Helps to improve management skills and expand the products and services of members.

2364 ■ Ohio State Society of Enrolled Agents Society Assistant (OSSEA)
85 Brent Hill Dr. NE
Newark, OH 43055
Contact: Bev Buttermore
Ph: (740)345-1269
Fax: (740)322-6400
E-mail: ossea4u@windstream.net
URL: http://www.ossea.org

Descr: Promotes ethical representation of the

financial position of taxpayers before government agencies. **Mem:** 275.

2365 ■ Small Business Development Center at Columbus State Community College
315 Cleveland Ave., Ste. 317
Columbus, OH 43215
Contact: Michael Bowers, Dir.
Ph: (614)287-5294
E-mail: sharri11@cscc.edu
URL: http://www.entrepreneurohio.org
Descr: Represents and promotes the small business sector. Provides management assistance to current and prospective small business owners. Helps to improve management skills and expand the products and services of members.

2366 ■ Small Business Development Center at Edison Community College
1973 Edison Ave.
Piqua, OH 45356
Contact: Jerry Alexander, Dir.
Ph: (937)381-1516
E-mail: jerry.alexander@edisonohio.edu
URL: http://www.entrepreneurohio.org
Descr: Represents and promotes the small business sector. Provides management assistance to current and prospective small business owners. Helps to improve management skills and expand the products and services of members.

2367 ■ Small Business Development Center at James A. Rhodes State College
Keese Hall
4240 Campus Dr.
Lima, OH 45804
Contact: Kathleen Keller, Dir.
Ph: (419)995-8184
E-mail: keller.k@rhodesstate.edu
URL: http://www.entrepreneurohio.org
Descr: Represents and promotes the small business sector. Provides management assistance to current and prospective small business owners. Helps to improve management skills and expand the products and services of members.

2368 ■ Small Business Development Center at Kent State University Stark Campus
Professional Education and Conference Ctr.
6000 Frank Ave. NW
Canton, OH 44720
Contact: Donald Schneck, Dir.
Ph: (330)244-3290
E-mail: dschneck@kent.edu
URL: http://www.entrepreneurohio.org
Descr: Represents and promotes the small business sector. Provides management assistance to current and prospective small business owners. Helps to improve management skills and expand the products and services of members.

2369 ■ Small Business Development Center at Kent State University Tuscarawas Campus
Science & Advance Technology Bldg.
330 University Dr. NE
New Philadelphia, OH 44663
Contact: Steve Schillig, Dir.
Ph: (330)308-7479
E-mail: sschil10@kent.edu
URL: http://www.entrepreneurohio.org
Descr: Represents and promotes the small business sector. Provides management assistance to current and prospective small business owners. Helps to improve management skills and expand the products and services of members.

2370 ■ Small Business Development Center at Lake County Economic Development Center
One Victoria Pl., Ste. 265A
Painesville, OH 44077
Contact: Allen Weaver, Dir.
Ph: (440)357-2290
E-mail: allenweaver@lcedc.org
URL: http://www.entrepreneurohio.org
Descr: Represents and promotes the small business sector. Provides management assistance to current

and prospective small business owners. Helps to improve management skills and expand the products and services of members.

2371 ■ Small Business Development Center at Marietta
308 Front St.
Marietta, OH 45750
Contact: Patricia Lankford, Dir.
Ph: (740)373-5150
E-mail: plankford@wscc.edu
URL: http://www.entrepreneurohio.org
Descr: Represents and promotes the small business sector. Provides management assistance to current and prospective small business owners. Helps to improve management skills and expand the products and services of members.

2372 ■ Small Business Development Center at Maumee Valley Planning Organization
Defiance County East Bldg.
1300 E 2nd St., Ste. 201
Defiance, OH 43512
Contact: Merry Beavers, Dir.
Ph: (419)782-6270
E-mail: nwsbdcoh@msn.com
URL: http://www.entrepreneurohio.org
Descr: Represents and promotes the small business sector. Provides management assistance to current and prospective small business owners. Helps to improve management skills and expand the products and services of members.

2373 ■ Small Business Development Center at Ohio University
The Ridges, Bldg. 20
20 E Circle Dr.
Athens, OH 45701
Contact: Shawn Mallett, Dir.
Ph: (740)593-1797
E-mail: jollickl@ohio.edu
URL: http://www.entrepreneurohio.org
Descr: Represents and promotes the small business sector. Provides management assistance to current and prospective small business owners. Helps to improve management skills and expand the products and services of members.

2374 ■ Small Business Development Center at The OSU South Centers
Endeavor Center
1864 Shyville Rd.
Piketon, OH 45661
Contact: Ryan Mapes, Dir.
Free: 800-860-7232
E-mail: obryant5@ag.osu.edu
URL: http://www.entrepreneurohio.org
Descr: Represents and promotes the small business sector. Provides management assistance to current and prospective small business owners. Helps to improve management skills and expand the products and services of members.

2375 ■ Small Business Development Center at University of Cincinnati
PNC Bldg.
7162 Reading Rd., Ste. 725
Cincinnati, OH 45237
Contact: Calvin Brown, Dir.
Ph: (513)556-2072
E-mail: jessica.foote@uc.edu
URL: http://www.entrepreneurohio.org
Descr: Represents and promotes the small business sector. Provides management assistance to current and prospective small business owners. Helps to improve management skills and expand the products and services of members.

2376 ■ Small Business Development Center at Wright State University
Rike Hall, Rm. 120
3640 Colonel Glenn Hwy.
Dayton, OH 45435
Contact: Michael Bodey, Dir.
Ph: (937)775-3487
E-mail: michael.bodey@wright.edu
URL: http://www.sbdcwsu.org

Descr: Represents and promotes the small business sector. Provides management assistance to current and prospective small business owners. Helps to improve management skills and expand the products and services of members.

2377 ■ Small Business Development Center at Youngstown State University
275 Fifth Ave.
Youngstown, OH 44502
Contact: Patricia Veisz, Dir.
Ph: (330)941-2140
E-mail: pkveisz@cboss.com
URL: http://www.entrepreneurohio.org
Descr: Represents and promotes the small business sector. Provides management assistance to current and prospective small business owners. Helps to improve management skills and expand the products and services of members.

2378 ■ Small Business Development Center at Zane State College
Willett-Pratt Training Ctr.
9900 Brick Church Rd.
Cambridge, OH 43725
Contact: Cindy Voorhies, Dir.
Ph: (740)432-6568
URL: http://www.entrepreneurohio.org
Descr: Represents and promotes the small business sector. Provides management assistance to current and prospective small business owners. Helps to improve management skills and expand the products and services of members.

2379 ■ SOCAP International - Ohio Chapter
325 Springside Dr.
Akron, OH 44333
Contact: Dana Allender, Pres.
Ph: (330)670-5141
Descr: Promotes customer care and customer management as a competitive advantage in business. Provides educational tools and professional resources to help members drive business transformation within their companies.

2380 ■ Tallmadge Business and Professional Women
143 Northwest Ave., Bldg. A
Tallmadge, OH 44278
Contact: Debby Catrone
Ph: (330)784-7522
E-mail: ohlibrarylady@yahoo.com
URL: http://www.bpwohio.org/tallmadge
Descr: Represents the interests of business and professional women. Elevates the standards for women in business and professional settings. Promotes equity for all women in the workplace through advocacy, education and information. Provides professional development, networking and career advancement opportunities for working women.

Oklahoma

2381 ■ Ada Business and Professional Women
16076 CR 3532
Ada, OK 74820
Contact: Dee Ann Jones
E-mail: webmaster@bpwada.org
URL: http://www.bpwada.org
Descr: Represents the interests of business and professional women. Elevates the standards for women in business and professional settings. Promotes equity for all women in the workplace through advocacy, education and information. Provides professional development, networking and career advancement opportunities for working women.

2382 ■ American Society of Appraisers, Oklahoma Chapter
2944 NW 50th St.
Oklahoma City, OK 73112
Contact: Lee R. Caesar Sr., Pres.
Ph: (405)942-2299

Fax: (405)942-3577
E-mail: lrcaesar@swbell.net
URL: http://old.appraisers.org/oklahoma_city
Descr: Serves as a professional appraisal educator, testing and accrediting society. Sponsors mandatory re-certification program for all members. Offers consumer information service to the public.

2383 ■ Carl Albert College Small Business Development Center
FL Holton Business Ctr., 3rd Fl.
1507 S McKenna St.
Poteau, OK 74953
Contact: Amy Lomon, Business Development Specialist
Ph: (918)647-1226
E-mail: alomon@carlalbert.edu
URL: http://www.osbdc.org
Descr: Represents and promotes the small business sector. Provides management assistance to current and prospective small business owners. Helps to improve management skills and expand the products and services of members.

2384 ■ Cimarron Business and Professional Women
1723 E Linda Ave.
Stillwater, OK 74075
Contact: Carey Warner, Pres.
E-mail: carey.warner@okstate.edu
URL: http://www.cimarronbpw.org
Descr: Represents the interests of business and professional women. Elevates the standards for women in business and professional settings. Promotes equity for all women in the workplace through advocacy, education and information. Provides professional development, networking and career advancement opportunities for working women.

2385 ■ East Central University Small Business Development Center
Administration Bldg., Rm. 251
E 12th St. & S Francis St.
Ada, OK 74820
Contact: Ann Ritter, Dir.
Ph: (580)436-3190
E-mail: aritter@mailclerk.ecok.edu
URL: http://www.osbdc.org
Descr: Represents and promotes the small business sector. Provides management assistance to current and prospective small business owners. Helps to improve management skills and expand the products and services of members.

2386 ■ Langston University Small Business Development Center
Oklahoma City Campus, Rm. 112
4205 N Lincoln Blvd.
Oklahoma City, OK 73105
Contact: Della Dean, Dir.
Ph: (405)962-1628
E-mail: dmdean@lunet.edu
URL: http://www.osbdc.org
Descr: Represents and promotes the small business sector. Provides management assistance to current and prospective small business owners. Helps to improve management skills and expand the products and services of members.

2387 ■ North American Securities Administrators Association, Oklahoma
First National Center, Ste. 860
120 N Robinson Ave.
Oklahoma City, OK 73102
Contact: Irving Faught, Admin.
Ph: (405)280-7700
Fax: (405)280-7742
Descr: Represents the interests of the state, provincial and territorial securities administrators in the U.S.

2388 ■ Northeastern State University Small Business Development Center - Broken Arrow
Bldg. A, Ste. 325
3100 E New Orleans St.

Broken Arrow, OK 74014
Contact: John Blue, Dir.
Ph: (918)449-6280
E-mail: bluejr@nsuok.edu
URL: http://www.osbdc.org
Descr: Represents and promotes the small business sector. Provides management assistance to current and prospective small business owners. Helps to improve management skills and expand the products and services of members.

2389 ■ Northeastern State University Small Business Development Center - Muskogee
2400 E Shawnee Rd.
Muskogee, OK 74403
Contact: Andy Livesay, Business Development Specialist
Ph: (918)458-0802
E-mail: livesaaj@nsuok.edu
URL: http://www.osbdc.org
Descr: Represents and promotes the small business sector. Provides management assistance to current and prospective small business owners. Helps to improve management skills and expand the products and services of members.

2390 ■ Northeastern State University Small Business Development Center Tahlequah
309 N Muskogee Ave.
Tahlequah, OK 74464
Contact: Andy Livesay, Business Development Specialist
Ph: (918)458-0802
E-mail: livesaaj@nsuok.edu
URL: http://www.osbdc.org
Descr: Represents and promotes the small business sector. Provides management assistance to current and prospective small business owners. Helps to improve management skills and expand the products and services of members.

2391 ■ Northwestern Oklahoma State University Small Business Development Center - Alva
Shockley Hall, Rm. 107
1038 8th St.
Alva, OK 73717
Contact: Jeanne Cole, Business Development Specialist
Ph: (580)327-8608
E-mail: jmcole@nwosu.edu
URL: http://www.osbdc.org
Descr: Represents and promotes the small business sector. Provides management assistance to current and prospective small business owners. Helps to improve management skills and expand the products and services of members.

2392 ■ Northwestern Oklahoma State University Small Business Development Center - Enid
2929 E Randolph Ave.
Enid, OK 73701
Contact: Bill Gregory, Dir.
Ph: (580)213-3197
E-mail: bwgregory@nwosu.edu
URL: http://www.osbdc.org
Descr: Represents and promotes the small business sector. Provides management assistance to current and prospective small business owners. Helps to improve management skills and expand the products and services of members.

2393 ■ Oklahoma AIFA
6051 N Brookline, Ste. 124
Oklahoma City, OK 73112
Contact: James Freudenberger, Pres.
Ph: (405)810-1989
Fax: (405)810-1799
E-mail: execvp@naifa-oklahoma.org
URL: http://www.okaifa.org
Descr: Represents the interests of insurance and financial advisors. Advocates for a positive legisla-

tive and regulatory environment. Enhances business and professional skills of members.

2394 ■ Oklahoma Chapter of the International Association of Assessing Officers
320 Robert S. Kerr Ave., Ste. 313
Oklahoma City, OK 73102
Contact: Mike Morrison, Pres.
Ph: (405)713-1200
Fax: (405)713-1853
E-mail: micmor@oklahomacounty.org
URL: http://ok-iaao.oklahomacounty.org
Descr: Represents state and local officials concerned with valuation of property for ad valorem property tax purposes. Works to improve standards and conduct research on tax assessment. Promotes innovation and excellence in property appraisal, assessment administration, and property tax policy through professional development, education, research, and technical assistance. **Fnd:** 1985.

2395 ■ Oklahoma City NAIFA (NAIFA-OKC)
6051 N Brookline Ave., Ste. 124
Oklahoma City, OK 73112-4286
Contact: Mary Garza, Association Exec.
Ph: (405)810-1989
Fax: (405)810-1799
E-mail: membersupport@naifa-okc.org
URL: http://naifa-okc.org
Descr: Represents the interest of insurance and financial advisors. Advocates for a positive legislative and regulatory environment. Enhances business and professional skills of members.

2396 ■ Oklahoma Society of Enrolled Agents
1700 Southwest Blvd.
Tulsa, OK 74107
Contact: James R. Adelman
Ph: (918)633-1120
Fax: (918)583-5637
E-mail: jadelman@swbell.net
Descr: Aims to improve the knowledge, skills and professionalism of members in all areas of taxation. Enhances the role of enrolled agents among government agencies, other professions and the public at large. Advocates for taxpayer rights and protects members' interests.

2397 ■ Rose State College Small Business Development Center
Professional Training and Education Center
1720 Hudiburg Dr.
Midwest City, OK 73110
Contact: Victoria Armstrong
Ph: (405)733-7348
E-mail: varmstrong@rose.edu
URL: http://www.osbdc.org
Descr: Represents and promotes the small business sector. Provides management assistance to current and prospective small business owners. Helps to improve management skills and expand the products and services of members.

2398 ■ Southeastern Oklahoma State University Small Business Development Center
301 W University Blvd.
Durant, OK 74701
Contact: Melinda Craige, Dir.
Ph: (580)745-2954
E-mail: mecraige@se.edu
URL: http://www.osbdc.org
Descr: Represents and promotes the small business sector. Provides management assistance to current and prospective small business owners. Helps to improve management skills and expand the products and services of members.

2399 ■ Southwestern Oklahoma State University Small Business Development Center
Center for Economic and Business Development
301 E Davis St.
Weatherford, OK 73096
Contact: Doug Misak, Coor.
Ph: (580)774-7095
E-mail: doug.misak@swosu.edu
URL: http://www.osbdc.org

Descr: Represents and promotes the small business sector. Provides management assistance to current and prospective small business owners. Helps to improve management skills and expand the products and services of members.

2400 ■ Waynoka Business and Professional Women
PO Box 24
Waynoka, OK 73860
Contact: Jeanne Cole, Treas.
E-mail: jmcole@nwosu.edu
URL: http://www.bpwwaynoka.org
Descr: Represents the interests of business and professional women. Elevates the standards for women in business and professional settings. Promotes equity for all women in the workplace through advocacy, education and information. Provides professional development, networking and career advancement opportunities for working women.

Oregon

2401 ■ Baker City Small Business Development Center
3275 Baker St.
Baker City, OR 97814
Ph: (541)523-9842
E-mail: bakercity@bizcenter.org
URL: http://www.bizcenter.org
Descr: Represents and promotes the small business sector. Provides management assistance to current and prospective small business owners. Helps to improve management skills and expand the products and services of members.

2402 ■ Blue Mountain Community College Small Business Development Center
PO Box 100
Pendleton, OR 97801
Ph: (541)276-6233
Fax: (541)276-6819
E-mail: pendleton@bizcenter.org
URL: http://www.bizcenter.org
Descr: Represents and promotes the small business sector. Provides management assistance to current and prospective small business owners. Helps to improve management skills and expand the products and services of members.

2403 ■ Central Oregon Community College Business Development Center
Boyle Education Center Bldg.
2600 NW College Way
Bend, OR 97701
Ph: (541)383-7290
Fax: (541)318-3751
E-mail: bend@bizcenter.org
URL: http://www.bizcenter.org
Descr: Represents and promotes the small business sector. Provides management assistance to current and prospective small business owners. Helps to improve management skills and expand the products and services of members.

2404 ■ Chemeketa Community College Small Business Development Center
Center for Business and Industry
365 Ferry St. SE
Salem, OR 97301
Ph: (503)399-5088
Fax: (503)581-6017
E-mail: salem@bizcenter.org
URL: http://www.bizcenter.org
Descr: Represents and promotes the small business sector. Provides management assistance to current and prospective small business owners. Helps to improve management skills and expand the products and services of members.

2405 ■ Clackamas Community College Small Business Development Center
OIT Bldg., Rm. 172
7736 SE Harmony Rd.
Milwaukie, OR 97222

Ph: (503)594-0738
Fax: (503)594-0726
E-mail: bizcenter@clackamas.edu
URL: http://www.bizcenter.org
Descr: Represents and promotes the small business sector. Provides management assistance to current and prospective small business owners. Helps to improve management skills and expand the products and services of members.

2406 ■ Clatsop Community College Small Business Development Center
1455 N Roosevelt Dr.
Seaside, OR 97138
Ph: (503)738-3346
Fax: (503)738-7843
E-mail: seaside@bizcenter.org
URL: http://www.bizcenter.org
Descr: Represents and promotes the small business sector. Provides management assistance to current and prospective small business owners. Helps to improve management skills and expand the products and services of members.

2407 ■ Columbia Gorge Community College Small Business Development Center
400 E Scenic Dr., Ste. 259
The Dalles, OR 97058
Ph: (541)506-6121
Fax: (541)506-6122
E-mail: thedalles@bizcenter.org
URL: http://www.bizcenter.org
Descr: Represents and promotes the small business sector. Provides management assistance to current and prospective small business owners. Helps to improve management skills and expand the products and services of members.

2408 ■ Eastern Oregon University Small Business Development Center
Integrated Services Bldg.
1607 Gekeler Ln.
La Grande, OR 97850
Ph: (541)962-1532
Fax: (541)962-1532
E-mail: lagrande@bizcenter.org
URL: http://www.bizcenter.org
Descr: Represents and promotes the small business sector. Provides management assistance to current and prospective small business owners. Helps to improve management skills and expand the products and services of members.

2409 ■ Financial Planning Association of Mid-Oregon Chapter
PO Box 1452
Eugene, OR 97440
Contact: Linda Barbara, Exec. Dir.
Ph: (541)284-9855
E-mail: lmbarba1@yahoo.com
URL: http://www.fpanet.org/chapters/midoregon
Descr: Provides educational and networking forum for Financial Service Professionals that increases public awareness of the benefits of the financial planning process and promotes high ethical standards.

2410 ■ Financial Planning Association of Oregon and SW Washington
PO Box 2126
Salem, OR 97308
Contact: Harvey Gail, Exec. Dir.
Ph: (503)286-8350
E-mail: info@fpa-or.org
URL: http://www.fpa-or.org
Descr: Fosters vital service, benefits, and lifelong value of professional financial planning. Promotes the CFP mark and enhance the financial planning profession for its members and the public through educational opportunities, professional interaction, and community involvement.

2411 ■ Greater Oregon Chapter of the Appraisal Institute (GOCAI)
PO Box 573
Salem, OR 97308-0573
Contact: Vicki Champ, Education Dir.

Ph: (503)316-1979
Fax: (503)585-8547
E-mail: aioregon@oregonappraisers.org
URL: http://www.oregonappraisers.org
Descr: Represents professional real estate appraisers. **Mem:** 23000. **Pub:** *Field Notes* (bimonthly).

2412 ■ Hermiston Small Business Development Center
980 SE Columbia Dr.
Hermiston, OR 97838
Ph: (541)567-1800
E-mail: hermiston@bizcenter.org
URL: http://www.bizcenter.org
Descr: Represents and promotes the small business sector. Provides management assistance to current and prospective small business owners. Helps to improve management skills and expand the products and services of members.

2413 ■ Lane Community College Business Development Center
Wildish Bldg.
1445 Willamette St., Ste. 1
Eugene, OR 97401
Ph: (541)463-5255
Fax: (541)686-0096
E-mail: eugene@bizcenter.org
URL: http://www.bizcenter.org
Descr: Represents and promotes the small business sector. Provides management assistance to current and prospective small business owners. Helps to improve management skills and expand the products and services of members.

2414 ■ Linn-Benton Community College Business Development Center
6500 Pacific Blvd. SW
Albany, OR 97321
Ph: (541)917-4929
Fax: (541)917-4831
E-mail: albany@bizcenter.org
URL: http://www.bizcenter.org
Descr: Represents and promotes the small business sector. Provides management assistance to current and prospective small business owners. Helps to improve management skills and expand the products and services of members.

2415 ■ Mt. Hood Community College Small Business Development Center
PGE Bldg.
323 NE Roberts Ave.
Gresham, OR 97030
Ph: (503)491-7658
Fax: (503)666-1140
E-mail: gresham@bizcenter.org
URL: http://www.bizcenter.org
Descr: Represents and promotes the small business sector. Provides management assistance to current and prospective small business owners. Helps to improve management skills and expand the products and services of members.

2416 ■ North American Securities Administrators Association, Oregon
350 Winter St. NE, Rm. 410
Salem, OR 97301
Contact: David Tatman, Admin.
Ph: (503)378-4387
Fax: (503)947-7862
Descr: Represents the interests of the state, provincial and territorial securities administrators in the U.S.

2417 ■ North County Recreation District Small Business Development Center
36155 9th St.
Nehalem, OR 97131
Ph: (503)368-8222
E-mail: nehalem@bizcenter.org
URL: http://www.bizcenter.org
Descr: Represents and promotes the small business sector. Provides management assistance to current and prospective small business owners. Helps to

improve management skills and expand the products and services of members.

2418 ■ Oregon Coast Community College Small Business Development Center
1206 SE 48th St.
Lincoln City, OR 97367
Ph: (541)994-4166
Fax: (541)996-4958
E-mail: lincolncity@bizcenter.org
URL: http://www.bizcenter.org

Descr: Represents and promotes the small business sector. Provides management assistance to current and prospective small business owners. Helps to improve management skills and expand the products and services of members.

2419 ■ Oregon Institute of Technology Small Business Development Center
3201 Campus Dr.
BH 119
Klamath Falls, OR 97601
Ph: (541)885-1760
Fax: (541)885-1761
E-mail: klamathfalls@bizcenter.org
URL: http://www.bizcenter.org

Descr: Represents and promotes the small business sector. Provides management assistance to current and prospective small business owners. Helps to improve management skills and expand the products and services of members.

2420 ■ Oregon Society of Enrolled Agents
631 SE Rose St.
Roseburg, OR 97470-4920
Contact: Susan Bladorn EA, Pres.
Ph: (541)672-4317
Fax: (541)672-6345
E-mail: rosest@rosenet.net
URL: http://www.naea.org/MemberPortal/StateAffiliates/Listing

Descr: Seeks to: foster professionalism and growth among members; be an advocate of taxpayer rights; protect the interests of members; and enhance the role of the enrolled agent among government agencies, other professions and the public at large, with an emphasis at the state and local levels.

2421 ■ Oregon Society of Enrolled Agents - Metro Area Chapter
2122 SE Harrison
Portland, OR 97214-4872
Contact: Marvin Carlson EA, Pres.
Ph: (503)731-8905
Fax: (503)235-2030
E-mail: mmcarl@earthlink.net

2422 ■ Oregon State AIFA
12690 NW Lorraine Dr.
Portland, OR 97229
Contact: Robert Buxman, Exec. Dir.
Ph: (503)718-0094
Fax: (866)791-3348
E-mail: associationmgmt@verizon.net
URL: http://209.61.156.20/main-pub.cfm?usr=400000

Descr: Represents the interests of insurance and financial advisors. Advocates for a positive legislative and regulatory environment. Enhances business and professional skills of members.

2423 ■ Pacific City Senior Center Small Business Development Center
34600 Cape Kiwanda Dr.
Pacific City, OR 97135
Ph: (503)965-6108
E-mail: pacificcity@bizcenter.org
URL: http://www.bizcenter.org

Descr: Represents and promotes the small business sector. Provides management assistance to current and prospective small business owners. Helps to

improve management skills and expand the products and services of members.

2424 ■ Portland Community College Small Business Development Center
2025 Lloyd Ctr.
Portland, OR 97232
Ph: (503)978-5080
Fax: (503)288-1366
E-mail: portland@bizcenter.org
URL: http://www.bizcenter.org

Descr: Represents and promotes the small business sector. Provides management assistance to current and prospective small business owners. Helps to improve management skills and expand the products and services of members.

2425 ■ Rogue AIFA
PO Box 4301
Medford, OR 97501
Contact: Ken Hedstrom, Exec. Dir.
Ph: (541)772-1116
Fax: (541)772-6927
URL: http://www.rogueaifa.org

Descr: Represents the interests of insurance and financial advisors. Advocates for a positive legislative and regulatory environment. Enhances business and professional skills of members.

2426 ■ Rogue Community College Small Business Development Center
214 SW 4th St.
Grants Pass, OR 97526
Ph: (541)956-7494
Fax: (541)471-3589
E-mail: grantspass@bizcenter.org
URL: http://www.bizcenter.org

Descr: Represents and promotes the small business sector. Provides management assistance to current and prospective small business owners. Helps to improve management skills and expand the products and services of members.

2427 ■ Southern Oregon University Small Business Development Center
673 Market St.
Medford, OR 97504
Ph: (541)772-3478
Fax: (541)779-0953
E-mail: medford@bizcenter.org
URL: http://www.bizcenter.org

Descr: Represents and promotes the small business sector. Provides management assistance to current and prospective small business owners. Helps to improve management skills and expand the products and services of members.

2428 ■ Southwestern Oregon Community College Business Development Center
2455 Maple Leaf Ln.
North Bend, OR 97459
Ph: (541)756-6866
Fax: (541)756-5735
E-mail: coosbay@bizcenter.org
URL: http://www.bizcenter.org

Descr: Represents and promotes the small business sector. Provides management assistance to current and prospective small business owners. Helps to improve management skills and expand the products and services of members.

2429 ■ Taxpayers Association of Oregon (TAO)
PO Box 23573
Tigard, OR 97281
Contact: Don McIntire, Pres.
Ph: (503)603-9009
E-mail: media@teleport.com
URL: http://www.oregonwatchdog.com

2430 ■ Tillamook Bay Community College Small Business Development Center
2510 1st St.
Tillamook, OR 97141
Ph: (503)842-8222
Fax: (503)842-2214

E-mail: tillamook@bizcenter.org
URL: http://www.bizcenter.org

Descr: Represents and promotes the small business sector. Provides management assistance to current and prospective small business owners. Helps to improve management skills and expand the products and services of members.

2431 ■ Treasure Valley Community College Small Business Development Center
Albertson Center
650 College Blvd.
Ontario, OR 97914
Ph: (541)881-8822
Fax: (541)881-2743
E-mail: treasurevalley@bizcenter.org
URL: http://www.bizcenter.org

Descr: Represents and promotes the small business sector. Provides management assistance to current and prospective small business owners. Helps to improve management skills and expand the products and services of members.

Pennsylvania

2432 ■ Adams County Taxpayers Association
824 Highland Ave.
Gettysburg, PA 17325
Ph: (717)337-1264

2433 ■ American Society of Appraisers, Philadelphia Chapter
8 Terrace Rd.
Plymouth Meeting, PA 19462
Contact: Robert Ardinger, Pres.
Ph: (610)277-1366
Fax: (610)277-1366
E-mail: riggscommercial.realestate@rcn.com
URL: http://www.asaphila.com/asaphila

Descr: Serves as a professional appraisal educator, testing and accrediting society. Sponsors mandatory recertification program for all members. Offers consumer information service to the public.

2434 ■ Association of Concerned Taxpayers - Pennsylvania
PO Box 106
Swarthmore, PA 19081
Ph: (215)543-4066

2435 ■ Bucknell University Small Business Development Center
112 Dana Engineering Bldg.
1 Dent Dr.
Lewisburg, PA 17837
Contact: Jon R. Vernam, Dir.
Ph: (570)577-1249
Free: 866-375-6010
Fax: (570)577-1768
E-mail: sbdc@bucknell.edu
URL: http://pasbdc.org/bucknell

Descr: Represents and promotes the small business sector. Provides management assistance to current and prospective small business owners. Helps to improve management skills and expand the products and services of members.

2436 ■ Business and Professional Women's Club of Canonsburg
297 Springfield Ave.
Washington, PA 15301
Contact: Alice Derian, Pres.
E-mail: info@canonsburgbpw.org
URL: http://www.canonsburgbpw.org

Descr: Represents the interests of business and professional women. Elevates the standards for women in business and professional settings. Promotes equity for all women in the workplace through advocacy, education and information. Provides professional development, networking and

career advancement opportunities for working women.

2437 ■ Business and Professional Women's Club, Lehigh Valley
PO Box 3457
Easton, PA 18043
Contact: Lilly Gioia, Pres.
E-mail: bpwlehighvalley@gmail.com
URL: http://www.bpwlehigh.org
Descr: Represents the interests of business and professional women. Elevates the standards for women in business and professional settings. Promotes equity for all women in the workplace through advocacy, education and information. Provides professional development, networking and career advancement opportunities for working women.

2438 ■ Central Bucks Taxpayers Association
1125 Maxwell Manor
Warminster, PA 18974
Ph: (215)694-1525
E-mail: jjgable@comcast.net

2439 ■ Clarion University Small Business Development Center
Clarion University of Pennsylvania
102 Still Hall
Clarion, PA 16214
Contact: Dr. Woodrow W. Yeaney, Dir.
Ph: (814)393-2060
Free: 877-292-1843
E-mail: sbdc@clarion.edu
URL: http://web.clarion.edu/sbdc
Descr: Represents and promotes the small business sector. Provides management assistance to current and prospective small business owners. Helps to improve management skills and expand the products and services of members.

2440 ■ Coatesville Taxpayers Alliance (CTA)
PO Box 72883
Thorndale, PA 19372
E-mail: casd@casdtaxpayeralliance.com

2441 ■ Daniel Boone Taxpayers Association (DBTA)
PO Box 527
Douglassville, PA 19518
E-mail: amitytaxes@yahoo.com

2442 ■ Duquesne University Small Business Development Center
108 Rockwell Hall
600 Forbes Ave.
Pittsburgh, PA 15282
Contact: Dr. Mary McKinney
Ph: (412)396-6233
Fax: (412)396-5884
E-mail: duqsbdc@duq.edu
URL: http://www.sbdc.duq.edu
Descr: Represents and promotes the small business sector. Provides management assistance to current and prospective small business owners. Helps to improve management skills and expand the products and services of members.

2443 ■ Financial Industry Regulatory Authority (FINRA)
1835 Market St., Ste. 1900
Philadelphia, PA 19103-2929
Contact: Robert B. Kaplan, Dir.
Ph: (215)665-1180
Fax: (215)496-0434
URL: http://www.finra.org
Descr: Serves as the primary private-sector regulator of America's securities industry.

2444 ■ Financial Planning Association of Central Pennsylvania (FPA)
2995 Round Hill Rd.
York, PA 17402
Contact: Lauren Scheib, Admin.
Ph: (717)668-2703
Fax: (717)755-8962

E-mail: laurenatfpa@aol.com
URL: http://www.fpacentralpa.org
Descr: Promotes the value of the financial planning process to the public. Provides professional education and networking opportunities for the financial planning community.

2445 ■ Financial Planning Association of Pittsburgh Chapter
PO Box 97795
Pittsburgh, PA 15227
Contact: Ann W. McKenna, Chapter Exec.
Ph: (412)653-1054
Fax: (412)653-1059
E-mail: fpa.pittsburgh@verizon.net
URL: http://www.fpapgh.org
Descr: Supports the financial planning process in order to help people achieve their goals and dreams. Promotes the value of the financial planning process and advances the financial planning profession.

2446 ■ Franklin County AIFA
421 Lincoln Way E
McConnellsburg, PA 17233
Contact: Phillip L. Lobaugh, Treas.
Free: 866-987-9955
Fax: (717)709-9083
URL: http://www.naifanet.com/franklincounty
Descr: Represents the interests of insurance and financial advisors. Advocates for a positive legislative and regulatory environment. Enhances business and professional skills of members.

2447 ■ Greater Downingtown Business and Professional Women's Club
1501 Robin Rd.
Coatesville, PA 19320
Contact: Paula Gambrill, Pres.
E-mail: bpwdowningtown@hotmail.com
URL: http://www.bpwdowningtown.tzo.org
Descr: Represents the interests of business and professional women. Elevates the standards for women in business and professional settings. Promotes equity for all women in the workplace through advocacy, education and information. Provides professional development, networking and career advancement opportunities for working women.

2448 ■ Huntingdon County Tax League
10674 Raystown Rd.
Huntingdon, PA 16652
Ph: (717)627-3933

2449 ■ Indiana Business and Professional Women's Club
PO Box 1165
Indiana, PA 15701
Contact: Regina Yanits, Pres.
Ph: (724)349-7366
E-mail: president@bpwindianapa.org
URL: http://www.bpwindianapa.org
Descr: Represents the interests of business and professional women. Elevates the standards for women in business and professional settings. Promotes equity for all women in the workplace through advocacy, education and information. Provides professional development, networking and career advancement opportunities for working women.

2450 ■ Indiana University of Pennsylvania Small Business Development Center
664 Pratt Dr., Ste. 108
Indiana, PA 15705
Contact: Tony Palamone, Dir.
Ph: (724)357-7915
Fax: (724)357-5985
E-mail: tpalamon@iup.edu
URL: http://www.eberly.iup.edu/msg/sbdc.htm
Descr: Represents and promotes the small business sector. Provides management assistance to current and prospective small business owners. Helps to

improve management skills and expand the products and services of members.

2451 ■ Jennersville Business and Professional Women
24 Mystery Rose Ln.
West Grove, PA 19390
Contact: Jackie Stenta, Pres.
Ph: (610)864-3100
E-mail: webmaster@bpwjennersville.org
URL: http://www.bpwjennersville.org
Descr: Represents the interests of business and professional women. Elevates the standards for women in business and professional settings. Promotes equity for all women in the workplace through advocacy, education and information. Provides professional development, networking and career advancement opportunities for working women.

2452 ■ Kutztown University Small Business Development Center (KU SBDC)
15155 Kutztown Rd.
Kutztown, PA 19530
Contact: Ernie Post, Dir.
Ph: (484)646-4002
Free: 866-458-7232
Fax: (484)646-4009
E-mail: sbdc@kutztownsbdc.org
URL: http://www.kutztownsbdc.org
Descr: Represents and promotes the small business sector. Provides management assistance to current and prospective small business owners. Helps to improve management skills and expand the products and services of members.

2453 ■ Latrobe Business and Professional Women
PO Box 545
Latrobe, PA 15650
Contact: Janice Merriman, Pres.
E-mail: latrobebpw@yahoo.com
URL: http://www.latrobebpw.org
Descr: Represents the interests of business and professional women. Elevates the standards for women in business and professional settings. Promotes equity for all women in the workplace through advocacy, education and information. Provides professional development, networking and career advancement opportunities for working women.

2454 ■ Lehigh University Small Business Development Center
College of Business and Economics
621 Taylor St., Rm. 395
Bethlehem, PA 18015
Contact: Alison McKechie
Ph: (610)758-3980
Fax: (610)758-5205
E-mail: insbdc@lehigh.edu
URL: http://www.lehigh.edu/~insbdc/index2.htm
Descr: Represents and promotes the small business sector. Provides management assistance to current and prospective small business owners. Helps to improve management skills and expand the products and services of members.

2455 ■ Lock Haven University Small Business Development Center
301 W Church St.
Lock Haven, PA 17745
Contact: Timothy J. Keohane, Dir.
Ph: (570)484-2589
E-mail: tkeohane@lhup.edu
URL: http://www.lhup.edu/sbdc
Descr: Represents and promotes the small business sector. Provides management assistance to current and prospective small business owners. Helps to improve management skills and expand the products and services of members.

2456 ■ NAIFA Altoona Area
1618 E Pleasant Valley Blvd.
Altoona, PA 16602
Contact: Robert E. Donlan, Treas.

Ph: (814)944-8849
Fax: (814)942-7185
E-mail: argyle@nb.net
URL: http://www.naifanet.com/altoona
Descr: Represents the interests of insurance and financial advisors. Advocates for a positive legislative and regulatory environment. Enhances business and professional skills of members.

2457 ■ NAIFA Crawford County
PO Box 372
Cochranton, PA 16314
Contact: Judy Shonnard
Ph: (814)425-2925
Fax: (814)425-7233
E-mail: ccaifa@verizon.net

Descr: Represents the interests of insurance and financial advisors. Advocates for a positive legislative and regulatory environment. Enhances business and professional skills of members.

2458 ■ NAIFA Erie
17550 Rte. 8
Union City, PA 16438
Contact: Gary L. Wells
Ph: (814)438-9325
Fax: (814)438-9325
E-mail: gwells1@metlife.com

Descr: Represents the interests of insurance and financial advisors. Advocates for a positive legislative and regulatory environment. Enhances business and professional skills of members.

2459 ■ North American Securities Administrators Association, Pennsylvania
Eastgate Office Bldg.
1010 N 7th St., 2nd Fl.
Harrisburg, PA 17102
Contact: Robert M. Lam
Ph: (717)787-8061
Fax: (717)783-5122
URL: http://www.psc.state.pa.us

Descr: Represents the interests of the state, provincial and territorial securities administrators in the U.S.

2460 ■ North Pennsylvania Taxpayers Association
PO Box 1576
Lansdale, PA 19446
Ph: (215)361-8208

2461 ■ Northwestern Pennsylvania AIFA
1741 Allegheny Blvd.
Box 333
Reno, PA 16343
Contact: Todd G. Williams, Sec.
Ph: (814)676-1246
Fax: (814)676-4558
E-mail: tg_williams@pa.rr.com

Descr: Represents the interest of insurance and financial advisors. Advocates for a positive legislative and regulatory environment. Enhances business and professional skills of members.

2462 ■ Penn State Small Business Development Center
3 Keller Bldg.
University Park, PA 16802
Contact: Linda Feltman
Ph: (814)863-4293
Fax: (814)865-6667
E-mail: sbdc@psu.edu
URL: http://www.sbdc.psu.edu

Descr: Represents and promotes the small business sector. Provides management assistance to current and prospective small business owners. Helps to improve management skills and expand the products and services of members.

2463 ■ Pennridge Community Taxpayers Association
324 Rte. 152
Perkasie, PA 18944

Ph: (215)257-8503
E-mail: jbolg@bellatlantic.net

2464 ■ Pennsylvania AIFA
777 E Park Dr., Ste. 200
Harrisburg, PA 17111
Contact: Albert E. Heiles, Pres.
Ph: (717)234-2523
Free: 800-552-7258
Fax: (717)234-5190
E-mail: al.heiles@zoominternet.net
URL: http://www.paifa.org
Descr: Represents the interests of insurance and financial advisors. Advocates for a positive legislative and regulatory environment. Enhances business and professional skills of members.

2465 ■ Pennsylvania Credit Union Association (PCUA)
4309 N Front St.
Harrisburg, PA 17110
Contact: Diana Roberts, Chair
Ph: (717)234-3156
Free: 800-932-0661
Fax: (717)234-2695
E-mail: info@pcua.coop
URL: http://www.pcua.coop
Staff: 41. **Descr:** Works to provide leadership in promoting credit unions and their philosophy. Serves credit card unions through products and services to meet the needs of their members; and maintains an organization that encourages growth and mutual respect of employees. **Fnd:** 1934. **Mem:** 836. **Pub:** *Keynotes* (bimonthly); *Keystone Extra* (weekly).

2466 ■ Pennsylvania Small Business Development Centers
University of Pennsylvania
Vance Hall, 4th Fl.
3733 Spruce St.
Philadelphia, PA 19104
Contact: Mr. William J. Cluck, Co-Chm.
Ph: (215)898-1219
Fax: (215)573-2135
E-mail: pasbdc@wharton.upenn.edu
URL: http://pasbdc.org
Descr: Represents and promotes the small business sector. Provides management assistance to current and prospective small business owners. Helps to improve management skills and expand the products and services of members.

2467 ■ Pennsylvania Society of Enrolled Agents
120 Park Dr.
Delmont, PA 15626
Contact: William P. Matesevac Jr., Pres.
Ph: (724)468-5086
Fax: (724)468-5245
E-mail: wpmatzea@alltel.net
URL: http://paenrolledagents.com/index.html
Descr: Promotes ethical representation of the financial position of taxpayers before government agencies.

2468 ■ Pittsburgh AIFA
1601 Penn Ave., No. 611
Pittsburgh, PA 15221
Contact: Christine Pikutis-Musuneggi, Pres.
Ph: (412)243-4315
Fax: (412)243-6104
E-mail: bud@cbmassoc.com
Descr: Represents the interest of insurance and financial advisors. Advocates for a positive legislative and regulatory environment. Enhances business and professional skills of members.

2469 ■ St. Vincent College Small Business Development Center
Center for Global Competitiveness
Aurelius Hall, 1st Fl.
300 Fraser Purchase Rd.
Latrobe, PA 15650
Contact: James H. Kunkel, Exec. Dir.
Ph: (724)537-4572
Free: 866-723-2242

Fax: (724)537-0919
E-mail: sbdc@stvincent.edu
URL: http://www.stvincent.edu/sbdc
Descr: Represents and promotes the small business sector. Provides management assistance to current and prospective small business owners. Helps to improve management skills and expand the products and services of members.

2470 ■ Shippensburg University Small Business Development Center
405 Grove Hall
1871 Old Main Dr.
Shippensburg, PA 17257
Contact: Michael H. Unruh, Dir.
Ph: (717)477-1935
Fax: (717)477-4010
E-mail: sbdc@ship.edu
URL: http://www.shipsbdc.org
Descr: Represents and promotes the small business sector. Provides management assistance to current and prospective small business owners. Helps to improve management skills and expand the products and services of members.

2471 ■ Small Business Development Center at Gannon University
120 W 9th St.
Erie, PA 16501
Contact: Debra Steiner, Dir.
Ph: (814)871-7232
Free: 877-258-6648
Fax: (814)871-7383
E-mail: gusbdc@gannon.edu
URL: http://www.sbdcgannon.org
Descr: Represents and promotes the small business sector. Provides management assistance to current and prospective small business owners. Helps to improve management skills and expand the products and services of members.

2472 ■ Small Business Development Center at St. Francis University
PO Box 600
Loretto, PA 15940
Contact: Ed Huttenhower, Dir.
Ph: (814)472-3200
Fax: (814)472-3202
E-mail: sbdc@francis.edu
URL: http://www.francis.edu/sbdc
Descr: Represents and promotes the small business sector. Provides management assistance to current and prospective small business owners. Helps to improve management skills and expand the products and services of members.

2473 ■ Small Business Development Center at The University of Scranton
Gallery House
411 Quincy Ave.
Scranton, PA 18510
Contact: Elaine M. Tweedy, Dir.
Ph: (570)941-7588
E-mail: sbdc@scranton.edu
URL: http://www.scrantonsbdc.com
Descr: Represents and promotes the small business sector. Provides management assistance to current and prospective small business owners. Helps to improve management skills and expand the products and services of members.

2474 ■ Small Business Development Center at the University of Pittsburgh
1800 Posvar Hall
230 S Bouquet St.
Pittsburgh, PA 15213
Contact: Raymond L. Vargo, Dir.
Ph: (412)648-1542
Fax: (412)648-1636
E-mail: rvargo@katz.pitt.edu
URL: http://www.pittentrepreneur.com/sbdc
Descr: Represents and promotes the small business sector. Provides management assistance to current and prospective small business owners. Helps to

improve management skills and expand the products and services of members.

2475 ■ SOCAP International - Greater Philadelphia Chapter
700 Indian Springs Dr.
Lancaster, PA 17601
Contact: Kelly Smedley, Pres.
Ph: (717)285-6262
URL: http://www.gphl-socap.org
Descr: Promotes customer care and customer management as a competitive advantage in business. Provides educational tools and professional resources to help members drive business transformation within their companies.

2476 ■ Temple Small Business Development Center
Beech Bldg.
1510 Cecil B. Moore Ave., Ste. 200
Philadelphia, PA 19121
Contact: Eustace Kangaju, Dir.
Ph: (215)204-7282
Fax: (215)204-4554
E-mail: sbdc@temple.edu
URL: http://sbm.temple.edu/sbdc
Descr: Represents and promotes the small business sector. Provides management assistance to current and prospective small business owners. Helps to improve management skills and expand the products and services of members.

2477 ■ Wharton Small Business Development Center (WSBDC)
Vance Hall
3733 Spruce St.
Philadelphia, PA 19104
Contact: Therese Flaherty
Ph: (215)898-4861
Fax: (215)898-1063
URL: http://whartonsbdc.wharton.upenn.edu
Descr: Represents and promotes the small business sector. Provides management assistance to current and prospective small business owners. Helps to improve management skills and expand the products and services of members.

2478 ■ Widener University Small Business Development Center
University Technology Park
1450 Edgmont Ave., Ste. 120
Chester, PA 19013
Contact: Glenn McAllister, Dir.
Ph: (610)610-8490
Fax: (610)619-8496
E-mail: info@widenersbdc.org
URL: http://www.widenersbdc.org
Descr: Represents and promotes the small business sector. Provides management assistance to current and prospective small business owners. Helps to improve management skills and expand the products and services of members.

2479 ■ Wilkes University Small Business Development Center
Innovation Center
7 S Main St., Ste. 200
Wilkes-Barre, PA 18701
Contact: Ruth C. Hughes
Ph: (570)408-4340
Fax: (570)408-9854
E-mail: sbdc@wilkes.edu
URL: http://www.wilkes.edu/sbdc
Descr: Represents and promotes the small business sector. Provides management assistance to current and prospective small business owners. Helps to improve management skills and expand the products and services of members.

2480 ■ Windber Business and Professional Women
2902 Jackson Ave.
Windber, PA 15963
Contact: Shannon Rugg, Pres.

Ph: (814)467-9131
E-mail: windberbpw@floodcity.net
URL: http://www.freewebs.com/windberbpw
Descr: Represents the interests of business and professional women. Elevates the standards for women in business and professional settings. Promotes equity for all women in the workplace through advocacy, education and information. Provides professional development, networking and career advancement opportunities for working women.

2481 ■ York County of Pennsylvania Taxpayers Council
1750 Wyndham Dr.
York, PA 17403
Ph: (717)845-4277
E-mail: jsears@yctc.us

Puerto Rico

2482 ■ Puerto Rico Small Business and Technology Development Centers
Edificio Union Plz., Piso 10
416 Ave. Ponce de Leon
San Juan, PR 00918
Contact: Carmen Marti, Exec. Dir.
Ph: (787)763-6811
Free: 888-300-7232
Fax: (787)763-4629
E-mail: inegron@inter.edu
URL: http://www.prsbtdc.org
Descr: Represents and promotes the small business sector. Provides management assistance to current and prospective small business owners. Helps to improve management skills and expand the products and services of members.

2483 ■ Puerto Rico Small Business and Technology Development Centers - Arecibo
PO Box 4050
Arecibo, PR 00614
Contact: Elidio Aldarondo, Dir.
Ph: (787)878-5475
Fax: (787)880-1624
E-mail: ealdarondo@arecibo.inter.edu
URL: http://www.prsbtdc.org
Descr: Represents and promotes the small business sector. Provides management assistance to current and prospective small business owners. Helps to improve management skills and expand the products and services of members.

2484 ■ Puerto Rico Small Business and Technology Development Centers - Caguas
PO Box 907
Caguas, PR 00726
Contact: Lorna Baez Amely, Dir.
Ph: (787)744-8833
Fax: (787)258-1797
E-mail: lbaez@prsbtdc.org
URL: http://www.prsbtdc.org
Descr: Represents and promotes the small business sector. Provides management assistance to current and prospective small business owners. Helps to improve management skills and expand the products and services of members.

2485 ■ Puerto Rico Small Business and Technology Development Centers - Fajardo
PO Box 70003
Fajardo, PR 00738
Contact: Carliana Carrasquillo, Dir.
Ph: (787)863-2390
Fax: (787)863-4711
E-mail: ccarrasq@inter.edu
URL: http://www.prsbtdc.org
Descr: Represents and promotes the small business sector. Provides management assistance to current and prospective small business owners. Helps to

improve management skills and expand the products and services of members.

2486 ■ Puerto Rico Small Business and Technology Development Centers - Ponce
Universidad Interamericana
Recinto de Ponce
104 Parque Industrial Turpo Rd., No. 1
Mercedita, PR 00715
Contact: Rafael Cepeda, Dir.
Ph: (787)284-1912
Fax: (787)842-0841
E-mail: recepeda@ponce.inter.edu
URL: http://www.prsbtdc.org
Descr: Represents and promotes the small business sector. Provides management assistance to current and prospective small business owners. Helps to improve management skills and expand the products and services of members.

2487 ■ Puerto Rico Small Business and Technology Development Centers - San German
PO Box 5100
San German, PR 00683
Contact: Brenda L. Rodriguez, Dir.
Ph: (787)264-1912
Fax: (787)892-6760
E-mail: blrodriguez@sg.inter.edu
URL: http://www.prsbtdc.org
Descr: Represents and promotes the small business sector. Provides management assistance to current and prospective small business owners. Helps to improve management skills and expand the products and services of members.

Rhode Island

2488 ■ Financial Planning Association of Rhode Island
Oceanstate Financial Services
401 Wampanoag Trail, Ste. 100
Riverside, RI 02915
Contact: Steve Grasso CFP, Chm.
Ph: (401)432-8855
E-mail: rpetrucci@oceanstatefinancial.com
URL: http://fpari.org
Descr: Supports the financial planning process in order to help people achieve their goals and dreams. Fosters the value of financial planning and advances the financial planning profession. Promotes the CFP mark and enhances the financial planning profession for its members and the public through educational opportunities, professional interaction, and community involvement.

2489 ■ International Association of Assessing Officers, Rhode Island
1170 Main St.
West Warwick, RI 02893
Contact: Raymond E. Beattie, Rep.
Ph: (401)827-9056
Fax: (401)822-9263
E-mail: rbeattie@westwarwickri.org
Descr: Represents state and local officials concerned with valuation of property for ad valorem property tax purposes. Works to improve standards and conduct research on tax assessment. Promotes innovation and excellence in property appraisal, assessment administration, and property tax policy through professional development, education, research, and technical assistance.

2490 ■ Lincoln Taxpayers Association (LTA)
11 Evergreen Rd.
Lincoln, RI 02865
E-mail: info@lincolntaxpayers.org
URL: http://www.lincolntaxpayers.org
Fnd: 2004.

2491 ■ Little Compton Taxpayers Association (LCTA)
PO Box 455
Adamsville, RI 02801
Contact: Bob Hayden, Chm.
E-mail: taxpayers@cox.net
URL: http://www.lctaxpayers.com

Fnd: 1990.

2492 ■ Newport Taxpayers Association
PO Box 485
Newport, RI 02840
Ph: (401)846-6872
Fax: (401)846-6872

2493 ■ North American Securities Administrators Association, Rhode Island
1511 Pontiac Ave.
Cranston, RI 02920
Contact: Maria D'Alessandro, Assoc. Dir.
Ph: (401)462-9500
Fax: (401)462-9532
URL: http://www.dbr.state.ri.us
Descr: Represents the interests of the state, provincial and territorial securities administrators in the U.S.

2494 ■ Rhode Island Commercial and Appraisal Board of Realtors
100 Bignall St.
Warwick, RI 02888
Contact: Claudia N. Chappelle, Exec. Off.
Ph: (401)432-6944
Fax: (401)941-5360
E-mail: cchappelle@riliving.com
Descr: Strives to develop real estate business practices. Advocates the right to own, use and transfer real property. Provides information about the real estate industry.

2495 ■ Rhode Island Credit Union League
20 Altieri Way
Warwick, RI 02888
Contact: Daniel F. Egan Jr., Pres.
Free: 800-842-1242
E-mail: degan@cucenter.org
URL: http://www.riculeague.org
Descr: Offers financial services to members. Provides legislative and public advocacy, education and training, product development and operational support. **Pub:** *Compliance Connection*; *Horizons* (monthly); Annual Report (annual).

2496 ■ Rhode Island Society of Enrolled Agents
35 High Gate Rd.
Cranston, RI 02920
Contact: Loretta E. Santagata
Ph: (401)942-4939
E-mail: lsantagata@verizon.net
Descr: Aims to improve the knowledge, skills and professionalism of members in all areas of taxation. Enhances the role of enrolled agents among government agencies, other professions and the public at large. Advocates for taxpayer rights and protects members' interests.

South Carolina

2497 ■ Aiken Area Small Business Development Center
Box 9
Aiken, SC 29801
Ph: (803)641-3646
URL: http://scsbdc.moore.sc.edu/AreaOffices.html#Aiken
Descr: Represents and promotes the small business sector. Provides management assistance to current and prospective small business owners. Helps to improve management skills and expand the products and services of members.

2498 ■ Aiken County Taxpayers' Association
981 Pineview Dr.
New Ellenton, SC 29809
Contact: Vicki Simons
Ph: (803)652-0923

2499 ■ American Society of Appraisers, South Carolina Chapter
201 Sunnyside Way
Summerville, SC 29485
Contact: Jan M. Goin, Pres.

Ph: (843)821-3669
Fax: (843)821-3617
E-mail: jgoin1@sc.rr.com
URL: http://old.appraisers.org/south_carolina
Descr: Serves as a professional appraisal educator, testing and accrediting society. Sponsors mandatory recertification program for all members. Offers consumer information service to the public.

2500 ■ Anderson County Taxpayers Association
500 Trail Rd.
Belton, SC 29627
Contact: Dan Harvell
Ph: (864)221-1221
E-mail: rileson@msn.com
URL: http://www.scatsc.org

2501 ■ Appraisal Institute, South Carolina Chapter
1516 Milford Rd.
Columbia, SC 29206
Contact: Caroline H. Stephenson, Exec. Sec.
Ph: (803)782-2922
Fax: (803)782-2923
E-mail: chapter@sc-ai.org
URL: http://www.sc-ai.org
Descr: General appraisers who hold the MAI or SRPA designations, and residential members who hold the SRA designation.

2502 ■ Beaufort Area Small Business Development Center
801 Carteret St.
Beaufort, SC 29902
Ph: (843)521-4143
URL: http://scsbdc.moore.sc.edu/AreaOffices.html#Beaufort
Descr: Represents and promotes the small business sector. Provides management assistance to current and prospective small business owners. Helps to improve management skills and expand the products and services of members.

2503 ■ Charleston Area Small Business Development Center
5900 Core Dr., Ste. 104
North Charleston, SC 29406
Ph: (843)740-6160
URL: http://scsbdc.moore.sc.edu/AreaOffices.html#Charleston
Descr: Represents and promotes the small business sector. Provides management assistance to current and prospective small business owners. Helps to improve management skills and expand the products and services of members.

2504 ■ Clemson Area Small Business Development Center
Clemson University
College of Business and Public Affairs
425 Sirrine Hall
Clemson, SC 29634-1392
Ph: (864)656-3227
URL: http://scsbdc.moore.sc.edu/AreaOffices.html#Clemson
Descr: Represents and promotes the small business sector. Provides management assistance to current and prospective small business owners. Helps to improve management skills and expand the products and services of members.

2505 ■ Colleton County Taxpayers Association
2584 Confederate Hwy.
Lodge, SC 29082
Ph: (843)866-2180

2506 ■ Dorchester County Taxpayers Association of South Carolina (DCTA)
PO Box 50522
Summerville, SC 29485

Contact: Joe Kress, VP
E-mail: jbraund7@bellsouth.net
URL: http://www.dcta.org

2507 ■ Florence Area Small Business Development Center
PO Box 100548
Florence, SC 29501-0548
Ph: (843)661-8256
URL: http://scsbdc.moore.sc.edu/AreaOffices.html#Florence
Descr: Represents and promotes the small business sector. Provides management assistance to current and prospective small business owners. Helps to improve management skills and expand the products and services of members.

2508 ■ Hilton Head Area Small Business Development Center
University of South Carolina - Beaufort South Campus
One University Blvd.
Bluffton, SC 29909
Ph: (843)208-8259
URL: http://scsbdc.moore.sc.edu/AreaOffices.html#HiltonHead
Descr: Represents and promotes the small business sector. Provides management assistance to current and prospective small business owners. Helps to improve management skills and expand the products and services of members.

2509 ■ Horry County Association of Taxpayers
255 Evergreen Ln.
Myrtle Beach, SC 29572
E-mail: info@wethepeopleofhorrycounty.org

2510 ■ International Association of Assessing Officers, South Carolina
PO Box 5762
Spartanburg, SC 29304
Contact: Guilford Bulman CAE, Rep.
Ph: (864)596-2548
E-mail: gbulman@spartanburgcounty.org
Descr: Represents state and local officials concerned with valuation of property for ad valorem property tax purposes. Works to improve standards and conduct research on tax assessment. Promotes innovation and excellence in property appraisal, assessment administration, and property tax policy through professional development, education, research, and technical assistance.

2511 ■ Lexington County Association of Taxpayers
709 N Eden Dr.
Cayce, SC 29033
Ph: (803)731-2466

2512 ■ Myrtle Beach Area Small Business Development Center
PO Box 261954
Conway, SC 29528-6054
Ph: (843)349-4010
URL: http://scsbdc.moore.sc.edu/AreaOffices.html#Myrtle
Descr: Represents and promotes the small business sector. Provides management assistance to current and prospective small business owners. Helps to improve management skills and expand the products and services of members.

2513 ■ Orangeburg Area Small Business Development Center
South Carolina State University
Campus Box 7176
Orangeburg, SC 29117
Ph: (803)536-8445
URL: http://scsbdc.moore.sc.edu/AreaOffices.html#Orangeburg
Descr: Represents and promotes the small business sector. Provides management assistance to current and prospective small business owners. Helps to

improve management skills and expand the products and services of members.

2514 ■ Pickens County Taxpayers Association

PO Box 92
Pickens, SC 29671
Ph: (864)878-0407
E-mail: whcgearman@charter.net

2515 ■ Richland County Association of Taxpayers

1812 Hi Sierra Dr.
Columbia, SC 29210
Ph: (803)772-2324
E-mail: jmccaulley@rr.sc.com

2516 ■ Rock Hill Area Small Business Development Center

Winthrop University
118 Thurmond Bldg.
Rock Hill, SC 29733
Ph: (864)323-2283
URL: http://scsbdc.moore.sc.edu/AreaOffices.html#Rockhill
Descr: Represents and promotes the small business sector. Provides management assistance to current and prospective small business owners. Helps to improve management skills and expand the products and services of members.

2517 ■ Saluda County Association of Taxpayers

115 Cheyenne Dr.
Leesville, SC 29070
Ph: (803)532-3389
E-mail: kerrywood@saludataxpayers.org
URL: http://www.scatsc.org

2518 ■ South Carolina Alliance of Taxpayer Organizations

218 Gold Finch Cir.
Greer, SC 29650
Ph: (864)268-0899
Fax: (864)268-0899

2519 ■ South Carolina Association of Taxpayers (SCAT)

PO Box 50799
Columbia, SC 29250
Contact: Don Weaver, Pres.
Ph: (803)748-9198
E-mail: sec.hailes@scatsc.org
URL: http://www.scatsc.org

2520 ■ South Carolina Society of Enrolled Agents

1309 N Blvd.
Anderson, SC 29621
Contact: Mr. W. Ray Partain
Ph: (864)224-4775
Fax: (864)231-6558
E-mail: ray@mcdougaldpartain.com
URL: http://www.scsea.org
Descr: Promotes ethical representation of the financial position of taxpayers before government agencies.

2521 ■ Spartanburg Small Business Development Center

Spartanburg Human Resource Ctr.
142 S Dean St., Ste. 216
Spartanburg, SC 29302
Ph: (864)316-9162
URL: http://scsbdc.moore.sc.edu/AreaOffices.html#Spartanburg
Descr: Represents and promotes the small business sector. Provides management assistance to current and prospective small business owners. Helps to improve management skills and expand the products and services of members.

2522 ■ Sumter Small Business Development Center

University of South Carolina - Sumter
200 Miller Rd., Rm. 216
Sumter, SC 29150

Ph: (803)938-3833
URL: http://scsbdc.moore.sc.edu/AreaOffices.html#Sumter
Descr: Represents and promotes the small business sector. Provides management assistance to current and prospective small business owners. Helps to improve management skills and expand the products and services of members.

2523 ■ University of South Carolina Small Business Development Center

Moore School of Business
1705 College St.
Columbia, SC 29208
Ph: (803)777-5118
Fax: (803)777-4403
E-mail: uscsbdc@moore.sc.edu
URL: http://mooreschool.sc.edu/moore/usc-sbdc/sbdc-index.htm
Descr: Represents and promotes the small business sector. Provides management assistance to current and prospective small business owners. Helps to improve management skills and expand the products and services of members.

South Dakota

2524 ■ Aberdeen City Small Business Development Center

416 Production St. N
Aberdeen, SD 57401
Contact: Kelly Weaver, Area Mgr.
Ph: (605)626-2565
Fax: (605)626-2667
E-mail: kweaver@midco.net
URL: http://www.usd.edu/sbdc
Descr: Represents and promotes the small business sector. Provides management assistance to current and prospective small business owners. Helps to improve management skills and expand the products and services of members.

2525 ■ NAIFA - Sioux Falls

4925 S Kalen Pl.
Sioux Falls, SD 57108
Contact: Margie Rolfing, Association Exec.
Ph: (605)339-0606
Fax: (605)339-0606
E-mail: sfrolfing@sio.midco.net
URL: http://www.naifanet.com/siouxfalls
Descr: Represents the interests of insurance and financial advisors. Advocates for a positive legislative and regulatory environment. Enhances business and professional skills of members.

2526 ■ North American Securities Administrators Association, South Dakota

445 E Capitol Ave.
Pierre, SD 57501
Contact: Gail Sheppick, Dir.
Ph: (605)773-4823
Fax: (605)773-5953
Descr: Represents the interests of the state, provincial and territorial securities administrators in the U.S.

2527 ■ Pierre Small Business Development Center

110 W Missouri Ave.
Pierre, SD 57501
Contact: Marcella Hurley, Area Mgr.
Ph: (605)773-2783
Fax: (605)773-2784
E-mail: marcella.hurley@usd.edu
URL: http://www.usd.edu/sbdc
Descr: Represents and promotes the small business sector. Provides management assistance to current and prospective small business owners. Helps to improve management skills and expand the products and services of members.

2528 ■ Rapid City Small Business Development Center

525 University Loop, Ste. 102
Rapid City, SD 57701
Contact: Dona Leavens, Area Mgr.

Ph: (605)394-5311
Fax: (605)394-6140
E-mail: dleavens@tie.net
URL: http://www.usd.edu/sbdc
Descr: Represents and promotes the small business sector. Provides management assistance to current and prospective small business owners. Helps to improve management skills and expand the products and services of members.

2529 ■ Sioux Falls Small Business Development Center

2329 N Career Ave., Ste. 106
Sioux Falls, SD 57107
Contact: Mark Slade, Area Mgr.
Ph: (605)367-5757
Fax: (605)367-5755
E-mail: mslade@usd.edu
URL: http://www.usd.edu/sbdc
Descr: Represents and promotes the small business sector. Provides management assistance to current and prospective small business owners. Helps to improve management skills and expand the products and services of members.

2530 ■ Watertown Small Business Development Center

PO Box 1207
Watertown, SD 57201
Contact: Belinda Engelhart, Area Mgr.
Ph: (605)882-5115
Fax: (605)882-5049
E-mail: bengelha@usd.edu
URL: http://www.usd.edu/sbdc
Descr: Represents and promotes the small business sector. Provides management assistance to current and prospective small business owners. Helps to improve management skills and expand the products and services of members.

2531 ■ Yankton Small Business Development Center

PO Box 687
Yankton, SD 57078
Contact: Sue Stoll, Area Mgr.
Ph: (605)665-0751
Fax: (605)665-0303
E-mail: suesbdc@districtiii.org
URL: http://www.usd.edu/sbdc
Descr: Represents and promotes the small business sector. Provides management assistance to current and prospective small business owners. Helps to improve management skills and expand the products and services of members.

Tennessee

2532 ■ American Society of Appraisers, Memphis Branch

Mercer Capital
5860 Ridgeway Center Pkwy., Ste. 400
Memphis, TN 38120
Contact: Timothy Robertson Lee, Chm.
Ph: (901)685-2120
Fax: (901)685-2199
E-mail: leet@mercercapital.com
URL: http://www.appraisers.org/memphis
Descr: Serves as a professional appraisal educator, testing and accrediting society. Sponsors mandatory recertification program for all members. Offers consumer information service to the public.

2533 ■ Benton County Business and Professional Women

50 Bounty Ln.
Camden, TN 38320
Contact: Gail Humphrey, Pres.
Ph: (731)584-5469
E-mail: ghumphrey55@hotmail.com
URL: http://www.bpwtn.org
Descr: Represents the interests of business and professional women. Elevates the standards for women in business and professional settings. Promotes equity for all women in the workplace through advocacy, education and information. Provides professional development, networking and

career advancement opportunities for working women.

2534 ■ Brentwood Business and Professional Women
6321 Noel Dr.
Brentwood, TN 37027
Contact: Wanda Carter Bates, Pres.
Ph: (615)373-4684
URL: http://www.bpwtn.org

Descr: Represents the interests of business and professional women. Elevates the standards for women in business and professional settings. Promotes equity for all women in the workplace through advocacy, education and information. Provides professional development, networking and career advancement opportunities for working women.

2535 ■ Chattanooga Business and Professional Women
4223 Highwood Dr.
Chattanooga, TN 37415
Contact: Mollie Flores, Pres.
Ph: (423)875-5357
E-mail: mollieflores@hotmail.com
URL: http://www.bpwtn.org

Descr: Represents the interests of business and professional women. Elevates the standards for women in business and professional settings. Promotes equity for all women in the workplace through advocacy, education and information. Provides professional development, networking and career advancement opportunities for working women.

2536 ■ Columbia Business and Professional Women
1023 E Valley Dr.
Columbia, TN 38401
Contact: Elizabeth Chrutcher, Pres.
Ph: (931)381-7183
E-mail: columbiabpw@gmail.com
URL: http://www.bpwtn.org

Descr: Represents the interests of business and professional women. Elevates the standards for women in business and professional settings. Promotes equity for all women in the workplace through advocacy, education and information. Provides professional development, networking and career advancement opportunities for working women.

2537 ■ Cookeville Business and Professional Women
3623 Shady Oak Cir.
Cookeville, TN 38501
Contact: Barbara Dean, Pres.
Ph: (931)528-4240
E-mail: tbmdean@frontiernet.net
URL: http://www.bpwtn.org

Descr: Represents the interests of business and professional women. Elevates the standards for women in business and professional settings. Promotes equity for all women in the workplace through advocacy, education and information. Provides professional development, networking and career advancement opportunities for working women.

2538 ■ Cumberland County Business and Professional Women
PO Box 228
Pleasant Hill, TN 38578
Contact: Bonnie Neveu, Pres.
Ph: (931)277-5682
E-mail: webmaster@bpwcumberland.org
URL: http://www.bpwcumberland.org

Descr: Represents the interests of business and professional women. Elevates the standards for women in business and professional settings. Promotes equity for all women in the workplace through advocacy, education and information. Provides professional development, networking and

career advancement opportunities for working women.

2539 ■ East Memphis Business and Professional Women
PO Box 34788
Bartlett, TN 38184-0788
Contact: Marlen Fulton, Pres.
E-mail: mfulton0371@hotmail.com
URL: http://www.eastmemphisbpw.org

Descr: Represents the interests of business and professional women. Elevates the standards for women in business and professional settings. Promotes equity for all women in the workplace through advocacy, education and information. Provides professional development, networking and career advancement opportunities for working women.

2540 ■ Elizabethon Business and Professional Women
PO Box 1625
Elizabethton, TN 37643
Contact: Joan Crow, Pres.
Ph: (423)543-1868
URL: http://www.bpwtn.org

Descr: Represents the interests of business and professional women. Elevates the standards for women in business and professional settings. Promotes equity for all women in the workplace through advocacy, education and information. Provides professional development, networking and career advancement opportunities for working women.

2541 ■ Fayette County Business and Professional Women
5845 Lagrange Rd.
Somerville, TN 38068
Contact: Cindy Marsh, Pres.
Ph: (901)937-1712
E-mail: cmarsh@csquared.biz
URL: http://www.bpwtn.org

Descr: Represents the interests of business and professional women. Elevates the standards for women in business and professional settings. Promotes equity for all women in the workplace through advocacy, education and information. Provides professional development, networking and career advancement opportunities for working women.

2542 ■ Financial Planning Association of Middle Tennessee
PO Box 150608
Nashville, TN 37215-0608
Contact: Douglas O'Rear CFP, Chm.
Ph: (615)473-1450
E-mail: fpamidtn@bellsouth.net
URL: http://www.fpa-midtn.org

Descr: Promotes financial planning profession through education, networking, and mentoring. Enhances public awareness of the value of the financial planning process. Provides forum for education and career development for its members.

2543 ■ Financial Planning Association of the Midsouth
Brandon Financial Planning
5101 Wheelis, Ste. 112
Memphis, TN 38117
Contact: Gary Lee Kieffner Jr., Pres.
Ph: (901)324-6600
Fax: (901)324-5743
E-mail: garykieffner@brandonplanning.com
URL: http://www.fpanet.org/chapters/midsouth

Descr: Promotes the value of the financial planning process to the public. Provides professional education and networking opportunities for the financial planning community.

2544 ■ Gallatin Business and Professional Women
849 Britton Ave.
Gallatin, TN 37066
Contact: Sara Clark Caldwell, Pres.

Ph: (615)452-8152
E-mail: kara7072@aol.com
URL: http://www.gallatinbpw.org

Descr: Represents the interests of business and professional women. Elevates the standards for women in business and professional settings. Promotes equity for all women in the workplace through advocacy, education and information. Provides professional development, networking and career advancement opportunities for working women.

2545 ■ Greater Nashville Business and Professional Women (GNBPW)
513 Four Lakes Dr.
Antioch, TN 37013
Contact: Susan Jakoblew, Pres.
Ph: (615)519-7498
E-mail: grtnashbpw@hotmail.com
URL: http://www.grtnashbpw.org

Descr: Represents the interests of business and professional women. Elevates the standards for women in business and professional settings. Promotes equity for all women in the workplace through advocacy, education and information. Provides professional development, networking and career advancement opportunities for working women.

2546 ■ Greater Tennessee Chapter of the Appraisal Institute
PO Box 60128
Nashville, TN 37206
Contact: Myra Withers, Exec.
Ph: (615)515-9700
Fax: (615)254-1186
E-mail: gtnchap@tds.net
URL: http://www.tnappraiser.org

Descr: Represents the interests of real estate appraisers.

2547 ■ Hardeman County Business and Professional Women
PO Box 868
Bolivar, TN 38008
Contact: Zulfat Suara, Pres.
Ph: (731)658-6808
E-mail: info@bpwhardeman.org
URL: http://www.bpwhardeman.org

Descr: Represents the interests of business and professional women. Elevates the standards for women in business and professional settings. Promotes equity for all women in the workplace through advocacy, education and information. Provides professional development, networking and career advancement opportunities for working women.

2548 ■ Heart of Tennessee Business and Professional Women
3015 Henderson Ln.
Murfreesboro, TN 37130
Contact: Cindy Burkitt, Pres.
Ph: (615)848-0857
Free: 800-819-0905
E-mail: cdburkitt@firstfleetinc.com
URL: http://www.heartoftnbpw.org

Descr: Represents the interests of business and professional women. Elevates the standards for women in business and professional settings. Promotes equity for all women in the workplace through advocacy, education and information. Provides professional development, networking and career advancement opportunities for working women.

2549 ■ Hendersonville Business and Professional Women
1000 Northview Dr.
Hendersonville, TN 37075
Contact: Jamie Marshall, Pres.
Ph: (615)207-5207
E-mail: thejamiemarshall@comcast.net
URL: http://www.bpwtn.org

Descr: Represents the interests of business and professional women. Elevates the standards for women in business and professional settings. Promotes equity for all women in the workplace through advocacy, education and information. Provides professional development, networking and career advancement opportunities for working women.

2550 ■ Jackson Business and Professional Women
1800 N Highland Ave.
Jackson, TN 38301
Contact: Jacque Hillman, Pres.
Ph: (731)554-1894
E-mail: jhillman@jacksonsun.com
URL: http://www.bpwtn.org
Descr: Represents the interests of business and professional women. Elevates the standards for women in business and professional settings. Promotes equity for all women in the workplace through advocacy, education and information. Provides professional development, networking and career advancement opportunities for working women.

2551 ■ Johnson City Business and Professional Women
3401 Sugartree Ct.
Johnson City, TN 37604
Contact: Laurel Karp, Pres.
Ph: (423)282-4311
E-mail: zlgk1@att.net
URL: http://www.bpwtn.org
Descr: Represents the interests of business and professional women. Elevates the standards for women in business and professional settings. Promotes equity for all women in the workplace through advocacy, education and information. Provides professional development, networking and career advancement opportunities for working women.

2552 ■ Kingsport Business and Professional Women
3245 Ashley St.
Kingsport, TN 37664
Contact: Anita Gulley, Pres.
Ph: (423)245-7272
URL: http://www.bpwtn.org
Descr: Represents the interests of business and professional women. Elevates the standards for women in business and professional settings. Promotes equity for all women in the workplace through advocacy, education and information. Provides professional development, networking and career advancement opportunities for working women.

2553 ■ La Follette Business and Professional Women
700 Howard Rd.
La Follette, TN 37766
Contact: China Willoughby, Pres.
Ph: (423)562-5024
E-mail: china.willoughby@state.tn.us
URL: http://www.bpwtn.org
Descr: Represents the interests of business and professional women. Elevates the standards for women in business and professional settings. Promotes equity for all women in the workplace through advocacy, education and information. Provides professional development, networking and career advancement opportunities for working women.

2554 ■ Laurelwood of Memphis Business and Professional Women
3871 Westridge Dr.
Bartlett, TN 38134
Contact: Pat Bartley, Pres.
Ph: (901)380-2332
URL: http://www.bpwtn.org
Descr: Represents the interests of business and professional women. Elevates the standards for women in business and professional settings. Promotes equity for all women in the workplace through advocacy, education and information.

Provides professional development, networking and career advancement opportunities for working women.

2555 ■ Lawrence County Business and Professional Women
1406 Massey Ave.
Lawrenceburg, TN 38464
Contact: Ruth Bryant, Pres.
Ph: (931)762-3585
URL: http://www.bpwtn.org
Descr: Represents the interests of business and professional women. Elevates the standards for women in business and professional settings. Promotes equity for all women in the workplace through advocacy, education and information. Provides professional development, networking and career advancement opportunities for working women.

2556 ■ Lebanon Business and Professional Women
24 Bond Rd.
Lebanon, TN 37090
Contact: Elizabeth Green, Pres.
Ph: (615)444-0426
E-mail: madmammy@aol.com
URL: http://www.lebanonbpw.org
Descr: Represents the interests of business and professional women. Elevates the standards for women in business and professional settings. Promotes equity for all women in the workplace through advocacy, education and information. Provides professional development, networking and career advancement opportunities for working women.

2557 ■ Lexington Business and Professional Women
153 Johnson St.
Lexington, TN 38351
Contact: Nancy Greenway, Pres.
Ph: (731)968-6394
E-mail: nancyg@netease.net
URL: http://www.bpwtn.org
Descr: Represents the interests of business and professional women. Elevates the standards for women in business and professional settings. Promotes equity for all women in the workplace through advocacy, education and information. Provides professional development, networking and career advancement opportunities for working women.

2558 ■ Manchester Business and Professional Women
615 Polk St.
Manchester, TN 37355
Contact: Marsha Dotson, Pres.
Ph: (931)454-2160
URL: http://www.bpwtn.org
Descr: Represents the interests of business and professional women. Elevates the standards for women in business and professional settings. Promotes equity for all women in the workplace through advocacy, education and information. Provides professional development, networking and career advancement opportunities for working women.

2559 ■ Maryville-Alcoa Business and Professional Women
3006 Wildwood Rd.
Maryville, TN 37804
Contact: Peggy Mobley, Pres.
Ph: (615)982-3211
E-mail: gran3006@aol.com
URL: http://www.bpwtn.org
Descr: Represents the interests of business and professional women. Elevates the standards for women in business and professional settings. Promotes equity for all women in the workplace through advocacy, education and information. Provides professional development, networking and

career advancement opportunities for working women.

2560 ■ McKenzie Business and Professional Women
2001 Cedar St.
McKenzie, TN 38201
Contact: Kathy Sacks, Pres.
Ph: (731)352-2070
E-mail: sacksk@bethel-college.edu
URL: http://www.bpwtn.org
Descr: Represents the interests of business and professional women. Elevates the standards for women in business and professional settings. Promotes equity for all women in the workplace through advocacy, education and information. Provides professional development, networking and career advancement opportunities for working women.

2561 ■ McMinnville Business and Professional Women
415 Collinwood Dr.
McMinnville, TN 37110
Contact: Jewell Walker, Pres.
Ph: (931)668-2987
E-mail: jewell.walker@secfed.net
URL: http://www.bpwtn.org
Descr: Represents the interests of business and professional women. Elevates the standards for women in business and professional settings. Promotes equity for all women in the workplace through advocacy, education and information. Provides professional development, networking and career advancement opportunities for working women.

2562 ■ Memphis AIFA
2542 Ridgeway Rd., No. 8
Memphis, TN 38119
Contact: Lisa Loden, Association Exec.
Ph: (901)360-1478
Fax: (901)366-0623
E-mail: naifamemphis@naifamemphis.org
URL: http://209.61.156.20/main-pub.cfm?usr=475780
Descr: Represents the interests of insurance and financial advisors. Advocates for a positive legislative and regulatory environment. Enhances business and professional skills of members.

2563 ■ Milan Business and Professional Women
116 Mathis Crossing Rd.
Milan, TN 38358
Contact: Denise Oliver, Pres.
Ph: (731)686-2964
E-mail: oliver60@bellsouth.net
URL: http://www.bpwtn.org
Descr: Represents the interests of business and professional women. Elevates the standards for women in business and professional settings. Promotes equity for all women in the workplace through advocacy, education and information. Provides professional development, networking and career advancement opportunities for working women.

2564 ■ NAIFA-Jackson
2038 Greyston Office Park
Jackson, TN 38305
Contact: Roderiv Wayne Parker, Pres.
Ph: (731)668-0767
Fax: (731)668-7141
E-mail: judy.a.beal@mwarerep.org
Descr: Represents the interest of insurance and financial advisors. Advocates for a positive legislative and regulatory environment. Enhances business and professional skills of members.

2565 ■ Nashville AIFA
PO Box 3230
Brentwood, TN 37024-3230
Contact: Ronald D. Morrow Jr., Pres.
Ph: (615)791-8011
Fax: (615)791-8011

E-mail: naifanashville@charter.net
URL: http://naifanet.com/nashville

Descr: Represents the interest of insurance and financial advisors. Advocates for a positive legislative and regulatory environment. Enhances business and professional skills of members.

2566 ■ Paris Business and Professional Women
1695 Hwy. 69 S
Paris, TN 38242
Contact: Nancy Snow, Pres.
Ph: (731)642-3204
E-mail: keensnow@wk.net
URL: http://www.bpwtn.org

Descr: Represents the interests of business and professional women. Elevates the standards for women in business and professional settings. Promotes equity for all women in the workplace through advocacy, education and information. Provides professional development, networking and career advancement opportunities for working women.

2567 ■ Rockwood Business and Professional Women
PO Box 1625
Rockwood, TN 37854
Contact: Ann Hiegel, Pres.
Ph: (865)354-0427
E-mail: hiegelma@comcast.net
URL: http://www.bpwtn.org

Descr: Represents the interests of business and professional women. Elevates the standards for women in business and professional settings. Promotes equity for all women in the workplace through advocacy, education and information. Provides professional development, networking and career advancement opportunities for working women.

2568 ■ Rogersville Business and Professional Women
164 Lena Dr.
Rogersville, TN 37857
Contact: Diane Woody, Pres.
Ph: (423)272-5065
E-mail: rdvwoody@chartertn.net
URL: http://www.bpwtn.org

Descr: Represents the interests of business and professional women. Elevates the standards for women in business and professional settings. Promotes equity for all women in the workplace through advocacy, education and information. Provides professional development, networking and career advancement opportunities for working women.

2569 ■ Tennessee Federation of Business and Professional Women
PO Box 70296
Nashville, TN 37207
Contact: Sharon Taylor, Pres.
Ph: (615)851-2275
E-mail: sharonlyrae@aol.com
URL: http://www.bpwtn.org

Descr: Represents the interests of business and professional women. Elevates the standards for women in business and professional settings. Promotes equity for all women in the workplace through advocacy, education and information. Provides professional development, networking and career advancement opportunities for working women.

2570 ■ Tennessee Small Business Development Centers, Austin Peay State University
106 Public Sq.
Clarksville, TN 37040
Ph: (931)221-1370
E-mail: rplatz@tsbdc.org
URL: http://www.tsbdc.org

Descr: Represents and promotes the small business sector. Provides management assistance to current and prospective small business owners. Helps to improve management skills and expand the products and services of members.

2571 ■ Tennessee Small Business Development Centers, Chattanooga State Technical Community College
Chattanooga Business Development Ctr.
100 Cherokee Blvd., Ste. 202
Chattanooga, TN 37405-0880
Ph: (423)756-8668
E-mail: kmaxfield@tsbdc.org
URL: http://www.tsbdc.org

Descr: Represents and promotes the small business sector. Provides management assistance to current and prospective small business owners. Helps to improve management skills and expand the products and services of members.

2572 ■ Tennessee Small Business Development Centers, Cleveland State Community College
Technologies Bldg., Rm.126
3535 Adkisson Dr.
Cleveland, TN 37320-3570
Ph: (423)614-8707
E-mail: rplatz@tsbdc.org
URL: http://www.tsbdc.org

Descr: Represents and promotes the small business sector. Provides management assistance to current and prospective small business owners. Helps to improve management skills and expand the products and services of members.

2573 ■ Tennessee Small Business Development Centers, Dyersburg State Community College
1510 Lake Rd.
Dyersburg, TN 38024-2411
Ph: (731)286-3201
E-mail: jfrakes@mail.tsbdc.org
URL: http://www.tsbdc.org

Descr: Represents and promotes the small business sector. Provides management assistance to current and prospective small business owners. Helps to improve management skills and expand the products and services of members.

2574 ■ Tennessee Small Business Development Centers, Jackson State Community College
Jackson Chamber of Commerce
197 Auditorium St.
Jackson, TN 38301
Ph: (731)424-5389
E-mail: racree@tsbdc.org
URL: http://www.tsbdc.org

Descr: Represents and promotes the small business sector. Provides management assistance to current and prospective small business owners. Helps to improve management skills and expand the products and services of members.

2575 ■ Tennessee Small Business Development Centers, Knoxville
737 Union Ave.
Memphis, TN 38103
Ph: (901)333-5085
E-mail: ddoyle@mail.tsbdc.org
URL: http://www.tsbdc.org

Descr: Represents and promotes the small business sector. Provides management assistance to current and prospective small business owners. Helps to improve management skills and expand the products and services of members.

2576 ■ Tennessee Small Business Development Centers, Memphis
555 Beale St.
Memphis, TN 38103
Ph: (901)526-9300
E-mail: ddoyle@tsbdc.org
URL: http://www.tsbdc.org

Descr: Represents and promotes the small business sector. Provides management assistance to current and prospective small business owners. Helps to

2577 ■ Tennessee Small Business Development Centers, Middle Tennessee State University
501 Memorial Blvd.
Murfreesboro, TN 37129
Ph: (615)898-2745
E-mail: rklika@tsbdc.org
URL: http://www.tsbdc.org

Descr: Represents and promotes the small business sector. Provides management assistance to current and prospective small business owners. Helps to improve management skills and expand the products and services of members.

2578 ■ Tennessee Small Business Development Centers, Middle Tennessee State University - Columbia
106 W 6th St.
Columbia, TN 38402
Ph: (931)388-2155
E-mail: gosekowsky@tsbdc.org
URL: http://www.tsbdc.org

Descr: Represents and promotes the small business sector. Provides management assistance to current and prospective small business owners. Helps to improve management skills and expand the products and services of members.

2579 ■ Tennessee Small Business Development Centers, Tennessee State University - Brentwood
Reliant Bank
1736 Carouthers Pkwy., Ste. 100
Brentwood, TN 37027-8167
Ph: (615)963-7179
E-mail: info@nashvillesbdc.org
URL: http://www.tsbdc.org

Descr: Represents and promotes the small business sector. Provides management assistance to current and prospective small business owners. Helps to improve management skills and expand the products and services of members.

2580 ■ Tennessee Small Business Development Centers, Tennessee State University - Nashville
330 10th Ave. N
Nashville, TN 37203-3401
Ph: (615)963-7179
E-mail: proberts@tsbdc.org
URL: http://www.tsbdc.org

Descr: Represents and promotes the small business sector. Provides management assistance to current and prospective small business owners. Helps to improve management skills and expand the products and services of members.

2581 ■ Tennessee Small Business Development Centers, Tennessee Tech University
PO Box 5025
Cookeville, TN 38505
Ph: (931)372-3670
E-mail: vhenley@tsbdc.org
URL: http://www.tsbdc.org

Descr: Represents and promotes the small business sector. Provides management assistance to current and prospective small business owners. Helps to improve management skills and expand the products and services of members.

2582 ■ Tennessee Small Business Development Centers, Volunteer State Community College
Gibson Hall
1480 Nashville Pike
Gallatin, TN 37066-3148
Ph: (615)230-4780
E-mail: calexander@tsbdc.org
URL: http://www.tsbdc.org

Descr: Represents and promotes the small business sector. Provides management assistance to current and prospective small business owners. Helps to

improve management skills and expand the products and services of members.

2583 ■ Tennessee Society of Enrolled Agents (TNSEA)
299 S Walnut Bend Rd., Ste. 202
Cordova, TN 38018
Contact: Wes Parker, Pres.
Ph: (901)794-3528
Fax: (901)794-8354
E-mail: wesparker5@gmail.com
URL: http://www.tnsea.com
Descr: Aims to improve the knowledge, skills and professionalism of members in all areas of taxation. Enhances the role of enrolled agents among government agencies, other professions and the public at large. Advocates for taxpayer rights and protects members' interests.

2584 ■ Tennessee Taxpayers Association
2075 Madison Ave.
Memphis, TN 38104
Ph: (901)272-0199
Fax: (901)726-1313

2585 ■ Tullahoma Business and Professional Women
PO Box 241
Tullahoma, TN 37388
Contact: Holly Slipher, Pres.
Ph: (931)409-6600
E-mail: holly@etla.us
URL: http://www.bpwtullahoma.org
Descr: Represents the interests of business and professional women. Elevates the standards for women in business and professional settings. Promotes equity for all women in the workplace through advocacy, education and information. Provides professional development, networking and career advancement opportunities for working women.

2586 ■ Union City Business and Professional Women
2469 Flippin Ln.
Union City, TN 38261
Contact: Dorothy Latimer, Pres.
Ph: (731)885-5289
URL: http://www.bpwtn.org
Descr: Represents the interests of business and professional women. Elevates the standards for women in business and professional settings. Promotes equity for all women in the workplace through advocacy, education and information. Provides professional development, networking and career advancement opportunities for working women.

Texas

2587 ■ Abilene Small Business Development Center
500 Chestnut St., Ste. 601
Abilene, TX 79602
Contact: Judy Wilhelm, Dir.
Ph: (325)670-0300
E-mail: j.wilhelm@ttusbdc.org
URL: http://www.ttusbdc.org/Abilene/index.htm
Descr: Represents and promotes the small business sector. Provides management assistance to current and prospective small business owners. Helps to improve management skills and expand the products and services of members.

2588 ■ American Society of Appraisers, Corpus Christi Chapter
Ehco Services Inc.
429 Colony Dr.
Corpus Christi, TX 78412
Contact: Edmund Herbert Hecht, Pres.
Ph: (361)994-6500
Fax: (361)994-6500
E-mail: ehecht@ehcoservices.com
Descr: Serves as a professional appraisal educator, testing and accrediting society. Sponsors mandatory

re-certification program for all members. Offers consumer information service to the public.

2589 ■ American Society of Appraisers, Dallas/Fort Worth Chapter
6009 Oakrest Rd.
Dallas, TX 75248
Contact: Alan L. Tolmas ASA, Pres.
Ph: (214)415-8842
E-mail: atolmas@tolmasconsulting.com
URL: http://www.rightvalue.org/Home_Page.html
Descr: Serves as a professional appraisal educator, testing and accrediting society. Sponsors mandatory re-certification program for all members. Offers consumer information service to the public.

2590 ■ American Society of Appraisers, El Paso Chapter
5857 N Mesa St., Ste. 19
El Paso, TX 79912-4653
Contact: Susan Eisen, VP
Ph: (915)584-0022
Fax: (915)584-2552
E-mail: lifetag@att.net
URL: http://www.appraisers.org/elpaso
Descr: Serves as a professional appraisal educator, testing and accrediting society. Sponsors mandatory recertification program for all members. Offers consumer information service to the public. **Fnd:** 1968.

2591 ■ American Society of Appraisers, Houston Chapter
Hill Schwartz Spilker Keller
5847 San Felipe St., Ste. 3100
Houston, TX 77057
Contact: David Smith, Pres.
Ph: (713)771-5011
Fax: (713)759-0968
E-mail: dsmith@hsskgroup.com
URL: http://www.appraisers.org/houston
Descr: Serves as a professional appraisal educator, testing and accrediting society. Sponsors mandatory re-certification program for all members. Offers consumer information service to the public.

2592 ■ American Society of Appraisers, San Antonio Chapter
The Hanke Group PC
10101 Reunion Pl., Ste. 750
San Antonio, TX 78216
Contact: Stanley Todd Burchett
Ph: (210)341-9400
Fax: (210)341-9434
E-mail: todd.burchett@thehankegroup.com
Descr: Serves as a professional appraisal educator, testing and accrediting society. Sponsors mandatory re-certification program for all members. Offers consumer information service to the public.

2593 ■ Angelina College Small Business Development Center
3500 S First St.
Lufkin, TX 75902
Contact: Brian McClain, Dir.
Ph: (936)633-5400
E-mail: bmcclain@angelina.edu
URL: http://www.angelina.cc.tx.us/SBDC/cs 20sbdc 20index.htm
Descr: Represents and promotes the small business sector. Provides management assistance to current and prospective small business owners. Helps to improve management skills and expand the products and services of members.

2594 ■ Angelo State University Small Business Development Center
ASU Station No. 10910
San Angelo, TX 76909
Contact: Dave Erickson, Dir.
Ph: (325)942-2098
Fax: (325)942-2096
E-mail: david.erickson@angelo.edu
URL: http://www.angelo.edu/services/sbdc
Descr: Represents and promotes the small business sector. Provides management assistance to current

and prospective small business owners. Helps to improve management skills and expand the products and services of members.

2595 ■ Aransas County Taxpayers Association
356 E Sagebrush St.
Rockport, TX 78382
Ph: (512)729-5923

2596 ■ Beaumont/Southeast Texas AIFA
PO Box 13007
Beaumont, TX 77726-3007
Contact: James E. Hughes Jr., Pres.
Ph: (409)832-5886
Fax: (409)832-5886
E-mail: beaumontaifa@yahoo.com
Descr: Represents the interest of insurance and financial advisors. Advocates for a positive legislative and regulatory environment. Enhances business and professional skills of members.

2597 ■ Best Southwest Small Business Development Center
207 N Cannady Dr.
Cedar Hill, TX 75104
Contact: Obie Greenleaf, Dir.
Ph: (972)860-7894
Fax: (972)291-1320
E-mail: vaw3704@dcccd.edu
URL: http://www.ntsbdc.org/bsw.html
Descr: Represents and promotes the small business sector. Provides management assistance to current and prospective small business owners. Helps to improve management skills and expand the products and services of members.

2598 ■ Big Bend Small Business Development Center
PO Box C-47
Alpine, TX 79832
Contact: Dave Wilson, Dir.
Ph: (915)837-8694
E-mail: dwilson@sulross.edu
URL: http://www.sulross.edu/~sbdc
Descr: Represents and promotes the small business sector. Provides management assistance to current and prospective small business owners. Helps to improve management skills and expand the products and services of members.

2599 ■ Blinn College Small Business Development Center
902 College Ave.
Brenham, TX 77833
Contact: Carol Doersom, Sec.
Ph: (979)830-4137
Fax: (979)830-4135
E-mail: sbdc@blinn.edu
URL: http://www.blinn.edu/sbdc/index.htm
Descr: Represents and promotes the small business sector. Provides management assistance to current and prospective small business owners. Helps to improve management skills and expand the products and services of members.

2600 ■ Brazos Valley Small Business Development Center
4001 E 29th St., Ste. 175
Bryan, TX 77805
Contact: James Pillans, Dir.
Ph: (979)260-5222
E-mail: jimp@bvsbdc.org
URL: http://www.bvsbdc.org
Descr: Represents and promotes the small business sector. Provides management assistance to current and prospective small business owners. Helps to improve management skills and expand the products and services of members.

2601 ■ Brazosport College Small Business Development Center
500 College Dr.
Lake Jackson, TX 77566
Contact: Jan Gooines, Dir.
Ph: (979)230-3380

E-mail: janice.goines@brazosport.edu
URL: http://www.brazosport.edu/sbdc

Descr: Represents and promotes the small business sector. Provides management assistance to current and prospective small business owners. Helps to improve management skills and expand the products and services of members.

2602 ■ Business and Professional Women of Dallas
PO Box 7885
Dallas, TX 75209
Contact: Anne Chastain, Pres.
Ph: (214)361-4086
E-mail: info@atsbpwdallasinc.org
URL: http://www.bpwdallasinc.org

Descr: Represents the interests of business and professional women. Elevates the standards for women in business and professional settings. Promotes equity for all women in the workplace through advocacy, education and information. Provides professional development, networking and career advancement opportunities for working women.

2603 ■ Collin County Taxpayers Association
PO Box 369
McKinney, TX 75069
Ph: (214)542-7657

2604 ■ Collin Small Business Development Center
4800 Preston Park Blvd., Ste. A126B
Plano, TX 75093
Contact: Marta Gomez Frey, Dir.
Ph: (972)985-3770
Fax: (972)985-3775
E-mail: gdaniel@ccccd.edu
URL: http://www.collinsbdc.com

Descr: Represents and promotes the small business sector. Provides management assistance to current and prospective small business owners. Helps to improve management skills and expand the products and services of members.

2605 ■ Corpus Christi Business and Professional Women's Club
PO Box 1677
Corpus Christi, TX 78403
Contact: Jo C. Naylor, Pres.
Ph: (361)643-3460
Fax: (361)992-9603
E-mail: joccbpw@yahoo.com
URL: http://www.ccbpw.com

Descr: Represents the interests of business and professional women. Elevates the standards for women in business and professional settings. Promotes equity for all women in the workplace through advocacy, education and information. Provides professional development, networking and career advancement opportunities for working women.

2606 ■ Corpus Christi Taxpayers Association
PO Box 8852
Corpus Christi, TX 78412
Ph: (361)857-0361
E-mail: cctaxcap@hotmail.com
URL: http://cctaxcap.org

2607 ■ Dallas Small Business Development Center
1402 Corinth St.
Dallas, TX 75215
Contact: Jeff Blatt, Dir.
Ph: (214)860-5865
Fax: (214)860-5867
E-mail: dsbdc@dcccd.edu
URL: http://www.ntsbdc.org/dallas.html

Descr: Represents and promotes the small business sector. Provides management assistance to current and prospective small business owners. Helps to

improve management skills and expand the products and services of members.

2608 ■ Del Mar College Small Business Development Center
101 Baldwin Blvd., CED 146
Corpus Christi, TX 78404
Contact: Ann Fierova, Dir.
Ph: (361)698-1021
Fax: (361)698-1024
E-mail: afierova@delmar.edu
URL: http://www.delmar.edu/sbdc

Descr: Represents and promotes the small business sector. Provides management assistance to current and prospective small business owners. Helps to improve management skills and expand the products and services of members.

2609 ■ Denton County Small Business Development Center
414 W Parkway St.
Denton, TX 76201
Contact: Pam Livingston
Ph: (940)380-1849
E-mail: nctcsbdc@denton-chamber.org
URL: http://www.nctc.edu/SBDC/sbdc.html

Descr: Represents and promotes the small business sector. Provides management assistance to current and prospective small business owners. Helps to improve management skills and expand the products and services of members.

2610 ■ El Paso Community College Small Business Development Center
1359 Lomaland Dr., Rm. 532
El Paso, TX 79925
Contact: Roque Segura
Ph: (915)831-7743
E-mail: rsegur12@epcc.edu
URL: http://www.elpasosbdc.biz

Descr: Represents and promotes the small business sector. Provides management assistance to current and prospective small business owners. Helps to improve management skills and expand the products and services of members.

2611 ■ Financial Planning Association of Austin
PO Box 28268
Austin, TX 78755-8268
Contact: Michael Orf, Pres.
Ph: (512)261-4159
Fax: (512)261-4159
E-mail: admin@austinfpa.org
URL: http://www.austinfpa.org

Descr: Fosters the value of the financial planning process and its ethical practice through professional growth, networking, education and mentoring.

2612 ■ Financial Planning Association of Dallas/Fort Worth Chapter
PO Box 261750
Plano, TX 75026-1750
Contact: Melisa Hall, Exec. Dir.
Ph: (972)747-0407
Fax: (972)747-0409
E-mail: execdir@fpadfw.org
URL: http://www.fpadfw.org

Descr: Supports the financial planning process in order to help people achieve their goals and dreams. Fosters excellence in the practice of financial planning and promotes the value of the CFP designation. **Mem:** 830.

2613 ■ Financial Planning Association of Houston
PO Box 261690
Plano, TX 75026-1690
Contact: Melisa L. Hall, Exec. Dir.
Ph: (713)518-1785
Fax: (972)747-0409
E-mail: execdir@fpahouston.org
URL: http://www.fpahouston.org

Descr: Supports the financial planning process in order to help people achieve their goals and dreams.

Promotes the value of the financial planning process and advances the financial planning profession.

2614 ■ Financial Planning Association of San Antonio and South Texas
PO Box 34036
San Antonio, TX 78265
Contact: Birdie P. Sanchez, Exec. Dir.
Ph: (210)822-6600
Fax: (210)822-6600
E-mail: admin@fpasatx.org
URL: http://www.fpasatx.org

Descr: Promotes financial planning profession through education, networking, and mentoring. Enhances public awareness of the value of the financial planning process. Provides forum for education and career development for its members. **Mem:** 200.

2615 ■ Galveston County Small Business Development Center
8419 Emmett F. Lowry Expy.
Texas City, TX 77591
Contact: Susan Moore, Acting Dir.
Ph: (409)933-1414
E-mail: susan@gcea.us
URL: http://www.gcsbdc.com

Descr: Represents and promotes the small business sector. Provides management assistance to current and prospective small business owners. Helps to improve management skills and expand the products and services of members.

2616 ■ Grayson Small Business Development Center
6101 Grayson Dr.
Denison, TX 75020
Contact: Karen Stidam, Dir.
Ph: (903)463-8787
Free: 800-316-7232
Fax: (903)463-5437
E-mail: stidhamk@grayson.edu
URL: http://www.ntsbdc.org/grayson.html

Descr: Represents and promotes the small business sector. Provides management assistance to current and prospective small business owners. Helps to improve management skills and expand the products and services of members.

2617 ■ Houston AIFA
3100 S Gessner Rd., Ste. 216
Houston, TX 77063
Contact: Alyson J. Guest, Exec. Dir.
Ph: (713)526-5331
Fax: (713)526-2911
E-mail: aguest@metlife.com
URL: http://www.naifahouston.org

Descr: Represents the interests of insurance and financial advisors. Advocates for a positive legislative and regulatory environment. Enhances business and professional skills of members.

2618 ■ Houston Taxpayers Coalition
PO Box 8642
Houston, TX 77249
Ph: (713)869-1654

2619 ■ Kilgore Small Business Development Center
911 NW Loop 281, No. 209
Longview, TX 75604
Contact: Brad Bunt, Dir.
Ph: (903)757-5857
Free: 800-388-7232
Fax: (903)753-7920
E-mail: bradbunt@aol.com
URL: http://www.kilgore.edu/sbdc.asp

Descr: Represents and promotes the small business sector. Provides management assistance to current and prospective small business owners. Helps to improve management skills and expand the products and services of members.

2620 ■ Lamar State College Small Business Development Center
1401 Procter St.
Port Arthur, TX 77640

Contact: Linda Tait, Dir.
Ph: (409)984-6531
E-mail: linda.tait@lamarpa.edu
URL: http://www.portarthur.com/sbdc
Descr: Represents and promotes the small business sector. Provides management assistance to current and prospective small business owners. Helps to improve management skills and expand the products and services of members.

2621 ■ Lamar University Small Business Development Center
850 Georgia Ave.
Beaumont, TX 77705
Contact: David Mulcahy, Dir.
Ph: (409)880-2367
E-mail: david.mulcahy@lamar.edu
URL: http://www.lamar.edu/sbdc
Descr: Represents and promotes the small business sector. Provides management assistance to current and prospective small business owners. Helps to improve management skills and expand the products and services of members.

2622 ■ Lampasas County Taxpayers Association
PO Box 122
Kempner, TX 76539
Ph: (512)932-3559

2623 ■ Lavaca County Taxpayers League
PO Box 95R
Hallettsville, TX 77964
Ph: (512)798-3320

2624 ■ Lee College Small Business Development Center
700 Rollingbrook Dr., Ste. B
Baytown, TX 77521
Contact: Steve McCorquodale, Consultant
Ph: (281)425-6309
E-mail: thathawa@lee.edu
URL: http://www.lee.edu/sbdc
Descr: Represents and promotes the small business sector. Provides management assistance to current and prospective small business owners. Helps to improve management skills and expand the products and services of members.

2625 ■ Lubbock Small Business Development Center
2579 S Loop 289
Lubbock, TX 79423
Contact: Efren Villanueva, Interim Dir.
Ph: (806)745-1637
Free: 800-992-7232
Fax: (806)745-6717
E-mail: e.villanueva@nwtsbdc.org
URL: http://www.ttusbdc.org/lubbock
Descr: Represents and promotes the small business sector. Provides management assistance to current and prospective small business owners. Helps to improve management skills and expand the products and services of members.

2626 ■ McLennan Small Business Development Center
McLennan Community College
1400 College Dr.
Waco, TX 76708
Contact: Belinda Pillow, Dir.
Ph: (254)299-8141
Free: 800-349-7232
Fax: (254)299-8054
E-mail: bpillow@mclennan.edu
URL: http://www.ntsbdc.org/mclennan.html
Descr: Represents and promotes the small business sector. Provides management assistance to current and prospective small business owners. Helps to improve management skills and expand the products and services of members.

2627 ■ Midwestern State University Small Business Development Center
3410 Taft Blvd.
Wichita Falls, TX 76308
Contact: Vanda Wright, Dir.

Ph: (940)397-4372
E-mail: vanda.wright@mwsu.edu
URL: http://www.msusbdc.org
Descr: Represents and promotes the small business sector. Provides management assistance to current and prospective small business owners. Helps to improve management skills and expand the products and services of members.

2628 ■ Milam County Association of Taxpayers
RR 3, Box 52-C
Cameron, TX 76520
Ph: (817)697-3868

2629 ■ Montague County Small Business Development Center
810 S Mill St.
Bowie, TX 76230
Contact: Cathy Keeler
Ph: (940)688-4220
E-mail: ckeeler@nctc.edu
URL: http://www.nctc.edu/SBDC/sbdc.html
Descr: Represents and promotes the small business sector. Provides management assistance to current and prospective small business owners. Helps to improve management skills and expand the products and services of members.

2630 ■ NAIFA-Austin
PO Box 201298
Austin, TX 78720-1298
Contact: Kim Kieschnick, Exec. Dir.
Ph: (512)401-6412
Fax: (512)401-6413
E-mail: kieschnick@austin.rr.com
URL: http://209.61.156.20/main-pub. cfm?usr=485852
Descr: Represents the interest of insurance and financial advisors. Advocates for a positive legislative and regulatory environment. Enhances business and professional skills of members.

2631 ■ NAIFA-Dallas
9101 LBJ Freeway, Ste. 450
Dallas, TX 75243
Contact: Karen H. True, Exec. VP
Ph: (972)991-2364
Fax: (972)934-1217
E-mail: memberservices@naifadallas.org
URL: http://www.naifanet.com/main-pub. cfm?usr=485884
Descr: Represents the interests of insurance and financial advisors. Advocates for a positive legislative and regulatory environment. Enhances business and professional skills of members. **Fnd:** 1913.

2632 ■ NAIFA East Texas
National Western Life
PO Box 100
Easton, TX 75641
Contact: Douglas A. Jackson, Pres.
Ph: (903)753-8636
Fax: (903)758-4667
E-mail: doug-jackson@sbcglobal.net
URL: http://www.naifanet.com/oilbelt
Descr: Represents the interest of insurance and financial advisors. Advocates for a positive legislative and regulatory environment. Enhances business and professional skills of members.

2633 ■ NAIFA-San Antonio
7800 IH10 W, Ste. 100
San Antonio, TX 78230
Contact: Robert Kinally, Pres.
Ph: (210)568-1560
E-mail: info@naifasanantoinio.org
URL: http://www.naifasanantonio.org
Descr: Represents the interests of insurance and financial advisors. Advocates for a positive legisla-

tive and regulatory environment. Enhances business and professional skills of members.

2634 ■ Navarro Small Business Development Center
Navarro College
3200 W 7th Ave.
Corsicana, TX 75110
Contact: Robin Lasher, Dir.
Ph: (903)875-7667
Fax: (903)875-7468
E-mail: sbdc@navarrocollege.edu
URL: http://www.ntsbdc.org/navarro.html
Descr: Represents and promotes the small business sector. Provides management assistance to current and prospective small business owners. Helps to improve management skills and expand the products and services of members.

2635 ■ North American Securities Administrators Association, Texas
208 E 10th St., 5th Fl.
Austin, TX 78701
Contact: Denise Voigt Crawford
Ph: (512)305-8300
Fax: (512)305-8310
Descr: Represents the interests of the state, provincial and territorial securities administrators in the U.S.

2636 ■ North Central Texas College - Corinth Small Business Development Center
1500 N Corinth St., Rm. 172
Corinth, TX 76208
Contact: Joyce Dillon
Ph: (940)668-4220
E-mail: ckeeler@nctc.edu
URL: http://www.nctc.edu/SBDC/sbdc.html
Descr: Represents and promotes the small business sector. Provides management assistance to current and prospective small business owners. Helps to improve management skills and expand the products and services of members.

2637 ■ North Central Texas Small Business Development Center
North Central Texas College
1525 W California St.
Gainesville, TX 76240
Contact: Catherine Keeler, Dir.
Ph: (940)668-4220
Free: 800-351-7232
Fax: (940)668-6049
E-mail: nctcsbdc@ntc.edu
URL: http://www.ntsbdc.org/n_cent.html
Descr: Represents and promotes the small business sector. Provides management assistance to current and prospective small business owners. Helps to improve management skills and expand the products and services of members.

2638 ■ North Harris Montgomery Community College Small Business Development Center
5000 Research Forest Dr.
The Woodlands, TX 77381
Contact: Sal Mira, Dir.
Ph: (832)813-6673
E-mail: sal.mira@nhmccd.edu
URL: http://sbdc.lonestar.edu
Descr: Represents and promotes the small business sector. Provides management assistance to current and prospective small business owners. Helps to improve management skills and expand the products and services of members.

2639 ■ Northeast Texas Small Business Development Center
PO Box 1307
Mount Pleasant, TX 75455
Contact: Bob Wall, Dir.
Ph: (903)897-2956
Free: 800-357-7232
Fax: (903)897-1106
E-mail: sbdcnetcc@aol.com
URL: http://www.ntsbdc.org/northeast.html
Descr: Represents and promotes the small business sector. Provides management assistance to current

and prospective small business owners. Helps to improve management skills and expand the products and services of members.

2640 ■ Nueces Canyon Taxpayers Association
17939 S State Hwy. 55
Barksdale, TX 78828
Ph: (512)234-3351

2641 ■ Paris Small Business Development Center
Paris Junior College
2400 Clarksville St.
Paris, TX 75460
Contact: Patricia Bell, Dir.
Ph: (903)782-0223
Fax: (903)782-0219
E-mail: pbell@parisjc.edu
URL: http://www.ntsbdc.org/paris.html
Descr: Represents and promotes the small business sector. Provides management assistance to current and prospective small business owners. Helps to improve management skills and expand the products and services of members.

2642 ■ Plano Area Enrolled Agents
210 S Elm St., Ste. C
Denton, TX 76201
Contact: Griff Moore, Pres.
Ph: (972)727-5650
Fax: (972)867-5278
E-mail: glinke@aroundtuitllc.com
URL: http://www.plano-ea.com
Descr: Aims to improve the knowledge, skills and professionalism of members in all areas of taxation. Enhances the role of enrolled agents among government agencies, other professions and the public at large. Advocates for taxpayer rights and protects members' interests.

2643 ■ Prairie View A & M Small Business Development Center
Hobart Taylor Hall, Rm. 1B
117 T.R. Soloman St.
Prairie View, TX 77446
Contact: Carol Herrington, Dir.
Ph: (936)261-9242
E-mail: mcherrington@pvamu.edu
URL: http://www.wallercountysbdc.org
Descr: Represents and promotes the small business sector. Provides management assistance to current and prospective small business owners. Helps to improve management skills and expand the products and services of members.

2644 ■ Richardson Business and Professional Women's Club
3421 Lilac Ln.
Rowlett, TX 75089
Contact: Cheryl Harris
E-mail: info@richardsonbpw.com
URL: http://www.richardsonbpw.org
Descr: Represents the interests of business and professional women. Elevates the standards for women in business and professional settings. Promotes equity for all women in the workplace through advocacy, education and information. Provides professional development, networking and career advancement opportunities for working women.

2645 ■ Sam Houston State University Small Business Development Center
2424 Sam Houston Ave., Bldg. A
Huntsville, TX 77341
Contact: Robert A. Barragan, Dir.
Ph: (936)294-3737
E-mail: sbd_rab@shsu.edu
URL: http://www.shsu.edu/~sbd_www
Descr: Represents and promotes the small business sector. Provides management assistance to current and prospective small business owners. Helps to

improve management skills and expand the products and services of members.

2646 ■ San Angelo Business and Professional Women
4105 Green Meadow Dr.
San Angelo, TX 76904
Contact: Tricia Affleck, Ed.
E-mail: hseals1@cox.net
URL: http://www.bpwsanangelo.org
Descr: Represents the interests of business and professional women. Elevates the standards for women in business and professional settings. Promotes equity for all women in the workplace through advocacy, education and information. Provides professional development, networking and career advancement opportunities for working women.

2647 ■ San Antonio Small Business Development Center
501 W Durango Blvd.
San Antonio, TX 78207
Contact: Morrison Woods
Ph: (210)458-2460
E-mail: morrison.woods@utsa.edu
URL: http://sasbdc.iedtexas.org
Descr: Represents and promotes the small business sector. Provides management assistance to current and prospective small business owners. Helps to improve management skills and expand the products and services of members.

2648 ■ San Jacinto College Small Business Development Center
2006 E Broadway, Ste. 101
Pearland, TX 77581
Contact: Mike Moore, Dir.
Ph: (281)485-5214
E-mail: michael.moore@sjcd.edu
URL: http://www.sjcd.edu/about_us_sbdc.html
Descr: Represents and promotes the small business sector. Provides management assistance to current and prospective small business owners. Helps to improve management skills and expand the products and services of members.

2649 ■ Smith County Taxpayers Association
PO Box 132205
Tyler, TX 75713
E-mail: jafleming3@juno.com

2650 ■ SOCAP International - Houston Chapter
900 Grand Plaza Dr.
Houston, TX 77067
Contact: Daniel Thompson
Ph: (832)235-1803
Descr: Promotes customer care and customer management as a competitive advantage in business. Provides educational tools and professional resources to help members drive business transformation within their companies.

2651 ■ Society of Consumer Affairs Professionals in Business, Dallas-Fort Worth Chapter
Telerx
9019 Clayco Dr.
Dallas, TX 75243
Contact: Linda Dickey, Pres.
Ph: (214)221-1144
E-mail: dale.conwell@telerx.com
URL: http://www.geocities.com/socapdfwchapter
Descr: Works to advance customer care through education and networking. Serves consumer affairs professionals in Texas, Oklahoma, Louisiana and Arkansas.

2652 ■ South West Texas Border Region Small Business Development Center
501 W Durango Blvd.
San Antonio, TX 78207-4415
Contact: Irene Mireles
Ph: (210)458-2450
Fax: (210)458-2464

URL: http://txsbdc.org/component/option,com_frontpage/Itemid,71
Descr: Represents and promotes the small business sector. Provides management assistance to current and prospective small business owners. Helps to improve management skills and expand the products and services of members.

2653 ■ SRSU Rio Grande College Small Business Development Center
Box 1200
Eagle Pass, TX 78852
Contact: Luis Urbina, Dir.
Ph: (830)758-5025
E-mail: lurbina@sulross.edu
URL: http://rgc.sulross.edu/pages/106.asp
Descr: Represents and promotes the small business sector. Provides management assistance to current and prospective small business owners. Helps to improve management skills and expand the products and services of members.

2654 ■ Tarleton State University Small Business Development Center
Box T-0650
Stephenville, TX 76402
Contact: Ron Beck, Dir.
Ph: (254)968-9330
Fax: (254)968-9329
E-mail: beck@tarleton.edu
URL: http://www.tsusbdc.org
Descr: Represents and promotes the small business sector. Provides management assistance to current and prospective small business owners. Helps to improve management skills and expand the products and services of members.

2655 ■ Tarrant Small Business Development Center
1150 South Fwy., Ste. 229
Fort Worth, TX 76104
Contact: David Edmonds, Dir.
Ph: (817)871-6028
Fax: (817)332-6417
E-mail: david.edmonds@tccd.edu
URL: http://www.ntsbdc.org/tarrant.html
Descr: Represents and promotes the small business sector. Provides management assistance to current and prospective small business owners. Helps to improve management skills and expand the products and services of members.

2656 ■ Texas Society of Enrolled Agents (TxSEA)
9100 Tourney St.
San Antonio, TX 78254
Contact: Deborah J. Cope
Ph: (210)521-2963
Fax: (210)680-9355
E-mail: txsea@earthlink.net
URL: http://www.txsea.org
Descr: Aims to improve the knowledge, skills and professionalism of members in all areas of taxation. Enhances the role of enrolled agents among government agencies, other professions and the public at large. Advocates for taxpayer rights and protects members' interests.

2657 ■ Texas Society of Enrolled Agents - Dallas/Fort Worth Chapter
2001 Hunter Glade Ln.
Arlington, TX 76012
Contact: Mr. David Dickerson EA, Pres.
E-mail: xskip@msn.com
URL: http://www.txsea.org

2658 ■ Texas Society of Enrolled Agents - San Antonio Jalapeno Chapter
1 Fl., Conference Rm.
Independence Plz. 1
14400 Northbrook Dr.

San Antonio, TX 78232
Contact: Nettie Johnson EA
URL: http://www.txsea.org

2659 ■ Texas State University - San Marcos Small Business Development Center
1555 University Blvd.
Round Rock, TX 78665
Contact: Larry Lucero, Dir.
Ph: (512)716-4800
Fax: (512)716-4810
E-mail: sbdc@txstate.edu
URL: http://txsbdc.org/austin/-san-marcos-sbdc.htm
Descr: Represents and promotes the small business sector. Provides management assistance to current and prospective small business owners. Helps to improve management skills and expand the products and services of members.

2660 ■ Trinity Valley Small Business Development Center
100 Cardinal Dr.
Athens, TX 75751
Contact: Michael Ellsberry, Dir.
Ph: (903)675-7403
Fax: (903)675-5199
E-mail: mellsberry@tvcc.edu
URL: http://www.ntsbdc.org/trinity.html
Descr: Represents and promotes the small business sector. Provides management assistance to current and prospective small business owners. Helps to improve management skills and expand the products and services of members.

2661 ■ Tyler Small Business Development Center
Tyler Junior College
1530 S Southwest Loop 323, No. 100
Tyler, TX 75701
Contact: Donald Proudfoot, Dir.
Ph: (903)510-2975
E-mail: dpro@tjc.edu
URL: http://www.ntsbdc.org/tyler.html
Descr: Represents and promotes the small business sector. Provides management assistance to current and prospective small business owners. Helps to improve management skills and expand the products and services of members.

2662 ■ University of Houston - Coastal Plains Small Business Development Center
2200 7th St., Ste. 300
Bay City, TX 77414
Contact: G. Allen Maffett, Dir.
Ph: (979)244-8466
E-mail: sbdc@wcnet.net
URL: http://sbdcnetwork.uh.edu/10.htm
Descr: Represents and promotes the small business sector. Provides management assistance to current and prospective small business owners. Helps to improve management skills and expand the products and services of members.

2663 ■ University of Houston - Fort Bend Small Business Development Center
2440 Texas Pkwy., Ste. 220
Missouri City, TX 77489
Contact: Joseph Decker, Dir.
Ph: (281)499-9787
E-mail: decker@uh.edu
URL: http://sbdcnetwork.uh.edu/14.htm
Descr: Represents and promotes the small business sector. Provides management assistance to current and prospective small business owners. Helps to improve management skills and expand the products and services of members.

2664 ■ University of Houston - Victoria Small Business Development Center
3402 N Ben Wilson St.
Victoria, TX 77901
Contact: Keith Mudd, Dir.
Ph: (361)575-8944
E-mail: muddk@uhv.edu
URL: http://www.sbdcvictoria.com
Descr: Represents and promotes the small business sector. Provides management assistance to current

and prospective small business owners. Helps to improve management skills and expand the products and services of members.

2665 ■ University of Texas Pan American Small Business Development Center
ASA Rm. 160
1201 W University Dr.
Edinburg, TX 78539
Contact: Maria Juarez, Dir.
Ph: (956)292-7535
Fax: (956)292-7561
E-mail: mariaj2@panam.edu
URL: http://txsbdc.org/edinburg.htm
Descr: Represents and promotes the small business sector. Provides management assistance to current and prospective small business owners. Helps to improve management skills and expand the products and services of members.

2666 ■ University of Texas of the Permian Basin Small Business Development Center
4901 E University Blvd.
Odessa, TX 79762
Contact: Tommy Baker, Dir.
Ph: (432)552-2455
Fax: (432)552-2455
E-mail: sbdc@utpb.edu
URL: http://www.utpbsbdc.org
Descr: Represents and promotes the small business sector. Provides management assistance to current and prospective small business owners. Helps to improve management skills and expand the products and services of members.

2667 ■ Waco AIFA
7111 Bosque Blvd.
Waco, TX 76710
Contact: Rick Abbe, Pres.
Ph: (254)399-0803
E-mail: rick@lakewoodassociates.net
URL: http://www.naifanet.com/waco
Descr: Represents the interest of insurance and financial advisors. Advocates for a positive legislative and regulatory environment. Enhances business and professional skills of members.

2668 ■ West Texas A & M University Small Business Development Center
701 S Taylor St., Ste. 118
Amarillo, TX 79101
Contact: P.J. Pronger
Ph: (806)372-5151
E-mail: pj@wtsbdc.com
URL: http://www.smallbusinessdevelopmentcenter.com
Descr: Represents and promotes the small business sector. Provides management assistance to current and prospective small business owners. Helps to improve management skills and expand the products and services of members.

2669 ■ Wichita Falls Area AIFA
4210 Kell Blvd., Ste. 106
Wichita Falls, TX 76309
Contact: Tracey W. Denson, Pres.
Ph: (940)689-0044
E-mail: tracey.denson.sq91@statefarm.com
URL: http://www.naifanet.com/wichita
Descr: Represents the interests of insurance and financial advisors. Advocates for a positive legislative and regulatory environment. Enhances business and professional skills of members.

2670 ■ Wichita Falls Business and Professional Women
PO Box 964
Wichita Falls, TX 76307
Contact: Doris Lackey, Corresponding Sec.
Ph: (940)766-1388
Fax: (940)766-5396
E-mail: mkennedy@sw.rr.com
URL: http://wichitafallsbpw.com
Descr: Represents the interests of business and professional women. Elevates the standards for women in business and professional settings.

Promotes equity for all women in the workplace through advocacy, education and information. Provides professional development, networking and career advancement opportunities for working women.

United States Virgin Islands

2671 ■ University of the Virgin Islands Small Business Development Center - St. Croix
Sunshine Mall, Ste. 104
Frederiksted, VI 00840
Contact: Karen Jones, Dir.
Ph: (340)692-5270
Fax: (340)692-5629
E-mail: kjones2@uvi.edu
URL: http://sbdcvi.org
Descr: Represents and promotes the small business sector. Provides management assistance to current and prospective small business owners. Helps to improve management skills and expand the products and services of members.

2672 ■ University of the Virgin Islands Small Business Development Center - St. Thomas/St. John
8000 Nisky Ctr., Ste. 720
St. Thomas, VI 00801
Contact: Leonor Dottin, Dir.
Ph: (340)776-3206
Fax: (340)775-3756
E-mail: ldottin@uvi.edu
URL: http://sbdcvi.org
Descr: Represents and promotes the small business sector. Provides management assistance to current and prospective small business owners. Helps to improve management skills and expand the products and services of members.

Utah

2673 ■ American Society of Appraisers, Salt Lake City Chapter
132 Pierpont Ave., Ste. 250
Salt Lake City, UT 84101
Contact: Robert S. Sly Jr., Pres.
Ph: (801)328-2011
Fax: (801)328-2015
E-mail: rsly@wsrp.com
URL: http://old.appraisers.org/saltlake
Descr: Serves as a professional appraisal educator, testing and accrediting society. Sponsors mandatory recertification program for all members. Offers consumer information service to the public.

2674 ■ Appraisal Institute, Utah Chapter
PO Box 1287
Centerville, UT 84014
Contact: Sheri Zaugg, Exec. Dir.
Ph: (801)924-6715
Fax: (801)924-6716
E-mail: execdir@ai-utah.com
URL: http://www.ai-utah.com
Descr: General appraisers who hold the MAI or SRPA designations, and residential members who hold the SRA designation.

2675 ■ Blanding Small Business Development Center
College of Eastern Utah - San Juan Campus
639 W 100 S
Blanding, UT 84511
Contact: Bill Olderog, Dir.
Ph: (435)678-8102
E-mail: billolderog@sjc.ceu.edu
URL: http://www.utahsbdc.org
Descr: Represents and promotes the small business sector. Provides management assistance to current and prospective small business owners. Helps to

improve management skills and expand the products and services of members.

2676 ■ Cedar City Small Business Development Center
351 W Center St.
Cedar City, UT 84720
Contact: Craig Isom, Dir.
Ph: (435)586-5400
E-mail: isom@suu.edu
URL: http://www.utahsbdc.org
Descr: Represents and promotes the small business sector. Provides management assistance to current and prospective small business owners. Helps to improve management skills and expand the products and services of members.

2677 ■ Ephraim Small Business Development Center
Snow College
150 E College Ave.
Ephraim, UT 84627
Ph: (435)283-7372
E-mail: sbdc@snow.edu
URL: http://www.snow.edu/~sbdc
Descr: Represents and promotes the small business sector. Provides management assistance to current and prospective small business owners. Helps to improve management skills and expand the products and services of members.

2678 ■ Financial Planning Association of Utah
3236 Cameron Park Ct.
South Jordan, UT 84095
Contact: Chuck R. Newton, Pres.
Ph: (801)446-2849
Fax: (801)446-2849
E-mail: chair@fpautah.org
URL: http://www.utahfpa.org
Descr: Promotes the value of the financial planning process and advances the financial planning profession with the CFP-TM mark as its cornerstone. Fosters competent, committed and ethical members with a shared vision. Provides a forum for productive interactions among industry peers. Promotes meaningful educational development.

2679 ■ International Association of Assessing Officers, Utah
Salt Lake County Assessor's Office
2001 S State St. N 3300
Salt Lake City, UT 84190
Contact: Lee Gardner, Rep.
Ph: (801)468-2165
Fax: (801)468-2249
E-mail: lgardner@slco.org
Descr: Represents state and local officials concerned with valuation of property for ad valorem property tax purposes. Works to improve standards and conduct research on tax assessment. Promotes innovation and excellence in property appraisal, assessment administration, and property tax policy through professional development, education, research, and technical assistance.

2680 ■ Kaysville Small Business Development Center
Davis Applied Technology Center
450 S Simmons Way, Ste. 202
Kaysville, UT 84037
Ph: (801)593-2202
E-mail: meiklebh@datc.edu
URL: http://www.utahsbdc.org
Descr: Represents and promotes the small business sector. Provides management assistance to current and prospective small business owners. Helps to improve management skills and expand the products and services of members.

2681 ■ Logan Small Business Development Center
Utah State University
UMC 8330
1330 E 700 N
Logan, UT 84322-8330
Contact: Frank Prante, Dir.

Ph: (435)797-2277
Fax: (435)797-3317
E-mail: fprante@ext.usu.edu
URL: http://www.usu.edu/sbdc/index.html
Descr: Represents and promotes the small business sector. Provides management assistance to current and prospective small business owners. Helps to improve management skills and expand the products and services of members.

2682 ■ NAIFA-Utah
PO Box 17956
Salt Lake City, UT 84117
Contact: Rick E. Nelson CLU, Pres.
Ph: (801)424-2564
Fax: (801)424-2388
E-mail: naifa-utah@comcast.net
URL: http://209.61.156.20/main-pub.cfm?usr=490000
Descr: Represents the interests of insurance and financial advisors. Advocates for a positive legislative and regulatory environment. Enhances business and professional skills of members.

2683 ■ North American Securities Administrators Association, Utah
160 E 300 S, 2nd Fl.
Salt Lake City, UT 84114
Contact: Thad Levar, Acting Dir.
Ph: (801)530-6600
Fax: (801)530-6980
Descr: Represents the interests of the state, provincial and territorial securities administrators in the U.S.

2684 ■ Ogden Small Business Development Center
Weber State University
3806 University Cir.
Ogden, UT 84408-3806
Contact: Beverly King, Dir.
Ph: (801)626-7051
Fax: (801)626-7423
E-mail: bking1@weber.edu
URL: http://community.weber.edu/sbdc/Default.html
Descr: Represents and promotes the small business sector. Provides management assistance to current and prospective small business owners. Helps to improve management skills and expand the products and services of members.

2685 ■ Orem/Provo Small Business Development Center
Utah Valley State College
800 W University Pkwy.
Orem, UT 84058
Ph: (801)626-7232
E-mail: sbdcinfo@uvsc.edu
URL: http://www.uvsc.edu/sbdc
Descr: Represents and promotes the small business sector. Provides management assistance to current and prospective small business owners. Helps to improve management skills and expand the products and services of members.

2686 ■ Price Small Business Development Center
Southeastern Applied Technology College
375 S Carbon Ave.
Price, UT 84501
Ph: (435)613-1438
E-mail: emigliori@ceu.edu
URL: http://www.utahsbdc.org
Descr: Represents and promotes the small business sector. Provides management assistance to current and prospective small business owners. Helps to improve management skills and expand the products and services of members.

2687 ■ Richfield Small Business Development Center
Snow College
800 W 200 S, Rm. 155W
Richfield, UT 84701
Ph: (435)893-2252

E-mail: keith.church@snow.edu
URL: http://www.utahsbdc.org
Descr: Represents and promotes the small business sector. Provides management assistance to current and prospective small business owners. Helps to improve management skills and expand the products and services of members.

2688 ■ Utah Society of Enrolled Agents (UT-SEA)
PO Box 26
Layton, UT 84041
Contact: Dee Murray EA, Pres.
Ph: (801)571-2870
Fax: (801)547-1170
E-mail: bob-dudley@att.net
Fnd: 1999. **Mem:** 53.

2689 ■ Utah State Business and Professional Women
1524 S 1100 E
Salt Lake City, UT 84105
Contact: Kelli Charlton, Pres.
E-mail: kellicharlton@infowest.com
URL: http://www.bpwut.org
Descr: Represents the interests of business and professional women. Elevates the standards for women in business and professional settings. Promotes equity for all women in the workplace through advocacy, education and information. Provides professional development, networking and career advancement opportunities for working women.

2690 ■ Vernal Small Business Development Center
Utah State University
1680 W Hwy. 40
Vernal, UT 84078
Ph: (435)789-6100
E-mail: markh@ext.usu.edu
URL: http://www.utahsbdc.org
Descr: Represents and promotes the small business sector. Provides management assistance to current and prospective small business owners. Helps to improve management skills and expand the products and services of members.

Vermont

2691 ■ International Association of Assessing Officers, Vermont
2718 VT Rte. 100
Warren, VT 05674
Contact: Priscilla Robinson, Rep.
Ph: (802)496-6629
Fax: (802)496-2418
E-mail: lister@madriver.com
Descr: Represents state and local officials concerned with valuation of property for ad valorem property tax purposes. Works to improve standards and conduct research on tax assessment. Promotes innovation and excellence in property appraisal, assessment administration, and property tax policy through professional development, education, research, and technical assistance.

2692 ■ NAIFA - Vermont (NAIFA VT)
325 Ethan Allen Pkwy.
Burlington, VT 05401
Contact: Helen Hossley, Exec. Dir.
Ph: (802)660-9639
E-mail: naifavt@gmail.com
URL: http://www.naifanet.com/vermont
Descr: Represents the interests of insurance and financial advisors. Advocates for a positive legislative and regulatory environment. Enhances business and professional skills of members. **Pub:** *Vermont Advisor* (monthly).

2693 ■ North American Securities Administrators Association, Vermont
89 Main St.
Montpelier, VT 05620
Contact: Anna Drummond

Ph: (802)828-3420
URL: http://www.bishca.state.vt.us
Descr: Represents the interests of the state, provincial and territorial securities administrators in the U.S.

2694 ■ Vermont Bankers Association (VBA)
PO Box 587
Montpelier, VT 05601-0587
Contact: Christopher D'Elia, Pres./Treas.
Ph: (802)229-0341
Fax: (802)223-5078
E-mail: vtbanker@sover.net
URL: http://www.vtbanker.com
Staff: 2. **Descr:** National and state chartered savings and commercial banks; federally chartered savings and loan associations. **Fnd:** 1909. **Mem:** 28.
Pub: Directory (annual); Bulletin (semiannual).

2695 ■ Vermont Business and Professional Women
PO Box 843
Montpelier, VT 05601
Contact: Mary Bushey, Pres.
Ph: (802)524-3073
E-mail: marybushey@comcast.net
URL: http://www.vermontbpw.org
Descr: Represents the interests of business and professional women. Elevates the standards for women in business and professional settings. Promotes equity for all women in the workplace through advocacy, education and information. Provides professional development, networking and career advancement opportunities for working women.

2696 ■ Vermont Small Business Development Center, Addison County
1590 Rte. 7 S, Ste. No. 2
Middlebury, VT 05753
Contact: Steve Paddock
Ph: (802)388-7953
Fax: (802)388-0119
E-mail: spaddock@vtsbdc.org
URL: http://www.vtsbdc.org
Descr: Represents and promotes the small business sector. Provides management assistance to current and prospective small business owners. Helps to improve management skills and expand the products and services of members.

2697 ■ Vermont Small Business Development Center, Caledonia County
PO Box 630
St. Johnsbury, VT 05819
Contact: Ross Hart, Area Business Advisor
Ph: (802)748-1014
Fax: (802)748-1223
E-mail: rhart@vtsbdc.org
URL: http://www.vtsbdc.org
Descr: Represents and promotes the small business sector. Provides management assistance to current and prospective small business owners. Helps to improve management skills and expand the products and services of members.

2698 ■ Vermont Small Business Development Center, Franklin County
PO Box 786
Burlington, VT 05402-0786
Contact: Steve Densham, Area Business Advisor
Ph: (802)658-9228
E-mail: sdensham@vtsbdc.org
URL: http://www.vtsbdc.org
Descr: Represents and promotes the small business sector. Provides management assistance to current and prospective small business owners. Helps to improve management skills and expand the products and services of members.

2699 ■ Vermont Small Business Development Center, Grand Isle County
PO Box 213
North Hero, VT 05474-0213
Contact: Pat Travers, Area Business Advisor
Ph: (802)372-8400

E-mail: ptravers@vtsbdc.org
URL: http://www.vtsbdc.org
Descr: Represents and promotes the small business sector. Provides management assistance to current and prospective small business owners. Helps to improve management skills and expand the products and services of members.

2700 ■ Vermont Small Business Development Center, Lamoille County
PO Box 455
Morrisville, VT 05661-0455
Contact: Dave Rubel, Area Business Advisor
Ph: (802)888-4542
Fax: (802)888-7612
E-mail: drubel@vtsbdc.org
URL: http://www.vtsbdc.org
Descr: Represents and promotes the small business sector. Provides management assistance to current and prospective small business owners. Helps to improve management skills and expand the products and services of members.

2701 ■ Vermont Small Business Development Center, Rutland County
112 Quality Ln.
Rutland, VT 05701
Contact: Chris Herriman
Ph: (802)773-9147
Fax: (802)773-8009
E-mail: mherriman@vtsbdc.org
URL: http://www.vtsbdc.org
Descr: Represents and promotes the small business sector. Provides management assistance to current and prospective small business owners. Helps to improve management skills and expand the products and services of members.

2702 ■ Vermont Small Business Development Center, Southeastern Vermont
14 Clinton Sq., Ste. 7
Springfield, VT 05156
Contact: Joan Goldstein
Ph: (802)885-2071
Fax: (802)885-3027
E-mail: jgoldstein@vtsbdc.org
URL: http://www.vtsbdc.org
Descr: Represents and promotes the small business sector. Provides management assistance to current and prospective small business owners. Helps to improve management skills and expand the products and services of members.

2703 ■ Vermont Small Business Development Center, Washington County
PO Box 1439
Montpelier, VT 05601-1439
Contact: Dave Rubel, Area Business Advisor
Ph: (802)223-4654
E-mail: drubel@vtsbdc.org
URL: http://www.vtsbdc.org
Descr: Represents and promotes the small business sector. Provides management assistance to current and prospective small business owners. Helps to improve management skills and expand the products and services of members.

2704 ■ Vermont Small Business Development Center, Windham County
76 Cotton Mill Hill, C-1
Brattleboro, VT 05301
Contact: David Dunn, Area Business Advisor
Ph: (802)257-7731
Fax: (802)257-0294
E-mail: ddunn@vtsbdc.org
URL: http://www.vtsbdc.org
Descr: Represents and promotes the small business sector. Provides management assistance to current and prospective small business owners. Helps to improve management skills and expand the products and services of members.

Virginia

2705 ■ Alexandria Small Business Development Center
Alexandria Chamber of Commerce
801 N Fairfax St., Ste. 402
Alexandria, VA 22314
Contact: Bill Reagan, Dir.
Ph: (703)778-1292
Fax: (703)778-1293
E-mail: billr@alexandriasbdc.org
URL: http://www.alexandriasbdc.org
Descr: Represents and promotes the small business sector. Provides management assistance to current and prospective small business owners. Helps to improve management skills and expand the products and services of members.

2706 ■ American Society of Appraisers, Richmond Chapter
Mark C. Grove Inc.
985 Glennwood Station Ln.
Charlottesville, VA 22901
Contact: Mark C. Grove, VP
Ph: (434)964-1403
Fax: (434)964-1403
E-mail: mark@mgrove.com
URL: http://www.appraisers.org/richmond
Descr: Serves as a professional appraisal educator, testing and accrediting society. Sponsors mandatory recertification program for all members. Offers consumer information service to the public. **Pub:** Newsletter (monthly).

2707 ■ Arlington County Taxpayers Association (ACTA)
PO Box 5335
Arlington, VA 22205
Contact: Tim Wise, Pres.
Ph: (703)351-9300
E-mail: info@acta.us
URL: http://www.acta.us

2708 ■ Arlington Small Business Development Center
George Mason University
901 S Highland St., Ste. 326
Arlington, VA 22204
Contact: Nailing Jain, Dir.
Ph: (703)892-1560
Fax: (703)892-1542
E-mail: nissan@gmu.edu
URL: http://www.arlingtonsbdc.org
Descr: Represents and promotes the small business sector. Provides management assistance to current and prospective small business owners. Helps to improve management skills and expand the products and services of members.

2709 ■ Blue Ridge Chapter Virginia Society of Enrolled Agents
The Tax Depot
2322 Orange Ave. NE
Roanoke, VA 24012
Contact: Rebecca Donehew, Pres.
Ph: (540)342-1120
Fax: (540)342-0972
E-mail: bdonehew@aol.com
URL: http://www.brcea.org
Descr: Aims to improve the knowledge, skills and professionalism of members in all areas of taxation. Enhances the role of enrolled agents among government agencies, other professions and the public at large. Advocates for taxpayer rights and protects members' interests.

2710 ■ Blue Ridge Community College Small Business Development Center
50 Lodge Ln.
Verona, VA 24482
Contact: Sandy Showalter, Dir.
Ph: (540)248-0600
Fax: (540)234-8102
E-mail: browsers@brcc.edu
URL: http://www.jmu.edu/sbdcenter
Descr: Represents and promotes the small business sector. Provides management assistance to current

and prospective small business owners. Helps to improve management skills and expand the products and services of members.

2711 ■ Business and Professional Women of Greater Fairfax
PO Box 494
Annandale, VA 22003
Contact: Jocelyn Colvin-Donald, Pres.
E-mail: bpwfairfax@yahoo.com
URL: http://bpwfairfax.org
Descr: Represents the interests of business and professional women. Elevates the standards for women in business and professional settings. Promotes equity for all women in the workplace through advocacy, education and information. Provides professional development, networking and career advancement opportunities for working women.

2712 ■ Central Virginia AIFA
PO Box 6746
Charlottesville, VA 22906-6746
Contact: John A. Martin, Pres.
Ph: (434)977-0566
Fax: (434)977-6508
E-mail: sva81707@allstate.com
Descr: Represents the interest of insurance and financial advisors. Advocates for a positive legislative and regulatory environment. Enhances business and professional skills of members.

2713 ■ Central Virginia Small Business Development Center
210 Ridge/McIntire Rd., Ste. 500
Charlottesville, VA 22902
Contact: Nora Gillespie, Dir.
Fax: (434)295-8198
E-mail: sbdc@cstone.net
URL: http://www.avenue.org/sbdc
Descr: Represents and promotes the small business sector. Provides management assistance to current and prospective small business owners. Helps to improve management skills and expand the products and services of members.

2714 ■ Covington Business and Professional Women
PO Box 1003
Covington, VA 24426
Contact: Margaret Phillips, Pres.
E-mail: webmaster@bpwcovington.org
URL: http://www.bpwcovington.org
Descr: Represents the interests of business and professional women. Elevates the standards for women in business and professional settings. Promotes equity for all women in the workplace through advocacy, education and information. Provides professional development, networking and career advancement opportunities for working women.

2715 ■ Fairfax County Taxpayers Alliance (FCTA)
PO Box 356
Fairfax, VA 22038
Contact: Arthur Purves, Pres.
E-mail: webmaster@fcta.org
URL: http://www.fcta.org
Fnd: 1956.

2716 ■ Fairfax Small Business Development Center
George Mason University
4031 University Dr., Ste. 200
Fairfax, VA 22030
Contact: John Casey, Dir.
Ph: (703)277-7700
Fax: (703)277-7722
E-mail: jcasey1@gmu.edu
URL: http://www.sbdc.org
Descr: Represents and promotes the small business sector. Provides management assistance to current and prospective small business owners. Helps to

improve management skills and expand the products and services of members.

2717 ■ Fauquier Business and Professional Women
PO Box 1102
Warrenton, VA 20188-1102
Contact: Colette Reynolds, Pres.
Ph: (540)347-1239
URL: http://www.fauquierbpw.org
Descr: Represents the interests of business and professional women. Elevates the standards for women in business and professional settings. Promotes equity for all women in the workplace through advocacy, education and information. Provides professional development, networking and career advancement opportunities for working women.

2718 ■ Financial Planning Association of Central Virginia
18563 Willoughby Heights Ln.
Rockville, VA 23146
Contact: Mila Spaulding, Exec. Dir.
Ph: (804)749-8149
E-mail: fpacva@gmail.com
URL: http://www.fpacva.org
Descr: Aims to be the community that fosters the value of financial planning and advances the financial planning profession. Promotes the CFP mark and enhance the financial planning profession for its members and the public through educational opportunities, professional interaction, and community involvement.

2719 ■ Financial Planning Association of the National Capital Area Chapter (FPA NCA)
12816 Tewksbury Dr.
Herndon, VA 20171
Contact: Peggy Nelson, Exec. Dir.
Ph: (703)620-1712
Fax: (703)620-9722
E-mail: peggynelson@cox.net
URL: http://www.fpanca.org
Descr: Promotes the value of the financial planning process and advances the financial planning profession. Provides a forum for education and career development for its members while adhering to the highest ethical and professional standards.

2720 ■ Greater Richmond Small Business Development Center
600 E Main St., Ste. 700
Richmond, VA 23219-2118
Contact: Mike Leonard, Dir.
Ph: (804)783-9314
Fax: (804)783-9366
E-mail: mike.leonard@grcc.com
URL: http://www.grsbdc.com
Descr: Represents and promotes the small business sector. Provides management assistance to current and prospective small business owners. Helps to improve management skills and expand the products and services of members.

2721 ■ International Association of Assessing Officers, Virginia
PO Box 911
Charlottesville, VA 22902
Contact: Roosevelt Barbour RES, Rep.
Ph: (434)970-3136
Fax: (434)970-3232
E-mail: barbouro@charlottesville.org
Descr: Represents state and local officials concerned with valuation of property for ad valorem property tax purposes. Works to improve standards and conduct research on tax assessment. Promotes innovation and excellence in property appraisal, assessment administration, and property tax policy through professional development, education, research, and technical assistance.

2722 ■ James Madison University Small Business Development Center
1598 S Main St., MSC 5502
Harrisonburg, VA 22807

Contact: Henry Reeves, Dir.
Ph: (540)568-3227
Fax: (540)801-8469
E-mail: reevesha@jmu.edu
URL: http://www.jmu.edu/sbdcenter
Descr: Represents and promotes the small business sector. Provides management assistance to current and prospective small business owners. Helps to improve management skills and expand the products and services of members.

2723 ■ Longwood University Small Business Development Center - Crater
PO Box 1808
Petersburg, VA 23805
Contact: Diane Howerton, Dir.
Ph: (804)518-2003
Fax: (804)518-2004
E-mail: dhowerton@cpd.state.va.us
URL: http://www.longwood.edu/sbdc
Descr: Represents and promotes the small business sector. Provides management assistance to current and prospective small business owners. Helps to improve management skills and expand the products and services of members.

2724 ■ Longwood University Small Business Development Center - Danville
300 Ringgold Industrial Pkwy.
Danville, VA 24540
Contact: Diane Arnold, Dir.
Ph: (434)791-7321
Fax: (434)791-7341
E-mail: arnoldjd@longwood.edu
URL: http://www.longwood.edu/sbdc
Descr: Represents and promotes the small business sector. Provides management assistance to current and prospective small business owners. Helps to improve management skills and expand the products and services of members.

2725 ■ Longwood University Small Business Development Center - Farmville
515 Main St.
Farmville, VA 23909
Contact: Sheri McGuire, Dir.
Ph: (434)395-2086
Fax: (434)395-2359
E-mail: mcguiresr@longwood.edu
URL: http://www.longwood.edu/sbdc
Descr: Represents and promotes the small business sector. Provides management assistance to current and prospective small business owners. Helps to improve management skills and expand the products and services of members.

2726 ■ Longwood University Small Business Development Center - Martinsville
PO Box 709
Martinsville, VA 24114
Contact: Richard G. Ephgrave Sr., Dir.
Ph: (276)632-4462
Fax: (276)632-5059
E-mail: ephgraverg@longwood.edu
URL: http://www.longwood.edu/sbdc
Descr: Represents and promotes the small business sector. Provides management assistance to current and prospective small business owners. Helps to improve management skills and expand the products and services of members.

2727 ■ Longwood University Small Business Development Center - South Boston
515 Broad St.
South Boston, VA 24592
Contact: Larry Harris, Dir.
Ph: (434)572-4533
Fax: (434)572-1733
E-mail: harrislb@longwood.edu
URL: http://www.longwood.edu/sbdc
Descr: Represents and promotes the small business sector. Provides management assistance to current and prospective small business owners. Helps to

improve management skills and expand the products and services of members.

2728 ■ Lord Fairfax Small Business Development Center - Culpeper
18121 Technology Dr.
Culpeper, VA 22701
Contact: Ruth Cope, Business Counselor
Ph: (540)937-2919
E-mail: rcope@lfsbdc.org
URL: http://www.lfsbdc.org

Descr: Represents and promotes the small business sector. Provides management assistance to current and prospective small business owners. Helps to improve management skills and expand the products and services of members.

2729 ■ Lord Fairfax Small Business Development Center - Fauquier
6480 College St.
Warrenton, VA 20187
Contact: David Reardon, Dir.
Ph: (540)351-1595
Fax: (540)351-1597
E-mail: dreardon@lfsbdc.org
URL: http://www.lfsbdc.org

Descr: Represents and promotes the small business sector. Provides management assistance to current and prospective small business owners. Helps to improve management skills and expand the products and services of members.

2730 ■ Lord Fairfax Small Business Development Center - Middletown
7718 Valley Ave.
Middletown, VA 22645
Contact: Bill Sirbaugh, Dir.
Ph: (540)868-7093
Fax: (540)868-7095
E-mail: bsirbaugh@lfsbdc.org
URL: http://www.lfsbdc.org

Descr: Represents and promotes the small business sector. Provides management assistance to current and prospective small business owners. Helps to improve management skills and expand the products and services of members.

2731 ■ Loudon County Taxpayers Association
PO Box 604
Ashburn, VA 20146
Ph: (703)430-9111
Fax: (202)393-5510

2732 ■ Loudoun County Small Business Development Center
21145 Whitfield Pl., Ste. 104
Sterling, VA 20165
Contact: Robin Suomi, Dir.
Ph: (703)430-7222
Fax: (703)430-7258
E-mail: rsuomi@loudounsbdc.org
URL: http://www.loudounsbdc.org

Descr: Represents and promotes the small business sector. Provides management assistance to current and prospective small business owners. Helps to improve management skills and expand the products and services of members.

2733 ■ Lynchburg Small Business Development Center
Business Development Centre
147 Mill Ridge Rd.
Lynchburg, VA 24502
Contact: Niro Rasanayagam, Dir.
Ph: (434)582-6170
Fax: (434)582-6106
E-mail: sbdcdir@lbdc.com
URL: http://www.lbdc.com

Descr: Represents and promotes the small business sector. Provides management assistance to current and prospective small business owners. Helps to

improve management skills and expand the products and services of members.

2734 ■ Mountain Empire Small Business Development Center
Mountain Empire Community College
3441 Mountain Empire Rd.
Big Stone Gap, VA 24219
Contact: Tim Blankenbecler, Dir.
Ph: (276)523-6529
Fax: (276)523-8139
E-mail: tblankenbecler@me.vccs.edu
URL: http://www.me.cc.va.us/sbdc

Descr: Represents and promotes the small business sector. Provides management assistance to current and prospective small business owners. Helps to improve management skills and expand the products and services of members.

2735 ■ Norfolk AIFA
295 Bendix Rd.
Virginia Beach, VA 23452
Contact: Kenneth Sholar, Pres.
Ph: (757)490-4848
E-mail: kenneth_sholar@us.aflac.com
URL: http://naifanet.com/norfolk

Descr: Represents the interest of insurance and financial advisors. Advocates for a positive legislative and regulatory environment. Enhances business and professional skills of members.

2736 ■ Northern Piedmont AIFA
14367 Clearview Ave.
Gainesville, VA 20155
Contact: Gail Harris, Sec.
Ph: (703)753-6535
Fax: (703)753-6535
E-mail: bgh1931@aol.com

Descr: Represents the interests of insurance and financial advisors. Advocates for a positive legislative and regulatory environment. Enhances business and professional skills of members.

2737 ■ Northern Virginia AIFA (NVAIFA)
14062 Hawkeye Run Ct.
Bristow, VA 20136
Contact: Jane E. Leckert, Exec. Dir.
Ph: (703)393-9493
Fax: (703)393-9423
E-mail: nvaifa@mindspring.com
URL: http://209.61.156.20/main-pub.cfm?usr=516244

Descr: Represents the interests of insurance and financial advisors. Advocates for a positive legislative and regulatory environment. Enhances business and professional skills of members.

2738 ■ Prince William Taxpayers Alliance
10024 Island Fog Ct.
Bristow, VA 20136
Ph: (703)335-8122
E-mail: rhendrix@comcast.net

2739 ■ Rappahannock Region Small Business Development Center - Fredericksburg
University of Mary Washington
College of Graduate and Profession
121 University Blvd.
Fredericksburg, VA 22406
Contact: Brian Baker, Dir.
Ph: (540)286-8060
Fax: (540)286-8042
E-mail: bbaker@umw.edu
URL: http://www.rrsbdc.biz

Descr: Represents and promotes the small business sector. Provides management assistance to current and prospective small business owners. Helps to improve management skills and expand the products and services of members.

2740 ■ Rappahannock Region Small Business Development Center - Warsaw
PO Box 490
Warsaw, VA 22572
Contact: Joy Corprew, Dir.
Ph: (804)333-0286

Free: 800-524-8915
Fax: (804)333-0187
E-mail: jcorprew@umw.edu
URL: http://www.rrsbdc.biz

Descr: Represents and promotes the small business sector. Provides management assistance to current and prospective small business owners. Helps to improve management skills and expand the products and services of members.

2741 ■ Richmond AIFA
7231 Forest Ave., Ste. 300
Richmond, VA 23226
Contact: Devon Cury, Pres.
Ph: (804)287-0253
Fax: (804)285-3134
E-mail: devon.cury@axa-advisors.com
URL: http://www.naifanet.com/richmond

Descr: Represents the interests of insurance and financial advisors. Advocates for a positive legislative and regulatory environment. Enhances business and professional skills of members.

2742 ■ Roanoke Regional Small Business Development Center
Roanoke Regional Chamber of Commerce
212 S Jefferson St.
Roanoke, VA 24011
Contact: Roy Baldwin, Dir.
Ph: (540)983-0717
Fax: (540)983-0723
E-mail: rbaldwin@roanokechamber.org
URL: http://www.rrsbdc.org

Descr: Represents and promotes the small business sector. Provides management assistance to current and prospective small business owners. Helps to improve management skills and expand the products and services of members.

2743 ■ Roanoke Valley AIFA
PO Box 1004
Vinton, VA 24179
Contact: John C. Brake, Pres.
Ph: (540)563-5000
Fax: (540)563-5000
E-mail: rvaifa@roanokemail.com
URL: http://www.naifanet.com/roanoke

Descr: Represents the interest of insurance and financial advisors. Advocates for a positive legislative and regulatory environment. Enhances business and professional skills of members.

2744 ■ SOCAP International - Washington, D.C. Area Chapter
4427 Holly Ave.
Fairfax, VA 22030
Contact: Mike Ebhardt, Pres.
Ph: (703)322-9645

Descr: Promotes customer care and customer management as a competitive advantage in business. Provides educational tools and professional resources to help members drive business transformation within their companies.

2745 ■ South Fairfax Small Business Development Center
7001 Loisdale Rd., 2nd Fl.
Springfield, VA 22150
Contact: Brenda Quiroz-Maday, Acting Dir.
Ph: (703)768-1440
Fax: (703)768-0547
E-mail: brenda@cbponline.org
URL: http://www.cbponline.org

Descr: Represents and promotes the small business sector. Provides management assistance to current and prospective small business owners. Helps to improve management skills and expand the products and services of members.

2746 ■ Southwest Virginia Small Business Development Center
PO Box SVCC
Richlands, VA 24641
Contact: Joyce Kinder, Dir.
Ph: (276)964-7345

Fax: (276)964-7575
E-mail: joyce.kinder@sw.edu
URL: http://www.sw.edu

Descr: Represents and promotes the small business sector. Provides management assistance to current and prospective small business owners. Helps to improve management skills and expand the products and services of members.

2747 ■ Virginia Beach Taxpayer Alliance (VBTA)
5225 S Lake Rd.
Virginia Beach, VA 23455
Contact: Sandy Linkous, Treas.
E-mail: robertkdean@cox.net
URL: http://www.vbtaxpayer.com

2748 ■ Virginia Highlands Small Business Development Center
Virginia Highlands Community College
150 VHCC Dr.
Abingdon, VA 24210
Contact: Jim Tilley, Dir.
Ph: (276)739-2474
Fax: (276)739-2577
E-mail: jtilley@vhcc.edu
URL: http://www.vhcc.edu/sbdc

Descr: Represents and promotes the small business sector. Provides management assistance to current and prospective small business owners. Helps to improve management skills and expand the products and services of members.

2749 ■ Virginia Society of Enrolled Agents, Fredericksburg Chapter
Century Small Business Solutions
2217 Princess Ann St.
Fredericksburg, VA 22401
Contact: W. Robert Brammer
Ph: (540)374-0545
URL: http://www.vasea.org/fredericksburg.php

Descr: Aims to improve the knowledge, skills and professionalism of members in all areas of taxation. Enhances the role of enrolled agents among government agencies, other professions and the public at large. Advocates for taxpayer rights and protects members' interests.

2750 ■ Virginia Society of Enrolled Agents - Hampton Roads Chapter (HRC VaSEA)
Walsh Enterprises, Ltd.
600 Norfolk Ave.
Virginia Beach, VA 23451
Contact: George Walsh EA, Pres.
Ph: (757)428-5258
E-mail: gwalsh9@aol.com
URL: http://www.vaeas.org/hampton-roads.php

Descr: Membership consists of Enrolled Agents and other interested parties. Offers monthly continuing education meetings featuring local speakers from the Internal Revenue Service, Virginia Department of Taxation as well as attorneys and accountants. **Fnd:** 1983. **Mem:** 200.

2751 ■ Virginia Society of Enrolled Agents - Northern Virginia Chapter
2108 N Military Rd.
Arlington, VA 22207
Contact: Alexander B. Thomson EA, Pres.
Ph: (703)524-1595
E-mail: al@thomsonmanagement.com
URL: http://www.vasea.org/northern-virginia.php

2752 ■ Virginia Society of Enrolled Agents, Richmond Chapter
Sage Bldg.
115 Jefferson Hwy.
Louisa, VA 23093
Contact: Jeffrey S. Bruce, Pres.
Ph: (540)967-2332
E-mail: jbruce@ns.gemlink.com
URL: http://www.vasea.org/richmond.php

Descr: Aims to improve the knowledge, skills and professionalism of members in all areas of taxation. Enhances the role of enrolled agents among government agencies, other professions and the public at large. Advocates for taxpayer rights and protects members' interests.

2753 ■ Virginia Taxpayers Association
PO Box 663
Lynchburg, VA 24505
Ph: (804)277-5255
Fax: (804)277-5255
E-mail: kwhite9472@aol.com

Washington

2754 ■ Aberdeen Small Business Development Center
Grays Harbor College
1620 Edward P. Smith Dr., Bldg. 200
Aberdeen, WA 98520
Contact: Erik Stewart, Business Advisor
Ph: (360)538-2530
E-mail: eriks@wsu.edu
URL: http://www.wsbdc.org

Descr: Represents and promotes the small business sector. Provides management assistance to current and prospective small business owners. Helps to improve management skills and expand the products and services of members.

2755 ■ American Society of Appraisers, Seattle Chapter
Moss Adams LLP
999 3rd Ave., Ste. 2800
Seattle, WA 98104-4057
Contact: Wayne D. Fjeld, VP
Ph: (206)302-6580
Fax: (206)233-9214
E-mail: wayne.fjeld@mossadams.com

Descr: Serves as a professional appraisal educator, testing and accrediting society. Sponsors mandatory re-certification program for all members. Offers consumer information service to the public.

2756 ■ Auburn Small Business Development Center
110 2nd St. SW, Ste. 135
Auburn, WA 98001
Contact: Deanna Burnett-Keener, Dir.
Ph: (253)333-4953
Fax: (253)333-4640
E-mail: dburnett@greenriver.edu
URL: http://www.wsbdc.org

Descr: Represents and promotes the small business sector. Provides management assistance to current and prospective small business owners. Helps to improve management skills and expand the products and services of members.

2757 ■ Bellevue Business and Professional Women
11714 N Creek Pkwy. N, No. 102
Bothell, WA 98011
Contact: Lisa M. Mikesell, Sec.-Treas.
Ph: (425)489-2139
E-mail: lisa.mikesell@hubinternational.com
URL: http://www.bpwbellevuewa.com

Descr: Represents the interests of business and professional women. Elevates the standards for women in business and professional settings. Promotes equity for all women in the workplace through advocacy, education and information. Provides professional development, networking and career advancement opportunities for working women.

2758 ■ Bellingham Small Business Development Center
119 N Commercial St., Ste. 195
Bellingham, WA 98225
Contact: Thomas Dorr, Dir.
Ph: (360)733-4014
Fax: (360)733-5092
E-mail: tom.dorr@wwu.edu
URL: http://www.wsbdc.org

Descr: Represents and promotes the small business sector. Provides management assistance to current and prospective small business owners. Helps to

improve management skills and expand the products and services of members.

2759 ■ Bremerton Small Business Development Center
345 6th St., Ste. 568
Bremerton, WA 98337
Contact: Rand Riedrich, Business Advisor
Ph: (360)307-4220
Fax: (360)337-4864
E-mail: rriedrich@oc.ctc.edu
URL: http://www.wsbdc.org

Descr: Represents and promotes the small business sector. Provides management assistance to current and prospective small business owners. Helps to improve management skills and expand the products and services of members.

2760 ■ Business and Professional Women, Washington
2720 W Marine View Dr.
Everett, WA 98201
Contact: Robyn Whitaker, Pres.-Elect
Ph: (425)483-3659
E-mail: robynwhitaker@aol.com
URL: http://home.earthlink.net/~wabusinesswoman

Descr: Represents the interests of business and professional women. Elevates the standards for women in business and professional settings. Promotes equity for all women in the workplace through advocacy, education and information. Provides professional development, networking and career advancement opportunities for working women.

2761 ■ Edmonds Small Business Development Center
728 134th St. SW, Ste. 128
Everett, WA 98204
Contact: Marjorie Tyson, Admin. Asst.
Ph: (425)640-1435
Fax: (425)743-5726
E-mail: marjorie.tyson@edcc.edu
URL: http://www.wsbdc.org

Descr: Represents and promotes the small business sector. Provides management assistance to current and prospective small business owners. Helps to improve management skills and expand the products and services of members.

2762 ■ Financial Planning Association of Puget Sound
PO Box 2016
Edmonds, WA 98020-9516
Contact: Cindy Byfield, Exec. Dir.
Ph: (206)686-4FPA
E-mail: info@fpapugetsound.org
URL: http://www.fpapugetsound.org

Descr: Supports the financial planning process in order to help people achieve their goals and dreams. Promotes the value of the financial planning process and advances the financial planning profession.

2763 ■ Greater Everett Business and Professional Women
PO Box 13292
Everett, WA 98206-3292
Contact: Frances Stewart, Pres.
Ph: (425)338-5298
E-mail: everettbpw@earthlink.net

Descr: Represents the interests of business and professional women. Elevates the standards for women in business and professional settings. Promotes equity for all women in the workplace through advocacy, education and information. Provides professional development, networking and career advancement opportunities for working women.

2764 ■ Highline Small Business Development Center
PO Box 98000
Des Moines, WA 98198
Contact: Rich Shockley, Business Advisor
Ph: (206)878-3710
Fax: (206)870-5929
URL: http://www.wsbdc.org

Descr: Represents and promotes the small business sector. Provides management assistance to current and prospective small business owners. Helps to improve management skills and expand the products and services of members.

2765 ■ International Association of Assessing Officers, Washington
2401 S 35th St., Rm. 142
Tacoma, WA 98409
Contact: Scott Peebles, Rep.
Ph: (253)798-7132
Fax: (253)798-3705
E-mail: speeble@co.pierce.wa.us

Descr: Represents state and local officials concerned with valuation of property for ad valorem property tax purposes. Works to improve standards and conduct research on tax assessment. Promotes innovation and excellence in property appraisal, assessment administration, and property tax policy through professional development, education, research, and technical assistance.

2766 ■ Lewis County Small Business Development Center
1611 N National Ave.
Chehalis, WA 98532
Contact: David Baria, Business Advisor
Ph: (360)748-0114
Fax: (360)748-1238
E-mail: dbaria@lewisedc.com
URL: http://www.wsbdc.org

Descr: Represents and promotes the small business sector. Provides management assistance to current and prospective small business owners. Helps to improve management skills and expand the products and services of members.

2767 ■ Longview Small Business Development Center
PO Box 3010
Longview, WA 98632
Contact: Susan Hoosier, Business Advisor
Ph: (360)442-2946
Fax: (360)422-2948
E-mail: shoosier@wsu.edu
URL: http://www.wsbdc.org

Descr: Represents and promotes the small business sector. Provides management assistance to current and prospective small business owners. Helps to improve management skills and expand the products and services of members.

2768 ■ Moses Lake Small Business Development Center
Bldg. 1800, Rm. 1857A
7662 Chanute St. NE
Moses Lake, WA 98837
Contact: Allan Peterson, Business Advisor
Ph: (509)793-2373
Fax: (509)762-4703
E-mail: allanp@bigbend.edu
URL: http://www.wsbdc.org

Descr: Represents and promotes the small business sector. Provides management assistance to current and prospective small business owners. Helps to improve management skills and expand the products and services of members.

2769 ■ Mount Vernon Small Business Development Center
204 W Montgomery St.
Mount Vernon, WA 98273
Contact: Traci Stark, Business Advisor
Ph: (360)336-6114
Fax: (360)336-6116
E-mail: traci@skagit.org
URL: http://www.wsbdc.org

Descr: Represents and promotes the small business sector. Provides management assistance to current and prospective small business owners. Helps to

improve management skills and expand the products and services of members.

2770 ■ NAIFA-Northwest Washington
PO Box 5343
Bellingham, WA 98227
Contact: Paul D. Twedt CLU, Pres.
Ph: (360)647-2321
Fax: (360)647-2327
E-mail: paul.twedt@nwfn.com
URL: http://naifanet.com/nwwashington

Descr: Represents the interests of insurance and financial advisors. Advocates for a positive legislative and regulatory environment. Enhances business and professional skills of members.

2771 ■ NAIFA-Snohomish County
3324 Bickford Ave.
Snohomish, WA 98290-9287
Contact: Robert N. Reuter, Pres.
Ph: (425)377-0281
Fax: (425)377-0284
E-mail: naifa.snohomish@integra.net
URL: http://www.naifanet.com/snohomishcounty

Descr: Represents the interest of insurance and financial advisors. Advocates for a positive legislative and regulatory environment. Enhances business and professional skills of members.

2772 ■ NAIFA-Spokane
PO Box 11212
Spokane, WA 99211
Contact: Randy Kimm
Ph: (509)362-1714
E-mail: dave@kofcagent.com
URL: http://www.naifa-spokane.com

Descr: Represents the interest of insurance and financial advisors. Advocates for a positive legislative and regulatory environment. Enhances business and professional skills of members.

2773 ■ North 5 Business and Professional Women
1181 Sudden Valley
Bellingham, WA 98229
Contact: Carolyn Leeper, Sec.-Treas.
Ph: (360)714-8901
Fax: (360)714-8901
E-mail: cdleeper@hotmail.com
URL: http://www.north5bpw.org

Descr: Represents the interests of business and professional women. Elevates the standards for women in business and professional settings. Promotes equity for all women in the workplace through advocacy, education and information. Provides professional development, networking and career advancement opportunities for working women.

2774 ■ North American Securities Administrators Association, Washington
150 Israel Rd. SW
Tumwater, WA 98501
Contact: Michael E. Stevenson, Dir.
Ph: (360)902-8760
Fax: (360)902-0524

Descr: Represents the interests of the state, provincial and territorial securities administrators in the U.S.

2775 ■ Okanogan Small Business Development Center
320 Omak Ave.
Omak, WA 98841
Contact: Lewis Blakeney, Business Advisor
Ph: (509)826-5107
Fax: (509)826-7425
E-mail: blakeney@methow.com
URL: http://www.wsbdc.org

Descr: Represents and promotes the small business sector. Provides management assistance to current and prospective small business owners. Helps to

improve management skills and expand the products and services of members.

2776 ■ Olympia Small Business Development Center
665 Woodland Sq. SE, Ste. 201
Lacey, WA 98503
Contact: Celia Nightingale, Business Advisor
Ph: (360)407-0014
Fax: (360)407-0012
E-mail: cnightingale@spscc.ctc.edu
URL: http://www.wsbdc.org

Descr: Represents and promotes the small business sector. Provides management assistance to current and prospective small business owners. Helps to improve management skills and expand the products and services of members.

2777 ■ Port Angeles Small Business Development Center
Lincoln Center
905 S B St., Ste. 128
Port Angeles, WA 98363
Contact: Kathleen Purdy, Dir.
Ph: (360)417-5657
Fax: (360)344-3079
E-mail: kpurdy@olympus.net
URL: http://www.wsbdc.org

Descr: Represents and promotes the small business sector. Provides management assistance to current and prospective small business owners. Helps to improve management skills and expand the products and services of members.

2778 ■ Port Townsend Small Business Development Center
PO Box 1849
Port Townsend, WA 98368
Contact: Kathleen Purdy, Business Advisor
Ph: (360)334-3078
Fax: (360)344-3079
E-mail: kpurdy@olympus.net
URL: http://www.wsbdc.org

Descr: Represents and promotes the small business sector. Provides management assistance to current and prospective small business owners. Helps to improve management skills and expand the products and services of members.

2779 ■ Pullman Small Business Development Center
PO Box 641802
Pullman, WA 99164-1802
Contact: Terry Cornelison, Business Advisor
Ph: (509)335-8081
Fax: (509)335-8082
E-mail: tlcornelison@wsu.edu
URL: http://www.wsbdc.org

Descr: Represents and promotes the small business sector. Provides management assistance to current and prospective small business owners. Helps to improve management skills and expand the products and services of members.

2780 ■ Renton Business and Professional Women
Box 2972
Renton, WA 98056
Contact: Irene Roberts, Pres.
Ph: (425)277-2434
E-mail: irene@rentonbpw.org
URL: http://www.rentonbpw.org

Descr: Represents the interests of business and professional women. Elevates the standards for women in business and professional settings. Promotes equity for all women in the workplace through advocacy, education and information. Provides professional development, networking and career advancement opportunities for working women.

2781 ■ Renton Small Business Development Center
Bldg. J, Ste. 214
3000 NE 4th St.
Renton, WA 98056
Contact: Kevin Hoult

Ph: (425)235-7819
E-mail: kevin.hoult@wsbdc.org
URL: http://www.wsbdc.org

Descr: Represents and promotes the small business sector. Provides management assistance to current and prospective small business owners. Helps to improve management skills and expand the products and services of members.

2782 ■ Republic, Washington Business and Professional Women
179 Rose Valley Rd.
Republic, WA 99166
Contact: Jayne Jurgensen
Ph: (509)775-3819
E-mail: jjajurg@televar.com
URL: http://www.freewebs.com/republicbpw/index.htm

Descr: Represents the interests of business and professional women. Elevates the standards for women in business and professional settings. Promotes equity for all women in the workplace through advocacy, education and information. Provides professional development, networking and career advancement opportunities for working women.

2783 ■ Seattle Small Business Development Center
Washington State University
520 Pike St., Ste. 1101
Seattle, WA 98101
Contact: Michael Franz, Business Advisor
Ph: (206)428-3022
Fax: (206)448-1334
E-mail: mfranz@wsu.edu
URL: http://www.wsbdc.org

Descr: Represents and promotes the small business sector. Provides management assistance to current and prospective small business owners. Helps to improve management skills and expand the products and services of members.

2784 ■ Spokane Small Business Development Center
SIRTI Bldg.
665 N Riverpoint Blvd., Ste. 201
Spokane, WA 99202
Contact: Cindy Doyl, Program Coor.
Ph: (509)358-7890
Fax: (509)358-7896
E-mail: cdoyl@wsu.edu
URL: http://www.wsbdc.org

Descr: Represents and promotes the small business sector. Provides management assistance to current and prospective small business owners. Helps to improve management skills and expand the products and services of members.

2785 ■ Tacoma Small Business Development Center
1101 S Yakima Ave., M-123
Tacoma, WA 98405
Contact: John Rodenberg, Business Advisor
Ph: (253)680-7768
E-mail: jrodenberg@bates.ctc.edu
URL: http://www.wsbdc.org

Descr: Represents and promotes the small business sector. Provides management assistance to current and prospective small business owners. Helps to improve management skills and expand the products and services of members.

2786 ■ Tri-Cities Small Business Development Center
2600 N 20th Ave.
Pasco, WA 99301
Contact: Bruce Davis, Dir.
Ph: (509)542-5635
Fax: (509)546-0416
E-mail: bdavis@columbiabasin.edu
URL: http://www.wsbdc.org

Descr: Represents and promotes the small business sector. Provides management assistance to current and prospective small business owners. Helps to

improve management skills and expand the products and services of members.

2787 ■ Vancouver Small Business Development Center
12000 NE 95th St., Ste. 504
Vancouver, WA 98682
Contact: Jan Harte, Business Advisor
Ph: (360)260-6372
Fax: (360)260-6369
E-mail: jharte@vancouver.wsu.edu
URL: http://www.wsbdc.org

Descr: Represents and promotes the small business sector. Provides management assistance to current and prospective small business owners. Helps to improve management skills and expand the products and services of members.

2788 ■ Washington State Society of Enrolled Agents (WSSEA)
PO Box 7
South Bend, WA 98586
Contact: Dennis LeMaster, Admin.
Ph: (360)875-5555
Free: 800-613-2801
Fax: (360)875-5248
E-mail: lemacct@willapabay.org
URL: http://www.taxea.org

Descr: Aims to improve the knowledge, skills and professionalism of members in all areas of taxation. Enhances the role of enrolled agents among government agencies, other professions and the public at large. Advocates for taxpayer rights and protects members' interests.

2789 ■ Wenatchee Small Business Development Center
285 Technology Center Way, Ste. 101
Wenatchee, WA 98801
Contact: Jim Fletcher, Business Advisor
Ph: (509)682-6905
Fax: (509)665-0780
E-mail: sbdc@wvc.edu
URL: http://www.wsbdc.org

Descr: Represents and promotes the small business sector. Provides management assistance to current and prospective small business owners. Helps to improve management skills and expand the products and services of members.

2790 ■ Yakima Small Business Development Center
10 N 9th St.
Yakima, WA 98901
Contact: Linda Johnson, Business Advisor
Ph: (509)454-7612
Fax: (509)248-0601
E-mail: linda@yakima.org
URL: http://www.wsbdc.org

Descr: Represents and promotes the small business sector. Provides management assistance to current and prospective small business owners. Helps to improve management skills and expand the products and services of members.

West Virginia

2791 ■ Business and Professional Women, Charleston
Rte. 4, Box 171-1
Charleston, WV 25312
Contact: Pearl Watson, Pres.
Ph: (304)343-8801
Fax: (304)343-8817
E-mail: rramsey@logancorp.com
URL: http://www.bpwcharlestonareawv.org

Descr: Represents the interests of business and professional women. Elevates the standards for women in business and professional settings. Promotes equity for all women in the workplace through advocacy, education and information. Provides professional development, networking and

career advancement opportunities for working women.

2792 ■ Business Professional Women, Weirton
PO Box 2333
Weirton, WV 26062
Contact: Debbie Coletti Pearce, Pres.
E-mail: deb020562@aol.com
URL: http://www.bpwweirtonwv.org

Descr: Represents the interests of business and professional women. Elevates the standards for women in business and professional settings. Promotes equity for all women in the workplace through advocacy, education and information. Provides professional development, networking and career advancement opportunities for working women.

2793 ■ Business and Professional Women, West Virginia
200 Logan Ave.
Morgantown, WV 26502
Contact: Ann H. Parsons, Pres.
E-mail: gholland410@yahoo.com
URL: http://www.bpwwv.org

Descr: Represents the interests of business and professional women. Elevates the standards for women in business and professional settings. Promotes equity for all women in the workplace through advocacy, education and information. Provides professional development, networking and career advancement opportunities for working women.

2794 ■ Charleston Small Business Development Center
Bldg. 6, Rm. 652
1900 Kanawha Blvd. E
Charleston, WV 25305
Contact: Anne Lane, Business Analyst
Ph: (304)558-2960
Fax: (304)558-0127
E-mail: alane@wvsbdc.org
URL: http://www.sbdcwv.org

Descr: Represents and promotes the small business sector. Provides management assistance to current and prospective small business owners. Helps to improve management skills and expand the products and services of members.

2795 ■ Eastern Panhandle Small Business Development Center
142 N Queen St.
Martinsburg, WV 25401
Contact: Christina Lundberg, Mgr.
Ph: (304)596-6642
Fax: (304)596-6646
E-mail: clundber@blueridgectc.edu
URL: http://www.sbdcwv.org

Descr: Represents and promotes the small business sector. Provides management assistance to current and prospective small business owners. Helps to improve management skills and expand the products and services of members.

2796 ■ Eastern West Virginia Small Business Development Center
1929 State Rd., No. 55
Moorefield, WV 26836
Contact: Beth Ludewig, Mgr.
Ph: (304)434-8000
Fax: (304)434-7003
E-mail: mludewig@eastern.wvnet.edu
URL: http://www.sbdcwv.org

Descr: Represents and promotes the small business sector. Provides management assistance to current and prospective small business owners. Helps to improve management skills and expand the products and services of members.

2797 ■ Marshall University Small Business Development Center
348 15th St.
Huntington, WV 25701
Contact: Amber Wilson, Mgr.

Ph: (304)399-1040
Fax: (304)525-1467
E-mail: wilsona@marshall.edu
URL: http://www.sbdcwv.org

Descr: Represents and promotes the small business sector. Provides management assistance to current and prospective small business owners. Helps to improve management skills and expand the products and services of members.

2798 ■ Pierpont Community and Technical College of Fairmont State University Small Business Development Center
320 Adams St., Ste. G01
Fairmont, WV 26554
Contact: Vicki Karickhoff, Business Analyst
Ph: (304)367-4920
Fax: (304)367-2717
E-mail: vkarickhoff@fairmontstate.edu
URL: http://www.sbdcwv.org

Descr: Represents and promotes the small business sector. Provides management assistance to current and prospective small business owners. Helps to improve management skills and expand the products and services of members.

2799 ■ Pierpont Community and Technical College of Fairmont State University Small Business Development Center - Flatwoods
Braxton County Center
200 Jerry Burton Dr.
Sutton, WV 26601
Free: 888-982-7232
Fax: (304)558-0127
URL: http://www.sbdcwv.org

Descr: Represents and promotes the small business sector. Provides management assistance to current and prospective small business owners. Helps to improve management skills and expand the products and services of members.

2800 ■ Southern West Virginia Small Business Development Center
PO Box 2900
Mount Gay, WV 25637
Contact: Harold Patterson, Mgr.
Ph: (304)896-7451
Fax: (304)862-3071
E-mail: hpatterson@frontiernet.net
URL: http://www.sbdcwv.org

Descr: Represents and promotes the small business sector. Provides management assistance to current and prospective small business owners. Helps to improve management skills and expand the products and services of members.

2801 ■ West Virginia Bankers Association (WVBA)
120 Washington St. E
Charleston, WV 25301-1516
Contact: Donna Atkinson, Dir. of Education
Ph: (304)343-8838
Fax: (304)343-9749
E-mail: datkinson@wvbankers.org
URL: http://www.wvbankers.org

Descr: Commercial banks and trust companies. Promotes industry interests. Provides opportunities for exchange of information. **Fnd:** 1891. **Pub:** *Legislative Bulletin*; *WV Banker* (quarterly).

2802 ■ West Virginia Northern Community College Small Business Development Center
1704 Market St.
Wheeling, WV 26003
Contact: Donna Schramm, Mgr.
Ph: (304)214-8973
Fax: (304)233-5522
E-mail: dschramm@wvncc.edu
URL: http://www.sbdcwv.org

Descr: Represents and promotes the small business sector. Provides management assistance to current and prospective small business owners. Helps to

improve management skills and expand the products and services of members.

2803 ■ West Virginia University Small Business Development Center
PO Box 6884
Morgantown, WV 26506
Contact: Sharon Stratton, Mgr.
Ph: (304)293-5839
Fax: (304)225-2510
E-mail: sharon.stratton@mail.wvu.edu
URL: http://www.sbdcwv.org

Descr: Represents and promotes the small business sector. Provides management assistance to current and prospective small business owners. Helps to improve management skills and expand the products and services of members.

2804 ■ West Virginia University Small Business Development Center - Parkersburg
300 Campus Dr.
Parkersburg, WV 26104
Contact: Greg Hill, Mgr.
Ph: (304)424-8391
Fax: (304)424-8266
E-mail: greg.hill@mail.wvu.edu
URL: http://www.sbdcwv.org

Descr: Represents and promotes the small business sector. Provides management assistance to current and prospective small business owners. Helps to improve management skills and expand the products and services of members.

2805 ■ Workforce Small Business Development Center - Beckley
200 Value City Ctr., Ste. 601
Beckley, WV 25801
Contact: Kevin Twohig, Mgr.
Ph: (304)558-2960
Free: 888-982-7232
Fax: (304)558-0127
E-mail: ktwohig@wvsbdc.org
URL: http://www.sbdcwv.org

Descr: Represents and promotes the small business sector. Provides management assistance to current and prospective small business owners. Helps to improve management skills and expand the products and services of members.

2806 ■ Workforce Small Business Development Center - Summersville
830 Northside Dr., Ste. 166
Summersville, WV 26651
Contact: James Epling, Mgr.
Ph: (304)872-0020
Fax: (304)872-0020
E-mail: jepling@r1workforcewv.org
URL: http://www.sbdcwv.org

Descr: Represents and promotes the small business sector. Provides management assistance to current and prospective small business owners. Helps to improve management skills and expand the products and services of members.

Wisconsin

2807 ■ American Society of Appraisers, Wisconsin Chapter
America Appraisal Associates, Inc.
411 E Wisconsin Ave., Ste. 1900
Milwaukee, WI 53202-4466
Contact: Edward W. Raether, Pres.
Ph: (414)271-7240
Fax: (414)225-1900
E-mail: skellenberger@american-appraisal.com
URL: http://www.appraisers.org/wisconsin

Descr: Serves as a professional appraisal educator, testing and accrediting society. Sponsors mandatory recertification program for all members. Offers consumer information service to the public.

2808 ■ Appraisal Institute, Wisconsin Chapter
11801 W Silver Spring Dr., No. 200
Milwaukee, WI 53225
Contact: Steve Stiloski, Pres.
Ph: (414)271-6858

Fax: (414)464-0850
E-mail: info@wamllc.net
URL: http://www.wisai.com

Descr: Represents the interests of real estate appraisers. **Pub:** *Messenger* (quarterly).

2809 ■ Brown County Taxpayers Association
PO Box 684
Green Bay, WI 54305
E-mail: taxpayers@bctaxpayers.org
URL: http://www.bctaxpayers.org

2810 ■ Business and Professional Women, Waterford
PO Box 55
Waterford, WI 53185
Contact: Mary Schingeck, Pres.
E-mail: schingeck@msn.com
URL: http://www.bpw-waterford.org

Descr: Represents the interests of business and professional women. Elevates the standards for women in business and professional settings. Promotes equity for all women in the workplace through advocacy, education and information. Provides professional development, networking and career advancement opportunities for working women.

2811 ■ Douglas County Taxpayers Association (DCTA)
2016 Hill Ave.
Superior, WI 54880
Contact: Kevin Peterson, Chm.
Ph: (218)348-0912
E-mail: kdpsrp2@aol.com

2812 ■ Federation of Wisconsin Taxpayer Organizations
228 14th Ave.
South Milwaukee, WI 53172

2813 ■ Financial Planning Association of Southern Wisconsin (FPA-SW)
6949 N 100th St.
Milwaukee, WI 53224
Contact: J. Bernard Fiedler CFP, Pres.
Ph: (414)358-9260
Fax: (414)358-9261
E-mail: info@fpasw.org
URL: http://www.fpasw.org

Descr: Promotes financial planning profession through education, networking, and mentoring. Enhances public awareness of the value of the financial planning process. Provides forum for education and career development for its members.

2814 ■ International Association of Assessing Officers, Wisconsin
200 E Wells St., Rm. 507
Milwaukee, WI 53202
Contact: Mary P. Reavey, Rep.
Ph: (414)286-3101
Fax: (414)286-8447
E-mail: mreavey@milwaukee.gov

Descr: Represents state and local officials concerned with valuation of property for ad valorem property tax purposes. Works to improve standards and conduct research on tax assessment. Promotes innovation and excellence in property appraisal, assessment administration, and property tax policy through professional development, education, research, and technical assistance.

2815 ■ Madison Business and Professional Women
PO Box 628373
Middleton, WI 53562
Contact: Linda Jackson, Pres.
E-mail: bpwmadison@yahoo.com
URL: http://www.madisonbpw.com

Descr: Represents the interests of business and professional women. Elevates the standards for women in business and professional settings. Promotes equity for all women in the workplace through advocacy, education and information. Provides professional development, networking and

career advancement opportunities for working women.

2816 ■ Menominee County Taxpayers Association
PO Box 666
Keshena, WI 54135
Ph: (715)799-3484
E-mail: pender@ezwebtech.com

2817 ■ Mid Day of Appleton Business and Professional Women
PO Box 334
Appleton, WI 54912-0334
Contact: Robyn Gruner, Co-Pres.
Ph: (920)730-2593
URL: http://www.middaybpw.org
Descr: Represents the interests of business and professional women. Elevates the standards for women in business and professional settings. Promotes equity for all women in the workplace through advocacy, education and information. Provides professional development, networking and career advancement opportunities for working women.

2818 ■ NAIFA-Fond du Lac
525 N Peters Ave., Ste. 700
Fond du Lac, WI 54935
Contact: Rose Bertram, Pres.
Ph: (920)924-6751
Fax: (920)921-5834
E-mail: rose@rosebertram.com
Staff: 3. **Descr:** Represents the interests of insurance and financial advisors. Advocates for a positive legislative and regulatory environment. Enhances business and professional skills of members.

2819 ■ NAIFA-Northeastern Wisconsin
2460 Prairie Flower Ln.
De Pere, WI 54115
Ph: (920)632-4171
Fax: (920)632-7052
E-mail: naifa-new@new.rr.com
URL: http://naifanet.com/northeasternwisconsin
Descr: Represents the interests of insurance and financial advisors. Advocates for a positive legislative and regulatory environment. Enhances business and professional skills of members.

2820 ■ NAIFA-Western Wisconsin
505 King St., Ste. 42
La Crosse, WI 54601
Contact: Arne P. Fremstad, Pres.
Ph: (608)793-1400
E-mail: wwnaifa@prodigy.net
Descr: Represents the interest of insurance and financial advisors. Advocates for a positive legislative and regulatory environment. Enhances business and professional skills of members.

2821 ■ NAIFA - Wisconsin Big Rivers
PO Box 3188
Eau Claire, WI 54702-3188
Contact: Todd J. Robertson CFE, Pres.
Ph: (715)835-5113
E-mail: robertson.todd@principal.com
Staff: 3. **Descr:** Represents the interests of insurance and financial advisors. Advocates for a positive legislative and regulatory environment. Enhances business and professional skills of members.

2822 ■ NAIFA-Wisconsin-Fox River Valley
PO Box 1994
Appleton, WI 54912-1994
Contact: Scott Scheer, Pres.
Ph: (920)734-1310
Fax: (920)830-2458
E-mail: foxvalleyadvisors@new.rr.com
URL: http://naifanet.com/foxriver
Descr: Represents the interest of insurance and financial advisors. Advocates for a positive legisla-

tive and regulatory environment. Enhances business and professional skills of members.

2823 ■ North American Securities Administrators Association, Wisconsin
345 W Washington Ave., 4th Fl.
Madison, WI 53703
Contact: Patricia Struck, Admin.
Ph: (608)266-1064
Fax: (608)264-7979
Descr: Represents the interests of the state, provincial and territorial securities administrators in the U.S.

2824 ■ Northwestern Wisconsin AIFA
PO Box 252
Rice Lake, WI 54868-0252
Contact: Carmen K. Crotteau, Sec.
Ph: (715)736-2498
Fax: (715)736-4023
E-mail: ccrotteau@ruralins.com
URL: http://nwaifa.craigschroeder.com
Descr: Represents the interest of insurance and financial advisors. Advocates for a positive legislative and regulatory environment. Enhances business and professional skills of members.

2825 ■ Society of Consumer Affairs Professionals in Business, Wisconsin Chapter
Associated Bank
1305 Main St.
Stevens Point, WI 54481
Contact: Wendy Kumm, Treas.
Ph: (715)345-4584
E-mail: wendy.kumm@associatedbank.com
URL: http://www.socapwi.org
Descr: Works to provide the tools needed for corporations to reach their goal of maximum customer loyalty, excellent customer service and value-added innovations.

2826 ■ Southwestern Wisconsin Small Business Development Center (SWSBDC)
510 Pioneer Tower
Platteville, WI 53818-3099
Contact: Gary M. Smith, Program Dir.
Ph: (608)342-1038
Fax: (608)342-1599
E-mail: swsbdc@uwplatt.edu
URL: http://www.uwplatt.edu/swsbdc/index.html
Descr: Represents and promotes the small business sector. Provides management assistance to current and prospective small business owners. Helps to improve management skills and expand the products and services of members.

2827 ■ University of Wisconsin - Eau Claire Small Business Development Center
210 Water St.
Eau Claire, WI 54702-4004
Contact: Jim Mishefske, Dir.
Ph: (715)836-5811
Fax: (715)836-5263
E-mail: ask-sbdc@uwec.edu
URL: http://www.uwec.edu/ce/business/sbdc.htm
Descr: Represents and promotes the small business sector. Provides management assistance to current and prospective small business owners. Helps to improve management skills and expand the products and services of members.

2828 ■ University of Wisconsin - Green Bay Small Business Development Center
2420 Nicolet Dr.
Green Bay, WI 54311
Contact: Christina Trombley, Dir.
Ph: (920)496-2117
E-mail: tromblec@uwgb.edu
URL: http://www.uwgb.edu/sbdc/index.html
Descr: Represents and promotes the small business sector. Provides management assistance to current and prospective small business owners. Helps to

improve management skills and expand the products and services of members.

2829 ■ University of Wisconsin - La Crosse Small Business Development Center
1725 State St.
La Crosse, WI 54601
Contact: Jan Gallagher, Dir.
Ph: (608)785-8782
Fax: (608)785-6919
E-mail: sbdc@uwlax.edu
URL: http://www.uwlax.edu/sbdc/index.html
Descr: Represents and promotes the small business sector. Provides management assistance to current and prospective small business owners. Helps to improve management skills and expand the products and services of members.

2830 ■ University of Wisconsin - Madison Small Business Development Center
975 University Ave., No. 3260
Madison, WI 53706
Ph: (608)263-7680
Fax: (608)263-0818
URL: http://exed.wisc.edu/sbdc
Descr: Represents and promotes the small business sector. Provides management assistance to current and prospective small business owners. Helps to improve management skills and expand the products and services of members.

2831 ■ University of Wisconsin - Milwaukee Small Business Development Center
161 W Wisconsin Ave., Ste. 6000
Milwaukee, WI 53203
Contact: Kristine Kruepke, Program Mgr.
Ph: (414)227-3240
E-mail: sbdc@uwm.edu
URL: http://www4.uwm.edu/SCE/dci.cfm?id=15
Descr: Represents and promotes the small business sector. Provides management assistance to current and prospective small business owners. Helps to improve management skills and expand the products and services of members.

2832 ■ University of Wisconsin - Oshkosh Small Business Development Center
347 City Ctr.
Oshkosh, WI 54901-4825
Ph: (920)424-1453
Free: 800-232-8939
Fax: (920)424-2005
E-mail: sbdc@uwosh.edu
URL: http://www.uwosh.edu/sbdc
Descr: Represents and promotes the small business sector. Provides management assistance to current and prospective small business owners. Helps to improve management skills and expand the products and services of members.

2833 ■ University of Wisconsin - Parkside Small Business Development Center
2320 Renaissance Blvd.
Sturtevant, WI 53177
Contact: Matt Wagner
Ph: (262)898-7512
E-mail: mwagner@thecati.com
URL: http://www.parksidesbdc.com
Descr: Represents and promotes the small business sector. Provides management assistance to current and prospective small business owners. Helps to improve management skills and expand the products and services of members.

2834 ■ University of Wisconsin - River Falls Small Business Development Center
College of Business and Economics
South Hall, Rm. 128
410 S Third St.
River Falls, WI 54022
Contact: Steve DeWald, Dir.
Ph: (715)425-0620
Fax: (715)425-0707
E-mail: sbdc@uwrf.edu
URL: http://www.uwrf.edu/sbdc/sbdctext.html
Descr: Represents and promotes the small business sector. Provides management assistance to current

and prospective small business owners. Helps to improve management skills and expand the products and services of members.

2835 ■ University of Wisconsin - Stevens Point Small Business Development Center
032 Main Bldg.
410 S Third St.
Stevens Point, WI 54481
Contact: Vicki Lobermeier
Free: 800-898-9472
E-mail: vloberme@uwsp.edu
URL: http://www.uwsp.edu/conted/sbdc
Descr: Represents and promotes the small business sector. Provides management assistance to current and prospective small business owners. Helps to improve management skills and expand the products and services of members.

2836 ■ University of Wisconsin - Superior Small Business Development Center
PO Box 2000
Superior, WI 54880
Contact: Ms. Julianne Raymond, Dir.
Ph: (715)394-8351
Free: 800-410-8351
Fax: (715)394-8592
E-mail: jraymond@uwsuper.edu
URL: http://www.uwsuper.edu/cee/bed/sbdc/index.cfm
Descr: Represents and promotes the small business sector. Provides management assistance to current and prospective small business owners. Helps to improve management skills and expand the products and services of members.

2837 ■ University of Wisconsin - Whitewater Small Business Development Center
402 McCutchan Hall
Whitewater, WI 53190
Contact: Sheila Johnson, Office Mgr.
Ph: (262)472-3217
Fax: (262)472-1600
E-mail: ask-sbdc@uww.edu
URL: http://www.uww.edu/sbdc/default.htm
Descr: Represents and promotes the small business sector. Provides management assistance to current and prospective small business owners. Helps to improve management skills and expand the products and services of members.

2838 ■ Waukesha Taxpayers League
2404 Broken Hill Rd.
Waukesha, WI 53188
Contact: Chris Lufter, Pres.
Ph: (262)547-8715
E-mail: info@waukeshataxpayersleague.com
URL: http://www.waukeshataxpayersleague.com
Fnd: 1989.

2839 ■ West Allis Taxpayers Association
6227 W Greenfield Ave.
West Allis, WI 53214
Ph: (414)774-3373

2840 ■ Wisconsin Direct Marketing Association (WDMA)
PO Box 26275
Milwaukee, WI 53226-0275
Contact: Lena Stephenson, Pres.
Ph: (414)760-9362
Fax: (414)431-4195
E-mail: info@wdma.org
URL: http://www.wdma.org
Descr: Works to encourage professional standards and further education in all aspects of direct marketing. **Pub:** Newsletter (quarterly).

2841 ■ Wisconsin Nonprofits Association
PO Box 1662
Madison, WI 53701-1662
Contact: Deborah Blanks, Pres.
Ph: (608)772-5962
E-mail: info@wisconsinnonprofits.org
URL: http://www.wisconsinnonprofits.org
Descr: Aims to strengthen Wisconsin's nonprofit sector. Raises awareness among the statewide com-

munity about the economic, educational and civic impact of the nonprofit sector. Creates opportunities for collaboration among nonprofit, business, funding, education and government sectors.

Wyoming

2842 ■ International Association of Assessing Officers, Wyoming
Wyoming Department of Revenue
Ad Valorem Tax Div.
Herschler Bldg.
122 W 25th St., No. 2-W
Cheyenne, WY 82001
Contact: Kenneth C. Uhrich, Rep.
Ph: (307)777-5232
Fax: (307)777-3632
E-mail: kuhric@state.wy.us
Descr: Represents state and local officials concerned with valuation of property for ad valorem property tax purposes. Works to improve standards and conduct research on tax assessment. Promotes innovation and excellence in property appraisal, assessment administration, and property tax policy through professional development, education, research, and technical assistance.

2843 ■ North American Securities Administrators Association, Wyoming
State Capitol, Rm. 109
200 W 24th St.
Cheyenne, WY 82002
Contact: Karen Wheeler, Dir.
Ph: (307)777-7370
Fax: (307)777-5339
Descr: Represents the interests of the state, provincial and territorial securities administrators in the U.S.

2844 ■ Wyoming Association of Nonprofit Organizations
313 S 2nd St.
Laramie, WY 82070
Contact: George Gault, Dir.
Ph: (307)721-8300
Fax: (307)721-8333
E-mail: info@wynonprofit.org
URL: http://www.wynonprofit.org
Descr: Works to strengthen the leadership, skills, effectiveness and efficiency of Wyoming's nonprofit organizations. Addresses the needs of the nonprofit sector. Provides member services, public awareness and advocacy. **Fnd:** 2005.

2845 ■ Wyoming Small Business Development Center - Region I
1400 Dewar Dr., Ste. 205B
Rock Springs, WY 82901
Contact: Mark Atkinson, Dir.
Ph: (307)352-6894
Fax: (307)352-6876
E-mail: matkins2@uwyo.edu
Descr: Represents and promotes the small business sector. Provides management assistance to current and prospective small business owners. Helps to improve management skills and expand the products and services of members.

2846 ■ Wyoming Small Business Development Center - Region II
143 S Bent St., Ste. A
Powell, WY 82435
Contact: Bruce Morse, Dir.
Ph: (307)754-2139
Fax: (307)754-0368
E-mail: bmorse1@uwyo.edu
Descr: Represents and promotes the small business sector. Provides management assistance to current and prospective small business owners. Helps to improve management skills and expand the products and services of members.

2847 ■ Wyoming Small Business Development Center - Region III
300 S Wolcott St., Ste. 300
Casper, WY 82601

Contact: Leonard Holler, Dir.
Ph: (307)234-6683
Fax: (307)577-7014
E-mail: lholler@uwyo.edu
Descr: Represents and promotes the small business sector. Provides management assistance to current and prospective small business owners. Helps to improve management skills and expand the products and services of members.

2848 ■ Wyoming Small Business Development Center - Region IV
1400 E College Dr.
Cheyenne, WY 82007
Contact: Anya Petersen-Frey, Dir.
Ph: (307)632-6141
Fax: (307)632-6061
E-mail: apeter35@uwyo.edu
Descr: Represents and promotes the small business sector. Provides management assistance to current and prospective small business owners. Helps to improve management skills and expand the products and services of members.

2849 ■ Wyoming Small Business Development Center - Region V
201 W Lakeway Rd., Ste. 1004
Gillette, WY 82718
Contact: Jill Kline, Dir.
Ph: (307)682-5232
Fax: (307)686-5792
E-mail: jkline@uwyo.edu
Descr: Represents and promotes the small business sector. Provides management assistance to current and prospective small business owners. Helps to improve management skills and expand the products and services of members.

2850 ■ Wyoming Small Business Development Center - Region VI
213 W Main St., Ste. C
Riverton, WY 82501
Contact: Margie Rowell, Dir.
Ph: (307)857-1174
Fax: (307)857-0873
E-mail: mrowell@uwyo.edu
Descr: Represents and promotes the small business sector. Provides management assistance to current and prospective small business owners. Helps to improve management skills and expand the products and services of members.

2851 ■ Wyoming Taxpayers Association (WTA)
2410 Pioneer Ave.
Cheyenne, WY 82001
Contact: Erin Taylor, Exec. Dir.
Ph: (307)635-8761
Fax: (307)637-7556
E-mail: wyotax@wyotax.org
URL: http://www.wyotax.org
Fnd: 1937. **Pub:** *Tax Roundup* (quarterly).

Publications

2852 ■ *The 50 Best Science & Technology Stocks for Canadians*
John Wiley & Sons Inc.
111 River St.
Hoboken, NJ 07030-5774
Ph: (201)748-6000
Free: 800-825-7550
Fax: (201)748-6088
E-mail: info@wiley.com
URL: http://www.wiley.com
Key Personnel: Marco Den Ouden, Author. **URL(s):** http://as.wiley.com/WileyCDA/WileyTitle/productCd-1553350227.html **Covers:** 50 best science and technology stocks in Canada. **Entries include:** Company name, address, phone, description, financial highlights, ratings, analysis. **Freq:** Annual,

Published April, 2003. **Price:** $22.95, individuals, paperback.

2853 ■ *100 Best Mutual Funds You Can Buy*
Adams Media Corp.
57 Littlefield St.
Avon, MA 02322
Ph: (508)427-7100
Free: 800-872-5627
Fax: 800-872-5628
E-mail: rights@adamsmedia.com
URL: http://www.adamsmedia.com
Key Personnel: Gordon K. Williamson, Author. **Covers:** Approximately 100 mutual funds categorized by aggressive growth, balanced, corporate bond, global equity, government bond, growth, growth and income, health, high yield, metals and natural resources, money market, municipal bond, technology, utility stock, and world bond. **Entries include:** Contact information, Web address, information on total return performance, risk and volatility, management, expenses, and summary statement and profile. **Price:** $2.97, individuals, 35 used & new.

2854 ■ *100 Best Stocks You Can Buy*
Adams Media Corp.
57 Littlefield St.
Avon, MA 02322
Ph: (508)427-7100
Free: 800-872-5627
Fax: 800-872-5628
E-mail: rights@adamsmedia.com
URL: http://www.adamsmedia.com
Key Personnel: John Slatter, Author. **URL(s):** http://www.adamsmediastore.com/product/1107/3 **Covers:** Stock profiles, basic terminology, investment strategies, rationales, and mistakes. **Entries include:** contact information, stock symbol, external rating, overview, history, and company profile. **Freq:** Latest edition 2009. **Price:** $14.95, individuals, list price.

2855 ■ *ABA Bank Compliance*
American Bankers Association
1120 Connecticut Ave. NW
Washington, DC 20036
Ph: (202)663-5564
Fax: (202)663-7543
E-mail: custserv@aba.com
URL: http://www.aba.com
Freq: bimonthly. **Price:** $160 for members, $250 for nonmembers.

2856 ■ *ABA Banking Journal*
American Bankers Association
1120 Connecticut Ave. NW
Washington, DC 20036
Ph: (202)663-5564
Fax: (202)663-7543
E-mail: custserv@aba.com
URL: http://www.aba.com
Descr: Provides immediate access to banking's inner circles and the behind-the-scenes activities, which are shaping the banking industry. **Freq:** monthly. **Price:** $18/copy in U.S. and Canada, $75/copy outside U.S. and Canada, $295/year outside U.S. and Canada. **ISSN:** 0194-5947.

2857 ■ *ABI Annual Membership Directory*
American Bankruptcy Institute
44 Canal Center Plz., Ste. 400
Alexandria, VA 22314
Ph: (703)739-0800
Fax: (703)739-1060
E-mail: support@abiworld.org
URL: http://www.abiworld.org
Descr: Contains listing of member's addresses and telephone numbers. **Freq:** annual. **Price:** included in membership dues.

2858 ■ *ABI Journal*
American Bankruptcy Institute
44 Canal Center Plz., Ste. 400
Alexandria, VA 22314
Ph: (703)739-0800
Fax: (703)739-1060

E-mail: support@abiworld.org
URL: http://www.abiworld.org
Descr: Covers the entire range of insolvency issues, featuring timely articles written by some of the most knowledgeable professionals in the field. **Freq:** 10/year.

2859 ■ *ABI Update Newsletter*
American Bankruptcy Institute
44 Canal Center Plz., Ste. 400
Alexandria, VA 22314
Ph: (703)739-0800
Fax: (703)739-1060
E-mail: support@abiworld.org
URL: http://www.abiworld.org

2860 ■ *ACULetter*
Alabama Credit Union League
PO Box 380428
Birmingham, AL 35238-0428
Ph: (205)991-9710
Fax: (205)991-2576
E-mail: awhitman@acul.com
URL: http://www.acul.com
Descr: Outlining the accomplishments of our member credit unions. Also features articles and columns on issues facing the credit union membership. **Freq:** quarterly.

2861 ■ *Advantage*
Food Marketing Institute
2345 Crystal Dr., Ste. 800
Arlington, VA 22202-4801
Ph: (202)452-8444
Fax: (202)429-4519
URL: http://www.fmi.org
Freq: monthly. **ISSN:** 1542-247X.

2862 ■ *Alabama Credit Union League Annual Report*
Alabama Credit Union League
PO Box 380428
Birmingham, AL 35238-0428
Ph: (205)991-9710
Fax: (205)991-2576
E-mail: awhitman@acul.com
URL: http://www.acul.com
Freq: annual.

2863 ■ *American Financial Directory*
Accuity
4709 Golf Rd.
Skokie, IL 60076
Ph: (847)676-9600
Free: 800-321-3373
Fax: (847)933-8101
E-mail: custserv@accuitysolutions.com
URL: http://www.accuitysolutions.com
Key Personnel: Marideth Johnson, Mktg. Mgr. **URL(s):** http://www.accuitysolutions.com **Covers:** Approximately 23,000 banks, bank holding companies, credit unions, savings and loans, and other financial institutions and their approximately 56,000 branch offices. **Entries include:** Institution name, address, phone, fax, holding company affiliation, names and titles of key personnel, correspondent banks, FEDWIRE data and ABA number, balance sheet highlights, branches. **Freq:** Semiannual, January and July. **Price:** $635, individuals.

2864 ■ *American Stock Exchange—Annual Report*
American Stock Exchange
86 Trinity Pl.
New York, NY 10006
Ph: (212)306-1000
E-mail: amexfeedback@amex.com
URL: http://www.amex.com
Descr: Includes review of previous year's activities of the association with financial statement. **Freq:** annual. **Price:** free.

2865 ■ *AMEX Fact Book*
American Stock Exchange
86 Trinity Pl.
New York, NY 10006

Ph: (212)306-1000
E-mail: amexfeedback@amex.com
URL: http://www.amex.com
Descr: Features a statistical reference work covering equities and derivatives; includes directories of company trading statistics and corporate addresses. **Freq:** annual. **Price:** $12.50/copy, plus tax.

2866 ■ *Annual Review*
National Futures Association
300 S Riverside Plz., No. 1800
Chicago, IL 60606-6615
Ph: (312)781-1300
Fax: (312)781-1467
E-mail: information@nfa.futures.org
URL: http://www.nfa.futures.org
Freq: annual. **Price:** free.

2867 ■ *Annual Risk Management Buyers Guide*
Risk and Insurance Management Society Inc.
1065 Ave. of the Americas, 13th Fl.
New York, NY 10018
Ph: (212)286-9292
Fax: (212)986-9716
URL: http://www.rims.org
URL(s): http://www.rims.org; http://www.rimsbuyersguide.com **Covers:** Risk management service providers. Free to members of the Risk and Insurance Management Society. **Freq:** Annual.

2868 ■ *Appraisal Institute Directory of Designated Members*
Appraisal Institute
550 W Van Buren St., Ste. 1000
Chicago, IL 60607
Ph: (312)335-4100
Fax: (312)335-4400
E-mail: aiceo@appraisalinstitute.org
URL: http://www.appraisalinstitute.org
Freq: annual. **Price:** free.

2869 ■ *Appraisal Institute Directory of Members*
Chicago Chapter of the Appraisal Institute
205 W Wacker Dr., Ste. 202
Chicago, IL 60606
Ph: (312)616-9400
Fax: (312)616-9404
E-mail: laanderson@ccai.org
URL: http://www.ccai.org
Descr: Provides the best source for finding qualified appraisers. **Price:** included in membership dues.

2870 ■ *Appraisal Journal*
Chicago Chapter of the Appraisal Institute
205 W Wacker Dr., Ste. 202
Chicago, IL 60606
Ph: (312)616-9400
Fax: (312)616-9404
E-mail: laanderson@ccai.org
URL: http://www.ccai.org
Price: included in membership dues.

2871 ■ *The Appraisal Journal*
Appraisal Institute
550 W Van Buren St., Ste. 1000
Chicago, IL 60607
Ph: (312)335-4100
Fax: (312)335-4400
E-mail: aiceo@appraisalinstitute.org
URL: http://www.appraisalinstitute.org
Freq: quarterly. **Price:** free for members, $48 for nonmembers.

2872 ■ *Appraiser News in Brief*
Appraisal Institute
550 W Van Buren St., Ste. 1000
Chicago, IL 60607
Ph: (312)335-4100
Fax: (312)335-4400
E-mail: aiceo@appraisalinstitute.org
URL: http://www.appraisalinstitute.org

Freq: 8/year. **Price:** free for members, $30/year for students, $35/year for nonmembers.

2873 ■ Arizona Food Industry Directory
Arizona Food Marketing Alliance
120 E Pierce St.
Phoenix, AZ 85004
Ph: (602)252-9761
Fax: (602)252-9021
E-mail: droth@afmaaz.org
URL: http://www.afmaaz.org
Freq: annual.

2874 ■ Arizona Food Industry Journal
Arizona Food Marketing Alliance
120 E Pierce St.
Phoenix, AZ 85004
Ph: (602)252-9761
Fax: (602)252-9021
E-mail: droth@afmaaz.org
URL: http://www.afmaaz.org
Descr: Features information about trade. **Freq:** monthly. **Price:** $3.

2875 ■ ASA Professional Magazine
American Society of Appraisers
555 Herndon Pkwy., Ste. 125
Herndon, VA 20170
Ph: (703)478-2228
Fax: (703)742-8471
E-mail: asainfo@appraisers.org
URL: http://www.appraisers.org/ASAHome.aspx
Freq: quarterly. **Price:** free for members.

2876 ■ Bank Operations Bulletin
American Bankers Association
1120 Connecticut Ave. NW
Washington, DC 20036
Ph: (202)663-5564
Fax: (202)663-7543
E-mail: custserv@aba.com
URL: http://www.aba.com
Freq: monthly. **Price:** $75 for members, $110 for nonmembers.

2877 ■ Bankers News
American Bankers Association
1120 Connecticut Ave. NW
Washington, DC 20036
Ph: (202)663-5564
Fax: (202)663-7543
E-mail: custserv@aba.com
URL: http://www.aba.com
Descr: Covers national trends and developments in the banking industry, and legislative, regulatory, and judicial news related to banking. **Freq:** biweekly. **Price:** $48 for members, $96 for nonmembers.

2878 ■ Bargaining for Pay Equity: A Strategy Manual
National Committee on Pay Equity
555 New Jersey Ave. NW
Washington, DC 20001-2029
Ph: (703)920-2010
Fax: (703)979-6372
E-mail: fairpay@pay-equity.org
URL: http://www.pay-equity.org

2879 ■ Basic Business Appraisal
Institute of Business Appraisers
PO Box 17410
Plantation, FL 33318
Ph: (954)584-1144
Fax: (954)584-1184
E-mail: hqiba@go-iba.org
URL: http://www.go-iba.org
Descr: Features a self-study course.

2880 ■ Bibliography and Information Source Lists
CME Group
20 S Wacker Dr.
Chicago, IL 60606
Ph: (312)930-1000
E-mail: info@cmegroup.com
URL: http://www.cmegroup.com

Freq: annual.

2881 ■ Big Dreams Still Need Oversight: Missile Defense Testing & Financial Accountability Are Being Circumvented, 2002 Report
Project on Government Oversight
666 11th St. NW, Ste. 900
Washington, DC 20001-4542
Ph: (202)347-1122
Fax: (202)347-1116
E-mail: info@pogo.org
URL: http://www.pogo.org

2882 ■ Bond's Top 50 Service-Based Franchises
Source Book Publications
1814 Franklin St., Ste. 815
PO Box 12488
Oakland, CA 94612
Ph: (510)839-5471
Fax: (510)839-2104
URL: http://www.sourcebookpublications.com
Key Personnel: Robert Bond, Author. **URL(s):** http://www.sourcebookpublications.com **Covers:** 50 service-based franchises. **Entries include:** Detailed profile of each company. **Price:** $19.95, individuals.

2883 ■ Bond's Top 100 Franchises
Source Book Publications
1814 Franklin St., Ste. 815
PO Box 12488
Oakland, CA 94612
Ph: (510)839-5471
Fax: (510)839-2104
URL: http://www.sourcebookpublications.com
Key Personnel: Robert Bond, Author. **URL(s):** http://www.sourcebookpublications.com **Covers:** 100 franchise companies. **Entries include:** Detailed profile of each company. **Freq:** Latest edition 2006. **Price:** $19.95, individuals.

2884 ■ Branches of Your State
Sheshunoff Information Services
807 Las Cimas Pky., Ste. 300
Austin, TX 78746-6597
Ph: (512)472-2244
Free: 800-456-2340
Fax: (512)305-6575
E-mail: customercare.sis@sheshunoff.com
URL: http://www.sheshunoff.com
Covers: In separate state editions, banks, savings and loan branches, and credit unions. For those states without branch banking, individual banks, savings and loan institutions, and credit unions are listed. **Entries include:** Institution name, address, institution type, deposit totals, percent change over 12 months, percentage share of parent company's total deposits. **Freq:** Annual, February.

2885 ■ Brands and Their Companies
Gale
27500 Drake Rd.
Farmington Hills, MI 48331-3535
Ph: (248)699-4253
Free: 800-877-4253
E-mail: galeord@cengage.com
URL: http://www.gale.cengage.com
URL(s): http://www.gale.cengage.com **Covers:** Approximately 426,000 trade names, trademarks, and brand names of consumer-oriented products and their 115,000 manufacturers, importers, marketers, or distributors. **Entries include:** For trade names--Name, description of product, company name. For companies--Name, address, phone, fax, toll-free number, email, websites. **Freq:** Annual, Latest edition 34th. **Price:** $1,357, individuals.

2886 ■ Briefing Paper: The Wage Gap
National Committee on Pay Equity
555 New Jersey Ave. NW
Washington, DC 20001-2029
Ph: (703)920-2010
Fax: (703)979-6372

E-mail: fairpay@pay-equity.org
URL: http://www.pay-equity.org

2887 ■ Business Appraisal Practice
Institute of Business Appraisers
PO Box 17410
Plantation, FL 33318
Ph: (954)584-1144
Fax: (954)584-1184
E-mail: hqiba@go-iba.org
URL: http://www.go-iba.org
Freq: semiannual. **Price:** $60 for members, $90 for nonmembers.

2888 ■ Business Cycle Indicators
The Conference Board
845 3rd Ave.
New York, NY 10022
Ph: (212)759-0900
Fax: (212)980-7014
E-mail: nick.sutcliffe@conference-board.org
URL: http://www.conference-board.org
Freq: monthly.

2889 ■ Business Information Alert
Alert Publications Inc.
65 E Scott St., Ste. 12E
Chicago, IL 60610-5277
Ph: (312)337-1362
Fax: (312)337-1388
URL: http://www.alertpub.com
Key Personnel: Donna T. Heroy, Editor. **URL(s):** http://www.alertpub.com **Entries include:** Publisher name, address, phone, fax, e-mail, product reviews. **Publication includes:** List of publishers of books, databases, CD-ROM products, loose-leaf services, periodicals and journals, audio and video tapes, and microfilm covering the business and finance profession and reviewed or discussed in the issue. **Freq:** Ten issues per year. **Price:** $167, individuals, 10 issues a year; $114, per year for academic/public.

2890 ■ Business Review
Direct Marketing Association
1120 Ave. of the Americas
New York, NY 10036-6700
Ph: (212)768-7277
Fax: (212)302-6714
E-mail: presiden@the-dma.org
URL: http://www.the-dma.org
Descr: Provides up-to-date economic performance, indicators, and business trends. **Freq:** quarterly.

2891 ■ Business Valuation Review
American Society of Appraisers
555 Herndon Pkwy., Ste. 125
Herndon, VA 20170
Ph: (703)478-2228
Fax: (703)742-8471
E-mail: asainfo@appraisers.org
URL: http://www.appraisers.org/ASAHome.aspx
Freq: quarterly. **Price:** $50/year for nonmembers, $45 for members in U.S., $60 for members outside U.S. **ISSN:** 0882-2875.

2892 ■ Business Woman Resource Directory
BusinessWoman
3912 Abel Dr.
Columbia, PA 17512
Ph: (717)285-1350
Fax: (717)285-1360
E-mail: info@businesswomanpa.com
URL: http://businesswomanpa.com
URL(s): http://www.businesswomanpa.com **Covers:** Woman-owned businesses, organizations, community services, and companies in Central Pennsylvania. **Freq:** Latest edition 4th.

2893 ■ BusinessWoman
Business and Professional Women/USA
1620 Eye St. NW, Ste. 210
Washington, DC 20006
Ph: (202)293-1100
Fax: (202)861-0298
E-mail: memberservices@bpwusa.org
URL: http://www.bpwusa.org

Descr: Covers women's socioeconomic issues such as pay equity and child care; includes association news. **Freq:** quarterly. **Price:** included in membership dues, $20/year for nonmembers. **ISSN:** 0027-8831.

2894 ■ California Enrolled Agent
California Society of Enrolled Agents
3200 Ramos Cir.
Sacramento, CA 95827-2513
Ph: (916)366-6646
Fax: (916)366-6674
E-mail: info@csea.org
URL: http://www.csea.org

Descr: Contains technical information regarding tax and tax related issues and society news. **Freq:** 9/year. **Price:** $50/year.

2895 ■ Callahan's Credit Union Directory
Callahan & Associates Inc.
1001 Connecticut Ave. NW, 10th Fl.
Washington, DC 20036
Ph: (202)223-3920
Free: 800-446-7453
Fax: (202)223-6098
E-mail: callahan@creditunions.com
URL: http://callahan.com

Key Personnel: Chip Filson, President. **URL(s):** http://www.creditunions.com **Covers:** 10,710 credit unions in the United States. **Entries include:** Contact information; CEO name; state supervisors; state leagues; national, state, and regional association contact information; financial details; year in review; corporate credit unions data. **Freq:** Annual, Latest edition 2008.

2896 ■ Callahan's Credit Union Financial Yearbook
Callahan & Associates Inc.
1001 Connecticut Ave. NW, 10th Fl.
Washington, DC 20036
Ph: (202)223-3920
Free: 800-446-7453
Fax: (202)223-6098
E-mail: callahan@creditunions.com
URL: http://callahan.com

Covers: Year-end financial data on all credit unions in the U.S. **Entries include:** Credit union name, address, phone, fax, URL, names and titles of key personnel, key performance ratios, peer-averages for three years, two-year balance sheets, income statements, changes in assets, operating expenses, investment portfolio, loan analysis, capital growth, membership information, CUSO investments, credit union data processor and auditing firm. **Freq:** Annual, March.

2897 ■ Canadian MoneySaver
Canadian MoneySaver
5540 Loyalist Pky.
PO Box 370
Bath, ON, Canada K0H 1G0
Ph: (613)352-7448
Fax: (613)352-7700
E-mail: moneyinfo@canadianmoneysaver.ca
URL: http://www.canadianmoneysaver.ca

Key Personnel: Dale Ennis, Publisher/Ed.-in-Ch.; Betty Ennis, Circulation Mgr. **URL(s):** http://www.canadianmoneysaver.ca **Descr:** Magazine serving as personal finance guide with advice on profitable tax, investment and financial planning, wise consumer buys, understanding pension/benefits, and investment ideas that work. **Freq:** Monthly. **Price:** $15, individuals; $4.95, individuals; $19.95, members.

2898 ■ Canadian Tax Journal
Canadian Tax Foundation
595 Bay St., Ste. 1200
Toronto, ON, Canada M5G 2N5
Ph: (416)599-0283
Fax: (416)599-9283
E-mail: lchapman@ctf.ca
URL: http://www.ctf.ca

Freq: quarterly.

2899 ■ Cannabis Yields and Dosage
Business Alliance for Commerce in Hemp
PO Box 1716
El Cerrito, CA 94530
Ph: (510)215-8326
Fax: (510)234-4460
E-mail: chris@chrisconrad.com
URL: http://www.equalrights4all.org/bach/BACHcore.html

Descr: Features practical review of the basics of cultivating and using cannabis for medical purposes. Includes CA and other state laws on the subject. **Price:** $5.99 plus shipping and handling ($3).

2900 ■ CBA Report
Consumer Bankers Association
1000 Wilson Blvd., Ste. 2500
Arlington, VA 22209-3912
Ph: (703)276-1750
Fax: (703)528-1290
E-mail: membership@cbanet.org
URL: http://www.cbanet.org

Descr: Covers regulatory, legislative, judicial, and industry news. Includes index, books reviews, and membership profiles. **Freq:** monthly. **Price:** free for members and selected journalists.

2901 ■ Challenged America Newsletter
Disabled Businesspersons Association
3590 Camino del Rio N
San Diego, CA 92108-1716
Ph: (619)594-8805
Fax: (619)594-4208
E-mail: ahoy@challengedamerica.org
URL: http://www.ChallengedAmerica.org

Descr: Features recreational rehabilitation and adaptive-sailing program for the disabled. **Freq:** quarterly.

2902 ■ CMA Management Magazine
Society of Management Accountants of Canada
1 Robert Speck Pkwy., Ste. 1400
Mississauga, ON, Canada L4Z 3M3
Ph: (905)949-4200
Fax: (905)949-0888
E-mail: svieweg@cma-canada.org
URL: http://www.cma-canada.org

Descr: Serves as a business publication designed for management professionals. **Freq:** 9/year. **Price:** $15/year.

2903 ■ Commercial Lending Review
American Bankers Association
1120 Connecticut Ave. NW
Washington, DC 20036
Ph: (202)663-5564
Fax: (202)663-7543
E-mail: custserv@aba.com
URL: http://www.aba.com

Descr: Published by Institutional Investor (endorsed by ABA). **Freq:** quarterly. **Price:** $84 for members, $140 for nonmembers.

2904 ■ Companies and Their Brands
Gale
27500 Drake Rd.
Farmington Hills, MI 48331-3535
Ph: (248)699-4253
Free: 800-877-4253
E-mail: galeord@cengage.com
URL: http://www.gale.cengage.com

URL(s): http://www.gale.cengage.com **Covers:** Over 110,000 companies that manufacture, distribute, import, or otherwise market their 400,000 consumer-oriented products. **Entries include:** Company name, address, phone, fax, trade names, description, e-mail, URL, SIC and PTO codes. Based on "Brands and Their Companies". **Freq:** Annual, Latest edition 34th. **Price:** $911, individuals.

2905 ■ Compliance Connection
Rhode Island Credit Union League
20 Altieri Way
Warwick, RI 02888

E-mail: degan@cucenter.org
URL: http://www.riculeague.org

2906 ■ Connecting Point
Multi-Level Marketing International Association
11956 Bernardo Plaza Dr., No. 313
San Diego, CA 92128
Ph: (949)854-0484
Fax: (949)854-7687
E-mail: info@mlmia.com
URL: http://www.mlmia.com

Price: included in membership dues.

2907 ■ Consumer Credit Delinquency Bulletin
American Bankers Association
1120 Connecticut Ave. NW
Washington, DC 20036
Ph: (202)663-5564
Fax: (202)663-7543
E-mail: custserv@aba.com
URL: http://www.aba.com

Freq: quarterly.

2908 ■ Consumer Middle East
Euromonitor International
Business Reference Div.
224 S Michigan Ave., Ste. 1500
Chicago, IL 60604
Ph: (312)922-1115
Fax: (312)922-1157
E-mail: insight@euromonitorintl.com
URL: http://www.euromonitor.com

URL(s): http://www.euromonitor.com **Publication includes:** List of 10 countries in the Middle East. Principal content of publication is Information regarding the Middle East including regional marketing perimeters, consumer markets, demographics, economic indicators, standards of living, household characteristics, consumer expenditures, and service industries. **Freq:** Published February, 2004. **Price:** $995, individuals, U.S.D.

2909 ■ Consumer Products Source Directory
Drop Shipping News
PO Box 7838
New York, NY 10150
Ph: (212)688-8797
Fax: (212)688-8797
E-mail: nscheel@drop-shipping-news.com
URL: http://www.drop-shipping-news.com

Key Personnel: Nicholas T. Scheel, Editor, nscheel@drop-shipping-news.com. **URL(s):** http://www.drop-shipping-news.com **Publication includes:** Company name, address, phone, fax. Principal content of publication is the names and address of dozens of trade magazines along with the types of products related to each magazine. Product categories covered include Apparel, Appliances, Archery, Army-Navy Goods, Art, Automotive, Bathroom and Beauty Products, Bedding, Bicycles, Billiards, Boating, Bras, Camping Equipment, Candy, Chairs, Christmas Goods, Collectibles, Computers, Consumer Electronics, Sporting Goods, Watches and Clocks. **Price:** $15, individuals, post paid.

2910 ■ Corporate Directory - Support Directory
Multi-Level Marketing International Association
11956 Bernardo Plaza Dr., No. 313
San Diego, CA 92128
Ph: (949)854-0484
Fax: (949)854-7687
E-mail: info@mlmia.com
URL: http://www.mlmia.com

Freq: quarterly. **Price:** free for members only.

2911 ■ Council Newsletter
Direct Marketing Association
1120 Ave. of the Americas
New York, NY 10036-6700
Ph: (212)768-7277
Fax: (212)302-6714
E-mail: presiden@the-dma.org
URL: http://www.the-dma.org

Freq: quarterly.

2912 ■ *CourierNet*
Missouri Credit Union Association
2055 Craigshire Dr.
St. Louis, MO 63146-4009
Ph: (314)542-0555
Fax: (314)542-1312
E-mail: contact@mcua.org
URL: http://www.mcua.org
Freq: weekly.

2913 ■ *Credit*
American Financial Services Association
919 18th St. NW, Ste. 300
Washington, DC 20006-5517
Ph: (202)296-5544
Fax: (202)223-0321
E-mail: cstinebert@afsamail.org
URL: http://www.afsaonline.org
Freq: bimonthly.

2914 ■ *The Credit Reporter*
National Credit Reporting Association
125 E Lake St., Ste. 200
Bloomingdale, IL 60108
Ph: (630)539-1525
Fax: (630)539-1526
E-mail: tclemans@ncrainc.org
URL: http://www.ncrainc.org
Freq: bimonthly. **Price:** included in membership dues.

2915 ■ *Credit Union Directors Newsletter*
Credit Union National Association
PO Box 431
Madison, WI 53701-0431
Fax: (608)231-4263
URL: http://www.cuna.org
Descr: Provides ideas and advice on policy matters and considerations for the credit union's board of directors. **Freq:** monthly. **Price:** $88/year. **ISSN:** 1058-1561.

2916 ■ *Credit Union Directory*
National Credit Union Administration
1775 Duke St.
Alexandria, VA 22314-3428
Ph: (703)518-6300
Free: 800-755-1030
Fax: (703)518-6660
E-mail: oamail@ncua.gov
URL: http://www.ncua.gov
Key Personnel: James Leonard Skiles, Exec. Dir.; Larry Fazio, Deputy Exec. Dir. **URL(s):** http://www.ncua.gov/data/directory/cudir.html **Covers:** Federal credit unions and state-chartered credit unions that are insured by the National Credit Union Share Insurance Fund; coverage includes United States possessions. **Entries include:** Credit union name, address, phone, charter number, principal operating officer, year-end total assets, number of members. **Freq:** Annual, LAT 2008.

2917 ■ *Credit Union Executive Newsletter*
Credit Union National Association
PO Box 431
Madison, WI 53701-0431
Fax: (608)231-4263
URL: http://www.cuna.org
Descr: Includes monthly four-page supplement called the *Economic Report.* **Freq:** biweekly. **Price:** $210/year. **ISSN:** 1068-2120.

2918 ■ *Credit Union Magazine*
Credit Union National Association
PO Box 431
Madison, WI 53701-0431
Fax: (608)231-4263
URL: http://www.cuna.org
Descr: For credit union officials, management, staff, and committee members. Includes statistics and

employment listings. **Freq:** monthly. **Price:** $53/year. **ISSN:** 0011-1066.

2919 ■ *Credit Union Newswatch*
Credit Union National Association
PO Box 431
Madison, WI 53701-0431
Fax: (608)231-4263
URL: http://www.cuna.org
Descr: Contains news and information on legislative, regulatory affairs, industry development and association activities. **Freq:** weekly. **Price:** $125/year. **ISSN:** 0889-5597.

2920 ■ *Credit Union Report*
Credit Union National Association Inc.
Publications Dept.
5710 Mineral Point Rd.
PO Box 431
Madison, WI 53705-4454
Ph: (202)638-5777
Free: 800-356-9655
Fax: (608)231-4263
E-mail: dorothy@cuna.org
URL: http://www.cuna.org
Key Personnel: Tom Dunn, Contact, tdunn@cuna. com. **URL(s):** http://www.cuna.org/download/ curepj04.pdf, http://advice.cuna.org/download/ curepd05.pdf **Covers:** Credit union leagues, associations, for each of the 50 states, and the District of Columbia. **Entries include:** Organization name address, phone, name of executive officer. Provides aggregate credit union data. **Freq:** Annual, 2005.

2921 ■ *CU Connection*
Arkansas Credit Union League
PO Box 3446
Little Rock, AR 72203
Ph: (501)376-6508
Fax: (501)376-3206
E-mail: acul@sbcglobal.net
URL: http://www.acul.org
Descr: Contains Credit Union activities. **Freq:** bimonthly. **Price:** included in membership dues.

2922 ■ *Current and Crossroads*
Catalog and Multichannel Marketing Council
1120 Ave. of the Americas
New York, NY 10036-6700
Ph: (212)768-7277
Fax: (212)302-6714
E-mail: customerservice@the-dma.org
URL: http://www.the-dma.org
Descr: Provides information on direct marketing in non-US markets. **Freq:** monthly.

2923 ■ *Current Marketing Newsletter*
Rural Electricity Resource Council
PO Box 309
Wilmington, OH 45177-0309
Ph: (937)383-0001
Fax: (937)383-0003
E-mail: info@rerc.org
URL: http://www.rerc.org
Descr: Covers energy management and marketing programs, new technologies, and electrical farm applications of interest to electric power suppliers. **Freq:** bimonthly. **Price:** included in membership dues, $35 for nonmembers.

2924 ■ *Customer Relationship Management*
Society of Consumer Affairs Professionals in Business
675 N Washington St., Ste. 200
Alexandria, VA 22314
Ph: (703)519-3700
Fax: (703)549-4886
E-mail: socap@socap.org
URL: http://www.socap.org
Freq: quarterly. **Price:** available to members only.

2925 ■ *D & B Directory of Service Companies*
Dun & Bradstreet Corp.
103 JFK Pkwy.
Short Hills, NJ 07078

Ph: (973)921-5500
Free: 800-234-3867
E-mail: custserv@dnb.com
URL: http://www.dnb.com
Key Personnel: Allan Z. Loren, Chm. & Ch. Exec. Off.; Steven W. Alesio, Pres. & COO; Joanne B. Carson, VP, Communications. **URL(s):** http://www.dnb. com **Covers:** 50,000 U.S. businesses in the service sector, private and public, including accounting, auditing and bookkeeping, advertising and public relations, architecture and engineering, consumer services, executive search, health, hospitality, management consulting, motion pictures, repair, research, social services, and law. **Entries include:** DUNS number, company name, address, phone, year started, state of incorporation, sales volume, number of employees, primary and secondary Standard Industrial Classification (SIC) codes, names and titles of key personnel, principal bank, stock exchange symbol, accounting firm, line of business, trade name. **Freq:** Annual.

2926 ■ *Daily Futures Report*
New York Mercantile Exchange
World Financial Ctr.
1 N End Ave.
New York, NY 10282-1101
Ph: (212)299-2000
Fax: (212)301-4700
E-mail: exchangeinfo@nymex.com
URL: http://www.nymex.com

2927 ■ *Daily Options Report*
New York Mercantile Exchange
World Financial Ctr.
1 N End Ave.
New York, NY 10282-1101
Ph: (212)299-2000
Fax: (212)301-4700
E-mail: exchangeinfo@nymex.com
URL: http://www.nymex.com

2928 ■ *Data Tracker*
Direct Selling Association
1667 K St. NW, Ste. 1100
Washington, DC 20006
Ph: (202)452-8866
Fax: (202)452-9010
E-mail: info@dsa.org
URL: http://www.dsa.org
Freq: quarterly.

2929 ■ *Dateline: DMA*
Direct Marketing Association
1120 Ave. of the Americas
New York, NY 10036-6700
Ph: (212)768-7277
Fax: (212)302-6714
E-mail: presiden@the-dma.org
URL: http://www.the-dma.org
Freq: quarterly.

2930 ■ *DBA Advisor*
Disabled Businesspersons Association
3590 Camino del Rio N
San Diego, CA 92108-1716
Ph: (619)594-8805
Fax: (619)594-4208
E-mail: ahoy@challengedamerica.org
URL: http://www.ChallengedAmerica.org
Freq: quarterly.

2931 ■ *Direct Hit*
Midwest Direct Marketing Association
1821 University Ave. West, Ste. S256
St. Paul, MN 55104
Ph: (651)999-5351
Fax: (651)917-1835
E-mail: mdma@mdma.org
URL: http://www.mdma.org
Descr: Contains news of meetings, activities, local and regional events, articles and changes in legisla-

tion that affect the direct marketing industry. **Freq:** bimonthly.

2932 ■ *Direct Line: The DMA Newsletter Serving the Direct Marketing Industry*
Direct Marketing Association
1120 Ave. of the Americas
New York, NY 10036-6700
Ph: (212)768-7277
Fax: (212)302-6714
E-mail: presiden@the-dma.org
URL: http://www.the-dma.org
Descr: Reports on association activities and matters relevant to direct marketers. **Freq:** monthly. **Price:** free for members. **ISSN:** 0743-7625.

2933 ■ *Directory of Better Business Bureaus*
Council of Better Business Bureaus Inc.
4200 Wilson Blvd., Ste. 800
Arlington, VA 22203-1838
Ph: (703)276-0100
Fax: (703)525-8277
URL: http://www.cbbb.org
URL(s): http://lookup.bbb.org **Covers:** About 185 Better Business Bureaus in the United States and Canada. **Entries include:** Name, address, phone. **Freq:** Irregular.

2934 ■ *Directory to BPA Membership and Marketing Compatibility Programs*
BPA Worldwide
Two Corporate Dr., 9th Fl.
Shelton, CT 06484
Ph: (203)447-2800
Fax: (203)447-2900
E-mail: info@bpaww.com
URL: http://www.bpaww.com
Freq: annual.

2935 ■ *Directory of Professional Appraisal Services*
American Society of Appraisers
555 Herndon Pkwy., Ste. 125
Herndon, VA 20170
Ph: (703)478-2228
Fax: (703)742-8471
E-mail: asainfo@appraisers.org
URL: http://www.appraisers.org/ASAHome.aspx
Freq: annual.

2936 ■ *Directory of Securities*
Pacific Stock Exchange
115 Sansome St.
San Francisco, CA 94104
Ph: (415)393-4000
Fax: (415)954-5507
E-mail: info@pacificex.com
Freq: quarterly.

2937 ■ *Directory of Women's Association*
Business Women's Network
1990 M St. NW, Ste. 700
Washington, DC 20036
Ph: (202)466-8209
Fax: (202)833-1808
E-mail: inquire@tpag.com
URL: http://www.bwni.com
Price: $70.90 plus shipping and handling.

2938 ■ *The DMA Insider*
Direct Marketing Association
1120 Ave. of the Americas
New York, NY 10036-6700
Ph: (212)768-7277
Fax: (212)302-6714
E-mail: presiden@the-dma.org
URL: http://www.the-dma.org
Descr: Covers industry innovations, trends and emerging technologies. **Freq:** quarterly. **Price:** available to members only.

2939 ■ *DMA Insider*
Catalog and Multichannel Marketing Council
1120 Ave. of the Americas
New York, NY 10036-6700
Ph: (212)768-7277

Fax: (212)302-6714
E-mail: customerservice@the-dma.org
URL: http://www.the-dma.org
Descr: Provides DMA members with an opportunity to read articles from the beat practitioners in the industry. **Freq:** quarterly. **Price:** included in membership dues.

2940 ■ *DMA Washington Report: Federal and State Regulatory Issues of Concern*
Direct Marketing Association
1120 Ave. of the Americas
New York, NY 10036-6700
Ph: (212)768-7277
Fax: (212)302-6714
E-mail: presiden@the-dma.org
URL: http://www.the-dma.org
Descr: Reviews federal and state regulations affecting direct mail marketing, such as cable privacy laws, and trade rule violations. **Freq:** monthly. **Price:** free for members.

2941 ■ *Do You Really Need a Financial Advisor?*
Forum for Investor Advice
PO Box 3216
Mercerville, NJ 08619
Fax: (609)890-8037
E-mail: investoradvice@optonline.net
URL: http://www.investoradvice.org

2942 ■ *Dollars and Sense*
National Taxpayers Union
108 N Alfred St.
Alexandria, VA 22314
Ph: (703)683-5700
Fax: (703)683-5722
E-mail: ntu@ntu.org
URL: http://www.ntu.org
Descr: Provides updates on important legislation. **Freq:** bimonthly. **Price:** included in membership dues.

2943 ■ *EA Journal*
National Association of Enrolled Agents
1120 Connecticut Ave. NW, Ste. 460
Washington, DC 20036-3953
Ph: (202)822-6232
Fax: (202)822-6270
E-mail: info@naea.org
URL: http://www.naea.org
Descr: Provides current information on taxation and taxpayer representation issues. **Freq:** bimonthly. **Price:** included in membership dues, $48/year for nonmembers. **ISSN:** 8750-7072.

2944 ■ *E@lert*
National Association of Enrolled Agents
1120 Connecticut Ave. NW, Ste. 460
Washington, DC 20036-3953
Ph: (202)822-6232
Fax: (202)822-6270
E-mail: info@naea.org
URL: http://www.naea.org
Descr: Provides brief updates on the latest tax news. **Freq:** weekly. **Price:** included in membership dues.

2945 ■ *eMarketBeat*
Futures Industry Association
2001 Pennsylvania Ave. NW, Ste. 600
Washington, DC 20006
Ph: (202)466-5460
Fax: (202)296-3184
E-mail: info@futuresindustry.org
URL: http://www.futuresindustry.org
Descr: Delivers industry news, updates on legislative and regulatory actions affecting the industry, FIA division reports and events. **Freq:** weekly. **Price:** free.

2946 ■ *Enterprise*
Canada's Venture Capital and Private Equity Association
MaRS Centre
Heritage Bldg.
101 College St., Ste. 120 J

Toronto, ON, Canada M5G 1L7
Ph: (416)487-0519
Fax: (416)487-5899
E-mail: cvca@cvca.ca
URL: http://www.cvca.ca
Descr: Features investment statistics, news on new funds, industry activities, and various important industry happenings. **Freq:** quarterly.

2947 ■ *Erase the Bias: A Pay Equity Guide to Eliminating Race and Sex Bias from Wage Setting Systems*
National Committee on Pay Equity
555 New Jersey Ave. NW
Washington, DC 20001-2029
Ph: (703)920-2010
Fax: (703)979-6372
E-mail: fairpay@pay-equity.org
URL: http://www.pay-equity.org

2948 ■ *Everybody's Money*
Credit Union National Association
PO Box 431
Madison, WI 53701-0431
Fax: (608)231-4263
URL: http://www.cuna.org
Descr: Serves as a promotional piece for credit unions and an educational tool for their members. **Freq:** quarterly. **Price:** $99/year (minimum order of 100 subscriptions). **ISSN:** 0423-8710.

2949 ■ *The Exchange*
New York Stock Exchange
11 Wall St.
New York, NY 10005
Ph: (212)656-3000
E-mail: boardofdirectors@nyse.com
URL: http://www.nyse.com
Freq: monthly.

2950 ■ *Fact Book on Direct Marketing*
Direct Marketing Association
1120 Ave. of the Americas
New York, NY 10036-6700
Ph: (212)768-7277
Fax: (212)302-6714
E-mail: presiden@the-dma.org
URL: http://www.the-dma.org
Descr: Includes charts and graphs on every aspect of the DM industry from more than 100 different sources. **Freq:** annual. **Price:** $79.95 for members, $104.95 for nonmembers.

2951 ■ *Facts About Supermarket Development*
Food Marketing Institute
2345 Crystal Dr., Ste. 800
Arlington, VA 22202-4801
Ph: (202)452-8444
Fax: (202)429-4519
URL: http://www.fmi.org
Freq: annual.

2952 ■ *Fair and Equitable*
International Association of Assessing Officers
314 W 10th St.
Kansas City, MO 64105-1616
Ph: (816)701-8100
Fax: (816)701-8149
E-mail: daniels@iaao.org
URL: http://www.iaao.org
Freq: monthly. **Price:** $48 for nonmembers, free for members.

2953 ■ *Fair Play*
United for a Fair Economy
29 Winter St.
Boston, MA 02108
Ph: (617)423-2148
Fax: (617)423-0191
E-mail: info@faireconomy.org
URL: http://www.faireconomy.org

Freq: semiannual.

2954 ■ FIA Membership Directory
Futures Industry Association
2001 Pennsylvania Ave. NW, Ste. 600
Washington, DC 20006
Ph: (202)466-5460
Fax: (202)296-3184
E-mail: info@futuresindustry.org
URL: http://www.futuresindustry.org
Freq: annual.

2955 ■ FIA Membership Guide
Futures Industry Association
2001 Pennsylvania Ave. NW, Ste. 600
Washington, DC 20006
Ph: (202)466-5460
Fax: (202)296-3184
E-mail: info@futuresindustry.org
URL: http://www.futuresindustry.org

2956 ■ Field Notes
Greater Oregon Chapter of the Appraisal Institute
PO Box 573
Salem, OR 97308-0573
Ph: (503)316-1979
Fax: (503)585-8547
E-mail: aioregon@oregonappraisers.org
URL: http://www.oregonappraisers.org
Freq: bimonthly.

2957 ■ Fill 'Er Up: Back Door Deal for Boeing Will Leave the Taxpayer on Empty, 2002 Report
Project on Government Oversight
666 11th St. NW, Ste. 900
Washington, DC 20001-4542
Ph: (202)347-1122
Fax: (202)347-1116
E-mail: info@pogo.org
URL: http://www.pogo.org

2958 ■ Food Marketing Industry Speaks
Food Marketing Institute
2345 Crystal Dr., Ste. 800
Arlington, VA 22202-4801
Ph: (202)452-8444
Fax: (202)429-4519
URL: http://www.fmi.org
Freq: annual.

2959 ■ Forbes—Mutual Fund Survey Issue
Forbes Magazine
90 5th Ave.
New York, NY 10011
Ph: (212)366-8900
Free: 800-295-0893
URL: http://www.forbes.com
Key Personnel: Michael K. Ozanian, Contact; William Baldwin, Editor. **URL(s):** http://www.forbes.com **Entries include:** For funds--Name, investment results, performance ratings, total assets, other financial data. **Publication includes:** List of nearly 2,000 mutual funds rated according to historical performance (if time in business permits); list of mutual fund distributors. **Freq:** Semiannual, Latest edition 2009.

2960 ■ Forum
Canadian Payments Association
180 Elgin St., 12th Fl.
Ottawa, ON, Canada K2P 2K3
Ph: (613)238-4173
Fax: (613)233-3385
E-mail: info@cdnpay.ca
URL: http://www.cdnpay.ca
Descr: Contains information on the Association's activities and important payment developments. **Freq:** quarterly. **Price:** free.

2961 ■ Foundation Grants to Individuals
Foundation Center
79 5th Ave., 16th St.
New York, NY 10003-3076
Ph: (212)620-4230
Free: 800-424-9836
Fax: (212)807-3677

E-mail: communications@foundationcenter.org
URL: http://www.foundationcenter.org
URL(s): http://foundationcenter.org **Covers:** Over 8,300 foundations that make grants to individuals. **Entries include:** Foundation name, address, phone, contact person, total assets, total number and amount of grants, number and amount of grants to individuals, application information, grant limitations, description of grant program, publications. **Freq:** Annual, Latest edition 17th. **Price:** $99.95, individuals.

2962 ■ FPA Hawaii Newsletter
Financial Planning Association of Hawaii
516 Kawaihae St., Ste. E
Honolulu, HI 96825
Ph: (808)394-3451
Fax: (808)395-4417
E-mail: hayacyn@hawaii.rr.com
URL: http://www.fpahawaii.org
Freq: monthly. **Price:** free for members.

2963 ■ FPA This Week
Financial Planning Association
4100 E Mississippi Ave., Ste. 400
Denver, CO 80246-3053
Ph: (303)759-4900
Fax: (303)759-0749
E-mail: webfeedback@fpanet.org
URL: http://www.fpanet.org
Descr: Contains updates on FPA happenings and current industry events. **Freq:** weekly.

2964 ■ Franchise Opportunities Guide
International Franchise Association
1501 K St. NW, Ste. 350
Washington, DC 20005
Ph: (202)628-8000
Fax: (202)628-0812
E-mail: ifa@franchise.org
URL: http://www.franchise.org
Freq: semiannual. **Price:** $21.

2965 ■ Franchising World Magazine
International Franchise Association
1501 K St. NW, Ste. 350
Washington, DC 20005
Ph: (202)628-8000
Fax: (202)628-0812
E-mail: ifa@franchise.org
URL: http://www.franchise.org
Freq: bimonthly.

2966 ■ Free Money to Change Your Life
Information USA Inc.
12081 Nebel St.
Rockville, MD 20852
Free: 800-955-7653
URL: http://www.lesko.com
Key Personnel: Matthew Lesko, Publisher. **URL(s):** http://lesko.com **Covers:** Approximately 15,000 government programs and funding agencies providing nontraditional grants. **Entries include:** Contact information. **Price:** $69.95, individuals, CDR.

2967 ■ From Making a Profit to Making a Difference
Planning Communications
7215 Oak Ave.
River Forest, IL 60305-1935
Ph: (708)366-5200
Free: 888-366-5200
Fax: (708)366-5280
E-mail: info@planningcommunications.com
URL: http://www.planningcommunications.com/jf/index.htm
Key Personnel: Richard King, Author. **URL(s):** http://www.planningcommunications.com **Covers:** Jobs in non-profits, specifically how to transition from positions in for-profit organizations to non-profits, and how to make yourself marketable to non-profits. **Price:** $16.95, individuals, paperback; plus shipping; $29.95, individuals, hard cover; plus shipping.

2968 ■ Futures Industry
Futures Industry Association
2001 Pennsylvania Ave. NW, Ste. 600

Washington, DC 20006
Ph: (202)466-5460
Fax: (202)296-3184
E-mail: info@futuresindustry.org
URL: http://www.futuresindustry.org
Freq: bimonthly. **Price:** free for qualified individuals.

2969 ■ FYI Newsletter
My Own Business, Inc.
13181 Crossroads Pkwy. N, Ste. 190
City of Industry, CA 91746
Ph: (562)463-1800
Fax: (562)463-1802
E-mail: support@myownbusiness.org
URL: http://www.myownbusiness.org
Descr: Contains articles, columns, success stories and other news. **Freq:** quarterly. **Price:** free.

2970 ■ Get Out of Debt
Myvesta
701 E Gudie Dr.
Rockville, MD 20850
Ph: (301)762-5270
URL: http://myvesta.org

2971 ■ Getting Financial Aid
The College Board
45 Columbus Ave.
New York, NY 10023-6992
Ph: (212)713-8000
Fax: (212)649-8442
E-mail: publicaffairs@collegeboard.org
URL: http://www.collegeboard.com
Freq: annual.

2972 ■ Getting Help Made All the Difference
Forum for Investor Advice
PO Box 3216
Mercerville, NJ 08619
Fax: (609)890-8037
E-mail: investoradvice@optonline.net
URL: http://www.investoradvice.org

2973 ■ Global Network for Banking Innovation
Women's World Banking - USA
8 W 40th St., 9th Fl.
New York, NY 10018
Ph: (212)768-8513
Fax: (212)768-8519
E-mail: communications@swwb.org
URL: http://www.swwb.org

2974 ■ Gone, But Not Forgotten
Coalition for Economic Survival
514 Shatto Pl., Ste. 270
Los Angeles, CA 90020
Ph: (213)252-4411
Fax: (213)252-4422
E-mail: contactces@earthlink.net
URL: http://www.cesinaction.org
Descr: Documents a struggle against displacement due to redevelopment, linking it to LA's redevelopment history.

2975 ■ Great Big Book of Business Lists
Entrepreneur Media Inc.
Entrepreneur Press
2445 McCabe Way, Ste. 400
Irvine, CA 92614
Ph: (949)261-2325
Free: 800-864-6864
Fax: (949)261-7729
E-mail: press@entrepreneur.com
URL: http://www.entrepreneurpress.com
URL(s): http://www.entrepreneurpress.com/cgi-bin/books/00227.html **Covers:** Approximately 10,000 listings of business information. **Entries include:** Business' contact information. **Price:** $34.95, individuals, paperback.

2976 ■ Guelph Business Directory
City of Guelph
Guelph Economic Development
59 Carden St.
Guelph, ON, Canada N1H 3A1
Ph: (519)822-1260

E-mail: info@guelph.ca
URL: http://guelph.ca/business.cfm
URL(s): http://guelph.ca/business.cfm **Covers:** 1,100 businesses in the city of Guelph. **Price:** $30, individuals, print version; $50, individuals, CD version.

2977 ■ Guidelines for Creating a Business Plan
Pet Care Services Association
1702 E Pikes Peak Ave.
Colorado Springs, CO 80909-5717
Ph: (719)667-1600
Fax: (719)667-0116
E-mail: membership@petcareservices.org
URL: http://www.petcareservices.org
Price: $21 each.

2978 ■ Hawaii Credit Union Directory
Hawaii Credit Union League
1654 S King St.
Honolulu, HI 96826-2097
Ph: (808)941-0556
Fax: (808)945-0019
E-mail: info@hcul.org
URL: http://www.hcul.org
Freq: annual. **Price:** available to members only.

2979 ■ HCUL Journal
Hawaii Credit Union League
1654 S King St.
Honolulu, HI 96826-2097
Ph: (808)941-0556
Fax: (808)945-0019
E-mail: info@hcul.org
URL: http://www.hcul.org
Freq: semiweekly.

2980 ■ Heavy Lifting for Boeing: Sweetheart Deal Helps Defense Contractor & Hurts Taxpayer, 2001 Report
Project on Government Oversight
666 11th St. NW, Ste. 900
Washington, DC 20001-4542
Ph: (202)347-1122
Fax: (202)347-1116
E-mail: info@pogo.org
URL: http://www.pogo.org

2981 ■ Hemp, Lifeline to the Future
Business Alliance for Commerce in Hemp
PO Box 1716
El Cerrito, CA 94530
Ph: (510)215-8326
Fax: (510)234-4460
E-mail: chris@chrisconrad.com
URL: http://www.equalrights4all.org/bach/BACHcore.html
Price: $12.95 plus shipping and handling.

2982 ■ Higher Ground: Thoughts on taking it to the next level
National Association of Credit Union Services Organizations
PMB 3419 Via Lido, No. 135
Newport Beach, CA 92663
Ph: (949)645-5296
Fax: (949)645-5297
E-mail: info@nacuso.org
URL: http://www.nacuso.org

2983 ■ Horizons
Rhode Island Credit Union League
20 Altieri Way
Warwick, RI 02888
E-mail: degan@cucenter.org
URL: http://www.riculeague.org
Freq: monthly.

2984 ■ How to Start a Business in Alabama
Entrepreneur Media Inc.
Entrepreneur Press
2445 McCabe Way, Ste. 400
Irvine, CA 92614
Ph: (949)261-2325
Free: 800-864-6864
Fax: (949)261-7729

E-mail: press@entrepreneur.com
URL: http://www.entrepreneurpress.com
URL(s): http://www.entrepreneurpress.com/cgi-bin/books/00089.html **Entries include:** Detailed information on mailing addresses, Internet addresses, and telephone numbers of federal, state, local and private agencies. **Price:** $24.95, individuals, paperback.

2985 ■ How to Start a Business in Alaska
Entrepreneur Media Inc.
Entrepreneur Press
2445 McCabe Way, Ste. 400
Irvine, CA 92614
Ph: (949)261-2325
Free: 800-864-6864
Fax: (949)261-7729
E-mail: press@entrepreneur.com
URL: http://www.entrepreneurpress.com
URL(s): http://www.entrepreneurpress.com/cgi-bin/books/00090.html **Entries include:** Detailed information on mailing addresses, Internet addresses, and telephone numbers of federal, state, local and private agencies. **Freq:** Annual. **Price:** $24.95, individuals, paperback.

2986 ■ How to Start a Business in Arkansas
Entrepreneur Media Inc.
Entrepreneur Press
2445 McCabe Way, Ste. 400
Irvine, CA 92614
Ph: (949)261-2325
Free: 800-864-6864
Fax: (949)261-7729
E-mail: press@entrepreneur.com
URL: http://www.entrepreneurpress.com
URL(s): http://www.entrepreneurpress.com/cgi-bin/books/00094.html **Entries include:** Detailed information on mailing addresses, Internet addresses, and telephone numbers of federal, state, local and private agencies. **Freq:** Annual. **Price:** $24.95, individuals, paperback.

2987 ■ How to Start a Business in Delaware
Entrepreneur Media Inc.
Entrepreneur Press
2445 McCabe Way, Ste. 400
Irvine, CA 92614
Ph: (949)261-2325
Free: 800-864-6864
Fax: (949)261-7729
E-mail: press@entrepreneur.com
URL: http://www.entrepreneurpress.com
URL(s): http://www.entrepreneurpress.com/cgi-bin/books/00099.html **Entries include:** Detailed information on mailing addresses, Internet addresses, and telephone numbers of federal, state, local and private agencies. **Freq:** Annual. **Price:** $24.95, individuals, paperback.

2988 ■ How to Start a Business in District of Columbia
Entrepreneur Media Inc.
Entrepreneur Press
2445 McCabe Way, Ste. 400
Irvine, CA 92614
Ph: (949)261-2325
Free: 800-864-6864
Fax: (949)261-7729
E-mail: press@entrepreneur.com
URL: http://www.entrepreneurpress.com
URL(s): http://www.entrepreneurpress.com/cgi-bin/books/00100.html **Entries include:** Detailed information on mailing addresses, Internet addresses, and telephone numbers of federal, state, local and private agencies. **Freq:** Annual. **Price:** $24.95, individuals, paperback.

2989 ■ How to Start a Business in Hawaii
Entrepreneur Media Inc.
Entrepreneur Press
2445 McCabe Way, Ste. 400
Irvine, CA 92614
Ph: (949)261-2325
Free: 800-864-6864
Fax: (949)261-7729

E-mail: press@entrepreneur.com
URL: http://www.entrepreneurpress.com
URL(s): http://www.entrepreneurpress.com/cgi-bin/books/00103.html **Entries include:** Detailed information on mailing, Internet addresses and telephone numbers for federal, state, local and private agencies. **Freq:** Annual. **Price:** $24.95, individuals, paperback.

2990 ■ How to Start a Business in Idaho
Entrepreneur Media Inc.
Entrepreneur Press
2445 McCabe Way, Ste. 400
Irvine, CA 92614
Ph: (949)261-2325
Free: 800-864-6864
Fax: (949)261-7729
E-mail: press@entrepreneur.com
URL: http://www.entrepreneurpress.com
URL(s): http://www.entrepreneurpress.com/cgi-bin/books/00104.html **Entries include:** Detailed information on mailing addresses, Internet addresses, and telephone numbers of federal, state, local and private agencies. **Freq:** Annual. **Price:** $24.95, individuals, paperback.

2991 ■ How to Start a Business in Iowa
Entrepreneur Media Inc.
Entrepreneur Press
2445 McCabe Way, Ste. 400
Irvine, CA 92614
Ph: (949)261-2325
Free: 800-864-6864
Fax: (949)261-7729
E-mail: press@entrepreneur.com
URL: http://www.entrepreneurpress.com
URL(s): http://www.entrepreneurpress.com/cgi-bin/books/00107.html **Entries include:** Detailed information on mailing addresses, Internet addresses, and telephone numbers of federal, state, local and private agencies. **Price:** $24.95, individuals, paperback.

2992 ■ How to Start a Business in Kansas
Entrepreneur Media Inc.
Entrepreneur Press
2445 McCabe Way, Ste. 400
Irvine, CA 92614
Ph: (949)261-2325
Free: 800-864-6864
Fax: (949)261-7729
E-mail: press@entrepreneur.com
URL: http://www.entrepreneurpress.com
URL(s): http://www.entrepreneurpress.com/cgi-bin/books/00108.html **Entries include:** Detailed information on mailing addresses, Internet addresses, and telephone numbers of federal, state, local and private agencies. **Freq:** Annual. **Price:** $24.95, individuals, paperback.

2993 ■ How to Start a Business in Kentucky
Entrepreneur Media Inc.
Entrepreneur Press
2445 McCabe Way, Ste. 400
Irvine, CA 92614
Ph: (949)261-2325
Free: 800-864-6864
Fax: (949)261-7729
E-mail: press@entrepreneur.com
URL: http://www.entrepreneurpress.com
URL(s): http://www.entrepreneurpress.com/cgi-bin/books/00110.html **Entries include:** Detailed information on mailing addresses, Internet addresses, and telephone numbers of federal, state, local and private agencies. **Freq:** Annual. **Price:** $24.95, individuals, paperback.

2994 ■ How to Start a Business in Louisiana
Entrepreneur Media Inc.
Entrepreneur Press
2445 McCabe Way, Ste. 400
Irvine, CA 92614
Ph: (949)261-2325
Free: 800-864-6864
Fax: (949)261-7729
E-mail: press@entrepreneur.com
URL: http://www.entrepreneurpress.com

URL(s): http://www.entrepreneurpress.com/cgi-bin/books/00111.html **Entries include:** Detailed information on mailing addresses, Internet addresses, and telephone numbers of federal, state, local and private agencies. **Freq:** Annual. **Price:** $24.95, individuals, paperback.

2995 ■ How to Start a Business in Maine
Entrepreneur Media Inc.
Entrepreneur Press
2445 McCabe Way, Ste. 400
Irvine, CA 92614
Ph: (949)261-2325
Free: 800-864-6864
Fax: (949)261-7729
E-mail: press@entrepreneur.com
URL: http://www.entrepreneurpress.com
URL(s): http://www.entrepreneurpress.com/cgi-bin/books/00112.html **Entries include:** Detailed information on mailing addresses, Internet addresses, and telephone numbers of federal, state, local and private agencies. **Freq:** Annual. **Price:** $24.95, individuals, paperback.

2996 ■ How to Start a Business in Mississippi
Entrepreneur Media Inc.
Entrepreneur Press
2445 McCabe Way, Ste. 400
Irvine, CA 92614
Ph: (949)261-2325
Free: 800-864-6864
Fax: (949)261-7729
E-mail: press@entrepreneur.com
URL: http://www.entrepreneurpress.com
URL(s): http://www.entrepreneurpress.com/cgi-bin/books/00117.html **Entries include:** Detailed information on mailing addresses, Internet addresses, and telephone numbers of federal, state, local and private agencies. **Freq:** Annual. **Price:** $24.95, individuals, paperback.

2997 ■ How to Start a Business in Montana
Entrepreneur Media Inc.
Entrepreneur Press
2445 McCabe Way, Ste. 400
Irvine, CA 92614
Ph: (949)261-2325
Free: 800-864-6864
Fax: (949)261-7729
E-mail: press@entrepreneur.com
URL: http://www.entrepreneurpress.com
URL(s): http://www.entrepreneurpress.com/cgi-bin/books/00119.html **Entries include:** Detailed information on mailing addresses, Internet addresses, and telephone numbers of federal, state, local and private agencies. **Price:** $24.95, individuals, paperback.

2998 ■ How to Start a Business in Nebraska
Entrepreneur Media Inc.
Entrepreneur Press
2445 McCabe Way, Ste. 400
Irvine, CA 92614
Ph: (949)261-2325
Free: 800-864-6864
Fax: (949)261-7729
E-mail: press@entrepreneur.com
URL: http://www.entrepreneurpress.com
URL(s): http://www.entrepreneurpress.com/cgi-bin/books/00120.html **Entries include:** Detailed information on mailing addresses, Internet addresses, and telephone numbers of federal, state, local and private agencies. **Freq:** Annual. **Price:** $24.95, individuals, paperback.

2999 ■ How to Start a Business in Nevada
Entrepreneur Media Inc.
Entrepreneur Press
2445 McCabe Way, Ste. 400
Irvine, CA 92614
Ph: (949)261-2325
Free: 800-864-6864
Fax: (949)261-7729
E-mail: press@entrepreneur.com
URL: http://www.entrepreneurpress.com
URL(s): http://www.entrepreneurpress.com/cgi-bin/books/00121.html **Entries include:** Detailed informa-

tion on mailing addresses, Internet addresses, and telephone numbers of federal, state, local and private agencies. **Freq:** Annual. **Price:** $24.95, individuals, paperback.

3000 ■ How to Start a Business in New Mexico
Entrepreneur Media Inc.
Entrepreneur Press
2445 McCabe Way, Ste. 400
Irvine, CA 92614
Ph: (949)261-2325
Free: 800-864-6864
Fax: (949)261-7729
E-mail: press@entrepreneur.com
URL: http://www.entrepreneurpress.com
URL(s): http://www.entrepreneurpress.com/cgi-bin/books/00124.html **Entries include:** Detailed information on mailing addresses, Internet addresses, and telephone numbers of federal, state, local and private agencies. **Freq:** Annual. **Price:** $24.95, individuals, paperback.

3001 ■ How to Start a Business in New York City
Entrepreneur Media Inc.
Entrepreneur Press
2445 McCabe Way, Ste. 400
Irvine, CA 92614
Ph: (949)261-2325
Free: 800-864-6864
Fax: (949)261-7729
E-mail: press@entrepreneur.com
URL: http://www.entrepreneurpress.com
URL(s): http://www.entrepreneurpress.com/cgi-bin/books/00126.html **Entries include:** Detailed information on mailing addresses, Internet addresses, and telephone numbers of federal, state, local and private agencies. **Freq:** Annual. **Price:** $24.95, individuals, paperback.

3002 ■ How to Start a Business in North Dakota
Entrepreneur Media Inc.
Entrepreneur Press
2445 McCabe Way, Ste. 400
Irvine, CA 92614
Ph: (949)261-2325
Free: 800-864-6864
Fax: (949)261-7729
E-mail: press@entrepreneur.com
URL: http://www.entrepreneurpress.com
URL(s): http://www.entrepreneurpress.com/cgi-bin/books/00128.html **Entries include:** Detailed information on mailing addresses, Internet addresses, and telephone numbers of federal, state, local and private agencies. **Price:** $24.95, individuals, paperback.

3003 ■ How to Start a Business in Ohio
Entrepreneur Media Inc.
Entrepreneur Press
2445 McCabe Way, Ste. 400
Irvine, CA 92614
Ph: (949)261-2325
Free: 800-864-6864
Fax: (949)261-7729
E-mail: press@entrepreneur.com
URL: http://www.entrepreneurpress.com
URL(s): http://www.entrepreneurpress.com/cgi-bin/books/00129.html **Entries include:** Detailed information on mailing addresses, Internet addresses, and telephone numbers of federal, state, local and private agencies. **Freq:** Annual. **Price:** $24.95, individuals, paperback.

3004 ■ How to Start a Business in Oklahoma
Entrepreneur Media Inc.
Entrepreneur Press
2445 McCabe Way, Ste. 400
Irvine, CA 92614
Ph: (949)261-2325
Free: 800-864-6864
Fax: (949)261-7729
E-mail: press@entrepreneur.com
URL: http://www.entrepreneurpress.com
URL(s): http://www.entrepreneurpress.com/cgi-bin/books/00130.html **Entries include:** Detailed informa-

tion on mailing addresses, Internet addresses, and telephone numbers of federal, state, local and private agencies. **Freq:** Annual. **Price:** $24.95, individuals, paperback.

3005 ■ How to Start a Business in Rhode Island
Entrepreneur Media Inc.
Entrepreneur Press
2445 McCabe Way, Ste. 400
Irvine, CA 92614
Ph: (949)261-2325
Free: 800-864-6864
Fax: (949)261-7729
E-mail: press@entrepreneur.com
URL: http://www.entrepreneurpress.com
URL(s): http://www.entrepreneurpress.com/cgi-bin/books/00133.html **Entries include:** Detailed information on mailing addresses, Internet addresses, and telephone numbers of federal, state, local and private agencies. **Freq:** Annual. **Price:** $24.95, individuals, paperback.

3006 ■ How to Start a Business in South Dakota
Entrepreneur Media Inc.
Entrepreneur Press
2445 McCabe Way, Ste. 400
Irvine, CA 92614
Ph: (949)261-2325
Free: 800-864-6864
Fax: (949)261-7729
E-mail: press@entrepreneur.com
URL: http://www.entrepreneurpress.com
URL(s): http://www.entrepreneurpress.com/cgi-bin/books/00135.html **Entries include:** Detailed information on mailing addresses, Internet addresses, and telephone numbers of federal, state, local and private agencies. **Freq:** Annual. **Price:** $24.95, individuals, paperback.

3007 ■ How to Start a Business in Utah
Entrepreneur Media Inc.
Entrepreneur Press
2445 McCabe Way, Ste. 400
Irvine, CA 92614
Ph: (949)261-2325
Free: 800-864-6864
Fax: (949)261-7729
E-mail: press@entrepreneur.com
URL: http://www.entrepreneurpress.com
URL(s): http://www.entrepreneurpress.com/cgi-bin/books/00138.html **Entries include:** Detailed information on mailing addresses, Internet addresses, and telephone numbers of federal, state, local and private agencies. **Freq:** Annual. **Price:** $24.95, individuals, paperback.

3008 ■ How to Start a Business in Vermont
Entrepreneur Media Inc.
Entrepreneur Press
2445 McCabe Way, Ste. 400
Irvine, CA 92614
Ph: (949)261-2325
Free: 800-864-6864
Fax: (949)261-7729
E-mail: press@entrepreneur.com
URL: http://www.entrepreneurpress.com
URL(s): http://www.entrepreneurpress.com/cgi-bin/books/00139.html **Entries include:** Detailed information on mailing addresses, Internet addresses, and telephone numbers of federal, state, local and private agencies. **Freq:** Annual. **Price:** $24.95, individuals, paperback.

3009 ■ How to Start a Business in West Virginia
Entrepreneur Media Inc.
Entrepreneur Press
2445 McCabe Way, Ste. 400
Irvine, CA 92614
Ph: (949)261-2325
Free: 800-864-6864
Fax: (949)261-7729
E-mail: press@entrepreneur.com
URL: http://www.entrepreneurpress.com

URL(s): http://www.entrepreneurpress.com/cgi-bin/
books/00142.html **Entries include:** Detailed information on mailing addresses, Internet addresses, and telephone numbers of federal, state, local and private agencies. **Freq:** Annual. **Price:** $24.95, individuals, paperback.

3010 ■ *How to Start a Business in Wyoming*
Entrepreneur Media Inc.
Entrepreneur Press
2445 McCabe Way, Ste. 400
Irvine, CA 92614
Ph: (949)261-2325
Free: 800-864-6864
Fax: (949)261-7729
E-mail: press@entrepreneur.com
URL: http://www.entrepreneurpress.com
URL(s): http://www.entrepreneurpress.com/cgi-bin/
books/00144.html **Entries include:** Detailed information on mailing addresses, Internet addresses, and telephone numbers of federal, state, local and private agencies. **Freq:** Annual. **Price:** $24.95, individuals, paperback.

3011 ■ *IAFCI News*
International Association of Financial Crimes Investigators
1020 Suncast Ln., Ste. 102
El Dorado Hills, CA 95762
Ph: (916)939-5000
Fax: (916)939-0395
E-mail: admin@iafci.org
URL: http://www.iafci.org
Freq: quarterly.

3012 ■ *IBA Applicants Handbook*
Institute of Business Appraisers
PO Box 17410
Plantation, FL 33318
Ph: (954)584-1144
Fax: (954)584-1184
E-mail: hqiba@go-iba.org
URL: http://www.go-iba.org
Price: $20 for members, $35 for nonmembers.

3013 ■ *ICA Model Bylaws for a Worker Cooperative (version III)*
ICA Group
1 Harvard St., Ste. 200
Brookline, MA 02445
Ph: (617)232-8765
Fax: (617)232-9545
E-mail: ica@ica-group.org
URL: http://www.ica-group.org
Price: $95 book (plus $5.25 postage), $50 diskette.

3014 ■ *ICA News & Events*
ICA Group
1 Harvard St., Ste. 200
Brookline, MA 02445
Ph: (617)232-8765
Fax: (617)232-9545
E-mail: ica@ica-group.org
URL: http://www.ica-group.org
Freq: semiannual.

3015 ■ *Identity Theft: The Aftermath*
Identity Theft Resource Center
PO Box 26833
San Diego, CA 92196
Ph: (858)693-7935
E-mail: itrc@idtheftcenter.org
URL: http://www.idtheftcenter.org
Freq: periodic.

3016 ■ *IMAA News Group*
eBusiness Association
PO Box 500
Penfield, NY 14526
E-mail: eba_rochester@yahoo.com
URL: http://www.ebusinessassociation.org
Freq: quarterly. **Price:** free for members.

3017 ■ *Independent Credit Operations*
American Financial Services Association
919 18th St. NW, Ste. 300

Washington, DC 20006-5517
Ph: (202)296-5544
Fax: (202)223-0321
E-mail: cstinebert@afsamail.org
URL: http://www.afsaonline.org
Freq: quarterly.

**3018 ■ *Institute of Business Appraisers—
Newsletter***
Institute of Business Appraisers
PO Box 17410
Plantation, FL 33318
Ph: (954)584-1144
Fax: (954)584-1184
E-mail: hqiba@go-iba.org
URL: http://www.go-iba.org
Descr: Covers association and industry news. **Freq:** quarterly.

**3019 ■ *International Association of Financial
Crimes Investigators—Membership Directory***
International Association of Financial Crimes Investigators
1020 Suncast Ln., Ste. 102
El Dorado Hills, CA 95762
Ph: (916)939-5000
Fax: (916)939-0395
E-mail: members@iafci.org
URL: http://www.iafci.org/
URL(s): http://www.iafci.org **Covers:** About 3,500 firms and individuals engaged in investigation of fraudulent use of credit cards. **Entries include:** Name, title, firm name, address, phone. **Freq:** Annual, Latest edition 2007.

**3020 ■ *Internet Guide to Personal Finance
and Investment***
Greenwood Publishing Group Inc.
88 Post Rd. W
PO Box 5007
Westport, CT 06881
Ph: (203)226-3571
Fax: 877-231-6980
E-mail: webmaster@greenwood.com
URL: http://www.greenwood.com
Key Personnel: Qun G. Jiao, Author. **URL(s):** http://
www.greenwood.com/catalog/OXIRINVST.aspx **Covers:** Over 1,400 Websites regarding personal finance and investment. **Entries include:** Name of Website, URL, sponsor of site, and description of contents. **Price:** $75, single issue, Paperback; $51.95, single issue, UK sterling price.

3021 ■ *IRTA Dialogue*
International Reciprocal Trade Association
524 Middle St.
Portsmouth, VA 23704
Ph: (757)393-2292
Fax: (757)257-4014
E-mail: ron@irta.com
URL: http://www.irta.com
Descr: Covers association events and activities, industry news. **Freq:** quarterly.

3022 ■ *ISA Professional Appraisers Information Exchange*
International Society of Appraisers
737 N Michigan Ave., Ste. 2100
Chicago, IL 60611
Ph: (312)981-6778
Fax: (312)981-6787
E-mail: isa@isa-appraisers.org
URL: http://www.isa-appraisers.org
Price: $1.

3023 ■ *The Journal*
Kansas City Regional Chapter of the International Association of Assessing Officers
Johnson County Appraiser's Office
415 E 12th St., No. 1M
Kansas City, MO 64106
Ph: (816)881-3239
E-mail: ckoons@jacksongov.org
URL: http://www.kciaao.org

Freq: quarterly. **Price:** free for members.

3024 ■ *Journal of Agricultural Lending*
American Bankers Association
1120 Connecticut Ave. NW
Washington, DC 20036
Ph: (202)663-5564
Fax: (202)663-7543
E-mail: custserv@aba.com
URL: http://www.aba.com
Freq: quarterly. **Price:** $60 for members, $90 for nonmembers.

3025 ■ *Journal of Cost Analysis & Parametrics*
Society of Cost Estimating and Analysis
527 Maple Ave. E, Ste. 301
Vienna, VA 22180
Ph: (703)938-5090
Fax: (703)938-5091
E-mail: scea@sceaonline.org
URL: http://www.sceaonline.org
Descr: Presents scholarly papers on cost estimating and analysis and related disciplines. **Freq:** annual. **Price:** $40/year, $50 foreign subscription. **ISSN:** 1941-658X.

3026 ■ *The Journal of Derivatives*
International Association of Financial Engineers
347 5th Ave., Ste. 703
New York, NY 10016
Ph: (646)736-0705
Fax: (646)417-6378
E-mail: main@iafe.org
URL: http://www.iafe.org
Descr: Includes research articles on the field of financial engineering. **Freq:** quarterly. **Price:** included in membership dues.

3027 ■ *Journal of Financial Planning*
Financial Planning Association
4100 E Mississippi Ave., Ste. 400
Denver, CO 80246-3053
Ph: (303)759-4900
Fax: (303)759-0749
E-mail: webfeedback@fpanet.org
URL: http://www.fpanet.org
Freq: monthly. **Price:** included in membership dues.

3028 ■ *JumpStart Update*
JumpStart Coalition for Personal Financial Literacy
919 18th St. NW, Ste. 300
Washington, DC 20006
Ph: (202)466-8610
E-mail: info@jumpstart.org
URL: http://www.jumpstartcoalition.org
Descr: Features personal finance education tools, concepts and sample lesson plans for educators. **Freq:** quarterly.

3029 ■ *Keynotes*
Pennsylvania Credit Union Association
4309 N Front St.
Harrisburg, PA 17110
Ph: (717)234-3156
Fax: (717)234-2695
E-mail: info@pcua.coop
URL: http://www.pcua.coop
Descr: Covers significant credit union topics, feature stories and political coverage and compliance issues. **Freq:** bimonthly.

3030 ■ *Keystone Extra*
Pennsylvania Credit Union Association
4309 N Front St.
Harrisburg, PA 17110
Ph: (717)234-3156
Fax: (717)234-2695
E-mail: info@pcua.coop
URL: http://www.pcua.coop
Freq: weekly.

3031 ■ *League News*
Hawaii Credit Union League
1654 S King St.
Honolulu, HI 96826-2097

Ph: (808)941-0556
Fax: (808)945-0019
E-mail: info@hcul.org
URL: http://www.hcul.org
Freq: monthly.

3032 ■ *Legislative Bulletin*
West Virginia Bankers Association
120 Washington St. E
Charleston, WV 25301-1516
Ph: (304)343-8838
Fax: (304)343-9749
E-mail: datkinson@wvbankers.org
URL: http://www.wvbankers.org

3033 ■ *Legislative Updates*
American Bankruptcy Institute
44 Canal Center Plz., Ste. 400
Alexandria, VA 22314
Ph: (703)739-0800
Fax: (703)739-1060
E-mail: support@abiworld.org
URL: http://www.abiworld.org

3034 ■ *Limited Partners: An Examination of Elizabeth and Robert Dole's Investment in the Altenn Associates Tax Shelter*
Center for Public Integrity
910 17th St. NW, Ste. 700
Washington, DC 20006
Ph: (202)466-1300
Fax: (202)466-1101
E-mail: cristina@nhli.org
URL: http://www.publicintegrity.org
Price: $5.

3035 ■ *LIMRA's MarketFacts*
LIMRA International
300 Day Hill Rd.
Windsor, CT 06095
Ph: (860)688-3358
Fax: (860)298-9555
E-mail: customer.service@limra.com
URL: http://www.limra.com
Freq: quarterly.

3036 ■ *Living Economy Newsletter*
Business Alliance for Local Living Economies
165 11th St.
San Francisco, CA 94103
Ph: (415)255-1108
Fax: (415)863-1356
E-mail: info@livingeconomies.org
URL: http://www.livingeconomies.org
Freq: monthly.

3037 ■ *MAAO Newsletter*
Massachusetts Association of Assessing Officers
Assessors Office, City Hall
1305 Hancock St.
Quincy, MA 02169
Ph: (617)376-1171
Fax: (617)376-1185
E-mail: mfantucchio@ci.quincy.ma.us
URL: http://www.maao.org
Freq: semimonthly. **Price:** included in membership dues.

3038 ■ *Make the Money and Run*
Dash-Hill L.L.C.
3540 W Sahara Ave., Ste. 094
Las Vegas, NV 89102-5816
Ph: (212)591-0384
Free: 800-266-5564
E-mail: dashhillpress@yahoo.com
URL: http://www.giftscrolls4u.com
Key Personnel: Siriol Jameson, Author. **Covers:** 163 entries covering 18 main and 57 other businesses that offer high profits and require "little or no experience or start-up money." Offers step-by-step guides to start each business, and resources. **Entries include:** Resource contacts, including company

name, address, phone, URL. **Freq:** Published June 1, 2001. **Price:** $19.95, individuals.

3039 ■ *Managing Investment Risk*
Forum for Investor Advice
PO Box 3216
Mercerville, NJ 08619
Fax: (609)890-8037
E-mail: investoradvice@optonline.net
URL: http://www.investoradvice.org

3040 ■ *MarketSource*
Appraisal Institute
550 W Van Buren St., Ste. 1000
Chicago, IL 60607
Ph: (312)335-4100
Fax: (312)335-4400
E-mail: aiceo@appraisalinstitute.org
URL: http://www.appraisalinstitute.org
Freq: quarterly. **Price:** $100/year for members and affiliates, $150/year for nonmembers.

3041 ■ *MarketSource*
Chicago Chapter of the Appraisal Institute
205 W Wacker Dr., Ste. 202
Chicago, IL 60606
Ph: (312)616-9400
Fax: (312)616-9404
E-mail: laanderson@ccai.org
URL: http://www.ccai.org
Descr: Contains real estate market activity. **Freq:** quarterly. **Price:** included in membership dues.

3042 ■ *Mature Market Calendar of Events*
Mature Market Resource Center
1850 W Winchester Rd., Ste. 213
Libertyville, IL 60048
Ph: (847)816-8660
Fax: (847)816-8662
E-mail: seniorprograms@aol.com
URL: http://www.seniorprograms.com
Freq: annual.

3043 ■ *Mature Markets*
Mature Market Resource Center
1850 W Winchester Rd., Ste. 213
Libertyville, IL 60048
Ph: (847)816-8660
Fax: (847)816-8662
E-mail: seniorprograms@aol.com
URL: http://www.seniorprograms.com
Freq: annual.

3044 ■ *Mature Markets Online*
Mature Market Resource Center
1850 W Winchester Rd., Ste. 213
Libertyville, IL 60048
Ph: (847)816-8660
Fax: (847)816-8662
E-mail: seniorprograms@aol.com
URL: http://www.seniorprograms.com
Freq: annual.

3045 ■ *Membership Brochure*
Fixed Income Analysts Society
244 Fifth Ave., Ste. L230
New York, NY 10001
Ph: (212)726-8100
E-mail: fiasi@fiasi.org
URL: http://www.fiasi.org

3046 ■ *Membership Roster*
Antique Appraisal Association of America
386 Park Ave. S, No. 2000
New York, NY 10016
Ph: (212)889-5404
Fax: (212)889-5503
E-mail: appraisers@appraiserassoc.org
URL: http://www.appraisersassoc.org/
Freq: biennial.

3047 ■ *Membership Roster*
Direct Marketing Association
1120 Ave. of the Americas
New York, NY 10036-6700
Ph: (212)768-7277
Fax: (212)302-6714

E-mail: presiden@the-dma.org
URL: http://www.the-dma.org
Freq: annual.

3048 ■ *Mergent Bank and Finance Manual*
Mergent Inc.
580 Kingsley Park Dr.
Fort Mill, SC 29715
Ph: (704)527-2700
Free: 800-937-1398
URL: http://www.mergent.com
Key Personnel: Jonathan Worrall, CEO; Paul Starkey, Mng. Dir. **URL(s):** http://www.mergent.com **Covers:** In four volumes, over 12,000 national, state, and private banks, savings and loans, mutual funds, unit investment trusts, and insurance and real estate companies in the United States. **Entries include:** Company name, headquarters and branch offices, phones, names and titles of principal executives, directors, history, Moody's rating, and extensive financial and statistical data. **Freq:** Annual, July; supplements in 'Mergent Bank & Finance News Reports'. **Price:** $2,095, per year, including supplements.

3049 ■ *Mergent's Handbook of Common Stocks*
Mergent Inc.
580 Kingsley Park Dr.
Fort Mill, SC 29715
Ph: (704)527-2700
Free: 800-937-1398
URL: http://www.mergent.com
Key Personnel: Jonathan Worrall, CEO; Paul Starkey, Mng. Dir. **URL(s):** http://www.mergent.com; http://as.wiley.com **Covers:** 900 NYSE-listed issues. **Entries include:** Company name, address, phone, fax, officers names, web address, business summary, products, line of business, financial data, investor contact, recent splits and dividend changes. **Freq:** Quarterly, latest edition 2008. **Price:** $95.

3050 ■ *Messenger*
Appraisal Institute, Wisconsin Chapter
11801 W Silver Spring Dr., No. 200
Milwaukee, WI 53225
Ph: (414)271-6858
Fax: (414)464-0850
E-mail: info@wamllc.net
URL: http://www.wisai.com
Freq: quarterly.

3051 ■ *Minutes of Annual Meeting*
National Association of Consumer Credit Administrators
PO Box 20871
Columbus, OH 43220-0871
Ph: (614)326-1165
Fax: (614)326-1162
E-mail: nacca2007@sbcglobal.net
URL: http://www.naccaonline.org
Freq: annual.

3052 ■ *Missouri Courier*
Missouri Credit Union Association
2055 Craigshire Dr.
St. Louis, MO 63146-4009
Ph: (314)542-0555
Fax: (314)542-1312
E-mail: contact@mcua.org
URL: http://www.mcua.org
Descr: Covers stories about interest of Missouri credit unions. **Freq:** quarterly. **Price:** $1.

3053 ■ *The Money Instruction Book: A Wealth-Building Course in Personal Finance*
Institute of Consumer Financial Education
PO Box 34070
San Diego, CA 92163-4070
Ph: (619)239-1401
Fax: (619)923-3284

E-mail: icfe@cox.net
URL: http://www.financial-education-icfe.org

3054 ■ *MTC Review*
MultiState Tax Commission
444 N Capitol St. NW, Ste. 425
Washington, DC 20001-1512
Ph: (202)624-8699
Fax: (202)624-8819
E-mail: mtc@mtc.gov
URL: http://www.mtc.gov
Freq: periodic. **Price:** free.

3055 ■ *The MTS Journal*
American Society of Appraisers
555 Herndon Pkwy., Ste. 125
Herndon, VA 20170
Ph: (703)478-2228
Fax: (703)742-8471
E-mail: asainfo@appraisers.org
URL: http://www.appraisers.org/ASAHome.aspx
Freq: quarterly. **Price:** $40 for nonmembers, $25 for members. **ISSN:** 0897-960X.

3056 ■ *Multistate Tax Commission Review*
MultiState Tax Commission
444 N Capitol St. NW, Ste. 425
Washington, DC 20001-1512
Ph: (202)624-8699
Fax: (202)624-8819
E-mail: mtc@mtc.gov
URL: http://www.mtc.gov

3057 ■ *MyDMA*
Direct Marketing Association
1120 Ave. of the Americas
New York, NY 10036-6700
Ph: (212)768-7277
Fax: (212)302-6714
E-mail: presiden@the-dma.org
URL: http://www.the-dma.org
Price: free.

3058 ■ *NAIFAmn LifeNotes*
Minneapolis AIFA
1405 Lilac Dr. N, No. 121
Minneapolis, MN 55422
Ph: (763)544-8087
Fax: (763)544-1631
E-mail: naifa@naifa-mn.org
URL: http://209.61.156.20/page.cfm?usr=260000&pageid=2628
Freq: monthly.

3059 ■ *NASAA Reports in CCH*
North American Securities Administrators Association
750 1st St. NE, Ste. 1140
Washington, DC 20002-8034
Ph: (202)737-0900
Fax: (202)783-3571
E-mail: info@nasaa.org
URL: http://www.nasaa.org
Freq: monthly.

3060 ■ *National CUSO Directory*
National Association of Credit Union Services Organizations
PMB 3419 Via Lido, No. 135
Newport Beach, CA 92663
Ph: (949)645-5296
Fax: (949)645-5297
E-mail: info@nacuso.org
URL: http://www.nacuso.org
Freq: annual.

3061 ■ *National CUSO Directory*
Callahan & Associates Inc.
1001 Connecticut Ave. NW, 10th Fl.
Washington, DC 20036
Ph: (202)223-3920
Free: 800-446-7453
Fax: (202)223-6098
E-mail: callahan@creditunions.com
URL: http://callahan.com
Key Personnel: Chip Filson, President; Jay

Johnson, Exec. VP. **URL(s):** http://www.creditunions.com **Covers:** More than 600 credit union service organizations, the credit unions associated with them, and the financial, insurance, investment, operational and other services they offer. **Freq:** Annual, Latest edition 2007. **Price:** $165, individuals.

3062 ■ *National Estimator*
Society of Cost Estimating and Analysis
527 Maple Ave. E, Ste. 301
Vienna, VA 22180
Ph: (703)938-5090
Fax: (703)938-5091
E-mail: scea@sceaonline.org
URL: http://www.sceaonline.net
Freq: semiannual. **Price:** $30/year for nonmembers, free, for members only.

3063 ■ *National Futures Association—News Release*
National Futures Association
300 S Riverside Plz., No. 1800
Chicago, IL 60606-6615
Ph: (312)781-1300
Fax: (312)781-1467
E-mail: information@nfa.futures.org
URL: http://www.nfa.futures.org
Descr: Reports group events to financial and general news media. **Freq:** periodic. **Price:** free.

3064 ■ *Network News*
American Bankers Association
1120 Connecticut Ave. NW
Washington, DC 20036
Ph: (202)663-5564
Fax: (202)663-7543
E-mail: custserv@aba.com
URL: http://www.aba.com
Freq: 3/year. **Price:** included in membership dues.

3065 ■ *New York Stock Exchange: Another Century*
New York Stock Exchange
11 Wall St.
New York, NY 10005
Ph: (212)656-3000
E-mail: boardofdirectors@nyse.com
URL: http://www.nyse.com
Price: $75 each.

3066 ■ *The New York Stock Exchange: The First 200 Years*
New York Stock Exchange
11 Wall St.
New York, NY 10005
Ph: (212)656-3000
E-mail: boardofdirectors@nyse.com
URL: http://www.nyse.com
Price: $49.95 each.

3067 ■ *News, Facts, Actions*
National Futures Association
300 S Riverside Plz., No. 1800
Chicago, IL 60606-6615
Ph: (312)781-1300
Fax: (312)781-1467
E-mail: information@nfa.futures.org
URL: http://www.nfa.futures.org
Descr: Keeps businesspeople apprised of current regulations and issues affecting the operation of their commodity futures businesses. **Freq:** quarterly. **Price:** free.

3068 ■ *News from Neil*
Direct Selling Association
1667 K St. NW, Ste. 1100
Washington, DC 20006
Ph: (202)452-8866
Fax: (202)452-9010
E-mail: info@dsa.org
URL: http://www.dsa.org
Freq: monthly.

3069 ■ *NFA Manual*
National Futures Association
300 S Riverside Plz., No. 1800

Chicago, IL 60606-6615
Ph: (312)781-1300
Fax: (312)781-1467
E-mail: information@nfa.futures.org
URL: http://www.nfa.futures.org

3070 ■ *NFCC Directory of Members*
National Foundation for Credit Counseling
801 Roeder Rd., Ste. 900
Silver Spring, MD 20910
Ph: (301)589-5600
Fax: (301)495-5623
E-mail: nfcc@nfcc.org
URL: http://www.debtadvice.org/
Key Personnel: William Cullinan, Interim Pres. **Covers:** about 1,300 affiliated non-profit Consumer Credit Counseling Services in the United States, Puerto Rico, and Canada, which provide non-profit education, counseling, and debt management programs for financial and housing issues. **Entries include:** Member name, address, phone, fax, name and title of contact, subsidiary and branch names and locations, names and titles of key personnel, description. **Price:** $5, members; $10.50, nonmembers.

3071 ■ *North Carolina Appraiser*
Appraisal Institute, North Carolina Chapter
3717 W Market St., Ste. C
Greensboro, NC 27407
Ph: (336)297-9511
Fax: (336)297-9055
E-mail: ncai@bellsouth.net
URL: http://www.ncappraisalinstitute.org
Freq: quarterly. **Price:** free for members.

3072 ■ *Now and in the Future: NACUSO is Here to Stay*
National Association of Credit Union Services Organizations
PMB 3419 Via Lido, No. 135
Newport Beach, CA 92663
Ph: (949)645-5296
Fax: (949)645-5297
E-mail: info@nacuso.org
URL: http://www.nacuso.org

3073 ■ *Organizing Times*
Coalition for Economic Survival
514 Shatto Pl., Ste. 270
Los Angeles, CA 90020
Ph: (213)252-4411
Fax: (213)252-4422
E-mail: contactces@earthlink.net
URL: http://www.cesinaction.org
Freq: quarterly.

3074 ■ *Path to Happiness & Wealth*
Myvesta
701 E Gudie Dr.
Rockville, MD 20850
Ph: (301)762-5270
URL: http://myvesta.org

3075 ■ *Pay Equity Activity in the Public Sector, 1979-1989*
National Committee on Pay Equity
555 New Jersey Ave. NW
Washington, DC 20001-2029
Ph: (703)920-2010
Fax: (703)979-6372
E-mail: fairpay@pay-equity.org
URL: http://www.pay-equity.org

3076 ■ *Pay Equity: An Issue of Race, Ethnicity, and Sex*
National Committee on Pay Equity
555 New Jersey Ave. NW
Washington, DC 20001-2029
Ph: (703)920-2010
Fax: (703)979-6372

E-mail: fairpay@pay-equity.org
URL: http://www.pay-equity.org

3077 ■ Pay Equity Bibliography and Resource Listing
National Committee on Pay Equity
555 New Jersey Ave. NW
Washington, DC 20001-2029
Ph: (703)920-2010
Fax: (703)979-6372
E-mail: fairpay@pay-equity.org
URL: http://www.pay-equity.org

3078 ■ Pay Equity Makes Good Business Sense
National Committee on Pay Equity
555 New Jersey Ave. NW
Washington, DC 20001-2029
Ph: (703)920-2010
Fax: (703)979-6372
E-mail: fairpay@pay-equity.org
URL: http://www.pay-equity.org

3079 ■ Professional Accountant
Society of Professional Accountants of Canada
250 Consumers Rd., Ste. 1007
Toronto, ON, Canada M2J 4V6
Ph: (416)350-8145
Fax: (416)350-8146
E-mail: ceo@professionalaccountant.org
Freq: quarterly.

3080 ■ Rail Report
Consumers United for Rail Equity
1050 Thomas Jefferson St. NW, 7th Fl.
Washington, DC 20007
Ph: (202)298-1959
Fax: (202)338-2416
E-mail: sch@vnf.com
URL: http://www.railcure.org
Freq: monthly.

3081 ■ RCR Report
CME Group
20 S Wacker Dr.
Chicago, IL 60606
Ph: (312)930-1000
E-mail: info@cmegroup.com
URL: http://www.cmegroup.com
Freq: quarterly.

3082 ■ Response
Direct Marketing Association of Detroit
32621 Grand River Ave.
Farmington, MI 48336
Ph: (248)478-4888
Fax: (248)478-6437
E-mail: dmad@ameritech.net
URL: http://www.stayinvolved.com/frontdoor/main.asp?omID=94
Freq: monthly.

3083 ■ Sales Tax Report
Institute for Professionals in Taxation
600 Northpark Town Center
1200 Abernathy Rd., Ste. L-2
Atlanta, GA 30328-1040
Ph: (404)240-2300
Fax: (404)240-2315
E-mail: ipt@ipt.org
URL: http://www.ipt.org
Descr: Contains listings of publications of interest and new members and employment referral service. Freq: monthly. Price: free for members.

3084 ■ Sales and Use Taxation
Institute for Professionals in Taxation
600 Northpark Town Center
1200 Abernathy Rd., Ste. L-2
Atlanta, GA 30328-1040
Ph: (404)240-2300
Fax: (404)240-2315
E-mail: ipt@ipt.org
URL: http://www.ipt.org

Price: $75 for members, $100 for staff of IPT member companies, $175 for nonmembers.

3085 ■ Schedule of Classes
Center for Financial Training, Southeast Regional
126 W Adams St., Ste. 501
Jacksonville, FL 32202
Ph: (904)354-4830
Fax: (904)354-1834
E-mail: lisaphillipscft@bellsouth.net
URL: http://www.cft-flsc.org
Freq: periodic.

3086 ■ Securities Processing Digest
American Bankers Association
1120 Connecticut Ave. NW
Washington, DC 20036
Ph: (202)663-5564
Fax: (202)663-7543
E-mail: custserv@aba.com
URL: http://www.aba.com
Freq: quarterly. Price: $90 for members, $135 for nonmembers.

3087 ■ Share Owner
Canadian ShareOwners Association
4 King St. W, Ste. 806
Toronto, ON, Canada M5H 1B6
Ph: (416)595-9600
Fax: (416)595-0400
E-mail: customercare@shareowner.com
URL: http://www.shareowner.com/index.html
Descr: Features two Stock To Study articles. Freq: bimonthly.

3088 ■ Smart Card Talk
Smart Card Alliance
191 Clarksville Rd.
Princeton Junction, NJ 08550
Fax: (609)587-4248
E-mail: info@smartcardalliance.org
URL: http://www.smartcardalliance.org
Descr: Contains news about the activities of the Alliance and information on industry events around the world. Freq: monthly. Price: free for members.

3089 ■ Society of Consumer Affairs Professionals in Business—Membership Directory
Society of Consumer Affairs Professionals in Business
675 N Washington St., Ste. 200
Alexandria, VA 22314
Ph: (703)519-3700
Fax: (703)549-4886
E-mail: socap@socap.org
URL: http://www.socap.org
Freq: annual.

3090 ■ Spotlight
American Financial Services Association
919 18th St. NW, Ste. 300
Washington, DC 20006-5517
Ph: (202)296-5544
Fax: (202)223-0321
E-mail: cstinebert@afsamail.org
URL: http://www.afsaonline.org
Freq: monthly.

3091 ■ SRMC Journal
Society of Risk Management Consultants
330 S Executive Dr., Ste. 301
Brookfield, WI 53005-4275
E-mail: webmaster@srmcsociety.org
URL: http://www.srmcsociety.org

3092 ■ State of New Jersey Department of Banking and Insurance—Annual Statistical Report
Office of Solvency Regulation
New Jersey Department of Banking and Insurance
PO Box 325
Trenton, NJ 08625-0325
Ph: (609)292-5350
Free: 800-446-7467
Fax: (609)292-6765
URL: http://www.state.nj.us/dobi
Key Personnel: Steven M. Goldman, Commnr.

URL(s): http://www.state.nj.us/dobi/commissreport/carmenu.htm Covers: About 1,200 state-licensed insurance companies operating in New Jersey. Entries include: Company name, address, state in which incorporated, code indicating lines of insurance for which licensed, financial data. Freq: Annual, Latest edition 2007.

3093 ■ State Status Sheet
Direct Selling Association
1667 K St. NW, Ste. 1100
Washington, DC 20006
Ph: (202)452-8866
Fax: (202)452-9010
E-mail: info@dsa.org
URL: http://www.dsa.org
Freq: weekly.

3094 ■ Systems Resource Center Bulletins
Mississippi Credit Union Association
PO Box 9575
Jackson, MS 39286-9575
Ph: (601)981-4552
Fax: (601)981-4564
URL: http://www.mcus.com
Descr: Contains information on regulatory changes that affects credit unions.

3095 ■ Tax News
Marin United Taxpayers Association
PO Box 2214
Mill Valley, CA 94942
Ph: (415)456-7910
E-mail: info@marintaxpayers.org
URL: http://marintaxpayers.org
Freq: quarterly.

3096 ■ Tax Roundup
Wyoming Taxpayers Association
2410 Pioneer Ave.
Cheyenne, WY 82001
Ph: (307)635-8761
Fax: (307)637-7556
E-mail: wyotax@wyotax.org
URL: http://www.wyotax.org
Freq: quarterly.

3097 ■ Tax Savings Report
National Taxpayers Union
108 N Alfred St.
Alexandria, VA 22314
Ph: (703)683-5700
Fax: (703)683-5722
E-mail: ntu@ntu.org
URL: http://www.ntu.org
Descr: Provides income tax advice. Freq: 10/year. Price: $39.95/year.

3098 ■ Taxing Times
Howard Jarvis Taxpayers Association
621 S Westmoreland Ave., Ste. 202
Los Angeles, CA 90005
Ph: (213)384-9656
E-mail: info@hjta.org
URL: http://www.hjta.org
Freq: quarterly. Price: included in membership dues.

3099 ■ Taxpayer's Action Guide
National Taxpayers Union
108 N Alfred St.
Alexandria, VA 22314
Ph: (703)683-5700
Fax: (703)683-5722
E-mail: ntu@ntu.org
URL: http://www.ntu.org

3100 ■ Taxpayers Resource Book
National Taxpayers Union
108 N Alfred St.
Alexandria, VA 22314
Ph: (703)683-5700

Fax: (703)683-5722
E-mail: ntu@ntu.org
URL: http://www.ntu.org

3101 ■ *Ten Keys to Transitioning Investment Services from the CUSO*
National Association of Credit Union Services Organizations
PMB 3419 Via Lido, No. 135
Newport Beach, CA 92663
Ph: (949)645-5296
Fax: (949)645-5297
E-mail: info@nacuso.org
URL: http://www.nacuso.org

3102 ■ *Third-Party Drop Shipment Survey*
Institute for Professionals in Taxation
600 Northpark Town Center
1200 Abernathy Rd., Ste. L-2
Atlanta, GA 30328-1040
Ph: (404)240-2300
Fax: (404)240-2315
E-mail: ipt@ipt.org
URL: http://www.ipt.org
Freq: semiannual. **Price:** $175.

3103 ■ *To Your Credit*
Credit Institute of Canada
219 Dufferin St., Ste. 216C
Toronto, ON, Canada M6K 3J1
Ph: (416)572-2615
Fax: (416)572-2619
E-mail: geninfo@creditedu.org
URL: http://www.creditedu.org
Freq: 3/year. **Price:** free for members.

3104 ■ *Trust and Financial Advisor*
American Bankers Association
1120 Connecticut Ave. NW
Washington, DC 20036
Ph: (202)663-5564
Fax: (202)663-7543
E-mail: custserv@aba.com
URL: http://www.aba.com
Freq: quarterly. **Price:** $125 for members, $190 for nonmembers.

3105 ■ *Trust Letter*
American Bankers Association
1120 Connecticut Ave. NW
Washington, DC 20036
Ph: (202)663-5564
Fax: (202)663-7543
E-mail: custserv@aba.com
URL: http://www.aba.com
Freq: monthly. **Price:** $100 for members, $150 for nonmembers.

3106 ■ *Update*
Society of Consumer Affairs Professionals in Business
675 N Washington St., Ste. 200
Alexandria, VA 22314
Ph: (703)519-3700
Fax: (703)549-4886
E-mail: socap@socap.org
URL: http://www.socap.org
Descr: Contains information of interest to members.
Freq: monthly.

3107 ■ *Update*
Nebraska Bankers Association
PO Box 80008
Lincoln, NE 68501
Ph: (402)474-1555
Fax: (402)474-2946
E-mail: nba@nebankers.org
URL: http://www.nebankers.org
Freq: weekly.

3108 ■ *Valuation Insights and Perspectives*
Appraisal Institute
550 W Van Buren St., Ste. 1000
Chicago, IL 60607
Ph: (312)335-4100
Fax: (312)335-4400

E-mail: aiceo@appraisalinstitute.org
URL: http://www.appraisalinstitute.org
Freq: quarterly. **Price:** free for members, $30/year for students, $35/year for nonmembers.

3109 ■ *Vermont Advisor*
NAIFA - Vermont
325 Ethan Allen Pkwy.
Burlington, VT 05401
Ph: (802)660-9639
E-mail: naifavt@gmail.com
URL: http://www.naifanet.com/vermont
Freq: monthly.

3110 ■ *Volume Reports*
Futures Industry Association
2001 Pennsylvania Ave. NW, Ste. 600
Washington, DC 20006
Ph: (202)466-5460
Fax: (202)296-3184
E-mail: info@futuresindustry.org
URL: http://www.futuresindustry.org
Freq: monthly.

3111 ■ *Walker's Manual of Penny Stocks*
Walker's Manual Inc.
92 W Main St.
Freehold, NJ 07728
Ph: (732)431-6614
Free: 800-932-2922
Fax: (732)810-0297
E-mail: info@walkersmanual.com
URL: http://www.walkersmanual.com

URL(s): http://www.walkersmanual.com/p00book.htm **Covers:** 500 stocks priced under $5 from Nasdaq and all major exchanges. **Freq:** Annual. **Price:** $65, individuals, hardcover; plus shipping.

3112 ■ *Washington Alert*
Direct Marketing Association
1120 Ave. of the Americas
New York, NY 10036-6700
Ph: (212)768-7277
Fax: (212)302-6714
E-mail: presiden@the-dma.org
URL: http://www.the-dma.org

3113 ■ *Weekly Bulletin*
New York Stock Exchange
11 Wall St.
New York, NY 10005
Ph: (212)656-3000
E-mail: boardofdirectors@nyse.com
URL: http://www.nyse.com
Freq: weekly.

3114 ■ *Weekly Bulletin*
Futures Industry Association
2001 Pennsylvania Ave. NW, Ste. 600
Washington, DC 20006
Ph: (202)466-5460
Fax: (202)296-3184
E-mail: info@futuresindustry.org
URL: http://www.futuresindustry.org

3115 ■ *WFDSA Directory of Members*
World Federation of Direct Selling Associations
1667 K St. NW, Ste. 1100
Washington, DC 20006
Ph: (202)452-8866
Fax: (202)452-9010
E-mail: info@wfdsa.org
URL: http://www.wfdsa.org
Freq: annual.

3116 ■ *What Works*
Women's World Banking - USA
8 W 40th St., 9th Fl.
New York, NY 10018
Ph: (212)768-8513
Fax: (212)768-8519
E-mail: communications@swwb.org
URL: http://www.swwb.org

Freq: periodic.

3117 ■ *The Wisconsin Taxpayer*
Wisconsin Taxpayers Alliance
401 N Lawn Ave.
Madison, WI 53704-5033
Ph: (608)241-9789
Fax: (608)241-5807
E-mail: wistax@wistax.org
URL: http://www.wistax.org/
Key Personnel: Todd A. Berry, President, pres@wistax.org; Dale J. Knapp, Res. Dir., research@wistax.org **URL(s):** http://www.wistax.org/pubs/ **Descr:** Magazine providing information on state and local government and taxation. **Freq:** Monthly. **Price:** $16, individuals; $33, individuals, 3 years.

3118 ■ *Women and Diversity WOW! Facts 2002*
Business Women's Network
1990 M St. NW, Ste. 700
Washington, DC 20036
Ph: (202)466-8209
Fax: (202)833-1808
E-mail: inquire@tpag.com
URL: http://www.bwni.com

3119 ■ *Work and Family Policies: Options for the 90's and Beyond*
Business and Professional Women/USA
1620 Eye St. NW, Ste. 210
Washington, DC 20006
Ph: (202)293-1100
Fax: (202)861-0298
E-mail: memberservices@bpwusa.org
URL: http://www.bpwusa.org

3120 ■ *World Directory of Marketing Information Sources*
Euromonitor International
Business Reference Div.
224 S Michigan Ave., Ste. 1500
Chicago, IL 60604
Ph: (312)922-1115
Fax: (312)922-1157
E-mail: insight@euromonitorintl.com
URL: http://www.euromonitor.com

URL(s): http://www.euromonitor.com **Covers:** Approximately 6,000 marketing information sources including trade and business associations, journals, Websites, government bodies, non-official sources, and publishers. **Entries include:** Company name, address, phone; and detailed reviews of information provider. **Freq:** Published March, 2003. **Price:** $650, individuals, U.S.D.

3121 ■ *World Federation News*
World Federation of Direct Selling Associations
1667 K St. NW, Ste. 1100
Washington, DC 20006
Ph: (202)452-8866
Fax: (202)452-9010
E-mail: info@wfdsa.org
URL: http://www.wfdsa.org
Freq: bimonthly. **Price:** included in membership dues.

3122 ■ *World Trade Connections*
Consumers for World Trade
1707 L St. NW, Ste. 570
Washington, DC 20036
Ph: (202)293-2944
Fax: (202)293-0495
URL: http://www.cwt.org
Freq: semimonthly.

3123 ■ *WV Banker*
West Virginia Bankers Association
120 Washington St. E
Charleston, WV 25301-1516
Ph: (304)343-8838
Fax: (304)343-9749
E-mail: datkinson@wvbankers.org
URL: http://www.wvbankers.org
Freq: quarterly. **Price:** $26.50/year.

Multimedia Resources

3124 ■ The ABC's of Personal Finance: An Essential Management
Zenger Media
10200 Jefferson Blvd
Box 802
Culver City, CA 90232
Ph: (310)839-2436
Free: 800-421-4246
Fax: (310)839-2249
E-mail: service@zengermedia.com
URL: http://zengermedia.com
Format(s): Videocassette. **Descr:** Identifies for young buyers the advantages of being an education consumer and financial enemies such as inflation and taxes. **Length:** 24. **Price:** $39.95.

3125 ■ Acorn Entrepeneurs
Tapeworm Video Distributors
27833 Hopkins Ave., Unit 6
Valencia, CA 91355
Ph: (661)257-4904
Fax: (661)257-4820
E-mail: sales@tapeworm.com
URL: http://www.tapeworm.com
Format(s): Videocassette. **Descr:** Features interviews with eight children ages nine to seventeen who have started their own businesses. Covers such subjects as money management, working long hours, overcoming obstacles, knowing their customers and balancing school, friends and business. **Prod. Date:** 1998. **Price:** $14.95.

3126 ■ Bankruptcy
Instructional Video
2219 C St
Lincoln, NE 68502
Ph: (402)475-6570
Free: 800-228-0164
Fax: (402)475-6500
E-mail: feedback@insvideo.com
URL: http://www.insvideo.com
Format(s): Videocassette. **Descr:** Attorney Eugene Grossman offers financial and legal information about the new personal bankruptcy laws. **Length:** 100. **Price:** $29.95.

3127 ■ Brand Marketing: Why We Eat, Drink, and Wear Brand Names
The Learning Seed
330 Telser Rd
Lake Zurich, IL 60047
Free: 800-634-4941
Fax: (847)540-0854
E-mail: info@learningseed.com
URL: http://www.learningseed.com
Format(s): Videocassette. **Descr:** An in-depth look into the power of brand marketing on youth culture and the consumer society. Discusses brand equity, brand and line extensions, co-branding, and celebrities as brands. **Length:** 19. **Price:** $89.00.

3128 ■ Buy Now, Pay Later: Credit Basics
Zenger Media
10200 Jefferson Blvd
Box 802
Culver City, CA 90232
Ph: (310)839-2436
Free: 800-421-4246
Fax: (310)839-2249
E-mail: service@zengermedia.com
URL: http://zengermedia.com
Format(s): Videocassette. **Descr:** Explains the credit application process, hidden costs of financing, interest rates, credit reporting and adjustment of errors, legal rights, types of credit, and how to establish credit. **Length:** 23. **Price:** $89.00.

3129 ■ Charge It: Credit Card Secrets
The Learning Seed
330 Telser Rd
Lake Zurich, IL 60047
Free: 800-634-4941
Fax: (847)540-0854
E-mail: info@learningseed.com
URL: http://www.learningseed.com
Format(s): Videocassette. **Descr:** Teaches how to select the best credit cards, avoid the traps of marketing gimmicks, and use a credit card responsibly. **Length:** 24. **Price:** $89.00.

3130 ■ Credit Card Basics: Play Now Pay Forever
Cambridge Educational
c/o Films Media Group
PO Box 2053
Princeton, NJ 08843-2053
Free: 800-257-5126
Fax: (609)671-0266
E-mail: custserve@filmsmediagroup.com
URL: http://www.cambridgeol.com
Format(s): Videocassette. **Descr:** Defines terms and explains procedures associated with credit. Emphasizes the need to keep accounts current in order to maintain a good credit rating. **Prod. Date:** 1992. **Length:** 15. **Price:** $79.

3131 ■ Credit Card Cautions
Social Studies School Service
10200 Jefferson Blvd
Box 802
Culver City, CA 90232
Free: 800-421-4246
Fax: 800-944-5432
E-mail: access@socialstudies.com
URL: http://www.socialstudies.com
Format(s): Videocassette. **Descr:** Practical advice on why to have or not have credit cards and how to be financially responsible. Intended for use with Grades 9-12. **Prod. Date:** 2000. **Length:** 29. **Price:** $89.00.

3132 ■ Dollar$ & Sense: Personal Finance for the 21st Century
Coast Telecourses
11460 Warner Ave
Fountain Valley, CA 92708-2597
Ph: (714)241-6109
Free: 800-547-4748
Fax: (714)241-6286
E-mail: coastlearning@cccd.edu
URL: http://www.coastlearning.org
Format(s): Videocassette. **Descr:** Telecourse of 26 half-hour programs discusses long-range impact of financial decisions, setting financial goals, investing, estate planning, and how to identify and avoid fraud. **Prod. Date:** 2000. **Length:** 780.

3133 ■ Financial Management During Crisis
Aquarius Productions
Olde Medfield Sq
18 N Main St
Sherborn, MA 01770
Ph: (508)650-1616
Free: 888-440-2963
Fax: (508)650-1665
E-mail: tm@aquariusproductions.com
URL: http://www.aquariusproductions.com
Format(s): Videocassette. **Descr:** Health care providers, utility and credit companies and families talk about how to deal with your insurance, creditors and make a workable budget when dealing with a seriously or chronically ill child. **Prod. Date:** 2000. **Length:** 24. **Price:** $140.00.

3134 ■ How to Achieve Financial Success
Tapeworm Video Distributors
27833 Hopkins Ave., Unit 6
Valencia, CA 91355
Ph: (661)257-4904
Fax: (661)257-4820
E-mail: sales@tapeworm.com
URL: http://www.tapeworm.com
Format(s): Videocassette. **Descr:** Financial guru Ric Edelman shows you his fundamental and contrarian approaches to money and finance, with segments on: the biggest factor to your investment success, why you should never own municipal bonds, why your home is not an investment and the concept of leveraging your way to greater wealth. **Price:** $19.95.

3135 ■ How to Avoid Investment Scams
American Institute of Small Business (AISB)
426 Second Street
Excelsior, MN 55331
Free: 800-328-2906
E-mail: AISBOFMN@AOL.COM
URL: http://www.aisb.biz
Format(s): Videocassette. **Descr:** Do's and don'ts for smart investing. **Prod. Date:** ????. **Length:** 45. **Price:** $69.95.

3136 ■ Just Sign Here
New Orleans Video Access Center
4040 Tulane Ave
New Orleans, LA 70119-6888
Ph: (504)339-4350
E-mail: info@novacvideo.org
URL: http://www.novacvideo.org/
Format(s): Videocassette. **Descr:** A program designed to warn the consumer about the dangers of co-signing loans. **Length:** 15.

3137 ■ Money and Values: What Is Wealth?
The Learning Seed
330 Telser Rd
Lake Zurich, IL 60047
Free: 800-634-4941
Fax: (847)540-0854
E-mail: info@learningseed.com
URL: http://www.learningseed.com
Format(s): Videocassette. **Descr:** Explores the nature of money, how it is confused with basic needs, relates to happiness, and the difference between being rich and being truly wealthy. **Length:** 22. **Price:** $89.

3138 ■ Never Say Yes to a Stranger
Phoenix Learning Group
2349 Chaffee Dr
St. Louis, MO 63146
Ph: (314)569-0211
Free: 800-221-1274
Fax: (314)569-2834
URL: http://www.phoenixlearninggroup.com
Format(s): Videocassette. **Descr:** For children and young people, this series of vignettes outlines the necessity for awareness and avoidance of strangers. Based on Susan Newman's best-selling book. **Prod. Date:** 1985. **Length:** 20.

3139 ■ Paper Bandits: Checks, Counterfeit, Credit Cards
Phoenix Learning Group
2349 Chaffee Dr
St. Louis, MO 63146
Ph: (314)569-0211
Free: 800-221-1274
Fax: (314)569-2834
URL: http://www.phoenixlearninggroup.com
Format(s): Videocassette. **Descr:** A series of vignettes illuminate the massive credit card/forged check thievery in this country. **Prod. Date:** 1984. **Length:** 13.

3140 ■ A Penny Saved: How to Grow Money
The Learning Seed
330 Telser Rd
Lake Zurich, IL 60047
Free: 800-634-4941
Fax: (847)540-0854
E-mail: info@learningseed.com
URL: http://www.learningseed.com
Format(s): Videocassette. **Descr:** Introduces the concepts of basic interest, investing, compounding, the time value of money, inflation, liquidity, and yield. **Length:** 21. **Price:** $89.

3141 ■ Planning Your Wedding, Vol. 6: Meeting with Your Financial Advisor
Leslie T. McClure
PO Box 1223
Pebble Beach, CA 93953

Ph: (831)656-0553
Fax: (831)656-0555
URL: http://www.411videoinfo.com
Format(s): Videocassette. **Descr:** Part of a ten-volume series for brides- and grooms-to-be that follows the steps taken by a typical couple, Jeff and Lisa, in their preparation for the big event. **Prod. Date:** 1998. **Length:** 43. **Price:** $29.95.

3142 ■ *Repairing Your Credit*
International Video Projects, Inc.
6700 S. Florida Ave., Ste. 28
Lakeland, FL 33813
Ph: (863)647-2234
Free: 800-852-0662
Fax: (863)647-5406
E-mail: ivplknd@aol.com
URL: http://www.videoprojects.tv
Format(s): Videocassette. **Descr:** Offers information on how to improve credit ratings through the elimination of misinformation. **Length:** 40. **Price:** $16.95.

3143 ■ *Secrets of Successful Home-Based Businesses*
Dreamaster Productions
9320 Vista West Dr
West Jordan, UT 84088-8843
E-mail: charmaine@dreamastersvideo.com
Format(s): Videocassette. **Descr:** Discusses fundamentals of home business success, choosing a business concept, cost-effective marketing strategies, avoiding pitfalls and problems of working from home, and much more. **Prod. Date:** 2000. **Length:** 85. **Price:** $39.95.

3144 ■ *The Stanford Video Guide to Financial Statements*
Kantola Productions, LLC
55 Sunnyside Ave
Mill Valley, CA 94941-1935
Ph: (415)381-9363
Free: 800-989-8273
Fax: (415)381-9801
E-mail: info@kantola.com
URL: http://kantola.com
Format(s): Videocassette. **Descr:** Professor George Parker provides line-by-line explanations of the three key financial statements used by U.S. companies and approaches to interpreting what they reveal about value, profitability and ability to pay bills. Includes study guide. **Prod. Date:** 2000. **Length:** 51. **Price:** $189.00.

3145 ■ *That's Marketing: Understanding Consumer Behavior*
The Learning Seed
330 Telser Rd
Lake Zurich, IL 60047
Free: 800-634-4941
Fax: (847)540-0854
E-mail: info@learningseed.com
URL: http://www.learningseed.com
Format(s): Videocassette. **Descr:** Explains segmentation, market research, branding, packaging, variable pricing, and positioning for marketing and consumer education students. **Prod. Date:** ????. **Length:** 23. **Price:** $89.00.

3146 ■ *User Friendly Budgeting*
The Learning Seed
330 Telser Rd
Lake Zurich, IL 60047
Free: 800-634-4941
Fax: (847)540-0854
E-mail: info@learningseed.com
URL: http://www.learningseed.com
Format(s): Videocassette. **Descr:** Discusses developing a personal budget, setting financial goals, and conduct a self-audit to analyze spending habits. **Length:** 13. **Price:** $89.

3147 ■ *Why You Should Carry a Big, Long Mortgage*
Tapeworm Video Distributors
27833 Hopkins Ave., Unit 6
Valencia, CA 91355

Ph: (661)257-4904
Fax: (661)257-4820
E-mail: sales@tapeworm.com
URL: http://www.tapeworm.com
Format(s): Videocassette. **Descr:** Host Ric Edelman tells you why it is smarter to get the biggest and longest mortgage for your house and to never pay it off. He also reveals why you should never get a 15-year mortgage, the type of mortgage insurance you should never buy, and how to choose between a fixed-rate and adjustable-rate loan. **Prod. Date:** 199?. **Length:** ?. **Price:** $19.95.

3148 ■ *Your Financial Future with Jonathon Pond*
American Institute of Small Business (AISB)
426 Second Street
Excelsior, MN 55331
Free: 800-328-2906
E-mail: AISBOFMN@AOL.COM
URL: http://www.aisb.biz
Format(s): Videocassette. **Descr:** Explains how to prepare and invest for financial security. Covers stocks, bonds, mutual funds, real estate, and short-term investments. **Prod. Date:** ????. **Length:** 50. **Price:** $69.95.

Media Contacts

3149 ■ Bloomberg News
Bloomberg L.P.
731 Lexington Ave.
New York, NY 10022
Contact: Brad Keoun, Finance Reporter
Ph: (212)617-2310
E-mail: bkeoun@bloomberg.net
URL: http://www.bloomberg.com

3150 ■ Bloomberg News
Boston Bureau
Bloomberg L.P.
100 Summer St., Ste. 2810
Boston, MA 02110
Contact: Matthew Keenan, Investing Reporter
Ph: (617)210-4600
Fax: (617)482-0703
E-mail: mkeenan6@bloomberg.net
URL: http://www.bloomberg.com

3151 ■ Bloomberg News
Washington Bureau
Bloomberg L.P.
1399 New York Ave., 11th Fl.
Washington, DC 20005
Contact: Gregory Mott, Finance Editor
Ph: (202)624-4317
Fax: (202)624-1300
E-mail: gmott1@bloomberg.net
URL: http://www.bloomberg.com

3152 ■ Bloomberg News
Washington Bureau
Bloomberg L.P.
1399 New York Ave., 11th Fl.
Washington, DC 20005
Contact: Jesse Westbrook, Finance Reporter
Ph: (202)624-1889
Fax: (202)624-1800
URL: http://www.bloomberg.com

3153 ■ Bloomberg News
Washington Bureau
Bloomberg L.P.
1399 New York Ave., 11th Fl.
Washington, DC 20005
Contact: Margaret Chadbourn, Finance Reporter
Ph: (202)654-4316
Fax: (202)624-1800
E-mail: mchadbourn@bloomberg.net
URL: http://www.bloomberg.com

3154 ■ Bloomberg News
Washington Bureau
Bloomberg L.P.
1399 New York Ave., 11th Fl.
Washington, DC 20005

Contact: Joshua Gallu, Finance Reporter
Ph: (202)624-1810
Fax: (202)624-1800
E-mail: jgallu@bloomberg.net
URL: http://www.bloomberg.com

3155 ■ Bloomberg News
Washington Bureau
Bloomberg L.P.
1399 New York Ave., 11th Fl.
Washington, DC 20005
Contact: Jeff Plungis, Finance Editor
Ph: (202)624-1835
Fax: (202)624-1800
E-mail: jplungis@bloomberg.net
URL: http://www.bloomberg.com

3156 ■ Bloomberg News
Washington Bureau
Bloomberg L.P.
1399 New York Ave., 11th Fl.
Washington, DC 20005
Contact: Steven Geimann, Finance Editor
Ph: (202)624-1960
Fax: (202)624-1800
E-mail: sgeimann@bloomberg.net
URL: http://www.bloomberg.com

3157 ■ Bloomberg News
Washington Bureau
Bloomberg L.P.
1399 New York Ave., 11th Fl.
Washington, DC 20005
Contact: Charles Babcock, Enterprise Editor
Ph: (202)654-1268
Fax: (202)624-1800
E-mail: cbabcock@bloomberg.net
URL: http://www.bloomberg.com

3158 ■ *Forbes on Fox*
Fox News Channel
1211 Ave. of the Americas
New York, NY 10036
Contact: John Huber, Senior Producer
Ph: (212)301-3027
E-mail: john.huber@foxnews.com
URL: http://www.foxnews.com

3159 ■ *Investor's Business Daily*
19 W. 44th St., Ste. 804
New York, NY 10036
Contact: Marilyn Much, Consumer Products Reporter
Ph: (212)626-7692
E-mail: marilyn.much@investors.com
URL: http://www.investors.com

3160 ■ *Investor's Business Daily*
12655 Beatrice St.
Los Angeles, CA 90066
Contact: Joanne von Alroth, Mutual Funds Writer
Ph: (408)720-2112
E-mail: joanne.vonalroth@investors.com
URL: http://www.investors.com

3161 ■ MarketWatch.com
Dow Jones & Company, Inc.
201 California St., 13th Fl.
San Francisco, CA 94111
Contact: Chuck Jaffe, Personal Finance Columnist
Ph: (415)733-0500
E-mail: cjaffe@marketwatch.com
URL: http://www.marketwatch.com

3162 ■ MarketWatch.com
Dow Jones & Company, Inc.
201 California St., 13th Fl.
San Francisco, CA 94111
Contact: Marshall Loeb, Personal Finance Columnist
Ph: (781)383-6712
E-mail: mloeb@marketwatch.com
URL: http://www.marketwatch.com

3163 ■ MarketWatch.com
Dow Jones & Company, Inc.
201 California St., 13th Fl.
San Francisco, CA 94111
Contact: Jennifer Openshaw, Financial Advice Columnist

Ph: (415)439-6400
URL: http://www.marketwatch.com

3164 ■ MarketWatch.com
Dow Jones & Company, Inc.
Chicago Bureau
One S. Wacker Dr., Ste. 2250
Chicago, IL 60606
Contact: Jennifer Waters, Personal Finance/
Consumer Reporter
Ph: (312)750-4212
E-mail: jwaters@marketwatch.com
URL: http://www.marketwatch.com

3165 ■ MarketWatch.com
Dow Jones & Company, Inc.
201 California St., 13th Fl.
San Francisco, CA 94111
Contact: Paul Farrell, Mutual Funds Columnist
Ph: (415)439-6400
E-mail: paulbfarel@charter.net
URL: http://www.marketwatch.com

3166 ■ MarketWatch.com
Dow Jones & Company, Inc.
201 California St., 13th Fl.
San Francisco, CA 94111
Contact: Greg Morcroft, Financial News Editor
Ph: (212)416-2000
E-mail: gmorcroft@marketwatch.com
URL: http://www.marketwatch.com

3167 ■ MarketWatch.com
New York Bureau
Dow Jones & Company, Inc.
524 W. 57th St., Ste. 6331
New York, NY 10019
Contact: David Weidner, Financial Reporter
Ph: (212)416-2000
E-mail: dweidner@marketwatch.com
URL: http://www.marketwatch.com

3168 ■ MarketWatch.com
San Francisco Bureau
Dow Jones & Company, Inc.
825 Battery St.
San Francisco, CA 94111
Contact: Kristen Gerencher, Persoanl Finance
Reporter
Ph: (415)439-6400
E-mail: kgerencher@marketwatch.com
URL: http://www.marketwatch.com

3169 ■ Thomson Reuters
Reuters Bldg.
3 Times Sq.
New York, NY 10036
Contact: Vivianne Rodrigues, Stock Market Reporter
Ph: (646)223-6000
E-mail: vivianne.rodrigues@thomsonreuters.com
URL: http://www.thomsonreuters.com

3170 ■ Thomson Reuters
Reuters Bldg.
3 Times Sq.
New York, NY 10036
Contact: Jennifer Coogan, Stock Market Reporter
Ph: (646)223-6000
E-mail: jennifer.coogan@thomsonreuters.com
URL: http://www.thomsonreuters.com

3171 ■ Thomson Reuters
Reuters Bldg.
3 Times Sq.
New York, NY 10036
Contact: Cal Mankowski, Mutual Funds Reporter
Ph: (646)223-6132
E-mail: cal.mankowski@thomsonreuters.com
URL: http://www.thomsonreuters.com

3172 ■ Thomson Reuters
Reuters Bldg.
3 Times Sq.
New York, NY 10036
Contact: Ellis Mnyandu, Wall Street Reporter
Ph: (646)223-6085

E-mail: ellis.mnyandu@thomsonreuters.com
URL: http://www.thomsonreuters.com

3173 ■ Thomson Reuters
Reuters Bldg.
3 Times Sq.
New York, NY 10036
Contact: Caroline Valetkevitch, Stock Market Reporter
Ph: (646)223-6393
E-mail: caroline.valetkevitch@thomsonreuters.com
URL: http://www.thomsonreuters.com

3174 ■ *USA Today*
Gannett Co., Inc.
10960 Wilshire Blvd., Ste. 1000
Los Angeles, CA 90024
Contact: Matthew Krantz, Internet Stocks Reporter
Ph: (310)882-2402
E-mail: mkrantz@usatoday.com
URL: http://www.usatoday.com

3175 ■ *USA Today*
Gannett Co., Inc.
Magnavision Bldg.
535 Madison Ave.
New York, NY 10022
Contact: Kathy Chu, Wall Street Reporter
Ph: (212)715-2074
E-mail: kchu@usatoday.com
URL: http://www.usatoday.com

3176 ■ *The Wall Street Journal*
Dow Jones & Company
1211 Ave. of the Americas
New York, NY 10036
Contact: Elizabeth Seay, Home and Family Editor
Ph: (212)416-4960
E-mail: elizabeth.seay@wsj.com
URL: http://www.wsj.com

Alabama

3177 ■ *Birmingham News*
Newhouse Newspapers
2201 Fourth Ave. N.
Birmingham, AL 35203
Contact: Jerry Underwood, Business Editor
Ph: (205)325-3250
E-mail: junderwood@bhamnews.com
URL: http://www.bhamnews.com

3178 ■ *Birmingham News*
Newhouse Newspapers
2201 Fourth Ave. N.
Birmingham, AL 35203
Contact: Roy L. Williams, Small Bus./Consumer Issues Reporter
Ph: (205)325-2471
E-mail: rwilliams@bhamnews.com
URL: http://www.bhamnews.com

3179 ■ *The Huntsville Times*
Newhouse Newspapers
2317 S. Memorial Pkwy.
Huntsville, AL 35801
Contact: Steve Byers, Business Editor
Ph: (256)532-4167
E-mail: steve.byers@htimes.com
URL: http://www.htimes.com

3180 ■ *Press-Register*
Advance Publications, Inc.
PO Box 2488
Mobile, AL 36652-2488
Contact: K.A. Turner, Business Editor
Ph: (251)219-5644
Fax: (251)219-5799
E-mail: kturner@press-register.com
URL: http://www.press-register.com

Alaska

3181 ■ *Anchorage Daily News*
The McClathy Company
PO Box 149001

Anchorage, AK 99514-9001
Contact: Bill White, Business Editor
Ph: (907)257-4311
E-mail: bwhite@adn.com
URL: http://www.adn.com

Arizona

3182 ■ *Arizona Daily Star*
Lee Enterprises, Inc.
PO Box 26807
Tucson, AZ 85726-6807
Contact: Dale Quinn, Business Reporter
Ph: (520)629-9412
E-mail: dquinn@azstarnet.com
URL: http://www.azstarnet.com

3183 ■ *Arizona Daily Star*
Lee Enterprises, Inc.
PO Box 26807
Tucson, AZ 85726-6807
Contact: Daniel Sorenson, Business Reporter
Ph: (520)573-4185
E-mail: dsorenson@azstarnet.com
URL: http://www.azstarnet.com

3184 ■ *Arizona Daily Star*
Lee Enterprises, Inc.
PO Box 26807
Tucson, AZ 85726-6807
Contact: Norma Coile, Business Editor
Ph: (520)573-4400
URL: http://www.azstarnet.com

3185 ■ *Arizona Daily Star*
Lee Enterprises Inc.
PO Box 26807
Tucson, AZ 85714-6807
Contact: Joshua Brodesky, Real Estate Reporter
Ph: (520)573-4178
E-mail: jbrodesky@azstarnet.com
URL: http://www.azstarnet.com

3186 ■ *Arizona Republic*
Gannett Co., Inc.
PO Box 1950
Phoenix, AZ 85001
Contact: Ed Perkins, Business Online Manager
Ph: (602)444-8262
Free: 800-331-9303
Fax: (602)444-8274
URL: http://www.arizonarepublic.com

3187 ■ *Arizona Republic*
Gannett Co., Inc.
PO Box 1950
Phoenix, AZ 85001
Contact: Russ Wiles, Personal Finance Reporter
Ph: (602)444-8616
Free: 800-331-9303
Fax: (602)444-8274
E-mail: russ.wiles@arizonarepublic.com
URL: http://www.arizonarepublic.com

3188 ■ *Arizona Republic*
Gannett Co., Inc.
PO Box 1950
Phoenix, AZ 85001
Contact: Chad W. Graham, Business Reporter
E-mail: chad.graham@arizonarepublic.com
Ph: (602)444-8577
Free: 800-331-9303
Fax: (602)444-8274
URL: http://www.arizonarepublic.com

Arkansas

3189 ■ *Arkansas Democrat-Gazette*
PO Box 2221
Little Rock, AR 72203-2221
Contact: David Smith, Banking and Investments
Reporter
Ph: (501)378-3567

E-mail: dsmith@arkansasonline.com
URL: http://www.ardemgaz.com

3190 ■ *Arkansas Democrat-Gazette*
PO Box 2221
Little Rock, AR 72203-2221
Contact: Jack Weatherly, Business Editor
Ph: (501)378-3518
E-mail: jweatherly@arkansasonline.com
URL: http://www.ardemgaz.com

California

3191 ■ *Contra Costa Times*
Knight Ridder, Inc.
2640 Shadelands Dr.
Walnet Creek, CA 94595
Contact: Eva Mitchell, Personal Finance Reporter
E-mail: emitchell@cctimes.com
URL: http://www.contracostatimes.com

3192 ■ *Contra Costa Times*
Knight Ridder, Inc.
2640 Shadelands Dr.
Walnut Creek, CA 94598-2578
Contact: Drew Voros, Business Editor
Ph: (925)943-8099
E-mail: dvoros@cctimes.com
URL: http://www.contracostatimes.com

3193 ■ *The Fresno Bee*
The McClatchy Company
1626 E St.
Fresno, CA 93786-0001
Contact: Tim Sheehan, Economics Reporter
Ph: (559)441-6329
E-mail: tsheehan@fresnobee.com
URL: http://www.fresnobee.com

3194 ■ *The Fresno Bee*
The McClatchy Company
1626 E St.
Fresno, CA 93786-0001
Contact: Robert Rodriguez, Small Business Reporter
Ph: (559)441-6327
E-mail: brodriguez@fresnobee.com
URL: http://www.fresnobee.com

3195 ■ *The Fresno Bee*
The McClatchy Company
1626 E St.
Fresno, CA 93786-0001
Contact: Mike Nemeth, Business Editor
Ph: (559)441-6239
E-mail: mnemeth@fresnobee.com
URL: http://www.fresnobee.com

3196 ■ *Los Angeles Times*
Tribune Company
202 W. First St.
Los Angeles, CA 90012
Contact: Scott Reckard, Banking Reporter
Ph: (213)237-7163
E-mail: scott.reckard@latimes.com
URL: http://www.latimes.com

3197 ■ *Los Angeles Times*
Tribune Company
202 W. First St.
Los Angeles, CA 90012
Contact: Kathy M. Kristol, Personal Finance Columnist
Ph: (213)237-7795
URL: http://www.latimes.com

3198 ■ *Los Angeles Times*
Tribune Company
202 W. First St.
Los Angeles, CA 90012
Contact: John Corrigan, Business Editor
Ph: (213)237-7006
E-mail: john.corrigan@latimes.com
URL: http://www.latimes.com

3199 ■ *Orange County Register*
625 N. Grand Ave.
Santa Ana, CA 92701-4347

Contact: Julie Gallego, Money Team Leader
Ph: (714)796-7925
E-mail: jgallego@ocregister.com
URL: http://www.ocregister.com

3200 ■ *Orange County Register*
625 N. Grand Ave.
Santa Ana, CA 92701-4347
Contact: Andrew Galvin, Small Business Columnist
Ph: (714)796-7927
E-mail: agalvin@ocregister.com
URL: http://www.ocregister.com

3201 ■ *The Press-Enterprise*
3450 Fourteenth St.
Riverside, CA 92501
Contact: Mark Coast, Business Editor
Ph: (951)368-9556
E-mail: mcoast@pe.com
URL: http://www.pe.com

3202 ■ *The Press-Enterprise*
3450 Fourteenth St.
Riverside, CA 92501
Contact: Leslie Berkman, Business Reporter
Ph: (951)368-9423
E-mail: lberkman@pe.com
URL: http://www.pe.com

3203 ■ *San Diego Union-Tribune*
Copley Press, Inc.
PO Box 120191
San Diego, CA 92112-0191
Contact: Dean Calbreath, Economy/Stock Market Reporter
Ph: (619)293-1891
E-mail: dean.calbreath@uniontrib.com
URL: http://www.uniontrib.com

3204 ■ *San Diego Union-Tribune*
Copley Press, Inc.
PO Box 120191
San Diego, CA 92112-0191
Contact: Jim Watters, Business Editor
Ph: (619)293-2156
E-mail: jim.watters@uniontrib.com
URL: http://www.uniontrib.com

3205 ■ *San Diego Union-Tribune*
Copley Press, Inc.
PO Box 120191
San Diego, CA 92112-0191
Contact: Michael Freeman, Real Estate/Banking Editor
Ph: (760)476-8209
E-mail: mike.freeman@uniontrib.com
URL: http://www.uniontrib.com

3206 ■ *San Francisco Chronicle*
Hearst Newspapers
901 Mission St.
San Francisco, CA 94103-2988
Contact: Tom Abate, Innovation Business Reporter
Ph: (415)777-6213
E-mail: tabate@sfchronicle.com
URL: http://www.sfchronicle.com

3207 ■ *San Francisco Chronicle*
Hearst Newspapers
901 Mission St.
San Francisco, CA 94103-2988
Contact: Carolyn Said, Economics Reporter
Ph: (415)536-5112
E-mail: csaid@sfchronicle.com
URL: http://www.sfchronicle.com

3208 ■ *San Francisco Chronicle*
Hearst Newspapers
901 Mission St.
San Francisco, CA 94103-2988
Contact: John Batteiger, Small Business Reporter
Ph: (415)516-3031
E-mail: jbatteiger@sfchronicle.com
URL: http://www.sfchronicle.com

3209 ■ *San Francisco Chronicle*
Hearst Newspapers
901 Mission St.

San Francisco, CA 94103-2988
Contact: Suzanne Herel, Business Editor
Ph: (415)777-7947
E-mail: sherel@sfchronicle.com
URL: http://www.sfchronicle.com

Colorado

3210 ■ *Denver Post*
101 W. Colfax Ave.
Denver, CO 80202
Contact: Elizabeth Aquilera, Business Reporter
Ph: (303)954-1372
E-mail: eaquilera@denverpost.com
URL: http://www.denverpost.com

3211 ■ *Denver Post*
101 W. Colfax Ave.
Denver, CO 80202
Contact: David Migoya, Business Reporter
Ph: (303)954-1506
E-mail: dmigoya@denverpost.com
URL: http://www.denverpost.com

3212 ■ *Denver Post*
101 W. Colfax Ave.
Denver, CO 80202
Contact: Aldo Svaldi, Financial/Banking Reporter
Ph: (303)954-1410
E-mail: asvaldi@denverpost.com
URL: http://www.denverpost.com

3213 ■ *Denver Post*
101 W. Colfax Ave.
Denver, CO 80202
Contact: Steve McMillan, Business Reporter
Ph: (303)954-1695
E-mail: smcmillan@denverpost.com
URL: http://www.denverpost.com

Connecticut

3214 ■ *Greenwich Time*
20 E. Elm St.
Greenwich, CT 06830
Contact: Jim Zebora, Business Editor
Ph: (203)964-2420
E-mail: jim.zebora@scni.com
URL: http://www.greenwichtime.com

3215 ■ *Hartford Courant*
Tribune Company
285 Broad St.
Hartford, CT 06115
Contact: Kenneth R. Gosselin, Banking Reporter
Ph: (860)241-6765
E-mail: kgosselin@courant.com
URL: http://www.courant.com

3216 ■ *Hartford Courant*
Tribune Company
285 Broad St.
Hartford, CT 06115
Contact: Dan Haar, Business Editor
Ph: (860)241-6536
E-mail: dhaar@courant.com
URL: http://www.courant.com

District of Columbia

3217 ■ *BusinessWeek*
The McGraw-Hill Companies, Inc.
1200 G St. NW, Ste. 1100
Washington, DC 20005-3802
Contact: Theo Francis, Finance Correspondent
Ph: (202)383-2204
E-mail: theo.francis@businessweek.com
URL: http://www.businessweek.com

3218 ■ *The Washington Post*
1150 15th St., NW
Washington, DC 20071-0070
Contact: Greg Schneider, Business Editor
Ph: (202)334-4445

E-mail: schneiderg@washpost.com
URL: http://www.washingtonpost.com

3219 ■ *The Washington Post*
1150 15th St., NW
Washington, DC 20071-0070
Contact: Michelle Singletary, Color of Money Columnist
Ph: (202)334-4185
E-mail: singletarym@washpost.com
URL: http://www.washingtonpost.com

3220 ■ *The Washington Post*
1150 15th St., NW
Washington, DC 20071-0070
Contact: Lori Montgomery, Budgets/Fiscal Policy Reporter
Ph: (202)334-6822
E-mail: montgomeryl@washpost.com
URL: http://www.washingtonpost.com

3221 ■ *The Washington Post*
1150 15th St., NW
Washington, DC 20071-0070
Contact: Del Wilber, Air Security/Safety Reporter
Ph: (202)334-7320
E-mail: ahrensf@washpost.com
URL: http://www.washingtonpost.com

3222 ■ *The Washington Post*
1150 15th St., NW
Washington, DC 20071-0070
Contact: Frank Ahrens, Economics Reporter
Ph: (202)334-5158
E-mail: alexanderk@washpost.com
URL: http://www.washingtonpost.com

3223 ■ *The Washington Post*
1150 15th St., NW
Washington, DC 20071-0070
Contact: Nancy Trejos, Personal Finance Reporter
Ph: (202)334-6731
E-mail: trejosn@washpost.com
URL: http://www.washpost.com

3224 ■ *The Washington Times*
3600 New York Ave. NE
Washington, DC 20002
Contact: Patrice Hill, Tax and Budget Reporter
Ph: (202)636-3192
E-mail: phill@washingtontimes.com
URL: http://www.washingtontimes.com

3225 ■ *The Washington Times*
3600 New York Ave. NE
Washington, DC 20002
Contact: David Dickson, Business Reporter
Ph: (202)636-4869
E-mail: ddickson@washingtontimes.com
URL: http://www.washingtontimes.com

Florida

3226 ■ *The Florida Times-Union*
PO Box 1949
Jacksonville, FL 32231
Contact: Paul Mattson, Business Editor
Ph: (904)359-4521
E-mail: paul.mattson@jacksonville.com
URL: http://www.jacksonville.com

3227 ■ *The Florida Times-Union*
PO Box 1949
Jacksonville, FL 32231
Contact: David Bauerlein, Retail Reporter
Ph: (904)359-4308
Free: 800-553-0541
E-mail: david.bauerlein@jacksonville.com
URL: http://www.jacksonville.com

3228 ■ *The Florida Times-Union*
PO Box 1949
Jacksonville, FL 32231
Contact: Mark Basch, Investments/Labor Editor
Ph: (904)359-4308
Free: 800-553-0541

E-mail: mark.basch@jacksonville.com
URL: http://www.jacksonville.com

3229 ■ *The Miami Herald*
The McClatchy Company
One Herald Plaza
Miami, FL 33132-1693
Contact: Gregg Fields, "Money Talks" Columnist
Ph: (305)376-2001
E-mail: gfields@miamiherald.com
URL: http://www.herald.com

3230 ■ *Orlando Sentinel*
Tribune Company
633 N. Orange Ave.
Orlando, FL 32801-1349
Contact: Ned Popkins, Business Editor
Ph: (407)420-5051
E-mail: npopkins@orlandosentinel.com
URL: http://www.orlandosentinel.com

3231 ■ *Orlando Sentinel*
Tribune Company
633 N. Orange Ave.
Orlando, FL 32801-1349
Contact: Richard Burnett, Consumer Finance Reporter
Ph: (407)420-5256
E-mail: rburnett@orlandosentinel.com
URL: http://www.orlandosentinel.com

3232 ■ *Orlando Sentinel*
Tribune Company
633 N. Orange Ave.
Orlando, FL 32801-1349
Contact: Beth Kassab, Business Columnist
Ph: (407)420-5448
E-mail: bkassab@orlandosentinel.com
URL: http://www.orlandosentinel.com

3233 ■ *The Palm Beach Post*
Palm Beach Newspapers, Inc.
2751 S. Dixie Hwy.
West Palm Beach, FL 33405
Contact: Lori Becker, Small Business/Workplace Issues Reporter
Ph: (561)820-4410
E-mail: lori_becker@pbpost.com
URL: http://www.pbpost.com

3234 ■ *The Palm Beach Post*
Palm Beach Newspapers, Inc.
2751 S. Dixie Hwy.
West Palm Beach, FL 33405
Contact: Pat Beall, Assistant Business Editor
Ph: (561)820-4497
E-mail: pat_beall@pbpost.com
URL: http://www.pbpost.com

3235 ■ *The Palm Beach Post*
Palm Beach Newspapers, Inc.
PO Box 24700
West Palm Beach, FL 33416
Contact: Randolph Diamond, Financial Fraud Reporter
Ph: (561)820-4578
E-mail: randy.diamond@pbpost.com
URL: http://www.pbpost.com

3236 ■ *Sun Sentinel*
Tribune Company
200 E. Las Olas Blvd.
Fort Lauderdale, FL 33301-2293
Contact: Marcia Heroux Pounds, Small Business Reporter
Ph: (561)243-6650
E-mail: marciabiz@aol.com
URL: http://www.sun-sentinel.com

3237 ■ *Sun Sentinel*
Tribune Company
200 E. Las Olas Blvd.
Fort Lauderdale, FL 33301-2293
Contact: Harriet Brackey, Banking Reporter
Ph: (954)356-4660

E-mail: hjubrackey@sun-sentinel.com
URL: http://www.sun-sentinel.com

3238 ■ *Tampa Tribune*
Media General, Inc.
200 S. Parker St.
Tampa, FL 33606-2395
Contact: Michael Sasso, Economy Reporter
Ph: (813)259-7865
E-mail: msasso@tampatrib.com
URL: http://www.tampatrib.com

Georgia

3239 ■ *Atlanta Journal-Constitution*
Cox Newspapers, Inc.
72 Marietta St., NW
Atlanta, GA 30303
Contact: Peralte Paul, Bankruptcy Reporter
Ph: (404)526-5661
E-mail: pcpaul@ajc.com
URL: http://www.ajc.com

3240 ■ *Atlanta Journal-Constitution*
Cox Newspapers, Inc.
72 Marietta St., NW
Atlanta, GA 30303
Contact: Paul Donsky, Finance Reporter
Ph: (404)526-5151
E-mail: pdonsky@ajc.com
URL: http://www.ajc.com

Hawaii

3241 ■ *Honolulu Advertiser*
Gannett Co., Inc.
605 Kapiolani Blvd.
Honolulu, HI 96813
Contact: Andrew Gomes, Retail Reporter
Ph: (808)525-8065
E-mail: agomes@honoluluadvertiser.com
URL: http://www.honoluluadvertiser.com

Illinois

3242 ■ *The Chicago Sun-Times*
Hollinger International, Inc.
350 N. Orleans
Chicago, IL 60654
Contact: Terry Savage, Personal Finance Columnist
Ph: (312)266-1717
E-mail: savage@suntimes.com
URL: http://www.suntimes.com

3243 ■ *Chicago Tribune*
Tribune Company
435 N. Michigan Ave.
Chicago, IL 60611-4041
Contact: Francine Knowles, Labor/Personal Finance Reporter
Ph: (312)321-2854
E-mail: fknowles@tribune.com
URL: http://www.chicagotribune.com

3244 ■ *Chicago Tribune*
Tribune Company
435 N. Michigan Ave.
Chicago, IL 60611-4041
Contact: Mike Hughlett, Venture Funding Reporter
Ph: (312)222-3595
E-mail: mhughlett@tribune.com
URL: http://www.chicagotribune.com

3245 ■ *Chicago Tribune*
Tribune Company
435 N. Michigan Ave.
Chicago, IL 60611-4041
Contact: Andy Countryman, "Your Money" Editor
Ph: (312)222-5015
E-mail: acountryman@tribune.com
URL: http://www.chicagotribune.com

3246 ■ *Chicago Tribune*
Tribune Company
435 N. Michigan Ave.

Chicago, IL 60611-4041
Contact: Gail MarksJarvis, Personal Finance Columnist
Ph: (312)222-3352
E-mail: gmarksjarvis@tribune.com
URL: http://www.chicagotribune.com

3247 ■ The State Journal-Register
PO Box 219
Springfield, IL 62705-0219
Contact: Tim Landis, Business Editor
Ph: (217)788-1536
E-mail: tim.landis@sj-r.com
URL: http://www.sj-r.com

Iowa

3248 ■ Des Moines Register
Gannett Co., Inc.
PO Box 957
Des Moines, IA 50304
Contact: Lynn Hicks, Business Editor
Ph: (515)284-8290
E-mail: lhicks@dmreg.com
URL: http://www.DesMoinesRegister.com

3249 ■ Des Moines Register
Gannett Co., Inc.
PO Box 957
Des Moines, IA 50304
Contact: Jeff Eckhoff, Retailing Reporter
Ph: (515)284-8271
URL: http://www.DesMoinesRegister.com

Kansas

3250 ■ The Wichita Eagle
The McClatchy Company
PO Box 820
Wichita, KS 67201-0820
Contact: Dan Voorhis, Economy Reporter
Ph: (316)268-6577
E-mail: dvoorhis@wichitaeagle.com
URL: http://www.wichitaeagle.com

Kentucky

3251 ■ The Courier-Journal
Garrett Co., Inc.
PO Box 740031
Louisville, KY 40201-7431
Contact: Dan Blake, Business Editor
Ph: (502)582-4627
E-mail: dblake@courier-journal.com
URL: http://www.courier-journal.com

3252 ■ Lexington Herald-Leader
100 Midland Ave.
Lexington, KY 40508-1999
Contact: Scott Sloan, Business Reporter
Ph: (859)231-1447
E-mail: ssloan@herald-leader.com
URL: http://www.kentucky.com

Louisiana

3253 ■ New Orleans Times-Picayune
Newhouse Newspapers
3800 Howard Ave.
New Orleans, LA 70125
Contact: Kimberly Quillen, Money Editor
Ph: (504)826-3416
E-mail: kquillen@timespicayune.com
URL: http://www.nola.com

3254 ■ New Orleans Times-Picayune
Newhouse Newspapers
3800 Howard Ave.
New Orleans, LA 70125
Contact: Ronette King, Small Business/Retail Writer
Ph: (504)826-3308
E-mail: rking@timespicayune.com
URL: http://www.nola.com

Maryland

3255 ■ The Baltimore Sun
Tribune Company
501 N. Calvert St.
Baltimore, MD 21278
Contact: Andrea Walker, Morning Bell Reporter
Ph: (410)332-6879
E-mail: andrea.walker@baltsun.com
URL: http://www.baltimoresun.com

3256 ■ The Baltimore Sun
Tribune Company
501 N. Calvert St.
Baltimore, MD 21278
Contact: Jay Hancock, Business Columnist
Ph: (410)332-6000
E-mail: jay.hancock@baltsun.com
URL: http://www.baltimoresun.com

3257 ■ The Baltimore Sun
Tribune Company
501 N. Calvert St.
Baltimore, MD 21278
Contact: Eileen Ambrose, Personal Finance Columnist
Ph: (410)332-6984
E-mail: eileen.ambrose@baltsun.com
URL: http://www.sunspot.net

3258 ■ The Baltimore Sun
Tribune Company
501 N. Calvert St.
Baltimore, MD 21278
Contact: Jamie Smith Hopkins, Regional Economy Reporter
Ph: (410)332-6400
E-mail: jamie.smith.hopkins@baltsun.com
URL: http://www.sunspot.net

3259 ■ The Capital
Capital Gazette Newspapers
PO Box 911
Annapolis, MD 21404
Contact: Katie Arcieri, Business Reporter
Ph: (410)280-5930
E-mail: karcieri@capitalgazette.com
URL: http://HometownAnnapolis.com

Massachusetts

3260 ■ Boston Globe
The New York Times Company
135 Morrissey Blvd.
Boston, MA 02125
Contact: Scott Kirsner, Innovation Economy Columnist
Ph: (617)929-2916
E-mail: business@globe.com
URL: http://www.boston.com

3261 ■ Boston Globe
The New York Times Company
135 Morrissey Blvd.
Boston, MA 02125
Contact: Robert Gavin, Economy Reporter
Ph: (617)929-3129
E-mail: rgavin@globe.com
URL: http://www.boston.com

3262 ■ New England Cable News (NECN)
160 Wells Ave.
Newton, MA 02459-3302
Contact: Jonah Davis, "New England Business Day" Producer
Ph: (617)630-5000
Fax: (617)630-5050
URL: http://www.necm.com

Michigan

3263 ■ Detroit News
MediaNews Group
615 W. Lafayette Blvd.
Detroit, MI 48226
Contact: Brian O'Connor, Personal Finance Editor

Ph: (313)222-2145
E-mail: boconnor@detnews.com
URL: http://www.detnews.com

3264 ■ Detroit News
MediaNews Group
615 W. Lafayette Blvd.
Detroit, MI 48226
Contact: Daniel Howes, Business Columnist
Ph: (313)222-2106
E-mail: dchowes@detnews.com
URL: http://www.detnews.com

3265 ■ The Grand Rapids Press
155 Michigan St. NW
Grand Rapids, MI 49503
Contact: Nancy Crawley, Business Editor
Ph: (616)222-5452
E-mail: ncrawley@grpress.com
URL: http://www.mlive.com/grpress/

Minnesota

3266 ■ St. Paul Pioneer Press
MediaNews Group, Inc.
345 Cedar St.
St. Paul, MN 55101-1057
Contact: Nicole Garrison-Sprenger, Financial Services Reporter
Ph: (651)228-5580
E-mail: ngarrisonsprenger@pioneerpress.com
URL: http://www.pioneerpress.com

3267 ■ Star Tribune
McClatchy Newspapers, Inc.
425 Portland Ave., S.
Minneapolis, MN 55415
Contact: Dick Youngblood, Small Business Columnist
Ph: (612)673-4439
E-mail: yblood@startribune.com
URL: http://www.startribune.com

3268 ■ Star Tribune
McClatchy Newspapers, Inc.
425 Portland Ave., S.
Minneapolis, MN 55415
Contact: Kara McGuire, Personal Finance/Stocks Reporter
Ph: (612)673-7293
E-mail: kmcguire@startribune.com
URL: http://www.startribune.com

Missouri

3269 ■ The Kansas City Star
Knight Ridder, Inc.
1729 Grand Blvd.
Kansas City, MO 64108
Contact: Joyce Smith, Retail/Small Business Reporter
Ph: (816)234-4692
E-mail: jsmith@kcstar.com
URL: http://www.kansascity.com

3270 ■ The Kansas City Star
Knight Ridder, Inc.
1729 Grand Blvd.
Kansas City, MO 64108
Contact: Steve Rosen, Moneywise Editor
Ph: (816)234-4879
E-mail: srosen@kcstar.com
URL: http://www.kansascity.com

3271 ■ St. Louis Post-Dispatch
Lee Enterprises, Inc.
900 N. Tucker Blvd.
St. Louis, MO 63101
Contact: Jerri A. Stroud, Banking and Finance Reporter
Ph: (314)340-8384
E-mail: jstroud@post-dispatch.com
URL: http://www.stltoday.com

3272 ■ St. Louis Post-Dispatch
Lee Enterprises, Inc.
900 N. Tucker Blvd.

St. Louis, MO 63101
Contact: Christopher Boyce, Small Business Reporter
Ph: (314)340-8345
E-mail: cboyce@post-dispatch.com
URL: http://www.stltoday.com

Nebraska

3273 ■ Omaha World-Herald
1314 Douglas St., Ste. 900
Omaha, NE 68102
Contact: Joe Ruff, Retail Reporter
Ph: (402)444-1000
E-mail: joe.ruff@owh.com
URL: http://www.omaha.com

Nevada

3274 ■ Las Vegas Review Journal
PO Box 70
Las Vegas, NV 89125
Contact: Michael Hiesiger, Business Editor
Ph: (702)383-0249
E-mail: mhiesiger@reviewjournal.com
URL: http://www.reviewjournal.com

3275 ■ Las Vegas Review Journal
PO Box 70
Las Vegas, NV 89125
Contact: John Edwards, Investments Reporter
Ph: (702)383-0420
E-mail: jedwards@reviewjournal.com
URL: http://www.reviewjournal.com

New Jersey

3276 ■ Asbury Park Press
Gannett Co., Inc.
PO Box 1550
Neptune, NJ 07754-1551
Contact: Dennis Carmody, Business Editor
Ph: (732)643-4042
E-mail: dcarmody@app.com
URL: http://www.app.com

3277 ■ The Star-Ledger
Newhouse Newspapers
One Star-Ledger Plaza
Newark, NJ 07102-1200
Contact: Joseph R. Perone, Small Business Writer
Ph: (973)392-4262
E-mail: jperone@starledger.com
URL: http://www.nj.com

3278 ■ The Star-Ledger
Newhouse Newspapers
One Star-Ledger Plaza
Newark, NJ 07102-1200
Contact: Steven Crabill, Business and Financial Editor
Ph: (973)392-5856
E-mail: scrabill@starledger.com
URL: http://www.nj.com

3279 ■ The Star-Ledger
Newhouse Newspapers
One Star-Ledger Plaza
Newark, NJ 07102-1200
Contact: Kevin Shinkle, Business & Financial Editor
Ph: (973)392-1544
E-mail: kshinkle@starledger.com
URL: http://www.nj.com

New Mexico

3280 ■ Albuquerque Journal
Journal Publishing Company
PO Drawer J
Albuquerque, NM 87103
Contact: Kiera Hay, Business Writer
Ph: (505)992-6270

E-mail: journal@abqjournal.com
URL: http://www.abqjournal.com

3281 ■ Albuquerque Journal
Journal Publishing Company
PO Drawer J
Albuquerque, NM 87103
Contact: Mike Hartranft, Business Writer
Ph: (505)823-3947
E-mail: mhartranft@abqjournal.com
URL: http://www.abqjournal.com

3282 ■ Albuquerque Journal
Journal Publishing Company
PO Drawer J
Albuquerque, NM 87103
Contact: Rivkela Brodsky, Business Writer
Ph: (505)823-3879
Fax: (505)823-3994
E-mail: rbrodsky@abqjournal.com
URL: http://www.abqjournal.com

3283 ■ Albuquerque Journal
Journal Publishing Company
PO Drawer J
Albuquerque, NM 87103
Contact: Michael Murphy, Business Editor
Ph: (505)823-3830
Fax: (505)823-3994
E-mail: mmurphy@abqjournal.com
URL: http://www.abqjournal.com

3284 ■ The Santa Fe New Mexican
PO Box 2048
Santa Fe, NM 87054-2048
Contact: Bob Quick, Business Editor & Reporter
Ph: (505)986-3011
E-mail: bobquick@sfnewmexican.com
URL: http://www.santafenewmexican.com

New York

3285 ■ The Buffalo News
Berkshire Hathaway Inc.
PO Box 100
Buffalo, NY 14240
Contact: Jonathan Epstein, Banking/Insurance Reporter
Ph: (716)849-4434
Free: 800-777-8680
Fax: (716)856-5150
E-mail: jepstein@buffnews.com
URL: http://www.buffalo.com

3286 ■ The Journal News
Gannett Co., Inc.
One Gannett Dr.
White Plains, NY 10604
Contact: Jay Loomis, Finance and Banking Reporter
Ph: (914)694-5041
E-mail: jloomis@lohud.com
URL: http://www.lohud.com

3287 ■ The Journal News
Gannett Co., Inc.
One Gannett Dr.
White Plains, NY 10604
Contact: Jerry Gleeson, Economy Reporter
Ph: (914)694-5026
E-mail: jgleeson@lohud.com
URL: http://www.lohud.com

3288 ■ The Journal News
Gannett Co., Inc.
One Gannett Dr.
White Plains, NY 10604
Contact: Michael Bieger, Business Editor
Ph: (914)696-5015
E-mail: mbiegerr@thejournalnews.com
URL: http://www.lohud.com

3289 ■ Los Angeles Times
Tribune Company
Two Park Ave.
New York, NY 10016-5675
Contact: Walter Hamilton, Wall Street Reporter

Ph: (212)448-2848
URL: http://www.latimes.com

3290 ■ New York 1 News
Time Warner Entertainment Company, LP
75 9th Ave., 6th Fl.
New York, NY 10011
Contact: Annika Pergment, Fortune Business Reporter
Ph: (212)379-3381
E-mail: annika.pergament@ny1news.com
URL: http://www.ny1.com

3291 ■ The New York Times
620 Eighth Ave.
New York, NY 10018
Contact: Lawrence Ingrassia, Business/Financial Editor
Ph: (212)556-1472
E-mail: lingrassia@nytimes.com
URL: http://www.nytimes.com

3292 ■ The New York Times
620 Eighth Ave.
New York, NY 10018
Contact: Eric Dash, Banking Reporter
Ph: (212)556-8314
E-mail: edash@nytimes.com
URL: http://www.nytimes.com

3293 ■ The New York Times
620 Eighth Ave.
New York, NY 10018
Contact: Denise Gray, Health and Medicine Reporter
Ph: (212)556-7447
Free: 800-698-4637
E-mail: dgrady@nytimes.com
URL: http://www.nytimes.com

3294 ■ The New York Times
229 W. 43rd St.
New York, NY 10036
Contact: Louis Uchitelle, Economics Reporter
Ph: (212)556-1705
E-mail: louisu@nytimes.com
URL: http://www.nytimes.com

3295 ■ The New York Times
Tribune Company
620 Eighth Ave.
New York, NY 10018
Contact: Landon Thomas, Jr., Wall Street Reporter
Ph: (212)556-3821
Free: 800-698-4637
E-mail: lthomas@nytimes.com
URL: http://www.nytimes.com

3296 ■ The New York Times
620 Eighth Ave.
New York, NY 10018
Contact: Tara Siegel Bernard, Personal Finance Reporter
Ph: (212)556-1474
Free: 800-698-4637
URL: http://www.nytimes.com

3297 ■ The New York Times
620 Eighth Ave.
New York, NY 10018
Contact: Mary Williams Walsh, Pensions & Benefits Reporter
Ph: (212)556-4271
Free: 800-698-4637
E-mail: mwalsh@nytimes.com
URL: http://www.nytimes.com

3298 ■ The New York Times
620 Eighth Ave.
New York, NY 10018
Contact: Floyd Norris, Chief Financial Correspondent
Ph: (212)556-1783
Free: 800-698-4637
E-mail: norris@nytimes.com
URL: http://www.nytimes.com

3299 ■ The New York Times
620 Eighth Ave.
New York, NY 10018

Contact: Charles Duhigg, Financial Services Reporter
Ph: (212)556-7477
E-mail: cduhigg@nytimes.com
URL: http://www.nytimes.com

3300 ■ *The New York Times*
620 Eighth Ave.
New York, NY 10018
Contact: Ron Lieber, Your Money Columnist
Ph: (212)556-1474
URL: http://www.nytimes.com
Descr: Provides personal finance expertise.

3301 ■ *Newsday*
Tribune Company
235 Pinelawn Rd.
Melville, NY 11747-4250
Contact: Tom Incantalupo, Personal Finance/Consumer Reporter
Ph: (631)843-2795
E-mail: incantal@newsday.com
URL: http://www.newsday.com

3302 ■ *Newsday*
Tribune Company
235 Pinelawn Rd.
Melville, NY 11747-4250
Contact: Patricia Kitchen, Personal Finance Reporter
Ph: (631)843-2899
E-mail: kitchen@newsday.com
URL: http://www.newsday.com

3303 ■ *Newsday*
Tribune Company
235 Pinelawn Rd.
Melville, NY 11747-4250
Contact: Carrie Mason-Draffen, Business Reporter & Columnist
Ph: (631)843-2791
E-mail: carrie.draffen@newsday.com
URL: http://www.newsday.com

3304 ■ *Newsday*
Tribune Company
235 Pinelawn Rd.
Melville, NY 11747-4250
Contact: Gary Dymski, Small Business Columnist
Ph: (631)843-4670
E-mail: gary.dymski@newsday.com
URL: http://www.newsday.com

3305 ■ *The Post-Standard*
PO Box 4915
Syracuse, NY 13221-4915
Contact: Charley Hannagan, Big Business Reporter
Ph: (315)470-2161
E-mail: channagan@post-standard.com
URL: http://www.post-standard.com

3306 ■ *The Post-Standard*
PO Box 4915
Syracuse, NY 13221-4915
Contact: Marie Morelli, Business Editor
Ph: (315)470-2220
E-mail: business@post-standard.com
URL: http://www.post-standard.com

North Carolina

3307 ■ *The Charlotte Observer*
Knight Ridder, Inc.
PO Box 30308
Charlotte, NC 28230-0308
Contact: Rick Rothacker, Small Business/Banking Reporter
Ph: (704)358-5040
E-mail: rrothacker@charlotteobserver.com
URL: http://www.charlotte.com/observer

3308 ■ *The Charlotte Observer*
Knight Ridder, Inc.
PO Box 30308
Charlotte, NC 28230-0308
Contact: Christina Rexrode, Consumer Banking Reporter
Ph: (704)358-5170
E-mail: crexrode@charlotteobserver.com
URL: http://www.charlotte.com/observer

3309 ■ *The Charlotte Observer*
Knight Ridder, Inc.
PO Box 30308
Charlotte, NC 28230-0308
Contact: Patrick Scott, Business Editor
Ph: (704)358-5176
E-mail: pscott@charlotteobserver.com
URL: http://www.charlotte.com/observer

3310 ■ *Winston-Salem Journal*
PO Box 3159
Winston-Salem, NC 27102-3159
Contact: Richard Craver, Personal Finance/Banking Reporter
Ph: (336)727-7376
E-mail: rcraver@wsjournal.com
URL: http://www.journalnow.com

North Dakota

3311 ■ *The Bismarck Tribune*
Lee Enterprises, Inc.
PO Box 5516
Bismarck, ND 58506
Contact: Crystal Reid, Business Reporter
Ph: (701)250-8261
E-mail: crystal.reid@bismarcktribune.com
URL: http://www.bismarcktribune.com

Ohio

3312 ■ *Akron Beacon Journal*
Sound Publishing Holdings, Inc.
PO Box 640
Akron, OH 44309-0640
Contact: Larry Pantages, Business Editor
Ph: (330)996-3810
E-mail: lpantages@thebeaconjournal
URL: http://www.ohio.com

3313 ■ *Akron Beacon Journal*
Sound Publishing Holdings, Inc.
PO Box 640
Akron, OH 44309-0640
Contact: Paula Schleis, Small Business Reporter
Ph: (330)996-3741
Fax: (330)376-9235
E-mail: pschleis@thebeaconjournal.com
URL: http://www.ohio.com

3314 ■ *The Cincinnati Enquirer*
Gannett Co., Inc.
312 Elm St.
Cincinnati, OH 45202-2739
Contact: Jeff McKinney, Small Business Reporter
Ph: (513)768-8483
E-mail: jmckinney@enquirer.com
URL: http://www.enquirer.com

3315 ■ *Cincinnati Enquirer*
Gannett Co., Inc.
312 Elm St.
Cincinnati, OH 45202-2739
Contact: Alexander Coolidge, Personal Finance Reporter
Ph: (513)768-8377
E-mail: acoolidge@enquirer.com
URL: http://www.enquirer.com

3316 ■ *The Cincinnati Enquirer*
Gannett Co., Inc.
312 Elm St.
Cincinnati, OH 45202-2739
Contact: Lee Ann Hamilton, Business Editor
Ph: (513)768-8372
E-mail: thamilton@enquirer.com
URL: http://www.enquirer.com

3317 ■ *Cleveland Plain Dealer*
Newhouse Newspapers
1801 Superior Ave., NE
Cleveland, OH 44114-2198
Contact: Shaheen Samavati, Tech/Real Estate Reporter
Ph: (216)999-4331
E-mail: ssamavati@plaind.com
URL: http://www.plaindealer.com

3318 ■ *The Columbus Dispatch*
34 S. Third St.
Columbus, OH 43215-4241
Contact: Steve Wartenberg, Personal Finance Reporter
Ph: (614)461-1768
Fax: (614)461-7580
E-mail: letters@columbusdispatch.com
URL: http://www.dispatch.com

3319 ■ *The Columbus Dispatch*
34 S. Third St.
Columbus, OH 43215-4241
Contact: Ron Carter, Business Editor
Ph: (614)461-5156
E-mail: rcarter@dispatch.com
URL: http://www.dispatch.com

3320 ■ *Dayton Daily News*
Cox Newspapers, Inc.
1611 S. Main St.
Dayton, OH 45409
Contact: Mary Irby-Jones, Business Editor
Ph: (937)225-7311
URL: http://www.daytondailynews.com

3321 ■ *Dayton Daily News*
Cox Newspapers, Inc.
45 S. Ludlow St.
Dayton, OH 45402
Contact: Tim Tresslar, Small Business Reporter
Ph: (937)225-7317
E-mail: ttresslar@daytondailynews.com
URL: http://www.daytondailynews.com

Oklahoma

3322 ■ *The Oklahoman*
Oklahoma Publishing Company
9000 N. Broadway
Oklahoma City, OK 73114
Contact: Don Mecoy, Personal Finance Reporter
Ph: (405)475-3942
E-mail: dmecoy@oklahoman.com
URL: http://www.newsok.com

Oregon

3323 ■ *The Oregonian*
1320 SW Broadway
Portland, OR 97201
Contact: Bruce Hammond, Business Editor
Ph: (503)221-8200
E-mail: newsroom@news.oregonian.com
URL: http://www.oregonlive.com

3324 ■ *The Oregonian*
1320 SW Broadway
Portland, OR 97201
Contact: Laura Oppenheimer, Consumer Goods Reporter
Ph: (503)221-8200
E-mail: lauraoppenheimer@news.oregonian.com
URL: http://www.oregonlive.com

3325 ■ *The Oregonian*
1320 SW Broadway
Portland, OR 97201
Contact: Brent Hunsberger, Personal Finance Columnist
Ph: (503)221-8200
E-mail: brenthunsberger@news.oregonian.com
URL: http://www.oregonlive.com

3326 ■ *The Oregonian*
1320 SW Broadway
Portland, OR 97201
Contact: Jonathan Brinckman, Small Business Reporter
Ph: (503)221-8190

E-mail: jbrinckman@news.oregonian.com
URL: http://www.oregonlive.com

Pennsylvania

3327 ■ *The Philadelphia Inquirer*
Philadelphia Media Holdings LLC
400 N. Broad St.
Philadelphia, PA 19103
Contact: Joanne McLaughlin, Deputy Business Editor
Ph: (215)854-2699
E-mail: jmclaughlin@phillynews.com
URL: http://www.philly.com

3328 ■ *The Philadelphia Inquirer*
Philadelphia Media Holdings LLC
400 N. Broad St.
Philadelphia, PA 19101
Contact: Harold Brubaker, Financial Services Reporter
Ph: (215)854-4651
E-mail: hbrubaker@phillynews.com
URL: http://www.philly.com

3329 ■ *The Philadelphia Inquirer*
Philadelphia Media Holdings LLC
400 N. Broad St.
Philadelphia, PA 19101
Contact: Joseph DiStefano, Corporate Deals Reporter
Ph: (215)854-5194
E-mail: jdistefano@phillynews.com
URL: http://www.philly.com

3330 ■ *The Philadelphia Inquirer*
Philadelphia Media Holdings LLC
400 N. Broad St.
Philadelphia, PA 19103
Contact: Henry Holcomb, Small Business Reporter
Ph: (215)854-2450
E-mail: hholcomb@phillynews.com
URL: http://www.philly.com

3331 ■ *The Philadelphia Inquirer*
Philadelphia Media Holdings LLC
400 N. Broad St.
Philadelphia, PA 19103
Contact: Paul Schweizer, Personal Finance Editor
Ph: (215)854-2487
E-mail: pschweizer@phillynews.com
URL: http://www.philly.com

3332 ■ *Pittsburgh Post-Gazette*
Block Communications, Inc.
34 Blvd. of the Allies
Pittsburgh, PA 15222
Contact: Patricia Sabatini, Banking Reporter
Ph: (412)263-3066
E-mail: psabatini@post-gazette.com
URL: http://www.post-gazette.com

Rhode Island

3333 ■ *The Providence Journal*
A.H. Belo Corporation
75 Fountain St.
Providence, RI 02902
Contact: Lynn Arditi, Business Reporter
Ph: (401)277-7335
Fax: (401)277-7346
E-mail: larditi@projo.com
URL: http://www.projo.com

3334 ■ *The Providence Journal*
A.H. Belo Corporation
75 Fountain St.
Providence, RI 02902
Contact: John Kostrzewa, Business Editor
Ph: (401)277-7330
Fax: (401)277-7346

E-mail: jkostrze@projo.com
URL: http://www.projo.com

3335 ■ *The Providence Journal*
A.H. Belo Corporation
75 Fountain St.
Providence, RI 02902
Contact: Neil Downing, Business Columnist
Ph: (401)277-7640
Fax: (401)277-7346
E-mail: ndowning@projo.com
URL: http://www.projo.com

South Carolina

3336 ■ *Greenville News*
PO Box 1688
Greenville, SC 29602
Contact: Woody White, Business Editor
Ph: (864)298-4490
E-mail: rwwhite@greenvillenews.com
URL: http://www.greenvilleonline.com

3337 ■ *The Post & Courier*
134 Columbus St.
Charleston, SC 29403-4800
Contact: Bryce Donovan, "It Beats Working" Columnist
Ph: (843)937-5938
E-mail: bdonovan@postandcourier.com
URL: http://www.charleston.net

3338 ■ *The Post & Courier*
134 Columbus St.
Charleston, SC 29403-4800
Contact: John McDermott, Business Editor
Ph: (843)937-5572
E-mail: jmcdermott@postandcourier.com
URL: http://www.charleston.net

3339 ■ *The Post & Courier*
134 Columbus St.
Charleston, SC 29403-4800
Contact: Warren Wise, Business Reporter
Ph: (843)937-5524
E-mail: wwise@postandcourier.com
URL: http://www.charleston.net

3340 ■ *The State*
The McClatchy Company
PO Box 1333
Columbia, SC 29202-1333
Contact: Sara Svedberg, Business Editor
Ph: (803)225-1390
E-mail: ssvedberg@thestate.com
URL: http://www.thestate.com

Tennessee

3341 ■ *The Commercial Appeal*
The E.W. Scripps Company
495 Union Ave.
Memphis, TN 38103
Contact: James Overstreet, Business Editor
Ph: (901)529-5893
E-mail: joverstreet@commercialappeal.com
URL: http://www.commercialappeal.com

Texas

3342 ■ *Austin American-Statesman*
Cox Newspapers, Inc.
305 S. Congress Ave.
Austin, TX 78704
Contact: Kathy Warbelow, Executive Business Editor
Ph: (512)445-3662
E-mail: kwarbelow@statesman.com
URL: http://www.austin360.com/aas

3343 ■ *Austin American-Statesman*
Cox Newspapers, Inc.
305 S. Congress Ave.
Austin, TX 78704
Contact: Lori Hawkins, Startups/Venture Reporter
Ph: (512)912-5955

E-mail: lhawkins@statesman.com
URL: http://www.austin360.com/aas

3344 ■ *Dallas Morning News*
Belo Corp.
508 Young St.
Dallas, TX 75202
Contact: Brendan Case, Economy/Finance Reporter
Ph: (214)977-8389
E-mail: bcase@dallasnews.com
URL: http://www.dallasnews.com

3345 ■ *Dallas Morning News*
Belo Corp.
508 Young St.
Dallas, TX 75202
Contact: Peter Johnson, Markets Editor, Stocks
Ph: (214)977-8376
E-mail: pjohnson@dallasnews.com
URL: http://www.dallasnews.com

3346 ■ *Dallas Morning News*
Belo Corp.
508 Young St.
Dallas, TX 75202
Contact: Pamlea Yip, Personal Finance Reporter
Ph: (214)977-8595
E-mail: pyip@dallasnews.com
URL: http://www.dallasnews.com

3347 ■ *Fort Worth Star-Telegram*
400 W. Seventh St.
Fort Worth, TX 76102
Contact: Gordon Dickson, Transportation Writer
Ph: (817)390-7064
Fax: (817)390-7774
E-mail: gdickson@star-telegram.com
URL: http://www.star-telegram.com

3348 ■ *Fort Worth Star-Telegram*
PO Box 1870
Fort Worth, TX 76115
Contact: Scott Nishimura, Business Editor
Ph: (817)390-7808
E-mail: snishimura@star-telegram.com
URL: http://www.star-telegram.com

3349 ■ *Houston Chronicle*
Hearst Newspapers
801 Texas Ave.
Houston, TX 77002
Contact: Shannon Buggs, Personal Finance/Banking Reporter
Ph: (713)362-6834
E-mail: shannon.buggs@chron.com
URL: http://www.houstonchronicle.com

3350 ■ *Houston Chronicle*
Hearst Newspapers
801 Texas Ave.
Houston, TX 77002
Contact: David Kaplan, Small Bus./Retail Reporter
Ph: (713)362-7584
E-mail: david.kaplan@chron.com
URL: http://www.houstonchronicle.com

3351 ■ *San Antonio Express-News*
Hearst Newspapers
PO Box 2171
San Antonio, TX 78297-2171
Contact: David Hendricks, Business Columnist
Ph: (210)250-3242
E-mail: dhendricks@express-news.net
URL: http://www.mysa.com

3352 ■ *San Antonio Express-News*
Hearst Newspapers
PO Box 2171
San Antonio, TX 78297-2171
Contact: Bradley Lehman, Business Editor
Ph: (210)250-3000
E-mail: blehman@express-news.net
URL: http://www.mysa.com

Utah

3353 ■ Deseret Morning News
PO Box 1257
Salt Lake City, UT 84110
Contact: Julianne Basinger, Business Editor
Ph: (801)236-6096
E-mail: jbasinger@desnews.com
URL: http://www.deseretnews.com

3354 ■ The Salt Lake Tribune
90 S. 400 W., Ste. 700
Salt Lake City, UT 84101
Contact: Michael Limon, Business Editor
Ph: (801)257-8798
E-mail: mlimon@sltrib.com
URL: http://www.sltrib.com

Vermont

3355 ■ The Burlington Free Press
Gannett Co., Inc.
PO Box 10
Burlington, VT 05402
Contact: Dan McLean, Business Reporter
Ph: (802)651-4877
Fax: (802)660-1802
E-mail: dmclean@afp.burlingtonfreepress.com
URL: http://www.burlingtonfreepress.com

Virginia

3356 ■ Richmond Times-Dispatch
Media General, Inc.
PO Box 85333
Richmond, VA 23293
Contact: Emily C. Dooley, Economy Reporter
Ph: (804)649-6016
Fax: (804)775-8059
URL: http://www.timesdispatch.com

3357 ■ Richmond Times-Dispatch
Media General, Inc.
PO Box 85333
Richmond, VA 23293
Contact: John Hoke, Business Editor
Ph: (804)649-6000
Fax: (804)775-8059
URL: http://www.timesdispatch.com

Washington

3358 ■ Seattle Times
PO Box 70
Seattle, WA 98111
Contact: Amy Martinez, Banking Reporter
Ph: (206)464-2923
E-mail: amartinez@seattletimes.com
URL: http://www.seattletimes.com

3359 ■ Seattle Times
PO Box 70
Seattle, WA 98111
Contact: Drew DeSilver, Economy Reporter
Ph: (206)464-3145
E-mail: ddesilver@seattletimes.com
URL: http://www.seattletimes.com

3360 ■ Seattle Times
PO Box 70
Seattle, WA 98111
Contact: Karl Neice, Business Wire Editor
Ph: (206)464-2355
E-mail: kneice@seattletimes.com
URL: http://www.seattletimes.com

West Virginia

3361 ■ Charleston Daily Mail
MediaNews Group, Inc.
1001 Virginia St. E.
Charleston, WV 25301

Contact: George Hohmann, Business Editor
Ph: (304)348-4836
E-mail: business@dailymail.com
URL: http://www.dailymail.com

Corporate Contacts

3362 ■ American Express Co.
General Inquiries
PO Box 981540
El Paso, TX 79998-1540
Free: 800-528-4800
URL: http://www.americanexpress.com

3363 ■ AXA Equitable Co., Inc.
1290 Ave. of the Americas, 8th Fl.
New York, NY 10104
Contact: Anthony Sages, Div.Pres.
Ph: (212)554-1234
URL: http://www.equitable.com

3364 ■ Bank of America
100 N. Tryon St.
Charlotte, NC 28255
Free: 800-432-1000
URL: http://www.bankofamerica.com

3365 ■ The Bank of New York Mellon
BNY Mellon Center
500 Grant St.
Pittsburgh, PA 15258
Ph: (212)495-1784
URL: http://www.bnymellon.com

3366 ■ Bank United
Customer Service
7815 NW 148th St.
Miami Lakes, FL 33016
Free: 877-779-2265
E-mail: pmoret@bankunited.com
URL: http://www.bankunited.com

3367 ■ Chase Bank
1 Chase Plaza
New York, NY 10005
Ph: (212)270-6000
Free: 877-576-6616
URL: http://www.chase.com

3368 ■ Citigroup, Inc.
U.S. Service Center, Citi Inquiries
100 Citibank Dr.
San Antonio, TX 78245
Free: 800-950-5114
URL: http://www.citibank.com

3369 ■ Coldwell Banker Real Estate Corp.
One Campus Dr.
Parsippany, NJ 07054
Ph: (973)428-9700
Free: 877-373-3829
URL: http://www.coldwellbanker.com

3370 ■ Consumer Credit Counseling Service of Greater Washington, Inc.
15847 Crabbs Branch Way
Rockville, MD 20855
Ph: (301)590-1010
Free: 800-747-4222
E-mail: info@cccsdc.org
URL: http://www.cccsdc.org

3371 ■ Debt Consolidation Care
711 S. Carson St., Ste. 4
Carson City, NV 89701
Ph: (775)297-8585
Free: 800-332-8913
URL: http://www.debtconsolidationcare.com

3372 ■ Debt Management Credit Counseling Corporation (DMCC)
PO Box 9182
Uniondale, NY 48277-0288

Free: 866-618-DEBT
URL: http://www.dmcccorp.org/

3373 ■ Diners Club International
Customer Service
PO Box 6500
Sioux Falls, SD 57117
Ph: (702)797-5532
Free: 800-234-6377
Fax: (303)649-2891
URL: http://www.dinersclubinternational.com

3374 ■ Discover Financial Services, Inc.
2500 Lake Cook Rd.
Riverwoods, IL 60015-3851
Contact: David W. Nelms, CEO
Ph: (224)405-0900
Free: 800-347-2683
Fax: (224)405-4993
URL: http://www.discoverfinancial.com

3375 ■ DWS Scudder
Customer Service Dept.
PO Box 219669
Kansas City, MO 64121
Free: 800-225-5163
URL: http://www.dws-scudder.com

3376 ■ Equifax
Office of Consumer Affairs
PO Box 105851
Atlanta, GA 30348
Free: 800-685-1111
URL: http://www.equifax.com
Telecom. Svcs: For TTY toll-free, call (866)478-0030.

3377 ■ ETRADE Financial
PO Box 1542
Merrifield, VA 22116-1542
Ph: (916)636-2510
Free: 800-387-2331
Fax: (866)650-0003
E-mail: tellmemore@etrade.com
URL: http://us.etrade.com

3378 ■ Fidelity & Guarantee Co.
Policy Holder Service Center
PO Box 81497
Lincoln, NE 68501
Contact: Christopher Chapman, Pres./CEO
Free: 888-513-8797
Fax: 800-638-2255
URL: http://www.omfn.com

3379 ■ GreenPath Debt Solutions
38505 Country Club Dr., Ste. 210
Farmington Hills, MI 48331
Free: 800-550-1961
URL: http://www.greenpath.com/

3380 ■ H & R Block, Inc.
Customer Support
4400 Main St.
Kansas City, MO 64111-9986
Ph: (816)753-6900
Free: 800-472-5625
URL: http://www.hrblock.com

3381 ■ HSBC North America
26525 N. Riverwoods Blvd., 4NE
Mettawa, IL 60045
Ph: 800-975-HSBC
URL: http://www.hsbc.com/

3382 ■ ID Watchdog
535 16th St., Ste. 700
Denver, CO 80202
Free: 800-970-5182
URL: http://www.idwatchdog.com

3383 ■ J.P. Morgan Chase and Company
270 Park Ave.
New York, NY 10017

Ph: (212)270-6000
URL: http://www.jpmorganchase.com

3384 ■ LifeLock Identity Theft Protection
60 E. Rio Salado Pkwy., Ste. 400
Tempe, AZ 85281
Ph: (480)682-5100
Free: 800-543-3562
URL: http://www.lifelock.com

3385 ■ MasterCard International
PO Box 28468-0968
St. Louis, MO 63146-0968
Free: 800-622-7747
E-mail: CustomerServiceCenter@mastercard.com
URL: http://www.mastercard.com
Telecom. Svcs: For TDD/TTY toll-free, call (800)300-3069.

3386 ■ Merrill Lynch & Co., Inc.
4 World Financial Ctr., 250 Vesey St.
New York, NJ 10080
Ph: (212)449-1000
Free: 800-MERRILL
URL: http://www.merrilllynch.com

3387 ■ Midas Mutual Funds
PO Box 6110
Indianapolis, IN 46209-6110
Ph: (212)363-1100
Free: 800-400-6432
Fax: (212)363-1101
E-mail: info@MutualFunds.com
URL: http://www.mutualfunds.com

3388 ■ Mobil Oil Credit Corp.
11300 Corporate Ave.
Lenexa, KS 66219-1385
Contact: R.D. Bahr
Free: 800-344-4355

3389 ■ Morgan Stanley
1585 Broadway
New York, NY 10036
Ph: (212)761-4000
Free: 800-733-2307
URL: http://www.morganstanley.com

3390 ■ Nationwide Financial Network, Inc.
Corporate Compliance
300 Continental Dr.

Newark, DE 19713
Free: 888-753-7364
Fax: (302)452-7634
URL: http://www.mynfn.com

3391 ■ Noble Trading
50 Broad St., Ste. 408
New York, NY 10004
Ph: (212)812-5400
Free: 877-TRADE-11
Fax: (212)656-1195
E-mail: info@nobletrading.com
URL: http://www.nobletrading.com/
Descr: Seeks to provide direct access trading to the U.S. equity, option, and future markets to both individual traders and institutions alike.

3392 ■ PaineWebber, Inc.
1285 Avenue of the Americas
New York, NY 10019-6028
Ph: (212)713-2000
Free: 800-354-9103
Fax: (212)713-4889

3393 ■ Prudential Securities Inc.
Client Relations Dept.
One Seaport Plaza
New York, NY 10292
Ph: (212)778-1000
Free: 800-367-8701
Fax: (212)778-2899
URL: http://www.prudential.com

3394 ■ Smith Barney
77 Water St., 19th Fl.
New York, NY 10005
Ph: (212)816-6000
Fax: (212)723-2184
URL: http://www.smithbarney.com

3395 ■ Superior Debt Services, Inc.
2625 Redwing Dr., Ste. 140
Fort Collins, CO 80526
Ph: 888-366-3414
URL: http://www.superiordebtrelief.com

3396 ■ Trans Union, LLC
PO Box 1000
Chester, PA 19022
Ph: (610)546-4600
Free: 800-888-4213

Fax: (610)546-4605
URL: http://www.transunion.com

3397 ■ UBS Financial Services Inc.
Client Relations
PO Box 766
Union City, NJ 07087
Free: 888-279-3343
E-mail: comments@ubs.com
URL: http://financialservicesinc.ubs.com

3398 ■ U.S. Bancorp
U.S. Bancorp Center
800 Nicollet Mall
Minneapolis, MN 55402
Free: 800-872-2657
URL: http://www.usbank.com

3399 ■ ValueStar
Communications Division
360 22nd St., 4th Fl.
Oakland, CA 94612
Contact: Leslie Summers
Ph: (510)808-1311
Free: 800-310-6661
Fax: (510)808-1440
E-mail: lsummers@valuestar.com
URL: http://www.valuestar.com

3400 ■ Visa USA, Inc.
PO Box 8999
San Francisco, CA 94128-8999
Free: 800-VISA-911
URL: http://www.visa.com
Telecom. Svcs: Contact your issuing bank first.

3401 ■ Wachovia Corporation
Customer Service
1525 West W.T. Harris Blvd.
Charlotte, NC 28288-0376
Free: 800-922-4684
URL: http://www.wachovia.com

3402 ■ Western Union Financial Services, Inc.
Customer Relations
13022 Hollenberg Dr.
Bridgeton, MO 63044
Ph: (314)291-8000
Free: 800-634-1311
Fax: (314)291-5271
URL: http://www.westernunion.com

Internet Resources

3403 ■ Autism Society of America Home Page
Autism Society of America
7910 Woodmont Ave., Ste. 300
Bethesda, MD 20814-3067
Contact: Lee Grossman, Pres. and CEO
Ph: (301)657-0881
Free: 800-328-8476
Fax: (301)657-0869
URL(s): www.autism-society.org/ **Descr:** This site offers an introduction to the Autism Society, its aims and activities, including Conference information, membership information, current news relating to autism, research, and a mailing list. Parents and educators can also order information packages and other materials aimed at enhancing the lives of autistic children. Visitors will find informative articles on autism and how parents can cope with the pressures of living with an autistic child. **Type:** Full-text; Directory. **Updating freq.:** As needed. **Fees:** Free. **Searching routines or searchable elements:** Searching is available.

3404 ■ Careers and Colleges
CollegeXpress
2 LAN Dr., Ste. 100
Westford, MA 01886
Ph: (978)692-5092
Fax: (978)692-4174
E-mail: comments@careersandcolleges.com
URL: http://www.careersandcolleges.com/
Descr: Contains detailed information on a variety of loans and related financial assistance programs available to college students in the United States. Includes data on both government and private loans. Provides information on Stafford loans, Parent PLUS loans, consolidation loans, K-12 prep loans, alternative loans, and other forms of student loans. Includes information on loan source, contact information, application procedures, loan availability, repayment procedures, and more. Requires free registration for search. **Type:** Directory. **Fees:** Free. **Searching routines or searchable elements:** Provides keyword search functions.

3405 ■ Classroom Connect
Classroom Connect Inc.
6277 Sea Harbor Dr.
Orlando, FL 32887
Contact: Jim Bowler, Pres. & CEO
Ph: (650)589-8326
Free: 800-638-1639
Fax: 888-801-8299
E-mail: help@classroom.com
URL(s): www.classroom.net/ **Descr:** Classroom Connect is a rich resource that will help locate some of the most interesting and useful information that is available to K-12 educators online. This site is a cooperative effort between the staff of Classroom Connect (a print magazine) and educators around the globe. Classroom Connect aims to provide innovative, thought-provoking, interactive media and

services that make the Internet easy in the classroom. You can access projects like Classroom-Web, an archive of Schools on the Web, and ConferenceWeb, a constantly updated list of educational conferences. You can also access a Teacher Contact Database and an interactive Virtual Auditorium. Link on to Educational News groups for up-to-date educational discussions, as well as Ask The Webmaster for all of you that are trying your hand at html. Visitors can sign up for a free membership to access more information, or just visit anonymously. **Type:** Full-text; Software; Transactional; Directory. **Updating freq.:** Regularly. **Fees:** Free. **Searching routines or searchable elements:** Searching is not available.

3406 ■ The College Board Scholarship Search
The College Board
45 Columbus Ave.
New York, NY 10023-6917
Contact: Gaston Caperton, Pres.
Ph: (212)713-8000
Free: 800-323-7155
Fax: (212)713-8309
URL: http://www.collegeboard.org
URL(s): apps.collegeboard.com/cbsearch_ss/welcome.jsp **Descr:** Contains detailed information on more than 2300 undergraduate scholarships, internships, research grants, and loan programs available for students in the United States. Includes information on financial assistance programs for both U.S. residents and international students attending U.S. colleges. Provides data on minority scholarships and scholarships with special criteria, including student's religion, major, disability, parent status, employment, residence, club and organization memberships, military service, and more. Includes scholarship name, contact information, amount of award, qualification information, and more. **Type:** Directory. **Fees:** Free. **Searching routines or searchable elements:** Provides keyword search functions.

3407 ■ CollegeBoard.com
The College Board
45 Columbus Ave.
New York, NY 10023-6917
Ph: (212)713-8165
Fax: (212)713-8143
E-mail: store_help@collegeboard.org
URL(s): www.collegeboard.com/ **Descr:** The College Board site provides information for parents, students, and educators about planning for college, specific colleges, admissions standards, the SAT test and financial aid. Site highlights include a "question of the day" from the SAT to test your knowledge, SAT testing dates, online SAT registration, a college search engine, and more. **Type:** Image; Directory; Full-text. **Updating freq.:** Daily. **Fees:** Free. **Search-**

ing routines or searchable elements: Database is keyword searchable.

3408 ■ CollegeLink Scholarship Search
FASTWEB LLC
444 N Michigan Ave., Ste. 3000
Chicago, IL 60611
Contact: Amanda Joyner, VP/Gen.Mgr.
Free: 800-FAST-WEB
Fax: (312)467-0638
E-mail: info@FastWeb.com
URL: http://www.fastweb.com
URL(s): fastweb.monster.com/ **Descr:** Contains detailed information on approximately 7500 scholarships available to U.S. students pursuing a variety of different areas of study. Includes scholarship name, award amount, number of scholarships available, scholarship provider, addresses and contact information for scholarships, application procedures, information on qualifications, and more. Provides listings of scholarships in areas such as agriculture, animal study, business, education, communications, performing arts, languages, literature, the humanities, medicine, nursing, science, mathematics, social science, law, political science, allied health, and more. Requires free registration for search. **Type:** Directory. **Fees:** Free. **Searching routines or searchable elements:** Provides keyword search functions.

3409 ■ Commonwealth of Learning
1055 W. Hastings St., Ste. 1200
Vancouver, BC, Canada V6E 2E9
Contact: Sir John Daniel, Pres. & CEO
Ph: (604)775-8200
Fax: (604)775-8210
E-mail: info@col.org
URL: http://www.col.org
URL(s): www.col.org **Descr:** The idea of distance education--using technology to teach individuals in their own homeland, no matter how remote--first arose in the 1950s. Today, this explosion in technology has resulted in video conferencing, online universities, and the World Wide Web. One of the chief advocates of distance learning is the Commonwealth of Learning, a group of nations established by Commonwealth governments in September 1988 to create and widen access to opportunities for learning and to improve the quality of education. Distance education techniques and associated communications technologies are used to meet particular human resource development requirements of member countries. Through its homepage, the COL disseminates information about its activities and about current programs being undertaken by member countries. It also provides a glossary and links to other Commonwealth and distance education sites. **Type:** Image; Full-text. **Fees:** Free. **Searching routines or searchable elements:** Keyword searching is available.

3410 ■ EduPrep Scholarship Search
EduPrep
PO Box 46
Yarmouth Port, MA 02675

Free: 800-413-7737
Fax: (508)790-5836
E-mail: help@eduprep.com
URL: http://www.eduprep.com
URL(s): www.eduprep.com/Scholarship.asp **Descr:**
Contains detailed listings of more than 2.5 million
scholarship awards available to students in the
United States. Includes information on scholarships
for entering freshmen, current undergraduates, and
graduate students. Provides scholarship name,
contact information, application procedures, student
qualifications, and more. Requires free registration
to search. **Type:** Directory. **Fees:** Free. **Searching
routines or searchable elements:** Provides keyword search functions.

3411 ■ FastWeb Scholarship Search
FastWeb Inc.
444 N Michigan Ave., Ste. 3100
Chicago, IL 60611
Free: 800-FAS-TWEB
Fax: (312)467-0638
URL: http://www.fastweb.com
URL(s): fastweb.monster.com/ib/spikessa-4f **Descr:**
Contains detailed information on more than 600,000
scholarships totaling more than $1 billion available to
students throughout the United States. Includes
scholarship name, scholarship sponsor information,
award amount, number of awards available, brief
text description, deadline date, qualification information, and more. Includes links to scholarship sponsors' web sites. **Type:** Directory. **Fees:** Free. **Searching routines or searchable elements:** Provides
keyword search functions.

3412 ■ FreSch!
FreSch Information Services LLC
779 Denver Ave.
Calhan, CO 80808
Contact: Laura DiFiore, Founder
Ph: (719)347-2602
URL: http://www.freschinfo.com
Descr: Contains information on more than 2000
organizations offering approximately 170,000 scholarships and awards to U.S. students. Includes
information on financial assistance programs for U.S.
citizens and permanent legal residents. Provides
data on minority scholarships and scholarships with
special criteria, including student's religion, major,
disability, parent status, employment, sports participation, fraternity or sorority membership, residence,
clubs and organizations, military service, and more.
Includes scholarship name, contact information,
amount of award, qualification information, and more.
Type: Directory. **Fees:** Free. **Searching routines or
searchable elements:** Provides keyword search
functions.

3413 ■ Mach 25 Scholarship Search
Collegnet Inc.
805 SW Broadway, Ste. 1600
Portland, OR 97205
Ph: (503)973-5200
Fax: (503)973-5252
E-mail: sales@collegenet.com
URL: http://www.collegenet.com
URL(s): www.collegenet.com/mach25/ **Descr:** Con-
tains detailed information on more than 600,000 U.S.
scholarships and awards totaling more than $1.6
billion. Includes scholarship name, scholarship spon-
sor, award amount, contact information, require-
ments for scholarship, and more. **Type:** Directory.
Fees: Free. **Searching routines or searchable ele-
ments:** Provides keyword search functions.

3414 ■ SRN Express Scholarship Search
Scholarship Resource Network Inc.
44 Regatta View Dr.
Saratoga Springs, NY 12866
Ph: (518)580-1022
Fax: (518)584-7320
E-mail: srntech@srnexpress.com
URL: http://www.srnexpress.com
URL(s): www.srnexpress.com/login.cfm **Descr:**
Contains detailed information on more than 8000
U.S. scholarships and award programs offering more

than 150,000 awards worth more than $35 million.
Includes scholarship name, contact information,
amount of awards, application procedures, and more.
Includes information on student loan forgiveness
programs for graduates seeking alternate methods
of loan repayment. Requires free registration for
search. **Type:** Directory. **Fees:** Free. **Searching
routines or searchable elements:** Provides keyword search functions.

3415 ■ UTS Telecampus
The University of Texas at Austin
702 Colorado
CLB - Ste. 4.100
Austin, TX 78701
Contact: Dr. David Price, Exec. Vice Chancellor
Ph: (512)499-4323
Free: 888-839-2716
Fax: (512)499-4715
E-mail: TeleCampus@utsystem.edu
URL(s): www.telecampus.utsystem.edu **Descr:** The
UT Telecampus provides the support for the University of Texas' distance learning program. Online
learning is organized throughout this site and
information regarding admissions and courses, as
well as actual courses are available. Offers 100
courses through the site, in both graduate and
undergraduate degree programs. **Type:** Full-text; Image; Video; Audio; Directory. **Updating freq.:** As
needed. **Fees:** Free. **Searching routines or searchable elements:** Keyword and menu-based search
options are available.

Federal Government Agencies

3416 ■ Advisory Commission on Childhood Vaccines
Div. of Vaccine Injury Compensation (DVIC)
Healthcare Systems Bureau
Health Resources and Services Administration
5600 Fishers Ln., Rm. 11C-26
Rockville, MD 20857-0001
Contact: Geoffrey S. Evans MD, Exec.Sec.
Ph: (301)443-6295
Free: 800-338-2382
Fax: (301)443-8196
E-mail: mherzog@hrsa.gov
URL: http://www.hrsa.gov/vaccinecompensation
Staff: Support services are provided by the Division
of Vaccine Injury Compensation. Geoffrey S. Evans,
MD, Director, serves as executive secretary. **Descr:**
Commission advises the Secretary of Health and
Human Services on the implementation of the
National Vaccine Injury Compensation Program, and
changes in the Vaccine Injury Table. The Table lists
vaccines and injuries, resulting from the administration of such vaccines; and the time period in which
the first symptom or significant aggravation appears
after administration of the vaccine. Commission also
advises the Secretary in implementing the Secretary's responsibilities under Section 2127 of the PHS
Act regarding the need for childhood vaccination
products that result in fewer or no significant adverse
reactions. Commission surveys federal, state, and
local programs and activities relating to the gathering
of information of childhood vaccines and recommends to the Director of the National Vaccine
Program research related to vaccine injuries that
should be conducted. **Mem:** Commission comprises
12 members appointed by the Secretary of Health
and Human Services, as follows: three health professionals (at least two pediatricians) who are knowledgeable in health care of children, childhood
diseases, and adverse reactions associated with vaccines; three members of the general public, of whom
at least two are legal representatives of children who
have suffered a vaccine-related injury or death; and
three attorneys, of whom at least one specializes in
vaccine-related injury or death and at least one who
represents vaccine manufacturers. Ex-officio members include the Director of the National Institutes of
Health, the Assistant Secretary for Health, the Director of the Centers for Disease Control and Prevention, and the Commissioner of Food and Drugs,
Department of Health and Human Services. Mem-

bers serve three-year terms. Jeffrey Sconyers, JD,
attorney, Children's Hospital and Regional Medical
Center, chairs the Commission.

3417 ■ Advisory Committee on Construction Safety and Health
Directorate of Construction, Rm. N-3468
Occupational Safety & Health Admin.
Department of Labor
200 Constitution Ave. NW
Washington, DC 20210
Contact: Noah Connell, Designated Fed.Off.
Ph: (202)693-2020
Fax: (202)693-1689
URL: http://www.osha.gov/doc/accsh/index.html
Staff: Administrative support is provided by the Oc-
cupational Safety and Health Administration. Noah
Connell, Acting Director, Directorate of Construction,
serves as designated federal official. **Descr:** Committee advises the Secretary of Labor in the formulation of construction safety and health standards and
other regulations, and with respect to policy matters
arising in the administration of the safety and health
provisions of the Contract Work Hours and Safety
Act and the Occupational Safety and Health Act of
1970. **Mem:** Committee consists of 15 members;
five representing employers, five representing
employees, two representing state safety and health
agencies, two representing the public sector and one
member designated by Secretary of the Department
of Health and Human Services to represent the
federal sector. Committee chair is appointed by the
Assistant Secretary of labor for Occupational Safety
and Health. Michael J. Thibodeaux, MJT Consulting
for National Association of Home Builders, chairs the
Committee. **Pub:** Meeting minutes and transcripts
and ACCSH products and reports are available on
the Committee website.

3418 ■ Advisory Committee for Education and Human Resources
Directorate for Education and Human Resources
National Science Foundation
4201 Wilson Blvd., Rm. 805N
Arlington, VA 22230
Contact: Dr. Cora B. Marrett, Designated Found.Off.
Ph: (703)292-8600
Fax: (703)292-9179
URL: http://www.nsf.gov/ehr/advisory.jsp
Staff: Support services are provided by the Director-
ate for Education and Human Resources, National
Science Foundation. Dr. Cora B. Marrett, Assistant
Director for Education and Human Resources,
serves as designated foundation official. **Descr:**
Committee provides advice and recommendations to
the National Science Foundation concerning programs of support for education and human resources
in science, mathematics, engineering, and
technology. Committee evaluates program results
and overall program balance, and provides long-term
strategic planning. **Mem:** Committee consists of approximately 20-25 members from higher education
(a community college president and senior administrators), the science and engineering professoriate,
business and industry, and state-wide education and
policy-making communities. Members included:
research scientists, mathematicians, and engineers
of international stature; educational leaders in the
private and public sectors; key academic, industrial,
and state-level education administrators; administrators from major school systems, liberal arts colleges,
comprehensive universities and research
universities.

3419 ■ Advisory Committee on Persons with Disabilities
Office of Multilateral & Global Affairs
Bureau of Democracy, Human Rights and Labor
Department of State
2201 C St. NW, Rm. 7822
Washington, DC 20520
Contact: Stephanie Ortoleva, Designated Fed.Off.
Ph: (202)647-9551
Fax: (202)647-4344
URL: http://www.state.gov/documents/organization/
51128.pdf

Staff: Stephanie Ortoleva, Foreign Affairs Officer, Office of Multilateral and Global Affairs, Bureau of Democracy, Human Rights and Labor, serves as designated federal official. **Descr:** Committee advises the Secretary of State and Administrator, Agency for International Development, on all matters concerning U.S. foreign policy and foreign assistance as it relates to persons with disabilities. **Mem:** Committee is comprised of no more than eleven members, including former U.S. governmental officials, representatives of corporations, not-for-profit nongovernmental organizations, public policy organizations, academic institutions, and other experts on foreign policy or development issues related to persons with disabilities.

3420 ■ Advisory Committee on Student Financial Assistance
Policy, Planning & Innovation
Dept. of Education
80 F St. NW, Ste. 413
Washington, DC 20202-7582
Contact: Daniel T. Madzelan, Designated Fed.Off.
Ph: (202)219-2099
Fax: (202)219-2099
E-mail: acsfa@ed.gov
URL: http://www.ed.gov/about/bdscomm/list/acsfa/edlite-about.html
Staff: Support services are provided by the Department of Education. Daniel T. Madzelan, Forecasting and Policy Analysis Staff, Office of Policy, Planning and Innovation, serves as designated federal official. Dr. William J. Goggin (william.goggin@ed.gov) serves as executive director. **Descr:** Committee advises and makes recommendations to the Secretary of Education and the U.S. Congress concerning federal, state, and institutional programs of postsecondary student assistance; student financial matters; and access of postsecondary education for low- and middle-income students. Committee reviews all regulations affecting programs concerning student assistance and makes recommendations for studies, surveys, and analyses of student financial assistance programs, policies, and practices, including the special needs of low-income, disadvantaged, and "nontraditional" students. The Higher Education Opportunity Act makes additional assignments to the Committee in the form of special analyses and activities, as well as new functions. Congress has requested that the Committee also support the Secretary of Education, the Comptroller General, and a study group on a FAFSA simplification study. Committee also assists the Department of Education with an early information demonstration program. As a new function, Committee has been charged with reporting annually on the adequacy of need-based aid for lowand moderate-income students, as well as their postsecondary enrollment and graduation rates. A second new function is to develop and maintain an information clearinghouse to help institutions of higher education understand the regulatory impact of the federal government on institutions of higher education from all sectors. **Mem:** Committee consists of 11 members who are appointed by members of Congress and the Secretary of Education for a single term of four years. Four members are appointed by the Speaker of the House of Representatives (two each upon recommendation by the majority and minority leaders); four by the President pro tempore of the Senate (two each upon recommendation by the majority and minority leaders); and three by the Secretary of Education. Members are knowledgeable in fields of higher education and student aid administration, financing postsecondary education, student aid delivery, and the operations and financing of student loan guarantee agencies. Dr. Scott A. Giles, Vice President for Policy, Research and Planning, Vermont Student Assistance Corporation, chairs the Committee. **Pub:** Apply to Succeed: Ensuring Community College Students Benefit from Need-Based Financial Aid (September 2008); Transition Matters: Community College to Bachelor's Degree (May 2008); Mortgaging Our Future Policy Bulletin (May 2008); Turn the Page: Making College Textbooks More Affordable (May 2007); Mortgaging Our Future: How Financial Barriers to College

Undercut America's Global Competitiveness (September 2006); Reflections on College Access and Persistence: In Honor of the 40th Anniversary of the Higher Education Act; ACSFA Letter to Congress and Interim Legislative Recommendations for the Special Study of Simplification of Need Analysis and Application for Title IV Aid (June 2004); Omitted Variables and Sample Selection Issues in the NCES Research on Financial Aid and College Participation (June 2003); Draft Report: Review of NCES Research on Financial Aid and College Participation (March 2003); Empty Promises: The Myth of College Access in America (2002); Access Denied, Restoring the Nation's Commitment to Equal Educational Opportunity (February 2001).

3421 ■ Advisory Committee on VA Disability Compensation and Related Benefits
Compensation and Pension Service
Veterans Benefits Admin.
Department of Veterans Affairs
810 Vermont Ave. NW
Washington, DC 20420
Contact: Ersie Farber, Designated Fed.Off.
Ph: (202)461-9728
Fax: (202)275-1728
Staff: Support services are provided by the Compensation and Pension Service, Veterans Benefits Administration. **Descr:** Committee advises the Secretary of Veterans Affairs on establishing and supervising a schedule to conduct periodic reviews of each of the body systems in the VA Schedule for Rating Disabilities, and makes recommendations on the possible expansion of VA benefits to address the impact on quality of life, the need for transition assistance, and the potential for successful rehabilitation. **Mem:** Committee is composed of approximately 12 members who are selected from among recognized experts, veterans, and others with special competence in areas such as disability claims adjudication, vocational rehabilitation, disability programs management, workers' compensation, rehabilitative medicine, mental health research, military medical services management, veterans' benefits advocacy, and survivor benefits advocacy. Ex-officio members include designees from the Veterans Benefits Administration, Veterans Health Administration, and the Department of Defense. Lt. Gen. James T. Scott, USA (ret.), Partner, Watson and Associates, chairs the Committee.

3422 ■ Advisory Council on Dependents' Education
Department of Defense Education Activity
Department of Defense Dependents Schools (DoDDS)
4040 Fairfax Dr.
Arlington, VA 22203-1635
Contact: Charlie Toth, Designated Fed.Off.
Ph: (703)588-3105
Fax: (703)588-3702
URL: http://www.eu.dodea.edu/home/about.php?cId=2
Staff: Support services are provided by the Department of Defense Education Activities. Charlie Toth, Asst. Assoc. Director for Education, serves as designated federal official. **Descr:** Council advises the Secretary of Defense and the Director, Department of Defense Dependents Schools (DoDDS), on ways to achieve and maintain a high quality public educational program through secondary school for minor dependents in overseas areas. It makes policy recommendations with respect to curriculum, student activities, and resource management; provides information on educational programs and practices found to be effective by other federal agencies concerned with primary and secondary education; and performs other tasks as may be required by the Secretary. **Mem:** Council comprises 17 members including the Director, DoDDS, who serves as executive secretary; one designee each of the Secretaries of Defense and Education who serve as Council Cochairs; one additional representative each of the Secretaries of Defense and Education; and twelve individuals who are appointed jointly by the Secretaries of Defense and Education and who represent

professional employee organizations, school administrators, parents of dependents enrolled in Defense dependents' schools, and one student enrolled in this system. Michael Dominguez, Principal Deputy Under Secretary of Defense, chairs the Council. **Pub:** Committee does not publish separate reports; the recommendations to the decision maker are contained in the meeting minutes.

3423 ■ Advisory Panel on Medicare Education
Partnership & Promotion Group
Center for Beneficiary Choices
Centers for Medicare and Medicaid Services
7500 Security Blvd., Rm. S1-23-05
Baltimore, MD 21244-1850
Contact: Lynne G. Johnson, Staff Contact
Ph: (410)786-0090
Fax: (410)786-9665
URL: http://www.cms.hhs.gov/FACA/04_APME.asp#TopOfPage
Staff: Lynne G. Johnson, health insurance specialist, Division of Partnership Development, Beneficiary Services and Partnership Group, Center for Beneficiary Choices, CMS, serves as staff contact. **Descr:** Panel advises and makes recommendations to the Secretary of Health and Human Services and the Administrator of the CMS on opportunities for CMS to make more effective use of its National Medicare Education Program and other programs that help Medicare beneficiaries understand the expanded range of Medicare options available with the passage of the Medicare Choice Program. **Mem:** Panel consists of no more than twenty members representing disability and chronic disease interests, minority populations, health consumer interests, seniors' organizations, health communications and policy, research and philanthropic organizations, health insurers and plans, employer groups, and health providers.

3424 ■ Board of Scientific Counselors, National Institute for Occupational Safety and Health
Off. of the Director, NIOSH
Centers for Disease Control & Prevention
200 Independence Ave. SW, Mail Stop P12
Rm. 715H
Washington, DC 20201
Contact: Roger R. Rosa PhD, Exec.Sec.
Ph: (202)205-7856
Fax: (202)260-4464
URL: http://www.cdc.gov/niosh/BSC/
Staff: Support services are provided by the National Institute for Occupational Safety and Health. Roger R. Rosa, PhD, Senior Scientist, serves as executive secretary. **Descr:** Board provides advice to the Director, National Institute for Occupational Safety and Health, Centers for Disease Control and Prevention, on research programs of the Institute and provides oversight of the research programs to ensure scientific quality, timeliness, utility, and dissemination of results. **Mem:** Board currently comprises 15 members representing disciplines associated with research in occupational safety and health. Members serve four-year terms. Dr. Sarah A. Felknor, University of Texas School of Public Health, chairs the Board.

3425 ■ Bureau of Indian Affairs Advisory Board for Exceptional Children
Office of Indian Education Programs
Bureau of Indian Affairs
1011 Indian School Rd. NW, Suite 332
P.O. Box 829
Albuquerque, NM 87103
Contact: Gloria Yepa, Designated Fed.Off.
Ph: (505)563-5277
Fax: (505)563-5281
URL: http://enan.bia.edu/site_res_view_folder.aspx?id=4107d81d-2cf3-4942-836a-d472cf14 3a96
Staff: Gloria Yepa, Specialist, Bureau of Indian Affairs, serves as designated federal official. **Descr:** Board advises the Bureau of Indian Affairs on matters concerning education programs and services for American Indian and Alaskan Native disabled chil-

dren and youth. Specifically, Committee comments on the state plan for exceptional education, on proposed rules or regulations regarding the education of disabled children, and on procedures for the distribution of funds; advises the Secretary of the Interior through the Assistant Secretary--Indian Affairs on the unmet needs in the education of disabled Indian children; and assists in developing and reporting such information to help serve disabled Indian children. **Mem:** Board consists of 15 members appointed by the Secretary from tribal nominees for two-year terms. Membership is representative of disabled individuals, teachers and parents of the disabled, special education administrators and tribal education officials. Billi Kipp, PhD, Associate Scientist, Southwest Alcohol Research Group, University of New Mexico, chairs the Board.

3426 ■ Collegiate Education Advisory Committee
ROTC Cadet Command
ATCC-TR-L Bldg. 56
55 Patch Rd.
Ft. Monroe, VA 23651-5000
Contact: Hattonia Halliday, Exec.Dir.
Ph: (757)788-4594
Fax: (757)788-5454
URL: http://www.rotc.monroe.army.mil
Staff: Support services are provided by the U.S. Army ROTC Cadet Command. **Descr:** Panel was established to provide for a continuous exchange of views between the U.S. Army, the academic community, and the private sector on issues relating to Army ROTC (Reserve Officers' Training Corps) program. Scope of Panel activities is constituted primarily in addressing the current and future status of the Senior ROTC program. The deliberations include a continuous evaluation of recruiting, procurement, and training policies and the problems related to maintaining an effective interface between the Army's ROTC program and the academic community. **Mem:** Panel is composed of sixteen members selected by the Secretary of the Army. Eight members are affiliated with national educational associations, four are ROTC region representatives, two members represent historically black colleges and universities; and two are nationally prominent individuals from the private sector Members serve two-year terms. Dr. Alex Gonzalez chairs the Panel.

3427 ■ Council on Graduate Medical Education (COGME)
Division of Medicine & Dentistry
Bureau of Health Professions
Health Resources & Services Admin.
5600 Fishers Ln., RM. 9A-21
Rockville, MD 20857
Contact: Jerald M. Katzoff MD, Exec.Sec.
Ph: (301)443-4443
Fax: (301)443-8890
URL: http://cogme.gov
Staff: Support services are provided by the Division of Medicine & Dentistry, Bureau of Health Professions, Health Resources and Services Administration. **Descr:** Council provides advice and recommendations to the Secretary of Health and Human Services, the U.S. Senate Committee on Health, Education, Labor and Pensions and the U.S. House of Representatives Committee on Commerce with respect to the supply and distribution of physicians in the United States; the current and future shortages of physicians in medical and surgical specialties and subspecialties; issues relating to foreign medical graduates; appropriate Federal policies concerning changes in the financing and types of training in medical education programs; efforts to be carried out by medical and osteopathic schools, public and private hospitals, and accrediting bodies, with respect to the matters specified above including changes in medical education programs; and deficiencies in the needs for improvements in existing databases concerning supply and distribution of and training programs for physicians in the United States. **Mem:** Council comprises 17 members including designees of the Assistant Secretary for Health; Administrator of Health Care Financing, Department of Health and Human Services; the Chief Medical Director of the Department of Veterans Affairs; and 14 members appointed by the Secretary of Health and Human Services who represent national and specialty physician organizations, foreign medical graduates, medical student and house staff associations, primary care physicians, schools of medicine and osteopathy, public and private teaching hospitals, health insurers, business, and labor. Members appointed by the Secretary serve four-year terms. Russell G. Robertson, MD, Professor and Chair, Department of Family Medicine, Feinburg School of Medicine, Northwestern University, chairs the Council. **Pub:** State and Managed Care Support for Graduate Medical Education: Innovations and Implications for Federal Policy (2004); Collaborative Education to Ensure Patient Safety (September 2000); Council on Graduate Medical Education: What Is it? What Has it done? Where Is it Going? (2000). Council reports are available on the Committee website.

3428 ■ Federal Advisory Council on Occupational Safety and Health (FACOSH)
Off. of Federal Agency Programs
Directorate of Enforcement Programs
OSHA, Department of Labor
200 Constitution Ave. NW, Rm. N3112
Washington, DC 20210
Contact: Francis Yebesi, Designated Fed.Off.
Ph: (202)693-2233
Fax: (202)693-1685
E-mail: ofap@dol.gov
URL: http://www.osha.gov/dep/facosh/index.html
Staff: Administrative support is provided by the Office of Federal Agency Programs, Directorate of Enforcement Programs. Francis Yebesi, Director, serves as designated federal official. **Descr:** Council is the official advisory body to the Secretary of Labor on matters relating to the safety and health of federal employees. It attempts to reduce and keep to a minimum the number of injuries and illnesses in the federal service and encourages the establishment and maintenance of adequate and effective occupational safety and health programs in each federal department and agency. **Mem:** Council consists of 16 members, eight members from federal agencies and eight union members representing Federal employees, appointed by the Secretary of Labor for three-year terms.

3429 ■ Federal Mine Safety and Health Review Commission
601 New Jersey Ave. NW
Washington, DC 20001
Contact: Thomas Stock, Exec.Dir.
Ph: (202)434-9900
Fax: (202)434-9944
E-mail: fmshrc@fmshrc.gov
URL: http://www.fmshrc.gov
Descr: Commission conducts hearings and decides cases resulting from disputes of enforcement of mine safety and health regulations by the Department of Labor at the trial level and reviews administrative law judge decisions under the provisions of the Federal Mine Safety and Health Amendments Act of 1977. **Mem:** Commission comprises five members appointed by the President of the United States with the consent of the U.S. Senate. Members serve six-year terms. Michael F. Duffy chairs the Commission. **Pub:** Copies of the Commission's decisions are published every two months and are available through the Government Printing Office.

3430 ■ Historically Black Colleges and Universities Capital Financing Advisory Board
Office of Postsecondary Education
Department of Education
1990 K. St. NW, Rm. 6130
Washington, DC 20006-8511
Contact: Don E. Watson, Exec.Dir.
Ph: (202)219-7037
Fax: (202)502-7852
URL: http://www.ed.gov/about/bdscomm/list/hbcu-finance.html
Descr: Board provides advice and counsel to the Secretary of Education and the designated bonding authority as to the most effective and efficient means of implementing construction financing on historically Black college and university campuses and to advise Congress regarding the progress made in implementing the Historically Black Colleges and Universities Capital Financing Program, which provides financial insurance to guarantee academic construction loans to qualified historically Black colleges and universities. Specifically, the Board provides advice as to the capital needs of the colleges and universities, how those needs can be met through the Program, and what additional steps might be taken to improve the operation and implementation of the construction financing Program. **Mem:** Board consists of ten persons appointed by the Secretary of Education as follows: The Secretary or the Secretary's designee; three members who are presidents of private historically Black colleges and universities, two members who are presidents of public historically Black colleges and universities; the president of the United Negro College Fund; the President of the National Association for Equal Opportunity in Higher Education; and the Executive Firector of the White House Initiative on Historically Black Colleges and Universities. Each member serves for three years. Dr. Norman Francis, President, Xavier University, Louisiana, chairs the Board.

3431 ■ Maritime Advisory Committee for Occupational Safety and Health (MACOSH)
Maritime Office, Dir. of Standards and Guidance
Occupational Safety & Health Admin., Rm. N3609
Department of Labor
200 Constitution Ave. NW
Washington, DC 20210
Ph: (202)693-2086
Fax: (202)693-1663
Staff: Support services are provided by the Occupational Safety and Health Administration. **Descr:** Committee advises the Secretary of Labor on matters relating to occupational safety and health programs, policies, and standards in U.S. maritime industries. **Mem:** Committee consists of 15 members representing employers, employees, federal and state safety and health organizations, professional organizations, and national groups setting standards. James Thornton, Northrop Grumman Newport News Shipyard, chairs the Committee. **Pub:** Maritime Advisory Committee Recommendations to OSHA; Minutes for MACOSH Meetings in Norfolk, VA (December 2004); Agenda for MACOSH Meeting March 31-April 1, 2005 Washington, DC. MACOSH meeting notices, transcripts and recommendations can be accessed at www.osha.gov.

3432 ■ Mine Safety and Health Research Advisory Committee (MSHRAC)
National Institute for Occupational Safety and Health
Centers for Disease Control and Prevention
Pittsburg Research Laboratory
626 Cochrans Mill Rd.
Pittsburgh, PA 15236
Contact: Jeffrey Kohler PhD, Designated Fed.Off.
Ph: (412)386-5301
Fax: (412)386-5300
URL: http://www.cdc.gov/maso/facm/facmMSHRAC.htm
Staff: Jeffrey Kohler, PhD, Assoc. Dir., Mining and Construction, NIOSH, serves as designated federal official. **Descr:** Committee advises the Secretary of Health and Human Services, the Assistant Secretary for Health, the Director of the Centers for Disease Control and Prevention (CDC), and the Director of the National Institute for Occupational Safety and Health (NIOSH) on matters involving or relating to mine health and safety research, including grants and contracts for such research. **Mem:** Committee consists of 10 public members and three ex-officio members including minority and female representatives. Committee includes a balanced mix of members representing key mining stakeholder groups of labor and industry, as well as knowledgeable members from the health and safety community, the scientific arena, and academia. Ex-officio members include designees of the Director, Bureau of

Mines, Department of the Interior; Director, National Institute of Health, Director, National Science Foundation; and the Assistant Secretary for Mine Safety and Health (nonvoting members). Mary M. Poulton, PhD, Department of Mining and Geological Engineering, University of Arizona, chairs the Committee. **Pub:** No formal reports are required in the charter or legislation; committee provides advice and recommendations through various means other than formal reports.

3433 ■ National Advisory Committee on Occupational Safety and Health (NACOSH)
Occupational Safety & Health Admin., Rm. N-3641
Department of Labor
200 Constitution Ave. NW
Washington, DC 20210
Contact: Deborah P. Crawford, Designated Fed.Off.
Ph: (202)693-1932
Fax: (202)693-1641
URL: http://www.osha.gov/dop/nacosh/nacosh.html
Staff: Administrative support is provided by the Occupational Safety and Health Administration. **Descr:** Committee advises, consults with, and makes recommendations to the Secretary of Labor and the Secretary of Health and Human Services on matters relating to the administration of the Occupational Safety and Health Act of 1970. **Mem:** Committee is composed of twelve members appointed by the Secretary of Labor and the Secretary of Health and Human Services. NACOSH has two members representing management, two members representing labor, two members representing the occupational health professions, two members representing the occupational safety professions and four members representing the public. Two of the health representatives and two of the public members are designated by the Secretary of Health and Human Services, although actual appointment of these members, as well as all other members, is by the Secretary of Labor. The members serve two-year terms. Douglas Kalinowski, Director, Michigan Department of Labor and Economic Growth, chairs the Committee. **Pub:** Report and Recommendations related to OSHA'S Standards Development Process (2000).

3434 ■ National Advisory Council on Nurse Education and Practice
Div. of Nursing
Bureau of Health Professions
Health Resources & Services Admin.
5600 Fishers Lane, Rm. 9-35
Rockville, MD 20857
Contact: Nancy Douglas-Kersellius, Actg. Exec.Sec.
Ph: (301)443-0907
Fax: (301)443-0791
URL: http://www.bhpr.hrsa.gov/nursing/nacnep.htm
Staff: Management and support services are provided by the Division of Nursing, Bureau of Health Professions. **Descr:** Council advises the secretary, Department of Health and Human Services and Congress on administration of programs authorized by federal legislation for the improvement of nurse education and conducts final review of specified applications for nurse education funds. Principal subject area of interest is grants to aid schools of nursing and other eligible applicants. Council's role has changed dramatically, from focusing on nursing grant applications, to providing policy advice to the Secretary and Congress on national nursing workforce, education and practice improvement issues. **Mem:** Council consists of not more than 23 and not less than 21 members appointed by the Secretary of Health and Human Services. Of the appointed members, two are selected from full-time students enrolled in schools of nursing, two are selected from the general public, two are practicing professional nurses, and nine are selected from among authorities in the fields of nursing, higher and secondary education, and associate degree schools of nursing, and from representatives of advanced practice nursing groups, hospitals, institutions, and organizations which provide nursing services. Members serve overlapping four-year terms. Michele Richardson, MS, BS, RN, Director, Division of Nursing, Bureau of Health Professions, Health Resources and Services

Administration, chairs the Council. **Pub:** Collaborative Education to Ensure Patient Safety (December 31, 2000); A National Agenda for Nursing Workforce Racial/Ethnic Diversity (1999); Federal Support for the Preparation of the Clinical Nurse Specialist Workforce through Title VIII (1998).

3435 ■ National Asthma Education and Prevention Program Coordinating Committee
Off. of Prevention, Education, and Control
National Heart, Lung, & Blood Institute
31 Center Dr., MSC 2480
PO Box 30105
Bethesda, MD 20824-0105
Contact: Diana K. Schmidt MHP, Coord.
Ph: (301)592-8573
Fax: (301)592-8563
URL: http://www.nhlbi.nih.gov/about/naepp/naep_pd.htm
Staff: Diana K. Schmidt, National Education Program Coordinator for Asthma Education and Prevention, Office of Application of Research Discoveries, NHLBI, serves as staff contact. **Descr:** Committee coordinates the National Asthma Education and Prevention program which was established to raise awareness of patients, health professionals, and the public that asthma is a serious chronic disease; ensure the recognition of the symptoms of asthma by patients, families, and the public and the appropriate diagnosis by health professionals; and ensure effective control of asthma by encouraging a partnership among patients, physicians, and other health professionals through modern treatment and education programs. **Mem:** Committee consists of forty-one members representing major scientific, professional, governmental, and voluntary organizations interested in asthma. **Pub:** Committee has numerous publications available from the NHLBI Health Information Center, PO Box 30105, Bethesda, MD 20824-0105; phone: (301)592-8573; TTY (240)629-3255.

3436 ■ National Boating Safety Advisory Council (NBSAC)
Office of Boating Safety
U.S. Coast Guard
2100 Second St. SW
Washington, DC 20593-0001
Contact: Jeffrey A. Ludwig, Exec.Sec.
Ph: (202)372-1061
Fax: (202)372-1932
URL: http://homeport.uscg.mil/mycg/portal/ep/channelView.do?channelId=-33185&channelPage=252Fep252Fchannel252Fdefault.jsp&pageTypeId=13489
Staff: Staff support is provided by the Operations Policy Directorate of the Coast Guard. Jeffrey Ludwig, Regulatory Development Manager, serves as executive secretary. **Descr:** Council consults with and advises the Commandant, U.S. Coast Guard, regarding matters involving boat safety. Council assists in formulating and prescribing regulations and standards for boat safety required under the Federal Boat Safety Act. Principal subject areas of interest are boat and associated equipment standards and regulations, and safe operation of boats. **Mem:** Council is composed of 24 members equally divided among the following three groups: state officials responsible for state boating safety programs; boat and associated equipment manufacturers; and national recreational boating organizations and members of the public. Members are recommended by the Commandant of the U.S. Coast Guard for appointment by the Secretary of Homeland Security, and are selected for their expertise, knowledge, and experience in boating safety. James P. Muldoon, Vice President, United States Sailing Association, chairs the Council.

3437 ■ National Committee on Foreign Medical Education and Accreditation
U.S. Dept. of Education
Rm. 7005 - MS 7563
1990 K St. NW
Washington, DC 20006
Contact: Melissa Lewis, Exec.Dir.

Ph: (202)219-7009
Fax: (202)219-7008
URL: http://www.ed.gov/about/bdscomm/list/ncfmea.html
Staff: Staff support is provided by the Department of Education. **Descr:** Committee evaluates the standards of accreditation applied to medical schools by a number of foreign countries and determines the comparability of those standards to the standards of accreditation applied to U.S. medical schools. **Mem:** Committee consists of eleven members appointed by the Secretary of Education. Members are knowledgeable in foreign medical education and accreditation. Members serve three-year terms. Dr. J. Lee Dockery, Professor Emeritus, College of Medicine, University of Florida, Gainesville, Florida, chairs the Committee.

3438 ■ National Council on Disability
1331 F St. NW, Ste. 850
Washington, DC 20004
Contact: Mike Collins, Exec.Dir.
Ph: (202)272-2004
Fax: (202)272-2022
E-mail: ncd@ncd.gov
URL: http://www.ncd.gov

Descr: Council reviews all laws, programs, and policies of the federal government affecting disabled people and makes recommendations to the President of the United States, the U.S. Congress, the Secretary of Education, the Commissioner of the Rehabilitation Services Administration, and the Director of the National Institute of Disability and Rehabilitation Research. **Mem:** Council consists of fifteen members appointed by the President and confirmed by the U.S. Senate. NCD members are people with disabilities, parents or guardians of people with disabilities, or other people who have substantial knowledge or experience relating to disability policy or programs. Council is chaired by John R. Vaughn of Ft. Myers, FL, retired executive in the financial services industry and former commissioner of the Virginia Department of Rehabilitative Services and Commissioner of the Virginia Department for the Blind and Vision Impaired. **Pub:** Monthly electronic newsletter.

3439 ■ National High Blood Pressure Education Program Coordinating Committee
Office of Prevention, Education and Control
National Heart, Lung, & Blood Institute
31 Center Dr., MSC 2480
Bethesda, MD 20892-2480
Contact: Dr. Edward J. Roccella, Coord.
Ph: (301)496-1051
Free: 800-575-9355
Fax: (301)480-4907
E-mail: NHLBlinfo@rover.nhlbi.nih.gov
URL: http://www.nhlbi.nih.gov/about/nhbpep

Descr: Committee directs, examines issues, and develops strategies of the National High Blood Pressure Education Program. The Program was established to inform the general public of the wide prevalence of hypertension (especially among African-Americans and older Americans); of threats to life and health from uncontrolled hypertension; of the availability of effective measures for blood pressure control; of the benefits of getting adequate therapy and how high blood pressure can be prevented. Committee directs the policy development areas of the Program which includes professional and patient education, public education, information development and dissemination, operation of the NHLBI Health Information Network and community program development of hypertension. **Mem:** Committee comprises 38 members who represent national professional, public and voluntary health organizations and seven government agencies with an interest in the hypertension field. Elizabeth G. Nabel, MD, Director, National Heart, Lung, and Blood Institute, National Institutes of Health, chairs the Committee. **Pub:** Publications available upon request: National Heart, Lung, and

Blood Institute Health Information Center, PO Box 30105, Bethesda, MD, 20824-0105.

3440 ■ National Security Education Board

National Security Education Program, OSD (P & R)
Department of Defense
1101 Wilson Blvd., Ste. 1210
Rosslyn, VA 22209-2248
Contact: Dr. Robert O. Slater, Exec.Sec.
Ph: (703)696-1991
Fax: (703)696-5667
URL: http://www.ndu.edu/nsep/#BOARD

Descr: Board is tasked with developing criteria under the national Security Education Act of 1991 for awarding scholarships, fellowships, and grants to U.S. citizens and institutions; providing for a wide dissemination of information regarding the activities assisted under the Act; establishing qualifications for persons desiring scholarships or fellowships, and for institutions of higher education desiring grants under the Act. The awards support study in the disciplines of foreign languages, area studies, and other critical international areas currently under-served in higher education. **Mem:** Board consists of thirteen members: six presidential appointees; the Secretaries of Defense, Commerce, Education, Energy, and State; the Director of Central Intelligence; and the chair, National Endowment for the Humanities. Lt.Gen. Michael M. Dunn, President, National Defense University, chairs the Board. **Pub:** Annual Report to the President and Congress.

3441 ■ National Technical Advisory Council

Off. of Elementary & Secondary Education
Department of Education
400 Maryland Ave. SW., Rm. 3W246
Washington, DC 20202
Contact: Patrick Rooney, Designated Fed.Off.
Ph: (202)401-0113
Fax: (202)260-7764
URL: http://www.ed.gov/about/bdscomm/list/ntac/index.html

Staff: Support services are provided by the Department of Education. Patrick Rooney, Accountability Group Leader, serves as designated federal official. **Descr:** Council advises the Secretary of Education and the Assistant Secretary for Elementary and Secondary Education on the design and implementation of standards, assessments, and accountability systems consistent with Section 1111(b) of the Elementary and Secondary Education Act, as amended by the No Child Left Behind Act of 2001 and 34 CFR 200.1 through 200.20. Council provides guidance to help the Secretary and Assistant Secretary ensure that the assessment and accountability components of state accountability systems are based on sound technical decisions. **Mem:** Council consists of no more than 16 members, selected by the Secretary of Education, including academicians, researchers, and national, state, and local policymakers. The Secretary solicits recommendations for members from the public. Members are experts in assessment and accountability and at least one-third has experience working in or with state educational agencies or local educational agencies. Members serve three-year terms. Tom Fisher, Fisher Education Consulting, LLC, chairs the Council.

3442 ■ National Transportation Safety Board (NTSB)

Off. of Government and Industry Affairs
490 L'Enfant Plz. SW, Rm. 2164
Washington, DC 20594
Ph: (202)314-6121
Free: 800-877-6799
Fax: (202)314-6110
URL: http://www.ntsb.gov

Descr: Board promotes transportation safety by conducting independent investigations of accidents and other safety problems, and by formulating safety improvement recommendations. It is charged with investigating and determining the conditions and circumstances of: (1) civil aircraft accidents; (2) highway accidents, including railroad grade crossing accidents, that it selects in cooperation with states (3) railroad accidents in which there is a fatality or substantial property damage or involving a passenger train; (4) major marine casualties and any marine accident involving a public and nonpublic vessel; and (5) pipeline accidents in which there is a fatality or substantial property damage. In addition, Board is authorized to make safety recommendations, conduct special studies, and exercise oversight responsibility over other government agencies involved in transportation safety. It also evaluates safeguards used in the transportation of hazardous materials, assesses techniques and methods of accident investigation, and occasionally recommends procedures for accident investigation. **Mem:** Board consists of five members knowledgeable in areas of transportation safety. Members are appointed by the President of the United States and serve five-year terms. Maj. Gen. Mark V. Rosenker USAF (Ret.)serves as acting chairman of the Board. **Pub:** Lessons Learned and Lives Saved, 1975 - 2005. Publications of the Board deal with the safety aspects of accident investigation, analysis and determination of probable cause, accident prevention, and the promotion of air and surface safety.

3443 ■ National Voluntary Laboratory Accreditation Program (NVLAP)

National Institute of Standards & Technology
Standards Services Div.
100 Bureau Dr., MS 2140
Gaithersburg, MD 20899-2140
Contact: Vanda R. White, Quality Mgr.
Ph: (301)975-3592
Fax: (301)926-2884
E-mail: nvlap@nist.gov
URL: http://www.nist.gov/nvlap

Staff: Vanda R. White, Quality Manager, serves as staff contact. **Descr:** Program provides a national voluntary system to accredit private and public testing and calibration laboratories that serve regulatory and nonregulatory product and certification needs. NVLAP grants or denies accreditation of testing and calibration laboratories based on the Program's assessment of laboratories' competence to perform certain specified test and calibration methods. **Pub:** Online Directory of Accredited Laboratories; NIST Handbook 150: NVLAP Procedures and General Requirements; NVLAP News; and program-specific handbooks. Publications are available on the NVLAP website.

3444 ■ Navigation Safety Advisory Council (NAVSAC)

Waterways Management Directorate
Commandant (G-MWN), Rm. 1408
U.S. Coast Guard Headquarters
2100 2nd St. SW
Washington, DC 20593-0001
Contact: J. Michael Sollosi, Exec.Dir.
Ph: (202)372-1545
Fax: (202)372-1930

Staff: J. Michael Sollosi, Chief, Navigation Systems Division, U.S. Coast Guard, serves as executive director. **Descr:** Council was originally established to advise the Commandant, U.S. Coast Guard, on policy concerning Navigational Rules of the Road. Council made recommendations on matters relating to proposed changes to the Inland Rules and the International Regulations for Preventing Collisions at Sea (COLREGS), and provided industry and user input into the development of rules that comply with the mandate of the Convention on International Regulations for the Prevention of Collisions at Sea, 1972. The expanded Council advises, consults with and makes recommendations to the Secretary of Homeland Security on matters relating to the prevention of collisions, rammings, and groundings, including the Inland Rules of the Road, navigation regulations and equipment, routing measures, marine information, diving safety, and aids to navigation systems. **Mem:** Council is composed of up to twenty-one members appointed by the Secretary of Homeland Security for three-year terms. Members are selected from the following groups: persons having an active interest in the Rules of the Road and vessel and port safety; representatives of owners and operators of vessels, professional mariners, recreational boat owners, and the recreational boating industry; persons with an interest in maritime law; and federal and state officials with responsibility for vessel and port safety.

3445 ■ NIST Blue Ribbon Commission on Management and Safety

Off. of the Deputy Secretary of Commerce
Department of Commerce
14th St. & Constitution Ave. NW, Rm. 5838
Washington, DC 20230
Contact:Gen. Thomas L. Hemingway, Designated Fed.Off.
Ph: (202)482-8376
URL: http://www.nist.gov/director/blueribbon/

Staff: Support services were provided by the National Institute of Standards and Technology. Gen. Thomas L. Hemingway, Senior Advisor to the Deputy Secretary of Commerce, served as designated federal official. **Descr:** Commission investigated whether training, safety, security, response protocols, implementation of protocols and internal controls, and the management structure at the National Institute of Standards and Technology (NIST) are appropriate to ensure the safe operation of all NIST programs. **Mem:** Commission was composed of not more than seven members appointed by the Secretary of Commerce. Members included qualified experts with public or private sector experience in management and organizational structure, training and human resources operations, laboratory management and safety, hazardous materials safety, emergency medical response, environmental safety, environmental remediation, and security for hazardous materials. Dr. Charles V. Shank Sr., Fellow, Janelia Farm Research Center, and former Director, Lawrence Berkeley National Laboratory, chaired the Commission. **Pub:** Final Report of the NIST Blue Ribbon Commission on Management and Safety (November 2008).

3446 ■ Occupational Safety and Health Review Commission

1120 20th St. NW, 9th Fl.
Washington, DC 20036-3457
Contact: Ray H. Darling Jr., Exec.Sec.
Ph: (202)606-5400
Fax: (202)606-5050
E-mail: lt_gpo@oshrc.gov
URL: http://www.oshrc.gov

Descr: Commission rules on cases emanating from disagreements over the results of safety and health inspections performed by the Department's Occupational Safety and Health Administration. It functions essentially as a court from which cited employers and affected employees may seek a decision whenever they disagree with one or more aspects of an OSHA inspection. After the Review Commission is notified by OSHA that an inspection, is being contested, the case is docketed in the Review Commission's Washington office and assigned to an administrative law judge (ALJ). After a hearing or successful settlement negotiations, the ALJ issues an order affirming, modifying, or vacating the Secretary of Labor's citation and/or proposed penalty. Review Commission members may review the ALJ decision. Final decisions of the ALJ and Commission members may be appealed to the appropriate U.S. Court of Appeals. **Mem:** Commission comprises three members appointed by the President of the United States with the advice and consent of the U.S. Senate. Members serve six-year terms. Thomasina V. Rogers was designated by the President of the United States as acting chair of the Commission. **Pub:** No Fear Act Notice; No Fear Act; Regulations Implementing the Privacy Act of 1974, Final Rule; Policy for Personal Identity Verification at OSHRC; Instructions for Electronic Filing; Biennial report, Guide to Procedures; FAIR 2004 Inventory of Commercial and Inherently Governmental Activities; Settlement Part and Management and Administrative Initiatives to Support Settlement Part Implementation; Guide to Simplified Proceedings; Guide to Review Commission Procedures.

3447 ■ Overseas Schools Advisory Council (OSAC)
Off. of Overseas Schools, SA-1, Rm. H-328
Bureau of Administration
Department of State, A-OPR-OS
2401 E St. NW
Washington, DC 20522
Contact: John G. Osthaus, Designated Fed.Off.
Ph: (202)261-8208
Fax: (202)261-8224
E-mail: OverseasSchools@state.gov
URL: http://www.state.gov/m/a/os/c6971.htm
Staff: John G. Osthaus, Special Assistant, Office of Overseas Schools, Department of State, serves as designated federal official. **Descr:** Council provides advice with respect to policy guidance and financial support of American-sponsored elementary and secondary schools abroad that are assisted by the Department of State. Its function is to help these overseas schools become showcases for excellence in education and to help make service abroad more attractive to Americans with school-age children, both in the business community and in government. Specifically, Council coordinates efforts of American business firms and foundations with those of the Department toward providing needed educational facilities for dependents of American citizens abroad; facilitates obtaining maximum resources (funds, buildings, equipment, and supplies) from private and public agencies to assist those American-sponsored, independent community schools abroad which are assisted by the Department; and advises and consults with the Department on the relations between the U.S. government and private firms concerned with such schools. **Mem:** Council is composed of up to twenty-five public members who are appointed by the Assistant Secretary for Administration of the Department of State upon the recommendation of the Executive Secretary of the Council. Members are selected from among senior executives in the business, professional, and educational communities. A chairperson and two vice chairpersons are selected from the membership. Robert Wilson Jr., Vice President, Wealth Management, Smith Barney, chairs the Council.

3448 ■ President's Committee for People with Intellectual Disabilities
Department of Health and Human Services
The Aerospace Center, Suite 210
370 L'Enfant Promenade SW
Washington, DC 20447
Contact: Laverdia Taylor Roach, Acting Exec.Dir.
Ph: (202)619-0634
Fax: (202)205-9519
URL: http://www.acf.hhs.gov/programs/pcpid/index.html
Staff: Administrative support is provided by the Administration for Children and Families, Department of Health and Human Services. **Descr:** Committee acts in an advisory capacity to the President and the Secretary of Health and Human Services on matters relating to programs and services for persons with intellectual disabilities. It studies and evaluates governmental and private programs for people with intellectual disabilities, ascertains needs which government can help to meet, and suggests suitable measures for the President's consideration; promotes public awareness and action in combating intellectual disabilities; helps people with intellectual disabilities to develop to their full abilities; and provides liaison between federal activities and related state and local governments, foundations, and other private organizations. **Mem:** Committee consists of 21 citizen members and thirteen ex-officio members appointed by the President. Ex-officio members include the Secretaries of Health and Human Services, Education, Labor, Housing and Urban Development, Commerce, Transportation, the Interior, and Homeland Security; the Attorney General; the President and CEO of the Corporation for National and Community Service; the Chair of the Equal Employment Opportunity Commission; the

Chair of the National Council on Disability; and the Commissioner of the Social Security Administration. Members serve two-year terms. Steven C. Rhatigan chairs the Committee. **Pub:** Report to the President: Keeping the charge--Accessibility to Dental Care for People with Intellectual Disabilities (2005); Report to the President--A Charge We Have to Keep: A Road Map to Personal and Economic Freedom for Persons with Intellectual Disabilities (December 2004); Companion Booklet to Report to the President (December 2004); The Forgotten Generation: 1999 Report to the President.

3449 ■ Proposal Review Panel for Graduate Education
Division of Graduate Education
Directorate for Education and Human Resources
National Science Foundation
4201 Wilson Blvd., Rm. 875S
Arlington, VA 22230
Contact: Carol F. Stoel, Designated Found.Off.
Ph: (703)292-8624
Fax: (703)292-9048
URL: http://www.nsf.gov/div/index.jsp?div=DGE
Staff: Carol F. Stoel, Acting Director, Division of Graduate Education, serves as designated foundation official. **Descr:** Panel provides recommendations concerning proposals on graduate education submitted to the National Science Foundation for financial support, including Integrative Graduate Education and Research Training proposals, Graduate Research Fellowships Applications, Graduate Teaching Fellows in K-12 Education proposals and NATO Postdoctoral Fellowship applications. **Mem:** Panel comprises approximately 800 members selected for their knowledge in science and engineering and graduate education.

3450 ■ Proposal Review Panel for Research on Learning in Formal and Informal Settings
Research on Learning in Formal and Informal Settings
Directorate for Education and Human Resources
National Science Foundation
4201 Wilson Blvd., Rm. 885S
Arlington, VA 22230
Contact: Dr. Joan Ferrini-Mundy, Designated Found. Off.
Ph: (703)292-8620
Fax: (703)292-9044
Staff: Dr. Joan Ferrini-Mundy, Division Director, Research on Learning in Formal and Informal Settings, serves as designated foundation official. **Descr:** Panel provides advice and recommendations concerning proposals submitted to the National Science Foundation for financial support. **Mem:** Panel comprises approximately 600 members selected based on their expertise in various fields of mathematics and science, pedagogy, educational research, and specialized knowledge of school systems, schools, media, museums, community-based organizations, curriculum development, etc.

3451 ■ Proposal Review Panel for Undergraduate Education
Division of Undergraduate Education
Directorate for Education and Human Resources
National Science Foundation
4201 Wilson Blvd., Rm. 835N
Arlington, VA 22230
Contact: Dr. Linda L. Slakey, Designated Federal Official
Ph: (703)292-8670
Fax: (703)292-9015
E-mail: undergrad@nsf.gov
URL: http://fido.gov/facadatabase/committeeMenu.asp?cno=1213&FY=2009
Staff: Dr. Linda L. Slakey, Division Director, Division of Undergraduate Education, National Science Foundation, serves as Designated Federal Official. **Descr:** Panel provides advice and recommendations concerning proposals on undergraduate education submitted to the National Science Foundation for financial support. **Mem:** Panel comprises approximately 1,000 members selected for their expertise in

the fields of science, technology, engineering, mathematics, and education.

3452 ■ Railroad Safety Advisory Committee (RSAC)
Office of Safety
Federal Railroad Administration
Department of Transportation
1200 New Jersey Ave. SE
Washington, DC 20590
Contact: Larry W. Woolverton, Designated Fed.Off.
Ph: (202)493-6212
Fax: (202)493-6309
URL: http://rsac.fra.dot.gov/home.php
Staff: Larry Woolverton, Coordinator, Office of Safety, Federal Railroad Administration, serves as designated federal official. **Descr:** Committee was established to provide advice and make recommendations to the Federal Railroad Administration on railroad safety regulatory issues. **Mem:** Committee currently consists of 61 members representing railroad owners, manufacturers, labor groups, state government groups, and public interest associations; two associate members from agencies with rail responsibilities in Canada and Mexico; two advisory members representing the National Transportation Safety Board and the Federal Transit Administration, and a Federal Railroad Administration Chairperson.

3453 ■ Regional Office Committee on Educational Allowances
Department of Veterans Affairs
810 Vermont Ave. NW
Washington, DC 20420
URL: http://www.vba.va.gov
Descr: The Committee makes recommendations to the Director of the VA Regional Processing Office of jurisdiction in deciding in a specific case whether: (1) Educational assistance should be discontinued to all individuals enrolled in any course or courses an educational institution offers; and (2) If appropriate, whether approval of all further enrollments or reenrollments in the course or courses an educational institution offers should be denied to veterans, service members, reservists, or other eligible persons pursuing those courses under programs VA administers; or (3) Payment should be denied to all service members and veterans for taking a specific licensing or certification test. **Mem:** Committee is composed of three employees of the VA Regional Processing Office designated by the regional office director, at least one of whom is familiar with the adjudication of claims for benefits administered by the Veterans Benefits Administration.

3454 ■ Safe Routes to School Taskforce
Federal Highway Administration
Department of Transportation
1200 New Jersey Ave. SE
Washington, DC 20590
Contact: Tim Arnade, Designated Fed.Off.
Ph: (202)366-2205
Fax: (202)366-3222
E-mail: SRTS@tooledesign.com
URL: http://www.saferoutesinfo.org/task_force/
Staff: Support services were provided by the Office of Safety, Federal Highway Administration. Tim Arnade, Program Manager, Safe Routes to School, served as designated federal official. **Descr:** Task Force studied and developed a strategy for advancing Safe Routes to School Programs nationwide. **Mem:** Task Force members represented a cross-section of agencies, organizations, and individuals involved in Safe Routes to School activities and programs in the United States. Members are appointed by the Secretary of Transportation by recommendation of the Office of Safety, Federal Highway Administration. Donna Smallwood, Operations Manager, MassRIDES, chaired the task force. **Pub:** Safe Routes to School: A Transportation Legacy, A National Strategy to Increase Safety and Physical

Activity among American Youth, final report (July 2008).

3455 ■ State Councils on Developmental Disabilities
Admin. on Developmental Disabilities
Department of Health and Human Services
370 L'Enfant Promenade SW
Washington, DC 20447
Contact: Faith McCormick, Staff Contact
Ph: (202)690-6590
Fax: (202)690-6904
URL: http://www.acf.hhs.gov/programs/add/states/ddcs.html
Staff: Faith McCormick, Acting Commissioner, Office of Programs, Administration on Developmental Disabilities, serves as staff contact. **Descr:** Councils are established for each state that receives assistance under the Developmental Disabilities Act. Each Council develops a state plan for the provision of services for persons with developmental disabilities; monitors, reviews, and evaluates the implementation of the plan; and submits a report to the Secretary of Health and Human Services, through the governor, on its activities. **Mem:** Members of each Council are appointed by the governor of the state for which the Council was established. Up to 60
of the members are persons with developmental disabilities and up to 40
includes representatives from appropriate principal state agencies, local agencies, and nongovernmental agencies and private nonprofit groups concerned with services for persons with developmental disabilities in that state.

3456 ■ Veterans' Advisory Committee on Education
Education Service (ES)
Veterans Benefits Admin.
Department of Veterans Affairs
810 Vermont Ave. NW
Washington, DC 20420
Contact: Barrett Bogue, Designated Fed.Off.
Ph: (202)461-9812
Fax: (202)275-2636
URL: http://www1.va.gov/advisory/page.cfm?pg=2
Staff: Support services are provided by the Veterans Benefits Administration. **Descr:** Committee advises and consults with the Secretary of Veterans Affairs on the administration of education and training programs for veterans, servicepersons, reservists and guard personnel, and dependents of veterans. **Mem:** Committee currently consists of 20 members representing education, labor, management, and institutions that furnish education to veterans and their dependents. Ex officio members include the Assistant Secretary of Education for Postsecondary Education and the Assistant Secretary of Labor for Veterans Employment. James Bombard, President, National Association of State Approving Agencies, Inc., chairs the Committee. **Pub:** Veterans' Advisory Committee on Education Recommendations (February 2008).

Associations and Other Organizations

3457 ■ 100 Black Men of America
141 Auburn Ave.
Atlanta, GA 30303
Contact: John Hammond III, Pres./CEO
Ph: (404)688-5100
Free: 800-598-3411
Fax: (404)688-1028
E-mail: info@100bmoa.org
URL: http://www.100blackmen.org
Descr: Committed to improving the quality of life and enhance educational and economic opportunities for all African Americans. **Fnd:** 1987.

3458 ■ 129th Alumni and Heritage Association
6718 Zerillo Dr.
Riverbank, CA 95367-2122

Contact: Col. John L. Ruppel Jr., Pres.
Ph: (209)869-2879
E-mail: j-l.ruppel@worldnet.att.net
URL: http://www.129aha.org
Descr: Represents alumni and current members of the 129th Rescue Wing or any predecessor unit. Seeks to provide a historical perspective and documentation of the 129th Rescue Wing. Provides members with financial assistance and fraternal entity. **Fnd:** 1999. **Pub:** Newsletter.

3459 ■ Abilities!
201 I.U. Willets Rd.
Albertson, NY 11507-1599
Contact: Edmund L. Cortez, Pres./CEO
Ph: (516)465-1400
Fax: (516)465-1591
E-mail: webmaster@abilitiesonline.org
URL: http://www.ncds.org
Descr: Serves as a center providing educational, vocational, rehabilitation, and research opportunities for persons with disabilities. Work is conducted through the following: Abilities Health and Rehabilitation Services, a New York state licensed diagnostic and treatment center which offers comprehensive outpatient programs in physical therapy, occupational therapy, speech therapy, and psychological services; Career and Employment Institute, which evaluates, trains, and counsels more than 600 adults with disabilities each year, with the goal of productive competitive employment; Henry Viscardi School, which conducts early childhood, elementary, and secondary programs, as well as adult and continuing education programs; Research and Training Institute, which conducts research on the education, employment, and career development of persons with disabilities, and holds seminars and workshops for rehabilitation services professionals. Maintains library and speakers' bureau; compiles statistics; offers placement service; conducts research and educational programs. **Fnd:** 1952. **Pub:** Access Abilities! (quarterly).

3460 ■ Accreditation Commission for Acupuncture and Oriental Medicine (ACAOM)
7501 Greenway Center Dr., Ste. 760
Greenbelt, MD 20770
Contact: Dort S. Bigg JD, Exec. Dir.
Ph: (301)313-0855
Fax: (301)313-0912
E-mail: coordinator@acaom.org
URL: http://www.acaom.org
Staff: 6. **Descr:** Acts as an independent body to evaluate first professional master's degree and first professional master's level certificate and diploma programs in acupuncture and in Oriental medicine with concentrations in both acupuncture and herbal therapy for a level of performance, integrity and quality that entitles them to the confidence of the educational community and the public they serve. Evaluates doctoral programs in oriental medicine. Establishes accreditation criteria, arranges site visits, evaluates those programs that desire accredited status and publicly designates those programs that meet the criteria. **Fnd:** 1982. **Mem:** 73. **Pub:** ACAOM Policies and Procedures Manual; Acupuncture and Oriental Medicine Accreditation Newsletter (biennial); Preparing the Eligibility Report (MA Programs) Interim Guide for DAOM Eligibility Reports; Self Study Guide; Site Visitor Manual; Standards Manual.

3461 ■ ACT
PO Box 168
Iowa City, IA 52244-0168
Contact: Richard L. Ferguson, CEO/Chm.
Ph: (319)337-1000
Fax: (319)339-3020
E-mail: mediarelations@act.org
URL: http://www.act.org
Staff: 1100. **Descr:** Provides guidance-oriented assessment and research programs for students, schools, colleges, universities, vocational-technical institutes, and scholarship agencies. ACT Assessment Program, which consists of a profile questionnaire, interest inventory, and four 35-60 minute tests in English, mathematics, reading, and scientific

reasoning, is completed by more than 1,700,000 students annually. Provides colleges and universities with information used in admission, placement, and advising. ASSET and COMPASS, placement programs for two-year colleges, are completed by more than 1,600,000 students annually. Also offers eighth grade and tenth grade assessments; Work Keys, the nation's leading work skills testing system; and DISCOVER, an interactive educational and career planning program. Conducts more than 90 other assessment programs on behalf of organizations, and agencies. Conducts research, compiles statistics, and processes federal financial aid applications. **Fnd:** 1959. **State Groups:** 37. **Pub:** ACTivity (quarterly); Research Report Series (periodic); Brochures; Pamphlets; Reports.

3462 ■ Adult Higher Education Alliance (AHEA)
St. Edward's University
PACE Organizational Communication
3001 S Congress Ave.
Austin, TX 78704
Contact: Joan Dolamore, Pres.
Ph: (512)428-1333
E-mail: dolamorej@wit.edu
URL: http://www.ahea.org
Descr: Seeks to serve professionals and institutions offering alternative undergraduate and graduate degree programs for adults. Aims to help institutions of higher education develop and sustain learning environments and programs suitable for adults. Serves as a vehicle for cooperative consultation and collaboration among professionals in the field. Supports the professional development of members. **Pub:** Newsletter (quarterly).

3463 ■ Alliance for Fire and Smoke Containment and Control (AFSCC)
4 Brookhollow Rd. SW
Rome, GA 30165-6509
Contact: Mike Ashley, Exec. Dir.
Ph: (706)291-9355
Fax: (706)291-9355
E-mail: mwashley@afscc.org
URL: http://afscc.org
Descr: Promotes fire and smoke protection in a built environment. Educates and informs code officials and designers on fire and smoke protection issues. Facilitates fire fighting activities and fosters the practice and application of fire safety measures. **Fnd:** 1999. **Pub:** Articles; Reports.

3464 ■ Alliance for Full Participation (AFP)
202 Lexington Dr.
Silver Spring, MD 20901
Contact: Carol Walsh
Ph: (301)706-6252
E-mail: walshworks@verizon.net
URL: http://www.allianceforfullparticipation.org
Descr: Works, mobilizes and organizes with people with developmental disabilities, their families, and supporting communities and organizations to make the promise of inclusion, integration, productivity, independence and quality of life a reality in policy and practice. Focuses on employment and the factors that contribute to job retention such as education, housing, transportation and personal safety. **Fnd:** 2003.

3465 ■ Alliance for School Choice
1660 L St. NW, Ste. 1000
Washington, DC 20036
Contact: John Schilling, Interim Pres.
Ph: (202)280-1990
E-mail: info@allianceforschoolchoice.org
URL: http://www.allianceforschoolchoice.org
Descr: Aims to improve K-12 education. Promotes, implements and enhances the K-12 educational choice. Creates opportunities for systemic and sustainable educational reforms. Advances public policy that empowers parents to choose the education that is best for their children. **Pub:** School

Choice Activist (quarterly); *School Choice Digest* (quarterly); *Yearbook* (annual).

3466 ■ Alternative Religions Educational Network (AREN)
PO Box 1893
Trenton, FL 32693
Contact: Bill Kilborn
Ph: (321)243-2337
E-mail: aren1@aren.org
URL: http://www.aren.org
Descr: Religious freedom organization. Promotes earth centered religious and spiritual traditions, including witchcraft and paganism. **Fnd:** 1970. **Pub:** *ACTION.*

3467 ■ American Accreditation Healthcare Commission (URAC)
1220 L St. NW, Ste. 400
Washington, DC 20005
Contact: Bernard J. Mansheim MD, Chm.
Ph: (202)216-9010
Fax: (202)216-9006
E-mail: communications@urac.org
URL: http://www.urac.org
Staff: 24. **Descr:** Serves as an accreditation body for the managed health care industry. Seeks to establish and enforce standards for the managed care industry. Examines managed healthcare providers and bestows accreditation upon qualifying case management, health utilization management, health network, health plan, practitioner credentialing, credentials verification, workers' compensation utilization management, workers' compensation network, and health call center programs. **Fnd:** 1990. **Mem:** 300. **Pub:** *AccreditWatch* (quarterly); *Directory of Accredited Organizations* (annual); *Models of Care: Case Studies of Healthcare Delivery Innovation.*

3468 ■ American Association for Adult and Continuing Education (AAACE)
10111 Martin Luther King, Jr. Hwy., Ste. 200C
Bowie, MD 20720
Contact: Cle Anderson, Mgr.
Ph: (301)459-6261
Fax: (301)459-6241
E-mail: aaace10@aol.com
URL: http://www.aaace.org
Staff: 2. **Descr:** Provides leadership in advancing adult education as a lifelong learning process. Serves as a central forum for a wide variety of adult and continuing education special interest groups. Works to stimulate local, state, and regional adult continuing education efforts; encourages mutual cooperation and support; monitors proposed legislation and offers testimony to congress. **Fnd:** 1982. **Mem:** 4000. **Pub:** *Adult Education Quarterly* (quarterly); *Adult Learning* (bimonthly); *Adult Learning Magazine for Practitioners* (bimonthly); *Freedom Road*; *Workplace Literacy*; Membership Directory (annual); Reports.

3469 ■ American Association of Early Childhood Educators
3612 Bent Branch Ct.
Falls Church, VA 22041
Contact: Dr. William J. Tobin PhD, Exec. Dir.
Ph: (703)941-4329
Fax: (703)941-4329
Staff: 3. **Descr:** Represents directors, teachers, and teacher aides working in licensed childcare centers. **Fnd:** 1990. **Mem:** 5000. **Pub:** *AAECE First Class Educator* (quarterly).

3470 ■ American Association of People with Disabilities (AAPD)
1629 K St. NW, Ste. 503
Washington, DC 20006
Contact: Helena Berger, COO
Ph: (202)457-0046
Free: 800-840-8844
Fax: (202)457-0473
E-mail: aapd@aol.com
URL: http://www.aapd-dc.org
Staff: 10. **Descr:** Promotes economic and political empowerment of persons with disabilities; educating businesses and general public about disability issues. **Fnd:** 1995. **Mem:** 100000. **Pub:** *AAPD News* (quarterly); Annual Report (annual).

3471 ■ American Association of University Women (AAUW)
1111 16th St. NW
Washington, DC 20036
Contact: Ms. Linda D. Hallman, Exec. Dir.
Ph: (202)785-7700
Free: 800-326-2289
Fax: (202)872-1425
E-mail: info@aauw.org
URL: http://www.aauw.org
Staff: 90. **Descr:** Graduates of regionally accredited 4-year colleges, colleges, and universities. Engages in research and lobbying. Supports local branches involved in community action projects to foster advocation for girls. **Fnd:** 1881. **Mem:** 130000. **Reg. Groups:** 10. **State Groups:** 52. **Local Groups:** 1500. **Pub:** *AAUW Outlook* (periodic); *American Association of University Women--Action Alert* (periodic); Booklets; Brochures.

3472 ■ American Association of University Women Legal Advocacy Fund (AAUW/LAF)
1111 16th St. NW
Washington, DC 20036
Contact: Carolyn H. Garfein, Pres.
Ph: (202)785-7700
Free: 800-326-AAUW
Fax: (202)872-1425
E-mail: connect@aauw.org
URL: http://www.aauw.org/advocacy/laf//index.cfm
Descr: Promotes equity for women in higher education; supports discrimination lawsuits against colleges and universities; provides financial support for sex discrimination lawsuits; works to educate the university community about sex discrimination; aims to improve conditions through campus outreach; provides consulting with individuals on legal strategies, resources and potential lawsuits. **Fnd:** 1981. **Pub:** *LAF Update.*

3473 ■ American Association for Vocational Instructional Materials (AAVIM)
220 Smithonia Rd.
Winterville, GA 30683
Contact: Mr. Gary Farmer, Dir.
Ph: (706)742-5355
Free: 800-228-4689
Fax: (706)742-7005
E-mail: sales@aavim.com
URL: http://www.aavim.com
Staff: 5. **Descr:** Serves as an interstate organization of universities, colleges, and divisions of vocational education devoted to the improvement of teaching through better information and teaching aids. Purpose is to provide vocational instructional materials in a manner most useful to both teacher and student. **Fnd:** 1949. **Mem:** 7. **Pub:** Catalogs (annual).

3474 ■ American Consumer Credit Counseling (ACCC)
130 Rumford Ave., Ste. 202
Auburndale, MA 02466-1371
Contact: Steven R. Trumble, Pres./CEO
Ph: (617)559-5700
Free: 800-769-3571
Fax: (617)244-1116
URL: http://www.consumercredit.com
Descr: Offers confidential credit counseling and financial education services to consumers. Helps people regain control of their finances and plan for a debt free future. Provides professional financial solutions such as debt management plans, budget counseling, financial resources, and community education programs. **Fnd:** 1991.

3475 ■ American Council for Drug Education (ACDE)
164 W 74th St.
New York, NY 10023
Ph: (718)222-6641
E-mail: acde@phoenixhouse.org
URL: http://www.acde.org
Staff: 4. **Descr:** Doctors, mental health counselors, teachers, clergymen, policymakers, school librarians, parent groups, industry leaders, and concerned individuals. Disseminates information and research on all drugs of abuse. Makes available resource information kits that include both written and audiovisual materials. Provides prevention materials to colleges and high schools. **Fnd:** 1977. **Pub:** *Free Catalog*; Brochures; Handbooks.

3476 ■ American Council on Education (ACE)
1 Dupont Cir. NW
Washington, DC 20036-1193
Contact: Molly Corbett Broad, Pres.
Ph: (202)939-9300
Fax: (202)659-2212
E-mail: comments@ace.nche.edu
URL: http://www.acenet.edu
Staff: 175. **Descr:** A council of colleges and universities, educational organizations, and affiliates. Represents accredited, degree-granting postsecondary institutions directly or through national and regional higher education associations; advocates on their behalf before congress, the federal government, and federal and state courts. Advances education and educational methods through comprehensive voluntary action on the part of American educational associations, organizations, and institutions. Serves as an advocate for adult education and nationally administers the GED (General Education Development) high school equivalency exam. Provides college credit equivalency evaluations for courses taught outside the traditional campus classroom by corporations and the military. Maintains numerous commissions, committees, and councils. **Fnd:** 1918. **Mem:** 17500. **Pub:** *Accredited Institutions of Higher Education* (annual); *ACE/Praeger Series on Higher Education*; *Higher Education and National Affairs Headlines* (semiweekly); *The Presidency* (3/year); Yearbooks.

3477 ■ American Council on Rural Special Education (ACRES)
Montana Center on Disabilities/MSU-Billings
1500 University Dr.
Billings, MT 59101
Contact: Lori Garnes, Chair
Ph: (406)657-2312
Free: 888-866-3822
Fax: (406)657-2313
E-mail: inquiries@acres-sped.org
URL: http://www.acres-sped.org
Descr: Represents rural special educators and administrators, parents of students with disabilities, and university and state department personnel. Works to enhance direct services to rural individuals and agencies serving exceptional students and to increase educational opportunities for rural students with special needs; works to develop models for serving at-risk rural students, and a system for forecasting futures for rural special education and to plan creative service delivery alternatives. Provides professional development opportunities; disseminates information on the current needs of rural special education. Conducts task forces on specific rural problems and professional training. **Fnd:** 1981. **Mem:** 200. **Pub:** *Rural Special Education Quarterly* (quarterly); *RuraLink* (quarterly); Books.

3478 ■ American Counseling Association (ACA)
5999 Stevenson Ave.
Alexandria, VA 22304
Contact: Richard Yep, Exec. Dir.
Free: 800-347-6647
Fax: (703)823-0252
E-mail: ryep@counseling.org
URL: http://www.counseling.org
Descr: Counseling professionals in elementary and secondary schools, higher education, community agencies and organizations, rehabilitation programs, government, industry, business, private practice, career counseling, and mental health counseling.

Conducts professional development institutes and provides liability insurance. Maintains Counseling and Human Development Foundation to fund counseling projects. **Fnd:** 1952. **Mem:** 45000. **Reg. Groups:** 4. **State Groups:** 56. **Pub:** *Career Development Quarterly* (quarterly); *Counseling and Values* (3/year); *Journal of Addictions and Offender Counseling* (semiannual); *Journal of College Counseling* (semiannual); *Journal of Counseling and Development* (quarterly); *Journal of Employment Counseling* (quarterly); *The Journal of Humanistic Counseling, Education and Development* (quarterly); *Journal of Multicultural Counseling and Development* (quarterly).

3479 ■ American Medical Student Association (AMSA)
1902 Association Dr.
Reston, VA 20191
Contact: Carol Williams-Nickelson PsyD, Exec. Dir.
Ph: (703)620-6600
Free: 800-767-2266
Fax: (703)620-5873
E-mail: amsa@amsa.org
URL: http://www.amsa.org
Staff: 30. **Descr:** Medical students; local, state, and national organizations; premedical students, interns, and residents. Seeks to improve medical education by making it relevant to today's needs and by making the process by which physicians are trained more humanistic. Contributes to the improvement of health care of all people; involves its members in the social, moral, and ethical obligations of the profession of medicine. Serves as a mechanism through which students may actively participate in the fields of community health through various student health programs. Addresses political issues relating to the nation's health care delivery system and other medical and health issues. Maintains action committees and interest groups which publish newsletters, organize educational workshops, and initiate special projects. **Fnd:** 1950. **Mem:** 35000. **Local Groups:** 140. **Pub:** *Focus*; *Global Pulse: AMSA's International Health Journal*; *The Healer's Voice* (monthly); *The New Physician* (9/year).

3480 ■ America's Athletes with Disabilities (AAD)
2813 Spindle Ln.
Bowie, MD 20715-2136
Contact: David R. Williamson, Pres.
Ph: (301)464-3776
Fax: (301)464-3776
E-mail: drwmson@aol.com
URL: http://www.americasathletes.org
Descr: Strives to promote and sponsor sports, recreation, fitness and leisure events for children and adults with physical disabilities. Maintains a National Athlete Registry. **Fnd:** 1985. **Pub:** *Victory Voice*.

3481 ■ America's Edge
1212 New York Ave. NW, Ste. 300
Washington, DC 20005
Contact: Joey Weedon, Deputy Natl. Dir.
Ph: (202)408-9282
Fax: (202)776-0110
E-mail: jweedon@americasedge.org
URL: http://www.americasedge.org
Descr: Encourages business leaders to support education policies and initiatives aimed at providing all Americans the skills and knowledge essential for success in a competitive global marketplace. Facilitates exchange of information on best practices in business advocacy and support for education reform. Supports legislative changes in public policy and programs that will help build a qualified workforce. **Fnd:** 2007. **Pub:** Reports.

3482 ■ Ancient Coins for Education
PO Box 90193
Springfield, MA 01139
Contact: Mark Lehman, Dir.
E-mail: aceassist@comcast.net
URL: http://ancientcoinsforeducation.org
Descr: Promotes education and cultural apprecia-

tion of the classics and the ancient world through the study of ancient coins. Provides coins to students for study and attribution with the help of online and computer resources. **Fnd:** 2001.

3483 ■ Anesthesia Patient Safety Foundation (APSF)
8007 S Meridian St., Bldg. 1, Ste. 2
Indianapolis, IN 46217-2922
Contact: Robert K. Stoeolting MD, Pres.
Fax: (317)888-1482
E-mail: walker@apsf.org
URL: http://www.apsf.org
Descr: Promotes safer anesthesia, fosters investigations to provide understanding of preventable anesthetic injuries. **Fnd:** 1984. **Pub:** *Anesthesia Patient Safety, A Modern History*; Newsletter (quarterly).

3484 ■ Arc of the United States
1010 Wayne Ave., Ste. 650
Silver Spring, MD 20910
Contact: Lynne Cleveland, Pres.
Ph: (301)565-3842
Free: 800-433-5255
Fax: (301)565-5342
E-mail: info@thearc.org
URL: http://www.thearc.org
Staff: 20. **Descr:** Parents, professional workers, and others interested in individuals with mental retardation. Works on local, state, and national levels to promote services, research, public understanding, and legislation for people with mental retardation and their families. Strives to include all children and adults with cognitive, intellectual and developmental disabilities in every community. **Fnd:** 1950. **Mem:** 140000. **State Groups:** 46. **Local Groups:** 100000. **Pub:** *The Arc Now* (monthly); *The ARC's Government Report* (semimonthly); *InSight* (quarterly).

3485 ■ Asian American Legal Defense and Education Fund (AALDEF)
99 Hudson St., 12th Fl.
New York, NY 10013
Contact: Margaret Fung, Exec. Dir.
Ph: (212)966-5932
Free: 800-966-5946
Fax: (212)966-4303
E-mail: info@aaldef.org
URL: http://www.aaldef.org
Staff: 17. **Descr:** Attorneys, legal workers, and members of the community who seek to employ legal, advocacy, and educational methods to address civil rights issues in Asian American communities. Provides bilingual legal counseling and representation for people who cannot obtain access to legal assistance; areas of concern include immigration, employment, voting rights, racially-motivated violence against Asian Americans, affirmative action and language rights. Litigates cases that have the potential of improving the quality of life in the Asian American community. Monitors and reports on incidents of racial discrimination against Asian Americans. Sponsors training sessions to inform community workers and residents of their rights and benefits before legal problems arise. Conducts student intern program to provide law and undergraduate students with legal experience in a community setting; is supported by foundation and corporate grants, special events, and individuals. **Fnd:** 1974. **Pub:** *The Asian American Vote 2004: A Report on the Multilingual Exit Poll in the 2004 Presidential Election*; *Outlook* (semiannual); *Righting Wrongs* (monthly); Pamphlet.

3486 ■ Asociacion para la Educacion Teologica Hispana (AETH)
100 E 27th St.
Austin, TX 78705-5711
Contact: Dr. Jose Daniel Montanez, Exec. Dir.
Ph: (512)708-0660
Free: 877-778-2384
Fax: (512)708-0671
E-mail: aeth@austinseminary.edu
URL: http://www.aeth.org
Descr: Stimulates dialogue and collaboration among

theological educators, administrators of institutions for ministerial formation, and Christian ministerial students in the United States, Canada and Puerto Rico. Affirms and supports educational programs and academic projects directed to Hispanic theological education. Creates a forum for the discussion of issues which affect institutions engaged in theological education for Hispanic-Americans. **Fnd:** 1991. **Pub:** *Encuentro*.

3487 ■ Association for the Advancement of Blind and Retarded (AABR)
1508 College Point Blvd., 2nd Fl.
College Point, NY 11356
Contact: Audrey Sachs Jr., Pres.
Ph: (718)321-3800
Fax: (718)321-8774
E-mail: cweldon@aabr.org
URL: http://aabr.org
Staff: 560. **Descr:** Community groups and individuals interested in multi-handicapped blind and severely retarded adults. Operates 19 group residences providing intermediate care and individual residential alternative facilities for blind and retarded adults; two treatment centers for blind, multi-handicapped, and severely retarded adults; NYS approved special education program for autistic children from preschool to school age. Provides information and referral services. **Fnd:** 1956. **Pub:** *AABR Newsletter* (3/year).

3488 ■ Association of African Women Scholars (AAWS)
Indiana University
French and Women's Studies
Cavanaugh Hall, Rm. 001C
425 University Blvd.
Indianapolis, IN 46202
Contact: Dr. Obioma Nnaemeka, Pres.
Ph: (317)278-2038
Fax: (317)274-2347
E-mail: aaws@iupui.edu
URL: http://www.iupui.edu/~aaws
Descr: Individuals. Promotes scholarship among women of African descent worldwide. Seeks to form intellectual links among scholars studying Africa, colonialism, and related topics. Serves as a clearinghouse on African history, culture, economics, and development, particularly as these subjects impact women. Provides information and advice to policy makers; participates in advocacy work. Conducts research and educational programs. **Fnd:** 1995. **Mem:** 327. **Pub:** *AAWS Newsletter* (semiannual).

3489 ■ Association for Assessment in Counseling and Education (AACE)
5999 Stevenson Ave.
Alexandria, VA 22304-3300
Contact: Dr. Rick Balkin, Pres.-Elect
Free: 800-347-6647
Fax: 800-473-2329
E-mail: jwatson@meridian.msstate.edu
URL: http://www.theaaceonline.com
Descr: A division of the American Counseling Association. School and college counselors, career counselors, rehabilitation counselors, private practice counselors and counselor educators. Supports counselors with information and advice that will help them use assessments appropriately. Provides: information on trends, issues, and advances in assessment; reviews and evaluations of new or revised tests; guidelines and position papers on topics such as responsible test use, application of minimum competency tests, career assessments, and performance assessments. **Fnd:** 1965. **Mem:** 995. **State Groups:** 13. **Pub:** *Measurement and Evaluation in Counseling and Development* (quarterly); *Newsnotes* (quarterly).

3490 ■ Association for Career and Technical Education (ACTE)
1410 King St.
Alexandria, VA 22314
Contact: Janet Bray CAE, Exec. Dir./Sec.-Treas.
Ph: (703)683-3111
Free: 800-826-9972

Fax: (703)683-7424
E-mail: acte@acteonline.org
URL: http://www.acteonline.org
Staff: 32. **Descr:** Represents teachers, supervisors, administrators, and others interested in the development and improvement of vocational, Technical, and practical arts education. Areas of interest include: secondary, postsecondary, and adult vocational education; education for special population groups; cooperative education. Works with such government agencies as: Bureau of Apprenticeship in Department of Labor; Office of Vocational Rehabilitation in Department of Health and Human Services; Veterans Administration; Office of Vocational and Adult Education of the Department of Education. Maintains hall of fame. **Fnd:** 1926. **Mem:** 35000. **State Groups:** 57. **Pub:** *ACTE News* (monthly); *Career Tech Update* (semimonthly); *Legislative Alert*; *National Awards Program*; *Techniques* (8/year); *Vocational Education Journal* (monthly); Newsletter (weekly).

3491 ■ Association for Career and Technical Education Research (ACTER)
North Carolina State University
13 Ricks Hall
Box 7607 NCSU
Raleigh, NC 27695
Contact: Barry Croom, Pres.-Elect
Ph: (919)515-1759
Fax: (919)515-9060
E-mail: barry_croom@ncsu.edu
URL: http://www.agri.wsu.edu/acter
Descr: Vocational and other educators interested in supporting or conducting research in vocational education; graduate students in vocational education research. Promotes research and development activities in vocational education; encourages training programs for vocational education researchers. **Fnd:** 1966. **Mem:** 500. **Pub:** *The Beacon* (quarterly); *Career and Technical Education Research* (quarterly); Monographs.

3492 ■ Association for the Education of Children with Medical Needs (AECMN)
7065 Hillgreen Dr.
Dallas, TX 75214
Contact: Carla Hart MSEd, Pres.
Ph: (214)456-5930
E-mail: judy.einstein@childrens.com
URL: http://www.aecmn.org
Descr: Provides professional support to individuals involved in the education of children with chronic illnesses and medical challenges. Promotes quality education of children with medical needs. Links communities of professional educators, parents, caregivers, healthcare professionals and patients. Increases awareness of the challenges of children with medical needs. **Fnd:** 2003. **Mem:** 74. **Pub:** Newsletter (quarterly).

3493 ■ Association for Education and Rehabilitation of the Blind and Visually Impaired (AERBVI)
1703 N Beauregard St., Ste. 440
Alexandria, VA 22311
Contact: Jim Gandorf CAE, Exec. Dir.
Ph: (703)671-4500
Free: 877-492-2708
Fax: (703)671-6391
E-mail: jgandorf@aerbvi.org
URL: http://www.aerbvi.org
Staff: 4. **Descr:** Provides support and assistance to professionals who work in all phases of education and rehabilitation of blind and visually impaired persons of all ages. **Fnd:** 1984. **Mem:** 4000. **State Groups:** 44. **Pub:** *AER Report* (quarterly); *Association for Education and Rehabilitation of the Blind and Visually Impaired--Job Exchange* (monthly); *Visual Impairment & Blindness*.

3494 ■ Association on Higher Education and Disability (AHEAD)
107 Commerce Center Dr., Ste. 204
Huntersville, NC 28078
Contact: Stephan J. Smith, Exec. Dir.
Ph: (704)947-7779

Fax: (704)948-7779
E-mail: ahead@ahead.org
URL: http://www.ahead.org
Staff: 8. **Descr:** Individuals interested in promoting the equal rights and opportunities of disabled postsecondary students, staff, faculty, and graduates. Provides an exchange of communication for those professionally involved with disabled students; collects, evaluates, and disseminates information; encourages and supports legislation for the benefit of disabled students. Conducts surveys on issues pertinent to college students with disabilities; offers resource referral system and employment exchange for positions in disability student services. Conducts research programs; compiles statistics. **Fnd:** 1977. **Mem:** 2000. **Reg. Groups:** 17. **Pub:** *ALERT* (bimonthly); *Journal of Postsecondary Education and Disability*; Membership Directory.

3495 ■ Association of Independent Consumer Credit Counseling Agencies (AICCCA)
11350 Random Hills Rd., Ste. 800, PMB 626
Fairfax, VA 22030
Contact: David C. Jones PhD, Pres.
Ph: (703)934-6118
Free: 866-703-8787
Fax: (703)802-0207
E-mail: assoc@aiccca.org
URL: http://www.aiccca.org
Descr: Represents non-profit credit counseling companies that provide consumer credit counseling, debt management, and financial education services. Aims to set industry standards and provide consumer protection guidelines for members. Advocates for equity and fair interaction between creditors and the credit counseling industry. **Fnd:** 1993.

3496 ■ Association of Independent School Admission Professionals (AISAP)
170 Boston Post Rd., No. 160
Madison, CT 06443
Contact: Janice Crampton, Exec. Dir.
Ph: (203)421-7051
E-mail: info@aisap.org
URL: http://www.aisap.org
Descr: Supports the advancement of independent school professionals involved in all aspects of admission and enrollment management. Promotes the value of independent school education. Facilitates training and collaborative dialogue among professionals involved and responsible for enrollment management. **Fnd:** 2004. **Pub:** *The Interviewer* (periodic).

3497 ■ Association for Support of Graduate Students (ASGS)
PO Box 4698
Incline Village, NV 89450-4698
Contact: Dr. Ronda Dave
Ph: (775)831-1399
Fax: (775)831-1221
E-mail: ronda@asgs.org
URL: http://www.asgs.org
Descr: Aims to help students plan, initiate and complete their theses or dissertations, produce the highest quality research, write effectively in the proper editorial style, obtain their academic degree(s), and improve their lives throughout the process.

3498 ■ Association for Vaccine Damaged Children (AVDC)
201-3041 Anson Ave.
Coquitlam, BC, Canada V3B 2H6
Contact: Ted Kuntz
Ph: (604)942-7134
Fax: (604)942-3915
E-mail: tjkuntz@axion.net
Descr: Children suffering disability as a result of reaction to a vaccine, their families, and health care professionals working with vaccine-damaged children. Seeks to improve the quality of life of vaccine-damaged children and their families; promotes advancement in the prevention of adverse vaccine reactions. Provides support and services to

vaccine-damaged children and their families; conducts educational programs.

3499 ■ ATV Safety Institute/Division of Specialty Vehicle Institute of America (ASI)
2 Jenner St., Ste. 150
Irvine, CA 92618-3806
Contact: Tim Buche, Pres.
Ph: (949)727-3727
Free: 800-887-2887
URL: http://www.atvsafety.org
Descr: A division of Specialty Vehicle Institute of America. Promotes safe and responsible use of all-terrain vehicles (ATVs). Conducts rider safety programs and disseminates public information. **Fnd:** 1988. **Mem:** 8. **Pub:** *A Guide to Off-Highway Riding*; *Parents, Youngsters and ATVs*; *Tips and Practice Guide for the ATV Rider*.

3500 ■ Automatic Fire Alarm Association (AFAA)
PO Box 1569
Jasper, GA 30143
Contact: Shane M. Clary, Chair
Ph: (678)454-3473
Fax: (678)454-3474
E-mail: fire-alarm@afaa.org
URL: http://www.afaa.org
Staff: 4. **Descr:** Represents automatic fire detection and fire alarm systems industry. Membership is made up of state and regional member associations, manufacturers, installing distributors, authorities having jurisdiction, and end users. Promotes Life Safety in America through involvement in the codes and standards making process and by providing training seminars on a national basis. **Fnd:** 1953. **Reg. Groups:** 4. **Pub:** *Signifire* (quarterly); Manuals.

3501 ■ Aviation Safety Institute (ASI)
PO Box 690
Worthington, OH 43085
Contact: Charles Minshall, Special Projects Dir.
Ph: (614)885-4242
Fax: (614)793-1708
E-mail: 110364.3550@compuserve.com
URL: http://www.aviationsafetyinstitute.com
Staff: 7. **Descr:** Acts as an independent party not aligned with industry or government to promote and improve aviation safety. Activities include: operating an anonymous hazard reporting system; conducting safety education programs and seminars; maintaining a computerized safety information system; performing safety audits and consulting services; conducting aircraft accident investigations and research projects on topics such as pilot and crew fatigue. Conducts research. **Fnd:** 1973. **Mem:** 500. **Pub:** *Aviation Safety Institute--Monitor* (quarterly).

3502 ■ BACCHUS Network
PO Box 100430
Denver, CO 80250-0430
Contact: Drew Hunter MPA, Pres./CEO
Ph: (303)871-0901
Fax: (303)871-0907
E-mail: admin@bacchusnetwork.org
URL: http://www.bacchusgamma.org
Descr: Students, advisors, faculty, and staff of colleges and universities in the U.S., Canada, and Mexico. Aims to deliver alcohol abuse prevention and health education to college students and their communities. Promotes responsible decisions and healthy lifestyles and discourages irresponsible or illegal use of alcohol. Encourages year-round prevention and education programs and activities. Operates Project GAMMA (Greeks Advocating Mature Management of Alcohol), a cooperative effort between BACCHUS and national Greek-letter organizations to increase undergraduate participation in alcohol education programs; National Collegiate Alcohol Awareness Week; and Safe Spring Break. Offers the Certified Peer Educator Training Program, a skill-based training curriculum for students. **Fnd:**

1975. **Mem:** 32000. **Reg. Groups:** 12. **State Groups:** 32. **Pub:** *The Peer Educator* (bimonthly).

3503 ■ A Better Chance
240 W 35th St., 9th Fl.
New York, NY 10001-2506
Contact: Ms. Sandra E. Timmons, Pres.
Ph: (646)346-1310
Free: 800-562-7865
Fax: (646)346-1311
E-mail: stimmons@abetterchance.org
URL: http://www.abetterchance.org
Staff: 25. **Descr:** Identifies, recruits, and places academically talented and motivated minority students into leading independent secondary schools and selected public schools. Students receive need-based financial assistance from member schools. Prepares students to attend selective colleges and universities and encourages their aspirations to assume positions of responsibility and leadership in American society. Conducts research and provides technical assistance on expanded educational opportunities for minority group students in secondary and higher education. **Fnd:** 1963. **Pub:** *Alumni*; *Letters to Member Schools* (annual); Annual Report; Brochure.

3504 ■ Better School Food (BSF)
487 E Main St.
Mount Kisco, NY 10549
Contact: Mary Ann Petrilena, Pres.
Ph: (914)864-1293
E-mail: info@betterschoolfood.org
URL: http://www.betterschoolfood.org
Descr: Represents parents, educators, and health professionals who are working with local communities to improve school meals. Raises awareness of the connection between food and children's health, behavior, and learning. Helps create wellness policies and implements new food standards. **Pub:** Newsletter (bimonthly).

3505 ■ Beyondmedia Education
4001 N Ravenswood Ave., No. 204 C
Chicago, IL 60613
Contact: Salome Chasnoff, Exec. Dir.
Ph: (773)857-7300
Fax: (773)857-7301
E-mail: beyond@beyondmedia.org
URL: http://www.beyondmedia.org
Descr: Collaborates with underserved and underrepresented women, youth, and communities to tell and connect their stories. Promotes social justice through the creation and distribution of media arts. Promotes access to media tools and information. Influences public policy and generates social transformation. **Fnd:** 1996. **Pub:** Newsletter (annual).

3506 ■ Bicycle Helmet Safety Institute (BHSI)
4611 7th St. S
Arlington, VA 22204-1419
Contact: Randy Swart, Dir.
Ph: (703)486-0100
Fax: (703)486-0100
E-mail: info@helmets.org
URL: http://www.helmets.org
Staff: 5. **Descr:** A national consumer-supported advocacy program of the Washington Area Bicyclist Association. Promotes the use of helmets for bicyclists. Disseminates information to the public and press. Works on the ASTM helmet standards committee. Compiles statistics. Sends Toolkit for Helmet Promotion Programs to teachers and others at no charge. **Fnd:** 1989. **Pub:** *Helmet Update Newsletter* (periodic); *Toolkit for Helmet Promotion Programs* (periodic).

3507 ■ Big Picture Alliance (BPA)
4732 Stenton Ave.
Philadelphia, PA 19144
Contact: Jeffrey A. Seder, Chm./Co-Founder/Exec. Dir.
Ph: (215)381-2588
Fax: (215)381-2593
E-mail: info@bigpicturealliance.org
URL: http://www.bigpicturealliance.org

Staff: 9. **Descr:** Seeks to educate and support the efforts of disadvantaged and underserved youth to develop self-expression, life skills, and job skills by engaging students in the inspiring and collaborative process of creating communications projects and media arts. Partners with schools, community centers and arts organizations with programs that support students in accessing advanced technologies, including digital media, computer arts and the Internet; uses intensive, hands-on training to engage young people's interest in media and media making and thereby developing language and communication skills, critical thinking, teamwork and self-esteem. **Fnd:** 1976. **Mem:** 50. **Pub:** Newsletter (quarterly).

3508 ■ Braille Authority of North America (BANA)
1805 N Oakland St.
Arlington, VA 22207
Contact: Judith Dixon, Chair
Ph: (202)707-0722
Fax: (202)707-0712
E-mail: jdix@loc.gov
URL: http://www.brailleauthority.org
Descr: Braille publishers, producers, and transcribers; representatives of consumer groups; educators of the visually handicapped; professional organizations. Aims to promote and facilitate the use, teaching, and production of Braille texts and other Braille items. Promulgates rules, makes interpretations, and renders opinions concerning literary and technical Braille codes and related forms and formats of embossed materials for the blind. **Fnd:** 1976. **Mem:** 12. **Pub:** *Braille Textbook Code Formats and Techniques*; *English Braille, American Edition*; *Learning the Nemeth Code*; *Nemeth Code of Braille Mathematics and Scientific Notation*; Directory (annual).

3509 ■ Braille Revival League (BRL)
57 Grandview Ave.
Watertown, MA 02472
Contact: Kim Charlson
Ph: (617)926-9198
Free: 800-424-8666
Fax: (617)923-0004
E-mail: kimcharlson@earthlink.net
Descr: Blind and visually impaired persons; professionals interested in promoting the use, production, and teaching of Braille. Encourages blind people to read and write in Braille; advocates the mandatory use of Braille instruction in educational facilities for the blind; promotes use of Braille material available through libraries and printing houses. Lends support to the Braille Authority of North America. Conducts research into Braille efficiency. **Fnd:** 1981. **Mem:** 1000. **State Groups:** 6. **Pub:** *BRL Memorandum* (quarterly).

3510 ■ Canada Safety Council (CSC)
1020 Thomas Spratt Pl.
Ottawa, ON, Canada K1G 5L5
Contact: Jack Smith, Pres.
Ph: (613)739-1535
Fax: (613)739-1566
E-mail: canadasafetycouncil@safety-council.org
URL: http://safety-council.org
Descr: Individuals and organizations. Seeks to reduce accident rates on the roads, in the workplace, and in the home. Conducts research and educational programs. **Fnd:** 1968. **Pub:** *Living Safety* (quarterly).

3511 ■ Canadian Association for Child Neurology (CACN)
7015 Macleod Trail SW, Ste. 709
Calgary, AB, Canada T2H 2K6
Ph: (403)229-9544
Fax: (403)229-1661
E-mail: info@cnsfederation.org
URL: http://www.ccns.org
Staff: 8. **Descr:** Seeks to promote the advancement of knowledge of the sciences pertaining to the development of the nervous system from conception to adult life and advance knowledge of the disease in the nervous system in children. Aims to stimulate

prevention of neurological disease and to foster improved treatment and care of young people with neurological handicaps. **Fnd:** 1991. **Mem:** 110. **Pub:** *Canadian Journal of Neurological Sciences* (quarterly).

3512 ■ Canadian Association for Distance Education (CADE)
260 Dalhousie St., Ste. 204
Ottawa, ON, Canada K1N 7E4
Contact: Mr. Tim Howard, Dir. of Admin.
Ph: (613)241-0018
Fax: (613)241-0019
E-mail: cade-aced@csse.ca
URL: http://www.cade-aced.ca
Descr: Educators, students, and other individuals with an interest in distance education. Promotes advancement in the field of distance education. Encourages use of new technologies in distance education. **Fnd:** 1983. **Mem:** 600. **Pub:** *Asynchronous Learning Networks* (periodic); *Journal of Distance Education* (semiannual).

3513 ■ Canadian Association of Student Financial Aid Administrators (CASFAA)
University of New Brunswick
PO Box 4400
Fredericton, NB, Canada E3B 5A3
Contact: Shelley Clayton, Pres.
E-mail: clayton@unb.ca
URL: http://www.casfaa.ca
Descr: Administrators of student financial aid programs. Promotes increased access to financial aid for students at all educational levels. Makes available continuing professional development courses for members; serves as a clearinghouse on student financial aid. **Fnd:** 1984. **Mem:** 100.

3514 ■ Canadian Council for Exceptional Children (CCEC)
479 Kingsleigh Ct.
Milton, ON, Canada L9T 1X6
Contact: Helga Berger, Pres.
Ph: (905)878-2145
Fax: (905)878-2145
E-mail: hberger@gov.mb.ca
URL: http://canadian.cec.sped.org
Staff: 1. **Descr:** Educators, parents, and others with an interest in the education and development of children with special needs. Promotes effective and appropriate education for children with behavioral difficulties, attention deficits, or other characteristics. Conducts educational programs for educators; sponsors research; participates in charitable activities. Provides children's services; maintains speakers' bureau; compiles statistics. Holds competitions. **Fnd:** 1921. **Mem:** 3000. **Pub:** *Keeping in Touch* (quarterly).

3515 ■ Canadian Council on Health Services Accreditation (CCHSA)
1730 St. Laurent Blvd., Ste. 100
Ottawa, ON, Canada K1G 5L1
Contact: Wendy Nicklin, Pres./CEO
Ph: (613)738-3800
Free: 800-814-7769
Fax: (613)738-7755
E-mail: international@cchsa-ccass.ca
URL: http://www.accreditation.ca
Staff: 60. **Descr:** Agencies and organizations accrediting health care services including mental health care, cancer treatment centers, home health care, and community health. Seeks to ensure high standards of ethics, practice, and equipment and facilities among Canadian health services. Formulates and enforces standards; conducts research and educational programs. **Fnd:** 1958. **Mem:** 1541. **Pub:** *The Accreditation Standard* (quarterly); *Standards*.

3516 ■ Canadian Credit Institute Educational Foundation (CCIEF)
219 Dufferin St., Ste. 216C
Toronto, ON, Canada M6L 3J1
Contact: Reggie Delovtich, Gen. Mgr.
Ph: (416)572-2615
Free: 888-447-3324
Fax: (416)572-2619

E-mail: geninfo@creditedu.org
URL: http://www.creditedu.org

Descr: Financial institutions and providers of financial planning services. Promotes adherence to high standards of ethics and practice by members. Provides financial support to credit initiatives. **Fnd:** 1967.

3517 ■ Canadian Educational Standards Institute (CESI)
PO Box 3013
St. Catharines, ON, Canada L2R 7C3
Contact: Ms. Anne-Marie Kee, Exec. Dir.
Ph: (905)684-5658
Fax: (905)684-6723
E-mail: execdir@cesi.edu
URL: http://www.cesi.edu/wordpress

Staff: 2. **Descr:** Independent schools. Seeks to develop and to ensure maintenance of high educational standards at independent primary and secondary educational institutions. Evaluates and accredits independent elementary and secondary schools. **Fnd:** 1986. **Mem:** 43. **Pub:** *CESI Newsletter* (quarterly).

3518 ■ Canadian Fire Alarm Association (CFAA)
85 Citizen Ct., Unit 5
Markham, ON, Canada L6G 1A8
Contact: Stephen Ames, Pres.
Ph: (905)944-0030
Free: 800-529-0552
Fax: (905)479-3639
E-mail: admin@cfaa.ca
URL: http://www.cfaa.ca

Descr: Promotes improved fire safety through use of fire alarms. Facilitates communication and cooperation among members; represents members' commercial and regulatory interests; sponsors research and educational programs. **Fnd:** 1973.

3519 ■ Canadian Fire Safety Association (CFSA)
2175 Sheppard Ave. E, Ste. 310
North York, ON, Canada M2J 1W8
Contact: Carolyne Vigon, Admin.
Ph: (416)492-9417
Fax: (416)491-1670
E-mail: cfsa@taylorenterprises.com
URL: http://canadianfiresafety.com

Descr: Individuals and organizations with an interest in fire safety. Promotes increased awareness of fire safety. Sponsors research and educational programs. **Fnd:** 1971.

3520 ■ Canadian Home and School Federation (CHSF)
Fisher Park School
250 Holland Ave.
Ottawa, ON, Canada K1Y 0Y6
Contact: Beverly Mullin, Pres.
Ph: (613)798-2837
Fax: (613)798-2838
E-mail: chsf@bellnet.ca
URL: http://www.canadianhomeandschool.com

Descr: Advocates for quality education and the well-being of children and youth. Provides a forum and a voice for parents to discuss and present parental views to the federal government and the public. Encourages parent leadership; collaborates with stakeholders; and is the national resource center for parents. **Fnd:** 1895.

3521 ■ Canadian Institute of Child Health (CICH)
384 Bank St., Ste. 300
Ottawa, ON, Canada K2P 1Y4
Contact: Dr. Angus A. Bruneau, Chm.
Ph: (613)230-8838
Fax: (613)230-6654
E-mail: cich@cich.ca
URL: http://www.cich.ca

Staff: 25. **Descr:** Works to promote and protect the health, well-being and rights of all children and youth through monitoring, education and advocacy. **Fnd:**

1977. **Mem:** 600. **Pub:** *Child Health* (quarterly); *Rights of the Child in the Health Care System.*

3522 ■ Canadian Network of Toxicology Centres (CNTC)
Bovey Bldg., 2nd Fl.
Gordon St.
University of Guelph
Guelph, ON, Canada N1G 2W1
Contact: Dr. Len Ritter, Exec. Dir.
Ph: (519)824-4120
Fax: (519)837-3861
E-mail: dwarner@uoguelph.ca
URL: http://www.uoguelph.ca/cntc

Descr: University based toxicology research centers. Seeks to improve human and environmental health through increased understanding of toxic substances and their impact on the environment. Coordinates research efforts of research team members; advises government agencies and industrial organizations concerned with the release of toxic substances into the environment. Supports educational programs in toxicology at all levels. Serves as a clearinghouse on toxicology and environmental health issues. **Fnd:** 1988. **Mem:** 300. **Pub:** *Toxicology Educators Resource Guide for Secondary School Audiences*; Annual Report.

3523 ■ Canadian Paralympic Committee (CPC)
85 rue Albert St., Ste. 1401
Ottawa, ON, Canada K1P 6A4
Contact: Brian MacPherson, COO
Ph: (613)569-4333
Fax: (613)569-2777
E-mail: brian@paralympic.ca
URL: http://www.paralympic.ca

Staff: 13. **Descr:** Committed to delivering a variety of programs and services to strengthen the paralympic movement in Canada, including sending Canadian teams to the Paralympic Games. Seeks to empower persons with a physical disability through sports. **Fnd:** 1993. **Mem:** 41. **Pub:** *Paralympic Insider* (monthly).

3524 ■ Canadian Teachers' Federation (CTF)
2490 Don Reid Dr.
Ottawa, ON, Canada K1H 1E1
Contact: Dr. Calvin Fraser, Sec. Gen.
Ph: (613)232-1505
Free: 866-283-1505
Fax: (613)232-1886
E-mail: info@ctf-fce.ca
URL: http://www.ctf-fce.ca

Staff: 45. **Descr:** Provincial and territorial teachers' organizations. Works to ensure that teachers' opinions are considered when national government bodies debate educational legislation. Facilitates communication and cooperation among members. Conducts research, educational, and lobbying activities. **Fnd:** 1920. **Mem:** 16.

3525 ■ CarryOn.com
PO Box 40058
Fort Wayne, IN 46804-0058
Contact: Sania Faucher
E-mail: info@carryon.com
URL: http://www.carryon.com

Descr: Aims to improve Internet safety for children. Raises public awareness and serves as an advocate for online child safety. Advances the fight against the proliferation of online child pornography and sexual victimization of children. **Fnd:** 2007.

3526 ■ Center on Education and Training for Employment (CETE)
Ohio State University
1900 Kenny Rd.
Columbus, OH 43210-1016
Contact: Ronald Jacobs
Ph: (614)292-6991
Free: 800-848-4815
Fax: (614)292-1260
E-mail: chambers.2@osu.edu
URL: http://www.cete.org

Staff: 50. **Descr:** Aims to increase the ability of diverse agencies, institutions, and organizations to

solve educational problems relating to individual career planning, preparation, and progression. Conducts occupational analyses and staff training programs. Evaluates programs and agencies and provides technical assistance. Researches identified problems or needs. Develops databases, information systems, and occupational curricula. **Fnd:** 1965. **Pub:** *Centegram* (quarterly).

3527 ■ Center for the Education of Women (CEW)
330 E Liberty St.
Ann Arbor, MI 48104
Contact: Gloria Thomas, Dir.
Ph: (734)764-6005
Fax: (734)998-6203
E-mail: cew.mail@umich.edu
URL: http://www.umich.edu/~cew

Descr: Offers services, advocacy and research in the area of women's employment, education, leadership, career and life transitions, and women faculty. **Fnd:** 1964.

3528 ■ Center for Law and Education (CLE)
1875 Connecticut Ave. NW, Ste. 510
Washington, DC 20009
Contact: Kathleen Boundy, Co-Dir.
Ph: (202)986-3000
Fax: (202)986-6648
E-mail: cle@cleweb.org
URL: http://www.cleweb.org

Staff: 14. **Descr:** Provides support services on education issues to advocates working on behalf of low-income students and parents. **Fnd:** 1969. **Pub:** *CAPS Newsletter*; *School Improvement Catalogs* (3/year).

3529 ■ Center for Workers with Disabilities (CWD)
810 1st St. NE, Ste. 500
Washington, DC 20002
Contact: Nanette Relave, Proj. Dir.
Ph: (202)682-0100
Fax: (202)204-0071
E-mail: nrelave@aphsa.org
URL: http://cwd.aphsa.org

Descr: Aids participating states to implement provisions of "Ticket to Work and Work Incentives Improvement Act of 1999". **Fnd:** 2001. **Pub:** *Working for Tomorrow* (monthly); Report (periodic).

3530 ■ Centra Cam Vocational Training Association (CCVTA)
5502 - 46th St.
PO Box 1443
Camrose, AB, Canada T4V 1X4
Contact: Roxanna Skjonsberg, Exec. Dir.
Ph: (780)672-9995
Fax: (780)672-0534
E-mail: ccvta@centracam.ca
URL: http://www.centracam.ca/default2.html

Staff: 50. **Descr:** Individuals with an interest in the vocational training of adults with disabilities. Seeks to improve the quality of life of people with disabilities; encourages employers to hire qualified people with disabilities. Assists in the integration of adults with disabilities into society; sponsors training programs for people providing vocational education to individuals with disabilities. **Fnd:** 1979. **Mem:** 25.

3531 ■ Challenged Conquistadors
1110 Pine Cir.
Smackover, AR 71762
Contact: Shaun Best, Pres./Founder
Ph: (870)725-3612
E-mail: shaun_best_2000@yahoo.com
URL: http://www.SpeakersQuest.com/speakers/Best.htm

Staff: 1. **Descr:** Works to increase self preservation, reduce dependency, and eradicate negative stereotypes, myths, and stigmas about persons with brain injuries. Targets active, positive, challenged role models to show others that success is obtainable. Reinforces individual empowerment and capabilities to reveal the talents inherent in all challenged individuals and reap rewards as opposed to the "stagnation and destruction that many social programs have achieved." Offers educational and research programs. **Fnd:** 1993. **Mem:** 10000. **Local Groups:** 1.

3532 ■ C.H.A.S.E. for Life
PO Box 443
Little Silver, NJ 07739
Contact: Farley Boyle, Founder/Pres./Exec. Dir.
Free: 888-547-4460
E-mail: fboyle@chaseforlife.org
URL: http://www.chaseforlife.org
Descr: Seeks to save children's lives by teaching the basic life-saving skills needed to sustain a life until help can take over. Works to make the education of Infant/Child CPR and Choking Maneuvers free and readily available to the nation. Develops programs and community outreach initiatives that provide free education, resources and training to families, child care providers and the community at large. **Fnd:** 2005.

3533 ■ Children of the Earth United
PO Box 816
Columbia, MD 21044
Contact: Jennifer Reinfeld, Founder/Exec. Dir.
Ph: (443)321-4617
E-mail: info@childrenoftheearth.org
URL: http://www.childrenoftheearth.org
Descr: Aims to help foster a greater understanding and respect for the environment. Educates the general public on environmental issues and ecological concepts. Provides a forum for children and adults to share knowledge and ideas, and learn about animals, plants and the environment. Offers educational programs for children and educational information system accessible through the internet. **Fnd:** 1998.

3534 ■ Children's Advertising Review Unit (CARU)
70 W 36th St., 12th Fl.
New York, NY 10018
Contact: Wayne J. Keeley, Dir.
Free: 866-334-6272
E-mail: caru@caru.bbb.org
URL: http://www.caru.org
Staff: 6. **Descr:** Participants include advertisers and advertising agencies. Monitors and evaluates child-directed advertising in all media; reviews advertising prior to its release upon request. Seeks voluntary change when advertising is found to be inaccurate, misleading, or otherwise inconsistent with the association's Self-Regulatory Guidelines for Children's Advertising. Acts as arbitrator in cases where the truthfulness of advertising claims comes under question by a competitor and entertains consumer complaints. Maintains Advisory Board to gather and disseminate information on the ways in which children perceive and understand advertising, and to revisit guidelines to ensure they remain current. Provides a Safe Harbor program under COPPA for the association's supporters. **Fnd:** 1974. **Local Groups:** 1. **Pub:** *A Parent's Guide: Advertising and Your Child*; *Self-Regulatory Guidelines for Children's Advertising*.

3535 ■ Children's Defense Fund (CDF)
25 E St. NW
Washington, DC 20001
Contact: Marian Wright Edelman, Founder/Pres.
Ph: (202)628-8787
Free: 800-233-1200
Fax: (202)662-3560
E-mail: cdfinfo@childrensdefense.org
URL: http://www.childrensdefense.org
Descr: Provides systematic, long-range advocacy on behalf of the nation's children and teenagers. Engages in research, public education, monitoring of federal agencies, litigation, legislative drafting and testimony, assistance to state and local groups, and community organizing in areas of child welfare, child health, adolescent pregnancy prevention, child care and development, family income, family services, prevention of violence against and by children and child mental health. Works with individuals and

groups to change policies and practices resulting in neglect or maltreatment of millions of children. Advocates: access to existing programs and services; creation of new programs and services where necessary; consistent emphasis on prevention; enforcement of civil rights laws; program accountability; strong parent and community role in decision-making; adequate funding for essential programs for children. Compiles statistics. **Fnd:** 1973. **State Groups:** 9. **Local Groups:** 7. **Pub:** *America's Cradle to Prison Pipeline*.

3536 ■ Children's Eye Foundation (CEF)
1527 W State Hwy. 114, Ste. 500, No. 216
Grapevine, TX 76051
Contact: Dr. Robert D. Gross MD, Pres.
Ph: (817)891-1144
Fax: (817)329-5532
E-mail: info@childrenseyefoundation.org
URL: http://www.childrenseyefoundation.org
Staff: 3. **Descr:** Seeks to optimize the quality of life of infants, children, and families by fostering normal development and protection of vision through promoting programs of prevention, detection, treatment, research and education. **Fnd:** 1970. **Pub:** Annual Report (annual); Brochures.

3537 ■ Children's Grief Education Association (CGEA)
PO Box 21876
Denver, CO 80221
Contact: Mary M. Lyles, Exec. Dir.
Ph: (303)722-2319
Free: 877-722-2319
E-mail: support@childgrief.org
URL: http://www.childgrief.org
Descr: Serves the needs of grieving children and families. Provides grief education and support to bereaved children, their families and professionals in schools and community organizations. Offers outreach and training programs. **Fnd:** 2004. **Pub:** Newsletter.

3538 ■ Christian Overcomers (CO)
PO Box 2007
Garfield, NJ 07026
Contact: Debbie Neilley
Ph: (973)253-2343
E-mail: overcomers2007@optonline.net
URL: http://www.christian-overcomers.org
Staff: 3. **Descr:** Individuals with physical disabilities and volunteers. Provides holistic physical and spiritual guidance to help members live with their disabilities. Sponsors camp program that provides Bible study, worship, recreational and social activities, and encourages "commitment to Jesus Christ and each other." Functions as a resource for local groups that wish to conduct activities including athletic events, outings, dinners, and other socially oriented educational programs for physically disabled individuals. Maintains speakers' bureau. Provides volunteer training. **Fnd:** 1977. **Pub:** *Library Catalog* (annual); *The Overcomer* (quarterly); Brochure.

3539 ■ Citizens for Effective Schools (CES)
8209 Hamilton Spring Ct.
Bethesda, MD 20817
Contact: Gary Ratner, Founder/Exec. Dir.
Ph: (301)469-8000
E-mail: info@citizenseffectiveschools.org
URL: http://www.citizenseffectiveschools.org
Descr: Seeks to promote and advance the academic proficiency of public school students. Supports the provisions of federal funding of public schools on state and local levels. Encourages the public to advocate for changes in educational policy.

3540 ■ Clearinghouse on Disability Information (CDI)
Office of Special Education and Rehabilitative Services
Communication and Media Support Services
United States U.S. Department of of Education
500 12th St. SW, Rm. 5133
Washington, DC 20202-2550
Contact: Carolyn Corlett, Technical Asst.

Ph: (202)245-7307
Free: 800-437-0833
Fax: (202)245-7636
URL: http://www.ed.gov/about/offices/list/osers/codi.html
Staff: 4. **Descr:** Provides information to people with disabilities, or anyone requesting information, by doing research and providing documents in response to inquiries. Information provided includes areas of federal funding for disability-related programs. Clearinghouse staff is trained to refer requests to other sources of disability related information, if necessary. **Fnd:** 1973. **Pub:** *Pocket Guide to Federal Help for Individuals With Disabilities*.

3541 ■ Clinical Legal Education Association (CLEA)
New York University School of Law
245 Sullivan St., 5th Fl.
New York, NY 10012
Contact: Paula Galowitz, Sec.
Ph: (212)998-6441
Fax: (212)995-4031
E-mail: clea@cleaweb.org
URL: http://www.cleaweb.org
Descr: Promotes the interests and professional development of clinical teachers. Encourages the expansion and improvement of clinical legal education. Supports clinical research and scholarship. Disseminates information about issues and developments that affect clinical teachers. **Fnd:** 1992. **Pub:** *CLEA Newsletter*.

3542 ■ Coalition for Emotional Literacy (CEL)
10801 Old Manchaca Rd., Ste. 1908
Austin, TX 78748
Contact: Gayle Temkin, Founding Dir.
Ph: (512)351-5538
E-mail: contact@thecel.org
URL: http://www.coalitionforemotionalliteracy.org
Descr: Promotes emotional literacy by sharing resources and information that will help people in the self-management of their emotions. Offers support to people who need healing and self-improvement. Encourages every individual to make a connection with themselves (body, mind, and emotions), which will manifest optimal happiness, wellness, and productivity.

3543 ■ Coalition for Fire-Safe Cigarettes
1 Batterymarch Park
Quincy, MA 02169
Contact: Ms. Lorraine Carli, VP of Communications
Ph: (617)984-7275
E-mail: publicaffairs@nfpa.org
URL: http://www.firesafecigarettes.org
Descr: Represents fire service members, consumer and disability rights advocates, medical and public health practitioners, and others, coordinated by National Fire Protection Association (NFPA). Works to save lives and prevent injuries and devastation from cigarette-ignited fires. Encourages manufacturers to immediately produce and market only cigarettes that adhere to an established fire safety performance standard. Works to see that these standards for fire-safe cigarettes are required in every state in the country.

3544 ■ Coalition for Science After School (CSAS)
University of California
Lawrence Hall of Science
REA No. 5200
Berkeley, CA 94720
Contact: Jason Freeman, Dir.
Ph: (510)642-8106
E-mail: scienceafterschool@gmail.com
URL: http://www.scienceafterschool.org
Descr: Represents individuals and organizations from science, technology, engineering and mathematics (STEM) education, youth development and out-of-school time programs. Increases and improves opportunities for children to learn science, technol-

ogy, engineering and mathematics in after-school programs.

3545 ■ Cognitive Development Society (CDS)
Taylor and Francis
325 Chestnut St.
Philadelphia, PA 19106
Contact: Henry Wellman, Pres.
Free: 800-354-1420
Fax: (215)625-2940
E-mail: secretary@cogdevsoc.org
URL: http://www.cogdevsoc.org
Descr: Aims to provide a unified voice for the wide range of scholars, practitioners and others who are interested in change and continuity in the intellectual processes that support mental life. Seeks to understand ontogenetic processes in both humans and nonhumans. Provides a forum for innovative research and theory. **Fnd:** 1999.

3546 ■ The College Board (TCB)
45 Columbus Ave.
New York, NY 10023-6992
Contact:Governor Gaston Caperton, Pres.
Ph: (212)713-8000
Free: 866-392-3017
Fax: (212)649-8442
E-mail: publicaffairs@collegeboard.org
URL: http://www.collegeboard.com
Staff: 1000. **Descr:** Represents the schools, colleges, universities, and other educational organizations that seeks to connect members to success and opportunity. Serves students, parents, high schools, and colleges through major programs and services in college admission, guidance, assessment, financial aid, enrollment, and teaching and learning. **Fnd:** 1900. **Mem:** 5400. **Reg. Groups:** 6. **Pub:** *Campus Visits and College Interviews*; *CLEP Official Study Guide* (annual); *The College Application Essay*; *College Board Book of Majors* (biennial); *College Board College Handbook* (annual); *College Board Review* (3/year); *College Counseling Sourcebook* (annual); *College Scoop* (biennial); *CollegeEd Family Handbooks*; *CollegeEd Student Workbooks*; *CollegeEd Teachers Guides*; *Getting Financial Aid* (annual); *International Student Handbook* (annual); *Meeting College Costs*; *Official SAT Study Guide*; *Onboard*; *Scholarship Handbook* (annual); Proceedings (annual).

3547 ■ College Savings Plans Network (CSPN)
PO Box 11910
Lexington, KY 40578-1910
Contact: Jacqueline Williams, Chair
Ph: (859)244-8175
Free: 877-277-6496
E-mail: cspn@csg.org
URL: http://www.collegesavings.org
Descr: State sponsored savings plans allowing parents to set aside money for their children's postsecondary education. Promotes use of state savings plans to defray postsecondary educational costs. Serves as a clearinghouse on state educational savings plans. **Fnd:** 1991. **Mem:** 125.

3548 ■ Collegiate Equestrian Polo Association (CEPA)
20317 Coulson St.
Woodland Hills, CA 91367
Contact: Andres Huertas, Treas./Exec. Dir.
Ph: (818)346-7648
E-mail: andres@cepa-polo.org
URL: http://www.cepapolo.org
Descr: Promotes the spirit of safety, competition, sportsmanship, and friendship among polo players. Provides polo ponies, tack, equipment, money, and instructional materials and coaching. Maintains Clearing House Database of polo resources.

3549 ■ Committee for Children (CFC)
568 1st Ave. S, Ste. 600
Seattle, WA 98104-2804
Contact: Ed Rogan, Pres.
Ph: (206)343-1223
Free: 800-634-4449
Fax: (206)438-6765

E-mail: info@cfchildren.org
URL: http://www.cfchildren.org
Staff: 95. **Descr:** Promotes the safety, well-being, and social development of children by creating quality educational programs for educators, families, and communities. **Fnd:** 1981. **Mem:** 17. **Pub:** *A Family Guide to Second Step*; *Catalog of Committee for Children-Prevention Education Resources* (semiannual); *Prevention Update* (3/year); *Second Step: A Violence Prevention Curriculum*; Annual Report (annual).

3550 ■ Common Cause (CC)
1133 19th St. NW, 9th Fl.
Washington, DC 20036
Contact: Bob Edgar, Pres./CEO
Ph: (202)833-1200
Free: 800-926-1064
E-mail: causenet@commoncause.org
URL: http://www.commoncause.org
Staff: 85. **Descr:** Nonpartisan citizens' lobby. Dedicated to fighting for open, honest, and accountable government at the national, state, and local levels. Gathers and disseminates information on the effects of money in politics; lobbies for political finance and other campaign reforms. **Fnd:** 1970. **Mem:** 300000. **State Groups:** 41.

3551 ■ Commonwealth of Learning (COL)
1055 W Hastings St., Ste. 1200
Vancouver, BC, Canada V6E 2E9
Contact: Sir John Daniel, CEO/Pres.
Ph: (604)775-8200
Fax: (604)775-8210
E-mail: info@col.org
URL: http://www.col.org/Pages/default.aspx
Staff: 35. **Descr:** Education in the Commonwealth. Intergovernmental organization created by Commonwealth Heads of Government to encourage the development and sharing of open learning and distance education knowledge, resources and technologies; helps developing nations improve access to quality education and training. Seeks to increase the quality and availability of educational opportunity in the Commonwealth. Serves as a forum for the exchange of ideas and information among members. Maintains information resource center; formulates consultancy reports; sponsors internship and attachment programs; works with vocational and technical education programs. **Fnd:** 1988. **Mem:** 53. **Pub:** *Connections/EdTech News* (3/year); *Three-Year Plan, 2009-2012*.

3552 ■ Communities In Schools (CIS)
2345 Crytal Dr., Ste. 801
Arlington, VA 22202
Contact: William E. Milliken, Founder/Vice Chm.
Ph: (703)519-8999
Free: 800-CIS4-KIDS
E-mail: cis@cisnet.org
URL: http://www.cisnet.org
Staff: 65. **Descr:** Works to help kids succeed in school and prepare for life. Champions the connection of needed community resources with schools to help young people successfully learn, stay in school and prepare for life. **Fnd:** 1977. **Reg. Groups:** 5. **State Groups:** 16. **Local Groups:** 121. **Pub:** *CIS Network News* (quarterly); *Facts You Can Use* (quarterly); *Forward, March!* (quarterly); Annual Report (annual); Brochures; Manuals.

3553 ■ Communities Without Borders (CWB)
63 Pickwick Rd.
West Newton, MA 02465
Contact: Richard Bail, Pres.
Ph: (617)233-6071
E-mail: info@communitieswithoutborders.org
URL: http://www.communitieswithoutborders.org
Descr: Seeks to increase educational opportunities for children. Educates AIDS orphans and other vulnerable children. Fosters community-to-

community relationships to foster development activities. **Pub:** Newsletter.

3554 ■ Community Anti-Drug Coalitions of America (CADCA)
625 Slaters Ln., Ste. 300
Alexandria, VA 22314-1176
Contact: Arthur T. Dean, Chm.
Ph: (703)706-0560
Free: 800-54-CADCA
Fax: (703)706-0565
E-mail: info@cadca.org
URL: http://cadca.org
Staff: 30. **Descr:** Represents coalitions working to make America's communities safe, healthy and drug-free. **Fnd:** 1992. **Mem:** 5000. **State Groups:** 35. **Local Groups:** 5000. **Pub:** *Coalitions* (quarterly); Annual Report.

3555 ■ Community Learning and Information Network (CLIN)
1750 K St. NW, Ste. 1200
Washington, DC 20006
Contact: Brenda Purdy, VP, Operations and Finance
Ph: (202)857-2330
Fax: (202)835-0643
E-mail: bpurdy@clin.org
URL: http://www.clin.org
Staff: 8. **Descr:** Seeks to improve the global competitiveness of U.S. industry through employment of technology-based educational and training programs. Designs and implements model technology-based educational programs. Maintains network of Centers to coordinate technology-based educational programs throughout the United States; works with government agencies and educational organizations to increase availability of technology-based educational programs. **Fnd:** 1992. **Pub:** *CLINews* (quarterly).

3556 ■ Compete America
1341 G St. NW, Ste. 1100
Washington, DC 20005
Contact: Eric Thomas
E-mail: info@competeamerica.org
URL: http://www.competeamerica.org
Descr: Represents corporations, educators, research institutions and trade associations committed to ensuring that U.S. has the talent for continued innovation, job creation and economic expansion. Provides education and job training. Establishes a secure and efficient employment-based immigration system.

3557 ■ The Conference Board (TCB)
845 3rd Ave.
New York, NY 10022
Contact: Douglas R. Conant, Chm.
Ph: (212)759-0900
Fax: (212)980-7014
E-mail: nick.sutcliffe@conference-board.org
URL: http://www.conference-board.org
Staff: 200. **Descr:** Corporations, government agencies, libraries, colleges, and universities. Fact-finding institution that conducts research and publishes studies on business economics and management experience. Holds more than 100 conferences, council meetings, and seminars per year in the U.S., Asia, and Europe where members exchange ideas and keep abreast of business trends and developments. Makes research available to secondary schools, colleges, and universities at minimum cost. Disseminates research data to the public. **Fnd:** 1916. **Mem:** 3000. **Pub:** *Business Cycle Indicators* (monthly); *Conference Board Review* (10/year); *Consumer Confidence Survey* (monthly); *StraightTalk* (monthly); Newsletters.

3558 ■ Consumer Credit Counseling Services (CCCS)
100 Edgewood Ave., Ste. 1800
Atlanta, GA 30303
Contact: Suzanne Boas, Pres.
Free: 800-873-2227
E-mail: info@cccsinc.org
URL: http://www.cccsatl.org

Descr: Promotes financial education as an investment in the community. **Pub:** Newsletter.

3559 ■ Consumer Health Education Council (CHEC)
1100 13th St. NW, Ste. 878
Washington, DC 20005
Contact: Paul Frostin PhD, Dir.
Ph: (202)659-0670
Fax: (202)775-6312
E-mail: fronstin@ebri.org
URL: http://www.ebri.org/research/hrep

Descr: Seeks to reduce the number of uninsured Americans and improve public health.

3560 ■ Consumers Education and Protective Association International (CEPA)
6048 Ogontz Ave.
Philadelphia, PA 19141-1347
Contact: Tina Nelson, Exec. Dir.
Ph: (215)424-1441
Fax: (215)424-8045
E-mail: info@jewishceliacs.com
URL: http://www.cepa.us

Descr: Seeks to educate the consumer, combat fraud and other unscrupulous business activities, and strengthen the power of consumers to deal with economic problems affecting their interests. Engages in direct action, such as peaceful picketing, to expose consumer grievances. **Fnd:** 1966. **Local Groups:** 2.

3561 ■ Council of the Great City Schools (CGCS)
1301 Pennsylvania Ave. NW, Ste. 702
Washington, DC 20004
Contact: Michael D. Casserly, Exec. Dir.
Ph: (202)393-2427
Fax: (202)393-2400
E-mail: mcasserly@cgcs.org
URL: http://www.cgcs.org

Staff: 17. **Descr:** Large city school districts. Conducts studies of problems shared by urban schools; coordinates projects designed to provide solutions to these problems; uses the findings and recommendations of studies for the improvement of education in the great cities. Provides informational support for legislative activities. Conducts seminars, workshops, and special projects to provide forum for members to share successful projects and to learn new programs. Studies the educational needs of urban children exposed to the effects of discrimination; school financing; teacher preparation for urban schools; more functional approaches to outmoded urban schools; current status and needs in the areas of testing and technology. **Fnd:** 1956. **Mem:** 66. **Pub:** Council Directory (annual); Legislative Activity Report (biweekly); Roster of Board of Directors (periodic); Urban Educator (monthly); Urban Indicator (bimonthly); Annual Report (annual); Reports.

3562 ■ Council for Opportunity in Education (COE)
1025 Vermont Ave. NW, Ste. 900
Washington, DC 20005
Contact: Dr. Arnold L. Mitchem, Pres.
Ph: (202)347-7430
Fax: (202)347-0786
E-mail: arnold.mitchem@coenet.us
URL: http://www.coenet.us

Staff: 15. **Descr:** Institutions of higher education, administrators, counselors, and teachers. Works to advance educational opportunities for disadvantaged students in colleges and universities. Provides professional development and continuing education. Monitors federal legislation designed to serve disadvantaged students. Provides technical assistance to educational opportunity program personnel. Assists institutions in preparing competitive proposals for federal funding. Conducts workshops and training programs; encourages research. **Fnd:** 1981. **Mem:** 900. **Reg. Groups:** 10. **State Groups:** 54. **Pub:** Equality (quarterly); Opportunity

Outlook (semiannual); Directory (annual); Monograph (periodic).

3563 ■ Criminal Defense Investigation Training Council (CDITC)
800 E Ocean Blvd., Ste. D
Stuart, FL 34994
Contact: Brandon A. Perron, Natl. Dir.
Ph: (772)288-1485
Free: 800-465-5233
E-mail: bperron@aol.com
URL: http://www.defenseinvestigator.com

Descr: Strives to uphold the standards of professional competence and academic excellence in criminal defense investigation. Encourages dialogue between professionals and scholars involved in various aspects of criminal defense investigation. Serves as a forum for discussion of topics on investigative philosophy, methodology, education, and principles of ethical inquiry.

3564 ■ Dam Safety Coalition
101 Constitution Ave. NW, Ste. 375 E
Washington, DC 20001
Contact: Brian Pallasch, Co-Chm.
Ph: (202)789-7850
Free: 800-548-2723
E-mail: info@damsafetycoalition.org
URL: http://www.damsafetycoalition.org

Descr: Favors the creation of a federal funding program to repair the nation's unsafe dams. Strives to address the critical issue of deteriorating dam structures that pose a severe threat to many communities throughout the country. **Fnd:** 2004.

3565 ■ Danny Foundation (DF)
1451 Danville Blvd., Ste. 202
Alamo, CA 94507-1941
Contact: Jack Walsh, Exec.Dir.
Ph: (925)314-8130
Free: 800-833-2669
Fax: (925)314-8133
E-mail: info@dannyfoundation.org

Staff: 3. **Descr:** Educates the public about baby cribs and the nursery products industry. Conducts research and surveys; compiles statistics. Operates speakers' bureau; The foundation is named for Danny Lineweaver, the founders' son who was strangled and suffered massive brain damage when his T-shirt strap got caught on a crib post. **Fnd:** 1986. **Pub:** Crib Notes (quarterly); Is Your Crib Safe?.

3566 ■ Democrats for Education Reform (DFER)
140 E 45th St., 28 Fl.
New York, NY 10017
Contact: Joe Williams, Exec. Dir.
Ph: (212)763-8921
E-mail: beverly@dfer.org
URL: http://www.dfer.org

Descr: Aims to change the way Democrats approach education policy. Encourages dialogue within the Democratic Party to reform American public education. Works on all levels of government to educate elected officials and support reform-minded candidates for public office.

3567 ■ Department of Civil, Human and Women's Rights, AFL-CIO
815 16th St. NW
Washington, DC 20006
Contact: Arlene Holt Baker, Exec. VP
Ph: (202)637-5000
Fax: (202)637-5058
E-mail: feedback@aflcio.org
URL: http://www.aflcio.org

Descr: Staff arm AFL-CIO Civil Rights Committee. Serves as official liaison with women's and civil rights organizations and government agencies working in the field of equal opportunity; helps to implement state and federal laws and AFL-CIO civil rights policies; aids affiliates in the development of affirmative programs to expand opportunities for minorities and women; prepares and disseminates special materials on civil rights; speaks at union and civil rights institutes, conferences, and conventions; helps affili-

ates resolve complaints involving unions under Title VII of the 1964 Civil Rights Act and Executive Order 11246. **Fnd:** 1955. **Pub:** America @Work (monthly).

3568 ■ Developmental Delay Resources (DDR)
5801 Beacon St.
Pittsburgh, PA 15217
Contact: Patricia S. Lerner, Exec. Dir.
Free: 800-497-0944
Fax: (412)422-1374
E-mail: devdelay@mindspring.com
URL: http://www.devdelay.org

Descr: Meets needs of families with children with developmental delays in sensory motor, language, social, and emotional areas. **Fnd:** 1998. **Pub:** The Digest of Volume 1-7 of the DDR Newsletter New Developments; Networking Directory (annual); New Developments (quarterly).

3569 ■ Diabetes Action Research and Education Foundation
426 C St. NE
Washington, DC 20002
Contact: Patricia A. Faulkner, Chair
Ph: (202)333-4520
Fax: (202)558-5240
E-mail: info@diabetesaction.org
URL: http://www.diabetesaction.org

Descr: Works to improve quality of life for those affected by diabetes and its complications. **Fnd:** 1990. **Pub:** Diabetes Action (monthly); Managing Your Diabetes: Basics and Beyond.

3570 ■ Direct Selling Education Foundation (DSEF)
1667 K St. NW, Ste. 1100
Washington, DC 20006-1660
Contact: Charles L. Orr, Exec. Dir.
Ph: (202)452-8866
Fax: (202)452-9015
E-mail: info@dsef.org
URL: http://www.dsef.org

Staff: 4. **Descr:** Serves the public interest with education, information, and research, thereby enhancing acceptance and public awareness of direct selling in the global marketplace. **Fnd:** 1973. **Pub:** DSEF: A Foundation That Works; Moral Suasion.

3571 ■ Disability Central
4744 Adenmoor Ave.
Lakewood, CA 90713-2302
E-mail: docstein@disabilitycentral.com

Descr: People with disabilities. Promote disability awareness. Provide information and resources.

3572 ■ Disability Resources
4 Glatter Ln.
Centereach, NY 11720-1032
Contact: Avery Klauber, Co-Founder/Exec. Dir.
Ph: (631)585-0290
Fax: (631)585-0290
E-mail: info@disabilityresources.org
URL: http://www.disabilityresources.org

Staff: 2. **Descr:** Works to promote and improve awareness, availability and accessibility of information to help people with disabilities to live independently. Advises libraries, independent living centers, rehabilitation professionals, hospitals, health and social service organizations, and consumers of resources and publications concerning independent living. **Fnd:** 1993. **Pub:** An Enabling Collection for People with Disabilities; Disability Information at Your Fingertips, 3rd Edition; Disability Resources Monthly (monthly); Living Well with a Disability: How Libraries Can Help; Toy Story - How to Select and Buy Adaptive Toys.

3573 ■ Disability Rights Center (DRC)
PO Box 2007
Augusta, ME 04338-2007
Contact: Kim Moody, Exec. Dir.
Ph: (207)626-2774
Free: 800-452-1948
Fax: (207)621-1419

E-mail: advocate@drcme.org
URL: http://www.drcme.org

Descr: Represents public interest research group committed on educating society about the disability rights movement. Aims to inform the public, political activists, consumer activists, advocates, and students on the disability movement. Seeks to involve as many disabled citizens as possible in processes that directly affect their lives, to work closely with other disability-related, consumer-based advocacy groups, and to educate the public in the legitimate demands and needs of the disabled. Compiles statistics. **Fnd:** 1976. **Pub:** *Advance Health Care Directives*; *DRC News*; *Involuntary Hospitalization Laws*; *Parent Advocate Handbook*; *Your Rights Under the AMHI Consent Decree*.

3574 ■ Disability Rights Education and Defense Fund (DREDF)
2212 6th St.
Berkeley, CA 94710
Contact: Susan Henderson, Exec. Dir.
Ph: (510)644-2555
Free: 800-348-4232
Fax: (510)841-8645
E-mail: info@dredf.org
URL: http://www.dredf.org

Descr: Believes in the principle that people with disabilities have the right to lead full and integrated lives, with the freedom of choice and dignity. Seeks to educate the public and policymakers in order to further the civil rights and liberties of people with disabilities. Conducts educational activities such as: training state and local government officials, attorneys, and judges on disability rights compliance requirements such as the Americans with Disabilities Act; prepares materials pertaining to the right of children with disabilities to a free and appropriate public education. Houses the Disability Rights Clinical Legal Education Program which educates law students about disability rights laws and represents people with disabilities who have experienced unlawful discrimination. Provides technical assistance. **Fnd:** 1979. **Pub:** *Disability Rights News* (quarterly); *DREDF News* (periodic); *Explanation of the Contents of the ADA*; *Manuals*.

3575 ■ Disabled Womyn's Educational Project
PO Box 8773
Madison, WI 53708-8773
Contact: Catherine Odette, Exec. Off.
Ph: (608)256-8883
Fax: (608)256-8883
E-mail: catherine-odette@juno.com

Staff: 6. **Descr:** Lesbians with disabilities. Promotes members' interests. Supports legislation sensitive to members' needs. Maintains speakers' bureau. **Fnd:** 1988. **Pub:** *Building Community Through Access*; *Dykes, Disability, and Stuff* (quarterly); *The Time for Access is Now*.

3576 ■ Distance Education and Training Council (DETC)
1601 18th St. NW, Ste. 2
Washington, DC 20009
Contact: Michael P. Lambert, Exec. Dir./Sec.
Ph: (202)234-5100
Fax: (202)332-1386
E-mail: karen@detc.org
URL: http://www.detc.org

Staff: 6. **Descr:** Represents the interests of home study (correspondence) schools. Establishes standards for the operation of distance education institutions and serves as the accrediting agency for schools meeting these standards. Sponsors independent accrediting commission listed by the U.S. Department of of Education as a nationally recognized accrediting agency. Sponsors workshops and maintains small home study library. **Fnd:** 1926. **Mem:** 80. **Pub:** *DETC Accreditation Handbook* (annual); *DETC News* (semiannual); *Directory of Accredited Distance Education Institutions* (annual); *Facts About DETC*.

3577 ■ Division for Early Childhood of the Council for Exceptional Children (DEC CEC)
27 Ft. Missoula Rd., Ste. 2
Missoula, MT 59804
Contact: Sarah Mulligan, Exec. Dir.
Ph: (406)543-0872
Fax: (406)543-0887
E-mail: dec@dec-sped.org
URL: http://www.dec-sped.org

Staff: 4. **Descr:** Represents individuals who work with or on behalf of children with special needs, birth through age eight, and their families. Promotes policies and advances evidence-based practices that support families and enhance the optimal development of young children who have or are at risk for developmental delays and disabilities. **Fnd:** 1973. **Mem:** 5000. **State Groups:** 30. **Pub:** *Journal of Early Intervention* (quarterly); *Young Exceptional Children* (quarterly).

3578 ■ e-Learning for Kids
PO Box 754
Ardmore, PA 19003
Contact: Nick van Dam PhD, Founder/Chm.
Free: 888-399-3138
Fax: (610)300-4400
E-mail: info@e-learningforkids.org
URL: http://www.e-learningforkids.org

Descr: Promotes online learning for children 5 to 12 years old. Offers free courseware in math, science, reading and keyboarding. Provides a forum for parents and educators to share innovations and insights in childhood education. **Fnd:** 2004. **Pub:** Newsletter.

3579 ■ Educate Tomorrow
1717 N Bayshore Dr., Ste. 203
Miami, FL 33132
Contact: Virginia Emmons McNaught, Dir.
Ph: (305)374-3751
Free: 866-897-1564
E-mail: info@educatetomorrow.org
URL: http://www.educatetomorrow.org

Descr: Aims to make education an attainable goal for the most disadvantaged individuals. Promotes proper education and advanced learning. Provides inspiration, guidance and social assistance.

3580 ■ Education-A-Must
PO Box 216
East Derry, NH 03041
Contact: Dorothy French, Exec. Dir./Founder
Ph: (603)437-6286
Fax: (603)434-0371
E-mail: info@education-a-must.com
URL: http://education-a-must.com

Descr: Provides advocacy services for children or youth with physical, emotional, behavioral, or learning disabilities. Offers assistance to parents and caregivers of children with special needs. Works with school districts and local, state, and federal agencies in securing the educational needs of appropriate schooling, accommodations, and placement for individuals and children with special needs. **Fnd:** 1996.

3581 ■ The Education Coalition (TEC)
31 Segovia
San Clemente, CA 92672
Contact: Dr. Carla Lane EdD, Exec. Dir.
Ph: (949)369-3867
Fax: (949)369-3865
E-mail: carlalane@aol.com
URL: http://www.tecweb.org

Descr: Aims to serve the needs of the business and education communities. Promotes systemic educational reform through the use of multiple technologies. Works to create new public educational systems, models and partnerships. Serves as a focus for development, dissemination, research, advocacy and funding related to educational change and the use of technologies. **Fnd:** 1993. **Pub:** Newsletter.

3582 ■ Education Excellence Partnership
1615 L St. NW Ste. 1100
Washington, DC 20036
Contact: Susan Trainman, Dir.
Ph: (202)872-1260
Free: 800-BE-SMART

Descr: Seeks to create awareness about the need for education reform. Encourages people to take action to improve education. Sponsors public advertising campaign. **Fnd:** 1992.

3583 ■ Education Industry Association (EIA)
5909 Barbados Pl., Ste. 202
Rockville, MD 20852
Contact: Deborah M. McGriff, Pres.
Free: 800-252-3280
Fax: (301)468-3249
E-mail: spines@educationindustry.org
URL: http://www.educationindustry.org

Staff: 5. **Descr:** Educators in private practice and private educational institutions. Promotes "education reform through entrepreneurship." Facilitates communication and cooperation among members; conducts educational and advocacy activities. **Fnd:** 1990. **Mem:** 800. **Pub:** *Enterprising Educators* (quarterly); *Membership Directory* (annual).

3584 ■ Education Pioneers
300 Frank H. Ogawa Plz., Ste. 232
Oakland, CA 94612
Contact: Scott Morgan, Founder/CEO
Ph: (510)893-4374
Fax: (408)904-4873
E-mail: info@educationpioneers.org
URL: http://www.educationpioneers.org

Descr: Trains, connects, and inspires education leaders dedicated to transforming the educational system. Seeks to develop a pipeline of talented leaders from multiple disciplines who will significantly improve student outcomes in urban schools. Increases the capacity of existing schools, districts and education ventures to operate as high-performing organizations. **Fnd:** 2004.

3585 ■ Educational Fund to Stop Gun Violence
1424 L St. NW, Ste. 2-1
Washington, DC 20005-2602
Contact: Joshua Horwitz, Exec. Dir.
Ph: (202)408-0061
E-mail: csgv@csgv.org
URL: http://www.efsgv.org

Staff: 6. **Descr:** Examines and offers public education on handgun violence in the U.S., particularly as it affects children. Maintains Firearms Litigation Clearinghouse that provides assistance to litigants, victims, attorneys, and legal scholars. Participates in the development of materials and educational programs in an effort to promote youth alternatives to gun violence. Examines the impact of handguns on public health. Conducts research on handgun violence, firearms marketing and production, and the design of firearms. Maintains speakers' bureau; compiles statistics. **Fnd:** 1978. **Pub:** *Firearm Litigation Reporter* (quarterly); *Grass Roots Organizing*; *Kids and Guns: A National Disgrace*; *Stop Gun Violence News* (bimonthly).

3586 ■ Educational Records Bureau (ERB)
220 E 42nd St.
New York, NY 10017
Contact: Dr. David F. Clune, Pres.
Ph: (212)672-9800
Free: 800-989-3721
Fax: (212)370-4096
E-mail: info@erbtest.org
URL: http://www.erbtest.org

Staff: 15. **Descr:** Independent and nonpublic schools, international schools, and suburban public schools. Provides student testing services and research to member schools; ability/achievement test, writing assessment, and independent school admissions program. Plans student testing programs, scores tests, reports results to schools, prepares normative data, conducts research on test results, publishes research reports on testing, and assists schools in using test results in instruction and guidance. **Fnd:** 1927. **Mem:** 1500. **Pub:** *Catalog of Programs and Services* (annual); *The Evaluator* (quarterly).

3587 ■ Educational Research Analysts

PO Box 7518
Longview, TX 75607-7518
Ph: (903)753-5993
Fax: (903)753-8424
E-mail: info@textbookreviews.org
URL: http://www.textbookreviews.org
Staff: 3. **Descr:** Reviews and analyzes public school curricula, programs, and textbooks in order to reveal those that conflict with America's traditional values, including "censorship" of the Judeo-Christian ethic, free-enterprise economics, strict construction of the Constitution, and "scientific" flaws in the theory of evolution. Participates in Texas textbook review process. Identifies science texts that teach both strengths and weaknesses of evolutionary theory, reading programs that are true phonics, and traditional math programs. Rates textbooks and sends results to all Texas school districts and the nationwide mailing list. Maintains files of textbook and program reviews. **Fnd:** 1961. **Pub:** *The Mel Gablers' Newsletter* (semiannual); *Textbooks on Trial*; *What Are They Teaching Our Children?*.

3588 ■ Educational Testing Service (ETS)

Rosedale Rd.
Princeton, NJ 08541
Contact: Kurt Landgraf, Pres./CEO
Ph: (609)921-9000
Fax: (609)734-5410
E-mail: etsinfo@ets.org
URL: http://www.ets.org
Staff: 2500. **Descr:** Educational measurement and research organization, founded by merger of the testing activities of American Council on Education, Carnegie Foundation for the Advancement of Teaching, and The College Board. Provides tests and related services for schools, colleges, governmental agencies, and the professions; offers advisory services in the sound application of measurement techniques and materials; conducts educational, psychological, and measurement research. Offers a summer program in educational testing for scholars and educators from other countries, continuing education programs, and measurement, evaluation, and other instructional activities. **Fnd:** 1947. **Pub:** *ETS Developments* (quarterly); Articles; Reports.

3589 ■ ERIC Clearinghouse on Adult, Career, and Vocational Education (ERIC/ACVE)

College of Education
Center on Education & Training for Employment
1900 Kenny Rd.
Columbus, OH 43210-1090
Contact: Judy Wagner, Assoc.Dir.
Ph: (614)292-7069
Free: 800-848-4815
Fax: (614)292-1260
E-mail: ericacve@osu.edu
URL: http://ericacve.org/
Staff: 11. **Descr:** Promotes career and occupational preparation and advancement of youth and adults; provides services in the areas of adult and continuing education; career education, childhood through adult; vocational and technical education including employment and training. **Fnd:** 1966. **Pub:** *Adult Education for Social Change: From Center Stage to the Wings and Back Again*; *Applying Constructivism in Vocational and Career Education*; *ERIC Digest*; *Practice Application Briefs*; *Trends & Issues Alerts*; Newsletter.

3590 ■ Exodus Guild

9 Sherer Trail
Worcester, MA 01603
Contact: Funke Adenodi Akinbuli, Founder/Exec. Dir.
Ph: (617)777-9338

E-mail: reach@theexodusguild.org
URL: http://theexodusguild.org
Descr: Promotes the inclusion and welfare of Africans living with disability. Provides services such as configuring homes, schools or companies to become disability friendly and accessible. Coordinates, organizes, and executes disability forums including conferences and seminars. **Fnd:** 2005.

3591 ■ Family and Consumer Sciences Education Association (FCSEA)

Central Washington University
Dept. of Family & Consumer Science
400 E 8th University Way
Ellensburg, WA 98926-7565
Contact: Jan Bowers, Exec. Dir.
Ph: (509)963-2766
Fax: (509)963-2787
E-mail: hubbards@cwu.edu
URL: http://www.cwu.edu/~fandcs/fcsea
Staff: 1. **Descr:** Family and consumer sciences educators and interested persons. Dedicated to helping individuals to help themselves through understanding family and community life. Works with other organizations to develop public policy. Conducts educational programs. **Fnd:** 1927. **Mem:** 1500. **State Groups:** 50. **Pub:** *Education Reform in Family and Consumer Sciences*; *The Educator* (semiannual); *Implementing Family and Consumer Sciences Standards through Project-Based Learning*; *The Importance of Reading in Family and Consumer Sciences* (annual); *Importance of Reading in Family and Consumer Sciences*; *Positioning Family and Consumer Sciences in the 21st Century*; *Taking Action to Recruit Family and Consumer Sciences Teachers*.

3592 ■ Family Resource Center on Disabilities (FRCD)

20 E Jackson Blvd., Rm. 300
Chicago, IL 60604
Contact: Charlotte Des Jardins, Exec. Dir.
Ph: (312)939-3513
Free: 800-952-4199
Fax: (312)939-7297
E-mail: frcdptiil@ameritech.net
URL: http://www.frcd.org
Staff: 15. **Descr:** Parents, professionals, and volunteers seeking to improve services for all children with disabilities. Originally organized as a result of the 1969 Illinois law mandating the education of all children with disabilities and operates as a coalition to inform and activate parents. Provides information and referral services, individualized support services for low-income Chicago families, transition services, and special education rights training. **Fnd:** 1969. **Pub:** *How to Get Services by Being Assertive*; *How to Organize an Effective Parent/Advocacy Group and Move Bureaucracies*; *Rehabilitation Act Manual*.

3593 ■ Farm Safety 4 Just Kids (FS4JK)

11304 Aurora Ave.
Urbandale, IA 50322
Contact: Marilyn Adams, Pres.
Ph: (515)331-6506
Free: 800-423-5437
Fax: (515)331-2947
E-mail: fs4jk@fs4jk.org
URL: http://www.fs4jk.org
Staff: 9. **Descr:** Individuals, businesses, and organizations with an interest in the safety of children living on farms. Seeks to increase public awareness of hazards to children present on farms; empowers families to make their farms safe for children. Serves as a clearinghouse on farm safety; develops and distributes educational materials; sponsors local farm safety programs. **Fnd:** 1987. **Mem:** 3194. **Pub:** *Farm Safety Game and Activity Book*; *Let's Do a Farm Safety Day Camp*; *PAWS*; Articles.

3594 ■ Federation for Children with Special Needs (FCSN)

1135 Tremont St., Ste. 420
Boston, MA 02120
Contact: Richard J. Robison, Exec. Dir.
Ph: (617)236-7210

Free: 800-331-0688
Fax: (617)572-2094
E-mail: fcsninfo@fcsn.org
URL: http://www.fcsn.org
Staff: 48. **Descr:** Coalition of parents' organizations acting on behalf of children and adults with disabilities. Provides information and workshops on special education laws and resources, and how to obtain related services. Operates projects that help to increase and encourage parent involvement in the health care of children with disabilities or chronic illnesses; projects are: Parent Training and Information Project (PTI), which provides workshops in basic rights, parent consultations, and training, and an information service. **Fnd:** 1974. **Pub:** *Newsline* (quarterly).

3595 ■ Foundation for Science and Disability (FSD)

1700 SW 23rd Dr.
Gainesville, FL 32608
Contact: Richard Mankin, Pres.
Ph: (352)374-5774
Fax: (352)374-5804
E-mail: rmankin@nersp.nerdc.ufl.edu
URL: http://www.stemd.org
Descr: Disabled scientists and interested individuals. Offers consultation and advice concerning problems faced by persons with disabilities in scientific fields. **Fnd:** 1975. **Mem:** 206. **Pub:** *The Abled Disabled in Science* (periodic); *FSD News* (semiannual).

3596 ■ Friends: The National Association of Young People Who Stutter

38 S Oyster Bay Rd.
Syosset, NY 11791
Contact: Lee Caggiano
Free: 866-866-8335
E-mail: lcaggiano@aol.com
URL: http://www.friendswhostutter.org
Staff: 2. **Descr:** Children and teenagers who stutter; family members of young people who stutter; professionals working with people who stutter. Seeks to create a network of love and support for members; promotes increased self-esteem among young people who stutter. Facilitates communication among members. **Fnd:** 1998. **Pub:** *Reaching Out* (bimonthly).

3597 ■ Gifted Learning Project (GLP)

PO Box 481551
Kansas City, MO 64148-1551
Contact: Girard Sagmiller, CEO/Exec. Dir.
Ph: (816)803-4679
E-mail: theglp@yahoo.com
URL: http://giftedlearningproject.org
Descr: Aims to increase awareness and understanding about learning disabilities. Educates the general public about learning disabilities. Develops tools for people with learning disabilities to improve their comprehensive skills as well as their social skills and self-esteem. Approves and provides resources for parents, schools and teachers. Serves as a support network for individuals with learning disabilities by providing one-on-one mentoring. Offers scholarships to individuals (both adults and children) with learning disabilities. **Fnd:** 1999.

3598 ■ Girls Education International

PO Box 853
Lyons, CO 80540
Contact: Lizzy Scully, Exec. Dir./Founder
Ph: (303)903-2768
E-mail: girlsed@gmail.com
URL: http://www.girlsed.org
Descr: Seeks to expand and support educational opportunities for women and girls. Raises money to construct, support and maintain schools for girls throughout the world. Facilitates the hiring and housing of teachers and provision of scholarships and long-term funding. **Fnd:** 2006.

3599 ■ Girls Educational and Mentoring Services (GEMS)

298B W 149th St.
New York, NY 10039

Contact: Rachel Lloyd, Founder/Exec. Dir.
Ph: (212)926-8089
Fax: (212)926-7984
E-mail: info@gems-girls.org
URL: http://www.gems-girls.org
Descr: Focuses on serving girls and young women who have experienced commercial sexual exploitation and domestic trafficking. Provides young women with support and opportunities for positive change. Empowers young women, ages 12-21, who have experienced sexual exploitation and domestic trafficking to exit the commercial sex industry and develop their full potential. **Fnd:** 1999.

3600 ■ Girls Helping Girls (GHG)
45945 Sentinel Pl.
Fremont, CA 94539
Contact: Sejal Hathi, Founder/CEO/Exec. Dir.
Ph: (510)490-4459
E-mail: info@empoweragirl.org
URL: http://www.empoweragirl.org
Descr: Aims to eradicate poverty, increase access to education, improve health and promote peace. Encourages girls to engage in cultural exchange, gain global education and create and lead social change. Provides girls with the curriculum, toolkits and communication interface to discover their talents. **Fnd:** 2007.

3601 ■ Girls Learn International (GLI)
252 Seventh Ave., Ste. 3F
New York, NY 10001
Contact: Lisa Ann Alter, Pres.
Ph: (212)707-8577
Fax: (212)707-8317
E-mail: info@girlslearn.org
URL: http://www.girlslearninternational.org
Descr: Seeks to provide quality education for girls. Conducts educational, communication, advocacy and outreach projects. Helps girls develop their critical thinking and problem solving skills.

3602 ■ Girlstart
1400 W Anderson Ln.
Austin, TX 78757
Contact: Rachel Muir, Founder/Exec. Dir.
Ph: (512)916-4775
Free: 877-768-4775
Fax: (512)916-4776
E-mail: info@girlstart.org
URL: http://www.girlstart.org
Descr: Seeks to empower girls in math, science, engineering and technology. Provides hands-on learning in math, science, technology and engineering concepts to a diverse group of girls and their parents. Holds after-school clubs, free Saturday camps, science nights, family math nights, summer camps, and other educational events. **Fnd:** 1997. **Pub:** Newsletter (monthly).

3603 ■ Goodwill - The Amity Group
225 King William St.
Hamilton, ON, Canada L8R 1B1
Contact: Paul Chapin, Pres./CEO
Ph: (905)526-8482
Fax: (905)526-8949
E-mail: pchapin@goodwillonline.ca
URL: http://www.goodwillonline.ca
Staff: 200. **Descr:** Individuals with disabilities. Promotes employment and full participation in society by members. Operates businesses providing employment to people with disabilities; provides support and services to industries employing people with disabilities. **Fnd:** 1935.

3604 ■ Graduate Record Examinations Board (GRE BOARD)
PO Box 6000
Princeton, NJ 08541-6000
Contact: Dale Johnson, Chm.
Ph: (609)771-7670
Free: 866-473-4373
Fax: (610)290-8975
E-mail: gre-info@rosedale.org
URL: http://www.ets.org/gre
Descr: Participants are appointees of the Associa-

tion of Graduate Schools in Association of American Universities, the Council of Graduate Schools, and the GRE Board. Has responsibility for the Graduate Record Examinations Program (GRE) to assist in graduate school selection. Seeks to ensure that the program is carried out in the best interests of graduate education, the students, and the schools. Educational Testing Service provides technical advice, research expertise, professional counsel, and administers the GRE. Graduate Record Examinations, first administered in 1937, were initiated as a joint venture of the Carnegie Foundation for the Advancement of Teaching and the graduate school deans of four eastern U.S. universities. The examination and programs in which they were used became the responsibility of ETS when it began operating in 1948, until 1966, when the present structure was formed in order to give broader representation to the graduate education community. **Fnd:** 1966. **Pub:** *Directory of Graduate Programs* (biennial); *General Test Practice Book*; *General Test Preparation Software* (biennial); *GRE Information Bulletin* (annual); *Subject Tests Practice Books* (annual).

3605 ■ HEATH Resource Center
George Washington University
2134 G St. NW
Washington, DC 20052-0001
Contact: Donna Martinez, Dir.
Fax: (202)994-3365
E-mail: askheath@gwu.edu
URL: http://www.heath.gwu.edu
Staff: 5. **Descr:** National information Clearinghouse. Works to aid in the postsecondary education of people who are disabled. Provides information on educational support services, procedures, policies, adaptations, campus opportunities, vocational technical schools, adult education programs, and independent living centers. **Fnd:** 1977. **Pub:** *Fact Sheet* (quarterly); *Information* (3/year); *Information from HEATH* (quarterly); *Resource Directory* (biennial).

3606 ■ Help the Children
PO Box 911607
Los Angeles, CA 90091
Contact: Roger Presgrove, Pres./CEO
Ph: (323)980-9870
Free: 877-CNI-2AID
Fax: (323)980-9878
E-mail: info@helpthechildren.org
URL: http://www.helpthechildren.org
Descr: Represents individuals dedicated to help alleviate the suffering of children and their families throughout the United States and around the world. Provides disaster aid, clothing, medical and dental supplies, and food.

3607 ■ Hispanic Educational Technology Services (HETS)
PO Box 363255
San Juan, PR 00936-3255
Contact: Yubelkys Montalvo, Exec. Dir.
Ph: (787)766-1912
Fax: (787)250-7984
E-mail: yumontalvo@suagm.edu
URL: http://www.hets.org
Descr: Aims to promote, support and increase the capabilities of member institutions to enhance Hispanic/Latino student success and opportunities in higher education. Promotes collaboration among HETS members and the academic, government, and corporate sectors. Supports the acquisition and integration of new education-oriented technologies. **Fnd:** 1993. **Pub:** Newsletter.

3608 ■ Hospice Education Institute (HEI)
3 Unity Sq.
PO Box 98
Machiasport, ME 04655-0098
Ph: (207)255-8800
Free: 800-331-1620
Fax: (207)255-8008
E-mail: info@hospiceworld.com
URL: http://www.hospiceworld.org
Staff: 7. **Descr:** Provides educational and informational services to health professionals and the public

on subjects such as hospice and palliative care, death and dying, and bereavement counseling. Encourages educational exchange among hospice and palliative care professionals and volunteers. Offers advice and support to persons working to open local hospice programs. Organizes continuing education seminars on hospice care throughout the U.S. and abroad. **Fnd:** 1985. **Pub:** *Notes on Symptom Control in Hospice and Palliative Care*; Booklets.

3609 ■ I Create
6 Crest Ln.
Fanwood, NJ 07023
Contact: Harsh Bhargava, Co-Founder
Ph: (703)893-4751
E-mail: info@icreateinc.org
URL: http://www.icreateinc.org
Descr: Seeks to help disadvantaged youth to become entrepreneurs and acquire employability skills. Provides seed money to selected aspiring entrepreneurs who have taken the IC-NFTE entrepreneurship training. Equips women and youth with the practical knowledge and skills needed to start a business, generate income, and create employment for themselves and others. **Fnd:** 2000.

3610 ■ Innocents at Risk (IAR)
1101 30th St. NW, Ste. 500
Washington, DC 20007
Contact: Deborah Sigmund, Founder
Ph: (202)625-4338
Free: 888-373-7888
Fax: (202)625-4363
E-mail: dsigmund@eoc.net
URL: http://www.innocentsatrisk.org
Descr: Aims to protect and stop the trafficking of women and children. Raises awareness of human trafficking. Works with other NGOs to provide housing and care for human trafficking victims in the United States and around the world. **Fnd:** 2006.

3611 ■ Institute of Consumer Financial Education (ICFE)
PO Box 34070
San Diego, CA 92163-4070
Contact: Paul S. Richard RFC, Exec. Dir.
Ph: (619)239-1401
Fax: (619)923-3284
E-mail: icfe@cox.net
URL: http://www.financial-education-icfe.org
Staff: 2. **Descr:** Aims to encourage Americans to improve spending, saving, investing, insuring, and financial planning habits to lessen their dependence on Social Security, welfare, or other individuals. Provides financial education courses to junior high and high school. Maintains a resource section of videos, books and home study courses in personal finance. **Fnd:** 1982. **State Groups:** 50. **Pub:** *Do-It-Yourself Credit File Correction Guide*; *The Money Instruction Book: A Wealth-Building Course in Personal Finance, Revised 2002*.

3612 ■ Institute for Responsive Education (IRE)
Cambridge Colorado School of Education
80 Prospect St., 3rd Fl.
Cambridge, MA 02138
Contact: Jorge Cardoso, Exec. Dir.
Ph: (617)873-0610
Fax: (617)873-0273
E-mail: jorge.cardoso@cambridgecollege.edu
Staff: 10. **Descr:** Studies and assists the process of parent and citizen participation in education. Activities include research, evaluation, participation in national meetings, work with other national organizations, and writing about national issues. Provides technical assistance and training in parent and citizen involvement in education. **Fnd:** 1973. **Pub:** *New Schools, New Communities* (3/year); Books; Handbooks; Reports.

3613 ■ International Alliance for the Prevention of AIDS (IAPA)
1747 W Devonshire Ave.
Phoenix, AZ 85015
Contact: Sanjay Sinha, Co-Founder/Exec. Dir.

E-mail: allianceindia@gmail.com
URL: http://www.iapaindia.org

Descr: Strives to minimize the spread of HIV in India through educational initiatives in schools and communities. Promotes capacity building and cooperation among community based organizations and sound public health programs and measures. Supports the creation of a sustainable, multinational and multicultural effort to fight the disease. **Fnd:** 2004.

3614 ■ International Association of Audio Information Services (IAAIS)

Radio Talking Book Service Inc.
7101 Newport Ave., Ste. 205
Omaha, NE 68152
Contact: Kim Walsh, Pres.
Ph: (402)572-3003
Free: 800-280-5325
Fax: (402)572-3002
E-mail: fullertonj@rtbs.org
URL: http://www.iaais.org

Staff: 1. **Descr:** Helps members to provide access to current printed information not available to print disabled people. Represents volunteers broadcast daily newspapers, community news updates, grocery ads, and death notices. Advocates access to printed material as a key issue under the Americans with Disabilities Act and that the Internet needs to be accessible to people with disabilities. Compiles statistics; holds competitions; maintains speakers' bureau. **Fnd:** 1977. **Mem:** 140. **Pub:** *Directory of Radio Reading Services* (annual); *HEARSSAY* (quarterly); *IAAIS Newsletter* (quarterly); Membership Directory (annual).

3615 ■ International Association of Certified Surveillance Professionals (IACSP)

35 E Horizon Ridge Pkwy., No. 110
Henderson, NV 89002
Contact: Derk Boss CSP, Pres.
Ph: (702)539-7448
URL: http://www.iacsp.org

Descr: Aims to advance surveillance professionals through education and training. Establishes and facilitates professional standards for the surveillance profession. Provides information and networking opportunities to individuals involved in the surveillance profession and offers training and certification programs. **Fnd:** 2001.

3616 ■ International Association of Educators (INASED)

1965 S Orchard St.
Urbana, IL 61801
Contact: Nihat Gurel Kahveci PhD, Gen. Sec.
E-mail: secretary@inased.org
URL: http://www.inased.org

Descr: Aims to develop new pedagogies and alternative languages for cross-cultural communication and understanding. Promotes educational theory and practice. Fosters empirical research, theoretical statements, and philosophical arguments on the current issues and future conceptions of educational theory and practice. **Pub:** *International Journal of Progressive Education* (3/year).

3617 ■ International Association for Intelligence Education (IAFIE)

PO Box 10508
Erie, PA 16514
Contact: Thomas Carr, Chm.
Ph: (814)824-2131
Fax: (814)824-3335
E-mail: info@iafie.org
URL: http://www.iafie.org

Descr: Expands research, knowledge and professional development in intelligence education. Sets standards, builds resources and shares knowledge in intelligence studies. Provides a forum for the exchange of ideas and information about intelligence education. Fosters relationships and cultivates cooperation among intelligence professionals in academia, business and government. Develops, disseminates and promotes theory, curricula, methodologies and techniques for pure and applied intelligence. **Fnd:** 2004. **Pub:** Newsletter.

3618 ■ International Association for Learning Alternatives (IALA)

112103 Haering Cir.
Chaska, MN 55318
Contact: Wayne Jennings, Chair
Ph: (612)716-5620
Fax: (651)644-2020
URL: http://www.learningalternatives.net

Descr: Represents the interests of learning alternatives and choice options practitioners. Seeks to promote and support learning alternatives in education. Provides a forum for professional growth, technical and educational support, networking opportunities and dissemination of best practices in learning alternatives.

3619 ■ International Association for Teachers of Chinese to Speakers of Other Languages (IATCSOL)

9 E Loockerman St., Ste. 3A
Dover, DE 19901
Contact: Mr. Vincent C.S. Yang, Pres.
E-mail: president@tcsol.us.com
URL: http://www.tcsol.us

Descr: Promotes the study and teaching of the Chinese language. Seeks to enhance the professional development of Chinese teachers. Provides information on current methodologies and techniques in all areas of Chinese language teaching. **Fnd:** 2005. **Mem:** 5500.

3620 ■ International Association for Truancy and Dropout Prevention (IATDP)

10602 Holly Springs
Houston, TX 77042
Contact: Mark Sellers, Pres.
Ph: (713)293-9711
E-mail: hpryor@houstonisd.org
URL: http://www.iatdp.org

Descr: Professional society of school attendance and pupil personnel workers including school administrators, counselors, attendance officers, visiting teachers, and school social workers. Believes in the premise that all children have the right to an education. Objectives are: to increase the educational competence of pupil personnel; to provide leadership in the development of pupil personnel services, philosophy, theory, practice, and skills; to help administrators, teachers, and parents understand school problems that face children; to provide ways to improve school attendance and behavior; to enforce and support the educational objectives set forth in compulsory attendance laws; to provide new and improved social, employment, and educational opportunities for children; to collect and disseminate information regarding pupil personnel work. Conducts research programs. Monitors related legislative activities. Maintains speakers' bureau and consultant service. **Fnd:** 1911. **Mem:** 400. **Pub:** *The Journal for Truancy and Dropout Prevention* (semiannual); Membership Directory (annual).

3621 ■ International Brain Education Association (IBREA)

PO Box 582
New York, NY 10150
Contact: Ilchi Lee, Chm./Founder
Ph: (212)319-0848
Fax: (212)319-8671
E-mail: ibreaus@gmail.com
URL: http://ibreaus.org

Descr: Promotes excellence in brain education. Raises public awareness of brain and brain education. Certifies individuals to be instructors of brain education. **Pub:** Newsletter (monthly).

3622 ■ International Child Resource Institute (ICRI)

1581 LeRoy Ave.
Berkeley, CA 94708
Contact: Kenneth Jaffe, Exec. Dir.
Ph: (510)644-1000
Fax: (510)644-1115

E-mail: info@icrichild.org
URL: http://www.icrichild.org

Staff: 5. **Descr:** Individuals interested in issues regarding day care for children, including maternal and child health, child abuse prevention, neglect, and other children's issues. Organizations and companies that furnish or are engaged in child care. Implements model projects to gather information on techniques and practices involved in innovative forms of child care and child health. Provides technical assistance to individuals, corporations, and government agencies that wish to establish and maintain child care centers and other children's programs. Serves as a clearinghouse for information on children's issues. Maintains offices in Kenya, Ghana, Zimbabwe, Norway and Nepal. Conducts speakers' bureau. **Fnd:** 1981. **Reg. Groups:** 4. **Pub:** *News from ICRI*.

3623 ■ International Coalition for Addiction Studies Education (INCASE)

PO Box 224
Vermillion, SD 57069-0224
Contact: Dr. Kirk Bowden PhD, Pres.
Ph: (480)517-8522
Fax: (480)517-8449
E-mail: kirkbowdenphd@gmail.com
URL: http://incase-edu.net

Descr: Seeks to enhance the quality of training and education in addiction studies. Provides a global forum for the examination and debate of issues concerning post-secondary education in addiction studies. Aims to provide professional knowledge and share ideas regarding addiction studies and scholarship in the field of addiction studies. Works to develop standards and implement an accreditation process for addictions studies programs. **Fnd:** 1990. **Pub:** *Journal of Teaching Addictions*; *News Notes* (quarterly).

3624 ■ International Cultic Studies Association (ICSA)

PO Box 2265
Bonita Springs, FL 34133
Contact: Michael D. Langone PhD, Exec. Dir.
Ph: (239)514-3081
Fax: (305)393-8193
E-mail: mail@icsamail.com
URL: http://www.icsahome.com

Descr: Educational research organization seeking to understand and alleviate the problems caused to individuals, families, and society at large by people and groups that employ unethical forms of social influence. Reports on legal, medical, psychological, and social issues raised by cultism. **Fnd:** 1979. **Pub:** *Cult Observer* (quarterly); *Cultic Studies Journal* (annual); Books; Catalogs; Reports.

3625 ■ International Dyslexia Association (IDA)

40 York Rd., 4th Fl.
Baltimore, MD 21204-5202
Contact: Guinevere F. Eden PhD, Pres.
Ph: (410)296-0232
Free: 800-ABC-D123
Fax: (410)321-5069
E-mail: info@interdys.org
URL: http://www.interdys.org

Staff: 14. **Descr:** Offers free information to the public and referrals for diagnosis and treatment. Membership includes professionals in the fields of neurology, pediatrics, psychiatry, education, social work, and psychology; parents; other persons interested in the study, treatment, and prevention of the problems of specific language disability, often called developmental dyslexia or simply dyslexia. Provides a focal point for activities and ideas generated in various fields as they relate to problems of language development and learning. Establishes in memory of Dr. Samuel T. Orton, a pioneer in the field of dyslexia. Disseminates materials. Offers support groups. Presents seminars and conferences around the U.S. Advocates for appropriate educational policies. **Fnd:** 1949. **Mem:** 13000. **Reg. Groups:** 44. **Pub:** *Annals* of *Dyslexia* (annual); *Orton Emeritus Series*; *Perspectives* (quarterly).

3626 ■ International Federation of Engineering Education Societies (IFEES)
1818 N St. NW, Ste. 600
Washington, DC 20036-2476
Contact: Hans Jurgen Hoyer, Sec. Gen.
Ph: (202)331-3511
E-mail: h.hoyer@ifees.net
URL: http://www.ifees.net
Descr: Strives to strengthen engineering education worldwide. Aims to develop the locally pertinent and globally competent engineering professional. Helps establish policies to enhance education and innovation and support collaborative partnerships among global stakeholders. **Fnd:** 2006.

3627 ■ International Food Safety Council (IFSC)
175 W Jackson Blvd., Ste. 1500
Chicago, IL 60604-2814
Contact: Mary M. Adolf, Pres./CEO
Ph: (312)715-1010
Free: 800-765-2122
E-mail: info@restaurant.org
URL: http://www.nraef.org
Descr: Seeks to heighten the awareness of the importance of food safety education throughout the restaurant and foodservice industry. **Fnd:** 1993. **Pub:** *Food Safety Illustrated* (quarterly).

3628 ■ International Labor Communications Association, AFL-CIO/CLC (ILCA)
815 16th St. NW, 4 N
Washington, DC 20006
Contact: Mr. Steve Stallone, Pres.
Ph: (202)637-5068
Fax: (202)637-5069
E-mail: ilca@aflcio.org
URL: http://www.ilcaonline.org
Staff: 2. **Descr:** A professional support organization for labor communicators in North America, especially those of the AFL-CIO and the CLC. Works to strengthen and expand labor communications and to improve the professional and technical quality of member publications, websites, and media productions; it also maintains a Code of Ethics governing promotion and sale of advertising space. Holds a convention every two years immediately preceding each regular AFL-CIO convention. Officers are elected for two-year terms by convention delegates. **Fnd:** 1955. **Mem:** 672. **Reg. Groups:** 12. **State Groups:** 60. **Local Groups:** 600. **Pub:** *The ILCA Reporter* (bimonthly).

3629 ■ International Society of Air Safety Investigators (ISASI)
107 E Holly Ave., Ste. 11
Sterling, VA 20164
Contact: Frank S. Del Gandio, Pres.
Ph: (703)430-9668
Fax: (703)430-4970
E-mail: isasi@erols.com
URL: http://www.isasi.org
Staff: 1. **Descr:** Specialists who investigate and define the causes of aircraft accidents; persons who have made outstanding contributions to the promotion of air safety are honorary members. Encourages improvement of air safety and investigative procedures worldwide. **Fnd:** 1964. **Mem:** 1422. **Reg. Groups:** 10. **State Groups:** 9. **Pub:** *The Forum* (quarterly); *Membership Roster* (biennial).

3630 ■ InTouch Networks (ITN)
15 W 65th St.
New York, NY 10023
Contact: Lynne Thompson
Ph: (212)769-6270
Fax: (917)386-9811
E-mail: intouchinfo@jgb.org
URL: http://www.jgb.org/InTouch/default.asp
Staff: 5. **Descr:** Volunteer service that allows blind or physically impaired people to listen to readings of articles from more than 100 newspapers and magazines via closed-circuit radio. Broadcasts nationally

accessible on Galaxy 4 satellite. **Fnd:** 1974. **Mem:** 1000000. **Pub:** *Program Guide* (annual).

3631 ■ Inyana - League of Rwandan Children and Youth
230 Sunset Ridge
Rocky Hill, CT 06067
Contact: Kiji Mugisha, Founder
E-mail: thomas.k@inyanarwanda.org
URL: http://www.inyanarwanda.org
Descr: Seeks to bring hope, health, and education to Rwandan youth affected by war, genocide and disease. Educates the public about abuses caused by genocide in Rwanda. Conducts fundraising events and provides support for the schooling and shelter of children and youth in Rwanda. **Fnd:** 1999. **Pub:** Newsletter.

3632 ■ JBI International - Jewish Braille Institute of America (JBI)
110 E 30th St.
New York, NY 10016
Contact: Dr. Ellen Isler, Pres./CEO
Ph: (212)889-2525
Free: 800-433-1531
Fax: (212)689-3692
E-mail: admin@jbilibrary.org
URL: http://www.jbilibrary.org
Staff: 29. **Descr:** Serves the cultural, religious, educational and communal needs of the visually impaired and blind in over 50 countries, including the U.S., Israel and the former Soviet Union and in seven languages (English, Russian, Hebrew, Yiddish, Hungarian, Polish, Spanish). Distributes materials free on audiocassette, in large print and in Braille. Maintains a collection of 10,000 titles covering fiction and non-fiction, liturgical materials, and 7 monthly magazines. **Fnd:** 1931. **Pub:** *Hebrew Braille Bible*; *Hebrew Self-Taught*; *JBI Voice* (10/year); *Jerusalem Report* (bimonthly); *Jewish Reference Calendar* (annual); *Passover Haggadah*.

3633 ■ KaBOOM!
4455 Connecticut Ave. NW, Ste. B100
Washington, DC 20008
Contact: Darrell Hammond, Founder/CEO
Ph: (202)659-0215
URL: http://www.kaboom.org
Descr: Promotes safe and accessible playgrounds to America's children; links communities and corporations to build playgrounds. Sponsors the KaBOOM! Let Us Play Camp. **Fnd:** 1995. **Pub:** *Playtime*; Handbooks.

3634 ■ Laubach Literacy of Canada (LLC)
119 Ross Ave., Ste. 201
Ottawa, ON, Canada K1Y 0N6
Contact: Cheryl Ledgerwood, Acting Exec. Dir.
Ph: (613)759-4949
Fax: (613)759-4948
E-mail: cledgerwood@laubach.ca
URL: http://www.laubach.ca
Staff: 16. **Descr:** Volunteer literacy instructors, students, and other individuals with an interest in adult literacy. Promotes literacy. Conducts literacy programs. **Fnd:** 1990. **Mem:** 10000.

3635 ■ Leadership Conference Education Fund (LCEF)
1629 K St. NW, No. 1010
Washington, DC 20006
Ph: (202)466-3311
E-mail: comlcef@civilrights.org
URL: http://www.wecaretoo.com/Organizations/DC/lcef.html
Descr: Supports educational activities relevant to civil rights. **Fnd:** 1969. **Pub:** *Conference Reports*; Reports.

3636 ■ Learning Disabilities Association of America (LDA)
4156 Library Rd.
Pittsburgh, PA 15234-1349
Contact: Sheila Buckley, Exec. Dir.
Ph: (412)341-1515
Fax: (412)344-0224

E-mail: info@ldaamerica.org
URL: http://www.ldaamerica.org
Staff: 7. **Descr:** Parents of children with learning disabilities; interested professionals. Works to "advance the education and general well-being of children with adequate intelligence who have learning disabilities arising from perceptual, conceptual, or subtle coordinative problems, sometimes accompanied by behavior difficulties." Disseminates information to the public; provides assistance to state and local groups. These affiliated groups carry out direct services to parents and children, including schools, camps, recreation programs, parent education, information services, and publication of books and pamphlets. Offers information and referral services. **Fnd:** 1963. **Mem:** 40000. **State Groups:** 43. **Local Groups:** 300. **Pub:** *Advocacy Handbook: A Parent's Guide for Special Education*; *LDA Newsbriefs* (bimonthly); *Learning Disabilities: A Multidisciplinary Journal* (quarterly).

3637 ■ Learning Disabilities Association of Canada (LDAC)
250 City Centre Ave., Ste. 616
Ottawa, ON, Canada K1R 6K7
Contact: Judy Kerr, Exec. Dir.
Ph: (613)238-5721
Free: 877-238-5322
Fax: (613)235-5391
E-mail: info@ldac-taac.ca
URL: http://www.ldac-taac.ca
Staff: 6. **Descr:** Advocates in the areas of education, social development, legal rights, and general well being of individuals with learning disabilities; encourages early recognition, diagnosis, and treatment of individuals with learning disabilities; develops educational, social, recreational, and career-oriented programs; promotes legislation, research, and training of personnel in the field; initiates programs to increase public awareness and understanding of learning disabilities; advocates before government and other agencies on policies and programs affecting individuals with learning disabilities; provides support to provincial and territorial LDA network. Advocates for individuals before government and other agencies; develops parent support services to maximize parental involvement. **Fnd:** 1963. **Mem:** 10000. **State Groups:** 12. **Local Groups:** 150. **Pub:** *National* (quarterly).

3638 ■ Learning Disabilities Association - London Region (LDA-LR)
333 Horton St. E
London, ON, Canada N6B 1L5
Contact: Tracy Fawdry, Exec. Dir.
Ph: (519)438-6213
E-mail: ldainfo@ldalondon.ca
URL: http://www.ldalondon.ca
Descr: Seeks to increase public awareness and understanding of learning disabilities. Encourages early recognition, diagnosis and treatment of individuals with learning disabilities. Develops educational, social, recreational and career-oriented programs. Provides support services to individuals with learning disabilities.

3639 ■ Learning Disabilities Association of Toronto District (LDATD)
121 Willowdale Ave., Ste. 203
Toronto, ON, Canada M2N 6A3
Contact: Mimi Hoffman, Exec. Dir.
Ph: (416)229-1680
Fax: (416)229-1681
E-mail: admin@ldatd.on.ca
URL: http://www.ldatd.on.ca
Descr: Seeks to increase public awareness and understanding of learning disabilities. Encourages early recognition, diagnosis and treatment of individuals with learning disabilities. Develops educational, social, recreational and career-oriented programs. Provides support services to individuals with learning disabilities.

3640 ■ Libraries Without Borders (LWB)
PO Box 201849
New Haven, CT 06520

Contact: Paull Randt, Dir.
Ph: (203)430-7504
E-mail: contact@librarieswithoutborders.org
URL: http://www.librarieswithoutborders.org
Descr: Aims to facilitate the growth and improvement of libraries in Africa, Asia and the Americas. Supports education in developing and disaster affected areas. Provides children, students and adults with access to well-equipped, up-to-date and efficient libraries.

3641 ■ Lift Disability Network
4700 Millenia Blvd., Ste. 175
Orlando, FL 32839
Contact: Jim Hukill, Interim Exec. Dir.
Ph: (407)228-8343
Fax: (407)835-3601
E-mail: info@liftdisabilitynetwork.org
URL: http://www.liftdisabilitynetwork.org
Descr: Aims to connect the disability family through a collective voice of influence, innovative family support programs, and instructive learning initiatives. **Fnd:** 1989.

3642 ■ Logan Community Resources
2505 E Jefferson Blvd.
South Bend, IN 46615
Contact: James M. Lewis, Chm.
Ph: (574)289-4831
E-mail: logan@logancenter.org
URL: http://logancenter.org
Descr: Represents individuals, families, volunteers, neighbors, employers, donors. Strives to create opportunities for persons with developmental disabilities. Offers person directed planning.

3643 ■ Lutheran Braille Evangelism Association (LBEA)
1740 Eugene St.
White Bear Lake, MN 55110-3312
Contact: Carol McKitrick, Pres.
Ph: (651)426-0469
E-mail: lbea@qwest.net
URL: http://www.users.qwest.net/~lbea
Staff: 2. **Descr:** Fosters provision of religious material to the visually impaired in Braille, audio cassette, extra large print and digital formats. Supported by contributions of members. **Fnd:** 1952. **Mem:** 2000. **Pub:** *Braille Evangelism Bulletin* (quarterly); *Christian Magnifier* (11/year); *Tract Messenger* (11/year).

3644 ■ Lutheran Braille Workers (LBW)
PO Box 5000
Yucaipa, CA 92399
Contact:Rev. Phil Pledger, Exec. Dir.
Ph: (909)795-8977
Fax: (909)795-8970
E-mail: lbw@lbwinc.org
URL: http://www.lbwinc.org
Staff: 18. **Descr:** Volunteers staffing 206 work centers worldwide, through which they seek to bring the Bible to the blind and visually impaired. Assists sighted volunteers to transcribe printed material into Braille and large print. Produces and distributes free biblical and devotional material in Braille and large print in over 40 languages. Works to constantly upgrade the systems necessary for the production of Braille materials. **Fnd:** 1943. **Mem:** 7000. **Pub:** *Illuminations* (quarterly); *Lutheran Braille Workers-- Newsletter* (quarterly); *Work Center Directory* (annual); *Work Center Memo* (monthly).

3645 ■ Management Education Alliance (MEA)
300 Cumnock Hall
Boston, MA 02163
Contact: Francis J. Aguilar, Exec. Dir.
Ph: (617)495-6494
Fax: (617)495-8736
URL: http://www.mgteducationalliance.org
Descr: Seeks to help business schools that serve African-American and Hispanic-American students to provide the skills and knowledge that will lead to successful careers in management. Fosters the professional growth of faculty members, innovations in curriculum, and development of supporting institutional policies. Communicates and collaborates with

business schools and U.S. business corporations. **Fnd:** 1994. **Pub:** Newsletter.

3646 ■ Mexican American Legal Defense and Educational Fund (MALDEF)
634 S Spring St.
Los Angeles, CA 90014
Contact: Patricia A. Madrid, Chair
Ph: (213)629-2512
URL: http://www.maldef.org
Staff: 75. **Descr:** Funded through a range of sources including foundations, corporations, and individuals. Aims to protect the civil rights of Latinos, including Mexican-Americans. Has offices in Sacramento and Los Angeles, San Antonio, TX; Chicago, IL; and Washington, DC. Has been responsible for civil rights class-action litigation affecting Latinos. Areas of focus include education, employment, immigration, voting rights and public resource equity. Offers leadership training, parent leadership programs and higher education scholarships. **Fnd:** 1968. **Reg. Groups:** 4. **Pub:** *Leadership Program Newsletter* (3/ year); Annual Report (annual).

3647 ■ Military Impacted Schools Association (MISA)
1600 Hwy. 370
Bellevue, NE 68005
Contact: Dr. John F. Deegan, Exec. Dir.
Ph: (402)293-4005
Free: 800-291-MISA
Fax: (402)291-7982
URL: http://www.militaryimpactedschoolsassociation. org
Descr: Provides the educational needs of military families, including quality of life initiatives, community and school district support, and aid funding. **Fnd:** 1986.

3648 ■ Minority Access, Inc. (MAI)
5214 Baltimore Ave.
Hyattsville, MD 20781-2044
Contact: Andrea Mickle, CEO/Pres.
Ph: (301)779-7100
Fax: (301)779-9812
E-mail: klewis@minorityaccess.org
URL: http://www.minorityaccess.org
Descr: Focuses on improving diversity in education, employment and research. Teaches individuals, academic institutions, federal, state and local government agencies and various corporations to diversify campuses and work sites by improving the recruitment, retention and enhancement of minorities. Provides technical assistance to minorities and minority-serving institutions in order to improve the higher educational, professional and managerial employment of minorities. **Fnd:** 1995.

3649 ■ Mobility International USA (MIUSA)
132 E Broadway, Ste. 343
Eugene, OR 97401
Contact: Susan Sygall, CEO/Exec. Dir.
Ph: (541)343-1284
Fax: (541)343-6812
E-mail: info@miusa.org
URL: http://www.miusa.org
Descr: Focuses on empowering people with disabilities through international exchange opportunities. Organizes international exchange programs annually. Provides information on the range of international exchange opportunities available including work, study, research, and volunteering. Provides information to international exchange organizations on accessibility, homestays, recruiting and inclusion in international development programs. **Fnd:** 1981. **Pub:** *A World Awaits You: A Journal of Success of People with Disabilities in International Exchange*; *A World of Options: A Guide to International Educational Exchange, Community Service, and Travel for Persons with Disabilities*; *All Abroad!*; *Building an Inclusive Development Community: A Manual on Including People with Disabilities in International Development Programs*; *Building Bridges: A Manual on Including People with Disabilities in International Exchange Programs*; *Building Bridges: A Training Video on Including People with Disabilities in Interna-*

tional Exchange Programs; *Loud, Proud and Passionate*; *Loud, Proud and Passionate Including Women with Disabilities in International Development Programs* (quarterly); *Loud, Proud and Prosperous: Microcredit Projects By and For Women with Disabilities in South Africa*; *MIUSA's Global Impact* (semiannual); *Survival Strategies for Going Abroad: A Guide for People with Disabilities*.

3650 ■ Mommies Network
PO Box 472793
Charlotte, NC 28247-2793
Contact: Heather Meininger, Founder/Pres.
Ph: (704)470-4291
Free: 866-262-2320
E-mail: heather@themommiesnetwork.org
URL: http://www.themommiesnetwork.org
Descr: Aims to provide a place for mothers and fathers to find support and encouragement from other mothers and to empower them to be better women, parents and community leaders. **Fnd:** 2005.

3651 ■ Mothers Against Misuse and Abuse (MAMA)
5217 SE 28th Ave.
Portland, OR 97202
Contact: Sandee Burbank, Dir.
Ph: (503)233-4202
Fax: (503)233-8266
E-mail: mama@mamas.org
URL: http://www.mamas.org
Staff: 9. **Descr:** Promotes personal responsibility and informed decision making on issues of substance use, abuse, and misuse. **Fnd:** 1982. **Pub:** *Drug Consumer Safety*; *Using Alcohol Responsibly*.

3652 ■ Mothers And More
PO Box 31
Elmhurst, IL 60126
Contact: Joanne Brundage, Exec. Dir.
Ph: (630)941-3553
Fax: (630)941-3551
E-mail: nationaloffice@mothersandmore.org
URL: http://www.mothersandmore.org
Descr: Dedicated to improving the lives of mothers through support, education and advocacy. Addresses mothers' needs as individuals and members of society, and promotes the value of all the work mothers do. Provides nationwide network of local chapters for mothers who are, by choice or circumstance, altering their participation in the paid workplace over the course of their active parenting years. **Fnd:** 1987. **Mem:** 7500. **Local Groups:** 175. **Pub:** *The Forum* (bimonthly); Brochure.

3653 ■ Mutual Fund Education Alliance (MFEA)
100 NW Englewood Rd., Ste. 130
Kansas City, MO 64118
Contact: Michelle A. Smith, Managing Dir.
Ph: (816)454-9422
Fax: (816)454-9322
E-mail: mfea@mfea.com
URL: http://www.mfea.info
Staff: 5. **Descr:** Represents mutual fund marketers and distributors. Helps investors understand mutual funds and the benefits of long-term investing; members are America's leading mutual fund companies who collectively serve over eighty million shareholders and manage nearly 3 trillion in assets; approximately one half of all assets invested in mutual funds today. Maintains Mutual Fund Investor's Center, designed to serve as a resource for investors who want to use mutual funds to reach their financial goals; here investors can find "the largest collection of mutual fund companies, website links, fund listings and exclusive planning, tracking and monitoring tools available on the Internet." **Fnd:** 1971. **Mem:** 39.

3654 ■ NADD - An Association for Persons with Developmental Disabilities and Mental Health Needs
132 Fair St.
Kingston, NY 12401-4802
Contact: Dr. Robert J. Fletcher, CEO/Founder

Ph: (845)331-4336
Free: 800-331-5362
Fax: (845)331-4569
E-mail: info@thenadd.org
URL: http://www.thenadd.org
Staff: 4. **Descr:** People with developmental disabilities and mental health care needs; mental health professionals; other interested individuals. Promotes public and professional interest in developmental disability; seeks to improve access to mental health care. Supports research programs; facilitates exchange of information among mental health professionals and consumers; conducts advocacy to insure implementation of effective public mental health policies and legislation. Holds educational programs; maintains speakers' bureau. **Fnd:** 1983. **Mem:** 1300. **State Groups:** 6. **Pub:** NADD Bulletin (bimonthly).

3655 ■ Narcotic Educational Foundation of America (NEFA)
28245 Ave. Crocker, Ste. 230
Santa Clarita, CA 91355-1201
Contact: Lorraine White
Ph: (661)775-6960
Free: 877-775-6272
Fax: (661)775-1648
E-mail: info@cnoa.org
URL: http://www.cnoa.org/NEFA.htm
Descr: Conducts an education program revealing the dangers that result from the illicit and abusive use of narcotics and dangerous drugs, so that youth and adults will be protected from both mental and physical drug dependency and harm. **Fnd:** 1924. **Pub:** Alcohol-A Potent Drug; Am I Addicted or Dependent?; Designer Drugs: The Analog Game; The Heroin Story; Huffing: Inhalants; Lysergic Acid Diethylamide: Is it a Dream or Nightmare?; The PCP Story; Rohypnol: The Date Rape Drug; Speed: Amphetamines; The Story of Cocaine; Tobacco: Smoke or Chew; Understanding Anabolic Steroids; Use of Marijuana as a Medicine; Valium and Other Depressants; What About Marijuana?.

3656 ■ National Ability Center (NAC)
PO Box 682799
Park City, UT 84068
Contact: Meeche White, Co-Founder
Ph: (435)649-3991
Fax: (435)658-3992
E-mail: info@discovernac.org
URL: http://www.discovernac.org
Staff: 10. **Descr:** People with disabilities and their families. Promotes the development of lifetime skills for persons with disabilities and their families; works to increase the self-esteem of people with disabilities. Sponsors affordable sports and recreational activities, including cycling, skiing, challenge course, horseback riding, and river rafting, for members. **Fnd:** 1985. **Mem:** 5000. **State Groups:** 4. **Pub:** Ability Bulletin (quarterly).

3657 ■ National Abstinence Education Association (NAEA)
1701 Pennsylvania Ave. NW, Ste. 300
Washington, DC 20006
Contact: Valerie Huber, Exec. Dir.
Ph: (202)248-5420
Fax: (202)580-6559
E-mail: info@abstinenceassociation.org
URL: http://www.abstinenceassociation.org
Descr: Works to serve, support and represent individuals and organizations in the practice of abstinence education. Offers professional development opportunities for abstinence educators. Improves the public understanding and perception of abstinence education. Provides research and initiates studies that impact abstinence education. **Fnd:** 2006. **Mem:** 250.

3658 ■ National Academy for Teaching and Learning About Aging (NATLA)
PO Box 310919
Denton, TX 76203-0919
Contact: Don Louis PhD, Interim Dir.
Ph: (940)565-3450
Fax: (940)565-3141

E-mail: louis@scs.unt.edu
URL: http://www.cps.unt.edu/natla
Staff: 4. **Descr:** Professionals in gerontology, education, health care, and other fields interested in developing aging education and intergenerational programming. Seeks to dispel myths about aging and old age; encourages communication among generations and works to create a social environment where people of all ages can live together. Serves as a clearinghouse of information on issues of aging and intergenerational programs; provides consultation and presentation services to individuals or groups that wish to develop aging education programs. Maintains resources for aging education and intergenerational programming. **Fnd:** 1983. **Mem:** 250. **Pub:** AgeShare; Schools in an Aging Society.

3659 ■ National Accreditation Council for Agencies Serving the Blind and Visually Impaired (NAC)
7017 Pearl Rd.
Middleburg Heights, OH 44130
Contact: Steven K. Hegedeos, Exec. Dir.
Ph: (440)545-1601
E-mail: steve@nacasb.org
URL: http://www.nacasb.org
Staff: 2. **Descr:** Accredits schools, agencies and programs serving people who are blind or visually impaired. Constitutes with the broad-based support of national organizations in the field of blindness, many state and local organizations, and the U.S. Department of Health, Education and Welfare. Influences special schools and agencies that serve people who are blind or visually impaired to meet established standards that promote effective, sound, and publicly accountable education and rehabilitation programs. **Fnd:** 1966. **Mem:** 48. **Pub:** NAC News; The Standard-Bearer (annual).

3660 ■ National AfterSchool Association (NAA)
PO Box 34447
Washington, DC 20043
Contact: Mike English, CFO/COO
Free: 888-801-3622
Fax: 888-568-6590
E-mail: menglish@naaweb.org
URL: http://www.naaweb.org
Staff: 12. **Descr:** Professional providers of day care services for school age children outside of school hours. Seeks to advance the profession of school-age child care. Provides support and services to members including coalition building, networking, and group rates for video licensing. **Fnd:** 1981. **Mem:** 8000. **Reg. Groups:** 5. **Local Groups:** 35. **Pub:** AfterSchool Review; Caring, Stimulating, Responsive; NSACA News (quarterly).

3661 ■ National Alliance of Blind Students (NABS)
1155 15th St. NW, Ste. 1004
Washington, DC 20005
Contact: Cammie Vloedman, Pres.
Ph: (202)467-5081
Free: 800-424-8666
Fax: (202)467-5085
E-mail: rj.hodson@verizon.net
URL: http://acbstudents.org
Descr: Postsecondary students in academic, vocational, trade, and professional programs as well as disabled student service personnel. Aims to educate agencies, governments, institutions, and the public dealing with blind students as to their needs and educational pursuits in accredited postsecondary educational programs. Acts to protect rights and interests of blind students. Participates in annual National Student Seminar at the national convention of the American Council of the Blind. **Fnd:** 1974. **Mem:** 150. **State Groups:** 8. **Pub:** Student Advocate (quarterly).

3662 ■ National Alliance for Medicaid in Education (NAME)
1 Eagles Glen
Clifton Park, NY 12065

Contact: Amy Edwards, Pres.
Ph: (518)486-4887
E-mail: info@medicaidforeducation.org
URL: http://www.medicaidforeducation.org
Descr: Represents Medicaid and education agency staff and local education agency administrators who have programmatic responsibility for administering Medicaid's administrative claiming and/or direct billing of health related service programs in public schools. Provides an information network among the states on issues pertinent to the Medicaid programs in schools. Acts as a focal point of communication between the states.

3663 ■ National Alliance for Secondary Education and Transition (NASET)
University of Minnesota
Institute on Community Integration
150 Pillsbury Dr. SE
6 Pattee Hall
Minneapolis, MN 55455
Contact: David R. Johnson, Project Dir.
Ph: (612)624-1143
E-mail: johns042@umn.edu
URL: http://www.nasetalliance.org
Descr: Seeks to strengthen state and local capacity to improve secondary education and transition policies and practices for youth with disabilities and their families. Promotes effective secondary education and transition services. Develops standards that serve to guide policy development and professional practice. **Fnd:** 2003.

3664 ■ National Assessment of Educational Progress (NAEP)
1990 K St. NW, Rm. 8095
Washington, DC 20006
Contact: Peggy Carr, Assoc. Commissioner
Ph: (202)502-7321
Fax: (202)502-7440
E-mail: peggy.carr@ed.gov
URL: http://nces.ed.gov/nationsreportcard
Descr: A program of the Office for Educational Research and Improvement, under contract to Educational Testing Service. Objectives are to: provide census-like data on various educational levels; conduct national assessments of major learning areas; report results to professional public and educational decision-makers; continue ongoing research. Assessments have been conducted in reading, mathematics, science, writing, literature, citizenship, social studies, computer competence, career and occupational development, art, and music; areas are periodically reassessed. Financed through Department of Education. Provides reports on what American students know and can do; compiles statistics. **Fnd:** 1964. **Pub:** Reports.

3665 ■ National Association for Adults with Special Learning Needs (NAASLN)
1143 Tidewater Ct.
Westerville, OH 43082
Contact: Robyn Rennick, Pres.
Free: 888-562-2756
Fax: (614)392-1559
E-mail: naasln@aol.com
URL: http://www.naasln.org
Staff: 3. **Descr:** Works to organize and promote a coalition of individuals interested in educating adults with special learning needs. Fosters development and implementation of educational programs for adults. Promotes unification of adult education professionals. Encourages research and dissemination of information on adult education. Acts as a forum for the exchange of information on adult education. Seeks to unify adults with special learning needs. **Fnd:** 1989. **Mem:** 350. **Pub:** NAASLN Membership News and Views (monthly).

3666 ■ National Association for the Advancement of Colored People Legal Defense and Educational Fund (LDF)
99 Hudson St., Ste. 1600
New York, NY 10013
Contact: John Payton, Pres./Dir.-Counsel
Ph: (212)965-2200

E-mail: gworley@naacpldf.org
URL: http://www.naacpldf.org

Staff: 68. **Descr:** Legal arm of the civil rights movement, functioning independently from and no longer part of the National Association for the Advancement of Colored People since the mid-1950s. Works to provide and support litigation in behalf of blacks, other racial minorities, and women defending their legal and constitutional rights against discrimination in employment, education, housing, and other areas. Represents civil rights groups as well as individual citizens who have bonafide civil rights claims. Contributed funds are used to finance court actions for equality in schools, jobs, voting, housing, municipal services, land use, and delivery of health care services. Has organized litigation campaign for prison reform and the abolition of capital punishment. Maintains Herbert Lehman Education Fund, through which scholarships are awarded to black students attending state universities; sponsors Earl Warren Legal Training Program, which provides scholarships to black law students. Compiles statistics on capital punishment. Committee of 100, a voluntary cooperative group of individuals, has sponsored the appeal of the fund since 1943. **Fnd:** 1940. **Pub:** *Equal Justice* (quarterly); Annual Report (annual).

3667 ■ National Association on Alcohol, Drugs and Disability (NAADD)
2165 Bunker Hill Dr.
San Mateo, CA 94402-3801
Contact: John de Miranda, Exec. Dir.
Ph: (650)578-8047
Fax: (650)286-9205
E-mail: solanda@sbcglobal.net
URL: http://www.naadd.org

Descr: Promotes awareness and education about substance abuse among people with co-existing disabilities; aims to create public awareness of issues related to alcoholism, drug addiction, and substance abuse faced by persons with co-existing disabilities; provides a peer approach to enhance access to services, information, education and prevention through collaborative efforts of individuals and organizations. Sponsors the California Technology Assistance and Training Project. **Pub:** *The NAADD Report: The Newsletter on Alcohol, Drugs and Disability* (annual).

3668 ■ National Association for Continuing Education (NACE)
7860 Peters Rd., Ste. F111
Plantation, FL 33324
Contact: Sharon Graham, Pres.
Ph: (954)723-0057
Free: 866-266-6223
Fax: (954)723-0353
E-mail: info@naceonline.com
URL: http://www.naceonline.com

Descr: Provides learners in the fields of medicine, behavioral health, education and related disciplines with the most up-to-date science-based information that will enable them to increase their knowledge, competence and professional performance to ultimately benefit their patients' health. Provides opportunities for participants to learn evidenced-based information and acquire skills to improve competence and professional performance.

3669 ■ National Association of Councils on Developmental Disabilities (NACCD)
1660 L St. NW, Ste. 700
Washington, DC 20036
Contact: Karen Flippo, Exec. Dir.
Ph: (202)506-5813
Fax: (202)506-5846
E-mail: info@nacdd.org
URL: http://www.nacdd.org

Staff: 4. **Descr:** Promotes national policy which provides individuals with developmental disabilities the opportunity to make choices regarding the quality of their lives and be included in the community; and provides support and assistance to member Councils. **Fnd:** 1975. **Mem:** 40. **Pub:** *Council*

Chronicles; *Quiknews* (bimonthly); Monographs; Reports; Annual Report (annual).

3670 ■ National Association of Diversity Officers in Higher Education (NADOHE)
4440 PGA Blvd., Ste. 600
Palm Beach Gardens, FL 33410
Contact: William B. Harvey, Pres.
Ph: (561)472-8479
Fax: (561)472-8401
E-mail: dnolan@nadohe.org
URL: http://www.nadohe.org

Descr: Aims to lead higher education toward inclusive excellence through institutional transformation. Serves as the preeminent voice for diversity officers in higher education. Strives to produce and disseminate empirical evidence through research to inform diversity initiatives. Provides professional development opportunities for current and aspiring diversity officers. **Fnd:** 2006. **Pub:** *Journal of Diversity in Higher Education* (quarterly).

3671 ■ National Association for the Education of Young Children (NAEYC)
1313 L St. NW, Ste. 500
Washington, DC 20005
Contact: Mark R. Ginsberg PhD, Exec. Dir.
Ph: (202)232-8777
Free: 800-424-2460
Fax: (202)328-1846
E-mail: naeyc@naeyc.org
URL: http://www.naeyc.org

Staff: 125. **Descr:** Teachers and directors of preschool and primary schools, kindergartens, child care centers, and early other learning programs for young childhood; early childhood education and child development educators, trainers, and researchers and other professionals dedicated to young children's healthy development. **Fnd:** 1926. **Mem:** 104000. **Reg. Groups:** 400. **Pub:** *Early Childhood Research Quarterly* (quarterly); *Young Children* (bimonthly); Booklets; Videos; Books.

3672 ■ National Association for Episcopal Christian Education Directors (NAECED)
1406 University Dr.
Hammond, LA 70401
Contact: Kate Gillooly, Pres.
E-mail: staff@naeced.org
URL: http://naeced.org

Descr: Provides a forum for Christian educators to network with other leaders, explore issues of professionalism and give their input to the National Church as priority and budget are set. Strives to encourage Christian educators to seek out and embrace practices of spiritual reflection, theological studies and excellence in vocation. Aims to provide a national register of Christian Education Directors.

3673 ■ National Association for Government Training and Development (NAGTAD)
3565 E Presidential Dr.
Meridian, ID 83642
Contact: Laurette Burdyl, Pres.
Ph: (208)866-6200
Fax: (208)493-3086
E-mail: go2nagtad@cableone.net
URL: http://www.nagtad.org

Staff: 1. **Descr:** Training and development administrators and practitioners employed by governmental jurisdictions (local, state and federal). Seeks to advance the study and practice of public sector human resource training and development. Promotes growth and development of members. Encourages increased public understanding of the importance of training and development programs for public service employees. Facilitates networking and exchange of information among members; serves as a clearinghouse on public sector human resources development; provides research and technical support to public sector training and development programs.

Fnd: 1980. **Mem:** 94. **Reg. Groups:** 10. **State Groups:** 50.

3674 ■ National Association for Industry-Education Cooperation (NAIEC)
235 Hendricks Blvd.
Buffalo, NY 14226-3304
Contact: Dr. Donald M. Clark, Pres./CEO
Ph: (716)834-7047
Fax: (716)834-7047
E-mail: naiec@pcom.net

Staff: 4. **Descr:** Representatives of business, industry, education, government, labor, and the professions. Fosters industry-education collaboration in continuous school improvement and workforce preparation in order to develop responsive academic and vocational programs which will more effectively serve the needs of both the students and employers as well as further human resources and economic development. Provides technical assistance to schools implementing industry-education councils, high-performance sustainable education systems and business- or industry-sponsored programs. Promotes improved career and entrepreneurship education and supports school-based job placement. Provides staff development programs to improve instruction and curricula and the efficiency and effectiveness of educational management through use of corporate and volunteer services. Acts as national clearinghouse for information on industry involvement in education; serves as liaison between organizations involved in industry-education cooperation, including American Association for Career Education, National Research Center for Career and Technical, and American Society for Training and Development. Conducts research and policy studies. **Fnd:** 1948. **Mem:** 1180. **Pub:** Newsletter (bimonthly); Handbooks; Film.

3675 ■ National Association of Peoplecultural Rehabilitation Concerns (NAMRC)
Michigan State University
459 Erickson Hall
East Lansing, MI 48824
Contact: Stacia L. Robertson PhD, Pres.
E-mail: srbrtsn@siu.edu
URL: http://www.namrc.org

Descr: Rehabilitation professionals, human services providers, educators, researchers, students, and other individuals with an interest in rehabilitation and people with disabilities. Promotes increased awareness of the barriers created by cultural insensitivity; seeks to ensure availability and quality of rehabilitation services to people of all cultural and ethnic backgrounds. Conducts continuing education courses and certification programs for rehabilitation professionals; supports legislation that encourages multiculturalism in American society and benefits people with disabilities. **Fnd:** 1969. **Pub:** *Cultural Network Newsletter* (quarterly).

3676 ■ National Association of Private Special Education Centers (NAPSEC)
1522 K St. NW, Ste. 1032
Washington, DC 20005
Contact: Sherry L. Kolbe, CEO/Exec. Dir.
Ph: (202)408-3338
Fax: (202)408-3340
E-mail: napsec@aol.com
URL: http://www.napsec.org

Staff: 5. **Descr:** Represents over 300 private special programs nationally, and over 600 at the state level, through its Council of Affiliated State Associations. Serves private early intervention services, schools, residential therapeutic centers, and adult living centers. Promotes excellence in educational opportunities for children with disabilities by enhancing the role of private special education as a vital component of the nation's educational system. Strives to educate the public about the education and therapeutic services needed for individuals with disabilities. **Fnd:** 1971. **Mem:** 300. **State Groups:** 9.

Pub: *NAPSEC News* (3/year); *National Issues Service* (monthly); Membership Directory (biennial).

3677 ■ National Association for Professional Development Schools (NAPDS)
University of South Carolina
Coll. of Education
Wardlaw 252
Columbia, SC 29208
Contact: Alison Rutter, Pres.
Ph: (803)777-1515
Fax: (803)777-3035
E-mail: pdsconf@mailbox.sc.edu
URL: http://www.napds.org

Descr: Serves as an advocate for the educational community. Creates and sustains collaborative partnerships between P-12/higher education. Fosters equal representation of, and access for, all educators invested in improving education. Supports teacher leadership in the P-12/higher education community. **Fnd:** 2003. **Pub:** *PDS Partnerships* (3/year); *Scholarship University Partnerships* (semiannual).

3678 ■ National Association of Professional Educators (NAPE)
900 17th St., Ste. 300
Washington, DC 20006
Contact: Philip Strittmatter, Dir.
Ph: (202)848-8969
E-mail: acrocke@tenet.edu

Descr: Represents professional educators, school personnel, and other interested individuals. Establishes local and state organizations as alternatives to teacher unions. Maintains and ensures citizen control of public school systems. Promotes uninterrupted education of students during the school year. Fosters public confidence in state educational systems. Promotes professional status of compensation for educators and protects educators' individual freedoms. Improves and provides educational opportunities for educators. Monitors and takes part in related legislative activities. Prevents control of certification and decertification of educators by employee organizations. Conducts networking among related groups, legislators, school boards, and citizens. Makes available abstracts from databases on educational research. Drafted a code of ethics for professional educators. **Fnd:** 1972. **Reg. Groups:** 6. **State Groups:** 17. **Local Groups:** 36. **Pub:** *Professional Educator Newsletter* (7/year).

3679 ■ National Association of Special Education Teachers (NASET)
1250 Connecticut Ave. NW, Ste. 200
Washington, DC 20036
Contact: Dr. Roger Pierangelo, Co-Exec. Dir.
Free: 800-754-4421
E-mail: contactus@naset.org
URL: http://www.naset.org

Descr: Provides support and assistance to professionals who teach children with special needs. Fosters exceptional teaching for exceptional children. Seeks to promote standards of excellence and innovation in special education research, practice, and policy. **Pub:** *Classroom Management Series* (monthly); *The Special Educator e-Journal* (10/year); *Week in Review* (weekly).

3680 ■ National Association of State Directors of Vocational Technical Education Consortium (NASDVTEC)
8484 Georgia Ave., Ste. 320
Silver Spring, MD 20910
Contact: Ms. June Sanford, Pres.
Ph: (301)588-9630
Fax: (301)588-9631
E-mail: kgreen@nasdvtec.org
URL: http://infolit.org/members/nasdvte.htm

Staff: 2. **Descr:** Serves as a professional society of chief administrative officers for vocational education in each state and/or territory; assistant directors;

leaders in occupational education. **Fnd:** 1920. **Mem:** 220. **Pub:** *Technocrat* (monthly).

3681 ■ National Association of University-Model Schools (NAUMS)
3610 W Pioneer Pkwy., Ste. D
Arlington, TX 76013
Contact: Barbara Nicholson Freeman MEd, Exec. Dir.
Ph: (817)375-0800
Free: 866-760-9508
Fax: (817)299-0800
E-mail: info@naums.net
URL: http://www.naums.net

Descr: Serves as the centerpiece of the University-Model School Christian movement. Shares the vision, values, systems and structure of the University-Model School with Christian families around the world. **Fnd:** 2005.

3682 ■ National Association of University Women (NAUW)
1001 E St. SE
Washington, DC 20003
Contact: Mrs. Ollie D. Johnson, Pres./Chair
Ph: (202)547-3967
Fax: (202)547-5226
E-mail: info@nauw1910.org
URL: http://www.nauw1910.org

Descr: Women college or university graduates. Works to promote constructive work in education, civic activities, and human relations; studies educational conditions with emphasis on problems affecting women; encourages high educational standards and stimulate intellectual attainment among women generally. Theme is Women of Action: Reaching, Risking, Responding. Offers tutoring and sponsors After High School-What? youth development program. Maintains placement service. **Fnd:** 1924. **Mem:** 4000. **Reg. Groups:** 5. **Local Groups:** 92. **Pub:** *Directory of Branch Presidents and Members* (annual); *Journal of the National Association of University Women* (biennial); Bulletin (biennial); Newsletter (semiannual).

3683 ■ National Association of Women Highway Safety Leaders (NAWHSL)
NH Highway Safety Agency
117 Manchester St.
Concord, NH 03301
Contact: Debra H. Garvin, Pres.
Ph: (603)271-2131
Fax: (603)271-3790
E-mail: dgarvin@nhhsa.state.nh.us
URL: http://www.nawhsl.org

Descr: Women and representatives of women's organizations with interests in traffic safety. Seeks to reduce traffic crashes, injuries, and deaths by encouraging each political subdivision to assume its responsibility for highway safety. Aims to promote uniformity in traffic safety programs and regulations within the 50 states, the District of Columbia, Puerto Rico, St. Thomas, St. Croix, and American Samoa. Conducts educational programs including seminars and workshops; maintains speakers' bureau. **Fnd:** 1967. **Mem:** 100. **Reg. Groups:** 10. **State Groups:** 50. **Pub:** *Buckle Up*; *NEWS* (quarterly).

3684 ■ National Beep Baseball Association (NBBA)
3444 Limerick Ln. NE
Rochester, MN 55906
Contact: Stephen Guerra, Sec.
Ph: (507)208-8383
E-mail: secretary@nbba.org
URL: http://www.nbba.org

Descr: Blind and visually impaired athletes, sighted volunteers, and others interested in participating in beep baseball. (Beep baseball uses an adapted ball and two adapted bases that emit sounds. Once the batter hits the beeping ball, he or she must get to whichever base buzzes before one of the six defensive players fields the ball. The pitchers, catchers and defensive spotters are usually sighted volunteers.) Promotes the development of amateur beep baseball and other recreational and competi-

tive programs for the blind and visually impaired; improves independence, mobility, communication, and social skills of the blind and visually impaired; educates and promotes community awareness and interaction between the sighted and the blind/visually impaired; holds tournaments. Sponsors speakers' bureau; conducts research programs. **Fnd:** 1975. **Mem:** 500. **Local Groups:** 20. **Pub:** *Beep Baseball In A Nutshell* (annual); *History of NBBA*; *NBBA Newsletter* (quarterly).

3685 ■ National Black Graduate Student Association (NBGSA)
2400 6th St. NW
Washington, DC 20059
Contact: Nameka Bates, Pres.
Free: 800-471-4102
Fax: 800-471-4102
E-mail: nationaloffice@nbgsa.org
URL: http://www.nbgsa.org

Staff: 24. **Descr:** Commits to improve status of African Americans in higher education. **Fnd:** 1989. **Mem:** 500. **Reg. Groups:** 4. **Pub:** *The Voice* (quarterly); Membership Directory.

3686 ■ National Braille Association (NBA)
95 Allens Creek Rd., Bldg. 1, Ste. 202
Rochester, NY 14618
Contact: Mr. David W. Shaffer, Exec. Dir.
Ph: (585)427-8260
Fax: (585)427-0263
E-mail: nbaoffice@nationalbraille.org
URL: http://nationalbraille.org

Staff: 5. **Descr:** Provides continuing education to those who prepare Braille, and provides Braille materials to persons who are visually impaired. Cooperates with other organizations in developing and expanding use of advanced Braille codes; offers training workshops for transcribers and tactile illustrators. NBA Braille Book Bank maintains over 2000 titles and 500 standard technical tables in Braille for immediate duplication; offers a transcribing service for Braille readers. **Fnd:** 1945. **Mem:** 1500. **Pub:** *Braille Technical Table Catalog* (periodic); *National Braille Association--Bulletin* (quarterly); *National Braille Association--General Interest Catalog* (periodic); *National Braille Association--Music Catalog* (periodic); *National Braille Association--Textbook Catalog* (periodic); *NBA Publications*.

3687 ■ National Braille Press (NBP)
88 St. Stephen St.
Boston, MA 02115
Contact: Brian A. MacDonald, Pres.
Ph: (617)266-6160
Free: 888-965-8965
Fax: (617)437-0456
E-mail: orders@nbp.org
URL: http://www.nbp.org

Staff: 31. **Descr:** Publishes books and magazines in Braille, including booklets on computers, self-help, and children's books (also in print). Supported by private gifts and legacies. Sponsors Children's Braille Book Club, offering monthly selections of print-Braille books. **Fnd:** 1927. **Pub:** *National Braille Press Release* (3/year); *Our Special* (bimonthly); *Syndicated Columnists Weekly* (weekly); Annual Report (annual).

3688 ■ National Business and Disability Council (NBDC)
201 I.U. Willets Rd.
Albertson, NY 11507
Contact: Edmund L. Cortez, Pres./CEO
Ph: (516)465-1516
E-mail: lfrancis@abilitiesonline.org
URL: http://www.business-disability.com

Staff: 15. **Descr:** Acts as a resource for employers seeking to integrate people with disabilities into the workplace and companies seeking to reach them in the consumer market. **Fnd:** 1977. **Mem:** 195. **Reg. Groups:** 7. **Pub:** *The Americans with Disabilities Act Training Module*; *Emergency Evacuation Checklist to Include People with Disabilities*; *Giving Us the Tools: A Human Resources Training Package on Employing Individuals with Disabilities*; *Interviewing Individuals with Disabilities*; *NBDC News* (quarterly); *Steps* to Success: A Blueprint for Employing Individuals with Disabilities.

3689 ■ National Captioning Institute (NCI)
1900 Gallows Rd., Ste. 3000
Vienna, VA 22182
Contact: Gene Chao, Pres./CEO
Ph: (703)917-7600
Fax: (703)917-9853
E-mail: mail@ncicap.org
URL: http://www.ncicap.org

Staff: 160. **Descr:** Aims to caption television programs for the deaf and hard-of-hearing on behalf of public and commercial television broadcasters, cablecasters, and the home video industry. Makes available captioning services, making use of a "closed captioning" system that allows coded captions not visible on a normal television set to be decoded and made visible by the use of a special adapter which may be attached to a television set. **Fnd:** 1979. **Pub:** Newsletter (semiannual).

3690 ■ National Center for Fair and Open Testing
15 Court Sq., Ste. 820
Boston, MA 02108
Contact: Monty Neill EdD, Exec. Dir.
Ph: (857)350-8207
Fax: (857)350-8209
E-mail: info@fairtest.org
URL: http://www.fairtest.org

Staff: 6. **Descr:** Seeks to ensure that the 100 million standardized tests administered annually are fair, open, and educationally sound. Works to: eliminate racially, culturally, and sexually biased standardized tests, including aptitude tests, intelligence tests, and professional certification exams; replace multiple-choice tests, which the group feels do not adequately measure performance with educationally sound alternatives; prevent non-validated tests from being administered. Supports truth-in-testing requirements that compel test makers to publicly disclose test questions; encourages requiring test companies to publicize statistics about the reliability and validity of their tests. Opposes the use of experimental sections on tests without the test subjects' consent. Encourages withholding of test scores from institutions that misuse them. Holds educational programs. Maintains library and speakers' bureau; compiles statistics. **Fnd:** 1985. **Pub:** Annotated Bibliography on Assessment of Young Children; Annotated Bibliography on Performance Assessment; Annotated Bibliography on SAT Bias and Misuse; Beyond Standardized Tests: Admissions Alternatives That Work; Failing Our Children; FairTest Examiner (quarterly); Fallout From the Testing Explosion; Implementing Performance Assessments: A Guide to Classroom, School and System Reform; Principles and Indicators for Student Assessment Systems; The SAT Coaching Cover-up; Sex Bias in College Admissions Tests: Why Women Lose Out; Standardized Tests and Our Children: A Guide to Testing Reform; Standing Up to the SAT; Testing Our Children: A Report Card on State Assessment Systems.

3691 ■ National Center for Homeless Education (NCHE)
PO Box 5367
Greensboro, NC 27435
Contact: Diana Bowman, Dir.
Free: 800-755-3277
Fax: (336)315-7457
E-mail: homeless@serve.org
URL: http://www.serve.org/nche

Staff: 4. **Descr:** Aims to overcome barriers to education, strives to improve educational opportunities for homeless children and youth. **State Groups:** 54. **Pub:** Increasing School Stability for Students Experiencing Homelessness: Overcoming Challenges to Providing Transportation to the School of Origin; Parent Brochure; The State Coordinator's Handbook; Students on the Move: Reaching and Teaching Highly Mobile Children and Youth; Surviving on Your Own: Information for Youth on How Schools Can Help.

3692 ■ National Challenged Homeschoolers Associated Network (NATHHAN)
PO Box 310
Moyie Springs, ID 83845
Contact: Tom Bushnell, Co-Dir.
Ph: (208)267-6246
E-mail: nathanews@aol.com
URL: http://www.nathhan.com

Staff: 6. **Descr:** Christian homeschooling families with special needs children. Promotes more effective home study, with particular emphasis on the education of children with special needs. Serves as a clearinghouse on home study and special needs children; facilitates establishment of networks of families engaged in homeschooling; supports legal and advocacy campaigns protecting the right of families to teach their children at home. **Fnd:** 1992. **Mem:** 15000. **Pub:** Family Directory (annual); NATHHAN News (quarterly); Brochures.

3693 ■ National Child Support Enforcement Association (NCSEA)
1760 Old Meadow Rd., Ste. 500
McLean, VA 22102
Contact: Colleen Delaney Eubanks, Exec. Dir.
Ph: (703)506-2880
Fax: (703)506-3266
E-mail: colleeneubanks@ncsea.org
URL: http://www.ncsea.org

Staff: 6. **Descr:** Promotes the well-being of children through professional development of its membership, advocacy and public awareness. Membership includes: Judges, court masters, hearing officers, district attorneys, government attorneys, private attorneys, social workers, child support enforcement caseworkers, state and county child support offices, probation departments, and child support advocates. Conducts monthly Tele-Talks, annual Policy Forum & Training Conference, Annual Training Conference & Expo. **Fnd:** 1952. **Pub:** Child Support Quarterly (quarterly); Rapid Read (monthly); Membership Directory (annual); Annual Report (annual).

3694 ■ National Coalition for Campus Children's Centers (NCCCC)
University of Northern Iowa
Price Laboratory School No. 114E
Cedar Falls, IA 50614
Contact: Terri Kosik, Pres.
Free: 800-813-8207
Fax: (319)273-3109
E-mail: ncccc@uni.edu
URL: http://www.campuschildren.org

Descr: Promotes child care centers on college campuses and provides information on organizing and operating these centers. Believes that campus child care programs should be an integral part of higher education systems and should provide safe and healthy environments for children, developmentally sound educational programs, and services to both parents and campus programs. **Fnd:** 1980.

3695 ■ National Coalition for Consumer Education (NCCE)
1701 K St. NW, Ste. 1200
Washington, DC 20006
Contact: Jane King, Chair
Ph: (202)835-3323
Fax: (202)835-0747
E-mail: info@nclnet.org
URL: http://www.nclnet.org

Staff: 4. **Descr:** State representatives who coordinate consumer education programs in a 50-state network. Promotes consumer education at the local, state, and national levels. Sponsors consumer education activities in local communities, through the news media, and within the public sector. Seeks to motivate the public to become more involved in consumer education issues. Sponsors contests. **Fnd:** 1981. **Mem:** 500. **Pub:** Coalition Exchange (quarterly); Brochures.

3696 ■ National Coalition for Disability Rights (NCDR)
1701 Pennsylvania Ave. NW, Ste. 300
Washington, DC 20006
Contact: Jim Ward, Founder/Pres.
Ph: (202)448-9928
Fax: (202)478-0945
E-mail: info@ncdr.org
URL: http://ncdr.org

Descr: Represents national disability and allied civil rights and social justice organizations as well as recognized national, state and local disability rights leaders. Aims to advance inclusion, economic opportunity and social justice for children and adults with physical and mental disabilities. Strives to protect and advance the civil and human rights of children and adults with physical, mental, developmental, cognitive, intellectual and sensory disabilities. Pools expertise, resources and influence to build the capacity of civil rights and social justice organizations to further a National Agenda for Disability Rights. **Fnd:** 2001.

3697 ■ National Coalition for Public School Options (NCPSO)
PO Box 3230
Arlington, VA 22203-0230
Contact: Lori Cooney, Pres.
Free: 866-558-2874
E-mail: info@publicschooloptions.org
URL: http://www.publicschooloptions.org

Descr: Represents the alliance of parents that supports and defends parents' rights to access the best public school options for their children. Supports the creation of public school options including charter schools, online schools, magnet schools, open enrollment policies and other innovative education programs. Advocates for free and equal access without restrictions to these public schools for all children. Informs policymakers and the public about the benefits of public education options and innovative public schools.

3698 ■ National Coalition for Technology in Education and Training (NCTET)
Meetings and Events of Distinction, LLC
2724 Kenwood Ave.
Alexandria, VA 22302
Contact: Mary Ann Wolf PhD, Exec. Dir.
Ph: (703)626-1266
Fax: (703)998-0526
E-mail: adorman@meetingsandeventsofdistinction.com
URL: http://www.nctet.org

Descr: Represents education associations, corporations, and organizations and individuals with an interest in education technology. Promotes and supports the effective use of technology to improve education and training in America. Acts as a convener, catalyst and resource for relevant and timely information.

3699 ■ National Coalition for Women and Girls in Education (NCWGE)
1111 16th St. NW
Washington, DC 20036
Contact: Liza Maatz
Ph: (202)785-7793
Fax: (202)872-1425
E-mail: maatzl@aauw.org
URL: http://www.ncwge.org

Descr: Works to improve educational opportunities for women. Advocates for the strong enforcement of Title IX and other civil rights law; monitors federal agencies implementation of federal education programs; and provides a valuable forum to share information and strategies to advance educational equity. **Fnd:** 1975. **Mem:** 50. **Pub:** Catching Up: A Review of the Women's Educational Equity Act Program; Documenting the Success of Vocational Equity Programs for Women and Girls; Education for All: Women and Girls Speak Out on the National Education Goals; Exploring America's Families; The Higher Education Act: A Guide for Women; How Does the

SAT Score for Women?; *Title IX: A Practical Guide to Achieving Sex Equity in Education*; *Title IX at 30: Report Card on Gender Equity*; *Title IX at 25: Report Card on Gender Equity*; *Working Toward Equity: A Report on the Implementation of the Sex Equity Provisions of the Carl D. Perkins Vocational Education Act.*

3700 ■ National Council for Accreditation of Teacher Education (NCATE)
2010 Massachusetts Ave. NW, Ste. 500
Washington, DC 20036
Contact: James G. Cibulka, Pres.
Ph: (202)466-7496
Fax: (202)296-6620
E-mail: ncate@ncate.org
URL: http://www.ncate.org

Staff: 20. **Descr:** Representatives from constituent colleges and universities, state departments of education, school boards, teacher, and other professional groups. Voluntary accrediting body devoted exclusively to: evaluation and accreditation of institutions for preparation of elementary and secondary school teachers; preparation of school service personnel, including school principals, supervisors, superintendents, school psychologists, instructional technologists, and other specialists for school-oriented positions. **Fnd:** 1954. **Mem:** 575. **Pub:** *How Professional Development Schools Make a Difference: A Review of Research*; *Quality Teaching* (semiannual); *Standards, Procedures, and Policies for the Accreditation of Professional Education Units*; Handbooks; Papers.

3701 ■ National Council of Education Providers (NCEP)
910 17th St. NW, Ste. 1120
Washington, DC 20006
Contact: J.C. Huizenga, Chm.
Ph: (202)822-5076
URL: http://www.educationproviders.org

Descr: Advocates for equity, opportunity, innovation and performance in K-12 education. Promotes and supports parents in meeting the demands for quality education. Protects, enhances and furthers the educational opportunities made available to children. Fosters innovation in the structure, approach and content of teaching, learning and parental involvement in the schooling of children.

3702 ■ National Council of Japanese Language Teachers (NCJLT)
PO Box 3719
Boulder, CO 80307-3719
Contact: Suwako Watanabe, Pres.
E-mail: ncjlt@japaneseteaching.org
URL: http://www.ncjlt.org

Descr: Promotes Japanese language teaching at the elementary, secondary, and higher education levels across the United States. Fosters the study of Japanese language and culture at the Pre-K-16 levels. Provides professional development opportunities for Japanese language teachers. **Pub:** *Oshirase* (quarterly); Brochure.

3703 ■ National Council on Measurement in Education (NCME)
2810 Crossroads Dr., Ste. 3800
Madison, WI 53718
Contact: Plumer Lovelace III, Exec. Dir.
Ph: (608)443-2487
Fax: (608)443-2474
E-mail: plovelace@ncme.org
URL: http://www.ncme.org

Descr: University and test publishers; educational measurement specialists and educators interested in measurement of human abilities, personality characteristics, and educational achievement, and of the procedures appropriate for the interpretation and use of such measurements. **Fnd:** 1938. **Mem:** 2300. **Pub:** *Educational Measurement - Issues and Prac-*

tice (quarterly); *Journal of Educational Measurement* (quarterly); *NCME Newsletter* (quarterly).

3704 ■ National Council on Patient Information and Education (NCPIE)
4915 St. Elmo Ave., Ste. 505
Bethesda, MD 20814-6082
Contact: Leonard J. Linchtenfield MD, Chm.
Ph: (301)656-8565
Fax: (301)656-4464
E-mail: ncpie@ncpie.info
URL: http://www.talkaboutrx.org

Staff: 4. **Descr:** Health care professional organizations, pharmaceutical manufacturing organizations, federal agencies, voluntary health agencies, and consumer groups. Increases the availability of information and improves the dialogue between consumers and health care providers about prescription medicines; increases professional awareness of the need to give adequate information on prescription therapy; expands consumers' participation with health professionals on matters of drug therapy. Communicates with health care providers on the importance of giving consumers oral and written information on prescription medicines and encourages consumers to ask questions about medicines and explain factors that may affect their ability to follow prescriptions. **Fnd:** 1982. **Mem:** 160. **Pub:** *Alcohol and Medicine: Ask Before You Mix*; *Be MedWise: Use Over-the-Counter Medicines Wisely*; *Get the Answers Wallet Card*; *Get the Most From Your Medicines: Managing Side Effects*; *Medicine: Before You Take It, Talk About It*; *NCPIE E-News* (bi-monthly); *Talk About Prescriptions: Month Planning Kit* (annual); *Your Medicine: Play It Safe.*

3705 ■ National Council on Rehabilitation Education (NCRE)
California State University
5005 N Maple Ave., M/S ED 3
Fresno, CA 93725
Contact: Linda Holloway, Pres.
Ph: (559)278-0325
Fax: (559)278-0045
E-mail: charlesa@csufresno.edu
URL: http://www.rehabeducators.org

Staff: 2. **Descr:** Represents academic institutions and organizations, professional educators, researchers, and students. Goals are to: assist in the documentation of the effect of education in improving services to persons with disability; determine the skills and training necessary for effective rehabilitation services; develop models, standards, and uniform licensure and certification requirements for rehabilitation personnel; interact with consumers and public and private sector policy makers. Disseminates information and provides forum for discussion. Sponsors specialized education and placement service. Compiles statistics. Works closely with agencies and associations serving persons with disabilities. **Fnd:** 1955. **Mem:** 600. **Reg. Groups:** 10. **Pub:** *Rehabilitation Education* (quarterly); Newsletter (quarterly); Membership Directory (annual); Monographs; Report (quarterly).

3706 ■ National Council for Support of Disability Issues (NCSD)
3870 Mountain Rd.
Haymarket, VA 20169
Contact: Trisha Flink, Exec. Dir.
Ph: (703)753-9148
E-mail: tfink@ncsd.org
URL: http://www.ncsd.org

Descr: Works to strengthen legal rights and remedies, build networks among student groups, and expand education opportunities for students with disabilities. **Fnd:** 1995. **Pub:** *Parent Handbook*; Newsletter; Articles; Survey.

3707 ■ National Disability Rights Network (NDRN)
900 2nd St. NE, Ste. 211
Washington, DC 20002
Contact: Curtis L. Decker JD, Exec. Dir.
Ph: (202)408-9514
Fax: (202)408-9520

E-mail: info@ndrn.org
URL: http://www.napas.org

Descr: Executive directors and designees of state or territorial Developmental Disability, Mentally Ill Protection and Advocacy Systems, and Client Assistance Programs. Furthers the human, civil, and legal rights of persons with disabilities; advances the interests of protection and advocacy systems; facilitates coordination and mutual support among such systems and enhance their capacity to provide optimal services. Offers professional training; collects data. **Fnd:** 1980. **State Groups:** 57. **Pub:** *State Protection and Advocacy Agencies* (annual); Newsletter (periodic); Manuals; Reports.

3708 ■ National Disability Sports Alliance (NDSA)
25 W Independence Way
Kingston, RI 02881
Contact: Jerry McCole, Exec. Dir.
Ph: (401)792-7130
Fax: (401)792-7132
E-mail: info@ndsaonline.org
URL: http://www.ndsaonline.org

Staff: 4. **Descr:** Athletes with cerebral palsy, athletic officials including coaches and administrators, health care professionals, and other interested individuals. Seeks to offer competitive athletic opportunities for athletes with cerebral palsy or traumatic brain injury and stroke survivors; provides support and training assistance to athletes with varying degrees of disability. Organizes multi-sport competitions at the local, regional, national, and international levels; maintains 8-level classification system to ensure that competition is based on the functional level of participants rather than their neurological capability. Selects athletes to represent the U.S. in the Paralympic Games and other international competitions. Provides referral service to assist members in obtaining support for local sports programs; develops fund-raising programs. Operates Youth Sports Program, which provides guidelines and assistance to young people with special needs who wish to learn a sport. Conducts educational clinics and seminars. Compiles statistics; maintains speakers' bureau and library. Plans to make available to members liability insurance and reduced rates on special sports equipment. **Fnd:** 1986. **Mem:** 3000. **Reg. Groups:** 30. **State Groups:** 15. **Local Groups:** 100. **Pub:** *NDSA Classification and Rules Manual*; *Update* (quarterly).

3709 ■ National Dissemination Center for Children with Disabilities (NICHCY)
PO Box 1492
Washington, DC 20013-1492
Contact: Stephen D. Luke EdD, Dir.
Ph: (202)884-8200
Free: 800-695-0285
Fax: (202)884-8441
E-mail: nichcy@aed.org
URL: http://www.nichcy.org

Descr: Serves as central source of information on: IDEA, the nation's special education law; No Child Left Behind (as it relates to children with disabilities); and research-based information on effective educational practices; funded by the Office of Special Education Programs, U.S. Department of Education. **Fnd:** 1970.

3710 ■ National Down Syndrome Congress (NDSC)
1370 Center Dr., Ste. 102
Atlanta, GA 30338
Contact: David Tolleson, Exec. Dir.
Ph: (770)604-9500
Free: 800-232-6372
Fax: (770)604-9898
E-mail: info@ndsccenter.org
URL: http://www.ndsccenter.org

Staff: 9. **Descr:** Families of individuals with Down Syndrome; educators, health professionals, and other interested individuals. Works to promote the welfare of persons with Down Syndrome (DS), a chromosomal disorder which occurs in approximately one in every 800 to 1,100 births and usually causes delays in physical and intellectual development; its exact cause is unknown. Promotes the belief that persons with DS have the right to a normal and dignified life, particularly in the areas of education, medical care, employment, and human services. Examines issues of social policy and conditions that limit the full growth and potential of children and adults with DS. Assists parents on possible solutions to the needs of the child with DS; coordinates efforts and activities of local parents' organizations. Acts as clearinghouse for information on DS. **Fnd:** 1973. **Mem:** 10000. **Local Groups:** 600. **Pub:** *Alpha Fetoprotein and Prenatal Screening*; *Atlanto-Axial Instability*; *Depression in Persons with Down Syndrome*; *Doman-Delacato Treatment*; *Down Syndrome*; *Down Syndrome News*; *Management of Challenging Behaviors*; *Mega Vitamin Therapy*; *Quality Education for Students with Down Syndrome*; Articles; Bibliography; Films; Journals; Pamphlets.

3711 ■ National Down Syndrome Society (NDSS)

666 Broadway
New York, NY 10012
Contact: Jonathan Colman, Pres.
Ph: (212)460-9330
Free: 800-221-4602
Fax: (212)979-2873
E-mail: info@ndss.org
URL: http://www.ndss.org
Descr: Aims to benefit people with Down syndrome and their families through national leadership in education, research and advocacy. **Fnd:** 1979. **Pub:** *A Promising Future Together*; *Clinical Care Booklets*; *Down Syndrome: An Introduction*; *Inclusion, Making Plans, Transition, A Promising Future Together: A Guide for New and Expectant Parents*; *UpBeat*.

3712 ■ National Dropout Prevention Center/ Network (NDPC/N)

Clemson University
209 Martin St.
Clemson, SC 29631-1555
Contact: Dr. Jay Smink, Exec. Dir.
Ph: (864)656-2599
Fax: (864)656-0136
E-mail: ndpc@clemson.edu
URL: http://www.dropoutprevention.org
Staff: 12. **Descr:** Serves as a research center and resource network for practitioners, researchers, and policymakers to reshape school and community environments to meet the needs of youth in at-risk situations so these students receive the quality education and services necessary to succeed academically and graduate from high school. **Fnd:** 1986. **Mem:** 500. **Pub:** *Alternative Schools: Best Practices for Development and Evaluation*; *The Journal of At-Risk Issues* (quarterly); *National Dropout Prevention Newsletter* (quarterly); *National Dropout Prevention Update* (quarterly); *Straight Talk about Discipline*.

3713 ■ National Education Alliance for Borderline Personality Disorder (NEA-BPD)

PO Box 974
Rye, NY 10580
Contact: Perry D. Hoffman PhD, Pres.
Ph: (914)835-9011
E-mail: info@neabpd.org
URL: http://www.neabpd.org
Descr: Promotes medical research on borderline personality disorder (BPD). Provides educational materials and programs on BPD. Seeks to enhance the quality of life of those people affected by this mental illness. Raises public awareness on all aspects of BPD. **Fnd:** 2001. **Pub:** *A BPD Brief*; *NEA-BPD Update*; *Perspectives on Borderline Personality Disorder*; Articles.

3714 ■ National Education Association (NEA)

1201 16th St. NW
Washington, DC 20036-3290
Contact: John Wilson, Exec. Dir.
Ph: (202)833-4000
Fax: (202)822-7974
URL: http://www.nea.org
Staff: 600. **Descr:** Professional organization and

union of elementary and secondary school teachers, college and university professors, administrators, principals, counselors, and others concerned with education. **Fnd:** 1857. **Mem:** 3200000. **State Groups:** 53. **Local Groups:** 14000. **Pub:** *Almanac of Higher Education* (annual); *NEA Higher Education Advocate*; *NEA Today* (8/year); *Thought and Action*; Handbook (annual).

3715 ■ National Fire Protection Association (NFPA)

1 Batterymarch Park
Quincy, MA 02169-7471
Contact: James M. Shannon, Pres.
Ph: (617)770-3000
Free: 800-344-3555
Fax: (617)770-0700
E-mail: custserv@nfpa.org
URL: http://www.nfpa.org
Staff: 300. **Descr:** Represents individuals from the fire service, business and industry, health care, educational and other institutions, and individuals in the fields of insurance, government, architecture, and engineering. Develops, publishes, and disseminates standards. Conducts fire safety education programs for the general public. Provides information on fire protection, prevention, and suppression; compiles annual statistics on causes and occupancies of fires, fire deaths, and fire fighter casualties. Provides field service by specialists on electricity, flammable liquids and gases, and marine fire problems. Sponsors National Fire Prevention Week each October and public education campaigns featuring Sparky the Fire Dog. **Fnd:** 1896. **Mem:** 81000. **Reg. Groups:** 4. **Pub:** *Fire Protection Handbook*; *Fire Protection Reference Directory and Buyer's Guide* (annual); *Fire Technology* (quarterly); *Learn Not to Burn Curriculum*; *National Fire Codes* (annual); *National Fire Protection Association--Technical Committee Reports/Documentation* (semiannual); *NFPA Journal* (bimonthly); *NFPA News* (monthly); Catalog (quarterly); Yearbook; Reports.

3716 ■ National Floor Safety Institute (NFSI)

PO Box 92607
Southlake, TX 76092
Contact: Russell J. Kendzior, Exec. Dir./Founder
Ph: (817)749-1700
Fax: (817)749-1702
E-mail: info@nfsi.org
URL: http://www.nfsi.org
Staff: 1. **Descr:** Product manufacturers, insurance companies, and independent contractors. Aims to aid in the prevention of slip and fall accidents through education, training, and research. **Fnd:** 1997. **Mem:** 500. **Pub:** *A World of Safety*; *Slip and Fall Prevention Made Easy*; Newsletter; Articles.

3717 ■ National Foundation for Credit Counseling (NFCC)

801 Roeder Rd., Ste. 900
Silver Spring, MD 20910
Contact: Susan C. Keating, Pres./CEO
Ph: (301)589-5600
Free: 800-388-2227
Fax: (301)495-5623
E-mail: press@nfcc.org
URL: http://www.nfcc.org
Staff: 1. **Descr:** Umbrella group for 200 member services operating over 1,500 offices throughout the United States and Canada. Promotes the wise use of credit through education, counseling, and debt repayment programs. Member agencies provide teaching units and other money management educational materials to high schools, universities, employee assistance programs, and community groups. Sponsors confidential credit and budget and homeownership counseling. **Fnd:** 1951. **Mem:** 178. **Reg. Groups:** 5. **Pub:** *Directory of Member Agencies* (annual); *Money and You* (quarterly); *Synergy* (bimonthly); Pamphlets.

3718 ■ National Judicial Education Program (NJEP)

395 Hudson St.
New York, NY 10014-3669

Contact: Lynn Hecht Schafran Esq., Dir.
Ph: (212)925-6635
Fax: (212)226-1066
E-mail: njep@legalmomentum.org
URL: http://www.legalmomentum.org
Staff: 5. **Descr:** Serves as a project of the Legal Momentum in cooperation with the National Association of Women Judges. Works to eliminate gender bias in the courts by making judges aware of stereotypes, myths, and biases pertaining to the roles of men and women, and how those biases can affect judicial decision-making and the courtroom environment. Serves as a clearinghouse for data on gender bias in the courts. Conducts courses and other educational programs for judges, lawyers, and the public. Collaborates with state and national judicial colleges and state task forces; participates in legal conferences, law school programs, and continuing education projects. **Fnd:** 1980. **Pub:** *Adjudicating Allegations of Child Sexual Abuse When Custody is in Dispute*; *Understanding Sexual Violence: Prosecuting Adult Rape and Sexual Assault Cases*; *Understanding Sexual Violence: The Judicial Response to Stranger and Nonstranger Rape and Sexual Assault*; *When Bias Compounds: Insuring Equal Justice for Women of Color in the Courts*; Videos.

3719 ■ National Minorities with Disabilities Coalition (NMDC)

1213 Wyndhurst Dr.
Plainsboro, NJ 08536
Contact: Jane Dunhamn, Chair
E-mail: info@nmdc.us
URL: http://www.nmdc.us
Descr: Aims to respond to the needs of minorities with disabilities in America. Seeks to organize around issues of mutual concern and use collective strength to address disability issues from all communities of color. Uses strategies from the civil rights movement to seek personal growth, collective power and societal inclusion for people with disabilities. Creates opportunities for people of color with disabilities.

3720 ■ National Organization on Disability (NOD)

910 16th St. NW, Ste. 600
Washington, DC 20006
Contact: Carol Glazer, Pres.
Ph: (202)293-5960
Fax: (202)293-7999
E-mail: ability@nod.org
URL: http://nod.citysoft.org
Staff: 20. **Descr:** Works to promote the full and equal participation of people with disabilities in all aspects of life. **Fnd:** 1982.

3721 ■ National Patient Safety Foundation (NPSF)

268 Summer St., 6th Fl.
Boston, MA 02210
Contact: Diane C. Pinakiewicz MBA, Pres.
Ph: (617)391-9900
Fax: (617)391-9999
E-mail: info@npsf.org
URL: http://www.npsf.org
Descr: Works to improve the safety of patients. **Pub:** *Current Awareness Literature Alert* (semimonthly); *Focus on Patient Safety* (monthly); *Journal of Patient Safety* (quarterly); Annual Report (annual).

3722 ■ National PTA - National Congress of Parents and Teachers

541 N Fairbanks Ct., Ste. 1300
Chicago, IL 60611-3396
Contact: Byron Garrett, CEO
Ph: (312)670-6782
Free: 800-307-4PTA
Fax: (312)670-6783
E-mail: info@pta.org
URL: http://www.pta.org
Staff: 65. **Descr:** Parents, teachers, students, principals, administrators, and others interested in uniting the forces of home, school, and community on behalf of children and youth. Works for legislation benefiting children and youth through its Washington,

DC office. Maintains resource center. **Fnd:** 1897. **Mem:** 5897934. **Reg. Groups:** 8. **State Groups:** 54. **Local Groups:** 26000. **Pub:** *Annual Resources for PTAs* (annual); *Our Children* (bimonthly); *The PTA Story: A Century of Commitment to Children*.

3723 ■ National Right to Work Legal Defense and Education Foundation (NRTWLDEF)

8001 Braddock Rd.
Springfield, VA 22160
Contact: Mark A. Mix, Pres.
Ph: (703)321-8510
Free: 800-336-3600
Fax: (703)321-9613
E-mail: info@nrtw.org
URL: http://www.nrtw.org
Staff: 52. **Descr:** Assists employees whose human and civil rights are being violated under compulsory union membership arrangements. Provides free legal aid to individual workers and conducts in-depth research aimed at developing new legal theories based on existing law and legal precedents which may be effectively utilized to assist employees whose rights have been infringed by compulsory unionism. **Fnd:** 1968. **Pub:** *Foundation Action* (bimonthly).

3724 ■ National Rural Education Association (NREA)

Purdue University
Beering Hall of Liberal Arts and Education
100 N University St.
West Lafayette, IN 47907-2098
Contact: Dr. John Hill, Exec. Dir.
Ph: (765)494-0086
Fax: (765)496-1228
E-mail: jehill@purdue.edu
URL: http://www.nrea.net
Staff: 6. **Descr:** Rural educators; state, county, district, and local school administrators; teachers, board members, college faculty, representatives of state departments of education; education associations; lay leaders, federal administrators, parents, and others interested in rural and small schools. Seeks to: promote state and regional delivery systems; serve as an advocate and representative for rural education; stimulate discussion, research, and policy developments regarding equal education opportunities for all school children and those living in rural areas; provide coordination for rural education programs and brokering assistance of appropriate agencies and individuals to meet the needs of rural and small schools; encourage colleges and universities to develop materials and resources specifically for rural schools and train personnel to work more effectively in these schools; disseminate information relating to rural education as well as sharing services and resources among educational organizations and agencies; provide leadership for rural education related conferences and workshops. Acts as a forum for all those involved in rural education and stresses the need for public and private agencies to develop educational materials and technology appropriate for children in rural schools. Compiles statistics. **Fnd:** 1907. **Mem:** 1200. **State Groups:** 20. **Pub:** *Directory of Rural Education Programs and Centers* (periodic); *Rural Education News* (quarterly); *The Rural Educator* (3/year).

3725 ■ National Safety Council (NSC)

1121 Spring Lake Dr.
Itasca, IL 60143-3201
Contact: Joseph J. Ucciferro PhD, Chm.
Ph: (630)285-1121
Free: 800-621-7615
Fax: (630)285-1315
E-mail: info@nsc.org
URL: http://www.nsc.org
Staff: 270. **Descr:** Promotes injury reduction by providing a forum for the exchange of safety and health ideas, techniques, and experiences and the discussion of injury prevention methods. Offers courses in first aid, occupational safety and traffic safety. Maintains extensive library on health and safety subjects. **Fnd:** 1913. **Mem:** 16000. **Local Groups:** 45. **Pub:** *Accident Prevention Manual for Business and Industry; Family Safety and Health*

(quarterly); *Injury Facts* (annual); *Safe Driver* (monthly); *Safe Worker* (monthly); *Safety and Health* (monthly); *Traffic Safety* (monthly).

3726 ■ National Safety Management Society (NSMS)

PO Box 4460
Walnut Creek, CA 94596-0460
Contact: Dr. Jeffrey Chung PhD, Exec. Dir.
Free: 800-321-2910
Fax: (573)441-1765
E-mail: nsmsinc@yahoo.com
URL: http://www.nsms.us
Descr: Individuals with managerial responsibilities related to safety/loss control management, including professionals in the fields of education, medicine, computer technology, security, personnel, law, and other disciplines. Advances new concepts of accident prevention and loss control and promotes the role of safety management in the total management effort. Advises concentration in areas where a favorable cost/benefit return can be achieved with these new concepts while being cognizant of humanitarian considerations. Participates in local, state, and regional safety conferences; conducts regional management improvement and executive safety training seminars. **Fnd:** 1966. **Mem:** 500. **Pub:** *Journal of Safety Management* (quarterly); *NSMS Digest* (monthly).

3727 ■ National Scholarship Providers Association (NSPA)

101 Monroe St.
Denver, CO 80206
Contact: Amy Weinstein, Exec. Dir.
Ph: (720)941-4498
Fax: (720)941-4492
E-mail: aweinstein@scholarshipproviders.org
URL: http://www.scholarshipproviders.org
Descr: Advances the collective impact of scholarships. Provides opportunities for professional development and the exchange of best practices among scholarship providers. Facilitates collaboration and communication among scholarship providers. **Fnd:** 1999.

3728 ■ National Student Safety Program (NSSP)

Indiana University of Pennsylvania
Highway Safety Center
R&P Bldg.
Indiana, PA 15705
Contact: Devon Gregory, Pres.
Ph: (724)357-4051
Free: 800-896-7703
Fax: (724)357-7595
E-mail: dbowser@hsc.iup.edu
URL: http://www.adtsea.iup.edu/nssp
Staff: 11. **Descr:** Works to encourage and assist students in their efforts to initiate and implement safety activities within schools and communities on drug, alcohol, safe driving, and health issues. **Fnd:** 1956.

3729 ■ National Stuttering Association (NSA)

119 W 40th St., 14th Fl.
New York, NY 10018
Contact: Ernie Canadeo, Chm.
Ph: (212)944-4050
Free: 800-937-8888
Fax: (212)944-8244
E-mail: info@westutter.org
URL: http://www.WeStutter.org
Staff: 1. **Descr:** Serves as self-help organization of people who stutter, parents of children who stutter, and speech pathologists. Seeks to provide a safe, supportive environment for stutterers and their families through chapter meetings, special programs, workshops, tape series, and self-help groups. Concentrates on issues such as improving self-image and assuming personal responsibility rather than focusing on speech fluency. Educates the public about stuttering and functions as a referral service for those seeking professional help. (Does not provide speech therapy or trained therapists.) Offers consulting in program development and technical as-

sistance to school districts, speech clinics, hospitals, rehabilitation centers, and other agencies involved in speech services. Advises members on how to be wise consumers of speech and related therapies. Maintains speakers' bureau. **Fnd:** 1977. **Mem:** 4000. **Local Groups:** 79. **Pub:** *Letting Go, Care, Stutter Buddies* (bimonthly); *Letting Go, Stutter Buddies*; Audiotapes; Brochures; Pamphlets.

3730 ■ National Training and Information Center (NTIC)

810 N Milwaukee Ave.
Chicago, IL 60642-4103
Contact: George Goehl, Exec. Dir.
Ph: (312)243-3035
Fax: (312)243-7044
E-mail: ntic@ntic-us.org
URL: http://www.ntic-us.org
Staff: 13. **Descr:** Resource center dedicated to neighborhood revitalization. Offers community leaders and organizers "how to" courses dealing with issues such as housing, neighborhood reinvestment, community drug problems, block club organizing, issue development, and media usage. Provides on-site consultation services and technical assistance to local groups on organizing campaigns and revitalization efforts. Serves as an information clearinghouse. Researches mortgage and lending practices, utility rate increases, community development funding, insurance redlining and other issues, and uses the information to pressure industry and regulatory bodies as well as to inform legislative bodies and the public. Sponsors training sessions. **Fnd:** 1972. **Pub:** *Basics of Organizing: You Can't Build a Machine without Nuts and Bolts; Dynamics of Organizing - Building Power by Developing the Human Spirit*.

3731 ■ National Water Safety Congress (NWSC)

PO Box 1632
Mentor, OH 44061
Contact: Cecilia Duer, Exec. Dir.
Ph: (440)209-9805
Fax: (440)209-9805
E-mail: director@watersafetycongress.org
URL: http://www.watersafetycongress.org
Descr: Represents individuals, business firms, state and federal agencies, and safety organizations. Seeks to instill safe attitudes and behavior in recreational users of the nation's waters and waterways. Promotes water safety through education programs, water safety demonstrations and programs offered by civic and sportsmen's clubs, and cooperative actions between agencies. Encourages the inclusion of water safety concerns in the planning, design, and construction of structures and facilities in and along waterways. Promotes the formation of local water safety councils and provides continuing support and assistance to them. **Fnd:** 1951. **Mem:** 300. **Reg. Groups:** 8. **Pub:** *Water Safety Journal* (quarterly).

3732 ■ National Women's Studies Association (NWSA)

7100 Baltimore Ave., Ste. 502
College Park, MD 20740
Contact: Loretta Younger, Exec. Admin.
Ph: (301)403-0407
Fax: (301)403-4137
E-mail: nwsaoffice@nwsa.org
URL: http://www.nwsa.org
Staff: 5. **Descr:** Represents teachers, students, community activists, and interested individuals; academic and community-based programs, projects, and groups interested in feminist education. Works to further the social, political, and professional development of women's studies programs. Supports feminist causes. Compiles statistics. Conducts conferences to address topics such as: new developments and controversies in feminist research and theory in the humanities, social sciences, and sciences; curricular development; political and legal issues and strategies; intersection of race and gender; international women's studies. **Fnd:** 1977. **Mem:** 2000. **Reg. Groups:** 12. **Pub:** *Bridges on Power: Women's Multicultural Alliances; The Courage to*

Question: Women's Studies and Student Learning; Guide to Graduate Work in Women's Studies, 2000 Edition; National Report on the Women's Studies Major; NWSA Directory of Women's Studies Programs, Women's Centers, and Women's Research Centers; NWSAction (semiannual); Re-membering: NWSA 1977-1987; Students at the Center: Feminist Assessment.

3733 ■ Network of International Christian Schools (NICS)
3790 Goodman Rd. E
Southaven, MS 38672
Contact: Ellen L. Black
Ph: (662)892-4300
Free: 800-887-6427
Fax: (662)892-4310
URL: http://www.nics.org
Descr: Aims to establish a worldwide network of international Christian schools staffed by qualified Christian educators. Seeks to instill in each student a Biblical world-view in an environment of academic excellence and respect for people of all cultures and religions. Strives to strengthen the presence of Christian education in schools. **Pub:** *Core* (semiannual).

3734 ■ Networking Project for Young Adults with Disabilities (NPDWG)
50 Broadway, 13th Fl.
New York, NY 10004
Contact: Rennie Roberts, CEO
Ph: (212)755-4500
Fax: (212)838-1279
E-mail: info@ywcanyc.org
URL: http://www.ywcanyc.org
Staff: 3. **Descr:** A project of the Young Women's Christian Association of New York City. Aims to increase the educational, social, and career aspirations of adolescents with disabilities by linking them to successful, disabled role models. Provides support groups; offers advocacy training, pre-employment skills development, and one-to-one mentoring. Organizes visits to the role model's workplace. Operates in the New York City area and provides technical assistance to facilitate replication at several sites throughout the country. **Fnd:** 1984. **Pub:** *Replication Manual*; Books.

3735 ■ New Leaders for New Schools
30 W 26th St., 2nd Fl.
New York, NY 10010
Contact: Jon Schnur, CEO/Co-Founder
Ph: (646)792-1070
E-mail: info@nlns.org
URL: http://www.nlns.org/NLWeb/Index.jsp
Descr: Ensures high academic achievement for every student through its 'New Leaders for New Schools' program. Aims to build the next generation of outstanding leaders for urban public schools. Forms a partnership with different organizations which are devoted to improving urban schools through effective leadership. **Fnd:** 2000.

3736 ■ New Ways to Work (NWW)
103 Morris St., Ste. A
Sebastopol, CA 95472
Contact: Steve Trippe, Pres./Exec. Dir.
Ph: (707)824-4000
Fax: (707)824-4410
E-mail: newways@newwaystowork.org
URL: http://www.newwaystowork.org
Descr: Helps communities build systems that connect schools, community organizations and businesses, and improve the services, educational programs and support the community provides for its youth. Engages and supports local communities in the invention and renewal of connected, comprehensive youth-serving systems. **Fnd:** 1972. **Pub:** Reports.

3737 ■ Nonverbal Learning Disorders Association (NLDA)
507 Hopmeadow St.
Simsbury, CT 06070
Contact: Patricia Carrin, Pres.

Ph: (860)658-5522
Fax: (860)658-6688
E-mail: info@nlda.org
URL: http://www.nlda.org
Descr: Represents children and adults with Nonverbal Learning Disorders (NLD). Facilitates education, research and advocacy for children and adults who manifest disabilities associated with the syndrome of Nonverbal Learning Disorders. Strives to enhance the lives of all individuals with NLD by encouraging effective identification and intervention, fostering research, and protecting the rights of learning disabled individuals. **Fnd:** 2000. **Mem:** 3000. **Pub:** Newsletter (quarterly).

3738 ■ North America Missing Children Association (NAMCA)
186 Silistria Dr.
Dartmouth, NS, Canada B2W 6A7
Contact: Nancy Ernst
Ph: (902)463-6311
Free: 800-260-0753
Fax: (902)883-4447
E-mail: namca@nbnet.nb.ca
Descr: Volunteers working to locate missing, lost, or abducted children. Gathers and disseminates information on missing children to the public and police organizations.

3739 ■ North American Council on Adoptable Children (NACAC)
970 Raymond Ave., Ste. 106
St. Paul, MN 55114
Contact: Joe Kroll, Exec. Dir.
Ph: (651)644-3036
Fax: (651)644-9848
E-mail: info@nacac.org
URL: http://www.nacac.org
Descr: Members of citizen adoption groups (composed primarily of adoptive parents of "special needs" children) and other individuals from judicial, child welfare, and legislative areas. Advocates the right of every child to a permanent, loving home. Provides direct assistance to local and state advocacy efforts; acts as a clearinghouse for adoption information; liaises with other adoption organizations. Sponsors an annual national training conference. Also sponsors Adoption Awareness Month. Conducts extensive education and outreach through the media and pre- and post-adoptive support programs. Provides resources for local advocacy programs. **Fnd:** 1974.

3740 ■ North American Professional Driver Education Association (NAPDEA)
5180 N. Elston Ave.
Chicago, IL 60630
Contact: Charles Rumsfield
Ph: (773)777-9605
Staff: 2. **Descr:** Individuals and firms engaged in the driving school industry meeting association qualifications. Has developed: procedure to evaluate facilities, equipment, ethical standards, and instruction offered by schools; provides Qualified Driving School emblem to those meeting standards. Conducts research on automobiles, teaching techniques, selection, screening and training of teachers and supervisors, and business techniques. Offers courses for driver education teachers and school managers and workshops. Supports legislation relative to traffic safety and driver education. Maintains library of publications on highway safety and business and educational materials. **Fnd:** 1958. **Pub:** *Driver Training Bulletin* (semimonthly).

3741 ■ Nutrition and Education International (NEI)
2500 E Foothill Blvd., Ste. 200C
Pasadena, CA 91107
Contact: Mr. Hunseok Kang, Exec. Dir.
Ph: (626)744-0270
E-mail: contact@nei-intl.org
URL: http://nei-intl.org
Descr: Strives to fight malnutrition among women and children who live in high mortality rate areas in Afghanistan. Works to expand soy nutrition and cre-

ate sustainable livelihoods for the Afghan people. Collaborates with other like-minded organizations to bring proper nutrition in Afghanistan communities. **Pub:** Newsletter.

3742 ■ OneChildhood
PO Box 491053
Lawrenceville, GA 30049-0018
Contact: Katherine Conn, Exec. Dir.
Ph: (678)401-2559
E-mail: info@onechildhood.org
URL: http://www.onechildhood.org
Descr: Provides support and services to children who live in single-parent homes. **Fnd:** 2004.

3743 ■ Operation Respect
2 Penn Plz., 6th Fl.
New York, NY 10121
Contact: Kristen Sensenig, Office Mgr.
Ph: (212)904-5243
E-mail: info@operationrespect.org
URL: http://www.operationrespect.org
Descr: Promotes the academic, social and emotional development of children and youth. Offers assembly programs and professional development for educators. Fosters laws and regulations governing educational policies and practices to create safe and respectful environments. **Fnd:** 2000. **Pub:** Newsletter.

3744 ■ Parents Active for Vision Education (PAVE)
4135 54th Pl.
San Diego, CA 92105-2303
Contact: Robert Nurisio, Pres.
Ph: (619)287-0081
Free: 800-728-3988
Fax: (619)287-0084
E-mail: info@pavevision.org
URL: http://www.pavevision.org
Staff: 1. **Descr:** Parents and teachers with children in their homes and classrooms who suffer or have suffered from the effects of undiagnosed vision problems. Works to raise public awareness of learning related vision problems. Supports the development of comprehensive learning related vision screenings, vision education, and vision hygiene programs in schools and communities. Maintains speakers' bureau. **Fnd:** 1988. **Local Groups:** 1. **Pub:** *The Hidden Disability*; *The Hidden Disability: Undetected Vision Problems*; *PAVE Resource Book*; *Pavestones* (semiannual); *Some Heroes Are Small.*

3745 ■ Parents' Choice Foundation (PCF)
201 W Padonia Rd., Ste. 303
Timonium, MD 21093
Contact: Claire S. Green
Ph: (410)308-3858
Fax: (410)308-3877
E-mail: info@parents-choice.org
URL: http://www.parents-choice.org
Descr: Provides parents and professionals with a central source of information about videos, books, toys, games, music, television programs, movies, and computer software. Selections are made by parents, children, teachers, librarians, and other experts. **Fnd:** 1978.

3746 ■ Parents-Coaches Association (PCA)
PO Box 224
Odenton, MD 21113
Contact: Carole Brady, Pres.
Fax: (301)912-1039
E-mail: bowlingpcamaybe@aol.com
URL: http://www.pca-bowling.com
Descr: Provides opportunities for young bowlers to obtain scholarship money in order to attend college or technical schools upon graduation from high school. Offers a Saturday morning bowling program for children ages 5 to 22. Supports young bowlers

during national and international competitions. **Fnd:** 1992.

3747 ■ Parents and Teachers Against Violence in Education (PTAVE)
PO Box 1033
Alamo, CA 94507-7033
Contact: Jordan Riak, Exec. Dir./Founder
Ph: (925)831-1661
Fax: (925)838-8914
E-mail: feedback@nospank.net
URL: http://www.nospank.net

Descr: Works to promote universal acceptance of the belief that every child has the right to grow and learn in environments that are violence free. Opposes the use of corporal punishment or other types of violent punitive techniques for the management of children. Conducts outreach programs to public social service agencies, law enforcement, parents, the media and others to foster respect for the fundamental human rights of children. **Fnd:** 1978. **Pub:** *Plain Talking About Spanking.*

3748 ■ Partnership for Civil Justice Legal Defense and Education Fund (PCJ LDEF)
617 Florida Ave. NW
Washington, DC 20001-1852
Contact: Atty. Carl Messineo, Co-Founder
Ph: (202)232-1180
URL: http://www.justiceonline.org

Descr: Founded by civil rights attorneys in Washington, DC. Provides and supports exclusively charitable and educational activities that secure and advance civil rights under the law, and that work towards the elimination of discrimination and prejudice.

3749 ■ Partnership for Food Safety Education (PFSE)
50 F St. NW, 6th Fl.
Washington, DC 20001
Contact: Shelley Feist, Exec. Dir.
Ph: (202)220-0651
E-mail: info@fightbac.org
URL: http://www.fightbac.org

Descr: Educates the public about safe food handling through research-based, actionable consumer food safety initiatives that reduce foodborne illness. **Fnd:** 1997. **Mem:** 20.

3750 ■ Plan of Action for Challenging Times (PACT)
635 Divisadero St.
San Francisco, CA 94117
Contact: Dr. Henry Lucas, Pres.
Ph: (415)922-2550
Fax: (415)922-6305
E-mail: info@pactinc.org
URL: http://www.pactinc.org

Descr: Program to benefit first generation and low-income students who are U.S. citizens or permanent residents and who have not, in most cases, utilized their educational potential. Serves the city and county of San Francisco, CA. Provides college admissions, financial aid, and career counseling services; offers assistance with application forms; organizes campus visits, meetings between college recruiters and students, and visits to corporations and public institutions to observe various professions; conducts financial aid workshops; sponsors presentations to organizations, churches, and clubs. Supported by U.S. Department of Education under Educational Talent Search Program. **Fnd:** 1965. **Pub:** *Pact Times*; Annual Report (annual).

3751 ■ Planting Hope
PO Box 56
Montpelier, VT 05601
Contact: Darryl Bloom, Chair
E-mail: planting_hope@yahoo.com
URL: http://www.plantinghope.org

Descr: Aims to serve the communities of Nicaragua and United States. Creates opportunities for education, development and cultural exchange. Facilitates community development projects and service learning trips in Nicaragua and United States. **Pub:** Newsletter.

3752 ■ PRIDE Youth Programs (PYP)
4 W Oak St.
Fremont, MI 49412
Contact: Jay DeWispelaere, Pres./CEO
Ph: (231)924-1662
Free: 800-668-9277
Fax: (231)924-5663
E-mail: info@prideyouthprograms.org
URL: http://www.prideyouthprograms.org

Descr: Parents, youth groups, educators, law enforcement officials, community groups, and corporations. Promotes drug abuse prevention through education. Provides current research information on drug abuse and facilitates the organization of parent peer groups, parent-school teams, and community action groups to reduce adolescent drug abuse. Gathers and disseminates information on the latest medical and scientific findings on the effects of drugs on youth, current patterns of drug and alcohol use among youth, social and cultural pressures that encourage youth to use drugs, and institutional and legal efforts being made to prevent drug abuse, reduce drug supplies, and prosecute drug traffickers. Conducts the PRIDE Community Action Plan to assist communities in establishing an effective drug abuse program and the PRIDE's Parent Training Program to assist concerned parents. Offers America's PRIDE, ClubPRIDE, and PRIDE Junior youth programs. Develops workplace drug training programs for corporations. Sponsors the annual PRIDE World Drug Conference, which seeks to bring parents, youth, and the public into contact with scientists, physicians, and policymakers dealing with adolescent drug abuse; also sponsors a series of one-day conferences for local community teams who are trained to return to their neighborhoods to organize workshops. Operates speakers' bureau; conducts educational programs and children's services; compiles statistics. Maintains library. **Fnd:** 1977. **Pub:** *PRIDE Quarterly* (quarterly); *PYP Times.*

3753 ■ Professional and Organizational Development Network in Higher Education (POD Networ)
PO Box 3318
Nederland, CO 80466
Contact: Virginia S. Lee, Pres.
Ph: (303)258-9521
Fax: (303)258-7377
E-mail: podnetwork@podweb.org
URL: http://www.podnetwork.org

Staff: 1. **Descr:** Represents universities, colleges, and other professionals dedicated to advancing post-secondary teaching and learning through faculty, administrative, instructional, and such as: ethics, diversity, pedagogy, research, service, technology, scholarship of teaching and learning, Preparing Future Faculty, and assessment. Seeks to exchange information and ideas; forges supportive relationships; enhances professional skills. **Fnd:** 1975. **Mem:** 1600. **Reg. Groups:** 5. **Pub:** *Essays on Teaching Excellence* (semiannual); *POD Network News* (3/year); *Teaching Excellence* (8/year); *To Improve the Academy* (annual); Membership Directory (annual); Newsletter (quarterly).

3754 ■ Project Appleseed: The National Campaign for Public School Improvement
520 Melville Ave.
St. Louis, MO 63130-4506
Contact: Kevin S. Walker, Pres./Natl. Dir.
Ph: (314)225-7757
Fax: (314)725-2319
E-mail: headquarters@projectappleseed.org
URL: http://www.projectappleseed.org

Staff: 6. **Descr:** Advocates the improvement in public education by increasing parental involvement in all of the public school districts in the country. Offers competitions, statistics, educational, research, and charitable programs, and a speakers' bureau. **Fnd:** 1993. **Mem:** 3500. **State Groups:** 50. **Local Groups:** 2000. **Pub:** *Appleseed Today* (quarterly).

3755 ■ Project Baobab
555 Bryant St., No. 198
Palo Alto, CA 94301-1704
Contact: Clara Roa, Development Dir.
Ph: (650)328-9332
Fax: (650)328-2910
E-mail: clara@projectbaobab.org
URL: http://www.projectbaobab.org

Descr: Aims to provide free education as a means to escape an otherwise endless cycle of poverty. Provides free education and entrepreneurial grants to youth, especially women, through a specialized life skills and business curriculum in Kenya. **Fnd:** 1996. **Pub:** Newsletter.

3756 ■ Public Education Center (PEC)
1100 Connecticut Ave. NW, Ste. 1310
Washington, DC 20036-4119
Contact: Joseph Trento, Pres.
Ph: (202)466-4310
Fax: (202)466-4344
E-mail: info@publicedcenter.org
URL: http://www.storiesthatmatter.org

Descr: Works to educate citizens through the major media by developing comprehensive investigations on the environment and national security. **Fnd:** 1992. **Pub:** Newsletter (monthly).

3757 ■ Puerto Rican Legal Defense and Education Fund (PRLDEF)
99 Hudson St., 14th Fl.
New York, NY 10013-2815
Contact: Cesar A. Perales, Pres./Gen. Counsel
Ph: (212)219-3360
Free: 800-328-2322
Fax: (212)431-4276
E-mail: info@prldef.org
URL: http://www.prldef.org

Staff: 21. **Descr:** Seeks to secure, promote and protect the civil and human rights of the Puerto Rican and wider Latino community. (Three divisions, Legal, Policy and Education, carry out the core program areas - Civil and Human Rights, Civic Engagement and Empowerment, Civil Society and Culture and Equitable Educational Opportunities -the pursuit of a legal career for Puerto Ricans and other minorities via its LSAT prep course, Law Day and other programs). **Fnd:** 1972. **Pub:** *Justicia* (quarterly); *Politica Social*; *PRLDEF in the News.*

3758 ■ Pulp and Paper Safety Association (PPSA)
PO Box 531
Perry, FL 32348
Contact: John Sunderland, Sec.-Treas.
Ph: (850)584-1569
Fax: (850)584-1220
E-mail: john_sunderland@bkitech.com
URL: http://www.ppsa.org

Staff: 1. **Descr:** Represents technical safety and health advisers to manufacturers and converters of pulp, paper, paperboard, woodlands, plywood, and sawmills. Conducts technical safety activities by exchanging ideas on accident prevention, studying causes of accidents, and disseminating safety information. Sponsors courses in basic and advanced safety and in noise control. Compiles statistics. **Fnd:** 1942. **Mem:** 310. **Pub:** *Pulp and Paper Safety Association--Statistical Report* (quarterly); *Quarterly Review* (quarterly).

3759 ■ Reading Recovery Council of North America (RRCNA)
400 W Wilson Bridge Rd., Ste. 250
Worthington, OH 43085-5218
Contact: Jady Johnson, Exec. Dir.
Ph: (614)310-7323
Free: 877-883-READ
Fax: (614)310-7345
E-mail: jjohnson@readingrecovery.org
URL: http://www.readingrecovery.org

Descr: Serves as an advocate for Reading Recovery throughout North America. Works to ensure access to Reading Recovery for every child who needs its support. Provides a network of opportunities for leadership and professional development. Aims to sustain the integrity of Reading Recovery and expand its implementation by increasing the number of individuals who understand, support and collaborate. **Fnd:** 1995. **Mem:** 11000. **Pub:** *The Journal of Reading Recovery* (semiannual); *Literacy Teaching and Learning: An International Journal of Early Reading and Writing* (semiannual).

3760 ■ Recording for the Blind and Dyslexic (RFB&D)
20 Roszel Rd.
Princeton, NJ 08540
Contact: John Kelly, Pres./CEO
Ph: (609)520-8096
Free: 866-732-3585
Fax: (609)987-8116
E-mail: custserv@rfbd.org
URL: http://www.rfbd.org
Staff: 105. **Descr:** Provides library services, computerized books, books on audiotape, and other educational materials free of charge to individuals who are unable to read standard print because of a visual, physical, or perceptual disability. Materials are produced by 4800 volunteers at 31 recording studios throughout the U.S. Titles recorded supplement, but do not duplicate, those of the Library of Congress Talking Book program. **Fnd:** 1948. **Mem:** 40000. **Reg. Groups:** 31. **Pub:** *Disk Catalog* (quarterly); *Recorded Catalog* (quarterly); *Recording for the Blind--Catalog Supplement* (periodic); *RFB and D Impact* (quarterly); Annual Report (annual).

3761 ■ Rehabilitation Engineering and Assistive Technology Society of North America (RESNA)
1700 N Moore St., Ste. 1540
Arlington, VA 22209-1903
Contact: Greg McGrew, Pres.
Ph: (703)524-6686
Fax: (703)524-6630
E-mail: info@resna.org
URL: http://www.resna.org
Descr: Rehabilitation professionals, providers, and consumers. Serves as an interdisciplinary association for the advancement of rehabilitation and assistive technologies. Seeks to improve the quality of life for disabled persons through the application of science and technology; influence policy relating to delivery of technology to disabled persons. Works for the design and development of rehabilitation devices and the modification of housing and transportation systems. **Fnd:** 1979. **Pub:** *Assistive Technology* (semiannual); *Augmentative Communication: Finding a Voice.*

3762 ■ Research and Training Center on Independent Living (RTC/IL)
University of Kansas
Dole Center, Ste. 4089
1000 Sunnyside Ave.
Lawrence, KS 66045-7561
Contact: Dr. Glen W. White PhD, Dir.
Ph: (785)864-4095
Fax: (785)864-5063
E-mail: rtcil@ku.edu
URL: http://www.rtcil.org
Staff: 19. **Descr:** U.S. independent living centers helping individuals with severe disabilities lead independent lives. Works to: identify attributes of successful self-help support groups; develop and test instruments to assess social support levels within self-help support groups; implement and evaluate intervention strategies for accurate and positive portrayals of people with disabilities by the media; deter unlawful parking in handicapped-designated parking spaces and enhance public awareness of issues related to disability and independent living; establish accreditation standards to evaluate ILC programs, services and management. Has developed: Personal Attendant Care Management Training model in seven states to increase the ability of consumers to manage attendants and reduce management problems and institutionaliza-

tion; program to assist ILC consumers in identifying personal goals and initiating behavioral changes to attain them. Provides direct training and technical assistance to individuals, ILCs, state agencies, and consumers' groups; university courses, and presentations. Places an emphasis on the needs of underserved populations, including the mentally ill, patients with brain injuries, minorities, the elderly, and persons living in rural areas. **Fnd:** 1980. **Mem:** 180. **Pub:** *Action Letter Portfolio*; *Building Consumer Consensus on Independent Living*; *Catalogue of Publications* (annual); *Consumers as Collaborators in Research and Action*; *Guidelines for Reporting and Writing About People with Disabilities*; *How-to Guide: Condensing and Translating*; *The Self-Help Group Leader's Handbook: Leading Effective Meetings*; Manuals; Monographs.

3763 ■ Roadway Safety Foundation (RSF)
1101 14th St. NW, Ste. 750
Washington, DC 20005
Contact: Cathy Gillen
Ph: (202)857-1200
Fax: (202)857-1220
E-mail: cathygillen@roadwaysafety.org
URL: http://www.roadwaysafety.org
Staff: 2. **Descr:** Develops programs, awareness campaigns, publications regarding roadway safety issues and countermeasures. **Fnd:** 1997. **Mem:** 53. **Pub:** *Action Update* (quarterly); *Roadway Safety Reporter* (quarterly).

3764 ■ Rolling Readers
2911 Adams Ave., No. 17
San Diego, CA 92116
Contact: Sharon Lieder, Pres.
Ph: (619)516-4095
Fax: (619)516-4096
E-mail: admin@rollingreaders.org
URL: http://www.rollingreaders.org
Staff: 3. **Descr:** Represents volunteers who are promoting literacy to children and youth in distressed neighborhoods. **Fnd:** 1991. **State Groups:** 16. **Pub:** *Read-Aloud Training Manual* (semiannual); *Read-Aloud Training Video.*

3765 ■ Roots and Wings International
3220 Connecticut Ave. NW, No. 311
Washington, DC 20008
Contact: Erik Swanson, Founder/Exec. Dir.
Ph: (202)747-4946
E-mail: info@rootsandwingsintl.org
URL: http://www.rootsandwingsintl.org
Descr: Seeks to create educational opportunities to promote community development. Empowers students to connect their cultural identity with social and economic development. Encourages and promotes the importance of education for girls. **Fnd:** 2004. **Pub:** Newsletter (monthly).

3766 ■ Routes to Learning Canada (RLC)
4 Cataraqui St.
Kingston, ON, Canada K7K 1Z7
Contact: Cormac Evans, Business Development Mgr.
Free: 866-745-1690
Fax: (613)530-2096
E-mail: information@routestolearning.ca
URL: http://www.routestolearning.ca
Staff: 17. **Descr:** Offers short-term, affordable educational programs for adults through a global network of institutions. **Fnd:** 1986. **Pub:** *Elderhostel Canada* (quarterly).

3767 ■ The Rural Institute: Center for Excellence in Disability Education, Research and Service
University of Montana Rural Institute
52 Corbin Hall
Missoula, MT 59812
Contact: R. Timm Vogelsberg, Exec. Dir.
Ph: (406)243-5467
Free: 800-732-0323
Fax: (406)243-4730
E-mail: rural@ruralinstitute.umt.edu
URL: http://ruralinstitute.umt.edu
Descr: Aims to support the independence, productiv-

ity, and inclusion into the community of persons with disabilities and their families. **Fnd:** 1979. **Pub:** *Montana's Programs for Individuals with Disabilities.*

3768 ■ Secondary School Admission Test Board (SSATB)
CN 5339
Princeton, NJ 08543
Contact: Dr. James K. Scott, Chm.
Ph: (609)683-4440
Free: 800-442-SSAT
Fax: (609)683-4507
E-mail: info@ssat.org
URL: http://www.ssat.org
Staff: 17. **Descr:** Administers entrance examinations for 600 independent schools in the U.S. and in foreign countries to 50,000 candidates. The tests are administered at centers throughout the world. Offers professional services and training to educators in admission at independent schools. **Fnd:** 1957. **Mem:** 800. **Reg. Groups:** 1. **State Groups:** 1. **Local Groups:** 1. **Pub:** *About Applying*; *About SSAT*; *Interpretive Guide to the SSAT* (annual); *Memberanda Newsletter* (quarterly); *Preparing and Applying*; *Professional Services Guide*; Directory (annual).

3769 ■ SEIU, District 925, AFL-CIO
3647 Stone Way N
Seattle, WA 98103
Contact: Kim Cook, Pres.
Ph: (206)322-3010
Free: 866-734-8925
Fax: (206)632-7219
E-mail: kcook@seiu925.org
URL: http://www.seiu925.org
Staff: 20. **Descr:** National union of secretaries, stenographers, typists, clerks, and other office, technical, and professional workers in the U.S. Promotes collective bargaining for office workers and sponsors research and educational programs on pay equality, automation, and career advancement. Seeks to organize the nearly 20 million office workers in the U.S.; compiles statistics. **Fnd:** 1981. **Mem:** 7500. **Reg. Groups:** 4. **Pub:** *Stewards Manual*; Brochures; Bulletin (periodic); Reports.

3770 ■ Seton Hill University's E-magnify
Box 389F, Seton Hill University
Seton Hill Dr.
Greensburg, PA 15601
Contact: Ms. Jayne H. Huston, Dir.
Ph: (724)830-4625
Fax: (724)834-7131
E-mail: info@e-magnify.com
URL: http://www.e-magnify.com
Staff: 6. **Descr:** Promotes women and business ownership. Offers a variety of entrepreneurial resources, educational programs, advocacy initiatives and networking opportunities to women entrepreneurs. Works "to strengthen the economic impact of women business owners as a collective force and to advance their growth through innovative programming in entrepreneurship and new venture creation." Provides support, education and encouragement essential for the continued growth of women-owned businesses through its services. **Fnd:** 1992. **Mem:** 4500. **Pub:** *E-Magnify Extra!* (weekly).

3771 ■ Sex Information and Education Council of Canada (SIECCAN)
850 Coxwell Ave.
Toronto, ON, Canada M4C 5R1
Contact: Michael Barrett PhD, Research Coor.
Ph: (416)466-5304
Fax: (416)778-0785
E-mail: sieccan@web.net
URL: http://www.sieccan.org
Staff: 2. **Descr:** Individuals and organizations in fields including sex education, counselling, reproductive health and medicine, and rehabilitation and therapy. Fosters public and professional education about human sexuality. Facilitates networking among members. Maintains information service and speakers' bureau; conducts research programs; sponsors educational programs. **Fnd:** 1964. **Mem:** 800. **Pub:**

The Canadian Journal of Human Sexuality (quarterly); Newsletter (semiannual).

3772 ■ SMARTRISK
790 Bay St., Ste. 401
Toronto, ON, Canada M5G 1N8
Contact: Dr. Bob Baker, Pres./CEO
Ph: (416)977-7350
Free: 888-537-7777
Fax: (416)596-2700
E-mail: info@smartrisk.ca
URL: http://www.smartrisk.ca
Staff: 16. **Descr:** Works to reduce the number of injuries in Canada. Sponsors campaigns to raise public awareness of preventable causes of injury in all aspects of daily life. **Fnd:** 1992. **Pub:** *Heads Up* (monthly); *Will It Float.*

3773 ■ Society for Financial Education and Professional Development (SFEPD)
2120 Washington Blvd., Ste. 400
Arlington, VA 22204
Contact: Theodore R. Daniels, Pres./CEO/Founder
Ph: (202)842-3807
Fax: (703)920-3809
E-mail: tdaniels@sfepd.org
URL: http://www.sfepd.org
Descr: Aims to enhance the level of financial and economic literacy of individuals and households in the United States. Develops and presents customized financial education and professional development seminars and workshops. Works with organizations that support financial education and professional development programs. **Fnd:** 1998. **Pub:** *Financial Success* (quarterly); Brochure.

3774 ■ Society for Intercultural Education, Training and Research U.S.A. (SIETAR-USA)
603 Stewart St., Ste. 610
Seattle, WA 98101
Contact: Peggy Pusch, Exec. Dir.
Ph: (206)859-4351
Fax: (206)626-0392
E-mail: info@sietarusa.org
URL: http://www.sietarusa.org
Descr: Promotes and facilitates intercultural education, training, and research through professional exchange. Works to improve intercultural relations, both domestic and global, by supporting the development and diffusion of cross-cultural knowledge and intercultural skills and practices. Encourages highest ethical standards and conduct information clearinghouse, a core support system for professionals, and a reference service for linking resources to needs. Sponsors annual week-long summer institute; works to stimulate research and funding of research. **Fnd:** 1974. **Mem:** 400. **Reg. Groups:** 40. **Pub:** *S-USA News* (quarterly).

3775 ■ Society for Nutrition Education (SNE)
9100 Purdue Rd., Ste. 200
Indianapolis, IN 46268
Contact: Jackie Williams CPA, Exec. Dir.
Ph: (317)328-4627
Free: 800-235-6690
Fax: (317)280-8527
E-mail: info@sne.org
URL: http://www.sne.org
Staff: 5. **Descr:** Represents nutrition educators from the fields of dietetics, public health, home economics, medicine, industry and education (elementary, secondary, college, university and consumer affairs). Works toward the fulfillment of its vision of having healthy people in healthy communities. **Fnd:** 1967. **Mem:** 1000. **Reg. Groups:** 15. **Pub:** *Journal of Nutrition Education & Behavior* (bimonthly).

3776 ■ Special Olympics
1133 19th St. NW
Washington, DC 20036
Contact: Timothy P. Shriver PhD, Chm.
Ph: (202)628-3630
Free: 800-700-8585
Fax: (202)824-0200
E-mail: info@specialolympics.org
URL: http://www.specialolympics.org

Staff: 130. **Descr:** Changes lives by promoting understanding, acceptance and inclusion between people with and without intellectual disabilities through year-round sports training and athletic competition and other related programming for more than 2.25 million children and adults with intellectual disabilities in more than 150 countries, has created a model community that celebrates people's diverse gifts. Provides people with intellectual disabilities continuing opportunities to realize their potential, develop physical fitness, demonstrate courage and experience joy and friendship. **Fnd:** 1968. **Mem:** 2500000. **Reg. Groups:** 7. **State Groups:** 52. **Pub:** *Special Olympics Annual Report* (annual); *Spirit* (quarterly).

3777 ■ Special Recreation for disABLED International (SRDI)
701 Oaknoll Dr.
Iowa City, IA 52246-5168
Contact: Prof. John Arthur Nesbitt EdD, Pres./CEO
Ph: (319)466-3192
Fax: (319)351-6772
E-mail: john-nesbitt@uiowa.edu
URL: http://www.globalvisionproject.org
Staff: 1. **Descr:** Seeks to serve and advocate special and therapeutic play and recreation for infants, children, youth, adults, and seniors throughout the world. Services include advisory and consultation, awards, employment information, professional education, public education, publishing, research, resource information and referral, technical assistance on programs and management methods, and an international library. Does international service work to: collect and disseminate international information on special recreation services for disabled persons, special recreation programs, and personnel training; conduct, provide, and support international exchange of technical, professional, and general information on special recreation for the disabled; cooperate with both governmental and voluntary organizations on national and international levels. Offers career guidance and placement service. Maintains speakers' bureau; compiles statistics. **Fnd:** 1978. **Pub:** *Camping/Outdoor Recreation, National Institute on Camping for DisABLED*; *Community-Based Special Recreation, National Institute on New Models of Community-Based Special Recreation for DisABLED*; *Deaf-Blind, National Institute on Play and Recreation for Deaf-Blind*; *Mental Health, World Seminar on Special Recreation, World Congress of the World Federation for Mental Health, Manila, Philippines.*

3778 ■ Sportsmen's Association for Firearms Education (SAFE)
PO Box 343
Commack, NY 11725
Contact: John L. Cushman, Pres.
Ph: (631)475-8125
E-mail: jcushman@juno.com
URL: http://www.nysafe.org
Descr: Promotes lawful firearms ownership in the U.S. **Fnd:** 1992. **Mem:** 600. **Pub:** *SAFE Legislative Report* (monthly); Newsletter (monthly); Reports.

3779 ■ Student Affiliate Group (SAG)
University of Akron
Department of Psychology
Arts and Sciences Bldg.
Akron, OH 44325-4301
Contact: Sally Diegelman, Sec.-Treas.
Ph: (330)972-7280
Fax: (330)972-5174
E-mail: sag@uakron.edu
URL: http://www3.uakron.edu/sagweb
Descr: Strives to enhance communication between counseling professionals and students in counseling graduate programs. **Fnd:** 1977. **Pub:** *The Counseling Psychologist*; Newsletter.

3780 ■ Student/Farmworker Alliance (SFA)
PO Box 603
Immokalee, FL 34143
Contact: Meghan Cohorst
Ph: (239)657-8311

Fax: (239)657-5055
E-mail: organize@sfalliance.org
URL: http://www.sfalliance.org
Descr: Strives to eliminate "sweatshop conditions and modern-day slavery in the fields". Raises awareness of farm workers' struggles. Campaigns for better wages and working conditions of farm workers and for the democratization of agricultural labor conditions. **Fnd:** 2000.

3781 ■ Student Organization of North America (SONA)
PO Box 210300
Tucson, AZ 85721-0300
Contact: Jose Manuel Castellon, Co-Chm.
Ph: (520)626-4392
Fax: (520)626-2675
E-mail: joecastellon@hotmail.com
Descr: Fosters student awareness and personal involvement in North American regional collaboration. Promotes cross-cultural relations, respect and understanding across Canada, the United States and Mexico. Serves as a framework for student-led cooperation across national boundaries. Promotes opportunities for students to experience our North American Community. **Fnd:** 1999.

3782 ■ Student Press Law Center (SPLC)
1101 Wilson Blvd., Ste. 1100
Arlington, VA 22209
Contact: Frank LoMonte, Exec. Dir.
Ph: (703)807-1904
Fax: (703)807-2109
E-mail: splc@splc.org
URL: http://www.splc.org
Staff: 4. **Descr:** Supporters are high school and college student journalists and journalism educators. Aims to protect the First Amendment rights of high school and college journalists. Provides information clearinghouse for student editors and others interested in preserving press freedom at student level. Offers legal aid and advice to students and teachers experiencing censorship; acts as amicus curiae in major censorship cases. Monitors important litigation. Maintains speakers' bureau. **Fnd:** 1974. **Pub:** *Law of The Student Press*; *Rights, Restrictions and Responsibilities*; *Student Press Law Center--Report* (3/year); *Student Press Legal Center Legal Alert.*

3783 ■ Student Veterans of America (SVA)
PO Box 77673
Washington, DC 20013-8673
Contact: Derek Blumke, Pres.
Free: 866-320-3826
E-mail: contact@studentveterans.org
URL: http://www.studentveterans.org
Descr: Aims to improve the welfare of all student veterans and family members of veterans. Addresses the needs and concerns of veterans in higher education. Advocates for improvements in veteran educational benefits. **Fnd:** 2008.

3784 ■ Students Against Destructive Decisions, Students Against Drunk Driving (SADD)
255 Main St.
Marlborough, MA 01752
Contact: Penelope Wells, Pres./Exec. Dir.
Free: 877-SADD-INC
Fax: (508)481-5759
E-mail: info@sadd.org
URL: http://www.sadd.org
Descr: Students in middle and high school and college and concerned adults. Aims to end death and injury due to drinking and driving, underage drinking, and drug abuse among youth. Maintains speakers' bureau. **Fnd:** 1981. **Mem:** 350000. **State Groups:** 50. **Local Groups:** 25000. **Pub:** *Decisions* (3/year); *SADD and the Athlete*; *SADD in the College*; *SADD in the High School*; *SADD in the Junior High School*;

SADD Update (quarterly); Audiotapes; Books; Videos; Annual Report (annual).

3785 ■ Suicide Information and Education Collection (SIEC)
1202 Centre St. SE, Ste. 320
Calgary, AB, Canada T2G 5A5
Contact: Karen Kiddey, Library Coor.
Ph: (403)245-3900
Fax: (403)245-0299
E-mail: csp@suicideinfo.ca
URL: http://www.suicideinfo.ca
Staff: 3. **Descr:** Obtains and provides access to a comprehensive collection of more than 35,000 English language documents and references on suicide and suicidal behaviors. Provides information to all professions and the public on specific topics such as adolescent suicide and bereavement. **Fnd:** 1982. **Pub:** *Youth Suicide and You.*

3786 ■ TASH
1025 Vermont Ave. NW, Ste. 300
Washington, DC 20005
Contact: Barbara Trader, Exec. Dir.
Ph: (202)540-9020
Fax: (202)540-9019
E-mail: operations@tash.org
URL: http://www.tash.org
Descr: Teachers, therapists, parents, administrators, university faculty, lawyers, and advocates involved in all areas of service to people with severe disabilities. Seeks to ensure an autonomous, dignified lifestyle for all people with severe disabilities; advocates quality education, from birth through adulthood, for disabled individuals. Disseminates updated information on solutions to problems, research findings, trends, and practices relevant to people with severe disabilities. Provides information and referral service. **Fnd:** 1975. **Pub:** *Research & Practice for Persons with Severe Disabilities* (quarterly); *TASH Connections* (10/year).

3787 ■ Teaching for Change
PO Box 73038
Washington, DC 20056
Contact: Alicia Horton, Co-Chair
Ph: (202)588-7204
Free: 800-763-9131
Fax: (202)238-0109
E-mail: info@teachingforchange.org
URL: http://www.teachingforchange.org
Staff: 7. **Descr:** Promotes social and economic justice through "transformative, quality education for all learners." Seeks to create equitable relationships among families, students, school staff, and communities. Functions as a network linking teachers; makes available educational and cultural resources. **Fnd:** 1989. **Pub:** *Civil Right Teaching;* Catalog (semiannual); Newsletter; Annual Report (annual).

3788 ■ Team Success
PO Box 232311
Sacramento, CA 95823
Contact: Aaron Boyce, Founder
Free: 866-745-6966
E-mail: admin@teamsuccessinc.com
URL: http://www.teamsuccessinc.org
Descr: Promotes the education and improvement of youth throughout the United States. Seeks to improve the social development, life skills, employability, social skills and entrepreneurship abilities of youth. Assists the community by providing business related workshops, mentoring and job assistance. **Pub:** Magazine (quarterly).

3789 ■ TIPS Program
1101 Wilson Blvd., Ste. 1700
Arlington, VA 22209
Contact: Adam Chafetz, Pres./CEO
Free: 800-GET-TIPS
Fax: (703)524-1487
E-mail: info@gettips.com
URL: http://www.gettips.com
Descr: Provides all schools with awareness, training, evaluation, and technical assistance in the classroom. Assists students in meeting their responsibilities to help ensure the safety and welfare of themselves and others by utilizing protective strategies to reduce their vulnerability to crime. Teaches kindergarten through eighth grade students to positively resolve conflict, resist crime, and protect themselves and their property. Develops and distributes curricula and teaching strategies. Provides personnel to train teachers, administrators, and program instructors. (TIPS is the acronym for Teaching Individual Protective Strategies and Teaching Individuals Positive Solutions). **Fnd:** 1976.

3790 ■ Union Label and Service Trades Department, AFL-CIO (ULSTD)
815 16th St. NW
Washington, DC 20006
Contact: Rich Kline, Pres.
Ph: (202)508-3700
Fax: (202)508-3701
E-mail: ulstd@unionlabel.org
URL: http://www.unionlabel.org
Staff: 3. **Descr:** Works to promote the official emblems (union labels, shop cards, store cards, and service buttons) of 70 affiliated labor unions. Promotes purchase of union labeled goods and the patronage of union services. Supports boycotts sanctioned by the AFL-CIO Executive Council. **Fnd:** 1909. **Pub:** *Label Letter* (bimonthly); Bulletin (bimonthly).

3791 ■ United States Business and Industry Council Educational Foundation (USBICEF)
910 16th St. NW, Ste. 300
Washington, DC 20006
Contact: Kevin L. Kearns, Pres.
Ph: (202)728-1990
Fax: (202)728-1981
E-mail: usbicef@aol.com
URL: http://www.americaneconomicalert.org
Staff: 7. **Descr:** Serves the Americans to promote entrepreneurship, seeks deregulation of the U.S. economy, pushes for lower taxes and less government spending, and eliminate capital gains and estate taxes on family-owned businesses; promotes the global competitiveness of U.S. businesses. Fights to strengthen American and family values; promotes school choice; strives to combat political correctness and speech control on campus, eliminate multiculturalism in the academic curriculum, and combat all forms of media bias. Strives to define America's international interests, strengthen the economic and technological foundations of U.S. global leadership. Sponsors Campus Newspaper Program, Campus Cartoon Service, Krieble Editorial Service, Campus News Service, and Public Outreach Program. **Fnd:** 1968. **Mem:** 1500.

3792 ■ United States Student Association (USSA)
1211 Connecticut Ave. NW, Ste. 406
Washington, DC 20036
Contact: Carmen Berkley, Pres.
Ph: (202)640-6570
Free: 800-574-4243
Fax: (202)223-4005
E-mail: ussa@usstudents.org
URL: http://www.usstudents.org
Staff: 10. **Descr:** Confederation of student bodies at American colleges and universities represented through their democratically-elected student government and statewide student associations. Provides a voice for students before the Department of Education and Congress. Gives expression to student opinion; seeks to increase students' responsibility and contribution to the college community and society; works to strengthen relations between American and foreign students. Works with major educational and civil rights organizations; provides programming aids to members. Member services include credit card programs. **Fnd:** 1946. **Mem:** 425. **Pub:** *Access: A Student Activists' Guide to the U.S. Congress* (annual); *Advance: A Retention Organizing Manual; U.S. Student Association--Legislative Update* (monthly).

3793 ■ Urban Teacher Residency United (UTRU)
650 W Lake St., Ste. 340
Chicago, IL 60661
Contact: Anissa Listak, Managing Dir.
Ph: (312)382-8878
E-mail: contactus@utrunited.org
URL: http://www.utrunited.org
Descr: Promotes urban teacher residencies to accelerate student achievement through training, support and retention of excellent urban teachers. Provides resources for emerging residency programs. Develops and implements common program evaluations and pursues national policy initiatives to support the introduction and ongoing support of high-quality teacher residencies. **Fnd:** 2007.

3794 ■ USSA Foundation (USSAF)
1211 Connecticut Ave. NW, Ste. 406
Washington, DC 20036
Contact: Carmen Berkley, Pres.
Ph: (202)640-6570
Fax: (202)223-4005
E-mail: ussa@usstudents.org
URL: http://www.usstudents.org
Staff: 3. **Descr:** Educational organization working to increase student access, choice, and success in postsecondary education. Conducts higher education policy research from the student perspective; provides information on issues that affect students; conducts training for student representatives. Has collected and reproduced background material on areas in higher education including educational reform and governance and Title IX. Provides current resource material on issues such as students, student financial aid problems and developments, educational equity and women's concerns, consumer protection in postsecondary education, educational training, internship opportunities, and developing statewide student lobbies. Offers research and consultation service to institutional, state, and national boards, agencies, and committees; acts as distribution center for materials published by others; provides policy analysis of federal and state educational programs to student organizations; monitors activities of national higher educational associations and inserts a student perspective on programs and issues. **Fnd:** 1972.

3795 ■ Veterans Education Project (VEP)
PO Box 416
Amherst, MA 01004
Ph: (413)253-4947
E-mail: vep@vetsed.org
URL: http://www.vetsed.org
Descr: Informs veterans, including those with less than honorable discharges and those who are incarcerated, of their rights to veterans' benefits. Does not represent individual veterans. **Fnd:** 1982.

3796 ■ Windward Foundation
55 Windward Ln.
Klickitat, WA 98628
Ph: (509)369-2000
E-mail: windward@gorge.net
URL: http://www.windward.org
Staff: 3. **Descr:** Promotes self-reliance among homeless persons, single parents, and senior citizens through remedial work and hands-on programs. Focuses on food, communication, and personal growth. Conducts research. **Fnd:** 1976. **Mem:** 21. **Pub:** *Notes From Windward* (annual).

3797 ■ Woman Within International Ltd. (WWIL)
10051 E Highland Rd., Ste. 29-280
Howell, MI 48843-6317
Contact: Margaret Renaud, Exec. Admin.
Ph: (519)962-8512
Free: 800-732-0890
Fax: (519)728-3264
E-mail: info@womanwithin.org
URL: http://www.womanwithin.org

Descr: Creates educational opportunities for women to discover their own potentials and abilities. Encourages women to communicate with their families, in their workplaces and communities. Provides personal and professional development to members. **Pub:** Brochure.

3798 ■ Women's College Coalition (WCC)
1678 Asylum Ave.
West Hartford, CT 06117
Contact: Susan E. Lennon, Exec. Dir.
Ph: (860)231-5247
E-mail: colleges@womenscolleges.org
URL: http://www.womenscolleges.org
Staff: 2. **Descr:** Represents women's colleges and universities - public and private, independent and church-related, two-year and four-year - in the United States and Canada whose primary mission is the education and advancement of women. Makes the case for women's education to the higher education community, to policy makers, to the media and to the general public. Collects and disseminates information relating to the education of women and gender equity in education; other priority areas are the issues of recruitment and retention of women in math, science and engineering, and the development of women's leadership. **Fnd:** 1972. **Mem:** 58.

3799 ■ Women's Global Connection (WGC)
PO Box 34833
San Antonio, TX 78265
Contact: Dorothy Ettling PhD, Exec. Dir.
Ph: (210)832-3208
E-mail: wgcstaff@womensglobalconnection.org
URL: http://wgc.womensglobalconnection.org
Descr: Aims to promote the learning and leadership of women locally and globally. Provides trips, dialogue, information sharing and learning of women's wisdom, experience and spirituality for the purpose of creating a just and sustainable global community. **Fnd:** 2001.

3800 ■ Women's Legal Education and Action Fund (LEAF)
60 St. Clair Ave. E, Ste. 703
Toronto, ON, Canada M4T 1N5
Contact: Audrey M. Johnson, Exec. Dir.
Ph: (416)595-7170
Free: 888-824-5323
Fax: (416)595-7191
E-mail: info@leaf.ca
URL: http://www.leaf.ca
Staff: 5. **Descr:** Volunteer based national organization that promotes equality for women through test case litigation at the Appellate and Supreme Court of Canada levels, primarily based on the Charter of Rights and Freedoms. Provides public education programs on cases and case outcomes. **Fnd:** 1985. **Mem:** 2500. **Pub:** *LEAFLines* (annual); Annual Report (annual).

3801 ■ Work Fairness
39 W 14th St., Rm. 206
New York, NY 10011
Contact: Von dora Jordan, Co-Coor.
Ph: (212)633-6646
Fax: (212)633-2889
E-mail: iacenter@iacenter.org
URL: http://www.iacenter.org
Descr: Works on a grass roots basis to fight homelessness and unemployment. Sponsors educational programs. **Fnd:** 1992. **Pub:** Newsletter (periodic).

3802 ■ World Federation of Athletic Training and Therapy (WFATT)
UT Health Science Center at San Antonio
School of Allied Health Sciences
7703 Floyd Curl Dr.
San Antonio, TX 78229-3901
Contact: Catherine Ortega EdD, Pres.
Ph: (210)567-8755
Fax: (210)567-8774
E-mail: cathyo@wfatt.org
URL: http://www.wfatt.org
Descr: Represents health care professionals in the fields of sport, exercise, injury/illness prevention and

treatment. Aims to promote the highest quality of health care and functional activity through the collaborative efforts of members. Creates a global forum for exchanging non-binding information about health care for active populations, including academic preparation and professional practice through meetings and communications vehicles.

3803 ■ World Institute on Disability (WID)
510 16th St., Ste. 100
Oakland, CA 94612
Contact: Thomas Foley, Acting Exec. Dir.
Ph: (510)763-4100
Fax: (510)763-4109
E-mail: wid@wid.org
URL: http://www.wid.org
Staff: 18. **Descr:** International public policy center that conducts research on disability issues and overcoming obstacles to independent living for all people with disabilities. **Fnd:** 1983. **Pub:** *An Independent Living Approach to Disability Policy Studies; The Cost of Program Models Providing Personal Assistance Services for Independent Living; Ethical Issues in Disability and Rehabilitation: A Report on an International Conference; How to Create Disability Access to Technology: Best Practices in Electronic and Information Technical Companies; Treating Adults with Physical Disabilities: Access and Communication;* Reports.

3804 ■ World Organization and Public Education Corp. of the National Association for the Advancement of Psychoanalysis (WOPAC NAAP)
80 8th Ave., Ste. 1501
New York, NY 10011
Contact: Jennifer R. Harper, Pres.
Ph: (212)741-0515
Fax: (212)366-4347
E-mail: jrharpertx@aol.com
URL: http://www.naap.org
Staff: 6. **Descr:** Works for public education for the National Association for the Advancement of Psychoanalysis. **Fnd:** 1995. **Pub:** Brochure.

3805 ■ World Savvy
999 Sutter St., 4th Fl.
San Francisco, CA 94109
Contact: Dana Curran, Exec. Dir.
Ph: (415)292-7421
Fax: (415)614-9537
E-mail: info@worldsavvy.org
URL: http://worldsavvy.org
Descr: Seeks to educate and engage youth in community and world affairs. Prepares youth to learn, work and live as responsible citizens of the 21st century. Provides direct programs for youth aged 10-18 and professional development for 6th-12th grade teachers. **Fnd:** 2002. **Pub:** *World Savvy Monitor.*

3806 ■ World T.E.A.M. Sports
PO Box 15632
Boston, MA 02215
Contact: Chris Carrigg, Exec. Dir.
Ph: (617)512-7161
E-mail: ccarrigg@worldteamsports.org
URL: http://www.worldteamsports.org
Descr: Increases and promotes sports opportunities for people with disabilities. Promotes diversity and increases awareness, acceptance and integration of individuals with disabilities. Encourages disabled individuals to participate in lifetime sports. **Fnd:** 1990.

3807 ■ Yes I Can! Foundation for Exceptional Children
1110 N Glebe Rd., Ste. 300
Arlington, VA 22201-5704
Contact: Bill Bogdan, Pres.
Ph: (703)264-3660
Free: 800-224-6830
Fax: (703)264-9494
E-mail: yesican@cec.sped.org
Staff: 80. **Descr:** Advocates for quality education for all individuals with physical disabilities, multiple disabilities, and special health care needs served in

schools, hospitals, or home settings. Advocates for gifted and talented children and youth. Operates the ERIC Clearinghouse on Disabilities and Gifted Education, and the National Clearinghouse for Professions in Special Education. Develops programs to help teachers, administrators, and related services professionals improve their practice. **Fnd:** 1922. **Mem:** 50000. **State Groups:** 51. **Pub:** *DPHD Newsletter* (quarterly); *Exceptional Child Education Resources* (quarterly); *Exceptional Children* (quarterly); *Teaching Exceptional Children* (bimonthly); Audiotapes; Books; Films; Videos.

3808 ■ Youth Crime Watch of America (YCWA)
9200 S Dadeland Blvd., Ste. 417
Miami, FL 33156
Contact: Ellen G. Cohn PhD, Chair
Ph: (305)670-2409
Fax: (305)670-3805
E-mail: ycwa@ycwa.org
URL: http://www.ycwa.org
Descr: Seeks to empower youth to participate in addressing issues in their schools, neighborhoods, public housing sites, and recreational centers and parks; assists students to organize programs; strives to provide a drug-free environment for youth; instills positive values, citizenship, and self-confidence. **Fnd:** 1979. **Pub:** Annual Report (annual); Handbooks; Videos; Manuals.

State and Local Organizations and Agencies

Alabama

3809 ■ 100 Black Men of Greater Huntsville, Alabama
PO Box 5194
Huntsville, AL 35814
Contact: Earnest L. Starks, Pres.
Ph: (256)536-8050
Fax: (256)536-8054
E-mail: info@100ghc.org
URL: http://www.100ghc.org

3810 ■ Alabama Association for Career and Technical Education (AACTE)
660 Adams Ave., Ste. 154
Montgomery, AL 36104
Contact: Ann Gilmore, Dir.
Ph: (334)262-4694
Free: 877-239-3412
E-mail: alacte@mindspring.com
URL: http://www.alacte.net
Descr: Dedicated to the advancement of education that prepares the youth and adults for careers.

3811 ■ Alabama Branch of the International Dyslexia Association (ALIDA)
14011 Coys Dr. SE
Huntsville, AL 35803
Ph: (256)551-1442
Fax: (205)942-2688
E-mail: gibbsdenise@aol.com
Descr: Promotes public awareness and understanding of dyslexia. Seeks to develop and implement specialized methods to improve the quality of life for people who have dyslexia.

3812 ■ Alabama Counseling Association (ALCA)
217 Darryl St.
Livingston, AL 35470
Contact: Dr. Ervin L. Wood, Exec. Dir.
Ph: (205)652-1712
Free: 888-655-5460
Fax: (205)652-1576
E-mail: alca@alabamacounseling.org
URL: http://www.alabamacounseling.org
Descr: Represents counseling professionals working in education, private practice, community agencies, government, business and industry settings. Advo-

cates and promotes counseling. **Fnd:** 1966. **Mem:** 2000. **Pub:** Newsletter (quarterly).

3813 ■ Alabama Counseling Association, Chapter IV
2744 Shoemaker St.
Birmingham, AL 35235
Contact: Tracey Deal, Pres.
Ph: (205)531-0316
E-mail: lovepcgd@aol.com
URL: http://www.alcachapteriv.org

Descr: Promotes the practice of counseling. Provides opportunities for personal growth and professional development.

3814 ■ Alabama Counseling Association, Chapter IX
PO Box 516
Andalusia, AL 36420
Contact: Lisa Patterson, Pres.
Ph: (334)222-7094
E-mail: playtherapy@centurytel.net
URL: http://alcachapter9.tripod.com

Descr: Promotes the practice of counseling. Provides opportunities for personal growth and professional development.

3815 ■ Alabama Department of Education
Gordon Persons Office Bldg.
50 N. Ripley St.
PO Box 302101
Montgomery, AL 36104
Contact: Dr. Joseph B. Morton, Superintendent
Ph: (334)242-9700
Fax: (334)242-9708
E-mail: dmurray@alsde.edu
URL: http://www.alsde.edu/html/home.asp

3816 ■ Alabama Parent Teacher Association (APTA)
470 S Union St.
Montgomery, AL 36104-4330
Contact: Nakia Thomas, Exec. Dir.
Ph: (334)834-2501
Free: 800-328-1897
Fax: (334)396-7090
E-mail: al_office@pta.org
URL: http://www.alabamapta.org

Staff: 2. **Descr:** Parents, students, and teachers promoting cooperation and quality education. Holds leadership workshops. **Fnd:** 1911. **Mem:** 114155. **State Groups:** 1. **Local Groups:** 500. **Pub:** *Alabama PTA Bulletin* (quarterly).

3817 ■ American Medical Student Association, University of Alabama School of Medicine
Medical Student Services
VH 100
1530 3rd Ave. S
Birmingham, AL 35294
Contact: Reesha C. Shah, Pres.
Ph: (205)934-2330
Fax: (205)934-8724
E-mail: rrich@uab.edu
URL: http://main.uab.edu/uasom/show.asp?durki=2023

Descr: Promotes improvement in medical training and education. Advances the medicine profession. Contributes to the welfare of medical students, interns, residents and post-MD/DO trainees.

3818 ■ American Medical Student Association, University of South Alabama College of Medicine
MSB 3030
Mobile, AL 36688
Contact: Blake A. Mann
Ph: (251)460-6101
URL: http://www.southalabama.edu/com

Descr: Promotes improvement in medical training and education. Advances the medicine profession.

Contributes to the welfare of medical students, interns, residents and post-MD/DO trainees.

3819 ■ Arc of Alabama
PO Box 1206
Montgomery, AL 36102-1206
Contact: Thomas B. Holmes, Exec. Dir.
Ph: (334)262-7688
Free: 866-243-9557
Fax: (334)834-9737
E-mail: info@thearcofalabama.com
URL: http://www.TheArcofAlabama.com

Descr: Focuses on parents, professional workers, and others interested in individuals with mental retardation. Works to promote services, research, public understanding, and legislation for people with mental retardation and their families. **Fnd:** 1957.

3820 ■ Arc of Calhoun-Cleburne Counties
PO Box 1848
Anniston, AL 36202
Ph: (256)236-2857

Descr: Parents, professional workers, and others interested in individuals with mental retardation. Works to promote services, research, public understanding, and legislation for people with mental retardation and their families.

3821 ■ Arc of the Chattahoochee Valley
PO Box 416
Valley, AL 36854
Contact: Essie Mae Harris, Membership Chair
Ph: (334)756-2868
E-mail: valleyhaven@charterinternet.com
URL: http://www.valleyhavenschool.org/vh_ap.htm

3822 ■ Arc of Cullman County
926 Brentwood Dr. NE
Cullman, AL 35055
Contact: Fred Abt, Pres.
Ph: (256)339-6015
E-mail: ccarc@bellsouth.com

3823 ■ Arc of Dothan/Houston County
426 County Rd. 87
Midland City, AL 36350
Contact: Mitchell Breedlove, Pres.
Ph: (334)983-1130
URL: http://www.thearcofalabama.com/chapters/dothan.html

3824 ■ Arc of Franklin County - Alabama
PO Box 1456
Red Bay, AL 35582
Contact: Stacy Mansell Day, Dir.
Ph: (256)356-8855
Fax: (256)356-2255
URL: http://www.thearcofalabama.com/chapters/franklin.html

3825 ■ Arc of Lawrence County
1790 County Rd. 249
Moulton, AL 35650
Contact: Hadley Key, Pres.
Ph: (256)974-8136
URL: http://www.thearcofalabama.com/chapters/lawrence.html

3826 ■ Arc of Morgan County
401 14th St. SE, Bldg. 4E
Decatur, AL 35601
Contact: Johnna Breland, Pres.
Ph: (256)355-6192
Fax: (256)350-4502
E-mail: morgancountyarc@bellsouth.net
URL: http://www.thearcofalabama.com/chapters/morgan.html

3827 ■ Arc of North Talladega County
PO Box 797
Talladega, AL 35160
Contact: Stan Mitchell, Pres.
Ph: (256)761-2228
Fax: (256)761-2202

URL: http://www.thearcofalabama.com/chapters/ntalladega.html

3828 ■ Arc St. Clair County
225 Hunting Ridge Dr.
Cropwell, AL 35054
Contact: Randy Mason, Pres.
Ph: (205)338-1778
URL: http://www.thearcofalabama.com/chapters/stclair.html

3829 ■ Arc of Shelby County - Alabama
1960 Chandalar Dr., Ste. H
Pelham, AL 35124
Contact: Karen Stokes, Exec. Dir.
Ph: (205)664-9313
Fax: (205)664-1934
E-mail: sharc1960@bellsouth.net
URL: http://www.thearcofshelby.org

3830 ■ Arc of the Shoals
300 Roberts Dr.
Florence, AL 35634
Contact: Murray Townsend, Pres.
Ph: (256)762-7797
E-mail: murraytownsend@msn.com
URL: http://www.thearcofalabama.com/chapters/colbert.html

3831 ■ Arc of South Talladega County
1401 E Alice Dr.
Sylacauga, AL 35150
Contact: Kathy Russell, Pres.
Ph: (256)249-3200
URL: http://www.thearcofalabama.com/chapters/stalladega.html

3832 ■ Athens/Limestone Arc
427 Rogers St.
Athens, AL 35611
Contact: Thomas Saint, Pres.
Ph: (256)232-0366
URL: http://www.thearcofalabama.com/chapters/athens.html

3833 ■ Clarke County Arc (CCARC)
PO Box 100
Jackson, AL 36545
Contact: Norvelle Jones, Pres.
Ph: (251)246-3000
Fax: (251)246-3098
E-mail: ccarc@clarkearc.com
URL: http://www.clarkearc.com

3834 ■ Dekalb Arc
1117 County Rd. 108
Rainsville, AL 35986
Contact: Wayne Turner, Pres.
Fax: (256)845-0262
URL: http://www.thearcofalabama.com/chapters/dekalb.html

3835 ■ Fire Marshal Association of Alabama (FMAA)
PO Box 2701
Gulf Shores, AL 36547-2701
Contact: C.P. Martin II, Pres.
E-mail: efmaa-subscribe@yahoogroups.com
URL: http://www.firemarshalsassociationofalabama.org

Descr: Provides the highest quality codes, standards, products, and services for all concerned with the safety and performance of the built environment.

3836 ■ Geneva County Arc
2951 Travelers Rest Rd.
Samson, AL 36477
Contact: Barbara Atkinson, Pres.
Ph: (334)898-7641
URL: http://www.thearcofalabama.com/chapters/geneva.html

3837 ■ Learning Disabilities Association of Alabama (LDAA)
PO Box 11588
Montgomery, AL 36111

Contact: Harriette Dorosin, Recording Sec.
Ph: (334)277-9151
URL: http://www.ldaal.org

Descr: Works for individuals with learning disabilities, their parents and the professionals who serve them.

3838 ■ Marshall County Arc
5104 Porter Harvey Dr.
Guntersville, AL 35976
Contact: Joyce Bishop, Pres.
Ph: (256)582-5009
E-mail: mcarc@mindspring.com
URL: http://www.thearcofalabama.com/chapters/
marshall.html

3839 ■ Montgomery Arc - Alabama
527 Buckingham Dr.
Montgomery, AL 36116
Contact: Leland W.C. Conner, Dir.
Ph: (334)281-6938
Fax: (334)286-9102
E-mail: marcl@mindspring.com
URL: http://www.thearcofalabama.com/chapters/
montgomery.html

3840 ■ North Alabama Chapter of Autism Society of America (NALASA)
PO Box 2902
Huntsville, AL 35801
Contact: Teresa White, Pres.
Ph: (256)251-1005
E-mail: al-northalabama@autismsocietyofamerica.
org
URL: http://www.northalabamaautism.org

Descr: Seeks to improve the lives of individuals affected by autism. Promotes awareness and understanding of autism disorders. Aims to further the advancement of preventive studies, therapy and research of autism disorders.

3841 ■ Tennessee Valley Association for the Education of Young Children (TV-AEYC)
PO Box 7
Decatur, AL 35602
Contact: Deborah Preston, Pres.
Ph: (256)355-7843
E-mail: dpreston@cacdana.org
URL: http://www.
alabamaassociationforyoungchildren.org

Descr: Teachers and directors of preschool and primary schools, kindergartens, child care centers, and other early learning programs for young childhood; early childhood education and child development educators, trainers, and researchers and other professionals dedicated to young children's healthy development.

3842 ■ Winston/Marion County Arc
2825 Littleville Rd.
Haleyville, AL 35565
Contact: Bill Lakeman, Pres.
Ph: (205)486-3642
E-mail: blakeman@centurytel.net
URL: http://www.thearcofalabama.com/chapters/
winston.html

Alaska

3843 ■ Alaska Association for Career and Technical Education (AACTE)
PO Box 33361
Juneau, AK 99803-3361
Contact: John Egan, Pres.
Ph: (907)465-8704
Fax: (907)465-3240
E-mail: marcia_olson@eed.state.ak.us
URL: http://www.actealaska.org

Descr: Represents teachers, supervisors, administrators, and others interested in the development and improvement of vocational, technical, and practical arts education. Supports and promotes vocational education.

3844 ■ Alaska Department of Education and Early Development
801 W. 10th St., Ste. 200
PO Box 110500
Juneau, AK 99811-0500
Contact: Larry LeDoux, Commnr.
Ph: (907)465-2800
Fax: (907)465-4156
E-mail: eed.webmaster@alaska.gov
URL: http://www.eed.state.ak.us/

3845 ■ Alaska Parent Teacher Association
PO Box 201496
Anchorage, AK 99520-1496
Contact: Al Tamagni, Pres.
Ph: (907)279-9345
Free: 888-822-1699
Fax: (907)222-2401
E-mail: akpta@alaska.net
URL: http://www.alaskapta.org

3846 ■ Anchorage Association for the Education of Young Children (AAEYC)
PO Box 201301
Anchorage, AK 99520-1301
Contact: Cecilia Harmon, Admin. Asst.
Ph: (907)696-5884
Fax: (907)696-5884
E-mail: office@anchorageaeyc.org
URL: http://www.anchorageaeyc.org

Descr: Teachers and directors of preschool and primary schools, kindergartens, child care centers, cooperatives, church schools, and groups having similar programs for young children; early childhood education and child development educators, trainers, and researchers. Open to all individuals interested in serving and acting on behalf of the needs and rights of young children, with primary focus on the provision of educational services and resources.
Pub: Newsletter (bimonthly).

3847 ■ Arc of Anchorage
2211 Arca Dr.
Anchorage, AK 99508
Contact: Patti Saunders
Ph: (907)277-6677
Fax: (907)277-2009
URL: http://www.arc-anchorage.org

3848 ■ Association for the Education of Young Children-Southeast Alaska (AEYC-SEA)
PO Box 22870
Juneau, AK 99802
Contact: Kathleen Rhea, Chair
Ph: (907)789-1235
Free: 888-785-1235
Fax: (907)789-1238
E-mail: info@aeyc-sea.org
URL: http://www.aeyc-sea.org

Descr: Teachers and directors of preschool and primary schools, kindergartens, child care centers, and other early learning programs for young childhood; early childhood education and child development educators, trainers, and researchers and other professionals dedicated to young children's healthy development.

3849 ■ Autism Society of America Golden Heart Chapter
1002 D St.
Fairbanks, AK 99701
Contact: Heidi Hass, Pres.
Ph: (907)374-4421
E-mail: ak-goldenheart@autismsocietyofamerica.org

Descr: Seeks to improve the lives of individuals affected by autism. Promotes awareness and understanding of autism disorders. Aims to further the advancement of preventive studies, therapy and research of autism disorders.

3850 ■ Challenge Alaska
3350 Commercial Dr., Ste. 208
Anchorage, AK 99501

Contact: Beth Edmands, Exec. Dir.
Ph: (907)344-7399
Fax: (907)344-7349
URL: http://www.challengealaska.org

Descr: Provides sports and therapeutic recreation opportunities for people with disabilities. **Fnd:** 1980.

3851 ■ Fairbanks Association for the Education of Young Children
PO Box 72456
Fairbanks, AK 99707
Contact: Kathy Fitch, Pres.
Ph: (907)479-2214
URL: http://www.faeyc.org

Descr: Teachers and directors of preschool and primary schools, kindergartens, child care centers, and other early learning programs for young childhood; early childhood education and child development educators, trainers, and researchers and other professionals dedicated to young children's healthy development.

3852 ■ Fairbanks Education Association (FEA)
2118 S Cushman St.
Fairbanks, AK 99701
Contact: Nancy Duez, VP
Ph: (907)456-4435
Free: 888-456-4435
Fax: (907)456-2159
E-mail: fea@alaska.net
URL: http://www.alaska.net/~fea

Descr: Works to ensure quality educational programs and facilities in Fairbanks, AK. **Fnd:** 1946. **Mem:** 1014. **Reg. Groups:** 1. **State Groups:** 1. **Pub:** *FEAdback* (weekly).

3853 ■ National Education Association - Alaska
4100 Spenard Rd.
Anchorage, AK 99517
Contact: Lydia Garcia, Exec. Dir.
Ph: (907)274-0536
Fax: (907)274-0551
E-mail: info@ak.nea.org
URL: http://www.ak.nea.org

Staff: 26. **Descr:** Teachers, education support personnel, retired educators, and college students. Advocates for an excellent public education for each child in Alaska. Works to advance the interests of public school employees. **Fnd:** 1922. **Mem:** 11000. **Local Groups:** 65. **Pub:** *NEA-AKtivist*; *NEA-Alaska Orientation Handbook for Rural Educators*.

3854 ■ Special Olympics Alaska
3200 Mountain View Dr.
Anchorage, AK 99501
Contact: James D. Balamaci, Pres./CEO
Ph: (907)222-7625
Free: 888-499-SOAK
Fax: (907)222-6200
E-mail: jim@specialolympicsalaska.org
URL: http://www.specialolympicsalaska.org

Descr: Promotes physical fitness, sports training, and athletic competition for children and adults with mental retardation. Seeks to contribute to the physical, social, and psychological development of persons with mental retardation. Participants range in age from 8 years to adult and compete in track and field, swimming, gymnastics, bowling, ice skating, basketball, and other sports. **Fnd:** 1968.

Arizona

3855 ■ 100 Black Men of Phoenix
4802 E Ray Rd., Ste. 23-243
Phoenix, AZ 85044
Contact: Leonard Knight, Pres.
E-mail: president@100blackmenphx.org
URL: http://www.100blackmenphx.org

3856 ■ American Association of University Women of Arizona
7590 W Wikieup Ln.
Glendale, AZ 85308
Contact: Susan Youngdahl, Pres.

E-mail: president@aauwarizona.org
URL: http://www.aauwarizona.org
Descr: Advances equity for women and girls through advocacy, education, and research. Provides funds and a support system for women seeking judicial redress for sex discrimination in higher education.

3857 ■ American Association of University Women, Scottsdale Branch
7349 N Via Paseo del Sol, Ste. 515
Scottsdale, AZ 85258
Contact: Judy Hubbard, Pres.
E-mail: president@aauwscottsdale.org
URL: http://aauwscottsdale.org
Descr: Advances equity for women and girls through advocacy, education, and research. Provides funds and a support system for women seeking judicial redress for sex discrimination in higher education. **Mem:** 160.

3858 ■ American Association of University Women, Tucson Branch
PO Box 40822
Tucson, AZ 85717-0822
Contact: Connie Harrison, Pres.
E-mail: jnclarke@email.arizona.edu
URL: http://www.aauw-tucson.org
Descr: Advances equity for women and girls through advocacy, education, and research. Provides funds and a support system for women seeking judicial redress for sex discrimination in higher education.

3859 ■ American Medical Student Association, Arizona College of Osteopathic Medicine
19555 N 59th Ave.
Glendale, AZ 85308
Contact: Kathleen H. Goeppinger PhD, Pres./CEO
Ph: (623)572-3200
Descr: Promotes improvement in medical training and education. Advances the medicine profession. Contributes to the welfare of medical students, interns, residents and post-MD/DO trainees.

3860 ■ American Medical Student Association, The University of Arizona College of Medicine
PO Box 245017
Tucson, AZ 85724
Contact: Keith A. Joiner MD, Dean
Ph: (520)626-4555
URL: http://www.medicine.arizona.edu
Descr: Promotes improvement in medical training and education. Advances the medicine profession. Contributes to the welfare of medical students, interns, residents and post-MD/DO trainees.

3861 ■ Arc of Arizona
3839 N 3rd St., Ste. 105
Phoenix, AZ 85012
Contact: Joe Bonanno, Exec. Dir.
Ph: (602)234-2721
Fax: (602)234-5959
E-mail: thearcaz@gmail.com
URL: http://www.arcarizona.org
Descr: Parents, professional workers, and others interested in individuals with mental retardation. Works to promote services, research, public understanding, and legislation for people with mental retardation and their families. **Fnd:** 1958. **Mem:** 2000.

3862 ■ Arc of Tempe
PO Box 26014
Tempe, AZ 85285
Contact: Brenda Fox, Community Liaison
Ph: (480)966-8536
Fax: (480)736-2881
E-mail: community@tempearc.org
URL: http://www.tempearc.com

3863 ■ Arc of Tucson
PO Box 44324
Tucson, AZ 85733
Contact: Kelly McLear, Pres.
Ph: (520)570-1295
Free: 877-272-2270

Fax: (520)760-1570
URL: http://www.arcoftucson.org
Descr: People with developmental disabilities, their families, professionals and anyone concerned about people with developmental disabilities. Advocates for equal rights of disabled and their families with equal choices of where and how they learn, live, work and play. Provides education and information about prevention of developmental disabilities. Distributes donations of new and quality household items. **Fnd:** 1960. **Mem:** 600. **State Groups:** 1. **Local Groups:** 1000. **Pub:** *The Refresher* (quarterly).

3864 ■ Arc of Yuma County
PO Box 6830
Yuma, AZ 85366
Ph: (928)782-4791
E-mail: arcofyuma@yahoo.com
URL: http://www.arcarizona.org/local_chapters.html

3865 ■ Arizona Association for the Education of Young Children (AzAEYC)
8470 N Overfield Rd.
Coolidge, AZ 85228
Contact: Joanne Floth, Pres.
Ph: (520)494-5031
E-mail: joanne.floth@centralaz.edu
URL: http://www.azaeyc.net
Descr: Serves and acts on behalf of the needs, rights and well-being of all young children with primary focus on the quality of educational and developmental services for all children. Seeks to improve professional practice and working conditions in early childhood education.

3866 ■ Arizona Automatic Fire Alarm Association (AZAFAA)
PO Box 62681
Phoenix, AZ 85082
Contact: Cliff Emerson, Pres.
E-mail: cliff@afpc.com
URL: http://www.azafaa.org
Descr: Promotes the use of fire detection systems to protect life and property.

3867 ■ Arizona Branch of the International Dyslexia Association (IDA-AZ)
PO Box 6248
Scottsdale, AZ 85261-6284
Contact: Mary Wennersten, Pres.
Ph: (480)941-0308
E-mail: mwennersten2@cox.net
URL: http://www.dyslexia-az.org
Descr: Promotes public awareness and understanding of dyslexia. Seeks to develop and implement specialized methods to improve the quality of life for people who have dyslexia.

3868 ■ Arizona Department of Education
1535 W. Jefferson St.
Phoenix, AZ 85007
Contact: Tom Horne, Superintendent
Ph: (602)542-5393
Free: 800-352-4558
Fax: (602)542-5440
E-mail: ADEINBOX@ade.az.gov
URL: http://www.ade.az.gov/
Descr: Works to ensure academic excellence for all students.

3869 ■ Arizona Fire Marshals Association (AFMA)
797 E Ajo Way
Tucson, AZ 85713
Contact: Glenn T. D'Auria
Ph: (520)791-4502
Fax: (520)791-5346
E-mail: glenn.d'auria@tucsonaz.gov
URL: http://www.azfma.org
Descr: Provides the highest quality codes, standards, products, and services for all concerned with the safety and performance of the built environment.

3870 ■ Arizona PTA
2721 N 7th Ave.
Phoenix, AZ 85007

Contact: Vivian Vincent, Pres.
Ph: (602)279-1811
Fax: (602)279-1814
E-mail: office@azpta.org
URL: http://www.azpta.org
Staff: 2. **Descr:** Parents, teachers, students, and community members united to "speak on behalf of children, assist in the developing of parenting skills, and encourage involvement in the public schools." Conducts Reflections art competition. **Fnd:** 1906. **Mem:** 35000. **Pub:** *Arizona PTA NewsReport*.

3871 ■ Arizona School Age Coalition
700 W Campbell, Ste. 3
Phoenix, AZ 85013
Contact: Melanie W. McClintock, Exec. Dir.
Ph: (602)279-7100
Fax: (602)234-3943
E-mail: mmcclintock@azafterschool.org
URL: http://www.azsac.org
Descr: Fosters quality out-of-school time opportunities for children and youth. **Pub:** *AzSAC Advisor* (quarterly).

3872 ■ Association for Education and Rehabilitation of the Blind and Visually Impaired, Arizona Chapter (AZ AER)
6639 E Broadway Blvd., No. 207
Tucson, AZ 85710
Contact: Venetia Hayden, Pres.
Ph: (520)360-0642
E-mail: mark.brady@tusd1.org
URL: http://azaer.aerbvi.org
Descr: Develops and promotes professional excellence. Provides services to people with visual impairments through professional supports, continuing education, and career development. **Mem:** 165. **Pub:** *AERizona View*.

3873 ■ Autism Society of America - Pima County Chapter
PO Box 44156
Tucson, AZ 85733
Contact: Peter Earhart, Pres.
Ph: (520)770-1541
E-mail: asapcc@tucsonautism.org
URL: http://www.tucsonautism.org
Descr: Seeks to improve the lives of individuals affected by autism. Promotes awareness and understanding of autism disorders. Aims to further the advancement of preventive studies, therapy and research of autism disorders.

3874 ■ Chandler - Gilbert Arc
3250 N San Marcos Pl.
Chandler, AZ 85225
Contact: Ron Travis, Exec. Dir.
Ph: (480)892-9422
Fax: (480)497-0657
E-mail: cgarc@cgarc.org
URL: http://www.cgarc.org
Descr: Parents, professional workers, and others interested in individuals with mental retardation. Works to promote services, research, public understanding, and legislation for people with mental retardation and their families.

3875 ■ Communities In Schools of Arizona
4520 N Central Ave., Ste. 560
Phoenix, AZ 85012-1835
Contact: Cindy Vargo, Pres./CEO
Ph: (602)252-5312
Fax: (602)252-5314
E-mail: cisa@cisarizona.org
URL: http://www.cisarizona.org
Descr: Strives to champion the connection of needed community resources with schools to help young people learn, stay in school, and prepare for life. **Fnd:** 1994.

3876 ■ Douglas Arc
PO Box 252
Douglas, AZ 85608
Contact: Gary J. Clark, Exec. Dir.
Ph: (520)364-7473
Fax: (520)364-2236

E-mail: contact@douglasarc.org
URL: http://www.douglasarc.org
Descr: Parents, professional workers, and others interested in individuals with mental retardation. Works to promote services, research, public understanding, and legislation for people with mental retardation and their families.

3877 ■ Gila County Arc
PO Box 1262
Globe, AZ 85502
Contact: Debra Hammer, Exec. Dir.
Ph: (928)425-6053
E-mail: dlc@cybertrails.com
URL: http://www.arcarizona.org/local_chapters.html

3878 ■ Learning Disabilities Association of Arizona (LDA)
5757 W Eugie Ave., No. 1034
Glendale, AZ 85304
Contact: Rob Crawford, Pres.
Ph: (623)975-4551
Fax: (623)773-2788
E-mail: azlda@att.net
URL: http://old.ldaamerica.us/affiliates/az/welcome.htm

3879 ■ Marc Center of Mesa
924 N Country Club Dr.
Mesa, AZ 85201
Contact: Randy Gray, CEO
Ph: (480)969-3800
Fax: (480)644-1557
E-mail: randy.gray@marccenter.com
URL: http://www.marccenter.com
Staff: 400. **Descr:** Provides services to children and adults with developmental disabilities and/or mental illness. Works to promote services, research public understanding, and legislation for people with disabilities and their families. **Fnd:** 1957. **Pub:** *Independent Thinking*.

3880 ■ Mohave County Arc
2050 Airway Ave.
Kingman, AZ 86409
Contact: Norma Randall, Exec. Dir.
Ph: (928)757-1758
E-mail: mohavearc@hotmail.com
URL: http://www.arcarizona.org/local_chapters.html

3881 ■ Mothers and More McDowell Mountain Ranch, Chapter 300
10401 E McDowell Mountain Ranch Rd.
Box 2208
Scottsdale, AZ 85255
E-mail: info@mothersandmoreofmmr.org
URL: http://www.mothersandmoreofmmr.org

3882 ■ Northeastern Pinal County Arc
PO Box 535
Kearny, AZ 85237
Contact: Frances Chavez, Exec. Dir.
Ph: (520)363-5581
E-mail: francesarc@yahoo.com
URL: http://www.arcarizona.org/local_chapters.html

3883 ■ Northern Arizona Chapter of the Autism Society of America (NAzASA)
PO Box 2014
Flagstaff, AZ 86003
Contact: Jocelyn Van-Belle, Pres.
Ph: (928)523-4870
E-mail: nazasainformation@nazasa.org
URL: http://www.nazasa.org
Descr: Seeks to improve the lives of individuals affected by autism. Promotes awareness and understanding of autism disorders. Aims to further the advancement of preventive studies, therapy and research of autism disorders.

3884 ■ Recording for the Blind and Dyslexic Arizona Unit
3627 E Indian School Rd., Ste. 108
Phoenix, AZ 85018
Contact: Barbara Fenster, Exec. Dir.
Ph: (602)468-9144
Fax: (602)553-0226

E-mail: bfenster@rfbd.org
URL: http://www.rfbd.org/AZ
Descr: Serves individuals who cannot effectively read standard print because of visual impairment, dyslexia, or other physical disabilities. Creates educational opportunities for students with print disabilities through educational and outreach services. Provides and promotes the effective use of accessible educational materials.

3885 ■ Santa Cruz County Arc
PO Box 638
Nogales, AZ 85628
Ph: (520)287-6271
E-mail: sctpinc@theriver.com
URL: http://www.arcarizona.org/local_chapters.html

3886 ■ Southern Arizona Association for the Education of Young Children (SAzAEYC)
PO Box 86750
Tucson, AZ 85754
Contact: Jessica Brisson, Pres.
E-mail: sazzymanager@gmail.com
URL: http://www.sazaeyc.org
Descr: Serves and acts on behalf of the needs, rights and well-being of all young children with primary focus on the quality of educational and developmental services for all children. Seeks to improve professional practice and working conditions in early childhood education.

3887 ■ Valley of the Sun Association for the Education of Young Children (VSAEYC)
2850 N 24th St.
Phoenix, AZ 85008
Ph: (602)889-6145
URL: http://www.vsaeyc.org
Descr: Teachers and directors of preschool and primary schools, kindergartens, child care centers, and other early learning programs for young childhood; early childhood education and child development educators, trainers, and researchers and other professionals dedicated to young children's healthy development.

3888 ■ Y.E.S. The ARC
PO Box 1061
Cottonwood, AZ 86326
Contact: Penny Vigil, Exec. Dir.
Ph: (928)634-2049
Fax: (928)634-5187
E-mail: yesthearc@yesthearc.com
URL: http://www.yesthearc.com
Descr: Parents, professional workers, and persons with developmental disabilities, mental retardation, autism, or cerebral palsy. Seeks to provide the training and opportunities that will maximize that growth towards the greatest independence possible for each individual. Offers programs and services that support and enhance client independence, self-esteem, mutual respect, value, and dignity. Offers job training in community job placement, job coaching, contract work, and thrift store. Operates two female and two male residential homes. **Fnd:** 1974. **Mem:** 95.

Arkansas

3889 ■ American Counseling Association, Arkansas (ArCA)
2410 Spring Lake Rd.
Paragould, AR 72450
Contact: Janene Alexander, Pres.
Free: 888-562-0404
Fax: (870)236-3512
E-mail: stillwellpriscilla@hotmail.com
URL: http://www.arcounseling.com
Descr: Strives to enhance the quality of life by promoting the development of professional counselors and using the profession and practice of counseling. **Fnd:** 1946.

3890 ■ American Medical Student Association, University of Arkansas for Medical Sciences College of Medicine
4301 W Markham St.
Little Rock, AR 72205

Contact: Debra Fiser MD, Dean
Ph: (501)296-1100
URL: http://www.uams.edu/com/default.asp
Descr: Promotes improvement in medical training and education. Advances the medicine profession. Contributes to the welfare of medical students, interns, residents and post-MD/DO trainees.

3891 ■ Arkansas Association for Career and Technical Education
2105 W Union St.
Bald Knob, AR 72010
Contact: Debbie Anselmi, Exec. Dir.
Ph: (501)724-3689
Fax: (501)724-3689
E-mail: danselmi@centurytel.net
URL: http://www.arkansas-acte.org
Descr: Career and technical educators, administrators, counselors, support staff, and others concerned about career and technical education in Arkansas. Works with the Arkansas department of workforce education to provide in-service activities for educators, to promote career and technical education at all levels, and to plan and support legislation that will benefit the citizens of Arkansas. **Fnd:** 1937. **Mem:** 600. **Pub:** Newsletter (semiannual).

3892 ■ Arkansas Department of Education
Four Capitol Mall
Little Rock, AR 72201
Contact: Dr. Tom W. Kimbrell, Commnr.
Ph: (501)682-4475
Fax: (501)682-1079
E-mail: ADE.Communications@arkansas.gov
URL: http://arkansased.org/
Descr: Strives to ensure that all children in the state have access to quality education by providing educators, administrators, and staff with leadership, resources, and training.

3893 ■ Arkansas Governor's Developmental Disabilities Council
5800 W 10th St., Ste. 805
Little Rock, AR 72204
Contact: Mary L. Edwards, Coor.
Ph: (501)661-2589
Free: 800-462-0599
Fax: (501)661-2399
E-mail: mary.edwards@arkansas.gov
URL: http://www.ddcouncil.org
Descr: Aims to improve the lives of individuals with disabilities and their families. **Pub:** Newsletter (quarterly).

3894 ■ Arkansas Out of School Network (AOSN)
1400 W Markham St., Ste. 306
Union Sta.
Little Rock, AR 72201
Contact: Paul Kelly
Ph: (501)371-9678
Fax: (501)371-9681
URL: http://www.aosn.org/content/index.php

3895 ■ Arkansas Parent Teacher Association (ARPTA)
PO Box 1015
North Little Rock, AR 72115
Contact: Ginny Kurrus, Pres.
Ph: (501)753-5247
Free: 800-782-4782
E-mail: office@arkansaspta.org
URL: http://www.arkansaspta.org
Staff: 1. **Descr:** Parents and teachers of primary and secondary school students. Promotes high educational standards. Conducts seminars, leadership training, child advocacy. **Fnd:** 1925. **Mem:** 70000. **Pub:** Newsletter (5/year).

3896 ■ Arkansas Senior Olympics
PO Box 1577
Hot Springs, AR 71902
Contact: Gail Ezelle, Exec. Dir.
Ph: (501)321-1441
Free: 800-720-7276
E-mail: arsrolym@hotsprings.net

URL: http://www.srsports.org
Descr: Conducts senior Olympic programs.

3897 ■ Communities in Schools of Arkansas
523 S Louisiana St., Ste. 175
Little Rock, AR 72201
Ph: (501)370-9661
Fax: (501)375-8774
E-mail: cisa@alltel.net
URL: http://www.cisnet.org/arkansas
Descr: Strives to champion the connection of needed community resources with schools to help young people learn, stay in school, and prepare for life.

3898 ■ Learning Disabilities Association of Arkansas
PO Box 95255
North Little Rock, AR 72190-5255
Contact: Laura McNutt, Pres.
Ph: (501)666-8777
Staff: 1. **Descr:** Promotes better understanding of learning disabilities and the needs of learning disabled persons. Provides support to parents and the learning disabled. Provides information on various learning disabilities to adults, parents, teachers, and professionals. **Fnd:** 1963. **Mem:** 330. **Pub:** *LDAA Member Resource Directory* (semiannual); *Learning Disabilities Association of Arkansas Newsletter* (quarterly).

3899 ■ Nevada County Arc
PO Box 480
Prescott, AR 71857
Contact: Alan Fox, Pres.
Ph: (870)887-6675
E-mail: ptraczewitz@yahoo.com

3900 ■ Sevier County Arc
715 W Stillwell Ave.
De Queen, AR 71832
Contact: Verlaine Jones, Pres.
Ph: (870)642-6077

California

3901 ■ 100 Black Men of the Bay Area
1638 12th St.
Oakland, CA 94607
Ph: (510)763-3661
E-mail: dwhyte@altaalliancebank.com
URL: http://www.100blackmenba.org

3902 ■ 100 Black Men of Los Angeles
3701 Stocker St., Ste. 309
Los Angeles, CA 90008-5135
Contact: Dr. Anthony Asadullah Samad, Pres.
Ph: (323)294-7444
Fax: (323)294-7474
E-mail: info@100bmla.org
URL: http://100bmla.org

3903 ■ 100 Black Men of Sacramento
2251 Florin Rd., Ste. 140
Sacramento, CA 95822
Ph: (916)428-8203
E-mail: sac100blkmen@sbcglobal.net
URL: http://www.sac100.com

3904 ■ 100 Black Men of Silicon Valley
1101 S Winchester Blvd., No. H-188
San Jose, CA 95128
Contact: Fred Mitchem
Free: 888-855-1147
URL: http://www.100bmsv.org

3905 ■ American Association of University Women, Auburn Branch
PO Box 7872
Auburn, CA 95604
Contact: Judy Marston, Pres.
E-mail: rushton@cebridge.net
URL: http://www.auburnaauw.org
Descr: Advances equity for women and girls through advocacy, education, and research. Provides funds

and a support system for women seeking judicial redress for sex discrimination in higher education.

3906 ■ American Association of University Women, California (AAUW-CA)
PO Box 160067
Sacramento, CA 95816-0067
Contact: Judy Pfeil, Co-Pres.
Ph: (916)448-7795
Fax: (916)448-1729
E-mail: office@aauw-ca.org
URL: http://www.aauw-ca.org
Descr: Strives to promote equity for all women and girls, lifelong education, and positive societal change. **Mem:** 20000. **Local Groups:** 170. **Pub:** *California Perspective* (3/year).

3907 ■ American Association of University Women, Camarillo Branch
PO Box 862
Camarillo, CA 93011-0862
Contact: Nancy Grubb
E-mail: nancykayegrubb@yahoo.com
URL: http://www.aauw-brighterhorizons.org/cam_home.htm
Descr: Advances equity for women and girls through advocacy, education, and research. Provides funds and a support system for women seeking judicial redress for sex discrimination in higher education.

3908 ■ American Association of University Women, Clayton Branch
PO Box 316
Clayton, CA 94517
Contact: Jean Cain, Pres.-Elect
E-mail: membershipvp@aauw-da.org
URL: http://www.claytonaauw.org
Descr: Advances equity for women and girls through advocacy, education, and research. Provides funds and a support system for women seeking judicial redress for sex discrimination in higher education.

3909 ■ American Association of University Women, Corona-Norco Branch
4858 Wilton Pl.
Riverside, CA 92504
Contact: Maureen Macomber, Pres.
Ph: (951)736-2054
Fax: (909)737-6868
E-mail: president@aauw-coronanorco.org
Descr: Advances equity for women and girls through advocacy, education, and research. Provides funds and a support system for women seeking judicial redress for sex discrimination in higher education.

3910 ■ American Association of University Women, Danville-Alamo Branch
PO Box 996
Alamo, CA 94507
Contact: Tena Gallagher, Pres.
E-mail: president@aauw-da.org
URL: http://www.aauw-da.org
Descr: Advances equity for women and girls through advocacy, education, and research. Provides funds and a support system for women seeking judicial redress for sex discrimination in higher education. **Pub:** *The Advocate* (monthly).

3911 ■ American Association of University Women, Davis Branch
PO Box 4165
Davis, CA 95617
Contact: Rhonda Reed, Pres.
E-mail: info@aauwdavis.org
URL: http://www.aauwdavis.org
Descr: Advances equity for women and girls through advocacy, education, and research. Provides funds and a support system for women seeking judicial redress for sex discrimination in higher education.

3912 ■ American Association of University Women, Five Cities-Pismo Beach Branch
PO Box 1604
Pismo Beach, CA 93448-1604
Contact: Linda Lidberg, Pres.
Ph: (805)489-8893

E-mail: info@fivecitiesaauw.org
URL: http://www.fivecitiesaauw.org
Descr: Advances equity for women and girls through advocacy, education, and research. Provides funds and a support system for women seeking judicial redress for sex discrimination in higher education.

3913 ■ American Association of University Women, Gilroy Branch
PO Box 1962
Gilroy, CA 95020
Contact: Marianne Peoples, Sec.
Ph: (408)842-9022
E-mail: quiltldy@garlic.com
URL: http://www.gilroyaauw.org
Descr: Advances equity for women and girls through advocacy, education, and research. Provides funds and a support system for women seeking judicial redress for sex discrimination in higher education.

3914 ■ American Association of University Women, La Palma Cerritos Branch
18125 Bloomfield Ave.
Cerritos, CA 90703
Contact: Saurabh Deedwania, Pres./Chair
E-mail: saurabhji@worldnet.att.net
URL: http://web.mac.com/kmforsstrom/iWeb/LaPalma-Cerritos20AAUW/Home.html
Descr: Advances equity for women and girls through advocacy, education, and research. Provides funds and a support system for women seeking judicial redress for sex discrimination in higher education.

3915 ■ American Association of University Women, Lompoc-Vandenberg Branch
1432 Calle Primera
Lompoc, CA 93436
Contact: Jan Herber, Pres.
E-mail: mvossler@verizon.net
URL: http://willeyweb.com/aauw
Descr: Advances equity for women and girls through advocacy, education, and research. Provides funds and a support system for women seeking judicial redress for sex discrimination in higher education.

3916 ■ American Association of University Women, Los Gatos-Saratoga Branch
PO Box 2200
Los Gatos, CA 95031
Contact: Gladys Armstrong, Pres.
Ph: (408)395-5908
E-mail: gladysarmstrong@sbcglobal.net
URL: http://www.aauw-lgs.org
Descr: Advances equity for women and girls through advocacy, education, and research. Provides funds and a support system for women seeking judicial redress for sex discrimination in higher education.

3917 ■ American Association of University Women, Mission Viejo-Saddleback Valley Branch
42 Primrose
Aliso Viejo, CA 92656
Contact: Cathi Begg, Co-Pres.
Ph: (949)831-7642
E-mail: astone2@sbcglobal.net
URL: http://www.aauw-mvsv.org
Descr: Advances equity for women and girls through advocacy, education, and research. Provides funds and a support system for women seeking judicial redress for sex discrimination in higher education.

3918 ■ American Association of University Women, Napa County Branch
PO Box 10407
Napa, CA 94581
Contact: Gladys Johnson
E-mail: kim@medlin.com
Descr: Advances equity for women and girls through advocacy, education, and research. Provides funds

and a support system for women seeking judicial redress for sex discrimination in higher education.

3919 ■ American Association of University Women, Oxnard-Hueneme Branch
2960 Keel Way
Oxnard, CA 93035
Contact: Linda Stinebaugh, VP for Membership
E-mail: lstinebaugh@verizon.net
URL: http://www.aauw-brighterhorizons.org/hueneme_home.htm
Descr: Advances equity for women and girls through advocacy, education, and research. Provides funds and a support system for women seeking judicial redress for sex discrimination in higher education.

3920 ■ American Association of University Women, Palo Alto Branch
PO Box 60653
Palo Alto, CA 94306-0653
Contact: Liz Kniss
E-mail: info@aauw-paloalto.org
URL: http://www.aauw-paloalto.org
Descr: Advances equity for women and girls through advocacy, education, and research. Provides funds and a support system for women seeking judicial redress for sex discrimination in higher education.

3921 ■ American Association of University Women, Palos Verdes Peninsula Branch
PO Box 2443
Palos Verdes Peninsula, CA 90274
Contact: Eileen Edelson
E-mail: eileenedelson@cox.net
URL: http://www.palosverdes.com/aauw
Descr: Advances equity for women and girls through advocacy, education, and research. Provides funds and a support system for women seeking judicial redress for sex discrimination in higher education.

3922 ■ American Association of University Women, Petaluma Branch
PO Box 7054
Petaluma, CA 94955-7054
Contact: Rory Keller, Pres.
E-mail: president@aauwpetaluma.org
URL: http://www.aauwpetaluma.org
Descr: Advances equity for women and girls through advocacy, education, and research. Provides funds and a support system for women seeking judicial redress for sex discrimination in higher education.

3923 ■ American Association of University Women, Redlands Branch
PO Box 7678
Redlands, CA 92375-0678
Contact: Sheron Bealer, Pres.
E-mail: president@aauw-redlands-ca.org
URL: http://www.aauw-redlands-ca.org
Descr: Advances equity for women and girls through advocacy, education, and research. Provides funds and a support system for women seeking judicial redress for sex discrimination in higher education.

3924 ■ American Association of University Women, Roseville-South Placer Branch
7122 Lost Lake Ln.
Roseville, CA 95747
Contact: Susan Hall, Pres.
E-mail: cfedors@aauwrosevillesouthplacer.org
URL: http://www.aauwroseville.org
Descr: Advances equity for women and girls through advocacy, education, and research. Provides funds and a support system for women seeking judicial redress for sex discrimination in higher education.

3925 ■ American Association of University Women, Sacramento Branch
5777 Palmera Ln.
Sacramento, CA 95835-2123
Contact: Barbara Smith, Pres.
E-mail: bsmithfo@aol.com
URL: http://www.aauwsacramento.org
Descr: Advances equity for women and girls through advocacy, education, and research. Provides funds

and a support system for women seeking judicial redress for sex discrimination in higher education.

3926 ■ American Association of University Women, San Fernando Valley Branch
PO Box 570294
Tarzana, CA 91357-0274
Contact: Lee Lieberstein
Ph: (818)888-9744
E-mail: aauw@aauw-sfv.org
URL: http://www.aauw-sfv.org
Descr: Advances equity for women and girls through advocacy, education, and research. Provides funds and a support system for women seeking judicial redress for sex discrimination in higher education.
Mem: 150.

3927 ■ American Association of University Women, San Francisco Branch
PO Box 31405
San Francisco, CA 94131-0405
Contact: Marilyn Z. Smith, Co-Pres.
E-mail: smithmz@hotmail.com
URL: http://www.aauwsf.org
Descr: Advances equity for women and girls through advocacy, education, and research. Provides funds and a support system for women seeking judicial redress for sex discrimination in higher education.

3928 ■ American Association of University Women, San Jose Branch
1165 Minnesota Ave.
San Jose, CA 95125
Contact: Diane Trombeta, Membership VP
Ph: (408)294-2430
E-mail: karenfillmore@aol.com
URL: http://www.aauwsanjose.org
Descr: Advances equity for women and girls through advocacy, education, and research. Provides funds and a support system for women seeking judicial redress for sex discrimination in higher education.

3929 ■ American Association of University Women, San Mateo Branch
PO Box 1239
San Mateo, CA 94401
Contact: Cynthia Robbins-Roth
E-mail: biogodess@earthlink.net
URL: http://www.aauw-sanmateo.org
Descr: Advances equity for women and girls through advocacy, education, and research. Provides funds and a support system for women seeking judicial redress for sex discrimination in higher education.

3930 ■ American Association of University Women, Santa Rosa Branch
43 Oak Forest Pl.
Santa Rosa, CA 95409
Contact: Mariane Holt, Pres.
Ph: (707)539-9521
E-mail: president@aauwsantarosa.org
URL: http://www.aauwsantarosa.org
Descr: Advances equity for women and girls through advocacy, education, and research. Provides funds and a support system for women seeking judicial redress for sex discrimination in higher education.

3931 ■ American Association of University Women, Tehachapi Mountain Branch
PO Box 273
Tehachapi, CA 93581
Contact: Barbara Wood, Pres.-Elect
E-mail: webmaster@aauwtehachapi.org
URL: http://www.aauwtehachapi.org
Descr: Advances equity for women and girls through advocacy, education, and research. Provides funds and a support system for women seeking judicial redress for sex discrimination in higher education.

3932 ■ American Association of University Women, Thousand Oaks Branch
PO Box 4223
Thousand Oaks, CA 91359-1223
Contact: Narda Fargotstein, Pres.
Ph: (805)493-2138
URL: http://aauwto.org
Descr: Advances equity for women and girls through

advocacy, education, and research. Provides funds and a support system for women seeking judicial redress for sex discrimination in higher education.

3933 ■ American Association of University Women, Ventura County Branch
PO Box 7863
Ventura, CA 93006
Contact: Diane Ellis, Pres.
Ph: (805)650-8459
E-mail: clths4us@aol.com
URL: http://www.aauw-brighterhorizons.org
Descr: Advances equity for women and girls through advocacy, education, and research. Provides funds and a support system for women seeking judicial redress for sex discrimination in higher education.
Fnd: 1916.

3934 ■ American Association of University Women, Visalia-Sequoia Branch
PO Box 6
Visalia, CA 93279
Contact: Sally Childers, Pres.
E-mail: info@aauwvisalia.org
URL: http://www.aauwvisalia.org
Descr: Advances equity for women and girls through advocacy, education, and research. Provides funds and a support system for women seeking judicial redress for sex discrimination in higher education.

3935 ■ American Counseling Association, Western Region
15860 Poppy Ln., No. 2
Los Gatos, CA 95030
Contact: Dr. Robert Butziger PhD, Chm.
Ph: (408)395-0902
E-mail: butzigerm@comcast.net
Descr: Represents professional counselors who live and practice in the western part of the US.

3936 ■ American Medical Student Association, Keck School of Medicine of USC
1975 Zonal Ave., KAM 500
Los Angeles, CA 90033
Contact: Carmen A. Puliafito MD, Dean
Ph: (323)442-1100
E-mail: deanksom@usc.edu
URL: http://www.usc.edu/schools/medicine
Descr: Promotes improvement in medical training and education. Advances the medicine profession. Contributes to the welfare of medical students, interns, residents and post-MD/DO trainees.

3937 ■ American Medical Student Association, Loma Linda University School of Medicine
11234 Anderson St.
Loma Linda, CA 92354
Contact: Dr. Roger H. Hadley MD, Dean
Ph: (909)558-4467
E-mail: rhadley@llu.edu
URL: http://www.llu.edu/llu/medicine
Descr: Promotes improvement in medical training and education. Advances the medicine profession. Contributes to the welfare of medical students, interns, residents and post-MD/DO trainees.

3938 ■ American Medical Student Association, Stanford School of Medicine
300 Pasteur Dr.
Stanford, CA 94305
Contact: Philip A. Pizzo, Dean
Ph: (650)723-4000
URL: http://med.stanford.edu
Descr: Promotes improvement in medical training and education. Advances the medicine profession. Contributes to the welfare of medical students, interns, residents and post-MD/DO trainees.

3939 ■ American Medical Student Association, Touro University College of Osteopathic Medicine
1310 Johnson Ln.
Vallejo, CA 94592
Contact: Dr. Michael B. Clearfield DO, Dean
Ph: (707)638-5935
Fax: (707)638-5255

E-mail: michael.clearfield@touro.edu
URL: http://www.tu.edu/departments.php?id=43

Descr: Promotes improvement in medical training and education. Advances the medicine profession. Contributes to the welfare of medical students, interns, residents and post-MD/DO trainees.

3940 ■ American Medical Student Association, University of California, Davis School of Medicine
4610 X St.
Sacramento, CA 95817
Contact: Jana Katz-Bell, Asst. Dean
Ph: (530)752-0331
URL: http://www.ucdmc.ucdavis.edu/medschool

Descr: Promotes improvement in medical training and education. Advances the medicine profession. Contributes to the welfare of medical students, interns, residents and post-MD/DO trainees.

3941 ■ American Medical Student Association, University of California, Irvine School of Medicine
Office of Admissions and Outreach
Berk Hall, Rm. 100
Irvine, CA 92697
Contact: Ellena Peterson PhD, Assoc. Dean
Ph: (949)824-5388
Fax: (949)824-2485
E-mail: medadmit@uci.edu
URL: http://www.ucihs.uci.edu/som

Descr: Promotes improvement in medical training and education. Advances the medicine profession. Contributes to the welfare of medical students, interns, residents and post-MD/DO trainees.

3942 ■ American Medical Student Association, University of California, San Diego School of Medicine
9500 Gilman Dr.
La Jolla, CA 92093
Contact: David A. Brenner MD, Dean
Ph: (858)534-0830
Fax: (858)534-6573
E-mail: dbrenner@ucsd.edu
URL: http://som.ucsd.edu

Descr: Promotes improvement in medical training and education. Advances the medicine profession. Contributes to the welfare of medical students, interns, residents and post-MD/DO trainees.

3943 ■ American Medical Student Association, University of California, San Francisco School of Medicine
513 Parnassus Ave.
San Francisco, CA 94143-2205
Contact: Keith Yamamoto
Ph: (415)476-3128
Fax: (415)476-6129
E-mail: yamamoto@medsch.ucsf.edu
URL: http://medschool.ucsf.edu

Descr: Promotes improvement in medical training and education. Advances the medicine profession. Contributes to the welfare of medical students, interns, residents and post-MD/DO trainees.

3944 ■ Arc of Alameda County
2700A Merced St.
San Leandro, CA 94577
Contact: Ron Luter, Exec. Dir.
Ph: (510)357-2004
Fax: (510)357-1792
E-mail: ronluter@arcalameda.org
URL: http://www.tiw-alameda.com

3945 ■ Arc of Amador And Calaveras Counties
75 Academy Dr.
Sutter Creek, CA 95685
Ph: (209)267-5978

Descr: Parents, professional workers, and others interested in individuals with mental retardation. Works to promote services, research, public under-

standing, and legislation for people with mental retardation and their families.

3946 ■ Arc of Butte County
2030 Park Ave.
Chico, CA 95928
Contact: Ed Caldwell, Pres.
Ph: (530)891-5865
URL: http://www.arccalifornia.org/chapters.asp

3947 ■ Arc of California
1225 8th St., Ste. 210
Sacramento, CA 95814-2213
Contact: Pat Heineke, Pres.
Ph: (916)552-6619
Fax: (916)441-3494
E-mail: tanderson@arccalifornia.org
URL: http://www.arccalifornia.org

Descr: Parents, professional workers, and others interested in individuals with mental retardation. Works to promote services, research, public understanding, and legislation for people with mental retardation and their families.

3948 ■ Arc Fresno
4567 N Marty Ave.
Fresno, CA 93722
Contact: Lori Ramirez, Exec. Dir.
Ph: (559)226-6268
Fax: (559)226-6269
E-mail: loriramirez@arcfresno.org
URL: http://www.arcfresno.org

3949 ■ Arc - Imperial Valley
PO Box 1828
El Centro, CA 92244
Contact: Arturo Santos, CEO
Ph: (760)352-0180
Fax: (760)352-3269
E-mail: arcinfo@arciv.org
URL: http://www.arciv.org

Staff: 153. **Descr:** Provides programs and services to increase the independence of individuals with developmental and other related disabilities. **Fnd:** 1973. **Mem:** 350.

3950 ■ Arc of Riverside County
8138 Mar Vista Ct.
Riverside, CA 92504
Contact: Margie Lumbley, Pres.
Ph: (951)688-5141
Fax: (951)688-7207
URL: http://www.arcriversideca.org

3951 ■ Arc San Bernardino Area
796 E 6th St.
San Bernardino, CA 92410
Contact: Deanna Allender, Pres.
Ph: (909)844-6484
URL: http://www.arccalifornia.org/chapters.asp

3952 ■ Arc of San Diego
9575 Aero Dr.
San Diego, CA 92123
Contact: Tom Harmon, Chm.
Ph: (858)715-3780
Fax: (858)715-3788
E-mail: info@arc-sd.com
URL: http://www.arc-sd.com

Descr: Works with families and partnerships within the community. Committed to securing the opportunity to choose and realize their dreams and goals of where and how they learn, live, work and play for people with developmental disabilities. **Fnd:** 1951.

3953 ■ Arc of San Francisco
1500 Howard St.
San Francisco, CA 94103
Contact: Tim Hornbecker, Exec. Dir.
Ph: (415)255-7200
Fax: (415)225-9488
E-mail: info@thearcsf.org
URL: http://www.thearcsanfrancisco.org

Descr: Parents, professional workers, and others interested in individuals with mental retardation. Works to promote services, research, public under-

standing, and legislation for people with mental retardation and their families.

3954 ■ Arc Solano
3272 Sonoma Blvd., Ste. 4
Vallejo, CA 94590
Contact: Wanda Warren, Pres.
Ph: (707)552-2935
Fax: (707)644-6555
E-mail: thearcsolano@email.com
URL: http://www.thearcsolano.org

3955 ■ Arc of Southeast Los Angeles County
12049 Woodruff Ave.
Downey, CA 90241-5669
Contact: Kevin Macdonald, Exec. Dir.
Ph: (562)803-4606
Fax: (562)803-6550
E-mail: info@arcselac.org
URL: http://www.arcselac.org

Descr: Works to promote services, research, public understanding, and legislation for people with mental retardation and their families. **Fnd:** 1956.

3956 ■ Arc Taft
204 Van Buren St.
Taft, CA 93268
Contact: Stephanie House, Pres.
Ph: (661)763-1532
URL: http://www.arccalifornia.org/chapters.asp

3957 ■ Arc of Ventura County
5103 Walker St.
Ventura, CA 93003
Contact: Fred Robinson, CEO
Ph: (805)650-8611
Free: 800-501-4444
Fax: (805)644-7308
E-mail: frobinson@arcvc.org
URL: http://www.arcvc.org

3958 ■ Autism Society of America - Central California Chapter (ASACCC)
PO Box 13213
Fresno, CA 93794
Contact: Ana Bustos-Ponce, Pres.
Ph: (559)301-5763
E-mail: ca-centralcalifornia@autismsocietyofamerica.org
URL: http://www.asaccc.org

Descr: Seeks to improve the lives of individuals affected by autism. Promotes awareness and understanding of autism disorders. Aims to further the advancement of preventive studies, therapy and research of autism disorders.

3959 ■ Autism Society of America - Greater Long Beach/San Gabriel Valley Chapter
PO Box 15247
Long Beach, CA 90815
Contact: Rita Rubin
Ph: (562)943-3335
Fax: (562)943-3335
E-mail: ca-longbeach@autismsocietyofamerica.org

Descr: Seeks to improve the lives of individuals affected by autism. Promotes awareness and understanding of autism disorders. Aims to further the advancement of preventive studies, therapy and research of autism disorders.

3960 ■ Autism Society of America - Los Angeles (ASA-LA)
8939 S Sepulveda Blvd., Ste. 110-788
Los Angeles, CA 90045
Contact: Caroline Wilson RN, Pres.
Ph: (562)804-5556
Fax: (562)425-4940
E-mail: contact@asa-la.org
URL: http://www.asa-la.org

Descr: Seeks to improve the lives of individuals affected by autism. Promotes awareness and understanding of autism disorders. Aims to further the

advancement of preventive studies, therapy and research of autism disorders.

3961 ■ Autism Society of America - Santa Barbara Chapter (ASA SB)
PO Box 30364
Santa Barbara, CA 93130
Contact: Marcia Eichelberger, Co-Pres.
Ph: (805)560-3762
E-mail: info@asasb.org
URL: http://www.asasb.org
Descr: Seeks to improve the lives of individuals affected by autism. Promotes awareness and understanding of autism disorders. Aims to further the advancement of preventive studies, therapy and research of autism disorders.

3962 ■ Autism Society of America - Tulare County Chapter
3201 W Payson Ave.
Visalia, CA 93291
Contact: Lori Collins, Pres.
Ph: (559)747-2126
E-mail: lori10677@aol.com
Descr: Seeks to improve the lives of individuals affected by autism. Promotes awareness and understanding of autism disorders. Aims to further the advancement of preventive studies, therapy and research of autism disorders.

3963 ■ Autism Society of California
PO Box 1355
Glendora, CA 91740
Contact: Gregory Fletcher, Pres.
Free: 800-700-0037
E-mail: info@autism-society-ca.org
Descr: Seeks to improve the lives of individuals affected by autism. Promotes awareness and understanding of autism disorders. Aims to further the advancement of preventive studies, therapy and research of autism disorders.

3964 ■ Autism Society of Northern California (ASNC)
897 E 20th St., No. B
Chico, CA 95928
Contact: Dan McCampbell, Pres.
Ph: (530)897-0900
Fax: (530)897-0300
E-mail: meghann@autismsocietynca.org
URL: http://www.autismsocietynca.org
Descr: Seeks to improve the lives of individuals affected by autism. Promotes awareness and understanding of autism disorders. Aims to further the advancement of preventive studies, therapy and research of autism disorders.

3965 ■ A Better Chance, Northwest
436 14th St., Ste. 1015
Oakland, CA 94612-2710
Contact: Prasant Nukalapati, Program Coor.
Ph: (510)763-0333
Fax: (510)763-0434
E-mail: pnukalapati@abetterchance.org
Descr: Identifies, recruits, and places academically talented and motivated minority students into leading independent secondary schools and selected public schools.

3966 ■ A Better Chance, Southwest
3601 S Flower St.
Tyler Bldg., No. 201
Los Angeles, CA 90089
Contact: Carolyn Buenaflor, Program Coor.
Ph: (213)743-1757
Fax: (213)232-3773
E-mail: cbuenaflor@abetterchance.org
Descr: Identifies, recruits, and places academically talented and motivated minority students into leading independent secondary schools and selected public schools.

3967 ■ California AfterSchool Network
University of California, Davis
Davis, CA 95616
Contact: Debe Loxton, CEO
Ph: (530)754-0399
E-mail: info@afterschoolnetwork.org
URL: http://www.afterschoolnetwork.org

3968 ■ California Association for Career and Technical Education Chapter (CACTE)
1111 Van Ness Ave.
The Towers, Ste. 5
Fresno, CA 93721
Contact: Valerie Vuicich, Pres.
E-mail: vuicich@fcoe.k12.ca.us
URL: http://www.acteonline.org/content.aspx?id=776
Descr: Works year-round with education policymakers and organizations, building national support and funding for career and technical education in cities and towns from one end of the nation to the other.

3969 ■ California Association for the Education of Young Children (CAEYC)
950 Glenn Dr., Ste. 150
Folsom, CA 95630
Contact: Shelly Alcorn, Exec. Dir.
Ph: (916)486-7750
Fax: (916)932-0390
E-mail: shellya@caeyc.org
URL: http://www.caeyc.org
Staff: 16. **Descr:** Seeks to improve professional practice and working conditions, as well as to build public support for high-quality early childhood education. Resources are geared towards teachers and directors of preschool and primary schools, kindergartens, child care centers, cooperatives, church schools, and groups having similar programs for young children; early childhood education and child development educators, trainers, and researchers. Works to serve and act on behalf of the needs and rights of young children, focusing on the provision of educational services and resources. **Fnd:** 1980. **Mem:** 11000. **Local Groups:** 35.

3970 ■ California Department of Education
1430 N St.
Sacramento, CA 95814-5901
Contact: Jack O'Connell, State Superintendent
Ph: (916)319-0800
Fax: (916)319-0100
E-mail: joconnell@cde.ca.gov
URL: http://www.cde.ca.gov/
Descr: Mission is to create a dynamic, world-class education system that equips all students with the knowledge and skills to excel in college and careers, and excel as parents and citizens.

3971 ■ California School-Age Consortium (CalSAC)
657 Mission St., Ste. 601
San Francisco, CA 94105
Contact: Taylor Brady, Development Dir.
Ph: (415)957-9775
Fax: (415)957-9776
E-mail: cshirley@calsac.org
URL: http://www.calsac.org
Descr: Works to support and advance professionals and organizations in providing quality, affordable, and accessible school-age care programs. **Fnd:** 1982.

3972 ■ California State Council on Developmental Disabilities (SCDD)
1507 21st St., Ste. 210
Sacramento, CA 95814
Contact: Alan Kerzin, Exec. Dir.
Ph: (916)322-8481
Free: 866-802-0514
Fax: (916)443-4957
E-mail: council@scdd.ca.gov
URL: http://www.scdd.ca.gov
Descr: Advocates, promotes and implements policies and practices in order to achieve self-determination, independence, productivity and inclusion in all aspects of community life for Californians with developmental disabilities and their families. Comprises of individuals with a developmental disability, parents and family members of people with developmental disabilities, and representatives of

state agencies that provide services to individuals with developmental disabilities. **Mem:** 29.

3973 ■ California State Parents Teachers Association
2327 L St.
Sacramento, CA 95816-5014
Contact: Pam Brady, Pres.
Ph: (916)440-1985
Fax: (916)440-1986
URL: http://www.capta.org
Descr: Parents, teachers, students, principals, administrators, and others interested in uniting the forces of home, school, and community on behalf of children and youth.

3974 ■ Central California Branch of the International Dyslexia Association
2912 E Ryan Ln.
Fresno, CA 93720
Contact: Judy Gregory
Ph: (559)243-4047
E-mail: peterita@sbcglobal.net
Descr: Promotes public awareness and understanding of dyslexia. Seeks to develop and implement specialized methods to improve the quality of life for people who have dyslexia.

3975 ■ Central Coast Fire Prevention Association
200 E Branch St.
Arroyo Grande, CA 93421
Contact: Johnathan Richard Hurst
Ph: (805)473-5450
Fax: (805)473-5458
E-mail: jhurst@arroyogrande.org
Descr: Provides the highest quality codes, standards, products, and services for all concerned with the safety and performance of the built environment.

3976 ■ Coachella Valley Autism Society of America (CVASA)
77564 Country Club Dr., Ste. 228
Palm Desert, CA 92211
Contact: Gina Davis, Pres.
Ph: (760)772-1000
Fax: (760)772-1000
E-mail: cvasacoordinator@verizon.net
URL: http://www.coachellavalleyautism.org
Descr: Seeks to improve the lives of individuals affected by autism. Promotes awareness and understanding of autism disorders. Aims to further the advancement of preventive studies, therapy and research of autism disorders.

3977 ■ Common Cause California
3250 Wilshire Blvd., Ste. 1005
Los Angeles, CA 90010
Contact: JoAnn Fuller, Assoc. Dir.
Ph: (213)252-4552
Fax: (213)368-1615
E-mail: ca-info@commoncause.org
URL: http://www.commoncause.org/site/pp.asp?c=dkLNK1MQIwG&b=1416051
Staff: 4. **Descr:** Works to make public officials and public institutions accountable and responsive to citizens. **Fnd:** 1970. **Mem:** 200000. **State Groups:** 1. **Local Groups:** 10. **Pub:** Newsletter (semiannual); Newsletter (quarterly).

3978 ■ Contra Costa Association for Retarded Citizens
1340 Arnold Dr., Ste. 127
Martinez, CA 94553
Ph: (925)370-1818
Fax: (925)370-2048
E-mail: feedback@arcofcc.org
URL: http://www.contracostaarc.com
Descr: Parents, professional workers, and others interested in individuals with mental retardation. Works to promote services, research, public under-

standing, and legislation for people with mental retardation and their families. **Fnd:** 1965.

3979 ■ East Bay Learning Disabilities Association of California (EBLDA)
PO Box 5513
Berkeley, CA 94705
Contact: Dr. Shoshana Souza-Taubman PsyD, Pres.
Ph: (510)433-7934
Fax: (510)547-5306
E-mail: info@eastbaylda.org
URL: http://www.eastbaylda.org

Descr: Works to enhance the quality of life for all individuals with learning and attentional disabilities and their families, and to identify the causes and promote prevention of these disabilities. Seeks to accomplish these goals through awareness, advocacy, empowerment, education, service, and collaborative efforts across diverse communities. **Fnd:** 1966. **Mem:** 215. **State Groups:** 1. **Local Groups:** 12. **Pub:** *East Bay News* (quarterly).

3980 ■ Inland Empire Autism Society
2276 Griffin Way, Ste. 105-194
Corona, CA 92879
Contact: Beth Burt
Ph: (909)204-4142
E-mail: ca-inlandempire@autismsocietyofamerica.org

Descr: Seeks to improve the lives of individuals affected by autism. Promotes awareness and understanding of autism disorders. Aims to further the advancement of preventive studies, therapy and research of autism disorders.

3981 ■ Inland Empire Branch of the International Dyslexia Association (IEB/IDA)
5225 Canyon Crest Dr., No. 71
Box 308
Riverside, CA 92507-6301
Contact: Regina G. Richards, Pres.
Ph: (951)686-9837
E-mail: dyslexiainfo@gmail.com
URL: http://www.dyslexia-ca.org

Descr: Promotes public awareness and understanding of dyslexia. Seeks to develop and implement specialized methods to improve the quality of life for people who have dyslexia. **Fnd:** 1984. **Pub:** *The Resource* (semiannual).

3982 ■ Kern County Learning Disabilities Association (KCLDA)
PO Box 9191
Bakersfield, CA 93389
Contact: Daniel Marble, Pres.
Ph: (661)342-4323
URL: http://www.csub.edu/kclda/

3983 ■ Learning Disabilities Association of California, Los Angeles Chapter
PO Box 1067
Sierra Madre, CA 91025
Contact: Louise Fundenberg, Pres.
Ph: (626)355-0240
Free: 866-532-6322
Fax: (626)355-0109
E-mail: lalda@verizon.net
URL: http://www.ldaca.org

3984 ■ Learning Disabilities Association of California, Pomona Valley Chapter (LDA-CA)
PO Box 1114
Claremont, CA 91711
Contact: Arline Krieger
Ph: (909)621-1494
E-mail: pvlda@aol.com
URL: http://www.ldaca.org

3985 ■ Learning Disabilities Association of California, Sacramento Chapter
PO Box 276645
Sacramento, CA 95827

Ph: (949)673-6312
E-mail: info@sacramentolda.org
URL: http://www.ldaca.org

3986 ■ Learning Disabilities Association of California, San Diego Chapter
PO Box 421111
San Diego, CA 92142
Ph: (858)467-9158
E-mail: info@ldasandiego.org
URL: http://www.ldasandiego.org

3987 ■ Los Angeles County Branch of the International Dyslexia Association
PO Box 1808
Studio City, CA 91614
Contact: Jennifer C. Zvi PhD, Pres.
Ph: (818)506-8866
E-mail: dyslexiala@sbcglobal.net
URL: http://www.interdys.org/Branchdetail.aspx?bid=13

Descr: Promotes public awareness and understanding of dyslexia. Seeks to develop and implement specialized methods to improve the quality of life for people who have dyslexia. **Fnd:** 1981.

3988 ■ Northern California Branch of the International Dyslexia Association (NCBIDA)
PO Box 5010
San Mateo, CA 94402-0010
Contact: Leslie Lingaas Woodward, Pres.
Ph: (650)328-7667
Fax: (650)375-8504
E-mail: office@dyslexia-ncbida.org
URL: http://www.dyslexia-ncbida.org

Descr: Promotes public awareness and understanding of dyslexia. Seeks to develop and implement specialized methods to improve the quality of life for people who have dyslexia. **Pub:** Newsletter (3/year).

3989 ■ Orange County Autism Society
5591 Yuba Ave.
Westminster, CA 92683
Contact: Patti Arnold
Ph: (714)799-7500
E-mail: kungfuautism@yahoo.com
URL: http://www.autismsocietyca.org

Descr: Seeks to improve the lives of individuals affected by autism. Promotes awareness and understanding of autism disorders. Aims to further the advancement of preventive studies, therapy and research of autism disorders.

3990 ■ Recording for the Blind and Dyslexic Inland Empire/Orange County Unit
1844-C W 11th St., Unit C
Upland, CA 91786
Contact: Mike Davis, Exec. Dir.
Ph: (909)949-4316
Fax: (909)981-8457
E-mail: mdavis@rfbd.org
URL: http://www.rfbd.org/IEOC

Descr: Serves individuals who cannot effectively read standard print because of visual impairment, dyslexia, or other physical disabilities. Creates educational opportunities for students with print disabilities through educational and outreach services. Provides and promotes the effective use of accessible educational materials.

3991 ■ Recording for the Blind and Dyslexic Los Angeles Unit (RFB&D-LA)
5022 Hollywood Blvd.
Los Angeles, CA 90027-6192
Contact: Ms. Diane Kelber, Communications Dir.
Ph: (323)664-5525
Free: 800-221-4792
Fax: (323)664-1881
E-mail: los_angeles@rfbd.org

Descr: Serves individuals who cannot effectively read standard print because of visual impairment, dyslexia, or other physical disabilities. Creates educational opportunities for students with print disabilities through educational and outreach services.

Provides and promotes the effective use of accessible educational materials.

3992 ■ Recording for the Blind and Dyslexic Northern California Unit
488 W Charleston Rd.
Palo Alto, CA 94306
Contact: Matt Ward, Production Dir.
Ph: (650)493-3717
Free: 866-493-3717
Fax: (650)493-5513
E-mail: mward@rfbd.org

Descr: Serves individuals who cannot effectively read standard print because of visual impairment, dyslexia, or other physical disabilities. Creates educational opportunities for students with print disabilities through educational and outreach services. Provides and promotes the effective use of accessible educational materials.

3993 ■ Recording for the Blind and Dyslexic Santa Barbara Unit
5638 Hollister Ave., Ste. 210
Goleta, CA 93117
Contact: Tim Owens, Exec. Dir.
Ph: (805)681-0531
Fax: (805)681-0532
E-mail: towens@rfbd.org
URL: http://www.rfbd.org/SB

Descr: Serves individuals who cannot effectively read standard print because of visual impairment, dyslexia, or other physical disabilities. Creates educational opportunities for students with print disabilities through educational and outreach services. Provides and promotes the effective use of accessible educational materials.

3994 ■ SAFE Association - Southern California Chapter
Diversified Technical Systems
909 Electric Ave., Ste. 206
Seal Beach, CA 90740
Contact: Michael Beckage
Ph: (562)493-0158
Fax: (562)493-3158
E-mail: mike.beckage@web.com

Descr: Ensures personal safety and protection in land, sea, air and space environments. Fosters research and development in the fields of safety and survival. Provides a forum for the sharing of problems, ideas and information in the areas of safety, survival and crew systems.

3995 ■ San Diego County Chapter of the Autism Society of America (SDASA)
PO Box 420908
San Diego, CA 92142
Contact: Cherri Cary, Pres.
Ph: (858)715-0678
Fax: (858)712-1510
E-mail: info@sd-autism.org
URL: http://www.sd-autism.org

Descr: Seeks to improve the lives of individuals affected by autism. Promotes awareness and understanding of autism disorders. Aims to further the advancement of preventive studies, therapy and research of autism disorders.

3996 ■ San Francisco Bay Area Autism Society
PO Box 1207
San Carlos, CA 94070
Contact: Peggy Burwell
Ph: (650)637-7772
E-mail: ca-sanfrancisco@autismsocietyofamerica.org
URL: http://www.autismsocietyca.org

Descr: Seeks to improve the lives of individuals affected by autism. Promotes awareness and understanding of autism disorders. Aims to further the advancement of preventive studies, therapy and research of autism disorders.

3997 ■ Shared Adventures
90 Grandview St., Unit B101
Santa Cruz, CA 95060-3063

Contact: Foster Andersen, Founder/Pres.
Ph: (831)459-7210
Fax: (831)459-7210
E-mail: foster@sharedadventures.com
URL: http://www.sharedadventures.org
Descr: Improves the quality of life of people living with disabilities. **Fnd:** 1994.

3998 ■ Special Olympics, Northern California (SONC)
3480 Buskirk Ave., Ste. 340
Pleasant Hill, CA 94523
Contact: Richard E. Collett Jr., Pres./CEO
Ph: (925)944-8801
Fax: (925)944-8803
E-mail: rick@sonc.org
URL: http://www.sonc.org
Descr: Creates opportunities for athletes to develop physical fitness, demonstrate courage and participate in the sharing of skills and friendship with their families and the community. Provides sports training and competition in variety of Olympic-type sports for people with developmental disabilities in Northern California.

3999 ■ Special Olympics, San Diego County
10977 San Diego Mission Rd.
San Diego, CA 92108-2431
Contact: Teresa Contreras
Ph: (619)283-6100
Fax: (619)283-5171
E-mail: tcontreras@sosc.org
URL: http://www.specialolympicssandiego.com
Staff: 4. **Descr:** Provides year round sports training and competition opportunities to children and adults with intellectual disabilities (mental retardation). **Fnd:** 1969. **Mem:** 1450. **State Groups:** 1. **Pub:** Newsletter (monthly); Newsletter (semiannual).

4000 ■ Special Olympics Southern California
5875 Green Valley Cir., Ste. 200
Culver City, CA 90230-6901
Contact: Bill Shumard, Pres./CEO
Fax: (310)215-8388
E-mail: info@sosc.org
URL: http://www.sosc.org
Descr: Promotes physical fitness, sports training, and athletic competition for children and adults with mental retardation. Seeks to contribute to the physical, social, and psychological development of persons with mental retardation; participants range in age from 8 years to adult and compete in track and field, swimming, gymnastics, bowling, ice skating, basketball, and other sports. **Fnd:** 1995.

4001 ■ Tahoe Adaptive Ski School, Disabled Sports USA
6060 Sunrise Vista Dr., Ste. 2540
Citrus Heights, CA 95610
Contact: Bradley Harlan, Board Chm.
Ph: (916)722-6447
Fax: (916)722-2627
E-mail: dsusa@disabledsports.net
URL: http://www.dsusafw.org
Staff: 7. **Descr:** Persons in Northern California and Nevada with physical and mental disabilities. Improves the quality of life of people with disabilities by providing affordable inclusive sports which build self-esteem and confidence, enhancing active participation in community life. Offers alpine skiing, camping, water-skiing, sailing, rafting, fishing, and boating opportunities. **Fnd:** 1967. **Mem:** 1500. **Pub:** Newsletter (periodic).

4002 ■ Ventura County Autism Society (VCAS)
PO Box 2690
Ventura, CA 93002
Contact: Jennifer McNulty, Pres.
Ph: (805)496-1632
E-mail: ca-venturacounty@autismsocietyofamerica.org
URL: http://www.vcas.info
Descr: Seeks to improve the lives of individuals affected by autism. Promotes awareness and understanding of autism disorders. Aims to further the advancement of preventive studies, therapy and research of autism disorders.

4003 ■ VTC Enterprises
PO Box 1187
Santa Maria, CA 93456
Contact: Polly Huffer, Pres.
Ph: (805)928-5000
Fax: (805)349-8011
URL: http://www.vtc-sm.org
Staff: 175. **Descr:** Parents, professional workers, and others interested in individuals with mental retardation. Works to promote services, research, public understanding, and legislation for people with mental retardation and their families. **Fnd:** 1962.

Colorado

4004 ■ 100 Black Men of Denver
PO Box 300188
Denver, CO 80203
Contact: Paul Kelly, Pres.
Ph: (303)864-0945
E-mail: mhwhite@att.net
URL: http://www.100bmdenver.org

4005 ■ Adaptive Adventures
PO Box 2245
Evergreen, CO 80437
Contact: George Mannion, Chm.
Ph: (303)679-2770
Free: 866-679-2770
Fax: (303)670-8290
E-mail: info@adaptiveadventures.org
URL: http://www.adaptiveadventures.org
Descr: Works to advance the quality of life of people with disabilities through year-round outdoor sports and recreation. **Fnd:** 1999.

4006 ■ Adaptive Sports Association
PO Box 1884
Durango, CO 81302
Contact: Tim Kroes, Exec. Dir.
Ph: (970)259-0374
Fax: (970)259-2175
E-mail: info@asadurango.org
URL: http://www.asadurango.org
Staff: 11. **Descr:** Provides winter and summer outdoor sports opportunities to individuals with all types of physical and/or cognitive disabilities.

4007 ■ AG BELL, Colorado
PO Box 24906
Denver, CO 80224
Contact: Regina Squibbs, Pres.
Ph: (303)755-5183
E-mail: sportsmomreg@aol.com
URL: http://www.coloradoagbell.org
Descr: Represents the interests of educators, parents of children with hearing loss, adults with hearing loss and hearing health professionals. Provides governmental and education advocacy services.

4008 ■ American Association of University Women, Denver Branch
PO Box 100373-0373
Denver, CO 80250-0373
Contact: Valorie Yarbrough, Pres.
Ph: (303)757-6062
E-mail: valreey@msn.com
URL: http://www.coaauw.org/denver
Descr: Advances equity for women and girls through advocacy, education, and research. Provides funds and a support system for women seeking judicial redress for sex discrimination in higher education.

4009 ■ Arc of Adams County
11698 Huron St., Ste. 106
Northglenn, CO 80234
Contact: Linda Skaflen, Exec. Dir.
Ph: (303)428-0310
E-mail: info@arcadams.com
URL: http://www.arcadams.com
Descr: Parents, professional workers, and others interested in individuals with mental retardation.

Works to promote services, research, public understanding, and legislation for people with mental retardation and their families.

4010 ■ Arc of Arapahoe and Douglas
7430 E Caley Ave., Ste. 130
Centennial, CO 80111
Contact: Carol L. Meredith, Exec. Dir.
Ph: (303)220-9228
Fax: (303)220-0994
E-mail: carol@arcarapahoedouglas.org
URL: http://www.arcarapahoedouglas.org
Staff: 5. **Descr:** Works to include all children and adults with disabilities in their communities through advocacy and education. Provides support through one on one advocacy for individuals, families, and within the systems that serve the people with disabilities. **Fnd:** 1955. **Mem:** 300. **Pub:** *Dreams and Visions* (monthly).

4011 ■ Arc of Aurora
1342 S Chambers Rd.
Aurora, CO 80017
Contact: Aimee Pemberton, Pres.
Ph: (720)213-1420
E-mail: arcaurora@aol.com
URL: http://www.thearcofco.org/localarcs.html

4012 ■ Arc of Colorado
1580 Logan St., Ste. 730
Denver, CO 80203
Contact: Marijo Rymer, Exec. Dir.
Ph: (303)864-9334
Fax: (303)864-9330
E-mail: mrymer@thearcofco.org
URL: http://www.thearcofco.org

4013 ■ Arc of Denver
1905 Sherman St., Ste. 300
Denver, CO 80203
Contact: Aileen McGinley, Exec. Dir.
Ph: (303)831-7733
Fax: (303)839-5178
E-mail: advocacy@arcofdenver.org
URL: http://www.arcofdenver.org
Descr: Parents, professional workers, and others interested in individuals with mental retardation. Works to promote services, research, public understanding, and legislation for people with mental retardation and their families.

4014 ■ Arc in Jefferson County
8725 W 14th Ave., Ste. 100
Lakewood, CO 80215
Contact: Todd Lowther, Exec. Dir.
Ph: (303)232-1338
Fax: (303)232-9370
E-mail: info@arcjc.org
URL: http://www.arcjc.org
Descr: Parents, professional workers, and others interested in individuals with mental retardation. Works to promote services, research, public understanding, and legislation for people with mental retardation and their families. **Fnd:** 1961.

4015 ■ Arc of Larimer County
109 Coronado Ct., Bldg. 7
Fort Collins, CO 80525
Contact: Kimberly Spencer, Exec. Dir.
Ph: (970)204-6991
URL: http://arclc.org

4016 ■ Arc Mesa County
PO Box 2292
Grand Junction, CO 81502
Contact: Jana Colosimo, Pres.
Ph: (970)245-5775
E-mail: arcmesa@aol.com
URL: http://www.thearcofco.org/localarcs.html

4017 ■ Arc of the Pikes Peak Region
12 N Meade Ave.
Colorado Springs, CO 80909
Contact: Teddi Roberts, Exec. Dir.
Ph: (719)471-4800

Fax: (719)471-4828
E-mail: info@thearcppr.org
URL: http://thearcppr.org

4018 ■ **Arc of Pueblo Colorado**
2705 Vinewood Ln.
Pueblo, CO 81005
Contact: Stephanie Garcia, Exec. Dir.
Ph: (719)545-5845
E-mail: stephanie@arcofpueblo.org
URL: http://www.arcofpueblo.org

4019 ■ **Arc of Weld County**
3700 Golden St.
Evans, CO 80620
Ph: (970)353-5219
Descr: Parents, professional workers, and others interested in individuals with mental retardation. Works to promote services, research, public understanding, and legislation for people with mental retardation and their families.

4020 ■ **Association for Community Living in Boulder County (ACL)**
5744 N 71st St.
Longmont, CO 80503
Contact: Timothy L. Cairns, Exec. Dir.
Ph: (303)527-0888
E-mail: info@aclboulder.org
URL: http://www.aclboulder.org
Descr: Advocates children and adults with developmental disabilities. Develops, supports, and enhances efforts to bring people with developmental disabilities into the mainstream of community life.

4021 ■ **Autism Society of Boulder County (ASBC)**
PO Box 270300
Louisville, CO 80027
Contact: Gena Rieck, Pres.
Ph: (720)272-8231
Fax: (866)826-3995
E-mail: co-bouldercounty@autismsocietyofamerica.org
URL: http://www.autismboulder.org
Descr: Seeks to improve the lives of individuals affected by autism. Promotes awareness and understanding of autism disorders. Aims to further the advancement of preventive studies, therapy and research of autism disorders.

4022 ■ **Autism Society of Colorado (ASC)**
550 S Wadsworth Blvd., Ste. 100
Lakewood, CO 80226
Contact: Betty Lehman, Exec. Dir.
Ph: (720)214-0794
Free: 866-733-0794
Fax: (720)274-2744
E-mail: co-colorado@autismsocietyofamerica.org
URL: http://www.autismcolorado.org
Descr: Seeks to improve the lives of individuals affected by autism. Promotes awareness and understanding of autism disorders. Aims to further the advancement of preventive studies, therapy and research of autism disorders.

4023 ■ **Autism Society of Larimer County (ASLC)**
921 Province Rd.
Fort Collins, CO 80525
Contact: Phyllis Zimmerman, Pres.
Ph: (970)206-4979
E-mail: aslc@autismlarimer.org
URL: http://www.autismlarimer.org
Descr: Seeks to improve the lives of individuals affected by autism. Promotes awareness and understanding of autism disorders. Aims to further the advancement of preventive studies, therapy and research of autism disorders.

4024 ■ **Autism Society of the Pikes Peak Region (ASAPPR)**
PO Box 7802
Colorado Springs, CO 80933
Contact: Alison Seyler, Pres.
Ph: (719)216-7175

E-mail: info@asappr.org
URL: http://www.asappr.org
Descr: Seeks to improve the lives of individuals affected by autism. Promotes awareness and understanding of autism disorders. Aims to further the advancement of preventive studies, therapy and research of autism disorders.

4025 ■ **Breckenridge Outdoor Education Center (BOEC)**
PO Box 697
Breckenridge, CO 80424
Contact: Bob Bond, Wilderness Program Dir.
Ph: (970)453-6422
Free: 800-383-BOEC
Fax: (970)453-4676
E-mail: boec@boec.org
URL: http://www.boec.org
Staff: 25. **Descr:** Seeks to empower people of all abilities through high quality outdoor experiences. Provides four specific program areas: Adaptive Ski, Wilderness Program, Professional Challenge Program and an internship program. Programs provide individuals the opportunity to learn new skills, experience pristine natural areas, challenge themselves, and work together to enhance their health and self-confidence levels. **Fnd:** 1976. **Pub:** *Empowering News* (semiannual).

4026 ■ **Challenge Aspen**
PO Box M
Aspen, CO 81612
Contact: Houston Cowan, CEO
Ph: (970)923-0578
Fax: (970)923-7338
E-mail: possibilities@challengeaspen.com
URL: http://www.challengeaspen.com
Descr: Assists people with mental or physical disabilities in appreciating outdoor recreation and cultural activities. **Fnd:** 1995.

4027 ■ **Colorado AfterSchool Network**
450 Lincoln St., Ste. 100
Denver, CO 80203
Contact: Fred Franko, Program Dir.
Ph: (303)837-8466
E-mail: info@coloradoafterschoolnetwork.org
URL: http://www.coloradoafterschoolnetwork.org

4028 ■ **Colorado Association for Career and Technical Education (CACTE)**
170 Scenic Dr.
Loveland, CO 80537
Contact: Karla Rodie, Pres.
Ph: (970)669-4160
Fax: (970)669-4160
E-mail: coloradoacte@juno.com
URL: http://www.cacte.org
Fnd: 1917. **Mem:** 900.

4029 ■ **Colorado Association for the Education of Young Children (CAEYC)**
PO Box 631326
Highlands Ranch, CO 80163-1326
Contact: Linda Adams, Exec. Dir.
Ph: (303)791-2772
Free: 888-892-4453
Fax: (303)791-7597
E-mail: caeyc@coloradoaeyc.org
URL: http://www.coloradoaeyc.org
Staff: 1. **Descr:** Professionals in child care facilities and elementary schools; other professionals working with young children. Coordinates annual Month of the Young Child, and two state conferences. Promotes public policy and advocacy. **Fnd:** 1968. **Mem:** 1650. **State Groups:** 1. **Local Groups:** 18. **Pub:** *Young Children* (bimonthly); Directory (annual); Newsletter.

4030 ■ **Colorado Department of Education**
201 E. Colfax Ave.
Denver, CO 80203-1799
Contact: Dr. Dwight D. Jones, Commnr.
Ph: (303)866-6600
Fax: (303)830-0793

E-mail: commissioner@cde.state.co.us
URL: http://www.cde.state.co.us/
Descr: Mission is to provide all Colorado children equal access to quality, thorough, uniform, well-rounded educational opportunities in a safe, civil environment.

4031 ■ **Colorado Parent Teacher Association**
7859 W 38th Ave.
Wheat Ridge, CO 80033
Contact: Pamela Hurd-Keyzer, Pres.
Ph: (303)420-7820
Free: 888-225-8234
Fax: (303)420-7703
E-mail: office@copta.org
URL: http://www.copta.org
Descr: Works to support and speak on behalf of children and youth in schools, in the community, and before governmental bodies and other organizations that make decisions affecting children; assists parents in developing the skills needed to raise and protect their children; and encourages parental and public involvement in the public schools. **Fnd:** 1907. **Mem:** 33000.

4032 ■ **Fire Marshal's Association of Colorado**
1000 Englewood Pkwy.
Englewood, CO 80110
Contact: Doug Hall, Pres.
Ph: (303)762-2365
E-mail: dhall@ci.westminster.co.us
URL: http://www.co-fmac.org
Descr: Provides the highest quality codes, standards, products, and services for all concerned with the safety and performance of the built environment.

4033 ■ **Foresight Ski Guides**
PO Box 18944
Denver, CO 80218-0944
Contact: Mark G. Davis, Pres.
Ph: (303)832-1080
Free: 866-860-0972
Fax: (303)894-9383
E-mail: foresightskiguides@gmail.com
URL: http://www.foresightskiguides.org
Descr: Provides affordable access to skiing/snowboarding to blind or visually impaired people. **Fnd:** 2001.

4034 ■ **Learning Disability Association of Colorado**
2050 E Evans Ave., Ste. 30
Denver, CO 80208
Ph: (303)894-0992
Fax: (303)830-1645
E-mail: info@ldacolorado.com
URL: http://www.ldacolorado.com

4035 ■ **Mothers and More Central Denver, Chapter 218**
PO Box 100783
Denver, CO 80250
E-mail: mothersandmoredenver@yahoo.com
URL: http://www.mothersandmore.org/chapters/centraldenver

4036 ■ **Recording for the Blind and Dyslexic Rocky Mountain Unit**
1355 S Colorado Blvd., Ste. C-406
Denver, CO 80222
Contact: Robert Writz, Chm.
Ph: (303)757-0787
E-mail: bboudreau@rfbd.org
URL: http://www.rfbd.org/Denver_Unit.htm
Descr: Serves individuals who cannot effectively read standard print because of visual impairment, dyslexia, or other physical disabilities. Creates educational opportunities for students with print disabilities through educational and outreach services. Provides and promotes the effective use of accessible educational materials.

4037 ■ **Rocky Mountain Branch of the International Dyslexia Association (IDA-RMB)**
PO Box 46-1010
Glendale, CO 80246
Contact: Elenn Steinberg, Pres.

Ph: (303)721-9425
Fax: (303)557-9750
E-mail: ida_rmb@yahoo.com
URL: http://www.dyslexia-rmbida.org
Descr: Promotes public awareness and understanding of dyslexia. Seeks to develop and implement specialized methods to improve the quality of life for people who have dyslexia. **Mem:** 300.

4038 ■ Special Olympics, Colorado (SOCO)
410 17th St., Ste. 200
Denver, CO 80202
Contact: Mindy Watrous, Pres./CEO
Ph: (303)592-1361
Free: 800-777-5767
Fax: (303)592-1364
E-mail: mw@specialolympicsco.org
URL: http://www.specialolympicsco.org
Descr: Provides year-round sports training and athletic competition in a variety of Olympic-type sports for children and adults with developmental disabilities, eight years of age and older, giving them continuing opportunities to develop physical fitness, demonstrate courage, experience joy and participate in a sharing of gifts, skills and friendship with their families, other Special Olympics athletes and the community. **Fnd:** 1969.

Connecticut

4039 ■ American Association of University Women, Bridgeport Area Branch
PO Box 1043
Samp Mortar Sta.
Fairfield, CT 06825
Contact: Judith Polizzotti, VP for Membership
E-mail: members@aauwbridgeport.org
URL: http://www.aauwbridgeport.org
Descr: Advances equity for women and girls through advocacy, education, and research. Provides funds and a support system for women seeking judicial redress for sex discrimination in higher education.

4040 ■ American Association of University Women, Ridgefield Branch
128 W Mountain Rd.
Ridgefield, CT 06877
Contact: Sabina Slavin, Treas.
Ph: (203)438-3258
E-mail: sabinaslvn@aol.com
URL: http://www.aauw-ct-ridgefield.org
Descr: Advances equity for women and girls through advocacy, education, and research. Provides funds and a support system for women seeking judicial redress for sex discrimination in higher education.

4041 ■ American Medical Student Association, University of Connecticut School of Medicine
263 Farmington Ave.
Farmington, CT 06030
Ph: (860)679-2000
URL: http://medicine.uchc.edu
Descr: Promotes improvement in medical training and education. Advances the medicine profession. Contributes to the welfare of medical students, interns, residents and post-MD/DO trainees.

4042 ■ American Medical Student Association, Yale University School of Medicine
333 Cedar St.
New Haven, CT 06510
Ph: (203)785-2644
URL: http://info.med.yale.edu/ysm
Descr: Promotes improvement in medical training and education. Advances the medicine profession. Contributes to the welfare of medical students, interns, residents and post-MD/DO trainees.

4043 ■ Arc of Connecticut
43 Woodland St., Ste. 260
Hartford, CT 06105
Contact: Lynn Warner, Exec. Dir.
Ph: (860)246-6400
Fax: (860)246-6406

E-mail: lwarner@arcofct.org
URL: http://www.arcct.com
Descr: Works to protect the rights of mentally retarded people and other related disabilities and to promote opportunities for their full inclusion in the life of their communities.

4044 ■ Arc of the Farmington Valley
225 Commerce Dr.
PO Box 1099
Canton, CT 06019-1099
Contact: Stephen E. Morris MPA, Exec. Dir.
Ph: (860)693-6662
Fax: (860)693-8662
E-mail: favarh@favarh.org
URL: http://www.favarh.org
Descr: Strives to commit time, talents, and energy to support and empower individuals with developmental disabilities to enjoy a productive and independent life and to achieve his or her personal best. **Fnd:** 1958.

4045 ■ Arc of Greater New Haven
109 Sanford St.
Hamden, CT 06514
Contact: LouAnn McInnes, Exec. Dir.
Ph: (203)288-7932
Fax: (203)288-7925
E-mail: info@arcgnh.org
URL: http://www.arcgnh.org

4046 ■ Arc of Meriden-Wallingford
200 Research Pkwy.
Meriden, CT 06450
Contact: Pamela Fields, Exec. Dir.
Ph: (203)237-9975
Fax: (203)639-0946
E-mail: info@mwsinc.org
URL: http://www.arcmw.org

4047 ■ Arc of New London County
125 Sachem St.
Norwich, CT 06360
Contact: Diane Aubin, Pres.
Ph: (860)889-4435
Fax: (860)889-4662
E-mail: info@thearcnlc.org
URL: http://www.thearcnlc.org

4048 ■ Arc of Plainville
27 Sherman St., No. 1
Plainville, CT 06062
Contact: Jeannette Hinkson, Exec. Dir.
Ph: (860)747-4119
E-mail: hmtnn@aol.com
URL: http://216.36.57.72/506

4049 ■ Arc of Quinebaug Valley
687 Cook Hill Rd.
Danielson, CT 06239
Contact: Claire Griffith, Exec. Dir.
Ph: (860)774-2827
Fax: (860)774-4265
E-mail: clg@qvarc.org
URL: http://www.qvarc.org

4050 ■ Arc of Southington
201 W Main St.
Plantsville, CT 06479
Contact: Sandra A. Amato, Exec. Dir.
Ph: (860)628-9220
Fax: (860)621-2546
E-mail: advocacy@arcsouthington.org
URL: http://www.arcsouthington.org
Staff: 16. **Descr:** Enhances the quality of life for people with disabilities through education, empowerment, support, and advocacy. **Fnd:** 1954. **Mem:** 80.

4051 ■ Autism Society of Connecticut (AS-CONN)
PO Box 1404
Guilford, CT 06437
Contact: Sara Reed
Free: 888-453-4975
E-mail: asconn@sbcglobal.net
URL: http://www.autismsocietyofct.org
Descr: Seeks to improve the lives of individuals af-

fected by autism. Promotes awareness and understanding of autism disorders. Aims to further the advancement of preventive studies, therapy and research of autism disorders.

4052 ■ Common Cause Connecticut
55 Oak St.
Hartford, CT 06106
Contact: Andy Sauer, Exec. Dir.
Ph: (860)549-1220
E-mail: common.cause@snet.net
URL: http://www.commoncause.org/site/pp.asp?c=dkLNK1MQIwG&b=1699613
Descr: Works as a nonpartisan citizens' lobby. Fights for open, honest, and accountable government.

4053 ■ Connecticut After School Network
12 Melrose Ave.
Branford, CT 06405
Contact: Ms. Michelle Doucette Cunningham, Exec. Dir.
Ph: (203)483-1846
Fax: (203)481-7160
E-mail: info@ctafterschoolnetwork.org
URL: http://ctafterschoolnetwork.org/index.html
Staff: 7. **Descr:** Provides leadership, education and advocacy for excellence in after school programs for children and youth. Provides professional development that relates to program management and age appropriate constructive activities for directors and staff who work with children ages 5-18 in after school programs. **Fnd:** 1989. **Mem:** 1100.

4054 ■ Connecticut Branch of the International Dyslexia Association (CONNBIDA)
69 Hillspoint Rd.
Westport, CT 06889
Contact: Margie Bussmann Gillis, Pres.
Ph: (203)222-0413
E-mail: gillis@haskins.yale.edu
URL: http://connbida.org
Descr: Promotes public awareness and understanding of dyslexia. Seeks to develop and implement specialized methods to improve the quality of life for people who have dyslexia.

4055 ■ Connecticut Council on Developmental Disabilities
460 Capitol Ave.
Hartford, CT 06106-1308
Contact: Edward T. Preneta, Dir.
Ph: (860)418-6160
Free: 800-653-1134
Fax: (860)418-6003
E-mail: ed.preneta@ct.gov
URL: http://www.ct.gov/ctcdd/site/default.asp
Descr: Promotes education for children, meaningful work for adults, community living for all people with disabilities, and self-advocacy by people with disabilities and parents. **Fnd:** 1971.

4056 ■ Connecticut Parent Teacher Association (CT PTA)
60 Connolly Pkwy., Bldg. No. 12
Hamden, CT 06514
Contact: Lisa Whitney, Sec.-Treas.
Ph: (203)281-6617
Fax: (203)281-6749
E-mail: connecticut.pta@snet.net
URL: http://www.ctpta.org
Descr: Promotes the welfare of children and youth in home, school, community, and place of worship. Raises the standards of home life. Secures adequate laws for the care and protection of children and youth. Brings into closer relation the home and the school, that parents and teachers may cooperate intelligently in the education of children and youth. Develops between educators and the general public such unified efforts as will secure for all children and youth the highest advantages in physical, mental,

social and spiritual education. **Fnd:** 1900. **Mem:** 56000.

4057 ■ Connecticut State Department of Education
165 Capitol Ave.
Hartford, CT 06106-1630
Contact: Dr. Mark K. McQuillan, Commnr.
Ph: (860)713-6543
Free: 800-465-4014
Fax: (860)713-7001
E-mail: mark.mcquillan@ct.gov
URL: http://www.sde.ct.gov/
Descr: Provides leadership that promotes an educational system which supports all learners in reaching their full potential.

4058 ■ Hartford Association for the Education of Young Children (HAEYC)
11 Charter Oak Ave.
Hartford, CT 06106
Contact: Michelle Meace, Pres.
Ph: (860)509-3694
Fax: (860)246-3304
E-mail: info@hartfordaeyc.org
URL: http://www.hartfordaeyc.org
Descr: Teachers and directors of preschool and primary schools, kindergartens, child care centers, cooperatives, church schools, and groups having similar programs for young children; early childhood education and child development educators, trainers, and researchers. Open to all individuals interested in serving and acting on behalf of the needs and rights of young children, with primary focus on the provision of educational services and resources.

4059 ■ Litchfield County Arc (LARC)
314 Main St.
Torrington, CT 06790
Ph: (860)482-9364
Fax: (860)489-2492
E-mail: larc@litchfieldarc.org
URL: http://www.litchfieldarc.org

4060 ■ MARC of Manchester
376R W Middle Tpke.
Manchester, CT 06040
Contact: Ken Charpentier, Exec. Dir.
Ph: (860)646-5718
Fax: (860)645-9910
E-mail: info@marcct.org
URL: http://www.marcct.org
Descr: Supports people with disabilities in Manchester and surrounding towns. Dedicated to advocacy on the local, state and national level. Delivers diverse services to ensure that all people have the opportunity to live, work and enjoy their community according to their individual choices. **Fnd:** 1952.

4061 ■ Recording for the Blind and Dyslexic, New Haven
209 Orange St.
New Haven, CT 06510
Contact: Ms. Anne Fortunato, State Dir.
Ph: (203)624-4334
Fax: (203)865-0203
E-mail: connecticut@rfbd.org
URL: http://www.rfbd.org/CT/index.htm
Staff: 6. **Descr:** Volunteer members provide broad variety of educational resources for those with print, learning and physical disabilities through services and strategies incorporated with the used of audio textbooks into classroom learning. **Fnd:** 1959. **Mem:** 3000.

4062 ■ Tri-County Arc
65 Rte. 66 E
Columbia, CT 06237
Contact: Dennis Plante, Exec. Dir.
Ph: (860)228-2070
Descr: Parents, professional workers, and others interested in individuals with mental retardation. Works to promote services, research, public under-

standing, and legislation for people with mental retardation and their families.

4063 ■ Waterbury Arc (WARC)
1929 E Main St.
Waterbury, CT 06705
Contact: Marcy Kane PhD, Pres.
Ph: (203)575-0707
Fax: (203)596-0400
URL: http://www.waterburyarc.org

Delaware

4064 ■ Arc of Delaware
2 S Augustine St., Ste. B
Newport, DE 19804
Contact: Judy Govatos, Exec. Dir.
Ph: (302)996-9400
E-mail: jgovatos@arcde.org
URL: http://www.thearcofdelaware.org

4065 ■ Communities In Schools of Delaware
100 Campus Dr.
Dover, DE 19904
Contact: Jim Turcell, Pres.
Ph: (302)857-1744
E-mail: jpurcell@cisdelaware.org
URL: http://www.cisdelaware.org
Descr: Works to help kids succeed in school and prepare for life.

4066 ■ Delaware Department of Education
John G. Townsend Bldg.
401 Federal St.
Dover, DE 19901
Contact: Valerie A. Woodruff, Sec. of Educ.
Ph: (302)735-4000
Fax: (302)739-4654
E-mail: dedoe@doe.k12.de.us
URL: http://www.doe.state.de.us/

4067 ■ Developmental Disabilities Planning Council, Delaware (DDC)
Margaret M. O'Neill Bldg., 2nd Fl.
410 Federal St., Ste. 2
Dover, DE 19901
Contact: Patricia L. Maichle, Sr. Admin.
Ph: (302)739-3333
Free: 800-273-9500
Fax: (302)739-2015
E-mail: pat.maichle@state.de.us
URL: http://ddc.delaware.gov
Descr: Seeks to ensure that people with developmental disabilities can enjoy the same quality of life as the rest of society through system-wide advocacy, planning and demonstration projects.

4068 ■ Mid-Del Chapter of The Arc
PO Box 562
Dover, DE 19903
Contact: Judy Zingaro, Pres.
Ph: (302)736-6140
URL: http://www.thearcofdelaware.org

4069 ■ Special Olympics Delaware (SODE)
Univ. of Delaware
619 S College Ave.
Newark, DE 19716-1901
Contact: Ann Grunert, Exec. Dir.
Ph: (302)831-4653
Fax: (302)831-3483
E-mail: sode@sode.org
URL: http://www.sode.org
Descr: Promotes physical fitness, sports training, and athletic competition for children and adults with intellectual disabilities. Seeks to contribute to the physical, social, and psychological development of persons with intellectual disabilities. Participants range in age from 8 years to adult, and SODE offers 16 different sports.

District of Columbia

4070 ■ 100 Black Men of Greater Washington, DC
PO Box 70558
Washington, DC 20024
Contact: Mr. Michael Melton, Pres.
Ph: (202)289-8884
Fax: (301)515-9688
E-mail: info@100blackmendc.org
URL: http://www.100blackmendc.org

4071 ■ American Medical Student Association, Georgetown University Medical Center School of Medicine
37th and O St. NW
Washington, DC 20057
Contact: Tracey L. Henry, Co-Pres.
E-mail: dtk3@georgetown.edu
URL: http://som.georgetown.edu
Descr: Promotes improvement in medical training and education. Advances the medicine profession. Contributes to the welfare of medical students, interns, residents and post-MD/DO trainees. **Fnd:** 1950. **Mem:** 70000.

4072 ■ American Medical Student Association, Howard University College of Medicine
520 W St. NW
Washington, DC 20059
Contact: Robert E. Taylor MD
Ph: (202)806-6270
Fax: (202)806-7934
URL: http://www.med.howard.edu
Descr: Promotes improvement in medical training and education. Advances the medicine profession. Contributes to the welfare of medical students, interns, residents and post-MD/DO trainees.

4073 ■ American Medical Student Association, The George Washington University School of Medicine
2300 Eye St. NW, Ste. 713W
Washington, DC 20037
Contact: John F. Williams MD
Ph: (202)994-2987
URL: http://www.gwumc.edu/smhs
Descr: Promotes improvement in medical training and education. Advances the medicine profession. Contributes to the welfare of medical students, interns, residents and post-MD/DO trainees.

4074 ■ D.C. Capital Area Branch of the International Dyslexia Association
2327 40th St. NW, No. 1
Washington, DC 20007
Contact: Anthony Henley, Pres.
Ph: (703)827-9019
E-mail: ahenley@starpower.net
Descr: Promotes public awareness and understanding of dyslexia. Seeks to develop and implement specialized methods to improve the quality of life for people who have dyslexia.

4075 ■ District of Columbia Chapter of the Autism Society of America (DCASA)
5167 7th St. NE
Washington, DC 20011
Contact: Sondra K. Cunningham, Pres.
Ph: (202)561-5300
Fax: (202)561-5633
E-mail: dc-washington@autismsocietyofamerica.org
URL: http://www.autism-society.org/site/Clubs?club_id=1051&pg=main
Descr: Seeks to improve the lives of individuals affected by autism. Promotes awareness and understanding of autism disorders. Aims to further the advancement of preventive studies, therapy and research of autism disorders.

4076 ■ District of Columbia Public Schools
Union Sq.
825 N. Capitol St. NE, 9th Fl.
Washington, DC 20002
Contact: Michelle Rhee, Chancellor
Ph: (202)442-5885
Fax: (202)442-5026

E-mail: contactdcps@k12.dc.us
URL: http://www.k12.dc.us/
Descr: Mission is to educate all children in the District of Columbia, providing knowledge and skills they need to achieve academic success and choose a rewarding professional path.

4077 ■ Learning Disabilities Association of District of Columbia (LDA)
1518 Spring Pl. NW
Washington, DC 20010
Contact: Lorie Preheim
Ph: (202)232-7777
E-mail: lpreheim@evenstartdc.org

4078 ■ Recording for the Blind and Dyslexic of Metropolitan Washington
5225 Wisconsin Ave. NW, Ste. 312
Washington, DC 20015
Contact: Betsy Paull O'Connell, Exec. Dir.
Ph: (202)244-8990
Fax: (202)244-1346
E-mail: washingtondc@rfbd.org
URL: http://www.rfbd.org/dc
Descr: Serves individuals who cannot effectively read standard print because of visual impairment, dyslexia, or other physical disabilities. Creates educational opportunities for students with print disabilities through educational and outreach services. Provides and promotes the effective use of accessible educational materials.

4079 ■ Special Olympics, District of Columbia
900 2nd St. NE, Ste. 200
Washington, DC 20002
Contact: Stephen A. Hocker, Exec. Dir.
Ph: (202)408-2640
Fax: (202)408-2646
E-mail: wdcso@aol.com
URL: http://specialolympicsdc.org
Descr: Promotes physical fitness, sports training, and athletic competition for children and adults with mental retardation. Seeks to contribute to the physical, social, and psychological development of persons with mental retardation. Participants range in age from 8 years to adult and compete in track and field, swimming, gymnastics, bowling, ice skating, basketball, and other sports.

Florida

4080 ■ 100 Black Men of Jacksonville
PO Box 2065
Jacksonville, FL 32203
Contact: Robert Porter, Pres.
Ph: (904)924-2545
Free: 800-409-3764
Fax: (904)764-3262
E-mail: info@100blackmenjax.org
URL: http://www.100blackmenjax.org
Fnd: 1991.

4081 ■ 100 Black Men of South Florida
PO Box 530275
Miami Shores, FL 33153
Contact: Bobby L. Hall, Pres.
Ph: (305)620-2260
E-mail: info@100blackmensf.org
URL: http://www.100blackmensf.org

4082 ■ 100 Black Men of Tampa Bay, Florida
3837 N Dale Blvd., No. 165
Tampa, FL 33624
Contact: Henry L. Bell Jr., Pres.
Free: 877-636-6687
E-mail: vistors@100bmtb.org
URL: http://www.100bmtb.org

4083 ■ AG BELL, Florida
11457 Buck Lake Rd.
Tallahassee, FL 32317
Contact: Dennis K. Filloon, Pres.
Ph: (850)656-2570
E-mail: dennis5846@earthlink.net
URL: http://www.agbellflorida.org
Descr: Represents the interests of educators, parents of children with hearing loss, adults with hearing loss and hearing health professionals. Provides governmental and education advocacy services.

4084 ■ American Association of University Women, Gainesville Branch
3988 NW 23rd Cir.
Gainesville, FL 32605
Contact: Jackie Davison
Ph: (352)336-3591
E-mail: ladavison@msn.com
URL: http://www.afn.org/~aauwflgv
Descr: Advances equity for women and girls through advocacy, education, and research. Provides funds and a support system for women seeking judicial redress for sex discrimination in higher education.
Fnd: 1926.

4085 ■ American Association of University Women, Lee County Branch
8102 Pacific Beach Dr.
Fort Myers, FL 33919
Contact: Jean Schoenthaler, VP for Membership
E-mail: jeanschoenthaler@centuryfla.com
URL: http://www.aauwleeco.org
Descr: Advances equity for women and girls through advocacy, education, and research. Provides funds and a support system for women seeking judicial redress for sex discrimination in higher education.
Fnd: 1961.

4086 ■ American Association of University Women, Manatee County Branch
3707 118th St. W
Bradenton, FL 34210
Contact: Marilyn Steele, Co-Pres.
Ph: (941)792-5970
E-mail: tsteele19@tampabay.rr.com
URL: http://www.florida-aauw.org/Branches/manatee.htm
Descr: Advances equity for women and girls through advocacy, education, and research. Provides funds and a support system for women seeking judicial redress for sex discrimination in higher education.
Pub: *Manatee Messenger* (monthly).

4087 ■ American Association of University Women, Northern Palm Beach Branch
140 Ocean Pines Terr.
Jupiter, FL 33477
Contact: Sally Bailey, Finance Off.
Ph: (561)748-9909
E-mail: sallyb2@aol.com
URL: http://www.florida-aauw.org/Branches/norpalm.htm
Descr: Advances equity for women and girls through advocacy, education, and research. Provides funds and a support system for women seeking judicial redress for sex discrimination in higher education.
Pub: *Branch Out* (monthly).

4088 ■ American Association of University Women, Palm Beach County Branch
1734 S Congress Ave.
Palm Springs, FL 33461
Contact: Susan V. Berlin, Pres.
E-mail: svberlin@bellsouth.net
URL: http://www.florida-aauw.org/Branches/palmbch.htm
Descr: Advances equity for women and girls through advocacy, education, and research. Provides funds and a support system for women seeking judicial redress for sex discrimination in higher education.

4089 ■ American Association of University Women, Pompano Beach Branch
6361-2 Bay Club Dr., Bldg. No. 10
Fort Lauderdale, FL 33308-1645
Contact: Helen Elkiss, Pres.
Ph: (954)530-1443
E-mail: duchess143@yahoo.com
URL: http://www.florida-aauw.org/Branches/pompano.htm
Descr: Advances equity for women and girls through advocacy, education, and research. Provides funds and a support system for women seeking judicial redress for sex discrimination in higher education.

4090 ■ American Association of University Women, Stuart Branch
PO Box 3292
Stuart, FL 34995
Contact: Rosemary Carroll, Pres.
E-mail: fenglund@bellsouth.net
URL: http://stuartaauw.org
Descr: Advances equity for women and girls through advocacy, education, and research. Provides funds and a support system for women seeking judicial redress for sex discrimination in higher education.
Fnd: 1972.

4091 ■ American Association of University Women, Venice Branch
488 Marsh Creek Rd.
Venice, FL 34293
Contact: Anne Russell, Pres.
E-mail: annelruss@comcast.net
URL: http://www.florida-aauw.org/Branches/venice.htm
Descr: Advances equity for women and girls through advocacy, education, and research. Provides funds and a support system for women seeking judicial redress for sex discrimination in higher education.
Pub: *Venice Views* (monthly).

4092 ■ American Medical Student Association, Florida State University College of Medicine
1115 W Call St.
Tallahassee, FL 32306
Contact: J. Ocie Harris MD
Ph: (850)644-1855
Fax: (850)644-3735
E-mail: medinformation@med.fsu.edu
URL: http://med.fsu.edu
Descr: Promotes improvement in medical training and education. Advances the medicine profession. Contributes to the welfare of medical students, interns, residents and post-MD/DO trainees.

4093 ■ American Medical Student Association, Nova Southeastern University College of Osteopathic Medicine
College of Osteopathic Medicine
3200 S University Dr.
Fort Lauderdale, FL 33328
Contact: Alexandra R. Grace, Pres.
E-mail: agrace@nsu.nova.edu
URL: http://nsucomsga.nova.edu
Descr: Promotes improvement in medical training and education. Advances the medicine profession. Contributes to the welfare of medical students, interns, residents and post-MD/DO trainees.

4094 ■ American Medical Student Association, University of Miami Miller School of Medicine
University of Miami Medical Group
1150 NW 14th St., Ste. 610
Miami, FL 33136
Contact: Eduardo De Marchena MD, Chm.
Ph: (305)243-7100
Fax: (305)243-7141
E-mail: comments.ummg@med.miami.edu
URL: http://www.med.miami.edu
Descr: Promotes improvement in medical training and education. Advances the medicine profession. Contributes to the welfare of medical students, interns, residents and post-MD/DO trainees.

4095 ■ American Medical Student Association, University of South Florida College of Medicine
12901 Bruce B. Downs Blvd.
MDC 2
Tampa, FL 33612
Contact: Dr. Stephen K. Klasko, VP
Ph: (813)974-2196
E-mail: sklasko@health.usf.edu
URL: http://health.usf.edu/medicine/home.html
Descr: Promotes improvement in medical training and education. Advances the medicine profession.

Contributes to the welfare of medical students, interns, residents and post-MD/DO trainees.

4096 ■ Arc of Alachua County
3303 NW 83rd St.
Gainesville, FL 32606-6227
Contact: Mr. Dick Bradley, Exec. Dir.
Ph: (352)334-4060
Fax: (352)334-4059
URL: http://www.arcalachua.org
Staff: 250. **Descr:** Parents, professional workers, and others interested in individuals with developmental disabilities. Works to promote services, research, public understanding, and legislation for people with developmental disabilities and their families. **Fnd:** 1966.

4097 ■ Arc of Charlotte County
PO Box 495021
Port Charlotte, FL 33949
Contact: Robert Mungovan, Pres.
Ph: (941)627-8771
E-mail: bobm@ankoproducts.com
URL: http://www.arcflorida.org

4098 ■ Arc/Desoto
PO Box 787
Nocatee, FL 34268
Contact: Nancy Turner, Exec. Dir.
Ph: (863)494-2328
Fax: (863)494-0343
E-mail: arcdesot@strato.net
URL: http://www.arc-desoto.com
Descr: Parents, professional workers, and others interested in individuals with mental retardation. Works to promote services, research, public understanding, and legislation for people with mental retardation and their families.

4099 ■ ARC Flagler County
PO Box 354412
Palm Coast, FL 32135-4412
Contact: Theodora Wenstrom, Pres.
Ph: (386)446-2385

4100 ■ Arc/Florida
2898 Mahan Dr., Ste. 1
Tallahassee, FL 32308
Contact: Ms. Deborah Linton, Exec. Dir.
Ph: (850)921-0460
Fax: (850)921-0418
E-mail: arcofflorida@comcast.net
URL: http://www.arcflorida.org
Descr: Parents, professional workers, and others interested in individuals with mental retardation. Works to promote services, research, public understanding, and legislation for people with mental retardation and their families.

4101 ■ ARC Gateway
3932 N Tenth Ave.
Pensacola, FL 32503
Contact: Todd Torgersen, Pres.
Ph: (850)434-2638
Fax: (850)438-2180
E-mail: foundation@arc-gateway.org
URL: http://www.arc-gateway.org
Staff: 5. **Descr:** Increases the opportunities for persons with, or at risk of, developmental disabilities, to choose where, how and with whom they live, learn, work, and play. **Fnd:** 1954. **Pub:** Newsletter (monthly).

4102 ■ Arc of Jackson County - Florida
2944 Pennsylvania Ave., Ste. A
Marianna, FL 32448
Contact: Frances Henderson, Exec. Dir.
Ph: (850)526-7333
Fax: (850)526-2311
E-mail: jcarc@digitalexp.com
URL: http://www.arcflorida.org

4103 ■ Arc Jacksonville
1050 N Davis St.
Jacksonville, FL 32209
Contact: Jim Whittaker, Exec. Dir.

Ph: (904)355-0155
Fax: (904)355-9616
E-mail: thearc_jwhittaker@gbso.net
URL: http://www.arcflorida.org

4104 ■ Arc of Okeechobee
403 NW 2nd Ave.
Okeechobee, FL 34972
Contact: Tom Murphy, Pres.
Ph: (863)763-2419
E-mail: okrehab@okeechobee.com

4105 ■ Arc of Orange and Seminole Counties
PO Box 161250
Orlando, FL 32816
Contact: Jeannie Forthuber, Pres.
Ph: (407)823-6705
Fax: (407)823-1296
E-mail: jforthub@mail.ucf.edu
URL: http://www.arcflorida.org

4106 ■ Arc of Palm Beach County
1201 Australian Ave.
Riviera Beach, FL 33404
Contact: Debra Ruedisili, Pres.
Ph: (561)842-3213
Fax: (561)863-4352
E-mail: lhouston@arcpbc.org
URL: http://www.arcpbc.com
Descr: Works to improve the lives of children and adults who have developmental disabilities through services, advocacy and education. Offers services to meet the needs of people who are developmentally disabled. Works with lawmakers to promote appropriate legislation. Serves as an information and referral service for families. Collaborates with related agencies to assure complete services to prevent the incidence of mental retardation. Offers a speakers' bureau to promote community awareness and understanding. **Fnd:** 1958.

4107 ■ Arc of Putnam County
1209 Westover Dr.
Palatka, FL 32177
Contact: Jim Whittaker, Exec. Dir.
Ph: (386)325-2249
Fax: (386)325-3527
E-mail: thearc-jwhittaker@gbso.net
URL: http://www.arcflorida.org

4108 ■ Arc of St. Lucie County
PO Box 1016
Fort Pierce, FL 34954
Contact: Cheryl King, Exec. Dir.
Ph: (772)468-7879
Fax: (772)465-7050
E-mail: slarc@gate.net
URL: http://www.arcflorida.org

4109 ■ Arc Santa Rosa
6225 Dixie Rd.
Milton, FL 32570
Contact: Ann Smith, Exec. Dir.
Ph: (850)623-9320
Fax: (850)623-2877
E-mail: director@arcsantarosa.org
URL: http://www.arcflorida.org

4110 ■ Arc Suncoast
3201 Trident Terr.
New Port Richey, FL 34652
Contact: Lynn Hagaman, Pres.
Ph: (727)992-2771

4111 ■ Association for the Education of Young Children of the Palm Beaches
7937 Ambleside Way
Lake Worth, FL 33467
Contact: Barbara Turner, Pres.
Ph: (561)966-7937
E-mail: nturn79@aol.com
URL: http://64.90.169.16/details.aspx?ArticleId=21&PageID=70
Descr: Serves and acts on behalf of the needs, rights and well-being of all young children with primary focus on the quality of educational and developmental services for all children. Seeks to

improve professional practice and working conditions in early childhood education.

4112 ■ Autism Society of America - Broward Chapter
PO Box 450476
Sunrise, FL 33345
Contact: Denise Crosnick, Pres.
Ph: (954)577-4141
E-mail: info@asabroward.org
URL: http://www.asabroward.org
Descr: Seeks to improve the lives of individuals affected by autism. Promotes awareness and understanding of autism disorders. Aims to further the advancement of preventive studies, therapy and research of autism disorders.

4113 ■ Autism Society of America - Gulf Coast Florida Chapter
PO Box 21105
St. Petersburg, FL 33742
Contact: Filomena McDonald
Ph: (727)786-4292
Descr: Seeks to improve the lives of individuals affected by autism. Promotes awareness and understanding of autism disorders. Aims to further the advancement of preventive studies, therapy and research of autism disorders.

4114 ■ Autism Society of Florida (ASF)
PO Box 970646
Coconut Creek, FL 33097
Contact: Ven Sequenzia, Pres.
Ph: (954)349-2820
Fax: (954)571-2136
E-mail: fl-florida@autismsocietyofamerica.org
URL: http://www.autismfl.com
Descr: Seeks to improve the lives of individuals affected by autism. Promotes awareness and understanding of autism disorders. Aims to further the advancement of preventive studies, therapy and research of autism disorders.

4115 ■ Autism Society of Greater Orlando (ASGO)
4743 Hearthside Dr.
Orlando, FL 32837
Contact: Donna Lorman, Pres.
Ph: (407)855-0235
E-mail: contact@asgo.org
URL: http://www.asgo.org
Descr: Seeks to improve the lives of individuals affected by autism. Promotes awareness and understanding of autism disorders. Aims to further the advancement of preventive studies, therapy and research of autism disorders.

4116 ■ Autism Society of Miami-Dade Florida
PO Box 931405
Miami, FL 33283
Contact: Teresa Becerra, Pres.
Ph: (305)969-3900
E-mail: info@autismsocietymiami.org
URL: http://www.autismsocietymiami.org
Descr: Seeks to improve the lives of individuals affected by autism. Promotes awareness and understanding of autism disorders. Aims to further the advancement of preventive studies, therapy and research of autism disorders.

4117 ■ Autism Society of the Panhandle, Florida
PO Box 30213
Pensacola, FL 32503
Contact: Susan Byram, Exec. Dir.
Ph: (850)450-0656
E-mail: panhandleautism@bellsouth.net
URL: http://www.autismpensacola.org
Descr: Seeks to improve the lives of individuals affected by autism. Promotes awareness and understanding of autism disorders. Aims to further the

advancement of preventive studies, therapy and research of autism disorders.

4118 ■ Building Officials and Inspectors Educational Association of Broward County
100 W Atlantic Blvd.
Pompano Beach, FL 33061
Contact: Floyd Kelly
Ph: (954)786-4651
Fax: (954)786-4677
E-mail: floyd.kelly@copbfl.com

Descr: Provides codes, standards, products, and services to concerned individuals for the safety and effective performance in the built environment.

4119 ■ Charlotte County Association for the Education of Young Children (CCAEYC)
837 Cordele Ave.
Port Charlotte, FL 33948
Contact: Mary Coomer, Pres.
E-mail: mcoomer@charlottecountyaeyc.org
URL: http://www.charlottecountyaeyc.org

Descr: Serves and acts on behalf of the needs, rights and well-being of all young children with primary focus on the quality of educational and developmental services for all children. Seeks to improve professional practice and working conditions in early childhood education.

4120 ■ Common Cause/Florida
704 W Madison St.
Tallahassee, FL 32304
Contact: Ben Wilcox, Exec. Dir.
Ph: (850)222-3883
Fax: (850)222-3906
E-mail: cmncause@infionline.net
URL: http://www.commoncause.org/florida

Descr: Advocates government accessibility, ethics, and campaign finance reform. **Fnd:** 1974. **Mem:** 15000. **State Groups:** 1. **Local Groups:** 1. **Pub:** *Florida Frontline* (semiannual).

4121 ■ Communities In Schools of Florida
444 Appleyard Dr.
Tallahassee, FL 32304
Contact: Lois Gracey, Dir.
Ph: (850)201-9750
Free: 888-262-2031
Fax: (850)201-9757
E-mail: cis@cisfl.org
URL: http://www.cisfl.org

Descr: Provides stay in school and drop out prevention services to at-risk, and economically disadvantaged students in public schools.

4122 ■ Communities in Schools of Broward County (CIS Browar)
3217 NW 10th Terr., Ste. 3066
Oakland Park, FL 33309
Contact: Michael Flatley, Exec. Dir.
Ph: (954)337-1030
Fax: (954)335-2457
E-mail: mflatley@cisb.org
URL: http://www.cisnet.org/broward

Staff: 40. **Descr:** Creates and coordinates public and private sector partnerships to bring existing community resources into the public schools, improve the quality of public education and help children stay in school and prepare for life. **Fnd:** 1990.

4123 ■ Early Childhood Association of Sarasota
243 S Osprey Ave.
Sarasota, FL 34236
Contact: Susan Klein, Dir.
Ph: (941)345-6202
URL: http://www.ecaoffl.org

Descr: Serves and acts on behalf of the needs, rights and well-being of all young children with primary focus on the quality of educational and developmental services for all children. Seeks to

improve professional practice and working conditions in early childhood education.

4124 ■ Early Learning Coalition of Lake County (ELCLC)
1504 South St.
Leesburg, FL 34748
Contact: Lesha Coffield, Exec. Dir.
Ph: (352)435-0566
E-mail: lcoffield@elclc.org
URL: http://www.elclc.org

Descr: Serves and acts on behalf of the needs, rights and well-being of all young children with primary focus on the quality of educational and developmental services for all children. Seeks to improve professional practice and working conditions in early childhood education.

4125 ■ Emerald Coast Autism Society
8668 Navarre Pkwy., No. 216
Navarre, FL 32566
Contact: Amanda Whatley, Pres.
E-mail: ecautismsociety@yahoo.com
URL: http://www.ecautismsociety.com

Descr: Seeks to improve the lives of individuals affected by autism. Promotes awareness and understanding of autism disorders. Aims to further the advancement of preventive studies, therapy and research of autism disorders.

4126 ■ Florida Association for Career and Technical Education (FACTE)
1220 N Paul Russell Rd.
Tallahassee, FL 32301
Contact: Marsan Carr, Exec. Dir.
Ph: (850)878-6860
Free: 800-586-6860
Fax: (850)878-5476
E-mail: factexec@facte.org
URL: http://www.facte.org

Staff: 2. **Descr:** Vocational educators and vocational technology centers. Promotes vocational education. **Fnd:** 1926. **Mem:** 2800. **Pub:** *The Enlightener* (monthly).

4127 ■ Florida Branch of the International Dyslexia Association
3750 San Jose Pl., Ste. 35
Jacksonville, FL 32257
Contact: Dr. Gayle Cane, Pres.
Ph: (904)803-9591
E-mail: gaylefcacne@aol.com
URL: http://www.idafla.org

Descr: Promotes public awareness and understanding of dyslexia. Seeks to develop and implement specialized methods to improve the quality of life for people who have dyslexia. **Mem:** 350.

4128 ■ Florida Department of Education
Turlington Bldg., Ste. 1514
325 W. Gaines St.
Tallahassee, FL 32399
Contact: Dr. Eric J. Smith, Commissioner
Ph: (850)245-0505
Fax: (850)245-9667
E-mail: commissioner@fldoe.org
URL: http://www.fldoe.org/

4129 ■ Florida Developmental Disabilities Council (FDDC)
124 Marriott Dr., Ste. 203
Tallahassee, FL 32301-2981
Contact: Debra Dowds, Exec. Dir.
Ph: (850)488-4180
Free: 800-580-7801
Fax: (850)922-6702
E-mail: fddc@fddc.org
URL: http://www.fddc.org

Descr: Assures that individuals with developmental disabilities and their families participate in the design of and have access to needed community services, individualized supports, and other forms of assistance that promote self-determination, independence, productivity, and integration and inclusion in

all facets of community life, through culturally competent programs.

4130 ■ Florida Families of Children With Visual Impairments (FFCVI)
PO Box 730265
Ormond Beach, FL 32173-0265
Contact: Suzanne Townsend, Exec. Dir.
Ph: (386)677-7760
Fax: (813)926-0122
E-mail: ffcvi@yahoo.com
URL: http://www.ffcvi.org

Staff: 6. **Descr:** Represents individuals committed to providing support to the parents of children who have visual impairments. Promotes public understanding of the needs and rights of children who are visually impaired.

4131 ■ Florida Westcoast Fire Association
789 Providence Blvd.
Brooksville, FL 34601
Contact: Dennis Andrews
Ph: (352)754-4050
E-mail: dandrews@co.hernando.fl.us

Descr: Provides the highest quality codes, standards, products, and services for all concerned with the safety and performance of the built environment.

4132 ■ Gold Coast Down Syndrome Organization (GCDSO)
2255 Glades Rd., Ste. 342-W
Boca Raton, FL 33431
Ph: (561)912-1231
Fax: (561)912-1232
E-mail: gcdso@bellsouth.net
URL: http://www.goldcoastdownsyndrome.org

Staff: 1. **Descr:** Families of people with Down syndrome; educators; health care professionals. Makes available support, information, and advocacy services. **Fnd:** 1980. **Mem:** 225. **Pub:** *Gold Coast News* (quarterly).

4133 ■ Gulf County Arc
309 Williams Ave.
Port St. Joe, FL 32456
Contact: Dianna Harrison, Exec. Dir.
Ph: (850)229-6327
Fax: (850)227-2084
E-mail: garc@gtcom.net
URL: http://www.portstjoefl.com/gulfarc

4134 ■ Hardee Association for Retarded Citizens
PO Box 1372
Wauchula, FL 33873
Contact: Dr. Michael J. McCoy, Exec. Dir.
Ph: (863)735-1121
Fax: (863)735-1944
E-mail: hardeearc@hotmail.com
URL: http://www.arcflorida.org

4135 ■ Hillsborough Early Childhood Association (HECA)
PO Box 320205
Tampa, FL 33679
Contact: Sandy Spreadbury, Pres.
Ph: (813)842-9221
E-mail: sandyspr@verizon.net
URL: http://www.ecaoffl.org

Descr: Serves and acts on behalf of the needs, rights and well-being of all young children with primary focus on the quality of educational and developmental services for all children. Seeks to improve professional practice and working conditions in early childhood education.

4136 ■ Learning Disability Association of Florida (LDA-FL)
331 E Henry St.
Punta Gorda, FL 33950
Ph: (941)637-8957

Fax: (941)637-0617
E-mail: ldaf00@sunline.net
URL: http://www.lda-fl.org

4137 ■ Levy Association for Retarded Citizens
PO Box 86
Otter Creek, FL 32683
Contact: Betty Stockton-Walker, Exec. Dir.
Ph: (352)486-4293
Fax: (352)486-6851
E-mail: levyarc@bellsouth.net
URL: http://www.arcflorida.org

4138 ■ Manasota Arc
PO Box 9292
Bradenton, FL 34206-9292
Contact: Mike Hamrick, Pres.
Ph: (941)752-2976
Fax: (941)752-1635
E-mail: marc0001@tampabay.rr.com
Descr: Parents, professional workers, and others interested in individuals with mental retardation. Works to promote services, research, public understanding, and legislation for people with mental retardation and their families.

4139 ■ Mothers and More Beaches First Coast, Chapter 194
PO Box 330772
Atlantic Beach, FL 32233
Ph: (904)858-3372
E-mail: a.e.frank@worldnet.att.net
URL: http://www.geocities.com/mothersfirstcoast

4140 ■ North Florida Association for the Education of Young Children (NFAEYC)
PO Box 41244
Jacksonville, FL 32203-1244
Contact: Alva Isaac, Pres.
Ph: (904)358-1656
E-mail: northfloridaaeyc@hotmail.com
URL: http://www.ecaoffl.org
Descr: Serves and acts on behalf of the needs, rights and well-being of all young children with primary focus on the quality of educational and developmental services for all children. Seeks to improve professional practice and working conditions in early childhood education.

4141 ■ Pinellas Early Childhood Association
139 Riviere Rd.
Palm Harbor, FL 34683
Contact: Barbra Mastrota, Pres.
Ph: (727)786-1094
E-mail: ldy125@hotmail.com
URL: http://www.pinellaseca.org
Descr: Teachers and directors of preschool and primary schools, kindergartens, child care centers, and early other learning programs for young childhood; early childhood education and child development educators, trainers, and researchers and other professionals dedicated to young children's healthy development.

4142 ■ Southwest Florida Pods Angels Family Support Group
PO Box 60933
Fort Myers, FL 33906-6933
Contact: Mary Beth Pringle, Pres.
Ph: (239)392-0050
E-mail: pringleclan@msn.com
URL: http://www.swflpodsangels.org
Staff: 12. **Fnd:** 2000. **Mem:** 170. **Reg. Groups:** 2. **State Groups:** 2. **Local Groups:** 1. **Pub:** *Buddy Walk.*

4143 ■ Special Olympics Florida (SOFL)
1105 Citrus Tower Blvd.
Clermont, FL 34711
Contact: Mr. Monty Castevens, Pres./CEO
Ph: (352)243-9536
Fax: (352)243-9568
E-mail: montycastevens@sofl.org
URL: http://www.specialolympicsflorida.org
Staff: 25. **Descr:** Provides sports training and athletic competition to over 15,000 adults and children with intellectual disabilities throughout

Florida. **Fnd:** 1972. **Mem:** 19000. **Pub:** *SPIRIT* (quarterly).

4144 ■ Sunrise Arc of Lake County
35201 Radio Rd.
Leesburg, FL 34788
Contact: Neil Fischer Jr., Chm.
Ph: (352)787-3079
Fax: (352)787-5932
E-mail: information@sunrisearc.org
URL: http://www.sunrisearc.org
Descr: Committed to securing for all people with developmental disabilities the opportunity to choose and realize their goals of where and how they learn, live, work and play. Committed to reducing the incidence and limiting the consequence of developmental disabilities through early intervention, education, research, advocacy and the support of families, friends and community. Seeks to provide leadership in the field of developmental disabilities and develop necessary human and financial resources to attain its goal. **Fnd:** 1964.

4145 ■ Upper Pinellas Association for Retarded Citizens (UPARC)
1501 N Belcher Rd., Ste. 249
Clearwater, FL 33765
Ph: (727)799-3330
Fax: (727)799-4632
E-mail: veronica@uparc.com
URL: http://www.uparc.com

4146 ■ Volusia Arc
100 Jimmy Huger Cir.
Daytona Beach, FL 32117-5108
Contact: Mr. Jim King, Exec. Dir.
Ph: (386)274-4736
Fax: (386)274-1222
E-mail: jimarcv@cfl.rr.com
URL: http://www.arcvolusia.org
Descr: Serves and advocates for individuals with developmental disabilities so they may achieve independence and self-sufficiency. Parents, professional workers, and others interested in individuals with developmental disabilities. Works to promote services, research, public understanding, and legislation for people with developmental disabilities and their families. **Fnd:** 1962.

4147 ■ VSA arts of Florida
3500 E Fletcher Ave., Ste. 234
Tampa, FL 33613
Contact: Marian Winters, Exec. Dir.
Ph: (813)975-6962
Free: 888-844-2787
Fax: (813)975-6596
E-mail: mwinters@tempest.coedu.usf.edu
URL: http://www.vsafl.org
Staff: 8. **Descr:** Aims to create a society where people with disabilities can learn through participation and enjoy arts. **Fnd:** 1981.

Georgia

4148 ■ 100 Black Men of Augusta
PO Box 12275
Augusta, GA 30914
Contact: Mr. Winston Butler, Pres.
E-mail: 100bma@talk1consulting.com

4149 ■ 100 Black Men of Dekalb
1804 Bouldercrest Rd., Ste. 700
Atlanta, GA 30316
Contact: Mae Jones, Exec. Dir./CEO
Ph: (404)288-2772
Fax: (404)288-0107
E-mail: info@dekalb100blackmen.org
URL: http://www.dekalb100blackmen.org

4150 ■ 100 Black Men of Macon-Middle, Georgia
1680 Broadway
Macon, GA 31201

Contact: Tom Sands, Pres.
URL: http://www.100Blackmen-macon.com

4151 ■ 100 Black Men of North Metro
2300 Holcomb Bridge Rd., Ste. 103-215
Roswell, GA 30076
Contact: Harold Hamilton, Chm./Pres.
Ph: (678)688-4130
E-mail: harold.hamilton@northmetro100.org
URL: http://www.northmetro100.org
Fnd: 1992.

4152 ■ 100 Black Men of Rome
41 Washington Dr. SE
Rome, GA 30161-5566
URL: http://www.100bmor.org
Fnd: 1994.

4153 ■ 100 Black Men of South Metro
6338 Church St.
Riverdale, GA 30274
Contact: Mr. Charles Reddick, Pres.-Elect
Ph: (770)996-0314
Fax: (770)996-0315
E-mail: 100blksm@bellsouth.net
URL: http://www.100blackmensouthmetro.org
Fnd: 1991.

4154 ■ Albany Arc
PO Box 71026
Albany, GA 31708
Contact: Annette Bowling
Ph: (229)888-6852
E-mail: abowling@albanyarc.org
URL: http://www.thearcofgeorgia.org

4155 ■ American Association of University Women, Atlanta Branch
3542 Cedar Corners Pl.
Norcross, GA 30092
Contact: Diana Witt, Co-Pres.
Ph: (770)448-0887
E-mail: info@aauwatlanta.org
URL: http://www.aauwatlanta.org
Descr: Advances equity for women and girls through advocacy, education, and research. Provides funds and a support system for women seeking judicial redress for sex discrimination in higher education.

4156 ■ American Medical Student Association, Emory University School of Medicine
1440 Clifton Rd. NE
Atlanta, GA 30322
Contact: Thomas J. Lawley MD
Ph: (404)727-5640
Fax: (404)727-0473
URL: http://www.med.emory.edu/index.cfm
Descr: Promotes improvement in medical training and education. Advances the medicine profession. Contributes to the welfare of medical students, interns, residents and post-MD/DO trainees.

4157 ■ American Medical Student Association, Mercer University School of Medicine
1550 College St.
Macon, GA 31207
Contact: Dona L. Harris, Assoc. Dean
Free: 800-342-0841
E-mail: harris_d@mercer.edu
URL: http://medicine.mercer.edu
Descr: Promotes improvement in medical training and education. Advances the medicine profession. Contributes to the welfare of medical students, interns, residents and post-MD/DO trainees.

4158 ■ American Medical Student Association, Morehouse School of Medicine
720 Westview Dr. SW
Atlanta, GA 30310
Contact: John E. Maupin Jr., Pres.
Ph: (404)752-1500
URL: http://www.msm.edu
Descr: Promotes improvement in medical training and education. Advances the medicine profession.

Contributes to the welfare of medical students, interns, residents and post-MD/DO trainees.

4159 ■ Arc of Baldwin County - Georgia
PO Box 644
Milledgeville, GA 31059
Contact: Barbara Coleman, Exec. Dir.
Ph: (478)445-5726
E-mail: bcoleman@baldwinservicecenter.org

4160 ■ Arc of Bleckley County
PO Box 496
Cochran, GA 31014
Contact: Jerry Sapp, Pres.
Ph: (478)934-3578
E-mail: jsapp108@bellsouth.net
URL: http://www.thearcofgeorgia.org

4161 ■ Arc of Brooks County
1200 Roundtree St.
Quitman, GA 31643
Contact: Linda P. Peterson, Pres.
Ph: (229)263-9302
E-mail: lppeterson@dhr.state.us
URL: http://www.thearcofgeorgia.org

4162 ■ Arc of Carroll County - Georgia
PO Box 762
Carrollton, GA 30112
Contact: Bobby Holcombe, Exec. Dir.
Ph: (770)834-6232
E-mail: arccarroll@charterinternet.com
URL: http://www.thearcofgeorgia.org

4163 ■ Arc of Clayton County
5303 West St.
Forest Park, GA 30297
Contact: Virginia Ford, Pres.
Ph: (404)363-8494
E-mail: freemanvirginia@bellsouth.net

4164 ■ Arc of Effingham County
PO Box 219
Eden, GA 31307
Contact: Nina Dasher, Pres.
Ph: (912)748-4415
E-mail: dasherdasher9@aol.com

4165 ■ Arc of Georgia
PO Box 2987
Atlanta, GA 30301
Contact: Deirdre O'Brien, Exec. Dir.
Ph: (678)904-1967
Free: 888-303-0024
E-mail: info@thearcofgeorgia.org
URL: http://www.thearcofgeorgia.org

4166 ■ Arc of Liberty
PO Box 908
Hinesville, GA 31310
Ph: (912)320-7599
E-mail: glw.1950@gmail.com

4167 ■ Arc Macon
4664 Sheraton Dr.
Macon, GA 31210
Contact: Andy Harrell, Exec. Dir.
Ph: (478)477-7764
E-mail: aharrell@maconarc.org
URL: http://www.arc-macon.org

4168 ■ Arc of Northeast Georgia
PO Box 478
Demorest, GA 30535
Contact: Dorothy F. Parsons, Pres.
Ph: (706)776-8023
E-mail: jmcferrin@piedmont.edu

4169 ■ Arc of Satilla
PO Box 217
Waycross, GA 31502
Contact: Leslie Meeks, Pres.
Ph: (912)550-1160

E-mail: info@thearcofsatilla.org
URL: http://www.thearcofsatilla.org

4170 ■ Arc of Tattnall and Evans Counties
PO Box 266
Glennville, GA 30427
Contact: Janice A. Brannen
Ph: (912)654-4293
E-mail: jan@g-net.net
URL: http://www.thearcofgeorgia.org

4171 ■ Arc of Telfair County
PO Box 277
Helena, GA 31037
Ph: (229)868-0023
URL: http://www.thearcofgeorgia.org

4172 ■ Arc of Toombs County
PO Box 27
Lyons, GA 30436
Contact: Roy Stewart, Exec. Dir.
Ph: (912)526-3263

4173 ■ Arc of Upson County
PO Box 1093
Thomaston, GA 30286
Contact: Jim R. Aaron, Pres.
Ph: (706)647-5020
E-mail: gilmorec@windstream.net
URL: http://www.thearcofgeorgia.org

4174 ■ Arc of Walker County - Georgia
PO Box 438
La Fayette, GA 30728
Contact: Wesley Clark, Exec. Dir.
Ph: (706)638-0962
E-mail: arcwalker@windstream.net
URL: http://www.thearcofgeorgia.org

4175 ■ Autism Society of America - Greater Georgia Chapter (ASA-GGC)
PO Box 3707
Suwanee, GA 30024
Contact: Steve Doran, Pres.
Ph: (770)904-4474
Fax: (770)904-4476
E-mail: ga-greatergeorgia@autismsocietyofamerica.org
URL: http://www.asaga.com
Descr: Seeks to improve the lives of individuals affected by autism. Promotes awareness and understanding of autism disorders. Aims to further the advancement of preventive studies, therapy and research of autism disorders.

4176 ■ A Better Chance, Southeast
PO Box 43672
Atlanta, GA 30336
Contact: Ivonne A. Simms, Program Coor.
Ph: (404)344-9115
Fax: (678)302-6908
Descr: Identifies, recruits, and places academically talented and motivated minority students into leading independent secondary schools and selected public schools.

4177 ■ Common Cause Georgia
5115 New Peachtree Rd., Ste. 200
Atlanta, GA 30341
Contact: Bill Bozarth, Exec. Dir.
Ph: (770)986-4200
Fax: (678)547-0756
E-mail: ccga@commoncause.org
Descr: Aims to fight for open, honest, and accountable government at the national, state, and local levels. Gathers and disseminates information on the effects of money in politics; lobbies for political finance and other campaign reforms.

4178 ■ Communities in Schools of Georgia (CISGA)
600 W Peachtree St., Ste. 1200
Atlanta, GA 30308
Contact: Mr. Neil Shorthouse, Pres.
Ph: (404)888-5784
Free: 800-838-5784

Fax: (404)888-5789
E-mail: nshorthouse@cisga.org
URL: http://www.cisga.org
Staff: 33. **Descr:** Helps kids succeed in school and prepare them for life. **Fnd:** 1989.

4179 ■ Georgia AfterSchool Investment Council (GAIC)
100 Edgewood Ave. NE, 3rd Fl.
Atlanta, GA 30303
Contact: Jill J. Reimer, Exec. Dir.
Ph: (404)527-7250
Fax: (404)527-7353
E-mail: jreimer@afterschoolga.org
URL: http://www.afterschoolga.org

4180 ■ Georgia Association for Career and Technical Education (GACTE)
PO Box 443
Kennesaw, GA 30156
Contact: Tim Cockrell, Pres.
Ph: (678)461-0006
Fax: (706)628-4335
E-mail: cockrell-t@harris.k12.ga.us
URL: http://www.gacte.org
Descr: Conducts lobbying activities; represents members' interests. Delivers professional staff development. **Fnd:** 1923. **Mem:** 1200. **State Groups:** 10. **Pub:** *GACTE News* (quarterly).

4181 ■ Georgia Association on Higher Education and Disability
Georgia Perimeter College
555 N Indian Creek Dr.
Clarkston, GA 30021-2396
Contact: Elaine Manglitz PhD, Pres.
Ph: (678)891-3385
Fax: (404)298-3830
E-mail: elainemanglitz@mail.clayton.edu
URL: http://www.ga-ahead.org
Descr: Represents individuals interested in promoting the equal rights and opportunities of disabled postsecondary students, staff, faculty and graduates. Provides educational and professional development opportunities for persons with disabilities in postsecondary education. Encourages and supports legislation for the benefit of disabled students.

4182 ■ Georgia Association on Higher Education and Disability, Central Region
Columbus State University
4225 University Ave.
Columbus, GA 31907
Contact: Joy Norman, Rep.
Ph: (706)568-2330
Fax: (706)569-3096
E-mail: norman_joy@colstate.edu
URL: http://www.ga-ahead.org
Descr: Represents individuals interested in promoting the equal rights and opportunities of disabled postsecondary students, staff, faculty and graduates. Provides educational and professional development opportunities for persons with disabilities in postsecondary education. Encourages and supports legislation for the benefit of disabled students.

4183 ■ Georgia Association on Higher Education and Disability, Northeast Region
Clayton Station University
5900 N Lee St.
Morrow, GA 30260
Contact: Elaine Manglitz PhD, Pres.
Ph: (678)466-5448
Fax: (229)333-2153
E-mail: elainemanglitz@mail.clayton.edu
URL: http://www.ga-ahead.org
Descr: Represents individuals interested in promoting the equal rights and opportunities of disabled postsecondary students, staff, faculty and graduates. Provides educational and professional development opportunities for persons with disabilities in postsec-

ondary education. Encourages and supports legislation for the benefit of disabled students.

4184 ■ Georgia Association on Higher Education and Disability, Northwest Region
Berry College
Box 5043
Mount Berry, GA 30149
Contact: Martha Van Cise, Rep.
Ph: (706)233-4080
Fax: (706)368-6969
E-mail: mvancise@berry.edu
URL: http://www.ga-ahead.org
Descr: Represents individuals interested in promoting the equal rights and opportunities of disabled postsecondary students, staff, faculty and graduates. Provides educational and professional development opportunities for persons with disabilities in postsecondary education. Encourages and supports legislation for the benefit of disabled students.

4185 ■ Georgia Association on Higher Education and Disability, Southwest Region
PO Box 21
Tifton, GA 31793-2601
Contact: Cheryl Biggs, Rep.
Ph: (229)386-3489
Fax: (229)386-3579
E-mail: cbiggs@abac.edu
URL: http://www.ga-ahead.org
Descr: Represents individuals interested in promoting the equal rights and opportunities of disabled postsecondary students, staff, faculty and graduates. Provides educational and professional development opportunities for persons with disabilities in postsecondary education. Encourages and supports legislation for the benefit of disabled students.

4186 ■ Georgia Association on Young Children (GAYC)
368 Moreland Ave. NE, Ste. 240
Atlanta, GA 30307-1927
Contact: Hilda Tompkins, Pres.
Ph: (404)222-0014
Fax: (404)222-0107
E-mail: gayc@algxmail.com
URL: http://gayconline.org
Staff: 5. **Descr:** Works to address the needs of Georgia's children, birth through age eight. Provides members opportunities to increase their knowledge of young children and to enhance their professional experience through an annual conference, career counseling, child care center technical assistance, Director and Teacher Institutes, Training for Trainers course, seminars and "Month of the Young Child" outreach. **Fnd:** 1966. **Mem:** 1700. **Pub:** *Book of Forms*; *Careers in Childhood Care and Education*; *Young Children* (bimonthly).

4187 ■ Georgia Branch of the International Dyslexia Association
1951 Greystone Rd.
Atlanta, GA 30318
Contact: Ann Marie Lewis, Outreach Coor.
Ph: (404)256-1232
E-mail: info@idaga.org
URL: http://www.idaga.org
Descr: Promotes public awareness and understanding of dyslexia. Seeks to develop and implement specialized methods to improve the quality of life for people who have dyslexia. **Mem:** 300.

4188 ■ Georgia Department of Education
2054 Twin Towers E.
205 Jesse Hill Jr. Dr., SE
Atlanta, GA 30334
Contact: Kathy Cox, State Supt.
Ph: (404)656-2800
Free: 800-311-3627
Fax: (404)651-6867
E-mail: state.superintendent@doe.k12.ga.us
URL: http://public.doe.k12.ga.us/index.aspx

Pub: E-newsletter.

4189 ■ Georgia National Congress of Parents and Teachers
114 Baker St. NE
Atlanta, GA 30308-3366
Ph: (404)659-0214
Fax: (404)525-0210
E-mail: ga_office@pta.org

4190 ■ Georgia Unit of Recording for the Blind and Dyslexic
120 Florida Ave.
Athens, GA 30605
Contact: Lenora Martin, Exec. Dir.
Ph: (706)549-1313
E-mail: lmartin@rfbd.org
URL: http://www.rfbd.org/GA/index.html
Descr: Serves individuals who cannot effectively read standard print because of visual impairment, dyslexia, or other physical disabilities. Creates educational opportunities for students with print disabilities through educational and outreach services. Provides and promotes the effective use of accessible educational materials.

4191 ■ Governor's Council on Developmental Disabilities for Georgia
GCDD 2 Peachtree St., Ste. 26-240
Atlanta, GA 30303
Contact: Tom Seegmueller, Vice Chm.
Ph: (404)657-2126
Free: 888-275-4233
E-mail: info@gcdd.org
URL: http://www.gcdd.org
Descr: Collaborates with Georgia citizens, public and private advocacy organizations, and policy makers to positively influence public policies that enhance the quality of life for people with developmental disabilities and their families. Provides collaboration through education and advocacy activities, program implementation and funding, and public policy analysis and research.

4192 ■ Irwin County Arc
PO Box 614
Ocilla, GA 31774
Contact: Richard Murphy, Exec. Dir.
Ph: (229)468-9886
E-mail: icrcc@alltel.net

4193 ■ Learning Disabilities Association of Georgia (LDAG)
2566 Shallowford Rd., Ste. 104
PMB 353
Atlanta, GA 30345
Ph: (404)303-7774
Fax: (404)467-0190
E-mail: ldaga@bellsouth.net
URL: http://www.ldag.org
Descr: Parents, professionals, individuals with learning disabilities. Strives to advance the education and general well being of children and adults with learning disabilities and their families. Shares knowledge, disseminates information and seeks to affect policies related to learning disabilities. **Fnd:** 1966. **Pub:** *The LDAG Advocate*.

4194 ■ Newnan-Coweta Arc (NCARC)
61 Hospital Rd.
Newnan, GA 30263
Contact: Bobby W. Welch, Exec. Dir.
Ph: (770)253-1189
E-mail: bwelch@numail.org
URL: http://www.rutledgecenter.org
Staff: 18. **Descr:** Serves and promotes the general welfare of the mentally handicapped and developmentally disabled citizens. Advocates, obtains, and provides services, which will enhance development of human dignity and growth toward self-sufficiency.

Develops better public awareness and understanding of mental retardation. **Fnd:** 1968. **Mem:** 200.

4195 ■ South Eastern Association of Educational Opportunity Program Personnel (SAE-OPP)
Atlanta Metropolitan College
1630 Metropolitan Pkwy.
Atlanta, GA 30310
Contact: Camille Zeigler, Pres.
Ph: (404)756-4789
Fax: (404)756-4946
E-mail: czeigler@atlm.edu
URL: http://saeopp.org
Descr: Works to advance educational opportunities for disadvantaged students in colleges and universities. Provides professional development and continuing education. Monitors federal legislation designed to serve disadvantaged students.

4196 ■ Special Olympics Georgia (SOGA)
4000 Dekalb Technology Pkwy., Bldg. 400, Ste. 400
Atlanta, GA 30340
Contact: Georgia Milton-Sheats, CEO
Ph: (770)414-9390
Free: 800-866-4400
Fax: (770)216-8339
E-mail: georgia.milton-sheats@specialolympicsga.org
URL: http://www.specialolympicsga.org
Descr: Works to provide year-round sports training and athletic competition in a variety of Olympic-type sports for children and adults with intellectual disabilities, giving them continuing opportunities to develop physical fitness, demonstrate courage, experience joy, and participate in the sharing of gifts, skills, and friendship with their families, other Special Olympics athletes and the community. **Fnd:** 1970. **Pub:** *Olympian* (3/year).

Hawaii

4197 ■ American Medical Student Association, University of Hawaii at Manoa John A. Burns School of Medicine
651 Ilalo St.
Medical Education Bldg.
Honolulu, HI 96813
Contact: Gary Ostrander, Interim Dean
Ph: (808)692-1000
URL: http://jabsom.hawaii.edu/jabsom
Descr: Promotes improvement in medical training and education. Advances the medicine profession. Contributes to the welfare of medical students, interns, residents and post-MD/DO trainees.

4198 ■ Arc in Hawaii
3989 Diamond Head Rd.
Honolulu, HI 96816
Ph: (808)737-7995
Fax: (808)732-9531
E-mail: info@thearcinhawaii.org
URL: http://www.thearcinhawaii.org
Descr: Strives to improve the lives of people with mental retardation through advocacy, service delivery, education and prevention. **Fnd:** 1954.

4199 ■ Arc of Hilo
1099 Waianuenue Ave.
Hilo, HI 96720
Contact: Debora Cabarloc, Chief Financial Off.
Ph: (808)935-8534
Fax: (808)961-0148
E-mail: info@hiloarc.org
URL: http://www.hiloarc.org
Descr: Parents, professional workers, and others interested in individuals with mental retardation. Works to promote services, research, public understanding, and legislation for people with mental retardation and their families.

4200 ■ Arc of Kauai
3201 Akahi St.
Lihue, HI 96766
Contact: Ellen Ching, Exec. Dir.
Ph: (808)245-4132

E-mail: arckjamie@viphawaii.net
URL: http://www.thearcinhawaii.org

4201 ■ Arc of Maui
95 Mahalani St., Cameron Center
Wailuku, HI 96793
Ph: (808)242-5781
Descr: Parents, professional workers, and others interested in individuals with mental retardation. Works to promote services, research, public understanding, and legislation for people with mental retardation and their families.

4202 ■ Autism Society of Hawaii
PO Box 2995
Honolulu, HI 96802
Contact: Evelyn Akamine
Ph: (808)282-3676
E-mail: hi-hawaii@autismsocietyofamerica.org
Descr: Seeks to improve the lives of individuals affected by autism. Promotes awareness and understanding of autism disorders. Aims to further the advancement of preventive studies, therapy and research of autism disorders.

4203 ■ Hawaii Association for Career and Technical Education
2257 Kapahu St.
Honolulu, HI 96813
Contact: Mr. Dirk Soma, Pres.
Ph: (808)956-5714
Fax: (808)956-3918
E-mail: dirksoma@yahoo.com
URL: http://www.acteonline.org/content.aspx?id=782
Descr: Aims to advance education that prepares youth and adults for careers. **Pub:** *ACTE News* (monthly).

4204 ■ Hawaii Association for the Education of Young Children
1806 S King St., Ste. 30
Honolulu, HI 96826
Contact: Wayne Watkins, Pres.
Ph: (808)942-4708
Free: 888-224-2392
Fax: (808)955-2739
E-mail: info@hawaiiaeyc.org
URL: http://www.hawaiiaeyc.org
Descr: Strives to promote, support, and expand quality and professionalism in early childhood programs and services for young children (0-8) and their families. **Fnd:** 1974. **Mem:** 900. **Local Groups:** 4. **Pub:** *Young Children Journal* (bimonthly); Newsletter (quarterly).

4205 ■ Hawaii Association for the Education of Young Children, Hawaii Island Chapter (HAEYC-HIC)
PO Box 384807
Waikoloa, HI 96738
Contact: Hilda Gonzales
E-mail: bigisland@hawaiiaeyc.org
URL: http://www.hawaiiaeyc.org
Descr: Teachers and directors of preschool and primary schools, kindergartens, child care centers, and other early learning programs for young childhood; early childhood education and child development educators, trainers, and researchers and other professionals dedicated to young children's healthy development.

4206 ■ Hawaii Association for the Education of Young Children, Oahu Chapter
45-284 Pahikaua St.
Kaneohe, HI 96744
Contact: Robyn Chun, Rep.
E-mail: oahu@hawaiiaeyc.org
URL: http://www.hawaiiaeyc.org
Descr: Teachers and directors of preschool and primary schools, kindergartens, child care centers, and early other learning programs for young childhood; early childhood education and child development educators, trainers, and researchers and other

professionals dedicated to young children's healthy development.

4207 ■ Hawaii Branch of the International Dyslexia Association (HIDA)
1802A Ke'eaumoku St., Office No. 2
Honolulu, HI 96822
Contact: Sue Voit, Pres.
Ph: (808)538-7007
Free: 866-773-4432
Fax: (808)538-7009
E-mail: hida@dyslexia-hawaii.org
URL: http://www.dyslexia-hawaii.org
Descr: Promotes public awareness and understanding of dyslexia. Seeks to develop and implement specialized methods to improve the quality of life for people who have dyslexia. Provides services to those affected by dyslexia, attention disorders and other learning disabilities.

4208 ■ Hawaii Department of Education
PO Box 2360
Honolulu, HI 96804
Contact: Patricia Hamamoto, Superintendent
Ph: (808)586-3230
Fax: (808)586-3234
E-mail: doe_info@notes.k12.hi.us
URL: http://doe.k12.hi.us/
Mem: 14. **Pub:** *BOE Highlights*; *Na Lono Kula*; *InfoExchange*.

4209 ■ Hawaii State PTSA
PO Box 22878
Honolulu, HI 96823-2878
Contact: Valerie Sonoda, Pres.
Ph: (808)593-2042
Free: 877-834-7872
Fax: (808)593-2041
E-mail: hi_office@hawaiiantel.net
URL: http://www.hawaiiptsa.org
Descr: Strives to support and speak on behalf of young people, help parents to develop the skills in protecting and raising children and encourage parents in public involvement. **Fnd:** 1926.

4210 ■ Kona Arc
PO Box 127
Kealakekua, HI 96750
Ph: (808)323-2626
Descr: Parents, professional workers, and others interested in individuals with mental retardation. Works to promote services, research, public understanding, and legislation for people with mental retardation and their families.

4211 ■ Learning Disabilities Association of Hawaii (LDAH)
245 N Kukui St., Ste. 205
Honolulu, HI 96817
Contact: Michael K. Moore, Exec. Dir.
Ph: (808)536-9684
Free: 800-533-9684
Fax: (808)537-6780
E-mail: mmoore@ldahawaii.org
URL: http://www.ldahawaii.org

4212 ■ Special Olympics Hawaii
PO Box 3295
Honolulu, HI 96801
Contact: Nancy Bottelo, Pres./CEO
Ph: (808)943-8808
Free: 888-531-1888
Fax: (808)943-8814
E-mail: ceo@specialolympicshawaii.org
URL: http://www.specialolympicshawaii.org
Descr: Promotes physical fitness, sports training, and athletic competition for children and adults with mental retardation. Seeks to contribute to the physical, social, and psychological development of persons with mental retardation. Participants range in age from 8 years to adult and compete in track and field, swimming, gymnastics, bowling, ice skating, basketball, and other sports.

Idaho

4213 ■ AG BELL, Idaho
228 E Plaza St., Ste. B, PMB 210
Eagle, ID 83616
Contact: Pam Vannoy, Pres.
Ph: (208)939-3321
E-mail: mpvanfam@aol.com
URL: http://www.idahoagbell.org
Descr: Represents the interests of educators, parents of children with hearing loss, adults with hearing loss and hearing health professionals. Provides governmental and education advocacy services.

4214 ■ American Association of University Women, Boise Area Branch
2252 Interlachen Way
Meridian, ID 83646-9036
Contact: Noreen Pusey, Treas.
E-mail: pusey2@hotmail.com
URL: http://www.aauwidaho.org/boise.htm
Descr: Advances equity for women and girls through advocacy, education, and research. Provides funds and a support system for women seeking judicial redress for sex discrimination in higher education.

4215 ■ Arc of Latah County
1407 View St.
Moscow, ID 83843
Contact: Nancy Johansen, Pres.
Ph: (208)883-1469

4216 ■ Autism Society of America, Treasure Valley Chapter (ASATVC)
PO Box 44831
Boise, ID 83711
Contact: Paul Tierney
Ph: (208)336-5676
E-mail: info@asatvc.org
URL: http://www.asatvc.org
Descr: Seeks to improve the lives of individuals affected by autism. Promotes awareness and understanding of autism disorders. Aims to further the advancement of preventive studies, therapy and research of autism disorders.

4217 ■ Idaho Association for the Education of Young Children
1471 Shoreline Dr., Ste. 202
Boise, ID 83702
Contact: Karen Mason, Exec. Dir.
Ph: (208)344-6155
Free: 800-706-2320
Fax: (208)345-6569
E-mail: kmason@idahoaeyc.org
URL: http://www.idahoaeyc.org
Staff: 1. **Descr:** Represents teachers and directors of preschool and primary schools, kindergartens, child care centers, cooperatives, church schools, and groups having similar programs for young children; early childhood education and child development educators, trainers, and researchers. Open to all individuals interested in serving and acting on behalf of the needs and rights of young children, with primary focus on the provision of educational services and resources. **Fnd:** 1986. **Mem:** 500. **State Groups:** 1.

4218 ■ Idaho Department of Education
650 W. State St.
PO Box 83720
Boise, ID 83720-0027
Contact: Tom Luna, Superintendent
Ph: (208)332-6800
Free: 800-432-4601
Fax: (208)334-2228
E-mail: news@sde.state.id.us
URL: http://www.sde.idaho.gov/
Descr: Supports and promotes a system of public

education that delivers relevant academic and life skills.

4219 ■ Idaho State Council on Developmental Disabilities
802 W Bannock, Ste. 308
Boise, ID 83702-5840
Contact: Marilyn B. Sword, Exec. Dir.
Ph: (208)334-2178
Free: 800-544-2433
Fax: (208)334-3417
E-mail: icdd@icdd.idaho.gov
URL: http://www.icdd.idaho.gov

Descr: Promotes the capacity of people with developmental disabilities and their families to determine, access and direct the services and/or support they need to live the lives they choose, and to build the communities' ability to support their choices.

4220 ■ Learning Disabilities Association of Idaho
9797 N Circle Dr.
Hayden, ID 83835
Contact: Ginny Hughes
Ph: (208)762-2316
E-mail: connect4kids@imbris.com

4221 ■ Panhandle Autism Society (PAS)
PO Box 3950
Coeur d'Alene, ID 83816
Contact: Tracy Hofius, Exec. Dir.
Ph: (208)661-4950
E-mail: info@panhandleautism.org
URL: http://www.panhandleautism.org

Descr: Seeks to improve the lives of individuals affected by autism. Promotes awareness and understanding of autism disorders. Aims to further the advancement of preventive studies, therapy and research of autism disorders.

4222 ■ Special Olympics Idaho (SOID)
405 S 8th St., Ste. 1-201
Boise, ID 83702
Contact: Laurie LaFollette, CEO
Ph: (208)323-0482
Free: 800-234-3658
Fax: (208)323-0486
E-mail: llafollette@idso.org
URL: http://www.idso.org

Descr: Strives to provide year-round sports training and athletic competition in a variety of Olympic-type sports for persons 8 years old and older with mental retardation, to give them continuing opportunities to develop physical fitness, demonstrate courage, experience joy and participate in the sharing of gifts, skills and friendship with their families, other Special Olympic athletes and the community. Sports include alpine skiing, athletics, aquatics, basketball, bowling, cycling, equestrian, golf, Nordic skiing, powerlifting, snowshoeing and softball. **Fnd:** 1972. **Mem:** 1600. **Pub:** *Games Program* (3/year); *Torch Run* (annual); Annual Report (annual).

4223 ■ Sun Valley Adaptive Sports Programs (SVASP)
PO Box 6791
Ketchum, ID 83340
Contact: Mr. Tom Iselin, Exec. Dir.
Ph: (208)726-9298
Fax: (208)726-0957
E-mail: info@svasp.org
URL: http://www.svasp.org

Staff: 4. **Fnd:** 1999.

Illinois

4224 ■ 100 Black Men of Chicago
3473 S Martin Luther King Jr. Dr., Ste. 206
Chicago, IL 60616
Contact: Jeffrey L. Jackson, Pres.
Ph: (312)461-2673
Fax: (312)765-1750

E-mail: admin@100bmc.org
URL: http://www.100bmc.org

4225 ■ Access Living
115 W Chicago Ave.
Chicago, IL 60610
Contact: Marca Bristo, Pres./CEO
Ph: (312)640-2100
Free: 800-613-8549
Fax: (312)640-2101
E-mail: generalinfo@accessliving.org
URL: http://www.accessliving.org

Staff: 51. **Descr:** Fosters the dignity, inclusion, and independence of people with disabilities through peer oriented independent living services; public education and awareness; individualized and systematic advocacy; and enforcement of civil rights on behalf of people with disabilities. **Fnd:** 1980. **Pub:** *The Bullhorn* (3/year); *Shunted Aside Hidden and Ignored*; *Terri Schiavo Brief*; Annual Report; Brochures.

4226 ■ Access Services of Northern Illinois
7399 Forest Hills Rd.
Loves Park, IL 61111-3974
Contact: Matthew Toohey, Exec. Dir.
Ph: (815)282-8824
Fax: (815)282-8835
E-mail: info@accessni.com
URL: http://www.accessni.com

Staff: 1. **Descr:** Works to empower and assist individuals with developmental disabilities to participate as full citizens in their community by coordination and advocating for community services and supports of their choice.

4227 ■ American Association of University Women, Carbondale Branch
1 Hillcrest Dr.
Carbondale, IL 62901
Contact: Mary K. Cook-Wallace
Ph: (618)453-1961
E-mail: mreekat@siu.edu
URL: http://web.coehs.siu.edu/wed/wallace/aauw/ aauw page.htm

Descr: Advances equity for women and girls through advocacy, education, and research. Provides funds and a support system for women seeking judicial redress for sex discrimination in higher education.

4228 ■ American Association of University Women, Chicago Branch
2746 W Morse Ave.
Chicago, IL 60645
Contact: Lori Switzer, Pres.
Ph: (773)465-1148
E-mail: chicagoaauw@hotmail.com
URL: http://aauw-il.org/chicago

Descr: Advances equity for women and girls through advocacy, education, and research. Provides funds and a support system for women seeking judicial redress for sex discrimination in higher education. **Fnd:** 1889.

4229 ■ American Association of University Women, Decatur Branch
3776 Ashley Ct.
Decatur, IL 62526
Contact: Alice Huebner, Pres.
E-mail: ahuebner@prodigy.net
URL: http://www.millikin.edu/aauw

Descr: Advances equity for women and girls through advocacy, education, and research. Provides funds and a support system for women seeking judicial redress for sex discrimination in higher education.

4230 ■ American Association of University Women, Downers Grove Area Branch
PO Box 694
Downers Grove, IL 60515
Ph: (630)415-2531
E-mail: dgaauw@yahoo.com
URL: http://sites.google.com/site/dgaauw

Descr: Advances equity for women and girls through advocacy, education, and research. Provides funds and a support system for women seeking judicial

redress for sex discrimination in higher education. **Fnd:** 1949.

4231 ■ American Association of University Women, Lombard Area Branch
126 S Chase Ave.
Lombard, IL 60148-2904
Contact: Loretta Caputo, Pres.
E-mail: grannylori1@sbcglobal.net
URL: http://aauw-il.org/lombard

Descr: Advances equity for women and girls through advocacy, education, and research. Provides funds and a support system for women seeking judicial redress for sex discrimination in higher education. **Fnd:** 1959.

4232 ■ American Medical Student Association, Loyola University Chicago Stritch School of Medicine
2160 S 1st Ave.
Maywood, IL 60153
Ph: (708)216-3229

Descr: Promotes improvement in medical training and education. Advances the medicine profession. Contributes to the welfare of medical students, interns, residents and post-MD/DO trainees.

4233 ■ American Medical Student Association, Midwestern University's Chicago College of Osteopathic Medicine
555 31st St.
Downers Grove, IL 60515
Ph: (630)515-6470
URL: http://www.midwestern.edu/ccom

Descr: Promotes improvement in medical training and education. Advances the medicine profession. Contributes to the welfare of medical students, interns, residents and post-MD/DO trainees.

4234 ■ American Medical Student Association, Northwestern University, Feinberg School of Medicine
303 E Chicago Ave.
Chicago, IL 60611-3008
Ph: (312)503-0440
Fax: (312)503-0438
URL: http://www.feinberg.northwestern.edu

Descr: Promotes improvement in medical training and education. Advances the medicine profession. Contributes to the welfare of medical students, interns, residents and post-MD/DO trainees.

4235 ■ American Medical Student Association, Rosalind Franklin University of Medicine and Science
3333 Green Bay Rd.
North Chicago, IL 60064
Contact: Sarah R. Florence, Pres.
Ph: (847)578-3000
E-mail: amsa@rfums.org
URL: http://www.rosalindfranklin.edu

Descr: Promotes improvement in medical training and education. Advances the medicine profession. Contributes to the welfare of medical students, interns, residents and post-MD/DO trainees.

4236 ■ American Medical Student Association, Rush Medical College Rush University Medical Center
600 S Paulina St., Ste. 440
Chicago, IL 60612
Contact: Sara Englum
E-mail: sara_englum@rush.edu
URL: http://www.rushu.rush.edu/medcol

Descr: Promotes improvement in medical training and education. Advances the medicine profession. Contributes to the welfare of medical students, interns, residents and post-MD/DO trainees.

4237 ■ American Medical Student Association, Southern Illinois University School of Medicine
PO Box 19624
Springfield, IL 62794
Contact: Jason A. Kegg, Pres.
Ph: (217)545-2860
URL: http://www.siumed.edu

Descr: Promotes improvement in medical training and education. Advances the medicine profession. Contributes to the welfare of medical students, interns, residents and post-MD/DO trainees.

4238 ■ American Medical Student Association, University of Illinois College of Medicine at Chicago
1853 W Polk St.
MC 785
Chicago, IL 60612-7332
Contact: Shannon Stanley
Ph: (312)996-2450
E-mail: sestaley@uic.edu
URL: http://chicago.medicine.uic.edu

Descr: Promotes improvement in medical training and education. Advances the medicine profession. Contributes to the welfare of medical students, interns, residents and post-MD/DO trainees.

4239 ■ American Medical Student Association, University of Illinois College of Medicine at Urbana-Champaign
Office of Student Affairs
125 Medical Sciences Bldg.
506 S Mathews Ave.
Urbana, IL 61801
Contact: J.D. Cross, Co-Pres./Sec.
Ph: (217)333-8146
Fax: (217)333-2640
E-mail: jcross@nospamuiuc.edu
URL: http://www.med.uiuc.edu/studorg/amsa

Descr: Promotes improvement in medical training and education. Advances the medicine profession. Contributes to the welfare of medical students, interns, residents and post-MD/DO trainees.

4240 ■ American Medical Student's Association, The University of Chicago Pritzker School of Medicine
924 E 57th St., Ste. 104
Chicago, IL 60637-5415
Contact: Celine Goetz
E-mail: cgoetz@uchicago.edu
URL: http://pritzker.bsd.uchicago.edu

Descr: Promotes improvement in medical training and education. Advances the medicine profession. Contributes to the welfare of medical students, interns, residents and post-MD/DO trainees.

4241 ■ Arc of Adams County - Illinois
PO Box 3602
Quincy, IL 62305
Contact: Signe Oakley, Pres.
Ph: (217)224-8328
URL: http://www.thearcofil.org

4242 ■ Arc of Iroquois County
700 E Elm St.
Watseka, IL 60970
Ph: (815)432-5288
Fax: (815)432-5288
E-mail: info@thearcirq.org
URL: http://www.thearcirq.org

4243 ■ Arc of Lee County
PO Box 366
Dixon, IL 61021
Contact: Arlan McClain, Exec. Dir.
Ph: (815)288-6691
Fax: (815)288-1636
E-mail: adelmanc@kreiderservices.org
URL: http://www.thearcofil.org

4244 ■ Arc of Winnebago, Boone and Ogle
1222 E State St.
Rockford, IL 61104
Contact: Jackie Neil Boss, Exec. Dir.
Ph: (815)965-3455
Fax: (815)965-3673
E-mail: jackinb@arcwbo.org
URL: http://www.arcwbo.org

Descr: Parents, professional workers, and others interested in individuals with mental retardation. Works to promote services, research, public under-

standing, and legislation for people with mental retardation and their families.

4245 ■ Association for the Developmentally Disabled in Woodford County (ADDWC)
200 Moody St.
Eureka, IL 61530
Contact: Tanya Simpson
Ph: (309)467-3015
Fax: (309)467-5206
E-mail: addwc@mtco.com
URL: http://www.addwc.org

Descr: Parents, professional workers, and others interested in individuals with mental retardation. Works to promote services, research, public understanding, and legislation for people with mental retardation and their families.

4246 ■ Autism Society of America - Central Illinois Chapter (ASACIC)
PO Box 8781
Springfield, IL 62791
Contact: Ed Jankauski, Pres.
Ph: (217)241-2023
Fax: (217)241-2023
E-mail: info@asacic.org
URL: http://www.asacic.org

Descr: Seeks to improve the lives of individuals affected by autism. Promotes awareness and understanding of autism disorders. Aims to further the advancement of preventive studies, therapy and research of autism disorders.

4247 ■ Autism Society of America - Metropolitan Chicago Chapter
1550 W 88th St., No. 202A
Chicago, IL 60620
Contact: Grace Dyson, Pres.
Ph: (773)233-4210
E-mail: chicagochapter714@yahoo.com

Descr: Seeks to improve the lives of individuals affected by autism. Promotes awareness and understanding of autism disorders. Aims to further the advancement of preventive studies, therapy and research of autism disorders.

4248 ■ Autism Society of America - North Suburban Illinois Chapter
7503 Wilson Terr.
Morton Grove, IL 60053
Contact: Mr. Richard Fink
Ph: (847)583-5080
E-mail: il-northsuburbanillinois@autismsocietyofamerica.org

Descr: Seeks to improve the lives of individuals affected by autism. Promotes awareness and understanding of autism disorders. Aims to further the advancement of preventive studies, therapy and research of autism disorders.

4249 ■ Autism Society of America - Northeast Illinois Chapter
707 Crossland Dr.
Grayslake, IL 60030
Contact: Eric Smith, Pres./Treas.
Ph: (847)543-4502
E-mail: nechapasi@aol.com
URL: http://www.autism-society.org/site/Clubs?club_id=1160&pg=main

Descr: Seeks to improve the lives of individuals affected by autism. Promotes awareness and understanding of autism disorders. Aims to further the advancement of preventive studies, therapy and research of autism disorders.

4250 ■ Autism Society of America - Peoria Regional Chapter
507 E Armstrong Ave.
Peoria, IL 61615
Contact: Diane Parrish, Co-Pres.
Ph: (309)686-7755
E-mail: peoriaregionalchapterasa@gmail.com
URL: http://www.autism-society.org/site/Clubs?club_id=1460&pg=main

Descr: Seeks to improve the lives of individuals affected by autism. Promotes awareness and understanding of autism disorders. Aims to further the

advancement of preventive studies, therapy and research of autism disorders.

4251 ■ Autism Society of Illinois (ASI)
2200 S Main St., Ste. 205
Lombard, IL 60148
Contact: Constantine Bitsas, Exec. Dir.
Ph: (630)691-1270
Free: 888-691-1270
Fax: (630)691-5620
E-mail: info@autismillinois.org
URL: http://autismillinois.org

Descr: Seeks to improve the lives of individuals affected by autism. Promotes awareness and understanding of autism disorders. Aims to further the advancement of preventive studies, therapy and research of autism disorders.

4252 ■ Autism Society of Southern Illinois
PO Box 822
O'Fallon, IL 62269
Contact: Lois Hull Jordan, Pres.
Ph: (618)530-7894
E-mail: il-southernillinois@autismsocietyofamerica.org

Descr: Seeks to improve the lives of individuals affected by autism. Promotes awareness and understanding of autism disorders. Aims to further the advancement of preventive studies, therapy and research of autism disorders.

4253 ■ Blue Island Citizens for Developmental Disabilities
2155 Broadway
Blue Island, IL 60406
Contact: Anthony Di Vittorio, Exec. Dir.
Ph: (708)389-6578
Fax: (708)389-5086
E-mail: marianne.l@blue-cap.org
URL: http://www.blue-cap.org

Descr: Parents, professional workers, and others interested in individuals with mental retardation. Works to promote services, research, public understanding, and legislation for people with mental retardation and their families.

4254 ■ Champaign PTA Council
703 S New St.
Champaign, IL 61820
Contact: Ms. Nancy Hoetker, Pres.
Ph: (217)355-4891
E-mail: nhoetker@mac.com
URL: http://www.prairienet.org/cpta

Descr: Parents, teachers, students, and others interested in uniting the forces of home, school, and community. Promotes the welfare of children and youth.

4255 ■ Chicago/ARC (CARC)
8 S Michigan Ave., Ste. 1700
Chicago, IL 60603
Contact: Kristin V. Macrae, Pres./CEO
Ph: (312)346-6230
E-mail: relations@chgoarc.org
URL: http://carc.info

Descr: Parents, professional workers, and others interested in individuals with mental retardation. Works to promote services, research, public understanding, and legislation for people with mental retardation and their families. **Pub:** Newsletter (quarterly).

4256 ■ Chicago Metropolitan Association for the Education of Young Children
30 E Adams, Ste. 1000
Chicago, IL 60603
Contact: Gail Conway, Exec. Dir.
Ph: (312)427-5399
Fax: (312)427-5028
E-mail: moderator@chicagometroaeyc.org
URL: http://www.chicagometroaeyc.org

Staff: 8. **Descr:** Strives to improve the quality of services to young children and their families through advocacy, public education, and professional development. **Fnd:** 1962. **Mem:** 2200. **Local Groups:** 2. **Pub:** *Greatest 500 Books*.

4257 ■ Fox Valley Association for the Education of Young Children
2922 Deer Path Ln.
Carpentersville, IL 60110
Contact: Darlene Carlson, Pres.
Ph: (847)836-0116
E-mail: sdcarl817@aol.com
URL: http://www.foxvalleyaeyc.com

Descr: Teachers and directors of preschool and primary schools, kindergartens, child care centers, and other early learning programs for young childhood; early childhood education and child development educators, trainers, and researchers and other professionals dedicated to young children's healthy development.

4258 ■ Great Lakes Adaptive Sports Association (GLASA)
400 E Illinois Rd.
Lake Forest, IL 60045
Contact: Cindy Housner, Exec. Dir.
Ph: (847)283-0908
Fax: (847)283-0973
E-mail: info@glasa.org
URL: http://www.glasa.org

Descr: Aims to promote and support the optimal development and well being for youth and adults who have a primary physical or visual impairment through the provision of inclusive recreational, fitness and competitive sports activities. Seeks to offer opportunities for empowerment through education, leadership, and training in collaboration with community-based organizations. **Fnd:** 1993.

4259 ■ Illinois After-School Partnership
70 E Lake St., Ste. 720
Chicago, IL 60601
Contact: Jennifer Becker Mouhcine
Ph: (312)986-9200
Fax: (312)922-2277
E-mail: iasp@icvp.org
URL: http://www.illinoisafterschool.net
Mem: 250.

4260 ■ Illinois Association for Career and Technical Education (IACTE)
2450 Foundation Dr., Ste. 500
Springfield, IL 62703
Contact: Patti Kozlowski, Pres.
Ph: (217)585-9430
Fax: (217)585-9435
E-mail: info@iacte.org
URL: http://www.iacte.org

Staff: 1. **Descr:** Strives to provide unified, visionary leadership to advance and promote learning in career and technical education.

4261 ■ Illinois Association for the Education of Young Children
3180 Adloff Ln., Ste. 302
Springfield, IL 62703
Contact: Cindy Mahr, Pres.
Ph: (217)529-7732
Free: 800-773-0369
Fax: (217)529-7738
URL: http://www.illinoisaeyc.org

Descr: Advocates for the best childcare and education for all children in the state of Illinois. **Fnd:** 1969.

4262 ■ Illinois Association for Parents of Children with Visual Impairments (IPVI)
PO Box 2947
Naperville, IL 60567-2947
Contact: Mary Zabelski, Pres.
Free: 877-411-4784
E-mail: ipvi@ipvi.org
URL: http://www.ipvi.org

Descr: Represents individuals committed to providing support to the parents of children who have visual impairments. Promotes public understanding of the needs and rights of children who are visually impaired.

4263 ■ Illinois Branch of the International Dyslexia Association (IBIDA)
751 Roosevelt Rd., Ste. 116
Glen Ellyn, IL 60137-5905
Contact: Maureen O'Connor, Pres.
Ph: (630)469-6900
Fax: (630)469-6810
E-mail: info@ibida.org
URL: http://www.readibida.org

Descr: Promotes public awareness and understanding of dyslexia. Seeks to develop and implement specialized methods to improve the quality of life for people who have dyslexia. **Fnd:** 1978. **Pub:** *Toward A Common Goal*.

4264 ■ Illinois Council on Developmental Disabilities (ICDD)
100 W Randolph St., Ste. 10-600
Chicago, IL 60601
Contact: Sheila Romano, Exec. Dir.
Ph: (312)814-2080
Fax: (312)814-7141
E-mail: sromano@mail.state.il.us
URL: http://www.state.il.us/agency/icdd

Staff: 10. **Descr:** Represents parents, professional workers, and others interested in individuals with mental retardation. Works to promote services, research, public understanding, and legislation for people with mental retardation and their families. **Fnd:** 1974. **Mem:** 28.

4265 ■ Illinois Fire Inspectors Association (IFIA)
120 Lageschulte St., Ste. 104
Barrington, IL 60010
Contact: Mario Tristan, Pres.
Ph: (847)756-4750
Fax: (847)756-4752
E-mail: ifia@aol.com
URL: http://www.illinoisfireinspectors.org

Descr: Provides the highest quality codes, standards, products, and services for all concerned with the safety and performance of the built environment.

4266 ■ Illinois State Board of Education
100 N. First St.
Springfield, IL 62777
Contact: Dr. Christopher Koch, Superintendent
Ph: (217)782-4321
Free: 866-262-6663
Fax: (217)524-4928
E-mail: statesup@isbe.net
URL: http://www.isbe.net/

4267 ■ Independent Schools Association of the Central States (ISACS)
1165 N Clark St., Ste. 311
Chicago, IL 60610
Contact: Rick Belding, Pres.
Ph: (312)255-1244
Fax: (312)255-1278
E-mail: rbelding@isacs.org
URL: http://www.isacs.org

Staff: 5. **Descr:** Independent schools including, but not limited to, private prep, special education, boarding, religiously affiliated, and day schools. Strives to foster good relations and communication among member schools and between schools and governmental or public education agencies; promotes the interests and positive public image of independent schools; works to ensure that member schools are serving the public interest; assists member schools in preserving freedoms that enable them to practice their educational philosophies. Maintains and reviews an evaluation/accreditation program (schools are evaluated every seven years). Provides access to other independent school associations and organizations. Monitors relevant federal, state, and regional legislation, regulations, and judicial activity. Maintains speakers' bureau; compiles statistics; sponsors seminars and workshops. **Fnd:** 1909.

Mem: 230. **Pub:** *Accreditation Guide*; Membership Directory (annual).

4268 ■ International Code Council, Illinois State University Student Chapter
Dept. of Tech 5100
Turner Hall, Rm. 210
Campus Box 5100
Normal, IL 61790-5100
Contact: Richard Boser, Faculty Advisor
Ph: (309)438-3661
Fax: (309)438-8626
E-mail: raboser@ilstu.edu

Descr: Provides the highest quality codes, standards, products, and services for all concerned with the safety and performance of the built environment.

4269 ■ Learning Disabilities Association of Illinois
10101 S Roberts Rd., Ste. 205
Palos Hills, IL 60465
Contact: Louise Hullinger, Pres.
Ph: (708)430-7532
Fax: (708)430-7592
E-mail: ldaofil@ameritech.net
URL: http://www.ldail.org

Descr: Dedicated to the advancement of the education and general welfare of children and youth of normal or potentially normal intelligence who have learning disabilities of a perceptual, conceptual or coordinative nature or related problems. Present an annual fall conference. Members receive 4 newsletters a year from state LDA and 6 newsletters a year of national LDA.

4270 ■ Mothers and More DuPage County, Chapter 1
PO Box 2462
Glen Ellyn, IL 60138-2462
Ph: (630)415-0421
E-mail: dupagemandm@yahoo.com
URL: http://www.dupagemothersandmore.org

4271 ■ Mothers and More McHenry County, Chapter 34
PO Box 21
Crystal Lake, IL 60039-0021
Ph: (815)334-7813
URL: http://www.mchenrymothers.org
Fnd: 1990.

4272 ■ Victor C. Neumann Association
5547 N Bavenswood
Chicago, IL 60640
Contact: Sylvia Stuart PhD, Chair
Ph: (773)769-4313
Fax: (773)769-1476
E-mail: info@vcna.org
URL: http://www.neumannassociation.org

Descr: Parents, professional workers, and others interested in individuals with mental retardation. Works to promote services, research, public understanding, and legislation for people with mental retardation and their families. **Fnd:** 1949.

4273 ■ Northwest Passage Outing Club
1130 Greenleaf Ave.
Wilmette, IL 60091
Contact: Rick Sweitzer, Exec. Dir.
Ph: (847)256-4409
Free: 800-732-7328
Fax: (847)256-4476
E-mail: info@nwpassage.com
URL: http://www.nwpassage.com

Staff: 13. **Descr:** Works to enhance personal development, promote self-confidence and teach skills through adventure challenge while providing a safe and exciting environment for every participant. **Fnd:** 1984. **Mem:** 228. **Local Groups:** 1. **Pub:** *The Northwest NEWS* (bimonthly).

4274 ■ Options and Advocacy for McHenry County
365 Millenium Dr., Ste. A
Crystal Lake, IL 60012
Contact: Cindy Sullivan, Exec. Dir.
Ph: (815)477-4720

Fax: (815)477-4700
E-mail: cindy.sullivan@opad.org
URL: http://www.optionsandadvocacy.org
Descr: Parents, professional workers, and others interested in individuals with mental retardation. Works to promote services, research, public understanding, and legislation for people with mental retardation and their families.

4275 ■ Peoria Association for Retarded Citizens (PARC)
PO Box 3418
Peoria, IL 61612
Contact: Roy Rickitts, Pres./CEO
Ph: (309)691-3800
Fax: (309)689-3613
E-mail: rricketts@arcpeoria.org
URL: http://www.parcway.org
Descr: Parents, professional workers, and others interested in individuals with mental retardation. Works to promote services, research, public understanding, and legislation for people with mental retardation and their families. **Fnd:** 1950.

4276 ■ Recording for the Blind and Dyslexic Illinois Unit
180 N Michigan Ave., Ste. 620
Chicago, IL 60601
Contact: Janet Milkovich, Dir.
Ph: (312)236-8715
E-mail: jmilkovich@rfbd.org
Descr: Serves individuals who cannot effectively read standard print because of visual impairment, dyslexia, or other physical disabilities. Creates educational opportunities for students with print disabilities through educational and outreach services. Provides and promotes the effective use of accessible educational materials.

4277 ■ Rock Island County Arc
4016 Ninth St.
Rock Island, IL 61201
Contact: Kyle R. Rick, Exec. Dir.
Ph: (309)786-6474
Fax: (309)786-9861
E-mail: info@arcric.org
URL: http://www.arcric.org
Descr: Represents parents, professional workers, and others interested in individuals with mental retardation. Works to promote services, research, public understanding, and legislation for people with mental retardation and their families.

Indiana

4278 ■ AG BELL, Indiana
PO Box 347
Zionsville, IN 46077
Contact: Naomi Horton, Pres.
Ph: (317)828-0211
E-mail: info@hearindiana.org
URL: http://www.hearindiana.org
Descr: Represents the interests of educators, parents of children with hearing loss, adults with hearing loss and hearing health professionals. Provides governmental and education advocacy services.

4279 ■ American Association of University Women of Indiana
4305 Castleton Ct.
Muncie, IN 47304
Contact: E. Jean Amman, Pres.
Ph: (765)285-1333
Fax: (765)285-5198
E-mail: jamman@bsu.edu
URL: http://web.indstate.edu/aauw-in/home.html
Descr: Advances equity for women and girls through advocacy, education, and research. Provides funds and a support system for women seeking judicial redress for sex discrimination in higher education.

4280 ■ American Counseling Association, Indiana
899 S College Mall Rd., No. 375
Bloomington, IN 47401

Contact: John Donica, Exec. Dir.
Ph: (812)323-8680
Fax: 888-857-4974
E-mail: jdonica@indianacounseling.org
URL: http://www.indianacounseling.org
Staff: 3. **Descr:** Promotes the profession of counseling by providing opportunities for personal growth and professional development. **Fnd:** 1962. **Mem:** 950. **Reg. Groups:** 14. **Pub:** *Hoosier Counselor* (quarterly).

4281 ■ Arc of Bartholomew County
1531 13th St., Ste. 1320
Columbus, IN 47201
Ph: (812)372-0610
E-mail: arc@uwbarthco.org
URL: http://www.thearcbc.org

4282 ■ Arc, Bridges
2650 W 35th Ave.
Gary, IN 46408
Contact: Kris Prohl, Exec. Dir.
Ph: (219)884-1138
E-mail: mailbox@arcbridges.com
URL: http://www.arcbridges.com

4283 ■ Arc of Brown County
PO Box 185
Nashville, IN 47448
Contact: Mary McGrayel, Pres.
Ph: (812)988-2536
URL: http://www.arcind.org

4284 ■ Arc of Carroll County - Indiana
216 W Clem St.
Flora, IN 46929
Contact: Barbara Sterett, Pres.
Ph: (574)967-4252
E-mail: kinzrb@earthlink.net
URL: http://www.arcind.org

4285 ■ Arc of Decatur County
PO Box 126
Greensburg, IN 47240
Contact: Dale Crites, Pres.
Ph: (812)663-8587
E-mail: thooten2@verizon.net
URL: http://www.arcind.org

4286 ■ Arc of Hancock County
PO Box 93
Greenfield, IN 46140
Contact: Dennis Porter, Exec. Dir.
Ph: (317)462-3727
Fax: (317)462-3705
URL: http://www.arcind.org

4287 ■ Arc of Indiana
107 N Pennsylvania St., Ste. 300
Indianapolis, IN 46204
Contact: John Dickerson, Exec. Dir.
Ph: (317)977-2375
Free: 800-382-9100
Fax: (317)977-2385
E-mail: thearc@arcind.org
URL: http://www.arcind.org
Descr: Works to promote services, research, public understanding, and legislation for people with mental retardation and their families.

4288 ■ Arc of Indiana - Blackford
2724 S Carey St.
Marion, IN 46953
Contact: Mark Draves, Pres./CEO
Ph: (765)668-8961
Fax: (765)664-6747
URL: http://www.arcind.org

4289 ■ Arc of Indiana - Daviess
PO Box 249
Linton, IN 47441
Contact: Stephen Sacksteder, Exec. Dir.
Ph: (812)847-2231

Fax: (812)847-8836
URL: http://www.arcind.org

4290 ■ Arc of Indiana - Orange
PO Box 267
Paoli, IN 47454
Contact: William Smith, Exec. Dir.
Ph: (812)723-4486
Fax: (812)723-4487
URL: http://www.arcind.org

4291 ■ Arc of Jackson County - Indiana
2490 N County Rd. 925 W
Norman, IN 47264
Contact: Anne Baxter, Exec. Dir.
Ph: (812)522-4323
E-mail: arcbaxter@iquest.net
URL: http://www.arcind.org

4292 ■ Arc of North Central Indiana
Janus Developmental Services, Inc.
1555 Westfield Rd.
Noblesville, IN 46062
Ph: (317)773-8781
Fax: (317)773-8798
E-mail: abilities@janus-inc.org
URL: http://www.janus-inc.org

4293 ■ ARC Opportunities - Lagrance County
0235 W 300 N
Howe, IN 46746
Contact: Debra Seman, CEO
Ph: (260)463-2653
Fax: (260)463-2046
E-mail: info@arcopportunities.org
URL: http://www.arcopportunities.org
Staff: 40. **Descr:** Parents, professional workers, and others interested in individuals with mental retardation. Works to promote services, research, public understanding, and legislation for people with mental retardation and their families. **Fnd:** 1966.

4294 ■ Arc of Tippecanoe County
PO Box 1222
Lafayette, IN 47902
Contact: Gina Mundell, Exec. Dir.
Ph: (765)423-5531
Fax: (765)423-4235
URL: http://www.arcind.org

4295 ■ Arc of Wabash County
595 S Miami St.
Wabash, IN 46992
Contact: Nancy E. Hoffman, Exec. Dir.
Ph: (260)563-8411
Fax: (260)563-8413
E-mail: arc@arcwabash.org
URL: http://www.arcwabash.org
Fnd: 1954.

4296 ■ Autism Society of America - East Central Indiana Chapter
230 S Schroeder Rd.
Muncie, IN 47304
Contact: Ryan Hourigan PhD, Pres.
Ph: (765)702-7884
E-mail: rmhourigan@bsu.edu
URL: http://www.interlockin.org
Descr: Seeks to improve the lives of individuals affected by autism. Promotes awareness and understanding of autism disorders. Aims to further the advancement of preventive studies, therapy and research of autism disorders.

4297 ■ Autism Society of America - Northwest Indiana Chapter
13908 Delaware St.
Crown Point, IN 46307
Contact: Bonnie McCormick
Ph: (219)662-2668
E-mail: in-northwestindiana@ autismsocietyofamerica.org
Descr: Seeks to improve the lives of individuals affected by autism. Promotes awareness and understanding of autism disorders. Aims to further the

advancement of preventive studies, therapy and research of autism disorders.

4298 ■ Autism Society of America - Southwest Indiana Chapter
631 N Kluemper Rd.
Jasper, IN 47546
Contact: Kris Ketzner
Ph: (812)482-9495
E-mail: in-southwestindiana @ autismsocietyofamerica.org

Descr: Seeks to improve the lives of individuals affected by autism. Promotes awareness and understanding of autism disorders. Aims to further the advancement of preventive studies, therapy and research of autism disorders.

4299 ■ Common Cause Indiana
PO Box 1603
Indianapolis, IN 46206-1603
Contact: Stefanie Miller, Exec. Dir.
Ph: (317)254-0286
E-mail: info@commoncauseindiana.org
URL: http://www.commoncause.org/indiana

Descr: Aims to fight for open, honest, and accountable government at the national, state, and local levels. Gathers and disseminates information on the effects of money in politics; lobbies for political finance and other campaign reforms.

4300 ■ Easter Seals ARC of Northeast Indiana
4919 Coldwater Rd.
Fort Wayne, IN 46825
Ph: (260)456-4534
Free: 800-234-7811
Fax: (260)745-5200
URL: http://neindiana.easterseals.com

Descr: Serves people with disabilities and special needs and their families. Provides community services, intergenerational services, production and work training services, residential services, 24-hour medicaid waiver services, and employment services. **Fnd:** 1954.

4301 ■ Evansville Arc
PO Box 4089
Evansville, IN 47724
Contact: Deidra R. Conner, Pres.
Ph: (812)428-4500
Fax: (812)421-8537
E-mail: dconner@evansvillearc.org
URL: http://www.evansvillearc.org

4302 ■ Governor's Planning Council for People with Disabilities, Indiana
150 W Market St., No. 628
Indianapolis, IN 46204
Contact: Suellen Jackson-Boner, Exec. Dir.
Ph: (317)232-7770
Fax: (317)233-3712
E-mail: gpcpd@gpcpd.org
URL: http://www.in.gov/gpcpd

Descr: Federally funded council whose members are appointed by the governor to promote public policy which leads to the independence, productivity and inclusion of citizens with disabilities in all aspects of society. **Pub:** The Council; Newsletter (monthly).

4303 ■ Indiana Association on Higher Education and Disability
Ball State University
2000 W University Ave.
Muncie, IN 47306
Contact: Carlos Taylor, Pres.-Elect
E-mail: vicepresident@in-ahead.org
URL: http://www.in-ahead.org/indiana1.htm

Descr: Represents individuals interested in promoting the equal rights and opportunities of disabled postsecondary students, staff, faculty and graduates. Provides educational and professional development opportunities for persons with disabilities in postsec-

ondary education. Encourages and supports legislation for the benefit of disabled students.

4304 ■ Indiana Branch of the International Dyslexia Association (INIDA)
2511 E 46th St., Ste. O2
Indianapolis, IN 46205
Contact: Debbie Spinney, Co-Pres.
Ph: (317)926-1450
Fax: (317)705-2067
E-mail: contact@inbofida.com
URL: http://www.inbofida.com

Descr: Promotes public awareness and understanding of dyslexia. Seeks to develop and implement specialized methods to improve the quality of life for people who have dyslexia. **Fnd:** 1971.

4305 ■ Indiana Department of Education
151 W. Ohio St.
Indianapolis, IN 46204
Contact: Dr. Tony Bennett, Superintendent
Ph: (317)232-6610
Fax: (317)233-8004
E-mail: webmaster@doe.in.gov
URL: http://www.doe.in.gov
Pub: Education Matters (e-newsletter).

4306 ■ Johnson County Arc
PO Box 216
Franklin, IN 46131
Contact: Karen Luehmann, Exec. Dir.
Ph: (317)738-5500
Fax: (317)738-5522
URL: http://www.arcind.org

4307 ■ Knox County Association for Retarded Citizens (KCARC)
2525 N 6th St.
Vincennes, IN 47591
Contact: Mike Carney, Pres.
Ph: (812)895-0059
Fax: (812)895-0064
E-mail: info@knoxcountyarc.com
URL: http://www.knoxcountyarc.com

Descr: Parents, professional workers, and others interested in individuals with mental retardation. Works to promote services, research, public understanding, and legislation for people with mental retardation and their families. **Fnd:** 1972.

4308 ■ Lawrence County Arc
PO Box 393
Bedford, IN 47421
Contact: Kim Hodges, Exec. Dir.
Ph: (812)279-3229
URL: http://www.arcind.org

4309 ■ Learning Disabilities Association of Indiana
1508 E 86th St., No. 275
Indianapolis, IN 46240
Contact: Sharon Harris, Pres.
Free: 800-284-2519
URL: http://www.ldaofindiana.org

4310 ■ Spencer County ARC
PO Box 197
Rockport, IN 47635
Contact: Andrea Hayes, Pres.
E-mail: scarc@psci.net
URL: http://www.thearc.org/NetCommunity/Page. aspx?&pid=223&srcid=1314&chid=710

Descr: Provides leadership and resources for mentally handicapped individuals of Spencer County. Reduces the incidence and limiting the consequence of mental retardation through education, research, advocacy and the support of families, friends and community. Strives to provide leadership in the field of mental retardation and physical disabilities to develop necessary human and financial resources to attain its goals.

4311 ■ Stone Belt Arc
2815 E 10th St.
Bloomington, IN 47408
Contact: Beth Gazley, Pres.
Ph: (812)332-2168

Free: 888-332-2168
Fax: (812)323-4610
E-mail: development@stonebelt.org
URL: http://www.stonebelt.org

Iowa

4312 ■ American Association of University Women of Iowa
1302 W Boston Ave.
Indianola, IA 50125
Contact: Janet Heinicke, Pres.
Ph: (515)961-3174
E-mail: janetheinicke@earthlink.net
URL: http://www.aauwia.org

Descr: Advances equity for women and girls through advocacy, education, and research. Provides funds and a support system for women seeking judicial redress for sex discrimination in higher education.

4313 ■ American Medical Student Association, Des Moines University College of Osteopathic Medicine
3200 Grand Ave.
Des Moines, IA 50312
Contact: Terry Branstad, Pres.
Ph: (515)271-1400
Free: 800-240-2767
URL: http://www.dmu.edu/com

Descr: Promotes improvement in medical training and education. Advances the medicine profession. Contributes to the welfare of medical students, interns, residents and post-MD/DO trainees.

4314 ■ Arc of Allamakee
1270 Hwy. 9
Lansing, IA 52151
Contact: Bernadine Jones, Pres.
Ph: (563)568-3802
URL: http://www.thearcofiowa.org

4315 ■ Arc of Appanoose
1310 S 11th St.
Centerville, IA 52544
Contact: Judy Clark, Pres.
Ph: (641)856-5385
E-mail: dejmclark@mchsi.com
URL: http://www.thearcofiowa.org

4316 ■ Arc of Cedar County
604 Horizon Dr.
Tipton, IA 52772
Contact: Jeanne White, Pres.
Ph: (563)886-6226
URL: http://www.thearcofiowa.org

4317 ■ Arc of Delaware - Iowa
2567 180th Ave.
Manchester, IA 52057
Contact: JoAnn Besler, Pres.
Ph: (563)927-6882
URL: http://www.thearcofiowa.org

4318 ■ Arc of East Central Iowa
680 2nd St., Ste. 200
Cedar Rapids, IA 52401
Contact: Delaine Petersen, Exec. Dir.
Ph: (319)365-0487
Free: 800-843-0272
Fax: (319)365-9938
E-mail: dpetersen@arceci.org
URL: http://www.arceci.org

Descr: Parents, professional workers, and others interested in individuals with mental retardation. Works to promote services, research, public understanding, and legislation for people with mental retardation and their families. **Fnd:** 1953. **Pub:** The Challenger (monthly).

4319 ■ Arc of Grundy
105 Clark St.
Reinbeck, IA 50669
Contact: Evelyn Burdick, Pres.

Ph: (641)345-6474
URL: http://www.thearcofiowa.org

4320 ■ Arc of Hardin
1440 Georgetown Rd., Apt. 3
Iowa Falls, IA 50126
Contact: Ray Kline, Pres.
Ph: (641)648-2210
URL: http://www.thearcofiowa.org

4321 ■ Arc of Henry
PO Box 833
Mount Pleasant, IA 52641
Contact: Barbara Helt, Pres.
Ph: (319)668-2340
URL: http://www.thearcofiowa.org

4322 ■ Arc of Iowa
3821 71st St., Ste. A
Urbandale, IA 50322
Contact: Casey Westhoff, Exec. Dir.
Ph: (515)210-6686
Free: 800-362-2927
Fax: (515)309-0860
E-mail: casey@thearcofiowa.org
URL: http://thearcofiowa.org
Descr: Works to promote services, research, public understanding, and legislation for people with mental retardation and their families. **Pub:** *Initiative.*

4323 ■ Arc of Jackson, Iowa
4866 435th Ave.
Preston, IA 52069
Contact: Gary Trenkamp, Pres.
Ph: (563)689-6543
URL: http://www.thearcofiowa.org

4324 ■ Arc of Jefferson and Nearby
1176 Reed Ave.
Brighton, IA 52540
Contact: Sr. Janet Kreber, Pres.
E-mail: janet.kreber@gpaea.k12.ia.us
URL: http://www.thearcofiowa.org

4325 ■ Arc of Lucas
333 South Ave.
Chariton, IA 50049
Contact: Altha Offenburger, Pres.
Ph: (641)774-5493
E-mail: dandaoffy@iowatelecom.net
URL: http://www.thearcofiowa.org

4326 ■ Arc of Marshall
606 Ann Rutledge Rd.
Marshalltown, IA 50158
Contact: Al Fagerlund, Pres.
E-mail: al.fagerlund@emerson.com
URL: http://www.thearcofiowa.org

4327 ■ Arc Mitchell County
533 Chestnut St.
Osage, IA 50461
Contact: Karen Clark, Pres.
Ph: (641)732-4058

4328 ■ Arc of Poweshiek
1408 Summer St.
Grinnell, IA 50112
Contact: Karen Veeerhusen-Langerud, Pres.
E-mail: veerhuse@grinnell.edu
URL: http://www.thearcofiowa.org

4329 ■ Arc of Sac
3201 Taylor Ave.
Lake View, IA 51450
Contact: Dave Erpelding, Pres.
Ph: (712)657-2193
URL: http://www.thearcofiowa.org

4330 ■ Arc of Scott
4613 Hamilton Dr.
Davenport, IA 52807
Contact: Tina Harper, Pres.

E-mail: tinah45@aol.com
URL: http://www.thearcofiowa.org

4331 ■ Arc of Southeast Iowa
2620 Muscatine Ave.
Iowa City, IA 52240
Contact: Bill Reagan, Exec. Dir.
Ph: (319)351-5017
URL: http://www.thearcjc.org

4332 ■ Arc of Story County
PO Box 581
Ames, IA 50010
Contact: Jay D. Lettow, Exec. Dir.
Ph: (515)232-9330
E-mail: info@thearcstory.com
URL: http://www.thearcstory.org
Descr: Parents, professional workers, and others interested in individuals with mental retardation. Works to promote services, research, public understanding, and legislation for people with mental retardation and their families. **Fnd:** 1953.

4333 ■ Arc of Wayne
PO Box 45
Corydon, IA 50060
Contact: Delven Dressler, Pres.
Ph: (641)872-1658
URL: http://www.thearcofiowa.org

4334 ■ Arc of Winneshiek
1647 County Rd. W46
Decorah, IA 52101
Contact: Sue Lansing, Pres.
E-mail: dlansing@acegroup.cc
URL: http://www.thearcofiowa.org

4335 ■ Arc of Woodbury
3001 Malloy Rd.
Sioux City, IA 51103
Contact: Dr. Richard Owens, Pres.
E-mail: vrowens@earthlink.net
URL: http://www.thearcofiowa.org

4336 ■ Autism Society of America - East Central Iowa Chapter
3928 Terrace Hill Dr. NE
Cedar Rapids, IA 52402
Contact: Meg Oberreuter
Ph: (319)378-1241
E-mail: ia-eastcentraliowa@autismsocietyofamerica.org
URL: http://www.autism-society.org/site/Clubs?club_id=1166&pg=main
Descr: Seeks to improve the lives of individuals affected by autism. Promotes awareness and understanding of autism disorders. Aims to further the advancement of preventive studies, therapy and research of autism disorders.

4337 ■ Autism Society of America - Siouxland Chapter
137 Nimrod St.
Salix, IA 51052
Contact: Julie Case
Ph: (712)946-7847
E-mail: ia-siouxland@autismsocietyofamerica.org
Descr: Seeks to improve the lives of individuals affected by autism. Promotes awareness and understanding of autism disorders. Aims to further the advancement of preventive studies, therapy and research of autism disorders.

4338 ■ Autism Society of Iowa
4549 Waterford Dr.
West Des Moines, IA 50265
Contact: Michelle Hicks, Pres.
Ph: (515)327-9075
E-mail: autism50ia@aol.com
URL: http://www.autismia.org
Descr: Seeks to improve the lives of individuals affected by autism. Promotes awareness and understanding of autism disorders. Aims to further the

advancement of preventive studies, therapy and research of autism disorders.

4339 ■ Autism Society of the Quad Cities (ASQC)
PO Box 472
Bettendorf, IA 52722
Contact: Tom Crane, Pres.
Free: 888-722-4799
E-mail: asqc@mchsi.com
URL: http://www.autismqc.org
Descr: Seeks to improve the lives of individuals affected by autism. Promotes awareness and understanding of autism disorders. Aims to further the advancement of preventive studies, therapy and research of autism disorders.

4340 ■ Illinois/Iowa Association on Higher Education and Disability (ILLOWA AHE)
518 W Locust St.
Davenport, IA 52803
Contact: Jenifer Montag, Pres.
Ph: (563)333-6275
Fax: (563)333-6248
E-mail: jmontag@niu.edu
URL: http://www.ahead.org/affiliates/illinois-iowa
Descr: Represents individuals interested in promoting the equal rights and opportunities of disabled postsecondary students, staff, faculty and graduates. Provides educational and professional development opportunities for persons with disabilities in postsecondary education. Encourages and supports legislation for the benefit of disabled students.

4341 ■ Iowa AfterSchool Alliance (IAA)
200 10th St., 5th Fl.
Des Moines, IA 50309
Ph: (515)243-2000
Fax: (515)243-5943
E-mail: bfindley@sppq.com
URL: http://www.iowaafterschoolalliance.org

4342 ■ Iowa Association for the Education of Young Children (IAEYC)
5525 Meredith Dr., Ste. F
Des Moines, IA 50310
Contact: Barbara Merrill, Exec. Dir.
Ph: (515)331-8000
Fax: (515)331-8995
E-mail: info@iowaaeyc.org
URL: http://www.iowaaeyc.org
Staff: 1. **Descr:** Seeks to serve and act on behalf of the needs, rights, and well being of all young children, with primary focus on the promotion of educational and developmental services and resources for children, families, and communities. **Mem:** 1200. **Reg. Groups:** 1. **State Groups:** 1. **Local Groups:** 15. **Pub:** Newsletter (quarterly).

4343 ■ Iowa Branch of the International Dyslexia Association (IA-IDA)
PO Box 11188
Cedar Rapids, IA 52410-1188
Contact: Richard Bradford, Pres.
Free: 866-782-2930
E-mail: og-ida_tmjp@earthlink.net
URL: http://www.ida-ia.org
Descr: Promotes public awareness and understanding of dyslexia. Seeks to develop and implement specialized methods to improve the quality of life for people who have dyslexia.

4344 ■ Iowa Department of Education
Grimes State Office Bldg.
400 E. 14th
Des Moines, IA 50319-0146
Contact: Judy Jeffrey, Dir.
Ph: (515)281-5294
Fax: (515)281-4122

E-mail: judy.jeffrey@iowa.gov
URL: http://www.state.ia.us/educate/

4345 ■ Iowa Governor's Developmental Disabilities Council (GDDC)

617 E 2nd St.
Des Moines, IA 50309
Contact: Becky Maddy Harker, Exec. Dir.
Ph: (515)281-9082
Free: 800-452-1936
Fax: (515)281-9087
E-mail: fmorris@dhs.state.ia.us
URL: http://www.state.ia.us/government/ddcouncil
Staff: 4. **Descr:** Governor appointed council that identifies, develops, and promotes public policy and supportive practices through capacity building, advocacy, and systems change activities that ensure that people with disabilities and their families are included in planning, decision-making, and policy setting activities related to services and supports that affect their quality of life and full participation in the communities of their choice. **Fnd:** 1970. **Mem:** 21.

4346 ■ Iowa PTA

5619 NW 86th St., Ste. 600
Johnston, IA 50131-2955
Contact: Alda Helvey, Exec. Dir.
Ph: (515)225-4197
Free: 800-475-4782
Fax: (515)327-5050
E-mail: ia_office@pta.org
URL: http://www.iowapta.org
Descr: Serves as an active grassroots advocate for issues concerning the health, education, and safety of children and youth. The organization collaborates with other organizations across the state to improve the well-being and future of all children. Conducts a leadership conference held each fall to train local unit leaders and to update members on current issues. **Fnd:** 1900.

4347 ■ Learning Disabilities Association of Iowa (LDA-I)

321 E 6th St.
Des Moines, IA 50309
Contact: Dr. Richard Owens, Pres.
Ph: (515)280-8558
Free: 888-690-LDAI
Fax: (515)243-1902
E-mail: kathylda@askresource.org
URL: http://www.lda-ia.org

4348 ■ Special Olympics Iowa (SOIA)

PO Box 620
Grimes, IA 50111
Contact: Rich Fellingham, Pres./CEO
Ph: (515)986-5520
Fax: (515)986-5530
E-mail: rfellingham@soiowa.org
URL: http://www.soiowa.org
Descr: Provides sports training and competition in a variety of Olympic-type sports for individuals with mental retardation or closely related developmental disabilities, giving them continuing opportunities to develop physical fitness, demonstrate courage, experience joy and participate in a sharing of gifts, skills and friendship with their families, other athletes, and the community. **Fnd:** 1968. **Mem:** 1300.

Kansas

4349 ■ American Medical Student Association, The University of Kansas School of Medicine-Wichita

1010 N Kansas St.
Wichita, KS 67214
Contact: S. Edwards Dismuke MD, Dean
Ph: (316)293-2635
E-mail: kusmw@kumc.edu
URL: http://wichita.kumc.edu
Descr: Promotes improvement in medical training and education. Advances the medicine profession.

Contributes to the welfare of medical students, interns, residents and post-MD/DO trainees.

4350 ■ American Medical Student Association, University of Kansas School of Medicine

3901 Rainbow Blvd.
Mail Stop 1049
Kansas City, KS 66160
Contact: Barbara F. Atkinson MD, Exec. Vice Chancellor
Ph: (913)588-5200
URL: http://www.kumc.edu/som
Descr: Promotes improvement in medical training and education. Advances the medicine profession. Contributes to the welfare of medical students, interns, residents and post-MD/DO trainees. **Fnd:** 1905.

4351 ■ Arc of Butler County, Kansas

226 S Main St.
El Dorado, KS 67042
Contact: Nancy Olson, Pres.
Ph: (316)322-8777

4352 ■ Arc of Sedgwick County

2919 W Second St.
Wichita, KS 67203
Contact: Kevin Fish, Exec. Dir.
Ph: (316)943-1191
Fax: (316)943-3292
E-mail: arc@arc-sedgwickcounty.org
URL: http://www.arc-sedgwickcounty.org
Descr: Parents, professional workers, and others interested in individuals with mental retardation. Works to promote services, research, public understanding, and legislation for people with mental retardation and their families. **Pub:** *Sparks* (quarterly).

4353 ■ Association of Certified Fraud Examiners, Pittsburg St. University Student Chapter

1701 S Broadway St.
Pittsburg, KS 66762
Contact: Mrs. ReBekah Markham, Pres.
Ph: (620)235-4566
E-mail: obryan@pittstate.edu
Descr: Works to classify and examine financial crimes such as white-collar embezzlement, forgery, and fraud as well as their frequency and methodology to develop effective preventive plans and policies for businesses.

4354 ■ Autism Society of the Heartland (ASH)

PO Box 860984
Shawnee, KS 66286
Contact: Bill Robinson, Pres.
Ph: (913)706-0042
E-mail: bill@autismsocietyoftheheartland.org
URL: http://www.autismsocietyoftheheartland.org
Descr: Seeks to improve the lives of individuals affected by autism. Promotes awareness and understanding of autism disorders. Aims to further the advancement of preventive studies, therapy and research of autism disorders.

4355 ■ Douglas County Child Development Association (DCCDA)

935 Iowa St.
Lawrence, KS 66044
Contact: Anna Jenny, Exec. Dir.
Ph: (785)842-9679
Free: 866-352-1531
E-mail: ajenny@dccda.org
URL: http://www.dccda.org
Descr: Serves and acts on behalf of the needs, rights and well-being of all young children with primary focus on the quality of educational and developmental services for all children. Seeks to

improve professional practice and working conditions in early childhood education.

4356 ■ Hope Street Youth Development (HSYD)

1157 N Piatt
Wichita, KS 67214-3174
Contact: Melanie Anderson, CEO
Ph: (316)263-7325
Fax: (316)263-4835
URL: http://www.hopestreet.com
Descr: Provides intensive academic assistance which instills in youth a desire for knowledge and lifelong learning. **Fnd:** 1990.

4357 ■ Kansas Association of Agricultural Educators (KAAE)

575 River Falls Rd.
Edwardsville, KS 66111
Contact: Micheal Strohschein, Exec. Sec.-Treas.
Ph: (913)592-7365
E-mail: strohschein@ksaged.org
URL: http://www.ksaged.org
Staff: 3. **Descr:** Agriculture teachers in public schools; junior college vocational and technical staff. Promotes professional development and continuing education of teachers. **Mem:** 133. **Pub:** Directory (annual); Newsletter (quarterly).

4358 ■ Kansas Association for Career and Technical Education (K-ACTE)

1200 SW 10th Ave.
Topeka, KS 66604
Contact: Steve Kearney, Exec. Dir.
Ph: (785)233-2690
Fax: (785)234-2433
E-mail: skearney@kearneyandassociates.com
URL: http://www.k-acte.org
Descr: Career and technical educators, counselors, school administrators and teacher educators. Carries out a diverse array of programs that advance technical and school-to-careers education. **Fnd:** 1922. **Mem:** 655. **Pub:** *Forum* (semiannual).

4359 ■ Kansas Association on Higher Education and Disability (KanAHEAD)

Access Office
Johnson County Community College
12345 College Blvd.
Overland Park, KS 66210
Contact: Holly Dressler, Co-Pres.
Ph: (913)469-8500
E-mail: dressler@jccc.edu
URL: http://www.ahead.org/affiliates/kansas
Descr: Represents individuals interested in promoting the equal rights and opportunities of disabled postsecondary students, staff, faculty and graduates. Provides educational and professional development opportunities for persons with disabilities in postsecondary education. Encourages and supports legislation for the benefit of disabled students.

4360 ■ Kansas Council on Developmental Disabilities (KCDD)

Docking State Office Bldg.
915 SW Harrison, Rm. 141
Topeka, KS 66612-1570
Contact: Jane Rhys PhD, Exec. Dir.
Ph: (785)296-2608
Fax: (785)296-2861
E-mail: jane@kcdd.org
URL: http://www.kcdd.org
Staff: 4. **Descr:** Includes individuals who are appointed by the Governor, including representatives of the major agencies who provide services for individuals with developmental disabilities. At least 60 percent of the membership is composed of individuals with developmental disabilities or their immediate relatives. Strives to advocate for individuals with developmental disabilities (DD) to receive adequate supports to make choices about where they live,

work, and learn. **Fnd:** 1972. **Mem:** 19. **State Groups:** 1.

4361 ■ Kansas Counseling Association (KCA)
6565 W Foxridge Dr., Apt. 2024
Mission, KS 66202
Contact: Paul Kyle, Pres.
Ph: (785)488-7212
E-mail: danawoodkca@kc.rr.com
URL: http://www.kscounseling.org

Descr: Represents professional counselors in Kansas in a variety of private practice, community agency and religious institutions, elementary, secondary, and post-secondary schools and colleges, and university faculty settings; seeks to enhance human development through the lifespan and to promote the counseling profession. Publishes a quarterly newsletter, hosts annual conference, professional development CEU's, leadership development, public policy advocacy. **Mem:** 640. **Pub:** Newsletter (3/year).

4362 ■ Kansas Department of Education
120 SE 10th Ave.
Topeka, KS 66612-1182
Contact: Alexa Posny, Commnr.
Ph: (785)296-3201
Fax: (785)296-7933
E-mail: contact@ksde.org
URL: http://www.ksde.org/

Descr: Provides direction and leadership for the supervision of all state educational interests under its jurisdiction in Kansas.

4363 ■ Kansas Enrichment Network
1122 W Campus Rd.
320 Joseph R. Pearson Hall
Lawrence, KS 66045
Ph: (785)864-9665
Fax: (785)864-7457
URL: http://www2.ku.edu/~ken

4364 ■ Kansas National Education Association (KNEA)
715 SW 10th Ave.
Topeka, KS 66612-1686
Contact: Blake West, Pres.
Ph: (785)232-8271
Fax: (785)232-6012
E-mail: kneanews@knea.org
URL: http://www.knea.org

Descr: Promotes quality public schools through advance education. **Fnd:** 1863.

4365 ■ Learning Disabilities Association of Kansas (LDAK)
PO Box 4424
Topeka, KS 66604
Contact: Cindy Swarner MSED, Pres.
E-mail: cswarner@sbcglobal.net
URL: http://www.ldakansas.org

4366 ■ Mid-America Association for the Education of Young Children
PO Box 12922
Kansas City, KS 66112
Contact: Mary K. Walker, Admin.
Ph: (913)302-7452
Fax: (913)788-2916
E-mail: admin@mid-americaaeyc.org
URL: http://www.mid-americaaeyc.org

Descr: Serves and acts on behalf of the needs, rights and well-being of all young children with primary focus on the quality of educational and developmental services for all children. Seeks to improve professional practice and working conditions in early childhood education.

4367 ■ MO-KAN-NE Chapter of Mid-America Association of Educational Opportunity Program Personnel
Kansas State University
201 Holton Hall
Manhattan, KS 66506
Contact: Lora Boyer, Pres.
Ph: (785)532-6137
Fax: (785)532-6457
E-mail: lorajb@ksu.edu
URL: http://www.mokanne.org/mkn.html

Descr: Works to advance educational opportunities for disadvantaged students in colleges and universities. Provides professional development and continuing education. Monitors federal legislation designed to serve disadvantaged students.

4368 ■ Salina County Arc
PO Box 362
Salina, KS 67402
Contact: Linda Stack, Pres.
Ph: (785)826-9766

4369 ■ Topeka Association for Retarded Citizens (TARC)
2701 SW Randolph Ave.
Topeka, KS 66611
Contact: Mary Ann Keating, Exec. Dir.
Ph: (785)232-0597
Fax: (785)232-3770
E-mail: mkeating@tarcinc.org
URL: http://www.tarcinc.org

Kentucky

4370 ■ American Medical Student Association, University of Kentucky College of Medicine
800 Rose St.
Lexington, KY 40536-0298
Contact: Jay A. Perman, Dean
Ph: (859)323-5000
URL: http://www.mc.uky.edu/medicine

Descr: Promotes improvement in medical training and education. Advances the medicine profession. Contributes to the welfare of medical students, interns, residents and post-MD/DO trainees.

4371 ■ American Medical Student Association, University of Louisville Health Sciences Center School of Medicine
Student Affairs Office
323 E Chestnut St.
Louisville, KY 40202
Contact: Edward C. Halperin MD, Dean
Ph: (502)852-1499
Free: 800-334-8635
E-mail: meddean@louisville.edu
URL: http://louisville.edu/medschool

Descr: Promotes improvement in medical training and education. Advances the medicine profession. Contributes to the welfare of medical students, interns, residents and post-MD/DO trainees.

4372 ■ Arc of Barren County
123 E Washington St.
Glasgow, KY 42141
Contact: Rebecca Kingrey, Exec. Dir.
Ph: (270)659-0802
E-mail: arc@glasgow-ky.com

4373 ■ Arc of the Bluegrass
898 Georgetown St.
Lexington, KY 40511
Ph: (859)233-1483
Fax: (859)231-9695
E-mail: ellerbrk@mis.net
URL: http://www.hereweare.net/arcbluegrass.htm

Descr: Parents, professional workers, and others interested in individuals with mental retardation. Works to promote services, research, public understanding, and legislation for people with mental retardation and their families.

4374 ■ Arc of Lake Cumberland
PO Box 1421
Somerset, KY 42502
Contact: Patty Dempsey, Exec. Dir.
Ph: (606)679-7313

4375 ■ Arc of Madison County
PO Box 1863
Richmond, KY 40476
Contact: Michelle Gerken, Exec. Dir.
Ph: (859)622-2314

4376 ■ Arc of the Mountains
422 Clover St.
Harlan, KY 40831
Ph: (606)573-5777

4377 ■ ARHHC of Hardin County
PO Box 2013
Elizabethtown, KY 42702
Contact: Clara E. Harrison, Pres.
Ph: (270)737-1140
E-mail: arhhc@aol.com

4378 ■ Autism Society of the Bluegrass (ASBG)
453 Rookwood Pkwy.
Lexington, KY 40505
Contact: Sara Spragens, Pres.
Ph: (859)299-9000
E-mail: ky-lexington@autismsocietyofamerica.org
URL: http://asbg.org

Descr: Seeks to improve the lives of individuals affected by autism. Promotes awareness and understanding of autism disorders. Aims to further the advancement of preventive studies, therapy and research of autism disorders.

4379 ■ Autism Society of Kentuckiana (ASK)
PO Box 90
Pewee Valley, KY 40056
Contact: Laurie Spezzano
Ph: (502)222-4706
E-mail: lauriespezzano@insightbb.com
URL: http://www.ask-lou.org

Descr: Seeks to improve the lives of individuals affected by autism. Promotes awareness and understanding of autism disorders. Aims to further the advancement of preventive studies, therapy and research of autism disorders.

4380 ■ Autism Society of Western Kentucky
PO Box 1647
Henderson, KY 42419
Contact: Nancy Boyett
Ph: (270)826-0510
E-mail: ky-westernkentucky@autismsocietyofamerica.org

Descr: Seeks to improve the lives of individuals affected by autism. Promotes awareness and understanding of autism disorders. Aims to further the advancement of preventive studies, therapy and research of autism disorders.

4381 ■ Breckenridge County Educational Association for the Handicapped
PO Box 577
Hardinsburg, KY 40143
Contact: Herman Finn, Pres.
Ph: (270)756-1436
E-mail: bceahride@yahoo.com.au

4382 ■ Central Kentucky Counseling Association
105 Greenwing Ct.
Georgetown, KY 40324
Contact: Ms. Connie Morse, Pres.

Ph: (502)868-7202
E-mail: connie.morse@scott.kyschool.us
URL: http://www.kyca.org

Descr: Promotes the practice of counseling. Provides opportunities for personal growth and professional development.

4383 ■ Eastern Kentucky Counseling Association
405 Iron Furance Rd.
Wurtland, KY 41144
Contact: Mr. Mark Castro, Pres.
Ph: (606)836-4829
E-mail: mark.castro@russellind.kyschools.us
URL: http://www.kyca.org

Descr: Promotes the practice of counseling. Provides opportunities for personal growth and professional development.

4384 ■ Greater Louisville Metro Arc
3713 Fallen Timber Dr.
Louisville, KY 40241
Contact: Gail Lowe, Pres.
Ph: (502)339-8690
E-mail: gail619@bellsouth.net

4385 ■ Kentucky Association for Career and Technical Education (KACTE)
PO Box 4583
Frankfort, KY 40604-4583
Contact: Mr. Michael R. Stone, Exec. Dir.
Ph: (502)223-1823
Fax: (502)227-8082
E-mail: kmstone@mis.net
URL: http://kacteonline.org

Staff: 2. **Descr:** Provides professional development, meeting and membership-benefit services to professional educators working in career and technical (formerly called vocational) programs at middle schools, high schools, area technology centers and post-secondary institutions. **Fnd:** 1926. **Mem:** 600.

4386 ■ Kentucky Association of Educational Opportunity Program Personnel (KAEOPP)
Madisonville Community College
2000 College Dr.
Madisonville, KY 42431
Contact: Andy Ausenbaugh, Assoc. Dir.
Ph: (270)824-1738
Fax: (270)824-1881
E-mail: andy.ausenbaugh@kctcs.edu
URL: http://www.geocities.com/~kaeopp

Descr: Works to advance educational opportunities for disadvantaged students in colleges and universities. Provides professional development and continuing education. Monitors federal legislation designed to serve disadvantaged students.

4387 ■ Kentucky Association on Higher Education and Disability
University of Louisville
Disability Resource Center, Rm.120
Louisville, KY 40292
Contact: Cathy Patus, Dir.
Ph: (502)852-6938
Fax: (502)852-0924
URL: http://louisville.edu/disability

Staff: 9. **Descr:** Represents individuals interested in promoting the equal rights and opportunities of disabled postsecondary students, staff, faculty and graduates. Provides educational and professional development opportunities for persons with disabilities in postsecondary education. Encourages and supports legislation for the benefit of disabled students.

4388 ■ Kentucky Association of Technology Students
Lexington Community College
Cooper Dr.
Lexington, KY 40506
Contact: William Kevin Murphy, Faculty Advisor
Ph: (859)257-4872
E-mail: wkmurp0@uky.edu

Descr: Provides codes, standards, products, and

services to concerned individuals for the safety and effective performance in the built environment.

4389 ■ Kentucky Department of Education
500 Mero St.
Frankfort, KY 40601
Contact: Jon E. Draud, Commnr.
Ph: (502)564-4770
Fax: (502)564-3049
E-mail: webmaster@education.ky.gov
URL: http://www.education.ky.gov/

Descr: Provides technical assistance to schools and districts in the areas of finance, management, and curriculum; oversees the state's education technology system; and monitors school and district compliance with state and federal laws.

4390 ■ Kentucky National Congress of Parents and Teachers
PO Box 654
Frankfort, KY 40602-0654
Contact: Rose Babiak, Pres.
Ph: (502)226-6607
Fax: (502)226-6610
E-mail: ky_office@pta.org
URL: http://www.kypta.org

Staff: 2. **Descr:** Parents, teachers, students, principals, administrators, and others interested in uniting the forces of home, school, and community on behalf of children and youth. **Fnd:** 1918. **Mem:** 125000. **Reg. Groups:** 21. **State Groups:** 1. **Local Groups:** 420.

4391 ■ Kentucky PTA
PO Box 654
Frankfort, KY 40602-0654
Contact: Vicki Ensor, Office Staff
Ph: (502)226-6607
Fax: (502)226-6610
E-mail: ky_office@pta.org
URL: http://www.kypta.org

Descr: Promotes the welfare of children and youth in home, school, community and place of worship; secures adequate laws for the care and protection of children and youth; and raises the standards of home life. **Mem:** 150000.

4392 ■ Learning Disabilities Association of Kentucky (LDAOFKY)
2210 Goldsmith Ln., No. 118
Louisville, KY 40218
Ph: (502)473-1256
Free: 877-587-1256
Fax: (502)473-4695
E-mail: ldaofky@yahoo.com
URL: http://www.ldaofky.org

4393 ■ Mid Cumberland Counseling Association
811 Woods Edge Dr.
Somerset, KY 42503
Contact: Mr. James Powell, Pres.
Ph: (606)678-5874
E-mail: james.powell@pulaski.kyschools.us

Descr: Promotes the practice of counseling. Provides opportunities for personal growth and professional development.

4394 ■ Point/Arc of Northern Kentucky
104 W Pike St.
Covington, KY 41011
Ph: (859)491-9191
Fax: (859)491-0763
URL: http://www.thepointarc.org

Descr: Parents, professional workers, and others interested in individuals with mental retardation. Works to promote services, research, public understanding, and legislation for people with mental retardation and their families. **Fnd:** 1972.

4395 ■ Recording for the Blind and Dyslexic Kentucky Unit
240 Haldeman Ave.
Louisville, KY 40206
Contact: Sarah Trester, Exec. Dir.
Ph: (502)895-9068
Fax: (502)897-1145

E-mail: strester@rfbd.org
URL: http://www.rfbd.org/Kentucky_Unit.htm

Descr: Serves individuals who cannot effectively read standard print because of visual impairment, dyslexia, or other physical disabilities. Creates educational opportunities for students with print disabilities through educational and outreach services. Provides and promotes the effective use of accessible educational materials.

4396 ■ Special Olympics Kentucky (SOKY)
105 Lakeview Ct.
Frankfort, KY 40601-8749
Contact: Dave Kerchner, Pres./CEO
Ph: (502)695-8222
Free: 800-633-7403
Fax: (502)695-0496
E-mail: soky@soky.org
URL: http://www.soky.org

Descr: Promotes physical fitness, sports training, and athletic competition for children and adults with mental retardation. Seeks to contribute to the physical, social, and psychological development of persons with mental retardation. Participants range in age from 8 years to adult and compete in track and field, swimming, gymnastics, bowling, ice skating, basketball, and other sports.

4397 ■ Upper Cumberland Counseling Association, Kentucky
534 Virginia Ave.
Pineville, KY 40977
Contact: Ms. Kathy Warren, Pres.
Ph: (606)248-1794
E-mail: kathy.warren@bell.kyschools.us
URL: http://www.kyca.org

Descr: Promotes the practice of counseling. Provides opportunities for personal growth and professional development.

4398 ■ West Kentucky Counseling Association
1539 Gleneagles Dr.
Paducah, KY 42001
Contact: Ms. Deborah Curtis, Pres.
Ph: (270)444-5750
E-mail: dcurtis@mccracken.kentuckyschools.us
URL: http://www.kyca.org

Descr: Promotes the practice of counseling. Provides opportunities for personal growth and professional development.

Louisiana

4399 ■ 100 Black Men of New Orleans
305 Foxcroft
Slidell, LA 70461
Ph: (985)641-1477
E-mail: nlewis@100bmmno.org

4400 ■ American Association of University Women, Alexandria/Pineville Branch
3216 Skyline Dr.
Pineville, LA 71360
Contact: Helen Moore, Pres.
Ph: (318)448-4464
Fax: (318)442-7141
E-mail: ngrandquis@aol.com
URL: http://aauw_la.home.mindspring.com

Descr: Advances equity for women and girls through advocacy, education, and research. Provides funds and a support system for women seeking judicial redress for sex discrimination in higher education.

4401 ■ American Association of University Women, Baton Rouge Branch
6329 Double Tree Dr.
Baton Rouge, LA 70817-8915
Contact: Joan Houghton-Bonds, Treas.
Ph: (225)752-1326
E-mail: pbbaldwin47@hotmail.com
URL: http://aauw_br.home.mindspring.com

Descr: Advances equity for women and girls through advocacy, education, and research. Provides funds and a support system for women seeking judicial redress for sex discrimination in higher education.

4402 ■ American Association of University Women, Covington-Mandeville Branch
PO Box 1308
Lacombe, LA 70445-1308
Contact: Jean Lotz, Pres.
Ph: (985)893-2892
E-mail: info@aauw-covmande.org
URL: http://www.aauw-covmande.org
Descr: Advances equity for women and girls through advocacy, education, and research. Provides funds and a support system for women seeking judicial redress for sex discrimination in higher education. **Fnd:** 1964.

4403 ■ American Association of University Women of Louisiana (AAUW)
3208 Iowa Ave.
Kenner, LA 70065
Contact: Anne K. Taylor PhD, Pres.
Ph: (225)767-3565
Fax: (225)767-3565
E-mail: akt1208@bellsouth.net
URL: http://aauw_la.home.mindspring.com
Descr: Advances equity for women and girls through advocacy, education, and research. Provides funds and a support system for women seeking judicial redress for sex discrimination in higher education. **Mem:** 250.

4404 ■ American Medical Student Association, Louisiana State University School of Medicine in New Orleans
Student Admissions
1901 Perdido St.
Box P3-4
New Orleans, LA 70112
Contact: Steve Nelson MD, Dean
Ph: (504)568-6262
E-mail: snelso1@lsuhsc.edu
URL: http://www.medschool.lsuhsc.edu
Descr: Promotes improvement in medical training and education. Advances the medicine profession. Contributes to the welfare of medical students, interns, residents and post-MD/DO trainees.

4405 ■ American Medical Student Association, LSUHSC School of Medicine
PO Box 33932
Shreveport, LA 71130
Contact: John C. McDonald, Dean
Ph: (318)675-5206
Fax: (318)675-4758
E-mail: shvreg@lsuhsc.edu
URL: http://www.sh.lsuhsc.edu/medschool/index.html
Descr: Promotes improvement in medical training and education. Advances the medicine profession. Contributes to the welfare of medical students, interns, residents and post-MD/DO trainees.

4406 ■ American Medical Student Association, Tulane University School of Medicine
1430 Tulane Ave., SL 67
New Orleans, LA 70112
Contact: Benjamin P. Sachs, Sr. VP
Ph: (504)988-5187
Fax: (504)988-6462
URL: http://www.mcl.tulane.edu
Descr: Promotes improvement in medical training and education. Advances the medicine profession. Contributes to the welfare of medical students, interns, residents and post-MD/DO trainees.

4407 ■ Arc Baton Rouge
8326 Kelwood Ave.
Baton Rouge, LA 70806
Contact: Barry Meyer, Exec. Dir.
Ph: (225)927-0855
Fax: (225)924-3935
E-mail: bmeyer@arcbatonrouge.org
URL: http://www.arcbatonrouge.org

4408 ■ Arc of Caddo-Bossier
351 Jordan St.
Shreveport, LA 71101

Contact: Janet Parker, Exec. Dir.
Ph: (318)221-8392
Fax: (318)221-4262
E-mail: jparker@thearccaddobossier.org
URL: http://www.thearccaddobossier.org
Descr: Works to promote services, research, public understanding, and legislation for people with mental retardation and their families. **Fnd:** 1954.

4409 ■ Arc of Iberia
3716 Redwood Dr.
New Iberia, LA 70560
Contact: Kenny Patton, Exec. Dir.
Ph: (337)367-6813

4410 ■ Arc of Louisiana
606 Colonial Dr., Ste. G
Baton Rouge, LA 70806
Ph: (225)383-1033
Fax: (225)383-1092
E-mail: thearcla@thearcla.org
URL: http://www.thearcla.org

4411 ■ Arc - Morehouse
10640 Lucy Hudson Dr.
Bastrop, LA 71220
Contact: Ben Pitts, Exec. Dir.
Ph: (318)283-2338

4412 ■ Arc of North Webster
PO Box 351
Sarepta, LA 71071
Contact: Amy Vollmer, Exec. Dir.
Ph: (318)847-4356
E-mail: dg074@yahoo.com

4413 ■ Arc of Sabine
PO Box 1150
Many, LA 71449
Contact: Wayne Martinez, Exec. Dir.
Ph: (318)256-2025
E-mail: ssarc@cebridge.net

4414 ■ Assumption Arc
PO Drawer 1040
Napoleonville, LA 70390
Contact: Warren H. Gonzales, Exec. Dir.
Ph: (985)369-2907
E-mail: arcoa@bellsouth.net

4415 ■ Autism Society of Acadiana (ASAC)
PO Box 91553
Lafayette, LA 70509
Contact: Theron Pitre, Chm.
Ph: (337)369-2885
E-mail: la-lafayette@autismsocietyofamerica.org
URL: http://www.acadianaautism.org
Descr: Seeks to improve the lives of individuals affected by autism. Promotes awareness and understanding of autism disorders. Aims to further the advancement of preventive studies, therapy and research of autism disorders.

4416 ■ Autism Society of America - Bayou Louisiana Chapter
121 Callin Ct.
Morgan City, LA 70380
Contact: Dawn Spinella
Ph: (985)631-9823
E-mail: la-bayou@autismsocietyofamerica.org
URL: http://www.autism-society.org/site/Clubs?club_id=1324&pg=main
Descr: Seeks to improve the lives of individuals affected by autism. Promotes awareness and understanding of autism disorders. Aims to further the advancement of preventive studies, therapy and research of autism disorders.

4417 ■ Autism Society of America - Greater Baton Rouge Chapter
12854 Arlingford Ave.
Baton Rouge, LA 70815
Contact: Beryl Herbert
Ph: (225)907-5292
Descr: Seeks to improve the lives of individuals affected by autism. Promotes awareness and understanding of autism disorders. Aims to further the

advancement of preventive studies, therapy and research of autism disorders.

4418 ■ Autism Society of America - Northeast Louisiana Chapter
PO Box 682
Grayson, LA 71435
Contact: Anna Keith Foy
Ph: (318)649-7449
E-mail: la-northeastlouisiana@autismsocietyofamerica.org
Descr: Seeks to improve the lives of individuals affected by autism. Promotes awareness and understanding of autism disorders. Aims to further the advancement of preventive studies, therapy and research of autism disorders.

4419 ■ Autism Society of America - Northwest Louisiana Chapter
625 Red Chute Ln.
Bossier City, LA 71112
Contact: Alice Reynolds, Pres.
Ph: (318)747-1662
E-mail: ajrbcr2001@yahoo.com
URL: http://www.autism-society.org/site/Clubs?club_id=1261&pg=main
Descr: Seeks to improve the lives of individuals affected by autism. Promotes awareness and understanding of autism disorders. Aims to further the advancement of preventive studies, therapy and research of autism disorders.

4420 ■ Autism Society of America - Southwest Louisiana Chapter
PO Box 1805
Lake Charles, LA 70602
Contact: Barbara Greer, Pres.
Ph: (337)855-2068
E-mail: la-southwestlouisiana@autismsocietyofamerica.org
Descr: Seeks to improve the lives of individuals affected by autism. Promotes awareness and understanding of autism disorders. Aims to further the advancement of preventive studies, therapy and research of autism disorders.

4421 ■ Beauregard Arc
PO Box 13
DeRidder, LA 70634
Contact: Jackie L. Hickman, Exec. Dir.
Ph: (337)462-2513
Fax: (337)462-2513
E-mail: beauregardarc@hotmail.com
Descr: Parents, professional workers, and others interested in individuals with mental retardation. Works to promote services, research, public understanding, and legislation for people with mental retardation and their families.

4422 ■ Common Cause/Louisiana (CCLA)
PO Box 66687
Baton Rouge, LA 70896-6687
Contact: Ms. Dorothy Wise Wirth, Program Mgr.
Ph: (225)205-4235
E-mail: louisiana@commoncause.org
URL: http://www.commoncause.org/la
Staff: 1. **Descr:** Works as an active participant in the drive to make Louisiana government more open, ethical and accessible. **Mem:** 200. **State Groups:** 1. **Pub:** *From the State and the Nation* (quarterly).

4423 ■ Donaldsonville Arc
PO Box 624
Donaldsonville, LA 70346
Contact: Marlene Domingue, Exec. Dir.
Ph: (225)473-4516
E-mail: daarc@eatel.net

4424 ■ Greater New Orleans Arc
5700 Loyola Ave.
New Orleans, LA 70115
Contact: Cliff Doescher, Exec. Dir.
Ph: (504)837-5140
Fax: (504)899-0803
E-mail: arcgnoinfo@bellsouth.net
Descr: Works to increase public awareness of

people who have developmental disabilities; to encourage progressive legislation; to protect and advocate for the human and constitutional rights of each individual; to conduct valid assessments of each individual's health and human service needs; and to render services in compliance with professionally-developed standards. **Fnd:** 1953.

4425 ■ Greater New Orleans Autism Society of America (GNO-ASA)
PO Box 26057
New Orleans, LA 70186
Contact: Katherine Jefferson, Pres.
Ph: (251)802-8097
E-mail: gnoasachapter@yahoo.com
URL: http://www.autism-society.org/site/Clubs?club_id=1170&pg=main
Descr: Seeks to improve the lives of individuals affected by autism. Promotes awareness and understanding of autism disorders. Aims to further the advancement of preventive studies, therapy and research of autism disorders.

4426 ■ Iberville Arc
PO Box 201
Plaquemine, LA 70765
Contact: Paul Rhorer, Exec. Dir.
Ph: (225)687-4062
E-mail: arci@eatel.net

4427 ■ International Dyslexia Association - Louisiana Branch
149 Jefferson Oaks Dr.
Ruston, LA 71272
Contact: Alice Higginbotham, Pres.
Ph: (985)414-2575
E-mail: alicehigginbotham@hotmail.com
URL: http://www.interdys.org/Branchdetail.aspx?bid=26
Descr: Promotes public awareness and understanding of dyslexia. Seeks to develop and implement specialized methods to improve the quality of life for people who have dyslexia. Provides services to those affected by dyslexia, attention disorders and other learning disabilities.

4428 ■ Learning Disabilities Association of Louisiana (LDA)
67 Allard Blvd.
New Orleans, LA 70119
Contact: Jo Ann Lorusso
Ph: (504)482-1586
E-mail: ldalouisiana@yahoo.com
URL: http://www.ldalouisiana.org

4429 ■ Louisiana Association for Career and Technical Education (LACTE)
1914 S Carrollton Ave.
New Orleans, LA 70118
Contact: Barry Brantley, Exec. Dir.
Ph: (504)866-3855
Fax: (504)866-3853
E-mail: bbrantley@lacte.org
URL: http://www.lacte.org
Descr: Career and technical educators, administrators, counselors, support staff, and others concerned about career and technical education in Louisiana.

4430 ■ Louisiana Association for the Education of Young Children (LAEYC)
2515 Canal St.
New Orleans, LA 70119
Contact: Todd A. Battiste, Pres.
Ph: (504)827-6852
Fax: (504)827-6838
E-mail: toddb@unitedwaynola.org
URL: http://www.laeyc.org
Descr: Promotes excellence in early childhood education.

4431 ■ Louisiana Automatic Fire Alarm Association
C&S Safety
915 Granada Dr.
New Iberia, LA 70560
Contact: Gerald Faulk
Ph: (337)364-2212

Fax: (337)367-3417
E-mail: gerald@candssafety.com
Descr: Manufacturers, distributors, fire alarm installers, registered professional engineers, building and fire officials. Promotes cooperation and understanding among the professional involved in the fire alarm industry.

4432 ■ Louisiana Department of Education
1201 N. Third
PO Box 94064
Baton Rouge, LA 70804-9064
Contact: Paul G. Pastorek, Superintendent
Ph: (225)342-4411
Free: 877-453-2721
Fax: (225)342-0781
E-mail: customerservice@la.gov
URL: http://www.louisianaschools.net/index.html

4433 ■ Louisiana Developmental Disabilities Council
PO Box 3455
Baton Rouge, LA 70821-3455
Contact: Sandee Winchell, Exec. Dir.
Ph: (225)342-6804
Free: 800-450-8108
Fax: (225)342-1970
E-mail: swinchel@dhh.la.gov
URL: http://www.laddc.org
Staff: 8. **Descr:** Strives to promote the independence, productivity, integration and inclusion in the community of persons with developmental disabilities through systems change activities. **Mem:** 28. **Pub:** *Triangle* (quarterly).

4434 ■ Louisiana National Congress of Parents and Teachers
1543 Del Plaza Dr., Ste. 13
Baton Rouge, LA 70815
Contact: Chris Cohea, Pres.
Ph: (225)927-7382
Fax: (225)927-9497
E-mail: la_office@pta.org
Descr: Represents parents, teachers, students, principals, administrators, and others interested in uniting the forces of home, school, and community on behalf of children and youth.

4435 ■ Louisiana SADD (LA SADD)
3402 G Jackson St.
Alexandria, LA 71301
Contact: Janice Williams, Exec. Dir.
Ph: (318)561-2624
Free: 800-407-6343
Fax: (318)442-9433
E-mail: lasadd@aol.com
URL: http://www.lypservices.org

4436 ■ Louisiana Senior Olympic Games (LSOG)
PO Box 14748
Baton Rouge, LA 70898
Contact: Jody Thibodeaux, Pres.
Ph: (225)925-1748
Free: 800-799-8309
Fax: (225)925-3553
E-mail: lsog@lsog.net
URL: http://www.lsog.net
Descr: Promotes physical fitness and an improved quality of life for people over 50 through sports and physical training.

4437 ■ St. James Arc
29150 Health Unit St.
Vacherie, LA 70090
Contact: Latasha Lewis, Exec. Dir.
Ph: (225)265-7910
E-mail: stjamesarc@bellsouth.net

4438 ■ St. John Arc
101 Bamboo Rd.
La Place, LA 70068
Contact: Cherie DeBowes, Sec.
Ph: (985)652-8003
Free: 800-608-9776

E-mail: stjohnarc@comcast.net
URL: http://www.stjohnarc.org

4439 ■ Special Olympics Louisiana (SOLA)
1000 E Morris Ave.
Hammond, LA 70403
Contact: Pat Carpenter, Pres./CEO
Ph: (985)345-6644
Free: 800-345-6644
Fax: (985)345-6649
URL: http://www.laso.org
Descr: Provides year-round sports training and athletic competition in a variety of Olympic-type sports for children and adults with developmental disabilities, eight years of age and older. **Fnd:** 1968.

4440 ■ TARC of Hammond
408 N Cypress St.
Hammond, LA 70401
Contact: Melinda Shaffett, Exec. Dir.
Ph: (985)345-8811
Free: 800-673-0556
Fax: (985)549-0743
E-mail: tarc@tarc-hammond.com
URL: http://www.tarchammond.com

4441 ■ Terrebonne Association for Retarded Citizens (TARC)
1 McCord Rd.
Houma, LA 70363
Ph: (985)876-4465
Fax: (985)223-7387
E-mail: tarc@terrebonnearc.org
URL: http://www.terrebonnearc.org

4442 ▼ Vermilion Arc
809 S Severin St.
Erath, LA 70533
Contact: Scottie J. Daigle, Exec. Dir.
Ph: (337)937-6113

Maine

4443 ■ Adoptive and Foster Families of Maine (AFFM)
294 Center St., Unit 1
Old Town, ME 04468
Contact: Bette Hoxie, Dir.
Ph: (207)827-2331
Free: 800-833-9786
Fax: (207)827-1974
E-mail: info@affm.net
URL: http://www.affm.net
Staff: 2. **Descr:** Provides support services for adoptive and foster parents, and kinship providers. Gives training, guidance, knowledge, and resources needed to handle complex issues as families open their hearts and homes to children. **Fnd:** 1997. **Mem:** 550. **Reg. Groups:** 2. **State Groups:** 1. **Local Groups:** 3. **Pub:** *Family Ties* (monthly).

4444 ■ American Association of University Women of Maine
109 Vassalboro Rd.
South China, ME 04358
Contact: Pat Rathbun, Pres.
Ph: (207)762-1791
E-mail: arathbun@maine.rr.com
URL: http://www.bairnet.org/organizations/aauw/s-default.htm
Descr: Advances equity for women and girls through advocacy, education, and research. Provides funds and a support system for women seeking judicial redress for sex discrimination in higher education.

4445 ■ American Medical Student Association, University of New England College of Medicine
University Campus
11 Hills Beach Rd.
Biddeford, ME 04005
Contact: Danielle N. Ripich PhD, Pres.
Ph: (207)283-0171
URL: http://www.une.edu/com
Descr: Promotes improvement in medical training and education. Advances the medicine profession.

Contributes to the welfare of medical students, interns, residents and post-MD/DO trainees.

4446 ■ Arc - Waban Projects
5 Dunaway Dr.
Sanford, ME 04073
Contact: Neal Meltzer, Exec. Dir.
Ph: (207)324-7955

4447 ■ Autism Society of Maine (ASM)
72B Main St.
Winthrop, ME 04364
Contact: Kim Humphrey, Pres.
Free: 800-273-5200
Fax: (207)377-9434
E-mail: info@asmonline.org
URL: http://www.asmonline.org
Descr: Seeks to improve the lives of individuals affected by autism. Promotes awareness and understanding of autism disorders. Aims to further the advancement of preventive studies, therapy and research of autism disorders.

4448 ■ Central Aroostook Arc
PO Box 1245
Presque Isle, ME 04769
Contact: Steven Richard, Exec. Dir.
Ph: (207)764-0134
Descr: Parents, professional workers, and others interested in individuals with mental retardation. Works to promote services, research, public understanding, and legislation for people with mental retardation and their families.

4449 ■ Community Living Association (CLA)
45 School St.
Houlton, ME 04730
Contact: Ron Langworthy, Exec. Dir.
Ph: (207)532-9446
Free: 866-343-4144
Fax: (207)532-1359
E-mail: rlangworthy@cla-maine.org
URL: http://www.cla-maine.org
Staff: 250. **Descr:** Provides day habilitation, employment and residential supports for individuals with intellectual disabilities. Works to promote services, public understanding, and legislation for people with intellectual disabilities and their families. **Fnd:** 1967.

4450 ■ Downeast Horizons
1200 State Hwy. 3
Bar Harbor, ME 04609
Contact: Anthony Zambrano, Exec. Dir.
Ph: (207)288-4234
Fax: (207)288-1056
URL: http://www.dehi.org
Staff: 5. **Descr:** Parents, professional workers, and others interested in individuals with mental retardation. Works to promote services, research, public understanding, and legislation for people with mental retardation and their families.

4451 ■ Learning Disabilities Association of Maine (LDAME)
PO Box 67
Oakland, ME 04963
Contact: Gene Kucinkas Jr., Pres.
Ph: (207)465-7700
Free: 877-208-4029
Fax: (207)465-4844
E-mail: info@ldame.org
URL: http://www.ldame.org

4452 ■ Maine Association for the Education of Young Children
PO Box 1065
Bath, ME 04530
Contact: Erika Neal, Pres.-Elect
E-mail: info@maineaeyc.org
URL: http://www.maineaeyc.org
Descr: Serves and acts on behalf of the needs, rights and well-being of all young children with primary focus on the quality of educational and developmental services for all children. Seeks to

improve professional practice and working conditions in early childhood education.

4453 ■ Maine Department of Education
23 State House Station
Augusta, ME 04333-0023
Contact: Susan A. Gendron, Commnr. of Educ.
Ph: (207)624-6600
Fax: (207)624-6700
E-mail: susan.gendron@maine.gov
URL: http://www.maine.gov/education/

4454 ■ Maine PTA
PO Box 1929
Bangor, ME 04402
Contact: Tammie Breen, Pres.
Ph: (207)852-6683
Fax: (207)990-2444
E-mail: tbreen@zoneradio.com
URL: http://www.mainepta.org
Descr: Local, state and national network of parents, teachers, students, principals, administrators, and others working to unite the forces of home, school, and community on behalf of children and youth. **Fnd:** 1916. **Mem:** 3500. **Local Groups:** 100. **Pub:** Newsletter (quarterly).

4455 ■ Special Olympics Maine
125 John Roberts Rd., Ste. 19
South Portland, ME 04106
Contact: Phil Geelhoed, Pres./CEO
Ph: (207)879-0489
Fax: (207)879-0672
E-mail: someemail@aol.com
URL: http://www.specialolympicsmaine.org
Descr: Promotes physical fitness, sports training, and athletic competition for children and adults with mental retardation. Seeks to contribute to the physical, social, and psychological development of persons with mental retardation. Participants range in age from 8 years to adult and compete in track and field, swimming, gymnastics, bowling, ice skating, basketball, and other sports. **Fnd:** 1968. **Mem:** 3000. **Reg. Groups:** 13.

4456 ■ Waban Projects
5 Dunnaway Dr.
Sanford, ME 04073
Contact: Gervaise Flynn, Asst. Exec. Dir.
Ph: (207)324-7955
Fax: (207)324-6050
E-mail: waban@waban.org
URL: http://www.waban.org
Descr: Parents, professional workers, and others interested in individuals with mental retardation. Works to promote services, research, public understanding, and legislation for people with mental retardation and their families. **Fnd:** 1966.

4457 ■ Work First
PO Box 86
Farmington, ME 04938
Contact: Linda Larue-Keniston, Exec. Dir.
Ph: (207)778-3200
Descr: Parents, professional workers, and others interested in individuals with mental retardation. Works to promote services, research, public understanding, and legislation for people with mental retardation and their families.

Maryland

4458 ■ American Association of University Women, Harford County Branch
313 Aiken Terr.
Abingdon, MD 21009
Contact: Hazel U. Hopkins
E-mail: mmdymond@comcast.net
URL: http://www.geocities.com/harfordaauw
Descr: Advances equity for women and girls through advocacy, education, and research. Provides funds

and a support system for women seeking judicial redress for sex discrimination in higher education.

4459 ■ American Association of University Women, Laurel Branch
6006 Wiss Dr.
Laurel, MD 20707-2655
Contact: Jan Loftus, Treas.
URL: http://www.erols.com/ementon/aauwlaurel.html
Descr: Advances equity for women and girls through advocacy, education, and research. Provides funds and a support system for women seeking judicial redress for sex discrimination in higher education.

4460 ■ American Medical Student Association, The Johns Hopkins School of Medicine
Office of Student Affairs
Broadway Research Bldg.
733 N Broadway, Ste. 137
Baltimore, MD 21205
Contact: Thomas W. Koenig MD
Ph: (410)955-3416
E-mail: tkoenig@jhmi.edu
URL: http://www.hopkinsmedicine.org/som/index.html
Descr: Promotes improvement in medical training and education. Advances the medicine profession. Contributes to the welfare of medical students, interns, residents and post-MD/DO trainees.

4461 ■ American Medical Student Association, University of Maryland School of Medicine
655 W Baltimore St.
Baltimore, MD 21201-1559
Contact: E. Albert Reece MD, Dean
Ph: (410)706-7410
Fax: (410)706-0235
E-mail: deanmed@som.umaryland.edu
URL: http://medschool.umaryland.edu
Descr: Promotes improvement in medical training and education. Advances the medicine profession. Contributes to the welfare of medical students, interns, residents and post-MD/DO trainees.

4462 ■ Anne Arundel County Chapter of the Autism Society of America (AACC-ASA)
PO Box 1304
Millersville, MD 21108
Contact: Linda Carter-Ferrier, Co-Pres.
Ph: (410)923-8800
E-mail: md-annearundelcounty@autismsocietyofamerica.org
URL: http://www.aaccsa.org
Descr: Seeks to improve the lives of individuals affected by autism. Promotes awareness and understanding of autism disorders. Aims to further the advancement of preventive studies, therapy and research of autism disorders.

4463 ■ Arc of Baltimore
7215 York Rd.
Baltimore, MD 21212-4499
Contact: Stephen H. Morgan, Exec. Dir.
Ph: (410)296-2272
Fax: (410)296-2394
E-mail: info@arcofbaltimore.org
URL: http://www.arcofbaltimore.org
Staff: 22. **Descr:** Strives to ensure that persons with mental retardation have maximum opportunities for full participation in all aspects of life in the community and to offer programs and services that assist and support them in becoming and being true members of the community.

4464 ■ Arc of Carroll County, Maryland
180 Kriders Church Rd.
Westminster, MD 21158
Contact: Donald Rowe, Exec. Dir.
Ph: (410)848-4124
Fax: (410)876-5317
E-mail: drowe@arccarroll.com
URL: http://www.arccarroll.com

4465 ■ Arc of the Central Chesapeake Region
931 Spa Rd.
Annapolis, MD 21401

Ph: (410)268-8085
Fax: (410)269-0091
E-mail: information_request@thearcccr.org
URL: http://www.thearcccr.org

4466 ■ Arc of Frederick County
620A Research Dr.
Frederick, MD 21703
Contact: Margie Allen, Pres.
Ph: (301)663-0909
Fax: (301)695-6454
E-mail: info@arcfc.org
URL: http://www.arcfc.org

4467 ■ Arc of Howard County
11735 Homewood Rd.
Ellicott City, MD 21042
Contact: Carol A. Beatty, Exec. Dir.
Ph: (410)730-0638
Fax: (410)730-1436
E-mail: info@archoward.org
URL: http://www.archoward.org
Staff: 8. **Descr:** Parents, professional workers, and others interested in individuals with mental retardation. Works to promote services, research, public understanding, and legislation for people with mental retardation and their families. **Fnd:** 1961.

4468 ■ Arc of Maryland (Arc/MD)
49 Old Solomon's Island Rd., Ste. 205
Annapolis, MD 21401
Contact: Cristine Boswell Marchand, Exec. Dir.
Ph: (410)571-9320
Free: 888-272-3449
Fax: (410)974-6021
E-mail: info@thearcmd.org
URL: http://www.thearcmd.org
Staff: 11. **Descr:** Works to protect the rights and promote the abilities of persons with mental retardation. Provides systems advocacy, information and referral, public awareness, and prevention campaigns. **Fnd:** 1950. **Mem:** 7000. **Local Groups:** 12. **Pub:** The Arc and the Dove (quarterly).

4469 ■ Arc of Montgomery County
11600 Nebel St.
Rockville, MD 20852-2554
Contact: Joyce Taylor, Exec. Dir.
Ph: (301)984-5777
Fax: (301)816-2429
E-mail: info@arcmontmd.org
URL: http://www.arcmontmd.org
Descr: Parents, professional workers, and others interested in individuals with mental retardation. Works to promote services, research, public understanding, and legislation for people with mental retardation and their families. **Fnd:** 1992. **Pub:** Newsletter (bimonthly).

4470 ■ Arc Northern Chesapeake Region
4513 Old Philadelphia Rd.
Aberdeen, MD 21001
Ph: (410)836-7177
Free: 888-836-7177
Fax: (410)893-3909
URL: http://www.arcncr.org

4471 ■ Arc of Prince George's County
1401 McCormick Dr.
Largo, MD 20774
Contact: Mac Ramsey, Exec. Dir.
Ph: (301)925-7050
Fax: (301)925-4387
URL: http://www.thearcofpgc.org
Staff: 13. **Descr:** Parents, professional workers, and others interested in individuals with mental retardation. Works to promote services, research, public understanding, and legislation for people with mental retardation and their families. **Fnd:** 1952. **Pub:** Update (bimonthly).

4472 ■ Arc of Southern Maryland
Administration, Finance and Human Resources
268 Merrimac Ct.
PO Box 1860
Prince Frederick, MD 20678

Contact: Mark Todd, Pres.
Ph: (410)535-2413
Fax: (410)535-1314
E-mail: info@arcsomd.org
URL: http://www.arcsomd.org
Staff: 300. **Descr:** Parents, professionals, and interested individuals. Provides support, services, education, empowerment, employment and independence for people with mental retardation/developmental disabilities and their families. Sponsors fundraising activities. **Fnd:** 1975. **Mem:** 150. **Pub:** The Arc News (quarterly).

4473 ■ Arc of Washington County, Maryland
820 Florida Ave.
Hagerstown, MD 21740
Ph: (301)733-3550
Fax: (301)745-5573
E-mail: webmaster@arcwc-md.org
URL: http://www.arcwc-md.org

4474 ■ Autism Society of America - Frederick County Chapter
6595 Ewald Ct.
Frederick, MD 21703
Contact: Shawna Capotosto
Ph: (301)746-8080
Fax: (301)695-1250
E-mail: md-frederickcounty@
autismsocietyofamerica.org
Descr: Seeks to improve the lives of individuals affected by autism. Promotes awareness and understanding of autism disorders. Aims to further the advancement of preventive studies, therapy and research of autism disorders.

4475 ■ Autism Society of America - Harford County Chapter
1315 Vanderbilt Rd.
Bel Air, MD 21014
Contact: Ruth Good, Pres.
Ph: (410)879-4643
E-mail: bkgood@comcast.net
Descr: Seeks to improve the lives of individuals affected by autism. Promotes awareness and understanding of autism disorders. Aims to further the advancement of preventive studies, therapy and research of autism disorders.

4476 ■ Baltimore-Chesapeake Chapter - Autism Society of America (BCC-ASA)
PO Box 10822
Baltimore, MD 21234
Contact: Heather Thoms-Chesley
Ph: (410)655-7933
Fax: (410)583-2247
E-mail: questions@bcc-asa.org
URL: http://www.bcc-asa.org
Descr: Seeks to improve the lives of individuals affected by autism. Promotes awareness and understanding of autism disorders. Aims to further the advancement of preventive studies, therapy and research of autism disorders.

4477 ■ Concerned United Birthparents, DC Metro (CUB)
PO Box 15258
Chevy Chase, MD 20825
Ph: (202)298-1011
E-mail: dcmetrocub@aol.com
URL: http://www.geocities.com/Heartland/Village/6789/first.html
Descr: Birthparents (parents who have surrendered children to adoption), adoptees and adoptive parents. Provides emotional support and search assistance to family members separated by adoption. Educates society about adoption myths and realities, and increases public understanding and awareness of the need for family preservation and adoption reform. Maintains speakers' bureau, has local branches throughout the country, publishes a newsletter, and holds an annual retreat. **Fnd:** 1976. **Mem:** 60. **Reg.**

Groups: 25. **State Groups:** 2. **Local Groups:** 1. **Pub:** Newsletter (bimonthly).

4478 ■ District of Columbia Association for Career and Technical Education
7502 Gambier Dr.
Upper Marlboro, MD 20772
Contact: Guy F. Tillman, Acting Exec. Dir.
Ph: (301)868-4104
E-mail: gfratil@yahoo.com
URL: http://www.acteonline.org/content.aspx?id=780

4479 ■ Education Association of St. Mary's County (EASMC)
PO Box 640
Lexington Park, MD 20653
Contact: Ms. Jan Emerson, Pres.
Ph: (301)863-9216
Fax: (301)862-3342
E-mail: jbailer@mstanea.org
URL: http://www.mstanea.org/easmc
Staff: 1. **Descr:** Labor organization of public school teachers, administrators, and supervisors. **Mem:** 856. **Reg. Groups:** 1. **State Groups:** 1. **Pub:** Newsletter (monthly).

4480 ■ Horizon Goodwill Industries (HGI)
14515 Pennsylvania Ave.
Hagerstown, MD 21742
Contact: Debra Carbaugh
Ph: (301)733-7330
Free: 800-435-2480
E-mail: dcarbaugh@goodwill-hgi.org
URL: http://www.horizongoodwill.org
Staff: 340. **Descr:** Provides vocational training, placement services, and employment opportunities to persons with disabling and disadvantaged conditions. **Fnd:** 1955. **Mem:** 135. **State Groups:** 2. **Local Groups:** 1. **Pub:** Goodwill News (quarterly).

4481 ■ Howard County Autism Society (HCAS)
10280 Old Columbia Rd., Ste. 215
Columbia, MD 21046
Contact: Kim Manning
Ph: (410)290-3466
Fax: (410)290-5455
E-mail: info@howard-autism.org
URL: http://www.howard-autism.org
Descr: Seeks to improve the lives of individuals affected by autism. Promotes awareness and understanding of autism disorders. Aims to further the advancement of preventive studies, therapy and research of autism disorders.

4482 ■ Learning Disabilities Association of Calvert County
PO Box 3126
Prince Frederick, MD 20678
Contact: Donna Bowling, Pres.
E-mail: calvertlda@aol.com
URL: http://www.ldamaryland.org

4483 ■ Learning Disabilities Association of Howard County
PO Box 271
Woodstock, MD 21163
Contact: Nanette Schweitzer, Pres.
E-mail: howardcountylda@aol.com
URL: http://www.ldamaryland.org

4484 ■ Learning Disabilities Association of Maryland (LDA-MD)
PO Box 744
Dunkirk, MD 20754
Contact: Aimee Fellows-Merkle
Free: 888-265-6459
E-mail: calvertlda@aol.com

4485 ■ Learning Disabilities Association of Montgomery County (LDAMC)
PO Box 623
Rockville, MD 20848
Contact: Judy Lantz, Pres.
Ph: (301)933-1076

E-mail: ldamc@ldamc.org
URL: http://www.ldamc.org

4486 ■ Learning Disabilities Association of St. Mary's County
PO Box 70
St. Inigoes, MD 20684
Contact: Peggy Densford, Pres.
E-mail: densford@earthlink.net
URL: http://www.ldamaryland.org

4487 ■ Maryland Branch of the International Dyslexia Association (MBIDA)
PO Box 792
Brooklandville, MD 21022
Contact: Lucinda Draine, Pres.
Ph: (443)839-9209
E-mail: info@mbida.org
URL: http://www.mbida.org
Descr: Promotes public awareness and understanding of dyslexia. Seeks to develop and implement specialized methods to improve the quality of life for people who have dyslexia.

4488 ■ Maryland Department of Education
200 W. Baltimore St.
Baltimore, MD 21201
Contact: Dr. Nancy S. Grasmick, State Superintendent
Ph: (410)767-0600
Fax: (410)333-6033
E-mail: rpeiffer@msde.state.md.us
URL: http://www.marylandpublicschools.org/MSDE
Descr: Provides leadership, support, and accountability for effective systems of public education, library services, and rehabilitation services.

4489 ■ Maryland Developmental Disabilities Council
217 E Redwood St., Ste. 1300
Baltimore, MD 21202
Contact: Brian Cox, Exec. Dir.
Ph: (410)767-3670
Free: 800-305-6441
Fax: (410)333-3686
E-mail: info@md-council.org
URL: http://www.md-council.org
Descr: Advocates for public policy and supportive practices and opportunities that promote the full inclusion of all people with developmental disabilities in community life.

4490 ■ Maryland PTA
5 Central Ave.
Glen Burnie, MD 21061
Contact: Debbie Ritchie, Pres.
Ph: (410)760-6221
Free: 800-707-7972
Fax: (410)760-6344
E-mail: office@mdpta.org
URL: http://www.mdpta.org
Staff: 2. **Descr:** Promotes the welfare of children in the home, school, community, and place of worship. **Fnd:** 1915. **Mem:** 210000. **Local Groups:** 1. **Pub:** *PTA Bulletin* (9/year); Newsletter (9/year).

4491 ■ Maryland Vocational Association
Linganore High School
12013 Old Annapolis Rd.
Frederick, MD 21701
Contact: Thomas C. Hawthorne, Exec. Dir.
URL: http://www.acteonline.org/content.aspx?id=786
Descr: Aims to provide leadership in developing an educated, prepared, and competitive workforce.

4492 ■ Montgomery County Maryland Chapter of the Autism Society of America (MCASA)
4125 Queen Mary Dr.
Olney, MD 20832
Contact: Elizabeth Roth
Ph: (301)652-3912
E-mail: autismmontgomerycounty@yahoo.com
URL: http://www.autismmontgomerycounty.com
Descr: Seeks to improve the lives of individuals affected by autism. Promotes awareness and understanding of autism disorders. Aims to further the

advancement of preventive studies, therapy and research of autism disorders.

4493 ■ Special Olympics Maryland (SOMD)
513 Progress Dr., Ste. P
Linthicum, MD 21090-2256
Contact: Patricia Krebs PhD, Pres./CEO
Ph: (410)789-6677
Free: 800-541-7544
Fax: (410)789-5955
E-mail: jnovak@somd.org
URL: http://www.somd.org
Descr: Promotes physical fitness, sports training, and athletic competition for children and adults with mental retardation. Seeks to contribute to the physical, social, and psychological development of persons with mental retardation. Participants range in age from 8 years to adult and compete in track and field, swimming, gymnastics, bowling, ice skating, basketball, and other sports.

4494 ■ Teachers Association of Baltimore County (TABCO)
305 E Joppa Rd.
Towson, MD 21286-3252
Contact: Cheryl Bost
Ph: (410)882-2604
E-mail: cbost@mstanea.org
URL: http://www.mstanea.org
Staff: 12. **Descr:** Teachers, Labor Organization. Serves as a voice for the teaching profession. Promotes educational excellence. Operates Kid Care, a program assisting children who cannot attend school because of lack of clothing and other problems of the same nature. Maintains Teachers Center for professional development. **Fnd:** 1918. **Mem:** 5600. **State Groups:** 1. **Local Groups:** 1. **Pub:** *TABCO Bulletin* (monthly); *TABCO Calendar/Handbook* (annual).

Massachusetts

4495 ■ AccessSportAmerica
119 High St.
Acton, MA 01720
Contact:Rev. Ross Lilley, Exec. Dir.
Ph: (978)264-0985
Free: 866-45-SPORT
E-mail: info@accesssportamerica.org
URL: http://www.windsurf.org
Staff: 10. **Descr:** Improves physical and mental capabilities and performance of persons with physical disabilities. **Fnd:** 1995.

4496 ■ AG BELL, Massachusetts
PO Box 53
Sharon, MA 02067
Contact: Joanne Travers, Pres.
E-mail: info@massagbell.org
URL: http://www.massagbell.org
Descr: Represents the interests of educators, parents of children with hearing loss, adults with hearing loss and hearing health professionals. Provides governmental and education advocacy services.

4497 ■ American Medical Student Association, Boston University School of Medicine
715 Albany St.
Boston, MA 02118
Ph: (617)638-5300
E-mail: busmdean@bu.edu
URL: http://www.bumc.bu.edu/busm
Descr: Promotes improvement in medical training and education. Advances the medicine profession. Contributes to the welfare of medical students, interns, residents and post-MD/DO trainees.

4498 ■ American Medical Student Association, Harvard Medical School
25 Shattuck St.
Boston, MA 02115
Contact: Stephanie W. Hu, Pres.
Ph: (617)432-1000
URL: http://www.med.harvard.edu

Descr: Promotes improvement in medical training and education. Advances the medicine profession. Contributes to the welfare of medical students, interns, residents and post-MD/DO trainees.

4499 ■ American Medical Student Association, University of Massachusetts Medical School
55 Lake Ave. N
Worcester, MA 01655
Contact: Wynne Morgan
Ph: (508)856-8989
E-mail: wynne.morgan@umassmed.edu
URL: http://www.umassmed.edu/index.aspx
Descr: Promotes improvement in medical training and education. Advances the medicine profession. Contributes to the welfare of medical students, interns, residents and post-MD/DO trainees.

4500 ■ Arc of Cape Cod
PO Box 428
Hyannis, MA 02601
Ph: (508)790-3667
E-mail: arcofcapecod@hotmail.com
URL: http://www.arcofcapecod.org

4501 ■ ARC Community Services
564 Main St.
Fitchburg, MA 01420
Contact: Terry William Kennedy, Pres./CEO
Ph: (978)343-6662
Fax: (978)343-8852
E-mail: info@arccommunityservices.org
URL: http://www.arccommunityservices.org
Descr: Provides advocacy and services to families and individuals with disabilities. **Fnd:** 1952. **Pub:** *The Crusader* (quarterly).

4502 ■ Arc of East Middlesex
20 Gould St.
Reading, MA 01867
Contact: Michael Berardo, Interim Exec. Dir.
Ph: (781)942-4888
Fax: (781)942-0820
E-mail: mberardo@theemarc.org
URL: http://www.theemarc.org

4503 ■ Arc of Greater Boston (ArcGB)
221 N Beacon St.
Boston, MA 02135
Contact: Terri Angelone, CEO
Ph: (617)783-3900
Fax: (617)783-9190
E-mail: info@arcgb.org
URL: http://www.arcgb.org

4504 ■ Arc of Greater Fall River
PO Box 1943
Fall River, MA 02722
Contact: Dan Smith, Exec. Dir.
Ph: (508)679-0001
Fax: (508)679-9375
E-mail: danarc29@msn.com
URL: http://www.arcmass.org

4505 ■ Arc of Massachusetts
217 South St.
Waltham, MA 02453
Contact: Leo V. Sarkissian, Exec. Dir.
Ph: (781)891-6270
Fax: (781)891-6271
E-mail: arcmass@arcmass.org
URL: http://www.arcmass.org

4506 ■ Arc Northern Bristol County
141 Park St.
Attleboro, MA 02703
Contact: Valerie Zagami, Pres.
Ph: (508)226-1445
Free: 888-343-3301
Fax: (508)226-1476
URL: http://www.arcnbc.org
Descr: Parents, professional workers, and others interested in individuals with mental retardation. Works to promote services, research, public understanding, and legislation for people with mental

retardation and their families. **Fnd:** 1959. **Pub:** Annual Reports (annual); Newsletters (quarterly).

4507 ■ Arc of Northern Essex
57 Wingate St., Ste. 301
Haverhill, MA 01832
Contact: Eileen Woelfel
Ph: (978)373-0552
Fax: (978)373-0557
E-mail: arc.nec@verizon.net
URL: http://arcmass.org
Staff: 25. **Descr:** Individuals with disabilities, professionals, parents, health care agencies, and others. Provides advocacy, support and services to people with mental retardation/developmental disabilities and their families. Advocates and lobbies for favorable legislation. Sponsors educational programs for members as well as the public. Offers information and referral services. **Fnd:** 1963. **Mem:** 240. **Reg. Groups:** 1. **State Groups:** 1. **Local Groups:** 23. **Pub:** *The ARC Community Connection* (monthly); *Monthly Activity Calendar.*

4508 ■ Arc of the South Shore
371 River St.
North Weymouth, MA 02191
Contact: Maria Traniello, Pres.
Ph: (781)335-3023
E-mail: info@arcsouthshore.org
URL: http://www.arcsouthshore.org

4509 ■ Berkshire County Arc (BCARC)
395 South St.
Pittsfield, MA 01201
Contact: Kenneth W. Singer, Exec. Dir.
Ph: (413)499-4241
E-mail: bcarc@bcarc.org
URL: http://www.bcarc.org
Descr: Offers a broad range of community-based services to persons with developmental disabilities. Assists and supports individuals in their quest to identify and realize their chosen lifestyles. **Fnd:** 1954.

4510 ■ Brockton Area Arc (BAARC)
1250 W Chestnut St.
Brockton, MA 02301
Ph: (508)583-8030
Fax: (508)583-1739
E-mail: baarc@comcast.net
URL: http://www.brocktonareaarc.org

4511 ■ CLASS/Arc of Greater Lawrence
1 Parker St.
Lawrence, MA 01843
Contact: Robert A. Harris, Pres./CEO
Ph: (978)975-8587
Fax: (978)975-0498
E-mail: bharris@classinc.org
URL: http://www.classinc.org

4512 ■ Common Cause Massachusetts
59 Temple Pl., Ste. 600
Boston, MA 02111
Contact: Pamela Wilmot, Exec. Dir.
Ph: (617)426-9600
Fax: (617)426-6855
E-mail: ccma@commoncause.org
URL: http://www.commoncause.org/ma
Staff: 2. **Descr:** Works for open and accountable government, campaign finance and ethics reform. **Fnd:** 1973. **Mem:** 10000. **Pub:** *State Newsletter* (semiannual).

4513 ■ Learning Disabilities Association of Massachusetts
216 Lowell St., Apt. 3L
Peabody, MA 01960
Contact: Aaron Smith
E-mail: asmith0704@curry.edu

4514 ■ Massachusetts AfterSchool Partnership
1250 Hancock St., Ste. 205N
Quincy, MA 02169
Contact: Gwynn Hughes, Exec. Dir.
Ph: (781)348-4275
Fax: (781)348-4280

E-mail: ghughes@massafterschool.org
URL: http://www.massafterschool.org

4515 ■ Massachusetts AfterSchool Partnership - Central Region
Child Care Connection
100 Grove St., Ste. 102
Worcester, MA 01605
Contact: Joanne Gravell
Ph: (508)757-1503
E-mail: jgravell@cccfscm.org
URL: http://www.massafterschool.org

4516 ■ Massachusetts AfterSchool Partnership - Greater Boston Region
BOSTnet
11 Beacon St., Ste. 1000
Boston, MA 02108
Contact: Maryellen Coffey
Ph: (617)720-1290
E-mail: coffey@bostnet.org
URL: http://www.massafterschool.org

4517 ■ Massachusetts AfterSchool Partnership - MetroWest Region
MetroWest YMCA
280 Old Connecticut Path
Framingham, MA 01701
Contact: Heidi Kaufman
Ph: (508)879-4420
E-mail: hkaufman@metrowestymca.org
URL: http://www.massafterschool.org

4518 ■ Massachusetts AfterSchool Partnership - Northeast Region
For Kids Only
201 Winthrop St.
Winthrop, MA 02152
Contact: Debbie Kneeland
Ph: (617)846-6654
E-mail: debbiekneeland@hotmail.com
URL: http://www.massafterschool.org

4519 ■ Massachusetts AfterSchool Partnership - Southeastern Region
Bldg. After School Excellence
130 Liberty St., Ste. 7
Brockton, MA 02301
Contact: Patty McGrath
Ph: (508)941-0300
E-mail: getonbase508@aol.com
URL: http://www.massafterschool.org

4520 ■ Massachusetts Association for Children With Learning Disabilities
PO Box 142
Weston, MA 02493
Contact: David Bradburn, Exec. Dir.
Ph: (781)890-5399
Fax: (781)890-0555
Descr: Parents of children with learning disabilities, learning disabled individuals, and professionals in the field. Promotes education and support services. **Fnd:** 1968. **Mem:** 15000. **Pub:** *Insights on Learning Disabilities* (biennial); *LDW Highlights.*

4521 ■ Massachusetts Association for the Education of Young Children
126 Phoenix Ave.
Lowell, MA 01852
Contact: Yvonne Beirne, Pres.
Ph: (978)654-6053
E-mail: massaeyc@yahoo.com
URL: http://www.massaeyc.com
Descr: Serves and acts on behalf of the needs, rights and well-being of all young children with primary focus on the quality of educational and developmental services for all children. Seeks to improve professional practice and working conditions in early childhood education. **Mem:** 2100. **Pub:** Newsletter (quarterly).

4522 ■ Massachusetts Branch of the International Dyslexia Association (MABIDA)
PO Box 662
Lincoln, MA 01773
Contact: Pamela Hook, Pres.
Ph: (617)650-0011

E-mail: rnabida@comcast.net
URL: http://www.dyslexia-ma.org
Descr: Promotes public awareness and understanding of dyslexia. Seeks to develop and implement specialized methods to improve the quality of life for people who have dyslexia. **Fnd:** 1971. **Mem:** 500. **Pub:** Newsletter (semiannual).

4523 ■ Massachusetts Department of Education
350 Main St.
Malden, MA 02148-5023
Contact: Mitchell D. Chester, Commnr.
Ph: (781)338-3000
Fax: (781)338-3395
E-mail: www@doe.mass.edu
URL: http://www.doe.mass.edu/

4524 ■ Massachusetts Developmental Disabilities Council (MDDC)
1150 Hancock St., Ste. 300
Quincy, MA 02169-4340
Contact: Daniel M. Shannon, Exec. Dir.
Ph: (617)770-7676
Fax: (617)770-1987
E-mail: dan.shannon@state.ma.us
URL: http://www.state.ma.us/mddc
Descr: Promotes education for children, meaningful work for adults, community living for all people with disabilities, and self-advocacy by people with disabilities and parents.

4525 ■ Massachusetts Parent Teacher Association
PO Box 421
Rehoboth, MA 02769
Contact: Dr. Erik Champy, Sec.
Ph: (508)347-7055
Fax: (860)537-4173
E-mail: info@masspta.org
URL: http://www.masspta.org
Descr: Provides a support network to local units and councils statewide through state and district PTA conferences, workshops, personalized schools of instruction, and numerous publications and materials. **Fnd:** 1910. **Mem:** 19000.

4526 ■ Minute Man Arc
1269 Main St.
Concord, MA 01742
Contact: Marty Martini, Pres.
Ph: (978)287-7900
E-mail: mmartini@minutemanarc.org
URL: http://www.minutemanarc.org

4527 ■ North Shore Arc (NSArc)
64 Holten St.
Danvers, MA 01923
Contact: Gerard McCarthy, Exec. Dir.
Ph: (978)762-4878
Fax: (978)777-6149
E-mail: jmccarthy@nsarc.org
URL: http://www.arcmass.org

4528 ■ Recording for the Blind and Dyslexic Boston Unit
2067 Massachusetts Ave.
Cambridge, MA 02140
Contact: Christina Raimo, Exec. Dir.
Ph: (617)577-1111
Fax: (617)577-1113
E-mail: traimo@rfbd.org
Descr: Serves individuals who cannot effectively read standard print because of visual impairment, dyslexia, or other physical disabilities. Creates educational opportunities for students with print disabilities through educational and outreach services. Provides and promotes the effective use of accessible educational materials.

4529 ■ Seven Hills Foundation
81 Hope Ave.
Worcester, MA 01603
Contact: David A. Jordan DHA, Pres./CEO
Ph: (508)755-2340
Fax: (508)849-3882

E-mail: djordan@sevenhills.org

URL: http://www.sevenhills.org

Descr: Parents, professional workers, and others interested in individuals with mental retardation. Works to promote services, research, public understanding, and legislation for people with mental retardation and their families. **Fnd:** 1951. **Pub:** Annual Report (annual).

4530 ■ South Norfolk County Arc (SNCARC)
789 Clapboardtree St.
Westwood, MA 02090
Contact: William F. Abel, CEO
Ph: (781)762-4001
Fax: (781)461-5950
E-mail: dwood@sncarc.org
URL: http://www.sncarc.org

4531 ■ Southern Worcester County ARC
PO Box 66
Southbridge, MA 01550
Contact: James Howard, Exec. Dir.
Ph: (508)764-4085
Fax: (508)765-0255
E-mail: info@thecenterofhope.org
URL: http://www.thecenterofhope.org

4532 ■ Special Olympics Massachusetts (SOMA)
450 Maple St., Bldg. 1
Danvers, MA 01923-4009
Contact: Robert A. Johnson, Pres./CEO
Ph: (978)774-1501
Fax: (978)750-4686
E-mail: bob.johnson@specialolympicsma.org
URL: http://www.specialolympicsma.org

Descr: Promotes physical fitness, sports training, and athletic competition for children and adults with mental retardation and other closely related developmental disabilities. Seeks to contribute to the physical, social, and psychological development of persons with mental retardation. Participants range in age from 8 years to adult and compete in track and field, swimming, gymnastics, bowling, ice skating, basketball, and other sports. **Fnd:** 1971. **Mem:** 16800.

4533 ■ Tufts American Medical Student Association
136 Harrison Ave.
Boston, MA 02110
Contact: Tushar R. Patel, Pres.
Ph: (617)636-7000
E-mail: med-info@tufts.edu
URL: http://www.tufts.edu/med

Descr: Promotes improvement in medical training and education. Advances the medicine profession. Contributes to the welfare of medical students, interns, residents and post-MD/DO trainees.

Michigan

4534 ■ 100 Black Men of Greater Detroit
1 Ford Pl.
Detroit, MI 48202
Contact: Randy Walker, Pres.
Ph: (313)874-4811
E-mail: info@100blackmendetroit.org
URL: http://www.100blackmendetroit.org

4535 ■ American Association of University Women, Ann Arbor Branch
PO Box 2806
Ann Arbor, MI 48106
Contact: Polly Pan, Pres.
Ph: (734)973-6287
E-mail: president@aauwaa.org
URL: http://www.aauwaa.org

Descr: Advances equity for women and girls through advocacy, education, and research. Provides funds and a support system for women seeking judicial redress for sex discrimination in higher education.

4536 ■ American Association of University Women of Michigan
45177 Horseshoe Cir.
Canton, MI 48187
Contact: Mickey Edell, Pres.
Ph: (734)981-7172
E-mail: mousemick1@comcast.net

Descr: Advances equity for women and girls through advocacy, education, and research. Provides funds and a support system for women seeking judicial redress for sex discrimination in higher education.

4537 ■ American Medical Student Association, Michigan State University College of Human Medicine
A110 E Fee Hall
East Lansing, MI 48824-1316
Contact: Drew William Engers
Ph: (734)761-8529
E-mail: engersdr@msu.edu
URL: http://www.chm.msu.edu

Descr: Promotes improvement in medical training and education. Advances the medicine profession. Contributes to the welfare of medical students, interns, residents and post-MD/DO trainees.

4538 ■ American Medical Student Association, University of Michigan Medical School
Office of Student Programs
1301 Catherine St.
5124 MS I
Ann Arbor, MI 48109-0611
Contact: Adam Castano, Co-Pres.
Ph: (734)764-0219
Fax: (734)936-3510
E-mail: acastano@umich.edu
URL: http://www.umich.edu/~amsa

Descr: Promotes improvement in medical training and education. Advances the medicine profession. Contributes to the welfare of medical students, interns, residents and post-MD/DO trainees.

4539 ■ American Medical Student Association, Wayne State University School of Medicine
Scott Hall
540 E Canfield St.
Detroit, MI 48201
Contact: Iuliana Dit, Pres.
E-mail: idit@med.wayne.edu
URL: http://www.med.wayne.edu/amsa

Descr: Promotes improvement in medical training and education. Advances the medicine profession. Contributes to the welfare of medical students, interns, residents and post-MD/DO trainees.

4540 ■ Arc Arenac Area
PO Box 805
Pinconning, MI 48650
Contact: Mike De Wyse, Pres.
Ph: (989)846-9829
E-mail: carole3@charter.net

4541 ■ Arc of Bay County
709 Columbus Ave.
Bay City, MI 48708
Contact: Sharolyn R. Meyer, Exec. Dir.
Ph: (989)893-1346
Fax: (989)893-1281
URL: http://www.arcbc.com

4542 ■ Arc of Calhoun County
217 Hamblin Ave. W, Ste. 3
Battle Creek, MI 49037
Contact: Kim Hommerding, Exec. Dir.
Ph: (269)966-2575
E-mail: financearc@aol.com

4543 ■ Arc of Central Michigan
PO Box 171
Mount Pleasant, MI 48804
Contact: Anne Marie Koelbel, Exec. Dir.
Ph: (989)773-8765
Fax: (989)773-8765

E-mail: director@arcofcentralmi.org
URL: http://www.arcofcentralmi.org

4544 ■ Arc Dearborn/Dearborn Heights
27325 W Warren St.
Dearborn Heights, MI 48127
Contact: Lisa M. Nygord, Exec. Dir.
Ph: (313)562-1787
E-mail: arcpdp@aol.com

4545 ■ Arc Delta County
PO Box 651
Escanaba, MI 49829
Contact: James Vicenzi, Pres.
Ph: (906)786-9212

4546 ■ Arc Detroit
51 W Hancock St.
Detroit, MI 48201
Contact: Henry Johnson, Exec. Dir.
Ph: (313)831-0202
E-mail: thearcdetroit@aol.com

4547 ■ Arc Downriver
4212 13th St.
Wyandotte, MI 48192
Contact: Kevin McGuckin, Exec. Dir.
Ph: (734)283-0710
E-mail: arcriver@sbcglobal.net

4548 ■ Arc Kent County
629 Michigan Ave. NE, Ste. D
Grand Rapids, MI 49503
Contact: Ms. Kathleen Allen, Exec. Dir.
Ph: (616)459-3339
Free: 800-649-3777
Fax: (616)459-5299
E-mail: info@arckent.org
URL: http://www.arckent.org

Staff: 3. **Descr:** Provides individuals with developmental disabilities the assistance to advocate for their own concerns. **Fnd:** 1950. **Mem:** 100.

4549 ■ Arc Livingston
1004 Durant Dr., Ste. 1
Howell, MI 48843
Contact: Sherri L. Boyd
Ph: (517)546-1228
E-mail: pnowak@arclivingston.org
URL: http://www.arclivingston.org

Descr: Seeks to ensure the rights of people with disabilities and build quality community life for them and their families. **Fnd:** 1954.

4550 ■ Arc Manistee
PO Box 545
Manistee, MI 49660
Contact: Leanne Witucki, Pres.
Ph: (231)723-6205
E-mail: beldridg@manistee-net.com

4551 ■ Arc Michigan
1325 S Washington Ave.
Lansing, MI 48910
Contact: Dohn Hoyle, Exec. Dir.
Ph: (517)487-5426
Free: 800-292-7851
Fax: (517)487-0303
E-mail: dhoyle@arcmi.org
URL: http://www.arcmi.org

4552 ■ Arc of Midland
220 W Main St., Ste. 101
Midland, MI 48640
Contact: Jan Lampman, Exec. Dir.
Ph: (989)631-4439
Fax: (989)832-5528
E-mail: arcadmin@thearcofmidland.org
URL: http://www.thearcofmidland.org

4553 ■ Arc of Monroe County, Michigan
752 S Monroe St., Ste. B
Monroe, MI 48161
Contact: Kristyn Theisen, Exec. Dir.

Ph: (734)241-5881
E-mail: arcmonroe@foxberry.net

4554 ■ Arc Montcalm
PO Box 1011
Stanton, MI 48888
Contact: Kay Pierce, Pres.
Ph: (989)831-5008

4555 ■ Arc/Muskegon
1145 E Wesley Ave.
Muskegon, MI 49442-2197
Contact: Margaret O'Toole, Exec. Dir.
Ph: (231)777-2006
Fax: (231)777-3507
E-mail: arcmusk@i2k.com
URL: http://www.arcmuskegon.org
Descr: Represents persons interested in the welfare of people with developmental disabilities. **Fnd:** 1952. **Mem:** 109. **Pub:** ARC/Muskegon News (quarterly).

4556 ■ Arc Newaygo County
PO Box 147
Fremont, MI 49412
Contact: Maggie Kolk, Pres.
Ph: (616)924-5840
E-mail: thearc@iserv.net

4557 ■ Arc of Northwest Wayne County
26049 5 Mile Rd.
Redford, MI 48239
Contact: Christine Lerchen, Exec. Dir.
Ph: (313)532-7915
Fax: (313)532-7488
E-mail: info@thearcnw.org
URL: http://thearcnw.org

4558 ■ Arc of Oakland County
1641 W Big Beaver Rd.
Troy, MI 48084
Contact: Thomas F. Kendziorski, Exec. Dir.
Ph: (248)816-1900
Fax: (248)816-1906
URL: http://www.thearcoakland.org

4559 ■ Arc Oceana County
PO Box 336
Whitehall, MI 49461
Contact: Ruth Pecott, Pres.
Ph: (231)894-4638
E-mail: trepecott@hotmail.com
URL: http://www.arcmi.org

4560 ■ Arc Ogemaw County
117 Somerset Terr.
Roscommon, MI 48653
Contact: Arlene Williams, Pres.
Ph: (989)275-9563

4561 ■ Arc of St. Clair County
1033 26th St.
Port Huron, MI 48060
Contact: Jim Fortushniak, Exec. Dir.
Ph: (810)982-3261
E-mail: arcscc@advnet.net

4562 ■ ARC Services of Macomb
44050 Gratiot Ave.
Clinton Township, MI 48036-1308
Contact: Lisa Piercey-Lepine, Assoc. Dir.
Ph: (586)469-1600
Fax: (586)469-2527
E-mail: rfkimball@arcservices.org
URL: http://www.arcservices.org
Descr: Represents people with disabilities, parents, friends, and professionals. Provides an array of services for people with disabilities in Macomb County. **Fnd:** 1953.

4563 ■ Arc of Shiawassee County
1905 W M-21
Owosso, MI 48867
Contact: Cynthia Mayhew, Exec. Dir.
Ph: (989)723-7377
Fax: (989)725-6113

E-mail: arcshia@michonline.net
URL: http://www.arcofshiawassee.org

4564 ■ Arc of Western Wayne County
2257 S Wayne Rd.
Westland, MI 48186
Contact: Cheryl S. Polite, Exec. Dir.
Ph: (734)729-9100
Fax: (734)729-9695
E-mail: info@thearcww.org
URL: http://www.thearcww.org
Descr: Represents parents, professional workers, and others interested in individuals with mental retardation. Works to promote services, research, public understanding, and legislation for people with mental retardation and their families. **Fnd:** 1954.

4565 ■ Association for Community Advocacy
1100 N Main St., Ste. 205
Ann Arbor, MI 48104
Contact: Sherry Fernandez, Pres./CEO
Ph: (734)662-1256
Fax: (734)662-2699
E-mail: info@washtenawaca.org
URL: http://www.washtenawaca.org
Descr: Parents, professional workers, and others interested in individuals with mental retardation. Works to promote services, research, public understanding, and legislation for people with mental retardation and their families.

4566 ■ Autism Society of America - Lansing Chapter
15507 Outer Dr.
Bath, MI 48808
Contact: Kimberly Maddox-Reihl
Ph: (517)420-3313
E-mail: autismsocietyoflansing@ymail.com
Descr: Seeks to improve the lives of individuals affected by autism. Promotes awareness and understanding of autism disorders. Aims to further the advancement of preventive studies, therapy and research of autism disorders.

4567 ■ Autism Society of America - Livingston County Chapter
PO Box 842
Brighton, MI 48116
Contact: Louis D. Scott Jr., Pres.
Ph: (810)360-0417
E-mail: mi-livingstoncounty@autismsocietyofamerica.org
Descr: Seeks to improve the lives of individuals affected by autism. Promotes awareness and understanding of autism disorders. Aims to further the advancement of preventive studies, therapy and research of autism disorders.

4568 ■ Autism Society of America - Newaygo County Chapter
PO Box 314
Fremont, MI 49412
Contact: Kellie Ashcroft
Ph: (231)834-0384
E-mail: mi-newaygocounty@autismsocietyofamerica.org
Descr: Seeks to improve the lives of individuals affected by autism. Promotes awareness and understanding of autism disorders. Aims to further the advancement of preventive studies, therapy and research of autism disorders.

4569 ■ Autism Society of America - Oakland County Chapter (ASA-OCC)
PO Box 70207
Rochester Hills, MI 48307
Contact: Anne Fleming, Pres.
Ph: (248)393-3131
E-mail: chapterinfo@asaoakland.org
URL: http://www.asaoakland.org
Descr: Seeks to improve the lives of individuals affected by autism. Promotes awareness and understanding of autism disorders. Aims to further the

advancement of preventive studies, therapy and research of autism disorders.

4570 ■ Autism Society of America - West Shore Michigan Chapter
PO Box 1054
Holland, MI 49422
Contact: Margie Broussard, Pres.
Ph: (616)395-3222
E-mail: asws_contact@yahoo.com
URL: http://www.asws.org
Descr: Seeks to improve the lives of individuals affected by autism. Promotes awareness and understanding of autism disorders. Aims to further the advancement of preventive studies, therapy and research of autism disorders.

4571 ■ Autism Society of Kalamazoo/Battle Creek
4606 Croyden Ave.
Kalamazoo, MI 49006
Contact: Katrina Wood, Pres.
Free: 800-628-6421
E-mail: twood@asa-kal.org
URL: http://www.asa-kal.org
Descr: Seeks to improve the lives of individuals affected by autism. Promotes awareness and understanding of autism disorders. Aims to further the advancement of preventive studies, therapy and research of autism disorders.

4572 ■ Autism Society of Kent County (ASK)
PO Box 150348
Grand Rapids, MI 49515
Contact: Richard Elias III, Pres.
Ph: (616)752-8577
E-mail: info@autismsocietyofkentcounty.org
URL: http://www.autismsocietyofkentcounty.org
Descr: Seeks to improve the lives of individuals affected by autism. Promotes awareness and understanding of autism disorders. Aims to further the advancement of preventive studies, therapy and research of autism disorders.

4573 ■ Autism Society of Southeast Wayne County Chapter (ASA/SE-WCC)
PO Box 1403
Taylor, MI 48180
Contact: Cecelia Hammond, Pres.
Ph: (734)287-8898
E-mail: se-wcc@comcast.com
URL: http://asasewcc.homestead.com
Descr: Seeks to improve the lives of individuals affected by autism. Promotes awareness and understanding of autism disorders. Aims to further the advancement of preventive studies, therapy and research of autism disorders.

4574 ■ Autism Society of Washtenaw County (ASW)
4755 Meridian Ct.
Saline, MI 48176
Contact: Barb Byers, Co-Pres.
Ph: (734)827-0814
E-mail: babmay11@prodigy.net
URL: http://autismsocietywash.tripod.com
Descr: Seeks to improve the lives of individuals affected by autism. Promotes awareness and understanding of autism disorders. Aims to further the advancement of preventive studies, therapy and research of autism disorders.

4575 ■ Cannonsburg Challenged Ski Association (CCSA)
PO Box 352
Ada, MI 49301
Contact: Ms. Jean Weygandt, Pres.
Ph: (616)874-3060
E-mail: ken@skiccsa.org
URL: http://www.skiccsa.org
Descr: Provides lessons and the use of adaptive downhill ski equipment to people with disabilities in West Michigan. Encourages family participation and

the maximum independence possible for each individual. **Fnd:** 1980.

4576 ■ Central Michigan Autism Society of America
502 E Deerfield Rd.
Mount Pleasant, MI 48858
Contact: Sherrie Sponseller, Pres.
Ph: (989)506-1367
E-mail: central_michiganasa@yahoo.com
Descr: Seeks to improve the lives of individuals affected by autism. Promotes awareness and understanding of autism disorders. Aims to further the advancement of preventive studies, therapy and research of autism disorders.

4577 ■ Common Cause of Michigan (CC/MI)
315 Second St., No. 401
Ann Arbor, MI 48103
Contact: John Chamberlin, Chm.
Ph: (734)763-0689
Fax: (734)763-9181
E-mail: johnch@umich.edu
URL: http://www.commoncause.org
Staff: 1. **Descr:** Represents individuals working for an ethical, open, and accountable government. Promotes campaign finance reform, voter registration, and open legislative meetings. **Fnd:** 1973. **Mem:** 7500. **Pub:** *Legislative Update* (3/year); *Links* (3/year).

4578 ■ Community Advocates for Persons with Developmental Disabilities
814 S Westnedge Ave.
Kalamazoo, MI 49008
Contact: Deb Russell, Pres./CEO
Ph: (269)342-9801
Fax: (269)342-4638
E-mail: drussell@communityadvocates.org
URL: http://www.communityadvocates.org

4579 ■ Learning Disabilities Association of Michigan (LDA of MI)
200 Museum Dr., Ste. 101
Lansing, MI 48933-1914
Contact: Florence Curtis Dewitt, Acting Exec. Dir.
Ph: (517)485-8160
Free: 888-597-7809
E-mail: info@ldaofmichigan.org
URL: http://www.ldaofmichigan.org
Descr: Seeks to enhance the quality of life for all individuals with learning disabilities and their families; to alleviate the restricting effects of learning disabilities; and to support endeavors to determine the causes of learning disabilities. Addresses its missions through advocacy, education, research, service and collaborative efforts. **Fnd:** 1965. **Mem:** 1300. **Pub:** *Outlook* (bimonthly).

4580 ■ Learning Disabilities Association of Michigan, Washtenaw County Chapter
200 Museum Dr. Ste. 101
Lansing, MI 48933
Contact: Kathleen Kosobud, Pres.
Ph: (517)485-8160
Free: 888-597-7809
E-mail: ldamich@sbcglobal.net
URL: http://www.ldaofmichigan.org

4581 ■ Macomb County Fire Prevention Association
18750 Common Rd.
Roseville, MI 48066
Contact: Craig Robertson
Ph: (586)445-5421
E-mail: crobertson@roseville-mi.com
Descr: Provides the highest quality codes, standards, products, and services for all concerned with the safety and performance of the built environment.

4582 ■ Macomb/St. Clair County Chapter of the Autism Society of America (MSCCC/ASA)
PO Box 182186
Shelby Township, MI 48318
Contact: Betsy Mickley, Pres.
Ph: (586)447-2235

E-mail: support@macombasa.org
URL: http://www.macombasa.org
Descr: Seeks to improve the lives of individuals affected by autism. Promotes awareness and understanding of autism disorders. Aims to further the advancement of preventive studies, therapy and research of autism disorders.

4583 ■ Michigan Adaptive Sports (MAS)
PO Box 569
Keego Harbor, MI 48320
Ph: (248)988-0156
URL: http://www.michiganadaptivesports.org
Descr: Adaptive snow and water skiing, kayaking, and hand cycling for individuals with disabilities. **Fnd:** 1981. **Mem:** 125. **Pub:** Newsletter (semiannual).

4584 ■ Michigan Association for Career and Technical Education (MI ACTE)
Education Service District
1025 N Shiawassee St.
Corunna, MI 48817
Contact: Brian Pyles, Pres.
E-mail: pyles@sresd.org
URL: http://www.acteonline.org/content.aspx?id=788
Descr: Works to advance vocational technical education.

4585 ■ Michigan Association for the Education of Young Children (MiAEYC)
Beacon Pl.
4572 S Hagadorn Rd., Ste. 1-D
East Lansing, MI 48823-5385
Contact: Keith Myers, Exec. Dir.
Ph: (517)336-9700
Free: 800-336-6424
Fax: (517)336-9790
E-mail: miaeyc@miaeyc.org
URL: http://www.miaeyc.org
Staff: 6. **Descr:** Teachers and administrators of day care centers and preschools; teachers and administrators of elementary schools; college faculty and social service workers; Head Start teachers and administrators. Promotes high standards for the care and education of young children and advocates on their behalf. Promotes continued study of the development of young children. Works to ensure the welfare of young children and their families. **Fnd:** 1974. **Mem:** 3000. **Local Groups:** 21. **Pub:** *Beacon* (3/year).

4586 ■ Michigan Branch of the International Dyslexia Association
983 Spaulding Ave. SE
Ada, MI 49301
Contact: Pat Frazier, Pres.
Ph: (616)717-2984
E-mail: postmaster@idamib.org
URL: http://www.idamib.org
Descr: Promotes public awareness and understanding of dyslexia. Seeks to develop and implement specialized methods to improve the quality of life for people who have dyslexia.

4587 ■ Michigan Communities In Schools (MCIS)
11172 Adams St.
Holland, MI 49423
Contact: Deanna DePree, Dir.
Ph: (616)396-7566
E-mail: mail@lifeservicessystem.org
Descr: Creates and coordinates public and private sector partnerships to bring existing community resources into the public schools. Improves the quality of public education and helps children stay in school and prepare for life. **Fnd:** 1994.

4588 ■ Michigan Department of Education
608 W. Allegan St.
PO Box 30008
Lansing, MI 48909
Contact: Mike P. Flanagan, Superintendent
Ph: (517)373-3324
Fax: (517)335-4565

E-mail: MDEweb@michigan.gov
URL: http://www.michigan.gov/mde/

4589 ■ Michigan Protection and Advocacy Service (MPAS)
4095 Legacy Pkwy., Ste. 500
Lansing, MI 48911-4263
Contact: Kathy McGeathy, Pres.
Ph: (517)487-1755
Free: 800-288-5923
Fax: (517)487-0827
E-mail: molson@mpas.org
URL: http://www.mpas.org
Staff: 55. **Descr:** Works to protect the rights of persons with developmental, mental health, and other disabilities. Advocate on their behalf through information and referral, advocacy services, legal and systemic reform, legislation, and litigation. **Fnd:** 1981. **Pub:** *Exchange* (annual).

4590 ■ Michigan Women's Studies Association (MWSA)
213 W Main St.
Lansing, MI 48933
Contact: Gladys Beckwith PhD, Pres.
Ph: (517)484-1880
Fax: (517)372-0170
E-mail: michiganwomen@sbcglobal.net
URL: http://www.michiganwomenshalloffame.org
Staff: 5. **Descr:** Represents educators, education institutions, and others interested in promoting women's studies in schools and universities. Disseminates information on American women. Aims to eliminate bias against and stereotyping of women. Promotes non-racist and non-sexist education in schools; encourages research by, for, and about women. Maintains Women's Hall of Fame and Women's Historical Center. **Fnd:** 1973. **Mem:** 1800. **Local Groups:** 1. **Pub:** *House Handbill* (quarterly); *Michigan Women: Firsts and Founders, Vol. I & Vol. II*; Membership Directory (periodic); Newsletter (quarterly).

4591 ■ SAFE Association - Great Lakes Chapter
47460 Galleon Dr.
Plymouth, MI 48170
Contact: Steve Goldner
Ph: (734)254-1248
Fax: (734)451-9549
E-mail: sgoldner@ftss.com
Descr: Ensures personal safety and protection in land, sea, air and space environments. Fosters research and development in the fields of safety and survival. Provides a forum for the sharing of problems, ideas and information in the areas of safety, survival and crew systems.

4592 ■ Saginaw Advocacy for Individuals with Disabilities (SAID)
A Division of SVRC Industries
919 Veterans Memorial Pkwy.
Saginaw, MI 48601
Ph: (989)752-6104
Fax: (989)752-3111
URL: http://www.svrcindustries.com

4593 ■ Southern Michigan Association for the Education of Young Children (SMAEYC)
PO Box 242
Jackson, MI 49204
Contact: Chris Hines, Pres.
E-mail: smaeyc@yahoo.com
Descr: Serves and acts on behalf of the needs, rights and well-being of all young children with primary focus on the quality of educational and developmental services for all children. Seeks to improve professional practice and working conditions in early childhood education.

4594 ■ Special Olympics Michigan (SOMI)
Central Michigan Univ.
Mount Pleasant, MI 48859
Contact: Lois Arnold, Pres./CEO
Ph: (989)774-3911
Free: 800-644-6404

Fax: (989)774-3034
E-mail: somi@somi.org
URL: http://www.somi.org
Descr: Promotes physical fitness, sports training, and athletic competition for children and adults with mental retardation. Seeks to contribute to the physical, social, and psychological development of persons with mental retardation. Participants range in age from 8 years to adult and compete in track and field, swimming, gymnastics, bowling, ice skating, basketball, and other sports.

4595 ■ Van Buren Arc
30755 White Oak Dr.
Bangor, MI 49013
Contact: Douglas De Leo, Exec. Dir.
Ph: (616)427-5056

Minnesota

4596 ■ AG BELL, Minnesota
PO Box 10624
White Bear Lake, MN 55110
Contact: Mignon Miller, Pres.
E-mail: agbellmn@yahoo.com
URL: http://www.agbell.org/MN
Descr: Represents the interests of educators, parents of children with hearing loss, adults with hearing loss and hearing health professionals. Provides governmental and education advocacy services. **Fnd:** 2001.

4597 ■ American Association of University Women, Minneapolis Branch
Gale Mansion
2115 Stevens Ave. S
Minneapolis, MN 55404-2534
Contact: Tamara Nelson, Pres.
Ph: (612)870-1661
Fax: (612)870-0949
E-mail: aauwmpls@qwest.net
URL: http://www.aauwmpls.org
Descr: Advances equity for women and girls through advocacy, education, and research. Provides funds and a support system for women seeking judicial redress for sex discrimination in higher education. **Mem:** 500.

4598 ■ American Association of University Women - Minnesota State (AAUW-MN)
11345 Neal Ave. N
Stillwater, MN 55082
Contact: Mary Parcheta, Co-Pres.
E-mail: mparch01@aol.com
URL: http://www.aauwmn.org
Descr: Promotes equity for all women and girls, lifelong education and positive societal change. Activities include providing funds for education, research and self-development, and support for women seeking judicial redress for sex discrimination. **Mem:** 2300.

4599 ■ American Association of University Women, Red Wing Area Branch
1844 Bohmbach Dr.
Red Wing, MN 55066
Contact: Pat Welke
Ph: (651)388-2100
E-mail: redwingaauw@rwab-aauw.org
URL: http://www.rwab-aauw.org
Descr: Advances equity for women and girls through advocacy, education, and research. Provides funds and a support system for women seeking judicial redress for sex discrimination in higher education.

4600 ■ American Association of University Women, Willmar Branch
PO Box 374
Willmar, MN 56201
Contact: Jeanette Carlson, Pres.
Ph: (320)214-7600
E-mail: beromosz@yahoo.com
URL: http://www.aauwmn.org/willmar.htm
Descr: Advances equity for women and girls through advocacy, education, and research. Provides funds

and a support system for women seeking judicial redress for sex discrimination in higher education.

4601 ■ American Medical Student Association, Mayo Medical School
200 1st St. SW
Rochester, MN 55905
Ph: (507)284-3671
Fax: (507)284-2634
URL: http://www.mayo.edu/mms
Descr: Promotes improvement in medical training and education. Advances the medicine profession. Contributes to the welfare of medical students, interns, residents and post-MD/DO trainees.

4602 ■ American Medical Student Association, University of Minnesota Medical School
415 Delaware St. SE
Minneapolis, MN 55455
Contact: Rhamy Magid, Pres.
Ph: (612)802-7433
E-mail: john3594@umn.edu
URL: http://www.med.umn.edu
Descr: Promotes improvement in medical training and education. Advances the medicine profession. Contributes to the welfare of medical students, interns, residents and post-MD/DO trainees.

4603 ■ Arc Central Minnesota
6112 322nd St.
St. Cloud, MN 56303
Contact: Bev Kaler, Exec. Dir.
Ph: (320)240-9550
Free: 800-775-3196
Fax: (320)240-9315
E-mail: arccentral5@aol.com
URL: http://www.thearcofminnesota.org

4604 ■ Arc Freeborn County
407 E William St.
Albert Lea, MN 56007
Contact: Jo Lowe, Exec. Dir.
Ph: (507)377-3469
Fax: (507)377-8927
E-mail: jlowe@smig.net
URL: http://www.thearcofminnesota.org

4605 ■ Arc, Greater Twin Cities
2446 University Ave. W, Ste. 110
St. Paul, MN 55114-1740
Contact: Kim Keprios, CEO
Ph: (952)920-0855
Fax: (952)920-1480
E-mail: info@arcgreatertwincities.org
URL: http://www.arcgreatertwincities.org

4606 ■ Arc Headwaters
1891 Bemidji Ave. N
Bemidji, MN 56601
Contact: Cass Robinson, Exec. Dir.
Ph: (218)759-0097
Free: 800-450-7338
Fax: (218)444-4272
E-mail: arcnw@paulbunyan.net
URL: http://www.thearcofminnesota.org

4607 ■ Arc Kandiyohi County
201 4th St. SW, No. 12
Willmar, MN 56201
Contact: Arlen Christianson, Exec. Dir.
Ph: (320)231-1777
E-mail: arckandi@clearwire.net

4608 ■ Arc, Midstate
PO Box 251
St. Cloud, MN 56302
Ph: (320)251-7272
Free: 877-251-7272
Fax: (320)253-6844
E-mail: info@arcmidstate.org
URL: http://www.arcmidstate.org

4609 ■ Arc Minnesota
800 Transfer Rd., Ste. 7A
St. Paul, MN 55114
Contact: Pat Mellenthin, Exec. Dir.
Ph: (651)523-0823

Free: 800-582-5256
Fax: (651)523-0829
E-mail: mail@arcmn.org
URL: http://www.thearcofminnesota.org
Staff: 15. **Descr:** Provides advocacy and support for people with developmental disabilities and their families. **Fnd:** 1955. **Mem:** 6300. **Local Groups:** 37. **Pub:** *FOCUS* (3/year).

4610 ■ Arc of Minnesota Southwest
17889 Bunker Ave.
Walnut Grove, MN 56180
Contact: Carol Flesner, Exec. Dir.
Ph: (507)629-4227
Fax: (507)532-2220
E-mail: tcflesz@rrcnet.org
URL: http://www.thearcofminnesota.org

4611 ■ Arc of Mower County
PO Box 744
Austin, MN 55912
Contact: Dawn Helgeson, Exec. Dir.
Ph: (507)433-8994
Fax: (507)433-9290
E-mail: office@arcmowercounty.org
URL: http://www.arcmowercounty.org

4612 ■ Arc Northland
424 W Superior St.
Ordean Bldg., Ste. 201
Duluth, MN 55802
Contact: Lynne Frigaard, Exec. Dir.
Ph: (218)726-4725
Free: 800-317-6475
Fax: (218)726-4732
E-mail: lfrigaard@arcnorthland.org
URL: http://www.arcnorthland.org

4613 ■ Arc Range
703 Garfield St.
Eveleth, MN 55734
Contact: Donna Haapala, Pres.
Ph: (218)750-1251
E-mail: miko@2z.net
URL: http://www.thearcofminnesota.org

4614 ■ Arc St. Cloud
PO Box 251
St. Cloud, MN 56302
Ph: (320)202-1941
Free: 877-251-7272
Fax: (320)253-6844
E-mail: cowen@arcmidstate.org
URL: http://www.arcmidstate.org
Descr: Parents, professional workers, and others interested in individuals with mental retardation. Works to promote services, research, public understanding, and legislation for people with mental retardation and their families.

4615 ■ Arc Stevens County
19032 480th Ave.
Morris, MN 56267
Contact: Liz Harris, Pres.
Ph: (320)589-3096
E-mail: harri088@tc.umn.edu
URL: http://www.thearcofminnesota.org

4616 ■ Arc of West Central Minnesota
810 4th Ave. S, Rm. 134
Moorhead, MN 56560
Contact: Donna Atherton, Exec. Dir.
Ph: (218)233-5949
E-mail: arccc@fargocity.com

4617 ■ Autism Society of Minnesota (AuSM)
2380 Wycliff St., Ste. 102
St. Paul, MN 55114
Contact: Pam Erickson, Exec. Dir.
Ph: (651)647-1083
Fax: (651)642-1230
E-mail: info@ausm.org
URL: http://www.ausm.org
Descr: Seeks to improve the lives of individuals affected by autism. Promotes awareness and understanding of autism disorders. Aims to further the

advancement of preventive studies, therapy and research of autism disorders.

4618 ■ Children's Defense Fund, Minnesota (CDF MN)
555 Park St.
St. Paul, MN 55103
Contact: Jim Koppel, Dir.
Ph: (651)227-6121
Fax: (651)227-2553
E-mail: cdf-mn@cdf-mn.org
URL: http://www.cdf-mn.org
Descr: Focuses on the needs of poor and minority children and people with disabilities. Educates the nation about the needs of children and encourages preventive investment. Works to shape federal, state and local policies through research. **Fnd:** 1985. **Pub:** *The Child Defender*.

4619 ■ Fire Marshals Association of Minnesota (FMAM)
Farmington Fire Dept.
325 Oak St.
Farmington, MN 55024
Contact: John Powers, Treas.
E-mail: jpowers@ci.farmington.mn.us
URL: http://www.fmam.org
Descr: Provides the highest quality codes, standards, products, and services for all concerned with the safety and performance of the built environment.

4620 ■ Learning Disabilities Association of Minnesota (LDA)
5354 Parkdale Dr., Ste. 200
St. Louis Park, MN 55416
Contact: Carol Brumwell, Pres.
Ph: (952)922-8374
Fax: (952)922-8102
E-mail: info@ldaminnesota.org
URL: http://www.ldaminnesota.org

4621 ■ Minnesota Association for Career and Technical Education (MnACTE)
Winona Stata University
Business Education Program
175 W Mark St.
PO Box 583
Savage, MN 55378
Contact: Dr. Jeanette A. Karjala, Pres.
E-mail: jkarjala@winona.edu
URL: http://www.acteonline.org/content.aspx?id=810
Descr: Represents individuals who teach, administer, coordinate and offer support services to students in secondary and post secondary career and technical education.

4622 ■ Minnesota Association for the Education of Young Children (MnAEYC)
1821 University Ave., Ste. 324-S
St. Paul, MN 55104
Contact: Brian Siverson-Hall, Exec. Dir.
Ph: (651)646-8689
Free: 800-711-5690
Fax: (651)636-9146
E-mail: mnaeyc@mnaeyc.org
URL: http://www.mnaeyc.org
Staff: 4. **Descr:** Early childhood educators, day care providers, and kindergarten and primary school teachers. Promotes high standards for the care and education of young children and advocates on their behalf. **Fnd:** 1938. **Mem:** 1600. **Reg. Groups:** 1. **Local Groups:** 2. **Pub:** *News* (quarterly); *Views*.

4623 ■ Minnesota Association on Higher Education and Disability (MN AHEAD)
Office for Students with Disabilities
Normandale Community Coll.
9700 France Ave. S
Bloomington, MN 55431-4399
Contact: Shiela Fox, Pres.
Ph: (952)487-7035
Fax: (952)487-7031
E-mail: debbie.tillman@normandale.edu
URL: http://www.ahead.org/affiliates/minnesota
Descr: Represents individuals interested in promoting the equal rights and opportunities of disabled postsecondary students, staff, faculty and graduates.

Provides educational and professional development opportunities for persons with disabilities in postsecondary education. Encourages and supports legislation for the benefit of disabled students. **Fnd:** 1994.

4624 ■ Minnesota Department of Education
1500 Hwy. 36 W.
Roseville, MN 55113-4266
Contact: Alice Seagren, Commnr.
Ph: (651)582-8200
Fax: (651)582-8727
E-mail: mde.commissioner@state.mn.us
URL: http://education.state.mn.us/mde/index.html
Descr: Mission is to improve educational achievement by establishing clear standards, measuring performance, assisting educators, and increasing opportunities for lifelong learning.

4625 ■ Minnesota Governor's Council on Developmental Disabilities
370 Centennial Office Bldg.
658 Cedar St.
St. Paul, MN 55155
Contact: Colleen Wieck PhD, Exec. Dir.
Ph: (651)296-4018
Free: 877-348-0505
Fax: (651)297-7200
E-mail: admin.dd@state.mn.us
URL: http://www.mncdd.org
Descr: Provides information, education, and training to build knowledge, develop skills, and change attitudes that will lead to increased independence, self determination, productivity, integration and inclusion of people with developmental disabilities and their families in the community. **Fnd:** 1971. **Mem:** 25.

4626 ■ Minnesota PTA
1667 Snelling Ave. N, Ste. 111
St. Paul, MN 55108
Contact: Rosie Loeffler-Kemp, Pres.
Ph: (651)999-7320
Free: 800-672-0993
Fax: (651)999-7321
E-mail: mnpta@mnpta.org
URL: http://www.mnpta.org
Descr: Seeks to support and speak on behalf of children and youth in the schools, in the community and before governmental bodies and other organizations that make decisions affecting children; to assist parents in developing the skills they need to raise and protect their children; and to encourage parent and public involvement in public schools. **Fnd:** 1923. **Mem:** 27500. **Pub:** Newsletter.

4627 ■ Minnesota School Age Care Alliance (MNSACA)
1821 University Ave. W, Ste. 324-S
St. Paul, MN 55104
Contact: Brian J. Siverson-Hall, Exec. Dir.
Ph: (651)646-8689
Fax: (651)636-9146
E-mail: brians@mnsaca.org
URL: http://mnsaca.org
Staff: 1. **Descr:** Child and youth focused professionals in the state of MN who provide school-age care in school, park, home, and agency settings during out-of-school hours. Promotes quality programs for children and youth through professional development and public advocacy. **Fnd:** 1985. **Mem:** 600. **Pub:** *MNSACA Field Trip Fun* (annual); *Network News* (quarterly).

4628 ■ Minnesota State Fire Chiefs
415 Jackson Ave.
Elk River, MN 55330
Contact: Bruce West
Free: 877-504-0911
Fax: (763)635-1117
E-mail: bwest@ci.elk-river.mn.us
Descr: Provides the highest quality codes, stan-

dards, products, and services for all concerned with the safety and performance of the built environment.

4629 ■ Mothers and More Central Minneapolis, Chapter 294
5224 Minnetonka Blvd.
Minneapolis, MN 55416
Ph: (952)221-1409
URL: http://www.orgsites.com/mn/mothersandmore_mpls/index.html
Fnd: 2004.

4630 ■ Mothers and More Saint Paul, Chapter 268
2027 Sherwood Ave.
St. Paul, MN 55119
Ph: (651)204-2107
E-mail: mothersandmorestpaul@yahoo.com
URL: http://www.orgsites.com/mn/mothersandmore-stpaul

4631 ■ Special Olympics Minnesota
100 Washington Ave. S, Ste. 550
Minneapolis, MN 55401
Contact: David Dorn, Pres.
Ph: (612)333-0999
Free: 800-783-7732
Fax: (612)333-8782
E-mail: info@somn.org
URL: http://www.specialolympicsminnesota.org
Descr: Provides a year-round program of sports training and competition in 20 Olympic-type sports for the benefit of individuals with mental disabilities. Individuals are eligible for participation at the age of 8, being diagnosed by a medical professional as having a mental disability or cognitive delay. **Fnd:** 1973. **Mem:** 6000. **Pub:** *Forerunner* (quarterly).

4632 ■ Upper Midwest Branch of the International Dyslexia Association (UMBIDA)
5021 Vernon Ave.
PMB 159
Minneapolis, MN 55436
Ph: (651)450-7589
E-mail: info@umbida.org
URL: http://www.umbida.org
Descr: Promotes public awareness and understanding of dyslexia. Seeks to develop and implement specialized methods to improve the quality of life for people who have dyslexia. **Pub:** Newsletter (quarterly).

4633 ■ VSA arts of Minnesota
Hennepin Center for the Arts
528 Hennepin Ave., Ste. No. 305
Minneapolis, MN 55403
Contact: Mr. Craig Dunn, Exec. Dir.
Ph: (612)332-3888
Free: 800-801-3883
Fax: (612)305-0132
E-mail: info@vsaartsmn.org
URL: http://www.vsaartsmn.org
Staff: 3. **Descr:** Promotes quality, accessible arts experiences for people with disabilities. Offers granting programs, artists-in-residence, gallery showings, access training and awards, networking for ASL-interpreted or audio-described performances and other opportunities for artists with disabilities. **Fnd:** 1986. **Pub:** *Artists' Pipeline* (biweekly); *Arts Access* (3/year).

Mississippi

4634 ■ 100 Black Men of Jackson
PO Box 9510
Jackson, MS 39286
Ph: (601)366-8301
Fax: (601)366-8393
E-mail: rgibbs@brunini.com
URL: http://100blackmenjackson.com
Fnd: 1990.

4635 ■ Adams County Arc - Mississippi
PO Box 1362
Natchez, MS 39121

Contact: Mary A. Foggo, Pres.
Ph: (601)442-2264

4636 ■ Arc Jones County
PO Box 1233
Laurel, MS 39441
Contact: Betty Busbea, Pres.
Ph: (601)426-2944

4637 ■ Arc of Lowndes County
PO Box 5387
Columbus, MS 39704
Contact: Norma Jones, Pres.
Ph: (662)245-1323
E-mail: arclowndescounty@hotmail.com

4638 ■ Arc of Mississippi
7 Lakeland Cir., No. 600
Jackson, MS 39216
Contact: Marvin Carpenter, Pres.
Ph: (601)982-1180
Free: 800-717-1180
Fax: (601)982-5792
E-mail: mslcar@aol.com
URL: http://www.arcms.org

4639 ■ Arc of Northeast Mississippi
403 S Commerce St.
Ripley, MS 38663
Contact: Sherry Dunnam, Pres.
Ph: (662)993-9486
E-mail: arc@dixie-net.com

4640 ■ Common Cause, Mississippi
PO Box 13651
Jackson, MS 39236
Contact: Dick Johnson, Chm.
Ph: (601)969-0302
Fax: (601)969-0302
E-mail: comcausems@aol.com
URL: http://www.commoncause.org
Staff: 4. **Descr:** Citizens promoting honest government through public awareness in Mississippi. Informs public on current issues and encourages involvement in the legislative and political process. **Fnd:** 1970. **Mem:** 350. **Pub:** Newsletter (periodic).

4641 ■ Forrest County Arc
PO Box 18800
Hattiesburg, MS 39404
Contact: Cindy Pennington, Exec. Dir.
Ph: (601)583-4251

4642 ■ Learning Disabilities Association of Mississippi (LDAMS)
PO Box 4477
Jackson, MS 39296
Ph: (601)362-1667
Fax: (601)362-9180
E-mail: ldams@bellsouth.net
URL: http://www.ldams.org

4643 ■ Learning Disabilities Association of Mississippi, Gulf Coast Chapter (LDAMS)
18041 Dedeaux Clan Rd.
Gulfport, MS 39503
Contact: Alice Dedeaux
Ph: (228)831-5151
E-mail: adedeaux@yahoo.com
URL: http://www.ldams.org

4644 ■ Learning Disabilities Association of Mississippi, Jackson Metro Chapter
314 Northridge Dr.
Brandon, MS 39042
Contact: Clarice Baker
Ph: (601)825-3888
E-mail: imteaching@yahoo.com
URL: http://www.ldams.org

4645 ■ Learning Disabilities Association of Mississippi, Northeast Chapter (LDAMS)
605 W Main St., Ste. 9
Tupelo, MS 38804
Contact: Lynn High
Ph: (662)842-0630

Fax: (662)842-0630
URL: http://www.ldams.org

4646 ■ Learning Disabilities Association of Mississippi, Pine Belt Chapter (LDAMS)
USM Box 5163
Hattiesburg, MS 39407
Contact: Camille M. Yates PhD
Ph: (601)266-5728
Free: 888-671-0051
Fax: (601)266-5114
E-mail: camille.yates@usm.edu
URL: http://www.ldams.org

4647 ■ Mississippi Association of Educators (MAE)
775 N State St.
Jackson, MS 39202
Contact: Kevin F. Gilbert, Pres.
Ph: (601)354-4463
Free: 800-530-7998
Fax: (601)352-7054
E-mail: kgilbert@nea.org
URL: http://www.ms.nea.org
Staff: 17. **Descr:** Serves as professional organization for teachers. **Fnd:** 1976. **Mem:** 13000. **Pub:** *Mississippi Educator* (monthly).

4648 ■ Mississippi Counseling Association (MCA)
PO Box 728
Collins, MS 39428
Contact: Christy Broome, Pres.
Ph: (601)517-6221
E-mail: mca@mscounselor.org
URL: http://www.mscounselor.org
Descr: Professional counselors working to promote positive development and adjustment among the children and adults whom they serve.

4649 ■ Mississippi State Department of Education
Central High School
359 N. West St.
PO Box 771
Jackson, MS 39205
Contact: Dr. Hank Bounds, Superintendent
Ph: (601)359-3513
Fax: (601)359-3242
E-mail: webhelp@mde.k12.ms.us
URL: http://www.mde.k12.ms.us/

4650 ■ Special Olympics Mississippi
15 Olympic Way
Madison, MS 39110
Contact: Helen C. Parish, Pres./CEO
Ph: (601)856-7748
Free: 800-655-6742
Fax: (601)856-8132
E-mail: janie.allen@specialolympicsms.org
URL: http://www.specialolympicsms.org/so/index.html
Staff: 5. **Descr:** Makes available sports training and the opportunity for athletic competition to people with mental retardation. **Fnd:** 1968. **Mem:** 13000. **Pub:** Yearbook; Newsletter (quarterly).

4651 ■ Warren County Arc - Mississippi
100 Smoky Ln.
Vicksburg, MS 39180
Contact: Kearney Waites, Exec. Dir.
Ph: (601)638-2761

4652 ■ Washington, Mississippi County Arc
PO Box 1733
Greenville, MS 38702
Contact: Agnes Johnson, Exec. Dir.
Ph: (662)332-3271

4653 ■ West Jackson Arc
7009 Red Bud Ln.
Ocean Springs, MS 39564
Contact: Reva Hopkins, Pres.
Ph: (228)818-0592

Missouri

4654 ■ 100 Black Men of Metropolitan St. Louis
4631 Delmar Blvd.
St. Louis, MO 63108
Ph: (314)367-7778
E-mail: president@100bmstl.org
URL: http://www.100bmstl.org
Fnd: 1986.

4655 ■ American Association of University Women, Creve Coeur Branch
440 Glan Tai Dr.
Manchester, MO 63011
Contact: Debbie McWard, VP for Membership
E-mail: rmcward01@earthlink.net
URL: http://www.g-cubed.info/crevecoeuraauw/index.asp
Descr: Advances equity for women and girls through advocacy, education, and research. Provides funds and a support system for women seeking judicial redress for sex discrimination in higher education.

4656 ■ American Association of University Women, Kansas City, Missouri Branch
PO Box 33009
Kansas City, MO 64114-0009
Contact: Jane Crigler, Pres.
E-mail: info@aauwkcmo.org
URL: http://www.aauwkcmo.org
Descr: Advances equity for women and girls through advocacy, education, and research. Provides funds and a support system for women seeking judicial redress for sex discrimination in higher education.

4657 ■ American Medical Student Association, Kansas City University of Medicine and Biosciences College of Osteopathic Medicine
1750 Independence Ave.
Kansas City, MO 64106
Contact: Karen Pletz, Pres.
Ph: (816)283-2000
Free: 800-234-4847
URL: http://www.kcumb.edu/kcolleges/com/com.asp
Descr: Promotes improvement in medical training and education. Advances the medicine profession. Contributes to the welfare of medical students, interns, residents and post-MD/DO trainees.

4658 ■ American Medical Student Association, Kirksville College of Osteopathic Medicine
800 W Jefferson St.
Kirksville, MO 63501
Contact: Jack Magruder, Pres.
Ph: (660)626-2121
Free: 866-626-2878
E-mail: admissions@atsu.edu
URL: http://www.atsu.edu/kcom
Descr: Promotes improvement in medical training and education. Advances the medicine profession. Contributes to the welfare of medical students, interns, residents and post-MD/DO trainees.

4659 ■ American Medical Student Association, St. Louis University School of Medicine
1402 S Grand Blvd.
St. Louis, MO 63104
Contact: Philip Alderson MD, Pres.
Ph: (314)977-9801
E-mail: slumd@slu.edu
Descr: Promotes improvement in medical training and education. Advances the medicine profession. Contributes to the welfare of medical students, interns, residents and post-MD/DO trainees.

4660 ■ American Medical Student Association, University of Missouri - Kansas City School of Medicine
2411 Holmes St.
Kansas City, MO 64108
Contact: Betty Drees MD, Dean
Ph: (816)235-1111
URL: http://www.med.umkc.edu
Descr: Promotes improvement in medical training and education. Advances the medicine profession.

Contributes to the welfare of medical students, interns, residents and post-MD/DO trainees.

4661 ■ American Medical Student Association, University of Missouri School of Medicine
MA213 Medical Sciences Bldg.
Columbia, MO 65212
Contact: William M. Crist MD, Dean
Ph: (573)882-2923
Fax: (573)884-2988
Descr: Promotes improvement in medical training and education. Advances the medicine profession. Contributes to the welfare of medical students, interns, residents and post-MD/DO trainees.

4662 ■ American Medical Student Association, Washington University in St. Louis School of Medicine
Campus Box 8023
St. Louis, MO 63110
Contact: Larry J. Shapiro MD, Pres.
Ph: (314)362-6854
URL: http://medschool.wustl.edu
Descr: Promotes improvement in medical training and education. Advances the medicine profession. Contributes to the welfare of medical students, interns, residents and post-MD/DO trainees. **Fnd:** 1891.

4663 ■ Arc of the Lake
PO Box 3166
Camdenton, MO 65020
Contact: Angela Gourley, Pres.
Ph: (573)552-6748
E-mail: agourley@arcofthelake.org

4664 ■ Arc of the United States, Missouri Chapter
PO Box 6787
Jefferson City, MO 65102
Contact: Maryetta Lane, Exec. Dir.
Ph: (573)556-0400
Free: 877-627-0400
E-mail: ilrcstephanie@earthlink.net

4665 ■ Association for the Education of Young Children of Missouri (AEYC-MO)
1400 Rock Quarry Rd.
Columbia, MO 65211-3280
Contact: Mike Abel, Pres.
Ph: (573)884-3374
Free: 877-296-2852
Fax: (573)884-0598
E-mail: info@aeyc-mo.org
URL: http://www.aeyc-mo.org
Staff: 1. **Descr:** Represents early childhood professionals fostering excellence in early childhood systems and programs through advocacy, education, and professional development. Aims to invest in early childhood education to ensure that every child begins school ready to succeed. Offers annual conference, The Update newsletter, media resource library, leadership development and advocacy training. **Fnd:** 1978. **Mem:** 1500. **Reg. Groups:** 10. **State Groups:** 1. **Local Groups:** 4. **Pub:** *The Update* (3/year).

4666 ■ Central Missouri Association for the Education of Young Children (CMAEYC)
Educare-Boone County
1400 Rock Quarry Rd.
Columbia, MO 65211
Contact: Kathy Wallace, Membership Chair
Ph: (573)884-1497
E-mail: wallacek@missouri.edu
URL: http://www.aeyc-mo.org
Descr: Serves and acts on behalf of the needs, rights and well-being of all young children with primary focus on the quality of educational and developmental services for all children. Seeks to improve professional practice and working conditions in early childhood education.

4667 ■ Fire Marshal's Association of Missouri (FMAM)
Florrisant Valley Fire Protection District
645 St. Catherine St.

Florissant, MO 63031
Contact: Steve Gettemeier, VP
Ph: (314)837-8790
E-mail: gett@fvfpd.com
URL: http://www.fmamonline.com
Descr: Provides the highest quality codes, standards, products, and services for all concerned with the safety and performance of the built environment.

4668 ■ Jefferson County Fire Marshal Association
2090 Elm Dr., Ste. A
Arnold, MO 63010
Contact: Lloyd Montgomery
Ph: (636)282-1500
Fax: (636)282-7677
E-mail: lmontgomery@rockfire-rescue.org
Descr: Provides the highest quality codes, standards, products, and services for all concerned with the safety and performance of the built environment.

4669 ■ Kansas/Missouri Branch of the International Dyslexia Association (KSMOIDA)
430 E Blue Ridge Blvd.
Kansas City, MO 64145
Contact: Trudy Stegelman, Pres.-Elect
Ph: (816)838-7323
E-mail: info@ksmoida.org
URL: http://www.ksmoida.org
Descr: Promotes public awareness and understanding of dyslexia. Seeks to develop and implement specialized methods to improve the quality of life for people who have dyslexia. Provides services to those affected by dyslexia, attention disorders and other learning disabilities.

4670 ■ Learning Disabilities Association of Missouri
PO Box 3303
Springfield, MO 65808
Contact: Eileen Huth, Pres.
Ph: (417)864-5110
Fax: (417)864-7290
E-mail: ldamo@cland.net
URL: http://www.ldamo.org
Descr: Provides information, awareness, support and understanding for disabled individuals and professionals through the aid of workshops, seminars and other related activities. **Pub:** *Perspectives* (bimonthly).

4671 ■ Metropolitan Fire Marshals Association (MFMA)
10 N Bemiston Ave.
Clayton, MO 63105
Contact: Jerry Ambrosecchia, Pres.
E-mail: pmercurio@wescofire.org
URL: http://www.mfmaonline.com
Descr: Provides the highest quality codes, standards, products, and services for all concerned with the safety and performance of the built environment.

4672 ■ Missouri AfterSchool Network (MASN)
807 Clark Hall
Columbia, MO 65211
Contact: Harry Kujath, Dir.
Free: 888-210-2469
Fax: (573)884-4225
E-mail: afterschool@moasn.org
URL: http://www.moasn.org

4673 ■ Missouri Association for Career and Technical Education (MO-ACTE)
213 E Capitol Ave.
PO Box 1955
Jefferson City, MO 65102
Contact: Donna Vossen, Exec. Dir.
Ph: (573)634-7366
Fax: (573)635-6258
E-mail: info@mo-acte.org
URL: http://www.mo-acte.org
Staff: 2. **Descr:** Promotes the development of vocational-technical education within the state of Missouri. Gives emphasis on continued support of vocational-technical education at the secondary, post-secondary, and adult levels, while fostering partnerships with business and industry in the train-

ing and retraining of the Missouri workforce. Provides an open forum for the study and discussion of all questions involved in career, practical arts, technical and vocational education. Works with other states and agencies for the advancement of career, practical arts, technical and vocational education, in the state, and in the United States, and as an ally of the Association of Career and Technical Education. Supports local, state and national legislation for career, practical arts, technical and vocational education. Members join one of twelve divisions. **Fnd:** 1955. **Mem:** 3900. **Pub:** *The Reporter* (quarterly).

4674 ■ Missouri Association on Higher Education and Disability
St. Louis University, DuBourg Hall, Rm. 36
221 N Grand Blvd.
St. Louis, MO 63103-2097
Contact: Adam Meyer, VP
Ph: (314)977-3838
Fax: (314)977-3735
E-mail: meyer@slu.edu
Descr: Represents individuals interested in promoting the equal rights and opportunities of disabled postsecondary students, staff, faculty and graduates. Provides educational and professional development opportunities for persons with disabilities in postsecondary education. Encourages and supports legislation for the benefit of disabled students.

4675 ■ Missouri Department of Elementary and Secondary Education
PO Box 480
Jefferson City, MO 65102
Contact: Dr. D. Kent King, Commnr.
Ph: (573)751-4212
Fax: (573)751-8613
E-mail: pubinfo@dese.mo.gov
URL: http://dese.mo.gov/

4676 ■ Missouri Planning Council for Developmental Disabilities (MPCDD)
1716 Four Seasons Dr., Ste. 103
Jefferson City, MO 65102
Contact: Susan Pritchard-Green, Dir.
Ph: (573)751-8611
Free: 800-500-7878
Fax: (573)526-2755
E-mail: spritchard-green@mpcdd.com
URL: http://www.mpcdd.com
Descr: Comprises of volunteers appointed by the Governor of MO. Plans, advocates and works to build community capacity and systems change to increase opportunities for people with developmental disabilities to live and participate in their community. **Mem:** 23.

4677 ■ Missouri PTA
2100 I 70 Dr. SW
Columbia, MO 65203
Contact: Mary Oyler, Pres.
Ph: (573)445-4161
Free: 800-328-7330
Fax: (573)445-4163
E-mail: office@mopta.org
URL: http://www.mopta.org
Staff: 8. **Descr:** Parents, teachers, students, and others interested in uniting the forces of home, school, and community. Promotes the welfare of children and youth. **Fnd:** 1915. **Mem:** 95000. **Reg. Groups:** 8. **Local Groups:** 465. **Pub:** *Contact* (7/year).

4678 ■ Missouri SADD
1683 W Union Chapel Rd.
Nixa, MO 65714
Contact: Zac Rantz
Ph: (417)725-0149
Fax: (417)724-8537
E-mail: zac@mosadd.org

4679 ■ Missouri School Age Community Coalition
PO Box 736
Columbia, MO 65205
Contact: Miguel Jaramillo, Pres.
Fax: (573)884-0598

E-mail: contact@mosac2.org
URL: http://www.mosac2.org
Descr: Supports and unifies professionals in providing quality out-of-school programs.

4680 ■ National Stuttering Association, Kansas City Chapter
PO Box 15118
Kansas City, MO 64106-0118
Contact: Rich Schwerdt, Chapter Leader
Ph: (816)792-9619
E-mail: apphkr@aol.com
URL: http://www.geocities.com/Athens/Agora/3215/index.html
Descr: Serves as a self-help organization for people who stutter, parents of children who stutter and the professionals who serve them. Increases public awareness of stuttering. Provides support, education and empowerment to children and adults who stutter.

4681 ■ St. Louis Arc
1816 Lackland Hill Pkwy., Ste. 200
St. Louis, MO 63146
Contact: Kathy Meath MSW, Exec. Dir.
Ph: (314)569-2211
Fax: (314)569-0778
E-mail: slarc@slarc.org
URL: http://www.slarc.org
Descr: Parents, professional workers, and others interested in individuals with mental retardation. Works to promote services, research, public understanding, and legislation for people with mental retardation and their families. **Fnd:** 1950. **Pub:** *Arctimes* (quarterly).

4682 ■ UMKC Dental Alumni Association
650 E 25th St.
Kansas City, MO 64108
Ph: (816)235-2021
Fax: (816)235-5892
URL: http://dentistry.umkc.edu
Descr: Represents the interests of dentists committed to the public's oral health, ethics and professional development. Encourages the improvement of the public's oral health and promotes the art and science of dentistry.

Montana

4683 ■ Autism Society of America - North Central Montana
PO Box 2506
Great Falls, MT 59403
Contact: Sandi Hursh
Ph: (406)454-9004
E-mail: mt-northcentralmontana@autismsocietyofamerica.org
Descr: Seeks to improve the lives of individuals affected by autism. Promotes awareness and understanding of autism disorders. Aims to further the advancement of preventive studies, therapy and research of autism disorders.

4684 ■ Disabled Sports U.S.A., Eagle Mount - Bozeman
6901 Goldenstein Ln.
Bozeman, MT 59715
Contact: Chris McGregor, Exec. Dir.
Ph: (406)586-1781
Fax: (406)586-5794
E-mail: eaglemount@eaglemount.org
URL: http://www.eaglemount.org
Descr: Provides therapeutic recreational activities including skiing, ice skating, horseback riding, aquatics, golf, and rafting to people with disabilities and young people with cancer. **Fnd:** 1982. **Pub:** *Special Edition* (quarterly).

4685 ■ Montana AfterSchool Network
901 N Benton Ave.
Helena, MT 59601
Ph: (406)443-4551

Fax: (406)443-4560
URL: http://www.mtafterschool.com

4686 ■ Montana Association for Career and Technical Education
Huntley Project High School
24191 Main St.
Worden, MT 59088
Contact: Mark Branger, Exec. Dir.
Ph: (406)967-2540
Fax: (406)967-2839
E-mail: mbranger@huntley.k12.mt.us
URL: http://www.montanaacte.org
Descr: Provides educational leadership in developing a competitive workforce.

4687 ■ Montana Congress of Parents and Teachers (MTPTA)
PO Box 6448
Great Falls, MT 59406
Contact: Beth Verlanic, Pres.
Ph: (406)268-7475
E-mail: montana_pta@gfps.k12.mt.us
URL: http://www.montanapta.org
Descr: Parents, teachers, students, principals, administrators, and others interested in uniting the forces of home, school, and community on behalf of children and youth enrolled in the state's school districts. Sponsors competitions. **Fnd:** 1914. **Mem:** 9400. **Local Groups:** 100. **Pub:** *MPTA Bulletin* (9/year).

4688 ■ Montana Office of Public Instruction
PO Box 202501
Helena, MT 59620-2501
Contact: Linda McCulloch, Superintendent
Ph: (406)444-3095
Free: 888-231-9393
Fax: (406)444-3924
E-mail: OPISupt@mt.gov
URL: http://www.opi.mt.gov/

4689 ■ Special Olympics Montana
PO Box 3507
Great Falls, MT 59403
Contact: Judith Magruder, Asst. Pres.
Ph: (406)216-5327
Free: 800-242-6876
Fax: (406)454-9043
E-mail: info@somt.org
URL: http://www.somt.org
Staff: 9. **Descr:** Provides year-round statewide programs of physical fitness, sports training, and athletic competition for children and adults with intellectual disabilities. Conducts fundraisers. **Fnd:** 1968. **Mem:** 2750. **State Groups:** 12. **Local Groups:** 166. **Pub:** *Spirit of Special Olympics* (quarterly).

Nebraska

4690 ■ American Medical Student Association, Creighton University School of Medicine
Office of Student Affairs
2500 California Plz.
Criss III, Rooms 470-490G
Omaha, NE 68178
E-mail: pmarsh@creighton.edu
URL: http://www2.creighton.edu/medschool
Descr: Promotes improvement in medical training and education. Advances the medicine profession. Contributes to the welfare of medical students, interns, residents and post-MD/DO trainees.

4691 ■ American Medical Student Association, University of Nebraska Medical Center College of Medicine
42nd and Emile
Omaha, NE 68198
Contact: John Gollan, Dean
Ph: (402)559-4000
URL: http://www.unmc.edu/dept/com
Descr: Promotes improvement in medical training and education. Advances the medicine profession.

Contributes to the welfare of medical students, interns, residents and post-MD/DO trainees.

4692 ■ Arc of Central Nebraska
2210 Gateway Ave.
Grand Island, NE 68803
Contact: Mike Follmer, Pres.
Ph: (308)384-6876
URL: http://www.arc-nebraska.org

4693 ■ Arc - Cheyenne County
1544 King St.
Sidney, NE 69162
Contact: Pat Von Seggern, Pres.
Ph: (308)254-5378
URL: http://www.arc-nebraska.org

4694 ■ Arc of Colfax County
1172 Rd. 6
Schuyler, NE 68661
Contact: Pam Barta, Pres.
Ph: (402)352-2879
E-mail: butchdot1172@dtnspeed.net

4695 ■ Arc - Custer
PO Box 34
Broken Bow, NE 68822
Contact: Carol A. Jones, Exec. Dir.
Ph: (308)872-6081

4696 ■ Arc Elkhorn Valley
800 Cornhusker Dr.
West Point, NE 68788
Contact: Tracy Merchen, Pres.
Ph: (402)372-2451
URL: http://www.arc-nebraska.org

4697 ■ Arc Hamilton-Merrick Counties
915 P St.
Aurora, NE 68818
Contact: Tom Wanek, Pres.
Ph: (402)694-3519
URL: http://www.arc-nebraska.org

4698 ■ Arc of Lincoln-Lancaster County
5609 S 49th St., Ste. 5
Lincoln, NE 68516
Contact: Teri Roberts, Exec. Dir.
Ph: (402)421-8866
Fax: (402)421-8922
E-mail: info@arclincoln.org
URL: http://www.arclincoln.org
Descr: Parents, professional workers, and others interested in individuals with mental retardation. Works to promote services, research, public understanding, and legislation for people with mental retardation and their families. **Pub:** *The Arc Voice* (quarterly).

4699 ■ Arc of Nebraska
1672 Van Dorn St.
Lincoln, NE 68502
Contact: Marla Fischer-Lempke, Exec. Dir.
Ph: (402)475-4407
E-mail: arcneb@inebraska.com
URL: http://www.arc-nebraska.org
Descr: People with developmental disabilities, their parents, other family members, interested citizens and dedicated human-service professionals. Seeks to improve the quality of life for all people with developmental disabilities. **Fnd:** 1954.

4700 ■ Arc of Norfolk
PO Box 32
Norfolk, NE 68702
Contact: Ami Stubben, Exec. Dir.
Ph: (402)379-1160
E-mail: arcnorfolk@conpoint.com

4701 ■ Arc of Platte Valley
PO Box 344
Sutherland, NE 69165

Contact: Char Rotert, Pres.
Ph: (308)386-8311
E-mail: rotert@gpcom.net

4702 ■ Arc - Saunders
1910 N Chestnut St.
Wahoo, NE 68066
Contact: Bud Larson, Pres.
Ph: (402)443-4694

4703 ■ Arc of Seward County
1396 Redwood Rd.
Seward, NE 68434
Contact: Deanna Portz, Pres.
Ph: (402)761-3462
URL: http://www.arc-nebraska.org

4704 ■ Arc - Southwest Nebraska
71705 Terrace Dr.
Culbertson, NE 69024
Contact: Linda Koch, Exec. Dir.
Ph: (308)334-7805

4705 ■ Association for Career and Technical Education of Nebraska (ACTEN)
PO Box 22607
Lincoln, NE 68542-2607
Contact: Lila Kulwicki, Exec. Sec.
E-mail: acte.nebraska@juno.com
URL: http://www.acteonline.org/content.aspx?id=812
Descr: Supports career and technical education to assure students' successful roles in families, communities and the workplace.

4706 ■ Autism Society of Nebraska
1672 Van Dorn St.
Lincoln, NE 68502
Contact: Georgann Albin, Exec. Dir.
Free: 877-375-0120
E-mail: autismsociety@autismnebraska.org
URL: http://www.autismnebraska.org
Descr: Seeks to improve the lives of individuals affected by autism. Promotes awareness and understanding of autism disorders. Aims to further the advancement of preventive studies, therapy and research of autism disorders.

4707 ■ Common Cause/Nebraska (CC/NE)
7221 South St., Ste. 17
Lincoln, NE 68506
Contact: Charlotte Manton, Chair
Ph: (402)476-9651
E-mail: char7221@aol.com

4708 ■ Learning Disabilities Association of Nebraska (LDA)
3135 N 93rd St.
Omaha, NE 68134
Ph: (402)348-1567
E-mail: ldaofneb@yahoo.com
URL: http://www.ldanebraska.org

4709 ■ Nebraska Branch of the International Dyslexia Association (NEIDA)
PO Box 6302
Lincoln, NE 68506-0302
Contact: Carolyn Brandle, Pres.
Ph: (402)434-6434
E-mail: cbrandle@huskeraccess.com
URL: http://www.ne-ida.com
Descr: Promotes public awareness and understanding of dyslexia. Seeks to develop and implement specialized methods to improve the quality of life for people who have dyslexia. **Fnd:** 1984. **Pub:** Newsletter (3/year).

4710 ■ Nebraska Department of Education
301 Centennial Mall S., 6th Fl.
PO Box 94987
Lincoln, NE 68509-4987
Contact: Roger Breed, Commnr.
Ph: (402)471-2295
Fax: (402)471-0117

E-mail: doug.christensen@nde.ne.us
URL: http://www.nde.state.ne.us/

4711 ■ Omaha Association for the Education of Young Children (OAEYC)
PO Box 641906
Omaha, NE 68164
Contact: Jen Haggart, Pres.
Ph: (402)541-4718
E-mail: omahaaeyc@yahoo.com
URL: http://www.omahaaeyc.org
Descr: Serves and acts on behalf of the needs, rights and well-being of all young children with primary focus on the quality of educational and developmental services for all children. Seeks to improve professional practice and working conditions in early childhood education.

4712 ■ Special Olympics Nebraska
11011 Q St., Ste. 104C
Omaha, NE 68137-3700
Contact: Charles A. Cooper, Pres./CEO
Ph: (402)331-5545
Free: 800-247-0105
Fax: (402)331-5964
E-mail: cchamberlin@sone.org
URL: http://www.sone.org
Staff: 9. **Descr:** Provides athletic competition and training for persons with mental retardation. Conducts charitable activities. **Fnd:** 1968. **Mem:** 8700. **Reg. Groups:** 6. **Local Groups:** 110. **Pub:** Newsletter (quarterly).

Nevada

4713 ■ American Medical Student Association, University of Nevada School of Medicine
2040 W Charleston Blvd.
Las Vegas, NV 89102
Contact: John A. McDonald MD, Dean
Ph: (702)671-2240
URL: http://www.medicine.nevada.edu
Descr: Promotes improvement in medical training and education. Advances the medicine profession. Contributes to the welfare of medical students, interns, residents and post-MD/DO trainees.

4714 ■ Churchill County Arc
PO Box 1641
Fallon, NV 89407
Contact: Leslie Spracklin, Exec. Dir.
Ph: (775)423-4760
E-mail: carc@cccomm.net

4715 ■ Learning Disabilities Association of Nevada
2970 Idlewild Dr.
Reno, NV 89509
Contact: Candy Von Ruden
E-mail: nevspedlaw@aol.com

4716 ■ Nevada Association for Career and Technical Education
Nevada Department of Education
Office of Career and Technical Education
700 E 5th St.
Carson City, NV 89701-5096
Contact: Mr. Jim Barbee, Pres.
Ph: (775)687-9218
Fax: (775)687-9114
E-mail: jbarbee@doe.nv.gov
URL: http://www.nacte.org/index.html
Descr: Supports vocational technical education that will assure students' successful roles in families, communities, and society.

4717 ■ Nevada Department of Education
700 E. Fifth St.
Carson City, NV 89701
Contact: Dr. Keith Rheault, Superintendent
Ph: (775)687-9200
Fax: (775)687-9101
E-mail: krheault@doe.nv.gov
URL: http://www.doe.nv.gov/

Pub: Newsletter (quarterly).

4718 ■ Nevada State Education Association (NSEA)
1890 Donald St.
Reno, NV 89502
Contact: Terry Hickman, Exec. Dir.
Ph: (775)828-6732
Free: 800-232-6732
Fax: (775)828-6745
E-mail: terry.hickman@nsea-nv.org
URL: http://www.nsea-nv.org
Descr: Represents the state's teachers and education support professionals. Promotes opportunities for professional awareness, growth, and empowerment. **Fnd:** 1888. **Mem:** 23000.

4719 ■ Northern Nevada Chapter of the Autism Society of America (NNASA)
3490 Southampton Dr.
Reno, NV 89509
Contact: Dinah Deane, Pres.
Ph: (775)786-9315
E-mail: pd1989@yahoo.com
URL: http://www.nnasa.org
Descr: Seeks to improve the lives of individuals affected by autism. Promotes awareness and understanding of autism disorders. Aims to further the advancement of preventive studies, therapy and research of autism disorders.

4720 ■ Opportunity Village Arc
6300 W Oakey Blvd.
Las Vegas, NV 89146
Contact: Mr. Edward R. Guthrie, Exec. Dir.
Ph: (702)259-3700
Fax: (702)259-3734
E-mail: guthrie@opportunityvillage.org
URL: http://www.opportunityvillage.org
Staff: 250. **Descr:** Parents, professional workers, and others interested in individuals with mental retardation. Works to promote services, research, public understanding, and legislation for people with mental retardation and their families. **Fnd:** 1954.

4721 ■ Ormsby Arc
PO Box 491
Carson City, NV 89702
Contact: Mary C. Winkler, Exec. Dir.
Ph: (775)882-8520

4722 ■ Reno Association for the Education of Young Children (RAEYC)
PO Box 11421
Reno, NV 89510-1421
Contact: Margaret Oberg, Pres.
E-mail: granmuna@yahoo.com
URL: http://www.nevaeyc.org/RAEYC.asp
Descr: Teachers and directors of preschool and primary schools, kindergartens, child care centers, and early other learning programs for young childhood; early childhood education and child development educators, trainers, and researchers and other professionals dedicated to young children's healthy development.

4723 ■ Special Olympics, Nevada (SONV)
5670 Wynn Rd., Ste. H
Las Vegas, NV 89118
Contact: Kim Gradisher, Coor.
Ph: (702)474-0690
E-mail: kimg@sonv.org
URL: http://www.sonv.org
Descr: Offers free sports training and competition opportunities every day, throughout the year in eleven different sports. Gives athletes continuing opportunities to develop physical fitness, demonstrate courage, experience joy and participate in the sharing of gifts, skill, and friendship with their families, other athletes and the community.

4724 ■ Washoe Arc
790 Sutro St.
Reno, NV 89512
Ph: (775)333-9272
Descr: Parents, professional workers, and others

interested in individuals with mental retardation. Works to promote services, research, public understanding, and legislation for people with mental retardation and their families.

New Hampshire

4725 ■ American Medical Student Association, Dartmouth Medical School
1 Rope Ferry Rd.
Hanover, NH 03755-1404
Ph: (603)650-1200
Free: 877-DMS-1797
Fax: (603)650-1202
URL: http://dms.dartmouth.edu
Descr: Promotes improvement in medical training and education. Advances the medicine profession. Contributes to the welfare of medical students, interns, residents and post-MD/DO trainees.

4726 ■ Arc of Greater Manchester
PO Box 3363
Manchester, NH 03105
Contact: Jan Larsen, Pres.
E-mail: president@arcmanchester.org
URL: http://www.arcmanchester.org

4727 ■ Autism Society of New Hampshire (ASNH)
PO Box 68
Concord, NH 03302
Contact: Michelle Jarvis, Pres.
Ph: (603)679-2424
E-mail: info@nhautism.com
URL: http://www.autism-society-nh.org
Descr: Seeks to improve the lives of individuals affected by autism. Promotes awareness and understanding of autism disorders. Aims to further the advancement of preventive studies, therapy and research of autism disorders.

4728 ■ Learning Disabilities Association of New Hampshire
PO Box 127
Concord, NH 03302
Contact: Gale Cossette, Pres.
E-mail: information@ldanh.org
URL: http://www.ldanh.org

4729 ■ National Education Association - New Hampshire (NEA-NH)
9 S Spring St.
Concord, NH 03301-2425
Contact: Debra Schwoch-Swoboda, Exec. Dir.
Ph: (603)224-7751
Fax: (603)224-2648
E-mail: dswoboda@nhnea.org
URL: http://www.neanh.org
Descr: Works to strengthen and support public education and to serve members' professional, political, economic and advocacy needs. **Fnd:** 1982.

4730 ■ New Hampshire Association for the Education of Young Children (NHAEYC)
PO Box 85
Lempster, NH 03605
Contact: Lorraine Harris, Pres.
Free: 888-225-4884
E-mail: info@nhaeyc.org
URL: http://www.nhaeyc.org
Descr: Serves and acts on behalf of the needs, rights and well-being of all young children with primary focus on the quality of educational and developmental services for all children. Seeks to improve professional practice and working conditions in early childhood education.

4731 ■ New Hampshire Branch of the International Dyslexia Association
PO Box 3724
Concord, NH 03302
Contact: Colleen Sliva, Pres.
Ph: (603)229-7355
E-mail: info@nhida.org
URL: http://www.nhida.org
Descr: Promotes public awareness and understand-

ing of dyslexia. Seeks to develop and implement specialized methods to improve the quality of life for people who have dyslexia. **Fnd:** 2002.

4732 ■ New Hampshire Department of Education
Hugh J. Gallan State Office Park
101 Pleasant St.
Concord, NH 03301-3860
Contact: Dr. Lyonel B. Tracy, Commnr.
Ph: (603)271-3494
Free: 800-339-9900
Fax: (603)271-1953
E-mail: ltracy@ed.state.nh.us
URL: http://www.ed.state.nh.us
Descr: Provides educational leadership and services which promote equal educational opportunites and practices and programs that enable New Hampshire residents to become fully productive members of society.

4733 ■ New Hampshire Developmental Disabilities Council
21 S Fruit St., Ste. 22
Concord, NH 03301-2451
Contact: W. Gordon Allen, Exec. Dir.
Ph: (603)271-3236
Free: 800-852-3345
Fax: (603)271-1156
E-mail: gordon.allen@ddc.nh.gov
URL: http://www.nhddc.org
Descr: Assists individuals to make right choices and decision in their life.

4734 ■ PlusTime New Hampshire
160 Dover Rd., Ste. 1
Chichester, NH 03258
Contact: Rick Gallin, Chm.
Ph: (603)798-5850
Fax: (603)798-5861
E-mail: info@plustime.org
URL: http://www.plustime.org
Staff: 15. **Fnd:** 1990. **Mem:** 60.

4735 ■ Special Olympics New Hampshire (SONH)
650 Elm St.
Manchester, NH 03101
Contact: Mike Quinn, Pres.
Ph: (603)624-1250
Free: 800-639-2608
Fax: (603)624-4911
URL: http://www.sonh.org
Descr: Promotes physical fitness, sports training, and athletic competition for children and adults with mental retardation. Seeks to contribute to the physical, social, and psychological development of persons with mental retardation. Participants range in age from 8 years to adult and compete in track and field, swimming, gymnastics, bowling, ice skating, basketball, and other sports. **Reg. Groups:** 7. **Local Groups:** 100.

4736 ■ Walter Haigh School PTA
24 School St.
Salem, NH 03079
Contact: Lynda Bramhall, Pres.
Ph: (603)894-4288
E-mail: mltnbram@comcast.net
URL: http://www.salemschooldistrictnh.com/schools/haigh/pta.htm
Descr: Parents, teachers, students, and others interested in uniting the forces of home, school, and community. Promotes the welfare of children and youth.

4737 ■ Westmoreland School PTA
Westmoreland School
40 Glebe Rd.
Westmoreland, NH 03467
Contact: Deb Hunter, Pres.
Ph: (603)399-4421
Fax: (603)399-7107
URL: http://www.westmoreland.k12.nh.us/pta/index.html
Descr: Parents, teachers, students, and others

interested in uniting the forces of home, school, and community. Promotes the welfare of children and youth.

New Jersey

4738 ■ AG BELL, New Jersey
PO Box 551
Piscataway, NJ 08855
Contact: Reed Kleinle, Pres.
E-mail: president@agbellnj.org
URL: http://www.agbellnj.org
Descr: Represents the interests of educators, parents of children with hearing loss, adults with hearing loss and hearing health professionals. Provides governmental and education advocacy services.

4739 ■ American Association of University Women, Atlantic County Branch
620 Damstadt Ave.
Egg Harbor City, NJ 08215
Contact: Judy Page, VP for Membership
E-mail: stpage1@verizon.net
URL: http://www.aauwacnj.org
Descr: Advances equity for women and girls through advocacy, education, and research. Provides funds and a support system for women seeking judicial redress for sex discrimination in higher education.

4740 ■ American Association of University Women, Mountain Lakes NJ Area Branch
18 Lake Dr.
Boonton, NJ 07005
Contact: Marti Weinstein, VP for Membership
E-mail: marti7@aol.com
URL: http://www.aauwmlnj.org
Descr: Advances equity for women and girls through advocacy, education, and research. Provides funds and a support system for women seeking judicial redress for sex discrimination in higher education.

4741 ■ American Association of University Women of New Jersey
714 Joseph Ave.
Lanoka Harbor, NJ 08734
Contact: Joanne Messina, VP Membership
Ph: (732)431-1608
E-mail: messinajoanne@yahoo.com
URL: http://www.aauwnj.org
Descr: Advances equity for women and girls through advocacy, education, and research. Provides funds and a support system for women seeking judicial redress for sex discrimination in higher education.

4742 ■ American Medical Student Association, Robert Wood Johnson Medical School
675 Hoes Ln.
Piscataway, NJ 08854
Contact: Danielle M. Salovich, Co-Pres.
E-mail: salovidm@umdnj.edu
URL: http://www2.umdnj.edu/amsapweb/amsapweb.html
Descr: Promotes improvement in medical training and education. Advances the medicine profession. Contributes to the welfare of medical students, interns, residents and post-MD/DO trainees.

4743 ■ Arc of Atlantic County
6550 Delilah Rd., Ste. 101
Egg Harbor Township, NJ 08234
Contact: Deborah Davies PhD, CEO
Ph: (609)485-0800
Fax: (609)407-6282
E-mail: info@arcatlantic.org
URL: http://www.arcatlantic.org
Descr: Parents, professional workers, and others interested in individuals with mental retardation. Works to promote services, research, public understanding, and legislation for people with mental retardation and their families.

4744 ■ Arc of Bergen and Passaic Counties
223 Moore Ave.
Hackensack, NJ 07601
Contact: Kathy Walsh, Exec. Dir.

Ph: (201)343-0322
Fax: (201)343-0401
E-mail: arcbp@aol.com
URL: http://www.arcbergenpassaic.org
Staff: 250. **Descr:** Provides advocacy, services, and support to individuals with disabilities and to their families as well. Programs include early intervention, vocational residential, recreation, and family support. **Fnd:** 1947. **Mem:** 1000. **State Groups:** 1. **Local Groups:** 2. **Pub:** *Parents' Voice* (quarterly).

4745 ■ Arc of Burlington County
115 E Broad St.
Burlington, NJ 08016
Contact: Tom Parente, Exec. Dir.
Ph: (609)531-0211
Fax: (609)386-2244
E-mail: info@arcofburlington.org
URL: http://www.arcofburlington.org
Staff: 4. **Descr:** Parents, professional workers, and others interested in individuals with mental retardation. Works to promote services, research, public understanding, and legislation for people with mental retardation and their families. **Fnd:** 1956.

4746 ■ Arc of Camden County
215 W White Horse Pike
Berlin, NJ 08009
Ph: (856)767-3650
Fax: (856)767-1378
E-mail: arcotc@arccamden.org
URL: http://www.arccamden.org

4747 ■ Arc of Cumberland County, New Jersey
1680 W Sherman Ave.
Vineland, NJ 08360
Contact: Derek Nye, Exec. Dir.
Ph: (856)691-9138
Fax: (856)563-0221
E-mail: dnye@comcast.net
URL: http://www.arccumberland.org

4748 ■ ARC of Essex County
123 Naylon Ave.
Livingston, NJ 07039
Contact: Robert Laurino Esq, Pres.
Ph: (973)535-1181
Fax: (973)535-9507
E-mail: info@arcessex.org
URL: http://www.arcessex.org
Descr: Provides direct service to those with developmental disabilities and their families and acts as an advocate by advancing their interests. Committed to reducing the incidence of mental retardation through education and public information. **Fnd:** 1948.

4749 ■ Arc Gloucester
1555 Gateway Blvd.
Woodbury, NJ 08096
Contact: Robert H. Weir, Pres.
Ph: (856)848-8648
URL: http://www.thearcgloucester.org
Staff: 260. **Descr:** Serves people with intellectual and related developmental disabilities and their families through education, advocacy and direct services. **Fnd:** 1957. **Mem:** 900. **State Groups:** 1. **Local Groups:** 19.

4750 ■ Arc of Hudson County
405 36th St.
Union City, NJ 07087
Contact: Nadia Cabana, Exec. Dir.
Ph: (201)319-9229

4751 ■ Arc of Hunterdon County, New Jersey
1322 State Rte. 31, Ste. 5
Annandale, NJ 08801
Contact: Jeff Mattison, Exec. Dir.
Ph: (908)730-7827
Fax: (908)730-7726
E-mail: jeff@archunterdon.org
URL: http://www.archunterdon.org
Staff: 120. **Descr:** Persons with mental or developmental retardation; their friends and families; medical professionals; interested others. Provides support, information, and quality of life improvement

services. **Fnd:** 1954. **Mem:** 150. **Pub:** *The Archive* (quarterly).

4752 ■ Arc Mercer, New Jersey
180 Ewingville Rd.
Ewing, NJ 08638
Contact: Dennis Micai, Exec. Dir.
Ph: (609)406-0181
E-mail: arc@arcmercer.org

4753 ■ Arc of Middlesex County
219 Black Horse Ln., Ste. 1
North Brunswick, NJ 08902
Contact: Richard F. Sheridan, Exec. Dir.
Ph: (732)821-1199
Fax: (732)247-5590
E-mail: rsheridan@arc-middlesex.org
URL: http://www.arc-middlesex.org
Descr: Parents, professional workers, and others interested in individuals with mental retardation. Works to promote services, research, public understanding, and legislation for people with mental retardation and their families. **Fnd:** 1949. **Mem:** 371. **Pub:** *Catalyst* (quarterly); *Opportunities* (periodic).

4754 ■ ARC of Monmouth
1158 Wayside Rd.
Tinton Falls, NJ 07712
Contact: Mary E. Scott, Exec. Dir.
Ph: (732)493-1919
Fax: (732)493-3604
E-mail: info@arcofmonmouth.org
URL: http://www.arcofmonmouth.org
Staff: 240. **Descr:** Provides programs and services for people with mental retardation. **Fnd:** 1949. **Mem:** 650. **Local Groups:** 1. **Pub:** *The Turning Point* (quarterly); Annual Report (annual).

4755 ■ Arc of New Jersey
985 Livingston Ave.
North Brunswick, NJ 08902
Contact: Bruce Bird, Pres.
Ph: (732)246-2525
Fax: (732)214-1834
E-mail: info@arcnj.org
URL: http://www.arcnj.org
Descr: Parents, professional workers, and others interested in individuals with mental retardation. Works to promote services, research, public understanding, and legislation for people with mental retardation and their families. **Fnd:** 1947. **Local Groups:** 19.

4756 ■ Arc Ocean County Chapter
815 Cedar Bridge Ave.
Lakewood, NJ 08701
Contact: Laura Williams, Exec. Dir.
Ph: (732)363-3335
Fax: (732)363-2285
E-mail: laura.williams@arcocean.org
URL: http://www.arcocean.org

4757 ■ Arc of Somerset County
142 S Main St.
Manville, NJ 08835
Contact: Lauren Panarella, Exec. Dir.
Ph: (908)725-8544
Fax: (908)704-0850
E-mail: tarat@thearcotsomerset.org
URL: http://www.thearcofsomerset.org
Descr: Parents, professional workers, and others interested in individuals with mental retardation. Works to promote services, research, public understanding, and legislation for people with mental retardation and their families.

4758 ■ Arc Warren County Chapter
PO Box 389
Washington, NJ 07882
Contact: Robert Pruznick, Exec. Dir.
Ph: (908)689-7525
Fax: (908)689-4898
E-mail: info@arcwarren.org
URL: http://www.arcwarren.org
Descr: Parents, professional workers, and others interested in individuals with mental retardation.

Works to promote services, research, public understanding, and legislation for people with mental retardation and their families. **Fnd:** 1954.

4759 ■ Communities In Schools of New Jersey (CISNJ)
200 Washington St.
Newark, NJ 07102-2921
Contact: Gwendolyn Corrin, Interim State Dir.
Ph: (973)242-0706
URL: http://www.cisnj.org
Descr: Offers a proven long-term comprehensive framework to help children succeed and stay in school. **Fnd:** 1990.

4760 ■ Learning Disabilities Association of New Jersey
PO Box 492
Towaco, NJ 07082
Contact: Terry Cavanaugh, Pres.
Ph: (973)265-4303
Fax: (973)265-4303
E-mail: ldanj@optonline.net

4761 ■ New Jersey Branch of the International Dyslexia Association (NJIDA)
PO Box 32
Long Valley, NJ 07853
Contact: Susan Tramaglini, Pres.
Ph: (908)876-1179
Fax: (908)876-3621
E-mail: riegpainting@msn.com
URL: http://www.interdys.org/Branchdetail.aspx?bid=30
Descr: Promotes public awareness and understanding of dyslexia. Seeks to develop and implement specialized methods to improve the quality of life for people who have dyslexia.

4762 ■ New Jersey Council on Developmental Disabilities (NJCDD)
PO Box 700
20 W State St., 6th Fl.
Trenton, NJ 08625-0700
Contact: Allison M. Lozano PhD, Exec. Dir.
Ph: (609)292-3745
Free: 800-792-8858
Fax: (609)292-7114
E-mail: njcdd@njcdd.org
URL: http://www.njcdd.org
Descr: New Jersey's official planning body for developmental disabilities. **Pub:** *Monday Morning Newsletter* (weekly); *People & Families* (quarterly); *People with Disabilities*.

4763 ■ New Jersey Department of Education
PO Box 500
Trenton, NJ 08625-0500
Contact: Lucille E. Davy, Commnr.
Ph: (609)292-4469
Fax: (609)777-4099
URL: http://www.state.nj.us/education/
Descr: Provides leadership to prepare all students for their role as citizens and for the career opportunities of the 21st century.

4764 ■ New Jersey Fire Prevention and Protection Association
PO Box 357
Springfield, NJ 07081-0357
Contact: Stanley Sickels, Pres.
Free: 866-596-1780
Fax: (866)596-1780
E-mail: contact@njfppa.org
URL: http://www.njfppa.org
Descr: Provides the highest quality codes, standards, products, and services for all concerned with the safety and performance of the built environment.

4765 ■ New Jersey Parent Teacher Association (NJPTA)
900 Berkeley Ave.
Trenton, NJ 08618-5322
Contact: Paula Henry, Honorary Pres.
Ph: (609)393-6709
Fax: (609)393-8471

E-mail: njptaoffice@njpta.org
URL: http://www.njpta.org

Descr: Provides a support network to local units and councils statewide through state and district PTA conferences, workshops, personalized schools of instruction, and numerous publications and materials.

4766 ■ New Jersey Unit of Recording for the Blind and Dyslexic (RFB&D-NJ)
69 Mapleton Rd.
Princeton, NJ 08540
Contact: Stephanie Campbell, Exec. Dir.
Ph: (609)750-1830
Fax: (609)750-9653
E-mail: scampbell@rfbd.org
URL: http://www.rfbdnj.org

Descr: Serves individuals who cannot effectively read standard print because of visual impairment, dyslexia, or other physical disabilities. Creates educational opportunities for students with print disabilities through educational and outreach services. Provides and promotes the effective use of accessible educational materials. **Fnd:** 1957.

4767 ■ Sussex Arc
11 US Rte. 206, Ste. 100
Augusta, NJ 07822
Contact: Richard C. Lecher PhD, CEO
Ph: (973)383-7442
Fax: (973)383-8330
E-mail: rlecher@scarc.org

Descr: Parents, professional workers, and others interested in individuals with mental retardation. Works to promote services, research, public understanding, and legislation for people with mental retardation and their families.

4768 ■ Vocational Educators Association of New Jersey (VEANJ)
Pemberton Township High School
Arneys Mount Rd.
Pemberton, NJ 08068
Contact: John Hillard, Pres.
Ph: (609)893-8141
E-mail: jhillard@pemb.org

Descr: Represents teachers, supervisors, administrators, and others interested in the development and improvement of vocational, technical, and practical arts education. Supports and promotes vocational education.

4769 ■ VSA arts of New Jersey (VSA NJ)
703 Jersey Ave.
New Brunswick, NJ 08901
Contact: Vanessa Young, Exec. Dir.
Ph: (732)745-3885
Fax: (732)745-4524
E-mail: info@vsanj.org
URL: http://www.vsanj.org

Descr: Provides arts opportunities to individuals with and without disabilities. **Fnd:** 1978. **Mem:** 6.

New Mexico

4770 ■ Adaptive Ski Program
1595 Camino La Canada
Santa Fe, NM 87501
Contact: Katya Franzgen, Exec. Dir.
Ph: (505)995-9858
E-mail: adaptiveski@msn.com
URL: http://www.adaptiveski.org

Descr: Provides safe and supportive ski lessons for physically and/or developmentally challenged adults and children. **Fnd:** 1985.

4771 ■ American Association of University Women, Albuquerque Branch
PO Box 92643
Albuquerque, NM 87199
Contact: Cynthia Wise, Pres.
URL: http://aauw-nm.org/abq_branch/index.html

Descr: Advances equity for women and girls through advocacy, education, and research. Provides funds and a support system for women seeking judicial redress for sex discrimination in higher education.

4772 ■ American Association of University Women of New Mexico
7305 Golden Glow Way
Albuquerque, NM 87113
Contact: Antje Muir, Membership Coor.
Ph: (505)821-7966
E-mail: antjehuep1@msn.com
URL: http://www.aauw-nm.org

Descr: Advances equity for women and girls through advocacy, education, and research. Provides funds and a support system for women seeking judicial redress for sex discrimination in higher education.

4773 ■ American Medical Student Association, University of New Mexico School of Medicine
MSC09 5300
1 University of New Mexico
Albuquerque, NM 87131
Contact: Paul B. Roth MD, Dean
Ph: (505)272-3414
Fax: (505)272-8239
URL: http://hsc.unm.edu/som

Descr: Promotes improvement in medical training and education. Advances the medicine profession. Contributes to the welfare of medical students, interns, residents and post-MD/DO trainees.

4774 ■ Arc of Cibola County
1040 Sakelares Blvd.
Grants, NM 87020
Contact: Monique Gibson, Exec. Dir.
Ph: (505)285-3445

4775 ■ Arc of Las Cruces
2225 E Griggs Ave.
Las Cruces, NM 88001
Contact: Nik Hutchins, Pres.
Ph: (505)525-3811
Fax: (505)525-8364
URL: http://www.arcnm.org

4776 ■ Arc of Luna County
2020 Columbus Rd.
Deming, NM 88030
Contact: G.G. Gore, Pres.
Ph: (505)546-0463
Fax: (505)544-8473
URL: http://www.arcnm.org

4777 ■ Arc of New Mexico
3655 Carlisle NE
Albuquerque, NM 87110-5564
Free: 800-358-6493

Descr: Parents, professional workers, and others interested in individuals with mental retardation. Works to promote services, research, public understanding, and legislation for people with mental retardation and their families.

4778 ■ Central New Mexico Association for the Education of Young Children
5029 Rockcress Dr. NW
Albuquerque, NM 87120
Contact: Tillie Sanchez, Rep.
Ph: (505)873-8512
E-mail: sanchez_til@aps.edu
URL: http://www.nmaeyc.org

Descr: Serves and acts on behalf of the needs, rights and well-being of all young children with primary focus on the quality of educational and developmental services for all children. Seeks to improve professional practice and working conditions in early childhood education.

4779 ■ Four Corners New Mexico Association for the Education of Young Children
1121 Chaco Ave.
Farmington, NM 87401
Contact: Vicki Bruno, Rep.
Ph: (505)634-3364
E-mail: vbruno@cptnet.com
URL: http://www.nmaeyc.org

Descr: Serves and acts on behalf of the needs,

rights and well-being of all young children with primary focus on the quality of educational and developmental services for all children. Seeks to improve professional practice and working conditions in early childhood education.

4780 ■ National Education Association, New Mexico (NEA-NM)
2007 Botulph Rd.
Santa Fe, NM 87505
Contact: Charles Bowyer, Exec. Dir.
Ph: (505)982-1916
Fax: (505)982-6719
E-mail: cbowyer@nea.org
URL: http://www.nea-nm.org

Staff: 12. **Descr:** Serves as an advocate for New Mexico Public Schools and their students and employees. **Fnd:** 1886. **Mem:** 8000. **Local Groups:** 111.

4781 ■ New Mexico Association for Career and Technical Education (NMACTE)
PO Box 866
Carlsbad, NM 88220
Contact: Carol McAlister, Exec. Dir.
Ph: (505)302-5458
Fax: (505)234-3367
E-mail: carol.mcalister@carlsbad.k12.nm.us
URL: http://www.nmacte.com

Descr: Supports vocational technical education that will assure students' successful roles in families, communities, and society.

4782 ■ New Mexico Association for the Education of Young Children (NMAEYC)
2201 Buena Vista SE, Ste. 424
Albuquerque, NM 87111-1651
Contact: Bobbie Bailey, Admin. Coor.
Ph: (505)243-5437
E-mail: drbailey2@aol.com
URL: http://www.nmaeyc.org

4783 ■ New Mexico Autism Society (NMAS)
PO Box 30955
Albuquerque, NM 87190
Contact: Connie Molecke, Pres.
Ph: (505)332-0306
E-mail: nmautism@nmautismsociety.org
URL: http://www.nmautismsociety.org

Descr: Seeks to improve the lives of individuals affected by autism. Promotes awareness and understanding of autism disorders. Aims to further the advancement of preventive studies, therapy and research of autism disorders.

4784 ■ New Mexico Fire Marshals Association
PO Box 20000
Las Cruces, NM 88004
Contact: Brown Travis
Ph: (505)528-4150
E-mail: tbrown@las-cruces.org
URL: http://www.iccsafe.org

Descr: Provides the highest quality codes, standards, products, and services for all concerned with the safety and performance of the built environment.

4785 ■ New Mexico Learning Disabilities Association (NM-LDA)
6301 Menaul Blvd. NE, No. 556
Albuquerque, NM 87110-3323
Contact: Selma Nevarez, Pres.
Ph: (505)821-2545
E-mail: epoel@nmsu.edu
URL: http://education.nmsu.edu/projects/NMLDA

Descr: Prevents learning disabilities through awareness, advocacy, empowerment, education, service and collaborative efforts.

4786 ■ New Mexico Senior Olympics (NMSO)
PO Box 2690
Roswell, NM 88202-2690
Contact: Cecilia Acosta, Exec. Dir.
Ph: (505)623-5777
Fax: (505)622-9244
E-mail: nmso@nmseniorolympics.org
URL: http://www.nmseniorolympics.org

Descr: Raises fund each year to match federal and state dollars. Promotes physical fitness, sports training, and athletic competition for adults.

4787 ■ New Mexico State Department of Education
Jerry Apodaca Education Bldg.
300 Don Gaspar
Santa Fe, NM 87501
Contact: Dr. Veronica C. Garcia, Sec.
Ph: (505)827-5800
Fax: (505)827-6520
E-mail: ped.webmaster@state.nm.us
URL: http://www.ped.state.nm.us/
Descr: Provides leadership, technical assistance, and quality assurance to improve student performance and close the achievement gap.

4788 ■ Northeast New Mexico Association for the Education of Young Children
2802 Calle Campeon
Santa Fe, NM 87505
Contact: Lynn Kelly, Rep.
Ph: (505)983-2803
E-mail: lynn@lacasita.edu
URL: http://www.nmaeyc.org
Descr: Serves and acts on behalf of the needs, rights and well-being of all young children with primary focus on the quality of educational and developmental services for all children. Seeks to improve professional practice and working conditions in early childhood education.

4789 ■ Southeast New Mexico Association for the Education of Young Children
901 Hermosa Dr.
Roswell, NM 88201
Contact: Katie Harton, Rep.
Ph: (505)623-9438
E-mail: kharton@zianet.com
URL: http://www.nmaeyc.org
Descr: Serves and acts on behalf of the needs, rights and well-being of all young children with primary focus on the quality of educational and developmental services for all children. Seeks to improve professional practice and working conditions in early childhood education.

4790 ■ Southern New Mexico Association for the Education of Young Children
1815 N Florida Ave.
Alamogordo, NM 88310
Contact: Judy Rogers, Rep.
Ph: (505)434-9553
E-mail: judroger@hotmail.com
URL: http://www.nmaeyc.org
Descr: Serves and acts on behalf of the needs, rights and well-being of all young children with primary focus on the quality of educational and developmental services for all children. Seeks to improve professional practice and working conditions in early childhood education.

4791 ■ Southwest Branch of the International Dyslexia Association (SWIDA)
3915 Carlisle Blvd. NE
Albuquerque, NM 87107
Contact: Linda Curry
Ph: (505)255-8234
E-mail: info@southwestida.com
URL: http://www.southwestida.com
Descr: Promotes public awareness and understanding of dyslexia. Seeks to develop and implement specialized methods to improve the quality of life for people who have dyslexia. **Fnd:** 1985. **Pub:** NEWSwida (3/year).

4792 ■ Southwest New Mexico Association for the Education of Young Children
PO Box 186
Silver City, NM 88062
Contact: Erica Gonzales, Rep.
Ph: (505)538-6344
E-mail: gonzaleser@yahoo.com
URL: http://www.nmaeyc.org
Descr: Serves and acts on behalf of the needs, rights and well-being of all young children with primary focus on the quality of educational and developmental services for all children. Seeks to improve professional practice and working conditions in early childhood education.

4793 ■ Special Olympics New Mexico (SONM)
6600 Palomas NE
Albuquerque, NM 87109
Contact: Randy Mascorella, Exec. Dir.
Ph: (505)856-0342
Free: 800-371-5525
Fax: (505)856-0346
E-mail: info@specialolympicsnewmexico.org
URL: http://www.sonm.org
Descr: Promotes physical fitness, sports training, and athletic competition for children and adults with mental retardation. Seeks to contribute to the physical, social, and psychological development of persons with mental retardation. Participants range in age from 8 years to adult and compete in track and field, swimming, gymnastics, bowling, ice skating, basketball, and other sports. **Fnd:** 1968.

4794 ■ Taos County Arc
1030 Salazar Rd.
Taos, NM 87571
Contact: Felipe A. Santistevan, Pres.
Ph: (505)758-4274
E-mail: info@taoscountyarc.org
Descr: Parents, professional workers, and others interested in individuals with mental retardation. Works to promote services, research, public understanding, and legislation for people with mental retardation and their families.

New York

4795 ■ 100 Black Men of Long Island
9 Centre St.
Hempstead, NY 11550
Contact: Edison Bramble, Pres.
Ph: (516)538-6318
E-mail: obmli@cs.com
URL: http://www.100blackmenofli.org

4796 ■ ACHIEVE
125 Cutler Pond Rd.
Binghamton, NY 13905-1596
Contact: Mary Jo Thorn, Exec. Dir.
Ph: (607)723-8361
Fax: (607)723-8338
E-mail: achievey@achieveny.org
URL: http://www.achieveny.org
Descr: Represents parents, professional workers, and others interested in individuals with mental retardation. Works to promote services, research, public understanding, and legislation for people with mental retardation and their families. **Fnd:** 1993. **Mem:** 6.

4797 ■ Adaptive Sports Foundation
PO Box 266
Windham, NY 12496
Contact: Cherisse Young, Exec. Dir.
Ph: (518)734-5070
Fax: (518)734-6740
E-mail: asfwindham@mhcable.com
URL: http://www.adaptivesportsfoundation.org
Staff: 9. **Descr:** Teaches winter and summer sports to people with both cognitive and physical disabilities. **Fnd:** 1984. **Mem:** 1300.

4798 ■ Albany Chapter of the Autism Society of America
PO Box 3847
Schenectady, NY 12303
Contact: Cindy Herrmann
Ph: (518)355-2191
Fax: (518)355-2191
E-mail: info@albanyautism.org
URL: http://www.albanyautism.org
Descr: Seeks to improve the lives of individuals affected by autism. Promotes awareness and understanding of autism disorders. Aims to further the advancement of preventive studies, therapy and research of autism disorders.

4799 ■ American Association of University Women, Greater Rochester Area Branch
494 East Ave.
Rochester, NY 14607
Contact: Beverly Barr Vaughan, Pres.
Ph: (585)244-8890
Fax: (585)244-5277
E-mail: rochaauw@frontiernet.net
URL: http://www.aauwrochester.org
Descr: Advances equity for women and girls through advocacy, education, and research. Provides funds and a support system for women seeking judicial redress for sex discrimination in higher education.

4800 ■ American Association of University Women, New York City Branch
111 E 37th St.
New York, NY 10016
Contact: Maria Ellis, Pres.
Ph: (212)684-6068
Fax: (212)684-6068
E-mail: aauwnyc1@aol.com
URL: http://www.aauwnyc.org
Descr: Advances equity for women and girls through advocacy, education, and research. Provides funds and a support system for women seeking judicial redress for sex discrimination in higher education.

4801 ■ American Association of University Women, Poughkeepsie Branch
PO Box 1908
Poughkeepsie, NY 12603
Contact: Linda Beyer, Pres.
Ph: (845)462-0345
E-mail: president@aauwpughkeepsie.org
URL: http://www.aauwpoughkeepsie.org
Descr: Advances equity for women and girls through advocacy, education, and research. Provides funds and a support system for women seeking judicial redress for sex discrimination in higher education.

4802 ■ American Association of University Women, Skaneateles Area Branch
4 Prentiss Dr.
Skaneateles, NY 13152
Contact: Fran McCormack, VP for Membership
Ph: (315)685-2140
URL: http://aauw-nys.org/branches/skaneateles.htm
Descr: Advances equity for women and girls through advocacy, education, and research. Provides funds and a support system for women seeking judicial redress for sex discrimination in higher education.

4803 ■ American Medical Student Association, Albany Medical College
43 New Scotland Ave.
Albany, NY 12208
Ph: (518)262-3125
URL: http://www.amc.edu/Academic
Descr: Promotes improvement in medical training and education. Advances the medicine profession. Contributes to the welfare of medical students, interns, residents and post-MD/DO trainees.

4804 ■ American Medical Student Association, Albert Einstein College of Medicine of Yeshiva University
1300 Morris Park Ave.
Bronx, NY 10461
Ph: (718)430-2000
E-mail: information@aecom.yu.edu
URL: http://www.aecom.yu.edu/home
Descr: Promotes improvement in medical training and education. Advances the medicine profession. Contributes to the welfare of medical students, interns, residents and post-MD/DO trainees.

4805 ■ American Medical Student Association, Columbia University College of Physicians and Surgeons
P&S Club
Bard Hall, Ste. 106
50 Haven Ave.
New York, NY 10032

Contact: Nicholas Donin
Ph: (212)304-7025
E-mail: nmd2113@columbia.edu
URL: http://www.cumc.columbia.edu/dept/ps/affairs/psclub/clubs/amsa.html
Descr: Promotes improvement in medical training and education. Advances the medicine profession. Contributes to the welfare of medical students, interns, residents and post-MD/DO trainees.

4806 ■ American Medical Student Association, CUNY The Sophie Davis School of Biomedical Education
160 Convent Ave., Rm. H-107
New York, NY 10031
Ph: (212)650-5275
Fax: (212)650-6696
URL: http://med.cuny.edu
Descr: Promotes improvement in medical training and education. Advances the medicine profession. Contributes to the welfare of medical students, interns, residents and post-MD/DO trainees.

4807 ■ American Medical Student Association, Mount Sinai School of Medicine
1 Gustave L. Levy Pl.
New York, NY 10029
Contact: Kenneth L. Davis, Pres.
Ph: (212)241-6500
E-mail: studentc@mssm.edu
URL: http://www.mountsinai.org
Descr: Promotes improvement in medical training and education. Advances the medicine profession. Contributes to the welfare of medical students, interns, residents and post-MD/DO trainees.

4808 ■ American Medical Student Association, New York College of Medicine of New York Institute of Technology
PO Box 8000
Old Westbury, NY 11568
Ph: (516)686-1329
Fax: (516)686-3831
URL: http://iris.nyit.edu/nycom/Index.htm
Descr: Promotes improvement in medical training and education. Advances the medicine profession. Contributes to the welfare of medical students, interns, residents and post-MD/DO trainees.

4809 ■ American Medical Student Association, New York Medical College
New York Medical College
95 Grasslands Rd., Bldg. 5
Valhalla, NY 10595
Contact: Karl P. Adler, Pres.
Ph: (914)594-4507
URL: http://www.nymc.edu
Descr: Promotes improvement in medical training and education. Advances the medicine profession. Contributes to the welfare of medical students, interns, residents and post-MD/DO trainees.

4810 ■ American Medical Student Association, Stony Brook University Medical Center School of Medicine
School of Medicine
HSC, L4, Rm. 170
Stony Brook, NY 11794
Ph: (631)444-6130
URL: http://www.stonybrookmedicalcenter.org/education/som.cfm
Descr: Promotes improvement in medical training and education. Advances the medicine profession. Contributes to the welfare of medical students, interns, residents and post-MD/DO trainees.

4811 ■ American Medical Student Association, SUNY Downstate Medical Center College of Medicine
450 Clarkson Ave.
Brooklyn, NY 11203
Ph: (718)270-2446
Fax: (718)270-4775
URL: http://www.hscbklyn.edu/college_of_medicine/default.html
Descr: Promotes improvement in medical training and education. Advances the medicine profession.

Contributes to the welfare of medical students, interns, residents and post-MD/DO trainees.

4812 ■ American Medical Student Association, University at Buffalo School of Medicine and Biomedical Sciences
45 Biomedical Education Bldg.
Buffalo, NY 14214
Contact: Erica Colligan, Pres.
Ph: (716)829-3466
E-mail: jjrosso@acsu.buffalo.edu
URL: http://www.smbs.buffalo.edu
Descr: Promotes improvement in medical training and education. Advances the medicine profession. Contributes to the welfare of medical students, interns, residents and post-MD/DO trainees.

4813 ■ American Medical Student Association, Weill Cornell Medical College
525 E 68th St.
New York, NY 10065
Ph: (212)746-1067
URL: http://www.med.cornell.edu
Descr: Promotes improvement in medical training and education. Advances the medicine profession. Contributes to the welfare of medical students, interns, residents and post-MD/DO trainees.

4814 ■ Arc, Adirondack
12 Mohawk St.
Tupper Lake, NY 12986
Contact: Lester G. Parker Jr., Exec. Dir.
Ph: (518)359-3351
E-mail: les@adirondackarc.org
URL: http://www.adirondackarc.org

4815 ■ Arc, Allegany
240 O'Connor St.
Wellsville, NY 14895
Contact: Carrie Redman, Development Dir.
Ph: (585)593-5700
Fax: (585)593-4529
E-mail: carrie.redman@alleganyarc.org
URL: http://www.alleganyarc.org

4816 ■ Arc, Cattaraugus
The Rehab Center
1439 Buffalo St.
Olean, NY 14760
Ph: (716)375-4747
E-mail: trcinfo@rehabcenter.org

4817 ■ Arc, Chemung
711 Sullivan St.
Elmira, NY 14901
Contact: Michael A. Doherty PhD, Exec. Dir.
Ph: (607)734-6151
E-mail: info@chemungarc.org
URL: http://www.chemungarc.org

4818 ■ Arc, Chenango
17 Midland Dr.
Norwich, NY 13815
Contact: John McHale, Exec. Dir.
Ph: (607)334-5366

4819 ■ Arc of Community League Wassaic
1 South St.
Beacon, NY 12508
Ph: (845)838-0515
Fax: (845)831-2034
E-mail: commleague@hvi.net
URL: http://www.geocities.com/communityleague
Fnd: 1950.

4820 ■ Arc, Dutchess
1435 Rte. 44
Pleasant Valley, NY 12569
Ph: (845)635-8084
E-mail: info@dutchess-arc.org

4821 ■ Arc, Montgomery County Chapter
43 Liberty Dr.
Amsterdam, NY 12010
Ph: (518)842-5080
Fax: (518)842-0143
URL: http://libertyarc.org

Descr: Parents, professional workers, and others interested in individuals with mental retardation. Works to promote services, research, public understanding, and legislation for people with mental retardation and their families.

4822 ■ Arc, Niagara
PO Box 360
Niagara Falls, NY 14304-0360
Ph: (716)297-6400
E-mail: jspira@buffnet.net
URL: http://www.thearc.org/NetCommunity/Page.aspx?&pid=321&srcid=207

4823 ■ Arc of Orleans County
PO Box 439
Albion, NY 14411
Ph: (585)589-5516
Fax: (585)589-5669
E-mail: kspychalski@arcoforleans.org
URL: http://www.arcoforleans.org

4824 ■ Arc of Oswego
7 Morrill Pl.
Fulton, NY 13069
Contact: Cherryl A. Grant, Program Dir.
Ph: (315)598-3108
E-mail: cgrant@oswegoind.org
URL: http://www.arcofoswegocounty.org

4825 ■ Arc, Otsego
PO Box 490
Oneonta, NY 13820
Contact: Lynne Sessions
Ph: (607)433-8595
Fax: (607)433-8430
E-mail: info@arcotsego.org
URL: http://www.arcotsego.org

4826 ■ Arc of Rockland
25 Hemlock Dr.
Congers, NY 10920
Contact: Karyl Caplan, Exec. Dir.
Ph: (845)267-2500
E-mail: kcaplan@rocklandarc.org
URL: http://www.rocklandarc.org

4827 ■ Arc, Schenectady
PO Box 2236
Schenectady, NY 12301-2236
Contact: Linda Lahaie, Exec. Dir.
Ph: (518)372-1160
Fax: (518)377-2189
E-mail: webintake@arcschenectady.org
URL: http://www.arcschenectady.org

4828 ■ Arc, Schoharie
PO Box 307
Schoharie, NY 12157
Contact: John DeSanto, Pres.
Ph: (518)295-8130
Fax: (518)295-8969
E-mail: info@schohariearc.org
URL: http://www.schohariearc.org
Fnd: 1965.

4829 ■ Arc of Schuyler County
203 12th St.
Watkins Glen, NY 14891
Contact: Mary Margeson
Ph: (607)535-6934
Fax: (607)535-2666
E-mail: manager@arcofschuyler.org
URL: http://www.arcofschuyler.org
Descr: Works for and with people with mental retardation and other developmental disabilities in New York. Committed to securing for all people with mental retardation the opportunity to chose and realize their goals of where and how they learn, live, work and play. Serves individuals with disabilities and their families through various day, residential and support service programs. **Fnd:** 1978. **Mem:** 64000. **Pub:** Annual Report; Newsletter.

4830 ■ Arc, Staten Island
1150 Forest Hill Rd., Bldg. L
Staten Island, NY 10314

Contact: Jerome Isaacs, Pres.
Ph: (609)448-8306
E-mail: j4msully@verizon.net

4831 ■ Arc of Steuben
1 Arc Way
Bath, NY 14810
Contact: Mischelle K. Shattuck, Pres.
Ph: (607)776-4146
Fax: (607)776-9366
E-mail: arcofsteuben@arcofsteuben.org
URL: http://arcofsteuben.org

4832 ■ Arc, Tioga County
56 Broadway
Owego, NY 13827-1271
Contact: Mary Jo Thorn, Exec. Dir.
Ph: (607)687-5140
Fax: (607)687-5179
E-mail: info@btarc.org
URL: http://www.btarc.org
Staff: 6. **Descr:** Represents parents, professional workers, and others interested in individuals with mental retardation. Works to promote services, research, public understanding, and legislation for people with mental retardation and their families. **Fnd:** 1993.

4833 ■ Arc, Yates
235 North Ave.
Penn Yan, NY 14527
Contact: David W. Milliman, Exec. Dir.
Ph: (315)536-7447

4834 ■ Association of Certified Fraud Examiners, Utica College Student Chapter
1600 Burrstone Rd.
Utica, NY 13502
Contact: Ms. Ashley M. Busa, Pres.
Ph: (315)792-3443
Descr: Works to classify and examine financial crimes such as white-collar embezzlement, forgery, and fraud as well as their frequency and methodology to develop effective preventive plans and policies for businesses.

4835 ■ Autism Society of America - Bronx Chapter
FSPDD at North Central Bronx Hospital
3424 Kossuth Ave., Rm. 15A11
Bronx, NY 10467
Contact: Monica Sanabria, VP
Ph: (718)519-4797
Fax: (718)519-3634
E-mail: ny-bronx@autismsocietyofamerica.org
Descr: Seeks to improve the lives of individuals affected by autism. Promotes awareness and understanding of autism disorders. Aims to further the advancement of preventive studies, therapy and research of autism disorders.

4836 ■ Autism Society of America - Brooklyn Chapter
225 Ave. S
Brooklyn, NY 11223
Contact: Terry Sciametta, Pres.
Ph: (718)336-9533
E-mail: terryasbm@aol.com
Descr: Seeks to improve the lives of individuals affected by autism. Promotes awareness and understanding of autism disorders. Aims to further the advancement of preventive studies, therapy and research of autism disorders.

4837 ■ Autism Society of America - Manhattan Chapter
370 E 76th St., No. C1208
New York, NY 10021
Contact: Carey Zuckerman, Pres.
Ph: (212)628-0669
E-mail: gdzucker@aol.com
Descr: Seeks to improve the lives of individuals affected by autism. Promotes awareness and understanding of autism disorders. Aims to further the

advancement of preventive studies, therapy and research of autism disorders.

4838 ■ Autism Society of America Western New York Chapter (ASAWNY)
19 Limestone Dr., Ste. 1
Buffalo, NY 14221
Contact: Kathy Eiss
Ph: (716)633-2275
E-mail: info@autismwny.org
URL: http://www.autismwny.com
Descr: Seeks to improve the lives of individuals affected by autism. Promotes awareness and understanding of autism disorders. Aims to further the advancement of preventive studies, therapy and research of autism disorders.

4839 ■ A Better Chance, New York Metro
240 W 35th St.
New York, NY 10001-2506
Contact: Yasmine Abdul-Mani, Program Coor.
Ph: (646)346-1310
Fax: (646)346-1311
E-mail: yabdulmani@abetterchance.org
Descr: Identifies, recruits, and places academically talented and motivated minority students into leading independent secondary schools and selected public schools.

4840 ■ Capital District Counseling Association
PO Box 13174
Albany, NY 12212
Contact: Betsy Schuhle, Pres.
E-mail: betsala@yahoo.com
URL: http://www.casdany.org/CDCA.html
Descr: Promotes the practice of counseling. Provides opportunities for personal growth and professional development.

4841 ■ Central New York Chapter of the Autism Society of America (CNY ASA)
4465 E Genesee St.
PMB 252
De Witt, NY 13214
Contact: Sharon Salvo, Pres.
Ph: (315)447-4466
E-mail: cnyasa@yahoo.com
URL: http://www.cnyasa.org
Descr: Seeks to improve the lives of individuals affected by autism. Promotes awareness and understanding of autism disorders. Aims to further the advancement of preventive studies, therapy and research of autism disorders.

4842 ■ Counselor and Student Service Association of Schuyler, Chemung and Tioga
Spencer-Van Etten JSHS
Rte. 34
Spencer, NY 14883
Contact: Daniel Hundycz, Pres.
Ph: (607)589-7144
Fax: (607)589-7158
E-mail: dhundycz@mail.sctboces.org
URL: http://www.nycounseling.org
Descr: Promotes the practice of counseling. Provides opportunities for personal growth and professional development.

4843 ■ Delaware County Chapter Nysarc
34570 State Hwy. 10
Walton, NY 13856
Contact: Glenn C. Rappleyea, Pres.
Ph: (607)865-7126
Fax: (607)865-7129
E-mail: k.heggins@delarc.org
URL: http://www.delawarecountyarc.org
Descr: Parents, professional workers, and others interested in individuals with mental retardation. Works to promote services, research, public under-

standing, and legislation for people with mental retardation and their families.

4844 ■ Down Syndrome Association of Central New York
PO Box 5
Manlius, NY 13104-0005
Ph: (315)682-4289
Descr: Supports one another in the challenges faced. Educates the community both in its knowledge and perception of Down syndrome. Advocates for children and to other parents. **Fnd:** 1993. **Mem:** 170. **Pub:** *Down Syndrome Association of Central New York, Inc. Newsletter* (quarterly).

4845 ■ Dutchess County Counseling Association
Arlington Middle School
Dutchess Tpke.
Poughkeepsie, NY 12603
Contact: Pamela Riggins, Pres.
Ph: (845)471-0090
E-mail: priggins@ams.ascd.dcboces.org
URL: http://www.nycounseling.org
Descr: Promotes the practice of counseling. Provides opportunities for personal growth and professional development.

4846 ■ Essex County Chapter Nysarc
10 St. Patricks Pl.
Port Henry, NY 12974
Contact: Dipu Basu, Exec. Dir.
Ph: (518)546-3381
Descr: Parents, professional workers, and others interested in individuals with mental retardation. Works to promote services, research, public understanding, and legislation for people with mental retardation and their families.

4847 ■ Genesee County Chapter NYSARC
PO Box 988
Batavia, NY 14021
Contact: Jane Meier, Pres.
Ph: (585)343-1123
E-mail: genarc@rochester.rr.com
URL: http://www.gencoarc.com

4848 ■ Greek Peak Adaptive Snowsports
208 Meeker Rd.
Vestal, NY 13850
Contact: Jim Cappellett
Ph: (607)785-8101
E-mail: jmcappellett@yahoo.com
URL: http://www.gpadaptive.org
Descr: Provides a snow sports experience for disabled people whose disabilities would not allow them to utilize the traditional snow sport teaching process.

4849 ■ Hudson Valley Autism Society
18 Jansen Rd.
Stone Ridge, NY 12484
Contact: Carol Hikade, Pres.
Ph: (845)331-2626
E-mail: ny-hudsonvalley@autismsocietyofamerica.org
URL: http://www.autism-society.org/site/Clubs?club_id=1223&pg=main
Descr: Seeks to improve the lives of individuals affected by autism. Promotes awareness and understanding of autism disorders. Aims to further the advancement of preventive studies, therapy and research of autism disorders.

4850 ■ Jefferson-Lewis Counseling Association
Indian River Middle School
32735 County Rte. 29
Philadelphia, NY 13673
Contact: Jennifer Bryant-Ulrecht, Pres.
Ph: (315)642-0125
URL: http://www.nycounseling.org
Descr: Promotes the practice of counseling. Pro-

vides opportunities for personal growth and professional development.

4851 ■ Learning Disabilities Association of the Capital District of New York
1190 Troy Schenectady Rd.
Latham, NY 12110
Contact: Mr. Richard L. Walley, Chief Operating Off.
Ph: (518)640-3300
Fax: (518)640-3401
E-mail: info@wildwood.edu
URL: http://www.ldanys.org

4852 ■ Learning Disabilities Association of Central New York (LDA/CNY)
722 W Manlius St.
East Syracuse, NY 13057
Contact: Aggie Glavin, Co-Exec. Dir./Programs
Ph: (315)432-0665
Fax: (315)431-0606
E-mail: ldacny@ldacny.org
URL: http://www.ldacny.org
Staff: 8. **Descr:** Aims to enhance the quality of life for children and adults with learning disabilities by providing advocacy, programs, and educational resources. Serves Cayuga, Cortland, Madison, Onondaga, and Oswego county. **Pub:** Newsletter (monthly).

4853 ■ Learning Disabilities Association of the Genesee Valley
339 East Ave., Ste. 420
Rochester, NY 14604
Contact: Brian Frierson, Pres.
Ph: (585)263-3323
Fax: (585)263-2461
E-mail: info@ldarochester.org
URL: http://www.ldagvi.org
Descr: Serves as a resource to individuals who are working for people with cognitive and developmental barriers to learning. **Fnd:** 1964. **Pub:** Report (annual).

4854 ■ Learning Disabilities Association of the Mohawk Valley
401 Columbia St.
Utica, NY 13502
Ph: (315)797-1253
Fax: (315)797-4006
URL: http://www.ldanys.org

4855 ■ Learning Disabilities Association of New York City
27 W 20th St., Ste. 303
New York, NY 10011
Contact: Martha B. Bernard, Pres.
Ph: (212)645-6730
Fax: (212)924-8896
E-mail: info@ldanyc.org
URL: http://www.ldanyc.org

4856 ■ Learning Disabilities Association of New York State (LDANYS)
1190 Troy Schenectady Rd.
Latham, NY 12110
Contact: Michael Helman, Pres.
Ph: (518)608-8992
Fax: (518)608-8993
E-mail: ldalongisland@yahoo.com
URL: http://www.ldanys.org

4857 ■ Learning Disabilities Association of the Southern Tier
112 Nanticoke Ave.
Endicott, NY 13760
Contact: Ann Gorski, Rep.
Ph: (607)754-3335
E-mail: ldastny@aol.com
URL: http://www.ldanys.org

4858 ■ Learning Disabilities Association of Western New York
2555 Elmwood Ave.
Kenmore, NY 14217
Ph: (716)874-7200
E-mail: information@ldaofwny.org
URL: http://www.ldaofwny.org

4859 ■ Lexington-Fulton County ARC
465 N Perry St.
Johnstown, NY 12095
Ph: (518)762-0024
Fax: (518)762-3533
E-mail: info@lexcenter.org
URL: http://www.lexingtoncenter.org

4860 ■ Long Island Branch of the International Dyslexia Association (LIBIDA)
728 Rte. 25A
Northport, NY 11768
Contact: Lynn Burke, Pres.
Ph: (631)261-7441
E-mail: information@lidyslexia.org
URL: http://www.lidyslexia.org
Descr: Promotes public awareness and understanding of dyslexia. Seeks to develop and implement specialized methods to improve the quality of life for people who have dyslexia.

4861 ■ Lounsbury Adaptive Ski Program
PO Box 370
Ellicottville, NY 14731
Contact: Mary Ellen Racich, Program Dir.
Ph: (716)699-3504
E-mail: ski@lounsburyadaptive.org
URL: http://www.lounsburyadaptive.org
Descr: Offers lessons to persons with virtually all disabilities, both physical and cognitive.

4862 ■ Mothers and More Rochester, Chapter 9
1191 Hook Rd.
Farmington, NY 14425
Ph: (585)234-6498
URL: http://www.mothersandmorerochester.org

4863 ■ Nassau Suffolk Chapter of the Autism Society of America
PO Box 1405
Melville, NY 11747
Contact: Chris Petrosino, Co-Pres.
Ph: (631)404-8217
E-mail: nypaac@yahoo.com
URL: http://www.nsasa.org
Descr: Seeks to improve the lives of individuals affected by autism. Promotes awareness and understanding of autism disorders. Aims to further the advancement of preventive studies, therapy and research of autism disorders.

4864 ■ National Education Association - New York (NEA/NY)
217 Lark St.
Albany, NY 12210
Contact: Robin Rapaport, Pres.
Ph: (518)462-6451
Free: 800-66N-EANY
Fax: (518)462-1731
URL: http://www.neany.org
Descr: Represents the interests of educational employees in the state's school districts. Promotes quality and excellence in public education. **Pub:** NEA Today (8/year).

4865 ■ New York Branch of the International Dyslexia Association (NYB-IDA)
71 W 23rd St., Ste. 1527
New York, NY 10010
Contact: Jo Haines, Exec. Dir.
Ph: (212)691-1930
Fax: (212)633-1620
E-mail: info@nybida.org
URL: http://www.nybida.org
Descr: Promotes public awareness and understanding of dyslexia. Seeks to develop and implement specialized methods to improve the quality of life for

people who have dyslexia. **Mem:** 1200. **Pub:** dyslexia discourse (3/year).

4866 ■ New York City Association for Counseling and Development
1 Cambridge Pl.
Brooklyn, NY 11238
Contact: J. Cameron Thornhill, Pres.
Ph: (718)857-7974
URL: http://www.nycounseling.org
Descr: Promotes the practice of counseling. Provides opportunities for personal growth and professional development.

4867 ■ New York City Association for the Education of Young Children (NYCAEYC)
66 Leroy St.
New York, NY 10014-3929
Contact: Teresa Del Priore, Co-Pres.
Ph: (212)807-0144
Fax: (212)807-1767
E-mail: office@nycaeyc.org
URL: http://nycaeyc.org
Descr: Teachers and directors of preschool and primary schools, kindergartens, childcare centers, cooperatives, church schools, and groups having similar programs for young children; early childhood education and child development educators, trainers, and researchers. Open to all individuals interested in serving and acting on behalf of the needs and rights of young children, with primary focus on the provision of educational services and resources.

4868 ■ New York Education Department
Education Bldg., Rm. 111
89 Washington Ave.
Albany, NY 12234
Contact: Dr. Richard P. Mills, Commnr.
Ph: (518)474-3852
Fax: (518)473-4909
E-mail: rmills@mail.nysed.gov
URL: http://www.nysed.gov/
Pub: List of publications online (usny.nysed.gov/publications.html).

4869 ■ New York State Association for Career and Technical Education (NYSACTE)
307 Park Hall
Oswego, NY 13126
Contact: William Ransom, Pres.
E-mail: membership@nysacte.org
URL: http://www.nysacte.org
Descr: Supports vocational technical education that will assure students' successful roles in families, communities, and society.

4870 ■ New York State Association for Education and Rehabilitation of the Blind and Visually Impaired (NYSAER)
5300 Powers Rd.
Orchard Park, NY 14127
Contact: Mary Ann Oyer, Pres.
Fax: (716)649-6779
E-mail: mmoyervi@adelphia.net
URL: http://nysaer.aerbvi.org
Descr: Works in all phases of education and rehabilitation of blind and visually impaired children and adults. **Mem:** 350. **Pub:** Fresh AER.

4871 ■ New York State Association for the Education of Young Children (NYSAEYC)
230 Washington Ave. Extension
Albany, NY 12203
Contact: Kristine Kerr, Exec. Dir.
Ph: (518)867-3517
Fax: (518)867-3520
E-mail: nysaeyc@capital.net
URL: http://www.nysaeyc.org
Staff: 6. **Descr:** Supports the development of professionals to promote quality care and education for the well-being of all children and their families. **Fnd:**

1965. **Mem:** 5500. **State Groups:** 1. **Local Groups:** 17. **Pub:** *Reporter* (3/year).

4872 ■ New York State Association of Retarded Citizens (NYSARC)
393 Delaware Ave.
Delmar, NY 12054
Contact: Marc N. Brandt, Exec. Dir.
Ph: (518)439-8311
Fax: (518)439-1893
E-mail: info@nysarc.org
URL: http://www.nysarc.org
Staff: 18000. **Descr:** Strives to improve the quality of life for persons with mental retardation and other developmental disabilities. **Fnd:** 1949. **Mem:** 64000. **Pub:** *Directory of Chapter Programs and Services* (biennial); *Our Voice Today* (annual).

4873 ■ New York State Fire Marshals and Inspectors Association
155 Hemlock Woods Ln.
Rochester, NY 14615
Contact: Rob Drexler, Pres.
Ph: (585)723-2309
Fax: (585)723-2457
E-mail: info@nysfma.org
URL: http://www.nysfma.org
Descr: Provides the highest quality codes, standards, products, and services for all concerned with the safety and performance of the built environment.

4874 ■ New York State PTA (NYSPTA)
One Wembley Ct.
Albany, NY 12205-3830
Contact: Susan Lipman, Pres.
Ph: (518)452-8808
Free: 877-569-7782
Fax: (518)452-8105
E-mail: pta.office@nypta.com
URL: http://www.nypta.com
Staff: 5. **Descr:** Parents and teachers. Promotes the welfare of children. Seeks to raise the standards of home life, secure adequate laws for child care and protection, and develop cooperation among educators and the public. **Fnd:** 1897. **Mem:** 370000. **Reg. Groups:** 16. **Local Groups:** 1600. **Pub:** *Fast Facts* (monthly); *Legislation Bulletin* (5/year); *New York Parent-Teacher* (bimonthly); *NYS PTA Research Guide*; *Regents Watch*; *What's Happening in Albany*.

4875 ■ New York State School Age Care Coalition (NYSSACC)
230 Washington Ave. Ext.
Albany, NY 12203
Contact: James Murphy, Exec. Dir.
Ph: (518)694-0660
Fax: (518)694-0661
E-mail: mail@nyssacc.org
URL: http://www.nyssacc.org

4876 ■ Niagara-Orleans Counseling Association
Lockport High School
250 Lincoln Ave.
Lockport, NY 14094
Contact: Lana Riester, Pres.
Ph: (716)478-4469
URL: http://www.nycounseling.org
Descr: Promotes the practice of counseling. Provides opportunities for personal growth and professional development.

4877 ■ Northeastern New York Association for Counseling and Development
4914 S Catherine St.
Plattsburgh, NY 12901
Contact: Christy Minck, Pres.
Ph: (518)561-0470
URL: http://www.nycounseling.org
Descr: Promotes the practice of counseling. Provides opportunities for personal growth and professional development.

4878 ■ Northern Zone Association for Counseling and Development
Banford Elementary Scholarship
99 State St.

Canton, NY 13617
Contact: Kelly Glasgow, Pres.
Ph: (315)386-8561
E-mail: kglasgow@cantonbsd.neric.org
URL: http://www.nycounseling.org
Descr: Promotes the practice of counseling. Provides opportunities for personal growth and professional development.

4879 ■ Oneida Lewis ARC
241 Genesee St.
Utica, NY 13501
Contact: Angela VanDerhoof, Exec. Dir.
Ph: (315)272-1606
Fax: (315)272-1780
E-mail: childsrvs@thearcolc.org
URL: http://www.thearcolc.org
Staff: 5. **Descr:** Provides educational, vocational, residential and recreational services to enable individuals with disabilities to achieve their potential and participate in the life of their community as independently as possible. **Fnd:** 1954. **Pub:** *News and Views* (quarterly).

4880 ■ Ontario ARC
3071 County Complex Dr.
Canandaigua, NY 14424
Contact: Kathryn A. Wegman, Pres.
Ph: (585)394-7500
Fax: (585)394-1987
E-mail: contact@ontarioarc.org
URL: http://www.nysarc.org

4881 ■ Orange County AHRC (OCAHRC)
249 Broadway
Newburgh, NY 12550
Contact: Gary Fox, Pres.
Ph: (845)561-0670
URL: http://www.orangeahrc.org

4882 ■ Putnam ARC (PARC)
31 International Blvd.
Brewster, NY 10509
Ph: (845)278-7272
Fax: (845)278-2151
E-mail: info@putnamarc.org
URL: http://www.putnamarc.org

4883 ■ Recording for the Blind and Dyslexic New York Unit
545 Fifth Ave.
New York, NY 10017
Contact: Diane Crupain, Exec. Dir.
Ph: (212)557-5720
E-mail: dcrupain@rfbd.org
Descr: Serves individuals who cannot effectively read standard print because of visual impairment, dyslexia, or other physical disabilities. Creates educational opportunities for students with print disabilities through educational and outreach services. Provides and promotes the effective use of accessible educational materials.

4884 ■ Rensselaer County ARC
79 102nd St., 3rd Fl.
Troy, NY 12180
Contact: Lori Lehmkul, Pres.
Ph: (518)274-3110
Fax: (518)274-1522
E-mail: info@renarc.org
URL: http://www.rensselaerarc.org

4885 ■ Rome Tri-County Arc
801 Cypress St.
Rome, NY 13440
Contact: Alfred Remington, Pres.
Ph: (315)853-5479
URL: http://www.nysarc.org

4886 ■ SAFE Association - East Coast Chapter
1175 Church St.
Bohemia, NY 11716
Contact: Bob Ufer
Ph: (631)244-6388
Fax: (631)589-6348
E-mail: rufer@tbtest.com
Descr: Ensures personal safety and protection in

land, sea, air and space environments. Fosters research and development in the fields of safety and survival. Provides a forum for the sharing of problems, ideas and information in the areas of safety, survival and crew systems.

4887 ■ Seneca-Cayuga Arc
1083 Waterloo Geneva Rd.
Waterloo, NY 13165
Contact: Kevin M. Smith, Exec. Dir.
Ph: (315)539-5067
Fax: (315)539-6269
E-mail: mail@sencayarc.org
URL: http://www.sencayarc.org
Descr: Parents, professional workers, and others interested in individuals with mental retardation. Works to promote services, research, public understanding, and legislation for people with mental retardation and their families.

4888 ■ Special Olympics New York (SONY)
504 Balltown Rd.
Schenectady, NY 12304-2290
Contact: Neal J. Johnson, Pres./CEO
Ph: (518)388-0790
Free: 800-836-6976
Fax: (518)388-0795
E-mail: johnsonn@nyso.org
URL: http://www.nyso.org
Staff: 3. **Descr:** Promotes physical fitness, sports training, and athletic competition for children and adults with mental retardation. Seeks to contribute to the physical, social, and psychological development of persons with mental retardation. Participants range in age from 8 years to adult and compete in track and field, swimming, gymnastics, bowling, ice skating, basketball, and other sports. **Fnd:** 1969.

4889 ■ Suffolk Association for the Help of Retarded Citizens
2900 Veterans Memorial Hwy.
Bohemia, NY 11716
Contact: Fred K. Salzberg, Pres.
Ph: (631)585-0100
E-mail: info@suffahrc.org
URL: http://www.ahrcsuffolk.org
Descr: Parents, professional workers, and others interested in individuals with mental retardation. Works to promote services, research, public understanding, and legislation for people with mental retardation and their families.

4890 ■ Sullivan Arc
162 E Broadway
Monticello, NY 12701
Contact: Stephen Miller, Pres.
Ph: (845)796-1350
Fax: (845)796-3213
E-mail: administration@sullivanarc.org
URL: http://www.sullivanarc.org

4891 ■ Wayne ARC - New York
150 Van Buren St.
Newark, NY 14513
Contact: Bret Vanzo, Pres.
Ph: (315)331-7741
URL: http://www.waynearc.org

4892 ■ Westchester Arc
121 Westmoreland Ave.
White Plains, NY 10606
Contact: Anne M. Majsak, Pres.
Ph: (914)949-9300
E-mail: info@westchesterarc.org
URL: http://www.westchesterarc.org
Descr: Parents, professional workers, and others interested in individuals with mental retardation. Works to promote services, research, public understanding, and legislation for people with mental retardation and their families.

4893 ■ Westchester Association for the Education of Young Children (WAEYC)
180 E Prospect Ave., No. 130
Mamaroneck, NY 10543
Contact: Olivia Hewitt, Co-Pres.

E-mail: waeycmembers@aol.com
URL: http://www.westchesteraeyc.com

Descr: Serves and acts on behalf of the needs, rights and well-being of all young children with primary focus on the quality of educational and developmental services for all children. Seeks to improve professional practice and working conditions in early childhood education.

4894 ■ Westchester County Fire Marshals and Fire Inspectors Association
177 Hillside Ave.
White Plains, NY 10607
Contact: Laurence V. Desimone
Ph: (914)993-1568
Fax: (914)993-1554
E-mail: ldesimone@greenburghny.com

Descr: Provides codes, standards, products, and services to concerned individuals for the safety and effective performance in the built environment.

4895 ■ Westchester-Putnam-Rockland Counseling Association
Manhattan College
2900 Purchase St.
Purchase, NY 10577
Contact: Barry Ward, Pres.
E-mail: ward@mville.edu
URL: http://www.nycounseling.org

Descr: Promotes the practice of counseling. Provides opportunities for personal growth and professional development.

4896 ■ Western New York Branch of International Dyslexia Association
2491 Emery Rd.
South Wales, NY 14139
Ph: (716)687-2030
E-mail: admin@wnyida.org

Descr: Promotes public awareness and understanding of dyslexia. Seeks to develop and implement specialized methods to improve the quality of life for people who have dyslexia.

4897 ■ Western New York Counseling Association
13 N Shore Dr.
Alden, NY 14004
Contact: Doreen Krestic, Pres.
Ph: (716)937-3462
E-mail: dkrestic@hotmail.com
URL: http://www.nycounseling.org

Descr: Promotes the practice of counseling. Provides opportunities for personal growth and professional development.

4898 ■ Western Suffolk Counseling Association
SUNY Farmingdale
Career Development Center
2350 Broadhollow Rd.
Farmingdale, NY 11735
Contact: Dolores Ciaccio, Pres.
Ph: (631)420-2488
Fax: (631)420-2163
E-mail: dolores.ciaccio@farmingdale.edu
URL: http://www.nycounseling.org

Descr: Promotes the practice of counseling. Provides opportunities for personal growth and professional development.

North Carolina

4899 ■ American Association of University Women, Brevard Branch
1123 S Country Club Rd.
Brevard, NC 28712
Contact: Betty Runion, Treas.
Ph: (828)883-4611
E-mail: info@aauwbrevardnc.org
URL: http://www.aauwbrevardnc.org

Descr: Advances equity for women and girls through advocacy, education, and research. Provides funds

and a support system for women seeking judicial redress for sex discrimination in higher education.

4900 ■ American Medical Student Association, Duke University School of Medicine
DUMC Box 3005
Durham, NC 27710
Contact: Zachary P. Boas, Pres.
Ph: (919)668-1670
Fax: (919)684-2593
URL: http://medschool.duke.edu

Descr: Promotes improvement in medical training and education. Advances the medicine profession. Contributes to the welfare of medical students, interns, residents and post-MD/DO trainees.

4901 ■ American Medical Student Association, The Brody School of Medicine at East Carolina University
600 Moye Blvd.
Greenville, NC 27834
Contact: Phyllis N. Horns RN
Ph: (252)744-1020
Free: 866-515-4573
URL: http://www.ecu.edu/med

Descr: Promotes improvement in medical training and education. Advances the medicine profession. Contributes to the welfare of medical students, interns, residents and post-MD/DO trainees.

4902 ■ American Medical Student Association, University of North Carolina School of Medicine
4030 Bondurant Hall, CB No. 7000
Chapel Hill, NC 27599
Contact: William L. Roper MD, Dean
Ph: (919)962-8335
E-mail: admissions@med.unc.edu
URL: http://www.med.unc.edu

Descr: Promotes improvement in medical training and education. Advances the medicine profession. Contributes to the welfare of medical students, interns, residents and post-MD/DO trainees.

4903 ■ Arc of Brunswick County
335 Auburn Ln. NW
Calabash, NC 28467
Contact: Joan Olanchalk, Pres.
Ph: (910)287-2300

4904 ■ Arc of Buncombe County
PO Box 1365
Asheville, NC 28802
Contact: Nicole Hinebaugh, Exec. Dir.
Ph: (828)253-1255
E-mail: arcbc@bellsouth.net
URL: http://72.167.22.100

4905 ■ Arc of Cabarrus County
PO Box 1367
Concord, NC 28026
Contact: Sue Price, Exec. Dir.
Ph: (704)788-1616
Fax: (704)784-5948
E-mail: sueprice@vnet.net
URL: http://arcofcabarrus.org

Descr: Committed to securing for all people with mental retardation the opportunity to choose and realize their goals of where and how they learn, live, work and play. Strives to provide leadership in the field of mental retardation and develop necessary human and financial resources to attain its goal.

4906 ■ Arc of Chatham County
362 West St.
Pittsboro, NC 27312
Contact: Janet Groce, Co-Chair
Ph: (919)542-2368
E-mail: janet.groce@ncmail.net
URL: http://72.167.22.100

4907 ■ Arc of Columbus County
777 Vinson Blvd.
Whiteville, NC 28472
Contact: Nancy Hill, Pres.

Ph: (910)642-6544
URL: http://72.167.22.100

4908 ■ Arc of Craven County
13 A. Mulberry Ln.
New Bern, NC 28562
Contact: Jeannie Smith, Pres.
Ph: (252)638-6519
E-mail: jeanniebshaggin@hotmail.com
URL: http://72.167.22.100

4909 ■ Arc of Davidson County, North Carolina
6 Vance Cir.
Lexington, NC 27292
Contact: Vera McRae, Exec. Dir.
Ph: (336)248-2842
E-mail: arclex@lexcominc.net
URL: http://72.167.22.100

4910 ■ Arc of Durham County
3500 Westgate Dr., Ste. 303
Durham, NC 27707
Ph: (919)493-8141

Descr: Parents, professional workers, and others interested in individuals with mental retardation. Works to promote services, research, public understanding, and legislation for people with mental retardation and their families.

4911 ■ Arc of Gaston County
200 E Franklin Blvd.
Gastonia, NC 28052
Contact: Sara Osborne, Exec. Dir.
Ph: (704)861-1036
Fax: (704)864-9464
URL: http://gastoncountyarc.org

4912 ■ Arc of Greensboro
207-M S Westgate Dr.
Greensboro, NC 27407
Ph: (336)373-1076
E-mail: top@arcg.org
URL: http://www.arcg.org

Descr: Parents, professional workers, and others interested in individuals with mental retardation. Works to promote services, research, public understanding, and legislation for people with mental retardation and their families.

4913 ■ Arc of Harnett County
PO Box 515
Buies Creek, NC 27506
Contact: Bonnie Larche
Ph: (910)893-2578
E-mail: harnettarc@yahoo.com
URL: http://72.167.22.100

4914 ■ Arc of High Point
153 E Bellevue Dr.
High Point, NC 27265
Contact: Tonya Fowler, Exec. Dir.
Ph: (336)883-0650
E-mail: tfowler@arc-of-hp.com
URL: http://www.arc-of-hp.com

4915 ■ Arc of Lee County, North Carolina
PO Box 4941
Sanford, NC 27331
Contact: Mark Neuman, Pres.
Ph: (919)776-4048
E-mail: mneuman@arcoflee.org
URL: http://72.167.22.100

4916 ■ Arc of Lincoln County, North Carolina
227 E Water St.
Lincolnton, NC 28092
Contact: Sherry Jones, Pres.
Ph: (704)736-1413

4917 ■ Arc of Montgomery County, North Carolina
694 Horseshoe Bend Rd.
Troy, NC 27371
Contact: Lois Callicutt

Ph: (910)428-4298
URL: http://72.167.22.100

4918 ■ Arc of North Carolina
343 E Six Forks Rd., Ste. 320
Raleigh, NC 27609
Contact: Mr. David Richard, Exec. Dir.
Ph: (919)782-4632
Free: 800-662-8706
Fax: (919)782-4634
E-mail: arcofnc@arcnc.org
URL: http://www.arcnc.org
Descr: Parents, professional workers, and others
interested in individuals with mental retardation.
Works to promote services, research, public under-
standing, and legislation for people with mental
retardation and their families.

4919 ■ Arc Of Cumberland County
3007 Ft. Bragg Rd.
Fayetteville, NC 28303
Contact: Vincent Francis, Pres.
Ph: (910)867-2141
E-mail: thearcofcumberland@nc.rr.com
URL: http://www.thearc.org/NetCommunity/Page.
aspx?&pid=223&srcid=1304&chid=432
Descr: Parents, professional workers, and others
interested in individuals with mental retardation.
Works to promote services, research, public under-
standing, and legislation for people with mental
retardation and their families.

4920 ■ Arc Of Forsyth County
1006 S Marshall St.
Winston-Salem, NC 27101
Ph: (336)777-0076
Staff: 6. **Descr:** Parents, professional workers, and
others interested in individuals with mental
retardation. Works to promote services, research,
public understanding, and legislation for people with
mental retardation and their families. **Fnd:** 1964.
Mem: 200.

4921 ■ Arc Of Moore County
PO Box 773
Southern Pines, NC 28388
Contact: Ms. Wendy Russell, Exec. Dir.
Ph: (910)692-8272
Free: 800-909-9272
Fax: (910)692-4343
E-mail: arcmoorewr@embarqmail.com
URL: http://www.thearcofmoore.org
Descr: Parents, professional workers, and others
interested in individuals with mental retardation.
Works to promote services, research, public under-
standing, and legislation for people with mental
retardation and their families. **Fnd:** 1960.

4922 ■ Arc of Orange County, North Carolina
208 N Columbia St., Ste. 100
Chapel Hill, NC 27514
Contact: Robin Baker, Exec. Dir.
Ph: (919)942-5119
Fax: (919)942-2119
E-mail: info@arcoforange.org
URL: http://www.arcoforange.org

4923 ■ Arc of Person County
PO Box 1182
Roxboro, NC 27573
Contact: Nancy Garrett, Exec. Dir.
Ph: (336)599-9658
URL: http://72.167.22.100

4924 ■ Arc of Pitt County
1311 W Arlington Blvd., Ste. 104
Greenville, NC 27834
Contact: Sandra Warren, Interim Pres.
Ph: (252)756-1056
Fax: (252)756-0057
E-mail: arcpitt@embarqmail.com
URL: http://www.arcpittnc.org

4925 ■ Arc of Robeson County
PO Box 3047
Lumberton, NC 28359

Contact: Phil Dudney, Pres.
Ph: (910)671-0818
URL: http://72.167.22.100

4926 ■ Arc of Rockingham County
PO Box 5223
Eden, NC 27289
Contact: Sharon Hairston, Pres.
Ph: (336)627-7565
E-mail: shairston003@triad.rr.com
URL: http://72.167.22.100

4927 ■ Arc of Rowan County
1918 W Innes St.
Salisbury, NC 28144
Ph: (704)637-1521
Fax: (704)637-9921
E-mail: arcrowan@cbi.net
URL: http://www.thearcrowan.org

4928 ■ Arc of Rutherford/Polk County
PO Box 501
Rutherfordton, NC 28139
Contact: Barbara Paulin, Pres.
Ph: (828)287-3695
E-mail: barb11@wildblue.net
URL: http://72.167.22.100

4929 ■ Arc of Stanly County
PO Box 2448
Albemarle, NC 28002-2448
Contact: Peggy Terhune, Exec. Dir.
Ph: (704)983-3911
Fax: (704)982-1264
E-mail: pterhune@arcofstanlync.org
URL: http://www.arcofstanlync.org
Descr: Parents, professional workers, and others
interested in individuals with mental retardation.
Works to promote services, research, public under-
standing, and legislation for people with mental
retardation and their families. **Fnd:** 1958. **Mem:** 365.

4930 ■ Arc of Stokes County
PO Box 566
King, NC 27021
Contact: Jo Ann Collins, Pres.
Ph: (336)773-4166
E-mail: jo_ann.collins@wachovia.com
URL: http://72.167.22.100

4931 ■ Arc of Union County, North Carolina
1653 Campus Park Dr., Ste. C
Monroe, NC 28112
Contact: Melinda Plue, Exec. Dir.
Ph: (704)261-1550
Fax: (704)261-1554
E-mail: mplue@thearcofunion.com
URL: http://www.thearcofunion.com

4932 ■ Arc of Vance County
946 W Andrews Ave., Ste. X
Henderson, NC 27536
Contact: Nancy Ormond, Pres.
Ph: (252)438-7627
E-mail: arcofvance@arcnc.org
URL: http://72.167.22.100

4933 ■ Arc of Wilson County
PO Box 3943
Wilson, NC 27895
Contact: Kay Bunch, Exec. Dir.
Ph: (252)237-8266
Fax: (252)237-1868
E-mail: arcwilco@nc.rr.com
URL: http://www.arcofwilson.org

4934 ■ Arc of Yadkin County
2236 Carson Dr.
Boonville, NC 27011
Contact: Vaun Hobson
Ph: (336)699-8861
URL: http://72.167.22.100

**4935 ■ Communities in Schools of North
Carolina (CISNC)**
222 N Person St.
Raleigh, NC 27601

Contact: Linda Harrill, Pres./CEO
Ph: (919)832-2700
Free: 800-849-8881
Fax: (919)832-5436
E-mail: gcrawford@cisnc.org
URL: http://www.cisnc.org
Descr: Helps young people learn, stay in school,
and prepare for life. **Fnd:** 1989. **Pub:** *The North
Carolina Network* (monthly).

**4936 ■ Communities in Schools of Thomas-
ville**
400 Turner St.
Thomasville, NC 27360-0548
Contact: Judy Younts, Dir.
Ph: (336)474-4233
Fax: (336)475-0356
E-mail: yountsj@tcs.k12.nc.us
Staff: 7. **Descr:** Addresses the multiple needs of
youth at highest risk of educational, social, and
economic failure. Brings community resources from
businesses, social/human service agencies, and
volunteer/community organizations into the schools,
to serve these youth and their families. **Fnd:** 1994.
State Groups: 1. **Local Groups:** 1.

**4937 ■ Learning disAbilities Association of
Charlotte (LDAC)**
PO Box 49306
Charlotte, NC 28277
Ph: (704)542-0470
E-mail: ldac@ldac.org
URL: http://www.ldac.org

**4938 ■ Learning Disabilities Association of
North Carolina (LDANC)**
1854A Hendersonville Rd., No. 239
Asheville, NC 28803
Contact: Kim Anderson, Office Mgr.
Fax: (919)489-0788
E-mail: ldanc@mindspring.com
URL: http://www.ldanc.org
Staff: 1. **Descr:** Works to improve the lives of, and
serving as the voice for, all persons in the state with
learning disabilities and/or attention disorders. **Pub:**
Keynotes (quarterly).

**4939 ■ North Carolina AfterSchool Coalition
(NCASC)**
134 Government Cir., Ste. 202
Jefferson, NC 28640
Contact: Linda Blackburn, Pres.
Ph: (336)219-2650
Fax: (336)219-2682
E-mail: linda_blackburn@ncsu.edu

**4940 ■ North Carolina Association on Higher
Education and Disability (NCAHEAD)**
Davidson College Student Counseling Center
Box 7188
Davidson, NC 28035-7188
Contact: Liz Johnston, Pres.-Elect
Ph: (704)894-2451
Fax: (704)894-2615
E-mail: nalongworth@davidson.edu
URL: http://www.ahead.org/affiliates/north-carolina
Staff: 12. **Descr:** Represents individuals interested
in promoting the equal rights and opportunities of
disabled postsecondary students, staff, faculty and
graduates. Provides educational and professional
development opportunities for persons with dis-
abilities in postsecondary education. Encourages
and supports legislation for the benefit of disabled
students.

**4941 ■ North Carolina Branch of the Interna-
tional Dyslexia Association (NCIDA)**
70 Whispering Oak Ct.
Fletcher, NC 28732
Contact: Diane Milner, Pres.
Free: 800-284-1990
E-mail: dmilner@cdschool.org
URL: http://www.nc-ida.org
Descr: Promotes public awareness and understand-
ing of dyslexia. Seeks to develop and implement
specialized methods to improve the quality of life for

people who have dyslexia. **Pub:** *The Tarheel Times* (monthly).

4942 ■ North Carolina Council on Developmental Disabilities (NCCDD)
3801 Lake Boone Trail, Ste. 250
Raleigh, NC 27607
Contact: Holly Riddle, Exec. Dir.
Ph: (919)420-7901
Free: 800-357-6916
Fax: (919)420-7917
E-mail: hriddle@nc-ddc.org
URL: http://www.nc-ddc.org
Descr: Assists people with developmental disabilities. Conducts activities for people with developmental disabilities and their families to participate in the design of and have access to culturally competent services. Provides assistance and opportunities that promote inclusive communities. **Fnd:** 1973. **Mem:** 34.

4943 ■ North Carolina Council of Educational Opportunity Programs (NCCEOP)
PO Box 35009
Charlotte, NC 28235
Contact: Deborah Kingsberry, Pres.
Ph: (704)330-6961
Fax: (704)330-6610
E-mail: deborah.kingsberry@cpcc.edu
URL: http://www.ncceop.appstate.edu
Descr: Works to advance educational opportunities for disadvantaged students in colleges and universities. Provides professional development and continuing education. Monitors federal legislation designed to serve disadvantaged students.

4944 ■ North Carolina Counseling Association (NCCA)
PO Box 20875
Raleigh, NC 27619
Contact: Terry Robinson, Pres.
Ph: (919)256-2521
Free: 888-308-6222
Fax: (919)782-9470
E-mail: ncca@nccounseling.org
URL: http://www.nccounseling.org
Staff: 10. **Descr:** Promotes professional standards and advocacy for the counseling profession. Conducts professional, educational, and scientific meetings and conferences for counselors. Encourages scientific research and creative activity in the field of counseling. **Fnd:** 1970. **Mem:** 1550. **Pub:** Newsletter (semiannual).

4945 ■ North Carolina County Fire Marshal's Association (NCCFMA)
230 Market Place Dr., Ste. 130
Wilmington, NC 28403
Contact: David A. Heath, Sec.-Treas.
Ph: (910)798-7414
E-mail: nccfma@yahoo.com
URL: http://www.nccfma.org
Descr: Provides the highest quality codes, standards, products, and services for all concerned with the safety and performance of the built environment.

4946 ■ North Carolina Department of Public Instruction
301 N. Wilmington St.
Raleigh, NC 27601
Contact: Dr. June Atkinson, Superintendent
Ph: (919)807-3300
Fax: (919)807-3445
E-mail: information@dpi.state.nc.us
URL: http://www.ncpublicschools.org/

4947 ■ North Carolina PTA (NC PTA)
3501 Glenwood Ave.
Raleigh, NC 27612-4934
Contact: Debra J. Horton, Pres.
Ph: (919)787-0534
Free: 800-255-0417
Fax: (919)787-0569
E-mail: office@ncpta.org
URL: http://www.ncpta.org
Descr: Unites the forces of home, school, and community on behalf of children and youth. **Fnd:** 1919.

Mem: 240000. **Pub:** *North Carolina Parent-Teacher Bulletin* (monthly).

4948 ■ North Carolina TASH (NC TASH)
905A N New Hope Dr.
Gastonia, NC 28054
Contact: Sally Abril, Pres.
E-mail: nctashboard@nctash.com
Descr: Aims to promote equality, inclusion and social justice for people with developmental disabilities. Advocates high quality community-based services for persons with developmental disabilities.

4949 ■ Special Olympics, North Carolina (SONC)
2200 Gateway Centre Blvd., Ste. 201
Morrisville, NC 27560
Contact: Keith L. Fishburne, Pres./CEO
Ph: (919)719-7662
Free: 800-843-6276
Fax: (919)719-7663
E-mail: sonc@sonc.net
URL: http://www.sonc.net
Staff: 20. **Descr:** Strives to provide year-round athletic training and sports competition in a variety of Olympic-type sports for children and adults with intellectual disabilities (mental retardation). Gives them continuing opportunities to develop physical fitness, demonstrate courage, experience joy and participate in sharing of gifts, skills and friendship with their families and other Special Olympics athletes and the community. **Fnd:** 1970. **Mem:** 36000. **Pub:** *Discover* (quarterly).

North Dakota

4950 ■ American Medical Student Association, University of North Dakota School of Medicine and Health Sciences
Memorial Union, Rm. 113
2901 University Ave., Stop 8385
Grand Forks, ND 58202
Contact: Kyle Hoffer, Pres.
Ph: (701)777-3030
E-mail: amsa_list@medicine.nodak.edu
URL: http://www.union.und.edu/involvement/studentorgs/OrgDetail.asp?orgNumber=224
Descr: Promotes improvement in medical training and education. Advances the medicine profession. Contributes to the welfare of medical students, interns, residents and post-MD/DO trainees.

4951 ■ Arc of Barnes County
141 2nd St. NE
Valley City, ND 58072
Contact: Ken Merkes, Pres.
Ph: (701)845-4189
E-mail: bigpandmrsg@csicable.net

4952 ■ Arc of Bismarck
1211 Park Ave.
Bismarck, ND 58504
Contact: Veronica Zietz, Exec. Dir.
Ph: (701)222-1854
Fax: (701)222-1854
E-mail: veronica.zietz@thearcofbismarck.org
URL: http://www.thearcofbismarck.org

4953 ■ Arc of Cass County
215 N University Dr.
Fargo, ND 58102
Contact: Janell Malpert, Exec. Dir.
Ph: (701)293-8191
Fax: (701)293-3095
E-mail: arccassnd@yahoo.com
URL: http://www.arccassnd.com
Descr: Improves the services, opportunities and public understanding of the needs of all people with mental retardation and related disabilities. Committed to securing for all people with mental retardation and related disabilities the opportunity to choose and realize their goals of where and how they learn, live, work and play. Reduces the incidence and limits the consequence of mental retardation through educa-

tion, advocacy and the support of families, friends and the community. **Fnd:** 1956.

4954 ■ Arc of North Dakota
PO Box 12420
Grand Forks, ND 58208-2420
Contact: Dianne Sheppard, Exec. Dir./CEO
Ph: (701)772-6191
Free: 877-250-2022
Fax: (701)772-2195
E-mail: thearc@arcuv.com
URL: http://www.thearcuppervalley.com
Descr: Parents, professional workers, and others interested in individuals with mental retardation. Works to promote services, research, public understanding, and legislation for people with mental retardation and their families.

4955 ■ Arc, Upper Valley
2500 DeMers Ave.
PO Box 12420
Grand Forks, ND 58208-2420
Contact: Dianne Sheppard, Exec. Dir./CEO
Ph: (701)772-6191
Free: 877-250-2022
Fax: (701)772-2195
E-mail: thearc@arcuv.com
URL: http://www.thearcuppervalley.com
Descr: Parents, professionals, and others interested in individuals with mental retardation. Works to promote services, research, public understanding, and legislation for people with mental retardation and their families. **Fnd:** 1955. **Pub:** *The Advocate* (quarterly).

4956 ■ Autism Society of North Dakota (AutismND)
628 6th Ave.
Alice, ND 58031
Contact: Jocelyn Sloan
Ph: (701)281-8254
E-mail: jocelyn@autismnd.org
URL: http://www.autismnd.org
Descr: Seeks to improve the lives of individuals affected by autism. Promotes awareness and understanding of autism disorders. Aims to further the advancement of preventive studies, therapy and research of autism disorders.

4957 ■ North Dakota Association for Career and Technical Education
State Capitol 15th Fl.
600 E Boulevard Ave., Dept. 270
Bismarck, ND 58505-0610
Contact: Wayne Kutzer, Dir.
Ph: (701)328-3180
Fax: (701)328-1255
E-mail: cte@nd.gov
URL: http://www.nd.gov/cte
Descr: Supports career and technical education that will assure students' successful roles in families, communities, and society.

4958 ■ North Dakota Association for the Education of Young Children (NDAEYC)
26 35th Ave. NE
Fargo, ND 58102
Contact: Linda Lembke, Pres.
Ph: (218)299-7025
Fax: (218)299-7547
E-mail: lindal@lakesandprairies.net
URL: http://www.ndaeyc.org
Descr: Serves and acts on behalf of the needs, rights and well-being of all young children with primary focus on the quality of educational and developmental services for all children. Seeks to improve professional practice and working conditions in early childhood education.

4959 ■ North Dakota Department of Public Instruction
600 E. Boulevard Ave., Dept. 201
Bismarck, ND 58505-0440
Contact: Dr. Wayne G. Sanstead, Superintendent
Ph: (701)328-2260
Fax: (701)328-2461

E-mail: wsanstead@nd.gov
URL: http://www.dpi.state.nd.us/

4960 ■ North Dakota State Council on Developmental Disabilities (NDSCDD)
Dacotah Found. Bldg.
600 S 2nd St.
Bismarck, ND 58504
Contact: Tom Wallner, Exec. Dir.
Ph: (701)328-8953
Free: 800-755-2745
Fax: (701)328-8969
E-mail: sowalt@state.nd.us
URL: http://165.234.216.166/proj/uapdis/home.html
Descr: Advocates policy change that will promote choice, independence, productivity and inclusion for all North Dakotans with developmental disabilities. Supports projects and activities that maximize opportunities in these areas for consumers and families.

4961 ■ Special Olympics, North Dakota (NDSO)
2616 S 26th St.
Grand Forks, ND 58201
Contact: Nancy Christensen, Chair
Ph: (701)746-0331
Fax: (701)772-1265
E-mail: sond@midconetwork.com
URL: http://www.specialolympicsnorthdakota.org/home
Staff: 8. **Descr:** Promotes physical fitness, sports training, and athletic competition for children and adults with mental retardation. Conducts charitable activities. **Fnd:** 1972. **Mem:** 1700.

Ohio

4962 ■ 100 Black Men of Central Ohio
1409 E Livingston Ave.
Columbus, OH 43205
Contact: Anthony B. Redic MBA, Pres.
Fax: (614)253-4448
E-mail: info@100bmco.org
URL: http://www.100bmco.org

4963 ■ American Association of University Women, Cincinnati Branch
1452 Gumbert Dr.
Amelia, OH 45102
Contact: Sarah Rose, Pres.
Ph: (513)665-6590
E-mail: aauwcinci@yahoo.com
URL: http://aauwcincinnati.tripod.com
Descr: Advances equity for women and girls through advocacy, education, and research. Provides funds and a support system for women seeking judicial redress for sex discrimination in higher education.

4964 ■ American Association of University Women, Logan County Branch
409 E Chillicothe Ave.
Bellefontaine, OH 43311
Contact: Amy Jones, VP for Membership
E-mail: amy@mikeandamy.org
URL: http://www.2access.net/logancoaauw
Descr: Advances equity for women and girls through advocacy, education, and research. Provides funds and a support system for women seeking judicial redress for sex discrimination in higher education.

4965 ■ American Association of University Women, Middletown Branch
PO Box 118
Middletown, OH 45042
Contact: Sharon Kesterman, VP for Membership
E-mail: skkwak1964@aol.com
URL: http://www.orgsites.com/oh/middletown-aauw
Descr: Advances equity for women and girls through advocacy, education, and research. Provides funds

and a support system for women seeking judicial redress for sex discrimination in higher education.

4966 ■ American Medical Student Association, Case Western Reserve University School of Medicine
2109 Adelbert Rd.
Cleveland, OH 44106-4920
Contact: Jeffrey M. Collins
Ph: (216)368-3450
Fax: (216)368-6011
URL: http://mediswww.cwru.edu
Descr: Promotes improvement in medical training and education. Advances the medicine profession. Contributes to the welfare of medical students, interns, residents and post-MD/DO trainees.

4967 ■ American Medical Student Association, Northeastern Ohio Universities Colleges of Medicine and Pharmacy
5151 Hayes Rd.
Ravenna, OH 44266
Contact: Akil Patel, VP
Ph: (419)320-1135
E-mail: apatel1@neoucom.edu
URL: http://www.neoucom.edu/Students/ProfDev/StuOrg/amsa.htm
Descr: Promotes improvement in medical training and education. Advances the medicine profession. Contributes to the welfare of medical students, interns, residents and post-MD/DO trainees.

4968 ■ American Medical Student Association, Ohio University College of Osteopathic Medicine
014 Grosvenor Hall
Athens, OH 45701
Contact: Seth A. Deatley, Pres.
Ph: (740)593-2156
E-mail: sd386105@ohi.edu
URL: http://www.oucom.ohiou.edu
Descr: Promotes improvement in medical training and education. Advances the medicine profession. Contributes to the welfare of medical students, interns, residents and post-MD/DO trainees.

4969 ■ American Medical Student Association, The Ohio State University College of Medicine
370 W 9th Ave.
Columbus, OH 43210
Contact: Matthew C. Lomeli, Pres.
Ph: (614)292-2220
E-mail: matthew.lomeli@osumc.edu
URL: http://medicine.osu.edu/amsa
Descr: Promotes improvement in medical training and education. Advances the medicine profession. Contributes to the welfare of medical students, interns, residents and post-MD/DO trainees.

4970 ■ American Medical Student Association, The University of Toledo College of Medicine
2801 W Bancroft St.
Toledo, OH 43606-3390
Contact: Laura Hall, Pres.
Free: 800-586-5336
URL: http://hsc.utoledo.edu/med/index.html
Descr: Promotes improvement in medical training and education. Advances the medicine profession. Contributes to the welfare of medical students, interns, residents and post-MD/DO trainees.

4971 ■ American Medical Student Association, University of Cincinnati College of Medicine
231 Albert Sabin Way
Cincinnati, OH 45267
Contact: James Schlotman, Co-Pres.
Ph: (513)558-7391
E-mail: schlotjm@email.uc.edu
URL: http://www.med.uc.edu
Descr: Promotes improvement in medical training and education. Advances the medicine profession.

Contributes to the welfare of medical students, interns, residents and post-MD/DO trainees.

4972 ■ American Medical Student Association, Wright State University Boonshoft School of Medicine
PO Box 927
Dayton, OH 45401
Contact: Melanie E. Golembiewski, Pres.
Ph: (937)775-2936
E-mail: golembiewski.2@wright.edu
URL: http://www.med.wright.edu
Descr: Promotes improvement in medical training and education. Advances the medicine profession. Contributes to the welfare of medical students, interns, residents and post-MD/DO trainees.

4973 ■ Arc of Allen County
546 S Collett St.
Lima, OH 45805
Contact: Brad Perrott, Exec. Dir.
Ph: (419)225-6285
E-mail: arc@wcoil.com
URL: http://www.arcallencounty.org
Descr: Parents, professional workers, and others interested in individuals with mental retardation. Works to promote services, research, public understanding, and legislation for people with mental retardation and their families. **Fnd:** 1953.

4974 ■ Arc of Ashtabula County
3412 State Rd.
Ashtabula, OH 44004
Contact: Terry Mate, Pres.
Ph: (440)997-9210

4975 ■ Arc of Athens County
1948 Mill St.
Albany, OH 45710
Contact: Margaret Demko, Pres.
Ph: (740)698-1315
E-mail: seobranch_arcohio@verizon.net
URL: http://www.thearcofohio.org

4976 ■ Arc of Butler County, Ohio
5645 Liberty-Fairfield Rd.
Liberty Township, OH 45011
Ph: (513)867-3735
URL: http://www.thearcofohio.org

4977 ■ Arc of Champaign County
PO Box 29
Urbana, OH 43078
Ph: (937)653-1320

4978 ■ Arc of Clark County, Ohio
PO Box 3011
Springfield, OH 45501
E-mail: thompsonj@glasscity.net
URL: http://www.thearcofohio.org

4979 ■ Arc of Erie County
4405 Galloway Rd., No. 112
Sandusky, OH 44870
Contact: Laura Heiberger, Exec. Dir.
Ph: (419)625-9677
Free: 800-491-4566
Fax: (419)625-3448
E-mail: lheiberger@arcoferie.org
URL: http://www.orgsites.com/oh/arc
Descr: Parents, professional workers, and others interested in individuals with mental retardation. Works to promote services, research, public understanding, and legislation for people with mental retardation and their families.

4980 ■ Arc of Greater Cleveland
1331 Euclid Ave.
Cleveland, OH 44115
Contact: Cynthia Norwood, Exec. Dir.
Ph: (216)622-0755
Fax: (216)622-0752

E-mail: cmr-clev@cmr-cleveland.org
URL: http://www.cmr-cleveland.org

4981 ■ Arc - Hamilton County, Ohio
801A W 8th St., Ste. 400
Cincinnati, OH 45203
Contact: Tom Eamoe, Exec. Dir.
Ph: (513)821-2113
Free: 877-423-6900
E-mail: thearc@archamilton.org
URL: http://www.archamilton.org

4982 ■ Arc of Lucas County
5605 Monroe St.
Sylvania, OH 43560
Contact: Charles Abood, Pres.
Ph: (419)882-0941
Fax: (419)882-0941
E-mail: thearc@arclucas.org
URL: http://www.arclucas.org

4983 ■ Arc of Mercer County, Ohio
PO Box 137
Celina, OH 45822
Contact: Matthew Overman, Pres.
E-mail: mjoverman@yahoo.com
URL: http://www.thearcofohio.org

4984 ■ Arc of Ohio - Southwest Branch
1075 Ohio Pike
Cincinnati, OH 45245
Contact: Jessica Ruebel, Assoc. Dir.
Ph: (513)752-4330
Free: 800-875-2723
Fax: (513)752-4339
E-mail: thearccb@aol.com
URL: http://www.thearcofohio.org

4985 ■ Arc of Shelby County - Ohio
PO Box 925
Sidney, OH 45365
Contact: Cathy Dulin, Exec. Dir.
Ph: (937)497-8155
E-mail: rcdulin@bright.net
URL: http://www.thearcofohio.org

4986 ■ Arc of Stark County
Belden Village Tower, Ste. 307
4450 Belden Village St. NW
Canton, OH 44718-2564
Contact: Ronald Klonowski Jr., Exec. Dir.
Ph: (330)492-5225
Fax: (330)492-0593
E-mail: info@arcstark.org
URL: http://www.arcstark.org
Descr: Parents, professional workers, and others interested in individuals with mental retardation. Works to promote services, research, public understanding, and legislation for people with mental retardation and their families. **Fnd:** 1952.

4987 ■ Arc of Summit and Portage Counties
3869 Darrow Rd., Ste.109
Stow, OH 44224
Contact: Leeanne M. Saro, Exec. Dir.
Ph: (330)836-5863
E-mail: arcscpc@worldnet.att.net
URL: http://www.arcsummitportage.org

4988 ■ Arc of Wood County
PO Box 264
Bowling Green, OH 43402
Contact: Margie Harris, Exec. Dir.
Ph: (419)353-1099
E-mail: tkharris@dacor.net
URL: http://www.thearcofohio.org

4989 ■ Autism Society of America - Southeastern Ohio Chapter
PO Box 460
Athens, OH 45701
Contact: Ms. Noriko Kantake
Ph: (740)592-6500
E-mail: info@autismseohio.org
Descr: Seeks to improve the lives of individuals affected by autism. Promotes awareness and understanding of autism disorders. Aims to further the

advancement of preventive studies, therapy and research of autism disorders.

4990 ■ Autism Society of Greater Cincinnati (ASGC)
PO Box 43027
Cincinnati, OH 45243
Contact: Ken Jones, Pres.
Ph: (513)561-2300
Fax: (513)561-4748
E-mail: asgc@cinci.rr.com
URL: http://www.autismcincy.org
Descr: Seeks to improve the lives of individuals affected by autism. Promotes awareness and understanding of autism disorders. Aims to further the advancement of preventive studies, therapy and research of autism disorders.

4991 ■ Autism Society of Greater Cleveland (ASGC)
PO Box 41066
Brecksville, OH 44141
Contact: Eileen Hawkins, Admin.
Ph: (216)556-4937
E-mail: support@asgc.org
URL: http://www.asgc.org
Descr: Seeks to improve the lives of individuals affected by autism. Promotes awareness and understanding of autism disorders. Aims to further the advancement of preventive studies, therapy and research of autism disorders.

4992 ■ Autism Society of Northwest Ohio (ASNO)
4848 Dorr St.
Toledo, OH 43615
Contact: Bonnie Kelly, Pres.
Ph: (419)578-2766
E-mail: asno.org@bex.net
URL: http://www.asno.org
Descr: Seeks to improve the lives of individuals affected by autism. Promotes awareness and understanding of autism disorders. Aims to further the advancement of preventive studies, therapy and research of autism disorders.

4993 ■ Central Ohio Branch of the International Dyslexia Association (COBIDA)
635 Park Meadow Rd., Ste. 213
Westerville, OH 43081
Contact: Cyndi Schultz, Pres.
Ph: (614)899-5711
E-mail: helpline@cobida.org
URL: http://www.cobida.org
Descr: Promotes public awareness and understanding of dyslexia. Seeks to develop and implement specialized methods to improve the quality of life for people who have dyslexia.

4994 ■ Central Ohio Chapter of the Autism Society of America
286 Weydon Rd.
Worthington, OH 43085
Contact: Pat Cloppert, Pres.
Ph: (614)487-4720
Free: 800-875-2723
E-mail: centralohioasa@yahoo.com
URL: http://www.autism-centralohio.com
Descr: Seeks to improve the lives of individuals affected by autism. Promotes awareness and understanding of autism disorders. Aims to further the advancement of preventive studies, therapy and research of autism disorders.

4995 ■ Central Ohio Senior Olympics
2100 Morse Rd., Ste. 4625
Columbus, OH 43229
Contact: John Zupp
Ph: (614)645-3320
Fax: (614)645-0647
E-mail: jdzupp@columbus.gov
URL: http://www.ohioseniorolympics.org

4996 ■ Cincinnati Association for the Education of Young Children (CAEYC)
PO Box 6483
Cincinnati, OH 45206

Contact: Kris Mooney, Pres.
E-mail: kmooney@cinciaeyc.org
URL: http://www.oaeyc.org/i4a/pages/index.cfm?pageid=3296
Descr: Serves and acts on behalf of the needs, rights and well-being of all young children with primary focus on the quality of educational and developmental services for all children. Seeks to improve professional practice and working conditions in early childhood education.

4997 ■ Dayton Association for Young Children (DAYC)
PO Box 60488
Dayton, OH 45406
Contact: Cheryl Butler, Pres.
Ph: (937)223-3292
E-mail: ssprinkle@daytonayc.org
URL: http://www.daytonayc.org
Descr: Serves and acts on behalf of the needs, rights and well-being of all young children with primary focus on the quality of educational and developmental services for all children. Seeks to improve professional practice and working conditions in early childhood education.

4998 ■ Dayton Autism Society (DAS)
PO Box 1013
Miamisburg, OH 45343
Contact: Nancy Bernotaitis, Pres.
Ph: (937)286-5615
Fax: (937)859-4964
E-mail: info@daytonautismsociety.org
URL: http://www.daytonautismsociety.org
Descr: Seeks to improve the lives of individuals affected by autism. Promotes awareness and understanding of autism disorders. Aims to further the advancement of preventive studies, therapy and research of autism disorders.

4999 ■ Greater Cincinnati Counseling Association (GCCA)
Xavier University
3800 Victory Pkwy.
Cincinnati, OH 45207-6612
Contact: Al Lewis, Pres.
E-mail: oconnell@xavier.edu
URL: http://www.cincycounseling.com

5000 ■ Learning Disabilities Association of Cuyahoga County (LDACC)
4800 E 131st St., Ste. B
Garfield Heights, OH 44105
Contact: Patty Kusinski, Co-Pres.
Ph: (216)581-4549
Fax: (216)581-7076
E-mail: info@ldacc.org
URL: http://www.ldacc.org

5001 ■ Learning Disabilities Association of Ohio
PO Box 784
Springfield, OH 45501
Contact: Nancy Andrews, Pres.
Ph: (937)325-1923
E-mail: nandrewbrkvll@aol.com

5002 ■ Lima Area Senior Olympics
3400 W Elm St.
Lima, OH 45807
Contact: Mary Lou Paisley
Ph: (419)991-8811
Fax: (419)991-3312
E-mail: info@ohioseniorolympics.org
URL: http://www.ohioseniorolympics.org

5003 ■ Miami Valley Counseling Association (MVCA)
255 Hadley Ave.
Dayton, OH 45419
Contact: Lisa Adler-Bacon, Pres.
Ph: (937)298-8084
Fax: (937)298-0013

E-mail: 4105-ssd@hcr-manorcare.com
URL: http://www.ohiocounseling.org

5004 ■ National Stuttering Association, Cleveland Chapter
PO Box 525
Gates Mills, OH 44040
Contact: Doug Havighurst
Ph: (216)381-6237
URL: http://www.geocities.com/Heartland/Acres/3564/clevnsp.htm

Descr: Serves as a self-help organization for people who stutter, parents of children who stutter and the professionals who serve them. Increases public awareness of stuttering. Provides support, education and empowerment to children and adults who stutter.

5005 ■ National Stuttering Association, Columbus Chapter
1125 Belden Rd.
Columbus, OH 43229-5136
Contact: Karen Iacovetta, Coor.
Ph: (614)431-0207
E-mail: kiacovetta@att.net
URL: http://www.geocities.com/nsacolumbus

Descr: Serves as a self-help organization for people who stutter, parents of children who stutter and the professionals who serve them. Increases public awareness of stuttering. Provides support, education and empowerment to children and adults who stutter.

5006 ■ North Central Ohio Chapter of the Autism Society of America (NCOC-ASA)
38940 Amberwood Dr.
Avon, OH 44011
Contact: Susan Carr, Pres.
Ph: (440)934-9989
E-mail: oh-northcentralohio@autismsocietyofamerica.org
URL: http://www.ncoc-asa.org

Descr: Seeks to improve the lives of individuals affected by autism. Promotes awareness and understanding of autism disorders. Aims to further the advancement of preventive studies, therapy and research of autism disorders.

5007 ■ North Central Ohio Counseling Association (NCOCA)
34355 Sherwood Dr.
Solon, OH 44139
Contact: Amanda Rovnak, Pres.
E-mail: ataylor8277@yahoo.com
URL: http://chdsw.educ.kent.edu/ncoca

5008 ■ North Eastern Ohio Education Association (NEOEA)
5422 E 90th St., Ste. 200
Garfield Heights, OH 44125-5330
Contact: Dale Kain, Pres.
Ph: (216)518-0200
Fax: (216)518-0202
URL: http://www.neoea.org

Staff: 3. **Descr:** Membership consists of teachers and support personnel in public K-12 schools, colleges, and MR/DD boards in the northeastern OH. Affiliate of the Ohio Education Association and the National Education Association. Seeks to improve professional standards and promote compensation and working conditions for members. Sponsors annual "NEOEA Day", on the second Friday of each school year, offering an extensive array of leadership, professional, and personal development workshops. **Fnd:** 1869. **Mem:** 34000. **Reg. Groups:** 1. **State Groups:** 1. **Local Groups:** 193. **Pub:** *News and Views* (7/year).

5009 ■ Northcoast (Lake County-Cleveland) Senior Olympics
11189 Spear Rd.
Concord Township, OH 44077
Contact: Karen Reis
Ph: (440)256-2126
Fax: (440)358-7280

E-mail: kreis@lakemetroparks.com
URL: http://www.ohioseniorolympics.org

5010 ■ Northern Ohio Branch of the International Dyslexia Association (NOB/IDA)
PO Box 2141
Hudson, OH 44236
Contact: Allyson Tonozzi, Exec. Dir.
Ph: (216)556-0883
URL: http://www.dyslexia-nohio.org

Staff: 1. **Descr:** Individuals interested in the study, treatment, and prevention of the problems of dyslexia or specific language disability. **Fnd:** 1989. **Mem:** 235. **Pub:** Newsletter (semiannual).

5011 ■ Northwest Ohio Counseling Association (NWOCA)
5151 Monroe St., Ste. 250
Toledo, OH 43623
Contact: Jean Underfer-Babalis
Ph: (419)508-9648
E-mail: jeanub@destinedformore.com
URL: http://www.ohiocounseling.org

5012 ■ Ohio AfterSchool Network (OAN)
6660 Doubletree Ave., Ste. 11
Columbus, OH 43229
Contact: Liz Nusken, Dir.
Ph: (614)396-5959
Free: 877-547-6978
Fax: (614)396-5960
E-mail: info@ohioafterschoolnetwork.org
URL: http://www.ohioafterschoolnetwork.org

5013 ■ Ohio Association for Career and Technical Education
38 Commerce Park Dr., Ste. D
Westerville, OH 43082
Contact: Christine Gardner, Exec. Dir.
Ph: (614)890-2283
Free: 800-522-5519
Fax: (614)890-1584
E-mail: admin@ohioacte.org
URL: http://www.ohioacte.org

Staff: 2. **Descr:** Comprises of career and technical educational teachers and administrators. Represents the field before governmental bodies; provides public relations services; promotes professional growth. **Fnd:** 1922. **Mem:** 3800. **Local Groups:** 14. **Pub:** Newsletter (quarterly).

5014 ■ Ohio Association for the Education of Young Children
PO Box 71
Mount Gilead, OH 43338
Contact: Kimberly Tice, Exec. Dir.
Ph: (419)946-6693
Free: 800-626-2392
Fax: (419)946-6515
E-mail: exedirector@oaeyc.org
URL: http://www.oaeyc.org

Descr: Aims to improve the well-being of young children, with particular focus on the quality of educational and developmental services for the children. **Pub:** *Focus*.

5015 ■ Ohio Department of Education
25 S. Front St.
Columbus, OH 43215-4183
Contact: Deborah S. Delisle, Superintendent
Ph: (614)466-4839
Free: 877-644-6338
Fax: (614)728-9300
E-mail: contact.center@ode.state.oh.us
URL: http://www.ode.state.oh.us/
Pub: List of publications on website.

5016 ■ Ohio Developmental Disabilities Planning Council (ODDC)
Ohio Developmental Disabilities Council
Atlas Bldg., 12th Fl.
8 E Long St.
Columbus, OH 43215
Contact: Peter Keiser, Chm.
Ph: (614)466-5205
Free: 800-766-7426

Fax: (614)466-0298
E-mail: peter.keiser@cchmc.org
URL: http://ddc.ohio.gov

Descr: People with developmental disabilities, families and guardians of people with developmental disabilities, representatives from state agencies, nonprofit organizations and agencies that serve people with developmental disabilities. National network of state councils serving people with developmental disabilities. **Mem:** 28. **Pub:** *DD Quarterly* (quarterly).

5017 ■ Ohio Fire Officials Association
5482 Mallard Dr.
Cincinnati, OH 45247
Contact: Michael Boeckermann
Ph: (513)598-1879
E-mail: boeckermann@fuse.net

Descr: Provides the highest quality codes, standards, products, and services for all concerned with the safety and performance of the built environment.

5018 ■ Ohio National Congress of Parents and Teachers
40 Northwoods Blvd.
Columbus, OH 43235
Contact: Sandy Nekoloff, Pres.
Ph: (614)781-6344
Fax: (614)781-6349
E-mail: oh_office@pta.org
URL: http://www.ohiopta.org

Descr: Parents, teachers, students, and others interested in uniting the forces of home, school, and community. Promotes the welfare of children and youth. **Pub:** *Ohio PTA - The News* (8/year).

5019 ■ Ohio Parents of Children with Visual Impairments (OPVI)
5786 Arlyne Ln.
Medina, OH 44256
Contact: Rachel Miller, Pres.
Ph: (330)722-6609
E-mail: rlmiller423@gmail.com
URL: http://www.spedex.com/napvi/chapters.html

Descr: Represents individuals committed to providing support to the parents of children who have visual impairments. Promotes public understanding of the needs and rights of children who are visually impaired.

5020 ■ Ohio Valley Branch of the International Dyslexia Association
317 E Fifth St.
Cincinnati, OH 45202
Contact: Barbara Buhrer
Ph: (513)651-4747
E-mail: webmaster@cincinnatidyslexia.org
URL: http://www.cincinnatidyslexia.org

Descr: Promotes public awareness and understanding of dyslexia. Seeks to develop and implement specialized methods to improve the quality of life for people who have dyslexia. Provides services to those affected by dyslexia, attention disorders and other learning disabilities.

5021 ■ SAFE Association - Wright Brothers Chapter
PO Box 33844
Wright Patterson AFB, OH 45433-0844
Contact: Doug Coppess, VP
E-mail: dacoppess@verizon.net
URL: http://209.240.147.198/chapters/wright/

Descr: Fosters professional interchange among members. Recognizes professional achievement in the areas of safety, survival and crew systems. Sponsors educational programs and technical and social events for members. **Mem:** 100.

5022 ■ Southeast Ohio Counseling Association (SEOCA)
222 W Washington St.
Athens, OH 45701
Contact: Yegan Pillay, Pres.

E-mail: pillay@ohio.edu
URL: http://www.ohiocounseling.org

5023 ■ Southwest Ohio Senior Olympics
805 Central Ave., Ste. 800
Cincinnati, OH 45202
Contact: Dina Hanks
Ph: (513)421-5222
Fax: (513)871-1935
E-mail: seniorolympics@cincinnati-oh.gov
URL: http://www.ohioseniorolympics.org

5024 ■ Special Olympics, Ohio
3303 Winchester Pike
Columbus, OH 43232
Contact: Bob Rickard, Exec. Dir.
Ph: (614)239-7050
Fax: (614)239-1873
E-mail: rwrsooh@aol.com
URL: http://www.sooh.org

Descr: Provides year-round sports training and
competition opportunities for children and adults with
intellectual disabilities.

5025 ■ Toledo Senior Olympics
Area Office on Aging
2155 Arlington Ave.
Toledo, OH 43609
Contact: Justin Moor
Ph: (419)382-0624
Fax: (419)382-4560
E-mail: jmoor@areaofficeonaging.com
URL: http://www.ohioseniorolympics.org

5026 ■ Tri County Autism Society
1749 S Raccoon Rd., Ste. 3
Austintown, OH 44515
Contact: Daniel Gallagher, Pres.
Ph: (330)720-2066
E-mail: triautism@aol.com
URL: http://www.triautism.org

Descr: Seeks to improve the lives of individuals affected by autism. Promotes awareness and understanding of autism disorders. Aims to further the
advancement of preventive studies, therapy and
research of autism disorders.

**5027 ■ Tru-Mah-Col Association for the Edu-
cation of Young Children**
PO Box 76
Girard, OH 44420
Contact: Judy Miller, Pres.
Ph: (330)545-0901
E-mail: information@trumahcolaeyc.org
URL: http://www.trumahcolaeyc.org

Descr: Serves and acts on behalf of the needs,
rights and well-being of all young children with
primary focus on the quality of educational and
developmental services for all children. Seeks to
improve professional practice and working conditions in early childhood education.

5028 ■ Trumbull County Arc
1400 Tod Ave. NW, Ste. L800
Warren, OH 44485
Ph: (330)369-4545
Fax: (330)369-4545
E-mail: arctrumbull@earthlink.net
URL: http://www.thearcofohio.org

Oklahoma

5029 ■ AG BELL, Oklahoma
PO Box 1426
Bethany, OK 73008
Contact: Tammie Burlison, Pres.
E-mail: tam4osu@aol.com
URL: http://www.agbell.org/ok

Descr: Represents the interests of educators,
parents of children with hearing loss, adults with
hearing loss and hearing health professionals.

Provides governmental and education advocacy
services.

**5030 ■ American Association of University
Women of Oklahoma**
PO Box 535
Weatherford, OK 73096-0535
Contact: Faye K. Henson, Pres.
Ph: (580)772-5984
E-mail: epita@cebridge.net
URL: http://www.aauwoklahoma.org

Descr: Advances equity for women and girls through
advocacy, education, and research. Provides funds
and a support system for women seeking judicial
redress for sex discrimination in higher education.

**5031 ■ American Association of University
Women, Tahlequah Branch**
1001 Gerri Dr.
Tahlequah, OK 74464
Contact: Jeanna Wing, Pres.
E-mail: west@nsuok.edu
URL: http://arapaho.nsuok.edu/~aauw

Descr: Advances equity for women and girls through
advocacy, education, and research. Provides funds
and a support system for women seeking judicial
redress for sex discrimination in higher education.

**5032 ■ American Association of University
Women, Tulsa Branch**
7024 E 48th St.
Tulsa, OK 74145
Contact: Linda Brooks, Pres.
Ph: (918)494-7720
E-mail: nm.hilliard@yahoo.com
URL: http://members.cox.net/tulsaauw

Descr: Advances equity for women and girls through
advocacy, education, and research. Provides funds
and a support system for women seeking judicial
redress for sex discrimination in higher education.

**5033 ■ American Medical Student Associa-
tion, Oklahoma State University Center for
Health Sciences College of Osteopathic Medi-
cine**
1111 W 17th St.
Tulsa, OK 74107
Contact: John Fernandes DO, Pres.
Ph: (918)582-1972
URL: http://www.healthsciences.okstate.edu/college/
index.cfm

Descr: Promotes improvement in medical training
and education. Advances the medicine profession.
Contributes to the welfare of medical students,
interns, residents and post-MD/DO trainees.

**5034 ■ American Medical Student Associa-
tion, The University of Oklahoma College of
Medicine**
PO Box 26901
Oklahoma City, OK 73126-0901
Contact: M. Dewayne Andrews MD, Exec. Dean
Ph: (405)271-2265
URL: http://www.medicine.ouhsc.edu

Descr: Promotes improvement in medical training
and education. Advances the medicine profession.
Contributes to the welfare of medical students,
interns, residents and post-MD/DO trainees.

**5035 ■ American Medical Student Associa-
tion, University of Oklahoma - Tulsa College
of Medicine**
4502 E 41st St.
Tulsa, OK 74135-2512
Contact: Gerard Clancy MD, Dean
Ph: (918)660-3000
URL: http://tulsa.ou.edu/medicine/index.htm

Descr: Promotes improvement in medical training
and education. Advances the medicine profession.
Contributes to the welfare of medical students,
interns, residents and post-MD/DO trainees.

**5036 ■ Autism Society of Central Oklahoma
(ASOCO)**
PO Box 720103
Norman, OK 73070
Contact: Deborah Decker, Pres.

Ph: (405)370-3220
E-mail: ok-centraloklahoma@
autismsocietyofamerica.org
URL: http://www.asofok.org

Descr: Seeks to improve the lives of individuals affected by autism. Promotes awareness and understanding of autism disorders. Aims to further the
advancement of preventive studies, therapy and
research of autism disorders.

**5037 ■ Fire Marshal's Association of Okla-
homa**
10 S Littler Ave.
Edmond, OK 73034
Contact: Ed Steiner
Ph: (405)359-4794
E-mail: ed.steiner@edmondok.com
URL: http://fmao.org

Descr: Provides the highest quality codes, standards, products, and services for all concerned with
the safety and performance of the built environment.

5038 ■ Homelife Association
PO Box 35903
Tulsa, OK 74153
Ph: (918)745-1114
E-mail: contact@homelifeok.org
URL: http://homelifeok.org

Descr: Parents, professional workers, and others
interested in individuals with mental retardation.
Works to promote services, research, public understanding, and legislation for people with mental
retardation and their families.

**5039 ■ Learning Disabilities Association of
Oklahoma (LDAO)**
PO Box 1134
Jenks, OK 74037
Contact: Linda Modenbach, Pres.
Ph: (918)298-1600
E-mail: ldao2002@sbcglobal.net
URL: http://www.ldao.org

**5040 ■ Oklahoma Association of Career and
Technology Education (OkACTE)**
4545 N Lincoln Blvd., Ste. 159
Oklahoma City, OK 73105
Contact: Patrick McGregor, Exec. Dir.
Ph: (405)525-8906
Fax: (405)525-8973
E-mail: dnewsom@okacte.org
URL: http://www.okacte.org

Staff: 4. **Descr:** Serves the profession of career and
technology education. **Fnd:** 1929. **Mem:** 3600.

**5041 ■ Oklahoma Association on Higher
Education and Disability (OK-AHEAD)**
PO Box 42152
Oklahoma City, OK 73123
Contact: Chimene Long, Treas.
E-mail: clweb@ok-ahead.org
URL: http://www.ok-ahead.org/index.html

Descr: Represents individuals interested in promoting the equal rights and opportunities of disabled
postsecondary students, staff, faculty and graduates.
Provides educational and professional development
opportunities for persons with disabilities in postsecondary education. Encourages and supports legislation for the benefit of disabled students.

**5042 ■ Oklahoma Division of Student As-
sistance (ODSA)**
Oklahoma State University
601 Elm Ave., Rm. 517
Norman, OK 73019-3104
Contact: Deborah Binkley-Jackson, Pres.
Ph: (405)325-2143
Fax: (405)325-7772
E-mail: dbjackson@ou.edu
URL: http://www.odsa.org

Descr: Works to advance educational opportunities
for disadvantaged students in colleges and
universities. Provides professional development and

continuing education. Monitors federal legislation designed to serve disadvantaged students.

5043 ■ Oklahoma Parents and Teachers Association
2801 N Lincoln Blvd., Ste. 214
Oklahoma City, OK 73105
Contact: Angela McKinney, Office Dir.
Ph: (405)681-0750
E-mail: director@okpta.org
URL: http://www.okpta.org
Descr: Promotes the welfare of children and youth in home, community, and place of worship.

5044 ■ Oklahoma State Department of Education
2500 N. Lincoln Blvd.
Oklahoma City, OK 73105-4599
Contact: Sandy Garrett, Superintendent
Ph: (405)521-3301
Fax: (405)521-6205
E-mail: sandy_garrett@sde.state.ok.us
URL: http://sde.state.ok.us/

5045 ■ Special Olympics Oklahoma (SOOK)
6835 S Canton Ave.
Tulsa, OK 74136-3433
Contact: Adrian DeWendt, Exec. Dir.
Ph: (918)481-1234
Free: 800-722-9004
Fax: (918)496-1515
E-mail: info@sook.org
URL: http://www.sook.org
Descr: Promotes physical fitness, sports training, and athletic competition for children and adults with mental retardation. Seeks to contribute to the physical, social, and psychological development of persons with mental retardation. Participants range in age from 8 years to adult and compete in track and field, swimming, gymnastics, bowling, ice-skating, basketball, and other sports. **Fnd:** 1972.

5046 ■ Tulsa Advocates for Rights of Citizens with Developmental Disabilities (TARC)
16 E 16th St., Ste. 405
Tulsa, OK 74119-4447
Contact: John F. Gajda, Exec. Dir.
Ph: (918)582-8272
Free: 800-688-8272
Fax: (918)582-3628
E-mail: tarc@ddadvocacy.net
URL: http://www.ddadvocacy.net
Descr: Parents, professional workers, and others interested in individuals with mental retardation. Works to promote services, research, public understanding, and legislation for people with mental retardation and their families. **Fnd:** 1952. **Pub:** TARC in Action (quarterly).

Oregon

5047 ■ American Association of University Women, Ashland Branch
1460 fielder St.
Ashland, OR 97520
Contact: Carol Custodio, Membership Co-Chair
E-mail: ccustodi@msn.com
URL: http://aauwashland.homestead.com
Descr: Advances equity for women and girls through advocacy, education, and research. Provides funds and a support system for women seeking judicial redress for sex discrimination in higher education.

5048 ■ American Association of University Women, Corvallis Branch
1095 NW Overlook Dr.
Corvallis, OR 97330
Contact: Mary Mills
E-mail: millsmaryr@msn.com
URL: http://www.corvallis-aauw.org
Descr: Advances equity for women and girls through advocacy, education, and research. Provides funds

and a support system for women seeking judicial redress for sex discrimination in higher education.

5049 ■ American Medical Student Association, Oregon Health and Science University School of Medicine
3181 SW Sam Jackson Park Rd.
Portland, OR 97239-3011
Contact: Red Hoffman, Rep.
Ph: (503)494-8220
URL: http://www.ohsu.edu/som
Descr: Promotes improvement in medical training and education. Advances the medicine profession. Contributes to the welfare of medical students, interns, residents and post-MD/DO trainees.

5050 ■ Arc of Benton County
414 NW 4th St.
Corvallis, OR 97330
Ph: (541)753-1711
Descr: Parents, professional workers, and others interested in individuals with mental retardation. Works to promote services, research, public understanding, and legislation for people with mental retardation and their families.

5051 ■ Arc of Multnomah County
619 SW 11th Ave., Ste. 106
Portland, OR 97205-2692
Contact: Robert Shook, Exec. Dir.
Ph: (503)223-7279
Fax: (503)223-1488
E-mail: info@thearcmult.org
URL: http://www.thearcmult.org
Staff: 12. **Descr:** Parents, professional workers, and others interested in individuals with mental retardation. Works to promote services, research, public understanding, and legislation for people with mental retardation and their families.

5052 ■ Arc of Oregon
1745 State St.
Salem, OR 97301
Contact: Marcie Ingledue, Exec. Dir.
Ph: (503)581-2726
Free: 877-581-2726
Fax: (503)363-7168
E-mail: info@arcoregon.org
URL: http://www.arcoregon.org
Descr: Advocates to enhance the dignity, expand the opportunities, and protect the rights of persons with mental retardation and related developmental disabilities and their families. **Fnd:** 1954. **Mem:** 2000.

5053 ■ Arc of Washington County
4450 SW 184th Ave.
Aloha, OR 97007-1630
Ph: (503)649-6110
Descr: Parents, professional workers, and others interested in individuals with mental retardation. Works to promote services, research, public understanding, and legislation for people with mental retardation and their families.

5054 ■ Central Oregon Arc
1720 NE 4th St.
Bend, OR 97701
Ph: (541)388-3060
Descr: Parents, professional workers, and others interested in individuals with mental retardation. Works to promote services, research, public understanding, and legislation for people with mental retardation and their families.

5055 ■ Learning Disabilities Association of Oregon
PO Box 34
Marylhurst, OR 97036
Contact: Myrna Soule, Pres.
Ph: (503)968-0140
E-mail: mtsoule@ix.netcom.com
URL: http://www.ldaor.org

5056 ■ Oregon Adaptive Sports
PO Box 1737
Bend, OR 97709

Contact: Kendall Cook, Dir.
Ph: (541)848-9390
E-mail: oas@gmail.com
URL: http://www.oregonadaptivesports.org
Fnd: 1996.

5057 ■ Oregon Association for Career and Technical Education (OACTE)
2814 Dahlia Ln.
Eugene, OR 97404
Contact: Thelma Clemons, Exec. Sec.
Ph: (541)688-8774
Fax: (541)688-0738
E-mail: oacte@mindspring.com
URL: http://www.oregonacte.org
Descr: Promotes and supports quality career and technical education opportunities through leadership, advocacy, professional development, and partnerships.

5058 ■ Oregon Association for the Education of Young Children (OAEYC)
PO Box 1455
Tualatin, OR 97062-1455
Contact: Merrily Haas, Exec. Dir.
Ph: (503)233-0190
Free: 800-452-3610
Fax: (503)233-0185
E-mail: oregonaeyc@covad.net
URL: http://www.oregonaeyc.org
Staff: 3. **Descr:** Advocates for high quality care and education for every young child; strives to meet the professional needs and interests of the diverse early childhood community. **Fnd:** 1956. **Mem:** 1300. **State Groups:** 1. **Local Groups:** 13. **Pub:** OAEYC Member Update (semiannual).

5059 ■ Oregon Council on Developmental Disabilities (OCDD)
540 24th Pl. NE
Salem, OR 97301-4517
Contact: Bill Lynch, Exec. Dir.
Ph: (503)945-9941
Free: 800-292-4154
Fax: (503)945-9947
E-mail: ocdd@ocdd.org
URL: http://www.ocdd.org
Staff: 10. **Descr:** Aims to join with Oregonians with development disabilities and their families to promote change through self-determination leading to a more accessible, inclusive and culturally responsive world. **Fnd:** 1973. **Mem:** 30. **Pub:** The Oregon Clarion (quarterly).

5060 ■ Oregon Department of Education
255 Capitol St., NE
Salem, OR 97310-0203
Contact: Susan Castillo, Superintendent
Ph: (503)947-5600
Fax: (503)378-5156
E-mail: ode.frontdesk@state.or.us
URL: http://www.ode.state.or.us/

5061 ■ Oregon Fire Marshals Association (OFMA)
727 Center St. NE, Ste. 300
Salem, OR 97301
Contact: Eric McMullen, Pres.
Ph: (503)612-7010
Fax: (503)612-7003
E-mail: eric.mullen@tvfr.com
URL: http://www.ofma.net
Descr: Provides the highest quality codes, standards, products, and services for all concerned with the safety and performance of the built environment. **Mem:** 300.

5062 ■ Oregon National Congress of Parents and Teachers
4506 SE Belmont St., Ste. 108B
Portland, OR 97215
Contact: Anita Olsen, Pres.
Ph: (503)234-3928
Fax: (503)234-6024
E-mail: or_office@pta.org
URL: http://www.oregonpta.org

Staff: 1. **Descr:** Supports children. **Fnd:** 1905. **Mem:** 22000. **State Groups:** 1. **Local Groups:** 260.

5063 ■ Special Olympics, Oregon
5901 SW Macadam Ave., Ste. 100
Portland, OR 97239
Contact: Margaret Hunt, CEO
Ph: (503)248-0600
Free: 800-452-6079
Fax: (503)248-0603
E-mail: mhunt@soor.org
URL: http://www.soor.org
Descr: Offers year-round program offering 14 different Olympic-style sports to athletes with intellectual disabilities. **Fnd:** 1972.

Pennsylvania

5064 ■ American Association of University Women, Allentown Branch
5825 Ricky Ridge Trail
Orefield, PA 18069
Contact: Meghan Godorov, VP for Membership
Ph: (610)776-8270
E-mail: contactus@aauwallentownpa.org
URL: http://www.aauwallentownpa.org
Descr: Advances equity for women and girls through advocacy, education, and research. Provides funds and a support system for women seeking judicial redress for sex discrimination in higher education.

5065 ■ American Association of University Women, Harrisburg Branch
PO Box 1625
Harrisburg, PA 17105-1625
Contact: Toni Lee Neikens, Pres.
Ph: (717)233-8227
E-mail: info@aauwharrisburg.org
URL: http://www.aauwharrisburg.org
Descr: Advances equity for women and girls through advocacy, education, and research. Provides funds and a support system for women seeking judicial redress for sex discrimination in higher education.

5066 ■ American Association of University Women, Philadelphia Branch
1420 Locust St., Ste. 420
Philadelphia, PA 19102
Contact: Claudette Dia-Taylor, Program VP
Ph: (215)545-4903
Fax: (215)545-2270
E-mail: members@aauwphila.org
URL: http://www.aauwphila.org
Staff: 9. **Descr:** Promotes equity for all women and girls, lifelong education and positive social change. Offers programs promoting the AAUW Educational Foundation, the AAUW Legal Advocacy Fund, book group, dinner with authors or expert on gender equity, diversity, public policy, tours and cultural events. **Fnd:** 1886.

5067 ■ American Association of University Women, State College Branch
1189 Smithfield St.
State College, PA 16801
Contact: Harriet Feinstein, VP for Membership
E-mail: bubbie14@verizon.net
URL: http://aauwstatecollege.org
Descr: Advances equity for women and girls through advocacy, education, and research. Provides funds and a support system for women seeking judicial redress for sex discrimination in higher education. **Fnd:** 1916.

5068 ■ American Association of University Women, West Chester-Chester County Branch
1311 Robynwood Ln.
West Chester, PA 19380
Contact: Barbara Leone, VP for Membership
Ph: (610)429-4520
E-mail: leone219@verizon.net
Descr: Advances equity for women and girls through advocacy, education, and research. Provides funds

and a support system for women seeking judicial redress for sex discrimination in higher education.

5069 ■ American Medical Student Association, Drexel University College of Medicine
2900 W Queen Ln.
Philadelphia, PA 19129
Ph: (215)991-8100
URL: http://www.drexelmed.edu
Descr: Promotes improvement in medical training and education. Advances the medicine profession. Contributes to the welfare of medical students, interns, residents and post-MD/DO trainees.

5070 ■ American Medical Student Association, Jefferson Medical College
1015 Walnut St.
Philadelphia, PA 19107
Contact: Devin T. Kato, Pres.
Ph: (215)955-6983
E-mail: jmc.admissions@jefferson.edu
URL: http://www.jefferson.edu/jmc
Descr: Promotes improvement in medical training and education. Advances the medicine profession. Contributes to the welfare of medical students, interns, residents and post-MD/DO trainees.

5071 ■ American Medical Student Association, Penn State College of Medicine
500 University Dr.
Hershey, PA 17033
Contact: Weston S. Fisher, Pres.
E-mail: studentaffairs@hmc.psu.edu
URL: http://www.hmc.psu.edu/college
Descr: Promotes improvement in medical training and education. Advances the medicine profession. Contributes to the welfare of medical students, interns, residents and post-MD/DO trainees.

5072 ■ American Medical Student Association, Philadelphia College of Osteopathic Medicine
4170 City Ave.
Philadelphia, PA 19131
Contact: Matthew Schure, Pres./CEO
Ph: (215)871-6100
E-mail: info@pcom.edu
URL: http://www.pcom.edu
Descr: Promotes improvement in medical training and education. Advances the medicine profession. Contributes to the welfare of medical students, interns, residents and post-MD/DO trainees.

5073 ■ American Medical Student Association, Temple University School of Medicine
3420 N Broad St.
Philadelphia, PA 19140
Contact: Beth L. Hart, Pres.
Ph: (215)707-7000
URL: http://www.temple.edu/medicine
Descr: Promotes improvement in medical training and education. Advances the medicine profession. Contributes to the welfare of medical students, interns, residents and post-MD/DO trainees.

5074 ■ American Medical Student Association, The University of Pittsburgh School of Medicine
Office of Student Affairs
401 Scaife Hall
3550 Terrace St.
Pittsburgh, PA 15261
Contact: Arthur S. Levine
Ph: (412)648-8975
Fax: (412)624-0290
URL: http://www.medschool.pitt.edu
Descr: Promotes improvement in medical training and education. Advances the medicine profession. Contributes to the welfare of medical students, interns, residents and post-MD/DO trainees.

5075 ■ American Medical Student Association, University of Pennsylvania School of Medicine
3600 Market St., Ste. 240
Philadelphia, PA 19104
Ph: (215)662-2560

Fax: (215)349-8312
URL: http://www.med.upenn.edu
Descr: Promotes improvement in medical training and education. Advances the medicine profession. Contributes to the welfare of medical students, interns, residents and post-MD/DO trainees.

5076 ■ Arc Armstrong County
320 Market St., Ste. 2
Kittanning, PA 16201
Contact: Carol Sell, Pres.
Ph: (724)545-3426
E-mail: thearcarmstrongco@penn.com
Descr: Parents, professional workers, and others interested in individuals with mental retardation. Works to promote services, research, public understanding, and legislation for people with mental retardation and their families.

5077 ■ Arc of Berks County
1829 New Holland Rd., Ste. 9
Reading, PA 19607
Contact: Thomas D. Dareneau, Exec. Dir.
Ph: (610)603-0227
Fax: (610)603-0229
E-mail: berksarc@aol.com
Staff: 3. **Descr:** Supports, coordinates, and mediates with individuals, their families, agencies, and schools to help ensure that individuals receive appropriate services and maintain individual rights. **Fnd:** 1961. **Pub:** *Mental Retardation.*

5078 ■ Arc of Butler County
Pullman Commerce Ctr.
112 Hollywood Dr., Ste. 202
Butler, PA 16001
Contact: Philip Rosenbauer, Exec. Dir.
Ph: (724)282-1500
Descr: Parents, professional workers, and others interested in individuals with mental retardation. Works to promote services, research, public understanding, and legislation for people with mental retardation and their families.

5079 ■ Arc of Center County
1840 N Atherton St.
State College, PA 16803
Contact: Effie Jenks, Exec. Dir.
Ph: (814)238-1444
URL: http://taocc.org
Staff: 15. **Descr:** Dedicated to improving the lives of people with developmental disabilities. **Fnd:** 1953. **Pub:** Newsletter.

5080 ■ Arc of Chester County
900 Lawrence Dr.
West Chester, PA 19380
Contact: Allen Thomas, Pres.
Ph: (610)696-8090
Fax: (610)696-8300
E-mail: info@arcofchestercounty.org
URL: http://www.arcofchestercounty.org
Descr: Parents, professional workers, and others interested in individuals with mental retardation. Works to promote services, research, public understanding, and legislation for people with mental retardation and their families. **Fnd:** 1952.

5081 ■ Arc of Clarion County
319 Main St.
Clarion, PA 16214
Contact: Carrie Phillips, Exec. Dir.
E-mail: cphillips@thearcclarion.org
URL: http://www.thearcclarion.org

5082 ■ Arc of Crawford County
222 Chestnut St.
Meadville, PA 16335
Contact: Donna Smith, Pres.
Ph: (814)724-7346
Fax: (814)724-7373
E-mail: rlgorske@windstream.net
URL: http://www.arcofcrawfordcounty.org
Descr: Parents, professional workers, and others interested in individuals with mental retardation. Works to promote services, research, public under-

standing, and legislation for people with mental retardation and their families.

5083 ■ Arc of Dauphin and Lebanon Counties
2569 Walnut St.
Harrisburg, PA 17103
Contact: Barbara Jumper, Exec. Dir.
Ph: (717)920-2727
Fax: (717)920-2730
E-mail: information@arcofdc.org
URL: http://www.arcofdc.org
Descr: Parents, professional workers, and others interested in individuals with mental retardation. Works to promote services, research, public understanding, and legislation for people with mental retardation and their families. **Fnd:** 1953.

5084 ■ Arc of Franklin-Fulton
4351 Philadelphia Ave.
Chambersburg, PA 17201
Contact: Lorrie Barrows, Exec. Dir.
Ph: (717)264-9782
E-mail: frfuarc@innernet.net
Descr: Parents, professional workers, and others interested in individuals with mental retardation. Works to promote services, research, public understanding, and legislation for people with mental retardation and their families.

5085 ■ Arc of Indiana County Chapter
Regency Mall
1570 Oakland Ave., Ste. 290
Indiana, PA 15701
Contact: Barbara Telthorster, Exec. Dir.
Ph: (724)349-8230
Fax: (724)349-8230
E-mail: info@arcindiana.org
URL: http://www.arcindiana.org
Descr: Parents, professional workers, and others interested in individuals with mental retardation. Works to promote services, research, public understanding, and legislation for people with mental retardation and their families. **Fnd:** 1973.

5086 ■ Arc of Lackawanna County
115 Meadow Ave.
Scranton, PA 18505
Contact: Mr. Donald Broderick, Exec. Dir.
Ph: (570)346-4010
URL: http://www.thearcpa.org
Staff: 165. **Descr:** Individuals with mental retardation, family members, professionals in the field of disability and other concerned citizens. Committed to the welfare of all children and adults with mental retardation and their families. **Fnd:** 1955.

5087 ■ Arc of Lancaster County
630 Janet Ave.
Lancaster, PA 17601
Contact: Ellen J. Schellenberger, Exec. Dir.
Ph: (717)394-5251
Fax: (717)394-5257
E-mail: ellenrbb@dejazzd.com
URL: http://www.thearcoflancasterco.org
Descr: Parents, professional workers, and others interested in individuals with mental retardation. Works to promote services, research, public understanding, and legislation for people with mental retardation and their families.

5088 ■ Arc of Lehigh and Northampton Counties
2289 Ave. A
Bethlehem, PA 18017
Contact: Ron Eichenberg, Pres.
Ph: (610)849-8076
Fax: (610)849-6202
E-mail: thearc@ptd.net
URL: http://www.arcofl-n.org
Descr: Seeks to advocate, educate, and provide services to children and adults with mental retardation and their families. **Fnd:** 1967. **Mem:** 140000.

5089 ■ Arc of Luzerne County
183 Market St., Ste. 102
Kingston, PA 18704

Contact: Pamela Zotynia, Exec. Dir.
Ph: (570)714-6320
E-mail: pamelazotynia@thearcofluzernecounty.org
URL: http://thearcofluzernecounty.org
Descr: Parents, professional workers, and others interested in individuals with mental retardation. Works to promote services, research, public understanding, and legislation for people with mental retardation and their families.

5090 ■ Arc of Lycoming County
460 Market St., Ste. 115
Williamsport, PA 17701
Contact: Kristine Rainey-Wright, Pres.
Ph: (570)326-6997
Descr: Parents, professional workers, and others interested in individuals with mental retardation. Works to promote services, research, public understanding, and legislation for people with mental retardation and their families.

5091 ■ Arc Mercer County (MCAR)
850 N Hermitage Rd.
Hermitage, PA 16148
Contact: Robert R. Beach, CEO
Ph: (724)981-2950
Fax: (724)981-1877
E-mail: mcar@mercerarc.org
URL: http://www.nauticom.net/www/mcar
Descr: Seeks to provide quality, comprehensive services to people with mental retardation and/or developmental disabilities that afford them the opportunities to make choices about where they live, work and recreate, while assisting them to develop the necessary skills to function as vital members of the community. Strives to provide quality services to the individuals within the various programs; quality products to the industry contractors and local businesses; a positive work environment for the staff; and a positive presence in the community. **Fnd:** 1952.

5092 ■ Arc of Pennsylvania
101 S 2nd St., Ste. 8
Harrisburg, PA 17101
Contact: Stephen H. Suroviec, Exec. Dir.
Ph: (717)234-2621
Free: 800-692-7258
Fax: (717)234-7615
E-mail: ssuroviec@thearcpa.org
URL: http://www.thearcpa.org
Staff: 3. **Descr:** Parents, professional workers, and others interested in individuals with mental retardation. Works to promote services, research, public understanding, and legislation for people with mental retardation and their families.

5093 ■ Arc of Philadelphia
2350 W Westmoreland St.
Philadelphia, PA 19140
Contact: Bruce Hulick, Exec. Dir.
Ph: (215)229-4550
Fax: (215)225-1330
E-mail: contact@arcpddc.org
URL: http://www.arcpddc.org
Descr: Parents, professional workers, and others interested in individuals with mental retardation. Works to promote services, research, public understanding, and legislation for people with mental retardation and their families. **Fnd:** 1948.

5094 ■ Arc, Washington County Chapter
201 S Johnson Rd., Ste. 200
Houston, PA 15342
Contact: Mr. Michael L. Reardon, Exec. Dir.
Ph: (724)745-3010
Descr: Seeks to assist individuals to achieve personal and vocational independence. **Fnd:** 1952.

5095 ■ Arc Westmoreland
316 Donohoe Rd.
Greensburg, PA 15601
Contact: Mr. Paul Dumm, Exec. Dir.
Ph: (724)837-8159
Fax: (724)837-7453

E-mail: admin@arcwestmoreland.org
URL: http://www.arcwestmoreland.org
Descr: Committed to securing for all people with mental retardation and developmental disabilities and their families the opportunity to choose and realize their goals of where and how they learn, live, work and play. **Fnd:** 1954. **Mem:** 700.

5096 ■ Arc of Wyoming County
PO Box 338
Tunkhannock, PA 18657
Contact: Dianne Sheridan, Exec. Dir.
Ph: (570)836-4001
E-mail: arc@mymail.emcyber.com
Descr: Parents, professional workers, and others interested in individuals with mental retardation. Works to promote services, research, public understanding, and legislation for people with mental retardation and their families.

5097 ■ Arc of York County
497 Hill St.
York, PA 17403
Contact: Gregory Knox, Exec. Dir.
Ph: (717)846-6589
Fax: (717)852-8842
E-mail: mail@thearcofyorkcounty.org
URL: http://www.thearcofyorkcounty.org
Descr: Parents, professional workers, and others interested in individuals with mental retardation. Works to promote services, research, public understanding, and legislation for people with mental retardation and their families. **Fnd:** 1952.

5098 ■ Association of Certified Fraud Examiners, Bloomsburg University Student Chapter
400 E Second St.
Bloomsburg, PA 17815
Contact: Mike Shapeero, Faculty Advisor
Ph: (570)389-4913
E-mail: mshapeer@bloomu.edu
URL: http://cob.bloomu.edu/safe
Descr: Works to classify and examine financial crimes such as white-collar embezzlement, forgery, and fraud as well as their frequency and methodology to develop effective preventive plans and policies for businesses. **Fnd:** 2005.

5099 ■ Autism Society of America Lehigh Valley Chapter (ASA-LV)
PO Box 90448
Allentown, PA 18109
Contact: Sheri Miltenberger, Pres.
Ph: (610)778-9212
E-mail: pa-lehighvalley@autismsocietyofamerica.org
URL: http://autismsocietyofamerica-lehighvalleychapter.giving.officelive.com
Descr: Seeks to improve the lives of individuals affected by autism. Promotes awareness and understanding of autism disorders. Aims to further the advancement of preventive studies, therapy and research of autism disorders.

5100 ■ Autism Society of America - Midwestern Pennsylvania Chapter
2317 Gilmore St.
New Castle, PA 16102
Contact: Pamela A. Monteson, Pres.
Ph: (724)657-9943
E-mail: pa-midwesternpennsylvania@autismsocietyofamerica.org
Descr: Seeks to improve the lives of individuals affected by autism. Promotes awareness and understanding of autism disorders. Aims to further the advancement of preventive studies, therapy and research of autism disorders.

5101 ■ Autism Society of America - York
PO Box 20566
York, PA 17402
Contact: Amy Wallace
Ph: (717)801-1272
E-mail: pa-york@autismsocietyofamerica.org
Descr: Seeks to improve the lives of individuals affected by autism. Promotes awareness and understanding of autism disorders. Aims to further the

advancement of preventive studies, therapy and research of autism disorders.

5102 ■ Autism Society of Berks County
PO Box 6683
Wyomissing, PA 19610
Contact: Jackie Spohn, Pres.
Ph: (610)736-3739
E-mail: info@autismsocietyofberks.org
URL: http://www.autismsocietyofberks.org
Descr: Seeks to improve the lives of individuals affected by autism. Promotes awareness and understanding of autism disorders. Aims to further the advancement of preventive studies, therapy and research of autism disorders.

5103 ■ Autism Society of Butler County (ASBC)
PO Box 275
Evans City, PA 16033
Contact: Davy B. Wildman, Pres.
Ph: (724)538-4425
Fax: (724)538-5953
E-mail: autismsocietyofbutlercounty@yahoo.com
URL: http://autismsocietyofbutlercounty.tripod.com/id16.html
Descr: Seeks to improve the lives of individuals affected by autism. Promotes awareness and understanding of autism disorders. Aims to further the advancement of preventive studies, therapy and research of autism disorders.

5104 ■ Autism Society of Pittsburgh
4371 Northern Pike
Monroeville, PA 15146
Contact: Daniel A. Torisky, Pres.
Ph: (412)856-7223
Fax: (412)856-7428
E-mail: pa-pittsburgh@autismsocietyofamerica.org
URL: http://www.autismsocietypgh.org
Descr: Seeks to improve the lives of individuals affected by autism. Promotes awareness and understanding of autism disorders. Aims to further the advancement of preventive studies, therapy and research of autism disorders.

5105 ■ A Better Chance, Mid-Atlantic
PO Box 60491
King of Prussia, PA 19406-0491
Contact: Keith Wilkerson, Sr. Program Coor.
Ph: (610)992-0995
Fax: (215)893-5177
E-mail: kwilkerson@abetterchance.org
Descr: Identifies, recruits, and places academically talented and motivated minority students into leading independent secondary schools and selected public schools.

5106 ■ Communities in Schools of Pennsylvania
225 Blvd. of the Allies, Ste. 404
Pittsburgh, PA 15222
Contact: Nicole Molinaro, Exec. Dir.
Ph: (412)471-7911
Fax: (412)471-7882
E-mail: nmolinaro@cispac.org
URL: http://cispac.org
Descr: Leads the way in creating and managing school/community partnerships that meet students' academic and social needs. Identifies community resources and services, connects services to the school, students, and families, manages the delivery of the services, and monitors student participation and progress. Runs after school programming that integrates academics with fun activities to help students learn and succeed in school. **Fnd:** 1994.

5107 ■ Delaware Valley Association for the Education of Young Children (DVAEYC)
1608 Walnut St., Ste. 1400
Philadelphia, PA 19103
Contact: Ms. Sharon Easterling, Exec. Dir.
Ph: (215)893-0130
Fax: (215)893-0205
E-mail: members@dvaeyc.org
URL: http://www.dvaeyc.org

Staff: 24. **Descr:** Improves educational opportunities for young children by offering professional development and training to the early education community and by building public support for high-quality early childhood programs. **Fnd:** 1967. **Mem:** 1700. **Pub:** *Connection* (bimonthly).

5108 ■ Greater Harrisburg Area Chapter of the Autism Society of America (GHAC-ASA)
PO Box 101
Enola, PA 17025
Contact: Georgia Rackley, Pres.
Ph: (717)732-8408
Free: 800-244-2425
E-mail: georgia.rackley@verizon.net
URL: http://autismharrisburg.org
Descr: Seeks to improve the lives of individuals affected by autism. Promotes awareness and understanding of autism disorders. Aims to further the advancement of preventive studies, therapy and research of autism disorders.

5109 ■ Greene Arc
197 Dunn Station Rd.
Prosperity, PA 15329
Contact: Cynthia Dias, Exec. Dir.
Ph: (724)627-5511
Descr: Parents, professional workers, and others interested in individuals with mental retardation. Works to promote services, research, public understanding, and legislation for people with mental retardation and their families.

5110 ■ Learning Disabilities Association of Bucks County (BCLDA)
PO Box 1179
Southampton, PA 18966
Ph: (215)355-9601
E-mail: bclda@att.net
URL: http://www.geocities.com/bclda

5111 ■ Northwestern Pennsylvania Autism Society of America (NWPA-ASA)
PO Box 3923
Erie, PA 16508
Contact: Diane Baer, Pres.
Ph: (814)455-3540
E-mail: nwpaasa@verizon.net
URL: http://www.nwpa-asa.org
Descr: Seeks to improve the lives of individuals affected by autism. Promotes awareness and understanding of autism disorders. Aims to further the advancement of preventive studies, therapy and research of autism disorders.

5112 ■ Pennsylvania Association for the Education of Young Children (PennAEYC)
PO Box 653
Pine Grove Mills, PA 16868
Contact: Linda Ehrlich, Pres.
Ph: (717)213-0581
Free: 888-272-9267
E-mail: jaskins@pennaeyc.org
URL: http://www.pennaeyc.org
Descr: Works to achieve healthy development and quality childhood programs for young children and offers professional development, advocacy support, networking, leadership, and other opportunities for childhood professionals.

5113 ■ Pennsylvania Association of Educational Opportunity Program Personnel (PAE-OPP)
Student Support Services/Beekey 125
Kuztown University
PO Box 730
Kutztown, PA 19530
Contact: Angela Steffy, Pres.
E-mail: atrumbau@kutztown.edu
URL: http://www.paeopp.org
Descr: Works to advance educational opportunities for disadvantaged students in colleges and universities. Provides professional development and

continuing education. Monitors federal legislation designed to serve disadvantaged students.

5114 ■ Pennsylvania Branch of the International Dyslexia Association (PBIDA)
PO Box 251
Bryn Mawr, PA 19010
Contact: Jeannie Bowman, Pres.
Ph: (610)527-1548
E-mail: dyslexia@pbida.org
URL: http://www.pbida.org
Descr: Promotes public awareness and understanding of dyslexia. Seeks to develop and implement specialized methods to improve the quality of life for people who have dyslexia. Provides services to those affected by dyslexia, attention disorders and other learning disabilities.

5115 ■ Pennsylvania Department of Education
333 Market St.
Harrisburg, PA 17126-0333
Contact: Dr. Gerald L. Zahorchak, Sec.
Ph: (717)783-6788
Fax: (717)787-8445
E-mail: 00admin@state.pa.us
URL: http://www.pde.state.pa.us/
Descr: Mission is to lead and serve the educational community to enable each individual to grow into an inspired, productive, fulfilled lifelong learner.

5116 ■ Pennsylvania Developmental Disabilities Planning Council
Forum Bldg., Rm. 561
605 South Dr.
Harrisburg, PA 17120
Contact: Graham Mulholland, Exec. Dir.
Ph: (717)787-6057
Free: 877-685-4452
URL: http://www.paddc.org
Descr: Supports people with disabilities in taking control of their own lives. Ensures access to goods, services, and supports. Builds inclusive communities. Pursues a cross-disability agenda and changes negative societal attitudes towards people with disabilities.

5117 ■ Pennsylvania Family Support Alliance (PFSA)
2001 N Front St., Bldg. 1, Ste. 210
Harrisburg, PA 17102
Contact: Angela Fogle, Exec. Dir.
Ph: (717)238-0937
Fax: (717)238-4315
E-mail: afogle@pennsylvaniafamilysupportalliance.org
URL: http://www.pennsylvaniafamilysupportalliance.org
Staff: 8. **Descr:** Provides a wide range of services, including training, technical assistance, and various support services to affiliated agencies in statewide network. Provides a wide variety of publications geared to parents with unique challenges such as mental illness, drug and alcohol dependency, and parenting while incarcerated. **Fnd:** 1979. **State Groups:** 1.

5118 ■ Pennsylvania Parent Teacher Association
4804 Derry St.
Harrisburg, PA 17111-3440
Contact: Caroline Allen, Pres.
Ph: (717)564-8985
Fax: (717)564-9046
E-mail: info@papta.org
URL: http://www.papta.org
Descr: Aims to promote welfare of children and youth in home, school, community, and place of worship. Raises standards of home life. **Fnd:** 1899.

5119 ■ Pennsylvania Statewide AfterSchool/Youth Development Network (PSAYDN)
275 Grandview Ave., Ste. 200
Camp Hill, PA 17011
Contact: Kisha Bird, Dir.
Ph: (717)763-1661

E-mail: kbird@csc.csiu.org
URL: http://www.psaydn.org

5120 ■ Pittsburgh Association for the Education of Young Children (PAEYC)
5604 Solway St.
Pittsburgh, PA 15217
Contact: Michelle Figlar, Exec. Dir.
Ph: (412)421-3889
Fax: (412)421-7624
E-mail: mfiglar@pghaeyc.org
URL: http://www.pghaeyc.org
Staff: 3. **Descr:** Strives to support and maintain the high quality early care and education for young children through: professional development; collaboration with community resources; and advocacy for the needs and rights of children, their families, and the individual who work with them. **Fnd:** 1980. **Mem:** 650. **Pub:** Newsletter (bimonthly).

5121 ■ TASH, Pennsylvania
26 Gunpowder Rd.
Mechanicsburg, PA 17050-7363
Contact: Kathy Brill, Pres.
Ph: (717)691-8686
E-mail: ksbrill@comcast.net
URL: http://home.dejazzd.com/mcsouth/PaTASH_index.html
Descr: Provides service to people with disabilities. **Fnd:** 1975.

5122 ■ York Area Association for the Education of Young Children (YAAEYC)
800 E King St.
York, PA 17403
Contact: Mindy Miller, Pres.
Ph: (717)843-7884
E-mail: mmiller@yorkcoymca.org
URL: http://www.yaaeyc.org
Descr: Serves and acts on behalf of the needs, rights and well-being of all young children with primary focus on the quality of educational and developmental services for all children. Seeks to improve professional practice and working conditions in early childhood education.

Puerto Rico

5123 ■ American Medical Student Association, Universidad Central del Caribe School of Medicine
PO Box 60327
Bayamon, PR 00960
Contact: Jorge Colon Nevares, Pres.
Ph: (787)798-3001
URL: http://www.uccaribe.edu/index.php?action=page_display&PageID=83
Descr: Promotes improvement in medical training and education. Advances the medicine profession. Contributes to the welfare of medical students, interns, residents and post-MD/DO trainees.

5124 ■ American Medical Student Association, University of Puerto Rico School of Medicine
PO Box 365067
San Juan, PR 00936-5067
Ph: (787)765-2363
Fax: (787)756-8475
URL: http://www.md.rcm.upr.edu
Descr: Promotes improvement in medical training and education. Advances the medicine profession. Contributes to the welfare of medical students, interns, residents and post-MD/DO trainees.

5125 ■ Puerto Rico Association for Career and Technical Education
B-11 Calle 3
Fajardo, PR 00738-3765
Contact: Benigno Matta, Pres.
E-mail: mattamarquez@hotmail.com
URL: http://www.acteonline.org/content.aspx?id=794
Descr: Supports vocational technical education that

will assure students' successful roles in families, communities, and society.

5126 ■ Puerto Rico Association for the Education of Young Children
PO Box 193048
San Juan, PR 00919-3048
Contact: Maria de Lourdes Lopez-Cintron, Pres.
Ph: (787)409-7877
Fax: (787)793-3100
E-mail: producir9luly@hotmail.com
Descr: Serves and acts on behalf of the needs, rights and well-being of all young children with primary focus on the quality of educational and developmental services for all children. Seeks to improve professional practice and working conditions in early childhood education.

Rhode Island

5127 ■ AG BELL, Rhode Island
20 Maribeth Dr.
Johnston, RI 02919
Contact: Iraida Williams, Pres.
E-mail: riagbell@yahoo.com
URL: http://www.riagbell.org
Descr: Represents the interests of educators, parents of children with hearing loss, adults with hearing loss and hearing health professionals. Provides governmental and education advocacy services.

5128 ■ American Medical Student Association, Brown Medical School
Box G-A
Providence, RI 02912
Contact: Kirsten L. Spalding, Pres.
Ph: (401)863-3330
E-mail: medical_school@brown.edu
URL: http://bms.brown.edu
Descr: Promotes improvement in medical training and education. Advances the medicine profession. Contributes to the welfare of medical students, interns, residents and post-MD/DO trainees.

5129 ■ Association on Higher Education and Disability - New England (AHEAD-NE)
Johnson and Wales University
8 Abbott Park Pl.
Providence, RI 02903
Contact: Bette Nee, Treas.
Ph: (401)598-4754
Fax: (401)598-1743
E-mail: elizabeth.nee@jwu.edu
URL: http://www.ahead.org/affiliates/new-england
Descr: Represents individuals interested in promoting the equal rights and opportunities of disabled postsecondary students, staff, faculty and graduates. Provides educational and professional development opportunities for persons with disabilities in postsecondary education. Encourages and supports legislation for the benefit of disabled students.

5130 ■ Autism Society of America - Rhode Island Chapter
PO Box 16603
Rumford, RI 02916
Contact: Lisa Rego
Ph: (401)595-3241
E-mail: ri-rhodeisland@autismsocietyofamerica.org
Descr: Seeks to improve the lives of individuals affected by autism. Promotes awareness and understanding of autism disorders. Aims to further the advancement of preventive studies, therapy and research of autism disorders.

5131 ■ Blackstone Valley Arc
115 Manton St.
Pawtucket, RI 02861
Contact: John J. Padien III, CEO
Ph: (401)727-0150
Fax: (401)727-0153
E-mail: contact@bvcriarc.org
URL: http://bvcriarc.org/e107_plugins/content/content.php?content.1003

Descr: Parents, professional workers, and others interested in individuals with mental retardation. Works to promote services, research, public understanding, and legislation for people with mental retardation and their families.

5132 ■ Bristol County Chapter Arc
PO Box 61
Bristol, RI 02809
Contact: L. Pocci, Exec. Dir.
Ph: (401)253-5900
Descr: Works to promote and improve supports and services for people with mental retardation and their families. Fosters research and education regarding the prevention of mental retardation in infants and young children.

5133 ■ Common Cause/Rhode Island
245 Waterman St., Ste. 400A
Providence, RI 02906
Contact: Christine Lopes, Exec. Dir.
Ph: (401)861-2322
Fax: (401)331-9676
E-mail: contact@commoncauseri.org
URL: http://www.commoncauseri.org
Staff: 3. **Descr:** Fights for open, honest, and accountable government, voter education, and civic involvement. **Fnd:** 1970.

5134 ■ Cranston Arc
111 Comstock Pkwy.
Cranston, RI 02921
Contact: Thomas P. Kane, Pres./CEO
Ph: (401)941-1112
Fax: (401)941-2516
URL: http://www.cranstonarc.org
Descr: Parents, professional workers, and others interested in individuals with mental retardation. Works to promote services, research, public understanding, and legislation for people with mental retardation and their families. **Fnd:** 1965.

5135 ■ Down Syndrome Society of Rhode Island (DSSRI)
99 Bald Hill Rd.
Cranston, RI 02920
Contact: Claudia M. Lowe, Coor.
Ph: (401)463-5751
Fax: (401)463-5337
E-mail: coordinator@dssri.org
URL: http://www.dssri.org
Descr: Parents, professional workers, and others interested in individuals with Down syndrome. Promotes the rights, dignity and potential of all individuals with Down syndrome through advocacy, education, public awareness and support. Works to promote services, research, public understanding, and legislation for people with Down syndrome and their families. **Fnd:** 1982. **Pub:** DSSRI News (3/year).

5136 ■ Learning Disabilities Association of Rhode Island
11 Chaloner Ct.
Cranston, RI 02921
Contact: Linda Dicecco
Ph: (401)946-6968
E-mail: lindixx@email.com

5137 ■ National Education Association - Rhode Island (NEARI)
99 Bald Hill Rd.
Cranston, RI 02920
Contact: Lawrence E. Purtill Jr., Pres.
Ph: (401)463-9630
Fax: (401)463-5337
E-mail: lpurtill@nea.org
URL: http://www.neari.org
Descr: Works to provide quality public education for children in Rhode Island. **Mem:** 11000. **Pub:** Newsline (5/year).

5138 ■ Rhode Island Association for the Education of Young Children
655 Main St., Ste. 201
East Greenwich, RI 02818

Contact: Tammy Camillo, Dir.
Ph: (401)398-7605
Fax: (401)398-7604
E-mail: tcamillo@brightstars.org
URL: http://riaeyc.org
Descr: Serves and acts on behalf of the needs, rights and well-being of all young children with primary focus on the quality of educational and developmental services for all children. Seeks to improve professional practice and working conditions in early childhood education.

5139 ■ Rhode Island Branch of the International Dyslexia Association (RIBIDA)
16 Houson Ave.
Newport, RI 02840
Contact: Dawn Pigott, Pres.
Ph: (401)521-0020
Fax: (401)847-6720
E-mail: ribida@yahoo.com
URL: http://www.interdys.org/Branchdetail.aspx?bid=52
Descr: Promotes public awareness and understanding of dyslexia. Seeks to develop and implement specialized methods to improve the quality of life for people who have dyslexia.

5140 ■ Rhode Island Department of Elementary and Secondary Education
255 Westminster St.
Providence, RI 02903-3400
Contact: Peter McWalters, Commnr.
Ph: (401)222-4600
Fax: (401)222-6178
E-mail: maureen.dandrea@ride.ri.gov
URL: http://www.ride.ri.gov/

5141 ■ Rhode Island Developmental Disabilities Council
400 Bald Hill Rd., Ste. 515
Warwick, RI 02886
Contact: John Susa, Chm.
Ph: (401)737-1238
Fax: (401)737-3395
E-mail: riddc@riddc.org
URL: http://www.riddc.org
Descr: Represents parents, professional workers, and others interested in individuals with mental retardation. Works to promote services, research, public understanding, and legislation for people with mental retardation and their families.

5142 ■ VSA arts of Rhode Island
500 Prospect St.
Pawtucket, RI 02860
Contact: Jeannine L. Chartier, Exec. Dir.
Ph: (401)725-0247
Fax: (401)725-0397
E-mail: programs@vsartsri.org
URL: http://www.vsartsri.org
Staff: 2. **Descr:** Provides programs and opportunities for children, youth and adults with disabilities to participate in a variety of visual, performing and literary arts. **Fnd:** 1987.

5143 ■ Westerly Chariho Arc
93 Airport Rd.
Westerly, RI 02891
Contact: Anthony J. Velluci, Exec. Dir.
Ph: (401)596-2091
Fax: (401)596-3945
E-mail: info@oleancenter.org
URL: http://www.oleancenter.org
Descr: Parents, professional workers, and others interested in individuals with mental retardation. Works to promote services, research, public understanding, and legislation for people with mental retardation and their families. **Fnd:** 1966.

South Carolina

5144 ■ American Medical Student Association, Medical University of South Carolina College of Medicine
171 Ashley Ave.
Charleston, SC 29425

E-mail: nicholsk@musc.edu
URL: http://www.musc.edu/com1
Descr: Promotes improvement in medical training and education. Advances the medicine profession. Contributes to the welfare of medical students, interns, residents and post-MD/DO trainees.

5145 ■ American Medical Student Association, University of South Carolina School of Medicine
6311 Garners Ferry Rd.
Columbia, SC 29209
Contact: Alice Teich
Ph: (803)733-3200
E-mail: ateich@gw.med.sc.edu
URL: http://www.med.sc.edu
Descr: Promotes improvement in medical training and education. Advances the medicine profession. Contributes to the welfare of medical students, interns, residents and post-MD/DO trainees.

5146 ■ Communities in Schools of South Carolina (CISSC)
2712 Middleburg Dr., Ste. 207-B
Columbia, SC 29204
Contact: Ms. Andrenette F. Hudley, State Exec. Dir./CEO
Ph: (803)254-5520
Free: 800-574-9140
Fax: (803)254-5377
E-mail: ahudley@cissc.org
URL: http://www.cissc.org
Staff: 2. **Descr:** Assists and supports local CIS organizations throughout the state by forming state level partnerships, providing training, technical assistance, community development and assisting with financial and in-kind resources. **Fnd:** 1992. **Local Groups:** 13.

5147 ■ Plain Elementary PTA
506 Neely Ferry Rd.
Simpsonville, SC 29680
Contact: Debbie Mihalic, Principal
Ph: (864)355-7700
Fax: (864)355-7774
E-mail: dmihalic@greenville.k12.sc.us
URL: http://www.greenville.k12.sc.us/plaine
Descr: Parents, teachers, students, and others interested in uniting the forces of home, school, and community. Promotes the welfare of children and youth.

5148 ■ South Carolina AfterSchool Alliance
1611 Devonshire Dr., Ste. 101
Columbia, SC 29204
Contact: Zelda Q. Waymer, Exec. Dir.
Ph: (803)254-5454
Free: 866-237-5454
Fax: (803)254-5441
E-mail: moreinfo@scafterschool.com
URL: http://www.scafterschool.com

5149 ■ South Carolina Association for the Education of Young Children (SCAEYC)
PO Box 7111
Columbia, SC 29202
Contact: Evelyn Fields, Business Mgr.
Ph: (803)516-4728
Fax: (803)536-8895
E-mail: scaeyc2000@aol.com
Descr: Serves and acts on behalf of the needs, rights and well-being of all young children with primary focus on the quality of educational and developmental services for all children. Seeks to improve professional practice and working conditions in early childhood education.

5150 ■ South Carolina Autism Society (SCAS)
806 12th St.
West Columbia, SC 29169
Contact: Craig Stoxen, Pres./CEO
Ph: (803)750-6988
Free: 800-438-4790
Fax: (803)750-8121
E-mail: scas@scautism.org
URL: http://www.scautism.org

Descr: Seeks to improve the lives of individuals affected by autism. Promotes awareness and understanding of autism disorders. Aims to further the advancement of preventive studies, therapy and research of autism disorders.

5151 ■ South Carolina Branch of the International Dyslexia Association (SCBIDA)
Camperdown Academy
501 Howell Rd.
Greenville, SC 29615
Contact: Susan McLeod
Ph: (864)483-0707
E-mail: scbida@gmail.com
URL: http://www.interdys.org/Branchdetail.aspx?bid=40
Descr: Promotes public awareness and understanding of dyslexia. Seeks to develop and implement specialized methods to improve the quality of life for people who have dyslexia.

5152 ■ South Carolina Department of Education
1429 Senate St.
Columbia, SC 29201
Contact: Dr. Jim Rex, Superintendent
Ph: (803)734-8500
Fax: (803)734-3389
E-mail: info@ed.sc.gov
URL: http://ed.sc.gov/

5153 ■ South Carolina Developmental Disabilities Council
1205 Pendleton St., Ste. 450
Columbia, SC 29201
Contact: Mr. Charles Lang, Exec. Dir.
Ph: (803)734-0465
Fax: (803)734-0241
E-mail: clang@oepp.sc.gov
URL: http://www.scddc.state.sc.us
Staff: 7. **Descr:** Aims to provide leadership in advocating, funding and implementing initiatives which recognize the inherent dignity of each individual, and promote independence, productivity, respect and inclusion for all persons with disabilities and their families. **Fnd:** 1971. **Mem:** 26.

5154 ■ South Carolina Fire Marshals Association
403 E Curtis St.
Simpsonville, SC 29681
Contact: Eddie Watson
Ph: (864)967-9804
Fax: (864)962-1345
E-mail: firemarshal@simpsonvillefd.com
Descr: Provides codes, standards, products, and services to concerned individuals for the safety and effective performance in the built environment.

5155 ■ South Carolina National Congress of Parents and Teachers
1826 Henderson St.
Columbia, SC 29201-2619
Contact: Phil Clark, Pres.
Ph: (803)765-0806
Free: 800-743-3782
Fax: (803)765-0399
E-mail: sc_office@pta.org
URL: http://www.scpta.org
Descr: Aims to support and speak on behalf of children and youth in the schools, in the community, and before governmental bodies and other organizations that make decisions affecting children.

5156 ■ Special Olympics, South Carolina
Dutch Plz.
810 Dutch Square Blvd., Ste. 204
Columbia, SC 29210
Contact: Barry Coats, Pres./CEO
Ph: (803)772-1555
Free: 800-765-7276
Fax: (803)772-0094
E-mail: bcoats@so-sc.org
URL: http://www.so-sc.org
Staff: 12. **Descr:** Provides year-round training and competition sports organization for children and adults with mental retardation. **Fnd:** 1968. **Mem:**

15500. **Pub:** *Games Books* (3/year); *Special Edition* (3/year).

South Dakota

5157 ■ American Medical Student Association, Sanford School of Medicine of University of South Dakota
414 E Clark St.
Vermillion, SD 57069
Contact: Paul C. Bunger PhD, Dean of Medical Student Affairs
Ph: (605)677-5233
Fax: (605)677-5109
E-mail: usdsmsa@usd.edu
URL: http://www.usd.edu/med/md
Descr: Promotes improvement in medical training and education. Advances the medicine profession. Contributes to the welfare of medical students, interns, residents and post-MD/DO trainees.

5158 ■ Association for Career and Technical Education, South Dakota (SDACTE)
PO Box 730
Watertown, SD 57201
Contact: Dodie Bemis, Exec. Dir.
Ph: (605)882-5284
Fax: (605)886-7016
Descr: Supports and promotes vocational education. **Pub:** Newsletters.

5159 ■ Autism Society of the Black Hills
PO Box 2893
Rapid City, SD 57709
Contact: Sheri Perkins
Ph: (605)415-3739
E-mail: sheritony@rap.midco.net
URL: http://www.autismsd.com
Descr: Seeks to improve the lives of individuals affected by autism. Promotes awareness and understanding of autism disorders. Aims to further the advancement of preventive studies, therapy and research of autism disorders.

5160 ■ South Dakota Association for Career and Technical Education (SDACTE)
PO Box 730
Watertown, SD 57201
Contact: Dodie Bemis, Exec. Dir.
Ph: (605)886-7016
E-mail: bemisd@lakeareatech.edu
URL: http://www.lakeareatech.edu/sdacte
Descr: Promotes vocational technical education. **Fnd:** 1972. **Mem:** 413. **Pub:** *SDACTE Viewpoint* (3/year).

5161 ■ South Dakota Association for the Education of Young Children (SDAEYC)
PO Box 91634
Sioux Falls, SD 57109
Contact: Tami Skorczewski, Pres.
Ph: (605)367-4628
E-mail: tami.skorczewski@southeasttech.com
URL: http://www.sdaeyc.org
Descr: Serves and acts on behalf of the needs, rights and well-being of all young children with primary focus on the quality of educational and developmental services for all children. Seeks to improve professional practice and working conditions in early childhood education.

5162 ■ South Dakota Council on Developmental Disabilities
Hillsview Plaza, E Hwy. 34
500 E Capitol
Pierre, SD 57501-5070
Contact: Ms. Arlene Poncelet, Exec. Dir.
Ph: (605)773-6369
Fax: (605)773-5483
E-mail: infoddc@state.sd.us
URL: http://www.state.sd.us/dhs/ddc
Staff: 1. **Descr:** Seeks to provide a leadership role in South Dakota in helping individuals with developmental disabilities to achieve their maximum potential for independence, productivity and integration into

the community. **Fnd:** 1973. **Mem:** 22. **Pub:** *DCC Notes* (quarterly).

5163 ■ South Dakota Counseling Association, Central Chapter
631 N Huron Ave.
Pierre, SD 57501
Contact: Christine Bisek, Pres.
Ph: (605)224-5011
E-mail: cbisek@cacsnet.org
URL: http://www.sdcounseling.org

5164 ■ South Dakota Counseling Association, Cornbelt Chapter
6808 S Mogan Ave.
Sioux Falls, SD 57108
Contact: Kelly Jones, Pres.
Ph: (605)729-2541
E-mail: kelly.jones@k12.sd.us
URL: http://www.sdcounseling.org

5165 ■ South Dakota Counseling Association, Coteau Chapter
802 Skyline Dr.
Watertown, SD 57201
Contact: Bonnie Werpy-Rye, Pres.
Ph: (605)696-7601
E-mail: werpyrye@wat.midco.net
URL: http://www.sdcounseling.org

5166 ■ South Dakota Counseling Association, Interlakes Chapter
211 4th St.
Brookings, SD 57007
Contact: Theresa Plut, Pres.
Ph: (605)697-2850
E-mail: theresa.plut@ecmhcd.org
URL: http://www.sdcounseling.org

5167 ■ South Dakota Counseling Association, Lewis and Clark Chapter
PO Box 158
Gayville, SD 57031
Contact: Natalie Selchert, Pres.
Ph: (605)267-4476
E-mail: natalie.selchert@k12.sd.us
URL: http://www.sdcounseling.org

5168 ■ South Dakota Counseling Association, North Central Chapter
719 S Jay St.
Aberdeen, SD 57401
Contact: Heather Bakeberg, Pres.
Ph: (605)290-3888
E-mail: hbakeberg@nemhc.org
URL: http://www.sdcounseling.org

5169 ■ South Dakota Counseling Association, Palace/Pheasant Chapter
1021 S Courtland St.
Chamberlain, SD 57325
Contact: Margie Neugebauer, Pres.
Ph: (605)234-0115
Fax: (605)778-6231
E-mail: margie.neugebauer@k12.sd.us
URL: http://www.sdcounseling.org

5170 ■ South Dakota Counseling Association, Sioux Chapter (SDCA)
835 S Main St., No. 1
Sioux Falls, SD 57104
Contact: Melissa Hemmestad, Pres.-Elect
Ph: (605)362-3530
E-mail: mhemmestad@glory-house.org
URL: http://www.sdcounseling.org

5171 ■ South Dakota Department of Education
700 Governors Dr.
Pierre, SD 57501-2291
Contact: Tamara Darnell, Dir.
Ph: (605)773-3134

Fax: (605)773-6139
E-mail: deb.barnett@state.sd.us
URL: http://doe.sd.gov/

5172 ■ Special Olympics South Dakota (SOSD)
305 W 39th St.
Sioux Falls, SD 57105
Contact: Carol Husby, CEO/Dir.
Ph: (605)331-4117
Free: 800-585-2114
Fax: (605)331-4328
E-mail: chusby@sosd.org
URL: http://www.sosd.org
Staff: 3. **Descr:** Individuals with mental handicaps who are 8 years of age or older. Provides year-round athletic training and competition for citizens with mental retardation. Events include: Winter Games, February; Basketball, March; Summer Games, May; Equestrian, July; Softball, September; Bowling, November. **Fnd:** 1968. **Mem:** 3000. **Pub:** *Torch* (quarterly).

Tennessee

5173 ■ 100 Black Men of Chattanooga
PO Box 1201
Chattanooga, TN 37401
Contact: Rose M. Martin, Exec. Dir.
Ph: (423)756-0790
Fax: (423)756-2976
E-mail: contact@100blackmenofchat.org

5174 ■ 100 Black Men of Knoxville
PO Box 333
Knoxville, TN 37901
Ph: (865)531-7370
Fax: (865)531-7370
E-mail: ionehun@earthlink.net
URL: http://www.100blackmenofknoxville.org
Fnd: 1994.

5175 ■ 100 Black Men of Memphis (100 BMOM)
PO Box 617
Memphis, TN 38101-0617
Contact: Ayanna Buchanan, Managing Admin.
Ph: (901)626-3994
URL: http://www.100blackmenofmemphis.org
Fnd: 1986.

5176 ■ 100 Black Men of Middle Tennessee
1 Vantage Way, Ste. E-200
Nashville, TN 37228
Contact: Mr. Darrell Freeman, Pres.
Ph: (615)248-2721
Fax: (615)248-3156
E-mail: info@the100.org
URL: http://www.100blkmentn.org/collegiate.htm

5177 ■ American Association of University Women of Tennessee
740 Liberty Ct.
Cookeville, TN 38501
Contact: Monika Bowman, Pres.
Ph: (931)526-1927
E-mail: mbowman@tnaccess.com
URL: http://www.discoveret.org/aauwtn
Descr: Advances equity for women and girls through advocacy, education, and research. Provides funds and a support system for women seeking judicial redress for sex discrimination in higher education.

5178 ■ American Medical Student Association, East Tennessee State University Quillen College of Medicine
Box 70694
Johnson City, TN 37614-1710
Contact: Philip C. Bagnell MD
Ph: (423)439-6315
Fax: (423)439-8090
E-mail: forrestd@etsu.edu
URL: http://com.etsu.edu
Descr: Promotes improvement in medical training and education. Advances the medicine profession.

Contributes to the welfare of medical students, interns, residents and post-MD/DO trainees.

5179 ■ American Medical Student Association, The University of Tennessee Health Science Center College of Medicine
Academic Affairs
930 Madison Ave., No. 836
Memphis, TN 38103
Contact: Anthony Huang
E-mail: ahuang1@utmem.edu
URL: http://www.utmem.edu/Medicine
Descr: Promotes improvement in medical training and education. Advances the medicine profession. Contributes to the welfare of medical students, interns, residents and post-MD/DO trainees.

5180 ■ American Medical Student Association, Vanderbilt University School of Medicine
21st Ave. S and Garland Ave.
Nashville, TN 37232
Contact: Steven G. Gabbe MD, Dean
Ph: (615)322-5191
E-mail: steven.gabbe@vanderbilt.edu
URL: http://www.mc.vanderbilt.edu/medschool
Descr: Promotes improvement in medical training and education. Advances the medicine profession. Contributes to the welfare of medical students, interns, residents and post-MD/DO trainees.

5181 ■ Arc of Tennessee
151 Athens Way, Ste. 100
Nashville, TN 37228
Contact: Walter Rogers, Exec. Dir.
Ph: (615)248-5878
Free: 800-835-7077
Fax: (615)248-5879
E-mail: info@thearctn.org
URL: http://www.thearctn.org
Staff: 40. **Descr:** Offers advocacy, information and support to people with developmental disabilities and their families. Issues publications. **Fnd:** 1952. **Mem:** 3000. **Reg. Groups:** 20. **State Groups:** 1. **Local Groups:** 20. **Pub:** *The Arc Connection* (quarterly); *Legislative Monitor* (monthly).

5182 ■ Arc of Washington County
2700 S Roan St., Ste. 300B
Johnson City, TN 37601
Contact: Bill Schiers, Exec. Dir.
Ph: (423)928-9362
Fax: (423)928-7431
E-mail: kim@arcwc.org
URL: http://www.arcwc.org
Staff: 10. **Descr:** Strives to create partnerships that foster nurturing communities where persons with mental retardation and developmental disabilities can express, achieve and expand their vision of a valued live. **Fnd:** 1961. **Pub:** *The Advocate* (quarterly).

5183 ■ Autism Society of America - East Tennessee Chapter (ASA-ETC)
PO Box 30015
Knoxville, TN 37930
Contact: Brook Dickerson, Exec. Dir.
Ph: (865)824-2897
Fax: (865)824-2896
E-mail: asaetc@gmail.com
URL: http://asaetc.org
Descr: Seeks to improve the lives of individuals affected by autism. Promotes awareness and understanding of autism disorders. Aims to further the advancement of preventive studies, therapy and research of autism disorders.

5184 ■ Autism Society of Middle Tennessee (ASMT)
955 Woodland St.
Nashville, TN 37206
Contact: Amanda Peltz, Exec. Dir.
Ph: (615)385-2077
Fax: (615)383-1176
E-mail: asmt@tnautism.org
URL: http://www.tnautism.org
Descr: Seeks to improve the lives of individuals af-

fected by autism. Promotes awareness and understanding of autism disorders. Aims to further the advancement of preventive studies, therapy and research of autism disorders.

5185 ■ Chattanooga Area Association for the Education of Young Children (CAAEYC)
2300 Bailey Ave.
Chattanooga, TN 37404
Contact: Emily Perrine, Pres.
Ph: (423)629-4174
E-mail: mcroy@signalcenters.org
URL: http://www.taeyc.org
Descr: Serves and acts on behalf of the needs, rights and well-being of all young children with primary focus on the quality of educational and developmental services for all children. Seeks to improve professional practice and working conditions in early childhood education. **Pub:** Newsletter (quarterly).

5186 ■ Common Cause Tennessee
PO Box 150781
Nashville, TN 37215
Contact: Dick Williams, Chm.
Ph: (615)321-9072
E-mail: commoncause-tn@msn.com
URL: http://www.commoncause.org/site/pp.asp?c=dkLNK1MQIwG&b=1765981
Staff: 1. **Descr:** Works to make public officials and public institutions accountable and responsive to citizens. **Fnd:** 1972. **Mem:** 1500. **Pub:** Newsletter.

5187 ■ Cumberland Counseling Association (CCA)
305 S Holly, Ste. B
Monterey, TN 38574
Contact: Abby L. Eibel, Pres.
Ph: (931)839-7181
E-mail: abby.eibel@gmail.com
URL: http://www.tncounselors.org

5188 ■ Learning Disabilities Association of Tennessee
PO Box 40562
Memphis, TN 38174
Contact: Joy Sue Marsh, Pres.
E-mail: info@learningdisabilities-tn.org
URL: http://www.learningdisabilities-tn.org

5189 ■ Lookout Counseling Association (LCA)
Tyner Academy
6836 Tyner Rd.
Chattanooga, TN 37421
Contact: Rita Waller, Pres.
Ph: (423)855-2635
Fax: (423)855-9417
E-mail: waller_rita@hcde.org
URL: http://www.tncounselors.org

5190 ■ Mid-South Arc
3485 Poplar Ave., Ste. 210
Memphis, TN 38111
Contact: Carlene I. Leaper, Exec. Dir.
Ph: (901)327-2473
Fax: (901)327-1197
E-mail: msarc@arcmidsouth.net
URL: http://www.arcmidsouth.net
Staff: 25. **Descr:** Seeks to empower people with developmental disabilities to reach their full potential. Creates a higher quality of life for individuals with mental retardation. **Mem:** 500.

5191 ■ Recording for the Blind and Dyslexic Tennessee Unit
205 Badger Rd.
Oak Ridge, TN 37830
Contact: Stephanie Guthrie, Development Dir.
Ph: (865)482-3496
Fax: (865)483-9934
E-mail: sguthrie@rfbd.org
Descr: Serves individuals who cannot effectively read standard print because of visual impairment, dyslexia, or other physical disabilities. Creates educational opportunities for students with print disabilities through educational and outreach services.

Provides and promotes the effective use of accessible educational materials.

5192 ■ Special Olympics Tennessee
1900 12th Ave. S
Nashville, TN 37203
Contact: Alan Bolick, Pres.
Ph: (615)329-1375
Free: 800-383-8502
Fax: (615)327-1465
E-mail: sotnpres@aol.com
URL: http://www.specialolympicstn.org
Descr: Promotes physical fitness, sports training, and athletic competition for children and adults with mental retardation. Seeks to contribute to the physical, social, and psychological development of persons with mental retardation. Participants range in age from 8 years to adult and compete in track and field, swimming, gymnastics, bowling, ice skating, basketball, and other sports.

5193 ■ Tennessee Association on Higher Education and Disability
Middle Tennessee Station University
PO Box 7
Murfreesboro, TN 37132
Contact: Janet Norman, Pres.
Ph: (615)898-2099
E-mail: jnorman@mtsu.edu
URL: http://www.ahead.org/affiliates/tennessee
Descr: Provides professional support and development to post-secondary disability service providers in the state of Tennessee and to other individuals and organizations. Works to promote opportunities and affect change in the state of Tennessee that will be beneficial to qualified post-secondary students with disabilities.

5194 ■ Tennessee Branch of the International Dyslexia Association (TN IDA)
6113 Montcrest Dr.
Nashville, TN 37215
Contact: Latricia Phillips, Interim Pres.
Free: 877-836-6432
E-mail: phillipsl@hardingacademy.org
URL: http://www.tn-interdys.org
Descr: Promotes public awareness and understanding of dyslexia. Seeks to develop and implement specialized methods to improve the quality of life for people who have dyslexia. **Pub:** *The Volunteer Voice* (semiannual).

5195 ■ Tennessee Council on Developmental Disabilities
Andrew Jackson Bldg.
500 Deaderick St., Ste. 1310
Nashville, TN 37243-0228
Contact: Wanda Willis, Exec. Dir.
Ph: (615)532-6615
Fax: (615)532-6964
E-mail: tnddc@state.tn.us
URL: http://www.state.tn.us/cdd
Descr: Promotes public policies to increase and support the inclusion of individuals with developmental disabilities in their communities. Works with public and private groups across the State to find necessary supports for individuals with disabilities and their families, so that they may have equal access to public education, employment, housing, health care, and all other aspects of community life. Encourages individuals with developmental disabilities and their families to play decision-making roles in policies and programs that affect them.

5196 ■ Tennessee State Department of Education
Andrew Johnson Tower, Sixth Fl.
710 James Robertson Pkwy.
Nashville, TN 37243-0375
Contact: Dr. Tim Web, Actg.Commnr.
Ph: (615)741-2731
Fax: (615)532-4791
E-mail: Education.Comments@state.tn.us
URL: http://www.state.tn.us/education/
Pub: List of publications online (www.state.tn.us/education/mreport.shtml).

Texas

5197 ■ AG BELL, Texas
103 Tuleta Dr.
San Antonio, TX 78212
Contact: Julie Grisham, Pres.
Ph: (210)495-0398
E-mail: texasagbell@yahoo.com
URL: http://www.agbell.org/tx
Descr: Represents the interests of educators, parents of children with hearing loss, adults with hearing loss and hearing health professionals. Provides governmental and education advocacy services.

5198 ■ American Association of University Women, Dallas Branch
1555 Waterside Ct.
Dallas, TX 75218
Contact: Glenna Taite, Treas.
URL: http://www.aauwdallas.org
Descr: Advances equity for women and girls through advocacy, education, and research. Provides funds and a support system for women seeking judicial redress for sex discrimination in higher education.

5199 ■ American Association of University Women, McAllen Texas Branch
PO Box 720184
McAllen, TX 78504
Contact: Melba Zaremba, Pres.
Ph: (956)821-7614
E-mail: mmzaremba@yahoo.com
Descr: Advances equity for women and girls through advocacy, education, and research. Provides funds and a support system for women seeking judicial redress for sex discrimination in higher education.

5200 ■ American Association of University Women, Montgomery County Texas Branch
PO Box 130302
The Woodlands, TX 77393-0302
Contact: Linda G. Gilbert, Contact Dir.
E-mail: lingil@houston.rr.com
Descr: Advances equity for women and girls through advocacy, education, and research. Provides funds and a support system for women seeking judicial redress for sex discrimination in higher education.

5201 ■ American Association of University Women, Richardson Texas Branch
PO Box 251347
Plano, TX 75025-1347
Contact: Janice Schieffer, Treas.
Ph: (214)415-3476
E-mail: janice@schieffer.us
URL: http://web2.airmail.net/~alistair/aauw
Descr: Advances equity for women and girls through advocacy, education, and research. Provides funds and a support system for women seeking judicial redress for sex discrimination in higher education.
Pub: *The Branch Line* (bimonthly).

5202 ■ American Association of University Women, Tyler Branch
PO Box 7171
Tyler, TX 75711
Contact: Robin Insalaco, Pres.-Elect
Ph: (903)534-0088
E-mail: rins@tjc.edu
Descr: Advances equity for women and girls through advocacy, education, and research. Provides funds and a support system for women seeking judicial redress for sex discrimination in higher education.

5203 ■ American Association of University Women, West Harris County Branch
PO Box 821125
Houston, TX 77282-1125
Contact: Mary Edwards, Pres.
E-mail: info@aauw-whc.org
URL: http://www.aauw-whc.org
Descr: Advances equity for women and girls through advocacy, education, and research. Provides funds and a support system for women seeking judicial redress for sex discrimination in higher education.

5204 ■ American Medical Student Association, Baylor College of Medicine
1 Baylor Plz.
Houston, TX 77030
Contact: Peter G. Traber, Pres.
Ph: (713)798-4951
E-mail: admissions@bcm.tmc.edu
URL: http://www.bcm.edu
Descr: Promotes improvement in medical training and education. Advances the medicine profession. Contributes to the welfare of medical students, interns, residents and post-MD/DO trainees.

5205 ■ American Medical Student Association, Texas A and M Health Science Center College of Medicine
159 Reynolds Medical Bldg.
College Station, TX 77843
Ph: (979)845-7743
Fax: (979)845-5533
URL: http://medicine.tamhsc.edu
Descr: Promotes improvement in medical training and education. Advances the medicine profession. Contributes to the welfare of medical students, interns, residents and post-MD/DO trainees.

5206 ■ American Medical Student Association, Texas Tech University Health Sciences Center School of Medicine
Office of Student Affairs
3601 4th St.
Mail Stop 6222
Lubbock, TX 79430
Contact: John C. Baldwin MD, Pres.
Ph: (806)743-3005
Fax: (806)743-4165
E-mail: it.webmaster@ttuhsc.edu
URL: http://www.ttuhsc.edu/SOM
Descr: Promotes improvement in medical training and education. Advances the medicine profession. Contributes to the welfare of medical students, interns, residents and post-MD/DO trainees.

5207 ■ American Medical Student Association, University of North Texas Health Science Center Texas College of Osteopathic Medicine
3500 Camp Bowie Blvd.
Fort Worth, TX 76107
Contact: Marc B. Hahn DO, Dean
Ph: (817)735-2000
E-mail: deantcom@hsc.unt.edu
URL: http://www.hsc.unt.edu/education/tcom
Descr: Promotes improvement in medical training and education. Advances the medicine profession. Contributes to the welfare of medical students, interns, residents and post-MD/DO trainees.

5208 ■ American Medical Student Association, University of Texas Health Science Center at San Antonio School of Medicine
7703 Floyd Curl Dr.
San Antonio, TX 78229-3900
Contact: Francisco G. Cigarroa MD, Pres.
Ph: (210)567-7000
URL: http://som.uthscsa.edu
Descr: Promotes improvement in medical training and education. Advances the medicine profession. Contributes to the welfare of medical students, interns, residents and post-MD/DO trainees.

5209 ■ American Medical Student Association, University of Texas Medical Branch School of Medicine
301 University Blvd.
5.106 Administration Bldg.
Galveston, TX 77555-0100
Contact: Shonda Janke-Stedronsky, Pres.
Ph: (409)772-3967
URL: http://www.som.utmb.edu
Descr: Promotes improvement in medical training and education. Advances the medicine profession.

Contributes to the welfare of medical students, interns, residents and post-MD/DO trainees.

5210 ■ American Medical Student Association, University of Texas Southwestern Medical School
5323 Harry Hines Blvd.
Dallas, TX 75390
Ph: (214)648-3111
URL: http://www8.utsouthwestern.edu/home/education/medicalschool/index.html
Descr: Promotes improvement in medical training and education. Advances the medicine profession. Contributes to the welfare of medical students, interns, residents and post-MD/DO trainees.

5211 ■ Arc of the Capital Area
2818 San Gabriel
Austin, TX 78705
Contact: Susan Eason, Exec. Dir.
Ph: (512)476-7044
Fax: (512)476-9054
E-mail: information@arcofthecapitalarea.org
URL: http://www.arcofthecapitalarea.org
Descr: Provides services to children and adults with mental retardation and other developmental disabilities and their families in Austin, Texas and surrounding communities. **Fnd:** 1949.

5212 ■ Arc of Ector County
PO Box 13023
Odessa, TX 79768-3023
Contact: Clifford M. Ray, Pres.
Ph: (432)362-2702

5213 ■ Arc of Greater Beaumont
655 S 8th St.
Beaumont, TX 77701
Ph: (409)784-5556
E-mail: caitlin.kruger@stmhmr.org
URL: http://arcofbmt.org

5214 ■ Arc of Greater Houston (AOGH)
3737 Dacoma, Ste. E
PO Box 924168
Houston, TX 77292-4168
Contact: Judy Kantorczyk, Exec. Dir.
Ph: (713)957-1600
Fax: (713)957-1699
E-mail: information@thearcofgreaterhouston.com
URL: http://www.thearcofgreaterhouston.com
Descr: Works to include all children and adults with cognitive, intellectual and development disabilities in every community. **Fnd:** 1984. **Mem:** 717.

5215 ■ Arc of Greater Tarrant County
1300 W Lancaster Ave., Ste. 104
Fort Worth, TX 76102
Contact: Dr. Richard Garnett, Exec. Dir.
Ph: (817)877-1474
Fax: (817)877-1477
E-mail: richard.garnett@arcgtc.org
URL: http://www.arcgtc.org
Descr: Parents, professional workers, and others interested in individuals with mental retardation. Works to promote services, research, public understanding, and legislation for people with mental retardation and their families. **Pub:** *Arc Message* (monthly).

5216 ■ Arc of McLennan County
PO Box 3367
Waco, TX 76707
Contact: Tom Pearson, Exec. Dir.
Ph: (254)756-7491
Fax: (254)756-7504
E-mail: tpearson@hot.rr.com
URL: http://www.wacoarc.org
Descr: Parents, professional workers, and others interested in individuals with mental retardation. Works to promote services, research, public understanding, and legislation for people with mental retardation and their families. **Fnd:** 1954.

5217 ■ Arc of Texas
8001 Centre Park Dr.
Austin, TX 78754

Contact: Mike Bright, Exec. Dir.
Ph: (512)454-6694
Free: 800-252-9729
Fax: (512)454-4956
E-mail: secretary@thearcoftexas.org
URL: http://www.thearcoftexas.org

Staff: 20. **Descr:** Parents, professional workers, and others interested in individuals with mental retardation. Works to promote services, research, public understanding, and legislation for people with mental retardation and their families. **Fnd:** 1950. **Local Groups:** 39.

5218 ■ Arc of Tyler
810 Vine Heights
Tyler, TX 75701
Contact: Jacqueline Fowler, Exec. Dir.
Ph: (903)597-0995
E-mail: info@arcoftyler.org
URL: http://www.thearc.org/NetCommunity/Page. aspx?&pid=223&srcid=1315&chid=628

Descr: Parents, professional workers, and others interested in individuals with mental retardation. Works to promote services, research, public understanding, and legislation for people with mental retardation and their families.

5219 ■ Association on Higher Education and Disability in Texas
Box 2082
14781 Memorial Dr.
Houston, TX 77079
Contact: Steve Christopher, Pres.
Ph: (972)883-6104
E-mail: schris@austincc.edu
URL: http://www.ahead.org/affiliates/texas

Descr: Represents individuals interested in promoting the equal rights and opportunities of disabled postsecondary students, staff, faculty and graduates. Provides educational and professional development opportunities for persons with disabilities in postsecondary education. Encourages and supports legislation for the benefit of disabled students.

5220 ■ Austin Area Branch of the International Dyslexia Association
PO Box 92604
Austin, TX 78709-2605
Contact: Monica Clark, Pres.
Ph: (512)452-7658
URL: http://www.austinida.org

Descr: Promotes public awareness and understanding of dyslexia. Seeks to develop and implement specialized methods to improve the quality of life for people who have dyslexia.

5221 ■ Autism Society of America - Dallas Chapter
10503 Metric Dr.
Dallas, TX 75243
Contact: Ms. Pamela Lane, Pres.
Ph: (214)208-0792
E-mail: tx-dallas@autismsocietyofamerica.org

Descr: Seeks to improve the lives of individuals affected by autism. Promotes awareness and understanding of autism disorders. Aims to further the advancement of preventive studies, therapy and research of autism disorders.

5222 ■ Autism Society of America - Greater Tarrant County Chapter
PO Box 161516
Fort Worth, TX 76161
Contact: Karissa Rains, Office Mgr.
Ph: (817)390-2829
Fax: (817)498-6133
E-mail: tx-tarrantcounty@autismsocietyofamerica.org

Descr: Seeks to improve the lives of individuals affected by autism. Promotes awareness and understanding of autism disorders. Aims to further the

advancement of preventive studies, therapy and research of autism disorders.

5223 ■ Autism Society of America - Texas Gulf Coast Chapter (ASA-TGCC)
PO Box 57865
Webster, TX 77598
Contact: Kim Lindquist, Pres.
E-mail: romans2_6@hotmail.com
URL: http://asa-tgcc.org

Descr: Seeks to improve the lives of individuals affected by autism. Promotes awareness and understanding of autism disorders. Aims to further the advancement of preventive studies, therapy and research of autism disorders.

5224 ■ Autism Society of Collin County (ASCC)
PO Box 261209
Plano, TX 75026
Contact: Nagla Moussa
Ph: (214)925-2722
Fax: (972)379-3787
E-mail: ascc@autism-ascc.org
URL: http://autism-ascc.org

Descr: Seeks to improve the lives of individuals affected by autism. Promotes awareness and understanding of autism disorders. Aims to further the advancement of preventive studies, therapy and research of autism disorders.

5225 ■ Autism Society of Greater Austin (ASGA)
PO Box 160841
Austin, TX 78716
Contact: Ann Hart, Pres.
Ph: (512)479-4199
E-mail: tx-austin@autismsocietyofamerica.org
URL: http://www.autism-society.org/site/Clubs?club_id=1040&pg=main

Descr: Seeks to improve the lives of individuals affected by autism. Promotes awareness and understanding of autism disorders. Aims to further the advancement of preventive studies, therapy and research of autism disorders.

5226 ■ Autism Society of Greater San Antonio (ASGSA)
6914 Forest Park
San Antonio, TX 78240
Contact: Theresa Diaz, Pres.
Ph: (210)227-1710
E-mail: autismtdiaz@hotmail.com
URL: http://www.autismsocietysa.org

Descr: Seeks to improve the lives of individuals affected by autism. Promotes awareness and understanding of autism disorders. Aims to further the advancement of preventive studies, therapy and research of autism disorders.

5227 ■ Autism Society of Southeast Texas (ASSET)
PO Box 2228
Nederland, TX 77627
Contact: Denise Lindsey, Pres.
Ph: (409)727-5100
E-mail: info@assetx.org
URL: http://www.assetx.org

Descr: Seeks to improve the lives of individuals affected by autism. Promotes awareness and understanding of autism disorders. Aims to further the advancement of preventive studies, therapy and research of autism disorders.

5228 ■ Bay Area Counseling Association (BACA)
PO Box 1675
Galveston, TX 77553
Contact: Veronica Soileau, Pres.-Elect
E-mail: drozdl@lpisd.org
URL: http://www.tamug.edu/baca

5229 ■ Border Counseling Association
PO Box 451433
Laredo, TX 78041
Contact: Rosina M. Silva

Ph: (210)744-3202
URL: http://www.txca.org/tca/BORDER_CA. asp?SnID=72739

5230 ■ Capital of Texas Counseling Association (CTCA)
West Ridge MS
9201 Scenic Bluff Dr.
Austin, TX 78733
Contact: Roy Larson, Pres.
E-mail: salazar@capitalcounselors.org

5231 ■ Common Cause Texas
603 W 13th St., Ste. 2D
Austin, TX 78701
Contact: Suzy Woodford, Exec. Dir.
Ph: (512)474-2374
Fax: (512)474-5077
E-mail: comcause@ccsi.com
URL: http://www.commoncause.org/site/pp. asp?c=dkLNK1MQlwG&b=1697201

Descr: Works as a nonpartisan citizens' lobby. Fights for open, honest, and accountable government.

5232 ■ Communities In Schools Dallas Region (CISDR)
8700 N Stemmons Fwy., Ste. 125
Dallas, TX 75247-3725
Contact: Sandra G. Chavarria, Pres./CEO
Ph: (214)827-0955
Fax: (214)827-2198
E-mail: sandyc@cisdallas.org
URL: http://www.cisdallas.org

Staff: 7. **Descr:** Addresses the growing number of high school dropouts in Dallas and surrounding areas. Brings community resources into schools to work in the interest of at-risk children in a coordinated, caring and cost-effective way. Operates in 49 schools in seven school districts in Dallas, Collin and Ellis counties. **Fnd:** 1985.

5233 ■ Communities In Schools of North Texas (CISNT)
PO Box 295543
Lewisville, TX 75029-5543
Contact: Lori Anthony, Pres.
Ph: (972)436-6377
Fax: (972)436-6770
E-mail: ghenderson@cisnt.org
URL: http://www.cisnt.org

Staff: 13. **Descr:** Provides stay in school and dropout prevention services to at-risk, and economically disadvantaged students in public schools. Seeks to help children stay in school, pass their classes, be promoted to the next grade level, and ultimately graduate from high school. **Fnd:** 1994. **Mem:** 13. **State Groups:** 2. **Local Groups:** 4.

5234 ■ Communities In Schools of Texas
1701 N Congress Ave.
Austin, TX 78701
Contact: Nellie Reyes, Dir.
Ph: (512)936-5437
E-mail: nreyes@tea.state.tx.us
URL: http://www.tea.state.tx.us/cis

Descr: Works to help kids succeed in school and prepare for life.

5235 ■ Dallas Branch of the International Dyslexia Association (DBIDA)
14070 Proton Rd., Ste. 100
Dallas, TX 75244
Contact: Anna Burton, Pres.
Ph: (972)233-9107
Fax: (972)490-4219
E-mail: adminassistant@dbida.org
URL: http://www.dbida.org

Descr: Promotes public awareness and understanding of dyslexia. Seeks to develop and implement specialized methods to improve the quality of life for people who have dyslexia. Provides services to those affected by dyslexia, attention disorders and other learning disabilities.

5236 ■ Dallas Metro Counseling Association
12830 Hillcrest Rd., Ste. 206
Dallas, TX 75230

Contact: Candace Hyman, Pres.
E-mail: leocan2@sbcglobal.net
URL: http://www.dallasmetroca.org

5237 ■ Fort Bend County Fire Fighter's Association
112 Jackson St.
Richmond, TX 77469
Contact: Mike Hafer
Ph: (281)232-6871
Fax: (281)232-3538
E-mail: mikehafer@richmondfd.com
Descr: Provides codes, standards, products, and services to concerned individuals for the safety and effective performance in the built environment.

5238 ■ Greater Houston Chapter Autism Society of America (GHC ASA)
PO Box 2871
Houston, TX 77252
Contact: Vicki Fleming, Pres.
Ph: (713)513-7575
E-mail: ghcasapres@aol.com
URL: http://www.houstonchapterasa.org
Descr: Seeks to improve the lives of individuals affected by autism. Promotes awareness and understanding of autism disorders. Aims to further the advancement of preventive studies, therapy and research of autism disorders.

5239 ■ Greenbelt Counseling Association
1347 FM 2650
Wichita Falls, TX 76310
Contact: M. Deanee Moran, Pres.
Ph: (940)642-7067
E-mail: amharach@yahoo.com
URL: http://www.txca.org/tca/GREENBELT_CA.asp?SnID=1017638501

5240 ■ Gulf Coast Association for the Education of Young Children (GCAEYC)
PO Box 1064
La Marque, TX 77568
Contact: Lauren Holmes, Pres.
Ph: (281)332-4954
Fax: (281)332-4958
E-mail: gcaeyc@gcaeyc.org
URL: http://www.gcaeyc.org
Descr: Serves and acts on behalf of the needs, rights and well-being of all young children with primary focus on the quality of educational and developmental services for all children. Seeks to improve professional practice and working conditions in early childhood education.

5241 ■ Heart of Texas Counseling Association (HOTXCA)
624 Crestwood Dr.
Hewitt, TX 76643
Contact: Caroll Bonner, Pres.-Elect
Ph: (254)751-4180
Free: 866-627-7748
E-mail: info@hotxca.org
URL: http://sacosta.home.mindspring.com/hotca/index.htm

5242 ■ Houston Area Association for the Education of Young Children (HAAEYC)
5959 W Loop S, Ste. 150
Bellaire, TX 77401-3004
Contact: Aaron Carrara, Pres.
Ph: (713)781-2155
Fax: (713)665-2155
E-mail: haaeyc@haaeyc.org
URL: http://www.haaeyc.org
Descr: Serves and acts on behalf of the needs, rights and well-being of all young children with primary focus on the quality of educational and developmental services for all children. Seeks to improve professional practice and working conditions in early childhood education.

5243 ■ Houston Association for the Education of Young Children (HAAEYC)
5959 W Loop S, Ste. 150
Bellaire, TX 77401
Contact: Teresa Biggar, Program Dir.

Ph: (713)781-2155
Fax: (713)665-2155
E-mail: haaeyc@haaeyc.org
URL: http://www.haaeyc.org
Descr: Early childhood educators. Strives to improve professional practice and build public awareness, understanding, and support for high-quality early childhood care and education. Holds training conferences for early childhood educators, sponsors an annual Week of the Young Child Celebration, publishes a quarterly magazine for members, and holds four Network Nights a year where members are invited to an evening presentation on a specific aspect of quality child care and management and an opportunity for professional networking. **Pub:** The Advocate (quarterly).

5244 ■ Houston Branch of the International Dyslexia Association (HBIDA)
PO Box 540504
Houston, TX 77254-0504
Contact: Jim Carter, Pres.
Ph: (832)282-7154
E-mail: info@houstonida.org
URL: http://www.houstonida.org
Descr: Promotes public awareness and understanding of dyslexia. Seeks to develop and implement specialized methods to improve the quality of life for people who have dyslexia. **Fnd:** 1978. **Pub:** Newsletter (semiannual).

5245 ■ Houston Counseling Association
PO Box 22069
Houston, TX 77227
Contact: Lauren Askew, Pres.
Ph: (713)721-1808
E-mail: laskew@houstoncounselor.org
URL: http://www.houstoncounselor.org

5246 ■ Learning Disabilities Association of Texas (LDAT)
1011 W 31st St.
Austin, TX 78705
Ph: (512)458-8234
Free: 800-604-7500
Fax: (512)458-3826
E-mail: contact@ldat.org
URL: http://www.ldat.org
Staff: 1. **Descr:** Seeks to improve the quality of life of parents of children and adult with learning disabilities and the professionals who work with them using referral and information dissemination. **Fnd:** 1963. **Mem:** 2000. **Local Groups:** 26. **Pub:** Texas Key (quarterly).

5247 ■ Midland Association for Retarded Citizens (MARC)
2701 N A St.
Midland, TX 79705
Contact: Robert K. Rose, Exec. Dir.
Ph: (432)498-8590
Fax: (432)682-2606
E-mail: brose@arcmidlandtx.org
Descr: Strives to foster the prevention of mental retardation and to advance, through all resources, the total well-being, dignity and rights of citizens who have mental retardation. **Fnd:** 1959.

5248 ■ National Stuttering Association, Dallas Chapter
5004 Andover Dr.
Plano, TX 75023
Contact: Russ Hicks, Dir. of Public Relations
Ph: (972)881-1451
E-mail: russhicks@mail.com
URL: http://www.geocities.com/dallasnsa
Descr: Serves as a self-help organization for people who stutter, parents of children who stutter and the professionals who serve them. Increases public awareness of stuttering. Provides support, education and empowerment to children and adults who stutter.

5249 ■ Northern Metro Counseling Association
8911 Talon Ct.
McKinney, TX 75070

Contact: Karen Meyers
Ph: (214)536-9129
E-mail: info@northernmetroca.org
URL: http://www.northernmetroca.org

5250 ■ Northwest Houston Chapter of the Autism Society of America (NHC-ASA)
PO Box 1363
Cypress, TX 77410
Contact: Michelle Guppy, Pres.
Ph: (281)686-0103
E-mail: northwesthoustonchapterasa@yahoo.com
URL: http://www.autism-society.org/site/Clubs?club_id=1400&pg=main
Descr: Seeks to improve the lives of individuals affected by autism. Promotes awareness and understanding of autism disorders. Aims to further the advancement of preventive studies, therapy and research of autism disorders.

5251 ■ Park Cities Learning Disabilities Association (PCLDA)
PO Box 12064
Dallas, TX 75225
Contact: Linda Pepe, Pres.
Ph: (214)691-6166
E-mail: president@pclda.org
URL: http://www.pclda.org
Fnd: 1975.

5252 ■ Piney Woods Counseling Association
604 Cynthia St.
Longview, TX 75605
Contact: Cathy Sullivan, Pres.
E-mail: pfanning@lisd.org
URL: http://www.piney-woods-counseling.org

5253 ■ SAFE Association - Alamo Chapter
77 AESG/PSK
7980 Lindberg Landing, Bldg. 578
Brooks City Base, TX 78235-5119
Contact: Norma L. Kreutzkamp
Ph: (210)536-4919
Fax: (210)536-4365
E-mail: norma.kreutzkamp@brooks.af.mil
Descr: Ensures personal safety and protection in land, sea, air and space environments. Fosters research and development in the fields of safety and survival. Provides a forum for the sharing of problems, ideas and information in the areas of safety, survival and crew systems.

5254 ■ Southwest Chapter Autism Society of America
1340 Murchison Dr.
El Paso, TX 79902
Contact: Lisa Mitchell, Pres.
Ph: (915)772-9100
Fax: (915)772-9105
E-mail: swasa@sbcglobal.net
URL: http://www.swasa.com
Descr: Seeks to improve the lives of individuals affected by autism. Promotes awareness and understanding of autism disorders. Aims to further the advancement of preventive studies, therapy and research of autism disorders.

5255 ■ Texas Association for Parents of Children with Visual Impairments (TAPVI)
1100 W 45th St.
Austin, TX 78756
Contact: Shawna Tausch, Pres.
Ph: (512)398-6454
Free: 866-998-2784
E-mail: info@tapvi.org
Descr: Represents individuals committed to providing support to the parents of children who have visual impairments. Promotes public understanding of the needs and rights of children who are visually impaired. **Fnd:** 2003.

5256 ■ Texas Council for Developmental Disabilities (TCDD)
6201 E Oltorf, Ste. 600
Austin, TX 78741-7509
Contact: Ms. Lucy Walker, Public Information Specialist

Ph: (512)437-5432
Free: 800-262-0334
Fax: (512)437-5434
E-mail: lucy.walker@tcdd.state.tx.us
URL: http://www.txddc.state.tx.us
Descr: Twenty-seven-member board appointed by the governor of TX that works to create change so people with disabilities are fully included in their communities and exercise control over their own lives. **Pub:** *FYI* (quarterly).

5257 ■ Texas Counseling Association (TCA)
1204 San Antonio, Ste. 201
Austin, TX 78701
Contact: Jan Friese, Exec. Dir.
Ph: (512)472-3403
Free: 800-580-8144
Fax: (512)472-3756
E-mail: jan@txca.org
URL: http://www.txca.org
Staff: 4. **Descr:** Educates others about, and advocates for the understanding and delivery of effective counseling to all Texans. **Fnd:** 1945. **Mem:** 5000. **Reg. Groups:** 4. **Local Groups:** 32. **Pub:** *Guidelines* (monthly); Journal (semiannual).

5258 ■ Texas Education Agency
William B. Travis Bldg.
1701 N. Congress Ave.
Austin, TX 78701-1494
Contact: Robert Scott, Commnr. of Educ.
Ph: (512)463-9734
Fax: (512)463-9838
E-mail: commissioner@tea.state.tx.us
URL: http://www.tea.state.tx.us/
Descr: Mission is to provide leadership, guidance, and resources to help schools meet the educational needs of all students.

5259 ■ Texas Gulf Coast Fire Prevention Association
1500 S Gordon St.
Alvin, TX 77511
Contact: Martin Vela
Ph: (281)388-4370
Descr: Provides codes, standards, products, and services to concerned individuals for the safety and effective performance in the built environment.

5260 ■ Texas PTA
408 W 11th St.
Austin, TX 78701-2113
Contact: Kyle Ward, Exec. Dir.
Ph: (512)476-6769
Free: 800-825-5782
E-mail: txpta@txpta.org
URL: http://www.txpta.org
Staff: 20. **Descr:** Parents, teachers and anyone interested in bettering the world for children. Strives to improve the health, education and welfare of all children. **Fnd:** 1909. **Mem:** 630000. **Pub:** *The Voice*.

Utah

5261 ■ American Medical Student Association, University of Utah School of Medicine
30 N 1900 E
Salt Lake City, UT 84132
Contact: Barbara Cahill MD, Assoc. Dean
Ph: (801)581-7201
URL: http://medicine.utah.edu
Descr: Promotes improvement in medical training and education. Advances the medicine profession. Contributes to the welfare of medical students, interns, residents and post-MD/DO trainees.

5262 ■ Arc of Utah
155 S 300 W, Ste. 201
Salt Lake City, UT 84101
Contact: Douglas L. Hathaway, Exec. Dir.
Ph: (801)364-5060
Free: 800-371-5060
Fax: (801)364-6030
E-mail: execdirector@arcutah.org
URL: http://www.arcutah.org

Staff: 4. **Descr:** Represents members' interests; legislative advocacy by volunteer; sponsors Prevention Info (FAS) activities. Holds seminars and workshops. Provides information and referral, grants, systems advocacy, and individual advocacy when needed. **Fnd:** 1952. **Mem:** 800. **State Groups:** 45. **Local Groups:** 7. **Pub:** *Horizons* (bimonthly).

5263 ■ Fire Marshals' Association of Utah
80 S 300 W
Provo, UT 84601
Contact: Jim Guynn
Ph: (801)404-6375
Fax: (801)852-6330
E-mail: jguynn@provo.utah.gov
Descr: Provides the highest quality codes, standards, products, and services for all concerned with the safety and performance of the built environment.

5264 ■ Learning Disabilities Association of Utah (LDAU)
PO Box 900726
Sandy, UT 84090
Contact: Gaylia Tanner, Conference Chair
Ph: (801)553-9156
E-mail: lda.utah@gmail.com
URL: http://www.ldau.org

5265 ■ Special Olympics Utah
243 E 400 S, Ste. 111
Salt Lake City, UT 84111
Contact: John J. Donnelly, Pres./CEO
Ph: (801)363-1111
Free: 800-722-1589
Fax: (801)363-1524
E-mail: information@sout.org
URL: http://www.sout.org
Staff: 8. **Descr:** Promotes physical fitness, sports training, and athletic competition for children and adults with mental retardation. Seeks to contribute to the physical, social, and psychological development of persons with mental retardation. Participants range in age from 8 years to adult and compete in track and field, swimming, gymnastics, bowling, ice skating, basketball, and other sports. **Fnd:** 1970. **Mem:** 6200. **Pub:** Newsletter (quarterly).

5266 ■ Utah Association for Career and Technical Education (UACTE)
Taylorsville High School
5225 S Redwood Rd.
Salt Lake City, UT 84123
Contact: Judy Whitaker, Exec. Sec.
Ph: (801)646-5460
Fax: (801)646-5467
E-mail: judy.whitaker@granite.k12.ut.us
URL: http://www.uacte.org
Descr: Supports vocational technical education that will assure students' successful roles in families, communities, and society.

5267 ■ Utah Branch of the International Dyslexia Association (UBIDA)
PO Box 783
American Fork, UT 84003
Contact: Mary Russon, Pres.
E-mail: maryrusson@utwire.net
URL: http://www.uread.org
Descr: Promotes public awareness and understanding of dyslexia. Seeks to develop and implement specialized methods to improve the quality of life for people who have dyslexia.

5268 ■ Utah Governor's Council for People with Disabilities
155 S 300 W, Ste. 100
Salt Lake City, UT 84101
Contact: Claire Mantonya MA, Exec. Dir.
Ph: (801)533-3965
Free: 800-333-8824
Fax: (801)533-3968
E-mail: clairemantony@utah.gov
URL: http://www.gcpd.org
Descr: Promotes consumer and family directed

services that increase self-determination in individuals with disabilities and their families.

5269 ■ Utah State Office of Education
250 E. 500 S.
PO Box 144200
Salt Lake City, UT 84114-4200
Contact: Twila B. Affleck, Sec. of the Board
Ph: (801)538-7500
Fax: (801)538-7521
E-mail: twila.affleck@schools.utah.gov
URL: http://www.schools.utah.gov/

5270 ■ Washington County Arc
344 W Tabernacle, Ste. F
St. George, UT 84770
Contact: Terry Hawks, Exec. Dir.
Ph: (435)628-0393
E-mail: ednahenke2@gmail.com
URL: http://www.thearc.org/NetCommunity/Page.aspx?&pid=223&srcid=1315&chid=646
Descr: Advocates for people with cognitive disabilities. Works to alleviate the waiting list in Utah for people seeking services with the state and federal government. Seeks to educate families and community members on needs and opportunities for people with intellectual disabilities. **Mem:** 100.

Vermont

5271 ■ American Medical Student Association, University of Vermont College of Medicine
89 Beaumont Ave.
E-126 Given Bldg.
Burlington, VT 05405
Ph: (802)656-2156
Fax: (802)656-8577
URL: http://med.uvm.edu/HP-DEPT.asp?SiteAreaID=1283
Descr: Promotes improvement in medical training and education. Advances the medicine profession. Contributes to the welfare of medical students, interns, residents and post-MD/DO trainees.

5272 ■ Autism Society of Vermont (ASVT)
PO Box 978
White River Junction, VT 05001
Contact: Jenn Thody
Ph: (802)457-3764
Free: 800-559-7398
URL: http://www.autism-info.org
Descr: Seeks to improve the lives of individuals affected by autism. Promotes awareness and understanding of autism disorders. Aims to further the advancement of preventive studies, therapy and research of autism disorders.

5273 ■ Learning Disabilities Association of Vermont
PO Box 183
Grafton, VT 05146
Contact: Diana Lawrence
Ph: (802)869-6298
E-mail: greenmountaingardner@hotmail.com

5274 ■ Special Olympics Vermont (SOVT)
368 Ave. D, Ste. 30
Williston, VT 05495
Contact: William Porreca, Pres./CEO
Ph: (802)863-5222
Free: 800-639-1603
Fax: (802)863-3911
E-mail: wporreca@vtso.org
URL: http://www.vtso.org
Descr: Promotes physical fitness, sports training, and athletic competition for children and adults with mental retardation. Seeks to contribute to the physical, social, and psychological development of persons with mental retardation. Participants range in age from 8 years to adult and compete in track

and field, swimming, gymnastics, bowling, ice skating, basketball, and other sports.

5275 ■ Vermont Association for Career and Technical Education
Burlington Technical Ctr.
52 Institute Rd.
Burlington, VT 05401
Contact: Jane Donahue-Holt, Pres.
Ph: (802)864-8429
Fax: (802)864-8521
E-mail: jdonahue@bsdvt.org
Descr: Represents teachers, supervisors, administrators, and others interested in the development and improvement of vocational, technical, and practical arts education. Supports and promotes vocational education.

5276 ■ Vermont Association for the Education of Young Children (VAEYC)
PO Box 464
Waterbury, VT 05676-0464
Contact: Melissa Riegel-Garrett, Exec. Dir.
Ph: (802)244-6282
E-mail: inforequest@vaeyc.org
URL: http://www.vaeyc.org
Descr: Teachers and directors of preschool and primary schools, kindergartens, child care centers, cooperatives, church schools, and groups having similar programs for young children; early childhood education and child development educators, trainers, and researchers. Open to all individuals interested in serving and acting on behalf of the needs and rights of young children, with primary focus on the provision of educational services and resources.

5277 ■ Vermont Department of Education
120 State St.
Montpelier, VT 05620-2501
Contact: Richard Cate, Commnr.
Ph: (802)828-3135
Fax: (802)828-3140
E-mail: doe-edinfo@state.vt.us
URL: http://www.state.vt.us/educ/
Descr: Provides leadership and support to help all Vermont students achieve excellence.

5278 ■ Vermont Developmental Disabilities Council (VTDDC)
103 S Main St.
Waterbury, VT 05671-0206
Contact: Karen Schwartz, Exec. Dir.
Ph: (802)241-2613
Fax: (802)241-2989
E-mail: karen.schwartz@ahs.state.vt.us
Descr: Works to assure that all people with developmental disabilities receive the opportunities, assistance, and services necessary to live independently and productively in integrated and inclusive community settings.

5279 ■ Vermont National Education Association
10 Wheelock St.
Montpelier, VT 05602-3737
Contact: Joel D. Cook, Exec. Dir.
Ph: (802)223-6375
Free: 800-649-6375
Fax: (802)223-1253
E-mail: vtnea@together.net
URL: http://www.vtnea.org
Descr: Strives to support the work of educators, encourage the contribution of parents, and nurture the learning of children and young adults.

5280 ■ Vermont Out of School Time Network
PO Box 627
Montpelier, VT 05601
Contact: Barbara Christie-Garvin, Coor.
Ph: (802)229-9151
Fax: (802)229-2508
E-mail: info@voost.org
URL: http://www.voost.org

5281 ■ VSA arts of Vermont (VSAVT)
The Woolen Mill
20 Canal St., Ste. 7
Winooski, VT 05404
Contact: Judith Chalmer, Exec. Dir.
Ph: (802)655-7772
E-mail: info@vsavt.org
URL: http://www.vsavt.org
Fnd: 1986.

Virginia

5282 ■ American Association of University Women, Roanoke Valley Branch
6734 Peach Tree Cir.
Roanoke, VA 24018
Contact: Kathryn N. Koehler, Co-Pres.
Ph: (540)772-4264
E-mail: pamkc2@cox.net
URL: http://members.cox.net/aauwva/raauw.htm
Descr: Advances equity for women and girls through advocacy, education, and research. Provides funds and a support system for women seeking judicial redress for sex discrimination in higher education. **Fnd:** 1923.

5283 ■ American Association of University Women, Smith Mountain Branch
1300 Pats Dr.
Moneta, VA 24121
Contact: Josselyn Gregory, Pres.
Ph: (540)297-8970
E-mail: jsva03@aol.com
URL: http://www.aauwofva.org/branches/smithmountain.htm
Descr: Advances equity for women and girls through advocacy, education, and research. Provides funds and a support system for women seeking judicial redress for sex discrimination in higher education.

5284 ■ American Association of University Women of Virginia
4201 Wakerfield Ct.
Virginia Beach, VA 23455
Contact: Rosemary Plum, Pres.
Ph: (757)460-8369
E-mail: rplum@cox.net
URL: http://www.aauwofva.org
Descr: Advances equity for women and girls through advocacy, education, and research. Provides funds and a support system for women seeking judicial redress for sex discrimination in higher education.

5285 ■ American Medical Student Association, Eastern Virginia Medical School
PO Box 1980
Norfolk, VA 23501
Contact: Harry T. Lester, Pres.
Ph: (757)446-5600
URL: http://www.evms.edu
Descr: Promotes improvement in medical training and education. Advances the medicine profession. Contributes to the welfare of medical students, interns, residents and post-MD/DO trainees.

5286 ■ American Medical Student Association, University of Virginia School of Medicine
PO Box 800793
Charlottesville, VA 22908
Contact: Sharon L. Hostler MD, VP
Ph: (434)924-5118
E-mail: slh2m@virginia.edu
URL: http://www.healthsystem.virginia.edu/internet/som/home.cfm
Descr: Promotes improvement in medical training and education. Advances the medicine profession. Contributes to the welfare of medical students, interns, residents and post-MD/DO trainees.

5287 ■ American Medical Student Association, Virginia Commonwealth University School of Medicine
PO Box 980565
Richmond, VA 23298
Ph: (804)828-9629
E-mail: somume@vcu.edu
URL: http://www.medschool.vcu.edu
Descr: Promotes improvement in medical training and education. Advances the medicine profession.

Contributes to the welfare of medical students, interns, residents and post-MD/DO trainees.

5288 ■ Arc-Hanover County
PO Box 91
Ashland, VA 23005
Contact: Lucy Cantrell, Dir.
Ph: (804)798-2400
Fax: (804)798-0310
E-mail: info@hanoverarc.org
URL: http://www.hanoverarc.com
Descr: Parents, professional workers, and others interested in individuals with mental retardation. Works to promote services, research, public understanding, and legislation for people with mental retardation and their families.

5289 ■ Arc of Northern Shenandoah Valley (Arc/NSV)
119 Youth Development Ct.
Winchester, VA 22602
Ph: (540)665-0461
Staff: 2. **Descr:** Parents, professional workers, and others interested in individuals with mental retardation. Works to promote services, research, public understanding, and legislation for people with mental retardation and their families. **Mem:** 128. **Pub:** *The ArcNSV's News and Views.*

5290 ■ Arc of Rappahannock
1640 Lafayette Blvd., No. B
Fredericksburg, VA 22401-7065
Ph: (540)899-3789
Fax: (540)370-0179
E-mail: exec@arcr.vacoxmail.com
URL: http://arc.communitypoint.org
Descr: Parents, professional workers, and others interested in individuals with intellectual and developmental disabilities. Works to promote services, research, public understanding, and legislation for people with intellectual/developmental disabilities and their families.

5291 ■ Arc of The Piedmont
509 Park St.
Charlottesville, VA 22902
Contact: T. Lee Covington, Exec. Dir.
Ph: (434)977-4002
Free: 800-732-9507
Fax: (434)977-7864
E-mail: mail@thearcofthepiedmont.org
URL: http://www.thearcofthepiedmont.org
Descr: Parents, professional workers, and others interested in individuals with mental retardation. Works to promote services, research, public understanding, and legislation for people with mental retardation and their families. **Fnd:** 1954.

5292 ■ Arc of Virginia
2025 E Main St., Ste. 107
Richmond, VA 23223
Contact: Jamie Trosclair, Exec. Dir.
Ph: (804)649-8481
Fax: (804)649-3585
E-mail: jtrosclair@arcofva.org
URL: http://www.arcofva.org
Staff: 2. **Descr:** Works to promote services, research, public understanding, and legislation for people with mental retardation and their families.

5293 ■ Association on Higher Education and Disability in Virginia
J. Sargeant Reynolds Community College
Downtown Campus, Rm. 331
Richmond, VA 23285
Contact: Deborah Wilkerson, Pres.
E-mail: dwilkerson@jsr.vccs.edu
URL: http://www.aheadinva.org
Descr: Represents individuals interested in promoting the equal rights and opportunities of disabled postsecondary students, staff, faculty and graduates. Provides educational and professional development opportunities for persons with disabilities in postsec-

ondary education. Encourages and supports legislation for the benefit of disabled students.

5294 ■ Autism Society of America - Central Virginia Chapter
PO Box 29364
Richmond, VA 23242
Contact: Jennifer Vest, Co-Pres.
Ph: (804)257-0192
Fax: (804)290-0286
E-mail: asacv@aol.com
URL: http://www.asacv.org
Descr: Seeks to improve the lives of individuals affected by autism. Promotes awareness and understanding of autism disorders. Aims to further the advancement of preventive studies, therapy and research of autism disorders.

5295 ■ Autism Society of America - Northern Virginia Chapter (ASA-NV)
98 N Washington St.
Falls Church, VA 22046
Contact: Kymberly S. DeLoatche, Exec. Dir.
Ph: (703)495-8444
Fax: (703)532-3214
E-mail: asanv.ed@gmail.com
URL: http://www.autism-society.org/site/Clubs?club_id=1200&pg=main
Descr: Seeks to improve the lives of individuals affected by autism. Promotes awareness and understanding of autism disorders. Aims to further the advancement of preventive studies, therapy and research of autism disorders.

5296 ■ Learning Disabilities Association of Virginia (LDAV)
Randolph Towers, No. 505
4100 9th St. N
Arlington, VA 22203
Contact: Sharon Eak
Ph: (540)775-7947
E-mail: info@ldavirginia.org
URL: http://www.ldavirginia.org

5297 ■ Peninsula Autism Society
166 Devon Rd.
Williamsburg, VA 23188
Contact: Cynthia Favret
Ph: (757)565-6367
E-mail: va-peninsula@autismsocietyofamerica.org
Descr: Seeks to improve the lives of individuals affected by autism. Promotes awareness and understanding of autism disorders. Aims to further the advancement of preventive studies, therapy and research of autism disorders.

5298 ■ Recording for the Blind and Dyslexic Regional Unit of the Virginias and Carolinas
3500 Remson Ct.
Charlottesville, VA 22901
Contact: Christine Eure, Exec.Dir.
Ph: (434)293-4797
Free: 866-887-7323
Fax: (434)293-2153
E-mail: ceure@rfbdvanc.org
URL: http://www.rfbd.org/RUVC/index.htm
Descr: Serves individuals who cannot effectively read standard print because of visual impairment, dyslexia, or other physical disabilities. Creates educational opportunities for students with print disabilities through educational and outreach services. Provides and promotes the effective use of accessible educational materials.

5299 ■ Special Olympics Virginia (SOVA)
3212 Skipwith Rd., Ste. 100
Richmond, VA 23294
Contact: Rick Jeffrey, Pres.
Ph: (804)346-5544
Fax: (804)346-9633
E-mail: info@specialolympicsva.org
URL: http://www.specialolympicsva.org
Staff: 20. **Descr:** Works to provide sports training, education and athletic competition for individuals with mental retardation. **Fnd:** 1975. **Mem:** 13000.

Reg. Groups: 5. Local Groups: 24. Pub: *The Olympics Spirit* (annual).

5300 ■ Tidewater Chapter of the Autism Society of America (TASA)
6300 E Virginia Beach Blvd.
Norfolk, VA 23502
Contact: JoAnna Bryant, Pres.
Ph: (757)461-4474
E-mail: va-tidewater@autismsocietyofamerica.org
URL: http://www.tidewaterasa.org
Descr: Seeks to improve the lives of individuals affected by autism. Promotes awareness and understanding of autism disorders. Aims to further the advancement of preventive studies, therapy and research of autism disorders.

5301 ■ Virginia Association for Career and Technical Education (VACTE)
8020 River Stone Dr.
Fredericksburg, VA 22407
Contact: Dr. Dennis D. Parsons, Pres.
Ph: (540)834-2500
Fax: (540)834-2556
E-mail: dparsons@scs.k12.va.us
URL: http://www.vacte.net
Descr: Supports vocational technical education that will assure students' successful roles in families, communities, and society.

5302 ■ Virginia Association of Educational Opportunity Program Personnel (VAEOPP)
122 Hillcrest Hall, Rm. 0146
Blacksburg, VA 24061
Contact: Mr. Thomas Wilson, Pres.
Ph: (540)231-6911
Fax: (540)231-1266
E-mail: tgwilson@vt.edu
URL: http://www.vaeopp.org
Descr: Works to advance educational opportunities for disadvantaged students in colleges and universities. Provides professional development and continuing education. Monitors federal legislation designed to serve disadvantaged students.

5303 ■ Virginia Branch of International Dyslexia Association (VBIDA)
PO Box 17605
Richmond, VA 23226
Contact: Debra Farrar, Pres.
Fax: (804)272-0277
E-mail: info@vbida.org
URL: http://www.vbida.org
Descr: Dyslexics and their families; related professionals. Promotes public awareness and understanding of dyslexia and the development of effective teaching approaches; encourages research. Sponsors workshops, annual conferences, and teacher education programs. **Fnd:** 1976. **Mem:** 400. **Reg. Groups:** 4. **State Groups:** 1. **Pub:** *The Virginia Branch* (quarterly).

5304 ■ Virginia Department of Education
PO Box 2120
James Monroe Bldg.
101 N. 14th St.
Richmond, VA 23218
Contact: Dr. Patricia I. Wright, Superintendent
Ph: (804)225-2020
Free: 800-292-3820
Fax: (804)371-2455
E-mail: policy@doe.virginia.gov
URL: http://www.doe.virginia.gov/

5305 ■ Virginia Education Association (VEA)
116 S 3rd St.
Richmond, VA 23219
Contact: Kitty Boitnott, Pres.
Ph: (804)648-5801
Free: 800-552-9554
Fax: (804)775-8379
E-mail: jredford@veanea.org
URL: http://veaweteach.org
Descr: Labor union for teachers and educational personnel. Represents members' interests through lobbying. Offers workshops and seminars. **Fnd:**

1863. **Mem:** 56000. **Pub:** *The VEA News*; *Virginia Journal of Education* (10/year).

5306 ■ Virginia Fire Prevention Association (VFPA)
PO Box 7745
Woodbridge, VA 22195
Contact: Frank Teevan, Sec.-Treas.
Ph: (703)257-8455
E-mail: fteevan@ci.manassas.va.us
URL: http://www.vfpa.org
Descr: Provides the highest quality codes, standards, products, and services for all concerned with the safety and performance of the built environment.

Washington

5307 ■ American Association of University Women, Port Townsend Branch
PO Box 934
Port Townsend, WA 98368
Contact: Judy Blair, Co-Pres.
E-mail: porttownsend@aauw-wa.org
URL: http://www.aauwpt.org
Descr: Advances equity for women and girls through advocacy, education, and research. Provides funds and a support system for women seeking judicial redress for sex discrimination in higher education.

5308 ■ American Association of University Women, Tacoma Branch
PO Box 7648
Tacoma, WA 98406
Contact: Mary Trodden, Pres.
E-mail: tacomaaauw@aol.com
URL: http://www.aauw-tacoma.org
Descr: Advances equity for women and girls through advocacy, education, and research. Provides funds and a support system for women seeking judicial redress for sex discrimination in higher education.

5309 ■ American Association of University Women, Wenatchee Branch
127 S Mission St.
Wenatchee, WA 98801
Contact: Constance Dunkenberger, Pres.
E-mail: president@aauw-wa.org
URL: http://www.aauwmi.org
Descr: Advances equity for women and girls through advocacy, education, and research. Provides funds and a support system for women seeking judicial redress for sex discrimination in higher education.

5310 ■ American Medical Student Association, University of Washington School of Medicine
Box 356340
Seattle, WA 98195-6340
Contact: Dr. Carol F. MacLaren PhD, Assoc. Dean
Ph: (206)543-5560
Fax: (206)616-3341
URL: http://uwmedicine.washington.edu/Facilities/UWSchoolOfMedicine
Descr: Promotes improvement in medical training and education. Advances the medicine profession. Contributes to the welfare of medical students, interns, residents and post-MD/DO trainees.

5311 ■ Arc of Clark County
PO Box 2608
Vancouver, WA 98668-2608
Contact: Kay Parks, Pres.
Ph: (360)254-1562
Fax: (360)896-7382
URL: http://www.arcofclarkcounty.org
Descr: Works to promote services, research, public understanding, and legislation for people with mental retardation and their families.

5312 ■ Arc of Cowlitz Valley
1410 8th Ave., Rm. 15
Longview, WA 98632
Contact: Janice Hillman, Exec. Dir.
Ph: (360)425-5494
Fax: (360)425-3264

E-mail: mail@cowlitzarc.org

URL: http://www.cowlitzarc.org

Staff: 3. **Descr:** Guardianship services, surrogate parents and others interested in individuals with mental retardation. Works to promote services, research, public understanding, and legislation for people with mental retardation and their families. **Fnd:** 1953.

5313 ■ Arc of King County

233 6th Ave. N

Seattle, WA 98109

Contact: Sylvia Fuerstenberg, Exec. Dir.

Ph: (206)364-6337

Free: 877-964-0600

Fax: (206)364-8140

E-mail: info@arcofkingcounty.org

URL: http://www.arcofkingcounty.org

Descr: Advocates to support individuals with developmental disabilities such as mental retardation, cerebral palsy, epilepsy, autism and other similar cases. **Fnd:** 1936. **Pub:** *The Advocate* (monthly).

5314 ■ Arc of Kitsap and Jefferson Counties

3243 N Perry Ave.

Bremerton, WA 98310

Contact: Nina Dunning, Exec. Dir.

Ph: (360)377-3473

Fax: (360)792-8670

E-mail: nina@arckj.org

URL: http://www.arckj.org

Descr: Parents, professional workers, and others interested in individuals with mental retardation. Works to promote services, research, public understanding, and legislation for people with mental retardation and their families.

5315 ■ Arc of Snohomish County

2500 Hewitt Ave.

Everett, WA 98206

Ph: (425)258-2459

Descr: Parents, professional workers, and others interested in individuals with mental retardation. Works to promote services, research, public understanding, and legislation for people with mental retardation and their families.

5316 ■ Arc of Spokane

127 W Boone Ave.

Spokane, WA 99201

Contact: Greg Falk, Exec. Dir.

Ph: (509)328-6326

Fax: (509)328-6342

E-mail: gfalk@arc-spokane.org

URL: http://www.arc-spokane.org

Descr: Parents, professional workers, and others interested in individuals with mental retardation. Works to promote services, research, public understanding, and legislation for people with mental retardation and their families. **Fnd:** 1950. **Pub:** *Advocacy and Family Support* (bimonthly); *The ArcLite* (quarterly).

5317 ■ Arc of Washington State

2638 State Ave. NE

Olympia, WA 98506

Contact: Sue Elliot, Exec. Dir.

Ph: (360)357-5596

Free: 888-754-8798

Fax: (360)357-3279

E-mail: info@arcwa.org

URL: http://www.arcwa.org

Descr: Strives to promote the education, health, self-sufficiency, self-advocacy, inclusion and choices of individuals with developmental disabilities and their families. **Fnd:** 1936. **Local Groups:** 11. **Pub:** *The Arc Insider* (periodic); *The Arc News.*

5318 ■ Autism Society of Washington (ASW)

1101 Eastside St., Ste. B

Olympia, WA 98501

Contact: Patty Gee, Pres./Exec. Dir.

Free: 888-279-4968

E-mail: info@autismsocietyofwa.org

URL: http://www.autismsocietyofwa.org

Descr: Seeks to improve the lives of individuals af-

fected by autism. Promotes awareness and understanding of autism disorders. Aims to further the advancement of preventive studies, therapy and research of autism disorders.

5319 ■ Autism Society of Washington - Southwest Chapter (ASW-SWC)

PO Box 873573

Vancouver, WA 98687

Contact: Victoria Fitzsimmons

Ph: (360)980-4019

E-mail: aswswc@autismsocietyofwa.org

URL: http://www.autismsocietyofwa.org/ASWSWC. html

Descr: Seeks to improve the lives of individuals affected by autism. Promotes awareness and understanding of autism disorders. Aims to further the advancement of preventive studies, therapy and research of autism disorders.

5320 ■ Autism Society of Washington - Spokane Chapter (ASW-SC)

PO Box 8414

Spokane, WA 99203

Contact: Julie Parry, Pres.

Ph: (509)456-6204

E-mail: spokane@autismsocietyofwa.org

URL: http://www.autismsocietyofwa.org/ASW-SC. html

Descr: Seeks to improve the lives of individuals affected by autism. Promotes awareness and understanding of autism disorders. Aims to further the advancement of preventive studies, therapy and research of autism disorders.

5321 ■ Communities In Schools of Washington State

1904 Third Ave., Ste. 435

Seattle, WA 98101

Contact: Llynn Coriano, CEO

Ph: (206)461-8313

Fax: (206)461-8521

E-mail: info@ciswa.org

URL: http://www.ciswa.org

Descr: Strives to champion the connection of needed community resources with schools to help young people learn, stay in school, and prepare for life.

5322 ■ Learning Disabilities Association of Washington (LDA-WA)

16315 NE 87th St., No. B-4

Redmond, WA 98052

Contact: Cyd Imel, Exec. Dir.

Ph: (425)882-0820

Free: 800-536-2343

Fax: (425)861-4642

E-mail: cimel@ldawa.org

URL: http://www.ldawa.org

Descr: Provides services and support to maximize the quality of life for individuals and families affected by learning and attention disabilities. **Fnd:** 1965. **Mem:** 250. **Pub:** *The Missing Piece* (quarterly).

5323 ■ Pierce County Association for the Education of Young Children (PCAEYC)

PO Box 110607

Tacoma, WA 98411-0607

Contact: Wendy Newby, Pres.

Ph: (253)680-7320

E-mail: wnewby@bates.ctc.edu

URL: http://www.pcaeyc.org

Descr: Serves and acts on behalf of the needs, rights and well-being of all young children with primary focus on the quality of educational and developmental services for all children. Seeks to improve professional practice and working conditions in early childhood education.

5324 ■ PROVAIL - Life Opportunities for People with Disabilities

3670 Stone Way N

Seattle, WA 98103-8004

Contact: Mike Hatzenbeler, CEO

Ph: (206)363-7303

Free: 888-810-0745

Fax: (206)361-5628

E-mail: mikeh@provail.org

URL: http://www.provail.org

Descr: Aids persons with cerebral palsy and other disabilities, and their families. Prevents cerebral palsy, minimizes its effects, and improves the quality of life for persons with cerebral palsy and other disabilities, and their families. **Fnd:** 1942. **Pub:** *Connections* (quarterly).

5325 ■ School's Out Washington (SOWA)

801 23rd Ave. S

Seattle, WA 98144

Ph: (206)323-2396

Free: 888-419-9300

Fax: (206)323-7997

URL: http://schoolsoutwashington.org

5326 ■ Special Olympics, Washington (SOWA)

2150 N 107th Ave., Ste. 220

Seattle, WA 98133

Contact: Mark Shuken, Chm.

Ph: (206)362-4949

Free: 800-752-7559

Fax: (206)361-8158

URL: http://www.sowa.org

Staff: 25. **Descr:** Provides year-round sports training and athletic competition in a variety of Olympic-type sports for children and adults with intellectual disabilities, giving them continuing opportunities to develop physical fitness, demonstrate courage, experience joy and participate in the sharing of gifts, skills and friendship with their families, other Special Olympics athletes, and the community. **Fnd:** 1968. **Mem:** 8800. **State Groups:** 1.

5327 ■ Washington Association for Career and Technical Education (WA-ACTE)

PO Box 315

Olympia, WA 98507-0315

Contact: Kathleen Lopp, Exec. Dir.

Ph: (360)786-9286

Fax: (360)357-1491

E-mail: wa-acte@wa-acte.org

URL: http://www.wa-acte.org

Staff: 3. **Descr:** Teachers, administrators, career guidance specialists and counselors, university professors, state/local employees, and students at middle, secondary, and postsecondary educational levels. Supports vocational technical education that will assure students' successful roles in families, communities, and society. Provides a strong unified voice in support of legislation impact vocational technical education. Promotes mutually beneficial relationships with business, labor and community-based organizations. Provides assistance in marketing vocational technical education programs to students, families, educators, legislators, and the community. Assists members by providing professional development activities of members, students, and others who support the mission of vocational technical education. **Fnd:** 1946. **Mem:** 1800. **Reg. Groups:** 5. **State Groups:** 50. **Local Groups:** 11. **Pub:** *Do You Know the Players?* (annual); *National Executive Directors Association*; *Visions* (quarterly).

5328 ■ Washington Association for the Education of Young Children (WAEYC)

841 N Central Ave., Ste. 206

Kent, WA 98032

Contact: Agda Burchard, Exec. Dir.

Ph: (253)854-2565

Free: 800-727-3107

Fax: (253)813-3646

E-mail: waeyc@waeyc.org

URL: http://www.waeyc.org

Descr: Professionals working with children ages birth to 12 and their families, teachers and directors of preschool and primary schools, kindergartens, child care centers, cooperatives, church schools, and groups having similar programs for young children; early childhood education and child development educators, trainers, and researchers. Open to all individuals interested in serving and acting on behalf of the needs and rights of all young children, with primary focus on the provision of educational services and resources. **Fnd:** 1976. **Mem:** 2000. **Lo-**

cal Groups: 20. **Pub:** *Legislative Update* (weekly); *WAEYC News* (quarterly).

5329 ■ Washington Office of Superintendent of Public Instruction
Old Capitol Bldg.
600 S. Washington St., SE
PO Box 47200
Olympia, WA 98504-7200
Contact: Dr. Terry Bergeson, Superintendent
Ph: (360)725-6000
Fax: (360)753-6712
E-mail: webmaster@k12.wa.us
URL: http://www.k12.wa.us/

Descr: Leads, supports, and oversees K-12 education, ensuring the success of all students.

5330 ■ Washington State Association of Fire Marshals (WSAFM)
PO Box 2911
Olympia, WA 98507
Contact: Greg Rogers, Pres.
Ph: (360)876-8600
Fax: (360)586-5868
E-mail: grogers@skfr.org
URL: http://www.wsafm.com

Descr: Provides the highest quality codes, standards, products, and services for all concerned with the safety and performance of the built environment.

5331 ■ Washington State Branch of the International Dyslexia Association (WABIDA)
PO Box 1247
Mercer Island, WA 98040
Contact: Bonnie Meyer, Pres.
Ph: (206)382-1020
E-mail: info@wabida.org
URL: http://www.wabida.org

Descr: Promotes public awareness and understanding of dyslexia. Seeks to develop and implement specialized methods to improve the quality of life for people who have dyslexia. **Pub:** *The Communicator* (semiannual).

5332 ■ Washington State Developmental Disabilities Council (DDC)
PO Box 48314
2600 Martin Way, Ste. F
Olympia, WA 98504-8314
Contact: Edward M. Holen, Exec. Dir.
Ph: (360)586-3560
Free: 800-634-4473
Fax: (360)586-2424
E-mail: edh@cted.wa.gov
URL: http://www.ddc.wa.gov

Descr: Assures that individuals with developmental disabilities and their families have access to culturally competent, consumer/family-centered supports and other assistance that promotes independence, productivity, integration and inclusion into the community of their choice; and to promote this vision in the public policy and planning arena through system change, community capacity building and advocacy at the local, state and national level. **Mem:** 33.

5333 ■ Washington State PTA (WSPTA)
2003 65th Ave. W
Tacoma, WA 98466-6215
Contact: Laura Bay, Pres.
Ph: (253)565-2153
Free: 800-562-3804
Fax: (253)565-7753
E-mail: wapta@wastatepta.org
URL: http://www.wastatepta.org

Staff: 8. **Descr:** Parents, teachers, students, principals, administrators, and others interested in uniting the forces of home, school, and community on behalf of children and youth. Emphasis is placed on building a better world for all children. **Fnd:** 1905. **Mem:** 146000. **Reg. Groups:** 13. **Pub:** *The Child Advocate*; *Key Communicator*; *Money Matters*.

West Virginia

5334 ■ American Medical Student Association, Marshall University Joan C Edwards School of Medicine
1600 Medical Center Dr.
Huntington, WV 25701
Contact: Michael C. Binder, Pres.
E-mail: binder3@marshall.edu
URL: http://musom.marshall.edu/index2.asp?x=1024&y=768

Descr: Promotes improvement in medical training and education. Advances the medicine profession. Contributes to the welfare of medical students, interns, residents and post-MD/DO trainees.

5335 ■ American Medical Student Association, West Virginia University School of Medicine
PO Box 9100
Morgantown, WV 26506
Contact: Carolyn Wilhelm
E-mail: cwilhel1@mix.wvu.edu
URL: http://www.hsc.wvu.edu/som/index.asp

Descr: Promotes improvement in medical training and education. Advances the medicine profession. Contributes to the welfare of medical students, interns, residents and post-MD/DO trainees.

5336 ■ Arc of Mid Ohio Valley
521 Market St., No. 17
Parkersburg, WV 26101
Contact: Christina Smith, Exec. Dir.
Ph: (304)422-3151
Fax: (304)865-2072
E-mail: info@arcwd.org
URL: http://www.arcwd.org

Descr: Parents, professional workers, and others interested in individuals with mental retardation. Works to promote services, research, public understanding, and legislation for people with mental retardation and their families.

5337 ■ Autism Society of America - Hancock County West Virginia Chapter
277 Bennett Dr.
Weirton, WV 26062
Contact: Karen Randolph, Pres.
Ph: (304)564-4067
Fax: (304)748-0248
E-mail: jfair3@comcast.net

Descr: Seeks to improve the lives of individuals affected by autism. Promotes awareness and understanding of autism disorders. Aims to further the advancement of preventive studies, therapy and research of autism disorders.

5338 ■ Autism Society of America - Huntington Area Chapter
PO Box 1296
Huntington, WV 25714
Contact: Elaine Harvey
Ph: (304)736-1479
Fax: (304)736-5949
E-mail: wv-huntington@autismsocietyofamerica.org

Descr: Seeks to improve the lives of individuals affected by autism. Promotes awareness and understanding of autism disorders. Aims to further the advancement of preventive studies, therapy and research of autism disorders.

5339 ■ Autism Society of America - South Central West Virginia Chapter
706 Kanawha Ave. S
Nitro, WV 25143
Contact: Ginger McAllister, Pres.
Ph: (304)610-5203
Fax: (304)727-9543
E-mail: glee1989@suddenlink.net

Descr: Seeks to improve the lives of individuals affected by autism. Promotes awareness and understanding of autism disorders. Aims to further the

advancement of preventive studies, therapy and research of autism disorders.

5340 ■ Autism Society of West Virginia
PO Box 1024
Wayne, WV 25570
Contact: Kim Farley, Pres.
Ph: (304)272-9834
E-mail: wv-westvirginia@autismsocietyofamerica.org

Descr: Seeks to improve the lives of individuals affected by autism. Promotes awareness and understanding of autism disorders. Aims to further the advancement of preventive studies, therapy and research of autism disorders.

5341 ■ Common Cause West Virginia
1926 Big Sandy Rd.
Left Hand, WV 25251
Contact: Norie Huddle, Chair
Free: 877-321-7626
E-mail: commoncausewv@frontiernet.net

Descr: Aims to fight for open, honest, and accountable government at the national, state, and local levels. Gathers and disseminates information on the effects of money in politics; lobbies for political finance and other campaign reforms.

5342 ■ Marshall-Wetzel-Tyler Society
701 N Main St.
New Martinsville, WV 26155-1414
Contact: Dr. David F. Bridgeman
Ph: (304)455-2800
URL: http://www.wvdental.org

Descr: Represents professional association of dentists committed to the public's oral health, ethics, science and professional advancement. Promotes the art and science of dentistry through advocacy, education, research and the development of standards.

5343 ■ West Virginia Congress of Parents and Teachers (WV PTA)
PO Box 3557
Parkersburg, WV 26103
Contact: Linda Craig, Pres.
Ph: (304)420-9576
Fax: (304)420-9577
E-mail: wv_office@pta.org
URL: http://www.wvpta.net

Descr: Parents, teachers, students, principals, administrators, and others interested in uniting the forces of home, school, and community on behalf of children and youth enrolled in the school district. **Fnd:** 1923. **Mem:** 17000. **Reg. Groups:** 8. **State Groups:** 1. **Local Groups:** 125. **Pub:** *West Virginia Parent-Teacher Bulletin* (monthly).

5344 ■ West Virginia Department of Education
Bldg. 6, Rm. 358
1900 Kanawha Blvd. E.
Charleston, WV 25305-0330
Contact: Dr. Steven Paine, Superintendent
Ph: (304)558-2681
Fax: (304)558-0048
E-mail: dvermill@access.k12.wv.us
URL: http://wvde.state.wv.us/

Descr: Establishes policies and rules to assure implementation of education goals and to ensure the general supervision, oversight, and monitoring of a thorough and efficient educational system.

5345 ■ West Virginia Developmental Disabilities Council (WVDDC)
110 Stockton St.
Charleston, WV 25312
Contact: Jonathon Hankins, Office Mgr.
Ph: (304)558-0416
Fax: (304)558-0941
E-mail: swiseman@wvdhhr.org
URL: http://www.wvddc.org

Descr: Assures that West Virginians with developmental disabilities receive the services, supports and opportunities they need to achieve independence, productivity, integration and inclusion into the community of their choice.

Wisconsin

5346 ■ American Medical Student Association, Medical College of Wisconsin
8701 Watertown Plank Rd.
Milwaukee, WI 53226
Ph: (414)456-8296
URL: http://www.mcw.edu/display/router.asp?DocID=1
Descr: Promotes improvement in medical training and education. Advances the medicine profession. Contributes to the welfare of medical students, interns, residents and post-MD/DO trainees.

5347 ■ American Medical Student Association, University of Wisconsin School of Medicine and Public Health
750 Highland Ave.
Madison, WI 53705
Contact: Analisa M. Calderon, Pres.
Ph: (608)263-4925
URL: http://www.med.wisc.edu
Descr: Promotes improvement in medical training and education. Advances the medicine profession. Contributes to the welfare of medical students, interns, residents and post-MD/DO trainees.

5348 ■ Arc of Fox Cities
375 Winnebago Ave.
Menasha, WI 54952
Ph: (920)725-0943
Fax: (920)725-1513
E-mail: diane@arcfoxcities.com
URL: http://www.arcfoxcities.com

5349 ■ Associated Students of Madison (ASM)
800 Langdon St.
512 Mem Union
Madison, WI 53706
Contact: Brittany Wiegand, Chair
Ph: (608)265-4276
Fax: (608)265-5637
E-mail: blwiegand@wisc.edu
URL: http://www.asm.wisc.edu
Staff: 7. **Descr:** Promotes student participation in governance and policy development, events and activities, grievances, and actions to take for the welfare of the students and the university. **Fnd:** 1994. **Mem:** 40000. **State Groups:** 1.

5350 ■ Autism Society of America - Lakeshore Chapter
413 Waldo Blvd.
Manitowoc, WI 54220
Contact: Kelly Shariff
Ph: (920)683-9381
E-mail: wi-lakeshore@autismsocietyofamerica.org
Descr: Seeks to improve the lives of individuals affected by autism. Promotes awareness and understanding of autism disorders. Aims to further the advancement of preventive studies, therapy and research of autism disorders.

5351 ■ Autism Society of the Fox Valley (ASFV)
1800 Appleton Rd.
Menasha, WI 54952
Contact: Kelly Brodhagen, Pres.
Ph: (920)968-6829
E-mail: asfv@hotmail.com
URL: http://www.focol.org/asfv
Descr: Seeks to improve the lives of individuals affected by autism. Promotes awareness and understanding of autism disorders. Aims to further the advancement of preventive studies, therapy and research of autism disorders.

5352 ■ Autism Society of Northeast Wisconsin (ASNEW)
209 S Huron St.
De Pere, WI 54115
Contact: Lisa Dillhunt
Ph: (920)884-0216
E-mail: ldillhun@greenbay.k12.wi.us
URL: http://www.asnew.org
Descr: Seeks to improve the lives of individuals affected by autism. Promotes awareness and under-

standing of autism disorders. Aims to further the advancement of preventive studies, therapy and research of autism disorders.

5353 ■ Autism Society of Southeastern Wisconsin
9733 W St. Martins Rd.
Franklin, WI 53132
Contact: Emily Levine
Ph: (414)427-9345
Fax: (414)427-9395
E-mail: assew@assew.org
URL: http://www.assew.org
Descr: Seeks to improve the lives of individuals affected by autism. Promotes awareness and understanding of autism disorders. Aims to further the advancement of preventive studies, therapy and research of autism disorders.

5354 ■ Autism Society of Wisconsin (ASW)
PO Box 165
Two Rivers, WI 54241
Contact: Nancy Alar, Pres.
Ph: (920)553-0278
Free: 888-428-8476
Fax: (920)553-0034
E-mail: asw@asw4autism.org
Descr: Seeks to improve the lives of individuals affected by autism. Promotes awareness and understanding of autism disorders. Aims to further the advancement of preventive studies, therapy and research of autism disorders.

5355 ■ Chippewa Valley Autism Society (CVAS)
2415 Agnes St.
Eau Claire, WI 54701
Contact: Suzanne Gallagher, Co-Pres.
Ph: (715)836-9507
E-mail: wi-chippewavalley@autismsocietyofamerica.org
URL: http://www.geocities.com/wicvas
Descr: Seeks to improve the lives of individuals affected by autism. Promotes awareness and understanding of autism disorders. Aims to further the advancement of preventive studies, therapy and research of autism disorders.

5356 ■ Common Cause Wisconsin (CC/WI)
PO Box 2597
Madison, WI 53701-2597
Contact: Jay Heck, Exec. Dir.
Ph: (608)256-2686
Free: 866-252-3758
Fax: (866)252-3758
E-mail: ccwisjwh@itis.com
URL: http://www.commoncause.org/site/pp.asp?c=dkLNK1MQIwG&b=1776959
Staff: 2. **Descr:** Promotes government and political openness and accountability through research, advocacy, and lobbying. Campaigns finance, ethics and lobby reform, open meetings law and other issues concerning the promotion and maintenance of clean, open, responsive and accountable government. Works on issues at the state and federal levels. **Fnd:** 1975. **Mem:** 4300. **Pub:** *Common Sense* (quarterly).

5357 ■ Down Syndrome Association of Wisconsin (DSAW)
9401 W Beloit Rd., Ste. 311
Milwaukee, WI 53227
Contact: Angie Fech, Interim Exec. Dir.
Ph: (414)327-3729
Free: 866-327-DSAW
Fax: (414)327-1329
E-mail: info@dsaw.org
URL: http://www.dsaw.org
Staff: 3. **Descr:** Provides support to families and individuals with Down Syndrome through education, information, and the exchange of ideas and experiences. Offers many programs including newsletter, new parent information packets, parent match services, community education, and special events.

Fnd: 1990. **Mem:** 1100. **Pub:** *On the Up with Down Syndrome* (quarterly).

5358 ■ Green Bay Education Association (GBEA)
2256 Main St.
Green Bay, WI 54311
Contact: Keith Patt, Exec. Dir.
Ph: (920)468-4232
Fax: (920)468-6766
E-mail: gbea@gbea.org
URL: http://www.gbea.org
Staff: 4. **Descr:** Represents full-time and part-time certified teachers employed by the Green Bay, WI area public school district. Seeks to protect and advance the interests of teachers. Acts as collective bargaining agent. **Fnd:** 1912. **Mem:** 1800. **State Groups:** 1. **Pub:** *Calendar Handbook* (annual); *Common Ground, Common Voices; Counterpoint; Green Bay Education Association Perspective* (weekly).

5359 ■ Mothers and More Green Bay, Chapter 179
East Moravian Church
505 E Allouez Ave.
Green Bay, WI 54301
Free: 888-326-4394
E-mail: gbmothersandmore@onebox.com
URL: http://www.gbmothersandmore.org

5360 ■ Sheboygan Association for the Education of Young Children (SAEYC)
912 Roosevelt Ave.
Howards Grove, WI 53083-1019
Contact: Deborah Knoener, Pres.
Ph: (920)565-7600
E-mail: administrative@sheboyganaeyc.org
URL: http://www.sheboyganaeyc.org
Descr: Serves and acts on behalf of the needs, rights and well-being of all young children with primary focus on the quality of educational and developmental services for all children. Seeks to improve professional practice and working conditions in early childhood education.

5361 ■ Special Olympics Wisconsin (SOWI)
5900 Monona Dr., Ste. 301
Madison, WI 53716
Contact: Dennis H. Alldridge, Pres.
Ph: (608)222-1324
Free: 800-552-1324
Fax: (608)222-3578
E-mail: info@specialolympicswisconsin.org
URL: http://www.specialolympicswisconsin.org
Descr: Promotes physical fitness, sports training, and athletic competition for children and adults with mental retardation. Seeks to contribute to the physical, social, and psychological development of persons with mental retardation. Participants range in age from 8 years to adult and compete in 17 different sports. **Mem:** 25500. **Pub:** *Teammates* (quarterly).

5362 ■ VSA arts of Wisconsin
4785 Hayes Rd., Ste. 201
Madison, WI 53704-7364
Contact: Ms. Kathie Wagner, Pres.
Ph: (608)241-2131
Fax: (608)241-1982
E-mail: vsawis@vsawis.org
URL: http://www.vsawis.org
Descr: Works to expand the capabilities, confidence and quality of life for children and adults with disabilities by providing programs in dance, drama, creative writing, music and visual art.

5363 ■ Wisconsin AfterSchool Association
YMCA Pabst Farms
1750 Valley Rd.
Oconomowoc, WI 53066
Contact: Jen Kovach, Pres.
Ph: (262)567-9622
E-mail: jkovachj@oconymca.org

5364 ■ Wisconsin AfterSchool Network (WAN)
Wisconsin Dept. of Public Instruction
PO Box 7841

Madison, WI 53707-7841
Contact: Steve Fernan, Asst. Dir.
Ph: (608)266-3889
E-mail: steven.fernan@dpi.wi.gov
URL: http://dpi.state.wi.us/sspw/wan.html

5365 ■ Wisconsin Association for Career and Technical Education (WACTE)
518 Potomac Ln.
Madison, WI 53719-1115
Contact: Bette Lou Esser, Exec. Dir.
Ph: (608)833-5858
Fax: (608)833-3011
E-mail: wacteorg@chorus.net
URL: http://www.wacteonline.org
Descr: Supports vocational technical education that will assure students' successful roles in families, communities, and society.

5366 ■ Wisconsin Association of Educational Opportunity Program Personnel (WAEOPP)
PO Box 340123
Milwaukee, WI 53234-0123
Contact: Tori Nelson, Pres.
Ph: (414)828-7094
E-mail: nelsont@uwgb.edu
URL: http://www.waeopp.org
Descr: Works to advance educational opportunities for disadvantaged students in colleges and universities. Provides professional development and continuing education. Monitors federal legislation designed to serve disadvantaged students.

5367 ■ Wisconsin Branch of the International Dyslexia Association (WIBIDA)
PO Box 284
Baraboo, WI 53913
Contact: Lorinda Clary, Pres.
Ph: (608)355-0911
E-mail: wibida@gmail.com
URL: http://www.wibida.org
Descr: Promotes public awareness and understanding of dyslexia. Seeks to develop and implement specialized methods to improve the quality of life for people who have dyslexia.

5368 ■ Wisconsin Council on Developmental Disabilities (WCDD)
201 W Washington Ave., Ste. 110
Madison, WI 53703
Contact: Jennifer Ondrejka, Exec. Dir.
Ph: (608)266-7826
Free: 888-332-1677
Fax: (608)267-3906
E-mail: bpddhelp@wcdd.org
URL: http://www.wcdd.org
Descr: Plans ways to improve support for people with developmental disabilities, advocates for their civil rights, and plans ways that communities can increase their capacity to be welcoming, supportive, affirming places for people with developmental disabilities. Sponsors DAWN (Disability Advocates: Wisconsin Network), which works to establish a system of community supports and services that will enable all people with disabilities to enjoy the full rights and responsibilities that come with citizenship.

5369 ■ Wisconsin Department of Public Instruction
125 S. Webster St.
PO Box 7841
Madison, WI 53707-7841
Contact: Elizabeth Burmaster, State Superintendent
Ph: (608)266-3390
Free: 800-441-4563
E-mail: benson.gardner@dpi.state.wi.us
URL: http://www.dpi.wi.gov/

5370 ■ Wisconsin Early Childhood Association (WECA)
744 Williamson St., Ste. 200
Madison, WI 53703
Contact: Mary Babula, Dir. of Membership Services
Ph: (608)240-9880
Free: 800-783-9322
Fax: (608)663-1091

E-mail: weca@wecanaeyc.org
URL: http://www.wecanaeyc.org
Descr: Works to improve childcare and early education. **Pub:** *WECA Newsletter* (quarterly).

5371 ■ Wisconsin Fire Inspectors Association
W 140 N 7501 Rd.
Menomonee Falls, WI 53051
Contact: Tod Doebler, Pres.
Ph: (262)532-8810
Fax: (262)532-8829
E-mail: rdoebler@menomonee-falls.org
URL: http://wsfia.org
Descr: Provides the highest quality codes, standards, products, and services for all concerned with the safety and performance of the built environment.

5372 ■ Wisconsin National Congress of Parents and Teachers
4797 Hayes Rd., Ste. 102
Madison, WI 53704
Contact: Penny Larson, Pres.
Ph: (608)244-1455
Fax: (608)244-4785
E-mail: wi_office@pta.org
URL: http://www.wisconsinpta.org
Staff: 5. **Descr:** Works to improve the health and welfare of Wisconsin school children; focuses on issues such as parenting skills and drug abuse awareness. Offers leadership training and workshops; holds quarterly board meeting. **Fnd:** 1910. **Mem:** 50000. **Pub:** *Wisconsin Parent Teacher* (9/year).

5373 ■ Wisconsin Senior Olympics
125 N Executive Dr., Ste. 102
Brookfield, WI 53005
Contact: Tom Leidel, Pres.
Ph: (262)821-4444
E-mail: info@wiseniorolympics.com
URL: http://www.wiseniorolympics.com
Descr: Provides Wisconsin's older adults, men, and women age 50 and over, the opportunity to improve their overall fitness and wellness through recreational, social, and competitive events. **Fnd:** 1984.

Wyoming

5374 ■ American Association of University Women, Casper Branch
365 CY Ave.
Casper, WY 82601
Contact: Ruth Adelman, Co-Pres.
Ph: (307)234-0249
E-mail: cdadelman@bresnan.net
URL: http://www.aauw-wy.org
Descr: Advances equity for women and girls through advocacy, education, and research. Provides funds and a support system for women seeking judicial redress for sex discrimination in higher education.

5375 ■ American Association of University Women, Cheyenne Branch
4818 E 13th St.
Cheyenne, WY 82001
Contact: Nancy Albers Shore, Co-Pres.
Ph: (307)638-0078
E-mail: nancy_shore@lycos.com
URL: http://www.aauw-wy.org
Descr: Advances equity for women and girls through advocacy, education, and research. Provides funds and a support system for women seeking judicial redress for sex discrimination in higher education.

5376 ■ American Association of University Women, Cody Branch
1443 Bleistein Ave.
Cody, WY 82414
Contact: Nancy Backlund, Pres.
Ph: (307)587-4637
E-mail: nbacklund@hotmail.com
URL: http://www.aauw-wy.org
Descr: Advances equity for women and girls through advocacy, education, and research. Provides funds

and a support system for women seeking judicial redress for sex discrimination in higher education.

5377 ■ American Association of University Women, Powell Branch
1125 Ln. 9
Powell, WY 82435
Contact: Claudia Fisher, Pres.
Ph: (307)754-3643
E-mail: wy4fun@wir.net
URL: http://www.aauw-wy.org
Descr: Advances equity for women and girls through advocacy, education, and research. Provides funds and a support system for women seeking judicial redress for sex discrimination in higher education.

5378 ■ American Association of University Women, Sheridan Branch
424 S Main St.
Sheridan, WY 82801
Contact: Oma Birgenheir, Pres.
Ph: (307)752-8560
E-mail: obirgenheier@yahoo.com
URL: http://www.aauw-wy.org
Descr: Advances equity for women and girls through advocacy, education, and research. Provides funds and a support system for women seeking judicial redress for sex discrimination in higher education.

5379 ■ American Association of University Women, Wheatland Branch
4 Hayes Dr.
Wheatland, WY 82201
Contact: Diane Nein
Ph: (307)322-2803
E-mail: otnein@netcommander.com
URL: http://www.aauw-wy.org
Descr: Advances equity for women and girls through advocacy, education, and research. Provides funds and a support system for women seeking judicial redress for sex discrimination in higher education.

5380 ■ American Association of University Women of Wyoming
631 Ave. B
Powell, WY 82435
Contact: Shirley G. Smith, Pres.
Ph: (307)754-2021
E-mail: shirleyg6@msn.com
URL: http://www.aauw-wy.org
Descr: Advances equity for women and girls through advocacy, education, and research. Provides funds and a support system for women seeking judicial redress for sex discrimination in higher education.

5381 ■ Arc of Laramie County
PO Box 1812
Cheyenne, WY 82003
Ph: (307)632-1209
Descr: Parents, professional workers, and others interested in individuals with mental retardation. Works to promote services, research, public understanding, and legislation for people with mental retardation and their families.

5382 ■ Arc - Magic City Enterprises
1780 Westland Rd.
Cheyenne, WY 82001
Ph: (307)637-8869
Descr: Parents, professional workers, and others interested in individuals with mental retardation. Works to promote services, research, public understanding, and legislation for people with mental retardation and their families.

5383 ■ Arc - Weston County Children's Center
104 Stampede St.
Newcastle, WY 82701
Ph: (307)746-4560
Descr: Parents, professional workers, and others interested in individuals with mental retardation. Works to promote services, research, public under-

standing, and legislation for people with mental retardation and their families.

5384 ■ Governor's Planning Council on Developmental Disabilities, Wyoming
122 W 25th St.
Herschler Bldg., Rm. 1608
Cheyenne, WY 82002
Contact: Brenda Oswald, Exec. Dir.
Ph: (307)777-7230
Free: 800-438-5791
Fax: (307)777-5690
E-mail: boswal@state.wy.us
URL: http://ddcouncil.state.wy.us

Descr: Seeks and advocates for activities which promote self sufficiency, community involvement and educational opportunities for people with disabilities, their families, and the Wyoming community.

5385 ■ Lincoln-Uinta Child Development Association
PO Box 570
Mountain View, WY 82939
Ph: (307)782-6601

Descr: Parents, professional workers, and others interested in individuals with mental retardation. Works to promote services, research, public understanding, and legislation for people with mental retardation and their families.

5386 ■ NAMI-WYOMING
133 W 6th St.
Casper, WY 82601
Contact: Theresa Bush, Pres.
Free: 888-882-4968
E-mail: nami-wyo@qwest.net
URL: http://www.nami.org/sites/namiwyoming

Descr: Supports mentally ill persons and their families. Offers educational program, advocacy services, and self-help groups. **Fnd:** 1985. **Mem:** 195. **State Groups:** 1. **Local Groups:** 9. **Pub:** WYAMI Newsletter (bimonthly).

5387 ■ Special Olympics Wyoming
232 E 2nd St., Ste. 201
Casper, WY 82601
Contact: Priscilla Dowse, Pres./CEO
Ph: (307)235-3062
Free: 800-735-8345
Fax: (307)235-3063
E-mail: pdowse@specialolympicswy.org
URL: http://www.sowy.org

Descr: Promotes physical fitness, sports training, and athletic competition for children and adults with mental retardation. Seeks to contribute to the physical, social, and psychological development of persons with mental retardation. Participants range in age from 8 years to adult and compete in track and field, swimming, gymnastics, bowling, ice skating, basketball, and other sports.

5388 ■ VSA arts of Wyoming
239 W 1st St.
Casper, WY 82601
Contact: Judy Bower, Exec. Dir.
Ph: (307)237-8618
Fax: (307)237-1151
E-mail: vsaarts@tribcsp.com
URL: http://www.vsawyo.org

Staff: 5. **Descr:** Works to enhance education through arts. Fosters leadership in progressive programs by, with, and for people with disabilities. **Fnd:** 1974.

5389 ■ Wyoming Association of Fire Marshals
151 S Scott St.
Sheridan, WY 82801
Contact: Brian Songer
Ph: (307)674-6126
Fax: (307)674-5196
E-mail: fire-marshal@sheridanfirerescue.com

Descr: Provides the highest quality codes, stan-

dards, products, and services for all concerned with the safety and performance of the built environment.

5390 ■ Wyoming Department of Education
Hathaway Bldg., Second Fl.
2300 Capitol Ave.
Cheyenne, WY 82002-0050
Contact: Dr. Jim McBride, Superintendent
Ph: (307)777-7690
Fax: (307)777-6234
E-mail: supt@educ.state.wy.us
URL: http://www.k12.wy.us/index.asp

5391 ■ Wyoming Early Childhood Association (WECA)
PO Box 2062
Casper, WY 82602
Contact: Betsy Carlin, Pres.
Free: 877-234-3162
E-mail: weca@wyoming.com
URL: http://www.wyeca.org

Descr: Serves and acts on behalf of the needs, rights and well-being of all young children with primary focus on the quality of educational and developmental services for all children. Seeks to improve professional practice and working conditions in early childhood education.

Publications

5392 ■ *10 Things Every Parent, Teacher and Teenager Should Know About Marijuana*
Family Council on Drug Awareness
PO Box 1716
El Cerrito, CA 94530
Ph: (510)215-8326
Fax: (510)234-4460
E-mail: chris@fcda.org
URL: http://www.fcda.org

5393 ■ *414 Nevada Directory*
American Institute of Architects, Las Vegas and Nevada Chapters
UNLV Box 454018
4505 S Maryland Pkwy.
Las Vegas, NV 89154-4018
Ph: (702)895-0936
Fax: (702)895-4417
E-mail: rlavigne@aianevada.org
URL: http://aialasvegas.org

Freq: annual.

5394 ■ *AABR Newsletter*
Association for the Advancement of Blind and Retarded
1508 College Point Blvd., 2nd Fl.
College Point, NY 11356
Ph: (718)321-3800
Fax: (718)321-8774
E-mail: cweldon@aabr.org
URL: http://aabr.org

Descr: Contains donor update letter. **Freq:** 3/year. **Price:** free.

5395 ■ *AAECE First Class Educator*
American Association of Early Childhood Educators
3612 Bent Branch Ct.
Falls Church, VA 22041
Ph: (703)941-4329
Fax: (703)941-4329
Freq: quarterly.

5396 ■ *AAPD News*
American Association of People with Disabilities
1629 K St. NW, Ste. 503
Washington, DC 20006
Ph: (202)457-0046
Fax: (202)457-0473
E-mail: aapd@aol.com
URL: http://www.aapd-dc.org

Descr: Also available in Braille. **Freq:** quarterly. **Price:** included in membership dues.

5397 ■ *AAUW in Action*
American Association of University Women
1111 16th St. NW

Washington, DC 20036
Ph: (202)785-7700
Free: 800-326-2289
Fax: (202)872-1425
E-mail: editor@aauw.com
URL: http://www.aauw.org

Key Personnel: Jodi Lipson, Editor, editor@aauw.org. **Descr:** National magazine for AAUW members. Tabloid. **Freq:** Periodic. **Price:** Free, to members.

5398 ■ *AAUW Outlook*
American Association of University Women
1111 16th St. NW
Washington, DC 20036
Ph: (202)785-7700
Fax: (202)872-1425
E-mail: info@aauw.org
URL: http://www.aauw.org

Descr: Contains articles on issues such as equity in education and the workplace. Includes policy update on current legislative issues. **Freq:** periodic. **Price:** included in membership dues, $15/4 issues (institutes only).

5399 ■ *AAWS Newsletter*
Association of African Women Scholars
Indiana University
French and Women's Studies
Cavanaugh Hall, Rm. 001C
425 University Blvd.
Indianapolis, IN 46202
Ph: (317)278-2038
Fax: (317)274-2347
E-mail: aaws@iupui.edu
URL: http://www.iupui.edu/~aaws

Freq: semiannual.

5400 ■ *Ability Bulletin*
National Ability Center
PO Box 682799
Park City, UT 84068
Ph: (435)649-3991
Fax: (435)658-3992
E-mail: info@discovernac.org
URL: http://www.discovernac.org

Freq: quarterly.

5401 ■ *The Abled Disabled in Science*
Foundation for Science and Disability
1700 SW 23rd Dr.
Gainesville, FL 32608
Ph: (352)374-5774
Fax: (352)374-5804
E-mail: rmankin@nersp.nerdc.ufl.edu
URL: http://www.stemd.org

Freq: periodic.

5402 ■ *About Applying*
Secondary School Admission Test Board
CN 5339
Princeton, NJ 08543
Ph: (609)683-4440
Fax: (609)683-4507
E-mail: info@ssat.org
URL: http://www.ssat.org

5403 ■ *About SSAT*
Secondary School Admission Test Board
CN 5339
Princeton, NJ 08543
Ph: (609)683-4440
Fax: (609)683-4507
E-mail: info@ssat.org
URL: http://www.ssat.org

5404 ■ *Access: A Student Activists' Guide to the U.S. Congress*
United States Student Association
1211 Connecticut Ave. NW, Ste. 406
Washington, DC 20036
Ph: (202)640-6570
Fax: (202)223-4005
E-mail: ussa@usstudents.org
URL: http://www.usstudents.org

Freq: annual.

5405 ■ Access Abilities!
Abilities!
201 I.U. Willets Rd.
Albertson, NY 11507-1599
Ph: (516)465-1400
Fax: (516)465-1591
E-mail: webmaster@abilitiesonline.org
URL: http://www.ncds.org
Freq: quarterly.

5406 ■ Access and Education
International Association of Assistance Dog Partners
PO Box 1326
Sterling Heights, MI 48311
Ph: (586)826-3938
E-mail: iaadp@aol.com
URL: http://www.iaadp.org

5407 ■ Accident Prevention Manual for Business and Industry
National Safety Council
1121 Spring Lake Dr.
Itasca, IL 60143-3201
Ph: (630)285-1121
Fax: (630)285-1315
E-mail: info@nsc.org
URL: http://www.nsc.org
Descr: Contains two volumes per set.

5408 ■ Accreditation: A Quality Review and Enhancement Process
The Council on Quality and Leadership
100 West Rd., Ste. 406
Towson, MD 21204
Ph: (410)583-0060
Fax: (410)583-0063
E-mail: info@thecouncil.org
URL: http://www.thecouncil.org
Price: $25.

5409 ■ Accreditation Guide
Independent Schools Association of the Central States
1165 N Clark St., Ste. 311
Chicago, IL 60610
Ph: (312)255-1244
Fax: (312)255-1278
E-mail: rbelding@isacs.org
URL: http://www.isacs.org
Descr: Features a comprehensive description of ISACS Accreditation Program, 7-year cycle, including a full appendix of forms. Price: $18 for members, $25 for nonmembers.

5410 ■ The Accreditation Standard
Canadian Council on Health Services Accreditation
1730 St. Laurent Blvd., Ste. 100
Ottawa, ON, Canada K1G 5L1
Ph: (613)738-3800
Fax: (613)738-7755
E-mail: international@cchsa-ccass.ca
URL: http://www.accreditation.ca
Freq: quarterly.

5411 ■ Accredited Institutions of Higher Education
American Council on Education
1 Dupont Cir. NW
Washington, DC 20036-1193
Ph: (202)939-9300
Fax: (202)659-2212
E-mail: comments@ace.nche.edu
URL: http://www.acenet.edu
Descr: Lists accredited institutions of higher education in the U.S. Freq: annual.

5412 ■ Accredited Senior Centers: A Snapshot
National Institute of Senior Centers
1901 L St. NW, 4th Fl.
Washington, DC 20036
Ph: (202)479-1200
Fax: (202)479-0735

E-mail: info@ncoa.org
URL: http://www.ncoa.org/content.cfm?sectionID=44

5413 ■ AccreditWatch
American Accreditation Healthcare Commission
1220 L St. NW, Ste. 400
Washington, DC 20005
Ph: (202)216-9010
Fax: (202)216-9006
E-mail: communications@urac.org
URL: http://www.urac.org
Descr: Helps keep accredited organizations, regulators, and others in the health and managed care industry informed about the latest events. Freq: quarterly.

5414 ■ ACE/Praeger Series on Higher Education
American Council on Education
1 Dupont Cir. NW
Washington, DC 20036-1193
Ph: (202)939-9300
Fax: (202)659-2212
E-mail: comments@ace.nche.edu
URL: http://www.acenet.edu

5415 ■ ACTE News
Association for Career and Technical Education
1410 King St.
Alexandria, VA 22314
Ph: (703)683-3111
Fax: (703)683-7424
E-mail: acte@acteonline.org
URL: http://www.acteonline.org
Freq: monthly.

5416 ■ ACTE News
Hawaii Association for Career and Technical Education
2257 Kapahu St.
Honolulu, HI 96813
Ph: (808)956-5714
Fax: (808)956-3918
E-mail: dirksoma@yahoo.com
URL: http://www.acteonline.org/content.aspx?id=782
Descr: Features events and programs from ACTE.
Freq: monthly.

5417 ■ ACTION
Alternative Religions Educational Network
PO Box 1893
Trenton, FL 32693
Ph: (321)243-2337
E-mail: aren1@aren.org
URL: http://www.aren.org

5418 ■ Action Letter Portfolio
Research and Training Center on Independent Living
University of Kansas
Dole Center, Ste. 4089
1000 Sunnyside Ave.
Lawrence, KS 66045-7561
Ph: (785)864-4095
Fax: (785)864-5063
E-mail: rtcil@ku.edu
URL: http://www.rtcil.org
Price: $30.

5419 ■ Action Line
American Action Fund for Blind Children and Adults
1800 Johnson St., Ste. 100
Baltimore, MD 21230
Ph: (410)659-9315
Fax: (410)685-5653
E-mail: actionfund@actionfund.org
URL: http://www.actionfund.org
Freq: monthly.

5420 ■ Action Update
Roadway Safety Foundation
1101 14th St. NW, Ste. 750
Washington, DC 20005
Ph: (202)857-1200
Fax: (202)857-1220
E-mail: cathygillen@roadwaysafety.org
URL: http://www.roadwaysafety.org

Descr: Updates members on activities. Freq: quarterly. Price: included in membership dues.

5421 ■ ACTivity
ACT
PO Box 168
Iowa City, IA 52244-0168
Ph: (319)337-1000
Fax: (319)339-3020
E-mail: mediarelations@act.org
URL: http://www.act.org
Descr: Provides accounts of programs, services, and activities. Freq: quarterly. Price: free.

5422 ■ Adaptive Ski Teaching Methods
Disabled Sports USA
451 Hungerford Dr., Ste. 100
Rockville, MD 20850
Ph: (301)217-0960
Fax: (301)217-0968
E-mail: information@dsusa.org
URL: http://www.dsusa.org
Freq: quarterly.

5423 ■ Adjudicating Allegations of Child Sexual Abuse When Custody is in Dispute
National Judicial Education Program
395 Hudson St.
New York, NY 10014-3669
Ph: (212)925-6635
Fax: (212)226-1066
E-mail: njep@legalmomentum.org
URL: http://www.legalmomentum.org

5424 ■ Adult Education Quarterly
American Association for Adult and Continuing Education
10111 Martin Luther King, Jr. Hwy., Ste. 200C
Bowie, MD 20720
Ph: (301)459-6261
Fax: (301)459-6241
E-mail: aaace10@aol.com
URL: http://www.aaace.org
Freq: quarterly.

5425 ■ Adult Education for Social Change: From Center Stage to the Wings and Back Again
ERIC Clearinghouse on Adult, Career, and Vocational Education
College of Education
Center on Education & Training for Employment
1900 Kenny Rd.
Columbus, OH 43210-1090
Ph: (614)292-7069
Fax: (614)292-1260
E-mail: ericacve@osu.edu
URL: http://ericacve.org/

5426 ■ Adult Learning
American Association for Adult and Continuing Education
10111 Martin Luther King, Jr. Hwy., Ste. 200C
Bowie, MD 20720
Ph: (301)459-6261
Fax: (301)459-6241
E-mail: aaace10@aol.com
URL: http://www.aaace.org
Descr: Includes book reviews and calendar of events. Freq: bimonthly. Price: included in membership dues. ISSN: 0739-2915.

5427 ■ Adult Learning Magazine for Practitioners
American Association for Adult and Continuing Education
10111 Martin Luther King, Jr. Hwy., Ste. 200C
Bowie, MD 20720
Ph: (301)459-6261
Fax: (301)459-6241
E-mail: aaace10@aol.com
URL: http://www.aaace.org

Freq: bimonthly.

5428 ■ *Advance: A Retention Organizing Manual*
United States Student Association
1211 Connecticut Ave. NW, Ste. 406
Washington, DC 20036
Ph: (202)640-6570
Fax: (202)223-4005
E-mail: ussa@usstudents.org
URL: http://www.usstudents.org

5429 ■ *Advance Health Care Directives*
Disability Rights Center
PO Box 2007
Augusta, ME 04338-2007
Ph: (207)626-2774
Fax: (207)621-1419
E-mail: advocate@drcme.org
URL: http://www.drcme.org
Price: $4.

5430 ■ *Advocacy and Family Support*
Arc of Spokane
127 W Boone Ave.
Spokane, WA 99201
Ph: (509)328-6326
Fax: (509)328-6342
E-mail: gfalk@arc-spokane.org
URL: http://www.arc-spokane.org
Freq: bimonthly.

5431 ■ *Advocacy Handbook: A Parent's Guide for Special Education*
Learning Disabilities Association of America
4156 Library Rd.
Pittsburgh, PA 15234-1349
Ph: (412)341-1515
Fax: (412)344-0224
E-mail: info@ldaamerica.org
URL: http://www.ldaamerica.org
Price: free for members, $10 plus $2 shipping and handling.

5432 ■ *The Advocate*
American Association of University Women, Danville-Alamo Branch
PO Box 996
Alamo, CA 94507
E-mail: president@aauw-da.org
URL: http://www.aauw-da.org
Freq: monthly.

5433 ■ *The Advocate*
Arc of Washington County
2700 S Roan St., Ste. 300B
Johnson City, TN 37601
Ph: (423)928-9362
Fax: (423)928-7431
E-mail: kim@arcwc.org
URL: http://www.arcwc.org
Freq: quarterly.

5434 ■ *The Advocate*
Arc, Upper Valley
2500 DeMers Ave.
PO Box 12420
Grand Forks, ND 58208-2420
Ph: (701)772-6191
Fax: (701)772-2195
E-mail: thearc@arcuv.com
URL: http://www.thearcuppervalley.com
Descr: Contains information on the association and its members. Freq: quarterly.

5435 ■ *The Advocate*
Arc of King County
233 6th Ave. N
Seattle, WA 98109
Ph: (206)364-6337
Fax: (206)364-8140
E-mail: info@arcofkingcounty.org
URL: http://www.arcofkingcounty.org

Freq: monthly.

5436 ■ *The Advocate*
Houston Association for the Education of Young Children
5959 W Loop S, Ste. 150
Bellaire, TX 77401
Ph: (713)781-2155
Fax: (713)665-2155
E-mail: haaeyc@haaeyc.org
URL: http://www.haaeyc.org
Descr: Includes organizational news regarding both HAAEYC and TAEYC/NAEYC activities. Freq: quarterly. Price: $15/year.

5437 ■ *The Advocate*
Ohio Council for Home Care
1395 E Dublin-Granville Rd., Ste. 350
Columbus, OH 43229
Ph: (614)885-0434
Fax: (614)885-0413
E-mail: info@homecareohio.org
URL: http://www.homecareohio.org
Descr: Contains up-to-date information about the home care industry. Freq: weekly. Price: included in membership dues.

5438 ■ *The Advocate*
National Credit Reporting Association
125 E Lake St., Ste. 200
Bloomingdale, IL 60108
Ph: (630)539-1525
Fax: (630)539-1526
E-mail: tclemans@ncrainc.org
URL: http://www.ncrainc.org
Freq: bimonthly. Price: included in membership dues.

5439 ■ *AER Report*
Association for Education and Rehabilitation of the Blind and Visually Impaired
1703 N Beauregard St., Ste. 440
Alexandria, VA 22311
Ph: (703)671-4500
Fax: (703)671-6391
E-mail: jgandorf@aerbvi.org
URL: http://www.aerbvi.org
Descr: Contains information about blind and visually impaired persons. Includes legislative and membership news. Freq: quarterly. Price: included in membership dues.

5440 ■ *AFL-CIO Scholarship Guide*
AFL-CIO
815 16th St. NW, 5th Fl.
Washington, DC 20006
URL: http://www.aflcio.org
URL(s): http://www.aflcio.org

5441 ■ *AfterSchool Review*
National AfterSchool Association
PO Box 34447
Washington, DC 20043
Fax: 888-568-6590
E-mail: menglish@naaweb.org
URL: http://www.naaweb.org
Price: $10 for members, $12 for nonmembers.

5442 ■ *AG Bell Update*
Alexander Graham Bell Association for the Deaf and Hard of Hearing
3417 Volta Pl. NW
Washington, DC 20007
Ph: (202)337-5220
Fax: (202)337-8314
E-mail: info@agbell.org
URL: http://www.agbell.org
Freq: weekly.

5443 ■ *AgeShare*
National Academy for Teaching and Learning About Aging
PO Box 310919
Denton, TX 76203-0919
Ph: (940)565-3450
Fax: (940)565-3141

E-mail: louis@scs.unt.edu
URL: http://www.cps.unt.edu/natla

5444 ■ *Aging and Sensory Change: An Annotated Bibliography*
Gerontological Society of America
1220 L St. NW, Ste. 901
Washington, DC 20005
Ph: (202)842-1275
Fax: (202)842-1150
URL: http://www.geron.org

5445 ■ *AIA Florida Friday Facts*
American Institute of Architects - Florida Association
104 E Jefferson St.
Tallahassee, FL 32301
Ph: (850)222-7590
Fax: (850)224-8048
E-mail: vlong@aiafla.org
URL: http://www.aiafla.org
Descr: Keeps AIA Florida members aware of governmental concerns and issues affecting the profession. Freq: weekly.

5446 ■ *AIA Handbook*
American Institute of Architects New Jersey
414 River View Plz.
Trenton, NJ 08611
Ph: (609)393-5690
Fax: (609)393-9891
E-mail: info@aia-nj.org
URL: http://www.aia-nj.org
Freq: annual.

5447 ■ *AIA North Carolina Architext*
American Institute of Architects-North Carolina Chapter
115 W Morgan St.
Raleigh, NC 27601
Ph: (919)833-6656
Fax: (919)833-2015
E-mail: info@aianc.org
URL: http://www.aianc.org
Freq: bimonthly.

5448 ■ *AIA Nova News*
American Institute of Architects Northern Virginia Chapter
205 S Patrick St.
Alexandria, VA 22314
Ph: (703)549-9747
Fax: (703)549-9783
E-mail: aianova@aianova.org
URL: http://www.aianova.org
Descr: Contains news and information on local architecture programs. Freq: periodic. Price: $25.

5449 ■ *AIA Vermont*
American Institute of Architects Vermont
1662 Mill Brook Rd.
Fayston, VT 05673
Ph: (802)496-3761
Fax: (802)496-3294
E-mail: info@aiavt.org
URL: http://www.aiavt.org
Freq: monthly.

5450 ■ *AIA Yearbook Magazine*
American Institute of Architects, Philadelphia Chapter
1218 Arch St.
Philadelphia, PA 19107
Ph: (215)569-3186
Fax: (215)569-9226
E-mail: john@aiaphila.org
URL: http://www.aiaphiladelphia.org
Descr: Features award-winning and exhibited architectural projects, also includes the student work with architecture programs. Freq: annual.

5451 ■ *Alabama PTA Bulletin*
Alabama Parent Teacher Association
470 S Union St.
Montgomery, AL 36104-4330
Ph: (334)834-2501
Fax: (334)396-7090

E-mail: al_office@pta.org
URL: http://www.alabamapta.org
Freq: quarterly.

5452 ■ *Alateen-Hope for Children of Alcoholics*
Al-Anon Family Group Headquarters, World Service Office
1600 Corporate Landing Pkwy.
Virginia Beach, VA 23454-5617
Ph: (757)563-1600
Fax: (757)563-1655
E-mail: wso@al-anon.org
URL: http://www.al-anon.alateen.org
Price: $7/copy.

5453 ■ *Albricias!*
Sociedad Honoraria Hispanica
PO Box 10
Turbeville, SC 29162-0010
E-mail: bertiegreen@hotmail.com
Descr: Journal covering Hispanic educational issues. **Freq:** Quarterly. **Price:** Included in membership.

5454 ■ *ALERT*
Association on Higher Education and Disability
107 Commerce Center Dr., Ste. 204
Huntersville, NC 28078
Ph: (704)947-7779
Fax: (704)948-7779
E-mail: ahead@ahead.org
URL: http://www.ahead.org
Freq: bimonthly.

5455 ■ *All Abroad!*
Mobility International USA
132 E Broadway, Ste. 343
Eugene, OR 97401
Ph: (541)343-1284
Fax: (541)343-6812
E-mail: info@miusa.org
URL: http://www.miusa.org
Descr: Available with or without audio description and with captions; for People with Disabilities Interested in International Exchange. **Price:** $49.

5456 ■ *Almanac of Higher Education*
National Education Association
1201 16th St. NW
Washington, DC 20036-3290
Ph: (202)833-4000
Fax: (202)822-7974
URL: http://www.nea.org
Freq: annual. **Price:** included in membership dues.

5457 ■ *Alternative Schools: Best Practices for Development and Evaluation*
National Dropout Prevention Center/Network
Clemson University
209 Martin St.
Clemson, SC 29631-1555
Ph: (864)656-2599
Fax: (864)656-0136
E-mail: ndpc@clemson.edu
URL: http://www.dropoutprevention.org

5458 ■ *Alternatives in Medical Education*
Physicians Committee for Responsible Medicine
5100 Wisconsin Ave. NW, Ste. 400
Washington, DC 20016
Ph: (202)686-2210
Fax: (202)686-2216
E-mail: pcrm@pcrm.org
URL: http://www.pcrm.org

5459 ■ *Alumni*
A Better Chance
240 W 35th St., 9th Fl.
New York, NY 10001-2506
Ph: (646)346-1310
Fax: (646)346-1311
E-mail: stimmons@abetterchance.org
URL: http://www.abetterchance.org

Price: $79 deluxe edition, $69 standard edition.

5460 ■ *Alumni News*
Guide Dogs for the Blind
PO Box 151200
San Rafael, CA 94915-1200
Ph: (415)499-4000
Fax: (415)499-4035
E-mail: information@guidedogs.com
URL: http://www.guidedogs.com
Descr: Contains information on graduates.

5461 ■ *American Annals of the Deaf—Reference Issue*
Conference of Educational Administrators Serving the Deaf
Gallaudet University Press
Denison House
Washington, DC 20002
Ph: (202)651-5488
Fax: (202)651-5489
E-mail: valencia.simmons@gallaudet.edu
Key Personnel: Mary Ellen Carew, Mng. Ed., mary.carew@gallaudet.edu; Donald F. Moores, Editor. **Entries include:** Generally, name of sponsoring organization, address, and description of programs offered. School listings include staff and enrollment data. **Publication includes:** Lists of educational programs and services, supportive and rehabilitation programs and services, and research and information programs and services focusing on the deaf and aurally handicapped. **Freq:** Annual, April. **Price:** $50, individuals; $95, institutions; $45, members.

5462 ■ *American Association of University Women—Action Alert*
American Association of University Women
1111 16th St. NW
Washington, DC 20036
Ph: (202)785-7700
Fax: (202)872-1425
E-mail: info@aauw.org
URL: http://www.aauw.org
Descr: Covers legislative news and other issues, including pay equity, child care, and family law. **Freq:** periodic. **Price:** $20/year.

5463 ■ *American Teacher*
Women's Rights Committee
Human Rights Department
555 New Jersey Ave. NW
Washington, DC 20001
Ph: (202)879-4400
E-mail: assocmbr@aft.org
URL: http://www.aft.org
Freq: monthly.

5464 ■ *America's Cradle to Prison Pipeline*
Children's Defense Fund
25 E St. NW
Washington, DC 20001
Ph: (202)628-8787
Fax: (202)662-3560
E-mail: cdfinfo@childrensdefense.org
URL: http://www.childrensdefense.org

5465 ■ *America's Top Jobs for College Graduates: Detailed Information on 114 Jobs for People with Four-Year and Higher Degrees*
JIST Publishing
875 Montreal Way
Saint Paul, MN 55102
Ph: (317)613-4200
Free: 800-648-5478
Fax: 800-547-8329
E-mail: info@jist.com
URL: http://www.jist.com
Key Personnel: Michael Farr, Author. **URL(s):** http://www.jist.com **Publication includes:** List of 114 jobs that require 4-year college degrees or higher and jobs that are held by college graduates but that do not require a degree. Principal content of publication is information on job descriptions, job search advice

and career planning, and labor trends. **Price:** $15.95.

5466 ■ *Anesthesia Patient Safety, A Modern History*
Anesthesia Patient Safety Foundation
8007 S Meridian St., Bldg. 1, Ste. 2
Indianapolis, IN 46217-2922
Fax: (317)888-1482
E-mail: walker@apsf.org
URL: http://www.apsf.org
Descr: Contains substantive articles from the APSF Newsletter. **Price:** $25 includes postage.

5467 ■ *Annals of Dyslexia*
International Dyslexia Association
40 York Rd., 4th Fl.
Baltimore, MD 21204-5202
Ph: (410)296-0232
Fax: (410)321-5069
E-mail: info@interdys.org
URL: http://www.interdys.org
Descr: Features current research on dyslexia. **Freq:** annual. **Price:** included in membership dues, $35 for nonmembers. **ISSN:** 0736-9387.

5468 ■ *Annotated Bibliography on Assessment of Young Children*
National Center for Fair and Open Testing
15 Court Sq., Ste. 820
Boston, MA 02108
Ph: (857)350-8207
Fax: (857)350-8209
E-mail: info@fairtest.org
URL: http://www.fairtest.org

5469 ■ *Annotated Bibliography on Performance Assessment*
National Center for Fair and Open Testing
15 Court Sq., Ste. 820
Boston, MA 02108
Ph: (857)350-8207
Fax: (857)350-8209
E-mail: info@fairtest.org
URL: http://www.fairtest.org

5470 ■ *Annotated Bibliography on SAT Bias and Misuse*
National Center for Fair and Open Testing
15 Court Sq., Ste. 820
Boston, MA 02108
Ph: (857)350-8207
Fax: (857)350-8209
E-mail: info@fairtest.org
URL: http://www.fairtest.org
Price: $8.

5471 ■ *An Annotated Summary of the Regulations for Title IX of the Education Amendments of 1972*
Legal Momentum: Advancing Women's Rights
395 Hudson St., 5th Fl.
New York, NY 10014
Ph: (212)925-6635
Fax: (212)226-1066
E-mail: policy@legalmomentum.org
URL: http://www.legalmomentum.org

5472 ■ *Annual Resources for PTAs*
National PTA - National Congress of Parents and Teachers
541 N Fairbanks Ct., Ste. 1300
Chicago, IL 60611-3396
Ph: (312)670-6782
Fax: (312)670-6783
E-mail: info@pta.org
URL: http://www.pta.org
Descr: Contains resources for PTAs. **Freq:** annual.

5473 ■ *APCO Membership Directory*
Association of Public-Safety Communications Officials - International
351 N Williamson Blvd.
Daytona Beach, FL 32114-1112
Ph: (386)322-2500
Fax: (386)322-2501

E-mail: apco@apcointl.org
URL: http://www.apco911.org
Freq: annual.

5474 ■ *APH News*
American Printing House for the Blind
1839 Frankfort Ave.
PO Box 6085
Louisville, KY 40206-0085
Ph: (502)895-2405
Fax: (502)899-2274
E-mail: info@aph.org
URL: http://www.aph.org
Descr: Contains information on the products, services and training opportunities of the organization. **Freq:** monthly.

5475 ■ *APH Slate*
American Printing House for the Blind
1839 Frankfort Ave.
PO Box 6085
Louisville, KY 40206-0085
Ph: (502)895-2405
Fax: (502)899-2274
E-mail: info@aph.org
URL: http://www.aph.org
Descr: Provides information on new products for the visually impaired; includes organization news and activities. **Freq:** quarterly. **Price:** free. **ISSN:** 1081-5198.

5476 ■ *APH Technology Update: Technology for People Who Are Visually Impaired*
American Printing House for the Blind
1839 Frankfort Ave.
PO Box 6085
Louisville, KY 40206-0085
Ph: (502)895-2405
Fax: (502)899-2274
E-mail: info@aph.org
URL: http://www.aph.org
Descr: Covers computer and other high-tech products designed for blind persons. **Freq:** annual. **Price:** free. **ISSN:** 1081-518X.

5477 ■ *Appleseed Today*
Project Appleseed: The National Campaign for Public School Improvement
520 Melville Ave.
St. Louis, MO 63130-4506
Ph: (314)225-7757
Fax: (314)725-2319
E-mail: headquarters@projectappleseed.org
URL: http://www.projectappleseed.org
Freq: quarterly.

5478 ■ *Applying Constructivism in Vocational and Career Education*
ERIC Clearinghouse on Adult, Career, and Vocational Education
College of Education
Center on Education & Training for Employment
1900 Kenny Rd.
Columbus, OH 43210-1090
Ph: (614)292-7069
Fax: (614)292-1260
E-mail: ericacve@osu.edu
URL: http://ericacve.org/

5479 ■ *The ARC Community Connection*
Arc of Northern Essex
57 Wingate St., Ste. 301
Haverhill, MA 01832
Ph: (978)373-0552
Fax: (978)373-0557
E-mail: arc.nec@verizon.net
URL: http://arcmass.org
Freq: monthly. **Price:** free.

5480 ■ *The Arc Connection*
Arc of Tennessee
151 Athens Way, Ste. 100
Nashville, TN 37228
Ph: (615)248-5878
Fax: (615)248-5879

E-mail: info@thearctn.org
URL: http://www.thearctn.org
Descr: Contains information on disabilities. **Freq:** quarterly. **Price:** free.

5481 ■ *The Arc and the Dove*
Arc of Maryland
49 Old Solomon's Island Rd., Ste. 205
Annapolis, MD 21401
Ph: (410)571-9320
Fax: (410)974-6021
E-mail: info@thearcmd.org
URL: http://www.thearcmd.org
Descr: Compilation of issues and new developments of concern to people with disabilities. **Freq:** quarterly. **Price:** free for members.

5482 ■ *The Arc Insider*
Arc of Washington State
2638 State Ave. NE
Olympia, WA 98506
Ph: (360)357-5596
Fax: (360)357-3279
E-mail: info@arcwa.org
URL: http://www.arcwa.org
Descr: Provides alerts for Federal and State legislation impacting citizens with developmental disabilities. **Freq:** periodic.

5483 ■ *Arc Message*
Arc of Greater Tarrant County
1300 W Lancaster Ave., Ste. 104
Fort Worth, TX 76102
Ph: (817)877-1474
Fax: (817)877-1477
E-mail: richard.garnett@arcgtc.org
URL: http://www.arcgtc.org
Freq: monthly.

5484 ■ *ARC/Muskegon News*
Arc/Muskegon
1145 E Wesley Ave.
Muskegon, MI 49442-2197
Ph: (231)777-2006
Fax: (231)777-3507
E-mail: arcmusk@i2k.com
URL: http://www.arcmuskegon.org
Freq: quarterly.

5485 ■ *The Arc News*
Arc of Washington State
2638 State Ave. NE
Olympia, WA 98506
Ph: (360)357-5596
Fax: (360)357-3279
E-mail: info@arcwa.org
URL: http://www.arcwa.org

5486 ■ *The Arc News*
Arc of Southern Maryland
Administration, Finance and Human Resources
268 Merrimac Ct.
PO Box 1860
Prince Frederick, MD 20678
Ph: (410)535-2413
Fax: (410)535-1314
E-mail: info@arcsomd.org
URL: http://www.arcsomd.org
Freq: quarterly.

5487 ■ *The Arc Now*
Arc of the United States
1010 Wayne Ave., Ste. 650
Silver Spring, MD 20910
Ph: (301)565-3842
Fax: (301)565-5342
E-mail: info@thearc.org
URL: http://www.thearc.org
Freq: monthly.

5488 ■ *The Arc Voice*
Arc of Lincoln-Lancaster County
5609 S 49th St., Ste. 5
Lincoln, NE 68516
Ph: (402)421-8866
Fax: (402)421-8922

E-mail: info@arclincoln.org
URL: http://www.arclincoln.org
Freq: quarterly.

5489 ■ *Architalk*
American Institute of Architects Northeast Illinois
412 Green Valley Dr.
Naperville, IL 60540
Ph: (630)527-8550
Fax: (630)357-4818
E-mail: exec@aianei.org
URL: http://www.aianei.com
Freq: monthly.

5490 ■ *Architrane*
American Institute of Architects, Huron Valley Chapter
PO Box 1412
Ann Arbor, MI 48106
Ph: (734)663-4189
Fax: (734)663-1770
E-mail: huronvalley@aiagv.net
URL: http://www.aiami.com/Chapters/Huron_Valley/chpt_hv_home.htm
Descr: Contains items of interest to architects in Ann Arbor, MI area. **Freq:** bimonthly.

5491 ■ *Archi.type*
American Institute of Architects, Delaware Chapter
220 W 9th St.
Wilmington, DE 19801
Ph: (302)654-9817
Fax: (302)654-7687
E-mail: info@aiadelaware.org
URL: http://www.aiadelaware.org
Freq: monthly.

5492 ■ *ArchiTypes*
American Institute of Architects Ohio
17 S High St., Ste. 200
Columbus, OH 43215
Ph: (614)221-1900
Fax: (614)221-1989
E-mail: aiaohio@assnoffices.com
URL: http://www.aiaohio.org
Descr: Contains information, updates, and profile regarding the organization.

5493 ■ *The Archive*
Arc of Hunterdon County, New Jersey
1322 State Rte. 31, Ste. 5
Annandale, NJ 08801
Ph: (908)730-7827
Fax: (908)730-7726
E-mail: jeff@archunterdon.org
URL: http://www.archunterdon.org
Freq: quarterly.

5494 ■ *The ArcLite*
Arc of Spokane
127 W Boone Ave.
Spokane, WA 99201
Ph: (509)328-6326
Fax: (509)328-6342
E-mail: gfalk@arc-spokane.org
URL: http://www.arc-spokane.org
Freq: quarterly.

5495 ■ *The ArcNSV's News and Views*
Arc of Northern Shenandoah Valley
119 Youth Development Ct.
Winchester, VA 22602
Ph: (540)665-0461
Descr: Contains advocacy related news, local events, and Arc happenings. **Price:** free to members and friends.

5496 ■ *The ARC's Government Report*
Arc of the United States
1010 Wayne Ave., Ste. 650
Silver Spring, MD 20910
Ph: (301)565-3842
Fax: (301)565-5342
E-mail: info@thearc.org
URL: http://www.thearc.org

Freq: semimonthly. **Price:** $72/year.

5497 ■ Arctimes
St. Louis Arc
1816 Lackland Hill Pkwy., Ste. 200
St. Louis, MO 63146
Ph: (314)569-2211
Fax: (314)569-0778
E-mail: slarc@slarc.org
URL: http://www.slarc.org
Freq: quarterly.

5498 ■ Arizona PTA NewsReport
Arizona PTA
2721 N 7th Ave.
Phoenix, AZ 85007
Ph: (602)279-1811
Fax: (602)279-1814
E-mail: office@azpta.org
URL: http://www.azpta.org
Descr: Provides information to local units for the upcoming convention.

5499 ■ Artists' Pipeline
VSA arts of Minnesota
Hennepin Center for the Arts
528 Hennepin Ave., Ste. No. 305
Minneapolis, MN 55403
Ph: (612)332-3888
Fax: (612)305-0132
E-mail: info@vsaartsmn.org
URL: http://www.vsaartsmn.org
Freq: biweekly.

5500 ■ Arts Access
VSA arts of Minnesota
Hennepin Center for the Arts
528 Hennepin Ave., Ste. No. 305
Minneapolis, MN 55403
Ph: (612)332-3888
Fax: (612)305-0132
E-mail: info@vsaartsmn.org
URL: http://www.vsaartsmn.org
Freq: 3/year.

5501 ■ A's & B's of Academic Scholarships
Octameron Associates
PO Box 2748
Alexandria, VA 22301-2748
Ph: (703)836-5480
Fax: (703)836-5650
E-mail: octameron@aol.com
URL: http://www.octameron.com
Key Personnel: Anna Leider, Author. **URL(s):** http://www.thinktuition.com; http://www.octameron.com/productsframe.html **Covers:** About 100,000 academic/honor/merit scholarships offered on a no-need basis by about 1,200 colleges and universities. **Entries include:** Sponsor name, address, name and description of program, eligibility requirements, deadlines. Useful primarily to students with a B average or higher and combined scholastic aptitude tests (SAT) of 900 or more, who are in the upper third of their class. **Freq:** Annual, Latest edition 26th, September 2007. **Price:** $13, individuals, plus $3 for shipping/handling.

5502 ■ The Asian American Vote 2004: A Report on the Multilingual Exit Poll in the 2004 Presidential Election
Asian American Legal Defense and Education Fund
99 Hudson St., 12th Fl.
New York, NY 10013
Ph: (212)966-5932
Fax: (212)966-4303
E-mail: info@aaldef.org
URL: http://www.aaldef.org

5503 ■ Association for Education and Rehabilitation of the Blind and Visually Impaired—Job Exchange
Association for Education and Rehabilitation of the Blind and Visually Impaired
1703 N Beauregard St., Ste. 440
Alexandria, VA 22311
Ph: (703)671-4500
Fax: (703)671-6391

E-mail: jgandorf@aerbvi.org
URL: http://www.aerbvi.org
Descr: Lists job openings in the field of services to blind and visually impaired children and adults. **Freq:** monthly. **Price:** free for members (online).

5504 ■ Asynchronous Learning Networks
Canadian Association for Distance Education
260 Dalhousie St., Ste. 204
Ottawa, ON, Canada K1N 7E4
Ph: (613)241-0018
Fax: (613)241-0019
E-mail: cade-aced@csse.ca
URL: http://www.cade-aced.ca
Freq: periodic.

5505 ■ Athletic Scholarships
Facts on File Inc.
132 W 31st St., 17th Fl.
New York, NY 10001
Ph: (212)967-8800
Free: 800-322-8755
Fax: 800-678-3633
E-mail: custserv@factsonfile.com
URL: http://factsonfile.infobasepublishing.com
Key Personnel: Andy Clark, Editor; Amy Clark, Editor; Karen Breslow, Gen. Ed. **URL(s):** http://www.factsonfile.com **Covers:** colleges and universities that award athletic scholarships. **Entries include:** Institution name, men's and women's athletic departments' addresses and phone numbers, sports played, scholarships available, brief description of institution. **Freq:** Irregular, Latest edition 4th; published 2000. **Price:** $38.50, individuals, Hardcover; $34.65, libraries.

5506 ■ Axis Journal
American Institute of Architects, Golden Empire Chapter
Ordiz Melby Architects
5500 Ming Ave., Ste. 280
Bakersfield, CA 93309
Ph: (661)832-5258
Fax: (661)836-4311
E-mail: info@aiage.org
URL: http://www.aiage.org
Descr: Provides information to clients and public leaders on architects' concerns and activities. **Freq:** monthly.

5507 ■ AzCA Journal
Arizona Counselors Association
PO Box 37603
Phoenix, AZ 85069-7603
Ph: (480)644-8162
E-mail: email@azca.org
URL: http://www.azca.org
Freq: annual.

5508 ■ AzCA Newsletter
Arizona Counselors Association
PO Box 37603
Phoenix, AZ 85069-7603
Ph: (480)644-8162
E-mail: email@azca.org
URL: http://www.azca.org
Freq: semiannual.

5509 ■ AzSAC Advisor
Arizona School Age Coalition
700 W Campbell, Ste. 3
Phoenix, AZ 85013
Ph: (602)279-7100
Fax: (602)234-3943
E-mail: mmcclintock@azafterschool.org
URL: http://www.azsac.org
Freq: quarterly.

5510 ■ Basics of Organizing: You Can't Build a Machine without Nuts and Bolts
National Training and Information Center
810 N Milwaukee Ave.
Chicago, IL 60642-4103
Ph: (312)243-3035
Fax: (312)243-7044

E-mail: ntic@ntic-us.org
URL: http://www.ntic-us.org
Price: $5.

5511 ■ The Beacon
Association for Career and Technical Education Research
North Carolina State University
13 Ricks Hall
Box 7607 NCSU
Raleigh, NC 27695
Ph: (919)515-1759
Fax: (919)515-9060
E-mail: barry_croom@ncsu.edu
URL: http://www.agri.wsu.edu/acter
Freq: quarterly.

5512 ■ Beacon
Michigan Association for the Education of Young Children
Beacon Pl.
4572 S Hagadorn Rd., Ste. 1-D
East Lansing, MI 48823-5385
Ph: (517)336-9700
Fax: (517)336-9790
E-mail: miaeyc@miaeyc.org
URL: http://www.miaeyc.org
Descr: Contains news, events, legislation, and people around the state. **Freq:** 3/year.

5513 ■ Best of The OARacle
Organization for Autism Research
2000 N 14th St., Ste. 710
Arlington, VA 22201
Ph: (703)243-9710
Fax: (703)243-9751
E-mail: oar@researchautism.org
URL: http://www.researchautism.org
Descr: Features a compilation of the most useful and relevant articles on autism and autism intervention published in The OARacle between 2002 and 2007. **Freq:** quinquennial.

5514 ■ Beyond the Basics: A Sourcebook for Sexual and Reproductive Health Education
Canadian Federation for Sexual Health
1 Nicholas St., Ste. 430
Ottawa, ON, Canada K1N 7B7
Ph: (613)241-4474
Fax: (613)241-7550
E-mail: admin@cfsh.ca
URL: http://www.cfsh.ca
Price: $70.

5515 ■ Beyond Standardized Tests: Admissions Alternatives That Work
National Center for Fair and Open Testing
15 Court Sq., Ste. 820
Boston, MA 02108
Ph: (857)350-8207
Fax: (857)350-8209
E-mail: info@fairtest.org
URL: http://www.fairtest.org

5516 ■ Bitter Earth: Child Sexual Abuse in Indian Country
National Indian Justice Center
5250 Aero Dr.
Santa Rosa, CA 95403
Ph: (707)579-5507
Fax: (707)579-9019
E-mail: nijc@aol.com
URL: http://www.nijc.org
Price: $49.

5517 ■ Black Student's Guide to Scholarships
Beckham Publications Group Inc.
13619 Cedar Creek Ln.
PO Box 4066
Silver Spring, MD 20904-5308
Ph: (301)384-7995
Free: 800-431-1579
Fax: (866)659-3306
E-mail: editor@beckhamhouse.com
URL: http://www.beckhamhouse.com
Covers: providers of financial aid for Black students pursuing a college education. **Entries include:**

Organization name, address, phone, name and title of contact, eligibility requirements, description of award or grant. **Freq:** Biennial, latest edition January 1997.

5518 ■ *Book of Forms*
Georgia Association on Young Children
368 Moreland Ave. NE, Ste. 240
Atlanta, GA 30307-1927
Ph: (404)222-0014
Fax: (404)222-0107
E-mail: gayc@algxmail.com
URL: http://gayconline.org

5519 ■ *BOSC Directory*
BOSC-Books on Special Children
PO Box 3378
Amherst, MA 01004-3378
Ph: (413)256-8164
Fax: (413)256-8896
E-mail: contact@boscbooks.com
Key Personnel: Irene Slovak, Editor, irene@boscbooks.com **URL(s):** http://www.boscbooks.com **Covers:** Schools and independent living programs; colleges and vocational training programs; clinics and centers agencies; and commercial consumer products of interest to professionals and parents of persons with disabilities. **Entries include:** Facility name, address, phone; name and title of contact; activities; courses and faculty; health care offered; student eligibility requirements; accommodations. **Freq:** Periodically.

5520 ■ *A BPD Brief*
National Education Alliance for Borderline Personality Disorder
PO Box 974
Rye, NY 10580
Ph: (914)835-9011
E-mail: info@neabpd.org
URL: http://www.neabpd.org
Descr: Provides an introductory overview of borderline personality disorder.

5521 ■ *Braille Book Review*
National Library Service for the Blind and Physically Handicapped
Library of Congress
1291 Taylor St. NW
Washington, DC 20011
Ph: (202)707-5100
Free: 888-657-7323
Fax: (202)707-0712
E-mail: nls@loc.gov
URL: http://www.loc.gov/nls/contact.html
URL(s): http://www.loc.gov/nls/bbr/index.html **Descr:** Bibliography of publications for the visually and physically handicapped (braille and large print). **Freq:** Bimonthly. **Price:** Free, to registered patrons of NLS.

5522 ■ *Braille Evangelism Bulletin*
Lutheran Braille Evangelism Association
1740 Eugene St.
White Bear Lake, MN 55110-3312
Ph: (651)426-0469
E-mail: lbea@qwest.net
URL: http://www.users.qwest.net/~lbea
Descr: Contains membership activities, and services and materials available. **Freq:** quarterly. **Price:** free.

5523 ■ *Braille Forum*
American Council of the Blind
1155 15th St. NW, Ste. 1004
Washington, DC 20005
Ph: (202)467-5081
Fax: (202)467-5085
E-mail: info@acb.org
URL: http://www.acb.org
Descr: Concerned with legislative developments, new products and services, medical and technological advances, and human interest stories for the

blind. **Freq:** monthly. **Price:** $25/year for companies or agencies.

5524 ■ *The Braille Forum*
American Council of the Blind Enterprises and Services
120 S 6th St., Ste. 1005
Minneapolis, MN 55402
Ph: (612)332-3242
Fax: (612)332-7850
E-mail: acbesall@ix.netcom.com
Descr: Contains information of interest both to ACB members and the general public. **Freq:** monthly.

5525 ■ *Braille Monitor*
National Federation of the Blind
1800 Johnson St.
Baltimore, MD 21230
Ph: (410)659-9314
Fax: (410)685-5653
E-mail: nfb@nfb.org
URL: http://www.nfb.org
Descr: Reports on action by the NFB on current legislative issues, legal cases, and social concerns affecting the blind; gives news of aids and appliances. **Freq:** 11/year. **Price:** included in membership dues, available to nonmembers by donation.

5526 ■ *Braille Monitor*
National Federation of the Blind
1800 Johnson St.
Baltimore, MD 21230
Ph: (410)659-9314
Fax: (410)685-5653
E-mail: nfb@nfb.org
URL: http://www.nfb.org
Key Personnel: Barbara Pierce, Editor, bpierce@nfb.org **URL(s):** http://www.nfb.org/nfb/Braille_Monitor.asp?SnID=997538716 **Descr:** Magazine covering news, activities, and programs of the National Federation of the Blind. **Freq:** 11/yr. **Price:** $25, individuals; $35, Canada; $75, other countries.

5527 ■ *Braille Technical Table Catalog*
National Braille Association
95 Allens Creek Rd., Bldg. 1, Ste. 202
Rochester, NY 14618
Ph: (585)427-8260
Fax: (585)427-0263
E-mail: nbaoffice@nationalbraille.org
URL: http://nationalbraille.org
Descr: Contains technical tables in the NBA collection; covers the fields of mathematics, statistics, chemistry, physics, computer science, and business. **Freq:** periodic. **Price:** free.

5528 ■ *Braille Textbook Code Formats and Techniques*
Braille Authority of North America
1805 N Oakland St.
Arlington, VA 22207
Ph: (202)707-0722
Fax: (202)707-0712
E-mail: jdix@loc.gov
URL: http://www.brailleauthority.org

5529 ■ *The Branch Line*
American Association of University Women, Richardson Texas Branch
PO Box 251347
Plano, TX 75025-1347
Ph: (214)415-3476
E-mail: janice@schieffer.us
URL: http://web2.airmail.net/~alistair/aauw
Freq: bimonthly.

5530 ■ *Branch Out*
American Association of University Women, Northern Palm Beach Branch
140 Ocean Pines Terr.
Jupiter, FL 33477
Ph: (561)748-9909
E-mail: sallyb2@aol.com
URL: http://www.florida-aauw.org/Branches/norpalm.htm

Descr: Includes announcements and upcoming events. **Freq:** monthly.

5531 ■ *BSA ChapterLetter*
Boston Society of Architects/American Institute of Architects
52 Broad St.
Boston, MA 02109
Ph: (617)951-1433
Fax: (617)951-0845
E-mail: njenner@architects.org
URL: http://www.architects.org

5532 ■ *Buckle Up*
National Association of Women Highway Safety Leaders
NH Highway Safety Agency
117 Manchester St.
Concord, NH 03301
Ph: (603)271-2131
Fax: (603)271-3790
E-mail: dgarvin@nhhsa.state.nh.us
URL: http://www.nawhsl.org

5533 ■ *Building Bridges: A Manual on Including People with Disabilities in International Exchange Programs*
Mobility International USA
132 E Broadway, Ste. 343
Eugene, OR 97401
Ph: (541)343-1284
Fax: (541)343-6812
E-mail: info@miusa.org
URL: http://www.miusa.org
Price: $20.

5534 ■ *Building Bridges: A Training Video on Including People with Disabilities in International Exchange Programs*
Mobility International USA
132 E Broadway, Ste. 343
Eugene, OR 97401
Ph: (541)343-1284
Fax: (541)343-6812
E-mail: info@miusa.org
URL: http://www.miusa.org
Descr: Available with captions and with or without audio description. **Price:** $49.

5535 ■ *Building Community Through Access*
Disabled Womyn's Educational Project
PO Box 8773
Madison, WI 53708-8773
Ph: (608)256-8883
Fax: (608)256-8883
E-mail: catherine-odette@juno.com

5536 ■ *Building Consumer Consensus on Independent Living*
Research and Training Center on Independent Living
University of Kansas
Dole Center, Ste. 4089
1000 Sunnyside Ave.
Lawrence, KS 66045-7561
Ph: (785)864-4095
Fax: (785)864-5063
E-mail: rtcil@ku.edu
URL: http://www.rtcil.org
Price: $1.35.

5537 ■ *Building an Inclusive Development Community: A Manual on Including People with Disabilities in International Development Programs*
Mobility International USA
132 E Broadway, Ste. 343
Eugene, OR 97401
Ph: (541)343-1284
Fax: (541)343-6812
E-mail: info@miusa.org
URL: http://www.miusa.org
Descr: Offers opinions, techniques and guidelines, resource lists, and examples of best practices from

around the world. **Price:** $40 plus $5 domestic and $12 international shipping.

5538 ■ *Building Links: Developer Initiatives for Financing Child Care*
Child Care Action Campaign
24808 Deepdale Ave.
Little Neck, NY 11362-1233
Ph: (212)239-0138
Fax: (212)268-6515
URL: http://www.childcareaction.org
Descr: Covers financing alternatives for child care and examines the ways in which communities have begun to involve real estate developers in child care. **Price:** $15 for members, $25 for nonmembers.

5539 ■ *California Perspective*
American Association of University Women, California
PO Box 160067
Sacramento, CA 95816-0067
Ph: (916)448-7795
Fax: (916)448-1729
E-mail: office@aauw-ca.org
URL: http://www.aauw-ca.org
Freq: 3/year. **Price:** included in membership dues.

5540 ■ *Campus Visits and College Interviews*
The College Board
45 Columbus Ave.
New York, NY 10023-6992
Ph: (212)713-8000
Fax: (212)649-8442
E-mail: publicaffairs@collegeboard.org
URL: http://www.collegeboard.com

5541 ■ *The Canadian Journal of Human Sexuality*
Sex Information and Education Council of Canada
850 Coxwell Ave.
Toronto, ON, Canada M4C 5R1
Ph: (416)466-5304
Fax: (416)778-0785
E-mail: sieccan@web.net
URL: http://www.sieccan.org
Freq: quarterly. **ISSN:** 1188-4517.

5542 ■ *Canadian Journal of Neurological Sciences*
Canadian Association for Child Neurology
7015 Macleod Trail SW, Ste. 709
Calgary, AB, Canada T2H 2K6
Ph: (403)229-9544
Fax: (403)229-1661
E-mail: info@cnsfederation.org
URL: http://www.ccns.org
Descr: Contains papers from all branches of neuroscience. **Freq:** quarterly. **Price:** $80/year for individuals.

5543 ■ *Canoeing and Kayaking for Persons with Physical Disabilities*
American Canoe Association
1340 Central Park Blvd., Ste. 210
Fredericksburg, VA 22401
Ph: (540)907-4460
Fax: (703)636-0296
E-mail: aca@americancanoe.org
URL: http://www.acanet.org

5544 ■ *CAPS Newsletter*
Center for Law and Education
1875 Connecticut Ave. NW, Ste. 510
Washington, DC 20009
Ph: (202)986-3000
Fax: (202)986-6648
E-mail: cle@cleweb.org
URL: http://www.cleweb.org

5545 ■ *Career College & Technology School Databook*
Chronicle Guidance Publications Inc.
66 Aurora St.
Moravia, NY 13118-3569
Ph: (315)497-0330
Free: 800-622-7284
Fax: (315)497-0339

E-mail: customerservice@chronicleguidance.com
URL: http://www.chronicleguidance.com
Key Personnel: Cheryl Fickeisen, Pres. & CEO; Gary Fickeisen, Vice President; Christopher Fickeisen, Asst. VP. **URL(s):** http://www.chronicleguidance.com **Covers:** Over 940 programs of study offered by more than 1,580 vocational schools. **Entries include:** School name, city and ZIP code, phone, programs offered, admissions requirements, costs, enrollment, financial aid programs, year established, and student services. **Freq:** Annual, latest edition 2009-2010. **Price:** $26.73, individuals, Softbound.

5546 ■ *Career Development Quarterly*
American Counseling Association
5999 Stevenson Ave.
Alexandria, VA 22304
Fax: (703)823-0252
E-mail: ryep@counseling.org
URL: http://www.counseling.org
Descr: Includes career counseling trends and reviews of current career counseling information. **Freq:** quarterly. **Price:** included in membership dues, $55/year for nonmembers, $100/year for institutions. **ISSN:** 0889-4019.

5547 ■ *Career Guidance*
Facts on File Inc.
132 W 31st St., 17th Fl.
New York, NY 10001
Ph: (212)967-8800
Free: 800-322-8755
Fax: 800-678-3633
E-mail: support@factsonfile.com
URL: http://factsonfile.infobasepublishing.com
URL(s): http://www.fofweb.com/subscription **Covers:** Approximately 1,200 career positions in 49 industries. **Entries include:** Information on educational institutions and programs, associations and unions, periodicals, Websites, books, and scholarships. **Freq:** Irregular.

5548 ■ *Career Planning and Employment Strategies for Postsecondary Students with Disabilities*
National Clearinghouse on Postsecondary Education for Individuals with Disabilities
2121 K St. NW, Ste. 220
Washington, DC 20052
Ph: (202)973-0904
Free: 800-544-3284
Fax: (202)973-0908
E-mail: heath@ace.nche.edu
URL: http://www.heath.gwu.edu/
Key Personnel: Robin Deykes, Editor; Rhona C. Hartman, Editor. **URL(s):** http://www.heath.gwu.edu **Covers:** about 30 educational institutions and organizations offering career placement programs for handicapped postsecondary students. **Entries include:** Institution name, address, phone, name and title of contact, program name, description of program. **Freq:** Annual. **Price:** Free.

5549 ■ *Career Tech Update*
Association for Career and Technical Education
1410 King St.
Alexandria, VA 22314
Ph: (703)683-3111
Fax: (703)683-7424
E-mail: acte@acteonline.org
URL: http://www.acteonline.org
Freq: semimonthly. **Price:** $139/year for nonmembers.

5550 ■ *Career and Technical Education Research*
Association for Career and Technical Education Research
North Carolina State University
13 Ricks Hall
Box 7607 NCSU
Raleigh, NC 27695
Ph: (919)515-1759
Fax: (919)515-9060

E-mail: barry_croom@ncsu.edu
URL: http://www.agri.wsu.edu/acter
Descr: Provides articles about training programs and research and development activities. **Freq:** quarterly. **Price:** included in membership dues, $57/year for nonmembers. **ISSN:** 0739-3369.

5551 ■ *Careers in Childhood Care and Education*
Georgia Association on Young Children
368 Moreland Ave. NE, Ste. 240
Atlanta, GA 30307-1927
Ph: (404)222-0014
Fax: (404)222-0107
E-mail: gayc@algxmail.com
URL: http://gayconline.org

5552 ■ *careLearning.com*
Arkansas Hospital Association
419 Natural Resources Dr.
Little Rock, AR 72205
Ph: (501)224-7878
Fax: (501)224-0519
E-mail: aha@arkhospitals.org
URL: http://www.arkhospitals.org
Freq: monthly.

5553 ■ *Caring, Stimulating, Responsive*
National AfterSchool Association
PO Box 34447
Washington, DC 20043
Fax: 888-568-6590
E-mail: menglish@naaweb.org
URL: http://www.naaweb.org

5554 ■ *The Case Against School Vouchers*
Americans for Religious Liberty
PO Box 6656
Silver Spring, MD 20916
Ph: (301)260-2988
Fax: (301)260-2989
E-mail: arlinc@verizon.net
URL: http://www.arlinc.org
Descr: Includes member and research news. **Price:** included in membership dues, $15.95 for nonmembers.

5555 ■ *Catalog of Committee for Children-Prevention Education Resources*
Committee for Children
568 1st Ave. S, Ste. 600
Seattle, WA 98104-2804
Ph: (206)343-1223
Fax: (206)438-6765
E-mail: info@cfchildren.org
URL: http://www.cfchildren.org
Freq: semiannual. **Price:** free.

5556 ■ *Catalog of Programs and Services*
Educational Records Bureau
220 E 42nd St.
New York, NY 10017
Ph: (212)672-9800
Fax: (212)370-4096
E-mail: info@erbtest.org
URL: http://www.erbtest.org
Freq: annual.

5557 ■ *Catalogue of Publications*
Research and Training Center on Independent Living
University of Kansas
Dole Center, Ste. 4089
1000 Sunnyside Ave.
Lawrence, KS 66045-7561
Ph: (785)864-4095
Fax: (785)864-5063
E-mail: rtcil@ku.edu
URL: http://www.rtcil.org
Descr: Lists publications available from the center; includes abstracts. **Freq:** annual.

5558 ■ *Catalyst*
Arc of Middlesex County
219 Black Horse Ln., Ste. 1
North Brunswick, NJ 08902
Ph: (732)821-1199

Fax: (732)247-5590
E-mail: rsheridan@arc-middlesex.org
URL: http://www.arc-middlesex.org
Freq: quarterly.

5559 ■ *Catching Up: A Review of the Women's Educational Equity Act Program*
National Coalition for Women and Girls in Education
1111 16th St. NW
Washington, DC 20036
Ph: (202)785-7793
Fax: (202)872-1425
E-mail: maatzl@aauw.org
URL: http://www.ncwge.org

5560 ■ *Catholic Schools: The Facts*
Americans for Religious Liberty
PO Box 6656
Silver Spring, MD 20916
Ph: (301)260-2988
Fax: (301)260-2989
E-mail: arlinc@verizon.net
URL: http://www.arlinc.org
Price: $10.

5561 ■ *Centegram*
Center on Education and Training for Employment
Ohio State University
1900 Kenny Rd.
Columbus, OH 43210-1016
Ph: (614)292-6991
Fax: (614)292-1260
E-mail: chambers.2@osu.edu
URL: http://www.cete.org
Descr: Features news on the center's current works and upcoming events. **Freq:** quarterly.

5562 ■ *Certification and Education Programs*
American Council on Exercise
4851 Paramount Dr.
San Diego, CA 92123
Ph: (858)279-8227
Fax: (858)279-8064
E-mail: support@acefitness.org
URL: http://www.acefitness.org

5563 ■ *CESI Newsletter*
Canadian Educational Standards Institute
PO Box 3013
St. Catharines, ON, Canada L2R 7C3
Ph: (905)684-5658
Fax: (905)684-6723
E-mail: execdir@cesi.edu
URL: http://www.cesi.edu/wordpress
Freq: quarterly. **Price:** free.

5564 ■ *The Challenger*
Arc of East Central Iowa
680 2nd St., Ste. 200
Cedar Rapids, IA 52401
Ph: (319)365-0487
Fax: (319)365-9938
E-mail: dpetersen@arceci.org
URL: http://www.arceci.org
Freq: monthly.

5565 ■ *Charrette*
American Institute of Architects San Mateo County
307 S B St., No. 5
San Mateo, CA 94401
Ph: (650)348-5133
Fax: (650)348-7427
E-mail: connieb@aiasmc.org
URL: http://www.aiasmc.org
Freq: quarterly.

5566 ■ *Charrette*
American Institute of Architects Orlando
930 Woodcock Rd., Ste. 226
Orlando, FL 32803
Ph: (407)898-7006
Fax: (407)892-3399
E-mail: info@aiaorlando.com
URL: http://www.aiaorlando.com

Descr: Features latest news and events in the organization.

5567 ■ *Charter Education*
Ethics Resource Center
2345 Crystal Dr., Ste. 201
Arlington, VA 22202
Ph: (703)647-2185
Fax: (703)647-2180
E-mail: ethics@ethics.org
URL: http://www.ethics.org

5568 ■ *Checkset*
Texas Society of Architects/ AIA
816 Congress Ave., Ste. 970
Austin, TX 78701-2443
Ph: (512)478-7386
Fax: (512)478-0528
E-mail: info@texasarchitect.org
URL: http://www.texasarchitect.org
Descr: Contains information about individual members' professional achievements and personal accomplishments. **Freq:** bimonthly. **Price:** included in membership dues.

5569 ■ *The Child Advocate*
Washington State PTA
2003 65th Ave. W
Tacoma, WA 98466-6215
Ph: (253)565-2153
Fax: (253)565-7753
E-mail: wapta@wastatepta.org
URL: http://www.wastatepta.org

5570 ■ *The Child Defender*
Children's Defense Fund, Minnesota
555 Park St.
St. Paul, MN 55103
Ph: (651)227-6121
Fax: (651)227-2553
E-mail: cdf-mn@cdf-mn.org
URL: http://www.cdf-mn.org

5571 ■ *Child Health*
Canadian Institute of Child Health
384 Bank St., Ste. 300
Ottawa, ON, Canada K2P 1Y4
Ph: (613)230-8838
Fax: (613)230-6654
E-mail: cich@cich.ca
URL: http://www.cich.ca
Freq: quarterly. **Price:** included in membership dues.

5572 ■ *Child Support Quarterly*
National Child Support Enforcement Association
1760 Old Meadow Rd., Ste. 500
McLean, VA 22102
Ph: (703)506-2880
Fax: (703)506-3266
E-mail: colleeneubanks@ncsea.org
URL: http://www.ncsea.org
Freq: quarterly.

5573 ■ *Children at Risk: Failure of the Federal Child Restraint Recall Program*
Center for Auto Safety
1825 Connecticut Ave. NW, Ste. 330
Washington, DC 20009-5708
Ph: (202)328-7700
E-mail: accounts@autosafety.org
URL: http://www.autosafety.org

5574 ■ *Children with Special Needs*
Toy Industry Association
1115 Broadway, Ste. 400
New York, NY 10010
Ph: (212)675-1141
E-mail: info@toyassociation.org
URL: http://www.toyassociation.org

5575 ■ *Children's Fashions and Special Needs*
P.R.I.D.E. Foundation - Promote Real Independence for the Disabled and Elderly
391 Long Hill Rd.
Groton, CT 06340-1293
Ph: (860)445-7320

Fax: (860)445-1448
E-mail: sewtique@aol.com
URL: http://www.sewtiqueonline.com/pride.htm

5576 ■ *Choosing Better Schools: A report on student transfers under the No Child Left Behind Act*
Citizens' Commission on Civil Rights
2000 M St. NW, Ste. 400
Washington, DC 20036
Ph: (202)659-5565
Fax: (202)223-5302
E-mail: citizen@cccr.org
URL: http://www.cccr.org

5577 ■ *Chronicle Two-Year College Databook*
Chronicle Guidance Publications Inc.
66 Aurora St.
Moravia, NY 13118-3569
Ph: (315)497-0330
Free: 800-622-7284
Fax: (315)497-0339
E-mail: customerservice@chronicleguidance.com
URL: http://www.chronicleguidance.com
URL(s): http://www.chronicleguidance.com **Covers:** Over 954 associate, certificate, occupational, and transfer programs offered by more than 2,509 technical institutes, two-year colleges, and universities in the United States. **Entries include:** College charts section gives college name, address, phone; accreditation, enrollment, admissions, costs, financial aid; accrediting associations' names, addresses, and phone numbers. **Freq:** Annual, latest edition 2008-2009. **Price:** $25.47, individuals, softbound.

5578 ■ *Church Schools and Public Money - the Politics of Parochiaid*
Americans for Religious Liberty
PO Box 6656
Silver Spring, MD 20916
Ph: (301)260-2988
Fax: (301)260-2989
E-mail: arlinc@verizon.net
URL: http://www.arlinc.org
Price: $14.95.

5579 ■ *CIS Network News*
Communities In Schools
2345 Crytal Dr., Ste. 801
Arlington, VA 22202
Ph: (703)519-8999
E-mail: cis@cisnet.org
URL: http://www.cisnet.org
Freq: quarterly. **Price:** free. **ISSN:** 1069-966X.

5580 ■ *Classroom Management Series*
National Association of Special Education Teachers
1250 Connecticut Ave. NW, Ste. 200
Washington, DC 20036
E-mail: contactus@naset.org
URL: http://www.naset.org
Descr: Provides teachers with practical guidelines covering a variety of topics and supportive information. **Freq:** monthly.

5581 ■ *CLEA Newsletter*
Clinical Legal Education Association
New York University School of Law
245 Sullivan St., 5th Fl.
New York, NY 10012
Ph: (212)998-6441
Fax: (212)995-4031
E-mail: clea@cleaweb.org
URL: http://www.cleaweb.org

5582 ■ *CLEP Official Study Guide*
The College Board
45 Columbus Ave.
New York, NY 10023-6992
Ph: (212)713-8000
Fax: (212)649-8442
E-mail: publicaffairs@collegeboard.org
URL: http://www.collegeboard.com

Freq: annual.

5583 ■ *CLINews*
Community Learning and Information Network
1750 K St. NW, Ste. 1200
Washington, DC 20006
Ph: (202)857-2330
Fax: (202)835-0643
E-mail: bpurdy@clin.org
URL: http://www.clin.org
Freq: quarterly.

5584 ■ *Coalition Exchange*
National Coalition for Consumer Education
1701 K St. NW, Ste. 1200
Washington, DC 20006
Ph: (202)835-3323
Fax: (202)835-0747
E-mail: info@nclnet.org
URL: http://www.nclnet.org
Descr: Reports on consumer education programs
and projects. **Freq:** quarterly.

5585 ■ *The College Application Essay*
The College Board
45 Columbus Ave.
New York, NY 10023-6992
Ph: (212)713-8000
Fax: (212)649-8442
E-mail: publicaffairs@collegeboard.org
URL: http://www.collegeboard.com

5586 ■ *College Board Book of Majors*
The College Board
45 Columbus Ave.
New York, NY 10023-6992
Ph: (212)713-8000
Fax: (212)649-8442
E-mail: publicaffairs@collegeboard.org
URL: http://www.collegeboard.com
Freq: biennial.

5587 ■ *The College Board College Cost and
Financial Aid Handbook*
College Board
45 Columbus Ave.
New York, NY 10023-6917
Ph: (212)713-8000
Free: 800-323-7155
Fax: (212)713-8143
E-mail: info@atl.collegeboard.com
URL: http://www.collegeboard.com
URL(s): http://store.collegeboard.com **Entries in-
clude:** Institution name, address, financial aid
programs, application deadline, need analysis docu-
ment, tuition, fees. **Publication includes:** List of
complete costs and financial aid availability at over
3,100 twoand four-year colleges and universities.
Principal content of publication is information on the
costs of college education and obtaining financial
aid. **Freq:** Annual, latest edition 2003.

5588 ■ *College Board College Handbook*
The College Board
45 Columbus Ave.
New York, NY 10023-6992
Ph: (212)713-8000
Fax: (212)649-8442
E-mail: publicaffairs@collegeboard.org
URL: http://www.collegeboard.com
Freq: annual.

5589 ■ *College Board Review*
The College Board
45 Columbus Ave.
New York, NY 10023-6992
Ph: (212)713-8000
Fax: (212)649-8442
E-mail: publicaffairs@collegeboard.org
URL: http://www.collegeboard.com
Descr: Covers fresh, provocative topics. **Freq:**
3/year. **Price:** $30/year, $55/2 years, $80/3 years.

5590 ■ *College and Career Programs for Deaf
Students*
Gallaudet Research Institute
Graduate School & Professional Programs

Gallaudet University
Hall Memorial Bldg., 4th Fl.
800 Florida Ave., NE South Wing
Washington, DC 20002-3695
Ph: (202)651-5575
Fax: (202)651-5746
E-mail: gri.offices@gallaudet.edu
URL: http://gri.gallaudet.edu
Key Personnel: Dr. Michael A. Karchmer, Director,
michael.karchmer@gallaudet.edu; Sally W Dunn,
Coord. of Special Projects, sally.dunn@gallaudet.
edu; Sue A. Hotto, Survey/Editorial Design Specialist, sue.hotto@gallaudet.edu. **URL(s):** http://gri.
gallaudet.edu/ccg **Covers:** Over 125 colleges and
universities in the U.S. available to interested, qualified deaf students. **Entries include:** programs
descriptions by state and a question and answer
section for students. Each program description
includes information about admissions, enrollment,
costs, and support services available. **Price:** $12.95,
individuals, fax or order on-line.

5591 ■ *College Counseling Sourcebook*
The College Board
45 Columbus Ave.
New York, NY 10023-6992
Ph: (212)713-8000
Fax: (212)649-8442
E-mail: publicaffairs@collegeboard.org
URL: http://www.collegeboard.com
Freq: annual.

5592 ■ *College Scoop*
The College Board
45 Columbus Ave.
New York, NY 10023-6992
Ph: (212)713-8000
Fax: (212)649-8442
E-mail: publicaffairs@collegeboard.org
URL: http://www.collegeboard.com
Freq: biennial.

5593 ■ *College Student's Guide to Merit and
Other No-Need Funding*
Reference Service Press
5000 Windplay Dr., Ste. 4
El Dorado Hills, CA 95762-9600
Ph: (916)939-9620
Fax: (916)939-9626
E-mail: info@rspfunding.com
URL: http://www.rspfunding.com
Key Personnel: Gail A. Schlachter, Author,
gailschlachter@rspfunding.com; R. David Weber,
Author. **URL(s):** http://www.rspfunding.com **Covers:**
More than 1,300 scholarship and financial aid op-
portunities available to college students regardless
of income. **Entries include:** Sponsor name, address,
phone, fax, email, website, description. **Freq:** Bien-
nial, Latest edition 2008-2010. **Price:** $32.50,
individuals, Hardcover.

5594 ■ *CollegeEd Family Handbooks*
The College Board
45 Columbus Ave.
New York, NY 10023-6992
Ph: (212)713-8000
Fax: (212)649-8442
E-mail: publicaffairs@collegeboard.org
URL: http://www.collegeboard.com

5595 ■ *CollegeEd Student Workbooks*
The College Board
45 Columbus Ave.
New York, NY 10023-6992
Ph: (212)713-8000
Fax: (212)649-8442
E-mail: publicaffairs@collegeboard.org
URL: http://www.collegeboard.com

5596 ■ *CollegeEd Teachers Guides*
The College Board
45 Columbus Ave.
New York, NY 10023-6992
Ph: (212)713-8000
Fax: (212)649-8442

E-mail: publicaffairs@collegeboard.org
URL: http://www.collegeboard.com

5597 ■ *Common Ground*
Common Ground
604 Mission St., 10th Fl.
San Francisco, CA 94105
Ph: (415)459-4900
Fax: (415)459-4974
E-mail: ads@commongroundmag.com
URL: http://www.commongroundmag.com/
Key Personnel: Baha'uddin Alpine, Publisher.
URL(s): http://www.commongroundmag.com **Covers:** Music schools; art instructors; educational
programs; conferences and festivals; natural and
health food restaurants and suppliers; medicine and
dentistry professionals who emphasize preventive
health care; holistic health practitioners; individuals
engaged in the psychic arts, psychology, and psychic
healing; retreat sites, camps, hot springs, and inns;
publications, book publishers, and other sources of
materials; gyms, dance studios, yoga instructors,
and instructors in the martial arts; palmists and
astrologists. All listings are paid. Coverage is
primarily of northern California. **Entries include:**
Generally, name, address, phone, name of contact,
description of services, program, or merchandise.
Freq: Quarterly, Latest edition 2009.

5598 ■ *Common Sense*
Common Cause Wisconsin
PO Box 2597
Madison, WI 53701-2597
Ph: (608)256-2686
Fax: (866)252-3758
E-mail: ccwisjwh@itis.com
URL: http://www.commoncause.org/site/pp.
asp?c=dkLNK1MQIwG&b=1776959
Descr: Features updates on issues and activities for
statewide membership. **Freq:** quarterly. **Price:** free.

5599 ■ *The Complete Scholarship Book*
Sourcebooks Inc.
1935 Brookdale Rd., Ste. 139
Naperville, IL 60563
Ph: (630)961-3900
Free: 800-432-7444
Fax: (630)961-2168
URL: http://www.sourcebooks.com
URL(s): http://www.sourcebooks.com **Covers:** More
than 3,000 scholarship sources. **Entries include:**
Source name, address, phone, scholarship major,
ethnicity, religion. **Freq:** Latest edition 2000. **Price:**
$18.95, individuals.

5600 ■ *Computer Access, Resource Manual*
Carroll Center for the Blind
770 Centre St.
Newton, MA 02458
Ph: (617)969-6200
Fax: (617)969-6204
E-mail: info@carroll.org
URL: http://www.carroll.org
Price: $20.

5601 ■ *Conference Reports*
Leadership Conference Education Fund
1629 K St. NW, No. 1010
Washington, DC 20006
Ph: (202)466-3311
E-mail: comlcef@civilrights.org
URL: http://www.wecaretoo.com/Organizations/DC/
lcef.html

5602 ■ *Connection*
Delaware Valley Association for the Education of
Young Children
1608 Walnut St., Ste. 1400
Philadelphia, PA 19103
Ph: (215)893-0130
Fax: (215)893-0205
E-mail: members@dvaeyc.org
URL: http://www.dvaeyc.org

Freq: bimonthly.

5603 ■ *Connections*
PROVAIL - Life Opportunities for People with Disabilities
3670 Stone Way N
Seattle, WA 98103-8004
Ph: (206)363-7303
Fax: (206)361-5628
E-mail: mikeh@provail.org
URL: http://www.provail.org
Freq: quarterly.

5604 ■ *Connections/EdTech News*
Commonwealth of Learning
1055 W Hastings St., Ste. 1200
Vancouver, BC, Canada V6E 2E9
Ph: (604)775-8200
Fax: (604)775-8210
E-mail: info@col.org
URL: http://www.col.org/Pages/default.aspx
Freq: 3/year.

5605 ■ *Consumers as Collaborators in Research and Action*
Research and Training Center on Independent Living
University of Kansas
Dole Center, Ste. 4089
1000 Sunnyside Ave.
Lawrence, KS 66045-7561
Ph: (785)864-4095
Fax: (785)864-5063
E-mail: rtcil@ku.edu
URL: http://www.rtcil.org
Price: $5.

5606 ■ *Contact*
Missouri PTA
2100 I 70 Dr. SW
Columbia, MO 65203
Ph: (573)445-4161
Fax: (573)445-4163
E-mail: office@mopta.org
URL: http://www.mopta.org
Freq: 7/year. **Price:** $7.

5607 ■ *Continuing Danger: A Study of Child Fatalities in NYC*
Children's Rights
330 7th Ave., 4th Fl.
New York, NY 10001
Ph: (212)683-2210
Fax: (212)683-4015
E-mail: info@childrensrights.org
URL: http://www.childrensrights.org

5608 ■ *Corporate Brochure*
Goodwill Industries International
15810 Indianola Dr.
Rockville, MD 20855
Ph: (301)530-6500
E-mail: contactus@goodwill.org
URL: http://www.goodwill.org
Freq: annual.

5609 ■ *The Cost of Program Models Providing Personal Assistance Services for Independent Living*
World Institute on Disability
510 16th St., Ste. 100
Oakland, CA 94612
Ph: (510)763-4100
Fax: (510)763-4109
E-mail: wid@wid.org
URL: http://www.wid.org
Price: $10.

5610 ■ *The Council*
Governor's Planning Council for People with Disabilities, Indiana
150 W Market St., No. 628
Indianapolis, IN 46204
Ph: (317)232-7770
Fax: (317)233-3712
E-mail: gpcpd@gpcpd.org
URL: http://www.in.gov/gpcpd

Descr: Describes the Council's responsibilities and activities.

5611 ■ *Council Chronicles*
National Association of Councils on Developmental Disabilities
1660 L St. NW, Ste. 700
Washington, DC 20036
Ph: (202)506-5813
Fax: (202)506-5846
E-mail: info@nacdd.org
URL: http://www.nacdd.org

5612 ■ *Council Directory*
Council of the Great City Schools
1301 Pennsylvania Ave. NW, Ste. 702
Washington, DC 20004
Ph: (202)393-2427
Fax: (202)393-2400
E-mail: mcasserly@cgcs.org
URL: http://www.cgcs.org
Freq: annual.

5613 ■ *The Counseling Psychologist*
Student Affiliate Group
University of Akron
Department of Psychology
Arts and Sciences Bldg.
Akron, OH 44325-4301
Ph: (330)972-7280
Fax: (330)972-5174
E-mail: sag@uakron.edu
URL: http://www3.uakron.edu/sagweb
Price: included in membership dues.

5614 ■ *Counseling and Values*
American Counseling Association
5999 Stevenson Ave.
Alexandria, VA 22304
Fax: (703)823-0252
E-mail: ryep@counseling.org
URL: http://www.counseling.org
Descr: Focuses on the role of values and religion in counseling. **Freq:** 3/year. **Price:** included in membership dues, $41/year for individuals, $50/year for institutions. **ISSN:** 0160-7960.

5615 ■ *The Courage to Question: Women's Studies and Student Learning*
National Women's Studies Association
7100 Baltimore Ave., Ste. 502
College Park, MD 20740
Ph: (301)403-0407
Fax: (301)403-4137
E-mail: nwsaoffice@nwsa.org
URL: http://www.nwsa.org
Descr: Features new research on multicultural learning, critical thinking, classroom dynamics, and integrating knowledge into life choice. **Price:** $17.

5616 ■ *The Crusader*
ARC Community Services
564 Main St.
Fitchburg, MA 01420
Ph: (978)343-6662
Fax: (978)343-8852
E-mail: info@arccommunityservices.org
URL: http://www.arccommunityservices.org
Descr: Contains information on the organization.
Freq: quarterly. **Price:** included in membership dues.

5617 ■ *Current Awareness Literature Alert*
National Patient Safety Foundation
268 Summer St., 6th Fl.
Boston, MA 02210
Ph: (617)391-9900
Fax: (617)391-9999
E-mail: info@npsf.org
URL: http://www.npsf.org
Freq: semimonthly.

5618 ■ *Dan Cassidy's Worldwide Graduate Scholarship Directory*
Career Press Inc.
3 Tice Rd.
PO Box 687
Franklin Lakes, NJ 07417

Ph: (201)848-0310
Free: 800-227-3371
Fax: (201)848-1727
E-mail: ronfry@careerpress.com
URL: http://www.careerpress.com
Key Personnel: Daniel J. Cassidy, Author, abrooks@careerpress.com. **URL(s):** http://www.careerpress.com **Covers:** private organizations providing financial aids for graduate students to study in the U.S. **Entries include:** Organization name, address, phone, amount awarded, deadlines for applications, fields of study awarded, brief description. **Freq:** Irregular, 5th ed.

5619 ■ *DCC Notes*
South Dakota Council on Developmental Disabilities
Hillsview Plaza, E Hwy. 34
500 E Capitol
Pierre, SD 57501-5070
Ph: (605)773-6369
Fax: (605)773-5483
E-mail: infoddc@state.sd.us
URL: http://www.state.sd.us/dhs/ddc
Descr: Lists informal items related to council meetings, website information and training events. **Freq:** quarterly.

5620 ■ *DD Quarterly*
Ohio Developmental Disabilities Planning Council
Ohio Developmental Disabilities Council
Atlas Bldg., 12th Fl.
8 E Long St.
Columbus, OH 43215
Ph: (614)466-5205
Fax: (614)466-0298
E-mail: peter.keiser@cchmc.org
URL: http://ddc.ohio.gov
Freq: quarterly.

5621 ■ *Dealing Creatively with Death: A Manual of Death Education and Simple Burial*
Funeral Consumers Alliance of Western Pennsylvania
PO Box 8974
Pittsburgh, PA 15221-0974
Ph: (412)241-0705
E-mail: fcawp@verizon.net
URL: http://www.funerals.org/affiliates/westernpa
Descr: Contains information and suggestions regarding burial arrangement. **Price:** $9.

5622 ■ *Decisions*
Students Against Destructive Decisions, Students Against Drunk Driving
255 Main St.
Marlborough, MA 01752
Fax: (508)481-5759
E-mail: info@sadd.org
URL: http://www.sadd.org
Freq: 3/year.

5623 ■ *DETC Accreditation Handbook*
Distance Education and Training Council
1601 18th St. NW, Ste. 2
Washington, DC 20009
Ph: (202)234-5100
Fax: (202)332-1386
E-mail: karen@detc.org
URL: http://www.detc.org
Descr: Contains the commission's policies, procedures and standards. **Freq:** annual. **Price:** $30/copy.

5624 ■ *DETC News*
Distance Education and Training Council
1601 18th St. NW, Ste. 2
Washington, DC 20009
Ph: (202)234-5100
Fax: (202)332-1386
E-mail: karen@detc.org
URL: http://www.detc.org
Descr: Includes information on accreditation, ethics and standards. Includes council news, book reviews,

calendar of events and research. **Freq:** semiannual. **Price:** free.

5625 ■ Diabetes Action
Diabetes Action Research and Education Foundation
426 C St. NE
Washington, DC 20002
Ph: (202)333-4520
Fax: (202)558-5240
E-mail: info@diabetesaction.org
URL: http://www.diabetesaction.org
Freq: monthly.

5626 ■ The Digest of Volume 1-7 of the DDR Newsletter New Developments
Developmental Delay Resources
5801 Beacon St.
Pittsburgh, PA 15217
Fax: (412)422-1374
E-mail: devdelay@mindspring.com
URL: http://www.devdelay.org
Descr: Indexed by subject and name.

5627 ■ Directory of Accredited Counseling Services
International Association of Counseling Services
101 S Whiting St., Ste. 211
Alexandria, VA 22304-3416
Ph: (703)823-9840
Fax: (703)823-9843
E-mail: iacsinc@earthlink.net
URL: http://www.iacsinc.org/
Key Personnel: Nancy E. Roncketti, Contact.
URL(s): http://iacsinc.org/iacsmem.html **Covers:** About 200 accredited services in the United States and Canada concerned with psychological, educational, and vocational counseling, including those at colleges and universities, and public and private agencies. **Entries include:** Name, address, phone, hours of operation, director's name, service, clientele served. **Freq:** Annual, September. **Price:** $50, payment with order. Institutional orders accepted.

5628 ■ Directory of Accredited Distance Education Institutions
Distance Education and Training Council
1601 18th St. NW, Ste. 2
Washington, DC 20009
Ph: (202)234-5100
Fax: (202)332-1386
E-mail: karen@detc.org
URL: http://www.detc.org
Descr: Lists schools and their courses accredited by the council. **Freq:** annual. **Price:** free.

5629 ■ Directory of Accredited Organizations
American Accreditation Healthcare Commission
1220 L St. NW, Ste. 400
Washington, DC 20005
Ph: (202)216-9010
Fax: (202)216-9006
E-mail: communications@urac.org
URL: http://www.urac.org
Freq: annual. **Price:** $39/copy.

5630 ■ Directory of Branch Presidents and Members
National Association of University Women
1001 E St. SE
Washington, DC 20003
Ph: (202)547-3967
Fax: (202)547-5226
E-mail: info@nauw1910.org
URL: http://www.nauw1910.org
Freq: annual.

5631 ■ Directory of Chapter Programs and Services
New York State Association of Retarded Citizens
393 Delaware Ave.
Delmar, NY 12054
Ph: (518)439-8311
Fax: (518)439-1893
E-mail: info@nysarc.org
URL: http://www.nysarc.org

Freq: biennial.

5632 ■ Directory of Financial Aids for Women
Reference Service Press
5000 Windplay Dr., Ste. 4
El Dorado Hills, CA 95762-9600
Ph: (916)939-9620
Fax: (916)939-9626
E-mail: info@rspfunding.com
URL: http://www.rspfunding.com
Key Personnel: Gail Ann Schlachter, Author, gailschlachter@rspfunding.com; R. David Weber, Author. **URL(s):** http://www.rspfunding.com; http://www.rspfunding.com/catalog/item/1414261/872134.htm **Covers:** More than 1,500 scholarships, fellowships, loan sources, grants, awards, internships, and state government educational assistance programs; includes annotated list of 60 financial aid directories. Sponsors include institutions, associations, businesses, government bodies, etc. **Entries include:** Program title, sponsor name, address, phone, fax, toll-free phone, purpose, candidate eligibility, financial details, duration, restrictions, application details and deadline, number awarded, etc. **Freq:** Biennial, latest edition 2009-2011. **Price:** $45, individuals, Hardcover.

5633 ■ Directory of Graduate Programs
Graduate Record Examinations Board
PO Box 6000
Princeton, NJ 08541-6000
Ph: (609)771-7670
Fax: (610)290-8975
E-mail: gre-info@rosedale.org
URL: http://www.ets.org/gre
Freq: biennial.

5634 ■ Directory of Member Agencies
National Foundation for Credit Counseling
801 Roeder Rd., Ste. 900
Silver Spring, MD 20910
Ph: (301)589-5600
Fax: (301)495-5623
E-mail: press@nfcc.org
URL: http://www.nfcc.org
Freq: annual. **Price:** $1/copy.

5635 ■ Directory of Rural Education Programs and Centers
National Rural Education Association
Purdue University
Beering Hall of Liberal Arts and Education
100 N University St.
West Lafayette, IN 47907-2098
Ph: (765)494-0086
Fax: (765)496-1228
E-mail: jehill@purdue.edu
URL: http://www.nrea.net
Freq: periodic.

5636 ■ Directory of Services for Blind and Visually Impaired Persons in the United States and Canada
American Foundation for the Blind
2 Penn Plaza, Ste. 1102
New York, NY 10121
Ph: (212)502-7600
Free: 800-232-5463
Fax: (212)502-7777
E-mail: afbdirectory@afb.net
URL: http://www.afb.org
URL(s): http://www.afb.org **Covers:** Information on more than 1,500 organizations and agencies that serve people who are blind or visually impaired. Lists schools, agencies, organizations, and programs in the governmental and private, nonprofit sectors that provide a wide variety of direct and indirect services, information, and other assistance to blind and visually impaired children and adults, their families, and professionals who work with them. **Entries include:** Name or organization, address, website address, phone, fax, general e-mail, contact persons, general information about agency (date of organization's establishment, mission statement, organization type, funding, budget, number of clients served, staff, ages served, geographic area served, fee structure, facil-

ity accessibility, program eligibility requirements, hours of operation, publications), description of services offered by the organization. **Freq:** Irregular. **Price:** $79.95, individuals.

5637 ■ Disability Awareness Guide
VSA arts
818 Connecticut Ave. NW, Ste. 600
Washington, DC 20006
Ph: (202)628-2800
Fax: (202)429-0868
E-mail: info@vsarts.org
URL: http://www.vsarts.org
Descr: Serves as an informational tool for those who want to gain additional knowledge about disability and tips for social etiquette. **Freq:** periodic.

5638 ■ Disability Information at Your Fingertips, 3rd Edition
Disability Resources
4 Glatter Ln.
Centereach, NY 11720-1032
Ph: (631)585-0290
Fax: (631)585-0290
E-mail: info@disabilityresources.org
URL: http://www.disabilityresources.org
Price: $10.

5639 ■ Disability Medicine
American Board of Independent Medical Examiners
6470-A Merritts Creek Rd.
Huntington, WV 25702
Ph: (304)733-0095
Fax: (304)733-5243
E-mail: info@abime.org
URL: http://www.abime.org
Freq: quarterly. **Price:** $100.

5640 ■ Disability Resources Monthly
Disability Resources
4 Glatter Ln.
Centereach, NY 11720-1032
Ph: (631)585-0290
Fax: (631)585-0290
E-mail: info@disabilityresources.org
URL: http://www.disabilityresources.org
Descr: Reports on and reviews resources for independent living. **Freq:** monthly. **Price:** $33/year in U.S., $43/year outside U.S. **ISSN:** 1070-7220.

5641 ■ Disability Rights News
Disability Rights Education and Defense Fund
2212 6th St.
Berkeley, CA 94710
Ph: (510)644-2555
Fax: (510)841-8645
E-mail: info@dredf.org
URL: http://www.dredf.org
Freq: quarterly.

5642 ■ Disabled Children in Physical Education: Learning Through Movement
Disabled Sports USA
451 Hungerford Dr., Ste. 100
Rockville, MD 20850
Ph: (301)217-0960
Fax: (301)217-0968
E-mail: information@dsusa.org
URL: http://www.dsusa.org
Descr: Overviews proper adapted physical education programs for disabled children. **Price:** $14.95.

5643 ■ Disabled Driver's Mobility Guide
American Automobile Association
1000 AAA Dr.
PO Box 28
Heathrow, FL 32746-5063
Ph: (407)444-4240
Free: 800-222-4357
Fax: (407)444-4247
URL: http://www.aaasouth.com
Key Personnel: Kay Hamada, Editor, khamada@national.aaa.com. **Covers:** approximately 550 driving aid manufacturers, driving schools, publishers, government agencies, universities, and other organizations and companies offering services and prod-

ucts to the disabled driver; over 20 VA-approved hand control and lift manufacturers, and augmented driving systems. **Entries include:** Organization, publisher, or manufacturer name, address, phone, code for products or services; travel tips and state insurance commissioners. **Freq:** Biennial, May of odd years.

5644 ■ *Do-It-Yourself Credit File Correction Guide*
Institute of Consumer Financial Education
PO Box 34070
San Diego, CA 92163-4070
Ph: (619)239-1401
Fax: (619)923-3284
E-mail: icfe@cox.net
URL: http://www.financial-education-icfe.org

5645 ■ *Do You Know the Players?*
Washington Association for Career and Technical Education
PO Box 315
Olympia, WA 98507-0315
Ph: (360)786-9286
Fax: (360)357-1491
E-mail: wa-acte@wa-acte.org
URL: http://www.wa-acte.org
Freq: annual.

5646 ■ *Documenting the Success of Vocational Equity Programs for Women and Girls*
National Coalition for Women and Girls in Education
1111 16th St. NW
Washington, DC 20036
Ph: (202)785-7793
Fax: (202)872-1425
E-mail: maatzl@aauw.org
URL: http://www.ncwge.org

5647 ■ *Don't Miss Out*
Octameron Associates
PO Box 2748
Alexandria, VA 22301-2748
Ph: (703)836-5480
Fax: (703)836-5650
E-mail: octameron@aol.com
URL: http://www.octameron.com
Key Personnel: Anna J. Leider, Author; Robert Leider, Author. **URL(s):** http://www.thinktuition.com; http://www.octameron.com **Covers:** Organizations, government agencies, and others offering financial aid and scholarships to college-bound and college students. **Entries include:** Name and description of program, eligibility requirements, and name and address of sponsor. **Freq:** Annual, latest edition 33rd, September 2008. **Price:** $13, individuals, plus $4 for shipping/handling.

5648 ■ *DPHD Newsletter*
Yes I Can! Foundation for Exceptional Children
1110 N Glebe Rd., Ste. 300
Arlington, VA 22201-5704
Ph: (703)264-3660
Fax: (703)264-9494
E-mail: yesican@cec.sped.org
Descr: Covers information regarding the education of individuals with physical disabilities and health impairments. **Freq:** quarterly. **Price:** included in membership dues.

5649 ■ *DRC News*
Disability Rights Center
PO Box 2007
Augusta, ME 04338-2007
Ph: (207)626-2774
Fax: (207)621-1419
E-mail: advocate@drcme.org
URL: http://www.drcme.org

5650 ■ *Dreams and Visions*
Arc of Arapahoe and Douglas
7430 E Caley Ave., Ste. 130
Centennial, CO 80111
Ph: (303)220-9228
Fax: (303)220-0994
E-mail: carol@arcarapahoedouglas.org
URL: http://www.arcarapahoedouglas.org

Descr: Contains articles of interest and events in the community that would be of interest to people with disabilities and their families. **Freq:** monthly. **Price:** free.

5651 ■ *DREDF News*
Disability Rights Education and Defense Fund
2212 6th St.
Berkeley, CA 94710
Ph: (510)644-2555
Fax: (510)841-8645
E-mail: info@dredf.org
URL: http://www.dredf.org
Freq: periodic.

5652 ■ *Driver Training Bulletin*
North American Professional Driver Education Association
5180 N. Elston Ave.
Chicago, IL 60630
Ph: (773)777-9605
Descr: Covers driver training, driver education, business management, teaching techniques, instructor training, and latest devices and materials. **Freq:** semimonthly. **Price:** $10.

5653 ■ *Drunk Driving: An Unacknowledged Form of Child Endangerment*
Mothers Against Drunk Driving
511 E John Carpenter Fwy., Ste. 700
Irving, TX 75062
Ph: (214)744-6233
Fax: (972)869-2206
E-mail: info@madd.org
URL: http://www.madd.org

5654 ■ *DSEF: A Foundation That Works*
Direct Selling Education Foundation
1667 K St. NW, Ste. 1100
Washington, DC 20006-1660
Ph: (202)452-8866
Fax: (202)452-9015
E-mail: info@dsef.org
URL: http://www.dsef.org
Descr: Highlights the DSEF contributions to the academic community and consumer advocacy with a variety of programs.

5655 ■ *DVS Guide*
Descriptive Video Service
WGBH
PO Box 55785
Boston, MA 02205-5875
Ph: (617)300-5400
E-mail: dvs@wgbh.org
URL: http://www.wgbh.org/about/contact.cfm
URL(s): http://main.wgbh.org/ **Descr:** Magazine listing updates and programs available from the Descriptive Video Service, a free national service that makes television programs, cable programming and movies accessible to blind or visually impaired individuals. **Freq:** Quarterly.

5656 ■ *Dykes, Disability, and Stuff*
Disabled Womyn's Educational Project
PO Box 8773
Madison, WI 53708-8773
Ph: (608)256-8883
Fax: (608)256-8883
E-mail: catherine-odette@juno.com
Descr: Available in the format of audiocassette, Braille, DOS diskette, large print, modem transfer, audio tape. **Freq:** quarterly. **Price:** $25/year.

5657 ■ *Dynamics of Organizing - Building Power by Developing the Human Spirit*
National Training and Information Center
810 N Milwaukee Ave.
Chicago, IL 60642-4103
Ph: (312)243-3035
Fax: (312)243-7044
E-mail: ntic@ntic-us.org
URL: http://www.ntic-us.org

Price: $25.

5658 ■ *dyslexia discourse*
New York Branch of the International Dyslexia Association
71 W 23rd St., Ste. 1527
New York, NY 10010
Ph: (212)691-1930
Fax: (212)633-1620
E-mail: info@nybida.org
URL: http://www.nybida.org
Freq: 3/year. **Price:** included in membership dues.

5659 ■ *e-Architext*
American Institute of Architects Cincinnati
700 W Pete Rose Way
Cincinnati, OH 45203
Ph: (513)421-4661
Fax: (513)421-4665
E-mail: aiacinti@fuse.net
URL: http://www.aiacincinnati.org
Freq: monthly.

5660 ■ *E-Magnify Extra!*
Seton Hill University's E-magnify
Box 389F, Seton Hill University
Seton Hill Dr.
Greensburg, PA 15601
Ph: (724)830-4625
Fax: (724)834-7131
E-mail: info@e-magnify.com
URL: http://www.e-magnify.com
Freq: weekly. **Price:** included in membership dues.

5661 ■ *E-source*
American Institute of Architects/Kansas
700 SW Jackson St., Ste. 209
Topeka, KS 66603-3758
Ph: (785)357-5308
E-mail: info@aiaks.org
URL: http://www.aiaks.org
Descr: Features current news. **Freq:** monthly.

5662 ■ *Eagle*
American Institute of Architects, Monterey Bay Chapter
PO Box 310
Monterey, CA 93940
Ph: (831)372-6527
Fax: (831)375-4535
E-mail: aiamb@sbcglobal.net
URL: http://www.aiamontereybay.org
Freq: quarterly.

5663 ■ *Eagle Flash Newsletter*
American Institute of Architects, Monterey Bay Chapter
PO Box 310
Monterey, CA 93940
Ph: (831)372-6527
Fax: (831)375-4535
E-mail: aiamb@sbcglobal.net
URL: http://www.aiamontereybay.org
Freq: monthly.

5664 ■ *Early Childhood Research Quarterly*
National Association for the Education of Young Children
1313 L St. NW, Ste. 500
Washington, DC 20005
Ph: (202)232-8777
Fax: (202)328-1846
E-mail: naeyc@naeyc.org
URL: http://www.naeyc.org
Descr: Provides research and scholarship on early childhood field related to care and education of children from birth to age 8. **Freq:** quarterly. **Price:** $40 for members, $95 for individual nonmember, $225 institutional. **ISSN:** 0885-2006.

5665 ■ *East Bay News*
East Bay Learning Disabilities Association of California
PO Box 5513
Berkeley, CA 94705
Ph: (510)433-7934

Fax: (510)547-5306
E-mail: info@eastbaylda.org
URL: http://www.eastbaylda.org
Freq: quarterly. **Price:** included in membership dues.

5666 ■ Eastwords
American Institute of Architects Eastern Illinois
PO Box 1476
Homewood, IL 60430
Ph: (708)895-4716
E-mail: p.radloff@rjaarchitects.com
URL: http://www.aiaeic.org
Freq: 9/year.

5667 ■ Education for All: Women and Girls Speak Out on the National Education Goals
National Coalition for Women and Girls in Education
1111 16th St. NW
Washington, DC 20036
Ph: (202)785-7793
Fax: (202)872-1425
E-mail: maatzl@aauw.org
URL: http://www.ncwge.org

5668 ■ Education & Law Journal
Carswell
One Corporate Plz.
2075 Kennedy Rd.
Toronto, ON, Canada M1T 3V4
Ph: (416)609-8000
Fax: (416)298-5141
E-mail: carswell.customerrelations@thomson.com
URL: http://www.carswell.com
Key Personnel: Greg Dickinson, Editor-in-Chief. **URL(s):** http://www.carswell.com/description. asp?docid=234 **Descr:** Professional journal covering law and education at the elementary, secondary and post-secondary levels. **Freq:** Annual. **Price:** $233. 01, individuals; $240, individuals.

5669 ■ Education Reform in Family and Consumer Sciences
Family and Consumer Sciences Education Association
Central Washington University
Dept. of Family & Consumer Science
400 E 8th University Way
Ellensburg, WA 98926-7565
Ph: (509)963-2766
Fax: (509)963-2787
E-mail: hubbards@cwu.edu
URL: http://www.cwu.edu/~fandcs/fcsea
Price: $10 plus shipping and handling.

5670 ■ Educational
International Society of Weighing and Measurement
9707 Key West Ave., Ste. 100
Rockville, MD 20850
Ph: (301)258-1115
Fax: (301)990-9771
E-mail: staff@iswm.org
URL: http://www.iswm.org

5671 ■ Educational Measurement - Issues and Practice
National Council on Measurement in Education
2810 Crossroads Dr., Ste. 3800
Madison, WI 53718
Ph: (608)443-2487
Fax: (608)443-2474
E-mail: plovelace@ncme.org
URL: http://www.ncme.org
Descr: Features articles that deal with the practical aspects of testing in educational settings. **Freq:** quarterly. **Price:** included in membership dues. **ISSN:** 0731-1745.

5672 ■ The Educator
Family and Consumer Sciences Education Association
Central Washington University
Dept. of Family & Consumer Science
400 E 8th University Way
Ellensburg, WA 98926-7565
Ph: (509)963-2766
Fax: (509)963-2787

E-mail: hubbards@cwu.edu
URL: http://www.cwu.edu/~fandcs/fcsea
Freq: semiannual. **Price:** included in membership dues.

5673 ■ Elderhostel Canada
Routes to Learning Canada
4 Cataraqui St.
Kingston, ON, Canada K7K 1Z7
Fax: (613)530-2096
E-mail: information@routestolearning.ca
URL: http://www.routestolearning.ca
Freq: quarterly.

5674 ■ Emergency Evacuation Checklist to Include People with Disabilities
National Business and Disability Council
201 I.U. Willets Rd.
Albertson, NY 11507
Ph: (516)465-1516
E-mail: lfrancis@abilitiesonline.org
URL: http://www.business-disability.com
Price: $70.

5675 ■ Employee Drug Education and Awareness and Supervisor Training: An Employer's Development and Implementation Guide
Institute for a Drug-Free Workplace
8614 Westwood Center Dr., Ste. 950
Vienna, VA 22182
Ph: (703)288-4300
URL: http://www.drugfreeworkplace.org
Price: $4.50.

5676 ■ An Employer's Guide to Child Care Consultants
Child Care Action Campaign
24808 Deepdale Ave.
Little Neck, NY 11362-1233
Ph: (212)239-0138
Fax: (212)268-6515
URL: http://www.childcareaction.org
Descr: Focuses on the reasons for using a child care consultant, services that consultants can offer, and how to choose the child care consultant for you. **Price:** $10 for members, $15 for nonmembers.

5677 ■ Empowering News
Breckenridge Outdoor Education Center
PO Box 697
Breckenridge, CO 80424
Ph: (970)453-6422
Fax: (970)453-4676
E-mail: boec@boec.org
URL: http://www.boec.org
Freq: semiannual. **Price:** free.

5678 ■ An Enabling Collection for People with Disabilities
Disability Resources
4 Glatter Ln.
Centereach, NY 11720-1032
Ph: (631)585-0290
Fax: (631)585-0290
E-mail: info@disabilityresources.org
URL: http://www.disabilityresources.org
Price: $2 in U.S., $3 outside U.S.

5679 ■ The Encyclopedia of Learning Disabilities
Facts on File Inc.
132 W 31st St., 17th Fl.
New York, NY 10001
Ph: (212)967-8800
Free: 800-322-8755
Fax: 800-678-3633
E-mail: custserv@factsonfile.com
URL: http://factsonfile.infobasepublishing.com
Key Personnel: Carol Turkington, Author; Joseph Harris, PhD, Author. **URL(s):** http://factsonfile. infobasepublishing.com/ **Descr:** Encyclopedic entries related to learning disabilities. **Entries include:** Name, address, phone. List of more than 650 types of disabilities. **Publication includes:** Resource directory of government agencies, helpful organizations and discussion groups and hotlines. **Freq:** Lat-

est edition 2nd, May 2006. **Price:** $75, individuals, Hardcover.

5680 ■ English Braille, American Edition
Braille Authority of North America
1805 N Oakland St.
Arlington, VA 22207
Ph: (202)707-0722
Fax: (202)707-0712
E-mail: jdix@loc.gov
URL: http://www.brailleauthority.org

5681 ■ The Enlightener
Florida Association for Career and Technical Education
1220 N Paul Russell Rd.
Tallahassee, FL 32301
Ph: (850)878-6860
Fax: (850)878-5476
E-mail: factexec@facte.org
URL: http://www.facte.org
Freq: monthly.

5682 ■ Enterprising Educators
Education Industry Association
5909 Barbados Pl., Ste. 202
Rockville, MD 20852
Fax: (301)468-3249
E-mail: spines@educationindustry.org
URL: http://www.educationindustry.org
Freq: quarterly.

5683 ■ EnVision
Lighthouse International
111 E 59th St.
New York, NY 10022-1202
Ph: (212)821-9200
Fax: (212)821-9707
E-mail: info@lighthouse.org
URL: http://www.lighthouse.org
Descr: Contains issues of visually impaired children.

5684 ■ ERIC Digest
ERIC Clearinghouse on Adult, Career, and Vocational Education
College of Education
Center on Education & Training for Employment
1900 Kenny Rd.
Columbus, OH 43210-1090
Ph: (614)292-7069
Fax: (614)292-1260
E-mail: ericacve@osu.edu
URL: http://ericacve.org/

5685 ■ Essays on Teaching Excellence
Professional and Organizational Development Network in Higher Education
PO Box 3318
Nederland, CO 80466
Ph: (303)258-9521
Fax: (303)258-7377
E-mail: podnetwork@podweb.org
URL: http://www.podnetwork.org
Freq: semiannual. **Price:** $120 for nonmembers, $100 for members.

5686 ■ Ethical Issues in Disability and Rehabilitation: A Report on an International Conference
World Institute on Disability
510 16th St., Ste. 100
Oakland, CA 94612
Ph: (510)763-4100
Fax: (510)763-4109
E-mail: wid@wid.org
URL: http://www.wid.org
Price: $10.

5687 ■ Ethics Education in American Business Schools
Ethics Resource Center
2345 Crystal Dr., Ste. 201
Arlington, VA 22202
Ph: (703)647-2185
Fax: (703)647-2180

E-mail: ethics@ethics.org
URL: http://www.ethics.org

5688 ■ ETS Developments
Educational Testing Service
Rosedale Rd.
Princeton, NJ 08541
Ph: (609)921-9000
Fax: (609)734-5410
E-mail: etsinfo@ets.org
URL: http://www.ets.org
Descr: Covers new products and services. **Freq:** quarterly. **Price:** free.

5689 ■ The Evaluator
Educational Records Bureau
220 E 42nd St.
New York, NY 10017
Ph: (212)672-9800
Fax: (212)370-4096
E-mail: info@erbtest.org
URL: http://www.erbtest.org
Descr: Highlights issues of educational interest, provides announcements of important upcoming events, and summarizes important developments. **Freq:** quarterly.

5690 ■ Evergreen Leader
American Association of University Women of Washington
PO Box 537
Liberty Lake, WA 99019
E-mail: president@aauw-wa.org
URL: http://www.aauw-wa.org
Freq: quarterly.

5691 ■ Exceptional Child Education Resources
Yes I Can! Foundation for Exceptional Children
1110 N Glebe Rd., Ste. 300
Arlington, VA 22201-5704
Ph: (703)264-3660
Fax: (703)264-9494
E-mail: yesican@cec.sped.org
Descr: Includes abstracts of book, nonprint media, and journal literature. **Freq:** quarterly.

5692 ■ Exceptional Children
Yes I Can! Foundation for Exceptional Children
1110 N Glebe Rd., Ste. 300
Arlington, VA 22201-5704
Ph: (703)264-3660
Fax: (703)264-9494
E-mail: yesican@cec.sped.org
Descr: Covers special education and research. **Freq:** quarterly. **Price:** included in membership dues, $58/year for nonmembers.

5693 ■ Exchange
American Institute of Architects, Kansas City Chapter
104 W 9th St., Ste. 101
Kansas City, MO 64105
Ph: (816)221-3485
Fax: (816)221-5653
E-mail: aia.of.kansascity@aiakc.org
URL: http://www.aiakc.org
Freq: bimonthly.

5694 ■ Explanation of the Contents of the ADA
Disability Rights Education and Defense Fund
2212 6th St.
Berkeley, CA 94710
Ph: (510)644-2555
Fax: (510)841-8645
E-mail: info@dredf.org
URL: http://www.dredf.org
Price: $118.

5695 ■ Exploring America's Families
National Coalition for Women and Girls in Education
1111 16th St. NW
Washington, DC 20036
Ph: (202)785-7793
Fax: (202)872-1425

E-mail: maatzl@aauw.org
URL: http://www.ncwge.org

5696 ■ Fact Sheet
HEATH Resource Center
George Washington University
2134 G St. NW
Washington, DC 20052-0001
Fax: (202)994-3365
E-mail: askheath@gwu.edu
URL: http://www.heath.gwu.edu
Freq: quarterly.

5697 ■ Facts About DETC
Distance Education and Training Council
1601 18th St. NW, Ste. 2
Washington, DC 20009
Ph: (202)234-5100
Fax: (202)332-1386
E-mail: karen@detc.org
URL: http://www.detc.org

5698 ■ Facts You Can Use
Communities In Schools
2345 Crytal Dr., Ste. 801
Arlington, VA 22202
Ph: (703)519-8999
E-mail: cis@cisnet.org
URL: http://www.cisnet.org
Freq: quarterly.

5699 ■ Failing Our Children
National Center for Fair and Open Testing
15 Court Sq., Ste. 820
Boston, MA 02108
Ph: (857)350-8207
Fax: (857)350-8209
E-mail: info@fairtest.org
URL: http://www.fairtest.org
Price: $30 full report, $10 summary.

5700 ■ FairTest Examiner
National Center for Fair and Open Testing
15 Court Sq., Ste. 820
Boston, MA 02108
Ph: (857)350-8207
Fax: (857)350-8209
E-mail: info@fairtest.org
URL: http://www.fairtest.org
Descr: Contains news on the testing reform movement and reports on lawsuits, research, policy changes, new exams, and conferences. **Freq:** quarterly. **Price:** $30/year for individuals, $45/year for institutions, $5 for postage outside U.S.

5701 ■ Fallout From the Testing Explosion
National Center for Fair and Open Testing
15 Court Sq., Ste. 820
Boston, MA 02108
Ph: (857)350-8207
Fax: (857)350-8209
E-mail: info@fairtest.org
URL: http://www.fairtest.org
Price: $12.

5702 ■ A Family Guide to Second Step
Committee for Children
568 1st Ave. S, Ste. 600
Seattle, WA 98104-2804
Ph: (206)343-1223
Fax: (206)438-6765
E-mail: info@cfchildren.org
URL: http://www.cfchildren.org

5703 ■ Farm Safety Game and Activity Book
Farm Safety 4 Just Kids
11304 Aurora Ave.
Urbandale, IA 50322
Ph: (515)331-6506
Fax: (515)331-2947
E-mail: fs4jk@fs4jk.org
URL: http://www.fs4jk.org

Price: $32 for members, $45 for nonmembers.

5704 ■ Farmworker Nutrition Education Resource Guide
Association of Farmworker Opportunity Programs
1726 M St. NW, Ste. 800
Washington, DC 20036
Ph: (202)826-6006
Fax: (202)826-6005
E-mail: afop@afop.org
URL: http://www.afop.org
Descr: Lists farmworker service providers nationwide. **Price:** $10.

5705 ■ Fast Facts
New York State PTA
One Wembley Ct.
Albany, NY 12205-3830
Ph: (518)452-8808
Fax: (518)452-8105
E-mail: pta.office@nypta.com
URL: http://www.nypta.com
Descr: Contains up-to-date information of interest to PTA presidents. **Freq:** monthly.

5706 ■ FEAdback
Fairbanks Education Association
2118 S Cushman St.
Fairbanks, AK 99701
Ph: (907)456-4435
Fax: (907)456-2159
E-mail: fea@alaska.net
URL: http://www.alaska.net/~fea
Freq: weekly. **Price:** free.

5707 ■ Final Reports on Cosmetic Ingredient Safety Assessments
Cosmetic Ingredient Review
1101 17th St. NW, Ste. 412
Washington, DC 20036-4702
Ph: (202)331-0651
Fax: (202)331-0088
E-mail: cirinfo@cir-safety.org
URL: http://www.cir-safety.org
Descr: Presents all available published and unpublished safety data and conclusions regarding the safety of cosmetic ingredients. **Freq:** quarterly.

5708 ■ Financial Aid for African Americans
Reference Service Press
5000 Windplay Dr., Ste. 4
El Dorado Hills, CA 95762-9600
Ph: (916)939-9620
Fax: (916)939-9626
E-mail: info@rspfunding.com
URL: http://www.rspfunding.com
Key Personnel: Gail Ann Schlachter, Author, gailschlachter@rspfunding.com; R. David Weber, Author. **URL(s):** http://www.rspfunding.com **Covers:** Nearly 1,250 scholarships, fellowships, loans, grants, awards, and internships available to African Americans from high school through the professional/postdoctoral level. **Entries include:** Program name, address, phone, fax, toll-free number, e-mail address, website, purpose, eligibility, financial data, duration, special features, limitations, number awarded, and deadline date. **Freq:** Biennial, Latest edition 2009-2011. **Price:** $42.50, individuals, Hardcover.

5709 ■ Financial Aid for Asian Americans
Reference Service Press
5000 Windplay Dr., Ste. 4
El Dorado Hills, CA 95762-9600
Ph: (916)939-9620
Fax: (916)939-9626
E-mail: info@rspfunding.com
URL: http://www.rspfunding.com
Key Personnel: Gail A. Schlachter, Author, gailschlachter@rspfunding.com; R. David Weber, Author. **URL(s):** http://www.rspfunding.com **Covers:** Nearly 1,000 scholarships, fellowships, loans, grants, awards, and internships available to Asian Americans from high school through the professional/postdoctoral level. **Entries include:** Program name, address, phone, fax, toll-free number, e-mail ad-

dress, website, purpose, eligibility, financial data, duration, special features, limitations, number awarded, and deadline date. **Freq:** Biennial, Latest edition 2009-2011. **Price:** $40, individuals, Hardcover.

5710 ■ *Financial Aid for the Disabled and Their Families*
Reference Service Press
5000 Windplay Dr., Ste. 4
El Dorado Hills, CA 95762-9600
Ph: (916)939-9620
Fax: (916)939-9626
E-mail: info@rspfunding.com
URL: http://www.rspfunding.com
Key Personnel: Sandy Perez, Member of Team; Gail A. Schlachter, Author; R. David Weber, Author. **URL(s):** http://www.rspfunding.com **Covers:** Over 1,300 scholarships, fellowships, grants, loans, and awards to disabled persons or their family members. **Entries include:** Program name, sponsor name, address, phone, description of program including purpose, financial data, and eligibility requirements. **Freq:** Biennial, Latest edition 2008-2010. **Price:** $40, individuals, Hardcover.

5711 ■ *Financial Aid for Hispanic Americans*
Reference Service Press
5000 Windplay Dr., Ste. 4
El Dorado Hills, CA 95762-9600
Ph: (916)939-9620
Fax: (916)939-9626
E-mail: info@rspfunding.com
URL: http://www.rspfunding.com
Key Personnel: Gail A. Schlachter, Author, gailschlachter@rspfunding.com; R. David Weber, Author. **URL(s):** http://www.rspfunding.com **Covers:** Over 1,200 scholarships, fellowships, loans, grants, awards, and internships available to Hispanic Americans from high school through the professional/postdoctoral level. **Entries include:** Program name, address, phone, fax, toll-free number, e-mail address, website, purpose, eligibility, financial data, duration, special features, limitations, number awarded, and deadline date. **Freq:** Biennial, Latest edition 2009-2011. **Price:** $42.50, individuals, Hardcover.

5712 ■ *Financial Aid for Native Americans*
Reference Service Press
5000 Windplay Dr., Ste. 4
El Dorado Hills, CA 95762-9600
Ph: (916)939-9620
Fax: (916)939-9626
E-mail: info@rspfunding.com
URL: http://www.rspfunding.com
Key Personnel: Gail A. Schlachter, Author, gailschlachter@rspfunding.com; R. David Weber, Author. **URL(s):** http://www.rspfunding.com **Covers:** Over 1,350 scholarships, fellowships, loans, grants, awards, and internships available to Native Americans from high school through the professional/postdoctoral level. **Entries include:** Program name, address, phone, fax, toll-free number, e-mail address, purpose, eligibility, financial data, duration, special features, limitations, number awarded, and deadline date. **Freq:** Biennial, Latest edition 2009-2011. **Price:** $45, individuals, Hardcover.

5713 ■ *Financial Success*
Society for Financial Education and Professional Development
2120 Washington Blvd., Ste. 400
Arlington, VA 22204
Ph: (202)842-3807
Fax: (703)920-3809
E-mail: tdaniels@sfepd.org
URL: http://www.sfepd.org
Freq: quarterly.

5714 ■ *Fire Alarm Manual*
International Municipal Signal Association
PO Box 539
Newark, NY 14513-0539
Ph: (315)331-2182
Fax: (315)331-8205

E-mail: info@imsasafety.org
URL: http://www.imsasafety.org

5715 ■ *Fire Protection Handbook*
National Fire Protection Association
1 Batterymarch Park
Quincy, MA 02169-7471
Ph: (617)770-3000
Fax: (617)770-0700
E-mail: custserv@nfpa.org
URL: http://www.nfpa.org

5716 ■ *Fire Protection Reference Directory and Buyer's Guide*
National Fire Protection Association
1 Batterymarch Park
Quincy, MA 02169-7471
Ph: (617)770-3000
Fax: (617)770-0700
E-mail: custserv@nfpa.org
URL: http://www.nfpa.org
Descr: Provides information on products, manufacturers and sales office, and services in the field of fire protection. Includes list of trade names. **Freq:** annual. **Price:** free for members, $25/copy for nonmembers.

5717 ■ *Fire Technology*
National Fire Protection Association
1 Batterymarch Park
Quincy, MA 02169-7471
Ph: (617)770-3000
Fax: (617)770-0700
E-mail: custserv@nfpa.org
URL: http://www.nfpa.org
Descr: Serves as a professional journal for the fire safety practitioner and the fire safety researcher. Describes advances in fire technology. **Freq:** quarterly. **Price:** $39.50/year. **ISSN:** 0015-2684.

5718 ■ *Firearm Litigation Reporter*
Educational Fund to Stop Gun Violence
1424 L St. NW, Ste. 2-1
Washington, DC 20005-2602
Ph: (202)408-0061
E-mail: csgv@csgv.org
URL: http://www.efsgv.org
Descr: Contains summary of important firearms liability cases, recent studies in medical and public health magazines, and firearms industry updates. **Freq:** quarterly. **Price:** $80/year.

5719 ■ *Firm Profile*
American Institute of Architects, Seattle Chapter
1911 1st Ave.
Seattle, WA 98101
Ph: (206)448-4938
Fax: (206)448-2562
E-mail: aia@aiaseattle.org
URL: http://www.aiaseattle.org
Descr: Lists AIA affiliate firms. **Freq:** annual.

5720 ■ *Fitness Programming and Physical Disabilities*
Disabled Sports USA
451 Hungerford Dr., Ste. 100
Rockville, MD 20850
Ph: (301)217-0960
Fax: (301)217-0968
E-mail: information@dsusa.org
URL: http://www.dsusa.org

5721 ■ *Florida Frontline*
Common Cause/Florida
704 W Madison St.
Tallahassee, FL 32304
Ph: (850)222-3883
Fax: (850)222-3906
E-mail: cmncause@infionline.net
URL: http://www.commoncause.org/florida
Freq: semiannual. **Price:** free to members.

5722 ■ *Focus*
Dayton/Miami Valley Safety Council
1 Chamber Plz.
Dayton, OH 45402-2400
Ph: (937)226-8227

Fax: (937)226-8254
E-mail: info@dacc.org
URL: http://www.daytonchamber.org
Freq: quarterly. **Price:** free for members.

5723 ■ *FOCUS*
Arc Minnesota
800 Transfer Rd., Ste. 7A
St. Paul, MN 55114
Ph: (651)523-0823
Fax: (651)523-0829
E-mail: mail@arcmn.org
URL: http://www.thearcofminnesota.org
Descr: Covers legislative issues affecting people with developmental disabilities and their families. **Freq:** 3/year. **Price:** included in membership dues.

5724 ■ *Focus*
Ohio Association for the Education of Young Children
PO Box 71
Mount Gilead, OH 43338
Ph: (419)946-6693
Fax: (419)946-6515
E-mail: exedirector@oaeyc.org
URL: http://www.oaeyc.org

5725 ■ *Focus on Patient Safety*
National Patient Safety Foundation
268 Summer St., 6th Fl.
Boston, MA 02210
Ph: (617)391-9900
Fax: (617)391-9999
E-mail: info@npsf.org
URL: http://www.npsf.org
Freq: monthly.

5726 ■ *Food Safety Illustrated*
International Food Safety Council
175 W Jackson Blvd., Ste. 1500
Chicago, IL 60604-2814
Ph: (312)715-1010
E-mail: info@restaurant.org
URL: http://www.nraef.org
Descr: Focuses on ways to enhance food safety practices and procedures. **Freq:** quarterly.

5727 ■ *Foreclosure Prevention Counseling*
National Consumer Law Center
7 Winthrop Sq.
Boston, MA 02110-1245
Ph: (617)542-8010
Fax: (617)542-8028
E-mail: consumerlaw@nclc.org
URL: http://www.consumerlaw.org
Price: $50.

5728 ■ *Forum*
Kansas Association for Career and Technical Education
1200 SW 10th Ave.
Topeka, KS 66604
Ph: (785)233-2690
Fax: (785)234-2433
E-mail: skearney@kearneyandassociates.com
URL: http://www.k-acte.org
Descr: Provides current information on issues and events affecting educators, institutions, and students. **Freq:** semiannual. **Price:** free for members, $15/year for nonmembers.

5729 ■ *Forum*
American Institute of Architects, Las Vegas and Nevada Chapters
UNLV Box 454018
4505 S Maryland Pkwy.
Las Vegas, NV 89154-4018
Ph: (702)895-0936
Fax: (702)895-4417
E-mail: rlavigne@aianevada.org
URL: http://aialasvegas.org
Freq: monthly. **Price:** free for members.

5730 ■ *The Forum*
International Society of Air Safety Investigators
107 E Holly Ave., Ste. 11
Sterling, VA 20164

Ph: (703)430-9668
Fax: (703)430-4970
E-mail: isasi@erols.com
URL: http://www.isasi.org
Freq: quarterly. **Price:** $24/year.

5731 ■ Forward, March!
Communities In Schools
2345 Crytal Dr., Ste. 801
Arlington, VA 22202
Ph: (703)519-8999
E-mail: cis@cisnet.org
URL: http://www.cisnet.org
Freq: quarterly.

5732 ■ Foundation Action
National Right to Work Legal Defense and Education Foundation
8001 Braddock Rd.
Springfield, VA 22160
Ph: (703)321-8510
Fax: (703)321-9613
E-mail: info@nrtw.org
URL: http://www.nrtw.org
Freq: bimonthly. **Price:** free.

5733 ■ Free Catalog
American Council for Drug Education
164 W 74th St.
New York, NY 10023
Ph: (718)222-6641
E-mail: acde@phoenixhouse.org
URL: http://www.acde.org
Descr: For parents, children, schools, and other professionals.

5734 ■ Free Money for College
Facts on File Inc.
132 W 31st St., 17th Fl.
New York, NY 10001
Ph: (212)967-8800
Free: 800-322-8755
Fax: 800-678-3633
E-mail: custserv@factsonfile.com
URL: http://factsonfile.infobasepublishing.com
Key Personnel: Laurie Blum, Contact. **URL(s):** http://www.factsonfile.com **Covers:** over 1,000 grants and scholarships. **Entries include:** Sponsor or contact name, address, phone; restrictions, dollar amount given, application deadlines. **Freq:** Irregular, Latest edition 5, published 1999. **Price:** $6.25, individuals.

5735 ■ Free Money for Graduate School
Facts on File Inc.
132 W 31st St., 17th Fl.
New York, NY 10001
Ph: (212)967-8800
Free: 800-322-8755
Fax: 800-678-3633
E-mail: custserv@factsonfile.com
URL: http://factsonfile.infobasepublishing.com
Key Personnel: Laurie Blum, Author. **URL(s):** http://www.factsonfile.com/ **Covers:** Over 1,000 grants and scholarships for graduate study. **Entries include:** Sponsor or contact name, address, phone; restrictions, dollar amount given, application deadlines. **Freq:** Irregular, Latest edition July 2000.

5736 ■ Freedom Road
American Association for Adult and Continuing Education
10111 Martin Luther King, Jr. Hwy., Ste. 200C
Bowie, MD 20720
Ph: (301)459-6261
Fax: (301)459-6241
E-mail: aaace10@aol.com
URL: http://www.aaace.org

5737 ■ From the State and the Nation
Common Cause/Louisiana
PO Box 66687
Baton Rouge, LA 70896-6687
Ph: (225)205-4235
E-mail: louisiana@commoncause.org
URL: http://www.commoncause.org/la

Descr: Contains membership news. **Freq:** quarterly. **Price:** free for members.

5738 ■ FSD News
Foundation for Science and Disability
1700 SW 23rd Dr.
Gainesville, FL 32608
Ph: (352)374-5774
Fax: (352)374-5804
E-mail: rmankin@nersp.nerdc.ufl.edu
URL: http://www.stemd.org
Freq: semiannual. **Price:** available to members only.

5739 ■ Fun Play, Safe Play
Toy Industry Association
1115 Broadway, Ste. 400
New York, NY 10010
Ph: (212)675-1141
E-mail: info@toyassociation.org
URL: http://www.toyassociation.org

5740 ■ FYI
Texas Council for Developmental Disabilities
6201 E Oltorf, Ste. 600
Austin, TX 78741-7509
Ph: (512)437-5432
Fax: (512)437-5434
E-mail: lucy.walker@tcdd.state.tx.us
URL: http://www.txddc.state.tx.us
Descr: Includes federal, state and council news; opportunities for input; and resources. **Freq:** quarterly.

5741 ■ The Mel Gablers' Newsletter
Educational Research Analysts
PO Box 7518
Longview, TX 75607-7518
Ph: (903)753-5993
Fax: (903)753-8424
E-mail: info@textbookreviews.org
URL: http://www.textbookreviews.org
Freq: semiannual. **Price:** donation.

5742 ■ GACTE News
Georgia Association for Career and Technical Education
PO Box 443
Kennesaw, GA 30156
Ph: (678)461-0006
Fax: (706)628-4335
E-mail: cockrell-t@harris.k12.ga.us
URL: http://www.gacte.org
Freq: quarterly.

5743 ■ Gardening with People with Disabilities
City Farmer Society
Box 74567
Kitsilano RPO
Vancouver, BC, Canada V6K 4P4
Ph: (604)685-5832
Fax: (604)685-5862
E-mail: cityfarm@interchange.ubc.ca
URL: http://www.cityfarmer.org
Price: $6.

5744 ■ General Test Practice Book
Graduate Record Examinations Board
PO Box 6000
Princeton, NJ 08541-6000
Ph: (609)771-7670
Fax: (610)290-8975
E-mail: gre-info@rosedale.org
URL: http://www.ets.org/gre

5745 ■ General Test Preparation Software
Graduate Record Examinations Board
PO Box 6000
Princeton, NJ 08541-6000
Ph: (609)771-7670
Fax: (610)290-8975
E-mail: gre-info@rosedale.org
URL: http://www.ets.org/gre
Freq: biennial.

5746 ■ Gerontology & Geriatrics Education
Gerontological Society of America
1220 L St. NW, Ste. 901
Washington, DC 20005

Ph: (202)842-1275
Fax: (202)842-1150
URL: http://www.geron.org

5747 ■ Giving Us the Tools: A Human Resources Training Package on Employing Individuals with Disabilities
National Business and Disability Council
201 I.U. Willets Rd.
Albertson, NY 11507
Ph: (516)465-1516
E-mail: lfrancis@abilitiesonline.org
URL: http://www.business-disability.com

5748 ■ God's Golden Children
Crigler-Najjar Association
3134 Bayberry St.
Wichita, KS 67226
E-mail: mauckc@msn.com
URL: http://www.criglernajjar.com
Descr: Features stories of people afflicted with Crigler-Najjar syndrome. **Price:** $9.95/copy.

5749 ■ The Government Financial Aid Book
Perpetual Press
PO Box 45628
Seattle, WA 98145-0628
Ph: (206)971-3708
Free: 800-793-8010
Fax: (206)971-3708
E-mail: marathon@blarg.com
URL(s): http://www.amazon.com **Covers:** Financial aid sources for college and undergraduates. **Entries include:** Contact information. **Freq:** Published 1996, second edition. **Price:** $9.95, individuals.

5750 ■ Grass Roots Organizing
Educational Fund to Stop Gun Violence
1424 L St. NW, Ste. 2-1
Washington, DC 20005-2602
Ph: (202)408-0061
E-mail: csgv@csgv.org
URL: http://www.efsgv.org

5751 ■ GRE Information Bulletin
Graduate Record Examinations Board
PO Box 6000
Princeton, NJ 08541-6000
Ph: (609)771-7670
Fax: (610)290-8975
E-mail: gre-info@rosedale.org
URL: http://www.ets.org/gre
Freq: annual.

5752 ■ Greatest 500 Books
Chicago Metropolitan Association for the Education of Young Children
30 E Adams, Ste. 1000
Chicago, IL 60603
Ph: (312)427-5399
Fax: (312)427-5028
E-mail: moderator@chicagometroaeyc.org
URL: http://www.chicagometroaeyc.org
Descr: Contains list of books developed as an "Excellence in Teaching" program.

5753 ■ Green Bay Education Association Perspective
Green Bay Education Association
2256 Main St.
Green Bay, WI 54311
Ph: (920)468-4232
Fax: (920)468-6766
E-mail: gbea@gbea.org
URL: http://www.gbea.org
Freq: weekly.

5754 ■ Guide to Accredited Camps
American Camp Association
5000 State Rd., 67 N
Martinsville, IN 46151-7902
Ph: (765)342-8456
Fax: (765)342-2065
E-mail: psmith@acacamps.org
URL: http://www.acacamps.org
Descr: Lists 2200 camps accredited by the ACA. Includes information on clientele, fees, and location

and a cross-reference guide to program activities. **Freq:** annual. **Price:** $19.95/copy.

5755 ■ A Guide to Off-Highway Riding
ATV Safety Institute/Division of Specialty Vehicle
Institute of America
2 Jenner St., Ste. 150
Irvine, CA 92618-3806
Ph: (949)727-3727
URL: http://www.atvsafety.org

5756 ■ Guide to U.S. Department of Education Programs and Resources
U.S. Department of Education
U.S. Office of Educational Research and Improvement
400 Maryland Ave. SW
Washington, DC 20202
Free: 800-872-5327
Fax: (202)401-0689
E-mail: customerservice@inet.ed.gov
URL: http://www.ed.gov
Key Personnel: Edward Ohnemus, Editor; Alfred B. Gaarder, Contact. **URL(s):** http://www.ed.gov; http://www.ed.gov/programs/gtep/index.html **Covers:** Programs of financial aid offered by the Department of Education. **Entries include:** Program title, sponsoring office name, contact name and address, type of assistance, purpose of program, eligibility requirements. **Freq:** Continuous, Latest edition 2008.

5757 ■ Guidelines
Texas Counseling Association
1204 San Antonio, Ste. 201
Austin, TX 78701
Ph: (512)472-3403
Fax: (512)472-3756
E-mail: jan@txca.org
URL: http://www.txca.org
Freq: monthly.

5758 ■ Guidelines for Reporting and Writing About People with Disabilities
Research and Training Center on Independent Living
University of Kansas
Dole Center, Ste. 4089
1000 Sunnyside Ave.
Lawrence, KS 66045-7561
Ph: (785)864-4095
Fax: (785)864-5063
E-mail: rtcil@ku.edu
URL: http://www.rtcil.org
Price: free.

5759 ■ Guidelines for Training of Group Psychotherapists
American Group Psychotherapy Association
25 E 21st St., 6th Fl.
New York, NY 10010
Ph: (212)477-2677
Fax: (212)979-6627
E-mail: info@agpa.org
URL: http://www.agpa.org
Descr: Includes calendar of events and research updates. **Freq:** quarterly. **Price:** included in membership dues.

5760 ■ Guilty Until Proven Innocent: A Manual for Surviving False Allegations of Child Abuse
National Child Abuse Defense and Resource Center
PO Box 638
Holland, OH 43528
Ph: (419)865-0513
Fax: (419)865-0526
E-mail: ncadrc@aol.com
URL: http://www.falseallegation.org
Price: $30.50.

5761 ■ Hawaii Senior Olympics Newsletter
Hawaii Senior Games Association
1493 Halekoa Dr.
Honolulu, HI 96815
Ph: (808)732-8805
Fax: (808)737-9017
E-mail: zeug@hawaii.rr.com
URL: http://www.hawaiiseniorolympics.com

Freq: semiannual.

5762 ■ The Health and Safety Report
Canadian Centre for Occupational Health and Safety
135 Hunter St. E
Hamilton, ON, Canada L8N 1M5
Ph: (905)572-2981
Fax: (905)572-2206
E-mail: clientservices@ccohs.ca
URL: http://www.ccohs.ca
Descr: Contains latest occupational health and safety news. **Freq:** monthly. **Price:** free.

5763 ■ Heart-to-Heart Part III: Children
Last Acts Partnership
1620 I St. NW, No. 202
Washington, DC 20006
Ph: (202)296-8071
Fax: (202)296-8352
URL: http://www.lastactspartnership.org
Price: $12.

5764 ■ HEATH Resource Directory
HEATH Resource Center
2134 G St. NW
Washington, DC 20052-0001
Ph: (202)973-0904
Free: 800-544-3284
Fax: (202)994-3365
E-mail: askheath@heath.gwu.edu
URL: http://www.heath.gwu.edu
Key Personnel: Dr. Pamela Ekpone, Dir.; Daniel B. Gardner, Publications Mgr. **URL(s):** http://www.heath.gwu.edu **Covers:** Over 180 organizations that provide information and resources on topics relevant to postsecondary education and disability. **Entries include:** Organization name, topic, address, phone, fax, talking telephone (TT) availability. **Freq:** Biennial. **Price:** Free.

5765 ■ Hebrew Braille Bible
JBI International - Jewish Braille Institute of America
110 E 30th St.
New York, NY 10016
Ph: (212)889-2525
Fax: (212)689-3692
E-mail: admin@jbilibrary.org
URL: http://www.jbilibrary.org

5766 ■ Hebrew Self-Taught
JBI International - Jewish Braille Institute of America
110 E 30th St.
New York, NY 10016
Ph: (212)889-2525
Fax: (212)689-3692
E-mail: admin@jbilibrary.org
URL: http://www.jbilibrary.org
Descr: Serves as a Braille primer.

5767 ■ Helmet Update Newsletter
Bicycle Helmet Safety Institute
4611 7th St. S
Arlington, VA 22204-1419
Ph: (703)486-0100
Fax: (703)486-0100
E-mail: info@helmets.org
URL: http://www.helmets.org
Freq: periodic. **Price:** free.

5768 ■ Helping in Child Protective Services: A Competency-based Casework Handbook
American Humane Association Children's Services
63 Inverness Dr. E
Englewood, CO 80112-5117
Ph: (303)792-9900
Fax: (303)792-5333
E-mail: info@americanhumane.org
URL: http://www.americanhumane.org

5769 ■ Helping Your Child Succeed After Divorce
Children's Rights Council
8181 Professional Pl., Ste. 240
Landover, MD 20785
Ph: (301)459-1220
Fax: (301)459-1227

E-mail: info@crckids.org
URL: http://www.gocrc.com
Price: $9.95.

5770 ■ The Hidden Disability
Parents Active for Vision Education
4135 54th Pl.
San Diego, CA 92105-2303
Ph: (619)287-0081
Fax: (619)287-0084
E-mail: info@pavevision.org
URL: http://www.pavevision.org
Price: $26 100 copies, includes shipping and handling.

5771 ■ The Hidden Disability: Undetected Vision Problems
Parents Active for Vision Education
4135 54th Pl.
San Diego, CA 92105-2303
Ph: (619)287-0081
Fax: (619)287-0084
E-mail: info@pavevision.org
URL: http://www.pavevision.org
Price: $65/copy, plus shipping and handling.

5772 ■ High School Senior's Guide to Merit and Other No-Need Funding
Reference Service Press
5000 Windplay Dr., Ste. 4
El Dorado Hills, CA 95762-9600
Ph: (916)939-9620
Fax: (916)939-9626
E-mail: info@rspfunding.com
URL: http://www.rspfunding.com
Key Personnel: Gail A. Schlachter, Author, gailschlachter@rspfunding.com; R. David Weber, Author. **URL(s):** http://www.rspfunding.com **Covers:** Approximately 1,100 scholarship and financial aid opportunities available to high school seniors for college students regardless of income. **Entries include:** Sponsor name, address, phone, fax, email, website, description. **Freq:** Biennial, Latest edition 2008-2010. **Price:** $29.95, individuals, Hardcover.

5773 ■ The Higher Education Act: A Guide for Women
National Coalition for Women and Girls in Education
1111 16th St. NW
Washington, DC 20036
Ph: (202)785-7793
Fax: (202)872-1425
E-mail: maatzl@aauw.org
URL: http://www.ncwge.org

5774 ■ Hoosier Counselor
American Counseling Association, Indiana
899 S College Mall Rd., No. 375
Bloomington, IN 47401
Ph: (812)323-8680
Fax: 888-857-4974
E-mail: jdonica@indianacounseling.org
URL: http://www.indianacounseling.org
Freq: quarterly. **Price:** included in membership dues.

5775 ■ Horizons
Arc of Utah
155 S 300 W, Ste. 201
Salt Lake City, UT 84101
Ph: (801)364-5060
Fax: (801)364-6030
E-mail: execdirector@arcutah.org
URL: http://www.arcutah.org
Freq: bimonthly. **Price:** included in membership dues, $20/year for nonmembers.

5776 ■ Household Safety Sourcebook
Omnigraphics Inc.
PO Box 31-1640
Detroit, MI 48231
Free: 800-234-1340
E-mail: info@omnigraphics.com
URL: http://www.omnigraphics.com
Key Personnel: Dawn D. Matthews, Editor. **URL(s):** http://www.omnigraphics.com **Publication includes:** List of hotline services, Environmental Protection

Agency hotline information, and poison center hotlines. Principal content of publication is information about preventing injuries in the home. **Price:** $84, individuals, hardcover.

5777 ■ How to Choose a College: Guide for the Student with a Disability
National Clearinghouse on Postsecondary Education for Individuals with Disabilities
2121 K St. NW, Ste. 220
Washington, DC 20052
Ph: (202)973-0904
Free: 800-544-3284
Fax: (202)973-0908
E-mail: heath@ace.nche.edu
URL: http://www.heath.gwu.edu/
Key Personnel: Jane Jarrow, Editor. **URL(s):** http://www.heath.gwu.edu **Entries include:** Name of publisher, address, title of publication, brief description of publication, fees. Principal content is a discussion of concerns of handicapped persons in choosing a college. **Publication includes:** List of about five publishers of information on college planning and admissions. **Freq:** Irregular, latest edition 1997. **Price:** $1, contact publisher for ordering multiple copies.

5778 ■ How Does the SAT Score for Women?
National Coalition for Women and Girls in Education
1111 16th St. NW
Washington, DC 20036
Ph: (202)785-7793
Fax: (202)872-1425
E-mail: maatzl@aauw.org
URL: http://www.ncwge.org

5779 ■ How to Find Out about Financial Aid and Funding
Reference Service Press
5000 Windplay Dr., Ste. 4
El Dorado Hills, CA 95762-9600
Ph: (916)939-9620
Fax: (916)939-9626
E-mail: findaid@aol.com
URL: http://www.rspfunding.com
Key Personnel: Sandy Perez, Member of Team; Gail A. Schlachter, Author, gailschlachter@rspfunding.com. **URL(s):** http://www.rspfunding.com **Covers:** Over 700 financial aid resources; print, electronic, or online. **Entries include:** Title, publisher name, address, phone, annotation, title changes, price. **Freq:** Biennial, latest edition 2nd; Published 2003-2005. **Price:** $37.50, individuals, Hardcover.

5780 ■ How to Get Services by Being Assertive
Family Resource Center on Disabilities
20 E Jackson Blvd., Rm. 300
Chicago, IL 60604
Ph: (312)939-3513
Fax: (312)939-7297
E-mail: frcdptiill@ameritech.net
URL: http://www.frcd.org
Price: $10 plus shipping and handling.

5781 ■ How to Organize an Effective Parent/Advocacy Group and Move Bureaucracies
Family Resource Center on Disabilities
20 E Jackson Blvd., Rm. 300
Chicago, IL 60604
Ph: (312)939-3513
Fax: (312)939-7297
E-mail: frcdptiill@ameritech.net
URL: http://www.frcd.org
Price: $10 plus shipping and handling.

5782 ■ How Professional Development Schools Make a Difference: A Review of Research
National Council for Accreditation of Teacher Education
2010 Massachusetts Ave. NW, Ste. 500
Washington, DC 20036
Ph: (202)466-7496
Fax: (202)296-6620
E-mail: ncate@ncate.org
URL: http://www.ncate.org

Price: $20.

5783 ■ How-to Guide: Condensing and Translating
Research and Training Center on Independent Living
University of Kansas
Dole Center, Ste. 4089
1000 Sunnyside Ave.
Lawrence, KS 66045-7561
Ph: (785)864-4095
Fax: (785)864-5063
E-mail: rtcil@ku.edu
URL: http://www.rtcil.org
Price: $5.

5784 ■ IADH News
International Association for Disability and Oral Health
High Lodge
Tedgness Rd.
Hope Valley
Grindleford, S32 2HX
Ph: (999)44 -1 433
E-mail: rblank@waitrose.com
URL: http://www.iadh.org
Freq: quarterly.

5785 ■ ICUC: I See You See
Looking Glass Publications
Box 3604
Quincy, IL 62305
E-mail: icuc62305@yahoo.com
Key Personnel: Linda Ann Hughes, Editor, lindah217@netscape.net. **Descr:** Consumer large print magazine for the visually impaired. **Freq:** Quarterly. **Price:** $20, individuals; $30, out of country; $6, single issue.

5786 ■ Implementing Family and Consumer Sciences Standards through Project-Based Learning
Family and Consumer Sciences Education Association
Central Washington University
Dept. of Family & Consumer Science
400 E 8th University Way
Ellensburg, WA 98926-7565
Ph: (509)963-2766
Fax: (509)963-2787
E-mail: hubbards@cwu.edu
URL: http://www.cwu.edu/~fandcs/fcsea
Price: $10 plus shipping and handling.

5787 ■ Implementing Performance Assessments: A Guide to Classroom, School and System Reform
National Center for Fair and Open Testing
15 Court Sq., Ste. 820
Boston, MA 02108
Ph: (857)350-8207
Fax: (857)350-8209
E-mail: info@fairtest.org
URL: http://www.fairtest.org
Price: $6 each, $25 for 5 copies, $40 for 10 copies, $75 for 25 copies.

5788 ■ The Importance of Reading in Family and Consumer Sciences
Family and Consumer Sciences Education Association
Central Washington University
Dept. of Family & Consumer Science
400 E 8th University Way
Ellensburg, WA 98926-7565
Ph: (509)963-2766
Fax: (509)963-2787
E-mail: hubbards@cwu.edu
URL: http://www.cwu.edu/~fandcs/fcsea
Freq: annual. **Price:** $10 plus shipping and handling.

5789 ■ Increasing School Stability for Students Experiencing Homelessness: Overcoming Challenges to Providing Transportation to the School of Origin
National Center for Homeless Education
PO Box 5367

Greensboro, NC 27435
Fax: (336)315-7457
E-mail: homeless@serve.org
URL: http://www.serve.org/nche
Descr: Reviews provisions related to transportation to the school of origin and provides recommendations for implementing the transportation mandate.

5790 ■ An Independent Living Approach to Disability Policy Studies
World Institute on Disability
510 16th St., Ste. 100
Oakland, CA 94612
Ph: (510)763-4100
Fax: (510)763-4109
E-mail: wid@wid.org
URL: http://www.wid.org
Price: $17.50.

5791 ■ Information
HEATH Resource Center
George Washington University
2134 G St. NW
Washington, DC 20052-0001
Fax: (202)994-3365
E-mail: askheath@gwu.edu
URL: http://www.heath.gwu.edu
Freq: 3/year.

5792 ■ Information from HEATH
HEATH Resource Center
George Washington University
2134 G St. NW
Washington, DC 20052-0001
Fax: (202)994-3365
E-mail: askheath@gwu.edu
URL: http://www.heath.gwu.edu
Freq: quarterly.

5793 ■ Informational Brochure
Just One Break
570 Seventh Ave.
New York, NY 10018
Ph: (212)785-7300
Fax: (212)785-4513
E-mail: jobs@justonebreak.com
URL: http://www.justonebreak.com

5794 ■ Initiative
Arc of Iowa
3821 71st St., Ste. A
Urbandale, IA 50322
Ph: (515)210-6686
Fax: (515)309-0860
E-mail: casey@thearcofiowa.org
URL: http://thearcofiowa.org

5795 ■ Injury Facts
National Safety Council
1121 Spring Lake Dr.
Itasca, IL 60143-3201
Ph: (630)285-1121
Fax: (630)285-1315
E-mail: info@nsc.org
URL: http://www.nsc.org
Descr: Contains data on unintentional injuries. **Freq:** annual. **Price:** included in membership dues.

5796 ■ InSight
Arc of the United States
1010 Wayne Ave., Ste. 650
Silver Spring, MD 20910
Ph: (301)565-3842
Fax: (301)565-5342
E-mail: info@thearc.org
URL: http://www.thearc.org
Descr: Contains updated information about the organization. **Freq:** quarterly. **Price:** $15/year.

5797 ■ Insights on Learning Disabilities
Massachusetts Association for Children With Learning Disabilities
PO Box 142
Weston, MA 02493
Ph: (781)890-5399
Fax: (781)890-0555

Freq: biennial. **Price:** included in membership dues.

5798 ■ Internal Membership Directory
Goodwill Industries International
15810 Indianola Dr.
Rockville, MD 20855
Ph: (301)530-6500
E-mail: contactus@goodwill.org
URL: http://www.goodwill.org
Freq: annual.

5799 ■ International Educational Congress of Dental Technology—Program
Dental Laboratory Association of the State of New York
1718 Broadway
Schenectady, NY 12306
Ph: (518)355-3183
E-mail: info@dlany.org
URL: http://www.dlany.org
Freq: annual.

5800 ■ International Fire Code
Southern Building Code Congress, International
500 New Jersey Ave. NW, 6th Fl.
Washington, DC 20001-2070
Fax: (703)379-2348
E-mail: webmaster@iccsafe.org
URL: http://www.iccsafe.org
Freq: triennial.

5801 ■ International Fire Code
International Code Council
500 New Jersey Ave. NW, 6th Fl.
Washington, DC 20001-2070
Ph: (562)699-0541
Fax: (202)783-2348
E-mail: webmaster@iccsafe.org
URL: http://www.iccsafe.org
Freq: triennial.

5802 ■ International Fire Code
Building Officials and Code Administrators International
Chicago District Office
4051 W Flossmoor Rd.
Country Club Hills, IL 60478
E-mail: webmaster@iccsafe.org
URL: http://www.iccsafe.org
Freq: triennial.

5803 ■ International Journal of Educational Reform
Scarecrow Education
4720 Boston Way, Ste. A
Lanham, MD 20706
Free: 800-352-8039
Fax: (301)429-5747
E-mail: tmiller@rowman.com
Key Personnel: Dr. Steve Permuth, Editor, permuth@tempest.coedu.usf.edu; Cindy Tursman, Acquisitions Editor, ctursman@scarecrowpress.com. **Descr:** Journal on educational reform in the U.S. and around the world. **Freq:** Quarterly. **Price:** $125, individuals; $33, single issue.

5804 ■ International Journal of Progressive Education
International Association of Educators
1965 S Orchard St.
Urbana, IL 61801
E-mail: secretary@inased.org
URL: http://www.inased.org
Freq: 3/year. **Price:** $35 for members, $45 for nonmembers, $35 for nonmembers - student, $140 for nonmembers - library/institution. **ISSN:** 1554-5210.

5805 ■ International Student Handbook
The College Board
45 Columbus Ave.
New York, NY 10023-6992
Ph: (212)713-8000
Fax: (212)649-8442
E-mail: publicaffairs@collegeboard.org
URL: http://www.collegeboard.com

Freq: annual.

5806 ■ Interpretive Guide to the SSAT
Secondary School Admission Test Board
CN 5339
Princeton, NJ 08543
Ph: (609)683-4440
Fax: (609)683-4507
E-mail: info@ssat.org
URL: http://www.ssat.org
Freq: annual.

5807 ■ Interstate Child Support
Women's Law Project
125 S 9th St., No. 300
Philadelphia, PA 19107
Ph: (215)928-9801
Fax: (215)928-9848
E-mail: info@womenslawproject.org
URL: http://www.womenslawproject.org/pages/contact_us.htm

5808 ■ The Interviewer
Association of Independent School Admission Professionals
170 Boston Post Rd., No. 160
Madison, CT 06443
Ph: (203)421-7051
E-mail: info@aisap.org
URL: http://www.aisap.org
Freq: periodic.

5809 ■ Interviewing Individuals with Disabilities
National Business and Disability Council
201 I.U. Willets Rd.
Albertson, NY 11507
Ph: (516)465-1516
E-mail: lfrancis@abilitiesonline.org
URL: http://www.business-disability.com

5810 ■ Investigating Acquaintance Sexual Assault Training Manual
National Center for Women and Policing
433 S Beverly Dr.
Beverly Hills, CA 90212
Ph: (310)556-2526
Fax: (310)556-2509
E-mail: womencops@feminist.org
URL: http://www.womenandpolicing.org
Price: $10/CD; includes shipping and handling.

5811 ■ Investing in the Future: Child Care Financing Options for the Public and Private Sectors
Child Care Action Campaign
24808 Deepdale Ave.
Little Neck, NY 11362-1233
Ph: (212)239-0138
Fax: (212)268-6515
URL: http://www.childcareaction.org
Descr: Highlights successful financing models, including grants and loans, bank reinvestment strategies, community initiatives, bonds and pension funds. **Price:** $15 for members, $25 for nonmembers.

5812 ■ Involuntary Hospitalization Laws
Disability Rights Center
PO Box 2007
Augusta, ME 04338-2007
Ph: (207)626-2774
Fax: (207)621-1419
E-mail: advocate@drcme.org
URL: http://www.drcme.org
Price: $2.65.

5813 ■ Iowa Chapter of APCO Newsletter
Association of Public-Safety Communications International, Iowa Chapter
25 E First St.
Des Moines, IA 50309
Ph: (515)237-1598

Fax: (515)237-1669
E-mail: ednevins@dmgov.org
URL: http://iowaapco.org

5814 ■ ISMP Medication Safety Alert! Acute Care Edition
Institute for Safe Medication Practices
200 Lakeside Dr., Ste. 200
Horsham, PA 19044-2321
Ph: (215)947-7797
Fax: (215)914-1492
E-mail: ismpinfo@ismp.org
URL: http://www.ismp.org
Freq: biweekly.

5815 ■ ISMP Medication Safety Alert! Community/Ambulatory Edition
Institute for Safe Medication Practices
200 Lakeside Dr., Ste. 200
Horsham, PA 19044-2321
Ph: (215)947-7797
Fax: (215)914-1492
E-mail: ismpinfo@ismp.org
URL: http://www.ismp.org
Freq: monthly.

5816 ■ ISMP Medication Safety Alert! Consumer Edition
Institute for Safe Medication Practices
200 Lakeside Dr., Ste. 200
Horsham, PA 19044-2321
Ph: (215)947-7797
Fax: (215)914-1492
E-mail: ismpinfo@ismp.org
URL: http://www.ismp.org

5817 ■ ISMP Medication Safety Alert! Nursing Edition
Institute for Safe Medication Practices
200 Lakeside Dr., Ste. 200
Horsham, PA 19044-2321
Ph: (215)947-7797
Fax: (215)914-1492
E-mail: ismpinfo@ismp.org
URL: http://www.ismp.org
Freq: monthly.

5818 ■ ISTA Advocate
Indiana State Teachers Association
150 W Market St., Ste. 900
Indianapolis, IN 46204-2875
Ph: (317)263-3400
Free: 800-382-4037
Fax: (317)655-3700
URL: http://www.ista-in.org
Key Personnel: Kathleen A. Berry, Asst. Ed., kberry@ista-in.org. **URL(s):** http://www.ista-in.org **Descr:** Trade magazine (tabloid) covering education issues and employees. **Freq:** 5/yr.

5819 ■ Jail Officers' Training Manual
National Sheriffs' Association
1450 Duke St.
Alexandria, VA 22314-3490
Ph: (703)836-7827
Fax: (703)683-6541
E-mail: nsamail@sheriffs.org
URL: http://www.sheriffs.org

5820 ■ Jewish Braille Review
JBI Intl.
110 E 30th St.
New York, NY 10016
Ph: (212)889-2525
Free: 800-433-1531
Fax: (212)689-3692
E-mail: admin@jbilibrary.org
URL: http://www.jbilibrary.org
URL(s): http://www.jewishbraille.org/home.html **Descr:** Magazine for the blind. Printed in braille. **Freq:** 12/yr. **Price:** Free.

5821 ■ Jewish Reference Calendar
JBI International - Jewish Braille Institute of America
110 E 30th St.
New York, NY 10016
Ph: (212)889-2525

Fax: (212)689-3692
E-mail: admin@jbilibrary.org
URL: http://www.jbilibrary.org
Descr: Comes in large print, 18-month with secular holidays and candle lighting times. **Freq:** annual.

5822 ■ Journal of Addictions and Offender Counseling
International Association of Addictions and Offender Counselors
PO Box 791006
Baltimore, MD 21279-1006
Fax: 800-473-2329
E-mail: info@iaaoc.org
URL: http://www.iaaoc.org
Freq: semiannual. **Price:** $30/copy. **ISSN:** 1055-3835.

5823 ■ Journal of Addictions and Offender Counseling
American Counseling Association
5999 Stevenson Ave.
Alexandria, VA 22304
Fax: (703)823-0252
E-mail: ryep@counseling.org
URL: http://www.counseling.org
Freq: semiannual. **Price:** included in membership dues, $22/year for nonmembers. **ISSN:** 1055-3835.

5824 ■ Journal of Chiropractic Education
Association of Chiropractic Colleges
4424 Montgomery Ave., Ste. 202
Bethesda, MD 20814
Fax: (301)913-9146
E-mail: info@chirocolleges.org
URL: http://www.chirocolleges.org
Freq: semiannual.

5825 ■ Journal of College Counseling
American Counseling Association
5999 Stevenson Ave.
Alexandria, VA 22304
Fax: (703)823-0252
E-mail: ryep@counseling.org
URL: http://www.counseling.org
Freq: semiannual. **Price:** $32/year. **ISSN:** 1099-0399.

5826 ■ Journal of Counseling and Development
American Counseling Association
5999 Stevenson Ave.
Alexandria, VA 22304
Fax: (703)823-0252
E-mail: ryep@counseling.org
URL: http://www.counseling.org
Freq: quarterly. **Price:** included in membership dues, $128/year for nonmembers and institutions. **ISSN:** 0748-9633.

5827 ■ Journal of Distance Education
Canadian Association for Distance Education
260 Dalhousie St., Ste. 204
Ottawa, ON, Canada K1N 7E4
Ph: (613)241-0018
Fax: (613)241-0019
E-mail: cade-aced@csse.ca
URL: http://www.cade-aced.ca
Freq: semiannual. **Price:** $40. **ISSN:** 0830-0445.

5828 ■ Journal of Early Intervention
Division for Early Childhood of the Council for Exceptional Children
27 Ft. Missoula Rd., Ste. 2
Missoula, MT 59804
Ph: (406)543-0872
Fax: (406)543-0887
E-mail: dec@dec-sped.org
URL: http://www.dec-sped.org
Descr: Provides information on current research and practice for individuals who work with young children with special needs. Includes book reviews. **Freq:** quarterly. **Price:** included in membership dues, $50/

year for individual nonmembers, $70/year for institutions. **ISSN:** 0885-3460.

5829 ■ Journal of Educational Measurement
National Council on Measurement in Education
2810 Crossroads Dr., Ste. 3800
Madison, WI 53718
Ph: (608)443-2487
Fax: (608)443-2474
E-mail: plovelace@ncme.org
URL: http://www.ncme.org
Descr: Contains original measurement research and provides reviews of measurement publications and reports. **Freq:** quarterly. **Price:** included in membership dues. **ISSN:** 0022-0655.

5830 ■ Journal of Employment Counseling
American Counseling Association
5999 Stevenson Ave.
Alexandria, VA 22304
Fax: (703)823-0252
E-mail: ryep@counseling.org
URL: http://www.counseling.org
Freq: quarterly. **Price:** included in membership dues, $38/year. **ISSN:** 0022-0787.

5831 ■ Journal of Food Science Education
Institute of Food Technologists
525 W Van Buren, Ste. 1000
Chicago, IL 60607
Ph: (312)782-8424
Fax: (312)782-8348
E-mail: info@ift.org
URL: http://www.ift.org

5832 ■ The Journal of Humanistic Counseling, Education and Development
American Counseling Association
5999 Stevenson Ave.
Alexandria, VA 22304
Fax: (703)823-0252
E-mail: ryep@counseling.org
URL: http://www.counseling.org
Freq: quarterly. **Price:** included in membership dues, $32/year for nonmembers. **ISSN:** 0735-6846.

5833 ■ Journal of Multicultural Counseling and Development
American Counseling Association
5999 Stevenson Ave.
Alexandria, VA 22304
Fax: (703)823-0252
E-mail: ryep@counseling.org
URL: http://www.counseling.org
Freq: quarterly. **Price:** included in membership dues, $21/year for nonmembers. **ISSN:** 0883-8534.

5834 ■ Journal of the National Association of University Women
National Association of University Women
1001 E St. SE
Washington, DC 20003
Ph: (202)547-3967
Fax: (202)547-5226
E-mail: info@nauw1910.org
URL: http://www.nauw1910.org
Freq: biennial.

5835 ■ Journal of Nutrition Education & Behavior
Society for Nutrition Education
9100 Purdue Rd., Ste. 200
Indianapolis, IN 46268
Ph: (317)328-4627
Fax: (317)280-8527
E-mail: info@sne.org
URL: http://www.sne.org
Descr: For educators, practitioners and researchers on nutrition education. Includes book reviews and employment opportunity listings. **Freq:** bimonthly. **Price:** included in membership dues, $119/year for individuals, $170/year for institutions, $60/year for individuals in-training.

5836 ■ Journal of Patient Safety
National Patient Safety Foundation
268 Summer St., 6th Fl.

Boston, MA 02210
Ph: (617)391-9900
Fax: (617)391-9999
E-mail: info@npsf.org
URL: http://www.npsf.org
Freq: quarterly. **Price:** $168/year for individuals, $248/year for institutions.

5837 ■ Journal of Physical Education, Recreation and Dance
American Association for Physical Activity and Recreation
1900 Association Dr.
Reston, VA 20191-1598
Ph: (703)476-3400
Fax: (703)476-9527
E-mail: aapar@aahperd.org
URL: http://www.aahperd.org/aapar
Freq: 9/year.

5838 ■ Journal of Postsecondary Education and Disability
Association on Higher Education and Disability
107 Commerce Center Dr., Ste. 204
Huntersville, NC 28078
Ph: (704)947-7779
Fax: (704)948-7779
E-mail: ahead@ahead.org
URL: http://www.ahead.org

5839 ■ The Journal of Reading Recovery
Reading Recovery Council of North America
400 W Wilson Bridge Rd., Ste. 250
Worthington, OH 43085-5218
Ph: (614)310-7323
Fax: (614)310-7345
E-mail: jjohnson@readingrecovery.org
URL: http://www.readingrecovery.org
Freq: semiannual. **Price:** included in membership dues.

5840 ■ Journal of Safety Management
National Safety Management Society
PO Box 4460
Walnut Creek, CA 94596-0460
Fax: (573)441-1765
E-mail: nsmsinc@yahoo.com
URL: http://www.nsms.us
Freq: quarterly.

5841. ■ Journal of School Health
American School Health Association
7263 State, Rte. 43
PO Box 708
Kent, OH 44240
Ph: (330)678-1601
Fax: (330)678-4526
E-mail: asha@ashaweb.org
URL: http://www.ashaweb.org
Key Personnel: Morgan R. Pigg, Jr., Editor. **URL(s):** http://www.ashaweb.org/i4a/pages/index.cfm?pageid=3341 **Descr:** Journal on health promotion in school settings. **Freq:** Monthly, (not published in June and July). **Price:** $130, Included in membership, professional, print and online; $75, Included in membership, basic, print and online; $40, Included in membership, student, print and online.

5842 ■ Journal of Teaching Addictions
International Coalition for Addiction Studies Education
PO Box 224
Vermillion, SD 57069-0224
Ph: (480)517-8522
Fax: (480)517-8449
E-mail: kirkbowdenphd@gmail.com
URL: http://incase-edu.net
Price: included in membership dues.

5843 ■ The Journal for Truancy and Dropout Prevention
International Association for Truancy and Dropout Prevention
10602 Holly Springs
Houston, TX 77042

Ph: (713)293-9711
E-mail: hpryor@houstonisd.org
URL: http://www.iatdp.org
Descr: Addresses the problem of student truancy and other school social welfare issues; includes conference proceedings, research reports, and news releases. **Freq:** semiannual. **Price:** included in membership dues, $35/year for libraries. **ISSN:** 0020-6016.

5844 ■ *Journal for Vocational Special Needs Education*
Journal for Vocational Special Needs Education
c/o Betsy Dillon
99 Woodland Dr.
Pittsburgh, PA 15228
Ph: (412)344-7854
Fax: (412)675-9067
Key Personnel: Betsy Dillon, Contact, eeb6@psu.edu. **Descr:** Journal covering vocational education and career development of persons with disabilities or economically/academically disadvantaged. **Freq:** 3/year. **Price:** Free, to members; $40, nonmembers.

5845 ■ *Just the Facts, Please!*
American Institute of Architects, Southern Arizona
4633 E Broadway Blvd., Ste. 101
Tucson, AZ 85711
Ph: (520)323-2191
Fax: (520)323-3399
E-mail: brent@aia-arizona.org
URL: http://www.aia-arizona.org/sacaia/index.html
Freq: weekly.

5846 ■ *Just For Us*
Children of Lesbians and Gays Everywhere SF/Bay Area
1550 Bryant St., Ste. 830
San Francisco, CA 94103
Ph: (415)861-5437
Fax: (415)255-8345
E-mail: director@colage.org
URL: http://www.colage.org/bayarea
Freq: semiannual.

5847 ■ *Justicia*
Puerto Rican Legal Defense and Education Fund
99 Hudson St., 14th Fl.
New York, NY 10013-2815
Ph: (212)219-3360
Fax: (212)431-4276
E-mail: info@prldef.org
URL: http://www.prldef.org
Freq: quarterly. **Price:** free.

5848 ■ *The K & W Guide to Colleges for the Learning Disabled*
Princeton Review Inc.
2315 Broadway
New York, NY 10024
Ph: (212)874-8282
Free: 800-333-0369
URL: http://www.princetonreview.com
Key Personnel: Marybeth Kravets, Mailing Contact; Imy F. Wax, Editor. **Covers:** 338 colleges and universities with specialized services and programs for learning-disabled students. A "Quick Contact" list provides program details for 1,000 other schools. **Entries include:** Institution name, address, phone, name of coordinator of learning-disabled programs, number of learning-disabled students, description of programs and services, and entrance criteria and procedures. **Freq:** Approximately biennial; latest edition 2003. **Price:** $18.87, individuals.

5849 ■ *Kaplan Scholarships*
Simon & Schuster Adult Publishing Group
1230 Ave. of the Americas
New York, NY 10020
Ph: (212)698-7000
Fax: (212)632-8099
E-mail: consumer.customerservice@simonandschuster.com
URL: http://www.simonsays.com
Key Personnel: Gail Ann Schlachter, Author; R. David Weber, Author; Carolyn Reidy, President.

URL(s): http://www.simonsays.com **Covers:** Private sources for college scholarships. **Entries include:** Web and e-mail address, fax, eligibility requirements. **Price:** $27, individuals.

5850 ■ *Keeping in Touch*
Canadian Council for Exceptional Children
479 Kingsleigh Ct.
Milton, ON, Canada L9T 1X6
Ph: (905)878-2145
Fax: (905)878-2145
E-mail: hberger@gov.mb.ca
URL: http://canadian.cec.sped.org
Freq: quarterly.

5851 ■ *Key Communicator*
Washington State PTA
2003 65th Ave. W
Tacoma, WA 98466-6215
Ph: (253)565-2153
Fax: (253)565-7753
E-mail: wapta@wastatepta.org
URL: http://www.wastatepta.org

5852 ■ *Keynotes*
Learning Disabilities Association of North Carolina
1854A Hendersonville Rd., No. 239
Asheville, NC 28803
Fax: (919)489-0788
E-mail: ldanc@mindspring.com
URL: http://www.ldanc.org
Freq: quarterly.

5853 ■ *Kids and Guns: A National Disgrace*
Educational Fund to Stop Gun Violence
1424 L St. NW, Ste. 2-1
Washington, DC 20005-2602
Ph: (202)408-0061
E-mail: csgv@csgv.org
URL: http://www.efsgv.org

5854 ■ *LAF Update*
American Association of University Women Legal Advocacy Fund
1111 16th St. NW
Washington, DC 20036
Ph: (202)785-7700
Fax: (202)872-1425
E-mail: connect@aauw.org
URL: http://www.aauw.org/advocacy/laf//index.cfm

5855 ■ *Large Print Book of Common Prayer*
Episcopal Society for Ministry on Aging
PO Box 3065
Meridian, MS 39303
Ph: (601)485-0311
URL: http://www.episcopalchurch.org/episcopal-life/RetClose.html

5856 ■ *Large Print Loan Library Catalog*
National Association for Visually Handicapped
22 W 21st St., 6th Fl.
New York, NY 10010
Ph: (212)889-3141
Fax: (212)727-2931
E-mail: navh@navh.org
URL: http://www.navh.org
Descr: Lists books in large print commercial publishers available from NAVH. **Freq:** biennial.

5857 ■ *Law of The Student Press*
Student Press Law Center
1101 Wilson Blvd., Ste. 1100
Arlington, VA 22209
Ph: (703)807-1904
Fax: (703)807-2109
E-mail: splc@splc.org
URL: http://www.splc.org
Descr: Covers press law for student journalists. **Price:** $18. **ISSN:** 0964-3574.

5858 ■ *LDA Newsbriefs*
Learning Disabilities Association of America
4156 Library Rd.
Pittsburgh, PA 15234-1349
Ph: (412)341-1515
Fax: (412)344-0224

E-mail: info@ldaamerica.org
URL: http://www.ldaamerica.org
Descr: Contains items of interest on learning disabilities. **Freq:** bimonthly. **Price:** $15/year. **ISSN:** 0739-909X.

5859 ■ *LDAA Member Resource Directory*
Learning Disabilities Association of Arkansas
PO Box 95255
North Little Rock, AR 72190-5255
Ph: (501)666-8777
Descr: Provides resources to members. **Freq:** semiannual. **Price:** for members only.

5860 ■ *The LDAG Advocate*
Learning Disabilities Association of Georgia
2566 Shallowford Rd., Ste. 104
PMB 353
Atlanta, GA 30345
Ph: (404)303-7774
Fax: (404)467-0190
E-mail: ldaga@bellsouth.net
URL: http://www.ldag.org
Price: included in membership dues.

5861 ■ *LDW Highlights*
Massachusetts Association for Children With Learning Disabilities
PO Box 142
Weston, MA 02493
Ph: (781)890-5399
Fax: (781)890-0555

5862 ■ *Leadership Program Newsletter*
Mexican American Legal Defense and Educational Fund
634 S Spring St.
Los Angeles, CA 90014
Ph: (213)629-2512
URL: http://www.maldef.org
Freq: 3/year.

5863 ■ *The Leading Edge*
National Association of State Motorcycle Safety Administrators
7881 S Wellington St.
Centennial, CO 80122
Ph: (303)797-2318
Fax: (303)703-3569
E-mail: smsabusinessmgr@smsa.org
URL: http://www.smsa.org
Price: included in membership dues.

5864 ■ *LEAFLines*
Women's Legal Education and Action Fund
60 St. Clair Ave. E, Ste. 703
Toronto, ON, Canada M4T 1N5
Ph: (416)595-7170
Fax: (416)595-7191
E-mail: info@leaf.ca
URL: http://www.leaf.ca
Freq: annual.

5865 ■ *Learn Not to Burn Curriculum*
National Fire Protection Association
1 Batterymarch Park
Quincy, MA 02169-7471
Ph: (617)770-3000
Fax: (617)770-0700
E-mail: custserv@nfpa.org
URL: http://www.nfpa.org

5866 ■ *Learning about Adoption (When Fertility is Your Goal)*
World Association for Children and Parents
315 S Second St.
Renton, WA 98057
Ph: (206)575-4550
Fax: (206)575-4148
E-mail: wacap@wacap.org
URL: http://www.wacap.org
Descr: Contains information about the adoption

process, focusing on the struggles that infertile couples face. **Price:** free.

5867 ■ *Learning Disabilities: A Multidisciplinary Journal*
Learning Disabilities Association of America
4156 Library Rd.
Pittsburgh, PA 15234-1349
Ph: (412)341-1515
Fax: (412)344-0224
E-mail: info@ldaamerica.org
URL: http://www.ldaamerica.org
Freq: quarterly. **Price:** $30/year for members in U.S., $60/year for nonmembers, $45/year for members outside U.S.

5868 ■ *Learning Disabilities Association of Arkansas Newsletter*
Learning Disabilities Association of Arkansas
PO Box 95255
North Little Rock, AR 72190-5255
Ph: (501)666-8777
Descr: Contains articles of interest in the area of learning disabilities, and a calendar. **Freq:** quarterly. **Price:** included in membership dues.

5869 ■ *Learning Disabilities Sourcebook*
Omnigraphics Inc.
PO Box 31-1640
Detroit, MI 48231
Free: 800-234-1340
E-mail: info@omnigraphics.com
URL: http://www.omnigraphics.com
Key Personnel: Joyce Brennfleck Shannon, Editor. **URL(s):** http://www.omnigraphics.com **Publication includes:** A directory of resources and information on learning disabilities. Principal content of publication is Consumer information about various learning disabilities, including ADD, ADHD, language and speech disorders, brain injury, Tourette Syndrome and others. Information focuses on facts, coping strategies, educational programs and research. **Freq:** latest edition 3rd, Published 2009. **Price:** $84, individuals, Hardcover.

5870 ■ *Learning Financial Literacy in Bankruptcy*
National Consumer Law Center
7 Winthrop Sq.
Boston, MA 02110-1245
Ph: (617)542-8010
Fax: (617)542-8028
E-mail: consumerlaw@nclc.org
URL: http://www.consumerlaw.org

5871 ■ *Learning to Look*
Blind Children's Fund
201 S University St.
Mount Pleasant, MI 48858
Ph: (989)779-9966
Fax: (989)779-0015
E-mail: bcf@blindchildrensfund.org
URL: http://www.blindchildrensfund.org
Descr: Contains specific suggestions on how to help your child use what vision she/he has or may have; for parents of severely visually impaired children. **Price:** $9.

5872 ■ *Learning the Nemeth Code*
Braille Authority of North America
1805 N Oakland St.
Arlington, VA 22207
Ph: (202)707-0722
Fax: (202)707-0712
E-mail: jdix@loc.gov
URL: http://www.brailleauthority.org

5873 ■ *Legislation Bulletin*
New York State PTA
One Wembley Ct.
Albany, NY 12205-3830
Ph: (518)452-8808
Fax: (518)452-8105
E-mail: pta.office@nypta.com
URL: http://www.nypta.com

Freq: 5/year. **Price:** $5 per year.

5874 ■ *Legislative Activity Report*
Council of the Great City Schools
1301 Pennsylvania Ave. NW, Ste. 702
Washington, DC 20004
Ph: (202)393-2427
Fax: (202)393-2400
E-mail: mcasserly@cgcs.org
URL: http://www.cgcs.org
Freq: biweekly.

5875 ■ *Legislative Alert*
Association for Career and Technical Education
1410 King St.
Alexandria, VA 22314
Ph: (703)683-3111
Fax: (703)683-7424
E-mail: acte@acteonline.org
URL: http://www.acteonline.org

5876 ■ *Legislative Monitor*
Arc of Tennessee
151 Athens Way, Ste. 100
Nashville, TN 37228
Ph: (615)248-5878
Fax: (615)248-5879
E-mail: info@thearctn.org
URL: http://www.thearctn.org
Freq: monthly.

5877 ■ *Legislative Update*
Common Cause of Michigan
315 Second St., No. 401
Ann Arbor, MI 48103
Ph: (734)763-0689
Fax: (734)763-9181
E-mail: johnch@umich.edu
URL: http://www.commoncause.org
Freq: 3/year.

5878 ■ *Legislative Update*
Washington Association for the Education of Young Children
841 N Central Ave., Ste. 206
Kent, WA 98032
Ph: (253)854-2565
Fax: (253)813-3646
E-mail: waeyc@waeyc.org
URL: http://www.waeyc.org
Freq: weekly.

5879 ■ *LERN Magazine*
Learning Resources Network
PO Box 9
River Falls, WI 54022
Ph: (715)426-9777
Free: 800-678-5376
Fax: 888-234-8633
E-mail: info@lern.org
URL: http://www.lern.org/
Key Personnel: William A. Draves, President, draves@lern.org. **URL(s):** http://www.lern.org/visitors_center/newsletters.htm **Descr:** Magazine covering continuing education. **Freq:** 10/yr. **Price:** $125, institutions, local; $125, individuals; $11.95, single issue.

5880 ■ *Let's Do a Farm Safety Day Camp*
Farm Safety 4 Just Kids
11304 Aurora Ave.
Urbandale, IA 50322
Ph: (515)331-6506
Fax: (515)331-2947
E-mail: fs4jk@fs4jk.org
URL: http://www.fs4jk.org
Price: $9 for members, $11.25 for nonmembers.

5881 ■ *Letters to Member Schools*
A Better Chance
240 W 35th St., 9th Fl.
New York, NY 10001-2506
Ph: (646)346-1310
Fax: (646)346-1311
E-mail: stimmons@abetterchance.org
URL: http://www.abetterchance.org

Freq: annual.

5882 ■ *Letting Go, Care, Stutter Buddies*
National Stuttering Association
119 W 40th St., 14th Fl.
New York, NY 10018
Ph: (212)944-4050
Fax: (212)944-8244
E-mail: info@westutter.org
URL: http://www.WeStutter.org
Descr: Benefits parents, children and adults. **Freq:** bimonthly. **Price:** $35.

5883 ■ *Letting Go, Stutter Buddies*
National Stuttering Association
119 W 40th St., 14th Fl.
New York, NY 10018
Ph: (212)944-4050
Fax: (212)944-8244
E-mail: info@westutter.org
URL: http://www.WeStutter.org
Descr: Publication for children. **Price:** included in membership dues.

5884 ■ *Library Resources for the Blind and Physically Handicapped*
National Library Service for the Blind and Physically Handicapped
Library of Congress
1291 Taylor St. NW
Washington, DC 20011
Ph: (202)707-5100
Free: 888-657-7323
Fax: (202)707-0712
E-mail: nls@loc.gov
URL: http://www.loc.gov/nls/contact.html
URL(s): http://www.loc.gov/nls **Covers:** 57 regional and 81 subregional libraries, and 4 machine-lending agencies in the United States, Puerto Rico, the U.S. Virgin Islands, and Guam that provide a free library service of Braille and recorded books and magazines to visually and physically handicapped persons; other agencies distributing Braille materials and talking book machines are also indicated. **Entries include:** Name of library, address, phone, fax, in-WATS number, e-mail address, TDD number (for the deaf), name of librarian, name of contact for machines (if any), hours of operation, list of book collections (includes disc, cassette, Braille, large type), list of special collections (films, foreign language cassettes), list of special services. **Freq:** Annual, Latest edition 2006.

5885 ■ *Links*
Common Cause of Michigan
315 Second St., No. 401
Ann Arbor, MI 48103
Ph: (734)763-0689
Fax: (734)763-9181
E-mail: johnch@umich.edu
URL: http://www.commoncause.org
Freq: 3/year.

5886 ■ *Literacy Teaching and Learning: An International Journal of Early Reading and Writing*
Reading Recovery Council of North America
400 W Wilson Bridge Rd., Ste. 250
Worthington, OH 43085-5218
Ph: (614)310-7323
Fax: (614)310-7345
E-mail: jjohnson@readingrecovery.org
URL: http://www.readingrecovery.org
Descr: Contains issues related to language acquisition, literacy development, and instructional theory and practice. **Freq:** semiannual. **Price:** included in membership dues.

5887 ■ *Living Safety*
Canada Safety Council
1020 Thomas Spratt Pl.
Ottawa, ON, Canada K1G 5L5
Ph: (613)739-1535
Fax: (613)739-1566
E-mail: canadasafetycouncil@safety-council.org
URL: http://safety-council.org

Freq: quarterly. **Price:** $10.95/copy.

5888 ■ Living Well with a Disability: How Libraries Can Help
Disability Resources
4 Glatter Ln.
Centereach, NY 11720-1032
Ph: (631)585-0290
Fax: (631)585-0290
E-mail: info@disabilityresources.org
URL: http://www.disabilityresources.org
Price: $2 in U.S., $3 outside U.S.

5889 ■ Loud, Proud and Passionate
Mobility International USA
132 E Broadway, Ste. 343
Eugene, OR 97401
Ph: (541)343-1284
Fax: (541)343-6812
E-mail: info@miusa.org
URL: http://www.miusa.org
Descr: Available with captions. **Price:** $49.

5890 ■ Loud, Proud and Passionate Including Women with Disabilities in International Development Programs
Mobility International USA
132 E Broadway, Ste. 343
Eugene, OR 97401
Ph: (541)343-1284
Fax: (541)343-6812
E-mail: info@miusa.org
URL: http://www.miusa.org
Descr: Available with captions. **Freq:** quarterly.
Price: $30.

5891 ■ Loud, Proud and Prosperous: Microcredit Projects By and For Women with Disabilities in South Africa
Mobility International USA
132 E Broadway, Ste. 343
Eugene, OR 97401
Ph: (541)343-1284
Fax: (541)343-6812
E-mail: info@miusa.org
URL: http://www.miusa.org
Descr: Available with captions. **Price:** $49.

5892 ■ Lutheran Braille Workers—Newsletter
Lutheran Braille Workers
PO Box 5000
Yucaipa, CA 92399
Ph: (909)795-8977
Fax: (909)795-8970
E-mail: lbw@lbwinc.org
URL: http://www.lbwinc.org
Descr: Covers association activities. **Freq:** quarterly.
Price: free.

5893 ■ Magazines in Special Media
National Library Service for the Blind and Physically Handicapped
Library of Congress
1291 Taylor St. NW
Washington, DC 20011
Ph: (202)707-5100
Free: 888-657-7323
Fax: (202)707-0712
E-mail: nls@loc.gov
URL: http://www.loc.gov/nls/contact.html
URL(s): http://www.loc.gov/nls **Entries include:** Name of publisher, address, price. Principal content is a bibliography of periodicals, with brief description, frequency, format, and price of each. **Publication includes:** List of over 100 public and private organizations that publish magazines in Braille, on cassette, on disc and computer diskette, or in large print or moon type for visually impaired and physically disabled individuals. **Freq:** Biennial, Latest edition 2005.

5894 ■ Making Headway
Active Minds
2647 Connecticut Ave. NW, Ste. 200
Washington, DC 20008
Ph: (202)332-9595
Fax: (413)502-1593

E-mail: info@activeminds.org
URL: http://www.activemindsoncampus.org

5895 ■ Managing Your Diabetes: Basics and Beyond
Diabetes Action Research and Education Foundation
426 C St. NE
Washington, DC 20002
Ph: (202)333-4520
Fax: (202)558-5240
E-mail: info@diabetesaction.org
URL: http://www.diabetesaction.org
Price: free.

5896 ■ Manatee Messenger
American Association of University Women, Manatee County Branch
3707 118th St. W
Bradenton, FL 34210
Ph: (941)792-5970
E-mail: tsteele19@tampabay.rr.com
URL: http://www.florida-aauw.org/Branches/manatee.htm
Descr: Contains latest updates on the organizations.
Freq: monthly.

5897 ■ Manual for Adaptive Fitness Instructors
Disabled Sports USA
451 Hungerford Dr., Ste. 100
Rockville, MD 20850
Ph: (301)217-0960
Fax: (301)217-0968
E-mail: information@dsusa.org
URL: http://www.dsusa.org

5898 ■ Manual for Adaptive Ski Instructors
Disabled Sports USA
451 Hungerford Dr., Ste. 100
Rockville, MD 20850
Ph: (301)217-0960
Fax: (301)217-0968
E-mail: information@dsusa.org
URL: http://www.dsusa.org

5899 ■ Maternal and Child Health Publications Catalog
National Maternal and Child Health Clearinghouse
U.S. Department of Health and Human Services
Parklawn Bldg.
5600 Fishers Ln.
Rockville, MD 20857
Ph: (301)443-2170
E-mail: ask@hrsa.gov
URL: http://www.ask.hrsa.gov/
Descr: Lists approximatley 350 volumes and ordering information. **Freq:** annual. **Price:** free.

5900 ■ Maternal and Child Health Thesaurus, Second Edition
National Maternal and Child Health Clearinghouse
U.S. Department of Health and Human Services
Parklawn Bldg.
5600 Fishers Ln.
Rockville, MD 20857
Ph: (301)443-2170
E-mail: ask@hrsa.gov
URL: http://www.ask.hrsa.gov/

5901 ■ Matrix
American Institute of Architects - Minnesota
275 Market St., Ste. 54
Minneapolis, MN 55405
Ph: (612)338-6763
Fax: (612)625-7525
E-mail: rcheng@umn.edu
URL: http://www.aia-mn.org
Freq: monthly.

5902 ■ MEA Voice
Michigan Education Association
1216 Kendale Blvd.
PO Box 2573
East Lansing, MI 48826-2573
Ph: (517)332-6551

Free: 800-292-1934
URL: http://www.mea.org
Key Personnel: Iris K. Salters, President, isalters@mea.org; Steven Cook, Vice President, stcook@mea.org. **URL(s):** http://www.mea.org/voice **Descr:** Educational magazine for teachers union. **Freq:** Quarterly. **Price:** Included in membership.

5903 ■ Measurement and Evaluation in Counseling and Development
Association for Assessment in Counseling and Education
5999 Stevenson Ave.
Alexandria, VA 22304-3300
Fax: (202)473-2329
E-mail: jwatson@meridian.msstate.edu
URL: http://www.theaaceonline.com
Descr: Contains articles focusing on research and applications in guidance and counseling. Intended for counselors and directors of research. **Freq:** quarterly. **Price:** included in membership dues, $60/year for nonmembers. **ISSN:** 0748-1756.

5904 ■ Meeting College Costs
The College Board
45 Columbus Ave.
New York, NY 10023-6992
Ph: (212)713-8000
Fax: (212)649-8442
E-mail: publicaffairs@collegeboard.org
URL: http://www.collegeboard.com

5905 ■ Memberanda Newsletter
Secondary School Admission Test Board
CN 5339
Princeton, NJ 08543
Ph: (609)683-4440
Fax: (609)683-4507
E-mail: info@ssat.org
URL: http://www.ssat.org
Descr: Reports on education at independent schools and issues of interest to educators in admission. **Freq:** quarterly. **Price:** included in membership dues.

5906 ■ Membership Roster
International Society of Air Safety Investigators
107 E Holly Ave., Ste. 11
Sterling, VA 20164
Ph: (703)430-9668
Fax: (703)430-4970
E-mail: isasi@erols.com
URL: http://www.isasi.org
Freq: biennial.

5907 ■ Mental Retardation
Arc of Berks County
1829 New Holland Rd., Ste. 9
Reading, PA 19607
Ph: (610)603-0227
Fax: (610)603-0229
E-mail: berksarc@aol.com

5908 ■ Migrant Education News
Migrant Legal Action Program
1001 Connecticut Ave. NW, Ste. 915
Washington, DC 20036
Ph: (202)775-7780
Fax: (202)775-7784
E-mail: mlap@mlap.org
URL: http://www.mlap.org
Freq: monthly. **Price:** $120.

5909 ■ John Milton Adult Lesson Quarterly
John Milton Society for the Blind - USA
370 Lexington Ave., Rm. 1007
New York, NY 10017-6503
Ph: (212)870-3335
Fax: (212)870-3226
E-mail: order@jmsblind.org
URL: http://www.jmsblind.org
Descr: Contains Bible studies in braille and on cassette tape. **Price:** free to blind persons.

5910 ■ John Milton Magazine
John Milton Society for the Blind - USA
370 Lexington Ave., Rm. 1007

New York, NY 10017-6503
Ph: (212)870-3335
Fax: (212)870-3226
E-mail: order@jmsblind.org
URL: http://www.jmsblind.org

Descr: Reprints of reading material offered in over 50 religiou s periodicals for the sighted. Available in large print. **Freq:** quarterly. **Price:** free to blind persons.

5911 ■ *Minnesota Educator*
Education Minnesota
41 Sherburne Ave.
Saint Paul, MN 55103-2196
Ph: (651)227-9541
Free: 800-652-9073
E-mail: webmaster@educationminnesota.org
URL: http://www.educationminnesota.org/

Key Personnel: Judy Berglund, Editor. **URL(s):** http://www.educationminnesota.org; http://www. educationminnesota.org **Descr:** Educational newspaper. **Freq:** Monthly.

5912 ■ *The Missing Piece*
Learning Disabilities Association of Washington
16315 NE 87th St., No. B-4
Redmond, WA 98052
Ph: (425)882-0820
Fax: (425)861-4642
E-mail: cimel@ldawa.org
URL: http://www.ldawa.org
Freq: quarterly.

5913 ■ *MIUSA's Global Impact*
Mobility International USA
132 E Broadway, Ste. 343
Eugene, OR 97401
Ph: (541)343-1284
Fax: (541)343-6812
E-mail: info@miusa.org
URL: http://www.miusa.org

Descr: Also available on audiocassette. **Freq:** semiannual. **Price:** included in membership dues.

5914 ■ *MNSACA Field Trip Fun*
Minnesota School Age Care Alliance
1821 University Ave. W, Ste. 324-S
St. Paul, MN 55104
Ph: (651)646-8689
Fax: (651)636-9146
E-mail: brians@mnsaca.org
URL: http://mnsaca.org

Descr: Contains field trip listings in MN. **Freq:** annual. **Price:** $15.

5915 ■ *Monday Morning Newsletter*
New Jersey Council on Developmental Disabilities
PO Box 700
20 W State St., 6th Fl.
Trenton, NJ 08625-0700
Ph: (609)292-3745
Fax: (609)292-7114
E-mail: njcdd@njcdd.org
URL: http://www.njcdd.org
Freq: weekly.

5916 ■ *Money Matters*
Washington State PTA
2003 65th Ave. W
Tacoma, WA 98466-6215
Ph: (253)565-2153
Fax: (253)565-7753
E-mail: wapta@wastatepta.org
URL: http://www.wastatepta.org

5917 ■ *Money and You*
National Foundation for Credit Counseling
801 Roeder Rd., Ste. 900
Silver Spring, MD 20910
Ph: (301)589-5600
Fax: (301)495-5623
E-mail: press@nfcc.org
URL: http://www.nfcc.org

Freq: quarterly.

5918 ■ *Montana's Programs for Individuals with Disabilities*
The Rural Institute: Center for Excellence in Disability Education, Research and Service
University of Montana Rural Institute
52 Corbin Hall
Missoula, MT 59812
Ph: (406)243-5467
Fax: (406)243-4730
E-mail: rural@ruralinstitute.umt.edu
URL: http://ruralinstitute.umt.edu

5919 ■ *Monthly Activity Calendar*
Arc of Northern Essex
57 Wingate St., Ste. 301
Haverhill, MA 01832
Ph: (978)373-0552
Fax: (978)373-0557
E-mail: arc.nec@verizon.net
URL: http://arcmass.org

5920 ■ *Moral Suasion*
Direct Selling Education Foundation
1667 K St. NW, Ste. 1100
Washington, DC 20006-1660
Ph: (202)452-8866
Fax: (202)452-9015
E-mail: info@dsef.org
URL: http://www.dsef.org

Descr: Describes how the member companies of the Direct Selling Association developed and enacted a code of ethics.

5921 ■ *MPTA Bulletin*
Montana Congress of Parents and Teachers
PO Box 6448
Great Falls, MT 59406
Ph: (406)268-7475
E-mail: montana_pta@gfps.k12.mt.us
URL: http://www.montanapta.org
Freq: 9/year. **Price:** $5.

5922 ■ *The NAADD Report: The Newsletter on Alcohol, Drugs and Disability*
National Association on Alcohol, Drugs and Disability
2165 Bunker Hill Dr.
San Mateo, CA 94402-3801
Ph: (650)578-8047
Fax: (650)286-9205
E-mail: solanda@sbcglobal.net
URL: http://www.naadd.org
Freq: annual.

5923 ■ *NAASLN Membership News and Views*
National Association for Adults with Special Learning Needs
1143 Tidewater Ct.
Westerville, OH 43082
Fax: (614)392-1559
E-mail: naasln@aol.com
URL: http://www.naasln.org
Freq: monthly.

5924 ■ *NADD Bulletin*
NADD - An Association for Persons with Developmental Disabilities and Mental Health Needs
132 Fair St.
Kingston, NY 12401-4802
Ph: (845)331-4336
Fax: (845)331-4569
E-mail: info@thenadd.org
URL: http://www.thenadd.org
Freq: bimonthly. **Price:** included in membership dues. **ISSN:** 1065-2574.

5925 ■ *NAPSEC News*
National Association of Private Special Education Centers
1522 K St. NW, Ste. 1032
Washington, DC 20005
Ph: (202)408-3338
Fax: (202)408-3340
E-mail: napsec@aol.com
URL: http://www.napsec.org

Descr: Reports association and member news. **Freq:** 3/year. **Price:** included in membership dues.

5926 ■ *National*
Learning Disabilities Association of Canada
250 City Centre Ave., Ste. 616
Ottawa, ON, Canada K1R 6K7
Ph: (613)238-5721
Fax: (613)235-5391
E-mail: info@ldac-taac.ca
URL: http://www.ldac-taac.ca
Freq: quarterly. **Price:** $20/year for nonmembers, $24.50 international, $5.35/copy.

5927 ■ *National Association of Health Unit Coordinators - Education Program Procedure Guide*
National Association of Health Unit Coordinators
1947 Madron Rd.
Rockford, IL 61107-1716
Ph: (815)633-4351
Fax: (815)633-4438
E-mail: office@nahuc.org
URL: http://www.nahuc.org

Descr: Provides information to assist in the development or evaluation of a formal educational program. **Price:** $30 for members, $50 for nonmembers.

5928 ■ *National Awards Program*
Association for Career and Technical Education
1410 King St.
Alexandria, VA 22314
Ph: (703)683-3111
Fax: (703)683-7424
E-mail: acte@acteonline.org
URL: http://www.acteonline.org

5929 ■ *National Braille Association—Bulletin*
National Braille Association
95 Allens Creek Rd., Bldg. 1, Ste. 202
Rochester, NY 14618
Ph: (585)427-8260
Fax: (585)427-0263
E-mail: nbaoffice@nationalbraille.org
URL: http://nationalbraille.org

Descr: Features articles of interest to members and persons working in the field of services to the visually impaired; contains calendar of events. **Freq:** quarterly. **Price:** included in membership dues, $50/year for nonmembers in U.S., $60/year for nonmembers outside U.S. **ISSN:** 0550-5666.

5930 ■ *National Braille Association—General Interest Catalog*
National Braille Association
95 Allens Creek Rd., Bldg. 1, Ste. 202
Rochester, NY 14618
Ph: (585)427-8260
Fax: (585)427-0263
E-mail: nbaoffice@nationalbraille.org
URL: http://nationalbraille.org

Descr: Topics include work, recreation, and daily living. **Freq:** periodic. **Price:** free.

5931 ■ *National Braille Association—Music Catalog*
National Braille Association
95 Allens Creek Rd., Bldg. 1, Ste. 202
Rochester, NY 14618
Ph: (585)427-8260
Fax: (585)427-0263
E-mail: nbaoffice@nationalbraille.org
URL: http://nationalbraille.org

Descr: Contains music titles available in Braille from NBA collection; available in print and Braille. **Freq:** periodic. **Price:** free.

5932 ■ *National Braille Association—Textbook Catalog*
National Braille Association
95 Allens Creek Rd., Bldg. 1, Ste. 202
Rochester, NY 14618
Ph: (585)427-8260
Fax: (585)427-0263
E-mail: nbaoffice@nationalbraille.org
URL: http://nationalbraille.org

Descr: Includes titles of Braille books from NBA collection of college-level and technical materials; available in print and Braille. **Freq:** periodic. **Price:** free.

5933 ■ National Braille Press Release
National Braille Press
88 St. Stephen St.
Boston, MA 02115
Ph: (617)266-6160
Fax: (617)437-0456
E-mail: orders@nbp.org
URL: http://www.nbp.org
Freq: 3/year.

5934 ■ National Directory of Four-Year Colleges, Two-Year Colleges and Post School Training Programs for Young People with Learning Disabilities
Partners in Publishing
3332 E 4th St.
PO Box 50347
Tulsa, OK 74112
Ph: (918)835-8258
Fax: (918)834-6365
Key Personnel: P.M. Fielding, Contact; P.M. Fielding, Editor. **Covers:** about 200 postsecondary institutions offering programs for learning disabled students. **Entries include:** School name, address, and name of contact; description of program including type of program, admission policies, courses offered and curriculum modifications; enrollment; percentage of learning disabled students completing the program; remedial clinic available. **Freq:** Irregular, latest edition January 1994.

5935 ■ National Dropout Prevention Newsletter
National Dropout Prevention Center/Network
Clemson University
209 Martin St.
Clemson, SC 29631-1555
Ph: (864)656-2599
Fax: (864)656-0136
E-mail: ndpc@clemson.edu
URL: http://www.dropoutprevention.org
Freq: quarterly.

5936 ■ National Dropout Prevention Update
National Dropout Prevention Center/Network
Clemson University
209 Martin St.
Clemson, SC 29631-1555
Ph: (864)656-2599
Fax: (864)656-0136
E-mail: ndpc@clemson.edu
URL: http://www.dropoutprevention.org
Freq: quarterly. **Price:** $1 for nonmembers, free for members.

5937 ■ National Executive Directors Association
Washington Association for Career and Technical Education
PO Box 315
Olympia, WA 98507-0315
Ph: (360)786-9286
Fax: (360)357-1491
E-mail: wa-acte@wa-acte.org
URL: http://www.wa-acte.org

5938 ■ National Fire Codes
National Fire Protection Association
1 Batterymarch Park
Quincy, MA 02169-7471
Ph: (617)770-3000
Fax: (617)770-0700
E-mail: custserv@nfpa.org
URL: http://www.nfpa.org
Descr: Features a compilation of over 300 fire codes, standards, recommended practices, manuals, and guides on fire protection. **Freq:** annual. **Price:** $759/12-volume set, $683 for members.

5939 ■ National Fire Protection Association— Technical Committee Reports/Documentation
National Fire Protection Association
1 Batterymarch Park
Quincy, MA 02169-7471

Ph: (617)770-3000
Fax: (617)770-0700
E-mail: custserv@nfpa.org
URL: http://www.nfpa.org
Descr: Includes committee reports and interim documents on the fire code and standards development process. **Freq:** semiannual.

5940 ■ National Issues Service
National Association of Private Special Education Centers
1522 K St. NW, Ste. 1032
Washington, DC 20005
Ph: (202)408-3338
Fax: (202)408-3340
E-mail: napsec@aol.com
URL: http://www.napsec.org
Descr: Contains legislative update and membership news. **Freq:** monthly.

5941 ■ National Report on the Women's Studies Major
National Women's Studies Association
7100 Baltimore Ave., Ste. 502
College Park, MD 20740
Ph: (301)403-0407
Fax: (301)403-4137
E-mail: nwsaoffice@nwsa.org
URL: http://www.nwsa.org
Descr: Includes program models and makes recommendations for strengthening the major. **Price:** $3 each.

5942 ■ NBDC News
National Business and Disability Council
201 I.U. Willets Rd.
Albertson, NY 11507
Ph: (516)465-1516
E-mail: lfrancis@abilitiesonline.org
URL: http://www.business-disability.com
Freq: quarterly.

5943 ■ NCME Newsletter
National Council on Measurement in Education
2810 Crossroads Dr., Ste. 3800
Madison, WI 53718
Ph: (608)443-2487
Fax: (608)443-2474
E-mail: plovelace@ncme.org
URL: http://www.ncme.org
Descr: Contains information on events pertinent to research and practice in educational measurement. **Freq:** quarterly.

5944 ■ NDSA Classification and Rules Manual
National Disability Sports Alliance
25 W Independence Way
Kingston, RI 02881
Ph: (401)792-7130
Fax: (401)792-7132
E-mail: info@ndsaonline.org
URL: http://www.ndsaonline.org

5945 ■ NEA-AKtivist
National Education Association - Alaska
4100 Spenard Rd.
Anchorage, AK 99517
Ph: (907)274-0536
Fax: (907)274-0551
E-mail: info@ak.nea.org
URL: http://www.ak.nea.org

5946 ■ NEA-Alaska Orientation Handbook for Rural Educators
National Education Association - Alaska
4100 Spenard Rd.
Anchorage, AK 99517
Ph: (907)274-0536
Fax: (907)274-0551
E-mail: info@ak.nea.org
URL: http://www.ak.nea.org

5947 ■ NEA-BPD Update
National Education Alliance for Borderline Personality Disorder
PO Box 974
Rye, NY 10580

Ph: (914)835-9011
E-mail: info@neabpd.org
URL: http://www.neabpd.org

5948 ■ NEA Higher Education Advocate
National Education Association
1201 16th St. NW
Washington, DC 20036-3290
Ph: (202)833-4000
Fax: (202)822-7974
URL: http://www.nea.org

5949 ■ NEA Today
National Education Association
1201 16th St. NW
Washington, DC 20036-3290
Ph: (202)833-4000
Fax: (202)822-7974
URL: http://www.nea.org
Descr: Covers news and events affecting public education. **Freq:** 8/year. **Price:** included in membership dues, $50/year for nonmembers.

5950 ■ NEA Today
National Education Association - New York
217 Lark St.
Albany, NY 12210
Ph: (518)462-6451
Fax: (518)462-1731
URL: http://www.neany.org
Descr: Features today's toughest teaching challenges and solutions. **Freq:** 8/year.

5951 ■ Nemeth Code of Braille Mathematics and Scientific Notation
Braille Authority of North America
1805 N Oakland St.
Arlington, VA 22207
Ph: (202)707-0722
Fax: (202)707-0712
E-mail: jdix@loc.gov
URL: http://www.brailleauthority.org

5952 ■ Network News
Minnesota School Age Care Alliance
1821 University Ave. W, Ste. 324-S
St. Paul, MN 55104
Ph: (651)646-8689
Fax: (651)636-9146
E-mail: brians@mnsaca.org
URL: http://mnsaca.org
Freq: quarterly.

5953 ■ Networking Directory
Developmental Delay Resources
5801 Beacon St.
Pittsburgh, PA 15217
Fax: (412)422-1374
E-mail: devdelay@mindspring.com
URL: http://www.devdelay.org
Freq: annual. **Price:** included in membership dues.

5954 ■ New Developments
Developmental Delay Resources
5801 Beacon St.
Pittsburgh, PA 15217
Fax: (412)422-1374
E-mail: devdelay@mindspring.com
URL: http://www.devdelay.org
Freq: quarterly. **Price:** included in membership dues.

5955 ■ New Schools, New Communities
Institute for Responsive Education
Cambridge Colorado School of Education
80 Prospect St., 3rd Fl.
Cambridge, MA 02138
Ph: (617)873-0610
Fax: (617)873-0273
E-mail: jorge.cardoso@cambridgecollege.edu
Descr: Covers developments in desegregation, bilingual education, and choice in public schools. Includes book reviews, case studies, and resource

summaries. **Freq:** 3/year. **Price:** $24/year. **ISSN:** 0882-3863.

5956 ■ *New Visions*
Aspire of Western New York
2356 N Forest Rd.
Getzville, NY 14068
Ph: (716)838-0047
Fax: (716)838-5925
E-mail: info@aspirewny.org
URL: http://www.aspirewny.org
Freq: bimonthly.

5957 ■ *New York Parent-Teacher*
New York State PTA
One Wembley Ct.
Albany, NY 12205-3830
Ph: (518)452-8808
Fax: (518)452-8105
E-mail: pta.office@nypta.com
URL: http://www.nypta.com
Descr: Focuses on topics of concern to parents, educators, and others interested in the well being of children and youth. **Freq:** bimonthly. **Price:** $10 per year.

5958 ■ *The New York Times Large Type Weekly*
The New York Times Co.
229 W 43rd St.
New York, NY 10036-3913
Ph: (212)556-1234
Free: 888-346-9867
Fax: (212)556-3535
URL: http://www.nytimes.com
Key Personnel: Tom Brady, Editor, brady@nytimes.com. **URL(s):** http://www.nytstore.com/ProdCode.aspx?prodcode=792 **Descr:** Newspaper published for persons with impaired vision. **Freq:** Weekly (Mon.). **Price:** $29, individuals.

5959 ■ *News*
Minnesota Association for the Education of Young Children
1821 University Ave., Ste. 324-S
St. Paul, MN 55104
Ph: (651)646-8689
Fax: (651)636-9146
E-mail: mnaeyc@mnaeyc.org
URL: http://www.mnaeyc.org
Descr: Features early childhood practitioners in the state of Minnesota. **Freq:** quarterly.

5960 ■ *NEWS*
National Association of Women Highway Safety Leaders
NH Highway Safety Agency
117 Manchester St.
Concord, NH 03301
Ph: (603)271-2131
Fax: (603)271-3790
E-mail: dgarvin@nhhsa.state.nh.us
URL: http://www.nawhsl.org
Freq: quarterly.

5961 ■ *News Brief*
American Association of University Women, Grand Rapids Branch
1740 Malvern Rd.
Jackson, MI 49203
Ph: (517)784-9523
E-mail: amvankat@comcast.net
URL: http://www.aauwmi.org
Freq: monthly. **Price:** free.

5962 ■ *News from ICRI*
International Child Resource Institute
1581 LeRoy Ave.
Berkeley, CA 94708
Ph: (510)644-1000
Fax: (510)644-1115

E-mail: info@icrichild.org
URL: http://www.icrichild.org

5963 ■ *News Notes*
International Coalition for Addiction Studies Education
PO Box 224
Vermillion, SD 57069-0224
Ph: (480)517-8522
Fax: (480)517-8449
E-mail: kirkbowdenphd@gmail.com
URL: http://incase-edu.net
Freq: quarterly. **Price:** included in membership dues.

5964 ■ *News and Views*
North Eastern Ohio Education Association
5422 E 90th St., Ste. 200
Garfield Heights, OH 44125-5330
Ph: (216)518-0200
Fax: (216)518-0202
URL: http://www.neoea.org
Freq: 7/year. **Price:** free.

5965 ■ *News and Views*
Oneida Lewis ARC
241 Genesee St.
Utica, NY 13501
Ph: (315)272-1606
Fax: (315)272-1780
E-mail: childsrvs@thearcolc.org
URL: http://www.thearcolc.org
Freq: quarterly.

5966 ■ *Newsline*
National Education Association - Rhode Island
99 Bald Hill Rd.
Cranston, RI 02920
Ph: (401)463-9630
Fax: (401)463-5337
E-mail: lpurtill@nea.org
URL: http://www.neari.org
Descr: Keeps members informed of activities and issues. **Freq:** 5/year.

5967 ■ *Newsline*
Federation for Children with Special Needs
1135 Tremont St., Ste. 420
Boston, MA 02120
Ph: (617)236-7210
Fax: (617)572-2094
E-mail: fcsninfo@fcsn.org
URL: http://www.fcsn.org
Freq: quarterly.

5968 ■ *Newsnotes*
Association for Assessment in Counseling and Education
5999 Stevenson Ave.
Alexandria, VA 22304-3300
Fax: 800-473-2329
E-mail: jwatson@meridian.msstate.edu
URL: http://www.theaaceonline.com
Descr: Contains state, regional, national, and international news and information. **Freq:** quarterly. **Price:** included in membership dues.

5969 ■ *NFPA Journal*
National Fire Protection Association
1 Batterymarch Park
Quincy, MA 02169-7471
Ph: (617)770-3000
Fax: (617)770-0700
E-mail: custserv@nfpa.org
URL: http://www.nfpa.org
Descr: Features technical, scientific and industrial applications of fire protection, suppression, investigations and education. **Freq:** bimonthly. **Price:** included in membership dues.

5970 ■ *NFPA News*
National Fire Protection Association
1 Batterymarch Park
Quincy, MA 02169-7471
Ph: (617)770-3000
Fax: (617)770-0700

E-mail: custserv@nfpa.org
URL: http://www.nfpa.org
Descr: Features news, calendar of events and committee openings. **Freq:** monthly. **Price:** free.

5971 ■ *NIJH Hospice Training Manual*
National Institute for Jewish Hospice
732 University St.
Valley Stream, NY 11581
E-mail: mlamm@nijh.org
URL: http://www.nijh.org
Price: $18.

5972 ■ *The North Carolina Network*
Communities in Schools of North Carolina
222 N Person St.
Raleigh, NC 27601
Ph: (919)832-2700
Fax: (919)832-5436
E-mail: gcrawford@cisnc.org
URL: http://www.cisnc.org
Freq: monthly.

5973 ■ *North Carolina Parent-Teacher Bulletin*
North Carolina PTA
3501 Glenwood Ave.
Raleigh, NC 27612-4934
Ph: (919)787-0534
Fax: (919)787-0569
E-mail: office@ncpta.org
URL: http://www.ncpta.org
Descr: Contains news, messages, events, and different articles. **Freq:** monthly.

5974 ■ *Not Too Small to Care: Small Businesses and Child Care*
Child Care Action Campaign
24808 Deepdale Ave.
Little Neck, NY 11362-1233
Ph: (212)239-0138
Fax: (212)268-6515
URL: http://www.childcareaction.org
Descr: Profiles 29 small businesses that have implemented child care benefits: on-or-near-site child care centers, employee subsidies, and parental leave. **Price:** $15 for members, $25 for nonmembers.

5975 ■ *NSACA News*
National AfterSchool Association
PO Box 34447
Washington, DC 20043
Fax: 888-568-6590
E-mail: menglish@naaweb.org
URL: http://www.naaweb.org
Freq: quarterly.

5976 ■ *NSMS Digest*
National Safety Management Society
PO Box 4460
Walnut Creek, CA 94596-0460
Fax: (573)441-1765
E-mail: nsmsinc@yahoo.com
URL: http://www.nsms.us
Descr: Contains news by and for members. **Freq:** monthly. **Price:** included in membership dues.

5977 ■ *NYS PTA Research Guide*
New York State PTA
One Wembley Ct.
Albany, NY 12205-3830
Ph: (518)452-8808
Fax: (518)452-8105
E-mail: pta.office@nypta.com
URL: http://www.nypta.com
Price: $12 plus shipping and handling.

5978 ■ *OAEYC Member Update*
Oregon Association for the Education of Young Children
PO Box 1455
Tualatin, OR 97062-1455
Ph: (503)233-0190
Fax: (503)233-0185
E-mail: oregonaeyc@covad.net
URL: http://www.oregonaeyc.org

Freq: semiannual. **Price:** included in membership dues.

5979 ■ *The OARacle*
Organization for Autism Research
2000 N 14th St., Ste. 710
Arlington, VA 22201
Ph: (703)243-9710
Fax: (703)243-9751
E-mail: oar@researchautism.org
URL: http://www.researchautism.org
Freq: monthly.

5980 ■ *The Oculus*
AIA Nebraska
PO Box 80045
Lincoln, NE 68501-0045
Ph: (402)472-1456
Fax: (402)472-1654
E-mail: skay2@unl.edu
URL: http://www.aiane.org
Freq: bimonthly.

5981 ■ *Oculus*
American Institute of Architects New York Chapter
Center for Architecture
536 LaGuardia Pl.
New York, NY 10012
Ph: (212)683-0023
Fax: (212)696-5022
E-mail: info@aiany.org
URL: http://www.aiany.org
Freq: quarterly. **Price:** $10.

5982 ■ *Office Newsletter*
American Institute of Architects St. Louis
911 Washington Ave., No. 100
St. Louis, MO 63101
Ph: (314)621-3484
Fax: (314)621-3489
E-mail: mswatek@aia-stlouis.org
URL: http://www.aia-stlouis.org
Freq: annual.

5983 ■ *Officers Directory*
American Association of University Women of Washington
PO Box 537
Liberty Lake, WA 99019
E-mail: president@aauw-wa.org
URL: http://www.aauw-wa.org
Freq: annual.

5984 ■ *Official SAT Study Guide*
The College Board
45 Columbus Ave.
New York, NY 10023-6992
Ph: (212)713-8000
Fax: (212)649-8442
E-mail: publicaffairs@collegeboard.org
URL: http://www.collegeboard.com

5985 ■ *Ohio PTA - The News*
Ohio National Congress of Parents and Teachers
40 Northwoods Blvd.
Columbus, OH 43235
Ph: (614)781-6344
Fax: (614)781-6349
E-mail: oh_office@pta.org
URL: http://www.ohiopta.org
Descr: Contains information about the Ohio PTA.
Freq: 8/year. **Price:** $12/year. **ISSN:** 0199-0918.

5986 ■ *Onboard*
The College Board
45 Columbus Ave.
New York, NY 10023-6992
Ph: (212)713-8000
Fax: (212)649-8442
E-mail: publicaffairs@collegeboard.org
URL: http://www.collegeboard.com

5987 ■ *Online Child Labor Monitor*
National Consumers League
1701 K St. NW, Ste. 1200
Washington, DC 20006
Ph: (202)835-3323

Fax: (202)835-0747
E-mail: info@nclnet.org
URL: http://www.nclnet.org
Freq: weekly. **Price:** free.

5988 ■ *Opportunities*
Arc of Middlesex County
219 Black Horse Ln., Ste. 1
North Brunswick, NJ 08902
Ph: (732)821-1199
Fax: (732)247-5590
E-mail: rsheridan@arc-middlesex.org
URL: http://www.arc-middlesex.org
Freq: periodic.

5989 ■ *Opportunity Outlook*
Council for Opportunity in Education
1025 Vermont Ave. NW, Ste. 900
Washington, DC 20005
Ph: (202)347-7430
Fax: (202)347-0786
E-mail: arnold.mitchem@coenet.us
URL: http://www.coenet.us
Freq: semiannual.

5990 ■ *The Oregon Clarion*
Oregon Council on Developmental Disabilities
540 24th Pl. NE
Salem, OR 97301-4517
Ph: (503)945-9941
Fax: (503)945-9947
E-mail: ocdd@ocdd.org
URL: http://www.ocdd.org
Descr: Contains stateside news of interest to Oregonians with developmental disabilities and families. **Freq:** quarterly.

5991 ■ *Oshirase*
National Council of Japanese Language Teachers
PO Box 3719
Boulder, CO 80307-3719
E-mail: ncjlt@japaneseteaching.org
URL: http://www.ncjlt.org
Descr: Contains news and updates on the organization's activities and other relevant information. **Freq:** quarterly. **Price:** included in membership dues.

5992 ■ *Our Children*
National PTA - National Congress of Parents and Teachers
541 N Fairbanks Ct., Ste. 1300
Chicago, IL 60611-3396
Ph: (312)670-6782
Fax: (312)670-6783
E-mail: info@pta.org
URL: http://www.pta.org
Descr: Provides useful information on parenting, education, and child health and welfare. **Freq:** bimonthly. **Price:** $12/year for members, $20/year for nonmembers. **ISSN:** 1083-3080.

5993 ■ *Our Voice Today*
New York State Association of Retarded Citizens
393 Delaware Ave.
Delmar, NY 12054
Ph: (518)439-8311
Fax: (518)439-1893
E-mail: info@nysarc.org
URL: http://www.nysarc.org
Freq: annual.

5994 ■ *Outlook*
Learning Disabilities Association of Michigan
200 Museum Dr., Ste. 101
Lansing, MI 48933-1914
Ph: (517)485-8160
E-mail: info@ldaofmichigan.org
URL: http://www.ldaofmichigan.org
Freq: bimonthly.

5995 ■ *Outlook*
Asian American Legal Defense and Education Fund
99 Hudson St., 12th Fl.
New York, NY 10013
Ph: (212)966-5932
Fax: (212)966-4303

E-mail: info@aaldef.org
URL: http://www.aaldef.org
Freq: semiannual. **Price:** free for members.

5996 ■ *Palmetto Leaf*
American Association of University Women, South Carolina
745 Tyson's Forest Dr.
Rock Hill, SC 29732
Ph: (803)328-8324
Fax: (704)529-1010
E-mail: bevjames1998@yahoo.com
URL: http://www.aauw-sc.org
Freq: quarterly. **Price:** for members.

5997 ■ *Parent Advocate Handbook*
Disability Rights Center
PO Box 2007
Augusta, ME 04338-2007
Ph: (207)626-2774
Fax: (207)621-1419
E-mail: advocate@drcme.org
URL: http://www.drcme.org

5998 ■ *Parent Brochure*
National Center for Homeless Education
PO Box 5367
Greensboro, NC 27435
Fax: (336)315-7457
E-mail: homeless@serve.org
URL: http://www.serve.org/nche
Descr: Explains the educational rights of children and youth and inform parents about ways in which to support their children.

5999 ■ *Parent Handbook*
National Council for Support of Disability Issues
3870 Mountain Rd.
Haymarket, VA 20169
Ph: (703)753-9148
E-mail: tfink@ncsd.org
URL: http://www.ncsd.org

6000 ■ *A Parent's Guide: Advertising and Your Child*
Children's Advertising Review Unit
70 W 36th St., 12th Fl.
New York, NY 10018
E-mail: caru@caru.bbb.org
URL: http://www.caru.org

6001 ■ *Parents' Voice*
Arc of Bergen and Passaic Counties
223 Moore Ave.
Hackensack, NJ 07601
Ph: (201)343-0322
Fax: (201)343-0401
E-mail: arcbp@aol.com
URL: http://www.arcbergenpassaic.org
Freq: quarterly. **Price:** free.

6002 ■ *Parents, Youngsters and ATVs*
ATV Safety Institute/Division of Specialty Vehicle Institute of America
2 Jenner St., Ste. 150
Irvine, CA 92618-3806
Ph: (949)727-3727
URL: http://www.atvsafety.org

6003 ■ *Partnering with Families to Reform Services: Managed Care in Child Welfare*
American Humane Association Children's Services
63 Inverness Dr. E
Englewood, CO 80112-5117
Ph: (303)792-9900
Fax: (303)792-5333
E-mail: info@americanhumane.org
URL: http://www.americanhumane.org

6004 ■ *PAVE Resource Book*
Parents Active for Vision Education
4135 54th Pl.
San Diego, CA 92105-2303
Ph: (619)287-0081
Fax: (619)287-0084

E-mail: info@pavevision.org
URL: http://www.pavevision.org

6005 ■ Pavestones
Parents Active for Vision Education
4135 54th Pl.
San Diego, CA 92105-2303
Ph: (619)287-0081
Fax: (619)287-0084
E-mail: info@pavevision.org
URL: http://www.pavevision.org
Freq: semiannual. **Price:** free.

6006 ■ PAWS
Farm Safety 4 Just Kids
11304 Aurora Ave.
Urbandale, IA 50322
Ph: (515)331-6506
Fax: (515)331-2947
E-mail: fs4jk@fs4jk.org
URL: http://www.fs4jk.org
Price: $.35 for members, $.50 for nonmembers, $.30 bulk.

6007 ■ PDS Partnerships
National Association for Professional Development Schools
University of South Carolina
Coll. of Education
Wardlaw 252
Columbia, SC 29208
Ph: (803)777-1515
Fax: (803)777-3035
E-mail: pdsconf@mailbox.sc.edu
URL: http://www.napds.org
Freq: 3/year.

6008 ■ The Peer Educator
BACCHUS Network
PO Box 100430
Denver, CO 80250-0430
Ph: (303)871-0901
Fax: (303)871-0907
E-mail: admin@bacchusnetwork.org
URL: http://www.bacchusgamma.org
Freq: bimonthly. **Price:** free for members, $49.

6009 ■ People with Disabilities
New Jersey Council on Developmental Disabilities
PO Box 700
20 W State St., 6th Fl.
Trenton, NJ 08625-0700
Ph: (609)292-3745
Fax: (609)292-7114
E-mail: njcdd@njcdd.org
URL: http://www.njcdd.org

6010 ■ People & Families
New Jersey Council on Developmental Disabilities
PO Box 700
20 W State St., 6th Fl.
Trenton, NJ 08625-0700
Ph: (609)292-3745
Fax: (609)292-7114
E-mail: njcdd@njcdd.org
URL: http://www.njcdd.org
Freq: quarterly.

6011 ■ Personal Student Identification Handbook
WeTip
PO Box 1296
Rancho Cucamonga, CA 91729-1296
E-mail: info@wetip.com
URL: http://www.wetip.com

6012 ■ Perspective
American Institute of Architects Houston
315 Capitol St., Ste. 120
Houston, TX 77002
Ph: (713)520-0155
Fax: (713)520-5134
E-mail: information@aiahouston.org
URL: http://www.aiahouston.org

Freq: bimonthly.

6013 ■ Perspective
American Institute of Architects, Southern Arizona
4633 E Broadway Blvd., Ste. 101
Tucson, AZ 85711
Ph: (520)323-2191
Fax: (520)323-3399
E-mail: brent@aia-arizona.org
URL: http://www.aia-arizona.org/sacaia/index.html
Freq: monthly.

6014 ■ Perspectives
Learning Disabilities Association of Missouri
PO Box 3303
Springfield, MO 65808
Ph: (417)864-5110
Fax: (417)864-7290
E-mail: ldamo@cland.net
URL: http://www.ldamo.org
Freq: bimonthly.

6015 ■ Perspectives on Borderline Personality Disorder
National Education Alliance for Borderline Personality Disorder
PO Box 974
Rye, NY 10580
Ph: (914)835-9011
E-mail: info@neabpd.org
URL: http://www.neabpd.org
Descr: Addresses the issues concerning borderline personality disorder.

6016 ■ Peterson's Colleges with Programs for Students with Learning Disabilities
Peterson's
Princeton Pike Corporate Ctr.
2000 Lenox Dr.
PO Box 67005
Lawrenceville, NJ 08648
Ph: (609)896-1800
Free: 800-338-3282
Fax: (609)896-4531
E-mail: custsvc@petersons.com
URL: http://www.petersons.com
URL(s): http://www.petersons.com **Covers:** Over 1,100 two-year and four-year U.S. colleges and universities with services and programs for students with such learning disabilities as aphasia, dyslexia, or minimal brain dysfunction; list of resource organizations. **Entries include:** Institution name, location, special services offered (note takers, diagnostic testing, special orientation, etc.); description of school, admission procedures, tutoring and advising offered, testing, housing, staff information, support groups available, financial assistance available. **Freq:** Irregular, latest edition 7th. **Price:** $23.96, individuals.

6017 ■ Peterson's Paying Less for College
Peterson's
Princeton Pike Corporate Ctr.
2000 Lenox Dr.
PO Box 67005
Lawrenceville, NJ 08648
Ph: (609)896-1800
Free: 800-338-3282
Fax: (609)896-4531
E-mail: custsvc@petersons.com
URL: http://www.petersons.com
URL(s): http://www.petersons.com/ **Covers:** Financial profiles of more than 1,500 accredited U.S. four-year colleges, as well as nearly 350 state and federal government-sponsored financial aid programs.

6018 ■ Peterson's Vocational and Technical Schools and Programs
Peterson's
Princeton Pike Corporate Ctr.
2000 Lenox Dr.
PO Box 67005
Lawrenceville, NJ 08648
Ph: (609)896-1800
Free: 800-338-3282
Fax: (609)896-4531

E-mail: custsvc@petersons.com
URL: http://www.petersons.com
URL(s): http://www.petersons.com/; http://www.petersons.com/services/petersons/gov_catalog.pdf; http://careerbookstore.com **Covers:** approximately 5,800 accredited vocational and technical schools that offer training programs in over 370 career fields. Available in separate eastern and western U.S. regional editions. **Entries include:** Institution name, address, phone, name and title of contact, type of institution, year founded, accreditation, enrollment, faculty-to-student ratio, registration fee, student body profile, programs offered, student services, financial aid. **Freq:** latest edition 8th. **Price:** $75, individuals, East and West volumes; $42, individuals, each volumes.

6019 ■ Place Magazine
American Institute of Architects, Michigan
553 E Jefferson Ave.
Detroit, MI 48226
Ph: (313)965-4100
Fax: (313)965-1501
E-mail: aiami@aiami.com
URL: http://aiami.com
Freq: quarterly.

6020 ■ Plain Talking About Spanking
Parents and Teachers Against Violence in Education
PO Box 1033
Alamo, CA 94507-7033
Ph: (925)831-1661
Fax: (925)838-8914
E-mail: feedback@nospank.net
URL: http://www.nospank.net
Price: free.

6021 ■ Pocket Guide to Federal Help for Individuals With Disabilities
Clearinghouse on Disability Information
Office of Special Education and Rehabilitative Services
Communication and Media Support Services
United States U.S. Department of of Education
500 12th St. SW, Rm. 5133
Washington, DC 20202-2550
Ph: (202)245-7307
Fax: (202)245-7636
URL: http://www.ed.gov/about/offices/list/osers/codi.html

6022 ■ POD Network News
Professional and Organizational Development Network in Higher Education
PO Box 3318
Nederland, CO 80466
Ph: (303)258-9521
Fax: (303)258-7377
E-mail: podnetwork@podweb.org
URL: http://www.podnetwork.org
Freq: 3/year. **Price:** included in membership dues.

6023 ■ Politica Social
Puerto Rican Legal Defense and Education Fund
99 Hudson St., 14th Fl.
New York, NY 10013-2815
Ph: (212)219-3360
Fax: (212)431-4276
E-mail: info@prldef.org
URL: http://www.prldef.org

6024 ■ Positioning Family and Consumer Sciences in the 21st Century
Family and Consumer Sciences Education Association
Central Washington University
Dept. of Family & Consumer Science
400 E 8th University Way
Ellensburg, WA 98926-7565
Ph: (509)963-2766
Fax: (509)963-2787
E-mail: hubbards@cwu.edu
URL: http://www.cwu.edu/~fandcs/fcsea

Price: $10 plus shipping and handling.

6025 ■ Potomac Valley Annual
American Institute of Architects Potomac Valley
3907 Metzerott Rd.
College Park, MD 20740-2078
Ph: (301)935-5544
Fax: (240)465-0253
E-mail: info@aiapvc.org
URL: http://www.aiapvc.org
Freq: annual.

6026 ■ Practice Application Briefs
ERIC Clearinghouse on Adult, Career, and Vocational
Education
College of Education
Center on Education & Training for Employment
1900 Kenny Rd.
Columbus, OH 43210-1090
Ph: (614)292-7069
Fax: (614)292-1260
E-mail: ericacve@osu.edu
URL: http://ericacve.org/

6027 ■ Preparing and Applying
Secondary School Admission Test Board
CN 5339
Princeton, NJ 08543
Ph: (609)683-4440
Fax: (609)683-4507
E-mail: info@ssat.org
URL: http://www.ssat.org

**6028 ■ Preschool Learning Activities for the
Visually Impaired Child: A Guide for Parents**
National Association for Parents of Children With
Visual Impairments
PO Box 317
Watertown, MA 02471
Ph: (617)972-7441
Fax: (617)972-7444
E-mail: napvi@perkins.org
URL: http://www.spedex.com/napvi
Price: $9.50 for nonmembers, $8 for members.

6029 ■ The Presidency
American Council on Education
1 Dupont Cir. NW
Washington, DC 20036-1193
Ph: (202)939-9300
Fax: (202)659-2212
E-mail: comments@ace.nche.edu
URL: http://www.acenet.edu
Descr: Provides information on critical issues that
affect higher education leaders. **Freq:** 3/year. **Price:**
$36 for members, $40 for nonmembers.

6030 ■ Prevention Update
Committee for Children
568 1st Ave. S, Ste. 600
Seattle, WA 98104-2804
Ph: (206)343-1223
Fax: (206)438-6765
E-mail: info@cfchildren.org
URL: http://www.cfchildren.org
Descr: Provides articles for professionals and teach-
ers in the field of prevention education. **Freq:** 3/year.
Price: free.

**6031 ■ Principles and Indicators for Student
Assessment Systems**
National Center for Fair and Open Testing
15 Court Sq., Ste. 820
Boston, MA 02108
Ph: (857)350-8207
Fax: (857)350-8209
E-mail: info@fairtest.org
URL: http://www.fairtest.org
Price: $10 each, $80 for 10 copies, $350 for 50 cop-
ies, $600 for 100 copies.

6032 ■ PRLDEF in the News
Puerto Rican Legal Defense and Education Fund
99 Hudson St., 14th Fl.
New York, NY 10013-2815
Ph: (212)219-3360

Fax: (212)431-4276
E-mail: info@prldef.org
URL: http://www.prldef.org

**6033 ■ Professional Practice Guidelines for
School Psychologists in Canada**
Canadian Psychological Association
141 Laurier Ave. W, Ste. 702
Ottawa, ON, Canada K1P 5J3
Ph: (613)237-2144
Fax: (613)237-1674
E-mail: cpa@cpa.ca
URL: http://www.cpa.ca
Freq: annual.

6034 ■ Professional Services Guide
Secondary School Admission Test Board
CN 5339
Princeton, NJ 08543
Ph: (609)683-4440
Fax: (609)683-4507
E-mail: info@ssat.org
URL: http://www.ssat.org

6035 ■ Profile
American Institute of Architects
1735 New York Ave. NW
Washington, DC 20006-5292
Ph: (202)626-7300
Fax: (202)626-7547
E-mail: infocentral@aia.org
URL: http://www.aia.org
Freq: annual.

6036 ■ Profile
American Institute of Architects, Portland Chapter
403 NW 11th Ave.
Portland, OR 97209
Ph: (503)223-8757
Fax: (503)220-0254
E-mail: stevens@aiaportland.org
URL: http://www.aiaportland.com
Freq: annual.

6037 ■ PTA Bulletin
Maryland PTA
5 Central Ave.
Glen Burnie, MD 21061
Ph: (410)760-6221
Fax: (410)760-6344
E-mail: office@mdpta.org
URL: http://www.mdpta.org
Freq: 9/year. **Price:** $6 plus .30 tax, $5 plus .25 tax.

**6038 ■ The PTA Story: A Century of Commit-
ment to Children**
National PTA - National Congress of Parents and
Teachers
541 N Fairbanks Ct., Ste. 1300
Chicago, IL 60611-3396
Ph: (312)670-6782
Fax: (312)670-6783
E-mail: info@pta.org
URL: http://www.pta.org
Descr: Contains a chronicle of the history of the
National PTA.

**6039 ■ Public Education, Democracy, Free
Speech: The Ideas That Define and Unite Us**
National Coalition Against Censorship
275 7th Ave., No. 1504
New York, NY 10001
Ph: (212)807-6222
Fax: (212)807-6245
E-mail: ncac@ncac.org
URL: http://www.ncac.org
Price: $2.50 plus shipping and handling.

**6040 ■ Public Schools Teach Religion Without
God**
Parents' Rights Organization
498 Woods Mill Rd.
Manchester, MO 63011
Ph: (636)686-7101
Fax: (636)686-7173
E-mail: citedfree@educational-freedom.org
URL: http://www.educational-freedom.org

Price: $5/copy.

6041 ■ PYP Times
PRIDE Youth Programs
4 W Oak St.
Fremont, MI 49412
Ph: (231)924-1662
Fax: (231)924-5663
E-mail: info@prideyouthprograms.org
URL: http://www.prideyouthprograms.org

6042 ■ Quality Teaching
National Council for Accreditation of Teacher Educa-
tion
2010 Massachusetts Ave. NW, Ste. 500
Washington, DC 20036
Ph: (202)466-7496
Fax: (202)296-6620
E-mail: ncate@ncate.org
URL: http://www.ncate.org
Freq: semiannual.

6043 ■ Quarterly Review
Pulp and Paper Safety Association
PO Box 531
Perry, FL 32348
Ph: (850)584-1569
Fax: (850)584-1220
E-mail: john_sunderland@bkitech.com
URL: http://www.ppsa.org
Descr: Contains safety statistics as submitted by
each member location for the preceding quarter as
well as year-to-date. **Freq:** quarterly. **Price:** included
in membership dues.

6044 ■ Quick Prep Careers
Ferguson Publishing Co.
132 W 31st St., 17th Fl.
New York, NY 10001
Free: 800-678-3633
Fax: 800-322-8755
E-mail: custserv@factsonfile.com
URL: http://ferguson.infobasepublishing.com

Key Personnel: Paul Phifer, Contact. **Publication
includes:** Lists of associations for further consultation for each of 75 jobs featured. Principal content of
publication is detailed information on each job. **Price:**
$18.95, individuals.

6045 ■ Quiknews
National Association of Councils on Developmental
Disabilities
1660 L St. NW, Ste. 700
Washington, DC 20036
Ph: (202)506-5813
Fax: (202)506-5846
E-mail: info@nacdd.org
URL: http://www.nacdd.org

Freq: bimonthly. **Price:** available to members only.

6046 ■ Rapid Read
National Child Support Enforcement Association
1760 Old Meadow Rd., Ste. 500
McLean, VA 22102
Ph: (703)506-2880
Fax: (703)506-3266
E-mail: colleeneubanks@ncsea.org
URL: http://www.ncsea.org

Freq: monthly.

6047 ■ RE:view
Heldref Publications
Helen Dwight Reid Educational Foundation
1319 18th St. NW
Washington, DC 20036-1802
Ph: (202)296-6267
Free: 866-802-7059
E-mail: revu@heldref.org
URL: http://www.heldref.org

URL(s): http://www.heldref.org/review.php **Descr:**
Journal for educators, researchers, parents, and others concerned with services for visually handicapped
children, youth, and adults. **Freq:** Quarterly. **Price:**
$130, institutions, print or online; $33, individuals,

online only; $35, individuals, print and online; $156, institutions, print and online.

6048 ■ Reaching Out: A Directory of National Organizations Related to Maternal and Child Health
National Maternal and Child Health Clearinghouse
U.S. Department of Health and Human Services
Parklawn Bldg.
5600 Fishers Ln.
Rockville, MD 20857
Ph: (301)443-2170
E-mail: ask@hrsa.gov
URL: http://www.ask.hrsa.gov/

6049 ■ Read-Aloud Training Manual
Rolling Readers
2911 Adams Ave., No. 17
San Diego, CA 92116
Ph: (619)516-4095
Fax: (619)516-4096
E-mail: admin@rollingreaders.org
URL: http://www.rollingreaders.org
Descr: Provides parents with resources and tips to stimulate their child's love of reading. **Freq:** semiannual.

6050 ■ Read-Aloud Training Video
Rolling Readers
2911 Adams Ave., No. 17
San Diego, CA 92116
Ph: (619)516-4095
Fax: (619)516-4096
E-mail: admin@rollingreaders.org
URL: http://www.rollingreaders.org

6051 ■ The Refresher
Arc of Tucson
PO Box 44324
Tucson, AZ 85733
Ph: (520)570-1295
Fax: (520)760-1570
URL: http://www.arcoftucson.org
Descr: Contains feature articles, updates on activities, calendar of events, etc. **Freq:** quarterly. **Price:** free.

6052 ■ Regents Watch
New York State PTA
One Wembley Ct.
Albany, NY 12205-3830
Ph: (518)452-8808
Fax: (518)452-8105
E-mail: pta.office@nypta.com
URL: http://www.nypta.com
Descr: Includes decisions made at Regents meetings and other related education issues.

6053 ■ Regulated Drug Legalization, Education, and Rehabilitation: A Framework for Safely Legalizing All Drugs
New Age Citizen
PO Box 419
Dearborn Heights, MI 48127
Ph: (313)704-0021
E-mail: newagecitizenx@comcast.net
URL: http://www.newagecitizen.com

6054 ■ Rehabilitation Act Manual
Family Resource Center on Disabilities
20 E Jackson Blvd., Rm. 300
Chicago, IL 60604
Ph: (312)939-3513
Fax: (312)939-7297
E-mail: frcdptiil@ameritech.net
URL: http://www.frcd.org
Price: $25 plus shipping and handling.

6055 ■ Rehabilitation Education
National Council on Rehabilitation Education
California State University
5005 N Maple Ave., M/S ED 3
Fresno, CA 93725
Ph: (559)278-0325
Fax: (559)278-0045
E-mail: charlesa@csufresno.edu
URL: http://www.rehabeducators.org

Descr: Features original contributions. **Freq:** quarterly. **Price:** included in membership dues.

6056 ■ Religion and Public Education - Common Sense and the Law
Americans for Religious Liberty
PO Box 6656
Silver Spring, MD 20916
Ph: (301)260-2988
Fax: (301)260-2989
E-mail: arlinc@verizon.net
URL: http://www.arlinc.org
Price: $5.

6057 ■ Replication Manual
Networking Project for Young Adults with Disabilities
50 Broadway, 13th Fl.
New York, NY 10004
Ph: (212)755-4500
Fax: (212)838-1279
E-mail: info@ywcanyc.org
URL: http://www.ywcanyc.org

6058 ■ Report of the Medical Committee on Aging Research & Education
American Academy of Anti-Aging Medicine
1510 W Montana St.
Chicago, IL 60614
Ph: (773)528-1000
Fax: (773)528-5390
E-mail: info@worldhealth.net
URL: http://www.worldhealth.net
Freq: quarterly.

6059 ■ The Reporter
Missouri Association for Career and Technical Education
213 E Capitol Ave.
PO Box 1955
Jefferson City, MO 65102
Ph: (573)634-7366
Fax: (573)635-6258
E-mail: info@mo-acte.org
URL: http://www.mo-acte.org
Freq: quarterly. **Price:** free.

6060 ■ Reporter
New York State Association for the Education of Young Children
230 Washington Ave. Extension
Albany, NY 12203
Ph: (518)867-3517
Fax: (518)867-3520
E-mail: nysaeyc@capital.net
URL: http://www.nysaeyc.org
Descr: Features articles on early care and education as well as affiliate information. **Freq:** 3/year.

6061 ■ Research & Practice for Persons with Severe Disabilities
TASH
1025 Vermont Ave. NW, Ste. 300
Washington, DC 20005
Ph: (202)540-9020
Fax: (202)540-9019
E-mail: operations@tash.org
URL: http://www.tash.org
Freq: quarterly. **Price:** included in membership dues.

6062 ■ Research Report Series
ACT
PO Box 168
Iowa City, IA 52244-0168
Ph: (319)337-1000
Fax: (319)339-3020
E-mail: mediarelations@act.org
URL: http://www.act.org
Freq: periodic.

6063 ■ Resource Directory
HEATH Resource Center
George Washington University
2134 G St. NW
Washington, DC 20052-0001
Fax: (202)994-3365
E-mail: askheath@gwu.edu
URL: http://www.heath.gwu.edu

Freq: biennial.

6064 ■ Rethinking Schools
Rethinking Schools
1001 E Keefe Ave.
Milwaukee, WI 53212
Ph: (414)964-9646
Free: 800-669-4192
Fax: (414)964-7220
E-mail: rsonline@execpc.com
URL: http://www.rethinkingschools.org/
Key Personnel: Mike Trokan, Business Mgr., rsmike@execpc.com; Fred McKissack, Managing Editor, fred.mckissack@gmail.com. **URL(s):** http://www.rethinkingschools.org; http://www.rethinkingschools.org/special_reports/bushplan/index.shtml **Descr:** Educational journal promoting reform of public schools. **Freq:** Quarterly. **Price:** $4.95, single issue; $17.95, individuals, U.S. 1 year; $22.95, Canada and Mexico, 1 year; $27.95, other countries, 1 year.

6065 ■ Righting Wrongs
Asian American Legal Defense and Education Fund
99 Hudson St., 12th Fl.
New York, NY 10013
Ph: (212)966-5932
Fax: (212)966-4303
E-mail: info@aaldef.org
URL: http://www.aaldef.org
Freq: monthly.

6066 ■ Rights of the Child in the Health Care System
Canadian Institute of Child Health
384 Bank St., Ste. 300
Ottawa, ON, Canada K2P 1Y4
Ph: (613)230-8838
Fax: (613)230-6654
E-mail: cich@cich.ca
URL: http://www.cich.ca

6067 ■ Rights, Restrictions and Responsibilities
Student Press Law Center
1101 Wilson Blvd., Ste. 1100
Arlington, VA 22209
Ph: (703)807-1904
Fax: (703)807-2109
E-mail: splc@splc.org
URL: http://www.splc.org

6068 ■ The Rising Tide
WAVE
525 School St. SW, Ste. 500
Washington, DC 20024-2795
Ph: (202)484-0103
Fax: (202)484-7595
E-mail: info@waveinc.org
URL: http://www.waveinc.org
Descr: Includes articles, drawings, poetry, and achievements written by the youth participants of WAVE programs. **Freq:** quarterly.

6069 ■ Roadway Safety Reporter
Roadway Safety Foundation
1101 14th St. NW, Ste. 750
Washington, DC 20005
Ph: (202)857-1200
Fax: (202)857-1220
E-mail: cathygillen@roadwaysafety.org
URL: http://www.roadwaysafety.org
Descr: Includes grassroots report and technology column. **Freq:** quarterly. **Price:** $100/year.

6070 ■ Roster of Board of Directors
Council of the Great City Schools
1301 Pennsylvania Ave. NW, Ste. 702
Washington, DC 20004
Ph: (202)393-2427
Fax: (202)393-2400
E-mail: mcasserly@cgcs.org
URL: http://www.cgcs.org

Freq: periodic.

6071 ■ Rural Education News
National Rural Education Association
Purdue University
Beering Hall of Liberal Arts and Education
100 N University St.
West Lafayette, IN 47907-2098
Ph: (765)494-0086
Fax: (765)496-1228
E-mail: jehill@purdue.edu
URL: http://www.nrea.net
Freq: quarterly.

6072 ■ The Rural Educator
National Rural Education Association
Purdue University
Beering Hall of Liberal Arts and Education
100 N University St.
West Lafayette, IN 47907-2098
Ph: (765)494-0086
Fax: (765)496-1228
E-mail: jehill@purdue.edu
URL: http://www.nrea.net
Freq: 3/year. **Price:** included in membership dues.

6073 ■ Rural Special Education Quarterly
American Council on Rural Special Education
Montana Center on Disabilities/MSU-Billings
1500 University Dr.
Billings, MT 59101
Ph: (406)657-2312
Fax: (406)657-2313
E-mail: inquiries@acres-sped.org
URL: http://www.acres-sped.org
Descr: Contains articles concerning federal and other events relevant to rural individuals with disabilities and progressive service delivery systems. **Freq:** quarterly. **Price:** $75/year for individuals, $100/year for libraries, $81/year (international). **ISSN:** 8756-8705.

6074 ■ RuraLink
American Council on Rural Special Education
Montana Center on Disabilities/MSU-Billings
1500 University Dr.
Billings, MT 59101
Ph: (406)657-2312
Fax: (406)657-2313
E-mail: inquiries@acres-sped.org
URL: http://www.acres-sped.org
Descr: Provides information on improving services to rural individuals with disabilities. Includes book reviews and calendar of events. **Freq:** quarterly. **Price:** free for members.

6075 ■ S-USA News
Society for Intercultural Education, Training and Research U.S.A.
603 Stewart St., Ste. 610
Seattle, WA 98101
Ph: (206)859-4351
Fax: (206)626-0392
E-mail: info@sietarusa.org
URL: http://www.sietarusa.org
Descr: Includes affiliate news, job listing, articles. **Freq:** quarterly. **Price:** included in membership dues.

6076 ■ SADD and the Athlete
Students Against Destructive Decisions, Students Against Drunk Driving
255 Main St.
Marlborough, MA 01752
Fax: (508)481-5759
E-mail: info@sadd.org
URL: http://www.sadd.org

6077 ■ SADD in the College
Students Against Destructive Decisions, Students Against Drunk Driving
255 Main St.
Marlborough, MA 01752

Fax: (508)481-5759
E-mail: info@sadd.org
URL: http://www.sadd.org

6078 ■ SADD in the High School
Students Against Destructive Decisions, Students Against Drunk Driving
255 Main St.
Marlborough, MA 01752
Fax: (508)481-5759
E-mail: info@sadd.org
URL: http://www.sadd.org

6079 ■ SADD in the Junior High School
Students Against Destructive Decisions, Students Against Drunk Driving
255 Main St.
Marlborough, MA 01752
Fax: (508)481-5759
E-mail: info@sadd.org
URL: http://www.sadd.org

6080 ■ SADD Update
Students Against Destructive Decisions, Students Against Drunk Driving
255 Main St.
Marlborough, MA 01752
Fax: (508)481-5759
E-mail: info@sadd.org
URL: http://www.sadd.org
Freq: quarterly.

6081 ■ Safe Cycling
Motorcycle Safety Foundation
2 Jenner St., Ste. 150
Irvine, CA 92618-3806
Ph: (949)727-3227
Fax: (949)727-4217
E-mail: msf@msf-usa.org
URL: http://www.msf-usa.org
Descr: Covers foundation activities and developments in the motorcycle safety field. **Freq:** quarterly. **Price:** free for members, $15/year for nonmembers.

6082 ■ SAFE Legislative Report
Sportsmen's Association for Firearms Education
PO Box 343
Commack, NY 11725
Ph: (631)475-8125
E-mail: jcushman@juno.com
URL: http://www.nysafe.org
Freq: monthly. **Price:** free for members.

6083 ■ Safe Worker
National Safety Council
1121 Spring Lake Dr.
Itasca, IL 60143-3201
Ph: (630)285-1121
Fax: (630)285-1315
E-mail: info@nsc.org
URL: http://www.nsc.org
Freq: monthly.

6084 ■ The Safety Advocate
Advocates for Highway and Auto Safety
750 1st St. NE, Ste. 901
Washington, DC 20002
Ph: (202)408-1711
Fax: (202)408-1699
URL: http://www.saferoads.org
Descr: Includes updates on local and national safety legislation. **Freq:** periodic.

6085 ■ San Antonio on Foot
American Institute of Architects San Antonio
816 Camaron, Ste. 211
San Antonio, TX 78212
Ph: (210)226-4979
Fax: (210)226-3062
E-mail: info@aiasa.org
URL: http://www.aiasa.org

6086 ■ San Antonio: Outpost of Empires
American Institute of Architects San Antonio
816 Camaron, Ste. 211
San Antonio, TX 78212
Ph: (210)226-4979

Fax: (210)226-3062
E-mail: info@aiasa.org
URL: http://www.aiasa.org

6087 ■ The SAT Coaching Cover-up
National Center for Fair and Open Testing
15 Court Sq., Ste. 820
Boston, MA 02108
Ph: (857)350-8207
Fax: (857)350-8209
E-mail: info@fairtest.org
URL: http://www.fairtest.org
Price: $10.

6088 ■ Save A Child
4 R Kids Sake
PO Box 77693
Corona, CA 92877
Ph: (951)278-1820
Fax: (951)737-2539
E-mail: information@4rkidssake.org
URL: http://www.4rkidssake.org

6089 ■ Scholarship Handbook
The College Board
45 Columbus Ave.
New York, NY 10023-6992
Ph: (212)713-8000
Fax: (212)649-8442
E-mail: publicaffairs@collegeboard.org
URL: http://www.collegeboard.com
Freq: annual.

6090 ■ Scholarship University Partnerships
National Association for Professional Development Schools
University of South Carolina
Coll. of Education
Wardlaw 252
Columbia, SC 29208
Ph: (803)777-1515
Fax: (803)777-3035
E-mail: pdsconf@mailbox.sc.edu
URL: http://www.napds.org
Freq: semiannual.

6091 ■ School Choice Activist
Alliance for School Choice
1660 L St. NW, Ste. 1000
Washington, DC 20036
Ph: (202)280-1990
E-mail: info@allianceforschoolchoice.org
URL: http://www.allianceforschoolchoice.org
Freq: quarterly.

6092 ■ School Choice Digest
Alliance for School Choice
1660 L St. NW, Ste. 1000
Washington, DC 20036
Ph: (202)280-1990
E-mail: info@allianceforschoolchoice.org
URL: http://www.allianceforschoolchoice.org
Freq: quarterly.

6093 ■ School Improvement Catalogs
Center for Law and Education
1875 Connecticut Ave. NW, Ste. 510
Washington, DC 20009
Ph: (202)986-3000
Fax: (202)986-6648
E-mail: cle@cleweb.org
URL: http://www.cleweb.org
Freq: 3/year. **Price:** free.

6094 ■ Schools in an Aging Society
National Academy for Teaching and Learning About Aging
PO Box 310919
Denton, TX 76203-0919
Ph: (940)565-3450
Fax: (940)565-3141
E-mail: louis@scs.unt.edu
URL: http://www.cps.unt.edu/natla
Descr: Features six interrelated curriculum guides

which provide education, for, with, and about older adults. **Price:** $55.

6095 ■ SDACTE Viewpoint
South Dakota Association for Career and Technical Education
PO Box 730
Watertown, SD 57201
Ph: (605)886-7016
E-mail: bemisd@lakeareatech.edu
URL: http://www.lakeareatech.edu/sdacte
Freq: 3/year.

6096 ■ S.D.T.A. Teacher Advocate
San Diego Teachers Association
10393 San Diego Mission Rd., No. 100
San Diego, CA 92108
Ph: (619)283-4411
Fax: (619)282-7659
URL: http://www.sdta.net
Key Personnel: Suzanne Emery, Editor; Steven Kaplan, Advertising Mgr. **Descr:** Publication (tabloid) devoted to education. **Freq:** Monthly.

6097 ■ The Self-Help Group Leader's Handbook: Leading Effective Meetings
Research and Training Center on Independent Living
University of Kansas
Dole Center, Ste. 4089
1000 Sunnyside Ave.
Lawrence, KS 66045-7561
Ph: (785)864-4095
Fax: (785)864-5063
E-mail: rtcil@ku.edu
URL: http://www.rtcil.org
Price: $5.

6098 ■ Sex Bias in College Admissions Tests: Why Women Lose Out
National Center for Fair and Open Testing
15 Court Sq., Ste. 820
Boston, MA 02108
Ph: (857)350-8207
Fax: (857)350-8209
E-mail: info@fairtest.org
URL: http://www.fairtest.org

6099 ■ Sharing Solutions
Lighthouse International
111 E 59th St.
New York, NY 10022-1202
Ph: (212)821-9200
Fax: (212)821-9707
E-mail: info@lighthouse.org
URL: http://www.lighthouse.org
Freq: 3/year. **Price:** free for members.

6100 ■ Sign Language Studies
Linstok Press
4020 Blackburn Ln.
Burtonsville, MD 20866-1167
Ph: (301)421-0268
Free: 800-475-4756
Fax: (301)421-0270
E-mail: signmedia@aol.com
URL: http://www.signmedia.com
Descr: Magazine concerning the use of primary and alternative sign languages. **Freq:** Quarterly. **Price:** $40, individuals; $50, institutions.

6101 ■ Signifire
Automatic Fire Alarm Association
PO Box 1569
Jasper, GA 30143
Ph: (678)454-3473
Fax: (678)454-3474
E-mail: fire-alarm@afaa.org
URL: http://www.afaa.org
Descr: Includes membership activities and technical industry information. **Freq:** quarterly. **Price:** included in membership dues, $24/year for nonmembers.

6102 ■ Silent Advocate
St. Rita School for the Deaf
1720 Glendale Milford Rd.
Cincinnati, OH 45215-1233

Ph: (513)771-7600
Fax: (513)326-8264
URL: http://www.srsdeaf.org
Key Personnel: Greg Ernst, Jr., Exec. Dir., gernstjr@srsdeaf.org. **URL(s):** http://www.srsdeaf.org/development/advocate.html **Descr:** Magazine reporting school activities and items for and about the deaf and hearing impaired. **Freq:** 3/yr.

6103 ■ Slip and Fall Prevention Made Easy
National Floor Safety Institute
PO Box 92607
Southlake, TX 76092
Ph: (817)749-1700
Fax: (817)749-1702
E-mail: info@nfsi.org
URL: http://www.nfsi.org
Price: $60.

6104 ■ Smith-Kettlewell Technical File
Smith-Kettlewell Eye Research Institute
2318 Fillmore St.
San Francisco, CA 94115
Ph: (415)345-2124
Fax: (415)345-8455
E-mail: rerc@skivs.ski.org
Key Personnel: William Gerrey. **Descr:** Magazine reporting on technology and devices for visually impaired persons. **Freq:** 4/2 years. **Price:** $16, diskette; $18, braille; $14, talking book.

6105 ■ Some Heroes Are Small
Parents Active for Vision Education
4135 54th Pl.
San Diego, CA 92105-2303
Ph: (619)287-0081
Fax: (619)287-0084
E-mail: info@pavevision.org
URL: http://www.pavevision.org
Price: $7.70/copy, plus shipping and handling.

6106 ■ Sources for Custom-produced Books
National Library Service for the Blind and Physically Handicapped
Library of Congress
1291 Taylor St. NW
Washington, DC 20011
Ph: (202)707-5100
Free: 888-657-7323
Fax: (202)707-0712
E-mail: nls@loc.gov
URL: http://www.loc.gov/nls/contact.html
URL(s): http://www.loc.gov/nls/ **Covers:** organizations and individuals who produce books for visually and physically handicapped persons. Includes proofreaders and special education specialists. **Entries include:** For organizations--Name, address, and phone; chairperson's name, address, phone; type of media, specialty. For individuals--Name, address, and phone.

6107 ■ Sparks
Arc of Sedgwick County
2919 W Second St.
Wichita, KS 67203
Ph: (316)943-1191
Fax: (316)943-3292
E-mail: arc@arc-sedgwickcounty.org
URL: http://www.arc-sedgwickcounty.org
Freq: quarterly.

6108 ■ Special Bible Study
John Milton Society for the Blind - USA
370 Lexington Ave., Rm. 1007
New York, NY 10017-6503
Ph: (212)870-3335
Fax: (212)870-3226
E-mail: order@jmsblind.org
URL: http://www.jmsblind.org
Descr: Available in braille. **Freq:** annual.

6109 ■ Special Edition
Disabled Sports U.S.A., Eagle Mount - Bozeman
6901 Goldenstein Ln.
Bozeman, MT 59715
Ph: (406)586-1781

Fax: (406)586-5794
E-mail: eaglemount@eaglemount.org
URL: http://www.eaglemount.org
Freq: quarterly. **Price:** free.

6110 ■ The Special Educator e-Journal
National Association of Special Education Teachers
1250 Connecticut Ave. NW, Ste. 200
Washington, DC 20036
E-mail: contactus@naset.org
URL: http://www.naset.org
Descr: Contains current information in the field of special education. **Freq:** 10/year. **Price:** included in membership dues.

6111 ■ Special Olympics Annual Report
Special Olympics
1133 19th St. NW
Washington, DC 20036
Ph: (202)628-3630
Fax: (202)824-0200
E-mail: info@specialolympics.org
URL: http://www.specialolympics.org
Descr: Includes a summary of the past year's program service accomplishments. **Freq:** annual.

6112 ■ Spirit of Special Olympics
Special Olympics Montana
PO Box 3507
Great Falls, MT 59403
Ph: (406)216-5327
Fax: (406)454-9043
E-mail: info@somt.org
URL: http://www.somt.org
Freq: quarterly.

6113 ■ Standardized Tests and Our Children: A Guide to Testing Reform
National Center for Fair and Open Testing
15 Court Sq., Ste. 820
Boston, MA 02108
Ph: (857)350-8207
Fax: (857)350-8209
E-mail: info@fairtest.org
URL: http://www.fairtest.org
Price: $4 each, $15 for 5 copies, $20 for 10 copies, $50 for 50 copies.

6114 ■ Standards, Procedures, and Policies for the Accreditation of Professional Education Units
National Council for Accreditation of Teacher Education
2010 Massachusetts Ave. NW, Ste. 500
Washington, DC 20036
Ph: (202)466-7496
Fax: (202)296-6620
E-mail: ncate@ncate.org
URL: http://www.ncate.org
Price: $20.

6115 ■ Standing Up to the SAT
National Center for Fair and Open Testing
15 Court Sq., Ste. 820
Boston, MA 02108
Ph: (857)350-8207
Fax: (857)350-8209
E-mail: info@fairtest.org
URL: http://www.fairtest.org

6116 ■ The State Coordinator's Handbook
National Center for Homeless Education
PO Box 5367
Greensboro, NC 27435
Fax: (336)315-7457
E-mail: homeless@serve.org
URL: http://www.serve.org/nche
Descr: Provides information and strategies compiled from State Coordinators across the country.

6117 ■ State Newsletter
Common Cause Massachusetts
59 Temple Pl., Ste. 600
Boston, MA 02111
Ph: (617)426-9600
Fax: (617)426-6855

E-mail: ccma@commoncause.org
URL: http://www.commoncause.org/ma
Descr: Contains legislative updates and citizen actions. **Freq:** semiannual. **Price:** $30 included in membership dues.

6118 ■ State Protection and Advocacy Agencies
National Disability Rights Network
900 2nd St. NE, Ste. 211
Washington, DC 20002
Ph: (202)408-9514
Fax: (202)408-9520
E-mail: info@ndrn.org
URL: http://www.napas.org
Freq: annual.

6119 ■ Statement on Clinical Nurse Specialist Practice and Education
National Association of Clinical Nurse Specialists
2090 Linglestown Rd., Ste. 107
Harrisburg, PA 17110
Ph: (717)234-6799
Fax: (717)234-6798
E-mail: nacnsorg@nacns.org
URL: http://www.nacns.org
Price: $15 for members, $25 for nonmembers.

6120 ■ STD Spotlight: Dedicated to Thought and Activity in STD Information-Education Programs
Citizens Alliance for VD Awareness
800 W Central Rd., Ste. 128
Mount Prospect, IL 60056
Ph: (847)398-3378
Fax: (847)398-7309
E-mail: cavdarx@earthlink.net
Freq: quarterly. **Price:** $24/year.

6121 ■ Steps to Success: A Blueprint for Employing Individuals with Disabilities
National Business and Disability Council
201 I.U. Willets Rd.
Albertson, NY 11507
Ph: (516)465-1516
E-mail: lfrancis@abilitiesonline.org
URL: http://www.business-disability.com

6122 ■ Stop Gun Violence News
Educational Fund to Stop Gun Violence
1424 L St. NW, Ste. 2-1
Washington, DC 20005-2602
Ph: (202)408-0061
E-mail: csgv@csgv.org
URL: http://www.efsgv.org
Descr: Provides information and advice for citizens to reduce gun violence in their communities. **Freq:** bimonthly. **Price:** free.

6123 ■ Strengthen Flexibility Exercises for All Types of Disabilities
Disabled Sports USA
451 Hungerford Dr., Ste. 100
Rockville, MD 20850
Ph: (301)217-0960
Fax: (301)217-0968
E-mail: information@dsusa.org
URL: http://www.dsusa.org

6124 ■ The Student
Christian Record Services
PO Box 6097
Lincoln, NE 68506-0097
Ph: (402)488-0981
Fax: (402)488-7582
E-mail: info@christianrecord.org
URL: http://www.christianrecord.org
Descr: Focuses on a particular book of the Bible. **Freq:** monthly.

6125 ■ Student Advocate
National Alliance of Blind Students
1155 15th St. NW, Ste. 1004
Washington, DC 20005
Ph: (202)467-5081
Fax: (202)467-5085

E-mail: rj.hodson@verizon.net
URL: http://acbstudents.org
Freq: quarterly. **Price:** free for members.

6126 ■ Student Loan Law
National Consumer Law Center
7 Winthrop Sq.
Boston, MA 02110-1245
Ph: (617)542-8010
Fax: (617)542-8028
E-mail: consumerlaw@nclc.org
URL: http://www.consumerlaw.org
Descr: Provides strategies for students delinquent on their loans; with CD-Rom.

6127 ■ Student Press Law Center—Report
Student Press Law Center
1101 Wilson Blvd., Ste. 1100
Arlington, VA 22209
Ph: (703)807-1904
Fax: (703)807-2109
E-mail: splc@splc.org
URL: http://www.splc.org
Descr: Provides news, information, and advice on such topics as libel, censorship, and freedom of information. **Freq:** 3/year. **Price:** $15/year, $28/2 years. **ISSN:** 0160-3825.

6128 ■ Student Press Legal Center Legal Alert
Student Press Law Center
1101 Wilson Blvd., Ste. 1100
Arlington, VA 22209
Ph: (703)807-1904
Fax: (703)807-2109
E-mail: splc@splc.org
URL: http://www.splc.org

6129 ■ Students at the Center: Feminist Assessment
National Women's Studies Association
7100 Baltimore Ave., Ste. 502
College Park, MD 20740
Ph: (301)403-0407
Fax: (301)403-4137
E-mail: nwsaoffice@nwsa.org
URL: http://www.nwsa.org
Descr: Includes practical advice about how to set up a student-centered, faculty driven assessment project on campus. **Price:** $13.

6130 ■ Students: Know Your Rights
American Civil Liberties Union, Ohio Affiliate
4506 Chester Ave.
Cleveland, OH 44103
Ph: (216)472-2200
Fax: (216)472-2210
E-mail: contact@acluohio.org
URL: http://www.acluohio.org

6131 ■ Students on the Move: Reaching and Teaching Highly Mobile Children and Youth
National Center for Homeless Education
PO Box 5367
Greensboro, NC 27435
Fax: (336)315-7457
E-mail: homeless@serve.org
URL: http://www.serve.org/nche
Descr: Synthesizes research on the education of various subpopulations of students.

6132 ■ Subject Tests Practice Books
Graduate Record Examinations Board
PO Box 6000
Princeton, NJ 08541-6000
Ph: (609)771-7670
Fax: (610)290-8975
E-mail: gre-info@rosedale.org
URL: http://www.ets.org/gre
Freq: annual.

6133 ■ The Surgeon General's Workshop on Self-Help and Public Health
National Maternal and Child Health Clearinghouse
U.S. Department of Health and Human Services
Parklawn Bldg.
5600 Fishers Ln.
Rockville, MD 20857

Ph: (301)443-2170
E-mail: ask@hrsa.gov
URL: http://www.ask.hrsa.gov/

6134 ■ Survival Strategies for Going Abroad: A Guide for People with Disabilities
Mobility International USA
132 E Broadway, Ste. 343
Eugene, OR 97401
Ph: (541)343-1284
Fax: (541)343-6812
E-mail: info@miusa.org
URL: http://www.miusa.org
Descr: Contains stories, tips and resources told by twenty experienced travelers with disabilities. **Price:** $16.95.

6135 ■ Surviving on Your Own: Information for Youth on How Schools Can Help
National Center for Homeless Education
PO Box 5367
Greensboro, NC 27435
Fax: (336)315-7457
E-mail: homeless@serve.org
URL: http://www.serve.org/nche
Descr: Explains how schools can help youth who are living on their own without a parent or guardian.

6136 ■ Synergy
National Foundation for Credit Counseling
801 Roeder Rd., Ste. 900
Silver Spring, MD 20910
Ph: (301)589-5600
Fax: (301)495-5623
E-mail: press@nfcc.org
URL: http://www.nfcc.org
Freq: bimonthly.

6137 ■ TABCO Bulletin
Teachers Association of Baltimore County
305 E Joppa Rd.
Towson, MD 21286-3252
Ph: (410)882-2604
E-mail: cbost@mstanea.org
URL: http://www.mstanea.org
Freq: monthly. **Price:** for members.

6138 ■ TABCO Calendar/Handbook
Teachers Association of Baltimore County
305 E Joppa Rd.
Towson, MD 21286-3252
Ph: (410)882-2604
E-mail: cbost@mstanea.org
URL: http://www.mstanea.org
Freq: annual.

6139 ■ Taking Action to Recruit Family and Consumer Sciences Teachers
Family and Consumer Sciences Education Association
Central Washington University
Dept. of Family & Consumer Science
400 E 8th University Way
Ellensburg, WA 98926-7565
Ph: (509)963-2766
Fax: (509)963-2787
E-mail: hubbards@cwu.edu
URL: http://www.cwu.edu/~fandcs/fcsea
Price: $10 plus shipping and handling.

6140 ■ Talking Book Topics
National Library Service for the Blind and Physically Handicapped
Library of Congress
1291 Taylor St. NW
Washington, DC 20011
Ph: (202)707-5100
Free: 888-657-7323
Fax: (202)707-0712
E-mail: nls@loc.gov
URL: http://www.loc.gov/nls/contact.html
Key Personnel: Jean M. Moss, Digital Proj. Coord., jemo@loc.gov. **URL(s):** http://www.loc.gov/nls/tbt/index.html **Descr:** Catalog of audio books and magazines available to the blind and disabled people through free program administered by the Library of

Congress. Recorded, online, and diskette editions also available. **Freq:** Bimonthly. **Price:** Free.

6141 ■ *TARC in Action*
Tulsa Advocates for Rights of Citizens with Developmental Disabilities
16 E 16th St., Ste. 405
Tulsa, OK 74119-4447
Ph: (918)582-8272
Fax: (918)582-3628
E-mail: tarc@ddadvocacy.net
URL: http://www.ddadvocacy.net
Descr: Informs individuals with disabilities, volunteers, and members and supporters about agency-related news and activities. **Freq:** quarterly. **Price:** included in membership dues.

6142 ■ *TASH Connections*
TASH
1025 Vermont Ave. NW, Ste. 300
Washington, DC 20005
Ph: (202)540-9020
Fax: (202)540-9019
E-mail: operations@tash.org
URL: http://www.tash.org
Freq: 10/year. **Price:** included in membership dues.

6143 ■ *Teacher Educator's Guide*
Family, Career and Community Leaders of America
1910 Association Dr.
Reston, VA 20191-1584
Ph: (703)476-4900
Fax: (703)860-2713
E-mail: mbenjamin@fcclainc.org
URL: http://www.fcclainc.org

6144 ■ *Teaching Excellence*
Professional and Organizational Development Network in Higher Education
PO Box 3318
Nederland, CO 80466
Ph: (303)258-9521
Fax: (303)258-7377
E-mail: podnetwork@podweb.org
URL: http://www.podnetwork.org
Descr: Includes scholarly essays on teaching excellence. **Freq:** 8/year. **Price:** $100/year for members, $120/year for nonmembers.

6145 ■ *Teaching Exceptional Children*
Yes I Can! Foundation for Exceptional Children
1110 N Glebe Rd., Ste. 300
Arlington, VA 22201-5704
Ph: (703)264-3660
Fax: (703)264-9494
E-mail: yesican@cec.sped.org
Descr: Includes classroom-oriented information about instructional methods, materials, and techniques for students of all ages with special needs. **Freq:** bimonthly. **Price:** included in membership dues, $58/year for nonmembers.

6146 ■ *Techniques*
Association for Career and Technical Education
1410 King St.
Alexandria, VA 22314
Ph: (703)683-3111
Fax: (703)683-7424
E-mail: acte@acteonline.org
URL: http://www.acteonline.org
Freq: 8/year. **Price:** $48/year for nonmembers in U.S., $81/year for nonmembers outside U.S.

6147 ■ *Technocrat*
National Association of State Directors of Vocational Technical Education Consortium
8484 Georgia Ave., Ste. 320
Silver Spring, MD 20910
Ph: (301)588-9630
Fax: (301)588-9631
E-mail: kgreen@nasdvtec.org
URL: http://infolit.org/members/nasdvte.htm
Descr: Covers association activities and legislative

activities affecting occupational education. **Freq:** monthly.

6148 ■ *Testing Our Children: A Report Card on State Assessment Systems*
National Center for Fair and Open Testing
15 Court Sq., Ste. 820
Boston, MA 02108
Ph: (857)350-8207
Fax: (857)350-8209
E-mail: info@fairtest.org
URL: http://www.fairtest.org
Price: $30 each, $125 for 5 copies.

6149 ■ *Texas Key*
Learning Disabilities Association of Texas
1011 W 31st St.
Austin, TX 78705
Ph: (512)458-8234
Fax: (512)458-3826
E-mail: contact@ldat.org
URL: http://www.ldat.org
Freq: quarterly.

6150 ■ *Textbooks on Trial*
Educational Research Analysts
PO Box 7518
Longview, TX 75607-7518
Ph: (903)753-5993
Fax: (903)753-8424
E-mail: info@textbookreviews.org
URL: http://www.textbookreviews.org

6151 ■ *Thought and Action*
National Education Association
1201 16th St. NW
Washington, DC 20036-3290
Ph: (202)833-4000
Fax: (202)822-7974
URL: http://www.nea.org

6152 ■ *Three-Year Plan, 2009-2012*
Commonwealth of Learning
1055 W Hastings St., Ste. 1200
Vancouver, BC, Canada V6E 2E9
Ph: (604)775-8200
Fax: (604)775-8210
E-mail: info@col.org
URL: http://www.col.org/Pages/default.aspx

6153 ■ *The Time for Access is Now*
Disabled Womyn's Educational Project
PO Box 8773
Madison, WI 53708-8773
Ph: (608)256-8883
Fax: (608)256-8883
E-mail: catherine-odette@juno.com

6154 ■ *Tips and Practice Guide for the ATV Rider*
ATV Safety Institute/Division of Specialty Vehicle Institute of America
2 Jenner St., Ste. 150
Irvine, CA 92618-3806
Ph: (949)727-3727
URL: http://www.atvsafety.org

6155 ■ *Title IX at 25: Report Card on Gender Equity*
National Coalition for Women and Girls in Education
1111 16th St. NW
Washington, DC 20036
Ph: (202)785-7793
Fax: (202)872-1425
E-mail: maatzl@aauw.org
URL: http://www.ncwge.org

6156 ■ *Title IX at 30: Report Card on Gender Equity*
National Coalition for Women and Girls in Education
1111 16th St. NW
Washington, DC 20036
Ph: (202)785-7793
Fax: (202)872-1425

E-mail: maatzl@aauw.org
URL: http://www.ncwge.org

6157 ■ *Title IX: A Practical Guide to Achieving Sex Equity in Education*
National Coalition for Women and Girls in Education
1111 16th St. NW
Washington, DC 20036
Ph: (202)785-7793
Fax: (202)872-1425
E-mail: maatzl@aauw.org
URL: http://www.ncwge.org

6158 ■ *To Improve the Academy*
Professional and Organizational Development Network in Higher Education
PO Box 3318
Nederland, CO 80466
Ph: (303)258-9521
Fax: (303)258-7377
E-mail: podnetwork@podweb.org
URL: http://www.podnetwork.org
Descr: Offers a range of materials on teaching and learning written by POD members. **Freq:** annual. **Price:** included in membership dues.

6159 ■ *Toolkit for Helmet Promotion Programs*
Bicycle Helmet Safety Institute
4611 7th St. S
Arlington, VA 22204-1419
Ph: (703)486-0100
Fax: (703)486-0100
E-mail: info@helmets.org
URL: http://www.helmets.org
Descr: Contains statistics, speakers' outline, sources, manual, and pamphlets. **Freq:** periodic. **Price:** free.

6160 ■ *Toxicology Educators Resource Guide for Secondary School Audiences*
Canadian Network of Toxicology Centres
Bovey Bldg., 2nd Fl.
Gordon St.
University of Guelph
Guelph, ON, Canada N1G 2W1
Ph: (519)824-4120
Fax: (519)837-3861
E-mail: dwarner@uoguelph.ca
URL: http://www.uoguelph.ca/cntc

6161 ■ *Tracings*
American Institute of Architects, Santa Clara Valley Chapter
325 S 1st St., Ste. 100
San Jose, CA 95113
Ph: (408)298-0611
Fax: (408)298-0619
E-mail: info@aiascv.org
URL: http://www.aiascv.org
Freq: monthly. **Price:** $40/year.

6162 ■ *Tracking, Diversity, and Educational Equity: What's New in the Research?*
Common Destiny Alliance
University of Maryland
2110 Benjamin Bldg.
College Park, MD 20742
Ph: (301)405-0639
Fax: (301)405-3573
E-mail: mh267@umail.umd.edu
URL: http://www.education.umd.edu/CODA/index.html
Price: $7.

6163 ■ *Treating Adults with Physical Disabilities: Access and Communication*
World Institute on Disability
510 16th St., Ste. 100
Oakland, CA 94612
Ph: (510)763-4100
Fax: (510)763-4109
E-mail: wid@wid.org
URL: http://www.wid.org

Price: $152.

6164 ■ Trends & Issues Alerts
ERIC Clearinghouse on Adult, Career, and Vocational Education
College of Education
Center on Education & Training for Employment
1900 Kenny Rd.
Columbus, OH 43210-1090
Ph: (614)292-7069
Fax: (614)292-1260
E-mail: ericacve@osu.edu
URL: http://ericacve.org/

6165 ■ Triangle
Louisiana Developmental Disabilities Council
PO Box 3455
Baton Rouge, LA 70821-3455
Ph: (225)342-6804
Fax: (225)342-1970
E-mail: swinchel@dhh.la.gov
URL: http://www.laddc.org
Freq: quarterly.

6166 ■ TSA Handbook
Texas Society of Architects/ AIA
816 Congress Ave., Ste. 970
Austin, TX 78701-2443
Ph: (512)478-7386
Fax: (512)478-0528
E-mail: info@texasarchitect.org
URL: http://www.texasarchitect.org
Descr: Includes contact information for all 5000 TSA members along with other material specific to the practice of architecture in Texas. **Freq:** annual. **Price:** free for members, $5 for nonmembers.

6167 ■ TSTA Advocate
Texas State Teachers Association
316 W 12th St.
Austin, TX 78701
Free: 877-275-8782
URL: http://www.tsta.org/
URL(s): http://www.tsta.org/news/current/advocate.shtml **Descr:** Educational journal. **Freq:** Quarterly.

6168 ■ The Turning Point
ARC of Monmouth
1158 Wayside Rd.
Tinton Falls, NJ 07712
Ph: (732)493-1919
Fax: (732)493-3604
E-mail: info@arcofmonmouth.org
URL: http://www.arcofmonmouth.org
Freq: quarterly. **Price:** free.

6169 ■ Turning the Tide: Journal of Anti-Racist Action, Research and Education
Anti-Racist Action-Los Angeles/People Against Racist Terror
PO Box 1055
Culver City, CA 90232-1055
Ph: (310)495-0299
E-mail: antiracistaction_la@yahoo.com
URL: http://www.antiracistaction.us
Descr: Covers youth-oriented, anti-racist activities. **Freq:** bimonthly. **Price:** $16/year for members, $26/year for institutions, $2/issue. **ISSN:** 1082-6491.

6170 ■ Understanding the Medical Diagnosis of Child Maltreatment
American Humane Association Children's Services
63 Inverness Dr. E
Englewood, CO 80112-5117
Ph: (303)792-9900
Fax: (303)792-5333
E-mail: info@americanhumane.org
URL: http://www.americanhumane.org

6171 ■ Understanding Sexual Violence: Prosecuting Adult Rape and Sexual Assault Cases
National Judicial Education Program
395 Hudson St.
New York, NY 10014-3669
Ph: (212)925-6635
Fax: (212)226-1066

E-mail: njep@legalmomentum.org
URL: http://www.legalmomentum.org

6172 ■ Understanding Sexual Violence: The Judicial Response to Stranger and Non-stranger Rape and Sexual Assault
National Judicial Education Program
395 Hudson St.
New York, NY 10014-3669
Ph: (212)925-6635
Fax: (212)226-1066
E-mail: njep@legalmomentum.org
URL: http://www.legalmomentum.org

6173 ■ UNIPACs: Hospice/Palliative Care Training for Physicians and Other Medical Professionals
American Academy of Hospice and Palliative Medicine
4700 W Lake Ave.
Glenview, IL 60025-1485
Ph: (847)375-4712
Fax: 877-734-8671
E-mail: info@aahpm.org
URL: http://www.aahpm.org

6174 ■ U.S. Student Association—Legislative Update
United States Student Association
1211 Connecticut Ave. NW, Ste. 406
Washington, DC 20036
Ph: (202)640-6570
Fax: (202)223-4005
E-mail: ussa@usstudents.org
URL: http://www.usstudents.org
Freq: monthly. **Price:** included in membership dues.

6175 ■ University Women Texas
American Association of University Women, Texas Branch
PO Box 27223
Austin, TX 78755
Ph: (512)458-2289
Fax: (512)453-4716
E-mail: lbconger@earthlink.net
URL: http://www.aauwtexas.org
Freq: quarterly. **Price:** included in membership dues.

6176 ■ The Update
Association for the Education of Young Children of Missouri
1400 Rock Quarry Rd.
Columbia, MO 65211-3280
Ph: (573)884-3374
Fax: (573)884-0598
E-mail: info@aeyc-mo.org
URL: http://www.aeyc-mo.org
Descr: Contains topical information. **Freq:** 3/year. **Price:** included in membership dues.

6177 ■ Update
Arc of Prince George's County
1401 McCormick Dr.
Largo, MD 20774
Ph: (301)925-7050
Fax: (301)925-4387
URL: http://www.thearcofpgc.org
Descr: Contains information on chapter activities. **Freq:** bimonthly.

6178 ■ Update
National Disability Sports Alliance
25 W Independence Way
Kingston, RI 02881
Ph: (401)792-7130
Fax: (401)792-7132
E-mail: info@ndsaonline.org
URL: http://www.ndsaonline.org
Freq: quarterly.

6179 ■ Urban Educator
Council of the Great City Schools
1301 Pennsylvania Ave. NW, Ste. 702
Washington, DC 20004
Ph: (202)393-2427
Fax: (202)393-2400

E-mail: mcasserly@cgcs.org
URL: http://www.cgcs.org
Freq: monthly.

6180 ■ Urban Indicator
Council of the Great City Schools
1301 Pennsylvania Ave. NW, Ste. 702
Washington, DC 20004
Ph: (202)393-2427
Fax: (202)393-2400
E-mail: mcasserly@cgcs.org
URL: http://www.cgcs.org
Freq: bimonthly.

6181 ■ Vaccine Safety Manual for Concerned Families and Health Practitioners
Think Twice Global Vaccine Institute
PO Box 9638
Santa Fe, NM 87504
Ph: (505)983-1856
Fax: (505)983-1856
E-mail: global@thinktwice.com
URL: http://thinktwice.com
Price: $21.95.

6182 ■ The VEA News
Virginia Education Association
116 S 3rd St.
Richmond, VA 23219
Ph: (804)648-5801
Fax: (804)775-8379
E-mail: jredford@veanea.org
URL: http://veaweteach.org
Price: $10 for nonmembers, free for members.

6183 ■ Venice Views
American Association of University Women, Venice Branch
488 Marsh Creek Rd.
Venice, FL 34293
E-mail: annelruss@comcast.net
URL: http://www.florida-aauw.org/Branches/venice.htm
Freq: monthly.

6184 ■ Victory Voice
America's Athletes with Disabilities
2813 Spindle Ln.
Bowie, MD 20715-2136
Ph: (301)464-3776
Fax: (301)464-3776
E-mail: drwmson@aol.com
URL: http://www.americasathletes.org

6185 ■ Video Training Network Directory
Tire Industry Association
1532 Pointer Ridge Pl., Ste. G
Bowie, MD 20716-1883
Ph: (301)430-7280
Fax: (301)430-7283
E-mail: info@tireindustry.org
URL: http://www.tireindustry.org

6186 ■ Views
Minnesota Association for the Education of Young Children
1821 University Ave., Ste. 324-S
St. Paul, MN 55104
Ph: (651)646-8689
Fax: (651)636-9146
E-mail: mnaeyc@mnaeyc.org
URL: http://www.mnaeyc.org

6187 ■ Vignette
American Institute of Architects San Antonio
816 Camaron, Ste. 211
San Antonio, TX 78212
Ph: (210)226-4979
Fax: (210)226-3062
E-mail: info@aiasa.org
URL: http://www.aiasa.org
Freq: monthly. **Price:** $500 for members (corporate).

6188 ■ Virginia Journal of Education
Virginia Education Association
116 S 3rd St.
Richmond, VA 23219

Ph: (804)648-5801
Fax: (804)775-8379
E-mail: jredford@veanea.org
URL: http://veaweteach.org
Freq: 10/year. **Price:** included in membership dues.

6189 ■ Visionary Philanthropy
Lighthouse International
111 E 59th St.
New York, NY 10022-1202
Ph: (212)821-9200
Fax: (212)821-9707
E-mail: info@lighthouse.org
URL: http://www.lighthouse.org

6190 ■ Visions
Washington Association for Career and Technical
Education
PO Box 315
Olympia, WA 98507-0315
Ph: (360)786-9286
Fax: (360)357-1491
E-mail: wa-acte@wa-acte.org
URL: http://www.wa-acte.org
Freq: quarterly. **Price:** included in membership dues.

6191 ■ Visions of Reality: What Fundamental-ist Schools Teach
Americans for Religious Liberty
PO Box 6656
Silver Spring, MD 20916
Ph: (301)260-2988
Fax: (301)260-2989
E-mail: arlinc@verizon.net
URL: http://www.arlinc.org
Price: $14.95.

6192 ■ Visual Assessment of Physical Child Abuse
American Humane Association Children's Services
63 Inverness Dr. E
Englewood, CO 80112-5117
Ph: (303)792-9900
Fax: (303)792-5333
E-mail: info@americanhumane.org
URL: http://www.americanhumane.org

6193 ■ Visual Impairment & Blindness
Association for Education and Rehabilitation of the
Blind and Visually Impaired
1703 N Beauregard St., Ste. 440
Alexandria, VA 22311
Ph: (703)671-4500
Fax: (703)671-6391
E-mail: jgandorf@aerbvi.org
URL: http://www.aerbvi.org
Descr: Includes scholarship information and forum
of ideas, controversies and discussion of issues.
Price: $99 in U.S., $124/year for institutions, outside
U.S.

6194 ■ Vocational Education Journal
Association for Career and Technical Education
1410 King St.
Alexandria, VA 22314
Ph: (703)683-3111
Fax: (703)683-7424
E-mail: acte@acteonline.org
URL: http://www.acteonline.org
Descr: Contains information about trends affecting
the workplace and programs that prepare students
for work. Includes advertisers index. **Freq:** monthly.
Price: included in membership dues, $3/year for
student members, $20/year for nonmembers. **ISSN:**
0164-9175.

6195 ■ The Voice
Texas PTA
408 W 11th St.
Austin, TX 78701-2113
Ph: (512)476-6769
E-mail: txpta@txpta.org
URL: http://www.txpta.org

6196 ■ The Voice
National Black Graduate Student Association
2400 6th St. NW

Washington, DC 20059
Fax: 800-471-4102
E-mail: nationaloffice@nbgsa.org
URL: http://www.nbgsa.org
Freq: quarterly.

6197 ■ WAEYC News
Washington Association for the Education of Young
Children
841 N Central Ave., Ste. 206
Kent, WA 98032
Ph: (253)854-2565
Fax: (253)813-3646
E-mail: waeyc@waeyc.org
URL: http://www.waeyc.org
Descr: Features articles on theory, practice, re-
search, and association information. **Freq:** quarterly.

6198 ■ Water Safety Journal
National Water Safety Congress
PO Box 1632
Mentor, OH 44061
Ph: (440)209-9805
Fax: (440)209-9805
E-mail: director@watersafetycongress.org
URL: http://www.watersafetycongress.org
Freq: quarterly.

6199 ■ WECA Newsletter
Wisconsin Early Childhood Association
744 Williamson St., Ste. 200
Madison, WI 53703
Ph: (608)240-9880
Fax: (608)663-1091
E-mail: weca@wecanaeyc.org
URL: http://www.wecanaeyc.org
Freq: quarterly.

6200 ■ Week in Review
National Association of Special Education Teachers
1250 Connecticut Ave. NW, Ste. 200
Washington, DC 20036
E-mail: contactus@naset.org
URL: http://www.naset.org
Descr: Features latest news in Special Education.
Freq: weekly.

6201 ■ West Virginia Parent-Teacher Bulletin
West Virginia Congress of Parents and Teachers
PO Box 3557
Parkersburg, WV 26103
Ph: (304)420-9576
Fax: (304)420-9577
E-mail: wv_office@pta.org
URL: http://www.wvpta.net
Freq: monthly. **Price:** $3/year.

6202 ■ What About Marijuana?
Narcotic Educational Foundation of America
28245 Ave. Crocker, Ste. 230
Santa Clarita, CA 91355-1201
Ph: (661)775-6960
Fax: (661)775-1648
E-mail: info@cnoa.org
URL: http://www.cnoa.org/NEFA.htm

6203 ■ What Are They Teaching Our Children?
Educational Research Analysts
PO Box 7518
Longview, TX 75607-7518
Ph: (903)753-5993
Fax: (903)753-8424
E-mail: info@textbookreviews.org
URL: http://www.textbookreviews.org

6204 ■ What's Happening in Albany
New York State PTA
One Wembley Ct.
Albany, NY 12205-3830
Ph: (518)452-8808
Fax: (518)452-8105

E-mail: pta.office@nypta.com
URL: http://www.nypta.com

6205 ■ When Bias Compounds: Insuring Equal Justice for Women of Color in the Courts
National Judicial Education Program
395 Hudson St.
New York, NY 10014-3669
Ph: (212)925-6635
Fax: (212)226-1066
E-mail: njep@legalmomentum.org
URL: http://www.legalmomentum.org

6206 ■ Where They Stand: A Digest of Organi-zational Policies on Child Care and Education
Child Care Action Campaign
24808 Deepdale Ave.
Little Neck, NY 11362-1233
Ph: (212)239-0138
Fax: (212)268-6515
URL: http://www.childcareaction.org
Descr: Provides a guide to 45 national organiza-
tions' policy positions on quality child care, early
childhood education, and education reform. **Price:**
$15 for members, $25 for nonmembers.

6207 ■ Will It Float
SMARTRISK
790 Bay St., Ste. 401
Toronto, ON, Canada M5G 1N8
Ph: (416)977-7350
Fax: (416)596-2700
E-mail: info@smartrisk.ca
URL: http://www.smartrisk.ca

6208 ■ Wisconsin Parent Teacher
Wisconsin National Congress of Parents and Teach-
ers
4797 Hayes Rd., Ste. 102
Madison, WI 53704
Ph: (608)244-1455
Fax: (608)244-4785
E-mail: wi_office@pta.org
URL: http://www.wisconsinpta.org
Freq: 9/year. **Price:** $9/year.

6209 ■ Without Warning
RID - U.S.A.
PO Box 520
Schenectady, NY 12301
Ph: (518)372-0034
Fax: (518)370-4917
E-mail: dwi@rid-usa.org
URL: http://www.rid-usa.org
Descr: Discusses alcohol poisoning and teen binge
drinking. **Price:** $95 plus shipping and handling.

6210 ■ Women's Education in the Global Economy (WedGE)
Women of Color Resource Center
1611 Telegraph Ave., No. 303
Oakland, CA 94612
Ph: (510)444-2700
Fax: (510)444-2711
E-mail: info@coloredgirls.org
URL: http://www.coloredgirls.org
Descr: Presents lessons, activities, games and skits
for better understanding of the impact of the global
economy on women worldwide. **Price:** $24.95.

6211 ■ WomenTech Educators
Institute for Women in Trades, Technology and Sci-
ence
1150 Ballena Blvd., Ste. 102
Alameda, CA 94501-3696
Ph: (510)749-0200
Fax: (510)749-0500
E-mail: info@iwitts.com
URL: http://www.iwitts.com
Descr: Contains information on preparing women for
technology careers. **Price:** free.

6212 ■ WomenTechWorld
Institute for Women in Trades, Technology and Science
1150 Ballena Blvd., Ste. 102

Alameda, CA 94501-3696
Ph: (510)749-0200
Fax: (510)749-0500
E-mail: info@iwitts.com
URL: http://www.iwitts.com
Descr: Contains tips for women to succeed in tech education. **Price:** free.

6213 ■ *Working!*
Goodwill Industries International
15810 Indianola Dr.
Rockville, MD 20855
Ph: (301)530-6500
E-mail: contactus@goodwill.org
URL: http://www.goodwill.org
Freq: quarterly.

6214 ■ *Working for Tomorrow*
Center for Workers with Disabilities
810 1st St. NE, Ste. 500
Washington, DC 20002
Ph: (202)682-0100
Fax: (202)204-0071
E-mail: nrelave@aphsa.org
URL: http://cwd.aphsa.org
Freq: monthly.

6215 ■ *Working Toward Equity: A Report on the Implementation of the Sex Equity Provisions of the Carl D. Perkins Vocational Education Act*
National Coalition for Women and Girls in Education
1111 16th St. NW
Washington, DC 20036
Ph: (202)785-7793
Fax: (202)872-1425
E-mail: maatzl@aauw.org
URL: http://www.ncwge.org

6216 ■ *Workplace Literacy*
American Association for Adult and Continuing Education
10111 Martin Luther King, Jr. Hwy., Ste. 200C
Bowie, MD 20720
Ph: (301)459-6261
Fax: (301)459-6241
E-mail: aaace10@aol.com
URL: http://www.aaace.org

6217 ■ *A World Awaits You: A Journal of Success of People with Disabilities in International Exchange*
Mobility International USA
132 E Broadway, Ste. 343
Eugene, OR 97401
Ph: (541)343-1284
Fax: (541)343-6812
E-mail: info@miusa.org
URL: http://www.miusa.org
Price: free.

6218 ■ *A World of Options*
Mobility International USA
132 E Broadway, Ste. 343
Eugene, OR 97401
Ph: (541)343-1284
Fax: (541)343-6812
E-mail: info@miusa.org
URL: http://www.miusa.org
Key Personnel: Susan Sygall, Exec. Dir.; Christa Bucks, Editor; Carole Patterson, Editor. **URL(s):** http://www.miusa.org **Covers:** Hundreds of educational programs, workcamps, transportation and travel advisory services for persons with disabilities. **Entries include:** Name, address, phone, geographical area served, financial data, eligibility requirements, descriptions of projects and services. Complete title is A World of Options: A Guide to International Educational Exchange, Community Service and Travel for Persons with Disabilities.

Phone number is also equipped with TTY. **Freq:** Irregular.

6219 ■ *A World of Options: A Guide to International Educational Exchange, Community Service, and Travel for Persons with Disabilities*
Mobility International USA
132 E Broadway, Ste. 343
Eugene, OR 97401
Ph: (541)343-1284
Fax: (541)343-6812
E-mail: info@miusa.org
URL: http://www.miusa.org
Price: $18.

6220 ■ *A World of Safety*
National Floor Safety Institute
PO Box 92607
Southlake, TX 76092
Ph: (817)749-1700
Fax: (817)749-1702
E-mail: info@nfsi.org
URL: http://www.nfsi.org

6221 ■ *WYAMI Newsletter*
NAMI-WYOMING
133 W 6th St.
Casper, WY 82601
E-mail: nami-wyo@qwest.net
URL: http://www.nami.org/sites/namiwyoming
Freq: bimonthly.

6222 ■ *Young Children*
Colorado Association for the Education of Young Children
PO Box 631326
Highlands Ranch, CO 80163-1326
Ph: (303)791-2772
Fax: (303)791-7597
E-mail: caeyc@coloradoaeyc.org
URL: http://www.coloradoaeyc.org
Freq: bimonthly.

6223 ■ *Young Children*
Georgia Association on Young Children
368 Moreland Ave. NE, Ste. 240
Atlanta, GA 30307-1927
Ph: (404)222-0014
Fax: (404)222-0107
E-mail: gayc@algxmail.com
URL: http://gayconline.org
Freq: bimonthly. **Price:** included in membership dues.

6224 ■ *Young Children*
National Association for the Education of Young Children
1313 L St. NW, Ste. 500
Washington, DC 20005
Ph: (202)232-8777
Fax: (202)328-1846
E-mail: naeyc@naeyc.org
URL: http://www.naeyc.org
Descr: Covers developments in the practice, research, and theory of early childhood education. Includes book reviews and calendar of events. **Freq:** bimonthly. **Price:** included in membership dues, $30/year for nonmembers and institutions. **ISSN:** 0044-0728.

6225 ■ *Young Children Journal*
Hawaii Association for the Education of Young Children
1806 S King St., Ste. 30
Honolulu, HI 96826
Ph: (808)942-4708
Fax: (808)955-2739
E-mail: info@hawaiiaeyc.org
URL: http://www.hawaiiaeyc.org
Freq: bimonthly. **Price:** included in membership dues.

6226 ■ *Young Exceptional Children*
Division for Early Childhood of the Council for Exceptional Children
27 Ft. Missoula Rd., Ste. 2

Missoula, MT 59804
Ph: (406)543-0872
Fax: (406)543-0887
E-mail: dec@dec-sped.org
URL: http://www.dec-sped.org
Descr: Provides information to teachers, early care and education personnel, administrators, therapists, family members, and others who work with children. **Freq:** quarterly. **Price:** included in membership dues, $20 individual nonmembers, $35 for institutions. **ISSN:** 1096-2506.

6227 ■ *Your Rights Under the AMHI Consent Decree*
Disability Rights Center
PO Box 2007
Augusta, ME 04338-2007
Ph: (207)626-2774
Fax: (207)621-1419
E-mail: advocate@drcme.org
URL: http://www.drcme.org

Multimedia Resources

6228 ■ *A to Z of Walking Safely*
AIMS Multimedia
20765 Superior St
Chatsworth, CA 91311-4409
Ph: (818)773-4300
Free: 800-367-2467
Fax: (818)341-6700
E-mail: info@aims.multimedia.com
URL: http://www.aims.multimedia.com
Format(s): Videocassette. **Descr:** An animated film in which the letters of the alphabet walk about ostensibly teaching safety hints. **Prod. Date:** 1983. **Length:** 10.

6229 ■ *Above AllKeep Your Head*
Film Library/Greater Los Angeles Safety Council
600 Wilshire Blvd., No. 1263
Los Angeles, CA 90017
Ph: (213)385-6461
Free: 800-421-9585
Fax: (213)385-8405
URL: http://www.lasafety.org
Format(s): Videocassette. **Descr:** Shows workers how to protect their head. The techniques and equipment for preventing injury to eyes, ears, nose, mouth, neck, throat, brain, and skin are demonstrated in typical workplaces. **Prod. Date:** 1988. **Length:** 9.

6230 ■ *Accident-Proof Kids*
Move Communications
804 Phoenix Dr
Ann Arbor, MI 48108
Ph: (734)973-0100
Fax: (734)973-0150
URL: http://www.movecommunications.com
Format(s): Videocassette. **Descr:** O.J. Anderson's characters, Cowboy Careful, Sergeant Stop-N-Go, and Louie the Lifeguard, teach safety lessons to kids in a fun way. **Prod. Date:** 1992. **Length:** 28. **Price:** $14.95.

6231 ■ *Accident Report*
Film Library/Greater Los Angeles Safety Council
600 Wilshire Blvd., No. 1263
Los Angeles, CA 90017
Ph: (213)385-6461
Free: 800-421-9585
Fax: (213)385-8405
URL: http://www.lasafety.org
Format(s): Videocassette. **Descr:** A film designed to make workers aware of the consequences of unsafe behavior and of the need to take responsibility for their own safety. **Prod. Date:** 198?. **Length:** 15.

6232 ■ *Accidentally Yours*
Film Library/Greater Los Angeles Safety Council
600 Wilshire Blvd., No. 1263
Los Angeles, CA 90017
Ph: (213)385-6461
Free: 800-421-9585

Fax: (213)385-8405
URL: http://www.lasafety.org
Format(s): Videocassette. **Descr:** Stresses consumer product safety as a husband and wife become involved in household accidents with glass doors and power mowers. **Prod. Date:** 198?. **Length:** 14.

6233 ■ Accidents Made Easy
Film Library/Greater Los Angeles Safety Council
600 Wilshire Blvd., No. 1263
Los Angeles, CA 90017
Ph: (213)385-6461
Free: 800-421-9585
Fax: (213)385-8405
URL: http://www.lasafety.org
Format(s): Videocassette. **Descr:** A group of supervisors find out about their employees' attitudes toward safety after reviewing a series of accidents that could have been avoided. **Prod. Date:** 198?. **Length:** 15.

6234 ■ The Adventures of Safety Frog Series
AIMS Multimedia
20765 Superior St
Chatsworth, CA 91311-4409
Ph: (818)773-4300
Free: 800-367-2467
Fax: (818)341-6700
E-mail: info@aims.multimedia.com
URL: http://www.aimsmultimedia.com
Format(s): Videocassette. **Descr:** The three films in this series feature entertaining muppets that teach children important safety rules that will protect them at home, in school, and in the car. **Prod. Date:** 1985. **Length:** 22.

6235 ■ Air to Breathe
Film Library/Greater Los Angeles Safety Council
600 Wilshire Blvd., No. 1263
Los Angeles, CA 90017
Ph: (213)385-6461
Free: 800-421-9585
Fax: (213)385-8405
URL: http://www.lasafety.org
Format(s): Videocassette. **Descr:** The effects of toxic gas on the human body, and the speed in which it can overpower a person are demonstrated. **Prod. Date:** 198?. **Length:** 21.

6236 ■ Air Purifying Respirator: Safety on the Job
AIMS Multimedia
20765 Superior St
Chatsworth, CA 91311-4409
Ph: (818)773-4300
Free: 800-367-2467
Fax: (818)341-6700
E-mail: info@aims.multimedia.com
URL: http://www.aimsmultimedia.com
Format(s): Videocassette. **Descr:** This program will help workers understand the importance of protecting themselves from hazardous substances in the workplace. They'll learn the cardinal rules of safe respirator use. **Prod. Date:** 1988. **Length:** 13.

6237 ■ All Aboard: A Collection of Music Videos for Children
Learning Station
3950 Bristol Ct
Melbourne, FL 32904
Ph: (407)728-8773
Free: 800-789-9990
Fax: (407)722-9121
E-mail: lrngstn@concentric.net
URL: http://www.lrngstn.com
Format(s): Videocassette. **Descr:** A set of programs designed to get children involved in building friendships, self-confidence, and safety awareness, all while promoting physical fitness. **Prod. Date:** 1991. **Length:** 30. **Price:** $14.95.

6238 ■ All of Us: Talking Together
Aquarius Productions
Olde Medfield Sq
18 N Main St
Sherborn, MA 01770

Ph: (508)650-1616
Free: 888-440-2963
Fax: (508)650-1665
E-mail: tm@aquariusproductions.com
URL: http://www.aquariusproductions.com
Format(s): Videocassette. **Descr:** Presents a sex education course geared for developmentally disabled youth. Covers reproductive anatomy, pregnancy, contraception, disease prevention, the difference between love and friendship, and public/private behavior. Available in Spanish version. **Prod. Date:** 1999. **Length:** 24. **Price:** $195.

6239 ■ Amy
Film Library/Greater Los Angeles Safety Council
600 Wilshire Blvd., No. 1263
Los Angeles, CA 90017
Ph: (213)385-6461
Free: 800-421-9585
Fax: (213)385-8405
URL: http://www.lasafety.org
Format(s): Videocassette. **Descr:** This film teaches young people how to become safety conscious baby sitters through demonstrations on fire safety, injury prevention and first aid. **Prod. Date:** 198?. **Length:** 17.

6240 ■ Anatomy of a Fall
Film Library/Greater Los Angeles Safety Council
600 Wilshire Blvd., No. 1263
Los Angeles, CA 90017
Ph: (213)385-6461
Free: 800-421-9585
Fax: (213)385-8405
URL: http://www.lasafety.org
Format(s): Videocassette. **Descr:** The most common excuses for slips and falls in industry and hospitals are examined. **Prod. Date:** 198?. **Length:** 15. **Price:** $430.00.

6241 ■ And Then There Were Two
Film Library/Greater Los Angeles Safety Council
600 Wilshire Blvd., No. 1263
Los Angeles, CA 90017
Ph: (213)385-6461
Free: 800-421-9585
Fax: (213)385-8405
URL: http://www.lasafety.org
Format(s): Videocassette. **Descr:** The correct work procedures and safety rules for erecting scaffolds and platforms are explained. **Prod. Date:** 198?. **Length:** 22.

6242 ■ Arc Welding: Safety and Operation
Film Library/Greater Los Angeles Safety Council
600 Wilshire Blvd., No. 1263
Los Angeles, CA 90017
Ph: (213)385-6461
Free: 800-421-9585
Fax: (213)385-8405
URL: http://www.lasafety.org
Format(s): Videocassette. **Descr:** The basic fundamentals and safety precautions of arc welding are demonstrated. **Prod. Date:** 198?. **Length:** 14. **Price:** $49.95.

6243 ■ Around Every Corner
ERI Safety Videos
374 Park Rd
Lexington, SC 29072
Ph: (803)356-4880
Free: 800-311-1143
Fax: (803)356-1946
URL: http://www.eri-safety.com
Format(s): Videocassette. **Descr:** The causes of accidents in the workplace are thoroughly uncovered. **Prod. Date:** 1982. **Length:** 16.

6244 ■ Back Chat
Film Library/Greater Los Angeles Safety Council
600 Wilshire Blvd., No. 1263
Los Angeles, CA 90017
Ph: (213)385-6461
Free: 800-421-9585
Fax: (213)385-8405
URL: http://www.lasafety.org

Format(s): Videocassette. **Descr:** The correct procedure for office workers to bend, lift, carry and reach to avoid back injuries is demonstrated. **Prod. Date:** 198?. **Length:** 22.

6245 ■ Back and Ergonomic Safety Procedures for Offshore Personnel
John Sabella & Associate
805 W. Emerson St
Seattle, WA 98119
Ph: (206)281-8626
Fax: (206)217-0899
E-mail: sales@johnsabella.com
URL: http://www.johnsabella.com
Format(s): Videocassette. **Descr:** Outlines safe work practices required for offshore personnel to work injury-free in the oil field environment, including lifting techniques, stretching and strengthening. **Prod. Date:** ?. **Length:** 40. **Price:** $375.00.

6246 ■ Back Injury Prevention Program
DuPont Safety Resources
PO Box 80013
Wilmington, DE 19880-0013
Free: 800-532-7233
Fax: 888-644-7233
E-mail: info@dupont.com
URL: http://www.dupont.com/safety
Format(s): Videocassette. **Descr:** Three educational modules discuss ways to improve back health and safety to prevent injuries and lost work time. Includes administrator's, leader's, and participant's guides as well as a back injury prevention booklet. **Prod. Date:** 1993. **Length:** ?. **Price:** $690.00.

6247 ■ Back Injury Prevention Through Ergonomics
Film Library/Greater Los Angeles Safety Council
600 Wilshire Blvd., No. 1263
Los Angeles, CA 90017
Ph: (213)385-6461
Free: 800-421-9585
Fax: (213)385-8405
URL: http://www.lasafety.org
Format(s): Videocassette. **Descr:** This is a demonstration of how a total ergonomics program can reduce workers' on-the-job injuries. **Prod. Date:** 198?. **Length:** 14.

6248 ■ Back Safety for Inland Waterways Personnel
John Sabella & Associate
805 W. Emerson St
Seattle, WA 98119
Ph: (206)281-8626
Fax: (206)217-0899
E-mail: sales@johnsabella.com
URL: http://www.johnsabella.com
Format(s): Videocassette. **Descr:** Demonstrates the proper working postures and strengthening exercises that inland water personnel should utilize in order to avoid injury. **Prod. Date:** ?. **Length:** 55. **Price:** $295.00.

6249 ■ Backfire
Film Library/Greater Los Angeles Safety Council
600 Wilshire Blvd., No. 1263
Los Angeles, CA 90017
Ph: (213)385-6461
Free: 800-421-9585
Fax: (213)385-8405
URL: http://www.lasafety.org
Format(s): Videocassette. **Descr:** This film is designed to inform employees how to do their work without risking a back injury. **Prod. Date:** 198?. **Length:** 15. **Price:** $420.00.

6250 ■ Bare Minimum
Film Library/Greater Los Angeles Safety Council
600 Wilshire Blvd., No. 1263
Los Angeles, CA 90017
Ph: (213)385-6461
Free: 800-421-9585
Fax: (213)385-8405
URL: http://www.lasafety.org
Format(s): Videocassette. **Descr:** In this film, a

safety director and his foreman offer several recommendations for the care and proper use of safety gear. **Prod. Date:** 198?. **Length:** 10.

6251 ■ Basic Guide to Shotguns
School-Tech Inc.
745 State Cir
PO Box 1941
Ann Arbor, MI 48106
Ph: (734)761-5072
Free: 800-521-2832
Fax: 800-654-4321
E-mail: service@school-tech.com
URL: http://www.schoolmasters.com
Format(s): Videocassette. **Descr:** Learn all about buying and using a shotgun in this video geared toward hunters from a living legend, John Satterwhite. **Prod. Date:** 1988. **Length:** 45. **Price:** $49.95.

6252 ■ The Be Safe, Be Smart Series
United Learning
1560 Sherman Ave., Ste. 100
PO Box 48718
Evanston, IL 60201
Ph: 888-892-3484
Fax: (847)328-6706
E-mail: info@interaccess.com
URL: http://www.unitedlearning.com
Format(s): Videocassette. **Descr:** Kids are made aware of dangerous situations in the home, on the street and in school, and are encouraged to think and be careful before they act. **Prod. Date:** 1989. **Length:** 13. **Price:** $225.

6253 ■ Bedside Safety
Film Library/Greater Los Angeles Safety Council
600 Wilshire Blvd., No. 1263
Los Angeles, CA 90017
Ph: (213)385-6461
Free: 800-421-9585
Fax: (213)385-8405
URL: http://www.lasafety.org
Format(s): Videocassette. **Descr:** Depicts several bedside accidents at a health care facility and how they could have been prevented. **Prod. Date:** 198?. **Length:** 13.

6254 ■ Better Than Cure
Film Library/Greater Los Angeles Safety Council
600 Wilshire Blvd., No. 1263
Los Angeles, CA 90017
Ph: (213)385-6461
Free: 800-421-9585
Fax: (213)385-8405
URL: http://www.lasafety.org
Format(s): Videocassette. **Descr:** This film demonstrates the need for protection from potential hazards around the office. **Prod. Date:** 198?. **Length:** 19.

6255 ■ Beware and Be Wise
Film Library/Greater Los Angeles Safety Council
600 Wilshire Blvd., No. 1263
Los Angeles, CA 90017
Ph: (213)385-6461
Free: 800-421-9585
Fax: (213)385-8405
URL: http://www.lasafety.org
Format(s): Videocassette. **Descr:** The importance of outdoor electrical safety especially around power lines is stressed. **Prod. Date:** 198?. **Length:** 15.

6256 ■ Beware the Rapist
Film Library/Greater Los Angeles Safety Council
600 Wilshire Blvd., No. 1263
Los Angeles, CA 90017
Ph: (213)385-6461
Free: 800-421-9585
Fax: (213)385-8405
URL: http://www.lasafety.org
Format(s): Videocassette. **Descr:** A dramatization of several incidents in which women ignored the fundamentals of rape protection. The film points out

how each woman could have avoided the situation. **Prod. Date:** 1977. **Length:** 20.

6257 ■ Bicycle Dancin'
Edwards Films
203 Center Rd
Eagle Bridge, NY 12057
Ph: (518)677-5720
E-mail: edfilms@worldnet.att.net
URL: http://home.att.net/~edfilms
Format(s): Videocassette. **Descr:** Learn how to pull your favorite stunts on bikes, and pick up some safety tips, too! **Prod. Date:** 1985. **Length:** 16. **Price:** $32.50.

6258 ■ Bicycle Safety Camp
Tapeworm Video Distributors
27833 Hopkins Ave., Unit 6
Valencia, CA 91355
Ph: (661)257-4904
Fax: (661)257-4820
E-mail: sales@tapeworm.com
URL: http://www.tapeworm.com
Format(s): Videocassette. **Descr:** Sam Sprocket teaches kids ages 6-12 to wear a helmet with pride and other tips on bicycle safety in this musical video. **Prod. Date:** 1990. **Length:** 25. **Price:** $14.95.

6259 ■ Big Red
Tapeworm Video Distributors
27833 Hopkins Ave., Unit 6
Valencia, CA 91355
Ph: (661)257-4904
Fax: (661)257-4820
E-mail: sales@tapeworm.com
URL: http://www.tapeworm.com
Format(s): Videocassette. **Descr:** Fire safety education program for kids looks at the job of a firefighter. Introduces preparation, tools, and fire trucks. **Prod. Date:** 1993. **Length:** 25. **Price:** $19.95.

6260 ■ Bike-Wise: To Be Sure
Film Library/Greater Los Angeles Safety Council
600 Wilshire Blvd., No. 1263
Los Angeles, CA 90017
Ph: (213)385-6461
Free: 800-421-9585
Fax: (213)385-8405
URL: http://www.lasafety.org
Format(s): Videocassette. **Descr:** Everything you need to know about bicycles from how to equip it to the rules of the road is explained. **Prod. Date:** 198?. **Length:** 14.

6261 ■ Boating Safety: Courtesy Afloat
Film Library/Greater Los Angeles Safety Council
600 Wilshire Blvd., No. 1263
Los Angeles, CA 90017
Ph: (213)385-6461
Free: 800-421-9585
Fax: (213)385-8405
URL: http://www.lasafety.org
Format(s): Videocassette. **Descr:** The courteous and safe operation of boats in swimming and fishing areas are demonstrated. **Prod. Date:** 198?. **Length:** 22.

6262 ■ Breakthroughs: How to Reach Students with Autism
Aquarius Productions
Olde Medfield Sq
18 N Main St
Sherborn, MA 01770
Ph: (508)650-1616
Free: 888-440-2963
Fax: (508)650-1665
E-mail: tm@aquariusproductions.com
URL: http://www.aquariusproductions.com
Format(s): Videocassette. **Descr:** Educator Karen Sewell demonstrates the techniques she has developed for teaching students with autism. Includes

teacher's manual. **Prod. Date:** 1998. **Length:** 25. **Price:** $99.00.

6263 ■ Breathe Safe, Breathe Clean
Film Library/Greater Los Angeles Safety Council
600 Wilshire Blvd., No. 1263
Los Angeles, CA 90017
Ph: (213)385-6461
Free: 800-421-9585
Fax: (213)385-8405
URL: http://www.lasafety.org
Format(s): Videocassette. **Descr:** The importance of wearing the proper respiratory equipment at work is presented in this film. **Prod. Date:** 198?. **Length:** 15.

6264 ■ Bulk Liquid Safety Concerns
Williams Learning Network
15400 Calhoun Dr
Rockville, MD 20855-2762
Ph: (301)315-6700
Free: 800-848-1717
Fax: (301)315-6880
E-mail: mait@willearn.com
URL: http://www.willearn.com
Format(s): Videocassette. **Descr:** Outlines techniques for the safe transfer of bulk liquids from storage facilities to transport facilities. Emphasis is on three basic tasks: weighing and spotting; making connections; and disconnecting and releasing. Also discusses five basic characteristics of safe transfer: toxicity, viscosity, volatility, temperature, and pressure. Includes Leader's Guide and 25 Program Guides. **Length:** 8.

6265 ■ The Cases of Detective Duncan
Marshmedia
PO Box 8082
Shawnee Mission, KS 66208
Ph: (816)523-1059
Free: 800-821-3303
Fax: (816)333-7421
E-mail: order@marshmedia.com
URL: http://www.marshmedia.com
Format(s): Videocassette. **Descr:** Detective Duncan solves the mystery of who tried to abuse two kids. **Prod. Date:** 1988. **Length:** 45. **Price:** $47.50.

6266 ■ Caution: Office Zone
Film Library/Greater Los Angeles Safety Council
600 Wilshire Blvd., No. 1263
Los Angeles, CA 90017
Ph: (213)385-6461
Free: 800-421-9585
Fax: (213)385-8405
URL: http://www.lasafety.org
Format(s): Videocassette. **Descr:** Test how safe your office is with this video checklist which also features how to make a work environment safer. **Prod. Date:** 198?. **Length:** 15.

6267 ■ Chains, Slings and Hoists
Film Library/Greater Los Angeles Safety Council
600 Wilshire Blvd., No. 1263
Los Angeles, CA 90017
Ph: (213)385-6461
Free: 800-421-9585
Fax: (213)385-8405
URL: http://www.lasafety.org
Format(s): Videocassette. **Descr:** The procedures and precautions for persons using cranes, slings, chains and hoists are demonstrated. **Prod. Date:** 198?. **Length:** 12.

6268 ■ The Challenge of Change: Creating a New Safety Culture
Core Media Training Solutions
1732 NW Quimby, Ste. 100
Portland, OR 97209
Free: 800-537-8352
URL: http://www.cmts.com
Format(s): Videocassette. **Descr:** Dan Petersen leads an introduction to safety culture. Includes graphics and short clips of company meetings. Must be used with accompanying workbook and software

program. **Prod. Date:** 1993. **Length:** ?. **Price:** $1995.00.

6269 ■ *The Challenge of Osteoporosis for People With Disabilities*
Aquarius Productions
Olde Medfield Sq
18 N Main St
Sherborn, MA 01770
Ph: (508)650-1616
Free: 888-440-2963
Fax: (508)650-1665
E-mail: tm@aquariusproductions.com
URL: http://www.aquariusproductions.com
Format(s): Videocassette. **Descr:** Leading experts present the risk factors for osteoporosis that people with physical disabilities face and prevention methods that have proven successful. **Prod. Date:** 2000. **Length:** 15. **Price:** $89.00.

6270 ■ *Chaos to Calm*
AIMS Multimedia
20765 Superior St
Chatsworth, CA 91311-4409
Ph: (818)773-4300
Free: 800-367-2467
Fax: (818)341-6700
E-mail: info@aims.multimedia.com
URL: http://www.aimsmultimedia.com
Format(s): Videocassette. **Descr:** For educators and administrators, keys and hints to prevent in-school violence are discussed. **Prod. Date:** 1986. **Length:** 25.

6271 ■ *Chemical Safety for General Service Workers*
Cornell University
Audio Visual Resource Center
Business & Technology Park
15 Thornwood Dr
Ithaca, NY 14850
Ph: (607)266-7866
Fax: (607)266-7876
E-mail: dist_cent@cce.cornell.edu
URL: http://www.cornell.edu
Format(s): Videocassette. **Descr:** Designed for custodial, construction or maintenance workers, this program shows the proper handling of dangerous chemicals. **Prod. Date:** 1986. **Length:** 15.

6272 ■ *Chemical Safety I: Proper Handling*
Tel-A-Train, Inc.
305 Crewdson Ave
Chattanooga, TN 37405
E-mail: wkingsb@pwpl.com
Format(s): Videocassette. **Descr:** Explains the rules for safe handling of chemical substances and their behaviors, material safety data sheets, labeling, and emergency procedures. **Prod. Date:** ????. **Length:** 20. **Price:** $410.00.

6273 ■ *Chemical Safety II: Health Hazards*
Tel-A-Train, Inc.
305 Crewdson Ave
Chattanooga, TN 37405
E-mail: wkingsb@pwpl.com
Format(s): Videocassette. **Descr:** Explains the effects of certain chemicals on human health, ways to avoid harmful effects, and accident procedures. **Prod. Date:** ????. **Length:** 20. **Price:** $410.00.

6274 ■ *Chemical Safety III: Fire and Explosion*
Tel-A-Train, Inc.
305 Crewdson Ave
Chattanooga, TN 37405
E-mail: wkingsb@pwpl.com
Format(s): Videocassette. **Descr:** Discusses characteristics of chemicals; flashpoint, reactivity, and vapor pressure. Demonstrates safe handling and storage of potentially hazardous substances. **Prod. Date:** ????. **Length:** 20. **Price:** $410.00.

6275 ■ *Chemicals Under Control*
ERI Safety Videos
374 Park Rd

Lexington, SC 29072
Ph: (803)356-4880
Free: 800-311-1143
Fax: (803)356-1946
URL: http://www.eri-safety.com
Format(s): Videocassette. **Descr:** The safe handling of industrial chemicals made easy. **Prod. Date:** 1985. **Length:** 18.

6276 ■ *Child Safety at Home*
KidSafety of America
6251 Schaefer Ave., Ste. B
Chino, CA 91710-9065
Ph: (909)902-1340
Free: 800-524-1156
Fax: (909)902-1343
E-mail: feedback@kidsafetystore.com
URL: http://www.kidsafetystore.com
Format(s): Videocassette. **Descr:** Nosebleeds, cuts and bites are all part of growing up. Aimed at parents, the video gives tips for preventing accidents, and what to do if prevention doesn't work. Includes information on more severe injuries such as burns, drowning and severed limbs. Also available in a Spanish language version. **Prod. Date:** 1992. **Length:** 28. **Price:** $19.95.

6277 ■ *Child Safety Outdoors with John Stossel*
Baker & Taylor Inc.
2709 Water Ridge Pkwy., Ste. 500
Charlotte, NC 28217
Ph: (704)357-3500
Free: 800-775-1800
E-mail: btinfo@btol.com
URL: http://www.btol.com
Format(s): Videocassette. **Descr:** Reenactments illustrate potential safety hazards and first aid techniques for increased outdoor awareness. Demonstrates child and infant CPR, and reviews carseat, seat belt, rollerblade, bicycle, pedestrian, playground, and pool safety. **Prod. Date:** 1994. **Length:** 40. **Price:** $29.95.

6278 ■ *Child Safety Seats: What to Look For*
Medical University of South Carolina
Division of Television Services
Health Communications Network
171 Ashley Ave
Charleston, SC 29425
Ph: (843)792-2300
URL: http://www.musc.edu
Format(s): Videocassette. **Descr:** Different types of child safety seats are demonstrated and discussed. Parents are told what to look for when purchasing a child safety seat. **Prod. Date:** 1981. **Length:** 7.

6279 ■ *Childproof: Home Safety Checklist*
Promedion
PO Box 3551
Austin, TX 78764
Ph: (512)282-9006
Fax: (512)282-9099
Format(s): Videocassette. **Descr:** A collection of tips and hints on how to keep the homestead safe for children. **Prod. Date:** 1992. **Length:** 50. **Price:** $49.95.

6280 ■ *Childproofing Your Guns*
Gun Video
4585 Murphy Canyon Rd
San Diego, CA 92123
Ph: (858)569-4000
Free: 800-942-8273
Fax: (858)569-0505
E-mail: info2@gunvideo.com
URL: http://www.gunvideo.com
Format(s): Videocassette. **Descr:** Covers all the latest methods for keeping guns out of the hands of children. Includes information on the technical, safety, and legal aspects of firearm accidents involv-

ing children. **Prod. Date:** 1991. **Length:** 30. **Price:** $29.95.

6281 ■ *Children: Play it Safe*
Meridian Education Corp.
2572 Brunswick Ave
Lawrenceville, NJ 08648-4128
Ph: (609)671-1000
Free: 800-727-5507
Fax: 888-340-5507
E-mail: custmserv@meridianeducation.com
URL: http://www.meridianeducation.com
Format(s): Videocassette. **Descr:** Addresses child-care providers and reviews eight situations which are potentially harmful including dealing with strangers, ex-spouse abduction, medical emergencies, appropriate/inappropriate play environments, sexual assault, leaving the home, answering the telephone, and getting lost. Offers suggestions on constructively dealing with these situations. **Prod. Date:** 1989. **Price:** $95.

6282 ■ *Chlorine Emergency Kit A*
Williams Learning Network
15400 Calhoun Dr
Rockville, MD 20855-2762
Ph: (301)315-6700
Free: 800-848-1717
Fax: (301)315-6880
E-mail: mait@willearn.com
URL: http://www.willearn.com
Format(s): Videocassette. **Descr:** Outlines the major parts of a chlorine cylinder and what it takes to stop cylinder leaks. Covers valve leaks, fusible plug thread and metal leaks, and sidewall leaks. Includes Leader's Guide and 25 Program Guides. **Length:** 17.

6283 ■ *Choices: A Driver Safety Program*
DuPont Safety Resources
PO Box 80013
Wilmington, DE 19880-0013
Free: 800-532-7233
Fax: 888-644-7233
E-mail: info@dupont.com
URL: http://www.dupont.com/safety
Format(s): Videocassette. **Descr:** Teaches employees that having the proper attitude and being aware of driving conditions can lead to fewer accidents on the road. Uses positive self-talk to create the positive attitude that will lead to safer driving. **Prod. Date:** 1993. **Length:** 21. **Price:** $440.00.

6284 ■ *Choose Your Weapon*
Gun Video
4585 Murphy Canyon Rd
San Diego, CA 92123
Ph: (858)569-4000
Free: 800-942-8273
Fax: (858)569-0505
E-mail: info2@gunvideo.com
URL: http://www.gunvideo.com
Format(s): Videocassette. **Descr:** A comprehensive look at gun types, operation, safety and usage. **Prod. Date:** 1991. **Length:** 90. **Price:** $49.95.

6285 ■ *Choosing the Best in Children's Video*
BMG Entertainment
1540 Broadway
New York, NY 10036-4039
Ph: (212)930-4000
URL: http://www.bmg.com
Format(s): Videocassette. **Descr:** A guide to assist parents, teachers and anyone concerned about the kind and quality of programs watched by children through the age of 12. Clips from more than 30 top videos, including "The Snowman," "The Electric Grandmother," "The Mouse and the Motorcycle," "Beauty and the Beast" and "Raffi in Concert" are featured. **Prod. Date:** 1991. **Length:** 35. **Price:** $14.98.

6286 ■ *Christmas Season Holiday Safety*
ERI Safety Videos
374 Park Rd
Lexington, SC 29072

Ph: (803)356-4880
Free: 800-311-1143
Fax: (803)356-1946
URL: http://www.eri-safety.com
Format(s): Videocassette. **Descr:** Holiday safety tips show the viewer how to avoid the hazards associated with Christmas tree lights and other situations. **Prod. Date:** 1987. **Length:** 17. **Price:** $425.00.

6287 ■ Classes of Fires and Fire Extinguishers
Williams Learning Network
15400 Calhoun Dr
Rockville, MD 20855-2762
Ph: (301)315-6700
Free: 800-848-1717
Fax: (301)315-6880
E-mail: mait@willearn.com
URL: http://www.willearn.com
Format(s): Videocassette. **Descr:** Describes the four types of fires and the four types of fire extinguishers and emphasizes the correct extinguisher for the type of fire being put out. Includes Leader's Guide and 25 Program Guides. **Prod. Date:** 19??. **Length:** 12.

6288 ■ Climbing Country
Film Library/Greater Los Angeles Safety Council
600 Wilshire Blvd., No. 1263
Los Angeles, CA 90017
Ph: (213)385-6461
Free: 800-421-9585
Fax: (213)385-8405
URL: http://www.lasafety.org
Format(s): Videocassette. **Descr:** A mountain climbing party goes on an excursion to demonstrate the hazards that can occur such as falls and sunburn. **Prod. Date:** 198?. **Length:** 28.

6289 ■ Close to Home
Film Library/Greater Los Angeles Safety Council
600 Wilshire Blvd., No. 1263
Los Angeles, CA 90017
Ph: (213)385-6461
Free: 800-421-9585
Fax: (213)385-8405
URL: http://www.lasafety.org
Format(s): Videocassette. **Descr:** In this program a group of General Motors employees describe the moment of carelessness that led to their on-the-job accident. **Prod. Date:** 198?. **Length:** 20.

6290 ■ Coal Dust: Hazards and Controls
Film Library/Greater Los Angeles Safety Council
600 Wilshire Blvd., No. 1263
Los Angeles, CA 90017
Ph: (213)385-6461
Free: 800-421-9585
Fax: (213)385-8405
URL: http://www.lasafety.org
Format(s): Videocassette. **Descr:** This is a detailed look at the hazards of coal mine dust to underground and surface workers. **Prod. Date:** 1980. **Length:** 19.

6291 ■ The Color of Danger
Film Library/Greater Los Angeles Safety Council
600 Wilshire Blvd., No. 1263
Los Angeles, CA 90017
Ph: (213)385-6461
Free: 800-421-9585
Fax: (213)385-8405
URL: http://www.lasafety.org
Format(s): Videocassette. **Descr:** A series of accidents, brought about by fork lift operators dramatizes the need for the safe operation of industrial fork lift trucks. **Prod. Date:** 198?. **Length:** 15.

6292 ■ Communications
Film Library/Greater Los Angeles Safety Council
600 Wilshire Blvd., No. 1263
Los Angeles, CA 90017
Ph: (213)385-6461
Free: 800-421-9585
Fax: (213)385-8405
URL: http://www.lasafety.org
Format(s): Videocassette. **Descr:** This film demon-
strates that the best method of preventing an accident is clear-precise communication between two people. **Prod. Date:** 198?. **Length:** 9.

6293 ■ Compressed Bases: Under Your Control
Film Library/Greater Los Angeles Safety Council
600 Wilshire Blvd., No. 1263
Los Angeles, CA 90017
Ph: (213)385-6461
Free: 800-421-9585
Fax: (213)385-8405
URL: http://www.lasafety.org
Format(s): Videocassette. **Descr:** The recommended procedures and equipment for safe handling and storage of compressed gases in the plant or the laboratory are demonstrated. **Prod. Date:** 198?. **Length:** 60.

6294 ■ Confined Space Hazards
Film Library/Greater Los Angeles Safety Council
600 Wilshire Blvd., No. 1263
Los Angeles, CA 90017
Ph: (213)385-6461
Free: 800-421-9585
Fax: (213)385-8405
URL: http://www.lasafety.org
Format(s): Videocassette. **Descr:** The safe and unsafe procedures for working in confined spaces are explained in this film. **Prod. Date:** 198?. **Length:** 15.

6295 ■ Confined Space Hazards in Construction
Film Library/Greater Los Angeles Safety Council
600 Wilshire Blvd., No. 1263
Los Angeles, CA 90017
Ph: (213)385-6461
Free: 800-421-9585
Fax: (213)385-8405
URL: http://www.lasafety.org
Format(s): Videocassette. **Descr:** Tragedy ensues when three construction workers fail to follow the correct safety procedures on the job. **Prod. Date:** 198?. **Length:** 17.

6296 ■ Confined Space Hazards in Factories
Film Library/Greater Los Angeles Safety Council
600 Wilshire Blvd., No. 1263
Los Angeles, CA 90017
Ph: (213)385-6461
Free: 800-421-9585
Fax: (213)385-8405
URL: http://www.lasafety.org
Format(s): Videocassette. **Descr:** A dramatization of what happens to a factory worker who defies the company's safety rules by entering a reactor vessel and is overcome by fumes. **Prod. Date:** 198?. **Length:** 16.

6297 ■ Confined Space Hazards in Shipbuilding
Film Library/Greater Los Angeles Safety Council
600 Wilshire Blvd., No. 1263
Los Angeles, CA 90017
Ph: (213)385-6461
Free: 800-421-9585
Fax: (213)385-8405
URL: http://www.lasafety.org
Format(s): Videocassette. **Descr:** A dramatization of an incident that shows how an excess of oxygen in the hold of a ship caused an explosion which resulted in a fire that killed the men working on the ship. **Prod. Date:** 198?. **Length:** 16.

6298 ■ Consumer Connection
PBS Home Video
Catalog Fulfillment Center
PO Box 751089
Charlotte, NC 28275-1089
Ph: 800-531-4727
Free: 800-645-4PBS
E-mail: info@pbs.org
URL: http://www.pbs.org
Format(s): Videocassette. **Descr:** This series is designed to help high school students become more
effective consumers, through the study of the common buying problems of young people. **Prod. Date:** 1986. **Length:** 20.

6299 ■ Contact
Film Library/Greater Los Angeles Safety Council
600 Wilshire Blvd., No. 1263
Los Angeles, CA 90017
Ph: (213)385-6461
Free: 800-421-9585
Fax: (213)385-8405
URL: http://www.lasafety.org
Format(s): Videocassette. **Descr:** This film demonstrates grounding techniques for electrical workers. **Prod. Date:** 198?. **Length:** 15.

6300 ■ Contraphon
Film Library/Greater Los Angeles Safety Council
600 Wilshire Blvd., No. 1263
Los Angeles, CA 90017
Ph: (213)385-6461
Free: 800-421-9585
Fax: (213)385-8405
URL: http://www.lasafety.org
Format(s): Videocassette. **Descr:** This is a survival guide for dealing with and protecting oneself excessive noise. **Prod. Date:** 198?. **Length:** 15.

6301 ■ Craneman
Film Library/Greater Los Angeles Safety Council
600 Wilshire Blvd., No. 1263
Los Angeles, CA 90017
Ph: (213)385-6461
Free: 800-421-9585
Fax: (213)385-8405
URL: http://www.lasafety.org
Format(s): Videocassette. **Descr:** The basic functions and safe operation of the over head travelling crane are demonstrated in this tape. **Prod. Date:** 198?. **Length:** 20.

6302 ■ Cutting, Bending and Teamwork
Film Library/Greater Los Angeles Safety Council
600 Wilshire Blvd., No. 1263
Los Angeles, CA 90017
Ph: (213)385-6461
Free: 800-421-9585
Fax: (213)385-8405
URL: http://www.lasafety.org
Format(s): Videocassette. **Descr:** The procedures for safely operating power squaring shears and power press brakes are demonstrated. **Prod. Date:** 198?. **Length:** 18.

6303 ■ Danger! Gas Under Pressure
ERI Safety Videos
374 Park Rd
Lexington, SC 29072
Ph: (803)356-4880
Free: 800-311-1143
Fax: (803)356-1946
URL: http://www.eri-safety.com
Format(s): Videocassette. **Descr:** Designed to teach the dangers of high and low pressure gases. **Prod. Date:** 1983. **Length:** 11.

6304 ■ Danger Zone—Your Back
Film Library/Greater Los Angeles Safety Council
600 Wilshire Blvd., No. 1263
Los Angeles, CA 90017
Ph: (213)385-6461
Free: 800-421-9585
Fax: (213)385-8405
URL: http://www.lasafety.org
Format(s): Videocassette. **Descr:** Concepts for safe lifting and carrying are demonstrated in this film. **Prod. Date:** 198?. **Length:** 19.

6305 ■ Danger Zone—Your Hands
Film Library/Greater Los Angeles Safety Council
600 Wilshire Blvd., No. 1263
Los Angeles, CA 90017
Ph: (213)385-6461
Free: 800-421-9585
Fax: (213)385-8405
URL: http://www.lasafety.org

Format(s): Videocassette. **Descr:** Encourages employees to protect their hands while on the job. **Prod. Date:** 198?. **Length:** 17.

6306 ■ Danger Zone—Your Head
Film Library/Greater Los Angeles Safety Council
600 Wilshire Blvd., No. 1263
Los Angeles, CA 90017
Ph: (213)385-6461
Free: 800-421-9585
Fax: (213)385-8405
URL: http://www.lasafety.org
Format(s): Videocassette. **Descr:** Emphasizes the importance of wearing the proper head protection on the job. **Prod. Date:** 198?. **Length:** 16.

6307 ■ The Dangerous Stranger (3rd Edition)
AIMS Multimedia
20765 Superior St
Chatsworth, CA 91311-4409
Ph: (818)773-4300
Free: 800-367-2467
Fax: (818)341-6700
E-mail: info@aims.multimedia.com
URL: http://www.aimsmultimedia.com
Format(s): Videocassette. **Descr:** Vignettes about child molesters and how they charm and win children are enacted in this cautionary film for kids. **Prod. Date:** 1983. **Length:** 10.

6308 ■ D.A.R.E. Safety Tips Volume 1
Navarre Corp.
7400 49th Ave. N
New Hope, MN 55428
Ph: (763)535-8333
Free: 800-728-4000
Fax: (763)533-2156
E-mail: info@navarre.com
URL: http://www.navarre.com
Format(s): Videocassette. **Descr:** Deals with safety issues in an entertaining yet effective manner such as following directions, why you shouldn't ride with strangers, what to do in an emergency, effects of tobacco and drugs, and more. **Prod. Date:** 2000. **Length:** 22. **Price:** $12.98.

6309 ■ Deadly Weapons
International Historic Films, Inc.
PO Box 5796
Chicago, IL 60680
Ph: (773)927-2900
Fax: (773)927-9211
E-mail: info@ihffilm.com
URL: http://www.IHFfilm.com
Format(s): Videocassette. **Descr:** A look at the capabilities of modern firearms--what they will and will not do. **Prod. Date:** 1985. **Length:** 106. **Price:** $49.95.

6310 ■ John Deere Safety Programs
Cornell University
Audio Visual Resource Center
Business & Technology Park
15 Thornwood Dr
Ithaca, NY 14850
Ph: (607)266-7866
Fax: (607)266-7876
E-mail: dist_cent@cce.cornell.edu
URL: http://www.cornell.edu
Format(s): Videocassette. **Descr:** Safety tips for people who work with John Deere equipment are demonstrated in this series. **Prod. Date:** 1987. **Length:** 72. **Price:** $18.00.

6311 ■ Defective Hand Tools
Film Library/Greater Los Angeles Safety Council
600 Wilshire Blvd., No. 1263
Los Angeles, CA 90017
Ph: (213)385-6461
Free: 800-421-9585
Fax: (213)385-8405
URL: http://www.lasafety.org
Format(s): Videocassette. **Descr:** The hazards to

look for when using hand tools in construction are discussed. **Prod. Date:** 198?. **Length:** 5.

6312 ■ Defend Yourself with Cynthia Rothrock
SyberVision Systems, Inc.
1 Sansome St., Ste. 810
San Francisco, CA 94104
Free: 800-648-5095
E-mail: customerservice1@sybervision.com
URL: http://www.sybervision.com
Format(s): Videocassette. **Descr:** Using the unique Sybervision body-learning techniques, Rothrock trains female viewers how to defend themselves against attackers. **Prod. Date:** 1986. **Length:** 60. **Price:** $39.95.

6313 ■ Destinos: Introduction to Spanish: Part I
PBS Home Video
Catalog Fulfillment Center
PO Box 751089
Charlotte, NC 28275-1089
Ph: 800-531-4727
Free: 800-645-4PBS
E-mail: info@pbs.org
URL: http://www.pbs.org
Format(s): Videocassette. **Descr:** Uses a story line about a young female lawyer from L.A. and cultural information from Latino countries to help students learn conversational Spanish. Thirteen hours on seven videocassettes. **Prod. Date:** 1998. **Length:** 110. **Price:** $199.95.

6314 ■ Developing Safety Sense in the Office
ERI Safety Videos
374 Park Rd
Lexington, SC 29072
Ph: (803)356-4880
Free: 800-311-1143
Fax: (803)356-1946
URL: http://www.eri-safety.com
Format(s): Videocassette. **Descr:** Learn how to avoid accidents and other dangerous happenings in the workplace. **Prod. Date:** 1987. **Length:** 15. **Price:** $425.00.

6315 ■ Disabilities in the Workplace: Working Out
Aquarius Productions
Olde Medfield Sq
18 N Main St
Sherborn, MA 01770
Ph: (508)650-1616
Free: 888-440-2963
Fax: (508)650-1665
E-mail: tm@aquariusproductions.com
URL: http://www.aquariusproductions.com
Format(s): Videocassette. **Descr:** Follows four disabled individuals as they attempt to find and maintain employment, as well as gain acceptance in the workplace. Designed for both the disabled and able-bodied. **Prod. Date:** 1993. **Length:** 24. **Price:** $90.00.

6316 ■ The Disorderly Worker
Film Library/Greater Los Angeles Safety Council
600 Wilshire Blvd., No. 1263
Los Angeles, CA 90017
Ph: (213)385-6461
Free: 800-421-9585
Fax: (213)385-8405
URL: http://www.lasafety.org
Format(s): Videocassette. **Descr:** A disorderly employee's sloppiness endangers the lives of his coworkers. **Prod. Date:** 198?. **Length:** 10.

6317 ■ Doin' It Right
Film Library/Greater Los Angeles Safety Council
600 Wilshire Blvd., No. 1263
Los Angeles, CA 90017
Ph: (213)385-6461
Free: 800-421-9585
Fax: (213)385-8405
URL: http://www.lasafety.org
Format(s): Videocassette. **Descr:** The procedures

for reducing worker's exposure to asbestos are demonstrated in this film. **Prod. Date:** 198?. **Length:** 20.

6318 ■ Donald's Fire Drill
Phoenix Learning Group
2349 Chaffee Dr
St. Louis, MO 63146
Ph: (314)569-0211
Free: 800-221-1274
Fax: (314)569-2834
URL: http://www.phoenixlearninggroup.com
Format(s): Videocassette. **Descr:** Live action Donald Duck in costume participates in a quiz show with two nine-year-olds to answer questions about fire safety. Stresses the importance of exit drills in the home (E.D.I.T.H.). **Prod. Date:** 1991. **Length:** 16. **Price:** $280.00.

6319 ■ Don't Drop the Ball
Film Library/Greater Los Angeles Safety Council
600 Wilshire Blvd., No. 1263
Los Angeles, CA 90017
Ph: (213)385-6461
Free: 800-421-9585
Fax: (213)385-8405
URL: http://www.lasafety.org
Format(s): Videocassette. **Descr:** The basic causes of forklift accidents are examined in detail. **Prod. Date:** 198?. **Length:** 17.

6320 ■ Don't Push Your Luck
Film Library/Greater Los Angeles Safety Council
600 Wilshire Blvd., No. 1263
Los Angeles, CA 90017
Ph: (213)385-6461
Free: 800-421-9585
Fax: (213)385-8405
URL: http://www.lasafety.org
Format(s): Videocassette. **Descr:** This is the true story of a man who lost his eyesight as the result of an accident. **Prod. Date:** 198?. **Length:** 15.

6321 ■ Don't Take Chances
Film Library/Greater Los Angeles Safety Council
600 Wilshire Blvd., No. 1263
Los Angeles, CA 90017
Ph: (213)385-6461
Free: 800-421-9585
Fax: (213)385-8405
URL: http://www.lasafety.org
Format(s): Videocassette. **Descr:** This film dramatizes a series of accidents caused by worker thoughtlessness and details the accident's effect on each victim. **Prod. Date:** 198?. **Length:** 15.

6322 ■ Don't Touch That Gun!
Crawford Productions, Inc.
Box 1192
New Smyrna Beach, FL 32170-1192
Ph: (904)427-6626
Free: 800-745-0363
Fax: (904)427-0977
E-mail: rusty@volusia.com
URL: http://www.volusia.com/crawford
Format(s): Videocassette. **Descr:** Children learn the dangers of playing with guns. Hosted by police officers, with a clear message of gun safety. **Prod. Date:** 1990. **Length:** 15. **Price:** $24.95.

6323 ■ Don't Touch That Gun, Part II
Crawford Productions, Inc.
Box 1192
New Smyrna Beach, FL 32170-1192
Ph: (904)427-6626
Free: 800-745-0363
Fax: (904)427-0977
E-mail: rusty@volusia.com
URL: http://www.volusia.com/crawford
Format(s): Videocassette. **Descr:** Contains four nonviolent stories that teach children not to touch guns and demonstrates what can happen if a gun is

handled. Used by sheriff's departments and schools nationwide. **Length:** 20. **Price:** $39.95.

6324 ■ *Dust in Dockyards*
Film Library/Greater Los Angeles Safety Council
600 Wilshire Blvd., No. 1263
Los Angeles, CA 90017
Ph: (213)385-6461
Free: 800-421-9585
Fax: (213)385-8405
URL: http://www.lasafety.org
Format(s): Videocassette. **Descr:** Offers some guidelines that employees should follow when working in a dust-filled environment. **Prod. Date:** 198?. **Length:** 22.

6325 ■ *Dyslexia*
Aquarius Productions
Olde Medfield Sq
18 N Main St
Sherborn, MA 01770
Ph: (508)650-1616
Free: 888-440-2963
Fax: (508)650-1665
E-mail: tm@aquariusproductions.com
URL: http://www.aquariusproductions.com
Format(s): Videocassette. **Descr:** Profiles the wide range of conditions that affect oral or written language and takes a look at the visual gifts that often accompany dyslexia. **Prod. Date:** 1997. **Length:** 28. **Price:** $149.

6326 ■ *Dyslexia: A Different Kind of Learning*
Aquarius Productions
Olde Medfield Sq
18 N Main St
Sherborn, MA 01770
Ph: (508)650-1616
Free: 888-440-2963
Fax: (508)650-1665
E-mail: tm@aquariusproductions.com
URL: http://www.aquariusproductions.com
Format(s): Videocassette. **Descr:** Explains that dyslexia is not a disease but a unique way that the mind operates which is often actually gifted and productive. Presents tips for teachers and students dealing with the condition. **Prod. Date:** 2000. **Length:** 24. **Price:** $99.00.

6327 ■ *Early Finish*
Film Library/Greater Los Angeles Safety Council
600 Wilshire Blvd., No. 1263
Los Angeles, CA 90017
Ph: (213)385-6461
Free: 800-421-9585
Fax: (213)385-8405
URL: http://www.lasafety.org
Format(s): Videocassette. **Descr:** This film details a transport accident on a construction site. **Prod. Date:** 1984. **Length:** 27.

6328 ■ *Earthquake Do's and Don't's*
Film Library/Greater Los Angeles Safety Council
600 Wilshire Blvd., No. 1263
Los Angeles, CA 90017
Ph: (213)385-6461
Free: 800-421-9585
Fax: (213)385-8405
URL: http://www.lasafety.org
Format(s): Videocassette. **Descr:** Ritter shows how pre-emergency planning for an earthquake can reduce panic and help save lives. **Prod. Date:** 198?. **Length:** 11.

6329 ■ *Earthquake Preparedness*
Gun Video
4585 Murphy Canyon Rd
San Diego, CA 92123
Ph: (858)569-4000
Free: 800-942-8273
Fax: (858)569-0505
E-mail: info2@gunvideo.com
URL: http://www.gunvideo.com
Format(s): Videocassette. **Descr:** A look at what to do before, during, and after an earthquake. Includes

tips on inexpensive measures to minimize injury and losses. **Length:** 60. **Price:** $29.95.

6330 ■ *Easy Does It*
Film Library/Greater Los Angeles Safety Council
600 Wilshire Blvd., No. 1263
Los Angeles, CA 90017
Ph: (213)385-6461
Free: 800-421-9585
Fax: (213)385-8405
URL: http://www.lasafety.org
Format(s): Videocassette. **Descr:** This is a demonstration of how improper lifting techniques can affect the spine. **Prod. Date:** 198?. **Length:** 10.

6331 ■ *Easy Way Out*
Film Library/Greater Los Angeles Safety Council
600 Wilshire Blvd., No. 1263
Los Angeles, CA 90017
Ph: (213)385-6461
Free: 800-421-9585
Fax: (213)385-8405
URL: http://www.lasafety.org
Format(s): Videocassette. **Descr:** The procedures for fighting a flammable liquids fire with foam in a vertical tank is demonstrated. **Prod. Date:** 198?. **Length:** 20.

6332 ■ *Electrical Safety in Construction Industries*
Film Library/Greater Los Angeles Safety Council
600 Wilshire Blvd., No. 1263
Los Angeles, CA 90017
Ph: (213)385-6461
Free: 800-421-9585
Fax: (213)385-8405
URL: http://www.lasafety.org
Format(s): Videocassette. **Descr:** This film presents a clear outline for electrical accident prevention on construction sites. **Prod. Date:** 198?. **Length:** 20.

6333 ■ *Electrical Safety in the Home*
RMI Media
1365 N. Winchester
Olathe, KS 66061
Ph: (913)768-1696
Fax: (913)768-0184
E-mail: actmedia@act.org
URL: http://www.rmimedia.com
Format(s): Videocassette. **Descr:** This program explains how to avoid common electrical problems in the home and how to safely use plugs and extension cords. **Prod. Date:** 1984. **Length:** 16.

6334 ■ *Electrical Safety in the Intensive Care Unit*
Format(s): Videocassette. **Descr:** Safety instruction around hospital electrical equipment is emphasized in this video. **Prod. Date:** 1987. **Length:** 12. **Price:** $250.00.

6335 ■ *Electrical Safety Related Work Practices*
Gulf Publishing Co.
PO Box 2608
Houston, TX 77252-2608
Ph: (713)520-4448
Free: 800-231-6275
Fax: (713)204-4433
E-mail: csv@gulfpub.com
URL: http://www.gulfpub.com
Format(s): Videocassette. **Descr:** Six-part training program that offers educational material on electrical safety. Centers on the new OSHA requirements for work performed on or near exposed energized and de-energized parts of electrical equipment, the use of electrical protective equipment, and the safe use of electrical equipment. **Prod. Date:** 1992. **Length:** ?. **Price:** $1495.00.

6336 ■ *Electrical Safety Series*
Gulf Publishing Co.
PO Box 2608
Houston, TX 77252-2608
Ph: (713)520-4448
Free: 800-231-6275

Fax: (713)204-4433
E-mail: csv@gulfpub.com
URL: http://www.gulfpub.com
Format(s): Videocassette. **Descr:** This series explains various safe work practices that are essential for safe industrial operations. **Prod. Date:** 1984. **Length:** 10. **Price:** $295.00.

6337 ■ *Electrical Safety in the Shop*
RMI Media
1365 N. Winchester
Olathe, KS 66061
Ph: (913)768-1696
Fax: (913)768-0184
E-mail: actmedia@act.org
URL: http://www.rmimedia.com
Format(s): Videocassette. **Descr:** This program describes the hazards at a school or factory shop and how problems can be prevented by understanding the behavior of electricity. **Prod. Date:** 1984. **Length:** 18.

6338 ■ *Elementary Body Mechanics*
Film Library/Greater Los Angeles Safety Council
600 Wilshire Blvd., No. 1263
Los Angeles, CA 90017
Ph: (213)385-6461
Free: 800-421-9585
Fax: (213)385-8405
URL: http://www.lasafety.org
Format(s): Videocassette. **Descr:** The proper means of lifting and correct posture for carrying heavy objects are demonstrated. **Prod. Date:** 198?. **Length:** 13.

6339 ■ *Emergency Evacuation Training: Preparing for the Future*
LearnCom HR Consulting and Training
38 Discovery, Ste. 250
Irvine, CA 92618
Ph: (515)440-0890
Free: 800-698-8263
Fax: (515)221-3149
E-mail: nhartline@learncom.com
URL: http://www.learncomhr.com
Format(s): Videocassette. **Descr:** Trainees are provided with step-by-step training in emergency evacuation procedures. An emphasis is placed on developing and coordinating an emergency plan. Includes a leader's guide. **Length:** 18. **Price:** $295.

6340 ■ *Emergent Reader—Day One: A Demonstration of Book Buddies in Action*
Guilford Publications, Inc.
72 Spring St
New York, NY 10012
Ph: (212)431-9800
Free: 800-365-7006
Fax: (212)966-6708
E-mail: info@guilford.com
URL: http://www.guilford.com
Format(s): Videocassette. **Descr:** Provides training and guidelines for reading professionals and tutors involved in early reading intervention. **Prod. Date:** 1998. **Length:** 51. **Price:** $29.95.

6341 ■ *Emergent Reader—Mid-Year: A Demonstration of Book Buddies in Action*
Guilford Publications, Inc.
72 Spring St
New York, NY 10012
Ph: (212)431-9800
Free: 800-365-7006
Fax: (212)966-6708
E-mail: info@guilford.com
URL: http://www.guilford.com
Format(s): Videocassette. **Descr:** Provides training and guidelines for reading professionals and tutors involved in early reading intervention. **Prod. Date:** 1998. **Length:** 44. **Price:** $29.95.

6342 ■ *Emerging Issues in Special Education*
Aquarius Productions
Olde Medfield Sq
18 N Main St
Sherborn, MA 01770

Ph: (508)650-1616
Free: 888-440-2963
Fax: (508)650-1665
E-mail: tm@aquariusproductions.com
URL: http://www.aquariusproductions.com
Format(s): Videocassette. **Descr:** Professionals, teachers parents, and others talk about key issues in meeting the needs of impaired children. Topics include standardized testing procedures, disproportionate representation, IEPs and more. **Prod. Date:** 2001. **Length:** 25. **Price:** $99.00.

6343 ■ Enforcing Safety Rules and Motivating Employees
ERI Safety Videos
374 Park Rd
Lexington, SC 29072
Ph: (803)356-4880
Free: 800-311-1143
Fax: (803)356-1946
URL: http://www.eri-safety.com
Format(s): Videocassette. **Descr:** This program was designed to look at a positive approach to causing employees to participate in a safety program. **Prod. Date:** 1983. **Length:** 15.

6344 ■ Engine Lathe
Film Library/Greater Los Angeles Safety Council
600 Wilshire Blvd., No. 1263
Los Angeles, CA 90017
Ph: (213)385-6461
Free: 800-421-9585
Fax: (213)385-8405
URL: http://www.lasafety.org
Format(s): Videocassette. **Descr:** This film demonstrates how to safely operate an engine lathe. **Prod. Date:** 198?. **Length:** 23.

6345 ■ Ergonomics: Low-Cost, Common-Sense Training Solutions
LearnCom HR Consulting and Training
38 Discovery, Ste. 250
Irvine, CA 92618
Ph: (515)440-0890
Free: 800-698-8263
Fax: (515)221-3149
E-mail: nhartline@learncom.com
URL: http://www.learncomhr.com
Format(s): Videocassette. **Descr:** A 3-tape guide to reducing cumulative trauma disorders (also known as repetitive motion illnesses), reduce stress, and increase productivity--all without costly engineering controls or job redesigns. A set of three tapes, complete with Leader's Guides and Participant Workbooks. **Prod. Date:** 1991. **Length:** 12.

6346 ■ Ergonomics at Work
Film Library/Greater Los Angeles Safety Council
600 Wilshire Blvd., No. 1263
Los Angeles, CA 90017
Ph: (213)385-6461
Free: 800-421-9585
Fax: (213)385-8405
URL: http://www.lasafety.org
Format(s): Videocassette. **Descr:** This tape looks at how ergonomics can aid in creating safer working conditions. **Prod. Date:** 198?. **Length:** 14.

6347 ■ Evaluating and Controlling Exposures to Chemicals
ERI Safety Videos
374 Park Rd
Lexington, SC 29072
Ph: (803)356-4880
Free: 800-311-1143
Fax: (803)356-1946
URL: http://www.eri-safety.com
Format(s): Videocassette. **Descr:** Learn how to tell whether each individual exposure to a chemical is serious or not. **Prod. Date:** 1987. **Length:** 11. **Price:** $325.00.

6348 ■ Everybody's Job
Film Library/Greater Los Angeles Safety Council
600 Wilshire Blvd., No. 1263
Los Angeles, CA 90017

Ph: (213)385-6461
Free: 800-421-9585
Fax: (213)385-8405
URL: http://www.lasafety.org
Format(s): Videocassette. **Descr:** This film shows how accidents that occur in the daily activities of a health care facility can be prevented. **Prod. Date:** 198?. **Length:** 20.

6349 ■ Everything to Lose
Film Library/Greater Los Angeles Safety Council
600 Wilshire Blvd., No. 1263
Los Angeles, CA 90017
Ph: (213)385-6461
Free: 800-421-9585
Fax: (213)385-8405
URL: http://www.lasafety.org
Format(s): Videocassette. **Descr:** This film shows what happens to a group of workers when they ignore shop safety rules. **Prod. Date:** 198?. **Length:** 20.

6350 ■ Excavations
Film Library/Greater Los Angeles Safety Council
600 Wilshire Blvd., No. 1263
Los Angeles, CA 90017
Ph: (213)385-6461
Free: 800-421-9585
Fax: (213)385-8405
URL: http://www.lasafety.org
Format(s): Videocassette. **Descr:** The general safety rules and the dangers inherent to excavations are presented herein. **Prod. Date:** 198?. **Length:** 9.

6351 ■ Eyes, Hands and Feet
Film Library/Greater Los Angeles Safety Council
600 Wilshire Blvd., No. 1263
Los Angeles, CA 90017
Ph: (213)385-6461
Free: 800-421-9585
Fax: (213)385-8405
URL: http://www.lasafety.org
Format(s): Videocassette. **Descr:** This silent film illustrates the importance of eye protection, awareness of hand traps and of wearing safety shoes. **Prod. Date:** 198?. **Length:** 10.

6352 ■ Faceplate Turning
Film Library/Greater Los Angeles Safety Council
600 Wilshire Blvd., No. 1263
Los Angeles, CA 90017
Ph: (213)385-6461
Free: 800-421-9585
Fax: (213)385-8405
URL: http://www.lasafety.org
Format(s): Videocassette. **Descr:** The safest procedures to follow when using a faceplate turning machine are demonstrated in this program **Prod. Date:** 198?. **Length:** 19.

6353 ■ Facing on the Lathe
Film Library/Greater Los Angeles Safety Council
600 Wilshire Blvd., No. 1263
Los Angeles, CA 90017
Ph: (213)385-6461
Free: 800-421-9585
Fax: (213)385-8405
URL: http://www.lasafety.org
Format(s): Videocassette. **Descr:** The safest procedures to follow when facing on a lathe are demonstrated in this program. **Prod. Date:** 198?. **Length:** 11. **Price:** $125.00.

6354 ■ Facts on Backs
Film Library/Greater Los Angeles Safety Council
600 Wilshire Blvd., No. 1263
Los Angeles, CA 90017
Ph: (213)385-6461
Free: 800-421-9585
Fax: (213)385-8405
URL: http://www.lasafety.org
Format(s): Videocassette. **Descr:** This tape shows Dr. Leonard Ring demonstrating situations where

workers can't bend their knees while lifting. **Prod. Date:** 198?. **Length:** 18.

6355 ■ Falls Can Cripple
Film Library/Greater Los Angeles Safety Council
600 Wilshire Blvd., No. 1263
Los Angeles, CA 90017
Ph: (213)385-6461
Free: 800-421-9585
Fax: (213)385-8405
URL: http://www.lasafety.org
Format(s): Videocassette. **Descr:** This is an illustrated lecture on the types of falls which result hospitalization and how they can be prevented. **Prod. Date:** 198?. **Length:** 14.

6356 ■ Fire Aboard Pleasure Boats
National Audiovisual Center
5285 Port Royal Rd
Springfield, VA 22161
Ph: (703)605-4603
Free: 800-553-6847
Fax: (703)321-8547
E-mail: orders@ntis.fedworld.gov
URL: http://www.ntis.gov/products/nac/index.asp
Format(s): Videocassette. **Descr:** The program stresses that ignoring danger signals on a boating trip can lead to disaster, even though safety precautions have previously been taken. **Prod. Date:** 1980. **Length:** 15.

6357 ■ Fire: Countdown to Disaster
National Fire Protection Association
1 Batterymarch Park
Quincy, MA 02169-7471
Ph: (617)770-3000
Free: 800-344-3555
Fax: (617)770-0700
E-mail: info@nfpa.org
URL: http://www.nfpa.org
Format(s): Videocassette. **Descr:** The dangers of flame and smoke spread in fires are explained in this program. **Prod. Date:** 1984. **Length:** 15.

6358 ■ Fire Emergency
American Media, Inc.
4621 121st St
Urbandale, IA 50323-2311
Ph: (515)224-0919
Free: 888-776-8268
Fax: (515)327-2555
E-mail: custsvc@ammedia.com
URL: http://www.ammedia.com
Format(s): Videocassette. **Descr:** Shows hospital workers the proper methods in which to handle a fire emergency, including the evacuation of patients. **Prod. Date:** 1990. **Length:** 16. **Price:** $395.00.

6359 ■ Fire Extinguishers and Smoke Detectors
Handel Film Corp.
8787 Shoreham Dr., Ste. 609
West Hollywood, CA 90069
Ph: (310)652-3887
Free: 800-395-8990
Fax: (310)657-2746
Format(s): Videocassette. **Descr:** This program discusses different types of smoke detectors and different classes of fire extinguishers. **Prod. Date:** 1981. **Length:** 18.

6360 ■ Fire Extinguishers: The ABC's
Emergency Film Group
Detrick Lawrence Corp
PO Box 1928
Edgartown, MA 02539
Ph: (508)627-8844
Free: 800-842-0999
Fax: (508)627-8863
E-mail: info@efilmgroup.com
URL: http://www.efilmgroup.com
Format(s): Videocassette. **Descr:** Aimed at anyone who needs to learn how to operate a fire extinguisher. Covers the different fire classifications as well as the best locations for extinguisher placement and many

other key points. **Prod. Date:** 19??. **Length:** 13. **Price:** $315.00.

6361 ■ *Fire at the MGM Grand*
National Fire Protection Association
1 Batterymarch Park
Quincy, MA 02169-7471
Ph: (617)770-3000
Free: 800-344-3555
Fax: (617)770-0700
E-mail: info@nfpa.org
URL: http://www.nfpa.org
Format(s): Videocassette. **Descr:** This program provides information on fire safety and escape for hotel patrons. **Prod. Date:** 1982. **Length:** 20.

6362 ■ *Fire Prevention*
Film Library/Greater Los Angeles Safety Council
600 Wilshire Blvd., No. 1263
Los Angeles, CA 90017
Ph: (213)385-6461
Free: 800-421-9585
Fax: (213)385-8405
URL: http://www.lasafety.org
Format(s): Videocassette. **Descr:** This film looks at how things burn and what actions can be taken to prevent a fire. **Prod. Date:** 198?. **Length:** 13.

6363 ■ *Fire Prevention at Home*
Williams Learning Network
15400 Calhoun Dr
Rockville, MD 20855-2762
Ph: (301)315-6700
Free: 800-848-1717
Fax: (301)315-6880
E-mail: mait@willearn.com
URL: http://www.willearn.com
Format(s): Videocassette. **Descr:** Explains that fire prevention begins in the home and carries over to the workplace. Concentrates on educating employees about fire prevention in the home discussing the areas that fires are most likely to start, including the kitchen, the garage, and the workshop with emphasis on being alert to hazards, reading labels on chemicals and solvents, proper storage of flammable materials, and properly responding to fires in the home. Includes Leader's Guide and 25 Program Guides. **Length:** 14.

6364 ■ *Fire Protection for Business & Industry*
Media Resources, Inc.
9012-B NW Holly Rd
Bremerton, WA 98321
Ph: (360)693-3344
Free: 800-666-0106
Fax: (360)693-1760
Format(s): Videocassette. **Descr:** A list of things that businesses can do to prevent or minimize the danger of a fire are on these tapes. **Prod. Date:** 1988. **Length:** 30. **Price:** $600.00.

6365 ■ *Fire Protection Systems*
Williams Learning Network
15400 Calhoun Dr
Rockville, MD 20855-2762
Ph: (301)315-6700
Free: 800-848-1717
Fax: (301)315-6880
E-mail: mait@willearn.com
URL: http://www.willearn.com
Format(s): Videocassette. **Descr:** Discusses the various types of fire protection systems used in industry with emphasis on how they work as well as what precautions should be taken when re-entering an area after one of these systems has gone off. Includes Leader's Guide and 25 Program Guides. **Length:** 12.

6366 ■ *Fire Safety: Fire Extinguishers*
Film Library/Greater Los Angeles Safety Council
600 Wilshire Blvd., No. 1263
Los Angeles, CA 90017
Ph: (213)385-6461
Free: 800-421-9585
Fax: (213)385-8405
URL: http://www.lasafety.org

Format(s): Videocassette. **Descr:** A demonstration of how to use a fire extinguisher in the home. **Prod. Date:** 1981. **Length:** 15. **Price:** $195.00.

6367 ■ *Fire Safety Tips for Kids*
Carousel Film & Video
250 5th Ave., Ste. 204
New York, NY 10001
Free: 800-683-1660
Fax: (212)683-1662
E-mail: carousel@pipeline.com
URL: http://www.carouselfilm.com
Format(s): Videocassette. **Descr:** Twelve-year-old Kira reports on what to do if trapped in a fire, a safety checklist to help avoid a fire, and what extra precautions should be taken during the holidays. **Prod. Length:** 6. **Price:** $75.00.

6368 ■ *Firearm Safety*
ERI Safety Videos
374 Park Rd
Lexington, SC 29072
Ph: (803)356-4880
Free: 800-311-1143
Fax: (803)356-1946
URL: http://www.eri-safety.com
Format(s): Videocassette. **Descr:** Everything you need to know about safely using guns is demonstrated. **Prod. Date:** 1987. **Length:** 30. **Price:** $425.00.

6369 ■ *First Step Invitation to a Fall*
Film Library/Greater Los Angeles Safety Council
600 Wilshire Blvd., No. 1263
Los Angeles, CA 90017
Ph: (213)385-6461
Free: 800-421-9585
Fax: (213)385-8405
URL: http://www.lasafety.org
Format(s): Videocassette. **Descr:** An explanation of the four principles people should use for avoiding falls on stairs. **Prod. Date:** 198?. **Length:** 15.

6370 ■ *Five Problems in Communication*
Film Library/Greater Los Angeles Safety Council
600 Wilshire Blvd., No. 1263
Los Angeles, CA 90017
Ph: (213)385-6461
Free: 800-421-9585
Fax: (213)385-8405
URL: http://www.lasafety.org
Format(s): Videocassette. **Descr:** This film shows how effective communication between supervisors and employees can help them avoid accidents. **Prod. Date:** 198?. **Length:** 5.

6371 ■ *Flag Warning Lines*
Film Library/Greater Los Angeles Safety Council
600 Wilshire Blvd., No. 1263
Los Angeles, CA 90017
Ph: (213)385-6461
Free: 800-421-9585
Fax: (213)385-8405
URL: http://www.lasafety.org
Format(s): Videocassette. **Descr:** This film is designed to make workers aware of the potential hazards of working near the edge of a roof. **Prod. Date:** 198?. **Length:** 7.

6372 ■ *Flashpoint*
Film Library/Greater Los Angeles Safety Council
600 Wilshire Blvd., No. 1263
Los Angeles, CA 90017
Ph: (213)385-6461
Free: 800-421-9585
Fax: (213)385-8405
URL: http://www.lasafety.org
Format(s): Videocassette. **Descr:** This is a reenactment of the events that lead to a chemical explosion and fire. **Prod. Date:** 198?. **Length:** 21.

6373 ■ *For Good Sound Reasons*
Film Library/Greater Los Angeles Safety Council
600 Wilshire Blvd., No. 1263
Los Angeles, CA 90017
Ph: (213)385-6461

Free: 800-421-9585
Fax: (213)385-8405
URL: http://www.lasafety.org
Format(s): Videocassette. **Descr:** This film reminds industrial workers of the hazards of continuous exposure to high noise levels. **Prod. Date:** 198?. **Length:** 17.

6374 ■ *For Jamie*
Film Library/Greater Los Angeles Safety Council
600 Wilshire Blvd., No. 1263
Los Angeles, CA 90017
Ph: (213)385-6461
Free: 800-421-9585
Fax: (213)385-8405
URL: http://www.lasafety.org
Format(s): Videocassette. **Descr:** this is a description of how to properly use the car safety seat for children. **Prod. Date:** 198?. **Length:** 24.

6375 ■ *Forgetter*
Film Library/Greater Los Angeles Safety Council
600 Wilshire Blvd., No. 1263
Los Angeles, CA 90017
Ph: (213)385-6461
Free: 800-421-9585
Fax: (213)385-8405
URL: http://www.lasafety.org
Format(s): Videocassette. **Descr:** This film shows how an employee endangers his fellow workers by forgetting to follow safety rules and procedures. **Prod. Date:** 198?. **Length:** 10.

6376 ■ *Forklift Operator Training*
Film Library/Greater Los Angeles Safety Council
600 Wilshire Blvd., No. 1263
Los Angeles, CA 90017
Ph: (213)385-6461
Free: 800-421-9585
Fax: (213)385-8405
URL: http://www.lasafety.org
Format(s): Videocassette. **Descr:** This course will train forklift operators in OSHA requirements. **Prod. Date:** 198?. **Length:** 14.

6377 ■ *Forklift Safety in 8 Minutes*
ERI Safety Videos
374 Park Rd
Lexington, SC 29072
Ph: (803)356-4880
Free: 800-311-1143
Fax: (803)356-1946
URL: http://www.eri-safety.com
Format(s): Videocassette. **Descr:** A shorter version of "Forklift Safety in Hazardous Areas." **Prod. Date:** 1987. **Length:** 8. **Price:** $325.00.

6378 ■ *Forklift Safety Checks*
Williams Learning Network
15400 Calhoun Dr
Rockville, MD 20855-2762
Ph: (301)315-6700
Free: 800-848-1717
Fax: (301)315-6880
E-mail: mait@willearn.com
URL: http://www.willearn.com
Format(s): Videocassette. **Descr:** Outlines the importance of forklift safety checks. Furnishes information on pre-start inspections and preventive maintenance including the battery, hydraulic systems, fluids, fuel, forks and backlift, wheels and tires, brakes and controls, overhead guard, seat belts, horns, and lights. Includes Leader's Guide and 25 Program Guides. **Length:** 12.

6379 ■ *Forklift Safety in Hazardous Areas*
ERI Safety Videos
374 Park Rd
Lexington, SC 29072
Ph: (803)356-4880
Free: 800-311-1143
Fax: (803)356-1946
URL: http://www.eri-safety.com
Format(s): Videocassette. **Descr:** Safety procedures

for forklift drivers are reviewed. **Prod. Date:** 1987. **Length:** 15. **Price:** $425.00.

6380 ■ French In Action: Part I
PBS Home Video
Catalog Fulfillment Center
PO Box 751089
Charlotte, NC 28275-1089
Ph: 800-531-4727
Free: 800-645-4PBS
E-mail: info@pbs.org
URL: http://www.pbs.org
Format(s): Videocassette. **Descr:** Uses a romantic story involving an American student and a young French woman as well as short clips from TV, movies and advertising to teach students conversational French. Thirteen hours on seven videocassettes. **Prod. Date:** 1998. **Length:** 110. **Price:** $199.95.

6381 ■ Fun 'n Fathoms
Film Library/Greater Los Angeles Safety Council
600 Wilshire Blvd., No. 1263
Los Angeles, CA 90017
Ph: (213)385-6461
Free: 800-421-9585
Fax: (213)385-8405
URL: http://www.lasafety.org
Format(s): Videocassette. **Descr:** A demonstration of basic safety procedures for scuba divers. **Prod. Date:** 198?. **Length:** 27.

6382 ■ Funnybones
GPN Educational Media
Box 80669
Lincoln, NE 68501-0669
Ph: (402)472-2007
Free: 800-228-4630
Fax: 800-306-2330
URL: http://gpn.unl.edu
Format(s): Videocassette. **Descr:** Funnybones the robot teaches kids about health, nutrition, safety, and drug abuse in this eight program series. Complete with teacher's guide. **Prod. Date:** 1994. **Length:** 15.

6383 ■ The Future Is in Your Hands
ERI Safety Videos
374 Park Rd
Lexington, SC 29072
Ph: (803)356-4880
Free: 800-311-1143
Fax: (803)356-1946
URL: http://www.eri-safety.com
Format(s): Videocassette. **Descr:** This program combines interest, entertainment and excitement into a compelling lesson in the fundamentals of hand and finger protection. **Prod. Date:** 1982. **Length:** 15.

6384 ■ General Electrical Safety in the Workplace
ERI Safety Videos
374 Park Rd
Lexington, SC 29072
Ph: (803)356-4880
Free: 800-311-1143
Fax: (803)356-1946
URL: http://www.eri-safety.com
Format(s): Videocassette. **Descr:** An instructional tape for the workplace regarding cautious handling of electrical equipment. **Prod. Date:** 1987. **Length:** 15. **Price:** $425.00.

6385 ■ Get a Grip! Self Management Skills: Student Workshop
Zenger Media
10200 Jefferson Blvd
Box 802
Culver City, CA 90232
Ph: (310)839-2436
Free: 800-421-4246
Fax: (310)839-2249
E-mail: service@zengermedia.com
URL: http://zengermedia.com
Format(s): Videocassette. **Descr:** Teaches students how to organize their schoolwork, manage time ef-

fectively, and systemize long-term assignments. **Prod. Date:** 2000. **Length:** 18. **Price:** $119.95.

6386 ■ Gift
Film Library/Greater Los Angeles Safety Council
600 Wilshire Blvd., No. 1263
Los Angeles, CA 90017
Ph: (213)385-6461
Free: 800-421-9585
Fax: (213)385-8405
URL: http://www.lasafety.org
Format(s): Videocassette. **Descr:** This film teaches retail employees how to recognize and eliminate potential hazards. **Prod. Date:** 198?. **Length:** 10.

6387 ■ Good Luck, Ed Duncan
Film Library/Greater Los Angeles Safety Council
600 Wilshire Blvd., No. 1263
Los Angeles, CA 90017
Ph: (213)385-6461
Free: 800-421-9585
Fax: (213)385-8405
URL: http://www.lasafety.org
Format(s): Videocassette. **Descr:** This tape shows the former members of a foreman's crew remembering how his safety rules saved them from accidents at his retirement dinner. **Prod. Date:** 198?. **Length:** 10.

6388 ■ The Great Betrayal
Film Library/Greater Los Angeles Safety Council
600 Wilshire Blvd., No. 1263
Los Angeles, CA 90017
Ph: (213)385-6461
Free: 800-421-9585
Fax: (213)385-8405
URL: http://www.lasafety.org
Format(s): Videocassette. **Descr:** In this dramatization, a lift truck operator's emotions can cause errors in judgment that lead to dangerous mistakes. **Prod. Date:** 198?. **Length:** 28.

6389 ■ The Grim Statistics
Film Library/Greater Los Angeles Safety Council
600 Wilshire Blvd., No. 1263
Los Angeles, CA 90017
Ph: (213)385-6461
Free: 800-421-9585
Fax: (213)385-8405
URL: http://www.lasafety.org
Format(s): Videocassette. **Descr:** This film shows how heavy equipment operators can increase their chances of getting injured when they violate common-sense safety practices. **Prod. Date:** 198?. **Length:** 20.

6390 ■ Growing Pains
Film Library/Greater Los Angeles Safety Council
600 Wilshire Blvd., No. 1263
Los Angeles, CA 90017
Ph: (213)385-6461
Free: 800-421-9585
Fax: (213)385-8405
URL: http://www.lasafety.org
Format(s): Videocassette. **Descr:** A cement worker learns a lesson in safe conduct from his 11-year-old son in this program. **Prod. Date:** 198?. **Length:** 33.

6391 ■ Guard Duty
Film Library/Greater Los Angeles Safety Council
600 Wilshire Blvd., No. 1263
Los Angeles, CA 90017
Ph: (213)385-6461
Free: 800-421-9585
Fax: (213)385-8405
URL: http://www.lasafety.org
Format(s): Videocassette. **Descr:** This tape features a discussion of the responsibilities that the foreman, workers, and management should keep in mind concerning equipment guards and other safety measures. **Prod. Date:** 198?. **Length:** 10.

6392 ■ Hand/Finger Safety in Manufacturing
ERI Safety Videos
374 Park Rd
Lexington, SC 29072

Ph: (803)356-4880
Free: 800-311-1143
Fax: (803)356-1946
URL: http://www.eri-safety.com
Format(s): Videocassette. **Descr:** A factory-aimed safety tape. **Prod. Date:** 1987. **Length:** 16. **Price:** $425.00.

6393 ■ Hand-Power Tool Safety
Film Library/Greater Los Angeles Safety Council
600 Wilshire Blvd., No. 1263
Los Angeles, CA 90017
Ph: (213)385-6461
Free: 800-421-9585
Fax: (213)385-8405
URL: http://www.lasafety.org
Format(s): Videocassette. **Descr:** This tape demonstrates how to safely use hammers, screwdrivers, wrenches, drills, saws and impact tools. **Prod. Date:** 198?. **Length:** 12.

6394 ■ Handguns and Home Survival
Gun Video
4585 Murphy Canyon Rd
San Diego, CA 92123
Ph: (858)569-4000
Free: 800-942-8273
Fax: (858)569-0505
E-mail: info2@gunvideo.com
URL: http://www.gunvideo.com
Format(s): Videocassette. **Descr:** Experienced instructors offer a step-by-step method for home security, from basic to advanced techniques. **Prod. Date:** 1991. **Length:** 60. **Price:** $39.95.

6395 ■ Handling Chemicals Safely
ERI Safety Videos
374 Park Rd
Lexington, SC 29072
Ph: (803)356-4880
Free: 800-311-1143
Fax: (803)356-1946
URL: http://www.eri-safety.com
Format(s): Videocassette. **Descr:** This tape is designed to teach employees to handle chemicals safely. **Prod. Date:** 1983. **Length:** 12.

6396 ■ Hands Off—Danger
Film Library/Greater Los Angeles Safety Council
600 Wilshire Blvd., No. 1263
Los Angeles, CA 90017
Ph: (213)385-6461
Free: 800-421-9585
Fax: (213)385-8405
URL: http://www.lasafety.org
Format(s): Videocassette. **Descr:** Dr. Leonard Ring demonstrates the importance of hand safety in this program. **Prod. Date:** 198?. **Length:** 17.

6397 ■ Hands at Work
Film Library/Greater Los Angeles Safety Council
600 Wilshire Blvd., No. 1263
Los Angeles, CA 90017
Ph: (213)385-6461
Free: 800-421-9585
Fax: (213)385-8405
URL: http://www.lasafety.org
Format(s): Videocassette. **Descr:** This is a demonstration of how workers can save their jobs and their lives by knowing how to recognize fire hazards. **Prod. Date:** 198?. **Length:** 20.

6398 ■ The Handtrap Test
Film Library/Greater Los Angeles Safety Council
600 Wilshire Blvd., No. 1263
Los Angeles, CA 90017
Ph: (213)385-6461
Free: 800-421-9585
Fax: (213)385-8405
URL: http://www.lasafety.org
Format(s): Videocassette. **Descr:** This film is designed to help workers prevent hand and finger

injuries both on and off the job. **Prod. Date:** 198?. **Length:** 20.

6399 ■ *Harry's Hot Permit*
Film Library/Greater Los Angeles Safety Council
600 Wilshire Blvd., No. 1263
Los Angeles, CA 90017
Ph: (213)385-6461
Free: 800-421-9585
Fax: (213)385-8405
URL: http://www.lasafety.org

Format(s): Videocassette. **Descr:** A producer making a film on unsafe work habits violates the procedures he intends to teach workers. **Prod. Date:** 198?. **Length:** 16.

6400 ■ *Have a Good Day, Dear*
Film Library/Greater Los Angeles Safety Council
600 Wilshire Blvd., No. 1263
Los Angeles, CA 90017
Ph: (213)385-6461
Free: 800-421-9585
Fax: (213)385-8405
URL: http://www.lasafety.org

Format(s): Videocassette. **Descr:** Examines potential hazards in the office such as poorly arranged furniture and top heavy filing cabinets. **Prod. Date:** 198?. **Length:** 19.

6401 ■ *The Hazard Awareness Training Series*
Genium Group Inc.
1171 Riverfront Center
Amsterdam, NY 12010
Ph: (518)842-4111
Free: 800-243-6486
Fax: (518)842-1843
E-mail: info@genium.com
URL: http://www.genium.com

Format(s): Videocassette. **Descr:** OSHA laws, how to read and label material safety data sheets, and other industrial health threats are covered in this series. **Prod. Date:** 1989. **Length:** 20. **Price:** $534.00.

6402 ■ *Hazardous Chemicals*
Film Library/Greater Los Angeles Safety Council
600 Wilshire Blvd., No. 1263
Los Angeles, CA 90017
Ph: (213)385-6461
Free: 800-421-9585
Fax: (213)385-8405
URL: http://www.lasafety.org

Format(s): Videocassette. **Descr:** This film looks into the world of chemicals, solvents and cleaning products most often used in industry. **Prod. Date:** 198?. **Length:** 12.

6403 ■ *He Forgot*
Film Library/Greater Los Angeles Safety Council
600 Wilshire Blvd., No. 1263
Los Angeles, CA 90017
Ph: (213)385-6461
Free: 800-421-9585
Fax: (213)385-8405
URL: http://www.lasafety.org

Format(s): Videocassette. **Descr:** Three crane operators discuss the reason for the absence of one of their regular group members who was hospitalized due to an accident. **Prod. Date:** 198?. **Length:** 15.

6404 ■ *Heads Up*
Film Library/Greater Los Angeles Safety Council
600 Wilshire Blvd., No. 1263
Los Angeles, CA 90017
Ph: (213)385-6461
Free: 800-421-9585
Fax: (213)385-8405
URL: http://www.lasafety.org

Format(s): Videocassette. **Descr:** Former NFL quarterback Pat Haden presents a set of safety guidelines for those who work near power lines. **Prod. Date:** 198?. **Length:** 20.

6405 ■ *Health Care Accident Prevention*
Film Library/Greater Los Angeles Safety Council
600 Wilshire Blvd., No. 1263
Los Angeles, CA 90017
Ph: (213)385-6461
Free: 800-421-9585
Fax: (213)385-8405
URL: http://www.lasafety.org

Format(s): Videocassette. **Descr:** A demonstration of the basic accident prevention procedures to use in a health care facility. **Prod. Date:** 198?. **Length:** 14.

6406 ■ *Hear What You Want to Hear*
National Safety Council
1121 Spring Lake Dr
Itasca, IL 60143-3201
Ph: (630)285-1121
Free: 800-621-7619
Fax: (630)285-1315
E-mail: info@nsc.org
URL: http://www.nsc.org

Format(s): Videocassette. **Descr:** This film teaches workers how hearing losses occur and what types of sounds are damaging. **Prod. Date:** 198?. **Length:** 10.

6407 ■ *Hearts*
Leslie T. McClure
PO Box 1223
Pebble Beach, CA 93953
Ph: (831)656-0553
Fax: (831)656-0555
URL: http://www.411videoinfo.com

Format(s): Videocassette. **Descr:** Provides instructions and strategies for playing the card game Hearts. **Prod. Date:** 1998. **Price:** $12.99.

6408 ■ *A Hell of a Way to Die*
Film Library/Greater Los Angeles Safety Council
600 Wilshire Blvd., No. 1263
Los Angeles, CA 90017
Ph: (213)385-6461
Free: 800-421-9585
Fax: (213)385-8405
URL: http://www.lasafety.org

Format(s): Videocassette. **Descr:** This is the story of a dock worker who is accidentally killed by a truck driver. The film describes the tragedy's effect on his family and co-workers. **Prod. Date:** 198?. **Length:** 22.

6409 ■ *Helmets*
Film Library/Greater Los Angeles Safety Council
600 Wilshire Blvd., No. 1263
Los Angeles, CA 90017
Ph: (213)385-6461
Free: 800-421-9585
Fax: (213)385-8405
URL: http://www.lasafety.org

Format(s): Videocassette. **Descr:** This film emphasizes the importance of wearing a helmet when riding on a motorcycle. **Prod. Date:** 198?. **Length:** 25.

6410 ■ *The High School Bus Passenger*
AIMS Multimedia
20765 Superior St
Chatsworth, CA 91311-4409
Ph: (818)773-4300
Free: 800-367-2467
Fax: (818)341-6700
E-mail: info@aims.multimedia.com
URL: http://www.aimsmultimedia.com

Format(s): Videocassette. **Descr:** The rules for proper bus conduct, safety precautions, and fighting vandalism are examined for kids. **Prod. Date:** 1981. **Length:** 9.

6411 ■ *High Voltage Hazards*
Williams Learning Network
15400 Calhoun Dr
Rockville, MD 20855-2762
Ph: (301)315-6700

Free: 800-848-1717
Fax: (301)315-6880
E-mail: mait@willearn.com
URL: http://www.willearn.com

Format(s): Videocassette. **Descr:** Outlines techniques that allow you to safely work with high voltage. Contains examples of an energized high voltage coil, isolating and grounding high voltage equipment for maintenance, and steps needed to safely discharge a transformer. Includes Leader's Guide and 25 Program Guides. **Length:** 10.

6412 ■ *Hola Amigos: Spanish for Kids*
PBS Home Video
Catalog Fulfillment Center
PO Box 751089
Charlotte, NC 28275-1089
Ph: 800-531-4727
Free: 800-645-4PBS
E-mail: info@pbs.org
URL: http://www.pbs.org

Format(s): Videocassette. **Descr:** Roung viewers will learn the basics of Spanish, including the words for colors, letters, numbers, pets and animals, musical instuments and sports. Uses the adventures of cartoon dog Paco to ease youngsters into the Spanish language. Two hours and 30 minutes on three videocassettes. **Prod. Date:** 1998. **Length:** 50. **Price:** $54.95.

6413 ■ *Home Safety*
ERI Safety Videos
374 Park Rd
Lexington, SC 29072
Ph: (803)356-4880
Free: 800-311-1143
Fax: (803)356-1946
URL: http://www.eri-safety.com

Format(s): Videocassette. **Descr:** Prevent fires, poisonings, and other potential household accidents. **Prod. Date:** 1987. **Length:** 15. **Price:** $425.00.

6414 ■ *Hospital Safety*
Film Library/Greater Los Angeles Safety Council
600 Wilshire Blvd., No. 1263
Los Angeles, CA 90017
Ph: (213)385-6461
Free: 800-421-9585
Fax: (213)385-8405
URL: http://www.lasafety.org

Format(s): Videocassette. **Descr:** Various safety concepts for health care facility personnel such as proper lifting of patients and identification of hazards are discussed. **Prod. Date:** 198?. **Length:** 13.

6415 ■ *Hospital Safety Series*
Health Sciences Consortium
300 Silver Cedar Ct
201 Silver Cedar Ct
Chapel Hill, NC 27514-1696
Ph: (919)942-8731
Fax: (919)942-3689
URL: http://www.healthsciencesconsortium.org

Format(s): Videocassette. **Descr:** Demonstrates hospital safety and preparedness in critical situations. **Prod. Date:** 1987. **Length:** 10.

6416 ■ *Hot Liquid Burns—The Seegar Story*
Film Library/Greater Los Angeles Safety Council
600 Wilshire Blvd., No. 1263
Los Angeles, CA 90017
Ph: (213)385-6461
Free: 800-421-9585
Fax: (213)385-8405
URL: http://www.lasafety.org

Format(s): Videocassette. **Descr:** The true story of 11-month-old Kirsty Seegar, who was severely burned from hot tap water, causing her to lose both her legs. **Prod. Date:** 198?. **Length:** 18.

6417 ■ *Hotel Fire Survival*
Gulf Publishing Co.
PO Box 2608
Houston, TX 77252-2608
Ph: (713)520-4448
Free: 800-231-6275

Fax: (713)204-4433
E-mail: csv@gulfpub.com
URL: http://www.gulfpub.com

Format(s): Videocassette. **Descr:** This program compares the unprepared and the prepared traveler and shows how the prepared person is more likely to survive a hotel fire. **Prod. Date:** 1984. **Length:** 30. **Price:** $95.00.

6418 ■ How to Avoid 16 OSHA Citations
Film Library/Greater Los Angeles Safety Council
600 Wilshire Blvd., No. 1263
Los Angeles, CA 90017
Ph: (213)385-6461
Free: 800-421-9585
Fax: (213)385-8405
URL: http://www.lasafety.org

Format(s): Videocassette. **Descr:** This tape describes how the supervisor can contribute to his company by reducing unsafe acts and procedures in his department. **Prod. Date:** 198?. **Length:** 20.

6419 ■ How to Involve Joe
Film Library/Greater Los Angeles Safety Council
600 Wilshire Blvd., No. 1263
Los Angeles, CA 90017
Ph: (213)385-6461
Free: 800-421-9585
Fax: (213)385-8405
URL: http://www.lasafety.org

Format(s): Videocassette. **Descr:** The supervisor of an assembly line motivates a careless employee towards safer work habits and procedures in this program. **Prod. Date:** 198?. **Length:** 10.

6420 ■ How Much Are Your Eyes Worth
Film Library/Greater Los Angeles Safety Council
600 Wilshire Blvd., No. 1263
Los Angeles, CA 90017
Ph: (213)385-6461
Free: 800-421-9585
Fax: (213)385-8405
URL: http://www.lasafety.org

Format(s): Videocassette. **Descr:** A group of workers describe how priceless their eyesight is and the need to protect it. **Prod. Date:** 198?. **Length:** 12.

6421 ■ How to Raise a Street Smart Child
HBO
1100 Ave. of the Americas
New York, NY 10036
Ph: (212)512-7400
Fax: (212)512-7498
URL: http://www.hbo.com

Format(s): Videocassette. **Descr:** Frank, practical advice about keeping children safe in today's world. Hosted and narrated by Daniel J. Travanti. **Prod. Date:** 1987. **Length:** 43. **Price:** $19.99.

6422 ■ How to Save Your Child or Baby
ActiVideo
857 W. Webster Ave
Chicago, IL 60614
Ph: (773)404-0030
Free: 800-323-3431
Fax: (773)404-0035

Format(s): Videocassette. **Descr:** The video covers lifesaving techniques for newborns through eight years. Includes demonstrations on child or baby CPR, drownings, burns, poisoning, and Sudden Infant Death Syndrome. **Prod. Date:** 1987. **Length:** 40.

6423 ■ How Streetproof Are You?
United Learning
1560 Sherman Ave., Ste. 100
PO Box 48718
Evanston, IL 60201
Ph: 888-892-3484
Fax: (847)328-6706
E-mail: info@interaccess.com
URL: http://www.unitedlearning.com

Format(s): Videocassette. **Descr:** This tape teaches children how to survive in an urban environment,

dealing with traffic, strangers, unsafe areas, shortcuts and other difficulties. **Prod. Date:** 1985. **Length:** 28.

6424 ■ How's Eddie?
Film Library/Greater Los Angeles Safety Council
600 Wilshire Blvd., No. 1263
Los Angeles, CA 90017
Ph: (213)385-6461
Free: 800-421-9585
Fax: (213)385-8405
URL: http://www.lasafety.org

Format(s): Videocassette. **Descr:** This tape looks at the safety problems that can occur in various construction trades. **Prod. Date:** 1985. **Length:** 27.

6425 ■ Hydrogen Sulfide Safety for the Offshore Industry
John Sabella & Associate
805 W. Emerson St
Seattle, WA 98119
Ph: (206)281-8626
Fax: (206)217-0899
E-mail: sales@johnsabella.com
URL: http://www.johnsabella.com

Format(s): Videocassette. **Descr:** Addresses the precautions that must be taken specifically for working in an offshore environment in which hydrogen sulfide may be present. Also details the hazards of hydrogen sulfide, its effects and symptoms of exposure. **Prod. Date:** ?. **Length:** 23. **Price:** $375.00.

6426 ■ I Can't See
Film Library/Greater Los Angeles Safety Council
600 Wilshire Blvd., No. 1263
Los Angeles, CA 90017
Ph: (213)385-6461
Free: 800-421-9585
Fax: (213)385-8405
URL: http://www.lasafety.org

Format(s): Videocassette. **Descr:** Tragedy results when a factory worker ignores his supervisor's and co-worker's advice that he should wear his safety goggles. **Prod. Date:** 198?. **Length:** 23.

6427 ■ I Was Only Doing My Job
Film Library/Greater Los Angeles Safety Council
600 Wilshire Blvd., No. 1263
Los Angeles, CA 90017
Ph: (213)385-6461
Free: 800-421-9585
Fax: (213)385-8405
URL: http://www.lasafety.org

Format(s): Videocassette. **Descr:** This program tells the story of a worker who is injured when he assists a senior machine operator in removing a guard. **Prod. Date:** 198?. **Length:** 21.

6428 ■ If It's Not Too Late
Film Library/Greater Los Angeles Safety Council
600 Wilshire Blvd., No. 1263
Los Angeles, CA 90017
Ph: (213)385-6461
Free: 800-421-9585
Fax: (213)385-8405
URL: http://www.lasafety.org

Format(s): Videocassette. **Descr:** This film teaches supervisors and managers how to identify and control incidents that could lead to accidents. **Prod. Date:** 198?. **Length:** 10.

6429 ■ If You Snooze, You Lose
Film Library/Greater Los Angeles Safety Council
600 Wilshire Blvd., No. 1263
Los Angeles, CA 90017
Ph: (213)385-6461
Free: 800-421-9585
Fax: (213)385-8405
URL: http://www.lasafety.org

Format(s): Videocassette. **Descr:** When a manager acts upon his employee's safety suggestions, he

discovers an upward swing in productivity and profits. **Prod. Date:** 198?. **Length:** 18.

6430 ■ Inclusion: Learning Together
GPN Educational Media
Box 80669
Lincoln, NE 68501-0669
Ph: (402)472-2007
Free: 800-228-4630
Fax: 800-306-2330
URL: http://gpn.unl.edu

Format(s): Videocassette. **Descr:** Series of 15 30-minute videos designed to aid teachers in the inclusion of disabled students in the traditional classroom. **Prod. Date:** 1998. **Length:** 450. **Price:** $900.

6431 ■ Industrial Eye Safety
ERI Safety Videos
374 Park Rd
Lexington, SC 29072
Ph: (803)356-4880
Free: 800-311-1143
Fax: (803)356-1946
URL: http://www.eri-safety.com

Format(s): Videocassette. **Descr:** A program which teaches industrial employees what they can do to save their eyes. **Prod. Date:** 1987. **Length:** 15. **Price:** $425.00.

6432 ■ Industrial Housekeeping
ERI Safety Videos
374 Park Rd
Lexington, SC 29072
Ph: (803)356-4880
Free: 800-311-1143
Fax: (803)356-1946
URL: http://www.eri-safety.com

Format(s): Videocassette. **Descr:** The consequences of leaving stuff around and not cleaning up, both in the home and on the job, are explained. **Prod. Date:** 1987. **Length:** 16. **Price:** $425.00.

6433 ■ Industrial Hygiene: Right Makes Safe
Film Library/Greater Los Angeles Safety Council
600 Wilshire Blvd., No. 1263
Los Angeles, CA 90017
Ph: (213)385-6461
Free: 800-421-9585
Fax: (213)385-8405
URL: http://www.lasafety.org

Format(s): Videocassette. **Descr:** This is a demonstration of the protective equipment to use in hazardous situations, and of the preventative measures that should be taken to insure employee safety. **Prod. Date:** 198?. **Length:** 20.

6434 ■ An Instant of Time
United Learning
1560 Sherman Ave., Ste. 100
PO Box 48718
Evanston, IL 60201
Ph: 888-892-3484
Fax: (847)328-6706
E-mail: info@interaccess.com
URL: http://www.unitedlearning.com

Format(s): Videocassette. **Descr:** This program examines the ways to prevent serious accidents involving small children. **Prod. Date:** 1988. **Length:** 14. **Price:** $215.

6435 ■ Insuring Electrical Safety in the Critical Care Setting
AJN Video Library/Lippincott Williams & Wilkins
American Journal of Nursing
345 Hudson St., 16th Fl
New York, NY 10014
Ph: (212)886-1200
Free: 800-256-4045
Fax: (212)886-1276
E-mail: info@nursingcenter.com
URL: http://www.nursingcenter.com

Format(s): Videocassette. **Descr:** Electrical safety

for nurses is the main topic of this tape. **Prod. Date:** 1989. **Length:** 28. **Price:** $275.00.

6436 ■ Intensive Care
Film Library/Greater Los Angeles Safety Council
600 Wilshire Blvd., No. 1263
Los Angeles, CA 90017
Ph: (213)385-6461
Free: 800-421-9585
Fax: (213)385-8405
URL: http://www.lasafety.org
Format(s): Videocassette. **Descr:** One of five workers with a bad safety attitude has an accident which puts one of them in the operating room. **Prod. Date:** 198?. **Length:** 22.

6437 ■ International Safety Management (ISM) Code
John Sabella & Associate
805 W. Emerson St
Seattle, WA 98119
Ph: (206)281-8626
Fax: (206)217-0899
E-mail: sales@johnsabella.com
URL: http://www.johnsabella.com
Format(s): Videocassette. **Descr:** Aimed at ship operators or managers who are in the process of implementing their International Safety Management programs, which provide an international standard for the safe management and operation of vessels and for pollution prevention. **Price:** $125.00.

6438 ■ Introduction to Hand Tools
Film Library/Greater Los Angeles Safety Council
600 Wilshire Blvd., No. 1263
Los Angeles, CA 90017
Ph: (213)385-6461
Free: 800-421-9585
Fax: (213)385-8405
URL: http://www.lasafety.org
Format(s): Videocassette. **Descr:** The proper and safe use of hand tools is discussed in this film. **Prod. Date:** 198?. **Length:** 11.

6439 ■ Introduction to the Hazard Communication Standard
ERI Safety Videos
374 Park Rd
Lexington, SC 29072
Ph: (803)356-4880
Free: 800-311-1143
Fax: (803)356-1946
URL: http://www.eri-safety.com
Format(s): Videocassette. **Descr:** This program features explanations of all that can be done to minimize the risk of someone getting hurt by chemicals. **Prod. Date:** 1987. **Length:** 16. **Price:** $250.00.

6440 ■ Introduction to Health Care Safety
Film Library/Greater Los Angeles Safety Council
600 Wilshire Blvd., No. 1263
Los Angeles, CA 90017
Ph: (213)385-6461
Free: 800-421-9585
Fax: (213)385-8405
URL: http://www.lasafety.org
Format(s): Videocassette. **Descr:** A vivid description of the hazards that health care facilities face and the routine safety practices that should be a part of every safety program. **Prod. Date:** 198?. **Length:** 14.

6441 ■ Introduction to Process Safety Management
Williams Learning Network
15400 Calhoun Dr
Rockville, MD 20855-2762
Ph: (301)315-6700
Free: 800-848-1717
Fax: (301)315-6880
E-mail: mait@willearn.com
URL: http://www.willearn.com
Format(s): Videocassette. **Descr:** Outlines chemical process safety with operating and maintenance procedures, employee training, and safe management practices. Includes Leader's Guide and 25 Program Guides. **Prod. Date:** 19??. **Length:** 12.

6442 ■ The Invisible Danger
Film Library/Greater Los Angeles Safety Council
600 Wilshire Blvd., No. 1263
Los Angeles, CA 90017
Ph: (213)385-6461
Free: 800-421-9585
Fax: (213)385-8405
URL: http://www.lasafety.org
Format(s): Videocassette. **Descr:** This program recommends different types of breathing apparatus to use when dangerous toxic gasses are present. **Prod. Date:** 198?. **Length:** 15.

6443 ■ Is There Anything I've Forgotten?
Film Library/Greater Los Angeles Safety Council
600 Wilshire Blvd., No. 1263
Los Angeles, CA 90017
Ph: (213)385-6461
Free: 800-421-9585
Fax: (213)385-8405
URL: http://www.lasafety.org
Format(s): Videocassette. **Descr:** This is a dramatization of an accident that occurred on a ship after a sailor makes a procedural mistake in isolating the vessel. **Prod. Date:** 198?. **Length:** 21.

6444 ■ It Always Happens to the Other Guy
Film Library/Greater Los Angeles Safety Council
600 Wilshire Blvd., No. 1263
Los Angeles, CA 90017
Ph: (213)385-6461
Free: 800-421-9585
Fax: (213)385-8405
URL: http://www.lasafety.org
Format(s): Videocassette. **Descr:** In this program, a Hollywood stuntman demonstrates the basic safety procedures for operating heavy construction equipment. **Prod. Date:** 198?. **Length:** 21.

6445 ■ It Can't Happen to Me—Anatomy of an Accident
Film Library/Greater Los Angeles Safety Council
600 Wilshire Blvd., No. 1263
Los Angeles, CA 90017
Ph: (213)385-6461
Free: 800-421-9585
Fax: (213)385-8405
URL: http://www.lasafety.org
Format(s): Videocassette. **Descr:** This is a re-enactment of an accident that occurred at the Kennedy Space Center demonstrating that carelessness can often lead to accidents. **Prod. Date:** 198?. **Length:** 23.

6446 ■ It Didn't Have to Happen
Film Library/Greater Los Angeles Safety Council
600 Wilshire Blvd., No. 1263
Los Angeles, CA 90017
Ph: (213)385-6461
Free: 800-421-9585
Fax: (213)385-8405
URL: http://www.lasafety.org
Format(s): Videocassette. **Descr:** This tape shows how a careless worker who frowns upon using safety devices on woodworking machinery endangers the lives of his co-workers. **Prod. Date:** 198?. **Length:** 14.

6447 ■ It's Not Thursday, Is It?
Film Library/Greater Los Angeles Safety Council
600 Wilshire Blvd., No. 1263
Los Angeles, CA 90017
Ph: (213)385-6461
Free: 800-421-9585
Fax: (213)385-8405
URL: http://www.lasafety.org
Format(s): Videocassette. **Descr:** A safety representative discovers his company's lackadaisical attitudes towards safety when an inspection is moved up a day ahead of schedule. **Prod. Date:** 198?. **Length:** 21.

6448 ■ It's Still Up to You
Film Library/Greater Los Angeles Safety Council
600 Wilshire Blvd., No. 1263
Los Angeles, CA 90017
Ph: (213)385-6461
Free: 800-421-9585
Fax: (213)385-8405
URL: http://www.lasafety.org
Format(s): Videocassette. **Descr:** This is the true story of a factory worker who had a preventable eye injury and of the agony that it caused him. **Prod. Date:** 198?. **Length:** 12.

6449 ■ It's Up to You, Charley
Film Library/Greater Los Angeles Safety Council
600 Wilshire Blvd., No. 1263
Los Angeles, CA 90017
Ph: (213)385-6461
Free: 800-421-9585
Fax: (213)385-8405
URL: http://www.lasafety.org
Format(s): Videocassette. **Descr:** Two different plants in the same town have different outlooks on emergency planning. **Prod. Date:** 198?. **Length:** 19.

6450 ■ I've Never Had an Accident in My Life
Film Library/Greater Los Angeles Safety Council
600 Wilshire Blvd., No. 1263
Los Angeles, CA 90017
Ph: (213)385-6461
Free: 800-421-9585
Fax: (213)385-8405
URL: http://www.lasafety.org
Format(s): Videocassette. **Descr:** This tape offers a detailed descripton of the causes of accidents and hazards in the meat industry. **Prod. Date:** 198?. **Length:** 18.

6451 ■ Jointer
Film Library/Greater Los Angeles Safety Council
600 Wilshire Blvd., No. 1263
Los Angeles, CA 90017
Ph: (213)385-6461
Free: 800-421-9585
Fax: (213)385-8405
URL: http://www.lasafety.org
Format(s): Videocassette. **Descr:** This is a demonstration of how to safely use the jointer machine. **Prod. Date:** 198?. **Length:** 12.

6452 ■ Just Around the Corner: Consumer Education
Prentice Hall
Pearson Education
One Lake St
Upper Saddle Ridge, NJ 07458
Ph: (201)236-7000
URL: http://vig.prenhall.com
Format(s): Videocassette. **Descr:** Gives advice on how to shop wisely. All aspects of the consumer world are explored. **Prod. Date:** 197?. **Length:** 30.

6453 ■ Keep It Clean for Safety's Sake
Film Library/Greater Los Angeles Safety Council
600 Wilshire Blvd., No. 1263
Los Angeles, CA 90017
Ph: (213)385-6461
Free: 800-421-9585
Fax: (213)385-8405
URL: http://www.lasafety.org
Format(s): Videocassette. **Descr:** Provides nine sensible safety practices that can be used in any housekeeping situation. **Prod. Date:** 198?. **Length:** 10.

6454 ■ Kid Safe
ActiVideo
857 W. Webster Ave
Chicago, IL 60614
Ph: (773)404-0030
Free: 800-323-3431
Fax: (773)404-0035
Format(s): Videocassette. **Descr:** The video teaches

children safety information, including how and when to call 911, emergency first aid, fire safety and prevention, and how to handle strangers at the door. **Prod. Date:** 1988. **Length:** 30.

6455 ■ *Kid Safe: The Video*
Tapeworm Video Distributors
27833 Hopkins Ave., Unit 6
Valencia, CA 91355
Ph: (661)257-4904
Fax: (661)257-4820
E-mail: sales@tapeworm.com
URL: http://www.tapeworm.com
Format(s): Videocassette. **Descr:** SCTV star Andrea Martin, takes children through several safety situations with Marty the Fireman, Tina the Paramedic, and Ernie the Policeman. The children learn some very important information such as 911 while they're having fun. **Length:** 30. **Price:** $19.95.

6456 ■ *Kids for Safety: A Guide to Bicycle, Fire and Personal Safety*
Monterey Home Video
566 St. Charles Dr
Thousand Oaks, CA 91360-3901
Ph: (805)494-7199
Free: 800-424-2593
Fax: (805)496-6061
URL: http://www.montereymedia.com
Format(s): Videocassette. **Descr:** Children are taught the safe way to approach bicycling, fire and personal habits. Music video and flash quizzes keep viewers on their toes. Includes a teacher's guide and activity sheets. **Prod. Date:** 1990. **Length:** 24.

6457 ■ *Kidzone Series: Street Smarts*
New Dimension Media, Inc.
680 N Lake Shore Dr., Ste. 900
Chicago, IL 60611
Ph: (312)642-9400
Free: 800-288-4456
Fax: (312)642-9805
E-mail: Info@NDMquestar.com
URL: http://www.ndmquestar.com
Format(s): Videocassette. **Descr:** Shows young people how to bike with a helmet for maximum safety. **Prod. Date:** 1992. **Length:** 7. **Price:** $110.

6458 ■ *Kitchen Safety and Sanitation*
RMI Media
1365 N. Winchester
Olathe, KS 66061
Ph: (913)768-1696
Fax: (913)768-0184
E-mail: actmedia@act.org
URL: http://www.rmimedia.com
Format(s): Videocassette. **Descr:** Stresses the importance of safety and sanitation in the kitchen and addresses accident and illness prevention. **Prod. Date:** 1987. **Length:** 18. **Price:** $89.00.

6459 ■ *Knowing's Not Enough*
Film Library/Greater Los Angeles Safety Council
600 Wilshire Blvd., No. 1263
Los Angeles, CA 90017
Ph: (213)385-6461
Free: 800-421-9585
Fax: (213)385-8405
URL: http://www.lasafety.org
Format(s): Videocassette. **Descr:** This is a revised version of the popular safety film about an accident and the search to discover why it happened. **Prod. Date:** 198?. **Length:** 25.

6460 ■ *Lab Spills and Waste*
Williams Learning Network
15400 Calhoun Dr
Rockville, MD 20855-2762
Ph: (301)315-6700
Free: 800-848-1717
Fax: (301)315-6880
E-mail: mait@willearn.com
URL: http://www.willearn.com
Format(s): Videocassette. **Descr:** Profiles techniques for cleaning up small and moderate spills in the lab and also discusses ways of disposing of lab

waste. Includes Leader's Guide and 25 Program Guides.

6461 ■ *Lab Ventilation*
Williams Learning Network
15400 Calhoun Dr
Rockville, MD 20855-2762
Ph: (301)315-6700
Free: 800-848-1717
Fax: (301)315-6880
E-mail: mait@willearn.com
URL: http://www.willearn.com
Format(s): Videocassette. **Descr:** Describes the safety importance of a good ventilation system in the laboratory with emphasis on fume hoods and biological storage cabinets. Includes Leader's Guide and 25 Program Guides.

6462 ■ *Laser Safety Comes to Light*
Williams Learning Network
15400 Calhoun Dr
Rockville, MD 20855-2762
Ph: (301)315-6700
Free: 800-848-1717
Fax: (301)315-6880
E-mail: mait@willearn.com
URL: http://www.willearn.com
Format(s): Videocassette. **Descr:** Outlines the American National Standards Institute's guidelines for the safe operation of lasers. Covers five hazards categories and appropriate precautions: access control, eye protection, skin protection, chemical exposure, and electrical shock. Includes "Guidelines for Developing a Laser Safety Program," "ANSI Z136.1," "Laser Safety Guide," and "Guide for the Selection of Laser Eye Protection." **Prod. Date:** 19??. **Length:** 20.

6463 ■ *Last One Picked...First One Picked On*
PBS Home Video
Catalog Fulfillment Center
PO Box 751089
Charlotte, NC 28275-1089
Ph: 800-531-4727
Free: 800-645-4PBS
E-mail: info@pbs.org
URL: http://www.pbs.org
Format(s): Videocassette. **Descr:** Host Richard Lavoie, a nationally recognized expert on learning disabilities, addresses the social problems that learning disabled children face and offers some practical solutions. **Prod. Date:** 1998. **Length:** 62. **Price:** $49.95.

6464 ■ *Lessons in Living Series*
Phoenix Learning Group
2349 Chaffee Dr
St. Louis, MO 63146
Ph: (314)569-0211
Free: 800-221-1274
Fax: (314)569-2834
URL: http://www.phoenixlearninggroup.com
Format(s): Videocassette. **Descr:** Bambi, Dumbo, Snow White, Mowgli and other Disney favorites teach children important lessons, including self-assertion, acceptance, honesty, change, cooperation, perseverance, and compromise. **Prod. Date:** 1990. **Length:** 8. **Price:** $155.

6465 ■ *Let George Do It*
Film Library/Greater Los Angeles Safety Council
600 Wilshire Blvd., No. 1263
Los Angeles, CA 90017
Ph: (213)385-6461
Free: 800-421-9585
Fax: (213)385-8405
URL: http://www.lasafety.org
Format(s): Videocassette. **Descr:** This tape chronicles a series of events that lead to a work injury because the worker assumed that the other guy did his part of the job safely. **Prod. Date:** 198?. **Length:** 10.

6466 ■ *Let Them Know*
Film Library/Greater Los Angeles Safety Council
600 Wilshire Blvd., No. 1263

Los Angeles, CA 90017
Ph: (213)385-6461
Free: 800-421-9585
Fax: (213)385-8405
URL: http://www.lasafety.org
Format(s): Videocassette. **Descr:** Emphasizes that safety training is the best training whenever there is a new job learning situation. **Prod. Date:** 198?. **Length:** 10.

6467 ■ *Let's Think and Be Safe*
AIMS Multimedia
20765 Superior St
Chatsworth, CA 91311-4409
Ph: (818)773-4300
Free: 800-367-2467
Fax: (818)341-6700
E-mail: info@aims.multimedia.com
URL: http://www.aimsmultimedia.com
Format(s): Videocassette. **Descr:** Seven vignettes point up accident prevention in schools. **Prod. Date:** 1981. **Length:** 10.

6468 ■ *Lift and Carry*
Film Library/Greater Los Angeles Safety Council
600 Wilshire Blvd., No. 1263
Los Angeles, CA 90017
Ph: (213)385-6461
Free: 800-421-9585
Fax: (213)385-8405
URL: http://www.lasafety.org
Format(s): Videocassette. **Descr:** This is a demonstration of proper lifting and carrying techniques with an emphasis on the two-man teamwork approach. **Prod. Date:** 198?. **Length:** 5.

6469 ■ *Little Things That Count*
Film Library/Greater Los Angeles Safety Council
600 Wilshire Blvd., No. 1263
Los Angeles, CA 90017
Ph: (213)385-6461
Free: 800-421-9585
Fax: (213)385-8405
URL: http://www.lasafety.org
Format(s): Videocassette. **Descr:** This film illustrates how everyday routine tasks can lead to big accidents. **Prod. Date:** 198?. **Length:** 10.

6470 ■ *Living with Dust*
Film Library/Greater Los Angeles Safety Council
600 Wilshire Blvd., No. 1263
Los Angeles, CA 90017
Ph: (213)385-6461
Free: 800-421-9585
Fax: (213)385-8405
URL: http://www.lasafety.org
Format(s): Videocassette. **Descr:** An illustration of the dangers of working in a dust-filled environment is offered in this program. **Prod. Date:** 198?. **Length:** 16.

6471 ■ *Look What You've Done!*
PBS Home Video
Catalog Fulfillment Center
PO Box 751089
Charlotte, NC 28275-1089
Ph: 800-531-4727
Free: 800-645-4PBS
E-mail: info@pbs.org
URL: http://www.pbs.org
Format(s): Videocassette. **Descr:** Dr. Robert Brooks, an expert on learning disabilities, offers parents strategies for helping children develop the skills they will need to succeed. **Prod. Date:** 1998. **Length:** 66. **Price:** $49.95.

6472 ■ *Loss-Control Dollars Make Sense*
Film Library/Greater Los Angeles Safety Council
600 Wilshire Blvd., No. 1263
Los Angeles, CA 90017
Ph: (213)385-6461
Free: 800-421-9585
Fax: (213)385-8405
URL: http://www.lasafety.org
Format(s): Videocassette. **Descr:** Shows how the costs of accidents, employee safety performance,

and near-accidents impinge upon profits. **Prod. Date:** 1988. **Length:** 60.

6473 ■ Low Voltage Safety
Film Library/Greater Los Angeles Safety Council
600 Wilshire Blvd., No. 1263
Los Angeles, CA 90017
Ph: (213)385-6461
Free: 800-421-9585
Fax: (213)385-8405
URL: http://www.lasafety.org
Format(s): Videocassette. **Descr:** This tape describes the safety precautions electricians should take when working with 660 volts or less. **Prod. Date:** 198?. **Length:** 14.

6474 ■ Machine Shop Safety & Basic Operations
Tel-A-Train, Inc.
305 Crewdson Ave
Chattanooga, TN 37405
E-mail: wkingsb@pwpl.com
Format(s): Videocassette. **Descr:** Four-tape course teaches safe machine shop practices, common operations and efficient work practices. Also shows proper use of bandsaws, drill presses, milling machines, and engine lathes. **Prod. Date:** ????. **Length:** 91. **Price:** $1,695.00.

6475 ■ Magic of Believing in Safety for Employees
Film Library/Greater Los Angeles Safety Council
600 Wilshire Blvd., No. 1263
Los Angeles, CA 90017
Ph: (213)385-6461
Free: 800-421-9585
Fax: (213)385-8405
URL: http://www.lasafety.org
Format(s): Videocassette. **Descr:** This tape discusses the importance of believing in safety, and of how it can spread to other workers as well as to the employee's family. **Prod. Date:** 198?. **Length:** 16.

6476 ■ The Magic of Believing in Safety for Management
Film Library/Greater Los Angeles Safety Council
600 Wilshire Blvd., No. 1263
Los Angeles, CA 90017
Ph: (213)385-6461
Free: 800-421-9585
Fax: (213)385-8405
URL: http://www.lasafety.org
Format(s): Videocassette. **Descr:** Two experts give a strong motivational talk on how managers can have an effect on their department's safety record in this film. **Prod. Date:** 198?. **Length:** 24.

6477 ■ Make Light of Lifting
Film Library/Greater Los Angeles Safety Council
600 Wilshire Blvd., No. 1263
Los Angeles, CA 90017
Ph: (213)385-6461
Free: 800-421-9585
Fax: (213)385-8405
URL: http://www.lasafety.org
Format(s): Videocassette. **Descr:** This is a demonstration of the right and wrong ways to use the body when handling heavy objects. **Prod. Date:** 198?. **Length:** 17.

6478 ■ Man and His Habits
Film Library/Greater Los Angeles Safety Council
600 Wilshire Blvd., No. 1263
Los Angeles, CA 90017
Ph: (213)385-6461
Free: 800-421-9585
Fax: (213)385-8405
URL: http://www.lasafety.org
Format(s): Videocassette. **Descr:** An employee's after hours safety habits start to carry over onto his job. **Prod. Date:** 198?. **Length:** 13.

6479 ■ Man in the Middle
Film Library/Greater Los Angeles Safety Council
600 Wilshire Blvd., No. 1263
Los Angeles, CA 90017

Ph: (213)385-6461
Free: 800-421-9585
Fax: (213)385-8405
URL: http://www.lasafety.org
Format(s): Videocassette. **Descr:** A safety supervisor faces a perilous dilemma when he is caught between management's production schedules and employees who have little interest in safety. **Prod. Date:** 198?. **Length:** 22.

6480 ■ The Man from OSHA
Film Library/Greater Los Angeles Safety Council
600 Wilshire Blvd., No. 1263
Los Angeles, CA 90017
Ph: (213)385-6461
Free: 800-421-9585
Fax: (213)385-8405
URL: http://www.lasafety.org
Format(s): Videocassette. **Descr:** This is an explanation of the OSHA program and what an OSHA inspector does. **Prod. Date:** 198?. **Length:** 25.

6481 ■ Man and Safety—Physical Limitations
Film Library/Greater Los Angeles Safety Council
600 Wilshire Blvd., No. 1263
Los Angeles, CA 90017
Ph: (213)385-6461
Free: 800-421-9585
Fax: (213)385-8405
URL: http://www.lasafety.org
Format(s): Videocassette. **Descr:** This is a detailed account of how exceeding one's physical capabilities is a major cause of accidents. **Prod. Date:** 198?. **Length:** 25.

6482 ■ Man's Shortcomings
Film Library/Greater Los Angeles Safety Council
600 Wilshire Blvd., No. 1263
Los Angeles, CA 90017
Ph: (213)385-6461
Free: 800-421-9585
Fax: (213)385-8405
URL: http://www.lasafety.org
Format(s): Videocassette. **Descr:** A man's personality quirks endangers both his own and other worker's safety. **Prod. Date:** 198?. **Length:** 13.

6483 ■ Material Safety Data Sheets (MSDS)
Williams Learning Network
15400 Calhoun Dr
Rockville, MD 20855-2762
Ph: (301)315-6700
Free: 800-848-1717
Fax: (301)315-6880
E-mail: mait@willearn.com
URL: http://www.willearn.com
Format(s): Videocassette. **Descr:** Summarizes OSHA's requirements for Material Safety Data Sheets (MSDS). Covers chemical names, physical properties, fire and explosion data, health hazards, first-aid procedures, and handling precautions. Includes Leader's Guide and 25 Program Guides. **Prod. Date:** 19??. **Length:** 16.

6484 ■ Materials Handling
Film Library/Greater Los Angeles Safety Council
600 Wilshire Blvd., No. 1263
Los Angeles, CA 90017
Ph: (213)385-6461
Free: 800-421-9585
Fax: (213)385-8405
URL: http://www.lasafety.org
Format(s): Videocassette. **Descr:** This is a detailed account of the many types of material handling hazards that can befall a worker. **Prod. Date:** 198?. **Length:** 12.

6485 ■ A Matter of Time
Film Library/Greater Los Angeles Safety Council
600 Wilshire Blvd., No. 1263
Los Angeles, CA 90017
Ph: (213)385-6461
Free: 800-421-9585
Fax: (213)385-8405
URL: http://www.lasafety.org
Format(s): Videocassette. **Descr:** This film shows

that although heavy construction equipment operators may get away with taking chances on the job, it only catches up to them in the end. **Prod. Date:** 198?. **Length:** 20.

6486 ■ Mickey Mouse: Safety Belt Expert
Phoenix Learning Group
2349 Chaffee Dr
St. Louis, MO 63146
Ph: (314)569-0211
Free: 800-221-1274
Fax: (314)569-2834
URL: http://www.phoenixlearninggroup.com
Format(s): Videocassette. **Descr:** Mickey's Safety Clubhouse holds court to show Mrs. Horn why she should always wear her seatbelt. **Prod. Date:** 1988. **Length:** 16. **Price:** $280.00.

6487 ■ Mickey's Safety Club Series
Phoenix Learning Group
2349 Chaffee Dr
St. Louis, MO 63146
Ph: (314)569-0211
Free: 800-221-1274
Fax: (314)569-2834
URL: http://www.phoenixlearninggroup.com
Format(s): Videocassette. **Descr:** Mickey teaches all aspects of safety in and out of the home. Included are lessons on street smarts, home safety, playground behavior and holiday hooligans. **Prod. Date:** 1989. **Length:** 15. **Price:** $280.00.

6488 ■ Mind over Matter
Film Library/Greater Los Angeles Safety Council
600 Wilshire Blvd., No. 1263
Los Angeles, CA 90017
Ph: (213)385-6461
Free: 800-421-9585
Fax: (213)385-8405
URL: http://www.lasafety.org
Format(s): Videocassette. **Descr:** This tape discusses the problems that safety personnel face when employees attempt to lift more than they are able to. **Prod. Date:** 198?. **Length:** 10.

6489 ■ Monday Night and Tuesday Morning
National Safety Council
1121 Spring Lake Dr
Itasca, IL 60143-3201
Ph: (630)285-1121
Free: 800-621-7619
Fax: (630)285-1315
E-mail: info@nsc.org
URL: http://www.nsc.org
Format(s): Videocassette. **Descr:** Demonstrates the safety hazards arising from hangovers on-the-job. **Prod. Date:** 1988. **Length:** 15.

6490 ■ Moods of Safety
Film Library/Greater Los Angeles Safety Council
600 Wilshire Blvd., No. 1263
Los Angeles, CA 90017
Ph: (213)385-6461
Free: 800-421-9585
Fax: (213)385-8405
URL: http://www.lasafety.org
Format(s): Videocassette. **Descr:** This film demonstrates how various types of moods can be detrimental to personal safety. **Prod. Date:** 198?. **Length:** 20.

6491 ■ More on Portable Circular Saws
Film Library/Greater Los Angeles Safety Council
600 Wilshire Blvd., No. 1263
Los Angeles, CA 90017
Ph: (213)385-6461
Free: 800-421-9585
Fax: (213)385-8405
URL: http://www.lasafety.org
Format(s): Videocassette. **Descr:** The safety problems associated with portable circular saws are examined herein. **Prod. Date:** 198?. **Length:** 5.

6492 ■ The Most of Your Money
United Learning
1560 Sherman Ave., Ste. 100

PO Box 48718
Evanston, IL 60201
Ph: 888-892-3484
Fax: (847)328-6706
E-mail: info@interaccess.com
URL: http://www.unitedlearning.com
Format(s): Videocassette. **Descr:** A consumer education course for disabled people is detailed. **Prod. Date:** 1988. **Length:** 28. **Price:** $199.

6493 ■ *Motivating Employees to Follow Safety Rules and Practices*
ERI Safety Videos
374 Park Rd
Lexington, SC 29072
Ph: (803)356-4880
Free: 800-311-1143
Fax: (803)356-1946
URL: http://www.eri-safety.com
Format(s): Videocassette. **Descr:** An explanation for industrial workers as to why they should follow safety precautions. **Prod. Date:** 1987. **Length:** 30. **Price:** $495.00.

6494 ■ *Motivation: A Means to Accident Prevention*
Film Library/Greater Los Angeles Safety Council
600 Wilshire Blvd., No. 1263
Los Angeles, CA 90017
Ph: (213)385-6461
Free: 800-421-9585
Fax: (213)385-8405
URL: http://www.lasafety.org
Format(s): Videocassette. **Descr:** Herein are some of the methods that supervisors can use to motivate employees towards safer work practices. **Prod. Date:** 198?. **Length:** 10.

6495 ■ *Multiple Choice*
Film Library/Greater Los Angeles Safety Council
600 Wilshire Blvd., No. 1263
Los Angeles, CA 90017
Ph: (213)385-6461
Free: 800-421-9585
Fax: (213)385-8405
URL: http://www.lasafety.org
Format(s): Videocassette. **Descr:** This film features a series of reconstructed accident situations wherein viewers are asked to spot the hazard that caused the accident. **Prod. Date:** 198?. **Length:** 24.

6496 ■ *Must We Fall?*
Film Library/Greater Los Angeles Safety Council
600 Wilshire Blvd., No. 1263
Los Angeles, CA 90017
Ph: (213)385-6461
Free: 800-421-9585
Fax: (213)385-8405
URL: http://www.lasafety.org
Format(s): Videocassette. **Descr:** A stunt man shares his secrets for performing hazardous stunts safely and tells how these methods can be used to prevent slips and falls. **Prod. Date:** 198?. **Length:** 17.

6497 ■ *My Son Jack*
Aquarius Productions
Olde Medfield Sq
18 N Main St
Sherborn, MA 01770
Ph: (508)650-1616
Free: 888-440-2963
Fax: (508)650-1665
E-mail: tm@aquariusproductions.com
URL: http://www.aquariusproductions.com
Format(s): Videocassette. **Descr:** Explores how a family copes with an autistic child as he ages. Discusses origins, diagnosis, and treatment options for children with Autism Spectrum Disorders. **Prod. Date:** 2002. **Length:** 30. **Price:** $90.

6498 ■ *Never Say Die*
Film Library/Greater Los Angeles Safety Council
600 Wilshire Blvd., No. 1263
Los Angeles, CA 90017
Ph: (213)385-6461

Free: 800-421-9585
Fax: (213)385-8405
URL: http://www.lasafety.org
Format(s): Videocassette. **Descr:** This film is designed to improve oil rig hands' attitudes towards safety. **Prod. Date:** 198?. **Length:** 25.

6499 ■ *New Hire Safety Orientation*
Film Library/Greater Los Angeles Safety Council
600 Wilshire Blvd., No. 1263
Los Angeles, CA 90017
Ph: (213)385-6461
Free: 800-421-9585
Fax: (213)385-8405
URL: http://www.lasafety.org
Format(s): Videocassette. **Descr:** This orientation film is designed to introduce new employees to basic safety concepts. **Prod. Date:** 198?. **Length:** 12.

6500 ■ *Nice to Hear*
Film Library/Greater Los Angeles Safety Council
600 Wilshire Blvd., No. 1263
Los Angeles, CA 90017
Ph: (213)385-6461
Free: 800-421-9585
Fax: (213)385-8405
URL: http://www.lasafety.org
Format(s): Videocassette. **Descr:** This demonstration shows the various types of hearing protection available for those who work in noisy environments. **Prod. Date:** 198?. **Length:** 10.

6501 ■ *No More Secrets*
Select Media, Inc.
P.O. Box 1084
Harriman, NY 10926
Free: 845-774-7335
Fax: (845)774-2945
E-mail: tyree@selectmedia.org
URL: http://www.selectmedia.org
Format(s): Videocassette. **Descr:** Provides children with the skills and information they need to avoid sexual abuse. Uses animation to demonstrate assertiveness. Includes book and discussion guide. **Prod. Date:** 1982. **Length:** 13. **Price:** $295.

6502 ■ *Nobody's Fault*
Film Library/Greater Los Angeles Safety Council
600 Wilshire Blvd., No. 1263
Los Angeles, CA 90017
Ph: (213)385-6461
Free: 800-421-9585
Fax: (213)385-8405
URL: http://www.lasafety.org
Format(s): Videocassette. **Descr:** In this dramatic presentation, a series of seemingly innocent on-the-job actions lead to a tragedy. **Prod. Date:** 198?. **Length:** 20.

6503 ■ *Noise You're in Control*
ERI Safety Videos
374 Park Rd
Lexington, SC 29072
Ph: (803)356-4880
Free: 800-311-1143
Fax: (803)356-1946
URL: http://www.eri-safety.com
Format(s): Videocassette. **Descr:** This program shows different types of machines, tools and materials which can cause hearing damage, the use of personal protection and company commitment to noise conservation and prevention of hearing damage to employees. **Prod. Date:** 1982. **Length:** 15.

6504 ■ *On Guard: Infection Control for Safety and Health Care Workers*
Pyramid Media
PO Box 1048/WEB
Santa Monica, CA 90406
Ph: (310)828-7577
Free: 800-421-2304
Fax: (310)453-9083
E-mail: info@pyramedia.com
URL: http://www.pyramidmedia.com
Format(s): Videocassette. **Descr:** A presentation on recommended procedures for reducing the risk of

infection. **Prod. Date:** 1990. **Length:** 30. **Price:** $325.00.

6505 ■ *On Top of the Pros*
Film Library/Greater Los Angeles Safety Council
600 Wilshire Blvd., No. 1263
Los Angeles, CA 90017
Ph: (213)385-6461
Free: 800-421-9585
Fax: (213)385-8405
URL: http://www.lasafety.org
Format(s): Videocassette. **Descr:** This tape dramatically demonstrates why workers should wear their hard hats. **Prod. Date:** 198?. **Length:** 12.

6506 ■ *One in Five*
Film Library/Greater Los Angeles Safety Council
600 Wilshire Blvd., No. 1263
Los Angeles, CA 90017
Ph: (213)385-6461
Free: 800-421-9585
Fax: (213)385-8405
URL: http://www.lasafety.org
Format(s): Videocassette. **Descr:** This program points out that manual laborers are just as susceptible to coronary disease as the white collar worker. **Prod. Date:** 1981. **Length:** 17.

6507 ■ *One Last Shock*
Film Library/Greater Los Angeles Safety Council
600 Wilshire Blvd., No. 1263
Los Angeles, CA 90017
Ph: (213)385-6461
Free: 800-421-9585
Fax: (213)385-8405
URL: http://www.lasafety.org
Format(s): Videocassette. **Descr:** When an electrical worker disregards all safety regulations to finish a job he becomes seriously injured as a result. **Prod. Date:** 198?. **Length:** 21.

6508 ■ *One Million Hours*
Film Library/Greater Los Angeles Safety Council
600 Wilshire Blvd., No. 1263
Los Angeles, CA 90017
Ph: (213)385-6461
Free: 800-421-9585
Fax: (213)385-8405
URL: http://www.lasafety.org
Format(s): Videocassette. **Descr:** The viewer joins a committee investigating an accident that occurred at a local factory. **Prod. Date:** 198?. **Length:** 22.

6509 ■ *One Step Ahead: A Film About Safety Awareness*
Leo Media, Inc.
110 W. Main
Urbana, IL 61801
Ph: (217)337-0700
Free: 800-421-6999
E-mail: info@leomedia.net
URL: http://www.leomedia.net
Format(s): Videocassette. **Descr:** A detailed presentation on how parents can anticipate and prevent accidents around the home. Also good for day care providers and babysitters. **Prod. Date:** 19??. **Length:** 18. **Price:** $325.00.

6510 ■ *Operation Teddy Bear: Child Safety Seats*
Medical University of South Carolina
Division of Television Services
Health Communications Network
171 Ashley Ave
Charleston, SC 29425
Ph: (843)792-2300
URL: http://www.musc.edu
Format(s): Videocassette. **Descr:** This program is designed to inform the general public of the importance of using safety seats for children under age four to prevent serious injury from automobile accidents. **Prod. Date:** 1981. **Length:** 30.

6511 ■ *Orientation to Basic Chemical Safety*
ERI Safety Videos
374 Park Rd

Lexington, SC 29072
Ph: (803)356-4880
Free: 800-311-1143
Fax: (803)356-1946
URL: http://www.eri-safety.com
Format(s): Videocassette. **Descr:** A complete introduction to working safely with chemicals. **Prod. Date:** 1987. **Length:** 18. **Price:** $425.00.

6512 ■ *Orientation and Indoctrination of Safe Workmen*
Film Library/Greater Los Angeles Safety Council
600 Wilshire Blvd., No. 1263
Los Angeles, CA 90017
Ph: (213)385-6461
Free: 800-421-9585
Fax: (213)385-8405
URL: http://www.lasafety.org
Format(s): Videocassette. **Descr:** This tape demonstrates how training new employees in accident prevention can be of value to a company. **Prod. Date:** 198?. **Length:** 25.

6513 ■ *Orientation & Safety for the Offshore Oil Industry*
John Sabella & Associate
805 W. Emerson St
Seattle, WA 98119
Ph: (206)281-8626
Fax: (206)217-0899
E-mail: sales@johnsabella.com
URL: http://www.johnsabella.com
Format(s): Videocassette. **Descr:** Explains the latest developments in safety requirements to workers new to the offshore oil industry. **Prod. Date:** ?. **Length:** 43. **Price:** $395.00.

6514 ■ *OSHA Electrical Safety for Non-Electrical Workers*
Williams Learning Network
15400 Calhoun Dr
Rockville, MD 20855-2762
Ph: (301)315-6700
Free: 800-848-1717
Fax: (301)315-6880
E-mail: mait@willearn.com
URL: http://www.willearn.com
Format(s): Videocassette. **Descr:** Describes basic electrical safety for employees with little or no training. Explains basic properties of electricity, avoidance of electrical hazards, and steps to take in an electrical emergency. Helps meet OSHA 29 CFR 1910.331-335 training requirements. Includes Leader's Guide and 25 Program Guides. **Prod. Date:** 19??. **Length:** 20.

6515 ■ *Our Own Best Advocates: Breast Health for Women with Disabilities*
Aquarius Productions
Olde Medfield Sq
18 N Main St
Sherborn, MA 01770
Ph: (508)650-1616
Free: 888-440-2963
Fax: (508)650-1665
E-mail: tm@aquariusproductions.com
URL: http://www.aquariusproductions.com
Format(s): Videocassette. **Descr:** Demonstrates techniques for self breast exams for women with upper body disabilities and their partners. **Prod. Date:** 2000. **Length:** 14. **Price:** $99.00.

6516 ■ *Outdoor Safety Series*
New Dimension Media, Inc.
680 N Lake Shore Dr., Ste. 900
Chicago, IL 60611
Ph: (312)642-9400
Free: 800-288-4456
Fax: (312)642-9805
E-mail: Info@NDMquestar.com
URL: http://www.ndmquestar.com
Format(s): Videocassette. **Descr:** Series features outdoor activities and safety factors. Each individual

program is highly acclaimed. **Prod. Date:** 1991. **Length:** 25. **Price:** $160.00.

6517 ■ *Parenting Children with Learning Differences: LD, AD/HD*
Sunburst Technology
400 Columbus Ave, Ste 160E
Valhalla, NY 10595-1349
Ph: (914)747-3310
Fax: (914)747-4109
E-mail: webmaster@snysunburst.com
URL: http://www.sunburst.com
Format(s): Videocassette. **Descr:** Teaches parents methods to help their children with learning disabilities or behavioral problems get the best education, deal with conflicts and more. **Prod. Date:** 2000. **Length:** 47. **Price:** $89.95.

6518 ■ *Particularly Poor Albert*
Film Library/Greater Los Angeles Safety Council
600 Wilshire Blvd., No. 1263
Los Angeles, CA 90017
Ph: (213)385-6461
Free: 800-421-9585
Fax: (213)385-8405
URL: http://www.lasafety.org
Format(s): Videocassette. **Descr:** A forklift operator tells the story of how his carelessness led to a near fatal accident which resulted in his hospitalization. **Prod. Date:** 198?. **Length:** 17.

6519 ■ *The Path of Least Resistance*
ERI Safety Videos
374 Park Rd
Lexington, SC 29072
Ph: (803)356-4880
Free: 800-311-1143
Fax: (803)356-1946
URL: http://www.eri-safety.com
Format(s): Videocassette. **Descr:** This program deals with the prevention of electrical equipment accidents. **Prod. Date:** 1982. **Length:** 15.

6520 ■ *Payday*
New Dimension Media, Inc.
680 N Lake Shore Dr., Ste. 900
Chicago, IL 60611
Ph: (312)642-9400
Free: 800-288-4456
Fax: (312)642-9805
E-mail: Info@NDMquestar.com
URL: http://www.ndmquestar.com
Format(s): Videocassette. **Descr:** A cautionary program for elementary-level students about proper bus-riding behavior. **Prod. Date:** 1985. **Length:** 18.

6521 ■ *People Who Keep You Safe*
Marshmedia
PO Box 8082
Shawnee Mission, KS 66208
Ph: (816)523-1059
Free: 800-821-3303
Fax: (816)333-7421
E-mail: order@marshmedia.com
URL: http://www.marshmedia.com
Format(s): Videocassette. **Descr:** Health E. Elf visits firemen, policemen, teachers, and other people who help keep kids safe. **Prod. Date:** 1988. **Length:** 45. **Price:** $47.50.

6522 ■ *Perfect Gift*
Film Library/Greater Los Angeles Safety Council
600 Wilshire Blvd., No. 1263
Los Angeles, CA 90017
Ph: (213)385-6461
Free: 800-421-9585
Fax: (213)385-8405
URL: http://www.lasafety.org
Format(s): Videocassette. **Descr:** A graphic demonstration of what can happen to unprotected infants in car crashes or sudden stops. **Prod. Date:** 1985. **Length:** 22.

6523 ■ *Permit to Work*
Film Library/Greater Los Angeles Safety Council
600 Wilshire Blvd., No. 1263

Los Angeles, CA 90017
Ph: (213)385-6461
Free: 800-421-9585
Fax: (213)385-8405
URL: http://www.lasafety.org
Format(s): Videocassette. **Descr:** A deadly accident occurs in the confined spaces of a chemical storage tank. **Prod. Date:** 198?. **Length:** 23.

6524 ■ *Personal Responsibility for Safety*
ERI Safety Videos
374 Park Rd
Lexington, SC 29072
Ph: (803)356-4880
Free: 800-311-1143
Fax: (803)356-1946
URL: http://www.eri-safety.com
Format(s): Videocassette. **Descr:** Play it safe when you're on the job. Find out some things you can do to avoid accidents. **Prod. Date:** 1987. **Length:** 15. **Price:** $425.00.

6525 ■ *Physical Limitations*
Film Library/Greater Los Angeles Safety Council
600 Wilshire Blvd., No. 1263
Los Angeles, CA 90017
Ph: (213)385-6461
Free: 800-421-9585
Fax: (213)385-8405
URL: http://www.lasafety.org
Format(s): Videocassette. **Descr:** Viewers learn how employee awareness of physical limitations can reduce accidents and prevent errors in judgment in this program. **Prod. Date:** 198?. **Length:** 10.

6526 ■ *Plan for Prevention*
Film Library/Greater Los Angeles Safety Council
600 Wilshire Blvd., No. 1263
Los Angeles, CA 90017
Ph: (213)385-6461
Free: 800-421-9585
Fax: (213)385-8405
URL: http://www.lasafety.org
Format(s): Videocassette. **Descr:** In this tape, a safety director and his foreman discover that good investigation and reportage can help in forming an effective plan against industrial accidents. **Prod. Date:** 198?. **Length:** 10.

6527 ■ *Planned Safety Inspections*
ERI Safety Videos
374 Park Rd
Lexington, SC 29072
Ph: (803)356-4880
Free: 800-311-1143
Fax: (803)356-1946
URL: http://www.eri-safety.com
Format(s): Videocassette. **Descr:** An instructional video which teaches managers how to run safety inspections. **Prod. Date:** 1987. **Length:** 16. **Price:** $425.00.

6528 ■ *Plans for Talks*
Film Library/Greater Los Angeles Safety Council
600 Wilshire Blvd., No. 1263
Los Angeles, CA 90017
Ph: (213)385-6461
Free: 800-421-9585
Fax: (213)385-8405
URL: http://www.lasafety.org
Format(s): Videocassette. **Descr:** This tape tells supervisors how to turn any encounter with workers into a safety talk to maintain safety awareness in his department. **Prod. Date:** 198?. **Length:** 10.

6529 ■ *Plant Emergency Organization*
Film Library/Greater Los Angeles Safety Council
600 Wilshire Blvd., No. 1263
Los Angeles, CA 90017
Ph: (213)385-6461
Free: 800-421-9585
Fax: (213)385-8405
URL: http://www.lasafety.org
Format(s): Videocassette. **Descr:** This is a demonstration of what a plant emergency organization is

and how to form one. **Prod. Date:** 198?. **Length:** 15.

6530 ■ *Play It Safe: Making Playtime Safe for Your Child*
Cambridge Educational
c/o Films Media Group
PO Box 2053
Princeton, NJ 08843-2053
Free: 800-257-5126
Fax: (609)671-0266
E-mail: custserve@filmsmediagroup.com
URL: http://www.cambridgeol.com
Format(s): Videocassette. **Descr:** Video guide for parents and educators demonstrates how to test toys for safety, and provide safe environments for play. **Prod. Date:** 1993. **Price:** $59.95.

6531 ■ *Pliers and Screwdrivers*
Film Library/Greater Los Angeles Safety Council
600 Wilshire Blvd., No. 1263
Los Angeles, CA 90017
Ph: (213)385-6461
Free: 800-421-9585
Fax: (213)385-8405
URL: http://www.lasafety.org
Format(s): Videocassette. **Descr:** This is a demonstration of how to properly use pliers and screwdrivers, and of the safety precautions that should be taken when they are used. **Prod. Date:** 198?. **Length:** 15.

6532 ■ *Pooh's Great School Bus Adventure*
Phoenix Learning Group
2349 Chaffee Dr
St. Louis, MO 63146
Ph: (314)569-0211
Free: 800-221-1274
Fax: (314)569-2834
URL: http://www.phoenixlearninggroup.com
Format(s): Videocassette. **Descr:** Winnie, Piglet, Tigger and the crowd sing songs about the safety rules for going to school that Christopher Robin has taught them. **Prod. Date:** 1990. **Length:** 14. **Price:** $285.00.

6533 ■ *Portable Circular Saws*
Film Library/Greater Los Angeles Safety Council
600 Wilshire Blvd., No. 1263
Los Angeles, CA 90017
Ph: (213)385-6461
Free: 800-421-9585
Fax: (213)385-8405
URL: http://www.lasafety.org
Format(s): Videocassette. **Descr:** This is a reenactment of an accident involving an unsupported cut. **Prod. Date:** 198?. **Length:** 5.

6534 ■ *Portable Fire Extinguisher Safety*
Tel-A-Train, Inc.
305 Crewdson Ave
Chattanooga, TN 37405
E-mail: wkingsb@pwpl.com
Format(s): Videocassette. **Descr:** Discussion of fires types: ordinary combustible; flammable liquid oil gas fires; electrical fires; and combustible metal fires. Details four classes of fire extinguishers (A, B, C and D) and their contents. **Prod. Date:** ????. **Length:** 26. **Price:** $410.00.

6535 ■ *Portable Grinder Safety*
ERI Safety Videos
374 Park Rd
Lexington, SC 29072
Ph: (803)356-4880
Free: 800-311-1143
Fax: (803)356-1946
URL: http://www.eri-safety.com
Format(s): Videocassette. **Descr:** Grinders are used to remove excess metal from casting or welding. However, they could also cause injury, so learn some

safety tips first. **Prod. Date:** 1987. **Length:** 10. **Price:** $325.00.

6536 ■ *Powder-Actuated Tools*
Film Library/Greater Los Angeles Safety Council
600 Wilshire Blvd., No. 1263
Los Angeles, CA 90017
Ph: (213)385-6461
Free: 800-421-9585
Fax: (213)385-8405
URL: http://www.lasafety.org
Format(s): Videocassette. **Descr:** This tape demonstrates the proper safety precautions to take when operating powder-actuated tools. **Prod. Date:** 198?. **Length:** 7.

6537 ■ *Power Tools*
Film Library/Greater Los Angeles Safety Council
600 Wilshire Blvd., No. 1263
Los Angeles, CA 90017
Ph: (213)385-6461
Free: 800-421-9585
Fax: (213)385-8405
URL: http://www.lasafety.org
Format(s): Videocassette. **Descr:** This tape give an overview of the use and misuse of the most common power tools in dangerous work areas. **Prod. Date:** 198?. **Length:** 5.

6538 ■ *Pressurized Gas Safety*
ERI Safety Videos
374 Park Rd
Lexington, SC 29072
Ph: (803)356-4880
Free: 800-311-1143
Fax: (803)356-1946
URL: http://www.eri-safety.com
Format(s): Videocassette. **Descr:** Impress your workers into following safety procedures when dealing with pressurized gas by showing them what might happen if they don't. **Prod. Date:** 1987. **Length:** 11. **Price:** $325.00.

6539 ■ *Prevent that Pain*
Film Library/Greater Los Angeles Safety Council
600 Wilshire Blvd., No. 1263
Los Angeles, CA 90017
Ph: (213)385-6461
Free: 800-421-9585
Fax: (213)385-8405
URL: http://www.lasafety.org
Format(s): Videocassette. **Descr:** Dr. Leonard Ring tells how hernias happen and how they can be avoided in this demonstration. **Prod. Date:** 198?. **Length:** 13.

6540 ■ *Preventable-Yes or No?*
National Safety Council
1121 Spring Lake Dr
Itasca, IL 60143-3201
Ph: (630)285-1121
Free: 800-621-7619
Fax: (630)285-1315
E-mail: info@nsc.org
URL: http://www.nsc.org
Format(s): Videocassette. **Descr:** On the job, employees can help prevent accidents, even if it isn't their own job; encourages such behavior. **Prod. Date:** 1988. **Length:** 10.

6541 ■ *Preventing Welding and Cutting Fires*
Film Library/Greater Los Angeles Safety Council
600 Wilshire Blvd., No. 1263
Los Angeles, CA 90017
Ph: (213)385-6461
Free: 800-421-9585
Fax: (213)385-8405
URL: http://www.lasafety.org
Format(s): Videocassette. **Descr:** This is an examination of the fire hazards that occur in cutting and welding operations and the precautions that can be

taken to prevent them. **Prod. Date:** 198?. **Length:** 12.

6542 ■ *Prevention of Drowning*
National Audiovisual Center
5285 Port Royal Rd
Springfield, VA 22161
Ph: (703)605-4603
Free: 800-553-6847
Fax: (703)321-8547
E-mail: orders@ntis.fedworld.gov
URL: http://www.ntis.gov/products/nac/index.asp
Format(s): Videocassette. **Descr:** This video, from the US Army, claims to teach one "how to keep from getting into a drowning situation and what to do if in one." **Prod. Date:** 1984. **Length:** 26. **Price:** $110.00.

6543 ■ *Prognosis: Safety*
Film Library/Greater Los Angeles Safety Council
600 Wilshire Blvd., No. 1263
Los Angeles, CA 90017
Ph: (213)385-6461
Free: 800-421-9585
Fax: (213)385-8405
URL: http://www.lasafety.org
Format(s): Videocassette. **Descr:** This film teaches health care personnel how to avoid being injured from falls, electric shock, radiation exposure and other hazards. **Prod. Date:** 198?. **Length:** 22.

6544 ■ *Protect Your Eyes on the Job*
Film Library/Greater Los Angeles Safety Council
600 Wilshire Blvd., No. 1263
Los Angeles, CA 90017
Ph: (213)385-6461
Free: 800-421-9585
Fax: (213)385-8405
URL: http://www.lasafety.org
Format(s): Videocassette. **Descr:** A man blinded in an industrial accident tells how the event affected himself and his family. **Prod. Date:** 198?. **Length:** 13.

6545 ■ *Protect Your Hearing*
Film Library/Greater Los Angeles Safety Council
600 Wilshire Blvd., No. 1263
Los Angeles, CA 90017
Ph: (213)385-6461
Free: 800-421-9585
Fax: (213)385-8405
URL: http://www.lasafety.org
Format(s): Videocassette. **Descr:** This is a demonstration of how the ear is vulnerable to noise attack, and of how to go about protecting your hearing. **Prod. Date:** 198?. **Length:** 15.

6546 ■ *Protecting Your Back*
Williams Learning Network
15400 Calhoun Dr
Rockville, MD 20855-2762
Ph: (301)315-6700
Free: 800-848-1717
Fax: (301)315-6880
E-mail: mait@willearn.com
URL: http://www.willearn.com
Format(s): Videocassette. **Descr:** Illustrates techniques to use to help protect your back from injury. Covers lifting, moving, and stacking loads with emphasis on the use of leg muscles to lift, keeping loads close to the body, and applying principles of mechanical advantage when turning valves and wrenches. Includes Leader's Guide and 25 Program Guides. **Length:** 6.

6547 ■ *RAD TV: The Sequel*
NSI Sound & Video Inc.
105 S Sparks St
Burbank, CA 91506
Ph: (818)848-1004
Free: 800-333-4674
Fax: (818)848-1571
URL: http://www.nsisound.com
Format(s): Videocassette. **Descr:** Freestyle biking is featured, along with how to perform tricks, safety tips

and new locations. **Prod. Date:** 1987. **Length:** 30. **Price:** $24.95.

6548 ■ *Reachin' for the Lightning*
Film Library/Greater Los Angeles Safety Council
600 Wilshire Blvd., No. 1263
Los Angeles, CA 90017
Ph: (213)385-6461
Free: 800-421-9585
Fax: (213)385-8405
URL: http://www.lasafety.org

Format(s): Videocassette. **Descr:** This tape demonstrates how workers can prevent themselves from becoming human lightning rods at work, home or play. **Prod. Date:** 198?. **Length:** 10.

6549 ■ *Readers Are Leaders*
PBS Home Video
Catalog Fulfillment Center
PO Box 751089
Charlotte, NC 28275-1089
Ph: 800-531-4727
Free: 800-645-4PBS
E-mail: info@pbs.org
URL: http://www.pbs.org

Format(s): Videocassette. **Descr:** An innovative program that teaches children to read and write using phononyms, or sounds of words. Package includes a teacher handbook, two workbooks, five student readers, phononym flash cards as well as paper and pencils. **Prod. Date:** 1998. **Length:** 30. **Price:** $89.98.

6550 ■ *Ready for Fire?*
Film Library/Greater Los Angeles Safety Council
600 Wilshire Blvd., No. 1263
Los Angeles, CA 90017
Ph: (213)385-6461
Free: 800-421-9585
Fax: (213)385-8405
URL: http://www.lasafety.org

Format(s): Videocassette. **Descr:** This is a detailed account of how three disastrous fires affected employees, business operations and the surrounding community. **Prod. Date:** 198?. **Length:** 18.

6551 ■ *Recipe For Safety*
Film Library/Greater Los Angeles Safety Council
600 Wilshire Blvd., No. 1263
Los Angeles, CA 90017
Ph: (213)385-6461
Free: 800-421-9585
Fax: (213)385-8405
URL: http://www.lasafety.org

Format(s): Videocassette. **Descr:** A demonstration of the correct and incorrect kitchen safety procedures to follow. **Prod. Date:** 198?. **Length:** 10.

6552 ■ *Recognizing Chemical Hazards*
ERI Safety Videos
374 Park Rd
Lexington, SC 29072
Ph: (803)356-4880
Free: 800-311-1143
Fax: (803)356-1946
URL: http://www.eri-safety.com

Format(s): Videocassette. **Descr:** After watching this tape, you should not only know how to recognize potential chemical hazards but teach your employees how to do the same. **Prod. Date:** 1987. **Length:** 10. **Price:** $325.00.

6553 ■ *Rescue Team Alert*
Film Library/Greater Los Angeles Safety Council
600 Wilshire Blvd., No. 1263
Los Angeles, CA 90017
Ph: (213)385-6461
Free: 800-421-9585
Fax: (213)385-8405
URL: http://www.lasafety.org

Format(s): Videocassette. **Descr:** This program describes how a rescue team can be effective in situ-

ations requiring the removal of injured persons in a factory. **Prod. Date:** 198?. **Length:** 22.

6554 ■ *Responding to a Fire Emergency*
Williams Learning Network
15400 Calhoun Dr
Rockville, MD 20855-2762
Ph: (301)315-6700
Free: 800-848-1717
Fax: (301)315-6880
E-mail: mait@willearn.com
URL: http://www.willearn.com

Format(s): Videocassette. **Descr:** Stresses the importance of following a company's fire emergency procedures with emphasis on swift and smart reaction by employees to help contain the fire and alert others about the emergency. Includes Leader's Guide and 25 Program Guides. **Prod. Date:** 19??. **Length:** 7.

6555 ■ *Responsibility to Act*
Film Library/Greater Los Angeles Safety Council
600 Wilshire Blvd., No. 1263
Los Angeles, CA 90017
Ph: (213)385-6461
Free: 800-421-9585
Fax: (213)385-8405
URL: http://www.lasafety.org

Format(s): Videocassette. **Descr:** This is a demonstration of why it is important for workers to be responsible for their own safety and the safety of the workplace. **Prod. Date:** 198?. **Length:** 18.

6556 ■ *The Responsible Hunter*
Phoenix Learning Group
2349 Chaffee Dr
St. Louis, MO 63146
Ph: (314)569-0211
Free: 800-221-1274
Fax: (314)569-2834
URL: http://www.phoenixlearninggroup.com

Format(s): Videocassette. **Descr:** This video encourages responsible attitudes towards hunting and firearms, and teaches that hunting must be done with the correct ethical attitude. **Prod. Date:** 1984. **Length:** 23. **Price:** $250.

6557 ■ *The Revised Consumer Education Series*
Journal Films, Inc.
1560 Sherman Ave., Ste. 100
Evanston, IL 60201
Ph: (847)328-6700
Free: 800-323-9084
Fax: (847)328-6706
E-mail: info@agcmedia.com
URL: http://www.agcmedia.com

Format(s): Videocassette. **Descr:** Series uses humor to teach savvy consumer skills. New footage is included in revised editions. **Prod. Date:** 1988. **Length:** 22. **Price:** $900.00.

6558 ■ *Reviving Ophelia*
Media Education Foundation
60 Masonic St
Northampton, MA 01060
Ph: (413)584-8500
Free: 800-897-0089
Fax: (413)586-8398
E-mail: info@mediaed.org
URL: http://www.mediaed.org

Format(s): Videocassette. **Descr:** Mary Pipher, Ph. D., discusses the challenges facing today's teenagers, especially girls. Offers ideas for teens, families and schools to help girls free themselves from harmful influences in modern culture. Special pricing available to high schools. **Length:** 35. **Price:** $250.

6559 ■ *Right-to-Know Training Video*
LearnCom HR Consulting and Training
38 Discovery, Ste. 250
Irvine, CA 92618
Ph: (515)440-0890
Free: 800-698-8263
Fax: (515)221-3149

E-mail: nhartline@learncom.com
URL: http://www.learncomhr.com

Format(s): Videocassette. **Descr:** Make sure you've protected your employer and your staff with these dynamic and easy to understand tapes covering all necessary information about work with hazardous materials. **Prod. Date:** 1991. **Length:** 22. **Price:** $295.00.

6560 ■ *R.I.P. Harry Sparks*
Film Library/Greater Los Angeles Safety Council
600 Wilshire Blvd., No. 1263
Los Angeles, CA 90017
Ph: (213)385-6461
Free: 800-421-9585
Fax: (213)385-8405
URL: http://www.lasafety.org

Format(s): Videocassette. **Descr:** The guardian angel of electrical workers, Harry Sparks, attempts to keep others from making the same mistake with electricity that he did. **Prod. Date:** 198?. **Length:** 20.

6561 ■ *The Risk Takers*
Film Library/Greater Los Angeles Safety Council
600 Wilshire Blvd., No. 1263
Los Angeles, CA 90017
Ph: (213)385-6461
Free: 800-421-9585
Fax: (213)385-8405
URL: http://www.lasafety.org

Format(s): Videocassette. **Descr:** A portrayal of what can happen when horseplay enters the job scene. A bridegroom inadvertently kills his best man while driving a forklift because he failed to follow safety regulations. **Prod. Date:** 1995. **Length:** 15. **Price:** $430.00.

6562 ■ *The Roll of Drums*
Film Library/Greater Los Angeles Safety Council
600 Wilshire Blvd., No. 1263
Los Angeles, CA 90017
Ph: (213)385-6461
Free: 800-421-9585
Fax: (213)385-8405
URL: http://www.lasafety.org

Format(s): Videocassette. **Descr:** This film demonstrates the risks careless employees take when working with heavy construction equipment. **Prod. Date:** 198?. **Length:** 20.

6563 ■ *Roscoe's Rules*
AIMS Multimedia
20765 Superior St
Chatsworth, CA 91311-4409
Ph: (818)773-4300
Free: 800-367-2467
Fax: (818)341-6700
E-mail: info@aims.multimedia.com
URL: http://www.aimsmultimedia.com

Format(s): Videocassette. **Descr:** A cop and his teddy bear teach kids basic safety rules. **Prod. Date:** 1981. **Length:** 10.

6564 ■ *Round Trip to Danger*
Film Library/Greater Los Angeles Safety Council
600 Wilshire Blvd., No. 1263
Los Angeles, CA 90017
Ph: (213)385-6461
Free: 800-421-9585
Fax: (213)385-8405
URL: http://www.lasafety.org

Format(s): Videocassette. **Descr:** A professional stuntman demonstrates how to safely operate such logging industry equipment as grapple and cable skidders in this program. **Prod. Date:** 198?. **Length:** 21.

6565 ■ *Run the Team*
Film Library/Greater Los Angeles Safety Council
600 Wilshire Blvd., No. 1263
Los Angeles, CA 90017
Ph: (213)385-6461
Free: 800-421-9585
Fax: (213)385-8405
URL: http://www.lasafety.org

Format(s): Videocassette. Descr: This tape tells how management can provide effective safety leadership in order to make an industrial accident prevention program successful. Prod. Date: 198?. Length: 10.

6566 ■ Safe and Awake
Film Library/Greater Los Angeles Safety Council
600 Wilshire Blvd., No. 1263
Los Angeles, CA 90017
Ph: (213)385-6461
Free: 800-421-9585
Fax: (213)385-8405
URL: http://www.lasafety.org
Format(s): Videocassette. Descr: This film is designed to motivate employees to change their attitudes about job safety. Prod. Date: 198?. Length: 15.

6567 ■ Safe Diving
Film Library/Greater Los Angeles Safety Council
600 Wilshire Blvd., No. 1263
Los Angeles, CA 90017
Ph: (213)385-6461
Free: 800-421-9585
Fax: (213)385-8405
URL: http://www.lasafety.org
Format(s): Videocassette. Descr: This film teaches offshore oil industry workers about the basics of diving. Prod. Date: 198?. Length: 22.

6568 ■ Safe Handling of Light Ends
Film Library/Greater Los Angeles Safety Council
600 Wilshire Blvd., No. 1263
Los Angeles, CA 90017
Ph: (213)385-6461
Free: 800-421-9585
Fax: (213)385-8405
URL: http://www.lasafety.org
Format(s): Videocassette. Descr: This tape demonstrates the correct techniques used in handling light ends. Prod. Date: 198?. Length: 20.

6569 ■ Safe as Houses
Film Library/Greater Los Angeles Safety Council
600 Wilshire Blvd., No. 1263
Los Angeles, CA 90017
Ph: (213)385-6461
Free: 800-421-9585
Fax: (213)385-8405
URL: http://www.lasafety.org
Format(s): Videocassette. Descr: When a builder's production schedule starts to lag due to job related accidents, he encourages safer work habits among his employees. Prod. Date: 198?. Length: 23.

6570 ■ Safe Lab Design
Williams Learning Network
15400 Calhoun Dr
Rockville, MD 20855-2762
Ph: (301)315-6700
Free: 800-848-1717
Fax: (301)315-6880
E-mail: mait@willearn.com
URL: http://www.willearn.com
Format(s): Videocassette. Descr: Illustrates ways of designing a laboratory with emphasis on safety. Includes Leader's Guide and 25 Program Guides.

6571 ■ Safe Lifting
Film Library/Greater Los Angeles Safety Council
600 Wilshire Blvd., No. 1263
Los Angeles, CA 90017
Ph: (213)385-6461
Free: 800-421-9585
Fax: (213)385-8405
URL: http://www.lasafety.org
Format(s): Videocassette. Descr: This is a demonstration of how the back and legs can best be used when lifting. Prod. Date: 198?. Length: 12.

6572 ■ Safe Operation of Pendant-Controlled Overhead Cranes
ERI Safety Videos
374 Park Rd
Lexington, SC 29072

Ph: (803)356-4880
Free: 800-311-1143
Fax: (803)356-1946
URL: http://www.eri-safety.com
Format(s): Videocassette. Descr: Safety techniques are explained for people who work with cranes. Prod. Date: 1987. Length: 8. Price: $425.00.

6573 ■ Safe Practices in Electrical Maintenance
Williams Learning Network
15400 Calhoun Dr
Rockville, MD 20855-2762
Ph: (301)315-6700
Free: 800-848-1717
Fax: (301)315-6880
E-mail: mait@willearn.com
URL: http://www.willearn.com
Format(s): Videocassette. Descr: Describes techniques in safe electrical maintenance practices. Covers the proper use of voltage detectors, arcing, fuses, and locking/tagging out a box. Contains a 12-step electrical maintenance scenario that illustrates proper electrical maintenance safety. Includes Leader's Guide and 25 Program Guides. Length: 9.

6574 ■ The S.A.F.E. Shooting Method
Gun Video
4585 Murphy Canyon Rd
San Diego, CA 92123
Ph: (858)569-4000
Free: 800-942-8273
Fax: (858)569-0505
E-mail: info2@gunvideo.com
URL: http://www.gunvideo.com
Format(s): Videocassette. Descr: Basic information on the safe use of firearms. Prod. Date: 1990. Length: 38. Price: $39.95.

6575 ■ Safe Welding and Cutting
ERI Safety Videos
374 Park Rd
Lexington, SC 29072
Ph: (803)356-4880
Free: 800-311-1143
Fax: (803)356-1946
URL: http://www.eri-safety.com
Format(s): Videocassette. Descr: Don't get hurt yourself when welding-learn the safe way. Prod. Date: 1987. Length: 15. Price: $325.00.

6576 ■ Safeguarding of Machine Tools
Film Library/Greater Los Angeles Safety Council
600 Wilshire Blvd., No. 1263
Los Angeles, CA 90017
Ph: (213)385-6461
Free: 800-421-9585
Fax: (213)385-8405
URL: http://www.lasafety.org
Format(s): Videocassette. Descr: A discussion of the major concepts for safeguarding of machine tools. Prod. Date: 198?. Length: 18.

6577 ■ Safely—Walk to School
AIMS Multimedia
20765 Superior St
Chatsworth, CA 91311-4409
Ph: (818)773-4300
Free: 800-367-2467
Fax: (818)341-6700
E-mail: info@aims.multimedia.com
URL: http://www.aimsmultimedia.com
Format(s): Videocassette. Descr: Viewers follow Greg and Laurie walk to school safely. Prod. Date: 1983. Length: 12. Price: $195.00.

6578 ■ Safer Cycling
School-Tech Inc.
745 State Cir
PO Box 1941
Ann Arbor, MI 48106
Ph: (734)761-5072
Free: 800-521-2832
Fax: 800-654-4321
E-mail: service@school-tech.com
URL: http://www.schoolmasters.com

Format(s): Videocassette. Descr: The ins and outs of bicycle safety and general maintenance are discussed. Prod. Date: 1980. Length: 22.

6579 ■ A Safer You
GPN Educational Media
Box 80669
Lincoln, NE 68501-0669
Ph: (402)472-2007
Free: 800-228-4630
Fax: 800-306-2330
URL: http://gpn.unl.edu
Format(s): Videocassette. Descr: 13 programs demonstrating proper safety practices for use on the school bus, playground, and home as well as pedestrian and fire safety. Teacher's guide available. Prod. Date: 1984. Length: 15. Price: $264.

6580 ■ Safety: A Household Word
Film Library/Greater Los Angeles Safety Council
600 Wilshire Blvd., No. 1263
Los Angeles, CA 90017
Ph: (213)385-6461
Free: 800-421-9585
Fax: (213)385-8405
URL: http://www.lasafety.org
Format(s): Videocassette. Descr: A young couple learns all about how to make their new home a safer place to live in. Prod. Date: 198?. Length: 10.

6581 ■ Safety Afoot
Film Library/Greater Los Angeles Safety Council
600 Wilshire Blvd., No. 1263
Los Angeles, CA 90017
Ph: (213)385-6461
Free: 800-421-9585
Fax: (213)385-8405
URL: http://www.lasafety.org
Format(s): Videocassette. Descr: The importance of wearing safety shoes in all hazardous areas on the job is demonstrated. Prod. Date: 198?. Length: 10.

6582 ■ Safety Aloft
Film Library/Greater Los Angeles Safety Council
600 Wilshire Blvd., No. 1263
Los Angeles, CA 90017
Ph: (213)385-6461
Free: 800-421-9585
Fax: (213)385-8405
URL: http://www.lasafety.org
Format(s): Videocassette. Descr: A demonstration of the Fall Protection System and how to correctly use safety equipment in the construction industry. Prod. Date: 198?. Length: 20.

6583 ■ Safety Attitudes
Film Library/Greater Los Angeles Safety Council
600 Wilshire Blvd., No. 1263
Los Angeles, CA 90017
Ph: (213)385-6461
Free: 800-421-9585
Fax: (213)385-8405
URL: http://www.lasafety.org
Format(s): Videocassette. Descr: An illustration of how workers' attitudes can either cause or prevent accidents. Prod. Date: 198?. Length: 10.

6584 ■ The Safety Connection
New Jersey Network
25 S. Stockton St
Trenton, NJ 08625-0777
Ph: (609)777-5000
Free: 800-792-8645
Fax: (609)633-2920
E-mail: njnvideo@njn.org
URL: http://www.njn.net
Format(s): Videocassette. Descr: Shows the value of wearing an automobile seat belt. Prod. Date: 1988. Length: 30.

6585 ■ Safety Consciousness
Film Library/Greater Los Angeles Safety Council
600 Wilshire Blvd., No. 1263
Los Angeles, CA 90017
Ph: (213)385-6461

Free: 800-421-9585
Fax: (213)385-8405
URL: http://www.lasafety.org
Format(s): Videocassette. **Descr:** An examination of how people develop safe attitudes at work and at play. **Prod. Date:** 198?. **Length:** 10.

6586 ■ The Safety Deck
LearnCom HR Consulting and Training
38 Discovery, Ste. 250
Irvine, CA 92618
Ph: (515)440-0890
Free: 800-698-8263
Fax: (515)221-3149
E-mail: nhartline@learncom.com
URL: http://www.learncomhr.com
Format(s): Videocassette. **Descr:** Provides an overview of 13 job safety issues along with general safety information. Comes with deck of cards and training manual. **Prod. Date:** 19??. **Length:** 24. **Price:** $495.00.

6587 ■ The Safety Essentials Series
United Learning
1560 Sherman Ave., Ste. 100
PO Box 48718
Evanston, IL 60201
Ph: 888-892-3484
Fax: (847)328-6706
E-mail: info@interaccess.com
URL: http://www.unitedlearning.com
Format(s): Videocassette. **Descr:** Examines all aspects of potential injuries to various parts of the body and encourages prevention. **Prod. Date:** 1990. **Length:** 15. **Price:** $225.00.

6588 ■ Safety Everywhere
Film Library/Greater Los Angeles Safety Council
600 Wilshire Blvd., No. 1263
Los Angeles, CA 90017
Ph: (213)385-6461
Free: 800-421-9585
Fax: (213)385-8405
URL: http://www.lasafety.org
Format(s): Videocassette. **Descr:** A safety conscious worker also causes a disaster at home while working on a remodeling job. **Prod. Date:** 198?. **Length:** 10.

6589 ■ Safety: Help Is Just a Phone Call Away
Marshmedia
PO Box 8082
Shawnee Mission, KS 66208
Ph: (816)523-1059
Free: 800-821-3303
Fax: (816)333-7421
E-mail: order@marshmedia.com
URL: http://www.marshmedia.com
Format(s): Videocassette. **Descr:** A program that shows kids who have to stay home alone how to recognize an emergency and how to cope with it. **Prod. Date:** 1988. **Length:** 45. **Price:** $45.50.

6590 ■ Safety in Highway Surveying
Film Library/Greater Los Angeles Safety Council
600 Wilshire Blvd., No. 1263
Los Angeles, CA 90017
Ph: (213)385-6461
Free: 800-421-9585
Fax: (213)385-8405
URL: http://www.lasafety.org
Format(s): Videocassette. **Descr:** An illustration of the functions of a survey party and the hazards they encounter in their daily work. **Prod. Date:** 198?. **Length:** 25.

6591 ■ Safety Is in Order
Film Library/Greater Los Angeles Safety Council
600 Wilshire Blvd., No. 1263
Los Angeles, CA 90017
Ph: (213)385-6461
Free: 800-421-9585
Fax: (213)385-8405
URL: http://www.lasafety.org
Format(s): Videocassette. **Descr:** This tape examines how good housekeeping methods and orderly

work practices will increase both safety and productivity. **Prod. Date:** 198?. **Length:** 10.

6592 ■ Safety in the Lab? Safety in the Lab!
Health Sciences Consortium
300 Silver Cedar Ct
201 Silver Cedar Ct
Chapel Hill, NC 27514-1696
Ph: (919)942-8731
Fax: (919)942-3689
URL: http://www.healthsciencesconsortium.org
Format(s): Videocassette. **Descr:** Short dramatizations describe safety procedures to lab technologists. **Prod. Date:** 1985. **Length:** 15.

6593 ■ Safety for Mechanics
Film Library/Greater Los Angeles Safety Council
600 Wilshire Blvd., No. 1263
Los Angeles, CA 90017
Ph: (213)385-6461
Free: 800-421-9585
Fax: (213)385-8405
URL: http://www.lasafety.org
Format(s): Videocassette. **Descr:** This is a safety refresher course for mechanics and maintenance personnel covering hand and power tool safety, lock and tag outs and other general safety tips. **Prod. Date:** 198?. **Length:** 13.

6594 ■ Safety in Milling, Drilling and Boring Operations
Film Library/Greater Los Angeles Safety Council
600 Wilshire Blvd., No. 1263
Los Angeles, CA 90017
Ph: (213)385-6461
Free: 800-421-9585
Fax: (213)385-8405
URL: http://www.lasafety.org
Format(s): Videocassette. **Descr:** This is a detailed account of the safety requirements for the construction, care and use of drilling, milling and boring machines. **Prod. Date:** 198?. **Length:** 17.

6595 ■ Safety Odds of See-Think-Do
Film Library/Greater Los Angeles Safety Council
600 Wilshire Blvd., No. 1263
Los Angeles, CA 90017
Ph: (213)385-6461
Free: 800-421-9585
Fax: (213)385-8405
URL: http://www.lasafety.org
Format(s): Videocassette. **Descr:** A demonstration of how workers can take a continuing role in on the job accident prevention. **Prod. Date:** 198?. **Length:** 10.

6596 ■ Safety Orientation for Construction Contractors
DuPont Safety Resources
PO Box 80013
Wilmington, DE 19880-0013
Free: 800-532-7233
Fax: 888-644-7233
E-mail: info@dupont.com
URL: http://www.dupont.com/safety
Format(s): Videocassette. **Descr:** Designed to raise and promote safety consciousness among construction contractors and their employees. Includes an administrator's guide and personal handbooks outlining site safety rules and work practices. **Prod. Date:** 1993. **Length:** 16. **Price:** $475.00.

6597 ■ Safety Orientation Employees
DuPont Safety Resources
PO Box 80013
Wilmington, DE 19880-0013
Free: 800-532-7233
Fax: 888-644-7233
E-mail: info@dupont.com
URL: http://www.dupont.com/safety
Format(s): Videocassette. **Descr:** Teaches safety to both new and current employees through a six-step philosophy. Reminds employees about the safety practices they should observe each day, reinforces the employees' role in creating a safe job environment, and confirms the company's safety philosophy.

Employees will learn to report safety hazards, follow safety procedures, and observe their work areas and actions. Includes a leader's guide and a package of 10 workbooks. **Prod. Date:** 1993. **Length:** ?. **Price:** $415.00.

6598 ■ Safety on Our School Bus
Encyclopedia Britannica
331 N. LaSalle St
Chicago, IL 60610
Ph: (312)347-7159
Free: 800-323-1229
Fax: (312)294-2104
URL: http://www.britannica.com
Format(s): Videocassette. **Descr:** Proper ways to get on and off the school bus, and six basic rules of safe bus riding are covered. Emergency evacuation drills are included. **Prod. Date:** 1980. **Length:** 13.

6599 ■ Safety Rules for School (2nd Edition)
AIMS Multimedia
20765 Superior St
Chatsworth, CA 91311-4409
Ph: (818)773-4300
Free: 800-367-2467
Fax: (818)341-6700
E-mail: info@aims.multimedia.com
URL: http://www.aimsmultimedia.com
Format(s): Videocassette. **Descr:** An animated puppet teaches youngsters about school safety. **Prod. Date:** 1986. **Length:** 11. **Price:** $195.00.

6600 ■ The Safety Secret
American Media, Inc.
4621 121st St
Urbandale, IA 50323-2311
Ph: (515)224-0919
Free: 888-776-8268
Fax: (515)327-2555
E-mail: custsvc@ammedia.com
URL: http://www.ammedia.com
Format(s): Videocassette. **Descr:** A dramatized training film devised to teach employees to conscientously follow rules of safety. **Prod. Date:** 1987. **Length:** 25. **Price:** $475.00.

6601 ■ Safety: Total Loss Control
Film Library/Greater Los Angeles Safety Council
600 Wilshire Blvd., No. 1263
Los Angeles, CA 90017
Ph: (213)385-6461
Free: 800-421-9585
Fax: (213)385-8405
URL: http://www.lasafety.org
Format(s): Videocassette. **Descr:** How industry can direct its accident prevention effort towards all incidents that may lead to an employee injury is shown. **Prod. Date:** 198?. **Length:** 10.

6602 ■ Safety Zone
Film Library/Greater Los Angeles Safety Council
600 Wilshire Blvd., No. 1263
Los Angeles, CA 90017
Ph: (213)385-6461
Free: 800-421-9585
Fax: (213)385-8405
URL: http://www.lasafety.org
Format(s): Videocassette. **Descr:** A demonstration of the preventative and corrective action techniques vital to every safety program. **Prod. Date:** 198?. **Length:** 27.

6603 ■ Say No to Strangers
Bennu Productions, Inc.
350 5th Ave
New York, NY 10118-0110
Fax: (212)563-8006
Format(s): Videocassette. **Descr:** Describes various techniques that help to teach children to say no to strangers and what to do if they are approached by a stranger. **Length:** 28. **Price:** $49.95.

6604 ■ Scaffolding
Film Library/Greater Los Angeles Safety Council
600 Wilshire Blvd., No. 1263
Los Angeles, CA 90017

Ph: (213)385-6461
Free: 800-421-9585
Fax: (213)385-8405
URL: http://www.lasafety.org
Format(s): Videocassette. **Descr:** A demonstration of how to safely erect a scaffold and what the primary causes of scaffold collapse are. **Prod. Date:** 198?.
Length: 11.

6605 ■ Scaffolds
Film Library/Greater Los Angeles Safety Council
600 Wilshire Blvd., No. 1263
Los Angeles, CA 90017
Ph: (213)385-6461
Free: 800-421-9585
Fax: (213)385-8405
URL: http://www.lasafety.org
Format(s): Videocassette. **Descr:** A discussion of the most commonly used internal and external scaffolds and why workers should report unsafe scaffold conditions. **Prod. Date:** 198?. **Length:** 5.

6606 ■ School Bus Safety
Phoenix Learning Group
2349 Chaffee Dr
St. Louis, MO 63146
Ph: (314)569-0211
Free: 800-221-1274
Fax: (314)569-2834
URL: http://www.phoenixlearninggroup.com
Format(s): Videocassette. **Descr:** How to evacuate a school bus safely is described. **Prod. Date:** 1987.
Length: 17. **Price:** $275.00.

6607 ■ School Bus Safety Seminar
WJER Video Services
646 Boulevard St
Dover, OH 44622-2081
Ph: (330)343-7755
Fax: (330)364-4538
E-mail: wjer@wjer.com
URL: http://www.wjer.com
Format(s): Videocassette. **Descr:** A thorough exposure of bus safety rules, with expert testimony, including a bus disaster simulation. **Prod. Date:** 1985. **Length:** 58.

6608 ■ School Lab Safety
Handel Film Corp.
8787 Shoreham Dr., Ste. 609
West Hollywood, CA 90069
Ph: (310)652-3887
Free: 800-395-8990
Fax: (310)657-2746
Format(s): Videocassette. **Descr:** This program points to more than 50 of the most common lab injuries and stresses the necessary precautions.
Prod. Date: 1980. **Length:** 20.

6609 ■ School and School Bus Safety
School-Tech Inc.
745 State Cir
PO Box 1941
Ann Arbor, MI 48106
Ph: (734)761-5072
Free: 800-521-2832
Fax: 800-654-4321
E-mail: service@school-tech.com
URL: http://www.schoolmasters.com
Format(s): Videocassette. **Descr:** Unsafe situations around school buses and schools in general are analyzed. Crowded corridors, stairways, second floor windows, and lockers are mentioned to ensure a safer school day. **Prod. Date:** 1980. **Length:** 22.

6610 ■ Schoolsite Learning Compared to Worksite Learning
University of Wisconsin at Madison
College of Engineering
Department of Engineering Professional Development
432 N. Lake St
Madison, WI 53706
Ph: (608)262-2061
Free: 800-462-0876

Fax: (608)263-3160
URL: http://www.engr.wisc.edu
Format(s): Videocassette. **Descr:** Explores the benefits of learning in an academic setting and in actual employment situations. **Prod. Date:** ????.
Length: 11. **Price:** $89.00.

6611 ■ The Science of Survival
Film Library/Greater Los Angeles Safety Council
600 Wilshire Blvd., No. 1263
Los Angeles, CA 90017
Ph: (213)385-6461
Free: 800-421-9585
Fax: (213)385-8405
URL: http://www.lasafety.org
Format(s): Videocassette. **Descr:** An indepth look at what an industrial hygienist does and how he works to eliminate hazards in the work environment. **Prod. Date:** 198?. **Length:** 10.

6612 ■ The Scoffer
Film Library/Greater Los Angeles Safety Council
600 Wilshire Blvd., No. 1263
Los Angeles, CA 90017
Ph: (213)385-6461
Free: 800-421-9585
Fax: (213)385-8405
URL: http://www.lasafety.org
Format(s): Videocassette. **Descr:** An employee who disregards safety rules and shows contempt for authority becomes involved in an accident. **Prod. Date:** 198?. **Length:** 10.

6613 ■ The Sea Can Kill
Film Library/Greater Los Angeles Safety Council
600 Wilshire Blvd., No. 1263
Los Angeles, CA 90017
Ph: (213)385-6461
Free: 800-421-9585
Fax: (213)385-8405
URL: http://www.lasafety.org
Format(s): Videocassette. **Descr:** A graphic dramatization of how some members of an oil rig survived when they were forced to abandon ship during a storm. **Prod. Date:** 198?. **Length:** 27.

6614 ■ A Second Chance
AIMS Multimedia
20765 Superior St
Chatsworth, CA 91311-4409
Ph: (818)773-4300
Free: 800-367-2467
Fax: (818)341-6700
E-mail: info@aims.multimedia.com
URL: http://www.aimsmultimedia.com
Format(s): Videocassette. **Descr:** A hermit happens upon two kids shooting birds and relives his own tragic, gun-related memories. **Prod. Date:** 1986.
Length: 27.

6615 ■ Sell Safety
Film Library/Greater Los Angeles Safety Council
600 Wilshire Blvd., No. 1263
Los Angeles, CA 90017
Ph: (213)385-6461
Free: 800-421-9585
Fax: (213)385-8405
URL: http://www.lasafety.org
Format(s): Videocassette. **Descr:** A description of how management can communicate safety to their employees and encourage around the clock safety awareness. **Prod. Date:** 198?. **Length:** 10.

6616 ■ Sexual Abuse Prevention: Five Safety Rules for Persons Who Are Mentally Handicapped
Agency for Instructional Technology (AIT)
1800 N. Stonelake Dr
Box A
Bloomington, IN 47402-0120
Ph: (812)339-2203
Free: 800-457-4509
Fax: (812)333-4218
E-mail: info@ait.net
URL: http://www.ait.net
Format(s): Videocassette. **Descr:** Five vignettes

designed to equip mentally impaired persons with the knowledge and skills needed to prevent sexual abuse in public and private areas. Safety rules include Your body belongs to you, Keep your clothes on in public, Say "No," Get away, and Tell someone. Instructor's manual available at additional cost. **Prod. Date:** 1987. **Length:** 25. **Price:** $150.00.

6617 ■ Shaking the Tree: Social Responsibility in Education
Moving Images Distribution
402 W. Pender St., Ste. 606
Vancouver, BC, Canada V6B 1T6
Ph: (604)684-3014
Fax: (604)684-7165
E-mail: mailbox@movingimages.ca
URL: http://www.movingimages.bc.ca
Format(s): Videocassette. **Descr:** Examines the Canadian educational system and its students. Racism, gender equality, body image, sexuality, violence and assimilation are questioned, as well as the quality and type of education students receive. **Prod. Date:** 1995. **Length:** 45.

6618 ■ Shape Up! Avoiding Back Injuries
ERI Safety Videos
374 Park Rd
Lexington, SC 29072
Ph: (803)356-4880
Free: 800-311-1143
Fax: (803)356-1946
URL: http://www.eri-safety.com
Format(s): Videocassette. **Descr:** This tape teaches proper lifting methods and do's and dont's for standing and sitting on the job. **Prod. Date:** 1983. **Length:** 17.

6619 ■ The Shield
Film Library/Greater Los Angeles Safety Council
600 Wilshire Blvd., No. 1263
Los Angeles, CA 90017
Ph: (213)385-6461
Free: 800-421-9585
Fax: (213)385-8405
URL: http://www.lasafety.org
Format(s): Videocassette. **Descr:** Contains testimonials from workers who have had their sight saved by wearing the proper eye protection. **Prod. Date:** 198?. **Length:** 14.

6620 ■ Shop Safety
Film Library/Greater Los Angeles Safety Council
600 Wilshire Blvd., No. 1263
Los Angeles, CA 90017
Ph: (213)385-6461
Free: 800-421-9585
Fax: (213)385-8405
URL: http://www.lasafety.org
Format(s): Videocassette. **Descr:** An examination of the most common hazards that occur in a vehicle maintenance shop and what safety precautions should be taken to avoid them. **Prod. Date:** 198?.
Length: 21.

6621 ■ Shop Safety Series
Meridian Education Corp.
2572 Brunswick Ave
Lawrenceville, NJ 08648-4128
Ph: (609)671-1000
Free: 800-727-5507
Fax: 888-340-5507
E-mail: custmserv@meridianeducation.com
URL: http://www.meridianeducation.com
Format(s): Videocassette. **Descr:** A series on accident prevention aimed at high-risk shop activities. The complete series includes a guide. **Prod. Date:** 1992. **Length:** ?. **Price:** $59.00.

6622 ■ Single-Surface Planner
Film Library/Greater Los Angeles Safety Council
600 Wilshire Blvd., No. 1263
Los Angeles, CA 90017
Ph: (213)385-6461
Free: 800-421-9585
Fax: (213)385-8405
URL: http://www.lasafety.org

Format(s): Videocassette. **Descr:** A demonstration of how to safely operate a single surface planner. **Prod. Date:** 198?. **Length:** 16.

6623 ■ *Skateboard Sense*
AIMS Multimedia
20765 Superior St
Chatsworth, CA 91311-4409
Ph: (818)773-4300
Free: 800-367-2467
Fax: (818)341-6700
E-mail: info@aims.multimedia.com
URL: http://www.aimsmultimedia.com

Format(s): Videocassette. **Descr:** Experts expound upon the proper techniques in skateboard riding to insure optimum safety and fun. **Prod. Date:** 1982. **Length:** 10.

6624 ■ *Ski Sense*
Film Library/Greater Los Angeles Safety Council
600 Wilshire Blvd., No. 1263
Los Angeles, CA 90017
Ph: (213)385-6461
Free: 800-421-9585
Fax: (213)385-8405
URL: http://www.lasafety.org

Format(s): Videocassette. **Descr:** A look at the causes behind many skiing accidents and what can be done to prevent them. **Prod. Date:** 198?. **Length:** 27.

6625 ■ *Skier's Choice*
Film Library/Greater Los Angeles Safety Council
600 Wilshire Blvd., No. 1263
Los Angeles, CA 90017
Ph: (213)385-6461
Free: 800-421-9585
Fax: (213)385-8405
URL: http://www.lasafety.org

Format(s): Videocassette. **Descr:** Offers some safety tips that beginning and intermediate skiers should keep in mind before hitting the slopes. **Prod. Date:** 198?. **Length:** 28.

6626 ■ *Lisa Sliwa's Common Sense Defense*
Artisan Entertainment
2700 Colorado Ave., Ste. 200
Santa Monica, CA 90404
Ph: (310)449-9200
Fax: (310)255-3730
URL: http://www.artisanent.com

Format(s): Videocassette. **Descr:** Guardian Angel Lisa Sliwa, wife of Curtis, demonstrates practical self-defense methods. **Prod. Date:** 1986. **Length:** 60. **Price:** $29.98.

6627 ■ *Smart Moves*
Film Library/Greater Los Angeles Safety Council
600 Wilshire Blvd., No. 1263
Los Angeles, CA 90017
Ph: (213)385-6461
Free: 800-421-9585
Fax: (213)385-8405
URL: http://www.lasafety.org

Format(s): Videocassette. **Descr:** A demonstration of how electrical linemen should use all available safety equipment to insure their personal safety. **Prod. Date:** 198?. **Length:** 10.

6628 ■ *So You Think You Can Drink and Drive*
National Safety Council
1121 Spring Lake Dr
Itasca, IL 60143-3201
Ph: (630)285-1121
Free: 800-621-7619
Fax: (630)285-1315
E-mail: info@nsc.org
URL: http://www.nsc.org

Format(s): Videocassette. **Descr:** Intended for school safety or driver education (high school level), this film explains the increased danger of accidents when drinking and driving. Comes with teacher materials. **Prod. Date:** 1988. **Length:** 19.

6629 ■ *Something to Do with Safety Reps*
Film Library/Greater Los Angeles Safety Council
600 Wilshire Blvd., No. 1263
Los Angeles, CA 90017
Ph: (213)385-6461
Free: 800-421-9585
Fax: (213)385-8405
URL: http://www.lasafety.org

Format(s): Videocassette. **Descr:** Two British safety reps discuss their attitudes towards their work. **Prod. Date:** 198?. **Length:** 22.

6630 ■ *The Sound of Sound*
Film Library/Greater Los Angeles Safety Council
600 Wilshire Blvd., No. 1263
Los Angeles, CA 90017
Ph: (213)385-6461
Free: 800-421-9585
Fax: (213)385-8405
URL: http://www.lasafety.org

Format(s): Videocassette. **Descr:** The importance of wearing proper hearing protection devices while on the job is emphasized. **Prod. Date:** 198?. **Length:** 17.

6631 ■ *Speaking from Experience*
Film Library/Greater Los Angeles Safety Council
600 Wilshire Blvd., No. 1263
Los Angeles, CA 90017
Ph: (213)385-6461
Free: 800-421-9585
Fax: (213)385-8405
URL: http://www.lasafety.org

Format(s): Videocassette. **Descr:** Victims of accidents describe their experiences to other workers so they will not make the same mistakes that they themselves made. **Prod. Date:** 198?. **Length:** 18.

6632 ■ *Speaking without Words*
Film Library/Greater Los Angeles Safety Council
600 Wilshire Blvd., No. 1263
Los Angeles, CA 90017
Ph: (213)385-6461
Free: 800-421-9585
Fax: (213)385-8405
URL: http://www.lasafety.org

Format(s): Videocassette. **Descr:** Provides suggestions for supervisors on how to use non-verbal communication to improve accident records. **Prod. Date:** 198?. **Length:** 10.

6633 ■ *Spills Happen: A Training Program for Small Spill Response*
LearnCom HR Consulting and Training
38 Discovery, Ste. 250
Irvine, CA 92618
Ph: (515)440-0890
Free: 800-698-8263
Fax: (515)221-3149
E-mail: nhartline@learncom.com
URL: http://www.learncomhr.com

Format(s): Videocassette. **Descr:** A video training program in how to respond to and clean up small-scale spills of hazardous substances, from moderate to severe. Includes a trainer's manual and participant hand-outs. **Prod. Date:** 1991. **Length:** 20. **Price:** $495.00.

6634 ■ *Sports Eye Safety Public Service Announcements*
Prevent Blindness America
211 W. Wacker Dr., Ste 1700
Chicago, IL 60606
Ph: (847)843-2020
Free: 800-331-2020
Fax: (847)843-8458
E-mail: info@preventblindness.org
URL: http://www.preventblindness.org

Format(s): Videocassette. **Descr:** A series of public service announcements which advocate the wearing of eye safety paraphernalia. **Prod. Date:** 1988. **Length:** ?. **Price:** $35.00.

6635 ■ *Sports Eye Safety Video News Release*
Prevent Blindness America
211 W. Wacker Dr., Ste 1700
Chicago, IL 60606
Ph: (847)843-2020
Free: 800-331-2020
Fax: (847)843-8458
E-mail: info@preventblindness.org
URL: http://www.preventblindness.org

Format(s): Videocassette. **Descr:** A 90-second news release about eye safety for athletes. **Prod. Date:** 1988. **Length:** 2. **Price:** $35.00.

6636 ■ *Staying Afloat*
National Safety Council
1121 Spring Lake Dr
Itasca, IL 60143-3201
Ph: (630)285-1121
Free: 800-621-7619
Fax: (630)285-1315
E-mail: info@nsc.org
URL: http://www.nsc.org

Format(s): Videocassette. **Descr:** Water emergencies are explained, with tips on how to avoid them, and how to get out of them. **Prod. Date:** 1988. **Length:** 10.

6637 ■ *Staying on the Safe Side*
Phoenix Learning Group
2349 Chaffee Dr
St. Louis, MO 63146
Ph: (314)569-0211
Free: 800-221-1274
Fax: (314)569-2834
URL: http://www.phoenixlearninggroup.com

Format(s): Videocassette. **Descr:** For children grades four to six, provides the basics in spotting and avoiding dangerous strangers and situations. **Prod. Date:** 1986. **Length:** 19.

6638 ■ *Stick It in Your Ear*
Film Library/Greater Los Angeles Safety Council
600 Wilshire Blvd., No. 1263
Los Angeles, CA 90017
Ph: (213)385-6461
Free: 800-421-9585
Fax: (213)385-8405
URL: http://www.lasafety.org

Format(s): Videocassette. **Descr:** A motivational film designed to get workers to wear their hearing protection devices. **Prod. Date:** 198?. **Length:** 15.

6639 ■ *STOP for Employees*
DuPont Safety Resources
PO Box 80013
Wilmington, DE 19880-0013
Free: 800-532-7233
Fax: 888-644-7233
E-mail: info@dupont.com
URL: http://www.dupont.com/safety

Format(s): Videocassette. **Descr:** A set of six videotapes which teach employees that safety is everyone's responsibility. Focuses on preventing injuries and illnesses through eliminating unsafe acts and conditions. This program should be implemented by supervisors. An administrator's and leader's guide, self-study workbooks, and a refresher workbook are available separately. **Prod. Date:** 1993. **Length:** ?. **Price:** $1850.00.

6640 ■ *STOP for Ergonomics*
DuPont Safety Resources
PO Box 80013
Wilmington, DE 19880-0013
Free: 800-532-7233
Fax: 888-644-7233
E-mail: info@dupont.com
URL: http://www.dupont.com/safety

Format(s): Videocassette. **Descr:** Teaches employees how to survey their surroundings and help prevent cumulative trauma disorders and back injuries. Gives examples of how to apply various concepts within the workplace. An administrator's and leader's guide and self-study workbooks are available separately. **Prod. Date:** 1993. **Length:** 15. **Price:** $850.00.

6641 ■ STOP for Supervision
DuPont Safety Resources
PO Box 80013
Wilmington, DE 19880-0013
Free: 800-532-7233
Fax: 888-644-7233
E-mail: info@dupont.com
URL: http://www.dupont.com/safety

Format(s): Videocassette. **Descr:** Set of four tapes teaches managers and line supervisors how to observe, correct, report, and prevent unsafe acts that occur in the workplace. Consists of seven training units that should be completed in between 14 and 28 weeks. An administrator's and leader's guide, self-study workbooks, and a refresher workbook are available separately. **Prod. Date:** 1993. **Length:** 9. **Price:** $1850.00.

6642 ■ Straight Talk on Eye Safety
Film Library/Greater Los Angeles Safety Council
600 Wilshire Blvd., No. 1263
Los Angeles, CA 90017
Ph: (213)385-6461
Free: 800-421-9585
Fax: (213)385-8405
URL: http://www.lasafety.org

Format(s): Videocassette. **Descr:** A frank discussion of how eye injuries occur in industry and how they can be prevented. **Prod. Date:** 198?. **Length:** 12.

6643 ■ Street Safety Tactics
Emergency Film Group
Detrick Lawrence Corp
PO Box 1928
Edgartown, MA 02539
Ph: (508)627-8844
Free: 800-842-0999
Fax: (508)627-8863
E-mail: info@efilmgroup.com
URL: http://www.efilmgroup.com

Format(s): Videocassette. **Descr:** Learn how to deal with secondary hazards of the job that can emerge as primary hazards like domestic violence, race riots, alcohol and drugs, and gang factors. Includes tactics to help achieve contact and control in such situations, as well as procedures to escape from violent actions. **Prod. Date:** 19??. **Length:** 35. **Price:** $250.00.

6644 ■ Street Smarts: Straight Talk for Kids, Teens and Parents
PBS Home Video
Catalog Fulfillment Center
PO Box 751089
Charlotte, NC 28275-1089
Ph: 800-531-4727
Free: 800-645-4PBS
E-mail: info@pbs.org
URL: http://www.pbs.org

Format(s): Videocassette. **Descr:** Detective speaks to children and their parents about drugs, child molesters, gangs, and thieves, offering advice that reduces the risk of hazardous situations. He also encourages parents to be aware and improve neighborhood conditions. Children share their personal stories. **Prod. Date:** 1993. **Length:** 60. **Price:** $59.95.

6645 ■ Strong Kids, Safe Kids
Paramount Home Video
5555 Melrose Ave
5555 Melrose Ave
Los Angeles, CA 90038
Ph: (323)956-5000
URL: http://www.paramount.com

Format(s): Videocassette. **Descr:** Henry Winkler, along with Scooby-Doo, Yogi Bear, and the Flintstones, teaches parents and children the skills that

are necessary to prevent sexual abuse. **Prod. Date:** 1984. **Length:** 42. **Price:** $12.95.

6646 ■ Student Workshop
Sunburst Technology
400 Columbus Ave, Ste 160E
Valhalla, NY 10595-1349
Ph: (914)747-3310
Fax: (914)747-4109
E-mail: webmaster@snysunburst.com
URL: http://www.sunburst.com

Format(s): Videocassette. **Descr:** Offers information for elementary school children to help them understand that staying healthy means taking care of their bodies and using only drugs that a doctor prescribes for them. Includes Teacher's Guide. **Prod. Date:** 2000. **Length:** 17. **Price:** $89.95.

6647 ■ Suddenly in Command
Film Library/Greater Los Angeles Safety Council
600 Wilshire Blvd., No. 1263
Los Angeles, CA 90017
Ph: (213)385-6461
Free: 800-421-9585
Fax: (213)385-8405
URL: http://www.lasafety.org

Format(s): Videocassette. **Descr:** Demonstrates boating emergencies and gives helpful tips on getting out of them. For the novice boater. **Prod. Date:** 1988. **Length:** 14.

6648 ■ Summer Safety
ERI Safety Videos
374 Park Rd
Lexington, SC 29072
Ph: (803)356-4880
Free: 800-311-1143
Fax: (803)356-1946
URL: http://www.eri-safety.com

Format(s): Videocassette. **Descr:** A mock television newscast which features stories about the dangers of lawn mowing, barbequeing, and other summer activities. **Prod. Date:** 1987. **Length:** 17. **Price:** $425.00.

6649 ■ Super Sitters: A Training Course
United Learning
1560 Sherman Ave., Ste. 100
PO Box 48718
Evanston, IL 60201
Ph: 888-892-3484
Fax: (847)328-6706
E-mail: info@interaccess.com
URL: http://www.unitedlearning.com

Format(s): Videocassette. **Descr:** Demonstrates quality child care and home safety for parents and sitters. The package includes the First Aid and Emergency Care Manual, Sitters Resource Guide, and Parents Resource Guide, as well as a memo board for emergency phone numbers. **Prod. Date:** 1990. **Length:** 30. **Price:** $99.95.

6650 ■ Supervision
Film Library/Greater Los Angeles Safety Council
600 Wilshire Blvd., No. 1263
Los Angeles, CA 90017
Ph: (213)385-6461
Free: 800-421-9585
Fax: (213)385-8405
URL: http://www.lasafety.org

Format(s): Videocassette. **Descr:** A demonstration of how a supervisor can effectively reduce on the job accidents. **Prod. Date:** 198?. **Length:** 8.

6651 ■ Superwelder
ERI Safety Videos
374 Park Rd
Lexington, SC 29072
Ph: (803)356-4880
Free: 800-311-1143
Fax: (803)356-1946
URL: http://www.eri-safety.com

Format(s): Videocassette. **Descr:** Safety precautions to be taken when welding or cutting are discussed in this program. Covered are such basics as protective clothing, eye protection, ventilation,

hearing protection, special considerations a welder may encounter, and specifics relating to both gas and electric operations. **Prod. Date:** 1980. **Length:** 15.

6652 ■ Surviving the Big One: How to Prepare for a Major Earthquake
Bennett Marine Video
2321 Abbot Kinney Blvd., Top Fl
Venice, CA 90291
Ph: (310)827-8064
Free: 800-733-8862
Fax: (310)827-8074
E-mail: general@bennettmarine.com
URL: http://www.bennettmarine.com

Format(s): Videocassette. **Descr:** KCET of California presents a comprehensive guide about what to do in case of an earthquake. This program answers questions on the most-asked-about scenarios as well as provides a plan for the most likely events to occur during an earthquake. Incredibly useful for anyone in possible danger from seismic activity. **Prod. Date:** 1991. **Length:** 58. **Price:** $29.95.

6653 ■ Take Nothing for Granted
Film Library/Greater Los Angeles Safety Council
600 Wilshire Blvd., No. 1263
Los Angeles, CA 90017
Ph: (213)385-6461
Free: 800-421-9585
Fax: (213)385-8405
URL: http://www.lasafety.org

Format(s): Videocassette. **Descr:** Harry Sparks, the guardian angel of electrical workers talks about how a combination of inattention and carelessness almost led to tragedy. **Prod. Date:** 198?. **Length:** 19.

6654 ■ Take Two for Safety
DuPont Safety Resources
PO Box 80013
Wilmington, DE 19880-0013
Free: 800-532-7233
Fax: 888-644-7233
E-mail: info@dupont.com
URL: http://www.dupont.com/safety

Format(s): Videocassette. **Descr:** A series about industrial safety precautions. **Prod. Date:** 1993. **Length:** 9.

6655 ■ Talk It Up
Film Library/Greater Los Angeles Safety Council
600 Wilshire Blvd., No. 1263
Los Angeles, CA 90017
Ph: (213)385-6461
Free: 800-421-9585
Fax: (213)385-8405
URL: http://www.lasafety.org

Format(s): Videocassette. **Descr:** A demonstration of the successful methods that management can use to motivate employees to improve the safety habits on the job. **Prod. Date:** 198?. **Length:** 10.

6656 ■ Talking of Safety
Film Library/Greater Los Angeles Safety Council
600 Wilshire Blvd., No. 1263
Los Angeles, CA 90017
Ph: (213)385-6461
Free: 800-421-9585
Fax: (213)385-8405
URL: http://www.lasafety.org

Format(s): Videocassette. **Descr:** How safety committees can improve the standards of health and safety on the job. **Prod. Date:** 198?. **Length:** 24.

6657 ■ Tanker Safety Depends on You
Film Library/Greater Los Angeles Safety Council
600 Wilshire Blvd., No. 1263
Los Angeles, CA 90017
Ph: (213)385-6461
Free: 800-421-9585
Fax: (213)385-8405
URL: http://www.lasafety.org

Format(s): Videocassette. **Descr:** A look at the causes of tanker fires and explosions and how to recognize safety threats. **Prod. Date:** 198?. **Length:** 13.

6658 ■ *Teaching Kids About AIDS*
Aquarius Productions
Olde Medfield Sq
18 N Main St
Sherborn, MA 01770
Ph: (508)650-1616
Free: 888-440-2963
Fax: (508)650-1665
E-mail: tm@aquariusproductions.com
URL: http://www.aquariusproductions.com
Format(s): Videocassette. **Descr:** Offers programs for teachers designed to teach children of all ages about AIDS and the HIV virus. **Prod. Date:** 1993. **Length:** 27. **Price:** $149.

6659 ■ *Teamwork in Manufacturing Safety*
ERI Safety Videos
374 Park Rd
Lexington, SC 29072
Ph: (803)356-4880
Free: 800-311-1143
Fax: (803)356-1946
URL: http://www.eri-safety.com
Format(s): Videocassette. **Descr:** Work together for better job safety. **Prod. Date:** 1987. **Length:** 12. **Price:** $425.00.

6660 ■ *Techniques for Avoiding Back Injuries*
ERI Safety Videos
374 Park Rd
Lexington, SC 29072
Ph: (803)356-4880
Free: 800-311-1143
Fax: (803)356-1946
URL: http://www.eri-safety.com
Format(s): Videocassette. **Descr:** Learn how to lift and move things at work without hurting yourself. **Prod. Date:** 1987. **Length:** 17. **Price:** $425.00.

6661 ■ *Techniques for Lifting*
Film Library/Greater Los Angeles Safety Council
600 Wilshire Blvd., No. 1263
Los Angeles, CA 90017
Ph: (213)385-6461
Free: 800-421-9585
Fax: (213)385-8405
URL: http://www.lasafety.org
Format(s): Videocassette. **Descr:** Offers tips for workers on how to properly lift loads of various sizes without risking a back injury. **Prod. Date:** 198?. **Length:** 10.

6662 ■ *That Feel of Falling*
Film Library/Greater Los Angeles Safety Council
600 Wilshire Blvd., No. 1263
Los Angeles, CA 90017
Ph: (213)385-6461
Free: 800-421-9585
Fax: (213)385-8405
URL: http://www.lasafety.org
Format(s): Videocassette. **Descr:** A discussion of some safeguards that can be taken to prevent stairway falls and bathtub slips and falls. **Prod. Date:** 198?. **Length:** 10.

6663 ■ *They Can Be Guarded*
Film Library/Greater Los Angeles Safety Council
600 Wilshire Blvd., No. 1263
Los Angeles, CA 90017
Ph: (213)385-6461
Free: 800-421-9585
Fax: (213)385-8405
URL: http://www.lasafety.org
Format(s): Videocassette. **Descr:** An examination of the safety equipment now used on press Drakes. **Prod. Date:** 198?. **Length:** 16.

6664 ■ *They're Just Kids*
Aquarius Productions
Olde Medfield Sq
18 N Main St
Sherborn, MA 01770
Ph: (508)650-1616

Free: 888-440-2963
Fax: (508)650-1665
E-mail: tm@aquariusproductions.com
URL: http://www.aquariusproductions.com
Format(s): Videocassette. **Descr:** Explores the advantages of including disabled children in the classroom, scouting and other extracurricular activities. **Prod. Date:** 1998. **Length:** 27. **Price:** $99.

6665 ■ *Think Snow!*
National Safety Council
1121 Spring Lake Dr
Itasca, IL 60143-3201
Ph: (630)285-1121
Free: 800-621-7619
Fax: (630)285-1315
E-mail: info@nsc.org
URL: http://www.nsc.org
Format(s): Videocassette. **Descr:** This is a dramatization of winter driving safety. Two accident-prone drivers learn to prepare themselves. **Prod. Date:** 1988. **Length:** 10.

6666 ■ *Thinking Through Safety: The Job Safety and Health Analysis*
LearnCom HR Consulting and Training
38 Discovery, Ste. 250
Irvine, CA 92618
Ph: (515)440-0890
Free: 800-698-8263
Fax: (515)221-3149
E-mail: nhartline@learncom.com
URL: http://www.learncomhr.com
Format(s): Videocassette. **Descr:** Supervisors are instructed in the proper way to improve health and safety processes. Techniques for gathering information, asking questions, writing job safety and health analyses, and setting up a logical sequence of problems are the focus. Includes a leader's guide and 10 workbooks. **Prod. Date:** 19??. **Length:** 15. **Price:** $295.00.

6667 ■ *The Thirteenth Floor*
Film Library/Greater Los Angeles Safety Council
600 Wilshire Blvd., No. 1263
Los Angeles, CA 90017
Ph: (213)385-6461
Free: 800-421-9585
Fax: (213)385-8405
URL: http://www.lasafety.org
Format(s): Videocassette. **Descr:** A group of office workers on the 13th floor of a building blame the unlucky number for the many accidents that happen to them. **Prod. Date:** 198?. **Length:** 9.

6668 ■ *To Cast a Lifetime*
Film Library/Greater Los Angeles Safety Council
600 Wilshire Blvd., No. 1263
Los Angeles, CA 90017
Ph: (213)385-6461
Free: 800-421-9585
Fax: (213)385-8405
URL: http://www.lasafety.org
Format(s): Videocassette. **Descr:** This film is designed to make employees aware that safety is in their own best interest. **Prod. Date:** 198?. **Length:** 18.

6669 ■ *To Keep Your Child Alive*
Phoenix Learning Group
2349 Chaffee Dr
St. Louis, MO 63146
Ph: (314)569-0211
Free: 800-221-1274
Fax: (314)569-2834
URL: http://www.phoenixlearninggroup.com
Format(s): Videocassette. **Descr:** Parents are taught how to prevent serious and fatal accidents to their children, and how to give emergency care should such an accident occur. **Prod. Date:** 1986. **Length:** 20. **Price:** $275.00.

6670 ■ *Too Smart for Strangers with Winnie the Pooh*
Walt Disney Home Video
500 S. Buena Vista St

Burbank, CA 91521
Ph: (818)265-6500
URL: http://disney.store.go.com
Format(s): Videocassette. **Descr:** Winnie the Pooh and Tigger, along with Tyne Daly and Gavin MacLeod present tips on how children can defend themselves against strangers. **Prod. Date:** 1985. **Length:** 40. **Price:** $29.95.

6671 ■ *Tools*
Film Library/Greater Los Angeles Safety Council
600 Wilshire Blvd., No. 1263
Los Angeles, CA 90017
Ph: (213)385-6461
Free: 800-421-9585
Fax: (213)385-8405
URL: http://www.lasafety.org
Format(s): Videocassette. **Descr:** A demonstration of the special safety precautions to be taken when operating today's more sophisticated tools. **Prod. Date:** 198?. **Length:** 6.

6672 ■ *Towhead Blows His Chance*
Film Library/Greater Los Angeles Safety Council
600 Wilshire Blvd., No. 1263
Los Angeles, CA 90017
Ph: (213)385-6461
Free: 800-421-9585
Fax: (213)385-8405
URL: http://www.lasafety.org
Format(s): Videocassette. **Descr:** An employee finds out that his poor safety record has kept him from receiving a job promotion. **Prod. Date:** 198?. **Length:** 10.

6673 ■ *Towhead Busts His Back*
Film Library/Greater Los Angeles Safety Council
600 Wilshire Blvd., No. 1263
Los Angeles, CA 90017
Ph: (213)385-6461
Free: 800-421-9585
Fax: (213)385-8405
URL: http://www.lasafety.org
Format(s): Videocassette. **Descr:** A film designed to teach workers to know the demands and limitations of their jobs. **Prod. Date:** 198?. **Length:** 10.

6674 ■ *Towhead the Gunslinger*
Film Library/Greater Los Angeles Safety Council
600 Wilshire Blvd., No. 1263
Los Angeles, CA 90017
Ph: (213)385-6461
Free: 800-421-9585
Fax: (213)385-8405
URL: http://www.lasafety.org
Format(s): Videocassette. **Descr:** An employee learns how to develop safe work habits after he injures his hand in an accident. **Prod. Date:** 198?. **Length:** 10.

6675 ■ *Towhead's Terrible Temper*
Film Library/Greater Los Angeles Safety Council
600 Wilshire Blvd., No. 1263
Los Angeles, CA 90017
Ph: (213)385-6461
Free: 800-421-9585
Fax: (213)385-8405
URL: http://www.lasafety.org
Format(s): Videocassette. **Descr:** An employee realizes that attitudes and actions have a great effect on the safety of his co-workers and himself. **Prod. Date:** 198?. **Length:** 10.

6676 ■ *Toxic Hazards in Industry*
Film Library/Greater Los Angeles Safety Council
600 Wilshire Blvd., No. 1263
Los Angeles, CA 90017
Ph: (213)385-6461
Free: 800-421-9585
Fax: (213)385-8405
URL: http://www.lasafety.org
Format(s): Videocassette. **Descr:** An illustration of the various methods workers can use to protect

themselves when working with toxic substances. **Prod. Date:** 198?. **Length:** 23.

6677 ■ *Training Wheel: Safety in Grinding Operations*
Film Library/Greater Los Angeles Safety Council
600 Wilshire Blvd., No. 1263
Los Angeles, CA 90017
Ph: (213)385-6461
Free: 800-421-9585
Fax: (213)385-8405
URL: http://www.lasafety.org
Format(s): Videocassette. **Descr:** An explanation of the safety requirements for the construction, care and use of grinding machines. **Prod. Date:** 198?. **Length:** 16.

6678 ■ *The Trouble with Strangers*
AIMS Multimedia
20765 Superior St
Chatsworth, CA 91311-4409
Ph: (818)773-4300
Free: 800-367-2467
Fax: (818)341-6700
E-mail: info@aims.multimedia.com
URL: http://www.aimsmultimedia.com
Format(s): Videocassette. **Descr:** A young girl forgets her parents' anti-stranger lessons, is abducted and rescued, and gets the lesson reinforced by a kindly cop. **Prod. Date:** 1983. **Length:** 10.

6679 ■ *Twenty-Eight Grams of Prevention*
Film Library/Greater Los Angeles Safety Council
600 Wilshire Blvd., No. 1263
Los Angeles, CA 90017
Ph: (213)385-6461
Free: 800-421-9585
Fax: (213)385-8405
URL: http://www.lasafety.org
Format(s): Videocassette. **Descr:** An in-depth look at potential laboratory hazards and the effective safety precautions that can be enforced. **Prod. Date:** 198?. **Length:** 23.

6680 ■ *Typical Plant Inspection*
Film Library/Greater Los Angeles Safety Council
600 Wilshire Blvd., No. 1263
Los Angeles, CA 90017
Ph: (213)385-6461
Free: 800-421-9585
Fax: (213)385-8405
URL: http://www.lasafety.org
Format(s): Videocassette. **Descr:** This is a demonstration of an OSHA federal compliance inspection of a factory. **Prod. Date:** 198?. **Length:** 15.

6681 ■ *Uncoupling the Twin Trailer*
Film Library/Greater Los Angeles Safety Council
600 Wilshire Blvd., No. 1263
Los Angeles, CA 90017
Ph: (213)385-6461
Free: 800-421-9585
Fax: (213)385-8405
URL: http://www.lasafety.org
Format(s): Videocassette. **Descr:** A demonstration of the best methods to use to avoid an accident when uncoupling a twin trailer. **Prod. Date:** 198?. **Length:** 11.

6682 ■ *Understanding ADHD*
Aquarius Productions
Olde Medfield Sq
18 N Main St
Sherborn, MA 01770
Ph: (508)650-1616
Free: 888-440-2963
Fax: (508)650-1665
E-mail: tm@aquariusproductions.com
URL: http://www.aquariusproductions.com
Format(s): Videocassette. **Descr:** Looks at the controversies surrounding Attention Deficit Hyperactivity Disorder, its correct diagnosis and strategies for

living with a child afflicted with the disorder. **Prod. Date:** 1996. **Length:** 21. **Price:** $120.

6683 ■ *Understanding Learning Disabilities*
Aquarius Productions
Olde Medfield Sq
18 N Main St
Sherborn, MA 01770
Ph: (508)650-1616
Free: 888-440-2963
Fax: (508)650-1665
E-mail: tm@aquariusproductions.com
URL: http://www.aquariusproductions.com
Format(s): Videocassette. **Descr:** Explains various learning disabilities and how they affect areas such as language, reading, math skills and behavior. **Prod. Date:** 1996. **Length:** 16. **Price:** $125.00.

6684 ■ *Understanding the Relationship Between Emotional Child Abuse and Workplace Dysfunction*
Aquarius Productions
Olde Medfield Sq
18 N Main St
Sherborn, MA 01770
Ph: (508)650-1616
Free: 888-440-2963
Fax: (508)650-1665
E-mail: tm@aquariusproductions.com
URL: http://www.aquariusproductions.com
Format(s): Videocassette. **Descr:** Explores aspects of workplace dysfunction such as interpersonal conflict, sexual harassment, drug/alcohol abuse, and murder/shootings in relation to an employee's connection or experience with child abuse. **Prod. Date:** 2000. **Length:** 23. **Price:** $110.00.

6685 ■ *Universal Precautions for School Staff*
AMS Distributors, Inc.
PO Box 658
Lady Lake, FL 32158
Free: 800-424-3464
URL: http://www.vpats.com
Format(s): Videocassette. **Descr:** Training program for school employees explains preventative measures to reduce risk of coming into contact with infectious diseases. **Prod. Date:** 1991. **Length:** 15.

6686 ■ *Unsafe Acts*
Film Library/Greater Los Angeles Safety Council
600 Wilshire Blvd., No. 1263
Los Angeles, CA 90017
Ph: (213)385-6461
Free: 800-421-9585
Fax: (213)385-8405
URL: http://www.lasafety.org
Format(s): Videocassette. **Descr:** Contains some interesting answers to the question of why people commit unsafe acts. **Prod. Date:** 198?. **Length:** 7.

6687 ■ *Unsafe Acts Caused by Others*
Film Library/Greater Los Angeles Safety Council
600 Wilshire Blvd., No. 1263
Los Angeles, CA 90017
Ph: (213)385-6461
Free: 800-421-9585
Fax: (213)385-8405
URL: http://www.lasafety.org
Format(s): Videocassette. **Descr:** A look at how plumbing, electrical acoustical and drywall subcontractors can affect job site safety. **Prod. Date:** 198?. **Length:** 6.

6688 ■ *Using Fire Extinguishers*
Williams Learning Network
15400 Calhoun Dr
Rockville, MD 20855-2762
Ph: (301)315-6700
Free: 800-848-1717
Fax: (301)315-6880
E-mail: mait@willearn.com
URL: http://www.willearn.com
Format(s): Videocassette. **Descr:** Outlines the safe and efficient use of fire extinguishers. Provides examples of firefighters demonstrating the correct procedures for the use of the different types of

extinguishers. Includes Leader's Guide and 25 Program Guides. **Prod. Date:** 19??. **Length:** 14.

6689 ■ *Using Hearing Protection*
ERI Safety Videos
374 Park Rd
Lexington, SC 29072
Ph: (803)356-4880
Free: 800-311-1143
Fax: (803)356-1946
URL: http://www.eri-safety.com
Format(s): Videocassette. **Descr:** A video about the importance of taking precautions to save your hearing. Aimed at industrial employees. **Prod. Date:** 1987. **Length:** 15. **Price:** $425.00.

6690 ■ *The Waldorf Promise*
Landfall Productions, Inc.
315 S. Sparks St
P.O. Box 605
Burbank, CA 91503
E-mail: estacey@landfallprods.com
URL: http://www.landfallprods.com
Format(s): Videocassette. **Descr:** Takes a look at eight public school teachers who started teaching using conventional methods, but switched to the Waldorf methods established in 1928. The teachers describe their current success with the Waldorf method. **Prod. Date:** 1998. **Length:** 53. **Price:** $39.95.

6691 ■ *Walking Home from School*
AIMS Multimedia
20765 Superior St
Chatsworth, CA 91311-4409
Ph: (818)773-4300
Free: 800-367-2467
Fax: (818)341-6700
E-mail: info@aims.multimedia.com
URL: http://www.aimsmultimedia.com
Format(s): Videocassette. **Descr:** Observation of your surroundings is important in maintaining safety when walking home from school. **Prod. Date:** 1970. **Length:** 12.

6692 ■ *Walking Safe*
The Media Guild
11722 Sorrento Valley Rd., Ste. E
San Diego, CA 92121
Ph: (858)755-9191
Free: 800-886-9191
Fax: (858)755-4931
E-mail: info@mediaguild.com
URL: http://www.mediaguild.com
Format(s): Videocassette. **Descr:** Aimed at protecting elementary school children walking to and from school. **Prod. Date:** 1978. **Length:** 10.

6693 ■ *A Way of Life*
Film Library/Greater Los Angeles Safety Council
600 Wilshire Blvd., No. 1263
Los Angeles, CA 90017
Ph: (213)385-6461
Free: 800-421-9585
Fax: (213)385-8405
URL: http://www.lasafety.org
Format(s): Videocassette. **Descr:** Several safety-conscious workers tell their stories of how they left themselves open to accidents when they're away from their jobs. **Prod. Date:** 198?. **Length:** 20.

6694 ■ *WCB's Wide World of Rescue*
Film Library/Greater Los Angeles Safety Council
600 Wilshire Blvd., No. 1263
Los Angeles, CA 90017
Ph: (213)385-6461
Free: 800-421-9585
Fax: (213)385-8405
URL: http://www.lasafety.org
Format(s): Videocassette. **Descr:** This film looks at several H2S rescues and explains why each attempt succeeds or fails. **Prod. Date:** 198?. **Length:** 10.

6695 ■ *Weld in Safety*
Film Library/Greater Los Angeles Safety Council
600 Wilshire Blvd., No. 1263

Los Angeles, CA 90017
Ph: (213)385-6461
Free: 800-421-9585
Fax: (213)385-8405
URL: http://www.lasafety.org
Format(s): Videocassette. **Descr:** A demonstration of the safety precautions that must be taken when using gas welding or cutting equipment. **Prod. Date:** 198?. **Length:** 23.

6696 ■ Welding Safety
Bergwall Productions, Inc.
1224 Baltimore Pike, Ste. 203
Kennett Square, PA 19317
Ph: (610)361-0334
Free: 800-934-8696
Fax: (610)361-0092
E-mail: bergwall@bergwall.com
URL: http://www.bergwall.com
Format(s): Videocassette. **Descr:** On two tapes, the importance of safety while welding is stressed. **Prod. Date:** 1982. **Length:** 27.

6697 ■ We'll See Tomorrow
Film Library/Greater Los Angeles Safety Council
600 Wilshire Blvd., No. 1263
Los Angeles, CA 90017
Ph: (213)385-6461
Free: 800-421-9585
Fax: (213)385-8405
URL: http://www.lasafety.org
Format(s): Videocassette. **Descr:** A careful worker gets an eye injury when he neglects to wear his safety goggles. **Prod. Date:** 198?. **Length:** 10.

6698 ■ We're Not Stupid
Aquarius Productions
Olde Medfield Sq
18 N Main St
Sherborn, MA 01770
Ph: (508)650-1616
Free: 888-440-2963
Fax: (508)650-1665
E-mail: tm@aquariusproductions.com
URL: http://www.aquariusproductions.com
Format(s): Videocassette. **Descr:** Discusses the problems and misconceptions of people who suffer from learning disabilities such as dyslexia and Attention Deficit Disorder. **Prod. Date:** 1998. **Length:** 15. **Price:** $125.

6699 ■ What Every School Bus Driver Should Know
WJER Video Services
646 Boulevard St
Dover, OH 44622-2081
Ph: (330)343-7755
Fax: (330)364-4538
E-mail: wjer@wjer.com
URL: http://www.wjer.com
Format(s): Videocassette. **Descr:** Excerpts from a day-long seminar cover such topics as maintaining order aboard the bus with assertive discipline, conducting effective bus evacuation drills, and a school bus disaster simulation demonstrating emergency procedures to be followed by the bus driver and passengers. **Prod. Date:** 1983. **Length:** 58.

6700 ■ What Happens Next?
Film Library/Greater Los Angeles Safety Council
600 Wilshire Blvd., No. 1263
Los Angeles, CA 90017
Ph: (213)385-6461
Free: 800-421-9585
Fax: (213)385-8405
URL: http://www.lasafety.org
Format(s): Videocassette. **Descr:** Four different accidents are dramatized to show the need for supervisors to take charge in an accident situation. **Prod. Date:** 198?. **Length:** 18.

6701 ■ What'Cha Gonna Do?
United Learning
1560 Sherman Ave., Ste. 100
PO Box 48718
Evanston, IL 60201

Ph: 888-892-3484
Fax: (847)328-6706
E-mail: info@interaccess.com
URL: http://www.unitedlearning.com
Format(s): Videocassette. **Descr:** By example, this program shows kids how to avoid and resist strangers' possible advances as efficiently as possible. **Prod. Date:** 1985. **Length:** 11.

6702 ■ Whatever Happened to Linda
School-Tech Inc.
745 State Cir
PO Box 1941
Ann Arbor, MI 48106
Ph: (734)761-5072
Free: 800-521-2832
Fax: 800-654-4321
E-mail: service@school-tech.com
URL: http://www.schoolmasters.com
Format(s): Videocassette. **Descr:** Dramatization of everyday issues young children face. Teaches how to avoid trouble and what to do when confronted with uncomfortable situations. **Prod. Date:** 19??. **Length:** ?. **Price:** $49.95.

6703 ■ When the World Stops
Film Library/Greater Los Angeles Safety Council
600 Wilshire Blvd., No. 1263
Los Angeles, CA 90017
Ph: (213)385-6461
Free: 800-421-9585
Fax: (213)385-8405
URL: http://www.lasafety.org
Format(s): Videocassette. **Descr:** A look at worker's compensation and what industry can do to help bring down costs through loss prevention and safety. **Prod. Date:** 198?. **Length:** 24.

6704 ■ Where There's Smoke
Film Library/Greater Los Angeles Safety Council
600 Wilshire Blvd., No. 1263
Los Angeles, CA 90017
Ph: (213)385-6461
Free: 800-421-9585
Fax: (213)385-8405
URL: http://www.lasafety.org
Format(s): Videocassette. **Descr:** A demonstration of the correct use and maintenance of respirators during a fire. **Prod. Date:** 198?. **Length:** 10.

6705 ■ Who Needs Office Safety?
Film Library/Greater Los Angeles Safety Council
600 Wilshire Blvd., No. 1263
Los Angeles, CA 90017
Ph: (213)385-6461
Free: 800-421-9585
Fax: (213)385-8405
URL: http://www.lasafety.org
Format(s): Videocassette. **Descr:** A clumsy office manager finds out the true meaning of office safety as he discovers hazards around the office. **Prod. Date:** 198?. **Length:** 10.

6706 ■ Why 55?
Film Library/Greater Los Angeles Safety Council
600 Wilshire Blvd., No. 1263
Los Angeles, CA 90017
Ph: (213)385-6461
Free: 800-421-9585
Fax: (213)385-8405
URL: http://www.lasafety.org
Format(s): Videocassette. **Descr:** A look at various aspects of the 55 mph speed limit from why it is in effect to the safety and economic benefits. **Prod. Date:** 198?. **Length:** 14.

6707 ■ Wide World of Records
Film Library/Greater Los Angeles Safety Council
600 Wilshire Blvd., No. 1263
Los Angeles, CA 90017
Ph: (213)385-6461
Free: 800-421-9585
Fax: (213)385-8405
URL: http://www.lasafety.org
Format(s): Videocassette. **Descr:** A look at the various aspects of servicing and supplying a drilling

operation with a special emphasis on safety. **Prod. Date:** 198?. **Length:** 17.

6708 ■ Wilber
Film Library/Greater Los Angeles Safety Council
600 Wilshire Blvd., No. 1263
Los Angeles, CA 90017
Ph: (213)385-6461
Free: 800-421-9585
Fax: (213)385-8405
URL: http://www.lasafety.org
Format(s): Videocassette. **Descr:** This is a silent film depicting the misadventures of Wilber, a careless supermarket employee. **Prod. Date:** 198?. **Length:** 10.

6709 ■ Winter Safety
ERI Safety Videos
374 Park Rd
Lexington, SC 29072
Ph: (803)356-4880
Free: 800-311-1143
Fax: (803)356-1946
URL: http://www.eri-safety.com
Format(s): Videocassette. **Descr:** A TV news program showing some of the many accidents that are likely to occur in winter. **Prod. Date:** 1987. **Length:** 17. **Price:** $425.00.

6710 ■ Winter Survival
National Film Board of Canada
1123 Broadway, Ste 307
New York, NY 10010
Ph: (212)629-8890
Free: 800-542-2164
Fax: (866)299-9928
URL: http://www.nfb.ca
Format(s): Videocassette. **Descr:** This program illustrates techniques for treating hypothermia and teaches how to take care of yourself outdoors. **Prod. Date:** 1982. **Length:** 15.

6711 ■ Wood Shaper
Film Library/Greater Los Angeles Safety Council
600 Wilshire Blvd., No. 1263
Los Angeles, CA 90017
Ph: (213)385-6461
Free: 800-421-9585
Fax: (213)385-8405
URL: http://www.lasafety.org
Format(s): Videocassette. **Descr:** A demonstration of how to safely use the wood shaper. **Prod. Date:** 198?. **Length:** 20.

6712 ■ Work-Based Learning: A School-to-Work Transition Activity
University of Wisconsin at Madison
College of Engineering
Department of Engineering Professional Development
432 N. Lake St
Madison, WI 53706
Ph: (608)262-2061
Free: 800-462-0876
Fax: (608)263-3160
URL: http://www.engr.wisc.edu
Format(s): Videocassette. **Descr:** Explains the offerings and benefits of job shadowing, workplace mentoring, and broad instruction in many facets of industry. **Length:** 15. **Price:** $89.00.

6713 ■ The Working Back
Film Library/Greater Los Angeles Safety Council
600 Wilshire Blvd., No. 1263
Los Angeles, CA 90017
Ph: (213)385-6461
Free: 800-421-9585
Fax: (213)385-8405
URL: http://www.lasafety.org
Format(s): Videocassette. **Descr:** A demonstration of simple sleeping, standing and sitting techniques

that will promote a healthy back. **Prod. Date:** 198?. **Length:** 11.

6714 ■ Working Safely with Hand and Power Tools
LearnCom HR Consulting and Training
38 Discovery, Ste. 250
Irvine, CA 92618
Ph: (515)440-0890
Free: 800-698-8263
Fax: (515)221-3149
E-mail: nhartline@learncom.com
URL: http://www.learncomhr.com

Format(s): Videocassette. **Descr:** A demonstration of the proper use and maintenance of hand and power tools, focusing on good safety habits and the ergonomics of proper tool use. A leader's guide and ten participant workbooks are included. **Prod. Date:** 1991. **Length:** 15. **Price:** $175.

6715 ■ Working Safely with Robots
Film Library/Greater Los Angeles Safety Council
600 Wilshire Blvd., No. 1263
Los Angeles, CA 90017
Ph: (213)385-6461
Free: 800-421-9585
Fax: (213)385-8405
URL: http://www.lasafety.org

Format(s): Videocassette. **Descr:** This is a detailed account of the potential hazards employees can encounter when working with robots. **Prod. Date:** 198?. **Length:** 10.

6716 ■ Would You Bet Your Life?
Film Library/Greater Los Angeles Safety Council
600 Wilshire Blvd., No. 1263
Los Angeles, CA 90017
Ph: (213)385-6461
Free: 800-421-9585
Fax: (213)385-8405
URL: http://www.lasafety.org

Format(s): Videocassette. **Descr:** A group of linemen tell about their own near fatal accidents to prove that an electrical worker gambles with his life when he ignores safety rules. **Prod. Date:** 198?. **Length:** 17.

6717 ■ You Always Hurt the One You Love
Film Library/Greater Los Angeles Safety Council
600 Wilshire Blvd., No. 1263
Los Angeles, CA 90017
Ph: (213)385-6461
Free: 800-421-9585
Fax: (213)385-8405
URL: http://www.lasafety.org

Format(s): Videocassette. **Descr:** A demonstration of the basic do's and don'ts of office safety. **Prod. Date:** 198?. **Length:** 13.

6718 ■ You Bet Your Eyes
Film Library/Greater Los Angeles Safety Council
600 Wilshire Blvd., No. 1263
Los Angeles, CA 90017
Ph: (213)385-6461
Free: 800-421-9585
Fax: (213)385-8405
URL: http://www.lasafety.org

Format(s): Videocassette. **Descr:** A film designed to motivate workers to wear eye protection every day on every job. **Prod. Date:** 198?. **Length:** 15.

6719 ■ You and What You Do
Film Library/Greater Los Angeles Safety Council
600 Wilshire Blvd., No. 1263
Los Angeles, CA 90017
Ph: (213)385-6461
Free: 800-421-9585
Fax: (213)385-8405
URL: http://www.lasafety.org

Format(s): Videocassette. **Descr:** A look at the dangers involved when workers do not comprehend

specific instructions or are not completely trained in a specific job. **Prod. Date:** 198?. **Length:** 10.

6720 ■ Your Body Is Only Human
Film Library/Greater Los Angeles Safety Council
600 Wilshire Blvd., No. 1263
Los Angeles, CA 90017
Ph: (213)385-6461
Free: 800-421-9585
Fax: (213)385-8405
URL: http://www.lasafety.org

Format(s): Videocassette. **Descr:** A demonstration of how tools and equipment can be used to augment strength or dexterity. **Prod. Date:** 198?. **Length:** 10.

6721 ■ Your Guardian Angel
Film Library/Greater Los Angeles Safety Council
600 Wilshire Blvd., No. 1263
Los Angeles, CA 90017
Ph: (213)385-6461
Free: 800-421-9585
Fax: (213)385-8405
URL: http://www.lasafety.org

Format(s): Videocassette. **Descr:** Harry Sparks, the guardian angel of electrical workers, looks at the hazards and characteristics of 600-volt lines and equipment. **Prod. Date:** 198?. **Length:** 15.

6722 ■ Your House in Order?
Film Library/Greater Los Angeles Safety Council
600 Wilshire Blvd., No. 1263
Los Angeles, CA 90017
Ph: (213)385-6461
Free: 800-421-9585
Fax: (213)385-8405
URL: http://www.lasafety.org

Format(s): Videocassette. **Descr:** Guidelines for those workers who are responsible for their own work area. **Prod. Date:** 198?. **Length:** 20.

6723 ■ Yours to Keep and Protect
Film Library/Greater Los Angeles Safety Council
600 Wilshire Blvd., No. 1263
Los Angeles, CA 90017
Ph: (213)385-6461
Free: 800-421-9585
Fax: (213)385-8405
URL: http://www.lasafety.org

Format(s): Videocassette. **Descr:** An examination of the protective devices for punch and power presses. **Prod. Date:** 198?. **Length:** 16.

Media Contacts

6724 ■ USA Today
Gannett Co., Inc.
7950 Jones Branch Dr.
McLean, VA 22108
Contact: Mary Beth Marklein, Higher Education Writer
Ph: (703)854-3684
E-mail: mmarklein@usatoday.com
URL: http://www.usatoday.com

6725 ■ USA Today
Gannett Co., Inc.
7950 Jones Branch Dr.
McLean, VA 22108
Contact: Greg Toppo, Education Writer
Ph: (703)854-3467
URL: http://www.usatoday.com

6726 ■ USA Today
Gannett Co., Inc.
7950 Jones Branch Dr.
McLean, VA 22108
Contact: Michelle Healy, "A Better Life" Columnist
Ph: (703)854-4485
E-mail: mhealy@usatoday.com
URL: http://www.usatoday.com

6727 ■ The Wall Street Journal
Dow Jones & Company
1211 Ave. of the Americas
New York, NY 10036

Contact: Anne-Marie Chaker, Education Reporter
Ph: (212)416-3189
URL: http://www.wsj.com

Alabama

6728 ■ Press-Register
Advance Publications, Inc.
PO Box 2488
Mobile, AL 36652-2488
Contact: Rena Havner, Education Reporter
Ph: (251)219-5624
Fax: (251)219-5799
E-mail: rhavner@press-register.com
URL: http://www.press-register.com

Arizona

6729 ■ Arizona Daily Star
Lee Enterprises, Inc.
PO Box 26807
Tucson, AZ 85726-6807
Contact: Rhonda Bodfield, Education Reporter
Ph: (520)573-4195
E-mail: rbodfield@azstarnet.com
URL: http://www.azstarnet.com

6730 ■ Arizona Daily Star
Lee Enterprises Inc.
PO Box 26807
Tucson, AZ 85714-6807
Contact: Aaron Mackey, Higher Educ. Reporter
Ph: (520)807-8012
E-mail: amackey@azstarnet.com
URL: http://www.azstarnet.com

Arkansas

6731 ■ Arkansas Democrat-Gazette
PO Box 2221
Little Rock, AR 72203-2221
Contact: Tara M. Manthey, Education Reporter
Ph: (501)378-3530
Fax: (501)372-4765
E-mail: tmanthey@arkansasonline.com
URL: http://www.arkansasonline.com

6732 ■ Arkansas Democrat-Gazette
PO Box 2221
Little Rock, AR 72203-2221
Contact: Cynthia Howell, Education Reporter
Ph: (501)378-3474
E-mail: chowell@arkansasonline.com
URL: http://www.ardemgaz.com

California

6733 ■ The Fresno Bee
The McClatchy Company
1626 E St.
Fresno, CA 93786-0001
Contact: Anne Ellis, K-12 Education Reporter
Ph: (559)441-6328
E-mail: aellis@fresnobee.com
URL: http://www.fresnobee.com

6734 ■ The Fresno Bee
The McClatchy Company
1626 E St.
Fresno, CA 93786-0001
Contact: Cyndee Fontana, Higher Educ. Reporter
Ph: (559)441-6311
E-mail: cfontana@fresnobee.com
URL: http://www.fresnobee.com

6735 ■ Los Angeles Times
Tribune Company
202 W. First St.
Los Angeles, CA 90012
Contact: Mitchell Landsberg, Education Writer
Ph: (213)237-7847

E-mail: mitchell.landsberg@latimes.com
URL: http://www.latimes.com

6736 ■ *Los Angeles Times*
Tribune Company
202 W. First St.
Los Angeles, CA 90012
Contact: Carla Rivera, Education Writer
Ph: (213)237-7847
E-mail: carla.rivera@latimes.com
URL: http://www.latimes.com

6737 ■ *Los Angeles Times*
Tribune Company
202 W. First St.
Los Angeles, CA 90012
Contact: Larry Gordon, Higher Education Writer
Ph: (213)237-3274
E-mail: larry.gordon@latimes.com
URL: http://www.latimes.com

6738 ■ *Los Angeles Times*
Tribune Company
202 W. First St.
Los Angeles, CA 90012
Contact: Beth Shuster, Education Editor
Ph: (213)237-7847
E-mail: beth.shuster@latimes.com
URL: http://www.latimes.com

6739 ■ *Los Angeles Times*
Tribune Company
202 W. First St.
Los Angeles, CA 90012
Contact: Howard Blume, Education Writer
Ph: (213)237-7847
E-mail: howard.blume@latimes.com
URL: http://www.latimes.com

6740 ■ *Los Angeles Times*
Tribune Company
202 W. First St.
Los Angeles, CA 90012
Contact: Jason Song, Education Writer
Ph: (213)237-7847
E-mail: jason.song@latimes.com
URL: http://www.latimes.com

6741 ■ *Los Angeles Times*
Tribune Company
202 W. First St.
Los Angeles, CA 90012
Contact: Evelyn Larrubia, Education Writer
Ph: (213)237-7847
E-mail: evelyn.larrubia@latimes.com
URL: http://www.latimes.com

6742 ■ *Orange County Register*
625 N. Grand Ave.
Santa Ana, CA 92701-4347
Contact: Marla Jo Fisher, Higher Education Reporter
Ph: (714)796-7994
E-mail: mfisher@ocregister.com
URL: http://www.ocregister.com

6743 ■ *Orange County Register*
625 N. Grand Ave.
Santa Ana, CA 92701-4347
Contact: Eric Carpenter, K-12 Education Reporter
Ph: (714)796-3769
E-mail: ecarpenter@ocregister.com
URL: http://www.ocregister.com

6744 ■ *The Press-Enterprise*
3450 Fourteenth St.
Riverside, CA 92501
Contact: Melanie C. Johnson, Education Reporter
Ph: (951)368-9489
E-mail: mjohnson@pe.com
URL: http://www.pe.com

6745 ■ *The Press-Enterprise*
3450 Fourteenth St.
Riverside, CA 92501
Contact: Michelle Klampe, Education Reporter

Ph: (951)375-3740
E-mail: mklampe@pe.com
URL: http://www.pe.com

6746 ■ *The Press-Enterprise*
3450 Fourteenth St.
Riverside, CA 92501
Contact: Imran Vittachi, Education Reporter
Ph: (951)368-9283
E-mail: ivittachi@pe.com
URL: http://www.pe.com

6747 ■ *The Press-Enterprise*
3450 Fourteenth St.
Riverside, CA 92501
Contact: Shirin Parsavand, Education Reporter
Ph: (951)368-9645
E-mail: sparsavand@pe.com
URL: http://www.pe.com

6748 ■ *San Diego Union-Tribune*
Copley Press, Inc.
PO Box 120191
San Diego, CA 92112-0191
Contact: Maureen Magee, K-12 Eduction Reporter
Ph: (619)293-1369
E-mail: maureen.magee@uniontrib.com
URL: http://www.uniontrib.com

6749 ■ *San Francisco Chronicle*
Hearst Newspapers
901 Mission St.
San Francisco, CA 94103-2988
Contact: Tanya Schevitz, Higher Education Reporter
Ph: (415)777-7154
E-mail: tschevitz@sfchronicle.com
URL: http://www.sfchronicle.com

Colorado

6750 ■ *Denver Post*
101 W. Colfax Ave.
Denver, CO 80202
Contact: Allison Sherry, Higher Education Writer
Ph: (303)954-1377
E-mail: asherry@denverpost.com
URL: http://www.denverpost.com

Florida

6751 ■ *The Florida Times-Union*
PO Box 1949
Jacksonville, FL 32231
Contact: Mary Kelli Palka, K-12 Education Writer
Ph: (904)359-4104
Free: 800-553-0541
E-mail: mary.palka@jacksonville.com
URL: http://www.jacksonville.com

6752 ■ *The Florida Times-Union*
PO Box 1949
Jacksonville, FL 32231
Contact: Adam Aasen, Higher Educ. Writer
Ph: (904)359-4247
E-mail: adam.aasen@jacksonville.com
URL: http://www.jacksonville.com

6753 ■ *Orlando Sentinel*
Tribune Company
633 N. Orange Ave.
Orlando, FL 32801-1349
Contact: Denise-Marie Balona, Education Reporter
Ph: (352)742-5000
E-mail: dbalona@orlandosentinel.com
URL: http://www.orlandosentinel.com

6754 ■ *Orlando Sentinel*
Tribune Company
633 N. Orange Ave.
Orlando, FL 32801-1349
Contact: Luis Zaragoza, Higher Education Reporter
Ph: (407)420-5718

E-mail: lzaragoza@orlandosentinel.com
URL: http://www.orlandosentinel.com

6755 ■ *Orlando Sentinel*
Tribune Company
633 N. Orange Ave.
Orlando, FL 32801-1349
Contact: Sal Recchi, Education Editor
Ph: (407)420-5000
E-mail: srecchi@orlandosentinel.com
URL: http://www.orlandosentinel.com

6756 ■ *Sun Sentinel*
Tribune Company
200 E. Las Olas Blvd.
Fort Lauderdale, FL 33301-2293
Contact: Akliah K. Johnson, Education Reporter
Ph: (954)356-4527
E-mail: akjohnson@sun-sentinel.com
URL: http://www.sun-sentinel.com

6757 ■ *Sun Sentinel*
Tribune Company
200 E. Las Olas Blvd.
Fort Lauderdale, FL 33301-2293
Contact: Kathy Bushouse, Education Reporter
Ph: (954)356-4667
E-mail: kbushouse@sun-sentinel.com
URL: http://www.sun-sentinel.com

6758 ■ *Tallahassee Democrat*
Gannett Co., Inc.
PO Box 990
Tallahassee, FL 32301
Contact: TaMaryn Waters, Education Reporter
Ph: (850)599-2162
E-mail: tlwaters@tallahassee.com
URL: http://www.tallahassee.com

Hawaii

6759 ■ *Honolulu Advertiser*
Gannett Co., Inc.
605 Kapiolani Blvd.
Honolulu, HI 96813
Contact: Loren Moreno, Education Reporter
Ph: (808)535-2455
E-mail: lmoreno@honoluluadvertiser.com
URL: http://www.honoluluadvertiser.com

Illinois

6760 ■ *The Chicago Sun-Times*
Hollinger International, Inc.
350 N. Orleans
Chicago, IL 60654
Contact: Maudlyne Ihejirika, Education Reporter
Ph: (312)321-2522
E-mail: mihejirika@suntimes.com
URL: http://www.suntimes.com

6761 ■ *Chicago Tribune*
Tribune Company
435 N. Michigan Ave.
Chicago, IL 60611-4041
Contact: Stephanie Banchero, State Education Reporter
Ph: (312)222-4346
E-mail: sbanchero@tribune.com
URL: http://www.chicagotribune.com

6762 ■ *Chicago Tribune*
Tribune Company
435 N. Michigan Ave.
Chicago, IL 60611-4041
Contact: Jodi S. Cohen, Higher Education Reporter
Ph: (312)222-3466
E-mail: jcohen@tribune.com
URL: http://www.chicagotribune.com

6763 ■ *The State Journal-Register*
PO Box 219
Springfield, IL 62705-0219
Contact: Chris Dettro, Higher Education Reporter

Ph: (217)788-1510
E-mail: chris.dettro@sj-r.com
URL: http://www.sj-r.com

6764 ■ The State Journal-Register
PO Box 219
Springfield, IL 62705-0219
Contact: Pete Sherman, K-12 Education Reporter
Ph: (217)788-1539
E-mail: pete.sherman@sj-r.com
URL: http://www.sj-r.com

Kentucky

6765 ■ The Courier-Journal
Garrett Co., Inc.
PO Box 740031
Louisville, KY 40201-7431
Contact: Nancy Rodriguez, Higher Education Reporter
Ph: (502)582-7079
URL: http://www.courier-journal.com

6766 ■ Courier-Journal
Gannett Co., Inc.
PO Box 740031
Louisville, KY 40201-7431
Contact: Toni Konz, Education Reporter
Ph: (502)582-4232
E-mail: tkonz@courier-journal.com
URL: http://www.courier-journal.com

Louisiana

6767 ■ New Orleans Times-Picayune
Newhouse Newspapers
3800 Howard Ave.
New Orleans, LA 70125
Contact: John Pope, Higher Education Reporter
Ph: (504)826-3317
E-mail: jpope@timespicayune.com
URL: http://www.nola.com

6768 ■ New Orleans Times-Picayune
Newhouse Newspapers
3800 Howard Ave.
New Orleans, LA 70125
Contact: Jenny Hurwitz, Education Reporter
Ph: (504)826-3784
E-mail: jhurwitz@timespicayune.com
URL: http://www.nola.com

Maryland

6769 ■ The Baltimore Sun
Tribune Company
501 N. Calvert St.
Baltimore, MD 21278
Contact: Liz Bowie, K-12 Education Reporter
Ph: (410)332-6100
E-mail: liz.bowie@baltsun.com
URL: http://www.baltimoresun.com

Massachusetts

6770 ■ Boston Globe
The New York Times Company
135 Morrissey Blvd.
Boston, MA 02125
Contact: Tracy Jan, Education Editor
Ph: (617)929-1542
E-mail: tjan@globe.com
URL: http://www.boston.com

6771 ■ Boston Globe
The New York Times Company
135 Morrissey Blvd.
Boston, MA 02125
Contact: Peter Schworm, Higher Education Reporter
Ph: (617)929-3056
E-mail: schworm@globe.com
URL: http://www.boston.com

Michigan

6772 ■ Detroit News
MediaNews Group
38701 Seven Mile Rd., Ste. 170
Livonia, MI 48152
Contact: Shawn D. Lewis, K-12 Education Reporter
Ph: (734)462-2190
E-mail: slewis@detnews.com
URL: http://www.detnews.com

Missouri

6773 ■ St. Louis Post-Dispatch
Lee Enterprises, Inc.
900 N. Tucker Blvd.
St. Louis, MO 63101
Contact: David Hunn, Education Reporter
Ph: (314)340-8411
E-mail: dhunn@post-dispatch.com
URL: http://www.stltoday.com

6774 ■ St. Louis Post-Dispatch
Lee Enterprises, Inc.
900 N. Tucker Blvd.
St. Louis, MO 63101
Contact: Kavita Kumar, Higher Education Reporter
Ph: (314)340-9017
E-mail: kkumar@post-dispatch.com
URL: http://www.stltoday.com

6775 ■ St. Louis Post-Dispatch
Lee Enterprises, Inc.
900 N. Tucker Blvd.
St. Louis, MO 63101
Contact: Paul W. Hampel, Education Reporter
Ph: (314)727-6234
E-mail: phampel@post-dispatch.com
URL: http://www.stltoday.com

Nebraska

6776 ■ Omaha World-Herald
1314 Douglas St., Ste. 900
Omaha, NE 68102
Contact: Jeff Robb, K-12 Education Reporter
Ph: (402)444-1000
E-mail: jeff.robb@owh.com
URL: http://www.omaha.com

6777 ■ Omaha World-Herald
1314 Douglas St., Ste. 900
Omaha, NE 68102
Contact: Michaela Saunders, K-12 Education Reporter
Ph: (402)444-1000
E-mail: michaela.saunders@owh.com
URL: http://www.omaha.com

6778 ■ Omaha World-Herald
1314 Douglas St., Ste. 900
Omaha, NE 68102
Contact: Matthew Hansen, Higher Education Reporter
Ph: (402)444-1000
E-mail: matthew.hansen@owh.com
URL: http://www.omaha.com

New Jersey

6779 ■ The Star-Ledger
Newhouse Newspapers
One Star-Ledger Plaza
Newark, NJ 07102-1200
Contact: Ana M. Alaya, Higher Education Reporter
Ph: (973)392-4258
E-mail: aalaya@starledger.com
URL: http://www.nj.com

New Mexico

6780 ■ The Santa Fe New Mexican
PO Box 2048
Santa Fe, NM 87054-2048

Contact: John Sena, Education Reporter
Ph: (505)986-3079
E-mail: jsena@sfnewmexican.com
URL: http://www.santafenewmexican.com

New York

6781 ■ The Buffalo News
Berkshire Hathaway Inc.
PO Box 100
Buffalo, NY 14240
Contact: Jay Rey, Higher Education Reporter
Ph: (716)849-5591
Free: 800-777-8680
Fax: (716)856-5150
E-mail: jrey@buffnews.com
URL: http://www.buffalo.com

6782 ■ The Daily News
450 W. 33rd St.
New York, NY 10001-2681
Contact: Erin Einhorn, Education Reporter
Ph: (212)210-6365
E-mail: eeinhorn@nydailynews.com
URL: http://www.nydailynews.com

6783 ■ The Daily News
450 W. 33rd St.
New York, NY 10001-2681
Contact: Kate Lucadamo, Education Reporter
Ph: (212)210-2214
E-mail: klucadamo@nydailynews.com
URL: http://www.nydailynews.com

6784 ■ The Journal News
Gannett Co., Inc.
One Gannett Dr.
White Plains, NY 10604
Contact: Randi Weiner, Education Editor
Ph: (845)578-2468
E-mail: rcweiner@thejournalnews.com
URL: http://www.lohud.com

6785 ■ Rochester Democrat and Chronicle
Gannett Co., Inc.
55 Exchange Blvd.
Rochester, NY 14614
Contact: Bennett Loudon, Higher Education Reporter
Ph: (585)258-2494
E-mail: bloudon@democratandchronicle.com
URL: http://www.democratandchronicle.com

North Carolina

6786 ■ The Charlotte Observer
Knight Ridder, Inc.
PO Box 30308
Charlotte, NC 28230-0308
Contact: Ann Helms, Education Reporter
Ph: (704)358-5033
E-mail: ahelms@charlotteobserver.com
URL: http://www.charlotte.com/observer

North Dakota

6787 ■ The Bismarck Tribune
Lee Enterprises, Inc.
PO Box 5516
Bismarck, ND 58506
Contact: Sara Kincaid, Education Reporter
Ph: (701)250-8251
E-mail: sara.kincaid@bismarcktribune.com
URL: http://www.bismarcktribune.com

Ohio

6788 ■ Akron Beacon Journal
Sound Publishing Holdings, Inc.
PO Box 640
Akron, OH 44309-0640
Contact: Carol Biliczky, Higher Educ. Reporter
Ph: (330)996-3729

Fax: (330)376-9235
E-mail: cbiliczky@thebeaconjournal.com
URL: http://www.ohio.com

6789 ■ Cincinnati Enquirer
Gannett Co., Inc.
312 Elm St.
Cincinnati, OH 45202-2739
Contact: Cindy Kranz, Education Reporter
Ph: (513)936-3365
E-mail: ckranz@enquirer.com
URL: http://www.enquirer.com

6790 ■ The Columbus Dispatch
34 S. Third St.
Columbus, OH 43215-4241
Contact: Jennifer Smith Richards, Education Issues Reporter
Ph: (614)461-8877
E-mail: jrichards@dispatch.com
URL: http://www.dispatch.com

6791 ■ The Columbus Dispatch
34 S. Third St.
Columbus, OH 43215-4241
Contact: Bill Bush, Education Reporter
E-mail: bbush@dispatch.com
URL: http://www.dispatch.com

6792 ■ Dayton Daily News
Cox Newspapers, Inc.
45 S. Ludlow St.
Dayton, OH 45402
Contact: Kevin Lamb, Healthcare Reporter
Ph: (937)225-2129
E-mail: klamb@daytondailynews.com
URL: http://www.daytondailynews.com

Oklahoma

6793 ■ The Oklahoman
Oklahoma Publishing Company
9000 N. Broadway
Oklahoma City, OK 73114
Contact: Wendy Kleinman, Education Reporter
Ph: (405)475-3637
E-mail: wkleinman@oklahoman.com
URL: http://www.newsok.com

Oregon

6794 ■ Statesman Journal
Gannett Co., Inc.
PO Box 13009
Salem, OR 97309-3009
Contact: Tracy Loew, Education Reporter
Ph: (503)399-6779
E-mail: tloew@statesmanjournal.com
URL: http://www.sj-r.com

6795 ■ Statesman Journal
Gannett Co., Inc.
PO Box 13009
Salem, OR 97309-3009
Contact: Beth Casper, Environment Reporter
Ph: (503)589-6994
E-mail: bcasper@statesmanjournal.com
URL: http://www.statesmanjournal.com

Pennsylvania

6796 ■ The Patriot-News
Newhouse Newspapers
PO Box 2265
Harrisburg, PA 17105
Contact: Ford Turner, Education Reporter
Ph: (717)255-8486
E-mail: fturner@patriot-news.com
URL: http://www.patriots-news.com

6797 ■ The Philadelphia Inquirer
Philadelphia Media Holdings LLC
400 N. Broad St.
Philadelphia, PA 19103
Contact: Susan Snyder, Higher Education Reporter

Ph: (215)854-4693
E-mail: ssnyder@phillynews.com
URL: http://www.philly.com

6798 ■ The Philadelphia Inquirer
Philadelphia Media Holdings LLC
400 N. Broad St.
Philadelphia, PA 19103
Contact: Kathy Boccella, Higher Education Reporter
Ph: (610)313-8000
E-mail: kboccella@phillynews.com
URL: http://www.philly.com

6799 ■ The Philadelphia Inquirer
Philadelphia Media Holdings LLC
400 N. Broad St.
Philadelphia, PA 19103
Contact: Rose Ciotta, Education Editor
Ph: (215)854-2771
E-mail: rciotta@phillynews.com
URL: http://www.philly.com

Rhode Island

6800 ■ The Providence Journal
A.H. Belo Corporation
75 Fountain St.
Providence, RI 02902
Contact: Jennifer D. Jordan, Education Reporter
Ph: (401)277-7254
Fax: (401)277-7346
E-mail: jjordan@projo.com
URL: http://www.projo.com

6801 ■ The Providence Journal
A.H. Belo Corporation
75 Fountain St.
Providence, RI 02902
Contact: Linda Borg, Education Reporter
Ph: (401)277-7823
Fax: (401)277-7346
E-mail: lborg@projo.com
URL: http://www.projo.com

South Carolina

6802 ■ The Post & Courier
134 Columbus St.
Charleston, SC 29403-4800
Contact: Diette Courrege, Education Reporter
Ph: (843)937-5546
E-mail: dcourrege@postandcourier.com
URL: http://www.charleston.net

6803 ■ The State
The McClatchy Company
PO Box 1333
Columbia, SC 29202-1333
Contact: James Hammond, Higher Education Reporter
Ph: (803)771-8395
E-mail: jhammond@thestate.com
URL: http://www.thestate.com

Texas

6804 ■ Austin American-Statesman
Cox Newspapers, Inc.
305 S. Congress Ave.
Austin, TX 78704
Contact: Ralph Haurwitz, Higher Education Writer
Ph: (512)445-3604
E-mail: rhaurwitz@statesman.com
URL: http://www.austin360.com/aas

6805 ■ Austin American-Statesman
Cox Newspapers, Inc.
305 S. Congress Ave.
Austin, TX 78704
Contact: Laura Heinauer, Education Reporter
Ph: (512)445-3694

E-mail: lheinauer@statesman.com
URL: http://www.austin360.com/aas

6806 ■ Dallas Morning News
Belo Corp.
508 Young St.
Dallas, TX 75202
Contact: Holly Hacker, Higher Educ. Reporter
Ph: (214)977-8749
E-mail: hhacker@dallasnews.com
URL: http://www.dallasnews.com

6807 ■ Fort Worth Star-Telegram
PO Box 1870
Fort Worth, TX 76115
Contact: Mark Agee, Education Reporter
Ph: (817)685-3821
E-mail: rmagee@star-telegram.com
URL: http://www.star-telegram.com

6808 ■ Fort Worth Star-Telegram
PO Box 1870
Fort Worth, TX 76115
Contact: Gene Trainor, Higher Education Editor
Ph: (817)685-3956
E-mail: gtrainor@star-telegram.com
URL: http://www.star-telegram.com

6809 ■ Fort Worth Star-Telegram
PO Box 1870
Fort Worth, TX 76101
Contact: Diane Smith, Education Reporter
Ph: (817)390-7400
E-mail: dianesmith@star-telegram.com
URL: http://www.star-telegram.com

6810 ■ Forth Worth Star-Telegram
The McClatchy Company
PO Box 1870
Fort Worth, TX 76101
Contact: Elizabeth Campbell, Education Reporter
Ph: (817)390-7696
Free: 800-776-7827
E-mail: liz@star-telegram.com
URL: http://www.star-telegram.com

6811 ■ Houston Chronicle
Hearst Newspapers
801 Texas Ave.
Houston, TX 77002
Contact: Jennifer Radcliffe, Education Reporter
Ph: (713)362-7129
E-mail: jennifer.radcliffe@chron.com
URL: http://www.houstonchronicle.com

6812 ■ San Antonio Express-News
Hearst Newspapers
PO Box 2171
San Antonio, TX 78297-2171
Contact: Melissa Ludwig, Higher Education Reporter
Ph: (210)250-3171
E-mail: mludwig@express-news.net
URL: http://www.mysa.com

6813 ■ San Antonio Express-News
Hearst Newspapers
PO Box 2171
San Antonio, TX 78297-2171
Contact: Jenny Lacoste-Caputo, Education Editor
Ph: (210)250-3171
E-mail: jcaputo@express-news.net
URL: http://www.mysa.com

6814 ■ San Antonio Express-News
Hearst Newspapers
PO Box 2171
San Antonio, TX 78297-2171
Contact: Michelle De La Rosa, Education Editor
Ph: (210)250-3171
E-mail: mdelarosa@express-news.net
URL: http://www.mysa.com

Utah

6815 ■ The Salt Lake Tribune
90 S. 400 W., Ste. 700
Salt Lake City, UT 84101

Contact: Roxana Orellana, Higher Education Reporter
Ph: (801)257-8693
E-mail: rorellana@sltrib.com
URL: http://www.sltrib.com

Vermont

6816 ■ *The Burlington Free Press*
Gannett Co., Inc.
PO Box 10
Burlington, VT 05402
Contact: Molly Walsh, Education Reporter
Ph: (802)660-1874
Fax: (802)660-1802
E-mail: mwalsh@afp.burlingtonfreepress.com
URL: http://www.burlingtonfreepress.com

Virginia

6817 ■ *Richmond Times-Dispatch*
Media General, Inc.
PO Box 85333
Richmond, VA 23293
Contact: Holly Prestidge, Education Reporter
Ph: (804)649-6945
Fax: (804)775-8059
E-mail: hprestidge@timesdispatch.com
URL: http://www.timesdispatch.com

Washington

6818 ■ *Seattle Post-Intelligencer*
Hearst Newspapers
PO Box 1909
Seattle, WA 98111
Contact: Jessica Blanchard, K-12 Education Reporter
Ph: (206)448-8322
E-mail: jessicablanchard@seattlepi.com
URL: http://www.seattlepi.com

6819 ■ *Seattle Times*
PO Box 70
Seattle, WA 98111
Contact: Linda Shaw, Education Issues Reporter
Ph: (206)464-2359
E-mail: lshaw@seattletimes.com
URL: http://www.seattletimes.com

6820 ■ *Seattle Times*
PO Box 70
Seattle, WA 98111

Contact: Nick Perry, Higher Education Reporter
Ph: (206)464-2204
E-mail: nperry@seattletimes.com
URL: http://www.seattletimes.com

Wyoming

6821 ■ *Wyoming Tribune-Eagle*
Cheyenne Newspapers, Inc.
702 W. Lincolnway
Cheyenne, WY 82001
Contact: Becky Orr, Education Writer
Ph: (307)633-3183
E-mail: borr@wyomingnews.com
URL: http://www.wyomingnews.com

Corporate Contacts

6822 ■ Arrow Educational Products
PO Box 1287
1423 Union Chapel Rd.
Pembroke, NC 28372
Ph: (910)258-8049
E-mail: reginald.oxendine@arrowinc.com
URL: http://www.arrowinc.com

Descr: Sells computer software, videotapes, audiotapes, books, and other literary programs to school systems in North Carolina and across the United States.

6823 ■ Brame School and Office Products
PO Box 271
Durham, NC 27702
Free: 800-533-2041
URL: http://www.brameco.com/

6824 ■ Discount School Supply
Customer Service
PO Box 6013
Carol Stream, IL 60197-6013
Free: 800-627-2829
URL: http://www.discountschoolsupply.com/

6825 ■ Houghton Mifflin Harcourt
School Division
9205 S. Park Center Loop
Orlando, FL 32819
Free: 800-225-5425

E-mail: HBSPCS@harcourt.com
URL: http://www.hmhco.com/

6826 ■ MeadWestvaco Consumer and Office Products
Consumer Relations
4751 Hempstead Station Rd.
Kettering, OH 45429
Free: 800-936-9811
URL: http://www.mead.com/

6827 ■ National School Products
101 E. Broadway
Maryville, TN 37804
Free: 800-627-9393
E-mail: CustomerService@NationalSchoolProducts.com
URL: http://nationalschoolproducts.com/

6828 ■ New Mexico School Products
3020 Princeton NE
PO Box 2126
Albuquerque, NM 87103
Ph: (505)884-1426
URL: http://www.newmexicoschoolproducts.com/

6829 ■ Primemedia Consumer Magazines
3585 Engineering Dr., Ste. 100
Norcross, GA 30092
Free: 800-216-1423
E-mail: information@primedia.com
URL: http://www.primedia.com

6830 ■ Pyramid School Products
6510 N. 54th St.
Tampa, FL 33610
Free: 800-792-2644
URL: http://www.pyramidspcatalog.com/

6831 ■ Rigby Education
Harcourt Achieve
Attn: Customer Service, 5th Fl.
9205 SouthPark Center Loop
Orlando, FL 32819
Free: 800-225-3362
Fax: 800-634-7568
E-mail: tradecustomerservice@hmhpub.com
URL: http://rigby.harcourtachieve.com

6832 ■ Tools for Teaching
174 Semoran Commerce Place A106
Apopka, FL 32703
Free: 800-394-9661
URL: http://www.toolsforteaching.com/

Internet Resources

6833 ■ American Home-Based Work Administration Online
American Home-Based Work Administration
PO Box 103
Edenville, MI 48620-0103
Ph: (810)958-0148, x-1
Fax: (810)958-0148, x-2
E-mail: management@ahbwa.com
URL(s): www.ahbwa.com/html2/index.php **Descr:** AHBWA has helped thousands of people make a transition to the home-based workplace. If you are a job seeker wanting to work full or part-time from home; an entrepreneur wanting to start your own home-based business; or an employer wanting to recruit unlimited home-based workers, this site is a good place to start. Links provided are Testimonials, Job Samples, FAQs, Featured Employers, and Employers by Industry. **Type:** Directory; Full-text. **Updating freq.:** As needed. **Searching routines or searchable elements:** Searching is available.

6834 ■ CalJOBS
California Employment Development Department
PO Box 826880, MIC 83
Sacramento, CA 94280-0001
Contact: Patrick W. Henning, Dir.
Free: 800-480-3287
URL(s): www.caljobs.ca.gov/ **Descr:** The California Employment Development Department (EDD) sponsors this electronic resource for employers and job seekers. After registering with some biographical information, job hopefuls can choose to look for jobs or enter their resume. Users can also find information about work topics such as unemployment or disability insurance, tax info, training, and more. Employers must also register and can post jobs, examine resumes, and look for employees on this site. Agencies in partnership with EDD are able to use this system to coordinate matches between job seekers and employers. **Type:** Full-text; Directory; Bulletin board. **Updating freq.:** Regularly. **Fees:** Free. **Searching routines or searchable elements:** Searching is Available for job seekers and employers. **Telecom. Svcs:** TTY: 800-563-2441.

6835 ■ Career and Program Support
University of Missouri, Columbia
Education Career Services
101 Hill Hall
Columbia, MO 65211
Contact: Michelle Bollinger, Coord.
Ph: (573)882-7772
Fax: (573)884-4024
E-mail: caps@missouri.edu
URL(s): http://education.missouri.edu/TDP/CAPS/index.php **Descr:** Housed at the University of Missouri College of Education, this database contains open job listings in the field of education in the state of Missouri, as well as offering related resources for job seekers and employers alike. Job seekers can post their resumes, search for library and education jobs, get career advice, find Missouri teacher certification information, and search jobs outside of Missouri as well. **Type:** Full-text; Directory. **Updating freq.:** Weekly. **Fees:** Free. **Searching routines or searchable elements:** Searching is available.

6836 ■ Careers-In-Business
Careers-In-Business, LLC
4101 N.W. Urbandale Dr.
Urbandale, IA 50322
Contact: Wendy Tunstall, Pres.
E-mail: bizjobs09l@gmail.com
URL(s): www.careers-in-business.com **Descr:** Careers-In-Business contains information on employment in the business sector, primarily in accounting, finance and consulting. Links to many corporations who hire extensively in this area are included for those wishing to make contacts and/or mail out resumes. Detailed information on job search aids and employer profiles provided. Links to many other career sites also available, as well as links to career-related books for sale through Amazon. **Type:** Full-text; Directory; Statistical. **Updating freq.:** Regularly. **Fees:** Free. **Searching routines or searchable elements:** Searching is not available

6837 ■ Dictionary of Occupational Titles
U.S. Department of Labor
200 Constitution Ave., NW
Washington, DC 20210
Contact: Hilda L. Solis, Sec.
Ph: (202)693-7300
Free: 866-487-2365
Fax: (202)693-7365
E-mail: OALJ-Questions@dol.gov
URL: http://www.dol.gov
URL(s): www.acsh.org/ **Descr:** Contains detailed and authoritative information on all types and levels of occupations in the United States. Provides in-depth descriptions of thousands of jobs in nine different categories, including professional, technical, and managerial; clerical and sales; service; agricultural, fishery, and forestry; processing; and benchwork occupations. Covers traditional occupations as well as such jobs as wafer breaker, pit steward, and nitroglycerin neutralizer. Includes details about all listed occupations, such as educational requirements, exertional demands, aptitudes, and various other requirements. Provides insight into how the government categorizes jobs in the United States and what conditions and qualities the government assigns to each occupation. Corresponds to the print *Dictionary of Occupational Titles*. **Type:** Full-text. **Updating freq.:** Annual. **Fees:** Free.

6838 ■ Dictionary of Occupations
U.S. Department of Labor
Employment and Training Administration
200 Constitution Ave.
Washington, DC 20210
Free: 877-US2-JOBS
E-mail: onet@ncmail.net
URL: http://www.onetcenter.org/whatsnew.html
URL(s): online.onetcenter.org/ **Descr:** Contains information more than 950 occupations commonly undertaken in the United States. Includes information on skills, abilities, knowledge, training, education, work activities, and interests associated with occupations. Provides information usable in career exploration, job searching, vocational counseling, developing job descriptions, personnel recruiting, and more. Includes information on the occupations' Standard Occupational Classification. Offers data on related occupations. Includes information on job accommodations for persons with disabilities or particular work needs. **Type:** Dictionary. **Fees:** Free. **Searching routines or searchable elements:** Provides keyword search functions.

6839 ■ 1st Steps in the Hunt: Daily News for Online Job Hunters
IBN: inerbiznet.com
PO Box 637
Mill Valley, CA 94941
Contact: Colleen Gildea
Ph: (415)377-2255
Fax: (415)380-8245
E-mail: colleen.gildea@gmail.com
URL(s): www.interbiznet.com/hunt/index.html **Descr:** This site provides a range of information on job hunting on the Internet, as well as links to many other sources of information. There are examples of online web page resumes, and links to information about publishing them. In addition, a listing (with links) to 4,000 companies with jobs is provided, along with an archive of material going back one year, links to related databases, job market news, and more. Users can download information in PDF format. **Type:** Full-text; Directory. **Updating freq.:** Daily. **Fees:** Free. **Searching routines or searchable elements:** Multiple search options are allowed, including one which searches all major web databases at once and removes duplicates.

6840 ■ Health Hazard Evaluations
U.S. National Institute for Occupational Safety and Health (NIOSH)
Robert A Taft Lab
4676 Columbia Pkwy.
Cincinnati, OH 45226
Contact: Paul Schulte PhD, Dir.
Ph: (513)533-8302
Free: 800-356-4674
Fax: (513)533-8347
E-mail: pubstaff@cdc.gov
URL: http://www.cdc.gov/niosh/homepage.html
URL(s): www.cdc.gov/niosh/hhe/ **Descr:** Contains detailed reports covering possible health hazards in the American workplace. Provides information on whether or not substances normally found in workplaces have potentially toxic or carcinogenetic qualities. Includes detailed studies of factories, manufacturing plants, industrial sites, and other relevant locations. Provides information on worker exposure to other hazards such as heat, noise, radiation, and musculoskeletal stresses. Includes information on Health Hazard Evaluations requested by employees, employee representatives, and

employers. Offers information on the legal and regulatory basis for conducting Health Hazard Evaluations. **Type:** Full-text. **Fees:** Free. **Searching routines or searchable elements:** Provides keyword search functions.

6841 ■ Job-Hunt.org
NETability, Inc.
PO Box 507
Marlborough, MA 01752-0507
Contact: Susan P. Joyce, Ed.
Ph: (508)624-6261
E-mail: info@job-hunt.org
URL: http://www.job-hunt.org
Descr: Offers information for people who have experienced job loss. Provides tips on job search basics, popular articles, job sites and career resources, and job searching by location and profession. **Type:** Full-text. **Searching routines or searchable elements:** Searching options are available.

6842 ■ Savvy Miss Career & Money
Savvy Miss, LCC
URL: http://www.savvymiss.com
URL(s): www.savvymiss.com/career-woman.html
Descr: Offers advice to women on career and money matters.

6843 ■ Work Force 50
NHC Group
PO Box 508
Marlborough, MA 01752
Contact: Gene Burnard, Publisher
Free: 888-501-0804
E-mail: publisher@seniorjobbank.org
URL: http://www.workforce50.com/
Descr: Internet site for people over 50 and seeking employment. **Fees:** $89 per posting. **Searching routines or searchable elements:** Searching options are available.

Federal Government Agencies

6844 ■ Advisory Council on Employee Welfare and Pension Benefit Plans
Employee Benefits and Security Administration
Department of Labor
200 Constitution Ave. NW, Ste. N-5677
Washington, DC 20210-1111
Contact: Larry I. Good, Exec.Sec.
Ph: (202)693-8668
Fax: (202)219-8141
URL: http://www.dol.gov/ebsa/aboutebsa/erisa_advisory_council.html
Staff: Support services are provided by the Employee Benefits Security Administration. **Descr:** Council was established to advise the Secretary of Labor regarding the technical aspects of the provisions of the Employee Retirement Income Security Act of 1974 and to submit recommendations with respect to its administration. **Mem:** Council consists of 15 members representing the insurance, corporate trust, actuarial counseling, investment counseling and investment management, and accounting fields, as well as employers, employee organizations, and the general public. No more than eight members are of the same political party. Members are appointed by the Secretary for three-year terms. **Pub:** Spend Down of Defined Contribution Assets at Retirement, issue paper (2008); Phased Retirement, issue paper (2008); Hard To Value Assets/Target Date Funds (issue paper, 2008); Financial Literacy of Plan Participants and the Role of the Employer (2007); Fiduciary Responsibilities and Revenue Sharing Practices (2007); Participant Benefit Statements (2007); Health Information Technology (2006); Plan Asset Rules, Exemptions And Cross-Trading (2006); Prudent Investment Process (2006); Retirement Distributions and Options (November 30, 2005); Health and Welfare Benefit Plans' Communications (November 30, 2005); Communications to Retirement Plan Participants (2005); Health and Welfare Form 5500 Requirements Working Group Report (2004); Fee and Related Disclosures to Participants Working

Group Report (2004); Plan Fees and Reporting on Form 5500 Working Group Report (2004); Health and Welfare Form 5500 Requirements (2004). Reports are available on EBSA's Homepage. **Rmks:** Council is also known as the ERISA Advisory Council.

6845 ■ Employee Thrift Advisory Council
Federal Retirement Thrift Investment Board
1250 H St. NW
Washington, DC 20005
Contact: David T. Toro, Designated Fed.Off.
Ph: (202)942-1642
Fax: (202)942-1676
URL: http://www.frtib.gov
Descr: Council advises the Federal Retirement Investment Board on matters related to investment and administrative policies for the Thrift Savings Plan (a savings and retirement fund for government employees established by P.L. 99-335) and performs other duties as the Board directs with respect to investment funds established in accordance with P.L. 99-335. **Mem:** Council comprises representatives of fourteen government organizations, appointed by the chairperson of the Federal Retirement Thrift Investment Board. Members include representatives of all major federal, Postal Service and Uniformed Services employees and retirees. They serve four-year terms. James W. Sauber, National Association of Letter Carriers, serves as chair.

6846 ■ Equal Employment Opportunity Commission
131 M St. NE
Washington, DC 20507
Contact: Stephen Llewellyn, Acting Exec.Sec.
Ph: (202)663-4900
Free: 800-669-4000
Fax: (202)663-4174
E-mail: info@eeoc.gov
URL: http://www.eeoc.gov
Staff: Stephen Llewellyn, Acting Executive Officer, serves as staff contact. **Descr:** Commission promotes equality of employment opportunity by enforcing the federal laws prohibiting employment discrimination. This is achieved through administrative and judicial actions, and education and technical assistance. EEOC enforces Title VII of the Civil Rights Act of 1964, as amended, which prohibits employment discrimination based on race, color, religion, sex, and national origin; the Age Discrimination in Employment Act of 1967 (ADEA), as amended, which prohibits employment discrimination against person 40 years of age or older; the Equal Pay Act of 1963 (EPA), as amended, which prohibits sex-based wage discrimination between men and women in the same establishment who are performing under similar working conditions; Title I of the Americans with Disabilities Act (ADA), which prohibits discrimination against people with disabilities in the private sector and state and local governments; Section 501 and 505 of the Rehabilitation Act of 1973, which prohibits discrimination affecting individuals with disabilities in the federal government; and sections of the Civil Rights Act of 1991, which amends the Civil Rights Act of 1964 to strengthen and improve federal civil rights laws. **Mem:** Commission comprises five members appointed by the President of the United States by and with the advice and consent of the Senate; not more than three members are of the same political party. Chair is the chief executive officer of the Commission. Members serve five-year staggered terms. The General Counsel serves a four-year term. Stuart J. Ishimaru currently chairs the Commission. **Pub:** Publications may be ordered from EEOC's Office of Communications and Legislative Affairs, at 202-663-4191 or TTY 202-663-4494.

6847 ■ Native American Employment and Training Council
Off. of Indian & Native American Programs
Employment & Training Admin.
Department of Labor
200 Constitution Ave. NW, Rm. S-4209
Washington, DC 20210

Contact: Evangeline Campbell, Staff Contact
Ph: (202)693-3737
Fax: (202)693-3817
URL: http://www.doleta.gov/dinap/cfml/adcouncil.cfm
Staff: Evangeline Campbell, Program Manager, Indian and Native American Program, Employment and Training Administration, serves as designated federal official. **Descr:** Council advises the Department of Labor regarding the overall operation and administration of Native American programs authorized under Title IV, Section 401 of the Job Training Partnership Act, as amended, and successor legislation, the Workforce Investment Act. It also provides advice on the implementation of other programs providing services to Native American youth and adults under the Act. **Mem:** Council consists of approximately 20 American Indians, Alaskan Natives, and Hawaiian Natives appointed by the Secretary of Labor from among individuals nominated by Indian tribes or American Indian, Alaskan Native, or Hawaiian Native organizations. Members represent all geographic areas of the United States with a substantial American Indian, Alaskan Native, or Hawaiian Native population and includes representatives of tribal governments and non-reservation Native American organizations that are service providers under the Act. Lorenda Sanchez, Region VI, Executive Director, California Indian Manpower Consortium, Inc., chairs the Committee.

6848 ■ Occupational Information Development Advisory Panel
3-E-26 Operations Bldg.
Social Security Administration
6401 Security Blvd.
Baltimore, MD 21235-0001
Contact: Debra Tidwell-Peters, Designated Fed.Off.
Ph: (410)965-9617
Fax: (410)597-0825
E-mail: OIDAP@ssa.gov
URL: http://www.ssa.gov/oidap/
Staff: Support services are provided by the Social Security Administration. Debra Tidwell-Peters, Social Insurance Specialist, serves as designated federal official. **Descr:** Panel provides advice and recommendations on plans and activities to replace the Dictionary of Occupational Titles used in the Social Security Administration's (SSA) disability determination process. Panel advises the SSA on creating an occupational information system tailored specifically for its disability programs and adjudicative needs. Panel will address medical and vocational analysis of disability claims; occupational analysis, including definitions, rating, and capture of physical and mental/cognitive demands of work, and other occupational information critical to the disability programs; data collection; use of occupational information in the disability programs; and any other areas related to the development of an occupational information system suited to its disability programs and improvement of medical-vocational adjudication policies and processes. **Mem:** Panel comprises not more than 12 members, including: representatives of academia with expertise in occupational analysis, vocational assessment, and physical and occupational rehabilitation; professional experts in vocational rehabilitation, forensic vocational assessment, and disability insurance programs; medical professionals with experience in occupational or physical rehabilitation medicine, psychiatry or psychology, and physical or occupational therapy; professional experts who represent or advocate on behalf of persons with disabilities; and a Social Security representative with expertise in SSA's disability program policies, processes, and systems. Members serve two-year terms.

6849 ■ U.S. Department of Labor (OSHA) Occupational Safety and Health Administration
Region 1 Office
JFK Federal Bldg., Rm. E340
Boston, MA 02203
Ph: (617)565-9860

Fax: (617)565-9827
URL: http://www.osha.gov/html/RAmap.html

**6850 ■ U.S. Department of Labor (OSHA)
Occupational Safety and Health Administration
Region 2 Office**
201 Varick St., Rm. 670
New York, NY 10014
Ph: (212)337-2378
Fax: (212)337-2371
URL: http://www.osha.gov/html/RAmap.html

**6851 ■ U.S. Department of Labor (OSHA)
Occupational Safety and Health Administration
Region 3 Office**
The Curtis Center, Ste. 740 W.
170 S. Independence Mall W.
Philadelphia, PA 19106-3309
Ph: (215)861-4900
Fax: (215)861-4904
URL: http://www.osha.gov/html/RAmap.html

**6852 ■ U.S. Department of Labor (OSHA)
Occupational Safety and Health Administration
Region 4 Office**
61 Forsyth Street, SW, Rm. 6T50
Atlanta, GA 30303
Ph: (404)562-2300
Fax: (404)562-2295
URL: http://www.osha.gov/html/RAmap.html

**6853 ■ U.S. Department of Labor (OSHA)
Occupational Safety and Health Administration
Region 5 Office**
230 S. Dearborn St., Rm. 3244
Chicago, IL 60604
Ph: (312)353-2220
Fax: (312)353-7774
URL: http://www.osha.gov/html/RAmap.html

**6854 ■ U.S. Department of Labor (OSHA)
Occupational Safety and Health Administration
Region 6 Office**
525 Griffin St., Ste. 602
Dallas, TX 75202
Ph: (972)850-4145
Fax: (972)850-4149
URL: http://www.osha.gov/html/RAmap.html

**6855 ■ U.S. Department of Labor (OSHA)
Occupational Safety and Health Administration
Region 7 Office**
Two Pershing Sq.Bldg.
2300 Main St., Ste. 1010
Kansas City, MO 64108
Ph: (816)283-8745
Fax: (816)283-0547
URL: http://www.osha.gov/html/RAmap.html

**6856 ■ U.S. Department of Labor (OSHA)
Occupational Safety and Health Administration
Region 8 Office**
1999 Broadway, Ste. 1690
Denver, CO 80202
Ph: (720)264-6550
Fax: (720)264-6585
URL: http://www.osha.gov/html/RAmap.html

**6857 ■ U.S. Department of Labor (OSHA)
Occupational Safety and Health Administration
Region 9 Office**
90 7th St., Ste. 18100
San Francisco, CA 94103
Ph: (415)625-2547
Free: 800-475-4022

Fax: (415)625-2534
URL: http://www.osha.gov/html/RAmap.html

**6858 ■ U.S. Department of Labor (OSHA)
Occupational Safety and Health Administration
Region 10 Office**
1111 Third Ave., Ste. 715
Seattle, WA 98101-3212
Ph: (206)553-5930
Fax: (206)553-6499
URL: http://www.osha.gov/html/RAmap.html

**6859 ■ U.S. Equal Employment Opportunity
Commission (EEOC)
Albuquerque Area Office**
505 Marquette, NW, Ste. 900, 9th Fl.
Albuquerque, NM 87102
Contact: Georgia Marchbanks, Dir.
Ph: (505)248-5201
Free: 800-669-4000
Fax: (505)248-5239
URL: http://www.eeoc.gov/albuquerque/index.html
Telecom. Svcs: TTY toll free number is (800)669-6820.

**6860 ■ U.S. Equal Employment Opportunity
Commission (EEOC)
Atlanta District Office**
Sam Nunn Atlanta Federal Center
100 Alabama St. SW, Ste. 4R30
Atlanta, GA 30303
Contact: Bernice Williams-Kimbrough, Dir.
Ph: (404)562-6800
Free: 800-669-4000
Fax: (404)562-6909
URL: http://www.eeoc.gov/atlanta/index.html
Telecom. Svcs: TTY toll free number is (800)669-6820.

**6861 ■ U.S. Equal Employment Opportunity
Commission (EEOC)
Baltimore District Office**
City Crescent Bldg.
10 S. Howard St., Third Fl.
Baltimore, MD 21201
Contact: Gerald Kiel, Dir.
Ph: (410)962-3932
Free: 800-669-4000
Fax: (410)962-4270
URL: http://www.eeoc.gov/baltimore/index.html
Telecom. Svcs: TTY toll free number is (800)669-6820.

**6862 ■ U.S. Equal Employment Opportunity
Commission (EEOC)
Birmingham District Office**
Ridge Park Pl.
1130 22nd St. S., Ste. 2000
Birmingham, AL 35205
Contact: Delner Franklin-Thomas, Dir.
Ph: (205)212-2100
Free: 800-669-4000
Fax: (205)212-2105
URL: http://www.eeoc.gov/birmingham/index.html
Telecom. Svcs: TTY toll free number is (800)669-6820.

**6863 ■ U.S. Equal Employment Opportunity
Commission (EEOC)
Boston Area Office**
John F. Kennedy Federal Bldg.
475 Government Center
Boston, MA 02203
Contact: Robert L. Sanders, Dir.
Ph: (617)565-3200
Free: 800-669-4000
Fax: (617)565-3196
URL: http://www.eeoc.gov/boston/index.html
Telecom. Svcs: TTY toll free number is (800)669-6820.

**6864 ■ U.S. Equal Employment Opportunity
Commission (EEOC)
Buffalo Local Office**
6 Fountain Plaza, Ste. 350
Buffalo, NY 14202
Contact: John E. Thompson Jr., Dir.

Ph: (716)551-4441
Free: 800-669-4000
Fax: (716)551-4387
URL: http://www.eeoc.gov/buffalo/index.html
Telecom. Svcs: TTY toll free number is (800)669-6820.

**6865 ■ U.S. Equal Employment Opportunity
Commission (EEOC)
Charlotte District Office**
129 W. Trade St., Ste. 400
Charlotte, NC 28202
Contact: Reuben Daniels Jr., Dir.
Ph: (704)344-6682
Free: 800-669-4000
Fax: (704)344-6734
URL: http://www.eeoc.gov/charlotte/index.html
Telecom. Svcs: TTY toll free number is (800)669-6820.

**6866 ■ U.S. Equal Employment Opportunity
Commission (EEOC)
Chicago District Office**
500 W. Madison St., Ste. 2000
Chicago, IL 60661
Contact: John P. Rowe, Dir.
Ph: (312)353-2713
Free: 800-669-4000
Fax: (312)886-1168
URL: http://www.eeoc.gov/chicago/index.html
Telecom. Svcs: TTY toll free number is (800)669-6820.

**6867 ■ U.S. Equal Employment Opportunity
Commission (EEOC)
Cincinnati Area Office**
John W. Peck Federal Office Bldg.
550 Main St., 10th Fl.
Cincinnati, OH 45202
Contact: Wilma L. Javey, Dir.
Ph: (513)684-2851
Free: 800-669-4000
Fax: (513)684-2361
URL: http://www.eeoc.gov/cincinnati/index.html
Telecom. Svcs: TTY toll free number is (800)669-6820.

**6868 ■ U.S. Equal Employment Opportunity
Commission (EEOC)
Cleveland District Office**
Anthony J. Celebrezze Federal Bldg.
1240 E. 9th St., Ste. 3001
Cleveland, OH 44119
Contact: Daniel Cabot, Dir.
Ph: (216)522-2003
Free: 800-669-4000
Fax: (216)522-7395
URL: http://www.eeoc.gov/cleveland/index.html
Telecom. Svcs: TTY toll free number is (800)669-6820.

**6869 ■ U.S. Equal Employment Opportunity
Commission (EEOC)
Dallas District Office**
207 S. Houston St., 3rd Fl.
Dallas, TX 75202
Contact: Mike Fetzer, Dir.
Ph: (214)253-2700
Free: 800-669-4000
Fax: (214)253-2720
URL: http://www.eeoc.gov/dallas/index.html
Telecom. Svcs: TTY toll free number is (800)669-6820.

**6870 ■ U.S. Equal Employment Opportunity
Commission (EEOC)
Denver District Office**
303 E. 17th Ave., Ste. 410
Denver, CO 80203
Contact: Nancy Sienko, Dir.
Ph: (303)866-1300
Free: 800-669-4000
Fax: (303)866-1085
URL: http://www.eeoc.gov/denver/index.html

Telecom. Svcs: TTY toll free number is (800)669-6820.

6871 ■ U.S. Equal Employment Opportunity Commission (EEOC)
Detroit District Office
Patrick V. McNamara Bldg.
477 Michigan Ave., Rm. 865
Detroit, MI 48226
Contact: Gail Cober, Dir.
Ph: (313)226-4600
Free: 800-669-4000
Fax: (313)226-4610
URL: http://www.eeoc.gov/detroit/index.html
Telecom. Svcs: TTY toll free number is (800)669-6820.

6872 ■ U.S. Equal Employment Opportunity Commission (EEOC)
El Paso Area Office
300 E. Main Dr., Ste. 500
El Paso, TX 79901
Contact: Teresa Tena-Anchondo, Dir.
Ph: (915)534-6700
Free: 800-669-4000
Fax: (915)534-6701
URL: http://www.eeoc.gov/elpaso/index.html
Telecom. Svcs: TTY toll free number is (800)669-6820.

6873 ■ U.S. Equal Employment Opportunity Commission (EEOC)
Fresno Local Office
2300 Tulare St., Ste. 215
Fresno, CA 93721
Contact: Melissa Barrios, Dir.
Ph: (559)487-5793
Free: 800-669-4000
Fax: (559)487-5053
URL: http://www.eeoc.gov/fresno/index.html
Telecom. Svcs: TTY toll free number is (800)669-6820.

6874 ■ U.S. Equal Employment Opportunity Commission (EEOC)
Greensboro Local Office
2303 W. Meadowview Rd., Ste. 201
Greensboro, NC 27407
Contact: Jose Rosenberg, Dir.
Ph: (336)547-4188
Free: 800-669-4000
Fax: (336)547-4032
URL: http://www.eeoc.gov/greensboro/index.html
Telecom. Svcs: TTY toll free number is (800)669-6820.

6875 ■ U.S. Equal Employment Opportunity Commission (EEOC)
Greenville Local Office
301 N. Main St., Ste. 1402
Greenville, SC 29601-9916
Contact: Patricia B. Fuller, Dir.
Ph: (864)241-4400
Free: 800-669-4000
Fax: (864)241-4416
URL: http://www.eeoc.gov/greenville/index.html
Telecom. Svcs: TTY toll free number is (800)669-6820.

6876 ■ U.S. Equal Employment Opportunity Commission (EEOC)
Honolulu Local Office
300 Ala Moana Blvd., Rm. 7-127
PO Box 50082
Honolulu, HI 96850-0051
Contact: Timothy Riera, Dir.
Ph: (808)541-3120
Free: 800-669-4000
Fax: (808)541-3390
URL: http://www.eeoc.gov/honolulu/index.html
Telecom. Svcs: TTY toll free number is (800)669-6820.

6877 ■ U.S. Equal Employment Opportunity Commission (EEOC)
Houston District Office
Mickey Leland Federal Bldg.
1919 Smith St., 6th Fl.

Houston, TX 77002-8049
Contact: R.J. Ruff Jr., Dir.
Ph: (713)209-3320
Free: 800-669-4000
Fax: (713)209-3381
URL: http://www.eeoc.gov/houston/index.html
Telecom. Svcs: TTY toll free number is (800)669-6820.

6878 ■ U.S. Equal Employment Opportunity Commission (EEOC)
Indianapolis District Office
101 W. Ohio St, Ste. 1900
Indianapolis, IN 46204
Contact: Danny G. Harter, Dir.
Ph: (317)226-7212
Free: 800-669-4000
Fax: (317)226-7953
URL: http://www.eeoc.gov/indianapolis/index.html
Telecom. Svcs: TTY toll free number is (800)669-6820.

6879 ■ U.S. Equal Employment Opportunity Commission (EEOC)
Jackson Area Office
Dr. A.H. McCoy Federal Bldg.
100 W. Capitol St., Ste. 207
Jackson, MS 39269
Contact: Wilma Scott, Dir.
Ph: (601)965-4537
Free: 800-669-4000
Fax: (601)948-8401
URL: http://www.eeoc.gov/jackson/index.html
Telecom. Svcs: TTY toll free number is (800)669-6820.

6880 ■ U.S. Equal Employment Opportunity Commission (EEOC)
Kansas City Area Office
Gateway Tower II
4th and State Ave., 9th Fl.
Kansas City, KS 66101
Contact: Billie Ashton, Dir.
Ph: (913)551-5655
Free: 800-669-4000
Fax: (913)551-6957
URL: http://www.eeoc.gov/kansascity/index.html
Telecom. Svcs: TTY toll free number is (800)669-6820.

6881 ■ U.S. Equal Employment Opportunity Commission (EEOC)
Little Rock Area Office
820 Louisiana St., Ste. 200
Little Rock, AR 72201
Contact: Wanda C. Milton, Dir.
Ph: (501)324-5060
Free: 800-669-4000
Fax: (501)324-5991
URL: http://www.eeoc.gov/littlerock/index.html
Telecom. Svcs: TTY toll free number is (800)669-6820.

6882 ■ U.S. Equal Employment Opportunity Commission (EEOC)
Los Angeles District Office
Roybal Federal Bldg.
255 E. Temple St., 4th Fl.
Los Angeles, CA 90012
Contact: Olophius E. Perry, Dir.
Ph: (213)894-1000
Free: 800-669-4000
Fax: (213)894-1118
URL: http://www.eeoc.gov/losangeles/index.html
Telecom. Svcs: TTY toll free number is (800)669-6820.

6883 ■ U.S. Equal Employment Opportunity Commission (EEOC)
Louisville Area Office
600 Dr. Martin Luther King, Jr. Pl., Ste. 268
Louisville, KY 40202
Contact: Marcia Hall-Craig, Dir.
Ph: (502)582-6082
Free: 800-669-4000
Fax: (502)582-5895
URL: http://www.eeoc.gov/louisville/index.html

Telecom. Svcs: TTY toll free number is (800)669-6820.

6884 ■ U.S. Equal Employment Opportunity Commission (EEOC)
Memphis District Office
1407 Union Ave., 9th Fl.
Memphis, TN 38104
Contact: Katharine Kores, Dir.
Ph: (901)544-0115
Free: 800-669-4000
Fax: (901)544-0111
URL: http://www.eeoc.gov/memphis/index.html
Telecom. Svcs: TTY toll free number is (800)669-6820.

6885 ■ U.S. Equal Employment Opportunity Commission (EEOC)
Miami District Office
One Biscayne Tower
2 S. Biscayne Blvd., Ste. 2700
Miami, FL 33131
Contact: Jacqueline McNair, Dir.
Ph: (305)536-4491
Free: 800-669-4000
Fax: (305)808-1855
URL: http://www.eeoc.gov/miami/index.html
Telecom. Svcs: TTY toll free number is (800)669-6820.

6886 ■ U.S. Equal Employment Opportunity Commission (EEOC)
Milwaukee District Office
Reuss Federal Plaza
310 W. Wisconsin Ave., Ste. 800
Milwaukee, WI 53203-2292
Contact: Rosemary Fox, Actg.Dir.
Ph: (414)297-1111
Free: 800-669-4000
Fax: (414)297-4133
URL: http://www.eeoc.gov/milwaukee/index.html
Telecom. Svcs: TTY toll free number is (800)669-6820.

6887 ■ U.S. Equal Employment Opportunity Commission (EEOC)
Minneapolis Area Office
Towle Bldg.
330 S. Second Ave., Ste. 720
Minneapolis, MN 55401-2224
Contact: Julie Schmid, Acting Dir.
Ph: (612)335-4040
Free: 800-669-4000
Fax: (612)335-4044
URL: http://www.eeoc.gov/minneapolis/index.html
Telecom. Svcs: TTY toll free number is (800)669-6820.

6888 ■ U.S. Equal Employment Opportunity Commission (EEOC)
Nashville Area Office
50 Vantage Way, Ste. 202
Nashville, TN 37228-9940
Contact: Sarah L. Smith, Dir.
Ph: (615)736-5820
Free: 800-669-4000
Fax: (615)736-2107
URL: http://www.eeoc.gov/nashville/index.html
Telecom. Svcs: TTY toll free number is (800)669-6820.

6889 ■ U.S. Equal Employment Opportunity Commission (EEOC)
New Orleans District Office
1555 Poydras St. Ste. 1900
New Orleans, LA 70112
Contact: Keith T. Hill, Dir.
Ph: (504)589-2329
Free: 800-669-4000
Fax: (504)595-2884
URL: http://www.eeoc.gov/neworleans/index.html

Telecom. Svcs: TTY toll free number is (504)595-2958.

6890 ■ U.S. Equal Employment Opportunity Commission (EEOC)
New York District Office
33 Whitehall St., 5th Fl.
New York, NY 10004
Contact: Spencer H. Lewis Jr., Dir.
Ph: (212)336-3620
Free: 800-669-4000
Fax: (212)336-3790
URL: http://www.eeoc.gov/newyork/index.html
Telecom. Svcs: TTY toll free number is (800)669-6820.

6891 ■ U.S. Equal Employment Opportunity Commission (EEOC)
Newark Area Office
One Newark Center, 21st Fl.
Raymond Blvd. at McCarter Hwy. (Rt. 21)
Newark, NJ 07102-5233
Contact: Corrado Gigante, Dir.
Ph: (973)645-6383
Free: 800-669-4000
Fax: (973)645-4524
URL: http://www.eeoc.gov/newark/index.html
Telecom. Svcs: TTY toll free number is (800)669-6820.

6892 ■ U.S. Equal Employment Opportunity Commission (EEOC)
Norfolk Area Office
Federal Bldg.
200 Granby St., Ste. 739
Norfolk, VA 23510
Contact: Herbert Brown, Dir.
Ph: (757)441-3470
Free: 800-669-4000
Fax: (757)441-6720
URL: http://www.eeoc.gov/norfolk/index.html
Telecom. Svcs: TTY toll free number is (800)669-6820.

6893 ■ U.S. Equal Employment Opportunity Commission (EEOC)
Oakland Local Office
1301 Clay St., Ste. 1170-N
Oakland, CA 94612-5217
Contact: Kristine Jensen, Dir.
Ph: (510)637-3230
Free: 800-669-4000
Fax: (510)637-3235
URL: http://www.eeoc.gov/oakland/index.html
Telecom. Svcs: TTY toll free number is (800)669-6820.

6894 ■ U.S. Equal Employment Opportunity Commission (EEOC)
Oklahoma Area Office
215 Dean A McGee Ave., 5th Fl.
Oklahoma City, OK 73102
Contact: Lloyd Vasquez , Actg. Area Dir.
Ph: (405)231-4911
Free: 800-669-4000
Fax: (405)231-4140
URL: http://www.eeoc.gov/oklahoma/index.html
Telecom. Svcs: TTY toll free number is (800)669-6820.

6895 ■ U.S. Equal Employment Opportunity Commission (EEOC)
Philadelphia District Office
801 Market St., Ste. 1300
Philadelphia, PA 19107-3127
Contact: Marie M. Tomasso, Dir.
Ph: (215)440-2600
Free: 800-669-4000
Fax: (215)440-2606
URL: http://www.eeoc.gov/philadelphia/index.html
Telecom. Svcs: TTY toll free number is (800)669-6820.

6896 ■ U.S. Equal Employment Opportunity Commission (EEOC)
Phoenix District Office
3300 N. Central Ave., Ste. 690
Phoenix, AZ 85012-2504

Contact: Rayford O. Irvin, Actg.Dir.
Ph: (602)640-5000
Free: 800-669-4000
Fax: (602)640-5071
URL: http://www.eeoc.gov/phoenix/index.html
Telecom. Svcs: TTY toll free number is (800)669-6820.

6897 ■ U.S. Equal Employment Opportunity Commission (EEOC)
Pittsburgh Area Office
William S. Moorhead Federal Bldg.
1000 Liberty Ave., Ste. 1112
Pittsburgh, PA 15222-4187
Contact: Joseph Hardiman, Dir.
Free: 800-669-4000
Fax: (412)395-5749
URL: http://www.eeoc.gov/pittsburgh/index.html
Telecom. Svcs: TTY toll free number is (412)395-5904.

6898 ■ U.S. Equal Employment Opportunity Commission (EEOC)
Raleigh Area Office
1309 Annapolis Dr.
Raleigh, NC 27608-2129
Contact: Thomas M. Colclough, Dir.
Ph: (919)856-4064
Free: 800-669-4000
Fax: (919)856-4151
URL: http://www.eeoc.gov/raleigh/index.html
Telecom. Svcs: TTY toll free number is (800)669-6820.

6899 ■ U.S. Equal Employment Opportunity Commission (EEOC)
Richmond Area Office
830 E. Main St., Ste. 600
Richmond, VA 23219
Contact: Patricia Glisson, Dir.
Ph: (804)771-2200
Free: 800-669-4000
Fax: (804)771-2222
URL: http://www.eeoc.gov/richmond/index.html
Telecom. Svcs: TTY toll free number is (800)669-6820.

6900 ■ U.S. Equal Employment Opportunity Commission (EEOC)
St. Louis District Office
Robert A. Young Federal Bldg.
1222 Spruce St., Rm. 8.100
St. Louis, MO 63103
Contact: James R. Neely Jr., Dir.
Ph: (314)539-7800
Free: 800-669-4000
Fax: (314)539-7894
URL: http://www.eeoc.gov/stlouis/index.html
Telecom. Svcs: TTY toll free number is (800)669-6820.

6901 ■ U.S. Equal Employment Opportunity Commission (EEOC)
San Antonio District Office
Mockingbird Plaza II
5410 Fredericksburg Rd., Ste. 200
San Antonio, TX 78229
Contact: Pedro Esquivel, Dir.
Ph: (210)281-7600
Free: 800-669-4000
Fax: (210)281-7690
URL: http://www.eeoc.gov/sanantonio/index.html
Telecom. Svcs: TTY toll free number is (800)669-6820.

6902 ■ U.S. Equal Employment Opportunity Commission (EEOC)
San Diego Area Office
555 W. Beech St., Ste. 504
San Diego, CA 92101
Contact: Tom McCammon, Dir.
Ph: (619)557-7235
Free: 800-669-4000
Fax: (619)557-7274
URL: http://www.eeoc.gov/sandiego/index.html

Telecom. Svcs: TTY toll free number is (800)669-6820.

6903 ■ U.S. Equal Employment Opportunity Commission (EEOC)
San Francisco District Office
350 The Embarcadero, Ste. 500
San Francisco, CA 94105-1260
Contact: Michael Baldonado, Dir.
Ph: (415)625-5600
Free: 800-669-4000
Fax: (415)625-5609
URL: http://www.eeoc.gov/sanfrancisco/index.html
Telecom. Svcs: TTY toll free number is (800)669-6820.

6904 ■ U.S. Equal Employment Opportunity Commission (EEOC)
San Jose Local Office
96 N. Third St., Ste. 200
San Jose, CA 95112
Contact: Hea Jung Atkins, Dir.
Ph: (408)291-7352
Free: 800-669-4000
Fax: (408)291-4539
URL: http://www.eeoc.gov/sanjose/index.html
Telecom. Svcs: TTY toll free number is (800)669-6820.

6905 ■ U.S. Equal Employment Opportunity Commission (EEOC)
San Juan Area Office
525 F.D. Roosevelt Ave.
Plaza Las Americas, Ste. 1202
San Juan, PR 00918-8001
Contact: William Sanchez, Dir.
Ph: (787)771-1464
Free: 800-669-4000
Fax: (787)771-1485
URL: http://www.eeoc.gov/sanjuan/index.html
Telecom. Svcs: TTY toll free number is (800)669-6820.

6906 ■ U.S. Equal Employment Opportunity Commission (EEOC)
Savannah Local Office
410 Mall Blvd., Ste. G
Savannah, GA 31406-4821
Contact: Mason D. Barrett, Dir.
Ph: (912)652-4234
Free: 800-669-4000
Fax: (912)652-4248
URL: http://www.eeoc.gov/savannah/index.html
Telecom. Svcs: TTY toll free number is (800)669-6820.

6907 ■ U.S. Equal Employment Opportunity Commission (EEOC)
Seattle District Office
Federal Office Bldg.
909 First Ave., Ste. 400
Seattle, WA 98104-1061
Contact: Luis Lucero, Dir.
Ph: (206)220-6883
Free: 800-669-4000
Fax: (206)220-6911
URL: http://www.eeoc.gov/seattle/index.html
Telecom. Svcs: TTY toll free number is (800)669-6820.

6908 ■ U.S. Equal Employment Opportunity Commission (EEOC)
Tampa Area Office
501 East Polk St., Ste. 1000
Tampa, FL 33602
Contact: Manuel Zurita, Dir.
Ph: (813)228-2310
Free: 800-669-4000
Fax: (813)228-2841
URL: http://www.eeoc.gov/tampa/index.html
Telecom. Svcs: TTY toll free number is (800)669-6820.

6909 ■ U.S. Equal Employment Opportunity Commission (EEOC)
Washington Field Office
131 M St., NE, 4th Fl., Ste. 4NW02F
Washington, DC 20507-0100

Contact: Mindy Weinstein, Actg.Dir.
Ph: (202)275-7377
Free: 800-669-4000
Fax: (202)419-0740
URL: http://www.eeoc.gov/washington/index.html
Telecom. Svcs: TTY toll free number is (800)669-6820.

Associations and Other Organizations

6910 ■ 60 Plus Association
1600 Wilson Blvd., Ste. 960
Arlington, VA 22209
Contact: James L. Martin, Pres.
Free: 888-560-7587
Fax: (703)807-2073
E-mail: info@60plus.org
URL: http://www.60plus.org
Staff: 7. **Descr:** Individuals aged 60 years or older. Promotes adoption of a "less government, less taxes" approach to seniors' issues. Conducts lobbying and advocacy activities. **Fnd:** 1992. **Mem:** 500000. **Pub:** *Scorecard* (periodic); *Senior Voice* (periodic).

6911 ■ AARP
601 E St. NW
Washington, DC 20049
Contact: William D. Novelli, CEO
Ph: (202)434-2560
Free: 888-OUR-AARP
E-mail: member@aarp.org
URL: http://www.aarp.org
Descr: Represents persons 50 years of age or older, working or retired. Seeks to improve every aspect of living for older people. Has targeted four areas of immediate concern: health care, women's initiative, worker equity, and minority affairs. Provides group health insurance program, discounts on auto rental and hotel rates, and a specially designed and priced motoring plan. Sponsors community service programs on crime prevention, defensive driving, and tax aid. Provides pre-retirement planning program; offers special services to retired teachers through National Retired Teachers Association. Sponsors mail order pharmacy services. **Fnd:** 1958. **Mem:** 39000000. **Local Groups:** 2500. **Pub:** *AARP News Bulletin* (11/year); *The Magazine* (biweekly); *Modern Maturity* (bimonthly); *Working Age* (bimonthly).

6912 ■ AARP Grief and Loss Program
601 E St. NW
Washington, DC 20049
Contact: Bill Novelli, CEO
Free: 888-687-2277
E-mail: ageline@aarp.org
URL: http://www.aarp.org/families/grief_loss
Staff: 7. **Descr:** Provides resources and information on grief and loss issues, as well as technical assistance in the development of local community bereavement programs. Provides widowed volunteers to assist new widows and widowers cope with the change. **Fnd:** 1973. **Local Groups:** 230. **Pub:** *Directory of Services for the Widowed in the U.S. and Canada* (periodic); *Final Details: A Guide for Survivors*; *On Being Alone*.

6913 ■ Alliance for Worker Freedom (AWF)
722 12th St. NW, 4th Fl.
Washington, DC 20005
Contact: Brian M. Johnson MPA, Exec. Dir.
Ph: (202)785-0266
Fax: (202)785-0261
E-mail: info@workerfreedom.org
URL: http://www.workerfreedom.org
Descr: Aims to combat anti-worker legislation and command-and-control policies which skew the labor market toward one group over another, and to educate the public about the plight to protect workers' rights. Utilizes research and education efforts to protect workers' rights and improve the right of ordinary workers. Informs the public and national legislators about the benefits and perils of decisions concerning workers' rights. **Fnd:** 2003. **Pub:** *Index*

of Worker Freedom: A National Report Card (annual); Newsletter (bimonthly).

6914 ■ American Professional Wedding Photographers Association (APWPA)
1155 Sherman St., No. 203
Denver, CO 80203
Contact: Andrew Clark, Founder/Pres.
Free: 800-725-1650
E-mail: info@apwpa.com
URL: http://www.apwpa.com
Descr: Represents the interests of professional wedding photographers in the United States. Promotes high artistic and technical standards in wedding photography. Works for the further development of its members' craft. **Fnd:** 2004.

6915 ■ American Staffing Association (ASA)
277 S Washington St., Ste. 200
Alexandria, VA 22314-3675
Contact: Mr. Richard Wahlquist, Pres./CEO
Ph: (703)253-2020
Fax: (703)253-2053
E-mail: asa@americanstaffing.net
URL: http://www.americanstaffing.net
Staff: 30. **Descr:** Promotes and represents the staffing industry through legal and legislative advocacy, public relations, education, and the establishment of high standards of ethical conduct. **Fnd:** 1966. **Mem:** 1600. **State Groups:** 69. **Pub:** *ASA Managers Guide to Employment Law*; *Co-Employment Guide*; *Membership and Resource Directory*; *Staffing Law*; *Staffing Success* (bimonthly); *Staffing Week* (weekly); Brochures; Reports; Audiotapes.

6916 ■ Association des Aides Familiales du Quebec (AAFQ)
2348, Jean talon est, Local 407
Montreal, QC, Canada H2E 1V7
Ph: (514)272-2670
Fax: (514)272-8338
E-mail: aafq@aafq.ca
URL: http://www.aafq.ca
Staff: 3. **Descr:** Domestic workers. Seeks to obtain optimal conditions of employment for members. Advocates for increased recognition of the rights of domestic workers; represents members in negotiations with employers. **Fnd:** 1975. **Mem:** 407. **Pub:** *Standing Tall* (bimonthly).

6917 ■ Association of Career Professionals International
204 E St. NE
Washington, DC 20002
Contact: Heather Trunbull, Pres.
Ph: (202)547-6377
Fax: (202)547-6348
E-mail: info@acpinternational.org
URL: http://www.iacmp.org
Descr: Promotes the global development of the career management profession. **Fnd:** 1989. **Mem:** 2000. **Pub:** *Career Voice International* (quarterly); Articles.

6918 ■ Association of Farmworker Opportunity Programs (AFOP)
1726 M St. NW, Ste. 800
Washington, DC 20036
Ph: (202)826-6006
Fax: (202)826-6005
E-mail: afop@afop.org
URL: http://www.afop.org
Descr: Represents farmworker organizations in 49 states and Puerto Rico that operate employment, training, educates on pesticide worker safety, and related supportive service programs for migrant and seasonal farmworkers. Manages the National Children in the Fields campaign to eliminate child labor in agriculture. Conducts research; issues policy statements and analyses on federal regulations and legislation affecting farmworkers. Provides consultation service; operates speakers' bureau; compiles statistics. Operates national direct AmeriCorps program in 20 states with 80 members. Maintains hall of fame. Manages national farmworkers database containing individual records on over 80,000

migrant and seasonal farmworkers. Maintains national library and photo gallery. **Fnd:** 1971. **Pub:** *A Taste of English*; *AFOP Washington Newsline* (bimonthly); *AmeriCorps. Reporter* (monthly); *English for Farm Safety*; *Farmworker Nutrition Education Resource Guide*; *Radio Nutricion*; *Radio Pesticides*; Annual Report (annual).

6919 ■ Association of Retired Americans (ARA)
6505 E 82nd St., No. 130
Indianapolis, IN 46250
Contact: John K. Smith, Pres.
Free: 800-806-6160
Fax: (317)915-2510
E-mail: ara@ara-usa.org
URL: http://www.ara-usa.org
Staff: 4. **Descr:** Comprises senior Americans age 45 or older interested in enhancing their lives through group benefits. Aims to offer programs of high quality, low-cost benefits and services to members. Provides services such as discounts on prescriptions, eyeglasses, and hearing aids; low interest credit cards; discounts on lodging, car rental, tours, cruises, and airfare; insurance benefits including emergency air medical transportation. Assists governmental bodies and agencies with the development of programs and legislation which benefit and promotes the well-being of mature Americans. **Fnd:** 1974. **Mem:** 25000. **Pub:** *Vintage Times* (quarterly).

6920 ■ Campaign for Working Families (CWF)
PO Box 97163
Washington, DC 20077
Contact: Gary L. Bauer, Chm.
Ph: (703)671-8800
Fax: (703)671-8899
E-mail: info@cwfpac.com
URL: http://www.cwfpac.com
Descr: Represents the interests and values of America's traditional families in the political arena. Works on electing pro-family, pro-life and pro-free enterprise candidates to federal and state offices. Conducts extensive media campaigns and distribution of literature. **Fnd:** 1996. **Pub:** *Campaign Watch*.

6921 ■ Canada's Association for the Fifty-Plus (CARP)
27 Queen St. E, Ste. 702
Toronto, ON, Canada M5C 2M6
Contact: Moses Znaimer, Exec. Dir.
Ph: (416)363-8748
Free: 888-363-2279
Fax: (416)363-8747
E-mail: support@carp.ca
URL: http://en.50plus.com
Staff: 20. **Descr:** Canadians who are at least 50 years old. Promotes the rights and seeks to improve the quality of life of older people. Provides products and services to members; represents members in public forums. **Fnd:** 1984. **Mem:** 400000. **Reg. Groups:** 14. **Pub:** *50 Plus* (bimonthly).

6922 ■ Canadian Alliance of British Pensioners (CABP)
202-605 Royal York Rd.
Toronto, ON, Canada M8Y 4G5
Contact: Peter Kennan, Chm.
Ph: (416)253-6402
Fax: (416)253-9031
E-mail: info@britishpensions.com
URL: http://www.britishpensions.com
Descr: Senior citizens and British expatriates in Canada. Works to safeguard the interests of senior citizens. Campaigns to end pension discrimination such as freezing of British pension for those residents in Canada. **Fnd:** 1991. **Pub:** *Justice* (quarterly).

6923 ■ Canadian Association for Internship Programs (CAIP)
243 Church St., Rm. 337
Toronto, ON, Canada M5B 2K3
Contact: Donald Tham, Treas.
Ph: (416)979-5000
E-mail: dtham@ryerson.ca
URL: http://www.cafip.ca

Descr: Educational institutions and businesses participating in student internship programs. Promotes internship as a means for students to gather work experience while still in school. Provides support and assistance to internship programs; serves as a clearinghouse on business internships.

6924 ■ Canadian Association of Pension Supervisory Authorities (CAPSA)
5160 Yonge St., 17th Fl.
Box 85
North York, ON, Canada M2N 6L9
Contact: Daniel Padro, Policy Mgr.
Ph: (416)590-7034
Fax: (416)590-7070
E-mail: capsa-acor@fsco.gov.on.ca
URL: http://www.capsa-acor.org
Staff: 2. **Descr:** Facilitates an efficient and effective pension regulatory system in Canada. Furthers the simplification and harmonization of pension law across Canada. **Fnd:** 1974. **Mem:** 13. **Pub:** *CAPSA Communique* (semiannual).

6925 ■ Canadian Corps of Commissionaires (CCC)
100 rue Gloucester St., Ste. 201
Ottawa, ON, Canada K2P 0A4
Contact: Jean-Guy Blanchard, Office Mgr.
Ph: (613)688-0710
Fax: (613)688-0719
E-mail: national@commissionaires.ca
URL: http://www.commissionaires.ca
Descr: Active and former military personnel. Promotes employment of ex-service people. Makes available employment services to ex-military and ex-RCMP personnel. **Fnd:** 1925. **Mem:** 16000. **Reg. Groups:** 17. **Pub:** *The Commissionaires*.

6926 ■ Canadian Labour Congress (CLC)
2841 Riverside Dr.
Ottawa, ON, Canada K1V 8X7
Contact: Ken Georgetti, Pres.
Ph: (613)521-3400
Fax: (613)521-4655
E-mail: president@clc-ctc.ca
URL: http://www.clc-ctc.ca
Staff: 100. **Descr:** Works to ensure that all Canadians are able to find employment at fair wages, with union representation and the right to collective bargaining, in a safe environment. Seeks to create a just and equitable society. Joins with other organizations for advocacy and action on behalf of working Canadians. Facilitates establishment of grass roots organizations. Conducts research and educational programs; maintains speakers' bureau; compiles statistics. **Fnd:** 1956. **Mem:** 23000000. **Reg. Groups:** 4. **Pub:** *C.L.C. Fax-Press* (weekly); *Sweatshop Alert* (periodic); *UI Bulletin* (periodic).

6927 ■ Canadian Payroll Association (CPA)
250 Bloor St. E, Ste. 1600
Toronto, ON, Canada M4W 1E6
Contact: Patrick Culhane, Pres./CEO
Ph: (416)487-3380
Free: 800-387-4693
Fax: (416)487-3384
E-mail: membership@payroll.ca
URL: http://www.payroll.ca
Staff: 40. **Descr:** Represents the payroll community in Canada; offers education programs, advocacy efforts, products and services to help members enhance and adapt payroll operations, meet new legislative requirements, address changing workplace needs and take advantage of emerging technologies. **Fnd:** 1978. **Mem:** 12000. **Pub:** *CPA E-Source* (bimonthly); *Dialogue Magazine* (bimonthly).

6928 ■ Canadian Pensioners Concerned (CPC)
6 Trinity Sq.
Toronto, ON, Canada M5G 1B1
Contact: Ms. Winnie Fraser MacKay, Pres.
Ph: (416)368-5222
Free: 888-822-6750
Fax: (416)368-0443

E-mail: info@canpension.ca
URL: http://www.canpension.ca
Descr: Retirees. Seeks to improve the quality of life of older people in Canada. Represents the interests of pensioners before government agencies and the public. **Fnd:** 1969. **Reg. Groups:** 9.

6929 ■ Canadian Union of Postal Workers (CUPW)
377 Bank St.
Ottawa, ON, Canada K2P 1Y3
Contact: Denis Lemelin, Natl. Pres.
Ph: (613)236-7238
Fax: (613)563-7861
URL: http://www.cupw-sttp.org
Staff: 150. **Descr:** Postal workers. Seeks to obtain optimal conditions of employment for members. Represents members in negotiations with employers. **Fnd:** 1965. **Mem:** 54000. **Reg. Groups:** 8. **Local Groups:** 209. **Pub:** *Perspective* (bimonthly).

6930 ■ Canadian Union of Public Employees (CUPE)
1375 St. Lauren Blvd.
Ottawa, ON, Canada K1G 0Z7
Contact: Paul Moist, Pres.
Ph: (613)237-1590
Fax: (613)237-5508
URL: http://cupe.ca
Staff: 725. **Descr:** Seeks to protect the rights and improve the conditions of employment of members. Promotes fairness in hiring and promotion without regard to race or gender. Represents members in collective bargaining; makes available legal, educational, research, job evaluation, and communications services. **Fnd:** 1963. **Mem:** 590000. **Pub:** *CUPE: It's Your Union*; *Organize* (periodic).

6931 ■ Career College Association (CCA)
1101 Connecticut Ave. NW, Ste. 900
Washington, DC 20036
Contact: Mr. Bruce Leftwich, VP of Government Relations
Ph: (202)336-6700
Free: 866-711-8574
Fax: (202)336-6828
E-mail: cca@career.org
URL: http://www.career.org
Staff: 25. **Descr:** Represents private post-secondary schools, institutes, colleges and universities that provide career-specific educational programs. **Fnd:** 1991. **Mem:** 1400. **Pub:** *Fact Book* (biennial); *The Link* (quarterly); Annual Report (annual).

6932 ■ Communications Workers of America/ Canada (CWA)
7B-1050 Baxter Rd.
Ottawa, ON, Canada K2C 3P1
Contact: Arnold Amber, Chm.
Ph: (613)820-9777
Free: 877-486-4292
Fax: (613)820-8188
E-mail: info@cwa-scacanada.ca
URL: http://www.cwa-scacanada.ca
Staff: 4. **Descr:** Primarily union of journalists and media workers in Canada, as well as social workers and employees in the manufacturing industry. **Fnd:** 1995. **Mem:** 8000. **Local Groups:** 31. **Pub:** *TNG Canada Today* (monthly).

6933 ■ Confederation of National Trade Unions (CNTU)
1601 Ave. de Lorimier
Montreal, QC, Canada H2K 4M5
Contact: Claudette Carbonneau, Pres.
Ph: (514)598-2121
E-mail: csnexecutif@csn.qc.ca
URL: http://www.csn.qc.ca
Staff: 600. **Descr:** National trade unions representing 235,000 workers. Promotes advancement of the Canadian labor movement. Represents workers in

collective bargaining. **Fnd:** 1921. **Mem:** 235000. **Reg. Groups:** 13. **Pub:** *Nouvelles CSN* (biweekly).

6934 ■ Elder Craftsmen (EC)
307 7th Ave., Ste. 1401
New York, NY 10001
Contact: Patricia Manzione, Exec. Dir./Sec.
Ph: (212)319-8128
Fax: (212)319-8141
E-mail: info@eldercraftsmen.org
URL: http://www.eldercraftsmen.org
Descr: Helps men and women 55 and older be creative, productive, and independent. Seeks broader recognition by the general public of the skills and capabilities of older people. Sponsors craft training workshops for representatives of Senior Centers. Sponsors community service projects with older adults making items for people in need. **Fnd:** 1955. **Pub:** *Elder Craftnotes* (semiannual); Brochure.

6935 ■ Employee Assistance Professionals Association (EAPA)
4350 N Fairfax Dr., Ste. 410
Arlington, VA 22203
Contact: Dave Worster, Pres.
Ph: (703)387-1000
Fax: (703)522-4585
E-mail: mbrdatadm@eapassn.org
URL: http://www.eap-association.com
Descr: Persons employed in the development or operation of employee assistance programs (EAPs) and/or services as administrators, consultants, or motivational advisors; persons with an interest in the field; individuals enrolled in courses leading to degrees in employee assistance-related disciplines; firms, institutions, and associations. Encourages the systematic development of employee assistance programs. Serves as an advocate with the public and private sectors for the support and development of the EAP movement. Conducts research and educational programs; offers certification; compiles statistics. **Fnd:** 1971. **Reg. Groups:** 5. **Local Groups:** 90. **Pub:** *Appendix to EAPA Program Standards*; *Employee Assistance Law Desk Book*; *Journal of Employee Assistance* (quarterly); *Role Delineation Study of Certified Employee Assistance Professionals*.

6936 ■ Employee Benefit Research Institute (EBRI)
1100 13th St. NW, Ste. 878
Washington, DC 20005-4058
Contact: Dallas L. Salisbury, Pres.
Ph: (202)659-0670
Fax: (202)775-6312
E-mail: info@ebri.org
URL: http://www.ebri.org
Staff: 14. **Descr:** Corporations, consulting firms, banks, insurance companies, unions, and others with an interest in the future of employee benefit programs. Purpose is to contribute to the development of effective and responsible public policy in the field of employee benefits through research, publications, educational programs, seminars, and direct communication. Sponsors a broad range of studies on retirement income, health, disability, and other benefit programs; disseminates study results. Maintains research library with information on employee benefit programs. **Fnd:** 1978. **Mem:** 142. **Pub:** *EBRI Databook on Employee Benefits* (periodic); *EBRI Issue Brief* (monthly); *EBRI Notes* (monthly); *EBRI Pension Investment Report* (periodic); *EBRI Policy Forums* (semiannual); *Washington Bulletin* (biweekly).

6937 ■ Employee Services Management Association (ESM)
568 Spring Rd., Ste. D
Elmhurst, IL 60126-3896
Contact: Renee Mula, Exec. Dir.
Ph: (630)559-0020
Fax: (630)559-0025
E-mail: esmahq@esmassn.org
URL: http://www.esmassn.org
Staff: 4. **Descr:** Corporations and governmental agencies that sponsor recreation, fitness, and service

programs for their employees; associate members are manufacturers and suppliers in the employee recreation market and distributors of consumer products and services. Serves as an information resource network for members nationwide. Implements and maintains a diverse range of employee services; believes that employee services, as practical solutions to work/life issues, are essential to sound business management. Conducts programs that improves relations between employees and management, increases overall productivity, boosts morale, and reduces absenteeism and turnover. Covers the 10 Components of a Well-Rounded Employee Services Program such as employee stores, convenience services, recognition programs, recreation programs, travel services, and special events. **Fnd:** 1941. **Mem:** 2000. **Local Groups:** 25. **Pub:** *Employee Services Management* (bimonthly).

6938 ■ Equal Employment Advisory Council (EEAC)

1501 M St. NW, Ste. 400
Washington, DC 20005
Contact: Jeffrey A. Norris, Pres.
Ph: (202)629-5650
Fax: (202)629-5651
E-mail: info@eeac.org
URL: http://www.eeac.org
Descr: Promotes and presents the mutual interests of employers and the public regarding affirmative action and equal employment opportunity practices. Provides members with regulatory and legislative developments. **Fnd:** 1976. **Pub:** *Member Services*; Manuals; Pamphlets; Reports (annual).

6939 ■ ESOP Association Canada

304 Stone Rd. W, Ste. 145
Guelph, ON, Canada N1G 4W4
Contact: John Kingston, Pres.
Free: 866-601-3081
E-mail: info@esop-canada.com
URL: http://esop-canada.com/ESOPCanada/index.php
Descr: Individuals and corporations. Promotes the concept of employee ownership of businesses. Gathers and disseminates information on existing employee ownership plans; conducts research and studies of emerging employee ownership schemes. Makes available advisory services; facilitates networking among members; sponsors lobbying campaigns; provides educational programs. **Fnd:** 1990.

6940 ■ Executive Women's Council (EWC)

425 6th Ave., Ste. 1860
Pittsburgh, PA 15219
Contact: Christine Kirby, Pres.
E-mail: info@ewcpittsburgh.org
URL: http://www.ewcpittsburgh.org
Staff: 1. **Descr:** Women who hold an executive position. Seeks to support and enrich members' careers through networking and education. **Fnd:** 1975. **Mem:** 100. **Pub:** Newsletter (monthly).

6941 ■ Experience Works

4401 Wilson Blvd., Ste. 1100
Arlington, VA 22203
Contact: Cynthia A. Metzler, Pres./CEO
Ph: (703)522-7272
Free: 866-EXP-WRKS
Fax: (703)522-0141
URL: http://www.experienceworks.org
Staff: 526. **Descr:** Provides training and employment services for mature workers. Reaches more than 125,000 mature individuals. **Fnd:** 1965. **State Groups:** 44. **Pub:** Annual Report (annual).

6942 ■ Family, Career and Community Leaders of America (FCCLA)

1910 Association Dr.
Reston, VA 20191-1584
Contact: Michael L. Benjamin CAE, Exec. Dir.
Ph: (703)476-4900
Free: 800-234-4425
Fax: (703)860-2713
E-mail: mbenjamin@fcclainc.org
URL: http://www.fcclainc.org

Staff: 23. **Descr:** Young men and women studying family and consumer sciences and related occupational courses in public and private schools through grade 12 in the U.S., Puerto Rico, and the Virgin Islands. Youth assume social roles in areas of personal growth, family life, vocational preparation, and community involvement. Sponsors STAR (Students Taking Action with Recognition) competitions. Cosponsors, with Youth for Understanding, 8-week summer scholarships to Japan for 10th and 11th graders. **Fnd:** 1945. **Mem:** 220000. **State Groups:** 53. **Local Groups:** 10000. **Pub:** *The Adviser* (semiannual); *Co-Curricular Guide for FCCLA Chapters*; *FCCLA is...*; *Guide for Middle Level FCCLA Chapters*; *Publications Catalog* (annual); *State Advisers' Bulletin* (11/year); *Teacher Educator's Guide*; *Teen Times* (quarterly).

6943 ■ Federal Employees Veterans Association (FEVA)

PO Box 183
Merion Station, PA 19066
Contact: Lester Harris III, Exec. Off.
Descr: Federal government employees who have veterans' preference in federal employment under the G.I. Bill. Works to maintain and increase veterans' preference in federal employment and prevent "the discrimination against the veteran that was rampant in federal agencies in the post-World War II era". **Fnd:** 1950. **Mem:** 12842.

6944 ■ Federation of Employers and Workers of America (FEWA)

2901 Bucks Bayou Rd.
Bay City, TX 77414
Contact: Scott Evans, Pres.
Ph: (979)245-7577
Free: 877-422-3392
E-mail: hinojosa@h2b-fewa.org
URL: http://www.fewaglobal.org
Descr: Provides members with educational and informational services related to labor management issues. Seeks to improve business conditions and provide services in the areas of labor retention and management. **Mem:** 7500.

6945 ■ Freelancers Union

20 Jay St., Ste. 700
Brooklyn, NY 11201
Contact: Sara Horowitz, Founder/Exec. Dir.
Ph: (718)532-1515
Free: 800-856-9981
Fax: (718)222-4440
E-mail: membership@freelancersunion.org
URL: http://www.freelancersunion.org
Descr: Represents the needs and concerns of independent workforce through information and service. Seeks to bring together independent workers for mutual support and advocacy. Advances the rights and interests of America's independent workers. Facilitates friendship and cooperation among members. **Fnd:** 2001.

6946 ■ Gay and Lesbian Association of Retiring Persons (GLARP)

10940 Wilshire Blvd., Ste. 1600
Los Angeles, CA 90024
Contact: Mary Thorndal, Exec. Dir.
Ph: (310)709-8743
Fax: (310)477-0707
E-mail: info@gaylesbianretiring.org
URL: http://www.gaylesbianretiring.org
Descr: Promotes, provides, and supports education on aging. Works to develop and operate retirement communities for LGBTs. Encourages LGBT individuals, partners, and businesses to enhance their aging experience. Fosters fun, friendship and continued relationships among LGBTs. **Fnd:** 1996. **Pub:** Newsletter (quarterly).

6947 ■ Goodwill Industries International (GII)

15810 Indianola Dr.
Rockville, MD 20855
Contact: Jim Gibbons, Pres./CEO
Ph: (301)530-6500
Free: 800-741-0186

E-mail: contactus@goodwill.org
URL: http://www.goodwill.org
Descr: Federation of Goodwill Industries organizations across North America and the world concerned primarily with providing employment, training, evaluation, counseling, placement, job training, and other vocational rehabilitation services and opportunities for individual growth for people with disabilities and other special needs. Collects donated goods and sell them in Goodwill retail stores as a means of providing employment and generating income. Conducts seminars and training programs; compiles statistics. **Fnd:** 1902. **Local Groups:** 2100. **Pub:** *Corporate Brochure* (annual); *Internal Membership Directory* (annual); *Working!* (quarterly); Annual Report.

6948 ■ Goodwill Industries Volunteer Services (GIVS)

15810 Indianola Dr.
Rockville, MD 20855
Contact: George W. Kessinger, Pres./CEO
Free: 800-741-0186
E-mail: contactus@goodwill.org
URL: http://www.goodwill.org
Descr: Persons interested in volunteer work in programs serving people with disabilities or other barriers to employment. Supports the efforts of national and local Goodwill Industries International, Inc., programs through volunteer services. Provides programs that vary according to local needs and includes such activities as direct program services, fundraising, and public relations. **Fnd:** 1933. **Mem:** 3000. **Local Groups:** 71. **Pub:** *Giving* (quarterly); *Goodwill Volunteer Services Directory* (annual); *Goodwill Volunteer Services Handbook* (annual); Annual Report (annual).

6949 ■ ICA Group

1 Harvard St., Ste. 200
Brookline, MA 02445
Contact: Newell Lessell, Pres.
Ph: (617)232-8765
Fax: (617)232-9545
E-mail: ica@ica-group.org
URL: http://www.ica-group.org
Staff: 7. **Descr:** Seeks to create and strengthen worker-owned and controlled businesses (worker cooperatives) in low income and blue-collar communities. Provides full business development assistance. Services include: initial feasibility review for a plant closing response, conversion, or start-up; financing advice and brokering; management assistance; advice on democratic decision-making structures; implementation of work force education programs. Works both directly with employee groups and through sponsoring organizations. Conducts work force education and board training to ICA client cooperatives. Develops labor/management cooperation programs. Believes that employee-owned companies show increased profits due partly to workers' attitudes, as they are working for themselves, not an outside owner; and that community economic development is enhanced, because as the work force owns the company, profits remain within the community, discouraging poverty and capital flight. **Fnd:** 1978. **Mem:** 800. **Pub:** *The Design of Governance Systems for Small Workers' Cooperatives*; *ICA Model Bylaws for a Worker Cooperative (version III)*; *ICA News & Events* (semiannual); *The Massachusetts Law for Worker Cooperatives: MGL Chapter 157A*; *Putting Democracy to Work: A Practical Guide for Starting Worker-Owned Businesses*; *Worker Cooperatives and Basic Orientation*.

6950 ■ Industrial Accident Prevention Association (IAPA)

Centre for Health & Safety Innovation
5110 Creekbank Rd., Ste. 300
Mississauga, ON, Canada L4W 0A1
Contact: Ms. Maureen Shaw, Pres./CEO
Ph: (905)614-4272
Free: 800-406-4272
Fax: (905)614-1414
E-mail: communications@iapa.ca
URL: http://www.iapa.ca

Descr: Strives to improve the quality of life in workplaces and communities by being an internationally recognized leader in providing programs, products and services for the prevention of injury and illness. **Fnd:** 1917. **Mem:** 50000. **Pub:** *Accident Prevention* (quarterly).

6951 ■ Institute for a Drug-Free Workplace
8614 Westwood Center Dr., Ste. 950
Vienna, VA 22182
Contact: Mark A. de Bernardo, Exec. Dir.
Ph: (703)288-4300
URL: http://www.drugfreeworkplace.org
Staff: 10. **Descr:** Businesses, organizations, and individuals united to preserve the rights of employers and employees involved in corporate drug abuse prevention programs. Seeks to influence public policy pertaining to drug-abuse prevention in the workplace. Conducts surveys. **Fnd:** 1989. **Mem:** 90. **Pub:** *Avoiding Legal Liability: The 25 Most Common Employer Mistakes in Addressing Drug Abuse; Does Drug Testing Work?; Drug and Alcohol Abuse Prevention and the ADA: An Employer's Guide; Drug Testing in the Workplace: Basic Issues, Answers, and Options for Employees; Employee Assistance Programs: An Employer's Development and Implementation Guide; Employee Drug Education and Awareness and Supervisor Training: An Employer's Development and Implementation Guide; Guide to Dangerous Drugs; Guide to State and Federal Drug Testing Laws* (annual); *International Guide to Workplace Substance Abuse Prevention; Policy on Drug and Alcohol Abuse Prevention: An Employer's Development and Implementation Guide; What Every Employee Should Know About Alcohol Abuse: Answer to 25 Good Questions.*

6952 ■ Institute for Women in Trades, Technology and Science (IWITTS)
1150 Ballena Blvd., Ste. 102
Alameda, CA 94501-3696
Contact: Donna Milgram, Exec. Dir.
Ph: (510)749-0200
Fax: (510)749-0500
E-mail: info@iwitts.com
URL: http://www.iwitts.com
Descr: Works to integrate women into the full range of trades, technology and science careers. **Fnd:** 1994. **Mem:** 17. **Pub:** *Women in Policing; WomenTech Educators; WomenTechWorld.*

6953 ■ International Alliance of Professional Hypnotists (IAPH)
RR 2, Box 2468
Laceyville, PA 18623-9417
Contact: Linda Otto, Exec. Dir.
Ph: (570)869-1021
Free: 800-553-6886
Fax: (570)869-1249
E-mail: info@hypnosisalliance.com
URL: http://www.hypnosisalliance.com
Descr: Represents individuals interested in the art and science of hypnosis. Provides a forum for the exchange of information and ideas among practitioners of traditional and nontraditional therapies and methodologies. Fosters unity among grassroots practitioners and those with advanced academic credentials.

6954 ■ Job Accommodation Network (JAN)
PO Box 6080
Morgantown, WV 26506-6080
Contact: D.J. Hendricks EdD, Project Mgr.
Ph: (304)293-7186
Free: 800-526-7234
Fax: (304)293-5407
E-mail: jan@jan.wvu.edu
URL: http://www.jan.wvu.edu
Staff: 31. **Descr:** A service of U.S. Department of Labor's Office of Disability Employment Policy. An international toll-free consulting service that provides information about job accommodation and the employability of people with disabilities. Calls are answered by consultants who understand the limitations associated with disabilities and who have instant access to the most comprehensive and up-to-date information about accommodation methods, devices, and strategies. **Fnd:** 1983. **Pub:** Newsletter (quarterly).

6955 ■ A Job is a Right Campaign (AJRC)
PO Box 06053
Milwaukee, WI 53206
Contact: Phil Wilayto, Coor.
Ph: (414)374-1034
Fax: (414)374-1034
E-mail: ajrc@execpc.com
URL: http://my.execpc.com/~ajrc
Descr: Strives to fight growing unemployment. Organizes protest marches, rallies, and demonstrations to oppose layoffs and plant closings. **Fnd:** 1993. **Pub:** Newsletter (periodic).

6956 ■ John A. Hartford Foundation (JAHF)
55 E 59th St., 16th Fl.
New York, NY 10022-1713
Contact: Corinne H. Rieder, Exec. Dir./Treas.
Ph: (212)832-7788
Fax: (212)593-4913
E-mail: mail@jhartfound.org
URL: http://www.jhartfound.org
Staff: 16. **Descr:** Works to promote health care, training, research, and service related to older adults. **Fnd:** 1929. **Mem:** 9. **Pub:** *The Hartford Foundation Report* (quarterly); Annual Report (annual).

6957 ■ Just One Break (JOB)
570 Seventh Ave.
New York, NY 10018
Contact: Edmund L. Cortez, Pres.
Ph: (212)785-7300
Fax: (212)785-4513
E-mail: jobs@justonebreak.com
URL: http://www.justonebreak.com
Staff: 8. **Descr:** Serves as an employment service for people with disabilities, to help them find jobs and lead to productive lives. Finds competitive employment for people with disabilities by bringing together leading employers and qualified JOB applicants. Concentrates efforts in New York, and is working to include New Jersey and Connecticut, but advises companies nationwide. Offers placement services, employment counseling, skills evaluation, college recruitment, resume writing assistance service referrals, and computer access. Provides JOB's Student Internship Program (SIP), a hands-on work experience for college students with disabilities and works in collaboration with college disability and career service offices. Provides on-site disability awareness training to support initiatives related to interviewing, hiring, and retaining employees with disabilities. **Fnd:** 1947. **Pub:** *Gale Journal* (annual); *Informational Brochure; Just One Breaking News* (periodic); Annual Report (annual).

6958 ■ Mature Outlook (MO)
PO Box 9390
Des Moines, IA 50306-9519
Free: 800-336-6330
Fax: (515)334-9247
Descr: Individuals over 50 years of age. **Fnd:** 1984. **Mem:** 600000. **Pub:** *Mature Outlook Magazine* (bimonthly).

6959 ■ Mennonite Association of Retired Persons (MARP)
23 Homestead Dr.
Lancaster, PA 17602
Contact: Jay L. Roth, Exec. Dir.
Ph: (717)201-8391
Free: 866-721-7730
E-mail: marp-soop@juno.com
URL: http://marp.mennonite.net
Staff: 1. **Descr:** Retired persons of the Mennonite faith. Promotes an active and healthy life for its members. **Fnd:** 1989. **Mem:** 4000. **Pub:** *PAGES* (quarterly).

6960 ■ Mocha Moms
PO Box 1995
Upper Marlboro, MD 20773
Contact: Donna Jackson, Pres.
E-mail: nationaloffice@mochamoms.org
URL: http://www.mochamoms.org
Descr: Works as a support group for mothers who have chosen not to work full-time outside of the home in order to devote more time to their families. Serves as an advocate for those mothers and encourages the spirit of community activism within its membership. Provides opportunities for mothers to gather and talk through support group meetings and community service projects. Fosters camaraderie and friendship among members. **Fnd:** 1997.

6961 ■ National Association of Barber Boards of America (NABBA)
2703 Pine St.
Arkadelphia, AR 71923
Contact: Charles Kirkpatrick, Exec. Off.
Ph: (501)682-2806
Fax: (501)682-5073
E-mail: nabba@iocc.com
URL: http://www.nationalbarberboards.com
Staff: 2. **Descr:** Represents state boards of barber examiners. Promotes the exchange of information among state barber boards and state agencies that examine, license, and regulate the barber industry. Improves standards and procedures for examining barbers and regulates the barber industry. Furthers continuing education and development of curricula for educating barbers. Devises procedures for ensuring that consumers are informed and protected. Maintains library. **Fnd:** 1935. **Mem:** 50. **Reg. Groups:** 200. **State Groups:** 50.

6962 ■ National Association of Certified Public Bookkeepers (NACPB)
162 W Baer Creek Dr.
Kaysville, UT 84037
Contact: David B. Bybee CPA, Pres./CEO
Free: 866-444-9989
Fax: (801)444-9386
E-mail: info@nacpb.org
URL: http://www.nacpb.org
Descr: Aims to protect the public interest by ensuring that only qualified individuals provide public bookkeeping services. Fosters the professional development of public bookkeepers. Offers certification programs in bookkeeping.

6963 ■ National Association of Older Worker Employment Services (NAOWES)
300 D St. SW, Ste. 801
Washington, DC 20024
Contact: James Firman, Pres./CEO
Ph: (202)479-1200
Fax: (202)479-0735
URL: http://www.ncoa.org
Staff: 1. **Descr:** A constituent unit of The National Council on the Aging. Works to ensure that all individuals, regardless of age, are allowed to use their skills and talents as productive and contributing members of the workforce. Through promotion of adequate funding and coordination among federally funded programs, and through other initiatives targeted to meeting the needs of the growing older worker pool, it helps to ensure that older workers are provided access to professional services throughout the country. **Fnd:** 1981.

6964 ■ National Association of Part-Time and Temporary Employees (NAPTE)
5800 Barton, Ste. 201
PO Box 3805
Shawnee, KS 66203
Contact: Preston L. Conner, Pres.
Ph: (913)962-7740
E-mail: napte-champion@worldnet.att.net
URL: http://www.members.tripod.com/~napte
Descr: Promotes the economic and social interests of persons working on a part-time, contingent, or temporary basis through research, advocacy, and member services. Offers short-term portable health

insurance. **Fnd:** 1994. **Pub:** *NAPTE Tempo* (bimonthly).

6965 ■ National Association of Social Workers National Committee on Lesbian, Gay and Bisexual Issues
750 First St. NE, Ste. 700
Washington, DC 20002-4241
Contact: Elizabeth J. Clark PhD, Exec. Dir.
Ph: (202)408-8600
Free: 800-742-4089
E-mail: membership@naswdc.org
URL: http://www.socialworkers.org/governance/cmtes/nclgbi.asp
Staff: 1. **Descr:** A committee of the National Association of Social Workers. Seeks to ensure equal employment opportunities for lesbian, gay and bisexual individuals. Informs the NASW about: domestic, racial, and antigay violence; civil rights; family and primary associations. Encourages the NASW to support legislation, regulations, policies, judicial review, political action, and other activities that seek to establish and protect equal rights for all persons without regard to affectional and/or sexual orientation. Advises government bodies and political candidates regarding the needs and concerns of social workers and lesbian and gay people; reviews proposed legislation. **Fnd:** 1976. **Mem:** 5. **State Groups:** 30. **Pub:** *Lesbian and Gay Issues: A Resource Manual.*

6966 ■ National Association of Working Seniors (NAWS)
1013 Gardenia Ave.
Lompoc, CA 93436
Contact: Steve Bridge, CEO/Chm.
Ph: (805)277-2191
Fax: (805)614-9099
E-mail: steve.bridge@verizon.net
URL: http://workingsenior.com
Descr: Represents working seniors in a multitude of issues. Addresses the needs and interests of working people age 50 and older. Seeks to enhance the quality of life for all senior workers by promoting independence, dignity and purpose. **Fnd:** 2004. **Pub:** *Connecting Today With Tomorrow.*

6967 ■ National Career Development Association (NCDA)
305 N Beech Cir.
Broken Arrow, OK 74012
Contact: Deneen Pennington, Exec. Dir.
Ph: (918)663-7060
Free: 866-367-6232
Fax: (918)663-7058
E-mail: dpennington@ncda.org
URL: http://www.ncda.org
Descr: Represents professionals and others interested in career development or counseling in various work environments. Supports counselors, education and training personnel, and allied professionals working in schools, colleges, business/industry, community and government agencies, and in private practice. Provides publications, support for state and local activities, human equity programs, and continuing education and training for these professionals. Provides networking opportunities for career professionals in business, education, and government. **Fnd:** 1913. **Mem:** 4600. **Pub:** *Career Convergence Web Magazine* (monthly); *Career Development Quarterly* (quarterly); *Career Developments* (quarterly); *Counselor's Guide to Career Assessment Instruments.*

6968 ■ National Pensioners and Senior Citizens Federation (NPSCF)
44 2nd Ave.
Trenton, ON, Canada K8V 5M6
Contact: Joyce Mitchell, Treas.
Ph: (613)394-0739
E-mail: mitchell2@bel.auracom.com
URL: http://npscf.ca
Descr: Senior citizens' and pensioners' clubs. Seeks to stimulate public interest in the welfare of older Canadians. Provides services to improve the quality of life of senior citizens, including counselling and

education. **Fnd:** 1945. **Pub:** *National News* (quarterly); Brochure; Papers.

6969 ■ National Right to Work Committee (NRTWC)
8001 Braddock Rd., Ste. 500
Springfield, VA 22160
Contact: Mark A. Mix, Pres.
Ph: (703)321-9820
Free: 800-325-7892
Fax: (703)321-7342
E-mail: members@nrtw.org
URL: http://www.right-to-work.org
Staff: 131. **Descr:** Individuals seeking to promote the principle that "everyone must have the right but not be compelled to join labor unions." Lobbies; maintains speakers' bureau; conducts research and educational programs. **Fnd:** 1955. **Mem:** 2000000. **Pub:** *National Right to Work Newsletter* (monthly); Brochures.

6970 ■ National Safe Workplace Institute/ SafeSpaces.com (NSWI)
3008 Bishops Ridge Ct.
Monroe, NC 28110
Contact: Joseph A. Kinney, Pres.
Ph: (704)282-1111
Fax: (704)550-5857
E-mail: info@safespaces.com
URL: http://www.safespaces.com
Descr: Provides research and education on issues related to occupational health and safety. Is concerned with safe and healthy work environments and workplace violence. Seeks to make workplace safety and health a priority. Monitors efforts of the public and private sectors in improving workplace safety. Conducts periodic studies of national and regional industry issues. **Fnd:** 1987. **Pub:** *Electronic Newsletter* (semimonthly); Newsletter (monthly).

6971 ■ National Union of Public and General Employees (NUPGE)
15 Auriga Dr.
Nepean, ON, Canada K2E 1B7
Contact: James Clancy, Natl. Pres.
Ph: (613)228-9800
Fax: (613)228-9801
E-mail: national@nupge.ca
URL: http://www.nupge.ca
Staff: 16. **Descr:** Labor union in Canada representing 325,000 provincial government employees, public and private sector workers, and workers at public health care and educational institutions. Functions as a clearinghouse of information on collective bargaining, labor legislation, and the labor movement; facilitates exchange of information among members; makes available consultation, advice, and financial support. Represents members' interests before Parliament and the media. Conducts research on collective bargaining and labor legislation. **Fnd:** 1976. **Mem:** 340000. **Reg. Groups:** 14.

6972 ■ NISH
8401 Old Courthouse Rd., Ste. 200
Vienna, VA 22182
Contact: Paul Atkinson, Pres./CEO
Ph: (571)226-4660
Fax: (703)849-8916
E-mail: info@nish.org
URL: http://www.nish.org
Descr: Provides employment opportunities for people with severe disabilities under the Javits-Wagner O'Day Act. Promotes their placement into competitive industry. Conducts research and development to identify to the government commodities and services, which are feasible for production and/or performance by work centers. (Work centers are nonprofit agencies that provide rehabilitative, training, and vocational services for persons with severe disabilities). Provides training and technical assistance in the form of industrial engineering, production planning, quality control, inventory management, cost analysis, procurement, and contract administration. Acts as a liaison between work centers and the federal government. **Fnd:**

1974. **Reg. Groups:** 6. **Pub:** *NISH News* (monthly); Annual Report; Brochure.

6973 ■ Organization of Professional Employees of the United States Department of Agriculture (OPEDA)
PO Box 381
Washington, DC 20044
Contact: Mr. Farook Sait, Pres.
Ph: (202)720-4898
Fax: (202)720-2799
E-mail: opeda@usda.gov
URL: http://www.usda.gov/opeda
Staff: 1. **Descr:** Professional, scientific, technical, and administrative personnel of U.S. Department of Agriculture and in government classified grades. Seeks to provide enlightened guidance and representation before Congress, the administration and the public on matters that promote efficient and effective operation of USDA agencies. **Fnd:** 1929. **Mem:** 3500. **Reg. Groups:** 28. **Pub:** *OPEDA News* (monthly).

6974 ■ Out and Equal Workplace Advocates
155 Sansome St., Ste. 450
San Francisco, CA 94104
Contact: Selisse Berry, Exec. Dir./Founder
Ph: (415)694-6500
Fax: (415)694-6530
E-mail: info@outandequal.org
URL: http://www.outandequal.org
Descr: Advocates for workplace equality regardless of sexual orientation, gender identity, expression, or characteristics. Educates and empowers organizations, human resources professionals, employee resource groups, and individual employees about equality in the workplace. Fosters harmonious relationships between the LGBT and non-LGBT communities. **Fnd:** 1999. **Pub:** *Working Out.*

6975 ■ Professionals in Workers' Compensation (PWC)
PO Box 4435
Federal Way, WA 98063
Contact: Colleen Boyd, Pres.
E-mail: contact@pwc.org
URL: http://www.pwc.org
Descr: Provides educational and skill-building programs to the workers' compensation community. Serves as a venue for establishing and maintaining relationships among members. Creates opportunities for networking and learning.

6976 ■ Recognition Professionals International (RPI)
1601 N Bond St., Ste. 303
Naperville, IL 60563
Contact: Tom Miller CRP, Pres.
Ph: (630)369-7783
Fax: (630)369-3773
E-mail: rpi@recognition.org
URL: http://www.recognition.org
Descr: Aims to enhance employee performance through recognition, including its strategies and related initiatives. Provides a medium for information, sharing, and resources to aid employees in establishing a better work environment.

6977 ■ Residential Construction Workers' Association (ASTRACOR)
3660D Wheeler Ave.
Alexandria, VA 22304
Contact: Clayton Sinyai PhD, Dir.
Ph: (703)212-8294
E-mail: info@astracor.org
URL: http://www.astracor.org
Descr: Represents the interests of residential construction workers. Aims to improve the lives of all workers employed in residential construction. Provides job and social service referrals. Informs work-

ers of their rights and benefits and provides training in different construction trades.

6978 ■ The Retired Enlisted Association (TREA)
1111 S Abilene Ct.
Aurora, CO 80012
Contact: Charlie Flowers, Natl. Pres.
Ph: (303)752-0660
Free: 800-338-9337
Fax: (303)752-0835
E-mail: treahq@trea.org
URL: http://www.trea.org
Staff: 15. **Descr:** Retirees who have served in the military as enlisted persons; medically retired persons or enlisted persons who have been on active duty for at least 10 years. Associate members are widows/widowers of retired enlisted persons. Supports the rights and benefits of retired enlisted persons and their families. Lobbies at national, state, and local levels for: issues concerning retired enlisted persons; keeping commissaries open; protecting unemployment compensation, Veterans Administration disability compensation, and cost-of-living allowances; encouraging the addition of national cemeteries; keeping medical facilities open. Sponsors cultural and social activities for members through local chapters. Conducts seminars and sponsors travel and insurance programs. **Fnd:** 1963. **Mem:** 100000. **Local Groups:** 48. **Pub:** *The Retired Enlisted Association--The Voice* (bimonthly); *The Voice e-Mag* (bimonthly).

6979 ■ Retirement Research Foundation (RRF)
8765 W Higgins Rd., Ste. 430
Chicago, IL 60631-4170
Contact: Edward J. Kelly, Board Member
Ph: (773)714-8080
Fax: (773)714-8089
E-mail: info@rrf.org
URL: http://www.rrf.org
Descr: Works to promote aging and retirement issues. Supports efforts that improve care for the aging, and enable older adults to live at home or in residential settings that facilitate independent living. **Fnd:** 1978.

6980 ■ Senior Community Service Employment Program (SCSEP)
U.S. Dept. of Labor, Employment and Training Administration
200 Constitution Ave. NW, Rm. N-4641
Washington, DC 20210
Contact: Christine D.K. Ollis, Admin.
Ph: (202)693-3842
Free: 866-4US-ADOL
E-mail: ollis.christine@dol.gov
URL: http://www.doleta.gov/seniors
Descr: Comprises eight employment programs organized under Title V of the Older Americans Act and funded by the federal government. Provides programs that are designed to provide on-the-job training in community service agencies for workers 55 years of age or older who are economically disadvantaged, in order that they might gain the experience needed to find permanent employment. Conducts individual programs that are sponsored by the U.S. Forest Service. **Fnd:** 1969.

6981 ■ SER - Jobs for Progress National
122 W John Carpenter Fwy., Ste. 200
Irving, TX 75039
Contact: Ignacio Salazar, Pres./CEO
Ph: (469)524-1200
Fax: (469)524-1287
E-mail: info@ser-national.org
URL: http://www.ser-national.org
Descr: Aims to provide employment training and opportunities for Spanish-speaking and disadvantaged Americans. Seeks to increase business and economic opportunities for minority communities and ensure optimum participation by the Hispanic community in public policy forums. Gives funds to SER performance contracts that are funded by the federal government. (The acronym SER stands for service,

employment, and redevelopment.) Organizes its own training and management program and is responsible for recruitment and selection of job trainees, counseling, pre-job orientation and vocational preparation, basic education, employer relations, and follow-up services to trainees after training and job placement. **Fnd:** 1965. **State Groups:** 19. **Pub:** *SER America* (quarterly); *SER--Jobs for Progress--Annual Report* (annual); *SER--Jobs for Progress--Network Directory* (annual).

6982 ■ Setting Priorities for Retirement Years (SPRY)
3916 Rosemary St.
Chevy Chase, MD 20815
Contact: Richard Browdie, Chm.
Ph: (301)656-3405
Fax: (301)656-6221
E-mail: morganr@spry.org
URL: http://www.spry.org
Descr: Aims to help older adults plan for a healthy and financially secure future. Works with top organizations in the field on aging, disseminates information to consumers and conducts applied research.

6983 ■ Tradeswomen
1433 Webster St.
Oakland, CA 94612
Contact: Bonnie Henriquez, Interim Coor.
Ph: (510)891-8773
Fax: (510)891-8775
E-mail: bonnie@tradeswomen.org
URL: http://tradeswomen.org
Descr: Women who work in nontraditional, blue-collar occupations including construction, transportation, and industrial work; women who seek to enter these fields or who support the right of others to do so. Serves as a network for women in the trades. Conducts social gatherings and local and regional forums on topics such as: health and safety on the job; racism and sexism in the trades; sexual harassment; working within unions. Maintains speakers' bureau. Compiles statistics. **Fnd:** 1979. **Pub:** *Little Tradeswomen Coloring Book*; *Tradeswomen Magazine*; Pamphlets; Videos; Newsletter (periodic).

6984 ■ U.S. Equal Employment Opportunity Commission (EEOC)
131 M St. NE
Washington, DC 20507
Contact: Naomi C. Earp, Chair
Ph: (202)663-4900
Free: 800-669-4000
E-mail: info@eeoc.gov
URL: http://www.eeoc.gov
Staff: 2400. **Descr:** Strives to promote equal opportunity in employment through administrative and judicial enforcement of the federal civil rights laws and through education and technical assistance. **Fnd:** 1965. **Pub:** *Compliance Manual*; *10 Reasons to Mediate*.

6985 ■ Verite
44 Belchertown Rd.
Amherst, MA 01002
Contact: Dan Viederman, Exec. Dir.
Ph: (413)253-9227
Fax: (413)256-8960
E-mail: verite@verite.org
URL: http://www.verite.org
Descr: Aims to improve the lives of workers and assists the corporations that employ these workers to better balance profitability with social responsibility. Monitors independent factories from different industry sectors to ensure that employees work under safe, fair, and legal labor conditions. Conducts research in all aspects of workplace conditions. Provides social audits, factory remediation, corporate training, labor research, and worker education worldwide. **Fnd:** 1995. **Pub:** *Monitor* (quarterly).

6986 ■ Voluntary Protection Programs Participants' Association (VPPPA)
7600-E Leesburg Pike, Ste. 100
Falls Church, VA 22043
Contact: R. Davis Layne, Exec. Dir.

Ph: (703)761-1146
Fax: (703)761-1148
E-mail: administration@vpppa.org
URL: http://www.vpppa.org
Staff: 14. **Descr:** Companies participating in Voluntary Protection Programs and other workplace environmental protection, health, and safety programs. Promotes cooperation between labor, management, and government agencies to insure safe and environmentally sustainable workplaces. Works closely with federal environmental and safety agencies to develop and implement cooperative programs; provides information on environmental health and workplace safety to congressional committees considering legislation. **Mem:** 1200. **Pub:** *The Leader* (quarterly); *On the Wire* (bimonthly); *Safety News Network* (biweekly); *Washington Update* (monthly).

6987 ■ WAVE
525 School St. SW, Ste. 500
Washington, DC 20024-2795
Contact: Larry Brown, Pres.
Ph: (202)484-0103
Free: 800-274-2005
Fax: (202)484-7595
E-mail: info@waveinc.org
URL: http://www.waveinc.org
Descr: Helps disadvantaged 16- to 21-year-old high school dropouts and students at risk of dropping out to find unsubsidized jobs and careers. Provides classes for students to prepare for their high school equivalency diplomas and to learn basic living skills, such as how to find an apartment, how to dress for a job interview, and how to balance a checkbook. Holds seminars and competitions that foster motivation and leadership and conducts national employment and training seminars for enrollees, and annual staff training institutes. **Fnd:** 1969. **Local Groups:** 150. **Pub:** *Annual Corporate Report* (annual); *The Rising Tide* (quarterly); Newsletter.

6988 ■ Welfare to Work Partnership
1129 20th St. NW, Ste. 800
Washington, DC 20036
Contact: Rodney J. Carroll, Pres./CEO
Ph: (202)955-3005
Fax: (202)955-1087
E-mail: info@welfaretowork.org
Descr: Provides solutions to companies through hiring welfare recipients, unemployed, or low-income workers.

6989 ■ Wider Opportunities for Women (WOW)
1001 Connecticut Ave. NW, Ste. 930
Washington, DC 20036
Contact: Joan A. Kuriansky Esq., Exec. Dir.
Ph: (202)464-1596
E-mail: vstaples@wowonline.org
URL: http://www.wowonline.org
Staff: 16. **Descr:** Expands employment opportunities for women through information, employment training, technical assistance, and advocacy. Works to overcome barriers to women's employment and economic equity, including occupational segregation, sex stereotyped education and training, discrimination in employment practices and wages. Sponsors Women's Work Force Network, a national network of 500 women's employment programs and advocates. Monitors current policies to increase the priority given to employment needs of women; provides information to congressional staffs to clarify the impact of various legislative proposals on women; issues public policy alerts and informational materials when relevant federal policy is being proposed or undergoing revision; conducts investigative projects to assess how legislative programs are implemented and their impact on women. Offers technical assistance to education institutions, government agencies, and private industry on programs to increase women's participation in non-traditional employment and training. Maintains National Commission on Working Women and Industry Advisory Councils. **Fnd:** 1964. **Pub:** *A More Promising Future: Strategies to Improve the Workplace*; *Growing Up in Prime Time: An*

Analysis of Adolescent Girls on Television; *Women at Work* (quarterly); Books; Pamphlets.

6990 ■ Wildcat Service Corporation (WSC)
2 Washington St., 3rd Fl.
New York, NY 10004
Contact: Mary Ellen Boyd, Pres.
Ph: (212)209-6000
URL: http://www.wildcatnyc.org
Staff: 250. **Descr:** Provides transitional employment and training for chronically unemployed persons (former substance abusers, ex-offenders, welfare mothers, out-of-school youth, and illiterate and delinquent youth). Systematically prepares and grooms employees to accept the full responsibility of full-time work within a 12-month time period. Placement rate of terminees is about 70
in a variety of industries. Operates clerical school in basic and advanced office practices; conducts specialized "life skills" educational program. Compiles statistics; maintains placement service. Operates three high schools. **Fnd:** 1972. **Pub:** *The Wildcatter.*

6991 ■ Women Employed Institute (WEI)
111 N Wabash, Ste. 1300
Chicago, IL 60602
Contact: Anne Ladky, Exec. Dir.
Ph: (312)782-3902
Fax: (312)782-5249
E-mail: info@womenemployed.org
URL: http://www.womenemployed.org
Staff: 15. **Descr:** Serves as a research and education division of Women Employed devoted to promoting economic equity for women. Analyzes government programs and employer policies; develops recommendations for public and corporate policy to promote equal opportunity. Sponsors advocacy programs to increase women's accessibility to vocational education and training for higher paying and nontraditional jobs. Develops model employment awareness/readiness programs for disadvantaged women. Conducts research projects; compiles statistics on women's economic status. **Fnd:** 1973. **Mem:** 2500. **Pub:** *Bridges to Careers for Low-Skilled Adults: A Program Development Guide*; *Directory of Work/Family Benefits Offered by Chicago-Area Employers*; *News Byte* (monthly); *Workers and Families: A Policy Guide for Employers.*

6992 ■ Workplace Fairness
2031 Florida Ave. NW, Ste. 500
Washington, DC 20009
Contact: Denise Knecht, Sec.
Ph: (202)243-7660
Fax: (240)282-8801
URL: http://www.workplacefairness.org
Descr: Promotes public policies that advance employee rights. **Fnd:** 2001. **Pub:** *Workplace Week*; Brochure.

State and Local Organizations and Agencies

Alabama

6993 ■ Alabama Department of Labor
100 N. Union St.
Montgomery, AL 36130-3500
Contact: Robin Hancock, Chief Child Labor Inspector
Ph: (334)242-3460
Fax: (334)240-3417
E-mail: robin.hancock@alalabor.alabama.gov
URL: http://www.alalabor.state.al.us
Descr: Promotes peaceful settlement of labor disputes and enforces state labor laws.

6994 ■ American Association of Retired Persons, Alabama
201 Monroe St., Ste. 1880
RSA Tower
Montgomery, AL 36104

Contact: Eric Olsen, Pres.
Ph: (334)954-3042
Free: 866-542-8167
Fax: (334)954-3050
E-mail: alaarp@aarp.org
Staff: 6. **Descr:** Seeks to improve every aspect of living for older people. Leads positive social change and delivers value to members through information, advocacy, and service.

Alaska

6995 ■ Alaska Department of Labor and Workforce Development
PO Box 111149
Juneau, AK 99811-1149
Contact: Click Bishop, Commnr.
Ph: (907)465-2700
Fax: (907)465-2784
E-mail: commissioner.labor@alaska.gov
URL: http://www.labor.state.ak.us

Arizona

6996 ■ Arizona Career Development Association (ACDA)
PO Box 27886
Tempe, AZ 85285
Contact: Maryjo Douglas Zunk, Pres.
E-mail: info@azcareers.org
URL: http://www.azcareers.org

6997 ■ Arizona Professional Recruiters Association (APRA)
PO Box 1735
Tempe, AZ 85280-1735
Contact: Jason Dupree, Pres.
Ph: (480)659-5875
E-mail: jason@meridiangroup.com
URL: http://www.apra-az.org
Descr: Facilitates the sharing of ideas and information relevant to technical recruiting. Provides members with opportunities to be kept informed of the developments, trends and issues related to the recruitment industry. Enhances the education and professional development of technical recruiters.

6998 ■ Arizona Staffing Professionals Association (ASPA)
Blaine Personnel, Inc.
1702 E Highland, Ste. 407
Phoenix, AZ 85016
Contact: Stephanie Clark, Pres.
Ph: (602)222-9910
Fax: (602)222-9924
E-mail: azaspa@aol.com
URL: http://www.azaspa.com
Descr: Represents and promotes the staffing industry through legal and legislative advocacy, public relations, education, and the establishment of high standards of ethical conduct.

6999 ■ Employee Assistance Professionals Association - Arizona Chapter
PO Box 67507
Phoenix, AZ 85082-7507
Contact: Tim Lee, Pres.
Ph: (480)348-4944
E-mail: leetimoa@wellsfargo.com
URL: http://www.eapa.info/ChaptBranch/AZ01/Arizona.htm

7000 ■ Employee Assistance Professionals Association - Southern Arizona Chapter
PO Box 64082
Tucson, AZ 85728
Contact: Ellen Ross, Pres.
Ph: (520)331-7869
Fax: (520)844-1156

E-mail: ejue716@msn.com
URL: http://www.eapa.info/ChaptBranch/AZ02/SouthernArizona.htm

7001 ■ Employee Services Management Association of Greater Phoenix
PO Box 42534
Phoenix, AZ 85080
Contact: Tim Johnson, Pres.
Ph: (602)358-8955
Fax: (602)358-8956
E-mail: admin@esmphx.org
URL: http://www.esmphx.org
Descr: Implements diverse range of employee services. Encourages employees to live balanced lives as they help the company achieve its goals. Maintains practical solutions to work and life issues for a sound business management.

7002 ■ Employee Services Management Association of Southern Arizona
PO Box 26852
Tucson, AZ 85726
Contact: Vivian Torres-Lopez, Pres.
E-mail: president@esmofsouthernaz.org
URL: http://www.esmofsouthernaz.org
Descr: Implements diverse range of employee services. Encourages employees to live balanced lives as they help the company achieve its goals. Maintains practical solutions to work and life issues for a sound business management.

7003 ■ Family, Career and Community Leaders of America, Arizona
Arizona Department of Education
1535 W Jefferson St., Bin No. 42
Phoenix, AZ 85007
Contact: Sheri Cone, Advisor
Ph: (602)542-3040
Fax: (602)542-5334
E-mail: sheri.cone@azed.gov
URL: http://www.azfccla.org
Descr: Young men and women studying family and consumer sciences and related occupational courses in public and private schools through grade 12. Youth assume social roles in areas of personal growth, family life, vocational preparation, and community involvement.

7004 ■ Industrial Commission of Arizona
800 W. Washington St.
Phoenix, AZ 85007
Contact: Laura L. McGrory, Dir.
Ph: (602)542-4411
Fax: (602)542-7889
E-mail: webmasterinternational communications agency.state.az.us
URL: http://www.ica.state.az.us

Arkansas

7005 ■ Arkansas Department of Labor
10421 W. Markham
Little Rock, AR 72205
Contact: James L. Salkeld, Dir.
Ph: (501)682-4500
Fax: (501)682-4535
E-mail: asklabor@arkansas.gov
URL: http://www.state.ar.us/labor/
Descr: Has nine divisions, which provide a wide variety of services to the public.

California

7006 ■ AARP California
200 S Los Robles Ave., Ste. 400
Pasadena, CA 91101
Free: 866-448-3615
Fax: (626)583-8500
E-mail: calosangeles@aarp.org
Descr: Persons 50 years of age or older, working or

retired. Seeks to improve every aspect of living for older people.

7007 ■ California Department of Industrial Relations
455 Golden Gate Ave.
San Francisco, CA 94102
Contact: John Duncan, Dir.
Ph: (415)703-5050
Fax: (415)703-5059
E-mail: info@dir.ca.gov
URL: http://www.dir.ca.gov/

7008 ■ California Staffing Professionals, Golden Gate
Artizen, Inc.
990 Industrial Rd., No. 201
San Carlos, CA 94070
Contact: Rosanna Medernach CAC, Pres.
Ph: (650)261-9400
Fax: (650)261-9410
E-mail: rmedernach@artizen.com
URL: http://www.cspnet.org

Descr: Represents and promotes the staffing industry through legal and legislative advocacy, public relations, education, and the establishment of high standards of ethical conduct.

7009 ■ California Staffing Professionals, Inland Empire
4345 E Lowell St., Ste. N
Ontario, CA 91761
Contact: Karen Carroll CAC, Pres.
Ph: (909)390-7743
Fax: (909)390-7744
E-mail: kccarrol@aol.com
URL: http://www.cspnet.org

Descr: Represents and promotes the staffing industry through legal and legislative advocacy, public relations, education, and the establishment of high standards of ethical conduct.

7010 ■ California Staffing Professionals, Los Angeles
Royal Staffing Services, Inc.
14011 Ventura Blvd., No. 214-W
Sherman Oaks, CA 91423
Contact: Joe Cummings, Pres.
Ph: (818)981-1080
Fax: (818)981-1338
E-mail: joe@royalstaffing.com
URL: http://www.cspnet.org

Descr: Represents and promotes the staffing industry through legal and legislative advocacy, public relations, education, and the establishment of high standards of ethical conduct.

7011 ■ California Staffing Professionals, Orange County
Bordwell and Associates
1400 Quail St., No. 100
Newport Beach, CA 92660
Contact: Sharon Berg Hannah CAC, Pres.
Ph: (949)724-1466
Fax: (949)724-1567
E-mail: bordwell@wedolegal.com
URL: http://www.cspnet.org

Descr: Represents and promotes the staffing industry through legal and legislative advocacy, public relations, education, and the establishment of high standards of ethical conduct.

7012 ■ California Staffing Professionals, Sacramento
Mainstay Business Solutions
605 Coolidge Dr., 2nd Fl.
Folsom, CA 95630
Contact: Jeanette Anderson, Pres.
Ph: (916)390-0766
Fax: (916)294-0520
E-mail: jeanette.anderson@mainstayca.com
URL: http://www.cspnet.org

Descr: Represents and promotes the staffing industry through legal and legislative advocacy, public

relations, education, and the establishment of high standards of ethical conduct.

7013 ■ California Staffing Professionals, San Diego
XL Staffing, Inc.
700 N Johnson Ave., Ste. C
El Cajon, CA 92020
Contact: Stacy Mackey CAC, Pres.
Ph: (619)276-8677
Fax: (619)276-6729
E-mail: stacy@xlstaffing.com
URL: http://www.cspnet.org

Descr: Represents and promotes the staffing industry through legal and legislative advocacy, public relations, education, and the establishment of high standards of ethical conduct.

7014 ■ California Staffing Professionals, Silicon Valley
Ryzen Solutions
111 N Market St., No. 820
San Jose, CA 95113
Contact: Julie Fleury, Pres.
Ph: (408)993-1282
E-mail: jfleury@ryzen.com
URL: http://www.cspnet.org

Descr: Represents and promotes the staffing industry through legal and legislative advocacy, public relations, education, and the establishment of high standards of ethical conduct.

7015 ■ Employee Assistance Professionals Association - Los Angeles Chapter
2525 Grand Ave.
Long Beach, CA 90815
Contact: Phil Eswein, Pres.
Ph: (562)225-1922
E-mail: peswein@aol.com
URL: http://www.eapa.info/ChaptBranch/CA03/LosAngeles.htm

7016 ■ Employee Assistance Professionals Association - San Fernando Valley Chapter
PO Box 57874
Sherman Oaks, CA 91413-2874
Contact: Michael Perlman, Pres.
Ph: (818)759-9999
E-mail: mailbox@sfveapa.com
URL: http://www.eapa.info/ChaptBranch/CA06/SanFernando.htm

Colorado

7017 ■ AARP Colorado
1301 Pennsylvania St., Ste. 200
Denver, CO 80203
Contact: Jon Loonet, Dir.
Free: 866-554-5376
Fax: (303)764-5999
E-mail: coaarp@aarp.org
URL: http://www.aarp.org/states/co

Descr: Works to enhance the quality of life for all. Strives to make positive social change and deliver value to members through information, advocacy and service. **Fnd:** 1958. **Mem:** 680000. **Pub:** Magazine (monthly); Bulletin (monthly).

7018 ■ Colorado Department of Labor and Employment
633 17th St., Ste. 201
Denver, CO 80202-3660
Contact: Donald J. Mares, Exec.Dir.
Ph: (303)318-8000
Fax: (303)318-8048
E-mail: donald.j.mares@state.co.us
URL: http://www.coworkforce.com/

7019 ■ Colorado Staffing Association (CSA)
1141 N 25th St., Ste. C
Grand Junction, CO 81501
Contact: Mr. Bill Rohr, Pres./VP of Legislative Committee
Ph: (970)263-4169
Fax: (970)263-4254
URL: http://www.coloradostaffing.org

Descr: Represents and promotes the staffing industry through legal and legislative advocacy, public relations, education, and the establishment of high standards of ethical conduct.

7020 ■ Denver 9to5
655 Broadway, Ste. 400
Denver, CO 80203
Contact: Linda Meric, Exec. Dir.
Ph: (303)628-0925
E-mail: lindam@9to5.org

7021 ■ Employee Assistance Professionals Association - Colorado Chapter
Denver United Way
2505 18th St.
Denver, CO 80211
Contact: Randi Wood, Pres.
Ph: (303)866-4318
E-mail: coloradoeapa@usa.net
URL: http://www.eapa.info/ChaptBranch/CO01/Colorado.htm

7022 ■ The Retired Enlisted Association Chapter 1 (TREA)
834 Emory Cir.
Colorado Springs, CO 80915-3402
Contact: Wally Jones, Pres.
Ph: (719)596-0927
Fax: (719)570-7363
E-mail: treach1@msn.com
URL: http://www.treachap1.us

Staff: 20. **Descr:** Strives to protect the benefits of retired enlisted personnel. **Fnd:** 1963. **Mem:** 2500. **State Groups:** 5. **Local Groups:** 2. **Pub:** Newsletter (monthly).

Connecticut

7023 ■ AARP Connecticut
Capitol Pl.
21 Oak St., Ste. 104
Hartford, CT 06106-8003
Contact: Ed Dale
Free: 866-295-7279
Fax: (860)249-7707
E-mail: ctaarp@aarp.org
URL: http://www.aarp.org/states/ct

Descr: Seeks to improve every aspect of living for older people. Addresses the needs and interests of older people, working or retired. Promotes positive social change and delivers value to members through information, advocacy and service. **Mem:** 600000.

7024 ■ Connecticut Association of Personnel Services (CAPS)
PO Box 848
Plainville, CT 06062
Contact: Kevin San Juan, Chm.
Free: 800-793-2674
Fax: (860)793-6044
E-mail: kevinsj@advmr.net
URL: http://www.caps.org

Descr: Represents the interests of the search and staffing industry. Promotes ethical practices and increases awareness of the value of personnel services. Provides training, certification and educational programs to the search staffing personnel.

7025 ■ Connecticut Labor Department
200 Folly Brook Blvd.
Wethersfield, CT 06109
Contact: Patricia H. Mayfield, Commnr.
Ph: (860)263-6000
Fax: (860)263-6529
E-mail: dol.webhelp@ct.gov
URL: http://www.ctdol.state.ct.us

7026 ■ New England Association of Personnel Services (NEAPS)
PO Box 278
Cheshire, CT 06410
Contact: Barbara Hickcox, Registration/Treas.
Ph: (203)272-0227
Fax: (203)272-1237

E-mail: barbarah@hobsonassoc.com
URL: http://www.neaps.org
Descr: Represents the interests of the search and staffing industry. Promotes ethical practices and increases awareness of the value of personnel services. Provides training, certification and educational programs to the search staffing personnel.

Delaware

7027 ■ AARP Delaware
1100 N Market St., Ste. 1201
Wilmington, DE 19801
Contact: Lucretia Young, State Dir.
Free: 866-227-7441
Fax: (302)571-1984
E-mail: destate@aarp.org
URL: http://www.aarp.org/de
Staff: 4. **Descr:** Persons 50 years of age or older, working or retired. Seeks to improve the life of older people. **Mem:** 146000. **State Groups:** 12. **Pub:** *AARP Delaware Connections.*

7028 ■ Delaware Department of Labor
4425 N. Market St.
Wilmington, DE 19802
Contact: John McMahon, Sec.
Ph: (302)761-8008
Fax: (302)761-6621
E-mail: dlabor@state.de.us
URL: http://www.delawareworks.com

District of Columbia

7029 ■ District of Columbia Department of Employment Services
64 New York Ave. NE, Ste. 3000
Washington, DC 20002
Contact: Joseph P. Walsh Jr., Dir.
Ph: (202)724-7000
Fax: (202)673-6993
E-mail: does@dc.gov
URL: http://does.dc.gov
Telecom. Svcs: TDD/TYY phone number is (202)673-6994.

Florida

7030 ■ Employee Assistance Professionals Association - Big Bend Chapter
1616 Physicians Dr.
Tallahassee, FL 32308
Contact: Melvina MacDonald, Pres.
Ph: (850)431-5190
Fax: (850)431-6150
E-mail: melvina.macdonald@tmh.org
URL: http://www.eapa.info/ChaptBranch/FL07/BigBend.htm

7031 ■ Employee Assistance Professionals Association - Central Florida Chapter
PO Box 450
Altamonte Springs, FL 32715
Contact: Janet LeBlanc, Pres.
Ph: (407)260-8533
Fax: (407)478-0942
E-mail: jmldbamcs@cs.com
URL: http://www.eapa.info/ChaptBranch/FL04/CentralFlorida.htm

7032 ■ Employee Assistance Professionals Association - Gold Coast Chapter
PO Box 9094
Jupiter, FL 33468
Contact: Kathleen Chalaire, Pres.
Ph: (561)796-5534
Fax: (561)842-8157
E-mail: kathleen.weaver@pw.utc.com
URL: http://www.eapa.info/ChaptBranch/FL06/GoldCoast.htm

7033 ■ Employee Assistance Professionals Association - South Florida Chapter
1725 Main St., Ste. 223
Weston, FL 33326

Contact: Joseph Gisondo PhD, Pres.
Ph: (954)415-8608
E-mail: jgisondo@msn.com
URL: http://www.eapa.info/ChaptBranch/FL01/SouthFlorida.htm

7034 ■ Employee Assistance Professionals Association - Southwest Florida Chapter
1404 14th St. W
Bradenton, FL 34205
Contact: Charles Ringling, Pres.
Ph: (941)782-4800
Fax: (941)782-4839
E-mail: ringlinc@manateeglens.com
URL: http://www.eapa.info/ChaptBranch/FL05/SouthwestFlorida.htm

7035 ■ Employee Services Management Association, Central Florida
Daniels Manufacturing Corp.
526 Thorpe Rd.
Orlando, FL 32824
Contact: Ralph R. Recht, Pres.
Ph: (407)855-6531
Fax: (407)855-6884
E-mail: ralphr@dmctools.com
URL: http://www.esmacfl.org
Descr: Implements diverse range of employee services. Encourages employees to live balanced lives as they help the company achieve its goals. Maintains practical solutions to work and life issues for a sound business management.

7036 ■ Florida Association of Personnel Services (FAPS)
2180 W State Rd. 434, Ste. 4160
Longwood, FL 32779
Contact: Megan McEnany, Exec. Admin.
Ph: (407)571-2181
Fax: (407)682-3321
E-mail: meganm@justrecruit.org
URL: http://www.justrecruit.org
Descr: Represents the interests of the search and staffing industry. Promotes ethical practices and increases awareness of the value of personnel services. Provides training, certification and educational programs to the search staffing personnel.

7037 ■ Florida Department of Business and Professional Regulation
1940 N. Monroe St.
Tallahassee, FL 32399-1027
Contact: Chuck Drago, Sec.
Ph: (850)487-1395
Fax: (850)487-1044
E-mail: call.center@dbpr.state.fl.us
URL: http://www.myfloridalicense.com/dbpr/

7038 ■ Florida Staffing Association
PO Box 8716
Port St. Lucie, FL 34985-8716
Contact: Jean Larsen, Sec.
Ph: (772)335-5582
Fax: (772)335-9586
E-mail: fsa@assoc-mgmt.com
URL: http://www.floridastaffing.org
Descr: Represents and promotes the staffing industry through legal and legislative advocacy, public relations, education, and the establishment of high standards of ethical conduct.

Georgia

7039 ■ Atlanta 9to5
501 Pulliam St. SW, No. 344
Atlanta, GA 30312
Contact: Claudia Lewis, Chair
Ph: (404)222-0037
Free: 800-522-0925
Fax: (404)222-0006
E-mail: activist@9to5.org
URL: http://www.9to5atlanta.org
Staff: 5. **Descr:** Building local networks and chapters, working for corporate and public policy change, and providing information, support, and resources to women experiencing discrimination, harassment, and

oppression. **Fnd:** 1974. **Mem:** 200. **State Groups:** 4. **Local Groups:** 1.

7040 ■ Georgia Association of Personnel Services (GAPS)
DDS Staffing Resources, Inc.
9755 Dogwood Rd., Ste. 200
Roswell, GA 30075
Contact: Michelle Lee, Pres.
Ph: (770)998-7779
Fax: (770)552-0176
E-mail: michellelee@ddsstaffing.com
URL: http://www.jobconnection.com
Descr: Represents the interests of the search and staffing industry. Promotes ethical practices and increases awareness of the value of personnel services. Provides training, certification and educational programs to the search staffing personnel.

7041 ■ Georgia Department of Labor
Sussex Pl., Rm. 600
148 International Blvd., NE
Atlanta, GA 30303
Contact: Michael L. Thurmond, Commnr.
Ph: (404)232-7300
Fax: (404)656-2683
URL: http://www.dol.state.ga.us

Hawaii

7042 ■ Employee Assistance Professionals Association - Hawaii Chapter
PO Box 893563
Mililani, HI 96789
Contact: Cheryl Prince, Pres.
Ph: (808)531-3271
Fax: (808)531-3277
E-mail: cprince@eapacific.com
URL: http://www.eapa.info/ChaptBranch/HI01/Hawaii.htm

7043 ■ Hawaii Association of Temporary and Staffing Services
CTA Staffing Services
550 Paiea St., Ste. 222
Honolulu, HI 96819
Contact: Ms. Judy Bishop, Pres.
Ph: (808)839-2200
Fax: (808)839-4844
Descr: Represents and promotes the staffing industry through legal and legislative advocacy, public relations, education, and the establishment of high standards of ethical conduct.

7044 ■ Hawaii Department of Labor and Industrial Relations
Princess Ruth Keelikolani Bldg.
830 Punchbowl St.
Honolulu, HI 96813
Contact: Darwin Ching, Dir.
Ph: (808)586-8842
Fax: (808)586-9099
E-mail: dlir.director@hawaii.gov
URL: http://dlir.state.hi.us/labor/index.shtml

Idaho

7045 ■ Career and Technical Educators of Idaho (CTEI)
Rigby High School
290 N 3800 W
Rigby, ID 83442
Contact: Robert Hale, Pres.
Ph: (208)745-7704
Fax: (208)745-7707
E-mail: rhale@d251.k12.id.us
URL: http://www.ctei.org
Descr: Represents career and technical educators of Idaho. Presents the views of career and technical educators to Congress and administrative officials.

Promotes opportunities for continual personal and professional development.

7046 ■ Idaho Career Development Association (ICDA)
Buhl High School
525 Sawtooth Ave.
Buhl, ID 83316
Contact: Angela Hoops, Pres.
Ph: (208)543-8262
E-mail: angela@d412.k12.id.us

7047 ■ Idaho Department of Labor
317 W. Main St.
Boise, ID 83735
Contact: Roger B. Madsen, Dir.
Ph: (208)332-3570
Fax: (208)334-6430
E-mail: www@labor.idaho.gov
URL: http://labor.idaho.gov

Illinois

7048 ■ Employee Assistance Professionals Association - Central Illinois Chapter
1011 W University Ave.
Urbana, IL 61801
Contact: Larry J. Schaer, Pres.
Ph: (309)682-7611
E-mail: lschaer@sbcglobal.net
URL: http://www.eapa.info/ChaptBranch/IL03/CentralIllinois.htm

7049 ■ Employee Assistance Professionals Association - Northern Illinois Chapter
PO Box 81673
Chicago, IL 60681-0673
Contact: Chester J Taranowski, Pres.
Ph: (312)458-9797
Fax: (847)998-6994
E-mail: nieapa@comcast.net
URL: http://www.eapa.info/ChaptBranch/IL01/NorthernIllinois.htm
Mem: 150.

7050 ■ Illinois Department of Labor
160 N. LaSalle St., Ste. C-1300
Chicago, IL 60601
Contact: Catherine Shannon, Dir.
Ph: (312)793-2800
Fax: (312)793-5257
E-mail: pio.dol@illinois.gov
URL: http://www.state.il.us/agency/idol
Telecom. Svcs: TTY phone number is (888)758-6053.

7051 ■ Retired Enlisted Association, 90 (TREA)
1291 Oakwood Ave.
Des Plaines, IL 60016
Contact: Al Ballok, Pres.
Ph: (630)469-0669
E-mail: skcaeb@comcast.net
URL: http://www.agelesswarriors.org
Descr: Works to enhance the quality of life of uniformed service enlisted personnel, families, and survivors; to stop the erosion of earned benefits through legislative efforts; to maintain esprit de corps, dedication, patriotism, and allegiance to country.

Indiana

7052 ■ Employee Assistance Professionals Association - Kentucky Chapter
Southern Hills Counseling Center
PO Box 769
Jasper, IN 47547-0769
Contact: Ted Larrison, Pres.
Ph: (812)482-3020
Free: 800-883-4020
Fax: (812)482-6409

E-mail: tedl@southerhills.org
URL: http://www.eapa.info/ChaptBranch/KY01/Kentucky.htm

7053 ■ Indiana Department of Labor
402 W. Washington St., Rm. W195
Indianapolis, IN 46204
Contact: Lori A. Torres, Commnr.
Ph: (317)232-2378
Free: 800-457-8283
Fax: (317)233-3790
E-mail: commissioner@dol.in.gov
URL: http://www.state.in.us/labor

7054 ■ Indiana Search and Staffing Association (ISSA)
Time Services, Inc.
6422 Lima Rd.
Fort Wayne, IN 46818
Contact: Deb Keller-Wise
Ph: (260)489-2020
E-mail: dkellerwise@timeservices.com
URL: http://www.issaweb.org
Descr: Represents and promotes the staffing industry through legal and legislative advocacy, public relations, education, and the establishment of high standards of ethical conduct.

Iowa

7055 ■ Employee Assistance Professionals Association - Illowa Chapter
PO Box 317
Bettendorf, IA 52722
Contact: Nancy Phelps, VP
E-mail: nphelps@famres.org
URL: http://www.eapa.info/ChaptBranch/IL02/ILLOWA.htm

7056 ■ Employee and Family Resources (EFR)
505 5th Ave., Ste. 930
Des Moines, IA 50309
Contact: Paul M. Hedquist PhD, CEO
Ph: (515)288-9020
E-mail: info@efr.org
URL: http://www.efr.org
Descr: Works for the prevention and treatment of alcoholism and other drug dependence through programs of public education, information, and public policy advocacy. **Fnd:** 1964. **Pub:** Report (annual).

7057 ■ Iowa Division of Labor Services
1000 E. Grand Ave.
Des Moines, IA 50319-0209
Contact: Dave Neil, Commnr.
Ph: (515)281-5387
Free: 800-562-4692
Fax: (515)281-7995
E-mail: IWD.CustomerService@iwd.iowa.gov
URL: http://www.iowaworkforce.org/labor/

Kansas

7058 ■ Kansas Department of Labor
401 SW Topeka Blvd.
Topeka, KS 66603-3182
Contact: Jim Garner, Sec.
Ph: (785)296-5000
Fax: (785)296-5286
E-mail: laborstats@dol.ks.gov
URL: http://www.dol.ks.gov/

Kentucky

7059 ■ AARP Kentucky
10401 Linn Station Rd., Ste. 121
Louisville, KY 40223
Contact: Phil Peters, Dir.
Free: 866-295-7275
Fax: (502)394-9918
E-mail: kyaarp@aarp.org
URL: http://www.aarp.org/states/ky
Descr: Seeks to improve every aspect of living for older people. Addresses the needs and interests of older people, working or retired. Promotes positive

social change and delivers value to members through information, advocacy and service. **Pub:** Newsletter.

7060 ■ Kentucky Labor Cabinet
1047 U.S. Hwy. 127 S., Ste. 4
Frankfort, KY 40601
Contact: J.R. Gray, Sec.
Ph: (502)564-3070
Fax: (502)564-5387
E-mail: susan.long@ky.gov
URL: http://labor.ky.gov
Descr: Goal is to create workplace environments that are safe and free of conflict, where all workers are properly trained and receive fair pay and benefits for a quality standard of living.

7061 ■ Kentucky Staffing Association
Labor Finders of Kentucky, Inc.
11501 Plantside Dr., Ste. 11
Jeffersontown, KY 40299
Contact: Mr. Waldo Tames, Pres.
Ph: (502)261-0441
Fax: (502)261-0434
URL: http://www.americanstaffing.net/chapters/chapterdetails.cfm?chapterIndex=7
Descr: Represents and promotes the staffing industry through legal and legislative advocacy, public relations, education, and the establishment of high standards of ethical conduct.

Louisiana

7062 ■ Employee Assistance Professionals Association - Greater New Orleans Chapter
PO Box 15029
New Orleans, LA 70175-5029
Contact: Lisa Clark, Pres.
Ph: (504)574-4002
E-mail: lisa.clark@wjmc.org
URL: http://www.eapagno.org

7063 ■ Louisiana Department of Labor
1001 N. 23rd St.
Baton Rouge, LA 70802
Contact: Curt Eysink, Exec.Dir.
Ph: (225)342-3111
Fax: (225)342-3778
E-mail: os@ldol.state.la.us
URL: http://www.ldol.state.la.us
Telecom. Svcs: TDD toll-free number is (800)259-5154.

Maine

7064 ■ AARP Maine
1685 Congress St.
Portland, ME 04102
Free: 866-554-5380
Fax: (207)775-5727
E-mail: me@aarp.org
URL: http://www.aarp.org/states/me
Descr: Seeks to improve every aspect of living for older people. Addresses the needs and interests of older people, working or retired. Promotes positive social change and delivers value to members through information, advocacy and service.

7065 ■ Employee Assistance Professionals Association - Maine Chapter
412 State St.
Bangor, ME 04401
Contact: Jim Owen, Pres.
Ph: (207)973-6768
Fax: (207)973-5981
E-mail: jowen@ahs.emh.org
URL: http://www.eapa.info/ChaptBranch/ME01/Maine.htm

7066 ■ Maine Career Development Association (MCDA)
University College at Rockland
91 Camden St., Ste. 402
Rockland, ME 04841
Contact: Beverly Bayer, Treas.

Ph: (207)596-6906
Free: 800-286-1594
E-mail: bayer@maine.edu
URL: http://www.maine-cda.org

7067 ■ Maine Department of Labor
54 State House Station
Augusta, ME 04333
Contact: Laura Fortman, Commnr.
Ph: (207)623-7900
Fax: (207)287-5292
E-mail: mdol@maine.gov
URL: http://www.state.me.us/labor

Telecom. Svcs: TTY toll-free number is (800)794-1110.

7068 ■ Maine Staffing Association
Labor Ready
290 Congress St.
Portland, ME 04101
Contact: Mr. Dave Lorenzatti, Pres.
Ph: (207)774-1500
Fax: (207)774-1051

Descr: Represents and promotes the staffing industry through legal and legislative advocacy, public relations, education, and the establishment of high standards of ethical conduct.

Maryland

7069 ■ Maryland Career Development Association (MCDA)
8831 Satyr Hill Rd., Ste. 308
Baltimore, MD 21234
Contact: Pamela Allen, Pres.
E-mail: pallen@umd.edu
URL: http://mcda.career-nsite.com

7070 ■ Maryland Department of Labor, Licensing & Regulation
Division of Workforce Development
1100 N. Eutaw St.
Baltimore, MD 21201
Contact: Andy Moser, Asst.Sec.
Ph: (410)230-6001
Fax: (410)767-2986
E-mail: det@dllr.state.md.us
URL: http://www.dllr.state.md.us

7071 ■ Maryland Staffing Association
2300 York Rd., Ste. 209
Timonium, MD 21093
Contact: K.C. Lycett, Treas.
Ph: (443)279-4550
E-mail: admin@marylandstaffing.org
URL: http://www.marylandstaffing.org

Descr: Represents and promotes the staffing industry through legal and legislative advocacy, public relations, education, and the establishment of high standards of ethical conduct.

Massachusetts

7072 ■ Employee Assistance Professionals Association - Massachusetts/Rhode Island Chapter
Adcare Hospital
107 Lincoln St.
Worcester, MA 01605
Contact: Daniel O'Connor, Pres.
Ph: (781)729-5240
E-mail: pesull@yahoo.com
URL: http://www.mari-eapa.org
Fnd: 1977.

7073 ■ Employee Assistance Professionals Association - Western New England Chapter
120 King St.
Northampton, MA 01060
Contact: Bart Nierenberg, Pres.
Ph: (413)565-2840

E-mail: bnieren@comcast.net
URL: http://www.eapa.info/ChaptBranch/MA02/WNewEngland.htm

7074 ■ Massachusetts Association of Personnel Services (MAPS)
Franklin Key Associates
831 Washington St.
Franklin, MA 02038-3323
Contact: Elizabeth Sacchetti, Pres.
Ph: (508)520-3500
Fax: (508)520-3535
E-mail: contact@mapsweb.org
URL: http://www.mapsweb.org

Descr: Represents the interests of the search and staffing industry. Promotes ethical practices and increases awareness of the value of personnel services. Provides training, certification and educational programs to the search staffing personnel.

7075 ■ Massachusetts Association of Personnel Services - Boston Region
Cleary Consultants, Inc.
Faneuil Hall
21 Merchants Row, 2nd Fl.
Boston, MA 02109
Contact: Mary Cleary, VP
Ph: (617)367-7189
Fax: (617)367-3202
E-mail: mc@clearyconsultants.com
URL: http://www.mapsweb.org

Descr: Represents the interests of the search and staffing industry. Promotes ethical practices and increases awareness of the value of personnel services. Provides training, certification and educational programs to the search staffing personnel.

7076 ■ Massachusetts Association of Personnel Services - North Region
Lighthouse Placement Services, LLC
34 Rogers Rd., 2nd Fl.
Bradford, MA 01835
Contact: Alison R. Fogel, VP
Ph: (978)373-2095
Fax: (978)945-6574
E-mail: afogel@lighthouseplacement.com
URL: http://www.mapsweb.org

Descr: Represents the interests of the search and staffing industry. Promotes ethical practices and increases awareness of the value of personnel services. Provides training, certification and educational programs to the search staffing personnel.

7077 ■ Massachusetts Association of Personnel Services - South Region
Target Consulting Group
Foxford Business Center
960 Turnpike St., 2nd Fl.
Canton, MA 02021
Contact: Peter Marinilli, VP
Fax: (781)297-3873
E-mail: pmarinilli@targetrecruiters.com
URL: http://www.mapsweb.org

Descr: Represents the interests of the search and staffing industry. Promotes ethical practices and increases awareness of the value of personnel services. Provides training, certification and educational programs to the search staffing personnel.

7078 ■ Massachusetts Association of Personnel Services - Worcestor/Western Region
Partnership Employment, Inc.
71 Elm St., Ste. No. 103
Worcester, MA 01609
Contact: Tanja Hayward, VP
Ph: (508)770-1777
Fax: (508)770-1771
E-mail: thayward@partnershipemployment.com
URL: http://www.mapsweb.org

Descr: Represents the interests of the search and staffing industry. Promotes ethical practices and increases awareness of the value of personnel

services. Provides training, certification and educational programs to the search staffing personnel.

7079 ■ Massachusetts Department of Labor and Work Force Development
One Ashburton Pl., Ste. 2112
Boston, MA 02108
Contact: Suzanne M. Bump, Sec.
Ph: (617)626-7122
Fax: (617)727-1090
E-mail: DOL@dia.state.ma.us
URL: http://www.mass.gov/dlwd

Telecom. Svcs: TTY phone number is (617)727-4404.

7080 ■ SER - Jobs for Progress, Southeastern Massachusetts Office
164 Bedford St.
Fall River, MA 02720
Contact: M. Paula Raposa, Exec.Dir.
Ph: (508)676-1916
Fax: (508)676-2330
E-mail: admin@ser-jobs.com

Descr: Works to provide employment training, education, referrals, and translation services. Sponsors annual graduation celebration. **Fnd:** 1979.

Michigan

7081 ■ Family, Career and Community Leaders of America, Michigan (FCCLA)
Eastern Michigan University
201 King Hall
Ypsilanti, MI 48197-0000
Contact: Mr. Brad Schmidt, Coor.
Ph: (734)487-8657
Fax: (734)487-4329
E-mail: bschmidt@emich.edu
URL: http://www.mifccla.org

Descr: Young men and women studying family and consumer sciences and related occupational courses in public and private schools through grade 12. Youth assume social roles in areas of personal growth, family life, vocational preparation, and community involvement.

7082 ■ Michigan Department of Energy, Labor & Economic Growth
PO Box 30004
Lansing, MI 48909
Contact: Skip Pruss, Dir.
Ph: (517)373-1820
Fax: (517)373-2129
E-mail: fastinfo@michigan.gov
URL: http://www.michigan.gov/cis

7083 ■ Western Michigan Technical Staffing Services
Technical Professional Services Inc.
8315 White Pine Dr.
Middleville, MI 49333
Contact: Mr. Arnaldo Rodriguez, Pres.
Ph: (616)891-9261
Fax: (616)891-9263

Descr: Represents and promotes the staffing industry through legal and legislative advocacy, public relations, education, and the establishment of high standards of ethical conduct.

Minnesota

7084 ■ Central Minnesota Chapter 115, The Retired Enlisted Association
906 Lookout Pl.
Elk River, MN 55330
Contact: Ralph Donais, Pres.
Ph: (763)441-2630
E-mail: r.l.donais@izoom.net
URL: http://www.trea115.org

Descr: Retirees who have served in the military as enlisted persons; medically retired persons. Supports the rights and benefits of retired enlisted persons and their families. **Pub:** *Eagle News* (3/ year).

7085 ■ Minnesota Career Development Association (MCDA)
2400 Ivy Ln.
Bloomington, MN 55431-2830
Contact: Irene Rossman, Pres.
Ph: (952)217-7711
Fax: (952)884-7234
E-mail: lois@careerplanningresources.com
URL: http://www.mcda.net
Descr: Career counselors, coaches, educators, training and development professionals, human resource professionals, outplacement consultants, psychologists and career planning and placement professionals. Aims to provide professional development and opportunities to impact the field of career development. Holds an annual spring conference, a fall professional development event and a winter seminar. **Fnd:** 1920. **Pub:** *The Communique* (quarterly).

7086 ■ Minnesota Department of Labor and Industry
443 Lafayette Rd., N.
St. Paul, MN 55155-4307
Contact: Steve Sviggum, Commnr.
Ph: (651)284-5005
Free: 800-342-5354
Fax: (651)284-5721
E-mail: DLI.Communications@state.mn.us
URL: http://www.doli.state.mn.us
Telecom. Svcs: TTY phone number is (651)297-4198.

7087 ■ Minnesota Recruiting And Staffing Association (MNRSA)
PO Box 921
Chanhassen, MN 55317
Contact: Jackie Engmark, Exec. Dir.
Fax: (952)974-3760
E-mail: info@mnrsa.org
URL: http://www.mnaps.org
Descr: Represents the interests of the search and staffing industry. Promotes ethical practices and increases awareness of the value of personnel services. Provides training, certification and educational programs to the search staffing personnel.

Mississippi

7088 ■ Family, Career and Community Leaders of America, Mississippi
PO Box 771
Jackson, MS 39205-0771
Contact: Jan Guyse, Advisor
Ph: (601)354-7792
Fax: (601)354-7788
E-mail: jguyse@mde.k12.ms.us
URL: http://www.cwctc.org/clubs/FCCLA.htm
Descr: Young men and women studying family and consumer sciences and related occupational courses in public and private schools through grade 12. Youth assume social roles in areas of personal growth, family life, vocational preparation, and community involvement. **Fnd:** 1945. **Mem:** 3767.

7089 ■ Mississippi Department of Employment Security
1235 Echelon Pkwy.
PO Box 1699
Jackson, MS 39215-1699
Contact: Tommye Dale Favre, Exec.Dir.
Ph: (601)321-6000
E-mail: rwhatley@mesc.state.ms.us
URL: http://www.mdes.ms.gov/

Missouri

7090 ■ AARP Missouri
700 W 47th St., Ste. 110
Kansas City, MO 64112-1805
Contact: Marla Sutton
Free: 866-389-5627

Fax: (816)561-3107
E-mail: moaarp@aarp.org
URL: http://www.aarp.org/states/mo
Descr: Volunteers in Missouri. Works to enhance the quality of life for older persons. Promotes independence, dignity, and a sense of purpose. Sponsors programs and services. Lobbies on behalf of older persons. **Fnd:** 1958. **Mem:** 37000000.

7091 ■ Employee Assistance Professionals Association - St. Louis Chapter
PO Box 410320
Creve Coeur, MO 63141-0320
Contact: Barbara Fotsch, Pres.
Ph: (636)230-9199
E-mail: fotsbl@stlo.smhs.com
URL: http://www.eapa.info/ChaptBranch/MO01/ Missouri.htm

7092 ■ Family, Career and Community Leaders of America, Missouri (FCCLA)
Dept. of Elementary and Secondary Education
PO Box 480
Jefferson City, MO 65102-0480
Contact: Christine Hollingsworth, State Advisor
Ph: (573)751-7964
Fax: (573)526-4261
E-mail: christine.hollingsworth@dese.mo.gov
URL: http://dese.mo.gov/divcareered/fccla.htm
Descr: Seeks to promote personal growth and leadership development through family and consumer sciences education. Strives to help members develop skills for life through character development, creative and critical thinking, interpersonal communication and vocational preparation by focusing on the multiple roles of family member, wage earner and community leader. **Fnd:** 1946. **Mem:** 13320. **Pub:** *The Adviser* (3/year); *Regional Officer's Handbook*; *Teen Times* (quarterly); *2004-05 FCCLA Member Handbook*.

7093 ■ Mid-America Association of Personnel and Staffing Services (MAPSS)
2405 Grand Blvd., Ste. 390
Kansas City, MO 64108
Contact: Dave McDowell, Pres.
Ph: (816)471-5575
Free: 888-888-0152
Fax: (816)471-6690
E-mail: dave@austintec.com
URL: http://moaps.com
Descr: Represents and promotes the staffing industry through legal and legislative advocacy, public relations, education, and the establishment of high standards of ethical conduct. **Fnd:** 1968.

7094 ■ Missouri Department of Labor and Industrial Relations
421 E. Dunklin St.
PO Box 504
Jefferson City, MO 65102-0504
Contact: Lawrence G. Rebman, Dir.
Ph: (573)751-9691
Fax: (573)751-4135
E-mail: diroffice@labor.mo.gov
URL: http://www.dolir.mo.gov/lirc

Montana

7095 ■ Montana Department of Labor and Industry
PO Box 1728
Helena, MT 59624-1728
Contact: Keith Kelly, Commnr.
Ph: (406)444-2840
Fax: (406)444-1394
E-mail: dliquestions@mt.gov
URL: http://www.dli.mt.gov/
Telecom. Svcs: TTY phone number is (406)444-0532.

Nebraska

7096 ■ Employee Assistance Professionals Association - Heartland Chapter
PO Box 1990
Kearney, NE 68848
Contact: Maureen O'Donnell MS, Pres.
Ph: (308)865-7515
Free: 866-271-5006
Fax: (308)865-2216
E-mail: maureen@arborfamilycounseling.com
URL: http://www.eapa.info/ChaptBranch/NE01/ Heartland.htm

7097 ■ Family Career and Community Leaders of Nebraska (FCCLA)
State Dept. of Education
301 Centennial Mall S
PO Box 94987
Lincoln, NE 68509-4987
Contact: Jan Brandt, Advisor
Ph: (402)471-4815
E-mail: janis.brandt@nebraska.gov
URL: http://www.nebraskafccla.org
Staff: 1. **Descr:** Middle/Secondary school students. Promotes personal growth and leadership development through family and consumer sciences education. Investigates career development and the work-family balance. Sponsors competitions. Conducts volunteer, community service, and leadership training programs. **Fnd:** 1945. **Mem:** 4400. **State Groups:** 1. **Local Groups:** 140. **Pub:** *Teen Talk* (periodic).

7098 ■ Nebraska Department of Labor
550 S. 16th St.
PO Box 94600
Lincoln, NE 68509-4600
Contact: Phillip A. Baker, Admin.
Ph: (402)471-2600
Fax: (402)471-9867
E-mail: lmi_ne@dol.state.ne.us
URL: http://www.nebraskaworkforce.com/

Nevada

7099 ■ AARP Nevada
5820 S Eastern Ave., No. 190
Las Vegas, NV 89119
Contact: Carla Sloan, State Dir.
Free: 866-389-5652
Fax: (702)938-3225
E-mail: nvaarp@aarp.org
URL: http://www.aarp.org/nv
Pub: *Magazine* (bimonthly); *Bulletin* (monthly).

7100 ■ Employee Assistance Professionals Association - Nevada Chapter
5456 Red Sun Dr.
Las Vegas, NV 89149
Contact: Patsy Molina, Pres.
Ph: (702)240-8750
Fax: (702)242-5864
E-mail: glover@sierrahealth.com
URL: http://www.eapa.info/ChaptBranch/NV01/ Nevada.htm

7101 ■ Employee Services Management Association, Southern Nevada Chapter
PO Box 94951
Las Vegas, NV 89193-4951
Contact: Kimberly Conde, Pres.
Ph: (702)388-9924
Fax: (702)384-9974
E-mail: esmassociation@gmail.com
URL: http://www.esmassociation.org
Descr: Implements diverse range of employee service. Encourages employee to live balanced lives as they help the company achieve its goals. Maintains practical solution to work and life issues for a sound business management.

7102 ■ Nevada Office of the Labor Commissioner
555 E. Washington Ave., Ste. 4100
Las Vegas, NV 89101

Contact: Michael Tanchek, Commnr.
Ph: (702)486-2650
Fax: (702)486-2660
E-mail: mail1@LaborCommissioner.com
URL: http://www.laborcommissioner.com/

New Hampshire

7103 ■ American Association of Retired Persons, New Hampshire
900 Elm St., Ste. 702
Manchester, NH 03101
Contact: Mr. Richard Chevrefils, State Dir.
Free: 866-542-8168
Fax: (603)629-0066
E-mail: nh@aarp.org
URL: http://www.aarp.org/states/nh
Descr: Seeks to improve every aspect of living for older people. Provides wide range of unique benefits, special products, and services.

7104 ■ Employee Assistance Professionals Association - Granite State Chapter
Exeter Hospital
5 Alumni Dr.
Exeter, NH 03833
Contact: Maureen Pecora, Pres.
Ph: (603)580-6688
E-mail: mpecora@ehr.org
URL: http://www.eapa.info/ChaptBranch/NH01/Granite.htm

7105 ■ New Hampshire Department of Labor
PO Box 2076
Concord, NH 03302
Contact: George N. Copadis, Commnr.
Ph: (603)271-3176
Fax: (603)271-2668
URL: http://www.labor.state.nh.us/
Descr: Mission is to protect the interests and dignity of the New Hampshire workforce.

7106 ■ New Hampshire Staffing Association (NHSA)
American Resource Staffing
165 S River Rd., Ste. C
Bedford, NH 03110
Contact: Mrs. Stephanie A. Richfield, Pres.
Ph: (603)606-5886
Fax: (603)606-4070
Descr: Represents and promotes the staffing industry through legal and legislative advocacy, public relations, education, and the establishment of high standards of ethical conduct.

7107 ■ Northern New England Association of Personnel Services (NNEAPS)
65 Belknap St.
Dover, NH 03820
Contact: April Metivier, Pres.
Ph: (603)742-8325
Fax: (603)743-3323
URL: http://www.nneaps.org
Descr: Represents the interests of the search and staffing industry. Promotes ethical practices and increases awareness of the value of personnel services. Provides training, certification and educational programs to the search staffing personnel.

New Jersey

7108 ■ Employee Assistance Professionals Association - New Jersey Chapter
5 Greenfield Dr.
Allentown, NJ 08501
Contact: Kevin O'Neill, Pres.
Ph: (856)614-7020
Fax: (856)614-7011
E-mail: kevscouter@hotmail.com
URL: http://www.njeapa.org

7109 ■ New Jersey Department of Labor
One John Fitch Plaza
PO Box 110
Trenton, NJ 08625-0110
Contact: David J. Socolow, Commnr.

Ph: (609)777-3200
Fax: (609)633-9271
E-mail: constituent.relations@dol.state.nj.us
URL: http://lwd.dol.state.nj.us/labor/index.shtml

New Mexico

7110 ■ American Association of Retired Persons, New Mexico
535 Cerrilos Rd., Ste. A
Santa Fe, NM 87501
Contact: Stan Cooper, Dir.
Free: 866-389-5636
Fax: (505)820-2889
E-mail: nmaarp@aarp.org
Descr: Persons 50 years of age or older, working or retired. Seeks to improve every aspect of living for older people.

7111 ■ New Mexico Department of Workforce Solutions
PO Box 1928
401 Broadway, NE
Albuquerque, NM 87103
Contact: Ken F. Ortiz, Sec.
Ph: (505)841-8450
Fax: (505)841-8491
E-mail: infodws@state.nm.us
URL: http://www.dws.state.nm.us/

7112 ■ New Mexico Staffing Association
Express Personnel Services
1903-A Wyoming Blvd. NE
Albuquerque, NM 87112
Contact: Mr. Garrett Hennessy III, Pres.
Ph: (505)298-4662
Fax: (505)298-8658
Descr: Represents and promotes the staffing industry through legal and legislative advocacy, public relations, education, and the establishment of high standards of ethical conduct.

New York

7113 ■ American Association of Retired Persons, New York
780 3rd Ave., 33rd Fl.
New York, NY 10017
Contact: Lois Aronstein, Dir.
Free: 866-227-7442
Fax: (212)644-6390
E-mail: nyaarp@aarp.org
URL: http://www.aarp.org/states/ny
Descr: Persons 50 years of age or older, working or retired. Seeks to improve every aspect of living for older people.

7114 ■ Employee Assistance Professionals Association - Central New York Chapter
3059 Seneca Tpke.
Canastota, NY 13032
Contact: Susan Jenkins CEAP, Pres.
Ph: (315)697-3949
Free: 800-834-3947
E-mail: sjenkins@bridges-mccasa.org
URL: http://www.eapa.info/ChaptBranch/NY09/CentralNewYork.htm
Mem: 46.

7115 ■ Employee Assistance Professionals Association - Greater Buffalo Chapter
111 Linwood Ave.
Jamestown, NY 14701
Contact: Carrie Spencer, Pres.
Ph: (716)499-2935
E-mail: carrieann.spencer@gmail.com
URL: http://www.eapa.info/ChaptBranch/NY02/GreaterBuffalo.htm

7116 ■ Employee Assistance Professionals Association - Greater Rochester Chapter
463 Cline Rd.
Victor, NY 14564
Contact: Bonnie D. Maute, Pres.
Ph: (585)324-0732
Fax: (585)924-9054

E-mail: bdmaute@localnet.com
URL: http://www.eapa.info/ChaptBranch/NY01/GreaterRochester.htm

7117 ■ Employee Assistance Professionals Association - Hudson Valley Chapter
Nyack Hospital EAP
560 Rte. 303, Ste. 219
Orangeburg, NY 10962
Contact: Kitty Callahan LCSW, Pres.
Ph: (845)638-8880
Fax: (845)638-8804
E-mail: kittycallahan@verizon.net
URL: http://www.hudsonvalleyeapa.com

7118 ■ Employee Assistance Professionals Association - New York City Chapter
PO Box 2079
New York, NY 10163
Contact: Frank King, Pres.
Ph: (212)969-8684
E-mail: fxking924@aol.com
URL: http://www.eapa.info/ChaptBranch/NY04/NewYorkCity.htm

7119 ■ Employee Assistance Professionals Association - Northeast New York Chapter
PO Box 16312
Albany, NY 12212-6312
Contact: Ian Biggi, Pres.
Ph: (518)474-9083
E-mail: ibiggi@mail.nysed.gov
URL: http://www.eapa.info/ChaptBranch/NY05/NorthEast.htm

7120 ■ Family, Career and Community Leaders of America, New York (FCCLA)
PO Box 288
Endicott, NY 13761
Contact: Abby Oliver, Pres.
Ph: (607)754-6785
E-mail: nysfha@aol.com
URL: http://nysfccla.org
Descr: Young men and women in family and consumer sciences education in public and private school through grade 12. Promotes personal growth and leadership development through family and consumer sciences education. Offers members the opportunity to expand leadership potential and develop skills for life through planning, goal setting, problem solving, decision making and interpersonal communication, necessary in the home and workplace.

7121 ■ New York Department of Labor
W. Averell Harriman State Office Campus
Bldg. 12
Albany, NY 12240
Contact: M. Patricia Smith, Commnr.
Ph: (518)457-9000
Free: 888-4NYSDOL
Fax: (518)457-6908
E-mail: nysdol@labor.state.ny.us
URL: http://www.labor.state.ny.us
Telecom. Svcs: TTY and TDD toll-free number is (800)662-1220.

7122 ■ Rochester Area Career Development Association (RACDA)
Rochester Institute of Technology
Cooperative Education and Career Services
57 Lomb Memorial Dr.
Rochester, NY 14623
Contact: Maria Richart, Coor.
Ph: (585)475-5479
Fax: (585)475-5476
E-mail: mardino@brockport.edu
URL: http://www.racda.org

North Carolina

7123 ■ American Association of Retired Persons, North Carolina
225 Hillsborough St., Ste. 440
Raleigh, NC 27603
Contact: Robert Jackson, State Dir.
Ph: (919)508-0290

Free: 866-389-5650
Fax: (919)755-9684
E-mail: ncaarp@aarp.org
URL: http://www.aarp.org/states/nc

Descr: Represents working and retired people ages 50 and older. Provides education, advocacy, and community service programs on issues of importance to people 50 and older. Offers variety of discounts as well as insurance, investment and credit card programs designed to meet the needs of those over the age of 50. **Pub:** *AARP Connections North Carolina* (monthly).

7124 ■ Family, Career and Community Leaders of America, North Carolina (FCCLA)
6360 Mail Service Center
Raleigh, NC 27699-6360
Contact: Ms. Janet Johnson, State Advisor
Ph: (919)807-3884
Fax: (919)807-3656
E-mail: jljohnson@dpi.state.nc.us
URL: http://www.NCFCCLA.com

Staff: 1. **Descr:** Young men and women studying family and consumer sciences and related occupational courses in public and private schools through grade 12. Youth assume social roles in areas of personal growth, family life, vocational preparation, and community involvement. **Fnd:** 1946. **Mem:** 5889. **Reg. Groups:** 9.

7125 ■ North Carolina Department of Labor
1101 Mail Service Center
Raleigh, NC 27699-1101
Contact: Cherie K. Berry, Commnr.
Ph: (919)807-2796
Free: 800-625-2267
Fax: (919)733-0223
E-mail: commissioners.office@nclabor.com
URL: http://www.nclabor.com

7126 ■ Triangle Technical Recruiters Association (TTRA)
329 Bailey Ridge Dr.
Morrisville, NC 27560
Contact: Ed Kato, Pres.
Ph: (919)678-1228
E-mail: jllaskey@bellsouth.net
URL: http://www.ttra.org

Descr: Provides leadership and information relevant to the recruitment industry. Creates networking opportunities and hiring support for corporate and agency recruiters. Develops and promotes awareness of issues concerning the technical and recruiting industry.

North Dakota

7127 ■ American Association of Retired Persons, North Dakota
107 W Main Ave., Ste. 125
Bismarck, ND 58501
Ph: (701)221-2274
Free: 866-554-5383
Fax: (701)255-2242
E-mail: ndaarp@aarp.org

Descr: Persons 50 years of age or older, working or retired. Seeks to improve every aspect of living for older people.

7128 ■ Family, Career and Community Leaders of America, North Dakota
600 E Boulevard Ave., Dept. 270
Bismarck, ND 58505-0610
Contact: Vicki L. Neuharth, Advisor
Ph: (701)328-3167
Fax: (701)328-1255
E-mail: vneuhart@nd.gov
URL: http://www2.edutech.nodak.edu/fccla

Descr: Young men and women studying family and consumer sciences and related occupational courses in public and private schools through grade 12. Youth assume social roles in areas of personal growth, family life, vocational preparation, and community

involvement. **Fnd:** 1946. **Mem:** 2100. **Reg. Groups:** 8. **State Groups:** 1. **Local Groups:** 75.

7129 ■ North Dakota Department of Labor
600 E. Blvd. Ave., Dept. 406
Bismarck, ND 58505-0340
Contact: Lisa Fair McEvers, Commnr.
Ph: (701)328-2660
Free: 800-582-8032
Fax: (701)328-2031
E-mail: labor@nd.us
URL: http://www.state.nd.us/labor/

Telecom. Svcs: TTY toll-free number is (800)366-6889.

7130 ■ North Dakota Staffing Association (NDSA)
Preference Personnel
2600 9th Ave. SW
Fargo, ND 58103
Contact: Mr. David Dietz, Pres.
Ph: (701)293-9349
E-mail: david@preferencepersonnel.com

Descr: Represents and promotes the staffing industry through legal and legislative advocacy, public relations, education, and the establishment of high standards of ethical conduct.

Ohio

7131 ■ Cincinnati 9to5
4969 Oakland Dr.
Cincinnati, OH 45227
Contact: Leonie Carter
Ph: (513)271-4524

7132 ■ Cleveland/Akron 9to5
215 Kenwood
Akron, OH 44313
Contact: Kathy Dean
Ph: (330)836-3217

7133 ■ Employee Assistance Professionals Association - Greater Toledo Chapter (EAPA-GTC)
PO Box 1981
Toledo, OH 43603
Contact: Karen Morse CEAP, Pres.
Ph: (419)539-4499
Fax: (419)539-4497
E-mail: kmorse@buckeye-access.com
URL: http://www.ohioeapa.com/eapa_014.htm

7134 ■ Employee Assistance Professionals Association - Northern Ohio Chapter (EAPA)
PO Box 5167
Cleveland, OH 44101-0167
Contact: Rochelle Keith CEAP, Pres.
Ph: (216)491-4626
E-mail: lachell2@sbcglobal.net
URL: http://www.ohioeapa.com/eapa_002.htm

7135 ■ Ohio Division of Labor and Worker Safety
6606 Tussing Rd.
PO Box 4009
Reynoldsburg, OH 43068-9009
Contact: Robert Kennedy, Superintendent
Ph: (614)644-2450
Fax: (614)728-8639
E-mail: webmaster@wagehour.com.state.oh.us
URL: http://www.com.ohio.gov/laws/

7136 ■ Warren, OH 9to5
1145 Miller St. SW
Warren, OH 44485
Contact: Gale Johnson
Ph: (330)395-6913

Oklahoma

7137 ■ AARP, Oklahoma Information Center
Crossroads Mall, Ste. 2055
7000 Crossroads Blvd.
Oklahoma City, OK 73149

Ph: (405)632-1945
Fax: (405)632-1955
E-mail: ok@aarp.org

Descr: Represents working and retired people ages 50 and older. Enhances the quality of life through education, advocacy and community service programs. **Pub:** *AARP Connections Oklahoma* (monthly).

7138 ■ Employee Assistance Professionals Association - Oklahoma City Chapter
200 NE 21st St., Rm. 3A-8
Oklahoma City, OK 73105
Contact: Nancy Graham MHR, Pres.
Ph: (405)522-3709
E-mail: nancy.graham@odot.org
URL: http://www.eapa.info/ChaptBranch/OK01/Oklahoma.htm

Descr: Encourages the systematic development of employee assistance programs.

7139 ■ Employee Assistance Professionals Association - Tulsa Chapter
Community Care
218 W 6th St.
Tulsa, OK 74119
Contact: Robert Hulsey, Pres.
Free: 800-774-2677
E-mail: khalvors@ccok.com
URL: http://www.eapa.info/ChaptBranch/OK02/Tulsa.htm

Descr: Encourages the systematic development of employee assistance programs.

7140 ■ Oklahoma Department of Labor
3017 N. Stiles, Ste. 100
Oklahoma City, OK 73105
Contact: Lloyd Fields, Commnr.
Ph: (405)521-6100
Free: 888-269-5353
Fax: (405)521-6018
E-mail: labor.info@oklaosf.state.ok.us
URL: http://www.ok.gov/odol/

Oregon

7141 ■ AARP Oregon
9200 SE Sunnybrook Blvd., Ste. 410
Clackamas, OR 97015
Free: 866-554-5360
Fax: (503)652-9933
E-mail: oraarp@aarp.org
URL: http://www.aarp.org/or

Descr: Persons 50 years of age or older, working or retired. Seeks to improve every aspect of living for older people.

7142 ■ Employee Assistance Professionals Association - Columbia River Chapter
PO Box 4905
Portland, OR 97208
Contact: Russ Walker LMFT, Pres.
Ph: (503)294-2180
E-mail: info@creapa.com
URL: http://www.eapa.info/ChaptBranch/OR01/ColumbiaRiver.htm

7143 ■ Oregon Bureau of Labor and Industries
800 NE Oregon St., Ste. 1045
Portland, OR 97232
Contact: Brad Avakian, Commnr.
Ph: (971)673-0761
Fax: (971)673-0762
E-mail: bolita.ta@state.or.us
URL: http://www.boli.state.or.us

Descr: Promotes the development of a highly skilled, competitive workforce in Oregon through partnerships with government, labor, business, and educational institutions. **Telecom. Svcs:** TTY phone number is (971)673-0766.

7144 ■ Oregon Staffing Association (OSA)
PO Box 10823
Portland, OR 97296
Contact: Becky Vanaken, Exec. Dir.
Ph: (503)546-0900

Fax: (503)210-6878
E-mail: oregonstaffing@verizon.net
Descr: Represents and promotes the staffing indus-try through legal and legislative advocacy, public relations, education, and the establishment of high standards of ethical conduct.

7145 ■ The Retired Enlisted Association, Chapter 7 (TREA Chapt)
PO Box 682
Beaverton, OR 97075-0682
Contact: Wayne Harvey
Ph: (503)590-2747
E-mail: armyboy222@aol.com

Pennsylvania

7146 ■ American Association of Retired Persons, Pennsylvania
30 N Third St., Ste. 750
Harrisburg, PA 17101
Contact: J. Shane Creamer, Pres.
Free: 866-389-5654
Fax: (717)236-4078
URL: http://www.aarp.org/states/pa
Descr: Persons 50 years of age or older, working or retired. Seeks to improve every aspect of living for older people.

7147 ■ Delaware Valley Total Recruiters Network (DVTRN)
PO Box 1347
Malvern, PA 19355
Contact: Jim Lauckner, Pres.
E-mail: president@dvtrn.org
URL: http://www.dvtrn.org
Descr: Seeks to enhance and promote the staffing and recruiting profession. Helps to enhance the skills and professional development of technical recruiters. Creates a forum for the exchange of ideas and experiences among members.

7148 ■ Employee Assistance Professionals Association - Greater Philadelphia Chapter
4 Green Briar Ct.
Pottstown, PA 19464
Contact: Jack Shirley, Pres.
Ph: (610)322-2420
E-mail: jack1eap@comcast.net
URL: http://www.eapa.info/ChaptBranch/PA01/Philadelphia.htm

7149 ■ Employee Assistance Professionals Association - Keystone Chapter
PO Box 61205
Harrisburg, PA 17106-1205
Contact: Alo Meyer, Pres.
Ph: (610)374-4963
E-mail: meyer@gaudenzia.org
URL: http://www.eapa.info/ChaptBranch/PA03/Keystone.htm

7150 ■ Employee Assistance Professionals Association - Pittsburgh Chapter
200 Cedar Ridge Dr., Ste. 208
Pittsburgh, PA 15205
Contact: Jaime Morgan, Pres.
E-mail: jaimewolf7@yahoo.com
URL: http://www.eapa.info/ChaptBranch/PA02/Pittsburgh.htm
Fnd: 1973.

7151 ■ Pennsylvania Association - Family, Career and Community Leaders of America (FCCLA)
333 Market St., 6th Fl.
Harrisburg, PA 17126-0333
Contact: Mrs. Sue L. Fisher, Facilitator
Ph: (717)783-6952
Fax: (717)783-6672
E-mail: sufisher@state.pa.us
URL: http://www.pafccla.org
Descr: Career and technical student organization that helps young men and women become leaders. Addresses important personal, family, work, and societal issues through family and consumer sciences education. **Fnd:** 1946. **Mem:** 2600. **Reg.**

Groups: 3. **State Groups:** 1. **Local Groups:** 100.
Pub: *The Hotline.*

7152 ■ Pennsylvania Department of Labor and Industry
651 Boas St., Rm. 1700
Harrisburg, PA 17121
Contact: Sandi Vito, Sec.
Ph: (717)787-5279
Fax: (717)787-8826
URL: http://www.dli.state.pa.us
Descr: Mission is to improve the quality of life and economic security for Pennsylvania workers and businesses, encourage labor-management cooperation, and prepare the Commonwealth's workforce for the jobs of the future.

7153 ■ Pennsylvania Family, Career, and Community Leaders of America (PA FCCLA)
333 Market St., 11th Fl.
Harrisburg, PA 17126-0333
Contact: Mrs. Sue Fisher, State Facilitator
Ph: (717)783-6952
Fax: (717)783-6672
E-mail: sufisher@state.pa.us
URL: http://www.pafccla.org
Descr: Young men and women studying family and consumer sciences and related occupational courses in public and private schools through grade 12. Youth assume social roles in areas of personal growth, family life, vocational preparation, and community involvement. **Fnd:** 1946. **Mem:** 2150. **Reg. Groups:** 3. **State Groups:** 1. **Local Groups:** 100. **Pub:** *The Hotline* (3/year).

7154 ■ Pennsylvania Staffing Association - Western Chapter
Industrial Employees, Inc.
429 Forbes Ave., Ste. 1102
Pittsburgh, PA 15219
Contact: Mary Lou Wetzel, Pres.
Ph: (412)642-7422
Fax: (412)642-9011
Descr: Represents and promotes the staffing indus-try through legal and legislative advocacy, public relations, education, and the establishment of high standards of ethical conduct.

7155 ■ Philadelphia Unemployment Project (PUP)
112 N Broad St., 11th Fl.
Philadelphia, PA 19102-1510
Contact: John Dodds, Dir.
Ph: (215)557-0822
Fax: (215)557-6981
E-mail: info@philaup.org
URL: http://www.philaup.org
Descr: Represents unemployed individuals to fight for economic justice. Aims to bring diverse groups together to bring about major changes that will benefit millions of unemployed and impoverished.

7156 ■ Retired Enlisted Association, 70
32 Darlin Dr.
Reading, PA 19609-1784
Contact: Larry Cohen
Ph: (610)678-5812
Fax: (610)670-7495
E-mail: trea70@hotmail.com

Rhode Island

7157 ■ American Association of Retired Persons, Rhode Island
10 Orms St., Ste. 200
Providence, RI 02904
Contact: Kathleen Connell, Dir.
Ph: (401)248-2671
Free: 866-542-8170
Fax: (401)272-0596
E-mail: ri@aarp.org
URL: http://www.aarp.org/states/ri
Descr: Persons 50 years of age or older, working or

retired. Seeks to improve every aspect of living for older people.

7158 ■ Rhode Island Department of Labor and Training
Center General Complex
1511 Pontiac Ave.
Cranston, RI 02920
Contact: Sandra M. Powell, Dir.
Ph: (401)462-8000
Fax: (401)462-8872
E-mail: rmmadonna@dlt.ri.gov
URL: http://www.dlt.state.ri.us/
Telecom. Svcs: TDD phone number is (401)462-8006.

7159 ■ Rhode Island Staffing Services Association (RISSA)
Adecco
235 Promenade St., Ste. 130
Providence, RI 02908
Contact: Lee A. Johnson, Pres.
Ph: (401)273-2300
Fax: (401)273-1451
Descr: Represents and promotes the staffing indus-try through legal and legislative advocacy, public relations, education, and the establishment of high standards of ethical conduct.

South Carolina

7160 ■ Employee Assistance Professionals Association - North Carolina Chapter
Duke Energy CN01MD
4800 Concord Rd.
York, SC 29745
Contact: Lindy Langston, Pres.
Ph: (803)831-3218
Fax: (803)831-3039
E-mail: lllangst@duke-energy.com
URL: http://www.eapa.info/ChaptBranch/NC01/NorthCarolina.htm

7161 ■ South Carolina Association of Personnel and Staffing (SCAPS)
1310 Broad River Rd., No. 313
Columbia, SC 29210
Contact: Patrick Pettengill, Pres.
Ph: (980)297-7800
Fax: (980)297-7801
E-mail: patrick.pettengill@argussearch.com
URL: http://www.scaps.org
Descr: Represents the interests of the search and staffing industry. Promotes ethical practices and increases awareness of the value of personnel services. Provides training, certification and educa-tional programs to the search staffing personnel.

7162 ■ South Carolina Association of Personnel and Staffing - Coastal Region
Dunhill Staffing Systems of Charleston
1459 Stuart Engals Blvd., Ste. 300
Mount Pleasant, SC 29464
Contact: Neil Whitman, Co-Dir.
Ph: (843)375-0031
Fax: (843)375-0035
E-mail: ngw@dunhillsc.com
URL: http://www.scaps.org
Descr: Represents the interests of the search and staffing industry. Promotes ethical practices and increases awareness of the value of personnel services. Provides training, certification and educa-tional programs to the search staffing personnel.

7163 ■ South Carolina Association of Personnel and Staffing - Rock Hill Region
Argus Search
852 Gold Hill Rd., Ste. 201B
Fort Mill, SC 29708
Contact: Stephen Kane, Co-Dir.
Ph: (980)297-7800
Fax: (980)297-7801
E-mail: patrick.pettengill@argussearch.com
URL: http://www.scaps.org
Descr: Represents the interests of the search and staffing industry. Promotes ethical practices and

increases awareness of the value of personnel services. Provides training, certification and educational programs to the search staffing personnel.

7164 ■ South Carolina Association of Personnel and Staffing - Upstate Region
GrandSouth Bank
381 Halton Rd.
Greenville, SC 29606
Contact: Steve Hall, Co-Dir.
Ph: (864)527-7186
Fax: (864)527-7127
E-mail: dougc@grandsouth.com
URL: http://www.scaps.org
Descr: Represents the interests of the search and staffing industry. Promotes ethical practices and increases awareness of the value of personnel services. Provides training, certification and educational programs to the search staffing personnel.

7165 ■ South Carolina Department of Labor, Licensing and Regulations
PO Box 11329
Columbia, SC 29211
Contact: Adrienne Riggins Youmans, Dir.
Ph: (803)896-4300
Fax: (803)896-4393
URL: http://www.llr.state.sc.us

South Dakota

7166 ■ South Dakota Association of Family, Career and Community Leaders of America (SD FCCLA)
2417 Whispering Shores Dr.
Fort Pierre, SD 57532
Contact: Shannon Schweitzer, Advisor
Ph: (605)494-0233
E-mail: shannonschweitzer@pie.midco.net
URL: http://www.sdfccla.org
Descr: Promotes personal growth and leadership development through family and consumer science education. Encourages individual and group involvement in helping achieve global cooperation and harmony. **Fnd:** 1946.

7167 ■ South Dakota Department of Labor
700 Governors Dr.
Pierre, SD 57501-2291
Contact: Pamela S. Roberts, Sec.
Ph: (605)773-3101
Fax: (605)773-6184
URL: http://dol.sd.gov/

Tennessee

7168 ■ American Association of Retired Persons, Tennessee
150 4th Ave. N, Ste. 180
Nashville, TN 37219
Contact: Margot Seay, Pres.
Ph: (615)726-5104
Free: 866-295-7274
Fax: (615)313-8414
E-mail: tnaarp@aarp.org
URL: http://www.aarp.org/tn
Descr: Non-profit service organization.

7169 ■ Tennessee Department of Labor & Workforce Development
220 French Landing Dr.
Nashville, TN 37243
Contact: James G. Neeley, Commnr.
Ph: (615)741-6642
Fax: (615)741-5078
E-mail: TDLWD@tn.gov
URL: http://www.state.tn.us/labor-wfd/

7170 ■ Tennessee Staffing Association
T and T Distribution Staffing
331 Waldron Rd., Ste. 200
La Vergne, TN 37086
Contact: Ms. Terry Goodman, Pres.
Ph: (615)793-3116
URL: http://www.tnstaffing.com
Descr: Represents and promotes the staffing indus-

try through legal and legislative advocacy, public relations, education, and the establishment of high standards of ethical conduct.

Texas

7171 ■ American Association of Retired Persons, Southwest Field
8144 Walnut Hill Ln., Ste. 700
Dallas, TX 75231
Contact: Elaine Ryan
Ph: (214)265-4078
Free: 888-227-7443
Fax: (214)265-4061
E-mail: txaarp@aapr.org
Descr: Seeks to improve every aspect of living for older people. Provides wide range of unique benefits, special products, and services.

7172 ■ American Association of Retired Persons, Texas
98 San Jacinto Blvd., Ste. 750
Austin, TX 78701
Free: 866-227-7443
Descr: Persons 50 years of age or older, working or retired. Seeks to improve every aspect of living for older people.

7173 ■ Association of Career Professionals International, Dallas/Fort Worth Chapter
PO Box 2114
Coppell, TX 75019
Contact: Don Carter, Pres.
Ph: (972)304-0034
E-mail: doncarter@cartgroup.com
URL: http://www.acpinternational-dfw.org
Descr: Represents the interests of career service professionals. Promotes the professional development of its members. Fosters support and collegial relationships among career professionals.

7174 ■ Career and Technology Association of Texas (CTAT)
1304 San Antonio, Ste. 106A
Austin, TX 78701
Contact: Robin Painovich, Exec. Dir.
Ph: (512)288-8666
Fax: (512)288-9998
E-mail: robin@ctat.org
URL: http://www.ctat.org
Descr: Promotes career and technology education and provides valuable benefits to members. **Fnd:** 1975. **Mem:** 210. **State Groups:** 1. **Pub:** Membership Directory (annual).

7175 ■ Dallas/Fort Worth Technical Recruiters Network (DFWTRN)
5015 Addison Cir., No. 342
Addison, TX 75001
Contact: Cathy Henesey, Pres.
E-mail: dfwtrn@verizon.net
URL: http://www.dfwtrn.org
Descr: Promotes sharing and networking among recruiters and human resource professionals. Educates and develops the professional skills of technical recruiters. Encourages camaraderie and professional discourse among members.

7176 ■ Employee Assistance Professionals Association - Houston Chapter
Employee Assistance Program Texas Children Hospital
1919 S Braeswood Blvd.
MC 4-4234
Houston, TX 77230
Contact: Brent LoCaste-Wilken, Pres.
Ph: (832)824-2155
Fax: (832)825-2142
E-mail: brlocast@texaschildrenshospital.org
URL: http://www.eapa.info/ChaptBranch/TX01/Houston.htm

7177 ■ Employee Assistance Professionals Association, Lone Star Chapter
Corphealth, Inc.
1300 Summit Ave., Ste. 800

Fort Worth, TX 76102
Contact: Susan C. Winn SAP, Pres.
Ph: (817)332-2519
Fax: (817)338-4989
E-mail: susan_winn@corphealth.com
URL: http://www.eapa.info/ChaptBranch/TX05/LoneStar.htm

7178 ■ Employee Assistance Professionals Association - North Texas Chapter
9304 Forest Ln., Ste. 100 S
Dallas, TX 75243
Contact: Shannon Purtell LPC, Pres.
Ph: (214)340-0208
E-mail: shannonpurtell@crtcounseling.com
URL: http://www.eapa.info/ChaptBranch/TX02/NorthTexas.htm

7179 ■ Employee Assistance Professionals Association - South Texas Chapter
PO Box 29012
San Antonio, TX 78229
Contact: Clifford B. Melton, Pres.
Ph: (210)524-8151
E-mail: cliffs3@sbcglobal.net
URL: http://www.eapa.info/ChaptBranch/TX08/SouthTexas.htm
Descr: Encourages the systematic development of employee assistance programs.

7180 ■ Employee Services Management Association of North Texas
PO Box 154161
Irving, TX 75015-4161
Contact: Helen Kerr, Pres.
Ph: (817)498-0844
Fax: (817)967-6659
E-mail: hekerr1@attg.net
URL: http://www.esmant.org
Descr: Implements diverse range of employee services. Encourages employees to live balanced lives as they help the company achieve its goals. Maintains practical solutions to work and life issues for a sound business management. **Fnd:** 1974.

7181 ■ Family, Career and Community Leaders of America, Texas
6513 Circle S Rd.
Austin, TX 78745
Contact: Sharon Reddell Pierce, State Advisor
Ph: (512)306-0099
Fax: (512)306-0041
E-mail: fccla@texasfccla.org
URL: http://www.texasfccla.org
Descr: Young men and women studying family and consumer sciences and related occupational courses in public and private schools through grade 12. Youth assume social roles in areas of personal growth, family life, vocational preparation, and community involvement.

7182 ■ LOMA Society of South Central Texas
PO Box 780131
San Antonio, TX 78278-0131
Contact: David Danchak, Pres.
E-mail: flmi@flmi-sct.com
URL: http://www.flmi-sct.com
Descr: Promotes greater understanding and appreciation of the life insurance and financial services industry. Seeks to encourage and aid participation in the LOMA Insurance Education Program. Advances the professional and educational interests of its members.

7183 ■ Texas Career and Technology Council (TCTC)
614 E 12th St.
Austin, TX 78701
Contact: Karen Grumbles
Ph: (512)472-3128
Fax: (512)472-0555
E-mail: karen@vatat.org
URL: http://www.texascareerandtechnology.org
Descr: Supports vocational technical education that

will assure students' successful roles in families, communities, and society.

7184 ■ Texas Workforce Commission
101 E. 15th St., Rm. 618
Austin, TX 78778
Contact: Larry Temple, Exec.Dir.
Ph: (512)463-0735
Fax: (512)475-2321
E-mail: larry.temple@twc.state.tx.us
URL: http://www.twc.state.tx.us
Descr: The Texas Workforce Commission (TWC) is the state government agency charged with overseeing and providing workforce development services to employers and job seekers of Texas.

Utah

7185 ■ Employee Assistance Professionals Association - Salt Lake City Chapter
10150 S Centennial Pkwy.
Sandy, UT 84070-4103
Contact: Phil Quigley LPC, Pres.
Ph: (801)256-7025
E-mail: quigleyp@aetna.com
URL: http://www.eapa.info/ChaptBranch/UT01/SaltLake.htm

7186 ■ Utah Association of Temporary and Staffing Services
SOS Staffing Services
2650 S Decker Lake Blvd., Ste. 500
Salt Lake City, UT 84119
Contact: Mr. Joel Steadman, Pres.
Ph: (801)982-2568
Fax: (801)924-0400
Descr: Represents and promotes the staffing industry through legal and legislative advocacy, public relations, education, and the establishment of high standards of ethical conduct.

7187 ■ Utah Labor Commission
160 E. 300 S., Ste. 300
PO Box 146600
Salt Lake City, UT 84114-6600
Contact: Sherrie Hayashi, Commnr.
Ph: (801)530-6800
Free: 800-530-5090
Fax: (801)530-6390
E-mail: laborcom@utah.gov
URL: http://laborcommission.utah.gov/

Vermont

7188 ■ Vermont Association of Staffing Services
Spherion
1233 Shelburne Rd., Ste. 300
South Burlington, VT 05403
Contact: Mr. Kenneth J. Ballard, Pres.
Ph: (802)864-5900
Fax: (802)862-8795
Descr: Represents and promotes the staffing industry through legal and legislative advocacy, public relations, education, and the establishment of high standards of ethical conduct.

7189 ■ Vermont Department of Labor
5 Green Mountain Dr.
PO Box 488
Montpelier, VT 05601-0488
Contact: Patricia Moulton Powden, Commnr.
Ph: (802)828-4000
Fax: (802)828-4022
E-mail: pmcdonald@labor.state.vt.us
URL: http://www.labor.vermont.gov
Telecom. Svcs: TDD phone number is (802)828-4203.

Virginia

7190 ■ Employee Assistance Professionals Association - Blue Ridge Chapter
213 McClanahan St., Ste. 201A
Roanoke, VA 24014

Contact: Ken Redick, Pres.
Ph: (540)981-8952
E-mail: kredick@carilion.com
URL: http://www.eapa.info/ChaptBranch/VA02/BlueRidge.htm

7191 ■ Employee Assistance Professionals Association - District of Columbia Chapter
200 N Glebe Rd., Ste. 316
Arlington, VA 22203
Contact: Ms. Geetha Desikan
Ph: (703)228-8722
Fax: (703)875-2185
E-mail: gdesikan@arlington.k12.va.us
URL: http://www.eapa.info/ChaptBranch/DC01/District.htm

7192 ■ Employee Assistance Professionals Association - Virginia Chapter
RR 1 - Box 549
Roseland, VA 22967
Contact: Charlie McIntire, Pres.
Ph: (434)325-7574
E-mail: jcmcintire@verizon.net
URL: http://www.eapa.info/ChaptBranch/VA01/Virginia.htm

7193 ■ National Career Development Association, Virginia (VCDA)
Hanover Center for Trades and Technology
10002 Learning Ln.
Mechanicsville, VA 23116
Contact: Sharon DeBragga, Pres.
Ph: (804)723-2038
E-mail: vcda@vcdaweb.org
URL: http://www.vcdaweb.org
Staff: 11. **Descr:** Strengthens the knowledge and skills of career development professionals. Increases the quality of career resources, education and services. Enhances the profession through increased awareness, collaboration and consultation. Benefits of membership include continued professional development through one-day workshops, networking, career development materials, promotion and support of the career professional, VCDA newsletter, and scholarships for students. Regular members include bachelor's degree holder and members of the Virginia Counselors' Association.

7194 ■ Virginia Department of Labor and Industry
Powers-Taylor Bldg.
13 S. 13th St.
Richmond, VA 23219
Contact: C. Ray Davenport, Commnr.
Ph: (804)371-2327
Fax: (804)786-9877
E-mail: webmaster@doli.virginia.gov
URL: http://www.doli.virginia.gov/
Descr: Mission is to make Virginia a better place in which to work, live, and conduct business. **Telecom. Svcs:** TDD phone number is (804)786-2376.

Washington

7195 ■ Employee Assistance Professionals Association - Inland Northwest Chapter
4407 N Division, Ste. 210
Spokane, WA 99207
Contact: Barb Strote, Pres.
Ph: (509)482-3686
E-mail: bstrote@lourdesonline.org
URL: http://www.eapa.info/ChaptBranch/WA02/InlandNorthwest.htm

7196 ■ Employee Assistance Professionals Association - Pacific Northwest Chapter
7683 SE 27th St., PMG 190
Mercer Island, WA 98040
Contact: Skip Wheeler, Pres.

E-mail: skip.wheeler@providence.org
URL: http://www.eapa.info/ChaptBranch/WA01/PacificNorthwest.htm

7197 ■ Employee Services Management Association, Greater Seattle Chapter
PO Box 24804
Seattle, WA 98124-0804
Contact: Marcia Lyman, Pres.
E-mail: esmseattle@msn.com
URL: http://www.esmseattle.org
Descr: Implements diverse range of employee services. Encourages employees to live balanced lives as they help the company achieve its goals. Maintains practical solutions to work and life issues for a sound business management.

7198 ■ The Retired Enlisted Association Chapter 86 (TREA)
PO Box 5567
Wenatchee, WA 98807-0567
Ph: (509)884-5972
Fax: (509)667-2016
E-mail: trea86@surfmydot.com
URL: http://www.surfmydot.com/trea/86/index.htm
Descr: Strives to enhance the quality of life for uniformed services enlisted personnel, their families and survivors-including active components, reserve components, and all retirees; to stop the erosion of earned benefits through legislative efforts; to maintain esprit de corps, dedication and patriotism; and to continue devotion and allegiance to God and Country.

7199 ■ Seattle Area Technical Recruiting Network (SATN)
5021 Ripley Ln. N, No. 302
Renton, WA 98056
Contact: Annette Frigard, Managing Chair
E-mail: annette@satrn.org
URL: http://www.satrn.org
Descr: Represents and promotes the interests of professional technical recruiters. Improves the skills of technical recruiting professionals. Provides opportunities to members to network and share ideas and experiences.

7200 ■ Washington Department of Labor and Industries
PO Box 44000
Olympia, WA 98504-4000
Contact: Judy Schurke, Dir.
Ph: (360)902-5316
Free: 866-219-7321
Fax: (360)902-5300
URL: http://www.lni.wa.gov
Telecom. Svcs: TDD phone number is (360)902-5797.

West Virginia

7201 ■ Construction Employers Association of North Central West Virginia
2794 White Hall Blvd.
White Hall, WV 26554
Contact: L. Robert Worcester, Exec. Dir.
Ph: (304)367-1290
Fax: (304)367-0126
E-mail: officemgr@ceawv.com
URL: http://www.ceawv.com
Staff: 2. **Descr:** Strives to negotiate and administrate collective bargaining agreements with trade unions. Provides a center for plans and specs of projects out for bid to association members. **Fnd:** 1969. **Mem:** 180. **State Groups:** 1. **Pub:** *News and Views* (quarterly).

7202 ■ Employee Assistance Professionals Association - West Virginia Chapter
FBI-CJIS Division
1000 Custer Hollow Rd.
Clarksburg, WV 26306
Contact: Cynthia J. Palagino, Pres.
Ph: (304)625-5802
Fax: (304)625-7997

E-mail: cjiseap@hotmail.com
URL: http://www.eapa.info/ChaptBranch/WV01/WestVirginia.htm

7203 ■ West Virginia Division of Labor Bureau of Commerce
749 B Bldg., Capitol Complex
Charleston, WV 25305
Contact: David Mullins, Commnr.
Ph: (304)558-7890
Fax: (304)558-2415
E-mail: b.m.mcclure@wv.gov
URL: http://www.wvlabor.org/newwebsite/pages/index.html

7204 ■ West Virginia Staffing Association
Express Personnel Services
47 RHL Blvd.
South Charleston, WV 25309
Contact: Tom Wirts, Pres.
Ph: (304)746-8888
Fax: (304)746-1112
URL: http://www.americanstaffing.net/chapters/chapterdetails.cfm?chapterIndex=59
Descr: Represents and promotes the staffing industry through legal and legislative advocacy, public relations, education, and the establishment of high standards of ethical conduct.

Wisconsin

7205 ■ 9to5 Poverty Network
207 E Buffalo St., No. 211
Milwaukee, WI 53202
Contact: Mildred Navedo
Free: 800-920-9925
Fax: 800-920-9925

7206 ■ Employee Assistance Professionals Association - South Central Wisconsin Chapter
PO Box 252
Madison, WI 53701-0252
Contact: David Rutter, Pres.
Ph: (608)240-5458
E-mail: david.rutter@doc.state.wi.us
URL: http://www.eapa.info/ChaptBranch/WI03/SCentralWisconsin.htm

7207 ■ Milwaukee 9to5
207 E Buffalo St., No. 211
Milwaukee, WI 53202
Contact: Donna Skenadore, Chair
Ph: (414)274-0925

7208 ■ Retired Enlisted Association, 77
3315 Curvue Rd.
Eau Claire, WI 54703-9205
Contact: John Olson
Ph: (715)874-4484
E-mail: mlrude@att.net

7209 ■ Wisconsin Association of Personnel Services (WAPS)
PO Box 316
Franksville, WI 53126
Contact: Terry Rohde, Pres.
Ph: (262)412-0586
E-mail: des2001@wi.rr.com
URL: http://www.waps.org
Descr: Represents the interests of the search and staffing industry. Promotes ethical practices and increases awareness of the value of personnel services. Provides training, certification and educational programs to the search staffing personnel.

7210 ■ Wisconsin Association of Staffing Services (WASS)
PO Box 26694
Wauwatosa, WI 53226-0694
Contact: Monica Morrissey, Coor.
Ph: (414)962-6788
Fax: (414)962-6788
E-mail: morrisseymonica@sbcglobal.net
URL: http://www.wass-wi.org
Descr: Represents and promotes the staffing industry through legal and legislative advocacy, public

relations, education, and the establishment of high standards of ethical conduct. **Fnd:** 1971.

7211 ■ Wisconsin Career Development Association (WCDA)
1305 Linden Dr., Rm. 349
Madison, WI 53706
Contact: Sybil Pressprich, Membership Chair
E-mail: membership@wcda.org
URL: http://www.wcda.org

7212 ■ Wisconsin Department of Workforce Development
PO Box 7946
Madison, WI 53707-7946
Contact: Roberta Glassman, Sec.
Ph: (608)266-3131
Fax: (608)266-1784
URL: http://www.dwd.state.wi.us/

Wyoming

7213 ■ Wyoming Department of Employment
1510 E. Pershing Blvd.
Cheyenne, WY 82002
Contact: Gary W. Child, Dir.
Ph: (307)777-7672
Fax: (307)777-5805
E-mail: gchild@state.wy.us
URL: http://wydoe.state.wy.us/

Publications

7214 ■ *25 Jobs That Have It All*
Facts on File Inc.
132 W 31st St., 17th Fl.
New York, NY 10001
Ph: (212)967-8800
Free: 800-322-8755
Fax: 800-678-3633
E-mail: custserv@factsonfile.com
URL: http://factsonfile.infobasepublishing.com
URL(s): http://ferguson.infobasepublishing.com/ **Entries include:** Name, address, phone, and email and Web addresses for groups that can provide more information. Principal content of publication is information regarding job duties; the types of tools, machinery, or equipment used; types of workers in the job environment; growing sub-fields or specialties; job requirements; and personal qualities recommended for the job. **Publication includes:** List of 25 jobs that pay salaries higher that the 2000 national average, fast growing jobs, and new jobs. **Price:** $12.95, individuals.

7215 ■ *2004-05 FCCLA Member Handbook*
Family, Career and Community Leaders of America, Missouri
Dept. of Elementary and Secondary Education
PO Box 480
Jefferson City, MO 65102-0480
Ph: (573)751-7964
Fax: (573)526-4261
E-mail: christine.hollingsworth@dese.mo.gov
URL: http://dese.mo.gov/divcareered/fccla.htm

7216 ■ *AARP Bulletin Today*
American Association of Retired Persons
601 East St. NW
Washington, DC 20049
Ph: (202)434-2277
Free: 888-687-2277
URL: http://www.aarp.org
Key Personnel: Robert Wilson, Editor. **URL(s):** http://bulletin.aarp.org/ **Descr:** Newspaper for mature Americans. **Freq:** Monthly.

7217 ■ *AARP Connections Oklahoma*
AARP, Oklahoma Information Center
Crossroads Mall, Ste. 2055
7000 Crossroads Blvd.
Oklahoma City, OK 73149
Ph: (405)632-1945
Fax: (405)632-1955
E-mail: ok@aarp.org

Freq: monthly.

7218 ■ *AARP Delaware Connections*
AARP Delaware
1100 N Market St., Ste. 1201
Wilmington, DE 19801
Fax: (302)571-1984
E-mail: destate@aarp.org
URL: http://www.aarp.org/de
Descr: Contains information about volunteers.

7219 ■ *AARP News Bulletin*
AARP
601 E St. NW
Washington, DC 20049
Ph: (202)434-2560
E-mail: member@aarp.org
URL: http://www.aarp.org
Freq: 11/year. **Price:** included in membership dues. **ISSN:** 0010-0200.

7220 ■ *Absolute Advantage*
Wellness Councils of America
9802 Nicholas St., Ste. 315
Omaha, NE 68114
Ph: (402)827-3590
Fax: (402)827-3594
E-mail: wellworkplace@welcoa.org
URL: http://www.welcoa.org
Descr: Contains tips, strategies, and insights from the nation's best minds in workplace wellness. **Freq:** 10/year. **Price:** $89/year.

7221 ■ *Active Adult*
Homes Publishing Group
178 Main St.
Unionville, ON, Canada L3R 2G9
Ph: (905)479-4663
Free: 800-363-4663
E-mail: info@activeadultmag.com
URL: http://www.homespublishinggroup.com
URL(s): http://www.activeadultmag.com/ **Descr:** Consumer magazine covering retirement and adult lifestyle communities in Ontario, Canada.

7222 ■ *Adams Electronic Job Search Almanac*
Adams Media Corp.
57 Littlefield St.
Avon, MA 02322
Ph: (508)427-7100
Free: 800-872-5627
Fax: 800-872-5628
E-mail: rights@adamsmedia.com
URL: http://www.adamsmedia.com
Key Personnel: Steven Graber, Editor. **URL(s):** http://www.adamsmedia.com **Covers:** Job listings on the Internet; bulletin boards, Web networking, and online services for finding a job. **Entries include:** Firm or organization name, address, phone, name and title of contact; description of organization, headquarters location, typical titles for entry and middle-level positions, educational backgrounds desired, fringe benefits offered, stock exchange listing, training programs, internships, parent company, number of employees, revenues, e-mail and web address, projected number of hires. **Freq:** Annual, latest edition 6th. **Price:** $0.67, individuals, 18 used & new.

7223 ■ *Adams Jobs Almanac*
Adams Media Corp.
57 Littlefield St.
Avon, MA 02322
Ph: (508)427-7100
Free: 800-872-5627
Fax: 800-872-5628
E-mail: rights@adamsmedia.com
URL: http://www.adamsmedia.com
URL(s): http://www.adamsmediastore.com/product/68/5 **Covers:** Job listings nationwide. **Entries include:** Firm or organization name, address, phone, name and title of contact; description of organization, headquarters location, typical titles for entry and middle-level positions, educational backgrounds desired, fringe benefits offered, stock exchange listing, training programs, internships, parent company,

number of employees, revenues, e-mail and web address, projected number of hires. **Freq:** Annual, Latest edition 9th. **Price:** $10, individuals, list price.

7224 ■ *The Adviser*
Family, Career and Community Leaders of America
1910 Association Dr.
Reston, VA 20191-1584
Ph: (703)476-4900
Fax: (703)860-2713
E-mail: mbenjamin@fcclainc.org
URL: http://www.fcclainc.org
Freq: semiannual. **Price:** $2/issue, $7/year.

7225 ■ *The Adviser*
Family, Career and Community Leaders of America, Missouri
Dept. of Elementary and Secondary Education
PO Box 480
Jefferson City, MO 65102-0480
Ph: (573)751-7964
Fax: (573)526-4261
E-mail: christine.hollingsworth@dese.mo.gov
URL: http://dese.mo.gov/divcareered/fccla.htm
Descr: Recognizes advisors' important roles in the organization and provides updates and ideas to help make their job easier. **Freq:** 3/year. **Price:** included in membership dues.

7226 ■ *AFOP Washington Newsline*
Association of Farmworker Opportunity Programs
1726 M St. NW, Ste. 800
Washington, DC 20036
Ph: (202)826-6006
Fax: (202)826-6005
E-mail: afop@afop.org
URL: http://www.afop.org
Descr: Informs members of issues pertaining to migrant and seasonal farmworkers and other rural poor; analysis of legislative and regulatory actions. **Freq:** bimonthly. **Price:** free to members, $295/year for nonmember organizations, $250/year for member organizations.

7227 ■ *America's Career InfoNet*
U.S. Department of Labor
Business Operations Center
Frances Perkins Bldg.
200 Constitution Ave. NW
Washington, DC 20210
Ph: (886)487-2365
Free: 877-889-5627
URL: http://www.dol.gov
URL(s): http://www.acinet.org/acinet **Covers:** Links to and information about job banks, employment service providers, career education, and nationwide employer contacts.

7228 ■ *America's Fastest Growing Jobs*
JIST Publishing
875 Montreal Way
Saint Paul, MN 55102
Ph: (317)613-4200
Free: 800-648-5478
Fax: 800-547-8329
E-mail: info@jist.com
URL: http://www.jist.com
Key Personnel: J. Michael Farr, Author. **URL(s):** http://www.jist.com **Publication includes:** List of 140 of the fastest growing jobs in the United States. Principal content of publication is information on each job, job outlook, earnings, related occupations, and practical advice on resume writing and interviews. **Price:** $10.37, individuals, eligible for free super saver shipping.

7229 ■ *America's Top White-Collar Jobs*
JIST Publishing
875 Montreal Way
Saint Paul, MN 55102
Ph: (317)613-4200
Free: 800-648-5478
Fax: 800-547-8329
E-mail: info@jist.com
URL: http://www.jist.com
Key Personnel: J. Michael Farr, Author. **URL(s):**

http://www.jist.com **Publication includes:** List of 112 white-collar jobs. Principal content of publication is information on job descriptions, labor market trends, career planning, and advice related to resume writing and interviews. **Price:** $16.95, individuals.

7230 ■ *AmeriCorps. Reporter*
Association of Farmworker Opportunity Programs
1726 M St. NW, Ste. 800
Washington, DC 20036
Ph: (202)826-6006
Fax: (202)826-6005
E-mail: afop@afop.org
URL: http://www.afop.org
Descr: Informs AmeriCorps members of progress and success with providing pesticide worker safety training and education to farmworkers. **Freq:** monthly.

7231 ■ *Appendix to EAPA Program Standards*
Employee Assistance Professionals Association
4350 N Fairfax Dr., Ste. 410
Arlington, VA 22203
Ph: (703)387-1000
Fax: (703)522-4585
E-mail: mbrdatadm@eapassn.org
URL: http://www.eap-association.com
Price: $20 for members, $25 for nonmembers.

7232 ■ *Bridges to Careers for Low-Skilled Adults: A Program Development Guide*
Women Employed Institute
111 N Wabash, Ste. 1300
Chicago, IL 60602
Ph: (312)782-3902
Fax: (312)782-5249
E-mail: info@womenemployed.org
URL: http://www.womenemployed.org

7233 ■ *Canadian Occupational Safety*
Clifford/Elliot Ltd.
240 Edward St.
Aurora, ON, Canada L4G 3S9
URL: http://www.clbmedia.ca
Key Personnel: Karen Lorimer, Gp. Publisher, klorimer@clbmedia.ca; Mari-Len De Guzman, Editor, mdeguzman@clbmedia.ca; Alice Chen, Production Coord., achen@clbmedia.ca. **URL(s):** http://www.cos-mag.com/ **Descr:** Industrial safety and health news magazine (tabloid). **Freq:** Bimonthly, 6/yr.

7234 ■ *Career Convergence Web Magazine*
National Career Development Association
305 N Beech Cir.
Broken Arrow, OK 74012
Ph: (918)663-7060
Fax: (918)663-7058
E-mail: dpennington@ncda.org
URL: http://www.ncda.org
Descr: Includes annual index. **Freq:** monthly. **Price:** included in membership dues, $45/year for nonmembers.

7235 ■ *Career Development Quarterly*
National Career Development Association
305 N Beech Cir.
Broken Arrow, OK 74012
Ph: (918)663-7060
Fax: (918)663-7058
E-mail: dpennington@ncda.org
URL: http://www.ncda.org
Descr: Includes annual index. **Freq:** quarterly. **Price:** included in membership dues, $65/year for nonmembers, $100/year for libraries. **ISSN:** 0889-4019.

7236 ■ *Career Developments*
National Career Development Association
305 N Beech Cir.
Broken Arrow, OK 74012
Ph: (918)663-7060
Fax: (918)663-7058
E-mail: dpennington@ncda.org
URL: http://www.ncda.org

Freq: quarterly.

7237 ■ *The Career Directory*
Mediacorp Canada Inc.
21 New St.
Toronto, ON, Canada M5R 1P7
Ph: (416)964-6069
Free: 800-361-2580
Fax: (416)964-3202
E-mail: tcd@mediacorp.ca
URL: http://www.mediacorp.ca
URL(s): http://www.mediacorp.ca/tcd **Covers:** Canada's 1,000 best employers. **Entries include:** name, address, phone, fax of companies and recruiters. name, address, phone, fax. **Freq:** Annual, Latest edition 2009. **Price:** $29.95, individuals.

7238 ■ *The Career Guide—Dun's Employment Opportunities Directory*
Dun & Bradstreet Corp.
103 JFK Pkwy.
Short Hills, NJ 07078
Ph: (973)921-5500
Free: 800-234-3867
E-mail: custserv@dnb.com
URL: http://www.dnb.com
URL(s): http://dnb.com/us **Covers:** more than 5,000 companies on leading employers throughout the U.S. that provide career opportunities in sales, marketing, management, engineering, life and physical sciences, computer science, mathematics, statistics planning, accounting and finance, liberal arts fields, and other technical and professional areas; based on data supplied on questionnaires and through personal interviews. Also covers personnel consultants; includes some public sector employers (governments, schools, etc.) usually not found in similar lists. **Entries include:** Company name, location of headquarters and other offices or plants; entries may also include name, title, address, and phone of employment contact; disciplines or occupational groups hired; brief overview of company, discussion of types of positions that may be available, training and career development programs, benefits offered, internship and work-study programs. **Freq:** Annual.

7239 ■ *Career Opportunities for Minority College Graduates*
Paoli Publishing Inc.
1708 E Lancaster Ave., Ste. 287
Paoli, PA 19301
E-mail: collegeindex@aol.com
Covers: over 900 companies, organizations and schools representing 24 occupational fields and five continuing educational alternatives. **Entries include:** Name, address, personnel contact name or department; phone and fax number listed in many entries. **Freq:** Annual, latest edition 12th, March 2002. **Price:** Free.

7240 ■ *Career Opportunities in the Retail and Wholesale Industry*
Facts on File Inc.
132 W 31st St., 17th Fl.
New York, NY 10001
Ph: (212)967-8800
Free: 800-322-8755
Fax: 800-678-3633
E-mail: custserv@factsonfile.com
URL: http://factsonfile.infobasepublishing.com
Key Personnel: Shelly Field, Author. **URL(s):** http://www.factsonfile.com **Covers:** 80 jobs in a variety of occupations in retail and wholesale, including salesperson, secretary, bookkeeper, property manager, Webmaster, artist, security, events coordinator, and advertising director. **Entries include:** Career profile details; appendixes list contact details for college and university programs, associations and other organizations. **Freq:** June 2001. **Price:** $49.50, individuals, Hardcover.

7241 ■ *Career Voice International*
Association of Career Professionals International
204 E St. NE
Washington, DC 20002
Ph: (202)547-6377

Fax: (202)547-6348
E-mail: info@acpinternational.org
URL: http://www.iacmp.org
Freq: quarterly.

7242 ■ *CareerMagazine*
Verticalnet Inc.
5 Walnut Grove Dr., No. 300
Horsham, PA 19044-2201
E-mail: sales@careermag.com

URL(s): http://www.careermag.com/ **Descr:** Consumer magazine covering career development and employment.

7243 ■ *Careers and the MBA*
BrassRing Diversity
170 High St.
Waltham, MA 02453-5914
Free: 800-CBA-FORU
Fax: (617)577-7799
E-mail: advertising@brassring.com

Key Personnel: Kathleen Grimes, Dir. of Publishing. **Descr:** Career resource magazine for MBA students featuring company profiles, feature articles, and career bios. **Freq:** Semiannual. **Price:** $12.95, single issue, plus 4.50 s/h.

7244 ■ *CareerXRoads*
MMC GROUP
105 Decker Ct., Ste. 150
Irving, TX 75062
Ph: (972)893-0100
Fax: (972)893-0099
E-mail: info@mmcgrp.com
URL: http://www.mmcgrp.com

Key Personnel: Gerry Crispin, Editor; Mark Mehler, Editor. **URL(s):** http://www.careerxroads.com/about **Covers:** Nearly 3,000 job and resume Websites with reviews and descriptions of the top 500. **Freq:** latest edition 2002.

7245 ■ *Chronicle Financial Aid Guide*
Chronicle Guidance Publications Inc.
66 Aurora St.
Moravia, NY 13118-3569
Ph: (315)497-0330
Free: 800-622-7284
Fax: (315)497-0339
E-mail: customerservice@chronicleguidance.com
URL: http://www.chronicleguidance.com

URL(s): http://www.chronicleguidance.com **Covers:** Over 1,770 financial aid programs offered primarily by private organizations, independent and AFL-CIO affiliated labor unions, and federal and state governments for high school students, undergraduate and graduate students, and adult learners. **Entries include:** Name of sponsoring organization, address, amount of aid, eligibility requirements, application, selection procedure. **Freq:** Annual, latest edition 2008-2009. **Price:** $25.49, individuals, softbound.

7246 ■ *Civil Right Teaching*
Teaching for Change
PO Box 73038
Washington, DC 20056
Ph: (202)588-7204
Fax: (202)238-0109
E-mail: info@teachingforchange.org
URL: http://www.teachingforchange.org

Descr: Includes interactive and interdisciplinary lessons, writings, photographs, graphics and interviews on teaching about the civil rights movement.

7247 ■ *C.L.C. Fax-Press*
Canadian Labour Congress
2841 Riverside Dr.
Ottawa, ON, Canada K1V 8X7
Ph: (613)521-3400
Fax: (613)521-4655
E-mail: president@clc-ctc.ca
URL: http://www.clc-ctc.ca

Freq: weekly.

7248 ■ *Co-Curricular Guide for FCCLA Chapters*
Family, Career and Community Leaders of America
1910 Association Dr.
Reston, VA 20191-1584
Ph: (703)476-4900
Fax: (703)860-2713
E-mail: mbenjamin@fcclainc.org
URL: http://www.fcclainc.org

7249 ■ *Co-Employment Guide*
American Staffing Association
277 S Washington St., Ste. 200
Alexandria, VA 22314-3675
Ph: (703)253-2020
Fax: (703)253-2053
E-mail: asa@americanstaffing.net
URL: http://www.americanstaffing.net
Price: $40 for members, $60 for nonmembers.

7250 ■ *College Majors and Careers*
Facts on File Inc.
132 W 31st St., 17th Fl.
New York, NY 10001
Ph: (212)967-8800
Free: 800-322-8755
Fax: 800-678-3633
E-mail: holli@inil.com
URL: http://factsonfile.infobasepublishing.com

Key Personnel: Paul Phifer, Author. **URL(s):** http://www.fergpubco.com **Entries include:** Organization name, address, phone. Principal content of publication is descriptions of 60 of the most popular major fields and discussions of their attributes. **Publication includes:** Lists of organizations and other sources of information on choosing a college field of concentration and a subsequent career path. **Freq:** Irregular, latest edition 6th, 2008. **Price:** $35, individuals, hardcover.

7251 ■ *College Money Handbook*
Peterson's
Princeton Pike Corporate Ctr.
2000 Lenox Dr.
PO Box 67005
Lawrenceville, NJ 08648
Ph: (609)896-1800
Free: 800-338-3282
Fax: (609)896-4531
E-mail: custsvc@petersons.com
URL: http://www.petersons.com

URL(s): http://www.petersons.com; http://www.petersons.com/services/petersons/gov_catalog.pdf **Covers:** Over $50 billion in financial aid, including jobs, loans, scholarships, and special aids programs, available at over 2,100 four-year accredited colleges in the U.S. **Freq:** Irregular, Latest edition 2009. **Price:** $24.32, individuals.

7252 ■ *The Commissionaires*
Canadian Corps of Commissionaires
100 rue Gloucester St., Ste. 201
Ottawa, ON, Canada K2P 0A4
Ph: (613)688-0710
Fax: (613)688-0719
E-mail: national@commissionaires.ca
URL: http://www.commissionaires.ca
Price: $29.95/copy.

7253 ■ *Compliance Manual*
U.S. Equal Employment Opportunity Commission
131 M St. NE
Washington, DC 20507
Ph: (202)663-4900
E-mail: info@eeoc.gov
URL: http://www.eeoc.gov

7254 ■ *CPA E-Source*
Canadian Payroll Association
250 Bloor St. E, Ste. 1600
Toronto, ON, Canada M4W 1E6
Ph: (416)487-3380
Fax: (416)487-3384

E-mail: membership@payroll.ca
URL: http://www.payroll.ca
Freq: bimonthly.

7255 ■ *CUPE: It's Your Union*
Canadian Union of Public Employees
1375 St. Lauren Blvd.
Ottawa, ON, Canada K1G 0Z7
Ph: (613)237-1590
Fax: (613)237-5508
URL: http://cupe.ca

7256 ■ *Dialogue Magazine*
Canadian Payroll Association
250 Bloor St. E, Ste. 1600
Toronto, ON, Canada M4W 1E6
Ph: (416)487-3380
Fax: (416)487-3384
E-mail: membership@payroll.ca
URL: http://www.payroll.ca
Freq: bimonthly. **Price:** $95/year.

7257 ■ *Directory of Nontraditional Training and Employment Programs*
Women's Bureau
Department of Labor
200 Constitution Ave. NW, Rm. S-3002
Washington, DC 20210
Ph: (202)693-6710
Free: 800-827-5335
Fax: (202)693-6725
URL: http://www.dol.gov/wb/

Covers: 125 programs in 32 states designed to assist women in obtaining training and employment in skilled nontraditional jobs. **Entries include:** Program name, address, phone, administrative agency, name and title of contact, program services, eligibility, program locations. **Freq:** Published 1991.

7258 ■ *Directory of Services for the Widowed in the U.S. and Canada*
AARP Grief and Loss Program
601 E St. NW
Washington, DC 20049
E-mail: ageline@aarp.org
URL: http://www.aarp.org/families/grief_loss
Freq: periodic.

7259 ■ *The Directory of Temporary Placement Firms for Executives, Managers, & Professionals*
Kennedy Information
1 Phoenix Mill Ln., 3rd Fl.
Peterborough, NH 03458
Ph: (603)924-1006
Free: 800-531-0007
Fax: (603)924-4460
E-mail: bookstore@kennedyinfo.com
URL: http://www.kennedyinfo.com

URL(s): http://impactpublications.com/ **Covers:** Over 1,900 temporary placement firms in the U.S and Canada. **Enries include:** Company name, address, phone, fax, e-mail, description, geographical area served, practice breakdown, functions, and industries. **Freq:** Biennial, Latest edition 9th. **Price:** $39.95, individuals, plus shipping charges.

7260 ■ *Directory of U.S. Labor Organizations*
BNA Books
1801 S Bell St.
Arlington, VA 22202
Ph: (703)341-5777
Free: 800-960-1220
Fax: (703)341-1610
E-mail: books@bna.com
URL: http://storefront.bnabooks.com/epages/bnastore.sf

Key Personnel: Court D. Gifford, Author. **URL(s):** http://storefront.bnabooks.com/epages/bnastore.sf **Covers:** Nearly 150 national unions and professional and state employees associations engaged in labor representation. **Entries include:** Name, address, phone, fax numbers, and URLs; names of nearly 2,500 elected officials and key staff members, publications, convention dates, membership figures, and list of locals. **Freq:** Annual, Latest edition 2008. **Price:** $145, individuals, soft cover.

7261 ■ Does Drug Testing Work?
Institute for a Drug-Free Workplace
8614 Westwood Center Dr., Ste. 950
Vienna, VA 22182
Ph: (703)288-4300
URL: http://www.drugfreeworkplace.org
Price: $36.

7262 ■ Drug Testing in the Workplace: Basic Issues, Answers, and Options for Employees
Institute for a Drug-Free Workplace
8614 Westwood Center Dr., Ste. 950
Vienna, VA 22182
Ph: (703)288-4300
URL: http://www.drugfreeworkplace.org
Price: $4.50.

7263 ■ EBRI Issue Brief
Employee Benefit Research Institute
1100 13th St. NW, Ste. 878
Washington, DC 20005-4058
Ph: (202)659-0670
Fax: (202)775-6312
E-mail: info@ebri.org
URL: http://www.ebri.org
Descr: Provides evaluations of evolving employee benefit issues and trends and analyses of employee benefit program policies and proposals. **Freq:** monthly. **Price:** $25/issue. **ISSN:** 0887-137X.

7264 ■ EBRI Notes
Employee Benefit Research Institute
1100 13th St. NW, Ste. 878
Washington, DC 20005-4058
Ph: (202)659-0670
Fax: (202)775-6312
E-mail: info@ebri.org
URL: http://www.ebri.org
Descr: Provides released employee benefit statistical findings. **Freq:** monthly. **Price:** $25/issue. **ISSN:** 1085-4452.

7265 ■ EBRI Pension Investment Report
Employee Benefit Research Institute
1100 13th St. NW, Ste. 878
Washington, DC 20005-4058
Ph: (202)659-0670
Fax: (202)775-6312
E-mail: info@ebri.org
URL: http://www.ebri.org
Descr: Provides data on assets in the private and public pension systems and the performance of pension investment. Covers historical data. **Freq:** periodic. **Price:** included in membership dues, $500/issue for nonmembers. **ISSN:** 0889-4396.

7266 ■ EBRI Policy Forums
Employee Benefit Research Institute
1100 13th St. NW, Ste. 878
Washington, DC 20005-4058
Ph: (202)659-0670
Fax: (202)775-6312
E-mail: info@ebri.org
URL: http://www.ebri.org
Freq: semiannual.

7267 ■ Education Job Finder
Planning Communications
7215 Oak Ave.
River Forest, IL 60305-1935
Ph: (708)366-5200
Free: 888-366-5200
Fax: (708)366-5280
E-mail: info@planningcommunications.com
URL: http://www.planningcommunications.com/jf/index.htm
Key Personnel: Daniel Lauber, Author, dl@planningcommunications.com; Deborah Verlench, Author. **URL(s):** http://www.planningcommunications.com/jf/index.htm **Covers:** Over 1,000 sources of jobs and internships in the education sector in the U.S., including job matching services, Internet job sites, online job and resume databases, job hotlines,

periodicals and directories, salary surveys, and databases. Also includes directories of grant opportunities and free updates online. **Entries include:** For services--Name, sponsor or operator name, address, phone, length of registration period, cost, description (including number of job vacancies listed). For publications--Title, publisher name, address, phone, frequency, price, description (including number of job vacancies listed). **Freq:** Triennial, Latest edition 2009. **Price:** $19.95, individuals, paperback; $32.95, individuals, hardcover.

7268 ■ Employee Assistance Programs: An Employer's Development and Implementation Guide
Institute for a Drug-Free Workplace
8614 Westwood Center Dr., Ste. 950
Vienna, VA 22182
Ph: (703)288-4300
URL: http://www.drugfreeworkplace.org
Price: $4.50.

7269 ■ Employee Services Management
Employee Services Management Association
568 Spring Rd., Ste. D
Elmhurst, IL 60126-3896
Ph: (630)559-0020
Fax: (630)559-0025
E-mail: esmahq@esmassn.org
URL: http://www.esmassn.org
Descr: Contains trends, information and research on employee stores, community services, convenience services, dependent care, recreation programs, etc. **Freq:** bimonthly. **Price:** free for members. **ISSN:** 0744-3676.

7270 ■ Employment Guide
Dominion Enterprises
150 Granby St.
Norfolk, VA 23510
Ph: (757)351-7000
E-mail: mediainfo@dominionenterprises.com
URL: http://www.dominionenterprises.com/
Key Personnel: Jennifer A. Butsch, Public Relation Mgr. **URL(s):** http://www.dominionenterprises.com **Descr:** Consists of separate editions for cities throughout the U.S. , including Akron, Atlanta, Baltimore, Birmingham, Boston, Charlotte, Chicago, Cincinnati, Cleveland, Columbus, Dallas, Dayton, Denver, Detroit, Fort Lauderdale, Hartford, High Point (North Carolina), Houston, Indianapolis, Inland Empire (California), Jacksonville, Kansas City, Las Vegas, Los Angeles, Louisville, Memphis, Miami, Milwaukee, Minneapolis, Nashville, New Orleans, New York, Oklahoma City, Omaha, Orange County (California), Orlando, Philadelphia, Phoenix, Pittsburgh, Portland, Providence, Raleigh, Richmond, Sacramento, Salt Lake City, San Antonio, San Diego, San Francisco, Seattle, St. Louis, Tampa, Tucson, and Washington, DC. **Entries include:** Job description, contact information.

7271 ■ Ethnoviolence in the Workplace: Summary of Major Findings
Prejudice Institute/Center for the Applied Study of Ethnoviolence
2743 Maryland Ave.
Baltimore, MD 21218
Ph: (410)366-9654
E-mail: prejinst@aol.com
URL: http://www.prejudiceinstitute.org
Price: $10/copy.

7272 ■ Fact Book
Career College Association
1101 Connecticut Ave. NW, Ste. 900
Washington, DC 20036
Ph: (202)336-6700
Fax: (202)336-6828
E-mail: cca@career.org
URL: http://www.career.org
Descr: Contains research and analysis of important

trends in the career college sector of higher education. **Freq:** biennial. **Price:** $24.95/copy.

7273 ■ Facts About Retiring in the United States
H.W. Wilson Co.
950 University Ave.
Bronx, NY 10452
Ph: (718)588-8400
Free: 800-367-6770
Fax: (718)590-1617
E-mail: custserv@hwwilson.com
URL: http://www.hwwilson.com
Key Personnel: Steven S. Shagrin, Editor; Philip Taylor, Director, ptaylor@hwwilson.com; Regina Williams, Manager, rwilliams@hwwilson.com. **URL(s):** http://www.hwwilson.com **Covers:** Resources, housing options, and amenities for senior citizens. **Entries include:** For housing--Name, address, phone, rates and accommodations, range of services offered, and licensing and accreditation. **Price:** $120, U.S. and Canada; $140, out of country.

7274 ■ FCCLA is..
Family, Career and Community Leaders of America
1910 Association Dr.
Reston, VA 20191-1584
Ph: (703)476-4900
Fax: (703)860-2713
E-mail: mbenjamin@fcclainc.org
URL: http://www.fcclainc.org

7275 ■ Federal Career Opportunities
Federal Research Service Inc.
PO Box 1708
Annandale, VA 22003
Ph: (703)914-JOBS
Free: 800-822-5027
Fax: (703)281-7639
E-mail: info@fedjobs.com
URL: http://www.fedjobs.com
URL(s): http://www.fedjobs.com/index.html **Covers:** more than 3,000 current federal job vacancies in the United States and overseas; includes permanent, part-time, and temporary positions. **Entries include:** Position title, location, series and grade, job requirements, special forms, announcement number, closing date, application address. **Freq:** Biweekly. **Price:** $19.97, members, per copy; $59.95, members, 6 issues; $99.95, members, 12 issues; $39.95, members, 26 issues.

7276 ■ Federal Jobs Digest
Federal Jobs Digest
326 Main St.
Emmaus, PA 18049
Free: 800-824-5000
E-mail: webmaster@jobsfed.com
URL: http://www.jobsfed.com
Key Personnel: Peter E. Ognibene, Contact. **URL(s):** http://www.jobsfed.com **Covers:** Over 10,000 specific job openings in the federal government in each issue. Vacancies from over 300 Federal Agencies are covered. **Entries include:** Position name, title, General Schedule (GS) grade, and Wage Grade (WG), closing date for applications, announcement number, application address, phone, and name of contact. **Freq:** 25x/yr. **Price:** $125, U.S.; $152.75, Canada; $183.75, individuals, Europe; $112.50, libraries.

7277 ■ Final Details: A Guide for Survivors
AARP Grief and Loss Program
601 E St. NW
Washington, DC 20049
E-mail: ageline@aarp.org
URL: http://www.aarp.org/families/grief_loss
Descr: Contains information on making decisions and taking action in the first few months after death.

7278 ■ The Financial Aid Book
Perpetual Press
PO Box 45628
Seattle, WA 98145-0628
Ph: (206)971-3708
Free: 800-793-8010

Fax: (206)971-3708
E-mail: marathon@blarg.com
Covers: Private financial sources of scholarships, grants, loans, fellowships, internships, research support, etc. , for higher education. **Entries include:** Contact information. **Freq:** Published 1996. **Price:** $19.95, individuals.

7279 ■ Flight Attendant Job Finder and Career Guide
Planning Communications
7215 Oak Ave.
River Forest, IL 60305-1935
Ph: (708)366-5200
Free: 888-366-5200
Fax: (708)366-5280
E-mail: info@planningcommunications.com
URL: http://www.planningcommunications.com/jf/index.htm
Key Personnel: Tim Kirkwood, Author. **URL(s):** http://www.planningcommunications.com **Covers:** Career opportunities for flight attendants or those wanting to become flight attendants, including information on the application process, job requirements, training, benefits, pay, and more. **Entries include:** Airline profiles, contacts. Includes directory of U.S. and Canadian airlines. **Freq:** Annual, latest edition 77th Anniversary Edition. **Price:** $12.71, individuals, paperback; plus shipping.

7280 ■ Greater Philadelphia Chamber of Commerce Job Fair Employer Handbook
Greater Philadelphia Chamber of Commerce
200 S Broad St., Ste. 700
Philadelphia, PA 19102
Ph: (215)545-1234
Fax: (215)790-3600
E-mail: memberrelations@greaterphilachamber.com
URL: http://www.greaterphilachamber.com
URL(s): http://www.gpcc.com **Covers:** Employers in the greater Philadelphia area. **Entries include:** Company profiles, key contact, address, phone, URL, e-mail, products, services, revenue, and number of employees. **Freq:** latest edition 2005.

7281 ■ Guide to Dangerous Drugs
Institute for a Drug-Free Workplace
8614 Westwood Center Dr., Ste. 950
Vienna, VA 22182
Ph: (703)288-4300
URL: http://www.drugfreeworkplace.org
Price: $2.40.

7282 ■ The Guide to Internet Job Searching
The McGraw-Hill Cos.
PO Box 182604
Columbus, OH 43272
Ph: (609)426-5793
Free: 877-833-5524
Fax: (614)759-3749
E-mail: customer.service@mcgraw-hill.com
URL: http://www.mcgraw-hill.com/
Key Personnel: Margaret Riley, Author; Frances Roehm, Author. **URL(s):** http://www.mhprofessional.com **Covers:** Websites, bulletin boards, and online career development resources for job seekers in a variety of fields, including business and government, worldwide. **Entries include:** Site address. **Freq:** Latest edition 2008-2009. **Price:** $16.95, individuals.

7283 ■ Guide for Middle Level FCCLA Chapters
Family, Career and Community Leaders of America
1910 Association Dr.
Reston, VA 20191-1584
Ph: (703)476-4900
Fax: (703)860-2713
E-mail: mbenjamin@fcclainc.org
URL: http://www.fcclainc.org

7284 ■ Headhunters Revealed
Hunter Arts Publishing
PO Box 66578E
Los Angeles, CA 90066
Ph: (310)842-8864
Fax: (310)842-8868

E-mail: publisher@hunterarts.com
URL: http://www.headhuntersrevealed.com/reviews.html
Key Personnel: Darrell W. Gurney, Editor. **URL(s):** http://www.headhuntersrevealed.com **Covers:** Online career sites, career associations, and organizations. **Freq:** Quarterly. **Price:** $14.95, individuals, sales tax, shipping and handling extra; $12.50, out of country.

7285 ■ The Hotline
Pennsylvania Family, Career, and Community Leaders of America
333 Market St., 11th Fl.
Harrisburg, PA 17126-0333
Ph: (717)783-6952
Fax: (717)783-6672
E-mail: sufisher@state.pa.us
URL: http://www.pafccla.org
Freq: 3/year. **Price:** included in membership dues.

7286 ■ The Hotline
Pennsylvania Association - Family, Career and Community Leaders of America
333 Market St., 6th Fl.
Harrisburg, PA 17126-0333
Ph: (717)783-6952
Fax: (717)783-6672
E-mail: sufisher@state.pa.us
URL: http://www.pafccla.org
Descr: Contains 8 pages chapter news. **Price:** free.

7287 ■ HR Yellow Pages
Ransom & Benjamin Publishers L.L.C.
44 Washington St., Ste. 221
PO Box 160
Mystic, CT 06355
Ph: (860)536-7656
Free: 800-334-3352
Fax: (860)536-7657
E-mail: rbpubs@aol.com
URL: http://www.hreditor.com
URL(s): http://www.hreditor.com **Descr:** Covers human resource organizations, agencies, suppliers and sources. **Entries include:** Name, address, phone, URL, and e-mail addresses. **Freq:** Annual. **Price:** $19.95, individuals.

7288 ■ IBEW Journal
International Brotherhood of Electrical Workers
900 7th St., NW
Washington, DC 20001
Ph: (202)833-7000
Fax: (202)728-7676
E-mail: journal@ibew.org
URL: http://www.ibew.org
URL(s): http://www.ibew.org **Descr:** Labor magazine for local union members. **Freq:** Monthly.

7289 ■ Industrial Hygiene News
Rimbach Publishing Inc.
St. 8650 Babcock Blvd.
Pittsburgh, PA 15237
Ph: (412)364-5366
Free: 800-245-3182
Fax: (412)369-9720
E-mail: info@rimbach.com
URL: http://www.rimbach.com/RimPub/PandS/ProdandServ.htm
Key Personnel: Norberta Rimbach, Publisher; Karen Galante, Circulation Mgr., karen@rimbach.com. **URL(s):** http://www.rimbach.com **Descr:** Magazine covering industrial hygiene, occupational health, and safety. **Freq:** Bimonthly. **Price:** Free to qualified subscribers.

7290 ■ Industrial Safety and Hygiene News
BNP Media
Energy & Power Management
2401 W Big Beaver Rd., Ste. 700
Troy, MI 48084-3333
Ph: (847)763-9534
Fax: (847)763-9538
E-mail: customerservice@ihsn.com
URL: http://www.energyandpowermanagement.com/
Key Personnel: Randy Green, Publisher, greenr@

bnpmedia.com; Bill Noone, Mng. Ed., Products Ed., nooneb@bnpmedia.com; Dave Johnson, Editor, djsafe@bellatlantic.net. **URL(s):** http://www.ihsn.com **Descr:** Magazine for corporate managers and specialists responsible for employee safety and health, environmental programs, and regulatory compliance. **Freq:** Monthly. **Price:** $64, individuals; $128, two years; $87, Canada; $173, Canada, 2 years.

7291 ■ International Job Finder
Planning Communications
7215 Oak Ave.
River Forest, IL 60305-1935
Ph: (708)366-5200
Free: 888-366-5200
Fax: (708)366-5280
E-mail: info@planningcommunications.com
URL: http://www.planningcommunications.com/jf/index.htm
Key Personnel: Daniel Lauber, Author; Kraig Rice, Author. **URL(s):** http://www.planningcommunications.com **Covers:** More than 1,200 Internet resources for jobs around the world, including job databases, resume banks, and employer databases. **Entries include:** URLs. **Freq:** Triennial, latest edition 2002 edition. **Price:** $19.95, individuals, paperback.

7292 ■ The Intersection Between Pay Equity and Workplace Representation
National Committee on Pay Equity
555 New Jersey Ave. NW
Washington, DC 20001-2029
Ph: (703)920-2010
Fax: (703)979-6372
E-mail: fairpay@pay-equity.org
URL: http://www.pay-equity.org

7293 ■ Job Hotlines USA
Career Communications
PO Box 169
Harleysville, PA 19438
URL: http://www.careerbookstore.com/how2order.shtml
Covers: over 1,000 government agencies, hospitals, colleges, companies, and federal job information centers that have employment hotlines. **Entries include:** company name, address, voice telephone number, job hotline number, and industry classification. **Freq:** Latest edition 1994.

7294 ■ JobWatch
Advanstar Communications
641 Lexington Ave., 8th Fl.
New York, NY 10022
Ph: (212)951-6600
Free: 800-346-0085
Fax: (212)951-6793
E-mail: info@advanstar.com
URL: http://web.advanstar.com
URL(s): http://www.centerwatch.com/careers/careers.html **Descr:** Publication covering employment in clinical trials industry. **Freq:** Monthly. **Price:** $89; $129, out of country; Free, to CenterWatch subscribers.

7295 ■ Journal of Employee Assistance
Employee Assistance Professionals Association
4350 N Fairfax Dr., Ste. 410
Arlington, VA 22203
Ph: (703)387-1000
Fax: (703)522-4585
E-mail: mbrdatadm@eapassn.org
URL: http://www.eap-association.com
Freq: quarterly. **Price:** available to members only.

7296 ■ Journal of Labor Research
George Mason University
Dept. of Economics
Enterprise Hall, 3rd Fl.
4400 University Dr.
Fairfax, VA 22030
Ph: (703)993-1000
E-mail: webmaster@gmu.edu
URL: http://www.gmu.edu/
Key Personnel: Dr. James T. Bennett, Editor,

jbennett@gmu.edu. **URL(s):** http://www.
thelockeinstitute.org/jolr.html **Descr:** Journal reporting on aspects of the employer/employee
relationship. **Freq:** Quarterly.

7297 ■ Journal of Workplace Rights
Baywood Publishing Company Inc.
26 Austin Ave.
PO Box 337
Amityville, NY 11701
Ph: (631)691-1270
Free: 800-638-7819
Fax: (631)691-1770
E-mail: info@baywood.com
URL: http://www.baywood.com
Key Personnel: Paul Adler, Editorial Board; Charles
J. Coleman, Assoc. Ed.; Joel Rudin, Editor. **URL(s):**
http://baywood.com/journals/previewjournals.
asp?id=jwr **Descr:** Peer-reviewed journal covering
employee and employer rights in the workplace.
Freq: 4/yr. **Price:** $329, institutions; $97, individuals.

7298 ■ Label Letter
Union Label and Service Trades Department, AFL-
CIO
815 16th St. NW
Washington, DC 20006
Ph: (202)508-3700
Fax: (202)508-3701
E-mail: ulstd@unionlabel.org
URL: http://www.unionlabel.org
Freq: bimonthly. **Price:** free for members. **ISSN:**
0161-9365.

7299 ■ Labor Arbitration in Government
American Arbitration Association
1633 Broadway, Fl. 10
New York, NY 10019
Ph: (212)716-5800
Free: 800-778-7879
Fax: (212)716-5905
E-mail: websitemail@adr.org
URL: http://www.adr.org
URL(s): http://www.adr.org/publicationsorder.asp **De-
scr:** Periodical covering arbitrator awards, statutes
and collective bargaining, absenteeism, grievances,
drug and alcohol abuse, and layoffs. Contains
arbitrator and subject indexes. **Freq:** Monthly. **Price:**
$142, individuals.

7300 ■ Las Vegas JobBank
Adams Media Corp.
57 Littlefield St.
Avon, MA 02322
Ph: (508)427-7100
Free: 800-872-5627
Fax: 800-872-5628
E-mail: rights@adamsmedia.com
URL: http://www.adamsmedia.com
Key Personnel: Steven Graber, Editor. **Covers:**
More than 4,000 companies in all industries, and 20
employment agencies throughout Nevada. **Entries
include:** Company name, address, phone, fax,
e-mail, URL, hiring manager name, positions, intern-
ships offered, benefits, resources. **Freq:** Published
May 1998. **Price:** $18.13, individuals, 4 used & new.

**7301 ■ Lesbian and Gay Issues: A Resource
Manual**
National Association of Social Workers National
Committee on Lesbian, Gay and Bisexual Issues
750 First St. NE, Ste. 700
Washington, DC 20002-4241
Ph: (202)408-8600
E-mail: membership@naswdc.org
URL: http://www.socialworkers.org/governance/
cmtes/nclgbi.asp

7302 ■ Liaison
Canadian Centre for Occupational Health and Safety
135 Hunter St. E
Hamilton, ON, Canada L8N 1M5
Ph: (905)572-2981
Fax: (905)572-2206
E-mail: clientservices@ccohs.ca
URL: http://www.ccohs.ca

Descr: Features product information, user tips, and
developments on the activities of the center. **Freq:**
quarterly.

7303 ■ The Link
Career College Association
1101 Connecticut Ave. NW, Ste. 900
Washington, DC 20036
Ph: (202)336-6700
Fax: (202)336-6828
E-mail: cca@career.org
URL: http://www.career.org
Descr: Contains useful information and news to the
career college community. **Freq:** quarterly.

7304 ■ The Magazine
AARP
601 E St. NW
Washington, DC 20049
Ph: (202)434-2560
E-mail: member@aarp.org
URL: http://www.aarp.org
Descr: Includes news and guidance on health,
travel, celebrities and food. Features insights and
inspiration. **Freq:** biweekly.

**7305 ■ Making Workplaces Work: Quality
Work Policies for Small Business**
Business and Professional Women/USA
1620 Eye St. NW, Ste. 210
Washington, DC 20006
Ph: (202)293-1100
Fax: (202)861-0298
E-mail: memberservices@bpwusa.org
URL: http://www.bpwusa.org
Descr: Details working family values. **Freq:** annual.
Price: $29.95 for members, $295 for businesses.

7306 ■ Member Services
Equal Employment Advisory Council
1501 M St. NW, Ste. 400
Washington, DC 20005
Ph: (202)629-5650
Fax: (202)629-5651
E-mail: info@eeac.org
URL: http://www.eeac.org

7307 ■ Membership and Resource Directory
American Staffing Association
277 S Washington St., Ste. 200
Alexandria, VA 22314-3675
Ph: (703)253-2020
Fax: (703)253-2053
E-mail: asa@americanstaffing.net
URL: http://www.americanstaffing.net

7308 ■ Modern Maturity
AARP
601 E St. NW
Washington, DC 20049
Ph: (202)434-2560
E-mail: member@aarp.org
URL: http://www.aarp.org
Descr: Contains articles on careers, the workplace,
science and health, investments, and personal
relationships. **Freq:** bimonthly. **Price:** included in
membership dues, $5/year for nonmembers.

7309 ■ Monitor
Verite
44 Belchertown Rd.
Amherst, MA 01002
Ph: (413)253-9227
Fax: (413)256-8960
E-mail: verite@verite.org
URL: http://www.verite.org
Descr: Features articles concerning issues about
global labor and manufacturing trends. **Freq:**
quarterly.

**7310 ■ A More Promising Future: Strategies
to Improve the Workplace**
Wider Opportunities for Women
1001 Connecticut Ave. NW, Ste. 930
Washington, DC 20036
Ph: (202)464-1596

E-mail: vstaples@wowonline.org
URL: http://www.wowonline.org

7311 ■ NAPTE Tempo
National Association of Part-Time and Temporary
Employees
5800 Barton, Ste. 201
PO Box 3805
Shawnee, KS 66203
Ph: (913)962-7740
E-mail: napte-champion@worldnet.att.net
URL: http://www.members.tripod.com/~napte
Freq: bimonthly. **Price:** included in membership
dues.

7312 ■ National Job Hotline Directory
Planning Communications
7215 Oak Ave.
River Forest, IL 60305-1935
Ph: (708)366-5200
Free: 888-366-5200
Fax: (708)366-5280
E-mail: info@planningcommunications.com
URL: http://www.planningcommunications.com/jf/
index.htm
Key Personnel: Sue Cubbage, Author; Marcia Williams, Author. **URL(s):** http://www.
planningcommunications.com **Covers:** 6,500 job
telephone hotlines. **Entries include:** Phone number
and description. **Price:** $6.78, individuals, paperback;
plus shipping; $13.18, individuals, hard cover; plus
shipping; $16.95, retail.

7313 ■ National JobBank
Adams Media Corp.
57 Littlefield St.
Avon, MA 02322
Ph: (508)427-7100
Free: 800-872-5627
Fax: 800-872-5628
E-mail: rights@adamsmedia.com
URL: http://www.adamsmedia.com

URL(s): http://www.adamsmedia.com **Covers:** Over
20,000 employers nationwide. **Entries include:** Firm
or organization name, address, local phone, toll-free
phone, fax, contact name and title, description of
organization, headquarters location, names of
management, number of employees, other locations,
subsidiaries, parent company, projected number of
hires, training offered, internships, hours, recorded
jobline, typical titles for common positions, educational backgrounds desired, stock exchange (if
listed), fringe benefits offered. Several state and
regional volumes are available and described
separately. **Freq:** Annual, Latest edition 2008. **Price:**
$475, individuals, payment with order.

7314 ■ National News
National Pensioners and Senior Citizens Federation
44 2nd Ave.
Trenton, ON, Canada K8V 5M6
Ph: (613)394-0739
E-mail: mitchell2@bel.auracom.com
URL: http://npscf.ca
Descr: Contains issues on seniors. **Freq:** quarterly.
Price: $10.

7315 ■ National Right to Work Newsletter
National Right to Work Committee
8001 Braddock Rd., Ste. 500
Springfield, VA 22160
Ph: (703)321-9820
Fax: (703)321-7342
E-mail: members@nrtw.org
URL: http://www.right-to-work.org
Freq: monthly. **Price:** free for members.

**7316 ■ New Guide for Occupational Explora-
tion**
JIST Publishing
875 Montreal Way
Saint Paul, MN 55102
Ph: (317)613-4200
Free: 800-648-5478
Fax: 800-547-8329

E-mail: info@jist.com
URL: http://www.jist.com
Key Personnel: Michael Farr, Author; Laurence Shatkin, PhD, Author. **URL(s):** http://www.jist.com **Publication includes:** List of occupations and job descriptions. Principal content of publication is information on occupational interests and skills, different occupational fields, additional information on the Occupations Information Network, and the Department of Labor's job resource. **Freq:** latest edition 3. **Price:** $49.95, individuals, hardcover; $33.95, individuals, softcover.

7317 ■ The New Relocating Spouse's Guide to Employment
Impact Publications
9104 Manassas Dr., Ste. N
Manassas Park, VA 20111-5211
Ph: (703)361-7300
Free: 800-361-1055
Fax: (703)335-9486
E-mail: info@impactpublications.com
URL: http://www.impactpublications.com
Key Personnel: Frances Bastress, Editor. **URL(s):** http://www.impactpublications.com/ **Entries include:** Organization name, address, phone. Principal content of publication is discussion of the job market, employment trends, and other useful information for those facing a move to a city where they have no job waiting. **Publication includes:** List of 133 professional associations and 54 federal job centers. **Freq:** Irregular, previous edition 1989; latest edition 4th; published 1993. **Price:** $32.95, individuals, hardcover.

7318 ■ New York Generator
Communication Workers of America
Local 1101, CWA, AFL-CIO
275 Seventh Ave., 17th Fl.
New York, NY 10001
Ph: (212)633-2666
Fax: (212)633-8337
URL: http://www.cwa1101.org
Key Personnel: Jack Du Mars, Editor; Tommy Smucker, Editor. **Descr:** Local trade union newspaper. **Freq:** Monthly. **Price:** $12, individuals.

7319 ■ News Byte
Women Employed Institute
111 N Wabash, Ste. 1300
Chicago, IL 60602
Ph: (312)782-3902
Fax: (312)782-5249
E-mail: info@womenemployed.org
URL: http://www.womenemployed.org
Freq: monthly.

7320 ■ News and Views
Construction Employers Association of North Central West Virginia
2794 White Hall Blvd.
White Hall, WV 26554
Ph: (304)367-1290
Fax: (304)367-0126
E-mail: officemgr@ceawv.com
URL: http://www.ceawv.com
Descr: Contains news for association members consisting of local, state, and national items surrounding the construction industry. **Freq:** quarterly. **Price:** free for members.

7321 ■ Newsbyte
Women Employed
111 N Wabash, Ste. 1300
Chicago, IL 60602
Ph: (312)782-3902
Fax: (312)782-5249
E-mail: info@womenemployed.org
URL: http://www.womenemployed.org
Freq: monthly.

7322 ■ NISH News
NISH
8401 Old Courthouse Rd., Ste. 200
Vienna, VA 22182
Ph: (571)226-4660

Fax: (703)849-8916
E-mail: info@nish.org
URL: http://www.nish.org
Descr: Reports on work centers employing persons with severe disabilities, and legislation and regulations affecting these centers. **Freq:** monthly. **Price:** free to participants of the J-W O'Day Program.

7323 ■ Nonprofits Job Finder
Planning Communications
7215 Oak Ave.
River Forest, IL 60305-1935
Ph: (708)366-5200
Free: 888-366-5200
Fax: (708)366-5280
E-mail: info@planningcommunications.com
URL: http://www.planningcommunications.com/jf/index.htm
Key Personnel: Daniel Lauber, Author, dl@planningcommunications.com; Deborah Verlench, Author. **URL(s):** http://www.planningcommunications.com/jf/index.htm **Covers:** Over 1,500 sources of jobs and internships in the nonprofit sector in the U.S., including job matching services, Internet job sites, online job and resume databases, job hotlines, periodicals and directories, salary surveys, and databases. Also includes directories of grant opportunities and coupons for over $225 in discounts on job resources. **Entries include:** For services--Name, sponsor or operator name, address, phone, length of registration period, cost, description (including number of job vacancies listed). For publications--Title, publisher name, address, phone, frequency, price, description (including number of job vacancies listed). **Freq:** Triennial, Latest edition 5th. **Price:** $19.95, individuals, paperback; $32.95, individuals, hardcover.

7324 ■ Occupational Health & Safety
Stevens Publishing Corp.
5151 Beltline Rd., 10th Fl.
Dallas, TX 75254
Ph: (972)687-6700
Fax: (972)687-6799
URL: http://www.stevenspublishing.com/home.html
Key Personnel: Jerry Laws, Editor, jlaws@1105media.com; Lynda Brown, Exec. Asst., lbrown@1105media.com. **URL(s):** http://www.ohsonline.com **Descr:** Magazine covering federal and state regulation of occupational health and safety. **Freq:** Monthly. **Price:** $99, individuals.

7325 ■ Occupational Outlook Handbook
U.S. Bureau of Labor Statistics
2 Massachusetts Ave. NE Ste. 2135
Washington, DC 20212-0001
Ph: (202)691-5200
Fax: (202)691-5745
E-mail: oohinfo@bls.gov
URL: http://www.bls.gov
Key Personnel: Chet Levine, Contact. **URL(s):** http://www.bls.gov/oco/home.htm **Entries include:** For organizations--Organization name, address. Principal content of publication is profiles of various occupations, which include description of occupation, educational requirements, job outlook, and expected earnings. **Publication includes:** Various occupational organizations that provide career information on hundreds of occupations. **Freq:** Biennial, January of even years; latest edition 2008-2009. **Price:** $22, individuals.

7326 ■ Ohio SERB Official Reporter
West Group
6111 Oak Tree Blvd.
PO Box 318063
Cleveland, OH 44131-8063
Ph: (216)520-6407
Fax: (216)520-5655
URL: http://west.thomson.com
URL(s): http://west.thomson.com/store/product.aspx?r=3220&product_id=22119997 **Descr:** Legal

magazine of the Ohio State Employment Relations Board. **Freq:** Monthly. **Price:** $702, individuals.

7327 ■ The Older American
Massachusetts Association of Older Americans
105 Chauncy St., 3rd Fl.
Boston, MA 02111
Ph: (617)426-0804
Fax: (617)426-0070
E-mail: advocacy@MAOAmass.org
Key Personnel: Chet Jakubiak, Editor, cjakubiak@MAOAmass.org **Descr:** Newspaper (tabloid) containing information on issues of concern to the elderly. **Freq:** Quarterly. **Price:** $15, free w/membership; $50, individuals, membership; $50, for organizations.

7328 ■ On Being Alone
AARP Grief and Loss Program
601 E St. NW
Washington, DC 20049
E-mail: ageline@aarp.org
URL: http://www.aarp.org/families/grief_loss
Descr: Provides a comprehensive guide for recently widowed men and women.

7329 ■ OPEDA News
Organization of Professional Employees of the United States Department of Agriculture
PO Box 381
Washington, DC 20044
Ph: (202)720-4898
Fax: (202)720-2799
E-mail: opeda@usda.gov
URL: http://www.usda.gov/opeda
Descr: Covers industry, association and chapter news, and legislative issues. **Freq:** monthly. **ISSN:** 0277-1993.

7330 ■ Oregon Teamster
Joint Council of Teamsters, No. 37
1872 North East 162nd Ave.
Portland, OR 97230-5642
Ph: (503)251-2339
Fax: (503)251-2303
E-mail: oregonteamster37@aol.com
Key Personnel: Mark Davison, Editor. **Descr:** Trade magazine for teamster members and retirees in Oregon, Southwest Washington and Southwest Idaho. **Freq:** Bimonthly. **Price:** Free to qualified subscribers.

7331 ■ Organize
Canadian Union of Public Employees
1375 St. Lauren Blvd.
Ottawa, ON, Canada K1G 0Z7
Ph: (613)237-1590
Fax: (613)237-5508
URL: http://cupe.ca
Freq: periodic.

7332 ■ Our Ontario
Ontario Public Service Employees Union
100 Lesmill Rd.
North York, ON, Canada M3B 3P8
Ph: (416)443-8888
Free: 800-268-7376
Fax: (416)443-9670
E-mail: opseu@opseu.org
URL: http://www.opseu.org
Key Personnel: Katie FitzRandolph, Contact, kfitzrandolph@opseu.org. **URL(s):** http://www.opseu.org/ourontario/index.htm **Descr:** Union magazine. **Freq:** Semiannual. **Price:** Free to qualified subscribers.

7333 ■ PAGES
Mennonite Association of Retired Persons
23 Homestead Dr.
Lancaster, PA 17602
Ph: (717)201-8391
E-mail: marp-soop@juno.com
URL: http://marp.mennonite.net

Freq: quarterly.

7334 ■ Pathways to Career Success for Minorities
CRC Publishing Co. - Eagle Rock Books
PO Box 22583
Kansas City, MO 64113-2583
Ph: (816)361-2059
Free: 800-268-2059
Fax: (816)361-2115
E-mail: crcpub@crn.org
Key Personnel: Tim Schaffert, Editor. **URL(s):** http://eric.ed.gov/ **Entries include:** Name, address, phone, Web address, and description of organization or opportunity. Principal content of publication is essays on minority issues. **Publication includes:** List of financial aid, organizations, and magazines, journals, newspapers, and Websites of relevance to minorities.

7335 ■ Perspective
Canadian Union of Postal Workers
377 Bank St.
Ottawa, ON, Canada K2P 1Y3
Ph: (613)236-7238
Fax: (613)563-7861
URL: http://www.cupw-sttp.org
Freq: bimonthly. **Price:** free.

7336 ■ Peterson's College Money Handbook
Peterson's
Princeton Pike Corporate Ctr.
2000 Lenox Dr.
PO Box 67005
Lawrenceville, NJ 08648
Ph: (609)896-1800
Free: 800-338-3282
Fax: (609)896-4531
E-mail: custsvc@petersons.com
URL: http://www.petersons.com
URL(s): http://www.petersons.com; http://www.petersons.com/books/ **Covers:** Over 2,100 accredited U.S. four-year colleges' costs and financial aid programs, including scholarships, loans, special aid packages, and money-saving options. **Entries include:** College name, address, tuition, fees, room and board, percentage of freshmen applying for and receiving aid, types of scholarships and loans, merit scholarships available. **Freq:** Annual, latest edition 2009. **Price:** $24.32, individuals.

7337 ■ Peterson's Internships
Peterson's
Princeton Pike Corporate Ctr.
2000 Lenox Dr.
PO Box 67005
Lawrenceville, NJ 08648
Ph: (609)896-1800
Free: 800-338-3282
Fax: (609)896-4531
E-mail: custsvc@petersons.com
URL: http://www.petersons.com
URL(s): http://www.petersons.com; http://e-catalog.thomsonlearning.com **Covers:** 50,000 career-oriented internship positions with over 2,000 organizations in the U.S. ranging from business to theater, communications to science. **Entries include:** Company name, address, phone, name and title of contact, types of internships available, number of internships offered, salary where applicable, qualifications, how to apply. **Freq:** Annual, latest edition 25, 2005.

7338 ■ Peterson's Summer Jobs for Students
Peterson's
Princeton Pike Corporate Ctr.
2000 Lenox Dr.
PO Box 67005
Lawrenceville, NJ 08648
Ph: (609)896-1800
Free: 800-338-3282
Fax: (609)896-4531
E-mail: custsvc@petersons.com
URL: http://www.petersons.com
URL(s): http://www.petersons.com/ **Covers:** over 650 camps, resorts, amusement parks, hotels, businesses, national parks, conference and training centers, ranches, and restaurants offering about 45,000 temporary summer jobs; listings are paid. **Entries include:** Name and address, length of employment, pay rate, fringe benefits, duties, qualifications, application deadline and procedure. **Freq:** Annual, Latest edition 2002. **Price:** $13.95, individuals.

7339 ■ Professional and Occupational Licensure in the United States
Greenwood Publishing Group Inc.
88 Post Rd. W
PO Box 5007
Westport, CT 06881
Ph: (203)226-3571
Fax: 877-231-6980
E-mail: webmaster@greenwood.com
URL: http://www.greenwood.com
Key Personnel: Robert L. Hollings, Author; Christal Pike-Nase, Author. **URL(s):** http://www.greenwood.com/catalog/GR0440.aspx **Publication includes:** Lists of state regulation agencies and nongovernmental interest groups. Principal content of publication is a guide to books and articles published since 1960 and pertaining to the practice, regulation, and public impact of professional and occupational licensure. **Price:** $98.95, single issue, Hardcover; $57.95, single issue, UK sterling price.

7340 ■ Professional's Job Finder
Planning Communications
7215 Oak Ave.
River Forest, IL 60305-1935
Ph: (708)366-5200
Free: 888-366-5200
Fax: (708)366-5280
E-mail: projf@planningcommunications.com
URL: http://www.planningcommunications.com/jf/index.htm
Key Personnel: Daniel Lauber, Author, dl@planningcommunications.com. **URL(s):** http://www.planningcommunications.com/jf/index.htm, http://www.planningcommunications.com **Covers:** Over 3,003 sources of jobs in the private sector of the United States, including job matching services, job hotlines, periodicals and directories, Internet job sites, salary surveys, databases, and electronic online job services. Includes coupons for over $200 in discounts and free job resources. **Entries include:** For job services--Name, sponsor or operator name, address, phone, length of registration period, cost, description (including number of job vacancies listed). For publications--Title, publisher name, address, phone, frequency of publication, price, description (including number of job vacancies listed). **Price:** $7.58, individuals, plus shipping charges; paperback; $18.95, retail.

7341 ■ Publications Catalog
Family, Career and Community Leaders of America
1910 Association Dr.
Reston, VA 20191-1584
Ph: (703)476-4900
Fax: (703)860-2713
E-mail: mbenjamin@fcclainc.org
URL: http://www.fcclainc.org
Freq: annual.

7342 ■ Radio Nutricion
Association of Farmworker Opportunity Programs
1726 M St. NW, Ste. 800
Washington, DC 20036
Ph: (202)826-6006
Fax: (202)826-6005
E-mail: afop@afop.org
URL: http://www.afop.org
Price: $50, $25 for supplement.

7343 ■ Reciprocity and Endorsement in Social Work Licensure
Association of Social Work Boards
400 S Ridge Pkwy., Ste. B
Culpeper, VA 22701
Ph: (540)829-6880
Fax: (540)829-0142
E-mail: info@aswb.org
URL: http://www.aswb.org

7344 ■ Regional Officer's Handbook
Family, Career and Community Leaders of America, Missouri
Dept. of Elementary and Secondary Education
PO Box 480
Jefferson City, MO 65102-0480
Ph: (573)751-7964
Fax: (573)526-4261
E-mail: christine.hollingsworth@dese.mo.gov
URL: http://dese.mo.gov/divcareered/fccla.htm

7345 ■ Resource Guide for the Self-Employed
Ingraham Computer Services
13439 Elevation Ln.
Herndon, VA 20171
Ph: (703)318-0634
Fax: (703)318-0634
E-mail: icsdci@erols.com
Key Personnel: Diane Ingraham, Author. **Covers:** 125 nationwide associations, government agencies, periodicals, books, catalogs and online services of interest to self-employed people. **Freq:** Latest edition November 1991; new edition expected.

7346 ■ Retirement Guides
Retirement Knowledge
8652 N Magnolia Ave., Ste. 27
Santee, CA 92071
Ph: (619)449-8833
Fax: (619)449-8868
Descr: 19 guides to retirement services and information for retirees. Each guide contains information specific to the geographic location, including information about health, further education, entertainment, employment, transportation, housing, personal safety, discounts, and more. **Entries include:** Contact details, calendar of events. **Freq:** published in 2002. **Price:** $29.95, Included in membership, per guide.

7347 ■ RILA Report: Human Resources
Retail Industry Leaders Association
1700 N Moore St., Ste. 2250
Arlington, VA 22209
Ph: (703)841-2300
Fax: (703)841-1184
E-mail: erin.byrne@rila.org
URL: http://www.retail-leaders.org
Descr: Covers workforce issues, ranging from retention to performance management systems to diversity issues. **Freq:** quarterly.

7348 ■ Role Delineation Study of Certified Employee Assistance Professionals
Employee Assistance Professionals Association
4350 N Fairfax Dr., Ste. 410
Arlington, VA 22203
Ph: (703)387-1000
Fax: (703)522-4585
E-mail: mbrdatadm@eapassn.org
URL: http://www.eap-association.com
Price: $49/copy.

7349 ■ RWDSU Record
Retail, Wholesale and Dept. Store Union-AFL-CIO
30 E 29th St.
New York, NY 10016
Fax: (212)779-2809
URL: http://www.rwdsu.info/
Key Personnel: Stuart Appelbaum, President. **URL(s):** http://www.rwdsu.info **Descr:** Labor union newspaper. **Freq:** Bimonthly.

7350 ■ Safety+Health
National Safety Council
1121 Spring Lake Dr.
Itasca, IL 60143-3201
Ph: (630)285-1121
Free: 800-621-7615
Fax: (630)285-1315
E-mail: customerservice@nsc.org
URL: http://www.nsc.org

Key Personnel: Suzanne Powills, Publisher, powillss@nsc.org; Tim Hodson, Editor, hodson@nsc.org **Descr:** Publication focusing on workplace safety and health issues. **Freq:** Monthly. **Price:** $56; $5, single issue.

7351 ■ *The Scholarship Advisor*
Random House Inc.
1745 Broadway
New York, NY 10019-4305
Ph: (212)782-9000
Free: 800-733-3000
Fax: (212)572-6066
E-mail: bwaypub@randomhouse.com
URL: http://www.randomhouse.com

Key Personnel: Christopher Vuturo, Editor. **URL(s):** http://www.randomhouse.com/catalog/display. pperl?0375762108 **Covers:** 500,000 scholarships available in the U.S. **Entries include:** Scholarship source, address, requirements. **Price:** $26, individuals.

7352 ■ *Sex Discrimination and the Sexually Charged Work Environment*
National Employment Law Project
80 Maiden Ln., Ste. 601
New York, NY 10038
Ph: (212)285-3025
Fax: (212)285-3044
E-mail: nelp@nelp.org
URL: http://www.nelp.org

7353 ■ *Solidarity*
International Union, U.A.W.
8000 E Jefferson Ave.
Detroit, MI 48214
Ph: (313)926-5000
E-mail: uawsolidarity@uaw.net
URL: http://www.uaw.org

Key Personnel: Larry Gabriel, Editor. **URL(s):** http://www.uaw.org **Descr:** Labor magazine. **Freq:** Bimonthly. **Price:** $5, individuals.

7354 ■ *Staffing Success*
American Staffing Association
277 S Washington St., Ste. 200
Alexandria, VA 22314-3675
Ph: (703)253-2020
Fax: (703)253-2053
E-mail: asa@americanstaffing.net
URL: http://www.americanstaffing.net

Descr: Monitors current trends in the industry, each issue focusing on a specific topic; also covers association activities; contains book reviews. **Freq:** bimonthly. **Price:** $360/year for nonmembers, $90/year for members, $120/year for business and education industry.

7355 ■ *Staffing Week*
American Staffing Association
277 S Washington St., Ste. 200
Alexandria, VA 22314-3675
Ph: (703)253-2020
Fax: (703)253-2053
E-mail: asa@americanstaffing.net
URL: http://www.americanstaffing.net
Freq: weekly.

7356 ■ *State Advisers' Bulletin*
Family, Career and Community Leaders of America
1910 Association Dr.
Reston, VA 20191-1584
Ph: (703)476-4900
Fax: (703)860-2713
E-mail: mbenjamin@fcclainc.org
URL: http://www.fcclainc.org
Freq: 11/year.

7357 ■ *Stewards Manual*
SEIU, District 925, AFL-CIO
3647 Stone Way N
Seattle, WA 98103
Ph: (206)322-3010
Fax: (206)632-7219

E-mail: kcook@seiu925.org
URL: http://www.seiu925.org

7358 ■ *Study of Whistleblower Protections for Federal Employees*
Government Accountability Project
1612 K St. NW, Ste. 1100
Washington, DC 20006
Ph: (202)408-0034
E-mail: info@whistleblower.org
URL: http://www.whistleblower.org

7359 ■ *Summary of Labor Arbitration Awards*
American Arbitration Association
1633 Broadway, Fl. 10
New York, NY 10019
Ph: (212)716-5800
Free: 800-778-7879
Fax: (212)716-5905
E-mail: websitemail@adr.org
URL: http://www.adr.org

URL(s): http://www.adr.org/publicationsorder.asp **Descr:** Periodical covering private sector arbitration decisions and collective bargaining issues. **Freq:** Monthly. **Price:** $142, individuals.

7360 ■ *Sweatshop Alert*
Canadian Labour Congress
2841 Riverside Dr.
Ottawa, ON, Canada K1V 8X7
Ph: (613)521-3400
Fax: (613)521-4655
E-mail: president@clc-ctc.ca
URL: http://www.clc-ctc.ca
Freq: periodic.

7361 ■ *A Taste of English*
Association of Farmworker Opportunity Programs
1726 M St. NW, Ste. 800
Washington, DC 20036
Ph: (202)826-6006
Fax: (202)826-6005
E-mail: afop@afop.org
URL: http://www.afop.org
Price: $125 1 teacher's manual and 5 student workbooks, $25 teacher's manual, $12 student workbook.

7362 ■ *They Make That Much*
Families U.S.A. Foundation
1201 New York Ave. NW, Ste. 1100
Washington, DC 20005-6100
Ph: (202)628-3030
Fax: (202)347-2417
E-mail: info@familiesusa.org
URL: http://www.familiesusa.org

Descr: Contains salaries of medical specialists, CEOs of drug and insurance companies and large hospitals. **Price:** $5.

7363 ■ *TNG Canada Today*
Communications Workers of America/Canada
7B-1050 Baxter Rd.
Ottawa, ON, Canada K2C 3P1
Ph: (613)820-9777
Fax: (613)820-8188
E-mail: info@cwa-scacanada.ca
URL: http://www.cwa-scacanada.ca
Freq: monthly.

7364 ■ *UI Bulletin*
Canadian Labour Congress
2841 Riverside Dr.
Ottawa, ON, Canada K1V 8X7
Ph: (613)521-3400
Fax: (613)521-4655
E-mail: president@clc-ctc.ca
URL: http://www.clc-ctc.ca
Freq: periodic.

7365 ■ *Union Advocate*
Union Advocate
411 Main St.
Rm. 202
Saint Paul, MN 55102-1044
Ph: (651)222-3787

Fax: (651)293-1989
E-mail: advocate@mtn.org
Key Personnel: Michael Kuchta, Editor. **Descr:** Labor newspaper. **Freq:** Semimonthly. **Price:** $15.00.

7366 ■ *The Union Register*
Western Council of Industrial Workers, AFL-CIO
12788 SE Stark St.
Portland, OR 97233-1539
Ph: (503)228-0235
Fax: (503)228-0245
URL: http://www.wciw.org/
URL(s): http://www.wciw.org/ **Descr:** Labor tabloid. **Freq:** Bimonthly.

7367 ■ *UTU News*
United Transportation Union
14600 Detroit Ave.
Cleveland, OH 44107-4250
Ph: (216)228-9400
Fax: (216)228-5755
E-mail: utunews@utu.org
URL: http://www.utu.org/worksite/contactoffice.htm
URL(s): http://www.utu.org/worksite/utunewsonline.htm **Descr:** Railroad, mass transit bus and other transportation labor newspaper (tabloid). **Freq:** 11/yr. **Price:** controlled.

7368 ■ *VGM's Careers Encyclopedia*
VGM Career Horizons
4255 W Touhy Ave.
Lincolnwood, IL 60646-1975
Ph: (847)679-5500
Free: 800-323-4900
Fax: (847)679-2494

Entries include: Association name, address. Principal content is information on 200 careers, including qualifications needed, educational requirements, and salary. Publisher also offers catalog cards kits for this title, 89 cents each. **Publication includes:** List of over 200 professional associations that provide career guidance information. **Freq:** Irregular, latest edition 5th, 2001; previous edition 1997. **Price:** $39.95, individuals.

7369 ■ *Vista Magazine—The Hispanic Scholarship Guide Issue*
Vista Magazine
1201 Brickell Ave., Ste. 360
Miami, FL 33131
Ph: (305)416-4644
Fax: (305)416-4344
E-mail: editor@vistamagazine.com
URL: http://www.vistamagazine.com
Covers: Scholarship opportunities for Hispanic Americans. **Freq:** Annual, August.

7370 ■ *Washington Bulletin*
Employee Benefit Research Institute
1100 13th St. NW, Ste. 878
Washington, DC 20005-4058
Ph: (202)659-0670
Fax: (202)775-6312
E-mail: info@ebri.org
URL: http://www.ebri.org

Descr: Includes information on congressional activities as they relate to employee benefits. **Freq:** biweekly. **Price:** included in membership dues.

7371 ■ *Weddle's Job-seekers Guide to Employment Web Sites*
AMACOM
1601 Broadway
New York, NY 10019-7434
Ph: (212)903-8060
Free: 877-566-9441
Fax: (518)891-0368
E-mail: customerservice@amanet.org
URL: http://www.amacombooks.org

Key Personnel: Peter D. Weddle, Author. **URL(s):** http://www.weddles.com/ **Covers:** Approximately 350 job-related Websites. **Entries include:** Site profile including occupations and industries represented, what types of jobs are posted on site, top salary ranges, regional territory, and links to relevant sites.

Freq: Latest edition 7, 2005/2006. **Price:** $12.95, individuals.

7372 ■ The Well Workplace
Wellness Councils of America
9802 Nicholas St., Ste. 315
Omaha, NE 68114
Ph: (402)827-3590
Fax: (402)827-3594
E-mail: wellworkplace@welcoa.org
URL: http://www.welcoa.org
Freq: monthly. **Price:** $.29/copy (minimum of 10).

7373 ■ What Every Employee Should Know About Alcohol Abuse: Answer to 25 Good Questions
Institute for a Drug-Free Workplace
8614 Westwood Center Dr., Ste. 950
Vienna, VA 22182
Ph: (703)288-4300
URL: http://www.drugfreeworkplace.org
Price: $2.30.

7374 ■ Women Employed News
Women Employed
111 N Wabash, Ste. 1300
Chicago, IL 60602
Ph: (312)782-3902
Fax: (312)782-5249
E-mail: info@womenemployed.org
URL: http://www.womenemployed.org
Freq: quarterly. **Price:** included in membership dues.

7375 ■ Women at Work
Wider Opportunities for Women
1001 Connecticut Ave. NW, Ste. 930
Washington, DC 20036
Ph: (202)464-1596
E-mail: vstaples@wowonline.org
URL: http://www.wowonline.org
Freq: quarterly.

7376 ■ Work-at-Home Sourcebook
Live Oak Publications
6003 N 51st St. No. 105
PO Box 2193
Boulder, CO 80306
URL: http://www.asaga.com/Info_NationalResources.html
URL(s): http://www.workathomesourcebook.com
Covers: Over 1,000 companies and home business franchises that employ home workers. **Entries include:** Company name, address, contact person, description of job position, pay scale, requirements, equipment, and training provided. **Freq:** latest edition 2002. **Price:** $12.97, individuals.

7377 ■ Work and Family in America
ABC-CLIO
130 Cremona Dr.
PO Box 1911
Santa Barbara, CA 93117-5599
Ph: (805)968-1911
Free: 800-368-6868
Fax: (805)685-9685
E-mail: customerservice@abc-clio.com
URL: http://www.abc-clio.com
Key Personnel: Leslie F. Stebbins, Author. **URL(s):** http://www.abc-clio.com/products/overview.aspx?productid=109734 **Descr:** Provides an overview of topics relating to families and the workplace since 1977. **Publication includes:** A directory of agencies and organizations working with work and family issues. **Price:** $45, individuals, print; $31.95, individuals.

7378 ■ Workers Compensation Data Reporting Handbook
Workers Compensation Insurance Organizations
Pennsylvania Compensation Rating Bur.
One S Penn Sq., Widener Bldg., 6th Fl.
Philadelphia, PA 19107-3577
Ph: (215)568-2371
E-mail: bpiacentino@pcrb.com
URL: http://www.iisprojects.com/WCIO

Descr: Serves as a guideline and reference for industry professionals.

7379 ■ Workers Compensation Data Specifications Manual
Workers Compensation Insurance Organizations
Pennsylvania Compensation Rating Bur.
One S Penn Sq., Widener Bldg., 6th Fl.
Philadelphia, PA 19107-3577
Ph: (215)568-2371
E-mail: bpiacentino@pcrb.com
URL: http://www.iisprojects.com/WCIO
Descr: Contains compilation of electronic and hard copy specifications developed under the direction of the managers of DCOs.

7380 ■ Workers' Compensation Journal of Ohio
West Group
6111 Oak Tree Blvd.
PO Box 318063
Cleveland, OH 44131-8063
Ph: (216)520-6407
Fax: (216)520-5655
URL: http://west.thomson.com
URL(s): http://west.thomson.com/store/product.aspx?r=2996&product_id=22114553 **Descr:** Journal covering new developments in workers' compensation and intentional tort law in Ohio. **Freq:** Bimonthly. **Price:** $369.96, individuals.

7381 ■ Workers and Families: A Policy Guide for Employers
Women Employed Institute
111 N Wabash, Ste. 1300
Chicago, IL 60602
Ph: (312)782-3902
Fax: (312)782-5249
E-mail: info@womenemployed.org
URL: http://www.womenemployed.org

7382 ■ Workers World
WW Publishers Inc.
55 W 17th St.
New York, NY 10011
Ph: (212)627-2994
Fax: (212)675-7869
E-mail: wwp@workers.org
URL: http://www.workers.org/wwp/
Key Personnel: Deirdre Griswold, Editor. **URL(s):** http://www.workers.org/wwp/ **Descr:** Community newspaper covering labor, economics, politics and government. **Freq:** Weekly. **Price:** $25, individuals, new; $25, individuals, renewal; $40, other countries, surface mail; $100, other countries, airmail.

7383 ■ Working Age
AARP
601 E St. NW
Washington, DC 20049
Ph: (202)434-2560
E-mail: member@aarp.org
URL: http://www.aarp.org
Descr: Includes research reports, case studies, legislative updates, and calendar of events. **Freq:** bimonthly. **Price:** free. **ISSN:** 0883-2714.

7384 ■ Working Out
Out and Equal Workplace Advocates
155 Sansome St., Ste. 450
San Francisco, CA 94104
Ph: (415)694-6500
Fax: (415)694-6530
E-mail: info@outandequal.org
URL: http://www.outandequal.org

7385 ■ Working USA
Blackwell Publishing Inc.
Wiley-Blackwell
350 Main St., Commerce Pl.
Malden, MA 02148
Ph: (781)388-8200
Fax: (781)388-8210
URL: http://www.blackwellpublishing.com/
Key Personnel: Heather Boushey, Assoc. Ed.; Immanuel Ness, Editor, iness@igc.org. **URL(s):** http://www.wiley.com/bw/journal.asp?ref=1089-

7011&site=1 **Descr:** Periodical focusing on the labor movement and related topics. **Freq:** Quarterly. **Price:** $47, individuals, print and online; $334, institutions, print and online; $304, institutions, online, print.

7386 ■ Workplace Health & Safety Sourcebook
Omnigraphics Inc.
PO Box 31-1640
Detroit, MI 48231
Free: 800-234-1340
E-mail: info@omnigraphics.com
URL: http://www.omnigraphics.com
Key Personnel: Chad T. Kimball, Editor. **URL(s):** http://www.omnigraphics.com **Publication includes:** List of organizational resources with Web address and email. Principal content of publication is information on workplace health and safety basics, lung issues, skin and eye issues, noise and hearing issues, preventing work-related musculoskeletal disorders, infectious disease issues, toxins and hazardous chemicals in the workplace, pregnancy issues, protective equipment, workplace violence, and child labor issues. **Price:** $84, individuals, hardcover.

7387 ■ Workplace Week
Workplace Fairness
2031 Florida Ave. NW, Ste. 500
Washington, DC 20009
Ph: (202)243-7660
Fax: (240)282-8801
URL: http://www.workplacefairness.org
Descr: Covers news and commentary on critical issues affecting employees and their advocates.

Multimedia Resources

7388 ■ Access Denied
Commonwealth Films, Inc.
223 Commonwealth Ave
Boston, MA 02116
Ph: (617)262-5634
Fax: (617)262-6948
E-mail: info@commonwealthfilms.com
URL: http://www.commonwealthfilms.com
Format(s): Videocassette. **Descr:** Deals with the issue of computer security in the corporate environment. Maintains that access issues are fundamental to computer crime. Provides tips on how to reduce chance of system infiltration. **Prod. Date:** 19??. **Length:** 23. **Price:** $525.

7389 ■ Accident Investigation: A Tool for Effective Prevention
LearnCom HR Consulting and Training
38 Discovery, Ste. 250
Irvine, CA 92618
Ph: (515)440-0890
Free: 800-698-8263
Fax: (515)221-3149
E-mail: nhartline@learncom.com
URL: http://www.learncomhr.com
Format(s): Videocassette. **Descr:** Provides accident investigation techniques for supervisors and managers. Includes Leader's Guide. **Prod. Date:** 1992. **Length:** 13.

7390 ■ And Then There Was One
LearnCom HR Consulting and Training
38 Discovery, Ste. 250
Irvine, CA 92618
Ph: (515)440-0890
Free: 800-698-8263
Fax: (515)221-3149
E-mail: nhartline@learncom.com
URL: http://www.learncomhr.com
Format(s): Videocassette. **Descr:** A look at the effect of accidents on the families of workers, using four case studies. The importance of safety awareness, protective equipment and understanding

potential hazards are all emphasized. **Prod. Date:** 1991. **Price:** $175.

7391 ■ *The Art of Resolving Conflicts in the Workplace*
Kantola Productions, LLC
55 Sunnyside Ave
Mill Valley, CA 94941-1935
Ph: (415)381-9363
Free: 800-989-8273
Fax: (415)381-9801
E-mail: info@kantola.com
URL: http://kantola.com
Format(s): Videocassette. **Descr:** Presents strategies for dealing with contention and conflict in the workplace brought about by growth and change, including segments on building cooperation, handling non-performing coworkers and resolving conflicting job assignments. Includes study guide. **Prod. Date:** 2000. **Length:** 37. **Price:** $89.95.

7392 ■ *Back Basics*
Williams Learning Network
15400 Calhoun Dr
Rockville, MD 20855-2762
Ph: (301)315-6700
Free: 800-848-1717
Fax: (301)315-6880
E-mail: mait@willearn.com
URL: http://www.willearn.com
Format(s): Videocassette. **Descr:** Provides information on back injuries and how to avoid them in the workplace. Covers three areas: good posture, proper lifting techniques, and exercise. Includes Leader's Guide and 25 Program Guides. **Length:** 14.

7393 ■ *Back to Basics for Safe Lifting*
Aspen Publishers
7201 McKinney Circ
Frederick, MD 21704
Ph: (301)644-3599
Free: 800-638-8437
Fax: (301)644-3550
URL: http://www.aspenpublishers.com
Format(s): Videocassette. **Descr:** A cautionary film for businesses about proper procedures for lifting heavy objects. **Prod. Date:** 1984. **Length:** 21. **Price:** $495.

7394 ■ *Back in Business*
LearnCom HR Consulting and Training
38 Discovery, Ste. 250
Irvine, CA 92618
Ph: (515)440-0890
Free: 800-698-8263
Fax: (515)221-3149
E-mail: nhartline@learncom.com
URL: http://www.learncomhr.com
Format(s): Videocassette. **Descr:** A look at the ergonomics of back problems, including causes, symptoms, and remedies. Designed to help train workers to find ways of preventing back stress and injuries. A leader's guide and participants' workbooks are included. **Prod. Date:** 1990. **Length:** 16. **Price:** $175.

7395 ■ *Back Care for Maritime Industry*
John Sabella & Associate
805 W. Emerson St
Seattle, WA 98119
Ph: (206)281-8626
Fax: (206)217-0899
E-mail: sales@johnsabella.com
URL: http://www.johnsabella.com
Format(s): Videocassette. **Descr:** Educates production and supervisory personnel on the hows and whys of back care and safety. Offers workers a visual guide to protecting themselves and provides supervisory personnel with an idea of the costs associated with back injuries, as well as a real-world program for reducing back injury risks. **Prod. Date:** 2000. **Price:** $225.

7396 ■ *The Banana Verdict*
Filmakers Library, Inc.
124 E. 40th St

New York, NY 10016
Ph: (212)808-4980
Free: 800-555-9815
Fax: (212)808-4983
E-mail: info@filmakers.com
URL: http://www.filmakers.com
Format(s): Videocassette. **Descr:** Documentary of the international banana trade. Raises issues of environmental and worker safety, labor unions, management, and business concerns. **Prod. Date:** 2000. **Length:** 50. **Price:** $350.

7397 ■ *Brace Your Space: Earthquake Safety in the Work Environment*
University of California Extension Ctr. for Media & Independent Learning
2000 Center St., 4th Fl
Berkeley, CA 94704
Ph: (510)642-0460
Fax: (510)643-9271
E-mail: mediaservices@ucxonline.berkeley.edu
URL: http://ucmedia1.ucxonline.berkeley.edu
Format(s): Videocassette. **Descr:** Uses earthquake footage from the 1989 Loma Prieta quake to demonstrate the need for seismic safety in the school and business workplace, including the three basic principles of earthquake workplace safety and simple techniques for bracing and securing common office equipment and furnishings. **Prod. Date:** 1993. **Length:** 15. **Price:** $150.00.

7398 ■ *Chemical Protective Clothing*
Emergency Film Group
Detrick Lawrence Corp
PO Box 1928
Edgartown, MA 02539
Ph: (508)627-8844
Free: 800-842-0999
Fax: (508)627-8863
E-mail: info@efilmgroup.com
URL: http://www.efilmgroup.com
Format(s): Videocassette. **Descr:** Discusses how to select, use, and maintain chemical protective clothing to make workers and emergency response crews safe. Accompanying book gives guidelines for a five-hour training program. **Prod. Date:** 1992. **Length:** 29.

7399 ■ *CHEMSAFE*
LearnCom HR Consulting and Training
38 Discovery, Ste. 250
Irvine, CA 92618
Ph: (515)440-0890
Free: 800-698-8263
Fax: (515)221-3149
E-mail: nhartline@learncom.com
URL: http://www.learncomhr.com
Format(s): Videocassette. **Descr:** A nine-module program designed to help companies comply with OSHA's Hazard Communication Standard. Each module covers a different type of chemical hazard. A leader's guide and participants' handouts are included. **Prod. Date:** 1991. **Price:** $175.

7400 ■ *Common Mistakes People Make in Interviews*
Zenger Media
10200 Jefferson Blvd
Box 802
Culver City, CA 90232
Ph: (310)839-2436
Free: 800-421-4246
Fax: (310)839-2249
E-mail: service@zengermedia.com
URL: http://zengermedia.com
Format(s): Videocassette. **Descr:** Uses a right way/wrong way scenario to show the best way to approach an interview, ways to prepare and follow up. **Length:** 40. **Price:** $79.95.

7401 ■ *Communicating PSM to Workers*
Williams Learning Network
15400 Calhoun Dr
Rockville, MD 20855-2762
Ph: (301)315-6700
Free: 800-848-1717

Fax: (301)315-6880
E-mail: mait@willearn.com
URL: http://www.willearn.com
Format(s): Videocassette. **Descr:** Details how to communicate process safety management results to workers. Emphasis is placed on contractor personnel. Includes Leader's Guide and 25 Program Guides. **Prod. Date:** 19??. **Length:** 9.

7402 ■ *Confined Space Entry*
Media Resources, Inc.
9012-B NW Holly Rd
Bremerton, WA 98321
Ph: (360)693-3344
Free: 800-666-0106
Fax: (360)693-1760
Format(s): Videocassette. **Descr:** Designed to help train workers on OSHA's proposed rule on Permit Required Confined Spaces. Includes information on pre-entry procedures, testing the atmosphere, self-rescue and more. Instructor guide, discussion questions and a quiz are included. **Prod. Date:** 1992. **Length:** 30. **Price:** $295.

7403 ■ *Confined Space Rescue*
Media Resources, Inc.
9012-B NW Holly Rd
Bremerton, WA 98321
Ph: (360)693-3344
Free: 800-666-0106
Fax: (360)693-1760
Format(s): Videocassette. **Descr:** Designed to train fire departments and businesses in OSHA's Permit Required Confined Spaces. Includes information on entering confined spaces, preparing protective clothing and respiratory protection, preparing a pre-incident plan and more. Instructor guide, discussion questions and a quiz are included. **Prod. Date:** 1992. **Length:** 30. **Price:** $150.

7404 ■ *Confined Space Training: A Program for Everyone*
LearnCom HR Consulting and Training
38 Discovery, Ste. 250
Irvine, CA 92618
Ph: (515)440-0890
Free: 800-698-8263
Fax: (515)221-3149
E-mail: nhartline@learncom.com
URL: http://www.learncomhr.com
Format(s): Videocassette. **Descr:** Two-part training program designed to make all workers aware of the dangers of confined spaces and the proper procedures to follow if they encounter emergency situations. Module 1 discusses the hazards that exist for the untrained and the permit violator. Module 2 illustrates the procedures to follow for these confined spaces. Includes Trainer's Manual and Employee Manual. **Prod. Date:** 1992. **Length:** 37.

7405 ■ *Confined Spaces, Deadly Places*
LearnCom HR Consulting and Training
38 Discovery, Ste. 250
Irvine, CA 92618
Ph: (515)440-0890
Free: 800-698-8263
Fax: (515)221-3149
E-mail: nhartline@learncom.com
URL: http://www.learncomhr.com
Format(s): Videocassette. **Descr:** Based on real-life incidents, trainees learn what hazzards threaten confined work space. Emphasis is given to how rescuers can also become victims of these hazards. Includes a trainer's manual and 10 employee manuals. Also available as part of the two-part series "Confined Space Training: A Program For Everyone." **Length:** 21. **Price:** $495.

7406 ■ *Control Factor: Overhead Hoists and Cranes (7ER-J01)*
Thomson National Education Training Group (NETg)
14624 N. Scottsdale Rd., Ste. 300
Phoenix, AZ 85254
Ph: (480)315-4000
Free: 800-265-1900

Fax: (480)315-4001
E-mail: info@netg.com
URL: http://www.netg.com
Format(s): Videocassette. **Descr:** Part of an integrated course which helps employees adhere to safety standards by giving them relevant information that can be applied to their jobs. **Prod. Date:** 1979. **Length:** 30.

7407 ■ *Danger If You Don't: Lockout/Tagout*
LearnCom HR Consulting and Training
38 Discovery, Ste. 250
Irvine, CA 92618
Ph: (515)440-0890
Free: 800-698-8263
Fax: (515)221-3149
E-mail: nhartline@learncom.com
URL: http://www.learncomhr.com
Format(s): Videocassette. **Descr:** A video program to train workers in the procedures for isolating hazardous materials, equipment, and energy sources during emergencies. A leader's guide and participants' workbooks are included. **Prod. Date:** 1991. **Length:** 12. **Price:** $175.

7408 ■ *Death on the Job*
Direct Cinema Ltd.
PO Box 10003
Santa Monica, CA 90410-1003
Ph: (310)636-8200
Free: 800-525-0000
Fax: (310)636-8228
E-mail: orders@directcinemalimited.com
URL: http://www.directcinema.com
Format(s): Videocassette. **Descr:** Industrial accidents claim about 10,000 lives/year, mainly because safety is a low priority at many businesses. Dramatic footage includes chemical plant explosion, shot by friends of the worker who was killed. Originally aired on HBO. Includes interviews. **Prod. Date:** 1993. **Length:** 48. **Price:** $495.

7409 ■ *Drum and Cylinder Handling*
Williams Learning Network
15400 Calhoun Dr
Rockville, MD 20855-2762
Ph: (301)315-6700
Free: 800-848-1717
Fax: (301)315-6880
E-mail: mait@willearn.com
URL: http://www.willearn.com
Format(s): Videocassette. **Descr:** Outlines safe techniques for moving drums and cylinders, preparing them for use, and removing them when they are empty. Includes Leader's Guide and 25 Program Guides. **Length:** 17.

7410 ■ *Working Safely with Electricity*
Bergwall Productions, Inc.
1224 Baltimore Pike, Ste. 203
Kennett Square, PA 19317
Ph: (610)361-0334
Free: 800-934-8696
Fax: (610)361-0092
E-mail: bergwall@bergwall.com
URL: http://www.bergwall.com
Format(s): Videocassette. **Descr:** Workers who treat hazardous materials carelessly may benefit from the concepts of electricity presented in this program. Details what happens when electrical currents flow through the body. Introduces the concepts of grounding and outlines proper emergency response. Available in English and Spanish. **Prod. Date:** 1992. **Length:** 64. **Price:** $329.

7411 ■ *Enclosed Space Entry*
John Sabella & Associate
805 W. Emerson St
Seattle, WA 98119
Ph: (206)281-8626
Fax: (206)217-0899
E-mail: sales@johnsabella.com
URL: http://www.johnsabella.com
Format(s): Videocassette. **Descr:** Explains hazards of confined or enclosed work spaces, personal

protective equipment, testing procedures, hot work and emergency procedures. **Price:** $125.

7412 ■ *Ergonomic Economics*
Williams Learning Network
15400 Calhoun Dr
Rockville, MD 20855-2762
Ph: (301)315-6700
Free: 800-848-1717
Fax: (301)315-6880
E-mail: mait@willearn.com
URL: http://www.willearn.com
Format(s): Videocassette. **Descr:** Eight-part program aimed at management and supervisory personnel who are in charge of worker-safety and ergonomic hazards. Covers adequate work station and task design and proper material handling equipment. Furnishes definitions, medical aspects, and workplace accident statistics. Includes Leader's Guide and 25 Program Guides. **Length:** 38.

7413 ■ *Ergonomics: Video Display Terminals*
LearnCom HR Consulting and Training
38 Discovery, Ste. 250
Irvine, CA 92618
Ph: (515)440-0890
Free: 800-698-8263
Fax: (515)221-3149
E-mail: nhartline@learncom.com
URL: http://www.learncomhr.com
Format(s): Videocassette. **Descr:** A presentation on how to set up a Video Display Terminal in such a way as to eliminate physical stress. Features a demonstration of five exercises to relieve stress. A leader's guide and workbooks are included. **Prod. Date:** 1991. **Price:** $175.

7414 ■ *Ergonomics and You*
Williams Learning Network
15400 Calhoun Dr
Rockville, MD 20855-2762
Ph: (301)315-6700
Free: 800-848-1717
Fax: (301)315-6880
E-mail: mait@willearn.com
URL: http://www.willearn.com
Format(s): Videocassette. **Descr:** Outlines the major causes of stress and injuries in the workplace and provides simple stretching and strengthening exercises that can be done on the job in just a few minutes. Covers sitting, standing, and lifting. Includes Leader's Guide and 25 Program Guides. **Length:** 20.

7415 ■ *The Extra Step*
E-mail: info@leomedia.net
URL: http://www.leomedia.net
Format(s): Videocassette. **Descr:** A program for both new and veteran employees about the potential danger in handling and working around chemicals. Emphasizes the need for proper safety attitudes and the importance of personal protection from chemical hazards. **Length:** 15. **Price:** $445.

7416 ■ *Fatal Distraction*
Bergwall Productions, Inc.
1224 Baltimore Pike, Ste. 203
Kennett Square, PA 19317
Ph: (610)361-0334
Free: 800-934-8696
Fax: (610)361-0092
E-mail: bergwall@bergwall.com
URL: http://www.bergwall.com
Format(s): Videocassette. **Descr:** Outlines the disastrous results caused by industrial workers forced to work over the Christmas holidays who cut corners dangerously so they can get home early. **Prod. Date:** 1992. **Length:** 9. **Price:** $69.

7417 ■ *Fire Basics in the Workplace*
LearnCom HR Consulting and Training
38 Discovery, Ste. 250
Irvine, CA 92618
Ph: (515)440-0890
Free: 800-698-8263
Fax: (515)221-3149

E-mail: nhartline@learncom.com
URL: http://www.learncomhr.com
Format(s): Videocassette. **Descr:** A step-by-step guide to the proper use of fire extinguishers combined with basic fire prevention. Includes a leader's guide. **Prod. Date:** 19??. **Length:** 18. **Price:** $395.00.

7418 ■ *Fire in the Workplace*
The Idea Bank
1139 Alameda Padre Serra
Santa Barbara, CA 93103
Free: 800-621-1136
Fax: (805)965-2275
E-mail: info@theideabank.com
URL: http://www.theideabank.com
Format(s): Videocassette. **Descr:** Outlines the ways managers and employers can prevent fires and save lives in the event of a blaze. Combines expert interviews with on-scene footage of fire disasters. Comes with reproducible reference guides. **Prod. Date:** 1994. **Length:** 25. **Price:** $195.00.

7419 ■ *Flexible Work Options*
Tapeworm Video Distributors
27833 Hopkins Ave., Unit 6
Valencia, CA 91355
Ph: (661)257-4904
Fax: (661)257-4820
E-mail: sales@tapeworm.com
URL: http://www.tapeworm.com
Format(s): Videocassette. **Descr:** A guide for working parents designed to help organize work schedules in order to make the most of personal time. Uses real life scenarios that working parents often encounter. **Prod. Date:** 1998. **Length:** 50. **Price:** $24.95.

7420 ■ *Forklift Basics*
Williams Learning Network
15400 Calhoun Dr
Rockville, MD 20855-2762
Ph: (301)315-6700
Free: 800-848-1717
Fax: (301)315-6880
E-mail: mait@willearn.com
URL: http://www.willearn.com
Format(s): Videocassette. **Descr:** Outlines the forklift and discusses the different types of forklifts, their uses, and important safety procedures that help to decrease injury to the operator and others. Covers narrow aisle straddlers, pallet jacks, standees, nameplate specs, start-up checks, seat belts, and rear wheel steering. Includes Leader's Guide and 25 Program Guides. **Length:** 18.

7421 ■ *Forklift Inspection Training*
LearnCom HR Consulting and Training
38 Discovery, Ste. 250
Irvine, CA 92618
Ph: (515)440-0890
Free: 800-698-8263
Fax: (515)221-3149
E-mail: nhartline@learncom.com
URL: http://www.learncomhr.com
Format(s): Videocassette. **Descr:** Forklift safety and inspection procedures are demonstrated and outlined for employees. Includes a leader's guide. **Length:** 23. **Price:** $295.

7422 ■ *Forklifts*
LearnCom HR Consulting and Training
38 Discovery, Ste. 250
Irvine, CA 92618
Ph: (515)440-0890
Free: 800-698-8263
Fax: (515)221-3149
E-mail: nhartline@learncom.com
URL: http://www.learncomhr.com
Format(s): Videocassette. **Descr:** A step-by-step overview of safe forklift operation that stresses proper maintenance and inspection, as well as good

driving habits. Includes a leader's guide and 10 workbooks. **Length:** 11. **Price:** $295.

7423 ■ *Goin' Through the Motions*
LearnCom HR Consulting and Training
38 Discovery, Ste. 250
Irvine, CA 92618
Ph: (515)440-0890
Free: 800-698-8263
Fax: (515)221-3149
E-mail: nhartline@learncom.com
URL: http://www.learncomhr.com

Format(s): Videocassette. **Descr:** A two-part program designed to help prevent repetitive motion disorders. Part I is for the employee, and Part II is for supervisors. **Prod. Date:** 1991. **Price:** $175.

7424 ■ *Good Housekeeping*
Williams Learning Network
15400 Calhoun Dr
Rockville, MD 20855-2762
Ph: (301)315-6700
Free: 800-848-1717
Fax: (301)315-6880
E-mail: mait@willearn.com
URL: http://www.willearn.com

Format(s): Videocassette. **Descr:** Stresses the importance of good housekeeping procedures in keeping a safe work environment. Covers spills, trash, flammable materials, good lighting, nameplates, labels and signs, tools, and packing materials. Includes Leader's Guide and 25 Program Guides. **Length:** 4.

7425 ■ *Gravity Flow and Hydraulic Conveying of Bulk Solids*
Williams Learning Network
15400 Calhoun Dr
Rockville, MD 20855-2762
Ph: (301)315-6700
Free: 800-848-1717
Fax: (301)315-6880
E-mail: mait@willearn.com
URL: http://www.willearn.com

Format(s): Videocassette. **Descr:** Explains two bulk solid handling systems: the gravity flow system and the hydraulic conveying system. Discusses the various safety problems associated with each system and how to shut down each. Includes Leader's Guide and 25 Program Guides. **Length:** 10.

7426 ■ *Handling Bulk Liquids in Barges*
Williams Learning Network
15400 Calhoun Dr
Rockville, MD 20855-2762
Ph: (301)315-6700
Free: 800-848-1717
Fax: (301)315-6880
E-mail: mait@willearn.com
URL: http://www.willearn.com

Format(s): Videocassette. **Descr:** Profiles the typical steps in product transfer, centering on the numerous slip, trip, and fall hazards associated with barge transfers. Covers unique safety hazards, unique safety equipment, and safe transfers involved with the use of a barge for bulk liquid transport. Includes Leader's Guide and 25 Program Guides. **Length:** 10.

7427 ■ *Handling Bulk Liquids in Tank Cars*
Williams Learning Network
15400 Calhoun Dr
Rockville, MD 20855-2762
Ph: (301)315-6700
Free: 800-848-1717
Fax: (301)315-6880
E-mail: mait@willearn.com
URL: http://www.willearn.com

Format(s): Videocassette. **Descr:** Illustrates the features of a tank car for use in transporting bulk liquids. Provides step-by-step example for loading bulk liquids into a tank car. Also discusses other load-

ing and unloading techniques. Includes Leader's Guide and 25 Program Guides. **Length:** 17.

7428 ■ *Handling Bulk Liquids in Tank Trucks*
Williams Learning Network
15400 Calhoun Dr
Rockville, MD 20855-2762
Ph: (301)315-6700
Free: 800-848-1717
Fax: (301)315-6880
E-mail: mait@willearn.com
URL: http://www.willearn.com

Format(s): Videocassette. **Descr:** Details the main features of a typical tank truck and explains procedures for various loading and unloading techniques. Provides step-by-step examples of loading and unloading procedures. Includes Leader's Guide and 25 Program Guides. **Length:** 15.

7429 ■ *Handling Bulk Solids*
Williams Learning Network
15400 Calhoun Dr
Rockville, MD 20855-2762
Ph: (301)315-6700
Free: 800-848-1717
Fax: (301)315-6880
E-mail: mait@willearn.com
URL: http://www.willearn.com

Format(s): Videocassette. **Descr:** Outlines the four areas of conveying bulk solids in a process plant: start-up, normal operation, dealing with abnormal conditions, and shut down. Includes Leader's Guide and 25 Program Guides. **Length:** 15.

7430 ■ *Handling Hazardous Chemicals Safely*
LearnCom HR Consulting and Training
38 Discovery, Ste. 250
Irvine, CA 92618
Ph: (515)440-0890
Free: 800-698-8263
Fax: (515)221-3149
E-mail: nhartline@learncom.com
URL: http://www.learncomhr.com

Format(s): Videocassette. **Descr:** Employees learn how to ensure a safer workplace by controlling risks and minimizing dangers associated with hazardous chemicals. Includes a leader's guide and 10 workbooks. **Length:** 16.

7431 ■ *Handling Hazardous Waste*
LearnCom HR Consulting and Training
38 Discovery, Ste. 250
Irvine, CA 92618
Ph: (515)440-0890
Free: 800-698-8263
Fax: (515)221-3149
E-mail: nhartline@learncom.com
URL: http://www.learncomhr.com

Format(s): Videocassette. **Descr:** A seven-module program designed to train workers how to deal effectively with hazardous waste. **Prod. Date:** 1991. **Price:** $175.

7432 ■ *Handy Tips*
Williams Learning Network
15400 Calhoun Dr
Rockville, MD 20855-2762
Ph: (301)315-6700
Free: 800-848-1717
Fax: (301)315-6880
E-mail: mait@willearn.com
URL: http://www.willearn.com

Format(s): Videocassette. **Descr:** Discusses how your hands work as a flexible, complex piece of precision equipment and explains how to protect them from injury. Also furnishes exercises to help strengthen and condition your hands. Includes Leader's Guide and 25 Program Guides. **Length:** 16.

7433 ■ *Hazardous Chemical Risks: Employees' Right to Know*
RMI Media
1365 N. Winchester
Olathe, KS 66061
Ph: (913)768-1696

Fax: (913)768-0184
E-mail: actmedia@act.org
URL: http://www.rmimedia.com

Format(s): Videocassette. **Descr:** This tape addresses Iowa's recently enacted law requiring employers to inform employees about hazardous chemicals in the workplace. Includes a question-and-answer session and a review of several companies in compliance with the law. **Prod. Date:** 1987. **Length:** 120.

7434 ■ *Hazardous Inheritance: Workplace Dangers to Reproductive Health*
Cambridge Documentary Films, Inc.
PO Box 390385
Cambridge, MA 02139-0004
Ph: (617)484-3993
Fax: (617)484-0754
E-mail: cdf@shore.net
URL: http://www.cambridgedocumentaryfilms.org

Format(s): Videocassette. **Descr:** Examines hazards in the workplace that can cause infertility, miscarriage, stillbirth, birth defects, and childhood cancer from a medical, legal and workplace health and safety perspective. **Prod. Date:** 1991. **Length:** 24. **Price:** $100.00.

7435 ■ *HazCom Labeling*
Williams Learning Network
15400 Calhoun Dr
Rockville, MD 20855-2762
Ph: (301)315-6700
Free: 800-848-1717
Fax: (301)315-6880
E-mail: mait@willearn.com
URL: http://www.willearn.com

Format(s): Videocassette. **Descr:** Describes major hazardous materials labeling with emphasis on the color and numerical codes of NFPA "Fire Diamonds" and HMIS hazard-warning systems. Also covers labeling codes from the Resource Conservation and Recovery Act (RCRA), OSHA, and the Dept. of Transportation. Considered to be the only program of this kind. Includes Leader's Guide and 25 Program Guides. **Length:** 11.

7436 ■ *How to Have an Accident at Work*
Phoenix Learning Group
2349 Chaffee Dr
St. Louis, MO 63146
Ph: (314)569-0211
Free: 800-221-1274
Fax: (314)569-2834
URL: http://www.phoenixlearninggroup.com

Format(s): Videocassette. **Descr:** This animated film gives viewers an important safety message in preventing on-the-job accidents. **Prod. Date:** 1987. **Length:** 8. **Price:** $170.

7437 ■ *How to be a Success at Work Video Series*
Zenger Media
10200 Jefferson Blvd
Box 802
Culver City, CA 90232
Ph: (310)839-2436
Free: 800-421-4246
Fax: (310)839-2249
E-mail: service@zengermedia.com
URL: http://zengermedia.com

Format(s): Videocassette. **Descr:** Three-video set explains attitudes and skills that will help young entry-level workers be successful at their chosen employment. **Prod. Date:** 1999. **Length:** 54. **Price:** $329.

7438 ■ *Identifying the UN/DOT Hazard Classes: Labels and Placards (Revised)*
Media Resources, Inc.
9012-B NW Holly Rd
Bremerton, WA 98321
Ph: (360)693-3344
Free: 800-666-0106
Fax: (360)693-1760

Format(s): Videocassette. **Descr:** Helps workers identify hazardous materials with labels and placards.

Highlights information on hazard classes, containers, packaging, and emergency information resources. Includes an instructor's guide, discussion questions, a quiz, and a study guide. A discount is available to those who trade-in the original version. **Prod. Date:** 1992. **Length:** 40. **Price:** $175.

7439 ■ *Implementing the OSHA Hazard Communication Standard*
Aspen Publishers
7201 McKinney Circ
Frederick, MD 21704
Ph: (301)644-3599
Free: 800-638-8437
Fax: (301)644-3550
URL: http://www.aspenpublishers.com
Format(s): Videocassette. **Descr:** Businesses need to know what they must do to avoid heavy OSHA penalties because of insufficient safety standards. **Prod. Date:** 1987. **Length:** 30. **Price:** $695.

7440 ■ *Industrial Firefighting Series*
Gulf Publishing Co.
PO Box 2608
Houston, TX 77252-2608
Ph: (713)520-4448
Free: 800-231-6275
Fax: (713)204-4433
E-mail: csv@gulfpub.com
URL: http://www.gulfpub.com
Format(s): Videocassette. **Descr:** Five-part fire training series that provides information on various firefighting topics common to the industrial environment. Also covers common types of firefighting equipment and the techniques used to fight various types of fires. **Price:** $1595.

7441 ■ *Industrial Safety*
Williams Learning Network
15400 Calhoun Dr
Rockville, MD 20855-2762
Ph: (301)315-6700
Free: 800-848-1717
Fax: (301)315-6880
E-mail: mait@willearn.com
URL: http://www.willearn.com
Format(s): Videocassette. **Descr:** Summarizes safety attitudes, responsibilities, and responses in an industrial environment. Emphasis is on common sense, causes of accidents, emergency response, and elimination of hazards. Includes Leader's Guide and 25 Program Guides. **Prod. Date:** 19??. **Length:** 7.

7442 ■ *Industrial Safety*
Agency for Instructional Technology (AIT)
1800 N. Stonelake Dr
Box A
Bloomington, IN 47402-0120
Ph: (812)339-2203
Free: 800-457-4509
Fax: (812)333-4218
E-mail: info@ait.net
URL: http://www.ait.net
Format(s): Videocassette. **Descr:** A series of ten programs about things that can be done to make the workplace safer. **Prod. Date:** 1986. **Length:** 140. **Price:** $1095.00.

7443 ■ *The Industrial Weightlifter 2*
International Film Bureau, Inc.
332 S. Michigan Ave
Chicago, IL 60604-4382
Ph: (312)427-4545
Fax: (312)427-4550
Format(s): Videocassette. **Descr:** How to lift heavy objects so injury does not occur is demonstrated. **Prod. Date:** 1982. **Length:** 11.

7444 ■ *The Inner Mind of Milton Whitty*
International Film Bureau, Inc.
332 S. Michigan Ave
Chicago, IL 60604-4382
Ph: (312)427-4545
Fax: (312)427-4550
Format(s): Videocassette. **Descr:** This program tells

the story of Milton Whitty, who as an employer has the highest accident rate in the business. As he is about to make a speech, he fantasizes about being on trial. **Length:** 19.

7445 ■ *Internet Careers: College Not Required*
Zenger Media
10200 Jefferson Blvd
Box 802
Culver City, CA 90232
Ph: (310)839-2436
Free: 800-421-4246
Fax: (310)839-2249
E-mail: service@zengermedia.com
URL: http://zengermedia.com
Format(s): Videocassette. **Descr:** People in the field discuss their work as webmasters, service providers, content providers, Web designers, graphic artists, and other Internet related careers. **Prod. Date:** 1998. **Length:** 28. **Price:** $169.00.

7446 ■ *Introduction to HazCom*
Williams Learning Network
15400 Calhoun Dr
Rockville, MD 20855-2762
Ph: (301)315-6700
Free: 800-848-1717
Fax: (301)315-6880
E-mail: mait@willearn.com
URL: http://www.willearn.com
Format(s): Videocassette. **Descr:** Outlines OSHA requirements for the Hazard Communication Standard. Covers determination of hazards, container labeling, maintaining MSDS, and written training programs. Explains the HMIS and NFPA warning systems. Includes Leader's Guide and 25 Program Guides. **Length:** 10.

7447 ■ *Invitation to a Virus*
Pyramid Media
PO Box 1048/WEB
Santa Monica, CA 90406
Ph: (310)828-7577
Free: 800-421-2304
Fax: (310)453-9083
E-mail: info@pyramedia.com
URL: http://www.pyramidmedia.com
Format(s): Videocassette. **Descr:** This program helps medical professionals in private practice comply with new OSHA requirements for infection control procedures and staff training. Iincluded is information on Hepatitis B, universal precautions, techniques for preventing cross-contamination, and cleanup and disposal techniques. **Prod. Date:** 1988. **Length:** 16. **Price:** $125.

7448 ■ *Job Briefings*
Williams Learning Network
15400 Calhoun Dr
Rockville, MD 20855-2762
Ph: (301)315-6700
Free: 800-848-1717
Fax: (301)315-6880
E-mail: mait@willearn.com
URL: http://www.willearn.com
Format(s): Videocassette. **Descr:** Illustrates procedures for doing an accurate, well-informed job briefing including reviewing the procedures and safe work practices, explaining the hazards and how to minimize or eliminate them, special precautions, and expectations. Includes Leader's Guide and 25 Program Guides.

7449 ■ *Job Safety Analysis*
ERI Safety Videos
374 Park Rd
Lexington, SC 29072
Ph: (803)356-4880
Free: 800-311-1143
Fax: (803)356-1946
URL: http://www.eri-safety.com
Format(s): Videocassette. **Descr:** A program which helps managers recognize potential hazards and also to investigate areas which have been accident

sites. **Prod. Date:** 1987. **Length:** 15. **Price:** $425.00.

7450 ■ *Job Site Power*
Film Library/Greater Los Angeles Safety Council
600 Wilshire Blvd., No. 1263
Los Angeles, CA 90017
Ph: (213)385-6461
Free: 800-421-9585
Fax: (213)385-8405
URL: http://www.lasafety.org
Format(s): Videocassette. **Descr:** This is an examination of basic 220V/100 amp temporary power systems. **Prod. Date:** 198?. **Length:** 6.

7451 ■ *Just that One Time*
E-mail: info@leomedia.net
URL: http://www.leomedia.net
Format(s): Videocassette. **Descr:** A portrayal of what can happen when a young father forgets to wear his safety glasses on the job. **Length:** 15. **Price:** $445.

7452 ■ *Lifting Properly*
LearnCom HR Consulting and Training
38 Discovery, Ste. 250
Irvine, CA 92618
Ph: (515)440-0890
Free: 800-698-8263
Fax: (515)221-3149
E-mail: nhartline@learncom.com
URL: http://www.learncomhr.com
Format(s): Videocassette. **Descr:** Shows how simple techniques and practices can prevent on-the-job injuries. Employees learn the correct way to lift objects and use equipment. Includes a leader's guide and 10 workbooks. **Length:** 13. **Price:** $295.

7453 ■ *Lifting Techniques and Body Mechanics*
Kinetic Film Enterprises Ltd.
255 Delaware Ave
Buffalo, NY 14202
Ph: (716)856-7631
E-mail: info@kineticinc.com
URL: http://www.kineticinc.com
Format(s): Videocassette. **Descr:** A program which cautions workers who must lift heavy or awkward objects. The possibilities of spine damage from using incorrect lifting techniques are warned against. **Prod. Date:** 1981. **Length:** 30.

7454 ■ *Listening Under Pressure*
Kantola Productions, LLC
55 Sunnyside Ave
Mill Valley, CA 94941-1935
Ph: (415)381-9363
Free: 800-989-8273
Fax: (415)381-9801
E-mail: info@kantola.com
URL: http://kantola.com
Format(s): Videocassette. **Descr:** Helps train employees to eliminate miscommunication, especially in situations that require fast action. **Prod. Date:** 2000. **Length:** 15. **Price:** $79.

7455 ■ *Lockout/Tagout Procedures*
Aspen Publishers
7201 McKinney Circ
Frederick, MD 21704
Ph: (301)644-3599
Free: 800-638-8437
Fax: (301)644-3550
URL: http://www.aspenpublishers.com
Format(s): Videocassette. **Descr:** A dramatic re-enactment of a man getting killed because of carelessness and lack of communication on the job. Don't let it happen to you. **Prod. Date:** 1987. **Length:** 10. **Price:** $425.

7456 ■ *Main Street: Your Right to Know*
LearnCom HR Consulting and Training
38 Discovery, Ste. 250
Irvine, CA 92618
Ph: (515)440-0890
Free: 800-698-8263

Fax: (515)221-3149
E-mail: nhartline@learncom.com
URL: http://www.learncomhr.com
Format(s): Videocassette. **Descr:** An instructional program designed to teach workers and managers about the provisions of the Hazard Communication Standard. **Prod. Date:** 1991. **Length:** 17. **Price:** $175.

7457 ■ *Making It Better: How Everyone Can Create a Safer Workplace*
LearnCom HR Consulting and Training
38 Discovery, Ste. 250
Irvine, CA 92618
Ph: (515)440-0890
Free: 800-698-8263
Fax: (515)221-3149
E-mail: nhartline@learncom.com
URL: http://www.learncomhr.com
Format(s): Videocassette. **Descr:** Shows examples of safety measures created and implemented by employees. Encourages employees to take an active role in workplace safety. Includes leader guide and 10 workbooks. **Prod. Date:** 19??. **Length:** 11. **Price:** $295.00.

7458 ■ *Material Handling*
Williams Learning Network
15400 Calhoun Dr
Rockville, MD 20855-2762
Ph: (301)315-6700
Free: 800-848-1717
Fax: (301)315-6880
E-mail: mait@willearn.com
URL: http://www.willearn.com
Format(s): Videocassette. **Descr:** Provides simple steps for safe and efficient material handling and equipment utilization to keep workers alert to overloading and other equipment-related hazards. Stresses three rules: understand what is being moved, know where it's going, and determine the easiest method of getting there avoiding back injury and other accidents. Includes Leader's Guide and 25 Program Guides. **Length:** 8.

7459 ■ *Minimizing Back Strain on the Job*
Tel-A-Train, Inc.
305 Crewdson Ave
Chattanooga, TN 37405
E-mail: wkingsb@pwpl.com
Format(s): Videocassette. **Descr:** This program outlines specific techniques to reduce back strain induced by bending, driving, lifting and sitting at a bench. **Prod. Date:** 1984. **Length:** 30.

7460 ■ *The Charlie Morecraft Story*
Emergency Film Group
Detrick Lawrence Corp
PO Box 1928
Edgartown, MA 02539
Ph: (508)627-8844
Free: 800-842-0999
Fax: (508)627-8863
E-mail: info@efilmgroup.com
URL: http://www.efilmgroup.com
Format(s): Videocassette. **Descr:** Chemical plant accident victim preaches the benefits of practicing safety. Rather than sulking about his fate, Charlie now tells others about safe ways in which chemicals can be handled, borrowing from his own experiences. **Length:** 20. **Price:** $349.

7461 ■ *Occupational Respiratory Protection Series*
Gulf Publishing Co.
PO Box 2608
Houston, TX 77252-2608
Ph: (713)520-4448
Free: 800-231-6275
Fax: (713)204-4433
E-mail: csv@gulfpub.com
URL: http://www.gulfpub.com
Format(s): Videocassette. **Descr:** A look at the operation of various self-contained breathing apparatuses and the hazards to their efficient operation. Includes a discussion of operation, maintenance and

inspection. **Prod. Date:** 1991. **Length:** 38. **Price:** $495.00.

7462 ■ *Office Ergonomics: Video Display Terminals*
LearnCom HR Consulting and Training
38 Discovery, Ste. 250
Irvine, CA 92618
Ph: (515)440-0890
Free: 800-698-8263
Fax: (515)221-3149
E-mail: nhartline@learncom.com
URL: http://www.learncomhr.com
Format(s): Videocassette. **Descr:** Employees learn how to reduce stress and possible injury while working at their terminals and workstations. Includes a leader's guide and 10 workbooks. **Length:** 11. **Price:** $395.

7463 ■ *On Your Own*
URL: *http://www.lasafety.org*
Format(s): Videocassette. **Descr:** A safety program for people who work outdoors without supervision, including postal and sanitation workers. **Length:** 15. **Price:** $445.

7464 ■ *OSHA Confined Space Entry*
Williams Learning Network
15400 Calhoun Dr
Rockville, MD 20855-2762
Ph: (301)315-6700
Free: 800-848-1717
Fax: (301)315-6880
E-mail: mait@willearn.com
URL: http://www.willearn.com
Format(s): Videocassette. **Descr:** Outlines OSHA regulations for permit required confined spaces covering such topics as isolating, testing, and preparing permit spaces; properly equipping workers; maintaining entry conditions and employee duties. Includes Leader's Guide and 25 Program Guides. **Prod. Date:** 1993. **Length:** 17.

7465 ■ *The OSHA File: Cases and Compliance*
Aspen Publishers
7201 McKinney Circ
Frederick, MD 21704
Ph: (301)644-3599
Free: 800-638-8437
Fax: (301)644-3550
URL: http://www.aspenpublishers.com
Format(s): Videocassette. **Descr:** A presentation of court cases drawn from OSHA files to illustrate safety management. What to do when employees neglect to wear safety gear or refuse to use safety devices is considered. **Prod. Date:** 1973. **Length:** 25.

7466 ■ *OSHA Lockout/Tagout*
Williams Learning Network
15400 Calhoun Dr
Rockville, MD 20855-2762
Ph: (301)315-6700
Free: 800-848-1717
Fax: (301)315-6880
E-mail: mait@willearn.com
URL: http://www.willearn.com
Format(s): Videocassette. **Descr:** Outlines OSHA's new regulations for the control of hazardous energy sources known as lockout/tagout and how it applies to electrical, hydraulic, pneumatic, and other energy sources. Includes Leader's Guide and 25 Program Guides. **Length:** 16.

7467 ■ *OSHA Trenching and Shoring*
Williams Learning Network
15400 Calhoun Dr
Rockville, MD 20855-2762
Ph: (301)315-6700
Free: 800-848-1717
Fax: (301)315-6880
E-mail: mait@willearn.com
URL: http://www.willearn.com
Format(s): Videocassette. **Descr:** Diagrams OSHA regulations for shoring principles and techniques used by workers in trenches or excavations. Covers ways of identifying problems including subsidence

and tension cracks, and discusses shoring techniques including the digging of side trenches to prevent flooding and trench site inspections. Includes Leader's Guide and 25 Program Guides. **Length:** 13.

7468 ■ *Personal Protection in the Lab*
Williams Learning Network
15400 Calhoun Dr
Rockville, MD 20855-2762
Ph: (301)315-6700
Free: 800-848-1717
Fax: (301)315-6880
E-mail: mait@willearn.com
URL: http://www.willearn.com
Format(s): Videocassette. **Descr:** Outlines personal protective equipment for lab workers including eye protection, clothing, and protection from air contamination. Includes Leader's Guide and 25 Program Guides.

7469 ■ *Pig Bird*
Salenger Films, Inc.
1635 12th St
Santa Monica, CA 90404-9988
Ph: (310)450-1300
Free: 800-775-5025
Fax: (310)450-1010
E-mail: salenger@aol.com
URL: http://salengerfilms.visualnet.com
Format(s): Videocassette. **Descr:** A short animated film depicting the importance of on-the-job safety. **Prod. Date:** 1981. **Length:** 6.

7470 ■ *PPE Levels of Protection*
Williams Learning Network
15400 Calhoun Dr
Rockville, MD 20855-2762
Ph: (301)315-6700
Free: 800-848-1717
Fax: (301)315-6880
E-mail: mait@willearn.com
URL: http://www.willearn.com
Format(s): Videocassette. **Descr:** Discusses the four levels of OSHA and EPA guidelines for the selection of personal protective equipment. Illustrates proper use of equipment and proper selection procedures. Includes Leader's Guide and 25 Program Guides. **Length:** 17.

7471 ■ *Preventing Slips, Trips, and Falls*
Bergwall Productions, Inc.
1224 Baltimore Pike, Ste. 203
Kennett Square, PA 19317
Ph: (610)361-0334
Free: 800-934-8696
Fax: (610)361-0092
E-mail: bergwall@bergwall.com
URL: http://www.bergwall.com
Format(s): Videocassette. **Descr:** Includes the three primary steps that all industrial workers should keep in mind when solid footing conditions are not available. Gives clothing advice for common tumble situations. **Prod. Date:** 1992. **Length:** 12. **Price:** $99.

7472 ■ *Process Hazards Analysis*
Williams Learning Network
15400 Calhoun Dr
Rockville, MD 20855-2762
Ph: (301)315-6700
Free: 800-848-1717
Fax: (301)315-6880
E-mail: mait@willearn.com
URL: http://www.willearn.com
Format(s): Videocassette. **Descr:** Outlines the "What-If" method, hazard and operability study, failure mode and effects analysis, and fault tree analysis to complete an OSHA approved hazards process. Includes Leader's Guide and 25 Program Guides. **Length:** 9.

7473 ■ *The Professional "How-To" Bartending Video*
Tapeworm Video Distributors
27833 Hopkins Ave., Unit 6

Valencia, CA 91355
Ph: (661)257-4904
Fax: (661)257-4820
E-mail: sales@tapeworm.com
URL: http://www.tapeworm.com

Format(s): Videocassette. **Descr:** Filmed at the Cocoa Beach Hilton, this video explains and demonstrates the professional techniques involved in preparing and mixing hundreds of famous cocktails in order to obtain a job in the bartending field. Includes sections on proper customer service, responsible serving, shooters and work stations. **Prod. Date:** 1993. **Length:** 50. **Price:** $19.95.

7474 ■ Protection from Ionizing Radiation
Format(s): Videocassette. **Descr:** A five-part program for teaching radiation protection to people working in various fields at various levels. **Prod. Date:** 1990. **Length:** 20. **Price:** $295.

7475 ■ Recognizing and Treating Chemical Exposure
Williams Learning Network
15400 Calhoun Dr
Rockville, MD 20855-2762
Ph: (301)315-6700
Free: 800-848-1717
Fax: (301)315-6880
E-mail: mait@willearn.com
URL: http://www.willearn.com

Format(s): Videocassette. **Descr:** Outlines techniques that help workers identify various ways that chemical exposure can occur in the lab. Also furnishes information on four common routes of chemical exposure, physical indications of exposure, and first aid steps to take in case of chemical exposure. Includes Leader's Guide and 25 Program Guides.

7476 ■ Respiratory Protection
ITC Learning Corp.
13515 Dulles Technology Dr
Herndon, VA 20171-3413
Ph: (703)793-0766
Free: 800-638-3757
Fax: (703)713-0065

Format(s): Videocassette. **Descr:** A series of training films for industrial workers, outlining the correct procedures for proper respiratory protection. **Prod. Date:** 1987. **Length:** 120.

7477 ■ Rigging Fundamentals - Block and Tackle
Williams Learning Network
15400 Calhoun Dr
Rockville, MD 20855-2762
Ph: (301)315-6700
Free: 800-848-1717
Fax: (301)315-6880
E-mail: mait@willearn.com
URL: http://www.willearn.com

Format(s): Videocassette. **Descr:** Discusses the mechanical advantages of the use of block and tackle when moving or lifting loads. Furnishes information on rigging and reeving techniques and the safe use of block and tackle. Features demonstration of the use of block and tackle. Includes Leader's Guide and 25 Program Guides. **Length:** 11.

7478 ■ Rigging Fundamentals - Knots and Knot Tying
Williams Learning Network
15400 Calhoun Dr
Rockville, MD 20855-2762
Ph: (301)315-6700
Free: 800-848-1717
Fax: (301)315-6880
E-mail: mait@willearn.com
URL: http://www.willearn.com

Format(s): Videocassette. **Descr:** Outlines techniques on proper and safe knot tying in the rigging industry. Covers basic terms associated with the parts of a rope and demonstrates slip knots, square knots, half hitches, and bowlines and shows how

each of these knots can be used. Includes Leader's Guide and 25 Program Guides. **Length:** 16.

7479 ■ Rigging Fundamentals - Planning the Job
Williams Learning Network
15400 Calhoun Dr
Rockville, MD 20855-2762
Ph: (301)315-6700
Free: 800-848-1717
Fax: (301)315-6880
E-mail: mait@willearn.com
URL: http://www.willearn.com

Format(s): Videocassette. **Descr:** Details the importance of proper planning with a rigging project. Includes Leader's Guide and 25 Program Guides. **Length:** 7.

7480 ■ The Right-to-Know Series
AMS Distributors, Inc.
PO Box 658
Lady Lake, FL 32158
Free: 800-424-3464
URL: http://www.vpats.com

Format(s): Videocassette. **Descr:** Five programs prepare school staff for possible hazards of handling chemical products. **Prod. Date:** 1989.

7481 ■ Right-to-Know: Working Around Hazardous Substances
LearnCom HR Consulting and Training
38 Discovery, Ste. 250
Irvine, CA 92618
Ph: (515)440-0890
Free: 800-698-8263
Fax: (515)221-3149
E-mail: nhartline@learncom.com
URL: http://www.learncomhr.com

Format(s): Videocassette. **Descr:** Employees learn how to properly handle hazardous chemicals to eliminate or minimize accidents. Includes a leader's guide and 10 workbooks. **Length:** 12. **Price:** $295.

7482 ■ Roughneck Training
University of Texas at Austin
Petroleum Extension Service, Bldg. 2
J.J. Pickle Research Campus
10100 Burnet Rd
Austin, TX 78758
Ph: (512)471-5940
Free: 800-687-4132
Fax: (512)471-9410
E-mail: petex@www.utexas.edu
URL: http://www.utexas.edu/cee/petex

Format(s): Videocassette. **Descr:** This series is designed to educate entry-level rotary helpers about proper care and handling of the drill system. **Prod. Date:** 1983. **Length:** 78. **Price:** $545.

7483 ■ Safe Forklift Operation
Williams Learning Network
15400 Calhoun Dr
Rockville, MD 20855-2762
Ph: (301)315-6700
Free: 800-848-1717
Fax: (301)315-6880
E-mail: mait@willearn.com
URL: http://www.willearn.com

Format(s): Videocassette. **Descr:** Discusses techniques used in the safe operation of a forklift. Provides information on experience, common sense, good eye/hand coordination, pallet and load condition, load lifting and moving, and proper stacking. Highlights the concept of the "stability triangle" with emphasis on the center of gravity and why it must remain in this "triangle." Includes Leader's Guide and 25 Program Guides. **Length:** 16.

7484 ■ Safety Action for Employees
Gulf Publishing Co.
PO Box 2608
Houston, TX 77252-2608
Ph: (713)520-4448
Free: 800-231-6275
Fax: (713)204-4433

E-mail: csv@gulfpub.com
URL: http://www.gulfpub.com
Format(s): Videocassette. **Descr:** Ten tapes reviewing safe performance of job tasks. **Prod. Date:** 1991. **Length:** 18. **Price:** $375.00.

7485 ■ Show You Know It
LearnCom HR Consulting and Training
38 Discovery, Ste. 250
Irvine, CA 92618
Ph: (515)440-0890
Free: 800-698-8263
Fax: (515)221-3149
E-mail: nhartline@learncom.com
URL: http://www.learncomhr.com

Format(s): Videocassette. **Descr:** This program is an excellent tool for kicking-off an effective campaign to motivate workers to obey all safety rules both on and off the job. **Prod. Date:** 1982. **Length:** 11.

7486 ■ Sounding the Alarm: Awareness Level Training
LearnCom HR Consulting and Training
38 Discovery, Ste. 250
Irvine, CA 92618
Ph: (515)440-0890
Free: 800-698-8263
Fax: (515)221-3149
E-mail: nhartline@learncom.com
URL: http://www.learncomhr.com

Format(s): Videocassette. **Descr:** Workers learn what actions to take if they are first on the scene of a chemical emergency. Includes a leader's guide and 10 workbooks. **Length:** 14. **Price:** $395.

7487 ■ Succeeding Without College: Skilled Technical Careers
The Learning Seed
330 Telser Rd
Lake Zurich, IL 60047
Free: 800-634-4941
Fax: (847)540-0854
E-mail: info@learningseed.com
URL: http://www.learningseed.com

Format(s): Videocassette. **Descr:** Focuses on apprenticeships, work-based learning, the armed services, and associate's degrees as career training. **Length:** 21. **Price:** $89.00.

7488 ■ Survival by Permit
LearnCom HR Consulting and Training
38 Discovery, Ste. 250
Irvine, CA 92618
Ph: (515)440-0890
Free: 800-698-8263
Fax: (515)221-3149
E-mail: nhartline@learncom.com
URL: http://www.learncomhr.com

Format(s): Videocassette. **Descr:** Provides step-by-step training in OSHA's confined space permit initiative. Viewers will see how one man's life was saved by proper training and preparation. Second part of the two-part series "Confined Space Training: A Program For Everyone." Includes a trainer's manual and 10 employee manuals. **Length:** 16. **Price:** $495.

7489 ■ That's What the Circus Is For
LearnCom HR Consulting and Training
38 Discovery, Ste. 250
Irvine, CA 92618
Ph: (515)440-0890
Free: 800-698-8263
Fax: (515)221-3149
E-mail: nhartline@learncom.com
URL: http://www.learncomhr.com

Format(s): Videocassette. **Descr:** A safety training program designed to teach employees not to take risks--that's what the circus is for. **Prod. Date:** 1991. **Price:** $175.

7490 ■ Tracks: Accident Investigation and Loss Control
Commonwealth Films, Inc.
223 Commonwealth Ave
Boston, MA 02116

Ph: (617)262-5634
Fax: (617)262-6948
E-mail: info@commonwealthfilms.com
URL: http://www.commonwealthfilms.com
Format(s): Videocassette. **Descr:** A film designed to help anyone who drives for a living do his job more safely. **Prod. Date:** 1985. **Length:** 30. **Price:** $450.

7491 ■ The Very Quick Job Search Video
Zenger Media
10200 Jefferson Blvd
Box 802
Culver City, CA 90232
Ph: (310)839-2436
Free: 800-421-4246
Fax: (310)839-2249
E-mail: service@zengermedia.com
URL: http://zengermedia.com
Format(s): Videocassette. **Descr:** Discusses nontraditional and creative approaches to getting the job you want. Simulates cold-calls, networking calls, and interviews with employers. **Prod. Date:** 1999. **Length:** 34. **Price:** $169.

7492 ■ Will Your Job Burn?
National Fire Protection Association
1 Batterymarch Park
Quincy, MA 02169-7471
Ph: (617)770-3000
Free: 800-344-3555
Fax: (617)770-0700
E-mail: info@nfpa.org
URL: http://www.nfpa.org
Format(s): Videocassette. **Descr:** Assembly line workers and plant managers in all industries should be consciously aware of fire prevention. Three industrial workers tell their stories of losing their jobs because of fire. **Prod. Date:** 197?. **Length:** 18.

7493 ■ Work Search: Solving the Puzzle
University of Wisconsin at Madison
College of Engineering
Department of Engineering Professional Development
432 N. Lake St
Madison, WI 53706
Ph: (608)262-2061
Free: 800-462-0876
Fax: (608)263-3160
URL: http://www.engr.wisc.edu
Format(s): Videocassette. **Descr:** Discusses work search techniques such as identifying skills, writing a resume, networking, cold calling, job leads, and meeting employers. **Length:** 22. **Price:** $69.95.

7494 ■ Work Search: The First Steps
University of Wisconsin at Madison
College of Engineering
Department of Engineering Professional Development
432 N. Lake St
Madison, WI 53706
Ph: (608)262-2061
Free: 800-462-0876
Fax: (608)263-3160
URL: http://www.engr.wisc.edu
Format(s): Videocassette. **Descr:** Provides insight on how to overcome obstacles when searching for a first job. **Length:** 27. **Price:** $69.95.

7495 ■ Work Search: Transitions
University of Wisconsin at Madison
College of Engineering
Department of Engineering Professional Development
432 N. Lake St
Madison, WI 53706
Ph: (608)262-2061
Free: 800-462-0876
Fax: (608)263-3160
URL: http://www.engr.wisc.edu
Format(s): Videocassette. **Descr:** Provides insight

on how to transition from unemployment to employment. **Length:** 28. **Price:** $69.95.

7496 ■ Working in the Hazard Zone
LearnCom HR Consulting and Training
38 Discovery, Ste. 250
Irvine, CA 92618
Ph: (515)440-0890
Free: 800-698-8263
Fax: (515)221-3149
E-mail: nhartline@learncom.com
URL: http://www.learncomhr.com
Format(s): Videocassette. **Descr:** An eight-module series containing detailed training to comply with training requirements of the Resource Conservation and Recovery Act. A trainer's manual and participants' manuals are included. **Prod. Date:** 1991. **Price:** $175.

7497 ■ Working Safely with Unibolt Couplings
University of Texas at Austin
Petroleum Extension Service, Bldg. 2
J.J. Pickle Research Campus
10100 Burnet Rd
Austin, TX 78758
Ph: (512)471-5940
Free: 800-687-4132
Fax: (512)471-9410
E-mail: petex@www.utexas.edu
URL: http://www.utexas.edu/cee/petex
Format(s): Videocassette. **Descr:** This tape explores safe and proper procedures when working with unibolt couplings. **Prod. Date:** 1983. **Length:** 15.

7498 ■ Workplace Ergonomics: A Better Way to Work
Tel-A-Train, Inc.
305 Crewdson Ave
Chattanooga, TN 37405
E-mail: wkingsb@pwpl.com
Format(s): Videocassette. **Descr:** Identifies ergonomic risk factors and hazards, recognizes symptoms and signs, and tells of actions employees can take to work in an ergonomically correct environment. **Prod. Date:** ????. **Length:** 15.

7499 ■ Your Potential Is Huge
University of Wisconsin at Madison
College of Engineering
Department of Engineering Professional Development
432 N. Lake St
Madison, WI 53706
Ph: (608)262-2061
Free: 800-462-0876
Fax: (608)263-3160
URL: http://www.engr.wisc.edu
Format(s): Videocassette. **Descr:** Helps people realize their potential and make a successful transitions from school to work. **Length:** 16. **Price:** $89.

Media Contacts

District of Columbia

7500 ■ National Public Radio
635 Massachusetts Ave. NW
Washington, DC 20001-3753
Contact: Frank Langfitt, Labor and Workplace Reporter
Ph: (202)513-2229
Fax: (202)513-3329
E-mail: flangfitt@npr.org
URL: http://www.npr.org

Illinois

7501 ■ Chicago Tribune
Tribune Company
435 N. Michigan Ave.
Chicago, IL 60611-4041
Contact: Steve Franklin, Work and Labor Reporter
Ph: (312)222-4324

E-mail: sfranklin@tribune.com
URL: http://www.chicagotribune.com

Maryland

7502 ■ The Baltimore Sun
Tribune Company
501 N. Calvert St.
Baltimore, MD 21278
Contact: Hanah Cho, Labor, Workplace Reporter
Ph: (410)332-6000
E-mail: hanah.cho@baltsun.com
URL: http://www.baltimoresun.com

Massachusetts

7503 ■ Boston Herald
Herald Media, Inc.
One Herald Sq.
Boston, MA 02106-2096
Contact: Jay Fitzgerald, Labor/Economy Reporter
Ph: (617)619-6625
E-mail: jfitz@bostonherald.com
URL: http://www.bostonherald.com

Michigan

7504 ■ Detroit News
MediaNews Group
615 W. Lafayette Blvd.
Detroit, MI 48226
Contact: Louis Aguilar, Economy/Real Estate Editor
Ph: (313)222-2760
E-mail: laguilar@detnews.com
URL: http://www.detnews.com

Minnesota

7505 ■ St. Paul Pioneer Press
MediaNews Group, Inc.
345 Cedar St.
St. Paul, MN 55101-1057
Contact: Julie Forster, Workplace Issues Reporter
Ph: (651)228-5189
E-mail: jforster@pioneerpress.com
URL: http://www.pioneerpress.com

Missouri

7506 ■ The Kansas City Star
Knight Ridder, Inc.
1729 Grand Blvd.
Kansas City, MO 64108
Contact: Diane Stafford, Workplace Issues Reporter
Ph: (816)234-4359
E-mail: stafford@kcstar.com
URL: http://www.kansascity.com

New York

7507 ■ The Buffalo News
Berkshire Hathaway Inc.
PO Box 100
Buffalo, NY 14240
Contact: Samantha Christmann, Labor Reporter
Ph: (716)849-4436
Free: 800-777-8680
Fax: (716)849-4434
E-mail: schristmann@buffnews.com
URL: http://www.buffalo.com

Ohio

7508 ■ The Cincinnati Enquirer
Gannett Co., Inc.
312 Elm St.
Cincinnati, OH 45202-2739
Contact: Stepfanie Romine, Workplace Reporter
Ph: (513)768-8505
E-mail: sromine@enquirer.com
URL: http://www.enquirer.com

Oklahoma

7509 ■ *The Oklahoman*
Oklahoma Publishing Company
9000 N. Broadway
Oklahoma City, OK 73114
Contact: Paula Erickson, Workplace/Careers Reporter
Ph: (405)475-3232
E-mail: perickson@oklahoman.com
URL: http://www.newsok.com

Oregon

7510 ■ *The Oregonian*
1320 SW Broadway
Portland, OR 97201
Contact: Anne Saker, Workplace/Economy Reporter
Ph: (503)294-7656
E-mail: annesaker@news.oregonian.com
URL: http://www.oregonlive.com

7511 ■ *The Oregonian*
1320 SW Broadway
Portland, OR 97201
Contact: Mark Graves, People & Jobs Path Columnist
Ph: (503)221-8200
E-mail: money@news.oregonian.com
URL: http://www.oregonlive.com

Pennsylvania

7512 ■ *The Patriot-News*
Newhouse Newspapers
PO Box 2265
Harrisburg, PA 17105
Contact: Dan Miller, Workplace Issues Reporter
Ph: (717)255-8216
E-mail: danmiller@patriot-news.com
URL: http://www.patriots-news.com

7513 ■ *The Philadelphia Inquirer*
Philadelphia Media Holdings LLC
400 N. Broad St.
Philadelphia, PA 19103
Contact: Stacey Burling, Health Care Economy Reporter
Ph: (215)854-2450
E-mail: sburling@phillynews.com
URL: http://www.philly.com

7514 ■ *The Philadelphia Inquirer*
Philadelphia Media Holdings LLC
400 N. Broad St.
Philadelphia, PA 19103
Contact: Jane Von Berrgen, Workplace & Health Insurers Reporter
Ph: (215)854-2769
E-mail: jvonbergen@phillynews.com
URL: http://www.philly.com

Texas

7515 ■ *Dallas Morning News*
Belo Corp.
508 Young St.
Dallas, TX 75202
Contact: Bob Moos, Older Workers Reporter
Ph: (214)977-8147
E-mail: bmoos@dallasnews.com
URL: http://www.dallasnews.com

Corporate Contacts

7516 ■ Aerotek Staffing
7301 Parkway Dr.
Hanover, MD 21076
Free: 800-237-6835
URL: http://www.aerotek.com

7517 ■ Ceridian Corp.
3311 E. Old Shakopee Rd.
Minneapolis, MN 55425
Ph: (952)853-8100
E-mail: information@corporate.ceridian.com
URL: http://www.ceridian.com

7518 ■ Kelly Services
999 W. Big Beaver Rd.
Troy, MI 48084-4782
Ph: (248)362-4444
E-mail: kfirst@kellyservices.com
URL: http://www.kellyservices.com

7519 ■ Labor Finders International
11426 N. Jog Rd.
Palm Beach Gardens, FL 33418
Free: 800-864-7749
URL: http://www.laborfinders.com

7520 ■ Labor Ready
PO Box 2910
Tacoma, WA 98401-2910
Free: 877-733-0399
URL: http://www.laborready.com

7521 ■ Manpower Inc.
100 Manpower Place
Milwaukee, WI 53212
URL: http://www.manpower.com

Internet Resources

7522 ■ All for Animals Online
All for Animals, Inc.
PO Box 3534
Santa Barbara, CA 93130
Contact: Karen Lee Stevens, Founder
Fax: (805)569-9810
E-mail: info@allforanimals.com
URL: http://www.allforanimals.com
Descr: Online resource for animal lovers that provides animal testing alternatives, listings of companies that test on animals and cruelty-free companies, and news articles. **Type:** Full-text.

7523 ■ American Rivers
1101 14th St. NW, Ste. 1400
Washington, DC 20005
Contact: Rebecca R. Wodder, Pres.
Ph: (202)347-7550
Fax: (202)347-9240
E-mail: outreach@americanrivers.org
URL(s): www.americanrivers.org/ **Descr:** Dedicated to the protection and restoration of this country's river systems, American Rivers is North America's leading national river conservation organization. Its website contains the latest news from the battle to save endangered U.S. rivers, such as the Lower Snake and the Pascagoula, two of American Rivers' "America's Most Endangered Rivers of 2009." There are reports on rivers being lost forever because of pollution and on others where the battle is being won. Here, visitors can learn what's being done and what they can do to help preserve some of the country's most valuable resources. **Type:** Image; Directory; Full-text. **Updating freq.:** Regularly. **Fees:** Free. **Searching routines or searchable elements:** Keyword searching is available.

7524 ■ Bay Area Junk Mail Reduction Campaign
Bay Area Recycling Outreach Coalition
Contact: Catherine Pandori, BayROC Campaign Coord.
Free: 877-786-7927
E-mail: acwma@stopwaste.org
URL(s): www.stopjunkmail.org/ **Descr:** Advises consumers on how to stop unwanted mail from coming to their homes. Provides letter templates addressed to companies it perceives as major producers of "junk mail."

7525 ■ A Consumer's Guide to Energy Efficient and Renewable Energy
DOE Office of Energy Efficiency and Renewable Energy
Mail Stop EE-1
Washington, DC 20585
Contact: John Mizroch, Actg.Asst.Sec.
Ph: (202)586-4940
Fax: (202)586-1233
URL: http://www.eere.energy.gov/consumer/
Descr: Offers a wide range of information on how consumers can "explore your options for saving energy and using renewable energy at home, at work, in your community, and while driving."

7526 ■ Environmental Working Group
1436 U St., NW, Ste. 100
Washington, DC 20009
Contact: Ken Cook, Pres.
Ph: (202)667-6982
URL(s): www.ewg.org/ **Descr:** Strives to bring environmental issues to public attention and to influence public policy. Provides a special focus to children's safety issues, informing parents of products that may contain potentially toxic or otherwise harmful ingredients.

7527 ■ Global Stewards
Global Stewards
E-mail: global.stewards@mindspring.com
URL: http://www.globalstewards.org/
Descr: Provides information on sustainable living. The Solutions link covers substainable living solutions for food, water, buildings, clothing, transportation, economy, and ecosystem restoration. The EcoTips page offers suggestions in the areas of reduce, reuse, recycling, energy and water conservation, gardening, and home finances. Website also has a calendar of global environmental events, tools for effective advocacy, and an online fair trade mall. **Type:** Full-text.

7528 ■ Green Living Online
Green Living Magazine
70 the Esplanade, Ste. 400
Toronto, ON, Canada M5E 1R2
Contact: Joanne Bell
Ph: (416)360-0044
Fax: (416)362-2387
E-mail: webmaster@greenlivingonline.com
URL(s): www.greenlivingonline.com/ **Descr:** Provides extensive information on environmentally friendly living in areas such as beauty and fashion, energy, home and garden, family, health and nutrition, and transportation. **Type:** Full-text.

7529 ■ Green Living Tips
Contact: Michael Bloch, Owner/Editor
URL(s): www.greenlivingtips.com/ **Descr:** Offers tips on living a more planet-friendly lifestyle, with articles on topics such as building, cleaning, clothing, energy, food, gadgets, gardening, health, home, pets, repairs, and transportation. Users are encouraged to share their own earth-friendly tips. **Type:** Full-text.

7530 ■ Ideal Bite
Ideal Bite, Inc.
Contact: Heather Stephenson, Co-Founder
URL: http://www.idealbite.com
Descr: Provides information on simple green living. Website has "ideas for real people who lead busy lives and want to make small changes that add up to big results." Small Changes page notes that, among other things, up to 11,973 members--called "Biters"-- kept their tires properly inflated, saving enough gas to drive a hybrid automobile around the circumference of the earth.

7531 ■ National Lead Information Center (NLIC)
422 S. Clinton Ave.
Rochester, NY 14620
Free: 800-424-5323
Fax: (585)232-3111
URL(s): www.epa.gov/lead/pubs/nlic.htm **Descr:** Strives to inform the public about the dangers of lead poisoning. Provides related news and prevention tips. Runs a lead hotline. **Rmks:** According to the website listed above, NLIC "operates under a contract with the U.S. Environmental Protection Agency (EPA), with funding from EPA, the Centers for Disease Control and Prevention, and the Department of Housing and Urban Development."

7532 ■ Sierra Club Online
Sierra Club
85 Second St., 2nd Floor
San Francisco, CA 94105
Ph: (415)977-5500
Fax: (415)977-5799
E-mail: information@sierraclub.org
URL: http://www.sierraclub.org
Descr: Provides information on environmental issues such as clean water, wildlands, commercial logging, ecosystems, and environmental law. **Type:** Full-text. **Searching routines or searchable elements:** Search options are available.

7533 ■ Water Environment Federation Online
Water Environment Federation
601 Wythe St.
Alexandria, VA 22314-1994
Contact: William Bertera, Exec.Dir.
Ph: (703)684-2400
Free: 800-666-0206
Fax: (703)684-2492
E-mail: csc@wef.org
URL: http://www.wef.org
Descr: Offers information on water quality issues, including hazardous waste, biosolids, recycling, and watershed management. Also provides product profiles, glossary of terms, and an online library. **Type:** Full-text. **Searching routines or searchable elements:** Searching options are available.

7534 ■ WildEarth Guardians
WildEarth Guardians
312 Montezuma
Santa Fe, NM 87501
Contact: John Horning, Exec.Dir.
Ph: (505)988-9126
Fax: (505)989-8623
E-mail: info@wildearthguardians.org
URL: http://www.wildearthguardians.org/
Descr: Online site of company that aims to protect and restore the native biological diversity and watersheds of the American Southwest; educate and enlist citizens to support protection of forests, rivers, deserts, and grasslands; advocate for the principles

of conservation biology in plans to restore degraded ecosystems and watersheds; enforce and strengthen environmental laws; support communities in efforts to protect their land and to practice and promote sustainable use of natural resources. Offers information on environmental news and programs. **Type:** Full-text. **Searching routines or searchable elements:** Search options are available.

Federal Government Agencies

7535 ■ Advisory Board on Radiation and Worker Health
Office of the Director
National Inst. for Occupational Safety & Health
1600 Clifton Rd. NE
Atlanta, GA 30333
Contact: Christine Branche PhD, Exec.Sec.
Ph: (202)245-0625
Fax: (404)929-2699
E-mail: ocas@cdc.gov
URL: http://www.cdc.gov/niosh/ocas/ocasadv.html
Staff: Administrative support is provided by the Department of Health and Human Services. Dr. Christine Branche, Principal Associate Director, National Institute for Occupational Safety and Health (NIOSH), serves as executive secretary. **Descr:** Board advises the Secretary of Health and Human Services on the Energy Employees Occupational Illness Compensation Program. Since World War II, many men and women have served in building the nation's nuclear defense and, in the course of this work, have been exposed to beryllium, ionizing radiation, and other hazards unique to nuclear weapons production and testing. The purpose of the Program is to provide for timely, uniform, and adequate compensation of covered employees and, where applicable, survivors of such employees, suffering from illnesses incurred in the performance of duty for the Department of Energy and certain of its contractors and subcontractors. Board will advise on the scientific validity and quality of dose reconstruction efforts performed; the class of employees at any DOE facility who were exposed to radiation, but for whom it is not feasible to estimate their radiation dose; and the reasonably likelihood that such radiation doses may have endangered the health and members of the class. **Mem:** Board currently consists of 12 members appointed by the President of the United States. Members include affected workers and their representatives, and representatives from scientific and medical communities. Dr. Paul L. Ziemer, Professor Emeritus, School of Health Sciences, Purdue University, chairs the Board.

7536 ■ Board of Trustees, National Environmental Education Foundation
4301 Connecticut Ave. NW, Ste. 160
Washington, DC 20008
Contact: Diane W. Wood, Pres.
Ph: (202)833-2933
Fax: (202)261-6464
E-mail: dan@neetf.org
URL: http://www.neefusa.org
Staff: Diane W. Wood, President, National Environmental Education Foundation, serves as secretary of the Board. **Descr:** Board oversees and assures that the activities of the National Environmental Education and Training Foundation are consistent with the intents and purposes of the Act. The Foundation was established to extend the contribution of environmental education and training to meeting critical environmental protection needs in the United States; to facilitate the cooperation, coordination, and contribution of public and private resources to create an environmentally conscious and responsible public; and to foster an open and effective partnership among federal, state, and local government, business, industry, academic institutions, and community-based environmental groups. **Mem:** Board consists of twelve members who are knowledgeable or experienced in the areas of environment, education, and/or training. Appointed members serve two four-year terms. Ex-officio membership includes fifteen representatives of other federal agencies and

departments. There are also eight honorary members. Arthur Gibson, Baxter Healthcare Corporation, chairs the Board. **Pub:** Annual report.

7537 ■ Chief of Engineers Environmental Advisory Board
Chief of Engineers, USACE
441 G St. NW
Washington, DC 20314-1000
Contact: Ms. Rennie H. Sherman, Designated Fed. Off.
Ph: (202)761-7771
Fax: (202)761-1500
URL: http://www.usace.army.mil/cw/hot_topics/eab.htm
Staff: Support services are provided by the U.S. Army Corps of Engineers. **Descr:** Board serves as environmental advisor to the Chief of Engineers to provide guidance for developing environmental policy and procedural matters for Corps programs. In performing this function, Board examines existing and proposed policies, programs, and activities from an environmental point of view to identify problems and weaknesses and to suggest how these can be remedied; advises on how the Corps can improve working relations with the conservation community and the general public; and advises on environmental problems or issues pertinent to specific plans or programs. **Mem:** Board consists of five to ten members, selected by the Chief of Engineers, representing a broad range of knowledge and experience in environmental matters. Dr. George F. Crozier, Executive Director, Dauphin Island Sea Lab, chairs the Committee. **Pub:** A report is filed and published following every meeting.

7538 ■ Collaborative Forest Restoration Program Technical Advisory Panel
Southwestern Region
Forest Service
333 Broadway SE
Albuquerque, NM 87102
Contact: Walter W. Dunn, Designated Fed.Off.
Ph: (505)842-3425
Fax: (505)842-3165
URL: http://www.fs.fed.us/r3/spf/cfrp
Staff: Administrative support is provided by the Forest Service. **Descr:** Collaborative Forest Restoration Program (CFRP) provides grants for forest restoration and small diameter tree utilization projects on public forest land. Panel reviews grant proposals and develops consensus funding recommendations for the Forest Service on which proposals best meet the program objectives. Panel also examines the effect of projects on long-term management. **Mem:** Panel consists of 12 to 15 members, as follows: a state natural resources official from New Mexico; at least two representatives from federal land management agencies; at least one tribal or Pueblo representative; at least two independent scientists with experience in forest ecosystem restoration; and equal representation from conservation interests, local communities, and commodities interests. Members serve two-year terms. Walter W. Dunn, Collaborative Forest Restoration Program, Southwest Region, Forest Service, chairs the Panel and serves as designated federal official.

7539 ■ Council on Environmental Quality (CEQ)
730 Jackson Pl. NW
Washington, DC 20503
Contact: Martin L. Hall, Chief of Staff
Ph: (202)456-6546
Fax: (202)456-2710
URL: http://www.whitehouse.gov/ceq
Descr: Council was established to analyze important environmental conditions and trends; review and appraise federal government programs having an impact upon the environment; recommend policies for protecting and improving the quality of the environment; prepare the President's annual report to Congress; and issue regulations for agencies to follow in meeting procedural requirements of the National Environmental Policy Act. **Mem:** Council consists of three members appointed by the Presi-

dent and approved by the Senate. James Laurence Connaughton currently chairs the Council. **Pub:** Environmental Quality Report and other substantive and statistical reports as events dictate.

7540 ■ Environmental Laboratory Advisory Board (ELAB)
National Environmental Laboratory Accreditation Conference
Office of the Science Advisor
Environmental Protection Agency
109 T. W. Alexander Dr. (E243-05)
Research Triangle Park, NC 27709
Contact: Lara P. Autry, Designated Fed.Off.
Ph: (919)541-5544
Fax: (919)541-4261
URL: http://www.epa.gov/elab/
Staff: Support services are provided by the National Environmental Laboratory Accreditation Conference. Lara P. Autry, Senior Advisor, Measurement and Laboratory Science Matters, serves as designated federal official. **Descr:** Board provides recommendations and comments on the process and procedures to develop and operate a National Environmental Laboratory Accreditation Conference (NELAC). **Mem:** Board comprises 20 members including seven representatives of laboratory associations, EPA's regulated community, local government, environmental interest groups, environmental engineering associations or firms, Indian nations, third party assessors, small laboratories (20 employees or less), and associations representing the laboratory community complying with EPA's Toxic Substance Control Act and Federal Insecticide, Fungicide, and Rodenticide Act. Dr. Jeff S. Flowers, President and Technical Director, Flowers Chemical Laboratories and Councilman for City of Maitland, FL, chairs the Board.

7541 ■ Environmental Management Site-Specific Advisory Board (EM SSAB)
Office of Environmental Management
U.S. Department of Energy
Forrestal Bldg.
1000 Independence Ave. SW, Rm. 5A-014
Washington, DC 20585-0113
Contact: Cate Alexander Brennan, Designated Fed. Off.
Ph: (202)586-7711
Fax: (202)586-6773
URL: http://www.em.doe.gov/Pages/ssab.aspx
Staff: Support services are provided by the Office of the Assistant Secretary for Environmental Management. **Descr:** Board provides advice and makes recommendations to the Assistant Secretary for Environmental Management concerning environmental management, environmental restoration, waste management, and technology development activities and projects, and on issues related to budget (including prioritization), accelerated cleanup, risk management, future use, economic development, worker health and safety, and public participation at the following locations: Hanford in Washington State, Idaho, Northern New Mexico, Nevada, Oak Ridge in Tennessee, Paducah in Kentucky, and Savannah River in South Carolina. **Mem:** Approximately 188 board members represent local government, Indian tribes, environmental and civic groups, labor organizations, universities, waste management and environmental restoration firms, and other interested parties who are directly affected by site cleanup activities. Representatives of the Department of Energy, Environmental Protection Agency, and state government serve ex-officio. Ten members co-chair the Board.

7542 ■ Environmental Services Advisory Committee
Office of Ecosystem Services and Markets
Office of the Secretary
Department of Agriculture
1400 Independence Ave.
Washington, DC 20250
Contact: Sarah D. Collins, Dir.
Ph: (202)205-1779
Descr: Committee advises the Secretary of Agriculture regarding issues related to establishing techni-

cal guidelines that outline science-based methods to measure the environmental services benefits from conservation and land management activities in order to facilitate the participation of farmers, ranchers and forest landowners in emerging environmental services markets. **Mem:** Committee consists of at least 15 and no more than 19 members appointed by the Secretary of Agriculture. Members have relevant expertise and represent a diversity of organizations including: (1) representatives from state natural resource agencies, environmental quality agencies, agriculture departments; (2) tribal governments; (3) farmers, ranchers, and forest landowners representing the various regions of the nation; (4) conservation and environmental organizations; (5) institutions of higher education; (6) financial institutions involved in environmental services trading; and (7) others as determined by the Secretary. Members serve two-year terms. The Director of the USDA Office of Ecosystem Services and Markets (or designee) serves as the chair.

7543 ■ EPA Science Advisory Board
Environmental Protection Agency
1025 F St. NW, Rm. 3600
Washington, DC 20004
Contact: Thomas Miller, Designated Fed.Off.
Ph: (202)343-9982
Fax: (202)233-0643
URL: http://yosemite.epa.gov/sab/sabpeople.nsf/WebCommittees/BOARD

Staff: Support services are provided by an in-house staff of the Board, directed by Thomas Miller. **Descr:** Board has overall responsibility for providing expert and independent advice to the Administrator of the Environmental Protection Agency on issues relating to the scientific and technical problems facing the Agency, the strategies devised to meet these problems, the technical programs to solve problems, and the priorities among these. This responsibility is discharged by coordinating the research and the activities of the scientific advisory committees (see below under Subsidiary Units) to see that they are fulfilling their responsibilities to make recommendations concerning needed research and development activities, assess the results of specific research efforts, and assist in identifying emerging environmental problems without overlapping with each other, and reviewing the scientific basis of Agency regulations, standards, criteria, and guidance. Board also provides advice to the Senate Committee on Environment and Public Works and the House Committee on Science and Technology. **Mem:** Board consists of approximately 125 members representing academia, private industry, public interest groups and scientific consulting organizations. Members are appointed by the Administrator, Environmental Protection Agency, for three-year terms and serve on one (or more) standing committees and may interact as a liaison with other standing committees. Dr. Deborah Swackhamer, University of Minnesota, Minneapolis, MN, chairs the Board. **Pub:** Monthly newsletter available on Home Page and by email; includes rolling two month calendar. Listserver available for automatic notification of meetings. Approximately 30 reports a year. Annual report available. All reports provided on website. Advice to EPA on Advancing the Science and Application of Ecological Risk Assessment in Environmental Decision Making: A Report of the U.S. EPA Science Advisory Board (2008); Hypoxia in the Northern Gulf of Mexico: An Update by the EPA Science Advisory Board(2008); Review of Office of Research and Development (ORD) Draft Assessment entitled, "Evaluation of the Carcinogenicity of Ethylene Oxide" (2008); SAB Advisory on EPA's Issues in Valuing Mortality Risk Reduction(2008); Review of the Environmental Economics Research Strategy of the US EPA (2004); Advisory Report on the Science and Research Budgets for the U.S.

Environmental Protection Agency for FY 2005; A Report by the EPA SAB (2004).

7544 ■ Governmental Advisory Committee to the United States Government Representative to the North American Commission on Environmental Cooperation
Off. of Cooperative Environmental Management
Environmental Protection Agency
1200 Pennsylvania Ave., NW (MC-1601M)
Washington, DC 20460
Contact: Oscar Carrillo, Designated Fed.Off.
Ph: (202)564-2294
Fax: (202)564-8129
URL: http://www.epa.gov/ocem/gac/index.html

Staff: Support services are provided by the Office of the Administrator, Environmental Protection Agency. **Descr:** Committee is responsible for providing advice to the U.S. Representative (who is the Administrator of EPA) on implementation and further elaboration of the NAAEC. Committee is responsible for providing recommendations to help assure that state, local, and tribal governments are represented in the development of U.S. policy positions regarding implementation of the NAAEC and NAFTA. **Mem:** Committee consists of twelve independent representatives drawn from among state, local and tribal government agencies. Members are knowledgeable in environment-related strategic, scientific, technological, regulatory, and economic issues relevant to the implementation of NAFTA and the Environmental Cooperation Agreement. Members are appointed by the Administrator, Environmental Protection Agency, for one-year terms. Jeffrey N. Wennberg, Commissioner, Vermont Department of Natural Resources, currently chairs the Committee.

7545 ■ Interagency Coordinating Committee on the Validation of Alternative Methods
NICEATM
NIEHS
PO Box 12233
Mall Drop K2-16
Research Triangle Park, NC 27709
Contact: Dr. William Stokes, Exec.Dir.
Ph: (919)541-2384
Fax: (919)541-0947
E-mail: niceatm@niehs.nih.gov
URL: http://iccvam.niehs.nih.gov

Descr: Committee works to increase the efficiency and effectiveness of federal agency test method review; optimize the utilization of scientific expertise outside the federal government; ensure that new and revised test methods are validated to meet the needs of federal agencies; and reduce, refine, or replace the use of animals in testing, where feasible. The responsibilities of the Committee are to consider petitions from the public for the review and evaluation of validated test methods; review and evaluate the validation status of new, revised, and alternative test methods; submit test recommendations to federal agencies; facilitate and provide guidance on test method development and validation criteria and processes; and facilitate the acceptance of scientifically valid test methods and interagency and international harmonization. **Mem:** Committee consists of the heads (or their designees) of the following 15 federal agencies: Agency for Toxic Substances and Disease Registry; Consumer Product Safety Commission; Departments of Agriculture, Defense, Energy, the Interior, and Transportation; Environmental Protection Agency; Food and Drug Administration; National Institute for Occupational Safety and Health; National Institutes of Health; National Cancer Institute; National Institute of Environmental Health Sciences; National Library of Medicine; Occupational Safety and Health Administration; and any other agency that develops, or employs tests or test data

using animals, or regulates on the basis of the use of animals in toxicology testing.

7546 ■ National Advisory Committee to the United States Representative to the North American Commission on Environmental Cooperation
Off. of Cooperative Environmental Management
Environmental Protection Agency
1200 Pennsylvania Ave. NW, MC-1601M
Washington, DC 20004
Contact: Oscar Carrillo, Designated Fed.Off.
Ph: (202)564-2294
Fax: (202)564-8129
URL: http://www.epa.gov/ocem/nac/index.html

Staff: Support services are provided by the Office of the Administrator, Environmental Protection Agency. **Descr:** Committee is responsible for providing advice to the United States Representative (who is the EPA Administrator) on implementation and further elaboration of the NAAEC, which is the environmental side agreement to the NAFTA. Committee is responsible for providing recommendations to help assure that U.S. civil society is represented in the development of U.S. policy positions regarding implementation of the NAAEC and the NAFTA. **Mem:** Committee consists of 12 members representing business and industry, educational institutions, and environmental groups. Members are knowledgeable in the areas of environment-related strategic, scientific, nongovernment, technological, regulatory, and economic issues addressed in the implementation of the NAAEC and NAFTA and the Environmental Cooperation Agreement. Members are appointed by the EPA Administrator and serve two-year terms. Delores Wesson, University of California at San Diego, chairs the Committee. **Pub:** Advice on Ten-Year Review of the NAAEC & CEC Council Deliverables (2004); Advice on CEC Operational Plan & Budget (2003).

7547 ■ National Advisory Council for Environmental Policy and Technology (NACEPT)
Office of Cooperative Environmental Management
Environmental Protection Agency
1200 Pennsylvania Ave. NW, Mail Code 1601M
Washington, DC 20460
Contact: Sonia Altieri, Designated Fed.Off.
Ph: (202)564-0243
Fax: (202)564-8129
URL: http://www.epa.gov/ocempage/nacept/

Staff: Support services are provided by the Office of Cooperative Environmental Management, Environmental Protection Agency. Sonia Altieri, Program Analyst, serves as designated federal official. Megan Moreau serves as Assistant Designated Federal Officer. **Descr:** Council provides a cost-effective and flexible forum that can quickly respond to continually evolving policy challenges. Council advises the Environmental Protection Agency Administrator on a wide spectrum of domestic and international environmental management policies, programs, and technologies. **Mem:** Council is a balanced panel of approximately 39 outside experts who represent diverse interests from academia, industry, nongovernmental organizations, and state, local and tribal governments. Members serve two-year terms. Erik Meyers, Vice President, Sustainable Programs, The Conservation Fund, serves as Interim Chair. **Pub:** Everyone's Business: Working Towards Sustainability Through Environmental Stewardship and Collaboration (March 2008); NACEPT Advice Letter on EPA's Draft 2009-2014 Strategic Plan Change Document (2008); NACEPT Environmental Technology Subcommittee Report on Venture Capital (2008); NACEPT Advice Letter on Integrated Modeling (2008); NACEPT's Review of EPA's Strategy for Improving Access to Environmental Information (2008); NACEPT's Third Advice Letter on Biofuels (2007); NACEPT's Initial Findings and Recommendations on EPA's Sustainable Infrastructure Watershed Pillar (2007); EPA Technology Programs: Engaging the Marketplace (2007); NACEPT's Initial Thoughts on EPA's Role in Biofuels 02/20/2007 (2007); Recommendations for Enhancing EPA's

Compliance Assistance Program (2004); NACEPT Superfund Subcommittee Final Report (2004); Advice Letter on EPA's Draft Report on the Environment (2003); The Environmental Future: Emerging Challenges and Future for EPA (2002); Advice Letters, EPA's Draft Strategic Architecture and Draft Strategic Plan; Advice Letter, National Environmental Technology Competition.

7548 ■ National Environmental Justice Advisory Council (NEJAC)
Off. of Environmental Justice
Environmental Protection Agency (Mail Code 2201A)
1200 Pennsylvania Ave., NW
Washington, DC 20460
Contact: Charles Lee, Designated Fed.Off.
Ph: (202)564-2515
Fax: (202)501-0740
URL: http://epa.gov/compliance/environmentaljustice/nejac/index.html
Staff: Support services are provided by the Office of Environmental Justice, Environmental Protection Agency. Charles Lee, Associate Director, Policy and Interagency Liaison, serves as designated federal official. **Descr:** Council provides advice and information to the Administrator, Environmental Protection Agency, on broad, cross-cutting domestic and international environmental justice policy issues. Council's advice and recommendations include evaluating EPA's progress, quality, and adequacy in planning, developing and implementing environmental justice strategies, projects and initiatives. It also provides advice on the adequacy of EPA's scientific research and demonstration projects relating to environmental justice. NEJAC work has focused on two major areas: (1) strategies to identify, mitigate, and/or prevent the disproportionate burden on communities of air pollution resulting from goods movement activities; and (2) key issues related to the integration of environmental justice considerations in EPA's programs, policies, and activities. **Mem:** Council consists of approximately 26 full Council members and subcommittee members who are stakeholders drawn from community-based groups; industry and business; federal, state, tribal, and local government organizations; academic and educational institutions; and nongovernmental and environmental groups. Members serve one- to three-year terms. Richard Moore, Southeast Network for Environmental and Economic Justice, Albuquerque, NM, chairs the Committee. **Pub:** Mechanisms to Enhance Future Stakeholder Involvement and Engagement to Address Environmental Justice (2006); The 2005 Gulf Coast Hurricanes and Vulnerable Populations: Recommendations for Future Disaster Preparedness and Response; The Unintended Impacts of Redevelopment and Revitalization Efforts in Five Environmental Justice Communities; Ensuring Risk Reduction in Communities with Multiple Stressors: Environmental Justice and Cumulative Risks/Impacts (2004); Environmental Justice, Urban Revitalization, and Brownfields; The Search for Authentic Signs of Hope; A Regulatory Strategy for Siting and Operating Waste Transfer Stations; The Model Plan for Public Participation; Environmental Justice in the Permitting Report; and The Environmental Justice and Community-Based Health Model Discussion and Recommendations Report.

7549 ■ Opal Creek Scenic Recreation Area Advisory Council
Opal Creek
Detroit Ranger District
HC73, Box 320
Mill City, OR 97360
Contact: Paul Matter, Designated Fed.Off.
Ph: (503)854-4200
Fax: (503)854-4239
URL: http://www.fs.fed.us/r6/willamette/manage/opalcreek/advisorycouncil.html
Staff: Paul Matter, Detroit District Ranger, Forest Service, serves as designated federal official. **Descr:** Council provides advice to the Secretary of Agriculture on the management of the Opal Creek Scenic Recreation Area. **Mem:** Council consists of 20 members, representing Marion County, City of Salem, State of Oregon, local communities, economic development, Indian tribes, environmental organizations, mining and timber industries, SRA inholder and public at large. **Pub:** Trails Subcommittee Recommendations for New Trails (2006); Pearl Greek Guard Station Preservation Subcommittee Report (2006).

7550 ■ TSCA Interagency Testing Committee (ITC)
Chemical Information and Testing Branch
Environmental Protection Agency
1200 Pennsylvania Ave. NW, Mail Code 7405M
Washington, DC 20460
Ph: (202)564-4780
Fax: (202)564-4765
URL: http://www.epa.gov/oppt/chemtest/pubs/whatitc.htm; http://www.epa.gov/opptintr/itc/
Descr: Committee selects and recommends chemicals and chemical groups for priority consideration for health effects, chemical fate, and ecological effects testing. It is concerned with chemicals or chemical groups for which the statutory, liaison organizations and others need data to assess health and environmental risks. These chemicals may: (1) present an unreasonable risk of injury to health or the environment, (2) reasonably be anticipated to enter the environment in substantial quantities, or (3) involve significant or substantial human exposure. At least every six months, the Committee furnishes the Administrator, EPA, with a revised *Priority Testing List* of chemicals or chemical groups recommended for testing. In preparing the *List*, the Committee reviews unpublished studies and data submitted by chemical manufacturers, processors, and distributors. Committee promotes the exchange of information on chemicals and coordinates testing of industrial chemicals sponsored or required by the federal government. **Mem:** Committee is composed of representatives from the following statutory agencies: Council on Environmental Quality, Department of Commerce, Environmental Protection Agency, National Cancer Institute, National Institute of Environmental Health Sciences, National Institute for Occupational Safety and Health, National Science Foundation, and Occupational Safety and Health Administration; and from the following liaison agencies: Agency for Toxic Substances and Diseases Registry, Consumer Product Safety Commission, Food and Drug Administration, National Library of Medicine, National Toxicology Program, and the Departments of Agriculture, Defense, and the Interior. **Pub:** ITC delivers reports to the EPA Administrator every six months. Most reports are delivered in May and November. ITC Reports are available on the ITC web site.

7551 ■ U.S. Environmental Protection Agency Region 1 Office
1 Congress St., Ste. 1100
Boston, MA 02114-2023
Ph: (617)918-1111
Free: 888-372-7341
Fax: (617)918-1809
URL: http://www.epa.gov/region01/

7552 ■ U.S. Environmental Protection Agency Region 2 Office
290 Broadway
New York, NY 10007-1866
Contact: George Pavlou, Actg.Reg.Admin.
Ph: (212)637-3660
Fax: (212)637-3526
URL: http://www.epa.gov/region02/

7553 ■ U.S. Environmental Protection Agency Region 3 Office
1650 Arch St. (3PM52)
Philadelphia, PA 19103-2029
Ph: (215)814-5000
Free: 800-438-2474
Fax: (215)814-5103
E-mail: r3public@epa.gov
URL: http://www.epa.gov/region03/

7554 ■ U.S. Environmental Protection Agency Region 4 Office
Sam Nunn Atlanta Federal Ctr.
61 Forsyth St., SW
Atlanta, GA 30303-8960
Ph: (404)562-9900
Free: 800-241-1754
Fax: (404)562-8174
URL: http://www.epa.gov/region04/

7555 ■ U.S. Environmental Protection Agency Region 5 Office
77 W. Jackson Blvd.
Chicago, IL 60604-3507
Ph: (312)353-2000
Free: 800-621-8431
Fax: (312)353-4135
E-mail: 5rhotline@epa.gov
URL: http://www.epa.gov/region5/

7556 ■ U.S. Environmental Protection Agency Region 6 Office
1445 Ross Ave., Ste. 1200
Dallas, TX 75202
Ph: (214)665-6444
Free: 800-887-6063
Fax: (214)665-7113
URL: http://www.epa.gov/region06/

7557 ■ U.S. Environmental Protection Agency Region 7 Office
901 N. 5th St.
Kansas City, KS 66101
Ph: (913)551-7003
Free: 800-223-0425
Fax: (913)551-7066
URL: http://www.epa.gov/region07/

7558 ■ U.S. Environmental Protection Agency Region 8 Office
8OC-EISC
1595 Wynkoop St.
Denver, CO 80202-1129
Ph: (303)312-6312
Free: 800-227-8917
Fax: (303)312-6339
E-mail: r8eisc@epa.gov
URL: http://www.epa.gov/region08/

7559 ■ U.S. Environmental Protection Agency Region 9 Office
75 Hawthorne St.
San Francisco, CA 94105
Ph: (415)947-8000
Free: 866-EPA-WEST
Fax: (415)947-3553
E-mail: r9.info@epa.gov
URL: http://www.epa.gov/region09/

7560 ■ U.S. Environmental Protection Agency Region 10 Office
1200 Sixth Ave., Ste. 900
Seattle, WA 98101
Ph: (206)553-1200
Free: 800-424-4372
Fax: (206)553-2955
URL: http://www.epa.gov/region10/

7561 ■ Veterans' Advisory Committee on Environmental Hazards
Department of Veterans Affairs
810 Vermont Ave. NW
Washington, DC 20420
Contact: Ersie Farber, Designated Fed.Off.
Ph: (202)461-9728
Fax: (202)275-1728
URL: http://www1.va.gov/advisory/page.cfm?pg=14
Staff: The Secretary of Veterans Affairs provides administrative and financial support for the Committee. **Descr:** P.L. 98-542, as amended, requires the Secretary of Veterans Affairs to prescribe regulations regarding certain disabilities of veterans who participated in atmospheric nuclear tests or with the American occupation of Hiroshima or Nagasaki, Japan, prior to July 1, 1946, and were exposed to

ionizing radiation from the detonation of a nuclear device. Committee evaluates scientific studies relating to possible adverse health effects of exposure to ionizing radiation and makes recommendations to the Secretary of Veterans Affairs regarding compensation for veterans. **Mem:** Committee currently comprises nine members who are appointed for three-year terms by the Secretary of Veterans Affairs in consultation with veteran organizations. Six of the nine members are recognized scientific or medical authorities in fields pertinent to understanding the health effects of exposure to ionizing radiation such as biomedicine, environmental science, and epidemiology. The remaining three members are from the general public, including at least one disabled veteran with an interest in and experience relating to veterans' concerns regarding ionizing radiation. The Under Secretary for Health and the Under Secretary for Benefits of the Department of Veterans Affairs, serve ex officio. Amir H. Soas, MD, PhD, Senior Health Specialist for Lighthouse Group, chairs the full Committee. Henry D. Royal, MD, Associate Director, Division of Nuclear Medicine, Mallinckrodt Institute of Radiology, and Professor of Radiology, Washington University School of Medicine, chairs the Scientific Council.

Associations and Other Organizations

7562 ■ Abundant Life Seeds (ALS)
PO Box 279
Cottage Grove, OR 97424
Ph: (541)767-9606
Fax: (866)514-7333
E-mail: info@abundantlifeseeds.com
URL: http://www.abundantlifeseeds.com
Staff: 6. **Descr:** Home gardeners, small farmers, students. Acquires, propagates, and preserves the plants and seeds of the Pacific Northwest, with particular emphasis on those species not commercially available, including rare and endangered species and heirlooms. Maintains permanent garden with seed saving as its primary purpose. **Fnd:** 1975. **Mem:** 1200. **Pub:** *Seed Midden* (3/year); Catalog (annual).

7563 ■ Active: Water
PO Box 37
Mattawan, MI 49071
Contact: Daren Wendell, Exec. Dir.
Ph: (269)492-6470
Fax: (269)375-4792
E-mail: info@activewater.org
URL: http://www.activewater.org
Descr: Promotes safe and clean water awareness. Raises funds to respond to the international water crises. Focuses on shaping individuals and groups to become life-saving instruments for people living in poverty. **Fnd:** 2006.

7564 ■ Algerian American Scientists Association (AASA)
1825 Madison Ave., Ste. 6H
New York, NY 10035
Contact: Azedine Medhkour, Pres.
Ph: (646)641-7615
E-mail: merghoub@gmail.com
URL: http://algerianamericanscientists.org
Descr: Aims to promote excellence among Algerian scientists and health care professionals in the United States. Fosters educational, scientific and health care cooperation between the USA and Algeria. Facilitates the advancement of science through scientific exchange, educational programs and networking. **Fnd:** 2007.

7565 ■ Alliance for Climate Protection
901 E St. NW, Ste. 610
Washington, DC 20004
Contact: Maggie L. Fox, Pres./CEO
Ph: (202)628-1999
Fax: (202)628-1445
URL: http://www.climateprotect.org

Descr: Focuses on educating the global community on the urgency of implementing comprehensive solutions to the climate crisis. Seeks to present choices and offer changes that will protect the planet for future generations. Brings together faces and voices in a way that diversifies and strengthens the national network of concerned individuals who want to take immediate action on climate issues. **Fnd:** 2006. **Mem:** 2000000.

7566 ■ Alliance to Save Energy (ASE)
1850 M St. NW, Ste. 600
Washington, DC 20036-5817
Contact: Kateri Callahan, Pres.
Ph: (202)857-0666
Fax: (202)331-9588
E-mail: info@ase.org
URL: http://www.ase.org
Staff: 60. **Descr:** Coalition of business, government, environmental, and consumer leaders who seek to increase the efficiency of energy use. Promotes energy efficiency worldwide to achieve a healthier economy, a cleaner environment, and a greater energy security. Conducts research, pilot projects, and educational programs. **Fnd:** 1977. **Mem:** 1500. **Pub:** Annual Report (annual).

7567 ■ Alliance for Sustainability
University of Minnesota
1521 University Ave. SE
Minneapolis, MN 55414
Contact: Sean Gosiewski, Program Dir.
Ph: (612)331-1099
Fax: (612)379-1527
E-mail: sean@afors.org
URL: http://www.allianceforsustainability.net
Descr: Development specialists, farmers, researchers, and other individuals; cooperatives and agricultural, consumer, and environmental groups. Aims to promote and contribute to the establishment of projects that are economically viable, ecologically sound, and socially just and humane. Sponsors programs in education, information dissemination, organizational support, network building, and policy. Promotes information sharing and cooperation through conferences, work exchanges, and organized tours. Furnishes technical expertise in farm practices, market development, and financial planning. Operates speakers' bureau; conducts workshops. Maintains resource center providing information on biological pest control, pesticides, and sustainable agriculture, sustainability and more. Conducts projects stressing the theme of sustainability: The Natural Step Framework Training Seminars, Junk Mail Tree Project, and Skiers Ending Hunger. **Fnd:** 1983. **Pub:** *Manna Newsletter* (monthly).

7568 ■ Alliance for Sustainable Jobs and the Environment (ASJE)
PO Box 1361
Eureka, CA 95502
Contact: Bob Borck, Labor Co-Chair
Ph: (707)498-4481
E-mail: bluegreen@asje.org
URL: http://www.asje.org
Descr: Aims to promote the protection of workers and the environment. Facilitates campaigns and educational programs that benefit workers and the environment. **Pub:** *Green Worker*; Magazine; Annual Report (annual).

7569 ■ Alternative Energy Resources Organization (AERO)
432 N Last Chance Gulch
Helena, MT 59601-5014
Contact: Jonda Crosby, Exec. Dir.
Ph: (406)443-7272
Fax: (406)442-9120
E-mail: aero@aeromt.org
URL: http://www.aeromt.org
Staff: 4. **Descr:** Promotes sustainable agriculture, resource conservation and transportation choices through community education and citizen representation. Provides current programs that focus on sustainable agriculture, farm improvement clubs,

beginning and retiring farmers, smart growth, and a more localized food system for greater community self-reliance. **Fnd:** 1974. **Mem:** 650. **Pub:** *Abundant Montana* (annual); *AERO Sun-Times* (quarterly); *Big Sky or Big Sprawl Montana at the Crossroads*; *Montana's Sustainable Agriculture Farming with Foresight*; *Sustainable Agriculture Curriculum-Grades 4-6*.

7570 ■ American Association of Pesticide Safety Educators (AAPSE)
Washington State University
PO Box 646382
Pullman, WA 99164-6382
Contact: Carol Ramsay, Pres.-Elect
Ph: (509)335-9222
Fax: (509)335-1009
E-mail: ramsay@wsu.edu
URL: http://www.aapse.org
Descr: Provides science-based pesticide safety education programs; seeks to protect human health and environment through education. **Pub:** *Journal of Pesticide Safety Education*; Position Papers.

7571 ■ American Council for an Energy-Efficient Economy (ACEEE)
529 14th St. NW, Ste. 600
Washington, DC 20045
Contact: Steven Nadel, Exec. Dir.
Ph: (202)507-4000
Fax: (202)429-2248
E-mail: info@aceee.org
URL: http://www.aceee.org
Staff: 22. **Descr:** Collects, evaluates, and disseminates information to encourage the implementation of energy-efficient technologies and practices. Conducts research on energy conservation and links to environmental and economic issues. Sponsors conferences to facilitate the exchange of information among all interested groups. Provides utilities, federal, state, and local energy officials, private industry, and consumers with information on energy efficiency. **Fnd:** 1980. **Pub:** *ACEEE Series on Energy Conservation and Energy Policy*; *ACEEE Summer Study on Energy Efficiency in Buildings* (biennial); *ACEEE's Green Book*; *Consumer Guide to Home Energy Savings*; *The Environmental Guide to Cars and Trucks*; Publications Catalog.

7572 ■ American Institute of Biomedical Climatology (AIBC)
1050 Eagle Rd.
Newtown, PA 18940-2818
Contact: George W.K. King, Sec.-Treas.
Ph: (215)968-4483
E-mail: info@aibc.cc
Staff: 3. **Descr:** Meteorologists, biologists, epidemiologists, physicians, atmospheric physicists, engineers, architects, physiologists, climatologists, and other professionals interested in investigating the influence of the outdoor and indoor environment on the health and diseases of man. Areas of interest include: global warming, indoor and outdoor air pollution, biological effects of electromagnetic fields, power lines, cell phones and cell towers, and beneficial and detrimental effects of climate and weather on health. **Fnd:** 1958. **Mem:** 45. **Pub:** *AIBC News Med-Clime Currents*; Membership List.

7573 ■ American Oil Chemists' Society (AOCS)
PO Box 17190
Urbana, IL 61803-7190
Contact: Jean Wills, Exec. VP
Ph: (217)359-2344
Fax: (217)351-8091
E-mail: general@aocs.org
URL: http://www.aocs.org
Staff: 6. **Descr:** Chemists, biochemists, chemical engineers, research directors, plant personnel, and others in laboratories and chemical process industries concerned with animal, marine, and vegetable oils and fats, and their extraction, refining, safety, packaging, quality control, and use in consumer and industrial products such as foods, drugs, paints, waxes, lubricants, soaps, and cosmetics. Sponsors short courses; certifies referee chemists; distributes

cooperative check samples; sells official reagents. Maintains 100 committees. Operates job placement service for members only. **Fnd:** 1909. **Mem:** 4700. **Local Groups:** 9. **Pub:** *INFORM* (monthly); *Journal of Surfactants and Detergents* (quarterly); *Lipids* (monthly); Journal (monthly); Membership Directory (annual); Monographs; Proceedings.

7574 ■ American Public Information on the Environment
PO Box 676
Northfield, MN 55057-0676
Free: 800-320-2743
Fax: (507)645-5724
E-mail: info@americanpie.org
URL: http://www.AmericanPIE.org

Staff: 7. **Descr:** Individuals, organizations, and businesses. Promotes "development of a land ethic and ecological consciousness essential to sustaining the environment". Gathers and disseminates information on "environmental quality, protection of natural resources and promotion of environmental health for all elements of the biotic community". **Fnd:** 1993. **Mem:** 700.

7575 ■ American Public Power Association (APPA)
1875 Connecticut Ave. NW, Ste. 1200
Washington, DC 20009
Contact: Maude Grantham-Richards, Chm.
Ph: (202)467-2900
Fax: (202)467-2910
E-mail: mrufe@appanet.org
URL: http://www.appanet.org

Staff: 60. **Descr:** Municipally owned electric utilities, public utility districts, state and county-owned electric systems, and rural cooperatives. Conducts research programs; compiles statistics; offers utility education courses; sponsors competitions. **Fnd:** 1940. **Mem:** 2000. **Reg. Groups:** 10. **Pub:** *Annual Directory and Statistical Report* (annual); *Public Power* (bimonthly); *Public Power Weekly* (weekly); Booklets; Manuals; Papers; Surveys.

7576 ■ American Resources Group (ARG)
374 Maple Ave. E, Ste. 310
Vienna, VA 22180-4751
Contact: Dr. Keith A. Argow
Ph: (703)255-2700
Free: 800-476-8733
Fax: (703)281-9200
E-mail: info@firetower.org
URL: http://www.firetower.org

Staff: 5. **Descr:** Conservation service organization providing land acquisition and forestry services for membership organizations. Engages in monitoring educational and research activities that promote a more sensible use of U.S. natural resources, especially small, private forestlands. Maintains speakers' bureau; compiles statistics; provides land acquisition services. Sponsors National Historic Lookout Register. **Fnd:** 1981. **Reg. Groups:** 4. **State Groups:** 32. **Pub:** *The Forestry Advantage* (quarterly); *National Woodlands Magazine* (quarterly).

7577 ■ American Slow Sand Association
49 Morgan St.
Ilion, NY 13357
Contact: Janet Darling, Sec.
Ph: (315)895-7711
Fax: (315)895-7196
E-mail: water@ilionny.com

Descr: Water districts, corporations, public authorities, and political subdivisions with a primary interest in the provision and distribution of potable water or in the treatment of wastewater using slow sand filtration systems. Promotes the establishment and operation of slow sand water filtration systems. Serves as a clearinghouse on slow sand filtration; conducts educational programs and research on wastewater treatment; provides advice to state legislative bodies

with an interest in water supply and treatment. **Fnd:** 1984. **Mem:** 97.

7578 ■ American Society for Microbiology (ASM)
1752 N St. NW
Washington, DC 20036
Contact: Michael I. Goldberg PhD, Exec. Dir.
Ph: (202)737-3600
Fax: (202)942-9333
E-mail: oed@asmusa.org
URL: http://www.asm.org

Staff: 115. **Descr:** Scientific society of microbiologists. Promotes the advancement of scientific knowledge in order to improve education in microbiology. Encourages the highest professional and ethical standards, and the adoption of sound legislative and regulatory policies affecting the discipline of microbiology at all levels. Communicates microbiological scientific achievements to the public. Maintains numerous committees and 23 divisions, and placement services; compiles statistics. **Fnd:** 1899. **Mem:** 42000. **Local Groups:** 36. **Pub:** *Abstracts of Annual Meeting*; *Antimicrobial Agents and Chemotherapy* (monthly); *Applied and Environmental Microbiology* (monthly); *ASM Directory of Members*; *ASM News* (monthly); *Clinical Microbiology Reviews* (quarterly); *Infection and Immunity* (monthly); *International Journal of Systematic Bacteriology* (quarterly); *Journal of Bacteriology* (semimonthly); *Journal of Clinical Microbiology* (monthly); *Journal of Virology* (monthly); *Microbiological Reviews* (quarterly); *Molecular and Cellular Biology* (monthly); Books; Manuals; Reprints.

7579 ■ American Solar Energy Society (ASES)
2400 Central Ave., Ste. A
Boulder, CO 80301
Contact: Bradley D. Collins, Exec. Dir.
Ph: (303)443-3130
Fax: (303)443-3212
E-mail: ases@ases.org
URL: http://www.ases.org

Staff: 4. **Descr:** Professional energy society organized to promote a wide utilization of solar energy through the application of science and technology. Encourages basic and applied research and development. Conducts workshops; organizes forums inviting researchers, policymakers, practitioners and consumers for discussion, analysis, and debate. Promotes education by compiling and disseminating information to schools, universities, and the community. **Fnd:** 1954. **Mem:** 4000. **Reg. Groups:** 26. **Pub:** *Advances in Solar Energy* (annual); *National Passive Conference Proceedings* (annual); *Solar Today* (bimonthly); Membership Directory; Manuals.

7580 ■ Animal Agriculture Alliance
PO Box 9522
Arlington, VA 22219
Contact: Ms. Kay Johnson, Exec. VP
Ph: (703)562-5160
E-mail: info@animalagalliance.org
URL: http://www.animalagalliance.org

Staff: 3. **Descr:** Provides educational information about U.S. animal agriculture's contribution to the American consumer's quality of life. Serves as umbrella organization for feed, livestock, and poultry groups to deliver consistent messages to consumers. Provides information on animal agriculture as it relates to animal well-being, food safety, and environmental safety. Works to dispel misconceptions that animals raised for food and other products are mistreated and that a diet containing meat, milk, and eggs is unhealthy. Encourages and sponsors scientific research and educational programs. **Fnd:** 1987. **Pub:** *Alliance Newsletter* (monthly); *Animal Agriculture: Myths and Facts*; *Show Animal Care and Handling Guide*.

7581 ■ Animal Law Coalition (ALC)
907 Hanshaw Rd., No. 213
Ithaca, NY 14850
Contact: Laura Allen, Founder/Exec. Dir.

Ph: (607)220-8938
URL: http://www.animallawcoalition.com

Descr: Works to stop animal cruelty and suffering through legislation, administrative agency action and litigation. Offers legal analysis of the difficult and controversial issues relating to animals. Promotes or opposes political candidates and lobbies without restriction for legislation in support of animal welfare.

7582 ■ Animal Rights Coalition (ARC)
2615 E Franklin Ave.
Minneapolis, MN 55406
Ph: (612)822-6161
E-mail: animalrightscoalition@msn.com
URL: http://www.animalrightscoalition.com

Descr: Seeks to end the suffering, abuse, and exploitation of non-human animals through information, education, and advocacy. **Fnd:** 1980. **Pub:** *Animal Rights Coalition News* (semiannual); *Children and Dogs*; *Dissection: Biology or Cruelty?*; *Factory Farming: Mechanized Madness*; *Kids: Lets Talk About Animal Rights*; *Pet Shops: Love for Sale*; *The Real Price of Fashion*.

7583 ■ Animal Rights International (ARI)
PO Box 1292
Middlebury, CT 06762
Ph: (203)598-0554
E-mail: info@ari-online.org
URL: http://www.ari-online.org

Staff: 2. **Descr:** Represents individuals and organizations united to: reduce or eliminate the use of animals in testing, research, and education, without compromising human safety. Promotes nonviolent food. Encourages companies that conduct tests on animals to sponsor research into devising substitute tests of equal or greater accuracy that do not require the use of animals, or that use fewer animals and minimize their pain and suffering; encourages agribusinesses to employ economically viable techniques that take into account the well-being of food animals. Develops fact sheets and position papers on topics related to alternative methods of testing. Promotes vegetarianism. **Fnd:** 1974. **Pub:** *Coordinator's Report* (periodic).

7584 ■ Animal Rights Network/Animals and Society Institute (ARN/ASI)
2512 Carpenter Rd., Ste. 201-A2
Ann Arbor, MI 48108
Ph: (734)677-9240
Fax: (734)677-9242
E-mail: info@animalsandsociety.org
URL: http://www.animalsandsociety.org

Staff: 3. **Descr:** Advances animal advocacy issues in public policy development by conducting scholarly research and analysis, providing education and training, and fostering cooperation with other social movements and interests. **Fnd:** 1979.

7585 ■ Association for Communication Excellence in Agriculture, Natural Resources, and Life and Human Sciences (ACE)
PO Box 110811
Gainesville, FL 32611
Contact: Frankie Gould, Pres.
Ph: (352)392-9588
Fax: (352)392-8583
E-mail: ace@ifas.ufl.edu
URL: http://www.aceweb.org

Staff: 1. **Descr:** Develops professional skills of education, government, and research communicators and information technologists to extend knowledge about agriculture, natural resources and human sciences. **Fnd:** 1912. **Mem:** 700. **Reg. Groups:** 4. **State Groups:** 50. **Pub:** *ACE Archives Directory*; *Journal of Applied Communications* (quarterly); *Signals* (bimonthly).

7586 ■ Association for the Environmental Health of Soils (AEHS)
150 Fearing St.
Amherst, MA 01002
Contact: Paul Kostecki PhD, Exec. Dir./Exec. Ed.
Ph: (413)549-5170
Free: 888-540-2347

Fax: (413)549-0579
E-mail: paul@aehs.com
URL: http://www.aehs.com

Descr: Individuals interested in soil contamination and the analysis, assessment, remediation, and regulation of soils. Seeks to facilitate communication and foster cooperation among members. Serves as a network linking members; serves as a clearinghouse on soil contamination and remediation; sponsors educational programs. Makes available discounts on books to members. **Fnd:** 1989. **Mem:** 600. **Pub:** *International Journal of Phytoremediation* (periodic); *Journal of Soil Contamination* (periodic); *Soil and Groundwater Cleanup Magazine* (9/year).

7587 ■ Association of Municipal Recycling Coordinators (AMRC)
127 Wyndham St. N, Ste. 100
Guelph, ON, Canada N1H 4E9
Contact: Vivian De Giovanni, Exec. Dir.
Ph: (519)823-1990
Fax: (519)823-0084
E-mail: amrc@amrc.ca
URL: http://www.amrc.ca

Staff: 3. **Descr:** Municipal waste management professionals. Promotes more effective and environmentally sustainable removal of solid wastes. Facilitates sharing of municipal waste management, reduction, recycling, and reuse information and facilities. Conducts continuing professional education courses for members; operates job hotline; represents members' interests before government agencies and the public. Sponsors research; compiles statistics. **Fnd:** 1987. **Mem:** 200. **Pub:** *For R Information* (quarterly); Brochure.

7588 ■ Association of Water Technologies (AWT)
9707 Key West Ave., Ste. 100
Rockville, MD 20850
Contact: Ms. Heidi Zimmerman, Exec. Dir.
Ph: (301)740-1421
Fax: (301)990-9771
E-mail: hzimmerman@awt.org
URL: http://www.awt.org

Staff: 3. **Descr:** Provides regional water treatment companies with technical education, industry communication, access to information, group purchasing discounts, legislative affairs, and sound management techniques. Also supplies certification of professional water technologists and regulatory monitoring. **Fnd:** 1985. **Mem:** 2000. **Pub:** *The Analyst* (quarterly); *Technical Reference and Training Manual*; Membership Directory; Papers.

7589 ■ Beauty Without Cruelty U.S.A. (BWC)
175 W. 12th St., No. 16-G
New York, NY 10011
Contact: Dr. Ethel Thurston, Chm.
Ph: (212)989-8073
Fax: (212)989-8073

Staff: 6. **Descr:** Opposes the painful and destructive use of animals in the production of apparel and toiletries. Informs the public of the suffering of both wild and farmed fur-bearing animals, of trapped wild animals, and of animals used to make products and animal testing of cosmetics. Sponsors fashion shows of simulated fur garments and other garments without fur to demonstrate the humane alternatives to real fur. Provides information on where to obtain cruelty-free apparel and toiletries. Maintains speakers' bureau and charitable program. **Fnd:** 1972. **Mem:** 7000. **Reg. Groups:** 3. **Pub:** *Action Alert* (3/year); *The Compassionate Shopper* (3/year); Directory (periodic).

7590 ■ Beyond Pesticides - National Coalition Against the Misuse of Pesticides (NCAMP)
701 E St. SE, Ste. 200
Washington, DC 20003
Contact: Jay Feldman, Exec. Dir.
Ph: (202)543-5450
Fax: (202)543-4791
E-mail: info@beyondpesticides.org
URL: http://www.beyondpesticides.org

Staff: 5. **Descr:** Individuals and consumer, environ-

mental, farming, health, labor, and church organizations concerned with pesticide hazards and safety. Seeks to advance national and international awareness of public health, environmental, and economic problems caused by pesticides; to protect individuals exposed to pesticides. Works to improve legislation, regulation, and enforcement affecting pesticide use and to stress a systematic approach emphasizing preventive public health measures to control pesticides from production through use and disposal. Promotes alternatives to pesticide use such as integrated pest management, which ensures reduced soil and water contamination and lower residues in food. Stresses that these alternatives will reduce environmental damage, ease economic burdens, and improve the general health of the public. Collects and disseminates information and monitors governmental activities. **Fnd:** 1981. **Mem:** 1400. **Pub:** *Legislative Alerts* (periodic); *Pest Control Without Toxic Chemicals*; *Pesticide Safety: Myths and Facts*; *Pesticides and You* (quarterly); *Poison Poles: Their Toxic Trail and the Safer Alternatives*; *Public Health Mosquito Management Strategy*; *Safety at Home: A Guide to the Hazards of Lawn and Garden Pesticides*; *Technical Report* (monthly); *Unnecessary Risks*; Reports; Brochures.

7591 ■ Bio-Integral Resource Center (BIRC)
PO Box 7414
Berkeley, CA 94707
Contact: William Quarles, Managing Ed.
Ph: (510)524-2567
Fax: (510)524-1758
E-mail: birc@igc.org
URL: http://www.birc.org

Descr: Provides publications and consultations for pest management professionals, farmers, foresters, park service resource managers, environmentalists, and interested individuals. Provides practical information on methods of managing pests and land resource problems. Evaluates and disseminates information on the least toxic method of managing weed, vertebrate, insect, and microbe pests in urban, agricultural, forestall, and veterinary environments. Develops integrated pest management programs for community groups, public agencies, and private institutions. (IPM involves integrating biological, horticultural, mechanical, and chemical strategies to suppress pest populations below levels causing economic, medical, or aesthetic damage.) Areas of technical assistance include: consultation of community pest problems; identification of pests and their natural enemies; pest control program evaluation; development of contract specifications; landscape design and design plan review; integration of IPM methods and sustainable agriculture. Reports on educational opportunities; sponsors workshops and lectures. **Fnd:** 1979. **Local Groups:** 19. **Pub:** *Common Sense Pest Control*; *Common Sense Pest Control Quarterly* (quarterly); *Directory of Least-toxic Pest Control Products*; *IPM Practitioner*.

7592 ■ Canadian Environmental Law Association (CELA)
130 Spadina Ave., Ste. 301
Toronto, ON, Canada M5V 2L4
Contact: Theresa McClenaghan, Exec. Dir./Counsel
Ph: (416)960-2284
Fax: (416)960-9392
E-mail: theresa@cela.ca
URL: http://www.cela.ca

Staff: 12. **Descr:** Protects and enhances public health and environmental quality throughout Canada. Advocates for comprehensive laws, standards and policies. Seeks to increase public participation in environmental decision-making. **Fnd:** 1970. **Pub:** *Intervenor* (quarterly).

7593 ■ Canadian Environmental Network (CEN)
300-945 Wellington St. W
Ottawa, ON, Canada K1Y 2X5
Contact: Ms. Susan Tanner, Exec. Dir.
Ph: (613)728-9810
Fax: (613)728-2963
E-mail: info@cen-rce.org

URL: http://www.cen-rce.org

Staff: 10. **Descr:** Environmental organizations. Seeks to advance the projects and activities of members. Promotes ecologically sustainable development. Serves as a clearinghouse on environmental issues; provides support and assistance to members. **Fnd:** 1988. **Mem:** 780. **Reg. Groups:** 12. **Pub:** *Canadian Environmental Network News* (annual).

7594 ■ Carbon Management Council
1211 Connecticut Ave. NW, Ste. 600
Washington, DC 20036
Contact: Jeffrey Serfass, Pres.
Ph: (202)457-0868
Fax: (202)223-5537
E-mail: info@carboncouncil.org
URL: http://www.carboncouncil.org

Descr: Aims to educate leaders on the opportunities in carbon management. Provides information on carbon management principles and practices to the public. Creates opportunities for business leaders, government organizations, policy makers, and researchers to implement sound carbon management solutions to reduce their carbon footprint. **Fnd:** 2007.

7595 ■ CarFree City, USA
PO Box 2841
Berkeley, CA 94702-0841
Contact: Eugene B. Yates, Pres.
Ph: (510)849-4412
Fax: (510)849-4412
URL: http://new.carfreecity.us

Descr: Works to create and promote a carfree city. Aims to enhance both local and global environmental quality. Encourages local agencies and elected officials to modify zoning and building codes and to support carfree development. **Fnd:** 2003.

7596 ■ Cement Kiln Recycling Coalition (CKRC)
PO Box 7553
Arlington, VA 22207
Contact: Mike Benoit, Exec. Dir.
Ph: (703)534-0892
URL: http://www.ckrc.org

Descr: Cement companies engaged in the use of fuel derived from hazardous waste; collectors, processors, managers, and marketers of cement kiln fuel derived from hazardous waste. Promotes environmentally responsible use of hazardous waste as fuel for cement kilns. Develops and enforces standards of conduct and practice for members; supports regulations and permit provisions for the use of fuel derived from hazardous waste that protect human and environmental health; works to create generally accepted environmental evaluation procedures for the cement kiln industry. **Mem:** 100.

7597 ■ Center for Alternative Mining Development Policy (CAMDP)
210 Avon St., Ste. 4
La Crosse, WI 54603
Contact: Al Gedicks, Exec. Dir.
Ph: (608)784-4399
Fax: (608)785-8486
E-mail: gedicks.al@uwlax.edu

Descr: Native Americans, farmers, and those living in urban areas concerned about threats to the environment of the Lake Superior region. Seeks to provide information and technical assistance to Indian tribes and rural communities affected by plans for mining development. Focuses on issues such as mining taxation, groundwater quality, hazards of uranium exploration, and the environmental impact of metallic sulfide mining. Operates speakers' bureau. Consults with similar international and national groups. **Fnd:** 1977. **Mem:** 600. **Pub:** *Anishinaabe Niijii (Friends of the Chippewa)*; *Keepers of the Water*; *LAND GRAB: The Corporate Theft of Wisconsin's Mineral Resources*; *The New Resource Wars*; *The New Resource Wars: Native and Environmental Struggles Against Multinational Corporations*; *Questions and Answers about BHP Billiton's Proposed Crandon Mine in Wisconsin*; *Resource Rebels:*

Native Challenges to Mining and Oil Corporations; Brochures.

7598 ■ Center for Clean Air Policy (CCAP)
750 First St. NE, Ste. 940
Washington, DC 20002
Contact: Ned Helme, Pres.
Ph: (202)408-9260
Fax: (202)408-8896
E-mail: communications@ccap.org
URL: http://www.ccap.org
Staff: 13. **Descr:** Participants are U.S. state governors and corporate, academic, and public interest leaders. Develops and analyzes approaches to resolving environmental and energy issues. Seeks to inform decision makers and the public of the underlying environmental and economic implications of air pollution controls. Organizes and mediates discussions between all parties with an interest in the environment and economic impacts of air pollution control legislation. Conducts study projects to measure the impact of acid rain control strategies and policies, energy conservation efforts, and economic, environmental, and waste management control options; is currently engaged in environmental exchange programs with Germany and the Czech Republic. **Fnd:** 1985. **Pub:** *A Natural Approach: Forestry and Global Climate Changes; Acid Rain: Road to a Middleground Solution; Air Quality and Electricity Restructuring; An Efficient Approach to Reducing Acid Rain: The Environment Benefits of Energy Conservation; Cooling the Greenhouse Effect: Options and Costs for Reducing CO2 Emissions from the American Electric Power Company; Strengthening Demand Side Management In Ohio; The Untold Story: The Silver Lining for West Virginia in Acid Rain Control; Wisconsin's Strategy: Cleaning the Air, Protecting the Climate, Sustaining the Economy.*

7599 ■ Center For Health, Environment and Justice (CHEJ)
PO Box 6806
Falls Church, VA 22040-6806
Contact: Lois Marie Gibbs, Exec. Dir./Founder
Ph: (703)237-2249
Fax: (703)237-8389
E-mail: chej@chej.org
URL: http://www.chej.org
Staff: 13. **Descr:** Promotes environmental justice and empowerment through community organization. **Fnd:** 1981. **Mem:** 27599. **Reg. Groups:** 50. **State Groups:** 250. **Local Groups:** 8000. **Pub:** *Everyone's Backyard* (quarterly); *Journal of the Grassroots Movement;* Books; Manuals; Handbooks; Catalog.

7600 ■ Center for Health and the Global Environment
Harvard Medical School
401 Park Dr., 2nd Fl. E
Boston, MA 02115
Contact: Kathleen Frith MS, Admin. Dir.
Ph: (617)384-8530
Fax: (617)384-8585
E-mail: chge@hms.harvard.edu
URL: http://chge.med.harvard.edu
Descr: Promotes human health consequences of global environmental change. **Fnd:** 1996. **Pub:** *Biodiversity: Its Importance to Human Health; Biological and Physical Signs of Climate Change: Focus on Mosquito-Borne Diseases; The Bulletin; Climate Change and U.S. Agriculture: The Impacts of Warming and Extreme Weather Events on Productivity, Plant Diseases, and Pests; Environment and Health: Species Loss and Ecosystem Disruption the Implications for Human Health; Is Global Warming Harmful to Health?; Marine Ecosystems: Emerging Diseases as Indicators of Change; Oil: A Life Cycle Analysis of its Health and Environmental Impacts;* Newsletter (semiannual).

7601 ■ Children's Environmental Health Network (CEHN)
110 Maryland Ave. NE, Ste. 505
Washington, DC 20002
Contact: Nsedu Obot Witherspoon, Exec. Dir.

Ph: (202)543-4033
Fax: (202)543-8797
E-mail: cehn@cehn.org
URL: http://www.cehn.org
Descr: Promotes the development of sound public health and child-focused national policy for children affected by exposures to environmental hazards. **Pub:** *Children's Environmental Health.*

7602 ■ Clean Air Trust (CAT)
1625 K St. NW, Ste. 790
Washington, DC 20006
Ph: (301)941-1987
E-mail: frank@cleanairtrust.org
URL: http://www.cleanairtrust.org
Descr: Aims to educate the public and policymakers about the value of the Clean Air Act; promotes effective enforcement of the Act. **Fnd:** 1995. **Pub:** Bulletins.

7603 ■ Climate Counts
PO Box 4844
Manchester, NH 03108
Contact: Wood Turner, Proj. Dir.
Ph: (603)216-3788
E-mail: info@climatecounts.org
URL: http://www.climatecounts.org
Descr: Aims to help stop global warming. Brings consumers and companies together in the fight against global climate change. Raises awareness of consumers and the public of their power to support companies that take climate change seriously. **Fnd:** 2006.

7604 ■ Climate Group
444 Park Ave. S, 2nd Fl.
New York, NY 10016
Contact: Neal McGrath, Dir. of Communications
Ph: (646)233-0550
Fax: (646)861-4606
E-mail: info@theclimategroup.org
URL: http://www.theclimategroup.org
Descr: Advances business and government leadership on climate change. Creates interest and effort to stop climate change. Works to accelerate international action on global warming. Promotes profitability and competitiveness among the government, business and non-profit sectors. **Fnd:** 2004. **Pub:** Bulletin (monthly).

7605 ■ Climate Registry
523 W 6th St., Ste. 445
Los Angeles, CA 90014
Contact: Diane Wittenberg, Exec. Dir.
Ph: (213)891-6922
Free: 866-523-0764
Fax: (213)623-6716
E-mail: info@theclimateregistry.org
URL: http://www.theclimateregistry.org
Descr: Works to provide an accurate, complete, consistent, transparent, and verified set of greenhouse gas emissions data supported by a robust reporting and verification infrastructure. Encourages concerted initiatives to reduce greenhouse gas emissions and supports future greenhouse gas reduction efforts across North America. Promotes full and public disclosure of greenhouse gas emissions reports.

7606 ■ Coalition for Responsible Waste Incineration (CRWI)
1615 L St. NW, Ste. 1350
Washington, DC 20036
Ph: (202)452-1241
Fax: (202)887-8044
E-mail: mel@crwi.org
URL: http://www.crwi.org
Descr: Manufacturing companies; academic institutions; interested individuals and organizations. Promotes responsible incineration of industrial wastes as part of an overall waste management strategy. Serves as a forum for exchange of information among members and supplies members with technical, safety, health, and environmental information concerning waste incineration. Provides information on industrial incineration systems to the public,

the media, and government officials at the local, state, and federal levels. Monitors and reports on the formulation of legislative and regulatory guidelines for industrial waste incineration. Encourages research in incineration. **Fnd:** 1987. **Mem:** 28. **Pub:** *CRWI Update* (monthly); Proceedings (annual).

7607 ■ Communications, Energy and Paperworkers Union of Canada (CEP)
301 Laurier Ave. W
Ottawa, ON, Canada K1P 6M6
Contact: Dave Coles, Pres.
Ph: (613)230-5200
Free: 877-230-5201
Fax: (613)230-5801
E-mail: info@cep.ca
URL: http://www.cep.ca
Staff: 176. **Descr:** Trade union. Organizes and conducts collective bargaining for individuals employed in the telecommunications, electrical, electronics, pulp and paper, energy, print and broadcast media, and chemical industries in Canada. **Fnd:** 1992. **Mem:** 160000.

7608 ■ Compassion Without Borders (CWOB)
PO Box 14995
Santa Rosa, CA 95402
Contact: Christi Payne, Founder
Ph: (707)474-3345
E-mail: info@cwob.org
URL: http://www.cwob.org
Descr: Seeks to alleviate the suffering of unwanted companion animals in Mexico and other low resource regions. Promotes international rescue efforts and spay/neuter campaigns. Provides humane education and humane euthanasia programs. **Fnd:** 2001.

7609 ■ Composting Council of Canada
16, rue Northumberland St.
Toronto, ON, Canada M6H 1P7
Contact: Susan Antler, Exec. Dir.
Ph: (416)535-0240
Free: 877-571-4769
Fax: (416)536-9892
E-mail: ccc@compost.org
URL: http://www.compost.org
Descr: Serves to advocate and advance composting and compost usage across Canada. Serves as the central resource and network for the composting industry in Canada. Contributes to the environmental sustainability of communities. Sponsors International Composting Awareness Week; "Plant a Row Grow a Row". Conducts seminars and educational programs. Compiles statistics, maintains speakers' bureau. **Fnd:** 1991. **Pub:** *Communique.*

7610 ■ The Conservative Caucus Research, Analysis and Education Foundation (TCCF)
450 Maple Ave. E
Vienna, VA 22180
Contact: Howard Phillips, Chm.
Ph: (703)281-6782
E-mail: corndorf@cais.com
URL: http://www.conservativeusa.org/TCCFMission.htm
Staff: 8. **Descr:** Conservative individuals interested in staying informed of the activities of the federal government. Disseminates information concerning the actions and expenditures of the federal government. Supports Accountability Project to monitor federal moneys given to political activist groups. **Fnd:** 1976. **Mem:** 6000. **Pub:** *Eye on Bureaucracy* (monthly); *Howard Phillips Issues and Strategy* (semimonthly); Monographs; Report.

7611 ■ Conservative Majority for Citizen's Rights (CMCR)
302 Briarwood Cir. NW
Fort Walton Beach, FL 32548-3904
Contact: James Stanley Harkins Sr., Pres.
Ph: (850)862-6211
E-mail: jharkins@americangospel.org
URL: http://www.americangospel.org
Staff: 20. **Descr:** International and national conservative organizations; individuals promoting a conservative government. Provides on-call citizen aid

through political advocacy. Supports and distributes literature on issues such as citizens' rights, separation of church and state, pro-life activities and stances, pro-traditional family, anti-pornography, a strong national defense, and equal rights for women. Conducts research and educational programs. Maintains speakers' bureau; sponsors charitable programs. Compiles statistics. **Fnd:** 1981. **Mem:** 30000. **Pub:** *The Angry Samaritan Chronicles*; *Conservative Majority Newsletter* (quarterly).

7612 ■ Consumer Energy Alliance (CEA)
2211 Norfolk St., Ste. 614
Houston, TX 77098-4044
Contact: David Holt, Pres.
Ph: (713)337-8800
E-mail: info@consumerenergyalliance.org
URL: http://consumerenergyalliance.org
Descr: Works to improve general understanding of energy security and the thoughtful development and utilization of energy resources. Provides a voice for consumers interested in vital public issues. Helps in the improvement of domestic and global energy security and stable prices for consumers.

7613 ■ Consumer Energy Council of America Research Foundation (CECA/RF)
2000 L St. NW, Ste. 802
Washington, DC 20036
Contact: Ellen Berman, Pres.
Ph: (202)659-0404
Fax: (202)659-0407
E-mail: outreach@cecarf.org
URL: http://www.cecarf.org
Staff: 8. **Descr:** Focuses on network industries. Strives to establish arenas in which domestic and international policymakers and business leaders can forge innovative solutions to economic, environmental, and educational challenges worldwide. Works for constructive involvement of government and private organizations in broad educational initiatives and in the creation of self-sustaining and socially responsible markets for essential services. Provides expertise in how government and corporate policies affect the public, and how public response will affect legislation and the vibrancy of new markets. **Fnd:** 1973.

7614 ■ Crude Accountability
217 Palos Verdes Blvd., No. 137
Redondo Beach, CA 90277
Contact: Kate Watters, Exec. Dir.
Ph: (310)621-8935
E-mail: michelle@crudeaccountability.org
URL: http://www.crudeaccountability.org
Descr: Seeks to protect the threatened ecosystems of the Caspian region. **Fnd:** 2003.

7615 ■ EarthSave Canada
SPEC Bldg.
2150 Maple St.
Vancouver, BC, Canada V6J 3T3
Contact: Dale Littlejohn, Pres.
Ph: (604)731-5885
Fax: (604)731-5805
URL: http://www.earthsave.ca
Staff: 2. **Descr:** Seeks to increase the awareness of the health, ethical, and environmental impacts of food choices. Promotes transition to a plant-based diet for optimum health, environmental sustainability, and compassion. **Fnd:** 1990. **Mem:** 570. **State Groups:** 3. **Local Groups:** 3. **Pub:** *Canada Earth-Saver* (bimonthly).

7616 ■ Ecojustice Canada
131 Water St., Ste. 214
Vancouver, BC, Canada V6B 4M3
Contact: Devon Page, Exec. Dir.
Ph: (604)685-5618
Free: 800-926-7744
Fax: (604)685-7813
E-mail: info@ecojustice.ca
URL: http://www.ecojustice.ca
Staff: 45. **Descr:** Represents attorneys and others with an interest in conservation and environmental law. Provides free legal advice and representation to

organizations and individuals seeking judgments in cases involving environmental protection. **Fnd:** 1990. **Mem:** 41. **Pub:** Annual Report.

7617 ■ Empowerment Society International (ESI)
4460 S Cobblestone St.
Gilbert, AZ 85297
Contact: Peter Adolphus Gbelia, Exec. Dir.
E-mail: execdir@empowermentsociety.com
URL: http://www.empowermentsociety.com
Descr: Strives to empower individuals by promoting sustainable development and renewable energy in sub-Saharan Africa. Treats and prevents AIDS and other diseases, combats illiteracy and eliminates poverty in sub-Saharan community. Works with the public, private and corporate sectors in building sustainable society. **Fnd:** 2003.

7618 ■ Empowerment Works (EW)
1801 Lincoln Blvd., No. 138
Venice, CA 90291
Contact: Melanie St. James MPA, Founder/Exec. Dir.
Ph: (310)392-6909
E-mail: info@empowermentworks.org
URL: http://www.empowermentworks.org
Descr: Focuses on promoting a sustainable global community through the advancement of community-based public and private partnerships and civic engagement. **Fnd:** 2001.

7619 ■ EndOil
4000 Long Beach Blvd., Ste. 249
Long Beach, CA 90807
Contact: Gisele Fong PhD, Exec. Dir.
Ph: (562)424-8200
URL: http://www.endoil.org
Descr: Seeks to end the country's dependency on oil. Advocates for a comprehensive national plan to free America from oil dependency. Strives to move individuals, governments and civil society towards non-petroleum sources of energy. **Fnd:** 2004.

7620 ■ Energy Bar Association (EBA)
1990 M St. NW, Ste. 350
Washington, DC 20036
Contact: Lorna Wilson, Exec. Dir.
Ph: (202)223-5625
Fax: (202)833-5596
E-mail: admin@eba-net.org
URL: http://www.eba-net.org
Descr: Attorneys practicing in the U.S. and its territories, districts, and possessions. Seeks to promote the proper administration of laws relating to production, development, conservation, transmission, and economic regulation of energy. Conducts educational programs. **Fnd:** 1946. **Mem:** 2400. **State Groups:** 3. **Pub:** *Committee Reports* (annual); *EBA Update* (quarterly); Membership Directory (annual).

7621 ■ Energy Probe Research Foundation (EPRF)
225 Brunswick Ave.
Toronto, ON, Canada M5S 2M6
Contact: Patricia Adams, Pres.
Ph: (416)964-9223
Fax: (416)964-8239
E-mail: webadmin@eprf.ca
URL: http://www.eprf.ca/eprf/index.html
Staff: 25. **Descr:** Seeks to inform public opinion on matters of environmental protection, energy resources and consumption, international development, and consumer policies. Promotes social change through participation in democratic political institutions. Functions as a watchdog organization, monitoring public and corporate policies related to energy production and consumption and environmental protection. Provides advice and information to government agencies and corporations in matters of energy and environmental protection. Conducts research and educational programs; makes avail-

able teaching aids and other informative materials. **Fnd:** 1989. **Mem:** 50000.

7622 ■ Energy Services Coalition (ESC)
Energy Systems Group
501 Union St., Ste. 300-B
Nashville, TN 37219
Contact: Ray Hinson, Pres.
Ph: (615)268-4812
Fax: (615)248-3681
E-mail: info@energyservicescoalition.org
URL: http://www.energyservicescoalition.org
Descr: Works to increase energy efficiency and building upgrades through energy savings performance contracting. Acts as a clearinghouse for information on state-level performance contracting including best industry practices, procurement and contracting processes, and relevant case studies. Educates all market segments on the benefits of energy performance contracting. **Mem:** 175.

7623 ■ Environmental Alliance for Senior Involvement (EASI)
5615 26th St. N
Arlington, VA 22207-1407
Ph: (703)241-4927
Fax: (703)538-5504
E-mail: easi@easi.org
URL: http://www.easi.org
Staff: 12. **Descr:** Works to promote environmental awareness among seniors to help preserve the environment for future generations. **Fnd:** 1991. **Pub:** *EASI Does It* (bimonthly); *Sustainable Communities Review* (biennial).

7624 ■ Environmental Defense
257 Park Ave. S
New York, NY 10010
Contact: Fred D. Krupp, Pres.
Ph: (212)505-2100
Free: 800-684-3322
Fax: (212)505-2375
E-mail: members@environmentaldefense.org
URL: http://www.environmentaldefense.org
Staff: 300. **Descr:** Links science, law, economics, and engineering to create innovative and economically viable solutions to environmental problems. Focuses on four areas such as: protecting and restoring biodiversity (with an emphasis on rivers and watersheds); stabilizing climate by developing policies to reduce dependence on fossil fuels; reducing risks to human health from exposure to toxic chemicals; and protecting oceans from pollution and overfishing. **Fnd:** 1967. **Mem:** 500000. **Reg. Groups:** 8. **State Groups:** 19. **Pub:** *Solutions* (bimonthly); Annual Report (annual).

7625 ■ Environmental Information Association (EIA)
6935 Wisconsin Ave., Ste. 306
Chevy Chase, MD 20815-6112
Contact: Brent Kynoch, Managing Dir.
Ph: (301)961-4999
Free: 888-343-4342
Fax: (301)961-3094
E-mail: info@eia-usa.org
URL: http://www.eia-usa.org
Staff: 5. **Descr:** Individuals and corporations concerned about environmental management and control. Collects and disseminates information concerning environmental risks in buildings to interested professionals, building owners, and the public. Serves as a clearinghouse of information on effective environmental management. Promotes high standards of professionalism among members. Maintains Asbestos Abatement Worker and Training Program and offers operations and maintenance programs for management. Provides consulting and referral service to members on health issues. Maintains speakers' bureau; compiles statistics. **Fnd:** 1983. **Mem:** 1000. **Reg. Groups:** 12. **Pub:** *Environmental Choices and a Technical Journal* (quarterly);

Technical Supplement (periodic); Membership Directory (annual).

7626 ■ Environmental Law Institute (ELI)
2000 L St. NW, Ste. 620
Washington, DC 20036
Contact: Leslie Carothers, Pres.
Ph: (202)939-3800
E-mail: law@eli.org
URL: http://www.eli.org
Staff: 55. **Descr:** Provides information services, training courses and seminars, and research programs. Works to develops effective solutions to pressing environmental problems. Governed by a board of directors who represent a "balanced mix of leaders within the environmental profession" and supported by individuals, foundations, government, corporations, law firms and other sources. Cosponsors environmental law conferences with the American Bar Association, American Law Institute, and the Smithsonian Institution. Conducts summer and annual internship programs for law students. Research division includes projects on air and water pollution; wetlands; economics; state environmental law; toxic substances and hazardous waste; land use; biodiversity; smart growth/sprawl. **Fnd:** 1969. **Mem:** 4000. **Pub:** *Environmental Forum* (bimonthly); *Environmental Law Reporter*; *National Wetlands Newsletter* (bimonthly); Books; Brochures; Reports.

7627 ■ Environmental Outreach and Stewardship Alliance
650 S Orcas St., Ste. 220
Seattle, WA 98108
Contact: Erick McWayne, Founder/Exec. Dir.
Ph: (206)762-2553
Fax: (206)762-1979
E-mail: emcwayne@eosalliance.org
URL: http://www.eosalliance.org
Descr: Aims to foster an ecologically sustainable world by improving public health and environmental quality through citizen engagement and stewardship. Provides green jobs and workforce development, home energy audits and weatherization, efficiency retrofits for buildings, habitat restoration, civic leadership training, youth environmental education and technical environmental training. **Fnd:** 2000.

7628 ■ Farm Sanctuary
PO Box 150
Watkins Glen, NY 14891
Contact: Mr. Gene Baur, Pres./Co-Founder
Ph: (607)583-2225
Fax: (607)583-2041
E-mail: info@farmsanctuary.org
URL: http://www.farmsanctuary.org
Staff: 50. **Descr:** Representatives working to end factory farm animal abuses. Works to: eliminate what the organization terms abusive animal agricultural practices; educate the public on factory farming; promote alternatives to factory farm products. Sponsors Farm Animal Alert to monitor and inform people of legislative efforts to end factory farming. Organizes Veal Boycott and Veal Calf Refuge campaign to protest the abuse of veal calves. Sponsors Adopt-A-Turkey campaigns to draw media attention to the problems of factory farming. Operates referral, placement, and shelter services for abused and abandoned farm animals; maintains educational center and speakers' bureau; conducts outreach and educational activities and training sessions on farm animal issues. **Fnd:** 1986. **Mem:** 150000. **Pub:** *Farm Sanctuary News* (quarterly); *Guide to Veg Living*; *Life Behind Bars*; Annual Report (annual); Videos.

7629 ■ Feminists for Animal Rights (FAR)
PO Box 10017
Berkeley, CA 94709
E-mail: contact@farinc.org
URL: http://www.farinc.org
Descr: Feminist vegetarians dedicated to ending all forms of violence against women and animals. Believes that violence against animals is directly related to violence against women and stems from the hierarchical system which works for the powerful against the powerless. Advocates a plant-based diet

as an actualization of the feminist belief that "the personal is political." Provides educational materials. Offers a rescue program for companion animals of battered women. **Fnd:** 1982. **Pub:** *The Ecofeminist Journal*; *Feminists for Animal Rights Newsletter* (semiannual); Bibliography; Brochure.

7630 ■ Forest Service Employees for Environmental Ethics (FSEEE)
PO Box 11615
Eugene, OR 97440-3815
Contact: Andy Stahl, Exec. Dir.
Ph: (541)484-2692
Fax: (541)484-3004
E-mail: fseee@fseee.org
URL: http://www.fseee.org
Staff: 9. **Descr:** Present, former, and retired U.S. Forest Service employees, workers from other land management agencies, and concerned citizens. Works to create a responsible value system for the Forest Service based on a land ethic that ensures ecologically and economically sustainable resource management. Seeks to revise and replace the Forest Service's present practice of encouraging overuse of public land by timber companies, mining firms, and cattle owners with a more ecological system of resource management. Acts as a support system for Forest Service employees who do not agree with the Service's present land management ethics. Provides a forum for exchange of information and ideas. Disseminates information on conservation and the misuse of the resources in national forests. Sponsors educational programs. **Fnd:** 1989. **Mem:** 12000. **Pub:** *Forest Magazine* (quarterly); Brochures.

7631 ■ GE Stockholders' Alliance for a Sustainable Nuclear-Free Future (GESASNFF)
7904 Charcrest Ct.
PO Box 754
Fair Oaks, CA 95628-0754
Contact: Robert Freehling, Chair
Ph: (916)863-1299
Fax: (916)863-1299
E-mail: rsf1@bigvalley.net
Descr: General Electric stockholders. Objectives are to convince GE management to phase out GE's nuclear-related businesses; expand research of biologically and environmentally safe, renewable energy systems; direct research and development at helping to solve problems of radioactive waste disposal; direct technical assistance at safely decommissioning nuclear power plants and other nuclear facilities. Emphasizes that its objectives are "pro-GE," working for the best interests of GE, its stockholders, and the consumer public. Conducts public education campaign regarding biological hazards and "diseconomy" of nuclear power, and "national insecurity" generated by nuclear weapons. Writes stockholder proposals and lobbies management of some principal stockholders. Maintains speakers' bureau. **Fnd:** 1980.

7632 ■ Global Environment Facility (GEF)
1818 H St. NW, MSN G6-602
Washington, DC 20433
Contact: Monique Barbut, CEO/Chair
Ph: (202)473-0508
Fax: (202)522-3240
E-mail: secretariat@thegef.org
URL: http://www.gefweb.org
Staff: 43. **Descr:** Seeks to address global environmental issues and sustainable development. Acts as a financial mechanism for international agreements on biodiversity, climate change, persistent organic pollutants and desertification. Supports the work of global agreements to protect international waters and the ozone layer. **Fnd:** 1991. **Pub:** *Talking Points*.

7633 ■ Global Environmental Management Initiative (GEMI)
1155 15th St. NW, Ste. 500
Washington, DC 20005
Contact: Steve Hellem, Exec. Dir.
Ph: (202)296-7449

Fax: (202)296-7442
E-mail: info@gemi.org
URL: http://www.gemi.org
Descr: Helps businesses foster environmental, health and safety excellence, and economic succes. Provides a forum for corporate environmental leaders to work together and share experiences and ideas. Shares tools and information to help businesses achieve environmental as well as health and safety excellence. **Fnd:** 1990. **Mem:** 40. **Pub:** *GEMI News* (monthly); Reports.

7634 ■ Global Sourcing Council (GSC)
317 Madison Ave., Ste. 1619
New York, NY 10017
Contact: Christine Bullen, Pres.
Ph: (914)479-5016
Fax: (631)980-4071
E-mail: christine.bullen@gscouncil.org
URL: http://www.gscouncil.org
Descr: Supports people and organizations with an interest in the social and economic effects of sourcing. Serves as a forum for the discussion of the social and economic impacts of global sourcing. Provides opportunities for professional networking and business development. Addresses issues relevant to any company involved in global business operations. **Fnd:** 2007.

7635 ■ Global Warming International Center (GWIC)
PO Box 50303
Palo Alto, CA 94303-0303
Contact: Dr. Sinyan Shen, Dir.
Ph: (630)910-1551
Fax: (630)910-1561
E-mail: gw17@globalwarming.net
URL: http://www.globalwarming.net
Staff: 17. **Descr:** Ministerial agencies and industrial corporations. Concerns with impacts and effects of global warming. Provides a focus for governments, the private sector, and academia to share information on global warming internationally. Coordinates training for personnel dealing with environmental issues, energy planning, and natural resource management through the Institute for World Resource Research. Establishes the Global Warming Index (GWI) and the Extreme Event Index (EEI) for international standardization. Maintains speaker's bureau; compiles statistics; operates placement service; conducts research and educational programs. **Fnd:** 1986. **Mem:** 12381. **Reg. Groups:** 5. **Pub:** *World Resource Review* (quarterly).

7636 ■ Grassroots Environmental Education (GEE)
52 Main St.
Port Washington, NY 11050
Contact: Patricia J. Wood, Exec. Dir.
Ph: (516)883-0887
Fax: (516)944-6586
E-mail: info@grassrootsinfo.org
URL: http://www.grassrootsinfo.org
Descr: Promotes environmental health education. Educates the public about the links between environmental exposures and human health problems. Seeks to empower individuals to act as catalysts for change within the community. **Fnd:** 2000.

7637 ■ Green Restaurant Association
89 South St., Ste. LL02
Boston, MA 02111
Ph: (858)452-7378
E-mail: gra@dinegreen.com
URL: http://www.dinegreen.com
Descr: Strives to help restaurants become more environmentally sustainable in ways that are convenient and cost effective. Focuses on research, environmental consulting, education, public relations and marketing, and community organizing and consumer activism. **Fnd:** 1990.

7638 ■ Green Seal
1001 Connecticut Ave. NW, Ste. 827
Washington, DC 20036-5525
Contact: Dr. Arthur Weissman PhD, Pres./CEO

Ph: (202)872-6400
Fax: (202)872-4324
E-mail: greenseal@greenseal.org
URL: http://www.greenseal.org

Staff: 6. **Descr:** Serves as an environmental certification and consumer education organization. Establishes criteria and standards for consumer products, conducts product testing, and awards a seal of approval to products meeting standards. Offers membership program; Environmental Partners in which organizations receive assistance with green procurement. **Fnd:** 1989. **Mem:** 250. **Pub:** *Campus Green Buying Guide*; *Choose Green Report* (monthly); *Office Green Buying Guide*.

7639 ■ Green Spa Network (GSN)
PO Box 451
Occidental, CA 95465
Contact: Michael Stusser, Founder
Free: 800-275-3045
E-mail: info@greenspanetwork.org
URL: http://greenspanetwork.org

Descr: Aims to bring sustainable operating practices to the spa industry. Promotes the natural connections between personal wellbeing, economic sustainability, and the health of the planet. Facilitates education, research and alliances in sustainable business practices.

7640 ■ Greenpeace Canada
33 Cecil St.
Toronto, ON, Canada M5T 1N1
Contact: Peter Bleyer, Chm.
Ph: (416)597-8408
Free: 800-320-7183
Fax: (416)597-8422
E-mail: greenpeace.toronto@dialb.greenpeace.org
URL: http://p2-raw.greenpeace.org/canada/en/about-greenpeace

Staff: 35. **Descr:** Canadian chapter of Greenpeace International. Aims to ensure the ability of the earth to nurture life by protecting biodiversity, preventing pollution and abuse of ocean, land, air, and fresh water, ending nuclear threats, and promoting peace, global disarmament, and non-violence. **Fnd:** 1971. **Mem:** 100000. **Pub:** *E-News* (monthly); *Reseau Vert* (3/year).

7641 ■ Hazardous Materials Training and Research Institute (HMTRI)
6301 Kirkwood Blvd. SW
Cedar Rapids, IA 52404
Contact: Doug Feil, Assoc. Dir.
Ph: (319)398-5893
Free: 800-464-6874
E-mail: hmtri@kirkwood.edu
URL: http://www.hmtri.org/hmtri/index_hmtri.htm

Descr: Recognized as a national center of excellence by several federal agencies; promotes environmental health and safety education and training. Promotes worker protection and the maintenance of a clean and safe environment. **Fnd:** 1987.

7642 ■ Health and Energy Institute (HEI)
615 Kennebec Ave.
Takoma Park, MD 20912
Contact: Kathleen M. Tucker, Pres.
Ph: (301)585-5831
Fax: (301)585-9474
E-mail: kitbob@erols.com

Staff: 1. **Descr:** Projects concerned about the impact of nuclear energy on health and the environment with emphasis on: radiation law; radiation danger to women; nuclear technology, whether used for power or as a weapon; nuclear testing and radiation experiments. Conducts research and educational programs geared toward the public on the effects of food irradiation and radiation and nuclear development for electric power or weapons. The project is supported by funds from foundations and the public. Maintains legal and scientific advisory boards. **Fnd:** 1978. **Mem:** 7000. **Pub:** *Bubble, Bubble, Toil and Trouble: Reprocessing Nuclear Spent Fuel*; *Food Irradiation: Who Wants It?* (1987); *Heat, High Water,*

and Rock Instability at Hanford; *Uranium and the Nuclear Cycle*.

7643 ■ Heaven on Earth Society for Animals
16045 Sherman Way, No. 234-H
Van Nuys, CA 91406
Contact: Ritchie Geisel, Pres./CEO
Ph: (818)474-2700
E-mail: info@heavenlypets.org
URL: http://www.heavenlypets.org

Descr: Aims to improve the quality of life for homeless animals, particularly those that are often overlooked because of special needs and low potential for adoption. Works to provide lifelong care for animals in a cageless sanctuary. Seeks to decrease the number of homeless animals through spay/neuter programs and by providing information to the public on the importance of having their pets sterilized. **Fnd:** 2000. **Pub:** Newsletter.

7644 ■ HIS Nets
1017 Elm Ave.
Norman, OK 73072
Contact: Jimmy Lewis, Pres.
Ph: (405)447-2471
Fax: (405)321-8322
E-mail: info@hisnets.org
URL: http://www.hisnets.org

Descr: Focuses on fighting the global malaria epidemic. Provides a Christian response to the malaria epidemic in sub-Saharan Africa. Raises awareness of this ongoing global crisis and mobilizes Christians and other caring groups to save lives and improve the quality of life of people in malarial areas of sub-Saharan Africa. **Fnd:** 2004.

7645 ■ Household Hazardous Waste Project (HHWP)
University of Missouri Extension
Columbia, MO 65211
Contact: Marie Steinwachs, Dir.
Ph: (573)882-5011
E-mail: owm@missouri.edu
URL: http://outreach.missouri.edu/owm/hhw.htm

Staff: 2. **Descr:** An education program of the University of Missouri Extension. Aids the public in making informed decisions about the use, storage, and disposal of hazardous household products. Assists communities in developing management plans. Provides education to other unregulated generators of hazardous wastes including small businesses, home businesses, schools, farms, artists, and crafts persons. Emphasizes source reduction, waste minimization, and preventive practices in an attempt to change consumers' behavior toward hazardous products. Develops educational tools and materials. Operates an information request and referral service. **Fnd:** 1987. **Pub:** *Guide to Hazardous Products Around the Home*; *Home Hazardous Product Survey*; *Household Hazardous Waste: Consumer Information*; *Lessons in Household Hazardous Waste Management*; *Material Safety Data Sheets: Identifying Product Hazards*; *Safe Use, Storage and Disposal of Paint*; *Safe Use, Storage and Disposal of Pesticides*; *Selecting Household Safety Equipment*; *Setting Up Collection Sites for Antifreeze*; *Setting Up Collection Sites for Used Oil*; *Stored Waste Abatement Program*; *What Your Home Haz*; Brochures.

7646 ■ Human Ecology Action League (HEAL)
PO Box 509
Stockbridge, GA 30281
Ph: (770)389-4519
Fax: (770)389-4520
E-mail: healnatnl@aol.com
URL: http://www.healnatl.org

Staff: 2. **Descr:** Individuals and organizations interested in the study of human ecology and multiple chemical sensitivities, specifically how human health may be affected by synthetic and natural substances in the environment. Seeks to collect and disseminate information on human ecology and ecological illness to persons suffering from such illness, and to government agencies scientists, and health care professionals; to raise public awareness about potential dangers from substances in the environment. **Fnd:**

1977. **Mem:** 10000. **Local Groups:** 50. **Pub:** *Directory of HEAL Members in the Healthcare Professions*; *Fragrance and Health*; *HEAL's Service List*; *Human Ecologist* (quarterly); Brochures.

7647 ■ INFORM
5 Hanover Sq., Fl. 19
New York, NY 10004
Contact: Virginia Ramsey, Pres.
Ph: (212)361-2400
Fax: (212)361-2412
E-mail: ramsey@informinc.org
URL: http://www.informinc.org

Staff: 14. **Descr:** Examines business practices, technologies and products that threaten the environment, waste the natural resources, or put human health at risk. Works constructively with companies, communities, government agencies, and environmental organizations. Identifies and promotes avenues of innovation that support environmentally sustainable economic growth. Works on: protecting public health against the unsafe use of toxic chemicals; promoting waste prevention and the design of less wasteful products; and advancing the shift to sustainable transportation. Informs public debates worldwide via published reports, expert testimony, conference and workshop presentations, and media and outreach initiatives. **Fnd:** 1974. **Mem:** 500. **Pub:** *Cleaning for Health: Products and Practices for a Safer Indoor Environment*; *Greening Garbage Trucks: New Technologies for Cleaner Air*; *INFORM Reports* (quarterly); *Waste in the Wireless World: The Challenge of Cell Phones*.

7648 ■ Institute for Local Self-Reliance (ILSR)
927 15th St. NW, 4th Fl.
Washington, DC 20005
Contact: Neil Seldman, Pres.
Ph: (202)898-1610
E-mail: info@ilsr.org
URL: http://www.ilsr.org

Staff: 20. **Descr:** Provides the conceptual framework, strategies, and information to aid the creation of ecologically-sound and economically equitable communities. Works with citizens, activists, policymakers, and entrepreneurs to design systems, policies and enterprises that meet local or regional needs; maximize local human, material, natural, and financial resources; and ensure that the benefits of these systems and resources accrue to all local citizens. **Fnd:** 1974. **Pub:** *The Home Town Advantage: How to Defend Your Main Street Against Chain Stores and Why It Matters*; *Recycling Economic Development Through Scrap-Based Manufacturing*.

7649 ■ Institute of Scrap Recycling Industries (ISRI)
1615 L St. NW, Ste. 600
Washington, DC 20036-5610
Contact: Robin Wiener, Pres.
Ph: (202)662-8500
Fax: (202)626-0900
E-mail: robinwiener@isri.org
URL: http://www.isri.org

Staff: 36. **Descr:** Represents processors, brokers, and consumers engaged in the recycling of ferrous, nonferrous, paper, plastics, glass, textiles, rubber and electronics scrap. Conducts specialized education and research programs. **Fnd:** 1987. **Mem:** 1250. **Local Groups:** 21. **Pub:** *Institute of Scrap Recycling Industries Directory of Members* (annual); *ISRI Digest* (bimonthly); *ISRI Focus*; *Scrap Magazine* (bimonthly).

7650 ■ Institute for Sustainable Communities (ISC)
535 Stone Cutters Way
Montpelier, VT 05602
Contact: George Hamilton, Pres.
Ph: (802)229-2900
Fax: (802)229-2919
E-mail: isc@iscvt.org
URL: http://www.iscvt.org

Staff: 28. **Descr:** Helps communities globally to address environmental, economic, and social challenges. Provides local communities with the training, advice, and grants needed to solve problems. **Fnd:** 1991. **Pub:** *The Key to Sustainable Cities*; Annual Report (annual).

7651 ■ International Bottled Water Association (IBWA)
1700 Diagonal Rd., Ste. 650
Alexandria, VA 22314
Contact: Joseph K. Doss, Pres.
Ph: (703)683-5213
Free: 800-WATER-11
Fax: (703)683-4074
E-mail: ibwainfo@bottledwater.org
URL: http://www.bottledwater.org
Staff: 14. **Descr:** Bottled water plants; distributors; manufacturers of bottled water supplies; international bottlers, distributors and suppliers. Conducts seminars and technical research. **Fnd:** 1958. **Mem:** 700. **Pub:** *Bottled Water Reporter* (bimonthly); *IBWA Audit Handbook*; *IBWA Membership Roster* (annual).

7652 ■ International Institute for Baubiologie and Ecology (IBE)
PO Box 387
Clearwater, FL 33757
Contact: Vicki Warren, Exec. Dir.
Ph: (727)461-4371
Fax: (727)441-4373
E-mail: baubiologie@earthlink.net
URL: http://www.buildingbiology.net
Staff: 5. **Descr:** Seeks to advance public awareness of health hazards in homes and workplaces; offers correspondence courses and consulting services. **Fnd:** 1987. **Local Groups:** 1. **Pub:** *EcoDwell Online*.

7653 ■ International Society for Animal Rights (ISAR)
PO Box F
Clarks Summit, PA 18411
Contact: Susan Dapsis, Pres.
Ph: (570)586-2200
Free: 800-543-ISAR
Fax: (570)586-9580
E-mail: contact@isaronline.org
URL: http://www.isaronline.org
Staff: 8. **Descr:** Promotes animal rights through educational programs and legislation. Seeks to prevent exploitation and abuse in animals. Provides and distributes literature on subjects of animal abuse and exploitation; circulates a documentary film collection to schools and colleges throughout the U.S.; sponsors seminars and organizes demonstrations. Serves as an information resource for the media, writers, and other humane organizations; drafts legislation and works actively to advance the animal rights cause. **Fnd:** 1959. **Mem:** 50000. **Pub:** *International Society for Animal Rights--Report* (quarterly); Pamphlets.

7654 ■ International Society of Sustainability Professionals (ISSP)
2515 NE 17th Ave., Ste. 300
Portland, OR 97212
Contact: Marsha Willard, Exec. Dir.
E-mail: mwillard@sustainabilityprofessionals.org
URL: http://sustainabilityprofessionals.org
Descr: Represents professionals committed to making sustainability a standard practice. Seeks to keep members informed about the changes and innovations in sustainability practice throughout the United States and around the world. Aims to keep the greater membership informed of current events and innovative sustainability practices and projects, trends, regulations, incentives and partnerships in the areas and regions in which ISSP members live and work. **Fnd:** 2006.

7655 ■ Interstate Professional Applicators Association (IPAA)
PO Box 13262
Salem, OR 97309
Contact: Debbie Ego, Sec.
Ph: (503)363-7205
Fax: (503)378-0864
E-mail: ipaa2002@hotmail.com
Descr: Companies engaged in the application of

horticultural spraying. Aims to insure a healthy and safe environment through proper pesticide usage. Works to acquire and disseminate technological information regarding the safe application of pesticides. Contributes to state research facilities. Sponsors seminars on entomology, pathology, safety, soils, business management, and employee relations. **Fnd:** 1953. **Mem:** 100. **State Groups:** 2. **Local Groups:** 1.

7656 ■ Izaak Walton League of America (IWLA)
707 Conservation Ln.
Gaithersburg, MD 20878
Contact: David W. Hoskins, Exec. Dir.
Ph: (301)548-0150
Free: 800-IKE-LINE
E-mail: general@iwla.org
URL: http://www.iwla.org
Staff: 35. **Descr:** Works to educate the public about conserving, maintaining, protecting, and restoring the soil, forest, water, and other natural resources of the U.S.; promotes the enjoyment and wholesome utilization of these resources. Sponsors environmental programs including Sustainability Education Project, Outdoor Ethics, Save Our Streams, Midwest Energy Efficiency Program, Sustainable Agriculture and Wetlands, and Hunter and Angler Issues Program. **Fnd:** 1922. **Mem:** 40000. **State Groups:** 21. **Local Groups:** 350.

7657 ■ Jews for Animal Rights (JAR)
255 Humphrey St.
Marblehead, MA 01945
Contact: Roberta Kalechofsky
Ph: (781)631-7601
E-mail: micah@micahbooks.com
URL: http://www.micahbooks.com/JAR.html
Staff: 2. **Descr:** Jews promoting animal rights and the alleviation of animal suffering. Believes that "the earth and all life is sacred because God created it". Encourages vegetarianism and preventive medicine and alternatives to animal research. Provides materials on celebrating bar/bat mitzvahs, confirmations, and other holidays. Sponsors community action organizations, discussion groups, and educational programs. Maintains speakers' bureau. Operates Micah as publishing arm. **Fnd:** 1985. **Pub:** *A Boy, A Chicken, and The Lion of Juelah - How Ari Became a Vegetarian*; *Autobiography of a Revolutionary: Essays on Animal and Human Rights*; *The Dark Face of Science*; *In Pity and in Anger*; *JAR Newsletter* (semiannual); *The Jewish Vegetarian Year Cookbook*; *Judaism and Animal Rights: Classical and Contemporary Responses*; *My Time*; *Rabbis and Vegetarianism: An Evolving Tradition*; *The 6th Day of Creation - A Prose Poem About Vivisection*; *Vegetarian Judaism: A Guide for Everyone*; Videos.

7658 ■ KEZA
PO Box 681381
Franklin, TN 37068-1381
Contact: Jared N. Miller, Founder/Pres.
E-mail: keza@keza.com
URL: http://www.keza.com
Descr: Seeks to develop sustainable fashion businesses from women's cooperatives in Africa. Works to help establish Africa's position in the luxury fashion industry and bring income and careers to those in need. Promotes equality between the rich and the poor. **Pub:** Newsletter.

7659 ■ Large Public Power Council (LPPC)
300 N Washington St., Ste. 405
Alexandria, VA 22314
Contact: Robert Johnston, Chm.
Ph: (703)740-1750
E-mail: lppc@lppc.org
URL: http://www.lppc.org
Descr: Represents operators of locally owned and controlled power systems. Works to advance consumer-oriented positions on national energy

issues. Seeks to educate legislative decision makers about matters pertaining to public power utilities.

7660 ■ Lawn Institute (LI)
2 E Main St.
East Dundee, IL 60118
Contact: Kirk Hunter, Exec. Dir.
Ph: (847)649-5555
Free: 800-405-8873
Fax: (847)649-5678
E-mail: info@thelawninstitue.org
URL: http://www.lawninstitute.com
Staff: 7. **Descr:** Producers of lawn seed and lawn products. Seeks to help bridge the gap between professional research and an increasingly sophisticated consumer. Promotes better lawns through use of quality materials, research, and education. **Fnd:** 1993. **Mem:** 1100. **Pub:** *Turf News* (annual).

7661 ■ Legal Environmental Assistance Foundation (LEAF)
1114 Thomasville Rd., Ste. E
Tallahassee, FL 32303-6290
Contact: Cynthia Valencic
Ph: (850)681-2591
Fax: (850)224-1275
E-mail: leaf@leaflaw.org
URL: http://www.leaflaw.org
Staff: 3. **Descr:** Promotes the protection of the environment and health of the community by enforcing environmental regulations, discouraging harmful toxic and hazardous waste dumping, and encouraging energy efficiency. Works to enforce facilities and companies to comply with environmental laws and regulations. Participates in federal and state policy making. Sues governmental agency and industry personnel who violate environmental laws. Conducts education and legal workshops for professionals and interested individuals. **Fnd:** 1979. **Mem:** 500. **Pub:** *LEAF Briefs* (quarterly).

7662 ■ Mailorder Gardening Association (MGA)
5836 Rockburn Woods Way
Elkridge, MD 21075
Contact: Barbara Emerson, Pres.
Ph: (410)540-9830
Fax: (410)540-9827
E-mail: info@mailordergardening.com
URL: http://www.mailordergardening.com
Descr: Mailorder gardening catalog companies and gardening magazine publishers. Promotes growth and development of the mailorder gardening industries. Facilitates exchange of information among members. Formulates standards of business practice and ethics for the industry. Monitors legislation and business practices of interest to members. Provides services to members including marketing and statistical data, supply source referrals, and consumer awareness campaigns. Makes available children's services; sponsors competitions. **Fnd:** 1934. **Pub:** *MGA Messenger*.

7663 ■ Mercury Policy Project (MPP)
1420 North St.
Montpelier, VT 05602
Contact: Michael Bender, Exec. Dir.
Ph: (802)223-9000
E-mail: info@mercurypolicy.org
URL: http://www.mercurypolicy.org
Descr: Seeks to promote public awareness regarding mercury contamination; promotes policies to eliminate mercury use, reduce the export and trafficking of mercury, and reduce exposures at local, national, and international levels. **Fnd:** 1998.

7664 ■ Midwest Center for Environmental Science and Public Policy (MCESPP)
1845 N Farewell Ave., Ste. 100
Milwaukee, WI 53202
Contact: Jeffery A. Foran PhD, Pres.
Ph: (414)271-7280
Fax: (414)273-7293
E-mail: mcespp@mcespp.org
Staff: 8. **Descr:** Works to reduce exposure to toxic substances in air, water, and land. Focuses on

research, public information, and advocacy, including formal and informal interaction with policy-making bodies on a state, regional, and national level. **Fnd:** 1971. **Mem:** 30000. **Reg. Groups:** 1. **Pub:** *CBE Review* (semiannual).

7665 ■ National Association of Exotic Pest Plant Councils (NAEPPC)
National Park Service
Florida/Caribbean EPMT
18001 Old Cuttler Rd., Ste. 419
Palmetto Bay, FL 33157
Contact: Tony Pernas, Chm.
Ph: (305)252-0347
Fax: (305)253-0463
E-mail: tony_pernas@nps.gov
URL: http://www.naeppc.org
Descr: Focuses on issues of exotic pest plants in natural areas and other wildlands. Seeks to improve the methods of prevention of new infestations of exotic pest plants from importation into the USA and through interstate movement. Aims to increase biological control funding. **Fnd:** 1995.

7666 ■ National Center for Environmental Health Strategies (NCEHS)
1100 Rural Ave.
Voorhees, NJ 08043
Contact: Mary Lamielle, Exec. Dir.
Ph: (856)429-5358
E-mail: info@ncehs.org
URL: http://www.ncehs.org
Staff: 2. **Descr:** Persons with environmental illnesses, including those with chemical sensitivity disorders; medical, legal, and scientific professionals; government agencies; environmentalists; interested others. Promotes public awareness of health problems caused by chemical and environmental pollutants, focusing on chemical sensitivity disorders. Testifies before government agencies on behalf of persons with such health problems. Encourages the development and implementation of programs and policies aimed at assisting victims of pollutants and preventing future public health problems. Conducts educational programs and research. Gathers information and compiles statistics on indoor and outdoor pollutants, less-toxic products, pesticides, natural foods, and environmental disabilities, including alternative employment, workplace accommodations, social security disability and workmen's compensation, and housing. Maintains speakers' bureau. Provides advocacy and technical, referral, and children's services. Acts as a clearinghouse. **Fnd:** 1986. **Mem:** 2000. **Pub:** *Chemical Sensitivity: A Report to the New Jersey Department of Health*; *The Delicate Balance* (quarterly).

7667 ■ National Council of Minorities in Energy (NCME)
PO Box 65783
Washington, DC 20035
Contact: Ezekiel Patten, Chm.
Free: 866-663-9045
Fax: (866)663-8007
E-mail: contact@minoritiesinenergy.org
URL: http://www.minoritiesinenergy.org
Descr: Advocates for development and utilization of minority and women-owned businesses in the energy sector and energy-related industries across the United States and in international markets. Provides information regarding opportunities in the energy industry. Advocates on regulatory and legislative issues at the federal, state and local levels. Presents methodologies to help implement access to capital and credit facilitation.

7668 ■ National Council on Radiation Protection and Measurements (NCRP)
7910 Woodmont Ave., Ste. 400
Bethesda, MD 20814-3076
Contact: David A. Schauer, Exec. Dir.
Ph: (301)657-2652
Free: 800-229-2652
Fax: (301)907-8768
E-mail: schauer@ncrponline.org
URL: http://www.ncrponline.org

Staff: 10. **Descr:** Represents scientists who share the belief that significant advances in radiation protection and measurement can be achieved through cooperative effort. Makes recommendations focused on safe occupational exposure levels and disseminates information. **Fnd:** 1929. **Mem:** 100. **Pub:** *NCRP Commentary* (periodic); *NCRP Report* (periodic); *NCRP Statement* (periodic); *Symposium Proceedings* (periodic).

7669 ■ National Environmental Education Foundation (NEEF)
4301 Connecticut Ave. NW, Ste. 160
Washington, DC 20008
Contact: Diane W. Wood, Pres.
Ph: (202)833-2933
Fax: (202)261-6464
E-mail: dianewood@neefusa.org
URL: http://www.neefusa.org
Descr: Aims to advance environmental literacy in its many forms. Has taken a nontraditional approach to environmental education, moving beyond the K-12 classroom emphasis and targeting professionals who are trusted by and have daily contact with the general public. Provides environmental education and training to those leaders whose occupations give them opportunities to make meaningful, practical environmental connections that in turn can be translated into responsible actions. Seeks to generate more savings and curtail environmental destruction by building an environmentally literate citizenry capable and motivated to care for the environment at home, at work, and in its communities. **Fnd:** 1990.

7670 ■ National Onsite Wastewater Recycling Association (NOWRA)
3540 Soquel Ave., Ste. A
Santa Cruz, CA 95062
Contact: Jerry Stonebridge PhD, Pres.
Ph: (831)454-4884
Free: 800-966-2942
Fax: (831)464-4881
E-mail: info@nowra.org
URL: http://www.nowra.org
Descr: Onsite wastewater treatment providers including manufacturers, installers, field practitioners, suppliers, engineers, designers, researchers and academicians, and government regulatory personnel. Seeks to advance and promote the onsite wastewater treatment industry. Gathers and disseminates information on wastewater treatment; conducts educational programs to increase public awareness on the value of wastewater treatment; formulates and enforces standards of ethics and practice for the wastewater treatment industry. Assists in the development of sound ecological practices in wastewater treatment; compiles industry statistics. **Fnd:** 1991. **Pub:** *Onsite Journal.*

7671 ■ National Pesticide Information Center (NPIC)
Oregon State University
333 Weniger Hall
Corvallis, OR 97331-6502
Contact: Dr. Terry L. Miller, Dir.
Free: 800-858-7378
Fax: (541)737-0761
E-mail: npic@ace.orst.edu
URL: http://npic.orst.edu
Staff: 12. **Descr:** Provides information on a wide variety of pesticide-related topics, including pesticide product information, information on the recognition and management of pesticide poisonings, toxicology, environmental chemistry, referrals for laboratory analyses, investigation of pesticide incidents, emergency treatment information, safety information, health and environmental effects, and clean-up and disposal procedures. **Pub:** Brochure; Annual Report (annual).

7672 ■ National Wildlife Rehabilitators Association (NWRA)
2625 Clearwater Rd., Ste. 110
St. Cloud, MN 56301
Contact: Wendy Fox, Pres.
Ph: (320)230-9920

Fax: (320)230-3077
E-mail: nwra@nwrawildlife.org
URL: http://www.nwrawildlife.org
Staff: 3. **Descr:** Wildlife rehabilitators and other interested individuals including state and federal agency personnel, conservationists, educators, naturalists, researchers, veterinarians, and zoo and humane society staff. Supports the science and profession of wildlife rehabilitation and its practitioners. (Wildlife rehabilitation is the practice of assisting injured, orphaned, diseased, or displaced animals, with the goal of enabling such wildlife to be returned to its natural habitat.) Works to improve the profession through the development of high standards of practice, ethics, and conduct. Disseminates and stimulate the growth of knowledge in the field. Fosters cooperation of professional and governmental agencies and other similar groups with the wildlife rehabilitation community. Develops the Minimum Standards for Wildlife Rehabilitation, in conjunction with the International Wildlife Rehabilitation Council, to encourage the development of outstanding rehabilitation programs. Provides research grants; conducts networking; offers consulting referrals. **Fnd:** 1982. **Mem:** 1900. **Pub:** *Wildlife Rehabilitation* (annual); *Wildlife Rehabilitation Bulletin* (semiannual); *The Wildlife Rehabilitator* (semiannual); Membership Directory (annual).

7673 ■ Native American Water Association (NAWA)
1662 Hwy. 395, Ste. 212
Minden, NV 89423
Contact: Tom Crawford
Ph: (775)782-6636
Free: 877-888-6292
Fax: (775)782-1021
E-mail: nawa@msn.com
URL: http://www.nawainc.org
Descr: Provides training and technical assistance to tribal water and wastewater operators, managers, utility commissions and tribal leadership. Works to strengthen tribal sovereignty and self-determination and to protect the environment and the overall health of Indian communities. Offers tribal water and wastewater operator certification programs, on-site training, utility ordinance development, operation and maintenance assessments. **Pub:** *The Source* (quarterly).

7674 ■ Natural Resources Defense Council (NRDC)
40 W 20th St.
New York, NY 10011
Contact: Frances G. Beinecke, Pres.
Ph: (212)727-2700
Fax: (212)727-1773
E-mail: nrdcinfo@nrdc.org
URL: http://www.nrdc.org
Descr: Uses law, science, and support of more than 550,000 members nationwide to protect the planet's wildlife and wild places and to ensure a safe and healthy environment for all living things. **Fnd:** 1970. **Mem:** 1200000. **Pub:** *Nature's Voice* (bimonthly); *OnEarth* (quarterly).

7675 ■ Nature Canada
75 Alberta St., Ste. 300
Ottawa, ON, Canada K1P 5E7
Contact: Ian Davidson, Exec. Dir.
Ph: (613)562-3447
Free: 800-267-4088
Fax: (613)562-3371
E-mail: info@naturecanada.ca
URL: http://www.naturecanada.ca
Staff: 22. **Descr:** Individuals and organizations with an interest in nature. Promotes conservation and environmental protection; seeks to increase public awareness of threats to the environment. Encourages participation in outdoor activities; conducts social and educational programs. **Fnd:** 1972. **Mem:** 25000.

7676 ■ NEHRP Coalition
101 Constitution Ave. NW, Ste. 375 E
Washington, DC 20001

Contact: Brian Pallasch, Co-Chm.
Ph: (202)789-7850
E-mail: info@nehrp.org
URL: http://www.nehrp.org
Descr: Represents scientists, engineers, architects and emergency response leaders of the earthquake community. Encourages comprehensive, realistic and affordable measures for reducing the harmful effects of earthquakes. Strives to seek full funding at the authorized levels for the NEHRP Program.

7677 ■ New Environment Association (NEA)
821 Euclid Ave.
Syracuse, NY 13210
Contact: Harry Schwarzlander
Ph: (315)446-8009
E-mail: hs38@mailbox.syr.edu
URL: http://www.newenvironment.org
Descr: Exploration of new approaches to a sustainable future through participatory projects and educational programs. **Fnd:** 1974. **Mem:** 45. **Pub:** *New Environment Bulletin* (monthly); *The New Environment Process*; Annual Report (annual).

7678 ■ New Water Supply Coalition
1750 H St. NW, Ste. 600
Washington, DC 20006
Contact: Hal Furman, Exec. Dir.
Ph: (202)737-0700
Fax: (202)737-0455
E-mail: newwatersupply@newwatersupply.org
URL: http://www.newwatersupply.org
Descr: Represents public water agencies and utilities throughout the United States. Encourages the development of coastal seawater and inland brackish groundwater desalination plants, water recycling projects and groundwater contamination clean-up projects. Raises the level of awareness in Congress concerning the urgent need to make the development of new water supply sources a national priority. **Mem:** 21. **Pub:** Newsletter.

7679 ■ NextGen Energy Council
200 Union Blvd., Ste. 105
Lakewood, CO 80228
Contact: Bob Hanfling, Chm.
Ph: (303)577-4627
Free: 866-786-4022
Fax: (303)496-0334
E-mail: info@nextgenenergy.org
URL: http://www.nextgenenergy.org
Descr: Supports continuing efforts to improve the efficiency and environmental performance of all advanced energy technologies. Educates the public about the need for balanced energy policies. Maintains and expands consumer access to reliable, affordable and diverse energy resources.

7680 ■ North American Bear Center (NABC)
1926 Hwy. 169
Ely, MN 55731
Contact: Dr. Lynn Rogers, Chair
Ph: (218)365-7879
URL: http://www.bear.org
Descr: Enhances the understanding of the general public of the habits, needs, and environment of bears in North America. **Fnd:** 1994. **Pub:** *Bear Facts* (quarterly).

7681 ■ North American Nature Photography Association (NANPA)
10200 W 44th Ave., Ste. 304
Wheat Ridge, CO 80033-2840
Contact: Sharon Cohen-Powers, Pres.
Ph: (303)422-8527
Fax: (303)422-8894
E-mail: info@nanpa.org
URL: http://www.nanpa.org
Staff: 3. **Descr:** Wildlife photographers and other individuals with an interest in outdoor photography, environmental education and protection, including educators, government workers, biologists, and editors and publishers. Seeks to insure professionalism and ethical conduct in the photographing of wildlife; promotes wildlife photography as an art form and educational tool. Represents the professional inter-

ests of wildlife photographers. Serves as a forum for the discussion of issues in wildlife photography and for the exchange of information among members. Serves as liaison between wildlife photographers and environmental protection agencies and organizations. Develops guidelines for environmentally and ethically responsible wildlife photography. **Fnd:** 1994. **Mem:** 2500. **Pub:** *American Photo* (bimonthly); *Currents* (bimonthly); *Membership Brochure*; *Nature Photographer* (quarterly); *Nature's Best* (quarterly); *Outdoor Photographer* (monthly); *Popular Photography* (monthly); *Ripples* (bimonthly); Membership Directory (annual).

7682 ■ Northeast Sustainable Energy Association (NESEA)
50 Miles St.
Greenfield, MA 01301
Contact: Bruce Coldham, Pres.
Ph: (413)774-6051
Fax: (413)774-6053
E-mail: nesea@nesea.org
URL: http://www.nesea.org
Staff: 9. **Descr:** Promotes energy conservation, non-polluting and renewable energy technologies. **Fnd:** 1974. **Pub:** *Northeast Sun* (semiannual).

7683 ■ NSF International
789 N Dixboro Rd.
PO Box 130140
Ann Arbor, MI 48113-0140
Contact: Nancy Quay, Exec. Dir.
Ph: (734)769-8010
Free: 800-NSF-MARK
Fax: (734)769-0109
E-mail: info@nsf.org
URL: http://www.nsf.org
Staff: 230. **Descr:** Specializes in the areas of public health and environmental quality focusing on water quality, food safety, indoor air health and the environment. Develops standards, operates product certification and listings programs for products that meet or exceed public health safety standards. Maintains a worldwide network of auditors who conduct unannounced inspections of manufacturer facilities to ensure compliance and to protect the integrity of the NSF Certification Mark. Provides special research and testing services to industry, government, and foundations. **Fnd:** 1944. **Pub:** *Bottled Water and Packaged Ice* (periodic); *Class II Biohazard Cabinetry* (periodic); *Drinking Water Additives-Health Effects* (periodic); *Drinking Water Treatment Units and Related Products, Components, and Materials* (periodic); *Environmental Management Systems Standards and Guidance Documents*; *Food Equipment and Related Products, Components, and Materials* (periodic); *Plastics Piping Components and Related Materials* (periodic); *Swimming Pools, Spas, and Hot Tubs* (periodic); *Wastewater Treatment Units and Related Products and Components* (periodic).

7684 ■ Nuclear Information and Resource Service (NIRS)
6930 Carroll Ave., Ste. 340
Takoma Park, MD 20912
Contact: Michael Mariotte, Exec. Dir.
Ph: (301)270-6477
Fax: (301)270-4291
E-mail: nirsnet@nirs.org
URL: http://www.nirs.org
Staff: 7. **Descr:** Represents antinuclear grassroots groups and individuals. Seeks to: assist individuals and organizations interested in and concerned about nuclear power issues; provide information, advice, materials, and speakers to people trying to halt the construction of nuclear power plants; promote all alternatives to nuclear power. Works with local activist groups, public officials, and attorneys representing concerned employees at nuclear plants; helps local groups "work their way through the maze of government regulations and roadblocks established to discourage public participation in nuclear decisions." Monitors the Nuclear Regulatory Commission, Congress, the nuclear industry, and legislative, judicial, and regulatory bodies; reports on developing issues and upcoming events. Conducts

research; provides technical assistance and referrals to legal aid and technical experts; facilitates Freedom of Information Act requests; answers inquiries for information on nuclear issues. Maintains extensive files on operating nuclear plants as well as nuclear reactors under construction, utility companies, radioactive waste, and general nuclear issues. **Fnd:** 1978. **Mem:** 7000. **Pub:** *Nuclear Monitor* (biweekly); Brochure; Pamphlets.

7685 ■ Ocean Renewable Energy Coalition (OREC)
12909 Scarlet Oak Dr.
Darnestown, MD 20878
Contact: Sean O'Neill, Pres.
Ph: (301)869-3790
Fax: (301)869-5637
E-mail: sean@oceanrenewable.com
URL: http://www.oceanrenewable.com
Descr: Promotes marine and hydrokinetic energy technologies from clean, renewable ocean resources. Encourages utilization of ocean renewable technologies and raises awareness of their vast potential to help secure an affordable, reliable, and environmentally friendly energy future. Seeks a legislative and regulatory regime that fosters the development of ocean renewable technologies, their commercial development, and support in the race to capture the rich energy potential of oceans. **Fnd:** 2005. **Mem:** 40. **Pub:** Reports.

7686 ■ Pembina Institute for Appropriate Development (PIAD)
Box 7558
Drayton Valley, AB, Canada T7A 1S7
Contact: Marlo Raynolds, Exec. Dir.
Ph: (403)269-3344
Fax: (780)542-6464
E-mail: info@pembina.org
URL: http://www.pembina.org
Staff: 37. **Descr:** Organizations and individuals with an interest in environmental protection and global development. Promotes increased public awareness of environmental and development issues. Conducts environmental research and educational programs; provides corporate environmental strategic management services, sponsors charitable activities. **Fnd:** 1985. **Mem:** 40.

7687 ■ People-Animals-Love (PAL)
4900 Massachusetts Ave. NW, Ste. 330
Washington, DC 20016
Contact: Rene Wallis, Exec. Dir.
Ph: (202)966-2171
Fax: (202)966-2172
E-mail: info@peopleanimalslove.org
URL: http://www.peopleanimalslove.org
Staff: 4. **Descr:** Brings people and animals together, brightening the lives of the lonely, easing the pain of the sick, and enriching the world of at-risk children. Its volunteer corps is made up of caring adults, children, and eager animals committed to bringing people and animals together in meaningful, mutually life-affirming ways. This is accomplished through programs that fall into two broad areas: pet visiting and at-risk youth education. **Fnd:** 1981. **Pub:** *PAL Companion* (quarterly).

7688 ■ People for the Ethical Treatment of Animals (PETA)
501 Front St.
Norfolk, VA 23510
Contact: Ingrid E. Newkirk, Pres.
Ph: (757)622-7382
Fax: (757)622-0457
E-mail: info@peta.org
URL: http://www.peta.org
Staff: 156. **Descr:** Educational and activist group that opposes all forms of animal exploitation. Seeks to educate the public against speciesism and human chauvinist attitudes toward animals through documentary films, slides, and pictures of current conditions in slaughterhouses and animal experimentation laboratories. Conducts rallies and demonstrations to focus attention on the four major institutionalized cruelty issues: the exploitation and abuse of animals

in experimentation, use of animals for clothing, abuse of animals in the entertainment industry, and slaughtering for human consumption. Offers children's services; conducts research and charitable programs; compiles statistics; maintains speakers' bureau. Provides low-cost spaying and neutering for local dogs and cats, free doghouses to locals with backyard dogs; provides hands-on rescue of local animals; provides services for students; maintains a print and an audio-visual library, and will provide information or other literature to the public. **Fnd:** 1980. **Mem:** 1000000.

7689 ■ Pesticide Action Network North America (PANNA)
49 Powell St., Ste. 500
San Francisco, CA 94102
Contact: Monica Moore, Co-Dir./Prog.Dir.
Ph: (415)981-1771
Fax: (415)981-1991
E-mail: panna@panna.org
URL: http://www.panna.org
Staff: 20. **Descr:** One of five PAN Regional Centers worldwide. Works to replace pesticide use with ecologically sound and socially just alternatives; links local and international consumer, labor, health, environment and agriculture groups as an international citizens' action group challenging proliferation of pesticides, defends basic rights to health and environmental quality. **Fnd:** 1983. **Reg. Groups:** 65. **Pub:** *Global Pesticide Campaigner* (3/year); *Partners Update*.

7690 ■ Pesticide Action Network North America Regional Center (PANNA RC)
49 Powell St., Ste. 500
San Francisco, CA 94102
Contact: Kathryn Gilje, Exec. Dir.
Ph: (415)981-1771
Fax: (415)981-1991
E-mail: panna@panna.org
URL: http://www.panna.org
Staff: 17. **Descr:** Part of an international coalition of citizens' groups and individuals who advocate adoption of ecologically sound practices in place of pesticide use. **Fnd:** 1984. **Pub:** *Alternatives to Methyl Bromide: Excerpts from the U.N. Methyl Bromide Technical Options Committee Assessment 1995*; *Demise of the Dirty Dozen Chart*; *Dirty Dozen Fact Sheets*; *Global Pesticide Campaigner* (quarterly); Booklets; Manuals.

7691 ■ Pitch-In Canada (PIC)
Box 45011, Ocean Park PO
White Rock, BC, Canada V4A 9L1
Contact: Inez Santos, Office Mgr.
Free: 877-474-8244
E-mail: pitch-in@pitch-in.ca
URL: http://www.pitch-in.ca
Descr: Individuals and organizations with an interest in community beautification and pollution control. Promotes reduction of packaging and other refuse discarded in public and wild places. Conducts educational and public relations programs to discourage littering and stimulate community-based clean-up campaigns, including annual Pitch-In Week. Makes available resources and other support and assistance to local anti-littering and clean-up projects. Sponsors research; compiles statistics. **Fnd:** 1967.

7692 ■ Pollution Probe (PPF)
625 Church St., Ste. 402
Toronto, ON, Canada M4Y 2G1
Contact: Bob Oliver, Exec. Dir.
Ph: (416)926-1907
Fax: (416)926-1601
E-mail: pprobe@pollutionprobe.org
URL: http://www.pollutionprobe.org
Staff: 14. **Descr:** Works to define environmental problems through research; seeks to raise public awareness of environmental issues through education; lobbies for environmental protection and remediation before government agencies and industrial associations. Focuses on smog and climate change, reduction and elimination of mercury in water, child health and the environment, indoor air quality, and

water quality. **Fnd:** 1969. **Mem:** 6500. **Pub:** *Probe-Abilities* (3/year).

7693 ■ Power Up Gambia
PO Box 1636
Wilmington, DE 19899
Contact: Kathryn Cunningham Hall
E-mail: info@powerupgambia.org
URL: http://www.powerupgambia.org
Descr: Seeks to transform healthcare through solar technology. Aims to provide electricity and water to healthcare facilities in Gambia through solar energy. **Fnd:** 2006.

7694 ■ Professional Lawn Care Association of America (PLCAA)
1000 Johnson Ferry Rd., Ste. C-135
Marietta, GA 30068-6071
Contact: Tom Delaney, Exec. VP
Ph: (770)977-5222
Free: 800-458-3466
Fax: (770)578-6071
E-mail: tomd@plcaa.org
URL: http://www.landcarenetwork.org/cms/home.html
Staff: 6. **Descr:** Corporations, firms, and individuals active in the lawn care business; industry suppliers and distributors. Promotes general business interests, high standards, and ethical practices in the lawn care industry and supports beneficial legislation. Conducts training programs, research, consumer education, and safety programs. Compiles statistics. Offers certified turfgrass professional correspondence course. **Fnd:** 1979. **Mem:** 1200. **State Groups:** 21. **Pub:** *Pro Source* (bimonthly); *Professional Lawn Care Association of America--Membership Directory and Resource Guide* (annual); Manual; Monographs.

7695 ■ Promise World Wide
173 Ivy Hill Way
Los Gatos, CA 95032
Contact: Jaya Basu
Ph: (408)358-0160
Fax: (309)404-4347
E-mail: info@promise-ww.org
URL: http://www.promiseworldwide.org
Descr: Aims to increase the global standard of living by developing self-sustaining micro economies in disadvantaged communities through the feeding, education and training of children in the slums. Helps children born in poverty to gain access to basic amenities and education to help them regain their childhoods and grow up to be responsible citizens. **Fnd:** 2003.

7696 ■ Protect All Children's Environment (PACE)
396 Sugar Cove Rd.
Marion, NC 28752
Contact: E.M.T. O'nan, Dir.
Ph: (828)724-4221
Fax: (828)724-4177
E-mail: pace@mcdowell.main.nc.us
URL: http://www.main.nc.us/pace
Descr: Provides support to persons poisoned by the pesticide Chlordane. **Fnd:** 1987.

7697 ■ Protect Our Winters (POW)
787 11th St.
Boulder, CO 80302-7512
Contact: Jeremy Jones, Founder/CEO
E-mail: info@protectourwinters.org
URL: http://protectourwinters.org
Descr: Aims to reverse the global warming crisis by uniting and mobilizing the winter sports community. Works to educate the next generation on becoming environmental leaders. Gives support to alternative energy projects and focuses on the fight against climate change. **Fnd:** 2007.

7698 ■ Public Citizen's Critical Mass Energy and Environment Program
215 Pennsylvania Ave. SE
Washington, DC 20003
Contact: Tyson Slocum, Dir.
Ph: (202)546-4996

E-mail: member@citizen.org
URL: http://www.citizen.org/CMEP
Staff: 11. **Descr:** Energy research and education arm of Public Citizen founded to oppose nuclear power and advocate energy alternatives. Promotes renewable energy and energy efficiency technologies, programs, and policies; prepares and disseminates reports; lobbies Congress; acts as a watchdog of key federal and state energy regulatory agencies; monitors nuclear power issues such as disposal and transport of nuclear waste; provides information and resources (including action alerts, testimony, fact sheets, and other energy policy information via internet) to citizens, activists, grassroots groups, local officials and national press. Works closely with other citizens' groups and individuals across the country, empowering them to participate in important decisions affecting their health, safety, and standard of living. Operates Coalition of Ratepayers for Affordable Green Electricity. **Fnd:** 1974. **Pub:** *The Dark at the End of the Tunnel: Federal Clean-up Standards for Nuclear Power Plants*; *Directory of Anti-Nuclear Activists* (semiannual); *Energy Audit II: A State-by-State Profile of Energy Consumption and Conservation*; *National Directory of Safe Energy Organizations* (annual); *Nuclear Legacy: An Overview of the Places, Problems and Politics of Radioactive Waste in the United States*; *Nuclear Lemons: An Assessment of America's Worst Commercial Nuclear Reactors*; *Payment Due: A Reactor-by-Reactor Assessment of the Nuclear Industry's $25+ Billion Decommissioning Bill*; *Renewable Energy: A National Directory of Resources, Contacts, and Companies*; *Renewable Energy Research and Development: An Alternative Budget for FY'1993 1995*.

7699 ■ Rachel Carson Council (RCC)
PO Box 10779
Silver Spring, MD 20914-0779
Contact: Dr. Diana Post VMD, Exec. Dir.
Ph: (301)593-7507
E-mail: rccouncil@aol.com
URL: http://www.rachelcarsoncouncil.org/site
Descr: Seeks to inform and advise people and institutions about the effects of pesticides that threaten the health, welfare, and survival of living organisms and biological systems. Promotes alternative, environmentally benign pest management strategies to encourage healthier life styles. Fosters a sense of wonder and respect towards nature. **Fnd:** 1965.

7700 ■ Radiation Research Society (RRS)
PO Box 7050
Lawrence, KS 66044
Contact: Peter M. Corry PhD, Pres.
Free: 800-627-0326
Fax: (785)843-1274
E-mail: info@radres.org
URL: http://www.radres.org
Descr: Professional society of biologists, physicists, chemists, and physicians contributing to knowledge of radiation and its effects. Promotes original research in the natural sciences relating to radiation; facilitates integration of different disciplines in the study of radiation effects. **Fnd:** 1952. **Mem:** 1600. **Pub:** *Radiation Research* (monthly); *rrNEWS* (quarterly); Membership Directory (annual).

7701 ■ Rainforest Action Network (RAN)
221 Pine St., 5th Fl.
San Francisco, CA 94104
Contact: James D. Gollin, Pres.
Ph: (415)398-4404
Fax: (415)398-2732
E-mail: answers@ran.org
URL: http://www.ran.org
Staff: 43. **Descr:** Seeks to protect the earth's rainforests and the rights of their inhabitants through education, grassroots organizing, and direct action. Current campaigns include the Old Growth Forest Campaign and the Campaign for a Sane Economy. **Fnd:** 1985. **Mem:** 35000. **Reg. Groups:** 150. **Pub:**

Action Alert (bimonthly); *Amazonia: Voices From the Rainforest; Cut Waste, Not Trees.*

7702 ■ Recycling Council of Alberta (RCA)
PO Box 23
Bluffton, AB, Canada T0C 0M0
Contact: Dean Brawn, Pres.
Ph: (403)843-6563
Fax: (403)843-4156
E-mail: info@recycle.ab.ca
URL: http://www.recycle.ab.ca
Staff: 2. **Descr:** Promotes and facilitates waste reduction, recycling and resource conservation in the province of Alberta. **Fnd:** 1987. **Mem:** 200. **Pub:** *Connector* (quarterly); *Enviro Business Guide.*

7703 ■ Redwood Alliance (RA)
PO Box 293
Arcata, CA 95518
Contact: Michael Welch, Office Coor.
Ph: (707)822-7884
E-mail: info@redwoodalliance.org
URL: http://www.redwoodalliance.org
Staff: 1. **Descr:** Promotes safe and efficient energy use and development. Supports: anti-nuclear energy work; renewable energy promotion; climate protection; consumer activism; environmental education; and progressive local, regional, and national policies. Influences the government for environmentally sound laws. Offers a referral service to other groups. Conducts research and educational programs. **Fnd:** 1978. **Mem:** 4000.

7704 ■ Renew the Earth
1900 Oracle Way, Ste. 717
Reston, VA 20190
Contact: Ms. Debbie Reed, Exec. Dir.
Ph: (703)689-4670
E-mail: information@renew-the-earth.org
URL: http://www.renew-the-earth.org
Staff: 3. **Descr:** Individuals and groups working toward a sustainable future by promoting a safe and healthy environment. Coordinates National Awards for Environmental Sustainability program to recognize positive environmental measures. Operates the Environmental Success Index, a clearinghouse of more than 1600 working environmental projects available to community groups, the media, businesses, policy makers, and individuals dedicated to implementing and promoting positive environmental change. Moving toward developing an international program. **Fnd:** 1989. **Mem:** 2000. **Pub:** *Environmental Success Index* (annual).

7705 ■ Residential Energy Services Network (RESNET)
PO Box 4561
Oceanside, CA 92052-4561
Contact: Steve Baden, Exec. Dir.
Ph: (760)806-3448
E-mail: info@natresnet.org
URL: http://www.resnet.us
Descr: Aims to uphold the national standards for home energy ratings. Provides services concerning policy issues that affect consumer demand and housing industry support for residential energy efficiency. Serves as the portal by which consumers, the home energy rating industry, residential energy and, and the housing and mortgage industry can secure up-to-date information on residential energy performance and energy efficient financing options and packages. **Fnd:** 1995. **Pub:** *RESNET Notes* (monthly); Annual Report.

7706 ■ Rising Tide North America (RTNA)
PO Box 3928
Oakland, CA 94609
Contact: Mike Hudema
Ph: (503)438-4697
E-mail: contact@risingtidenorthamerica.org
URL: http://www.risingtidenorthamerica.org
Descr: Fosters community-based solutions to the climate crisis. Aims to prevent catastrophic global warming by determining the root causes of climate change. Works to support direct action and encourages individuals and organizations to carry out

autonomous actions that are in line with these principles. **Pub:** Brochure.

7707 ■ River Fund
11155 Roseland Rd., No. 16
Sebastian, FL 32958
Contact: Jaya Canterbury-Counts MEd, Exec. Dir.
Ph: (772)589-5076
E-mail: info@riverfund.org
URL: http://www.riverfund.org
Descr: Provides physical, emotional, spiritual, educational support to those living with or affected by HIV/AIDS and other life challenging illnesses. **Fnd:** 1990.

7708 ■ River Management Society (RMS)
PO Box 9048
Missoula, MT 59807-9048
Contact: Caroline Kurz, Program Dir.
Ph: (406)549-0514
Fax: (406)542-6208
E-mail: rms@river-management.org
URL: http://www.river-management.org
Staff: 1. **Descr:** Individuals, organizations, and agencies with an interest in the conservation of riverine ecosystems. Seeks to advance the profession of river management. Serves as a clearinghouse on riverine conservation; conducts continuing professional development courses for river managers; functions as a liaison linking river managers with environmental protection organizations and government agencies. **Fnd:** 1996. **Mem:** 400. **Pub:** *Better Boater Bathrooms: A Sourcebook for River Managers; River Information Digest* (quarterly); Membership Directory (periodic).

7709 ■ Safe Energy Communication Council (SECC)
1717 Massachusetts Ave. NW, Ste. 106
Washington, DC 20036
Contact: Scott Denman, Exec.Dir.
Fax: (202)234-9194
Staff: 7. **Descr:** Coalition of ten national environmental, consumer, and public interest media organizations. Seeks to disseminate fair and accurate energy information through broadcast and print media. Provides expertise in nuclear energy, utility reform, development of renewable energy alternatives and energy efficiency, and public media access. Offers advice and training to environmental and consumer groups on media skills, strategy and access. Established in response to multi-million dollar pronuclear promotional campaigns by nuclear corporations and electric utilities to offset negative publicity resulting from the Three Mile Island accident. Has produced television and radio segments to counter this pronuclear media blitz. Activities include continued monitoring of pronuclear media campaigns, production of additional response messages for broadcast and print media, expansion of links with alternative energy groups across the country, energy outreach media tours, and increased public education on viable energy alternatives. **Fnd:** 1979. **Pub:** *ENfacts* (periodic); *MYTHBusters Series* (periodic); *VIEWPOINT* (periodic).

7710 ■ Save the Patient
260 E Chestnut St., No. 1712
Chicago, IL 60611-2455
Contact: Lenore Janecek, Pres.
Ph: (312)440-0630
Fax: (312)440-0631
E-mail: savethepatient@aol.com
URL: http://www.savethepatient.org
Descr: Aims to educate and empower patients and the public in making health care decisions. Provides health services to people of all ages, cultures and socio-economic backgrounds. Helps mitigate the imbalance between the wealth of medical information and technology. **Fnd:** 2001.

7711 ■ Saving Horses, Inc. (SHI)
8840 Hunter Pass
Alpine, CA 91901-2622
Contact: Audrey Reynolds, Founder
Ph: (619)445-2917

E-mail: audrey@savinghorsesinc.com
URL: http://www.savinghorsesinc.com
Descr: Aims to rescue horses from slaughter, abuse, neglect and abandonment. Provides homes and environments for rescued horses. **Fnd:** 2007.

7712 ■ Senior Action in a Gay Environment (SAGE)
305 7th Ave., 16th Fl.
New York, NY 10001
Contact: Michael Adams, Exec. Dir.
Ph: (212)741-2247
Fax: (212)366-1947
E-mail: info@sageusa.org
URL: http://www.sageusa.org
Descr: Professional social workers and trained volunteers including doctors, lawyers, psychologists, gerontologists, and others dedicated to meeting the needs of older gays and lesbians and ending the isolation that has kept them separate from each other, other gays, and from the larger community. Centered in the New York City area, provides: information and referral in areas of legal matters, assessments, and friendly visitor homebound program; individual and group counseling, including bereavement services; social activities to reduce loneliness, rebuild relationships, and establish supportive connections with the gay and lesbian community. Provides in-service training for agency members and institutions serving older gays. Educates professionals and the public with regard to lesbian and gay aging. Sponsors AIDS Service Program for the Elderly. Conducts weekly workshops and training programs for volunteers and social service agencies interested in issues of lesbian and gay aging. Maintains speakers bureau; conducts research programs; compiles statistics. **Fnd:** 1978. **Pub:** *SAGE Bulletin* (monthly).

7713 ■ Sierra Club of Canada (SCC)
412-1 Nicholas St.
Ottawa, ON, Canada K1N 7B7
Contact: Stephen Hazell, Exec. Dir.
Ph: (613)241-4611
Free: 888-810-4204
Fax: (613)241-2292
E-mail: info@sierraclub.ca
URL: http://www.sierraclub.ca
Descr: Individuals and organizations concerned about conservation and environmental protection. Promotes development of public policies mandating environmental responsibility. Seeks to raise public awareness of environmental protection issues. Conducts national campaigns on matters including: increased energy efficiency; clear-cutting of forests; health risks associated with pesticide use; protection of biodiversity. **Fnd:** 1963. **Mem:** 10000. **Reg. Groups:** 3. **State Groups:** 10.

7714 ■ Solar Energy Industries Association (SEIA)
575 7th St. NW, Ste. 400
Washington, DC 20004
Contact: Rhone Resch, Pres.
Ph: (202)682-0556
E-mail: info@seia.org
URL: http://www.seia.org
Staff: 14. **Descr:** Manufacturers, installers, distributors, contractors, and engineers of solar energy systems and components. Aims to accelerate and foster commercialization of solar energy conversion for economic purposes. Maintains Solar Energy Research and Education Foundation. Compiles statistics; offers computerized services. **Fnd:** 1974. **Mem:** 500. **State Groups:** 13. **Pub:** *Statistical Survey of Solar Collector Manufacturers and Suppliers* (quarterly).

7715 ■ Southwest Research and Information Center (SRIC)
PO Box 4524
Albuquerque, NM 87106
Contact: Don Hancock, Dir.
Ph: (505)262-1862
Fax: (505)262-1864

E-mail: info@sric.org
URL: http://www.sric.org
Descr: Provides educational and scientific information to citizens and community groups on subjects of public interest; current emphasis is on the health effects of: nuclear waste disposal, mining, waste management, toxics, oil and gas, water, and uranium mining issues in the Southwest. Acts as a consultant to community organizations. Sponsors National Campaign for Radioactive Waste Safety and Health and Radiation Projects. **Fnd:** 1971. **Pub:** *How Safe is Mexico's Atomic City*; *Public Land Private Profit*; *Uranium Mining and Milling: A Primer*; *Voices From The Earth* (3/year).

7716 ■ Steel Recycling Institute (SRI)
680 Andersen Dr.
Pittsburgh, PA 15220-2700
Contact: Mr. Gregory L. Crawford, VP of Operations
Ph: (412)922-2772
Free: 800-876-7274
E-mail: gcrawford@steel.org
URL: http://www.recycle-steel.org
Staff: 10. **Descr:** Educates the solid waste management industry, government, business and the consumer about the economic and environmental benefits of recycling steel. **Fnd:** 1988.

7717 ■ Sunstove Organization
3140 N Lilly Rd.
Brookfield, WI 53005
Contact: Richard C. Wareham, Managing Dir.
Ph: (262)781-1689
Fax: (262)781-0455
E-mail: info@sungravity.com
URL: http://www.sungravity.com/index.html
Descr: Disseminates information relating to clean water and solar cooking systems for rural communities worldwide. Provides in-depth information, drawings, and photographs on how to mass-produce solar cookers by hand.

7718 ■ Sustainable Agriculture Education (SAGE)
1625 Shattuck Ave., Ste. 210
Berkeley, CA 94709
Contact: Sibella Kraus, Pres./Founder
Ph: (510)526-1793
Fax: (510)524-7153
E-mail: info@sagecenter.org
URL: http://www.sagecenter.org
Descr: Seeks to develop urban edge agriculture and engage diverse regional populations with the sustainable agriculture movement. Develops projects for public agencies, developers, planners and community groups, and helps inspire informed action through entrepreneurial, collaborative approaches. Fosters and supports projects that link urban and rural places. **Fnd:** 2001.

7719 ■ Sustainable Buildings Industry Council (SBIC)
1112 16th St. NW, Ste. 240
Washington, DC 20036
Contact: Sophia Greenbaum, Exec. Dir.
Ph: (202)628-7400
Fax: (202)393-5043
E-mail: sbic@sbicouncil.org
URL: http://www.sbicouncil.org
Staff: 3. **Descr:** Works to advance the design, affordability, energy performance, and environmental soundness of commercial, institutional, and residential buildings nationwide. Offers professional training, consumer education, and energy analysis tools. Provides accurate, easy-to-use guidelines, software, and general information about energy conservation measures, energy efficient equipment and appliances, daylighting, and sustainable architecture. Active in presenting workshops and seminars geared toward improving building energy performance in cities and towns throughout the nation. **Fnd:** 1980. **Mem:** 100. **Pub:** *Buildings: Inside and Out* (periodic);

Passive Solar Design Strategies: Guidelines for Home Builders; *Savings From the Sun*.

7720 ■ Sustainable Furnishings Council (SFC)
PO Box 205
Chapel Hill, NC 27514
Contact: Susan Inglis, Exec. Dir.
Ph: (919)967-1137
E-mail: susan@sustainablefurniturecouncil.org
URL: http://www.sustainablefurniturecouncil.org
Descr: Seeks to address sustainability issues concerning home furnishings. Promotes sustainable practices among manufacturers, retailers, and consumers. Encourages companies to adopt acceptable business practices that foster eco-responsibility in the manufacture of home furnishings and other related products. **Fnd:** 2006. **Mem:** 250.

7721 ■ Sustainable Packaging Coalition (SPC)
600 E Water St., Ste. C
Charlottesville, VA 22902
Contact: Anne Johnson, Dir.
Ph: (434)817-1424
Fax: (434)817-1425
E-mail: spcinfo@greenblue.org
URL: http://www.sustainablepackaging.org
Descr: Aims to advocate and communicate a positive, robust environmental vision for packaging. Strives to support innovative, functional packaging materials and systems that promote economic and environmental health through supply chain collaboration. Provides a forum for members to discuss and share perspectives on the issues, practices and solutions related to the creation of more sustainable packaging systems. **Fnd:** 2004.

7722 ■ Two Cents of Hope (TCH)
2805-4 Brigadoon Dr.
Raleigh, NC 27606
Contact: Prem Swaroop, Pres.
Ph: (919)389-3430
E-mail: info@twocentsofhope.com
URL: http://www.twocentsofhope.com
Descr: Aims to create a responsible and self-sustaining society. Promotes education for the underprivileged. Makes education accessible to deserving candidates from the poorer sections of society. Provides education to the youth of India and creates opportunities for the recognition of potential.

7723 ■ Union of Concerned Scientists (UCS)
2 Brattle Sq.
Cambridge, MA 02238-9105
Contact: Kathleen M. Rest, Exec. Dir.
Ph: (617)547-5552
Fax: (617)864-9405
URL: http://www.ucsusa.org
Staff: 70. **Descr:** Advocacy organization concerned about the impact of advanced technology on society. Conducts research on energy policy, global environmental problems, transportation, biotechnology, and arms control. Disseminates research results to the public and assists members and the public in presenting their views before administrative agencies and the courts. Conducts public education programs including nationwide events, television and radio appearances, and speaking engagements. Sponsors annual nationwide educational campaign. **Fnd:** 1969. **Mem:** 60000. **Pub:** *A Scientist's Guide to Talking with the Media*; *Catalyst* (semiannual); *Earthwise* (quarterly); *Gone to Seed: Transgenic Contaminants in the Traditional Seed Supply*; *Greener Pastures: How Grass-fed Beef and Milk Contribute to Healthy Eating*; *How to Avoid Dangerous Climate Change*; *Nuclear Power in a Warming World*; *U.S. Nuclear Plants in the 21st Century: The Risk of a Lifetime*; *Walking a Nuclear Tightrope: Unlearned Lessons of Year-plus Reactor Outages*.

7724 ■ U.S. Business Council for Sustainable Development (USBCSD)
Bldg. II, Ste. 202
4425 S Mopac Expy.
Austin, TX 78735
Contact: Andrew Mangan, Co-Founder/Exec. Dir.
Ph: (512)892-6411

Fax: (512)892-6443
E-mail: info@usbcsd.org
URL: http://www.usbcsd.org
Descr: Provides a voice for business in the sustainable development field. Promotes the business value of sustainable development. Creates initiatives that foster sustainable development. Advances the public and agency credibility of members. Offers networking and partnership opportunities. **Fnd:** 2002. **Pub:** Newsletter (quarterly).

7725 ■ Water Quality Association (WQA)
4151 Naperville Rd.
Lisle, IL 60532-1088
Contact: Peter J. Censky, Exec. Dir.
Ph: (630)505-0160
Fax: (630)505-9637
E-mail: info@wqa.org
URL: http://www.wqa.org
Staff: 38. **Descr:** Individuals or firms engaged in the manufacture and/or assembly and distribution and/or retail selling of water treatment equipment, supplies, and services. Promotes the acceptance and use of industry equipment, products, and services. Provides activities, programs, and services designed to improve economy and efficiency within the industry. Conducts expositions and certification and equipment validation programs. Compiles statistics. **Fnd:** 1974. **Mem:** 2500. **Pub:** *Water Treatment Fundamentals*; *Water Treatment Fundamentals Seminar Audio Cassette Series*; *WQA NewsFax* (bimonthly).

7726 ■ Western Canada Wilderness Committee (WCWC)
227 Abbott St.
Vancouver, BC, Canada V6B 2K7
Contact: Andrea Reimer, Exec. Dir.
Ph: (604)683-8220
Free: 800-661-9453
Fax: (604)683-8229
E-mail: info@wildernesscommittee.org
URL: http://www.wildernesscommittee.org
Staff: 14. **Descr:** Individuals interested in preserving wilderness areas, with emphasis on old-growth forests, and their inhabitants. Promotes social justice as a prerequisite of environmental protection in developing regions. Conducts educational campaigns to raise public awareness of environmental protection issues and the dangers posed to the environment by economic development. Works with local environmental groups and indigenous people associations to insure appropriate and sustainable economic growth in developing regions. Maintains trails in unprotected temperate rainforests on the coast of British Columbia. Acts as hub for a global network of environmental groups. **Fnd:** 1980. **Mem:** 26000. **Reg. Groups:** 5. **Pub:** Newspaper (monthly).

7727 ■ The Wilderness Society (TWS)
1615 M St. NW
Washington, DC 20036
Contact: Brenda Davis, Chair
Free: 800-843-9453
E-mail: member@tws.org
URL: http://www.wilderness.org
Descr: Works for the establishment of the land ethic as a basic element of American culture and philosophy, and the education of a broader and more committed wilderness preservation and land protection constituency. Focuses on federal, legislative, and administrative actions affecting public lands, including national forests, parks, and wildlife refuges, and Bureau of Land Management lands. Encourages Congress to designate appropriate public lands as wilderness areas. Programs include grass roots organizing, economic analysis, lobbying, research, and public education. Compiles statistics. **Fnd:** 1935. **Pub:** *National Landscape Conservation System*; *WildAlert* (weekly); *Wilderness* (annual); *Wilderness Act Handbook-40th Anniversary Edition (2004)* (periodic); *Wilderness Report* (biweekly); *The Wilderness Society's Newsletter* (quarterly); Annual Report.

7728 ■ Windustry
2105 1st Ave. S
Minneapolis, MN 55404

Contact: Lisa Daniels, Exec. Dir./Founder
Ph: (612)870-3461
Free: 800-946-3640
Fax: (612)813-5612
E-mail: info@windustry.org
URL: http://www.windustry.org
Descr: Seeks to increase wind energy opportunities for rural landowners and communities. Responds to barriers to wind energy by building collaborations with rural landowners, local communities and utilities, as well as state, regional and non-profit organizations. Promotes family farms, rural communities and ecosystems through advocacy, research and education and science and technology. **Pub:** Newsletter (quarterly).

7729 ■ Women's Earth Alliance (WEA)
300 Broadway, Ste. 28
San Francisco, CA 94133
Contact: Melinda Kramer, Founder/Dir.
Ph: (415)788-3666
E-mail: info@womensearthalliance.org
URL: http://www.womensearthalliance.org
Descr: Represents female environmental advocates around the world. Works to protect and conserve the earth and all its inhabitants. Strives to enhance the social and environmental health of the earth. **Fnd:** 2005.

7730 ■ World of Good Development Organization
5900 Hollis St., Ste. X
Emeryville, CA 94608
Contact: Ella Silverman, Exec. Dir.
Ph: (510)528-9400
Fax: (510)528-8400
E-mail: info@worldofgood.org
URL: http://www.worldofgood.org
Descr: Focuses on building strategies to improve economic and social conditions for millions of women and adolescent girls in developing countries. Increases awareness among businesses and international organizations of the needs of homeworkers especially women and adolescent girls living in poverty. **Fnd:** 2004.

7731 ■ Yukon Conservation Society (YCS)
302 Hawkins St.
Whitehorse, YT, Canada Y1A 1X6
Ph: (867)668-5678
Fax: (867)668-6637
E-mail: ycs@ycs.yk.ca
URL: http://www.yukonconservation.org
Staff: 6. **Descr:** Seeks to protect Canada's natural environment; particularly that of the Yukon region. Encourages the conservation of Yukon wilderness, wildlife and natural resources. **Fnd:** 1968. **Mem:** 325. **Pub:** *Walk Softly* (quarterly).

State and Local Organizations and Agencies

Alabama

7732 ■ Alabama Department of Conservation and Natural Resources
64 N. Union St., Ste. 468
Montgomery, AL 36130
Contact: M. Barnett Lawley, Commnr.
Ph: (334)242-3486
E-mail: dcnr.commissioner@dcnr.alabama.gov
URL: http://www.dcnr.state.al.us/
Pub: *Outdoor Alabama Newsletter* (online).

7733 ■ Alabama Solar Association
2117 Rothmore Dr. SW
Huntsville, AL 35803-1431
Contact: A. Morton Archibald Jr.
Ph: (256)658-5189
E-mail: morton@knology.net
Descr: Brings together energy professionals to create a sustainable energy economy. Promotes solar energy education, public outreach, and advocacy. Increases the use of solar energy, energy efficiency

and other sustainable technologies in the United States.

Alaska

7734 ■ Alaska Department of Environment Conservation
410 Willoughby Ave., Ste. 303
PO Box 111800
Juneau, AK 99811-1800
Contact: Larry Hartig, Commnr.
Ph: (907)465-5066
Fax: (907)465-5070
E-mail: dec.commissioner@alaska.gov
URL: http://www.dec.state.ak.us/

7735 ■ Wilderness Society, Alaska
705 Christensen Dr.
Anchorage, AK 99501
Contact: Eleanor Huffines, Regional Dir.
Ph: (907)272-9453
E-mail: eleanor_huffines@tws.org
URL: http://www.tws.org
Descr: Works to deliver to future generations an unspoiled legacy of wild places.

Arizona

7736 ■ Alcoholics Anonymous World Services, River City Central Office
603 Marina Blvd.
Bullhead City, AZ 86439
Ph: (928)763-4499
Free: 800-864-1606
E-mail: central_office@rcco-aa.org
URL: http://www.rcco-aa.org
Descr: Individuals recovering from alcoholism. Maintains that members can solve their common problem and help others achieve sobriety through a twelve-step program that includes sharing their experience, strength, and hope with each other.

7737 ■ Arizona Department of Environmental Quality
1110 W. Washington St.
Phoenix, AZ 85007
Contact: Benjamin H. Grumbles, Dir.
Ph: (602)771-2300
Free: 800-234-5677
E-mail: owens.Stephen@azdeq.gov
URL: http://www.adeq.state.az.us/
Descr: Mission is to protect public health and the environment.

7738 ■ Arizona Solar Energy Association (ASEA)
PO Box 5583
Scottsdale, AZ 85261
Contact: Dan Aiello, Vice Chm.
Ph: (480)966-1380
Fax: (480)966-1516
E-mail: lanegarret@aol.com
URL: http://www.azsolarcenter.com/solarorg/asea1.html
Descr: Promotes education, networking and communication in solar energy, wind renewables and sustainability. Works for favorable legislation to promote renewable energy. Holds educational seminars.

7739 ■ Green Valley Association of Realtors
210 W Continental Rd., Ste. 244
Green Valley, AZ 85614
Contact: Catherine York, Pres.-Elect
Ph: (520)625-2600
Free: 888-701-0127
Fax: (520)625-3870
E-mail: info@gvar.com
URL: http://www.gvar.com
Descr: Helps members become more successful and profitable in their businesses. Strives to develop real estate business practices. Provides information about the real estate industry.

Arkansas

7740 ■ The Arc for the River Valley (TARV)
2414 S 57th St., Ste. 101
Fort Smith, AR 72903
Contact: Ms. Amber Breazzeal, Exec. Dir.
Ph: (479)783-5529
Fax: (479)783-5394
E-mail: tarv1959@sbcglobal.net
URL: http://www.thearchelps.org
Staff: 1. **Descr:** Parents, professional workers, and others interested in individuals with mental retardation. Works to promote services, research, public understanding, and legislation for people with mental retardation and their families. **Fnd:** 1959. **Mem:** 386. **Pub:** Newsletter (monthly).

7741 ■ Arkansas Department of Environmental Quality
5301 Northshore Dr.
Little Rock, AR 72118-5317
Contact: Teresa Marks, Dir.
Ph: (501)682-0744
Fax: (501)682-0798
E-mail: marks@adeq.state.ar.us
URL: http://www.adeq.state.ar.us/
Descr: Strives to protect and enhance the state's environment through regulatory programs, proactive programs, and education activities.

7742 ■ National Ovarian Cancer Coalition - River Valley Chapter
8805 Meadow Dr.
Fort Smith, AR 72908
Contact: Blanche West
Ph: (479)646-3431
E-mail: noccrivervalley@ovarian.org
Descr: Seeks to improve the overall survival and quality of life for women with ovarian cancer. Advances the prevention, diagnosis and treatment of ovarian cancer. Promotes and expands patient, public and professional ovarian cancer education and awareness.

California

7743 ■ American Cancer Society, Antelope Valley-Eastern Sierra Unit
1043 West Ave. M-4, Ste. B
Palmdale, CA 93551
Ph: (661)945-7585
Free: 800-227-2345
Fax: (661)945-9039
Descr: Strives to eliminate cancer as a major health problem by preventing cancer, saving lives and diminishing suffering from cancer. Conducts research, education, advocacy and service.

7744 ■ American Society of Heating, Refrigerating, and Air-Conditioning Engineers, Sierra Delta Chapter
Dehart Plumbing Heating and Air
209 Kerr Ave.
Modesto, CA 95354
Contact: John Hardin, Pres.
Ph: (209)523-4578
Fax: (209)549-5095
E-mail: john@dehartinc.com
URL: http://sierra-delta.ashraechapters.org
Descr: Works to advance the arts and sciences of heating, ventilating, air conditioning and refrigerating. **Pub:** Newsletter (monthly).

7745 ■ Appraisal Institute, Sacramento Sierra Chapter
2701 Cottage Way, No. 1
Sacramento, CA 95825
Contact: Emily Bernardis, Exec. Dir.
Ph: (916)972-9700
Fax: (916)972-9750
E-mail: emily@sac-ai.org
URL: http://www.sac-ai.org
Descr: General appraisers who hold the MAI or

SRPA designations, and residential members who hold the SRA designation. **Mem:** 200.

7746 ■ Butte-Sierra District Dental Society (BSDDS)
1469 Butte House Rd., Ste. G
Yuba City, CA 95993-2752
Contact: Ms. Jeannie Pittman, Exec. Dir.
Ph: (530)671-9312
Fax: (530)671-2460
E-mail: buttesierradds@sbcglobal.net
URL: http://www.buttesierradds.org
Descr: Represents the interests of dentists committed to the public's oral health, ethics, science and professional advancement. Promotes the art and science of dentistry through advocacy, education, research and the development of standards.

7747 ■ California Bottled Water Association (CBWA)
1731 Howe Ave., No. 469
Sacramento, CA 95825
Contact: Chuck Hurst, Pres.
Free: 866-786-3924
Fax: (805)489-5010
E-mail: chuck@eculligan.com
URL: http://www.cbwa.info
Descr: Promotes increased use of bottled water. Fosters and safeguards the general interests of the bottled water industry. Provides technical assistance to members in preparing the highest quality water to consumers.

7748 ■ California Council for Wildlife Rehabilitators (CCWR)
PO Box 434
Santa Rosa, CA 95402
Contact: Dawn Wilson-Kozicki, Pres.
Ph: (415)541-5090
URL: http://www.ccwr.org
Fnd: 1993.

7749 ■ California Environmental Protection Agency
1001 I St.
PO Box 2815
Sacramento, CA 95812-2815
Contact: Linda S. Adams, Sec.
Ph: (916)323-2514
E-mail: cepacomm@calepa.ca.gov
URL: http://www.calepa.ca.gov/
Descr: Mission is to restore, protect, and enhance the environment, to ensure public health, environmental quality, and economic vitality.

7750 ■ California Onsite Wastewater Association (COWA)
PO Box 6146
Santa Rosa, CA 95406
Contact: Karen McBride, Pres.
Ph: (707)579-4882
Fax: (707)579-0117
E-mail: cliffrt@msn.com
URL: http://www.cowa.org

7751 ■ California Solar Energy Industries Association (CALSEIA)
PO Box 782
Rio Vista, CA 94571
Contact: Sue Kateley, Exec. Dir.
Ph: (916)747-6987
Fax: (707)374-4767
E-mail: info@calseia.org
URL: http://www.calseia.org
Descr: Includes solar-related businesses. Serves as a forum for the discussion of the legal, economic and technical issues affecting the use of solar energy. Educates members and nonmembers about the application of clean and self-renewing energy available from the sun. **Fnd:** 1977.

7752 ■ Natural Resources Defense Council - San Francisco
111 Sutter St., 20th Fl.
San Francisco, CA 94104
Ph: (415)875-6100

Fax: (415)495-5996
E-mail: nrdcinfo@nrdc.org
URL: http://www.nrdc.org
Descr: Works to safeguard the earth, its people, its plants and animals, and the natural systems on which all life depends.

7753 ■ Northern California Solar Energy Association (NorCal Sol)
PO Box 3008
Berkeley, CA 94703
Contact: Ms. Liz Merry, Exec. Dir.
Ph: (530)852-0354
Fax: (530)852-0381
E-mail: solarinfo@norcalsolar.org
URL: http://www.norcalsolar.org
Descr: Seeks to activate community support for making solar energy a primary energy choice in the 21st century. Also supports the use of solar energy for the benefit of U.S. citizens and the global environment. **Fnd:** 1976. **Mem:** 438. **Pub:** *Northern California Sun* (quarterly); *Solar Energy Resource Guide* (annual); *Solar Enews* (bimonthly).

7754 ■ Pacific Water Quality Association (PWQA)
17300 17th St., Ste. J-266
Tustin, CA 92780-7918
Contact: Kristi Pihl, Admin. Asst.
Ph: (760)644-7348
Fax: (714)242-7715
E-mail: info@pwqa.org
URL: http://www.pwqa.org
Descr: Works to represent the water quality improvement industry: retailers, assemblers, manufacturers and supplies, as well as auxiliary member companies. Provides all consumers equal access to quality water options for home, business and commercial water treatment products. Strives to provide the very best water quality improvement devices, back by trained, professional staffs who understand how to improve the customer's existing water supplies with safe and sound cutting edge technologies. **Fnd:** 1957.

7755 ■ San Diego Renewable Energy Society (SDRES)
PO Box 1660
Julian, CA 92036
Contact: Richard Caputo, Dir.
E-mail: info@sdres.org
URL: http://sdres.org
Descr: Promotes a wide utilization of solar energy through the application of science and technology.

7756 ■ Sierra Association of Health Facilities
Golden Empire CH
121 Dorsey Dr.
Grass Valley, CA 95945-5201
Contact: Vicki Young, Pres.
Ph: (530)273-1316
Fax: (530)273-4809
URL: http://www.cahf.org
Descr: Promotes professionalism and ethical behavior of individuals providing long-term care delivery for patients and for the general public. Provides information, education and administrative tools to enhance the quality of long-term care. Improves the standards of service and administration of member nursing homes.

7757 ■ Sierra College Small Business Development Center
333 Sunrise Ave., Ste. 885
Roseville, CA 95661
Contact: Indria Gillespie, Program Mgr.
Ph: (916)781-6235
Fax: (916)781-6239
E-mail: sbdc@sierracollege.edu
URL: http://www.sbdcsierra.org
Descr: Represents and promotes the small business sector. Provides management assistance to current and prospective small business owners. Helps to

improve management skills and expand the products and services of members.

7758 ■ Union of Concerned Scientists California Office (UCS)
2397 Shattuck Ave., Ste. 203
Berkeley, CA 94704-1567
Contact: Kevin Knobloch, Pres.
Ph: (510)843-1872
Fax: (510)843-3785
E-mail: ucs@ucsusa.org
URL: http://www.ucsusa.org
Descr: Conducts research on energy policy, global environmental problems, transportation, biotechnology, and arms control. **Fnd:** 1969.

7759 ■ Wilderness Society - California/Nevada Regional Office
655 Montgomery St., Ste. 1000
San Francisco, CA 94111
Contact: Sara Barth, Dir.
Ph: (415)398-1111
Fax: (415)398-1632
E-mail: ca@tws.org
URL: http://www.wilderness.org
Descr: Works to protect America's wilderness and to develop a nationwide network of wild lands through public education, scientific analysis, and advocacy. Goal is to ensure that future generations enjoy the clean air and water, beauty, wildlife, and opportunities for recreation and spiritual renewal provided by the nation's pristine forests, rivers, deserts, and mountains. **Fnd:** 1935. **Pub:** *Wilderness* (annual); *The Wilderness Society* (quarterly).

Colorado

7760 ■ Colorado Council for Wildlife Rehabilitation (CCWR)
PO Box 68
Hygiene, CO 80533
Contact: Joyce Benesh-Williams, Pres.
Ph: (970)686-9217
E-mail: ccwr_4_members@msn.com
URL: http://www.ccwr-co.org

7761 ■ Colorado Department of Public Health and Environment
4300 Cherry Creek Dr. S.
Denver, CO 80246-1530
Contact: James B. Martin, Exec.Dir.
Ph: (303)692-2000
Free: 800-886-7689
E-mail: cdphe.information@state.co.us
URL: http://www.cdphe.state.co.us/
Descr: Mission is to protect and improve the health of Colorado's people and the quality of the environment. **Telecom. Svcs:** TDD phone number is (303)691-7700.

7762 ■ Colorado Professionals in Onsite Wastewater (CPOW)
PO Box 196
Wheat Ridge, CO 80034-0196
Contact: Warren Brown, Pres.
E-mail: wbrown@tchd.org
URL: http://www.cpow.net

7763 ■ Colorado Solar Energy Industries Association (CoSEIA)
PO Box 16
Lafayette, CO 80026
Contact: Beth Hart, Exec. Dir.
Ph: (303)333-7342
Free: 866-633-9764
E-mail: info@coseia.org
URL: http://www.coseia.org
Fnd: 1989.

7764 ■ Colorado Water Quality Association (CWQA)
PO Box 83
Lamar, CO 81052
Contact: John Rickert, Pres.
Ph: (303)660-9093

Fax: (303)429-4669
E-mail: cwqa_info@cwqa.org
URL: http://www.cwqa.org
Descr: Represents individuals or firms engaged in the manufacturing and/or assembly and distribution and/or retail selling of water treatment equipment, supplies, and services. Promotes the acceptance and use of industry equipment, products, and services. Provides activities, programs, and services designed to improve economy and efficiency within the industry. **Fnd:** 1959.

7765 ■ Izaak Walton League of America, Pikes Peak Chapter
450 Franceville Coal Mine Rd.
Colorado Springs, CO 80929-9313
Contact: Bill Bolch, Pres.
Ph: (719)683-4420
Fax: (719)683-5990
URL: http://www.pikespeakgunclub.org
Descr: Works to educate the public to conserve, maintain, protect, and restore the soil, forest, water, and other natural resources of the U.S.; promotes the enjoyment and wholesome utilization of these resources.

Connecticut

7766 ■ Connecticut Department of Environmental Protection
79 Elm St.
Hartford, CT 06106-5127
Contact: Regina McCarthy, Commnr.
Ph: (860)424-3000
Fax: (860)424-4051
E-mail: dep.webmaster@ct.gov
URL: http://www.ct.gov/dep/site/default.asp
Descr: Mission is to conserve, improve, and protect the natural resources and the environment of Connecticut in such a manner as to encourage the social and economic development and the life forms it supports in a delicate, interrelated, and complex balance, to the end that the state may fulfill its responsibility as trustee of the environment for present and future generations.

7767 ■ Connecticut Wildlife Rehabilitators Association (CWRA)
78 Sanford Rd.
Woodbury, CT 06798
Contact: Jayne Amico, Pres.
Ph: (203)389-4411
E-mail: info@cwrawildlife.org
URL: http://www.cwrawildlife.org

7768 ■ Greenwich Association of Realtors
1 Lafayette Pl.
Greenwich, CT 06830
Contact: Tracy Chester
Ph: (203)869-0240
Fax: (203)869-5619
E-mail: bubblestc@aol.com
URL: http://www.greenwichctonline.com
Descr: Real estate firms and individuals working to increase communications, education, and multiple listing services in the industry. Conducts charitable programs; makes available scholarships. **Fnd:** 1924. **Mem:** 750. **State Groups:** 1.

Delaware

7769 ■ Delaware Council of Wildlife Rehabilitators and Educators
110 Karl Dr.
Dover, DE 19901
Contact: Cathy Martin, Pres.
Ph: (302)674-9131
E-mail: cathytheark@comcast.net

7770 ■ Delaware Department of Natural Resources and Environmental Control
89 Kings Hwy.
Dover, DE 19901
Contact: David Small, Actg.Sec.
Ph: (302)739-9000

Free: 800-662-8802
Fax: (302)739-6242
E-mail: michael.globettis@state.de.us
URL: http://www.dnrec.delaware.gov/Pages/default.aspx
Descr: Mission is to protect and manage the state's vital natural resources, protect public health and safety, provide quality outdoor recreation, and to serve and educate the citizens of Delaware about the wise use, conservation, and enhancement of Delaware's environment.

7771 ■ Delaware On-Site Wastewater Recycling Association (DOWRA)
PO Box 1696
Dover, DE 19903
Contact: Mr. Ken Walsh, Pres.
E-mail: mks1@aol.com
URL: http://www.dowra.org

7772 ■ Delaware Wildlife Rehabilitators Association (DWRA)
276 Cambridge Rd.
Camden, DE 19934
Contact: Robin Coventry, Pres.
Ph: (302)698-1047
E-mail: coventrybird@verizon.net

Florida

7773 ■ Alcoholics Anonymous World Services, Nature Coast Intergroup
111 W Main St., Ste. 305
Inverness, FL 34450
Ph: (352)344-0290
E-mail: ncinterg@ncintergroup.com
URL: http://www.ncintergroup.com
Descr: Individuals recovering from alcoholism. Maintains that members can solve their common problem and help others achieve sobriety through a twelve-step program that includes sharing their experience, strength, and hope with each other.

7774 ■ American Heart Association, Nature Coast and Citrus
11207 Blue Heron Blvd. N
St. Petersburg, FL 33716
Contact: Cathy Hewlett
Free: 800-352-3824
Fax: (727)563-8107
Descr: Aims to reduce disability and death from cardiovascular diseases and stroke.

7775 ■ American Solar Energy Society at University of Florida
University of Florida
Department of Mechanical Engineering
MEB 237
PO Box 116300
Gainesville, FL 32611-6300
Contact: Mr. Shalabh Maroo, Pres.
Ph: (352)392-2328
Fax: (352)846-1630
E-mail: ases@grove.ufl.edu
Staff: 6. **Descr:** Works to promote the use of solar energy through community activities in the Gainesville area.

7776 ■ Arc of Indian River County
1375 16th Ave.
Vero Beach, FL 32960
Contact: Charles Bradley, Exec. Dir.
Ph: (772)562-6855
Fax: (772)562-6063
E-mail: charlesb@arcir.org
URL: http://www.arcir.org

7777 ■ Environmental Information Association, Florida Chapter
UF TREEO Ctr.
3900 SW 63rd Blvd.
Gainesville, FL 32608
Contact: J. Larry Back
Ph: (352)392-9570
Fax: (352)392-6910
Descr: Represents individuals and corporations

concerned about environmental management and control. Collects and disseminates information concerning environmental risks in buildings to interested professionals, building owners, and the public. Serves as a clearinghouse of information on effective environmental management.

7778 ■ Florida Department of Environmental Protection
3900 Commonwealth Blvd.
M.S. 49
Tallahassee, FL 32399
Contact: Michael W. Sole, Sec.
Ph: (850)245-2118
Fax: (850)245-2128
URL: http://www.dep.state.fl.us/
Descr: Protects, conserves, and manages Florida's natural resources and enforces the state's environmental laws.

7779 ■ Florida Keys Wild Bird Rehabilitation Center (FKWBC)
93600 Overseas Hwy.
Tavernier, FL 33070
Contact: Laura B. Quinn, Chief Exec.
Ph: (305)852-4486
Fax: (305)852-3186
E-mail: info@fkwbc.org
URL: http://www.fkwbc.org
Staff: 8. **Descr:** Offers emergency therapy, rehabilitation, medical, and convalescent services to sick and injured wild birds in the Florida Keys. Collects data in order to aid in the detection of potential environmental concerns in the Florida Keys. Plans to develop captive breeding program using permanently injured wading birds of special concern. Educates the public on how man impacts the environment of the various local birds by touring the facility. **Fnd:** 1984. **Pub:** *Footprints* (quarterly).

7780 ■ Florida Onsite Wastewater Association (FOWA)
PO Box 950368
Lake Mary, FL 32795-0368
Ph: (407)937-2228
Fax: (407)937-2229
E-mail: fowa@cfl.rr.com
URL: http://www.fowaonsite.com

7781 ■ Florida Renewable Energy Association (FREA)
101 Cove Lake Dr.
Longwood, FL 32779
Contact: Colleen Kettles
Ph: (407)786-1799
E-mail: info@cleanenergyflorida.org
URL: http://www.cleanenergyflorida.org
Descr: Promotes a wide utilization of solar energy through the application of science and technology.

7782 ■ Florida Solar Energy Industries Association (FlaSEIA)
231 W Bay Ave.
Longwood, FL 32750-4125
Contact: Mr. Bruce Kershner
Ph: (407)339-2010
Free: 800-426-5899
Fax: (407)260-1582
E-mail: bruce@flaseia.org
URL: http://www.flaseia.org
Staff: 3. **Descr:** Represents the solar energy industry in Florida. **Fnd:** 1977. **Mem:** 50. **Pub:** Newsletter (quarterly).

7783 ■ Florida Water Quality Association (FWQA)
PO Box 2531
Lakeland, FL 33806
Contact: Suzanne Trueblood, Exec. Sec.
Ph: (863)644-6622
Fax: (866)845-4988
E-mail: info@fwqa.com
URL: http://www.fwqa.com
Descr: Represents individuals or firms engaged in the manufacturing and/or assembly and distribution and/or retail selling of water treatment equipment, supplies, and services. Promotes the acceptance

and use of industry equipment, products, and services. Provides activities, programs, and services designed to improve economy and efficiency within the industry.

7784 ■ Florida Wildlife Rehabilitation Association (FWRA)
PO Box 1449
Anna Maria, FL 34216
Contact: Deb Anderson DVM, Pres.
Ph: (941)778-6324
URL: http://www.fwra.org
Fnd: 1988.

7785 ■ Indian River Laryngectomee Club
1535 28th Ave.
Vero Beach, FL 32960
Contact: James C. Gilbert
Ph: (772)567-0087
E-mail: jigjeg@bellsouth.net

Descr: Promotes and supports the total rehabilitation of persons who have had laryngectomies. Seeks to improve the relations among persons who, due to the removal of the larynx because of cancer or other reasons, have lost their natural voices. Encourages exchange of ideas and methods for training and teaching of alaryngeal methods of communication.

7786 ■ Izaak Walton League of America, Florida Keys Chapter
PO Box 236
Homestead, FL 33090-0236
Contact: Mr. Michael F. Chenoweth
Ph: (305)451-0993
Fax: (305)451-3627
E-mail: gladerunner@earthlink.net
URL: http://www.iwla.org

Descr: Works to educate the public to conserve, maintain, protect, and restore the soil, forest, water, and other natural resources of the U.S.; promotes the enjoyment and wholesome utilization of these resources.

7787 ■ Mental Health Association in Indian River County
777 37th Ave., Ste. D-104
Vero Beach, FL 32960
Contact: Barbara Hammond, Chair
Ph: (772)569-9788
Fax: (772)569-2088
E-mail: someperson@mfa.com
URL: http://www.mhairc.org

Descr: Seeks to promote mental health and prevent mental health disorders. Improves mental health of Americans through advocacy, public education, research and service. **Fnd:** 1958.

7788 ■ Nature Coast Chapter of Building Officials Association of Florida
789 Providence Blvd.
Brooksville, FL 34601-3043
Contact: Joe Creech
Ph: (352)754-4050
Fax: (352)754-4159
E-mail: jcreech@hernandocounty.us

Descr: Provides the highest quality codes, standards, products, and services for all concerned with the safety and performance of the built environment.

7789 ■ Realtors Association of Indian River County
2182 Ponce De Leon Cir.
Vero Beach, FL 32960
Contact: Carol Eisenmann GRI, Pres.
Ph: (772)567-3510
Fax: (772)778-6490
E-mail: receptionist@rairc.com
URL: http://www.rairc.com
Staff: 5. **Descr:** Strives to develop real estate business practices. Advocates the right to own, use and transfer real property. Provides a facility for professional development, research and exchange of information among members.

Georgia

7790 ■ Central Savannah River Area Chapter of the Georgia Nurses Association
4569 Waterford Dr.
Evans, GA 30809
Contact: Sandra L. Turner, Pres
Ph: (706)650-3060
E-mail: sturner@mcg.edu
URL: http://www.gna10.org
Descr: Works to advance the nursing profession. Seeks to meet the needs of nurses and health care consumers. Fosters high standards of nursing practice. Promotes the economic and general welfare of nurses in the workplace.

7791 ■ Georgia Chapter of the Environmental Information Association
PO Box 524
Loganville, GA 30052
Contact: Mr. Gordon Reynolds
Ph: (770)554-3600
Fax: (770)554-2865
E-mail: greynolds@axisonline.us
URL: http://www.eia-georgia.org
Descr: Represents individuals and corporations concerned about environmental management and control. Collects and disseminates information concerning environmental risks in buildings to interested professionals, building owners, and the public. Serves as a clearinghouse of information on effective environmental management.

7792 ■ Georgia Environmental Protection Division
2 Martin Luther King Jr. Dr., Ste. 1152 E. Tower
Atlanta, GA 30334
Contact: Carol A. Couch, Dir.
Ph: (404)657-5947
Free: 888-373-5947
Fax: (404)651-5778
URL: http://www.gaepd.org/
Descr: Pursues a sustainable environment that provides a foundation for a vibrant economy and healthy communities.

Hawaii

7793 ■ Hawaii Department of Land and Natural Resources
Kalanimoku Bldg.
1151 Punchbowl St., Rm. 130
Honolulu, HI 96813
Contact: Laura H. Thielen, Chair
Ph: (808)587-0400
Fax: (808)587-0390
E-mail: dlnr@hawaii.gov
URL: http://www.hawaii.gov/dlnr/

Idaho

7794 ■ Idaho Bureau of Hazardous Materials
4040 Guard St., Bldg. 600
Boise, ID 83705-5004
Contact: Bill Shawver, Dir.
Ph: (208)422-3040
Free: 800-632-8000
Fax: (208)422-3044
URL: http://www2.state.id.us/serc/index.html
Descr: Mission is to save life and to limit human suffering, injury to wildlife, damage to natural resources, private and public property, the environment, and the economy as a result of the harmful affects of natural and human-caused disasters, from all hazards, including terrorism and the use of weapons of mass destruction, in support of local governments and communities.

7795 ■ Idaho Water Quality Association
1445 E Lincoln Rd.
Idaho Falls, ID 83401
Contact: Brad Brady
Ph: (208)522-6763
Fax: (208)522-6787
Descr: Represents individuals or firms engaged in

the manufacturing and/or assembly and distribution and/or retail selling of water treatment equipment, supplies, and services. Promotes the acceptance and use of industry equipment, products, and services. Provides activities, programs, and services designed to improve economy and efficiency within the industry.

7796 ■ International Code Council, Snake River Chapter
2135 Ammon Rd.
Ammon, ID 83406
Contact: Charles Allen
Ph: (208)529-4211
Fax: (208)524-6602
E-mail: callen@ci.ammon.id.us
Descr: Provides the highest quality codes, standards, products, and services for all concerned with the safety and performance of the built environment.

7797 ■ Upper Snake River Dental Society
640 S Woodruff Ave.
Idaho Falls, ID 83401
Contact: Dr. Douglas Barnard, Pres.
Ph: (208)523-5400
Fax: (208)528-0565
E-mail: drdoug@ida.net
URL: http://www.isdaweb.com
Descr: Represents the interests of dentists committed to the public's oral health, ethics, science and professional advancement. Promotes the art and science of dentistry through advocacy, education, research and the development of standards.

7798 ■ Wilderness Society, Idaho
950 W Bannock St., Ste. 605
Boise, ID 83702
Contact: Craig Gehrke, Dir.
Ph: (208)343-8153
Descr: Works to protect America's wilderness and wildlife and to develop a nationwide network of wild lands through public education, scientific analysis, and advocacy. Aims to ensure that future generations will enjoy the clean air and water, wildlife, beauty, and opportunities for recreation and renewal that pristine forests, rivers, deserts, and mountains provide. **Fnd:** 1935.

Illinois

7799 ■ Fox River Valley Dental Society
718 McKinley Ave.
Geneva, IL 60134-1231
Contact: Ms. Maureen Emma, Exec. Dir.
Ph: (630)232-4229
Fax: (630)232-4240
E-mail: memma@frvds.org
URL: http://www.ada.org/ada/organizations/orgdetail.asp?OrganizationID=520
Descr: Represents the interests of dentists committed to the public's oral health, ethics, science and professional advancement. Promotes the art and science of dentistry through advocacy, education, research and the development of standards.

7800 ■ Illinois Environmental Protection Agency
1021 N. Grand Ave. E.
PO Box 19276
Springfield, IL 62794-9276
Contact: Douglas P. Scott, Dir.
Ph: (217)782-3397
URL: http://www.epa.state.il.us/
Descr: Mission of the IEPA is to safeguard environmental quality, consistent with the social and economic needs of the state, so as to protect health, welfare, property, and the quality of life.

7801 ■ Illinois Solar Energy Association (ISEA)
800 W Evergreen Ave.
Chicago, IL 60622
Contact: Mark Burger, Pres.
Ph: (312)401-4859
E-mail: contactisea@illinoissolar.org
URL: http://www.illinoissolar.org

Descr: Works to educate the public and promote the appropriate use of solar energy and other renewable energy sources. **Fnd:** 1975. **Pub:** *ISEA's Heliograph* (quarterly).

7802 ■ Izaak Walton League of America, Champaign County Chapter
107 E Florida Ave.
Urbana, IL 61801
Contact: James G. Sternburg
Ph: (217)367-9857

Descr: Works to educate the public to conserve, maintain, protect, and restore the soil, forest, water, and other natural resources of the U.S.; promotes the enjoyment and wholesome utilization of these resources.

7803 ■ Izaak Walton League of America, Kewanee Chapter
Rte. 2, Box 59
Toulon, IL 61483-9523
Contact: John D. Turnbull
Ph: (309)896-3506

Descr: Works to educate the public to conserve, maintain, protect, and restore the soil, forest, water, and other natural resources of the U.S.; promotes the enjoyment and wholesome utilization of these resources.

7804 ■ Izaak Walton League of America, Peoria Chapter
1677 State Rte. 26
Metamora, IL 61548-9576
Contact: Carol Purple
Ph: (309)822-8207

Descr: Works to educate the public to conserve, maintain, protect, and restore the soil, forest, water, and other natural resources of the U.S.; promotes the enjoyment and wholesome utilization of these resources.

7805 ■ Izaak Walton League of America, Walter Sherry Memorial Chapter
409 Oakview Ave.
Joliet, IL 60433-2027
Contact: Christine Campbell
Ph: (815)723-5065

Descr: Works to educate the public to conserve, maintain, protect, and restore the soil, forest, water, and other natural resources of the U.S.; promotes the enjoyment and wholesome utilization of these resources.

7806 ■ Rock River Valley Dietetic Association (RRVDA)
636 N Ninth St.
DeKalb, IL 60115
Contact: Lynda Nelson, Pres.
Ph: (815)754-5147
E-mail: mgrosch@niu.edu
URL: http://www.eatrightillinois.org/Districts/rrvda.asp#ROCK

Descr: Represents the interests of food and nutrition professionals. Seeks to improve the public's health and nutrition. Advances the profession of dietetics through research, education and advocacy.

7807 ■ Taxpayers United Greene County
214 W Bridgeport St.
White Hall, IL 62092
Ph: (217)374-2338
Fax: (217)374-2338

7808 ■ Wabash River Dental Society
119 W 12th St.
Mount Carmel, IL 62863-1201
Contact: James W. Henning, Pres.
Ph: (618)263-3515
E-mail: jwhenningdds@hotmail.com
URL: http://www.isds.org

Descr: Represents the interests of dentists committed to the public's oral health, ethics and professional development. Encourages the improvement of the public's oral health and promotes the art and science of dentistry.

Indiana

7809 ■ Indiana Department of Natural Resources
402 W. Washington St., Rm. W160A
Indianapolis, IN 46204
Contact: Robert E. Carter Jr., Dir.
Ph: (317)232-4200
Free: 877-463-6367
Fax: (317)233-8654
URL: http://www.state.in.us/dnr/

7810 ■ Indiana Onsite Wastewater Professionals Association (IOWPA)
133 W Market St., PMB 188
Indianapolis, IN 46204-2801
Contact: Scott Rexroth, Pres.
E-mail: info@iowpa.org
URL: http://www.iowpa.org

7811 ■ Indiana Water Quality Association (IWQA)
PO Box 2822
Elkhart, IN 46515
Contact: Elmer Parks, Pres.
Ph: (574)522-4159
Free: 888-761-0134
Fax: (574)522-4169
E-mail: indwqa@msn.com
URL: http://www.iwqa.org

Descr: Represents individuals or firms engaged in the manufacturing and/or assembly and distribution and/or retail selling of water treatment equipment, supplies, and services. Promotes the acceptance and use of industry equipment, products, and services. Provides activities, programs, and services designed to improve economy and efficiency within the industry.

7812 ■ Izaak Walton League of America, Alexandria Chapter
407 Walnut St.
Alexandria, IN 46001-1614
Contact: Julie A. Etchison
Ph: (765)724-3353

Descr: Works to educate the public to conserve, maintain, protect, and restore the soil, forest, water, and other natural resources of the U.S.; promotes the enjoyment and wholesome utilization of these resources.

7813 ■ Izaak Walton League of America, Grant County Chapter
4030 N Wilshire Dr.
Marion, IN 46952-8610
Contact: Richard Purvis
Ph: (765)664-0790

Descr: Works to educate the public to conserve, maintain, protect, and restore the soil, forest, water, and other natural resources of the U.S.; promotes the enjoyment and wholesome utilization of these resources.

7814 ■ Izaak Walton League of America, Howard County Chapter
1428 Tam O Shanter Ln.
Kokomo, IN 46902
Contact: Patrick D. Graham
Ph: (765)319-3640
E-mail: pdg45acp@aol.com

Descr: Works to educate the public to conserve, maintain, protect, and restore the soil, forest, water, and other natural resources of the U.S.; promotes the enjoyment and wholesome utilization of these resources.

7815 ■ Izaak Walton League of America, Indiana Division
2173 Pennsylvania St.
Portage, IN 46368-2444
Contact: Charles A. Siar, Pres.
Ph: (219)762-4876
E-mail: res08mep@verizon.net
URL: http://www.in-iwla.org

Descr: Aims to conserve, maintain, protect and restore the soil, forest, water and other natural resources of the Indiana; to promote means and op-

portunities for the education of the public with respect to such resources and their enjoyment and wholesome utilization.

7816 ■ Izaak Walton League of America, Wabash Chapter
10439 S Old State Rd. 13
Wabash, IN 46992-3711
Contact: Ned Vandegrift
Ph: (260)563-6069
E-mail: nvande@hotmail.com
URL: http://www.iwla.org/index.php?id=7

Descr: Promotes environmental resources conservation.

7817 ■ Mental Health America of Indiana, Greene County
RR No. 2
Solsberry, IN 47459-9420
Contact: Norman Sullivan
Ph: (812)825-7108
URL: http://www.mhai.net

Descr: Seeks to promote mental health and prevent mental health disorders. Improves mental health of Americans through advocacy, public education, research and service.

Iowa

7818 ■ Iowa Department of Natural Resources
502 E. 9th St.
Des Moines, IA 50319-0034
Contact: Richard Leopold, Dir.
Ph: (515)281-5918
Fax: (515)281-8895
E-mail: webmaster@dnr.iowa.gov
URL: http://www.iowadnr.com/

Descr: Mission is to conserve and enhance Iowa's natural resources in cooperation with individuals and organizations to improve the quality of life for Iowans and ensure a legacy for future generations. **Telecom. Svcs:** TTY toll free number is (800)735-2942.

7819 ■ Iowa Onsite Waste Water Association (IOWWA)
10927 Lincoln Ave.
Des Moines, IA 50325
Contact: George Dickerson, Pres.
E-mail: info@iowwa.com
URL: http://www.iowwa.com

7820 ■ Iowa Water Quality Association
524 E Grand Ave.
Des Moines, IA 50309
Contact: Jim Boyt
Ph: (515)282-9303
Fax: (515)282-1730

Descr: Represents individuals or firms engaged in the manufacturing and/or assembly and distribution and/or retail selling of water treatment equipment, supplies, and services. Promotes the acceptance and use of industry equipment, products, and services. Provides activities, programs, and services designed to improve economy and efficiency within the industry.

7821 ■ Iowa Wildlife Rehabilitators Association (IWRA)
PO Box 217
Osceola, IA 50213
Contact: Beth Brown, Treas.
Ph: (641)342-2783

7822 ■ Izaak Walton League of America, Boone Valley Chapter
703 Laura Ln.
Webster City, IA 50595-3032
Contact: Ken Tabor
Ph: (515)832-2624

Descr: Works to educate the public to conserve, maintain, protect, and restore the soil, forest, water, and other natural resources of the U.S.; promotes

the enjoyment and wholesome utilization of these resources.

7823 ■ Izaak Walton League of America, Clinton County Chapter
1013 23rd Ave.
Camanche, IA 52730-1437
Contact: Alan D. Murphy
Ph: (563)259-8956
Descr: Works to educate the public to conserve, maintain, protect, and restore the soil, forest, water, and other natural resources of the U.S.; promotes the enjoyment and wholesome utilization of these resources.

7824 ■ Izaak Walton League of America, Dubuque Chapter
2828 Central Ave.
Dubuque, IA 52001-1949
Contact: Mary Lou Zweibohmer
Ph: (563)582-9157
Descr: Works to educate the public to conserve, maintain, protect, and restore the soil, forest, water, and other natural resources of the U.S.; promotes the enjoyment and wholesome utilization of these resources.

7825 ■ Izaak Walton League of America, Emerson Hough Chapter
227 Blair St.
Kellogg, IA 50135
Contact: Dennis Stansbury
Ph: (641)526-8090
Descr: Works to educate the public to conserve, maintain, protect, and restore the soil, forest, water, and other natural resources of the U.S.; promotes the enjoyment and wholesome utilization of these resources.

7826 ■ Izaak Walton League of America, Fort Dodge/Phil Fox Chapter
2137 Richmill Rd.
Fort Dodge, IA 50501
Contact: Joyce O'Connell
Ph: (515)955-3258
Descr: Works for the preservation of soil, woods, waters, air and wildlife and promotes the wholesome utilization of them. Sponsors annual Kids Fish Day. **Fnd:** 1947. **Mem:** 57. **Pub:** *Outdoor America* (quarterly); Newsletter (monthly).

7827 ■ Izaak Walton League of America, Keokuk County Chapter
24471 210th St.
Harper, IA 52231
Contact: Randy Weber
Ph: (641)622-2623
Descr: Works to protect America's rich resources to ensure high quality of life for all people, now and in the future.

7828 ■ Izaak Walton League of America, Linn County Chapter
PO Box 74404
Cedar Rapids, IA 52407
Contact: Bob Godlove, Pres.
Ph: (319)393-6624
E-mail: info@izaak-walton.org
URL: http://www.izaak-walton.org
Descr: Works to educate the public to conserve, maintain, protect, and restore the soil, forest, water, and other natural resources of the U.S. and promotes the enjoyment and wholesome utilization of these resources. **Mem:** 600.

7829 ■ Izaak Walton League of America, Maquoketa Valley Chapter
707 W Summit St.
Maquoketa, IA 52060
Contact: Terry Bronson
Ph: (563)652-6061
Descr: Works to educate the public to conserve, maintain, protect, and restore the soil, forest, water, and other natural resources of the U.S.; promotes

the enjoyment and wholesome utilization of these resources.

7830 ■ Izaak Walton League of America, Muscatine Chapter
306 W 7th St.
Muscatine, IA 52761-3244
Contact: Robert Buster
Ph: (563)263-5201
Descr: Works to educate the public to conserve, maintain, protect, and restore the soil, forest, water, and other natural resources of the U.S.; promotes the enjoyment and wholesome utilization of these resources.

7831 ■ Izaak Walton League of America, Poweshiek County Chapter
4224 Porter Addition
Grinnell, IA 50112-8143
Contact: Kenneth Tedrick Sr.
Ph: (641)236-7058
Descr: Works to educate the public to conserve, maintain, protect, and restore the soil, forest, water, and other natural resources of the U.S.; promotes the enjoyment and wholesome utilization of these resources.

7832 ■ Izaak Walton League of America, Red Cedar Chapter
609 2nd Ave.
Vinton, IA 52349-1722
Contact: Irene Lewis
Ph: (319)472-4429
Descr: Works to educate the public to conserve, maintain, protect, and restore the soil, forest, water, and other natural resources of the U.S.; promotes the enjoyment and wholesome utilization of these resources.

7833 ■ Izaak Walton League of America, Sabula Chapter
43834 58th St.
Preston, IA 52069-9543
Contact: Charles Lane
Ph: (319)689-6225
Descr: Works to educate the public to conserve, maintain, protect, and restore the soil, forest, water, and other natural resources of the U.S.; promotes the enjoyment and wholesome utilization of these resources.

7834 ■ Izaak Walton League of America, United Counties Chapter
411 W 2nd St.
Storm Lake, IA 50588
Contact: Patricia Hampton
Ph: (712)732-9272
Descr: Works to educate the public to conserve, maintain, protect, and restore the soil, forest, water, and other natural resources of the U.S.; promotes the enjoyment and wholesome utilization of these resources.

7835 ■ Izaak Walton League of America, Wapsi Valley Chapter
2454 26th Ave.
De Witt, IA 52742
Contact: Leo T. Mullen
Ph: (563)659-8577
Descr: Works to educate the public to conserve, maintain, protect, and restore the soil, forest, water, and other natural resources of the U.S.; promotes the enjoyment and wholesome utilization of these resources.

7836 ■ Izaak Walton League of America, Wapsiketa Chapter
207 S Davis St.
Anamosa, IA 52205-1929
Contact: Atha Jensen
Ph: (319)462-4043
E-mail: aoj52205@yahoo.com
Descr: Works to educate the public to conserve, maintain, protect, and restore the soil, forest, water, and other natural resources of the U.S.; promotes

the enjoyment and wholesome utilization of these resources.

7837 ■ Izaak Walton League of America, Waterloo Chapter
3867 Cedar Terrace Dr.
Waterloo, IA 50702
Contact: Katherine Millet
Ph: (319)296-2004
E-mail: mammasue1229@mchsi.com
Descr: Works to educate the public to conserve, maintain, protect, and restore the soil, forest, water, and other natural resources of the U.S.; promotes the enjoyment and wholesome utilization of these resources.

7838 ■ Izaak Walton League of America, West Central Chapter
408 Main St.
Deloit, IA 51441-7542
Contact: Michael Fritz
Ph: (712)263-3740
Descr: Works to educate the public to conserve, maintain, protect, and restore the soil, forest, water, and other natural resources of the U.S.; promotes the enjoyment and wholesome utilization of these resources.

7839 ■ Izaak Walton League of America, Woodbury County Chapter
2105 Roosevelt St.
Sioux City, IA 51109-1247
Contact: Leroy A. Anderson
Ph: (712)233-1513
Descr: Works to educate the public to conserve, maintain, protect, and restore the soil, forest, water, and other natural resources of the U.S.; promotes the enjoyment and wholesome utilization of these resources.

7840 ■ Izaak Walton League of America, Worth County Chapter
PO Box 31
Kensett, IA 50448-0031
Contact: Donna M. Larson
Ph: (641)845-2339
Descr: Works to educate the public to conserve, maintain, protect, and restore the soil, forest, water, and other natural resources of the U.S.; promotes the enjoyment and wholesome utilization of these resources.

Kansas

7841 ■ Heartland Solar Energy Industry Association (HSEIA)
8214 W 75th St.
Overland Park, KS 66204
Contact: Bill Roush, Pres.
Ph: (816)868-9695
E-mail: billroush@gmail.com
Descr: Solar trade association regional chapter which promotes solar power equipment use in MO, IA, KS, and NE. Offers frequent email news exchanges. **Fnd:** 1995. **Mem:** 24.

7842 ■ Kansas Department of Health and Environment
Curtis State Office Bldg.
1000 SW Jackson
Topeka, KS 66612
Contact: Roderick L. Bremby, Sec.
Ph: (785)296-1500
Fax: (785)368-6368
E-mail: info@kdheks.gov
URL: http://www.kdhe.state.ks.us/
Descr: State agency whose vision is "healthier Kansans living in safe and sustainable environments."

7843 ■ Kansas Small Flows Association
PO Box 107
Mullinville, KS 67109-0107
Contact: Dale Hayse, Exec. Dir.
Ph: (620)548-2369

Fax: (620)548-2369
E-mail: haysemgt@havilandtelco.com
URL: http://www.ksfa.org

7844 ■ Kansas Water Quality Association
906 E 17th Ave.
Hutchinson, KS 67501
Contact: Jack Higgins
Ph: (620)662-8630
Fax: (620)662-8630
Descr: Represents individuals or firms engaged in the manufacturing and/or assembly and distribution and/or retail selling of water treatment equipment, supplies, and services. Promotes the acceptance and use of industry equipment, products, and services. Provides activities, programs, and services designed to improve economy and efficiency within the industry.

Kentucky

7845 ■ American Cancer Society, Bowling Green
952 Fairview Ave., Ste. 4
Bowling Green, KY 42101
Ph: (270)782-3654
Fax: (270)846-0202
Descr: Serves as a nationwide, community-based, voluntary health organization dedicated to eliminating cancer as a major health problem by preventing cancer, saving lives and diminishing suffering from cancer, through research, education, advocacy, and service.

7846 ■ Business and Professional Women, River City
PO Box 36004
Louisville, KY 40233-6004
Contact: Lorie Marcum, Pres.
Ph: (502)499-4420
E-mail: lmarcum@secc.org
URL: http://www.bpwrc.org
Descr: Represents the interests of business and professional women. Elevates the standards for women in business and professional settings. Promotes equity for all women in the workplace through advocacy, education and information. Provides professional development, networking and career advancement opportunities for working women.

7847 ■ Dix River Board of Realtors
PO Box 199
Crab Orchard, KY 40419-0199
Contact: Gracie Gilbert, Sec.
Ph: (606)365-3153
URL: http://www.kar.com
Descr: Strives to develop real estate business practices. Advocates the right to own, use and transfer real property. Provides a facility for professional development, research and exchange of information among members and to the general public.

7848 ■ Green River Counseling Association
732 W 3rd St.
Beaver Dam, KY 42320
Contact: Mr. Charles Patton, Pres.
Ph: (270)274-3366
E-mail: charles.patton@ohio.kyschools.us
URL: http://www.kyca.org
Descr: Promotes the practice of counseling. Provides opportunities for personal growth and professional development.

7849 ■ Henderson Audubon Board of Realtors
201 N Main St.
Henderson, KY 42420
Contact: Becky Ferguson East, Exec. Off.
Ph: (270)827-4505
Fax: (270)827-4568
E-mail: habor@insightbb.com
URL: http://www.henderson-realtors.com
Staff: 1. **Descr:** Strives to develop real estate business practices. Advocates the right to own, use and

transfer real property. Provides a facility for professional development, research and exchange of information among members and to the general public.

7850 ■ Kentucky Environmental and Public Protection Cabinet
500 Mero St., 5th Fl., CPT
Frankfort, KY 40601
Contact: Dr. Len Peters, Sec.
Ph: (502)564-3350
Fax: (502)564-7484
E-mail: Cynthia.schafert@ky.gov
URL: http://www.eec.ky.gov/

7851 ■ Kentucky Onsite Wastewater Association (KOWA)
PO Box 1424
Bowling Green, KY 42104
Ph: (270)715-0043
Fax: (270)796-8623
E-mail: kowai@bellsouth.net
URL: http://www.kentuckyonsite.org

7852 ■ Kentucky Solar Partnership (KSP)
2235 Gregory Woods Rd.
Frankfort, KY 40601
Contact: Andy McDonald, Coor.
Ph: (502)227-4562
Free: 888-576-6527
E-mail: solar@kysolar.org
URL: http://www.kysolar.org
Descr: Works towards the installation of solar electric and hot water systems in Kentucky. Educates the community and students on the benefits of solar energy use. Demonstrates appropriate, safe, and code approved solar installations.

Louisiana

7853 ■ Louisiana Department of Environmental Quality
PO Box 4301
Baton Rouge, LA 70821-4301
Contact: Harold Leggett Ph.D., Sec.
Ph: (225)219-3953
Fax: (225)219-3971
E-mail: DEQ-WWWOfficeoftheSecretaryContact@la.gov
URL: http://www.deq.louisiana.gov/portal/

7854 ■ Louisiana Solar Energy Society (LSES)
5261 Highland Rd., No. 217
Baton Rouge, LA 70808
Contact: Tony Adrian
E-mail: info@lses.org
URL: http://www.lses.org
Descr: Promotes and educates people about solar energy. Shares information regarding the solar activity in Louisiana. Facilitates networking and conducts education programs for the community.

7855 ■ Louisiana Wildlife Rehabilitators Association (LAWRA)
16925 George O'Neal Rd.
Baton Rouge, LA 70817
Ph: (985)789-1061
Fax: (985)624-9559
URL: http://www.lawraonline.com

Maine

7856 ■ Green Valley Arc
PO Box 127
Island Falls, ME 04747
Contact: Eric Quint, Exec. Dir.
Ph: (207)463-2156
Free: 877-463-2156
Fax: (207)463-2151
E-mail: equint@gva-me.org
URL: http://www.gva-me.org
Descr: Parents, professional workers, and others interested in individuals with mental retardation. Works to promote services, research, public under-

standing, and legislation for people with mental retardation and their families. **Fnd:** 1967.

7857 ■ Maine Department of Environmental Protection
17 State House Station
Augusta, ME 04333-0017
Contact: David P. Littell, Commnr.
Ph: (207)287-7688
Free: 800-452-1942
URL: http://www.state.me.us/dep/index.shtml
Pub: List of publications online (www.state.me.us/dep/publications.htm).

7858 ■ Maine Solar Energy Association (MESEA)
17 Rockwell Rd. SE
Jonesport, ME 04649
Contact: Richard J. Komp, Pres.
E-mail: sunwatt@juno.com
URL: http://www.mainesolar.org
Descr: Dedicated to promoting the public awareness and use of solar energy, energy conservation, other renewable energy sources and green building practices throughout the state of Maine. Organizes workshops and seminars on solar and other renewable topics. **Fnd:** 1976. **Mem:** 124. **Pub:** *Maine Sun* (quarterly).

7859 ■ ReMaine Wild
PO Box 113
Newcastle, ME 04553
Ph: (207)829-3356
E-mail: remainewild@remainewild.org
URL: http://www.remainewild.org

7860 ■ Wilderness Society, Northeast Regional Office
9 Union St., 3rd Fl.
Hallowell, ME 04347
Contact: Jeremy Sheaffer
Ph: (207)626-5553
E-mail: jeremy_sheaffer@tws.org
Descr: Works to protect America's wilderness and wildlife and to develop a nationwide network of wild lands through public education, scientific analysis, and advocacy. Goal is to ensure that future generations will enjoy the clean air and water, wildlife, beauty, and opportunities for recreation and renewal that pristine forests, rivers, deserts, and mountains provide. **Fnd:** 1935. **Mem:** 200000. **Pub:** *Wilderness Magazine* (annual); *Wilderness Society Newsletter* (quarterly).

Maryland

7861 ■ Izaak Walton League of America, Bethesda-Chevy Chase Chapter
PO Box 542
Poolesville, MD 20837-0542
Contact: Carol Efdimis, Membership Sec.
E-mail: membership@bcciwla.org
URL: http://bcciwla.org
Descr: Works to educate the public to conserve, maintain, protect, and restore the soil, forest, water, and other natural resources of the U.S.; promotes the enjoyment and wholesome utilization of these resources. **Fnd:** 1922. **Mem:** 850. **Pub:** Newsletter (monthly).

7862 ■ Izaak Walton League of America, Rockville Chapter
PO Box 2255
Germantown, MD 20875
Contact: Miles Greenbaum, Pres.
Ph: (301)972-1645
E-mail: info@iwla-rockville.com
URL: http://www.iwla-rockville.com
Descr: Promotes environmental resources conservation. **Fnd:** 1933. **Mem:** 400. **Pub:** *Rockville Chapter* (monthly).

7863 ■ Izaak Walton League of America, Southern Maryland Chapter
4200 Gardiner Rd.
Waldorf, MD 20601-4425

Contact: Rick Farrell, Pres.
Ph: (301)932-9949
E-mail: rental@iwlasomd.org
URL: http://www.iwlasomd.org
Descr: Works to educate the public to conserve, maintain, protect, and restore the natural resources of the U.S. **Fnd:** 1958.

7864 ■ Maine Department of the Environment
1800 Washington Blvd.
Baltimore, MD 21230
Contact: Kendl P. Philbrick, Sec.
Ph: (410)537-3000
Free: 800-633-6101
E-mail: webmaster@mde.state.md.us
URL: http://www.mde.state.md.us/
Descr: Mission is to protect and restore the quality of Maryland's air, water, and land resources, while fostering smart growth, economic development, healthy and safe communities, and quality environmental education for the benefit of the environment, public health, and future generations.

7865 ■ Maryland Wildlife Rehabilitators Association (MWRA)
6616A Debold Rd.
Sabillasville, MD 21780
Contact: Roxy Brandenburg, Treas.
E-mail: info@mwra.org
URL: http://www.mwra.org

7866 ■ MDV Solar Energy Industries Association (MDV SEIA)
4707 Elmhirst Ln.
Bethesda, MD 20814-3954
Contact: Peter Lowenthal, Exec. Dir.
Ph: (301)530-5343
Fax: (301)530-5343
E-mail: info@mdv-seia.org
URL: http://www.mdv-seia.org
Descr: Manufacturers, installers, distributors, contractors, and engineers of solar energy systems and components. Aims to accelerate and foster commercialization of solar energy conversion for economic purposes. Maintains Solar Energy Research and Education Foundation. Compiles statistics; offers computerized services. **Fnd:** 1984.

7867 ■ Potomac Region Solar Energy Association (PRSEA)
PO Box 809
Pasadena, MD 21123-0809
Contact: Jane Hager, Exec. Dir.
E-mail: info@prsea.org
URL: http://www.prsea.org
Descr: Promotes the economic, environmental and social fabric of the Potomac region. Furthers the development and use of solar energy and related arts, sciences and technologies. Conducts educational activities about solar energy.

Massachusetts

7868 ■ Greater Fall River Association of Realtors
580 Eastern Ave.
Fall River, MA 02723
Contact: Jennifer Preston, Pres.
Ph: (508)679-4300
Fax: (508)678-6061
E-mail: info@fallriverarearealtors.com
URL: http://www.fallriverarearealtors.com
Descr: Strives to develop real estate business practices. Advocates the right to own, use and transfer real property. Provides a facility for professional development, research and exchange of information among members. **Fnd:** 1927.

7869 ■ Massachusetts Department of Environmental Protection
One Winter St.
Boston, MA 02108
Contact: Laurie Burt, Commnr.
Ph: (617)292-5500
Free: 800-462-0444
Fax: (617)556-1049

E-mail: dep.help@state.ma.us
URL: http://www.mass.gov/dep/dephome.htm
Descr: Responsible for ensuring clean air and water, the safe management of toxics and hazards, the recycling of solid and hazardous wastes, the timely cleanup of hazardous waste sites and spills, and the preservation of wetlands and coastal resources.

7870 ■ River Management Society, Northeast Chapter
Coll. of the Holy Cross
Dept. of Math and Computer Science
Box 100A
Worcester, MA 01610
Contact: Catherine Roberts, VP
Ph: (508)793-2456
E-mail: croberts@holycross.edu

7871 ■ Wildlife Rehabilitators' Association of Massachusetts (WRAM)
26 Beagle Club Rd.
Attleboro, MA 02703
Ph: (978)448-2812
URL: http://www.wraminc.org

7872 ■ Yankee Onsite Wastewater Association (YOWA)
2 Blackburn Ctr.
Gloucester, MA 01930
Contact: Steven Corr, Pres.
Free: 800-969-2674
E-mail: yankeeonsite@gmail.com
URL: http://www.nowra.org/yowa

Michigan

7873 ■ Down River Association of Code Officials
16912 Keppen Ave.
Allen Park, MI 48101
Contact: Ardys D. Bennett
Ph: (313)274-3492
Fax: (313)943-2097
E-mail: adbennettap@comcast.net
Descr: Provides codes, standards, products, and services to concerned individuals for the safety and effective performance in the built environment.

7874 ■ Izaak Walton League of America, Lock City Chapter
1200 Kimball St.
Sault Ste. Marie, MI 49783-3236
Contact: Earl Spuhler
Ph: (906)632-2698
Descr: Works to educate the public to conserve, maintain, protect, and restore the soil, forest, water, and other natural resources of the U.S.; promotes the enjoyment and wholesome utilization of these resources.

7875 ■ Izaak Walton League of America, Michigan Division
6260 Blythefield Ave. NE
Rockford, MI 49341
Contact: John Trimberger, Pres.
Ph: (616)866-8475
E-mail: jtrimberger@comcast.net
Descr: Works to educate the public to conserve, maintain, protect, and restore the soil, forest, water, and other natural resources of the U.S.; promotes the enjoyment and wholesome utilization of these resources.

7876 ■ Michigan Department of Environmental Quality
Constitution Hall
525 West Allegan St.
PO Box 30473
Lansing, MI 48909-7973
Ph: (517)373-7917
Free: 800-292-4706
E-mail: deq-ead-env-assist@michigan.gov
URL: http://www.michigan.gov/deq

Descr: Mission is to protect and enhance Michigan's environment and public health.

7877 ■ Michigan Onsite Wastewater Recycling Association (MOWRA)
PO Box 708
Haslett, MI 48840-0708
Contact: Dan Milan, Pres.
Ph: (989)773-9938
Fax: (989)772-3415
E-mail: milantech@chartermi.net
URL: http://www.mowra.org

7878 ■ Michigan Water Quality Association (MWQA)
721 N Capitol Ave., Ste. 3
Lansing, MI 48906
Contact: Alan Jackson, Pres.
Ph: (517)487-6840
Fax: (517)487-0372
E-mail: info@miwqa.org
URL: http://www.miwqa.org
Descr: Represents individuals or firms engaged in the manufacturing and/or assembly and distribution and/or retail selling of water treatment equipment, supplies, and services. Promotes the acceptance and use of industry equipment, products, and services. Provides activities, programs, and services designed to improve economy and efficiency within the industry.

Minnesota

7879 ■ Izaak Walton League of America Midwest Office
1619 Dayton Ave., Ste. 202
St. Paul, MN 55104
Contact: David W. Hoskins, Exec. Dir.
Ph: (651)649-1446
Fax: (651)649-1494
E-mail: midwestoffice@iwla.org
URL: http://www.iwla.org
Descr: Strive to improve America's air quality. Works to lead a Power Plant Campaign focused on cleaning up outdated coal-burning power plants. **Pub:** *Outdoor America* (quarterly); *Sustainability Communicator* (bimonthly); *Water Courses* (semiannual).

7880 ■ Izaak Walton League of America, Minnesota Division
161 St. Anthony Ave., Ste. 910
St. Paul, MN 55103
Contact: Rolf Nordstrom, Pres.
Ph: (651)221-0251
E-mail: ikes@minnesotaikes.org
URL: http://www.minnesotaikes.org
Staff: 1. **Descr:** Conservation group devoted to protecting the environment. **Fnd:** 1932. **Mem:** 1300. **Pub:** *Waltonian* (quarterly).

7881 ■ Izaak Walton League of America, Rochester Chapter
PO Box 431
Byron, MN 55920
Contact: Chad Jorgensen, Dues Sec.
Ph: (507)288-5657
E-mail: ikes@minnesotaikes.org
URL: http://www.minnesotaikes.org/chapters/Rochester.html
Descr: Works to promote conservation of natural resources, clean water; improve fish and wildlife habitat; establish and protect public parks, forests, lakeshores, and refuges. **Fnd:** 1923. **Mem:** 70. **State Groups:** 1. **Local Groups:** 1. **Pub:** Newsletter.

7882 ■ Izaak Walton League of America, W.J. McCabe Chapter
2116 Columbus Ave.
Duluth, MN 55803-2221
Contact: Margo Zentner
Ph: (218)724-3926
E-mail: dzentner@charter.net
Descr: Works to educate the public to conserve, maintain, protect, and restore the soil, forest, water, and other natural resources of the U.S.; promotes

the enjoyment and wholesome utilization of these resources.

7883 ■ Minnesota Department of Natural Resources
500 Lafayette Rd.
St. Paul, MN 55155-4040
Ph: (651)296-6157
Free: 888-646-6367
E-mail: info@dnr.state.mn.us
URL: http://www.dnr.state.mn.us/index.html
Descr: Mission is to work with citizens to conserve and manage the state's natural resources, to provide outdoor recreation opportunities, and to provide for commercial uses of natural resources in a way that creates a sustainable quality of life. **Telecom. Svcs:** TTY toll free number is (800)657-3929.

7884 ■ Minnesota Onsite Wastewater Association (MOWA)
5200 Willson Rd., Ste. 300
Edina, MN 55424
Contact: Wayne James, Pres.
Free: 888-810-4178
E-mail: mowacarla@aol.com
URL: http://www.mowa-mn.com
Fnd: 1975.

7885 ■ Minnesota Renewable Energy Society (MRES)
2928 5th Ave. S
Minneapolis, MN 55408
Contact: David Boyce, Chm.
Ph: (612)308-4757
E-mail: info@mnrenewables.org
URL: http://www.mres-solar.org
Staff: 2. **Descr:** Helps to develop awareness and to promote the use of renewable energy resources. Sponsors activities that include conference on the use of solar energy in Minneapolis area. **Fnd:** 1978. **Pub:** *Solar Flare* (monthly).

7886 ■ Minnesota Water Quality Association (MWQA)
PO Box 48452
Minneapolis, MN 55448
Contact: Lori Jansen
Ph: (763)754-2123
Fax: (763)754-6206
E-mail: info@mwqa.com
URL: http://www.mwqa.com
Descr: Represents individuals or firms engaged in the manufacturing and/or assembly and distribution and/or retail selling of water treatment equipment, supplies, and services. Promotes the acceptance and use of industry equipment, products, and services. Provides activities, programs, and services designed to improve economy and efficiency within the industry. **Fnd:** 1956.

7887 ■ Minnesota Wildlife Assistance Cooperative (MWAC)
PO Box 130545
Roseville, MN 55113
Contact: Stacey Trapp, Pres.
E-mail: info@mnwildlife.org
URL: http://www.mnwildlife.org

7888 ■ Red River Nu-Voice Club
208 4th St. NE
Dilworth, MN 56529
Contact: Dennis J. Roy
Ph: (218)287-2278
E-mail: djroy@g.mail.com
Descr: Promotes and supports the total rehabilitation of persons who have had laryngectomies. Seeks to improve the relations among persons who, due to the removal of the larynx because of cancer or other reasons, have lost their natural voices. Encourages exchange of ideas and methods for training and teaching of alaryngeal methods of communication.

7889 ■ River Management Society, Midwest Chapter
National Park Service
111 E Kellogg Blvd.
St. Paul, MN 55101

Contact: Steve Johnson, Pres.
Ph: (651)290-3030
Fax: (651)290-3214
E-mail: steven_p_johnson@nps.gov

Mississippi

7890 ■ Greenwood Board of Realtors
229 W Market St.
Greenwood, MS 38930
Contact: Ron DuBard, Exec. Off.
Ph: (662)455-5885
Fax: (662)455-5550
E-mail: ron@dubard.com
URL: http://www.dubard.com
Descr: Strives to develop real estate business practices. Advocates the right to own, use and transfer real property. Provides a facility for professional development, research and exchange of information among members.

7891 ■ Mississippi Department of Environmental Quality
PO Box 2261
Jackson, MS 39225
Contact: Trudy D. Fisher, Exec.Dir.
Ph: (601)961-5171
Free: 888-786-0661
Fax: (601)354-6612
URL: http://www.deq.state.ms.us/MDEQ.nsf/page/Main_Home?OpenDocument
Descr: Mission is to safeguard the health, safety, and welfare of present and future generations of Mississippians by conserving and improving our environment and fostering wise economic growth through focused research and responsible regulation.

7892 ■ Pearl River Arc
PO Box 1816
Picayune, MS 39466
Contact: Joanie Miller, Pres.
E-mail: carlieo@bellsouth.net

7893 ■ Pearl River Board of Realtors
PO Box 1110
Picayune, MS 39466
Contact: Tracy McKay
Ph: (601)749-0650
Fax: (601)749-0650
E-mail: pearl_realtors@bellsouth.net
Descr: Strives to develop real estate business practices. Advocates the right to own, use and transfer real property. Provides a facility for professional development, research and exchange of information among members.

Missouri

7894 ■ Arc of the Ozarks
1501 E Pythian
Springfield, MO 65802
Contact: Gene Barnes, Pres./CEO
Ph: (417)864-7887
Fax: (417)864-4307
E-mail: info@thearcoftheozarks.org
URL: http://www.thearcoftheozarks.org
Descr: Strives to support individuals with disabilities in directing their own lives as valued members of the community. **Fnd:** 1963.

7895 ■ Heart of Ozarks Speech-Language-Hearing Association (HOSHLA)
Rte. No. 1, Box 2880
Dora, MO 65637
Contact: Virginia McMurtrey, Sec.-Treas.
Ph: (417)469-2472
Fax: (417)469-4320
E-mail: vmcmurtrey@tri-lakes.net
URL: http://www.showmemsha.org
Descr: Represents audiologists and speech-language pathologists. Provides educational and referral information on speech, language, and hearing disabilities. Seeks to increase public awareness and encourage scientific study of the processes of

individual language, speech, swallowing, and hearing.

7896 ■ Heartland Renewable Energy Society (HRES)
9013 E 65th Terr.
Raytown, MO 64133
Contact: Bill Roush
E-mail: hresadmin@heartland-res.org
URL: http://www.heartland-res.org
Descr: Works to further the development, use of, and support for renewable energy and related arts, sciences and technologies.

7897 ■ Learning Disabilities Association of the Ozarks
PO Box 4362
Springfield, MO 65808
Contact: Angelique Chaverri, Pres.
Ph: (417)882-2008
E-mail: info@ldaozarks.org
URL: http://www.ldaozarks.org

7898 ■ Missouri Department of Natural Resources
PO Box 176
Jefferson City, MO 65102
Contact: Connie Patterson, Dir.
Ph: (573)751-3443
Free: 800-361-4827
E-mail: contact@dnr.mo.gov
URL: http://www.dnr.mo.gov
Pub: List of publications online (www.dnr.mo.gov.pubs/index.html).

7899 ■ Missouri Smallflows Organization
PO Box 606
Kimberling City, MO 65686
Contact: David Casaletto, Exec. Dir.
Ph: (417)739-4100
Fax: (417)739-9889
E-mail: mso@lvbw.net
URL: http://www.mosmallflows.org

7900 ■ Missouri Water Quality Association (MWQA)
PO Box 873
Camdenton, MO 65020
Contact: Kelly Imhoff, Asst. Sec.-Treas.
Ph: (573)346-1919
Fax: (573)346-1717
E-mail: info@mowqa.org
URL: http://www.mowqa.org
Descr: Represents individuals or firms engaged in the manufacturing and/or assembly and distribution and/or retail selling of water treatment equipment, supplies, and services. Promotes the acceptance and use of industry equipment, products, and services. Provides activities, programs, and services designed to improve economy and efficiency within the industry.

7901 ■ Ozark Association for the Education of Young Children (OAEYC)
PO Box 4912
Springfield, MO 65808-4912
Contact: Kim Roam, Pres.
Ph: (417)836-4151
E-mail: kimroam@missouristate.edu
URL: http://www.aeyc-mo.org
Descr: Serves and acts on behalf of the needs, rights and well-being of all young children with primary focus on the quality of educational and developmental services for all children. Seeks to improve professional practice and working conditions in early childhood education.

7902 ■ River Bend Association for the Education of Young Children (RBAEYC)
PO Box 2136
Lee's Summit, MO 64063
Contact: Janice Jones, Pres.
Free: 800-210-2602
E-mail: rbaeyc@rbaeyc.org
URL: http://www.rbaeyc.org
Descr: Serves and acts on behalf of the needs, rights and well-being of all young children with

primary focus on the quality of educational and developmental services for all children. Seeks to improve professional practice and working conditions in early childhood education.

7903 ■ St. Louis Animal Rights Team (START)
PO Box 19734
St. Louis, MO 63144
Contact: Colleen Tilford, Sec.
Ph: (314)851-0928
E-mail: info@start4animals.org
Descr: Promotes the nutritional, economical, ecological, and ethical benefits of a vegetarian diet. Educates society on the rights of animals to live freely and die naturally. **Fnd:** 1988. **Mem:** 200. **Local Groups:** 1.

7904 ■ St. Louis Hosta Society
9904 Crestwood Dr.
St. Louis, MO 63126
Contact: Jeff Hall, Pres.
Ph: (314)962-7456
E-mail: awtempnt@mac.com
URL: http://www.stlouishosta.org

Montana

7905 ■ Montana Department of Environmental Quality
1520 E. Sixth Ave.
PO Box 200901
Helena, MT 59620-0901
Contact: Richard Opper, Dir.
Ph: (406)444-2544
Fax: (406)444-4386
E-mail: ropper@mt.gov
URL: http://www.deq.state.mt.us/
Descr: State government agency responsible for regulating Montana environmental quality.

7906 ■ Montana Water Quality Association
PO Box 7068
Missoula, MT 59807
Contact: Duane Friedrichs
Ph: (406)728-3590
Fax: (406)543-8467
Descr: Represents individuals or firms engaged in the manufacturing and/or assembly and distribution and/or retail selling of water treatment equipment, supplies, and services. Promotes the acceptance and use of industry equipment, products, and services. Provides activities, programs, and services designed to improve economy and efficiency within the industry.

Nebraska

7907 ■ Blue River Area Board of Realtors
316 S Lincoln Ave.
York, NE 68467
Contact: Patsy Haggadone, Exec. Off.
Ph: (402)362-1997
Fax: (402)362-4427
E-mail: golfin1@alltel.net
Descr: Strives to develop real estate business practices. Advocates the right to own, use and transfer real property. Provides information about the real estate industry.

7908 ■ Izaak Walton League of America, Eastern Nebraska Chapter
5015 S 69th St.
Lincoln, NE 68516-1566
Contact: Mr. Arthur Bryant, Pres.
Ph: (402)488-7781
E-mail: ab62359@alltel.net
Descr: Works to educate the public to conserve, maintain, protect, and restore the soil, forest, water, and other natural resources of the U.S.; promotes the enjoyment and wholesome utilization of these resources.

7909 ■ Izaak Walton League of America, Jessie Benton Fremont Chapter
2111 N Union St.
Fremont, NE 68025-2619
Contact: Ms. Joan J. Strimple
Ph: (402)721-3186
Descr: Fishermen concerned with the environment. Sponsors festivals by donating to the John C. Fremont Days. **Fnd:** 1953. **Mem:** 35. **State Groups:** 1. **Local Groups:** 1. **Pub:** Newsletter (periodic).

7910 ■ Izaak Walton League of America, Lancaster Chapter
4010 N 15th St.
Lincoln, NE 68521-1907
Contact: Roger Eilers
Ph: (402)435-8363
Descr: Works to educate the public to conserve, maintain, protect, and restore the soil, forest, water, and other natural resources of the U.S.; promotes the enjoyment and wholesome utilization of these resources.

7911 ■ Izaak Walton League of America, Ravenna Loup Valley Chapter
PO Box 212
Boelus, NE 68820-0212
Contact: Norine Nielsen
Ph: (308)996-4282
Descr: Works to educate the public to conserve, maintain, protect, and restore the soil, forest, water, and other natural resources of the U.S.; promotes the enjoyment and wholesome utilization of these resources.

7912 ■ Izaak Walton League of America, Seward County Chapter
441 E Roberts St.
Seward, NE 68434-1649
Contact: Lyle Mueller
Ph: (402)643-6074
Descr: Works to educate the public to conserve, maintain, protect, and restore the soil, forest, water, and other natural resources of the U.S.; promotes the enjoyment and wholesome utilization of these resources.

7913 ■ Izaak Walton League of America, Southwest Chapter
1420 Grant St.
Imperial, NE 69033
Contact: Tom Elder
Ph: (308)882-5119
Descr: Works to educate the public to conserve, maintain, protect, and restore the soil, forest, water, and other natural resources of the U.S.; promotes the enjoyment and wholesome utilization of these resources.

7914 ■ Izaak Walton League of America, Thayer County Chapter
858 Rd. 5500
Deshler, NE 68340-9860
Contact: Victor O. Sorge
Ph: (402)365-4216
Descr: Works to educate the public to conserve, maintain, protect, and restore the soil, forest, water, and other natural resources of the U.S.; promotes the enjoyment and wholesome utilization of these resources.

7915 ■ Izaak Walton League of America, Wisner Chapter
PO Box 273
Wisner, NE 68791-0273
Contact: Helen Ortmann
Ph: (402)529-3353
Descr: Works to educate the public to conserve, maintain, protect, and restore the soil, forest, water, and other natural resources of the U.S.; promotes

the enjoyment and wholesome utilization of these resources.

7916 ■ Nebraska Department of Environmental Quality
1200 N St., Ste. 400
PO Box 98922
Lincoln, NE 68509
Contact: Mike Linder, Dir.
Ph: (402)471-2186
Fax: (402)471-2909
E-mail: MoreInfo@NDEQ.state.NE.US
URL: http://www.deq.state.ne.us/
Descr: State environmental regulatory agency. **Pub:** Quality report (biannual); air quality report (annual); ground water monitoring report (annual); recycling directory; newletter.

7917 ■ Shady Choice Hosta Society
17952 Pioneer Trail
Plattsmouth, NE 68048-7293
Contact: Bernie Diesen, Pres.
Ph: (402)298-8884
E-mail: gh90258@altel.net

Nevada

7918 ■ Easter Seals Sierra Nevada
6100 Neil Rd., No. 201
Reno, NV 89511
Ph: (775)322-6555
Fax: (775)834-5933
URL: http://www.sierra.easterseals.com
Descr: Works to help individuals with disabilities and special needs, and their families. Conducts programs to assist people of all ages with disabilities. Provides outpatient medical rehabilitation services. Advocates for the passage of legislation to help people with disabilities achieve independence, including the Americans with Disabilities Act (ADA).

7919 ■ Nevada Division of Environmental Protection
901 S. Stewart St., Ste. 4001
Carson City, NV 89701-5249
Contact: Leo M. Drozdoff, Admin.
Ph: (775)687-4670
Free: 800-992-0900
Fax: (775)687-5856
E-mail: abiaggi@ndep.nv.gov
URL: http://ndep.nv.gov/
Descr: Mission is to protect and enhance the environment of the state, consistent with the public health and enjoyment, the propagation and protection of terrestrial and aquatic life, the operation of existing industries, the pursuit of agriculture, and economic development of the state.

7920 ■ Sierra Nevada Association of Realtors (SNAR)
300 S Curry St., Ste. 3
Carson City, NV 89703
Contact: Marilyn Koschella, Exec. Off.
Ph: (775)885-7200
Fax: (775)885-7203
E-mail: eo@sierranvar.com
URL: http://www.sierranvar.com
Descr: Strives to develop real estate business practices. Advocates for the right to own, use and transfer real property. Provides a facility for professional development, research and exchange of information among members and the general public.

7921 ■ Solar NV
10624 S Eastern Ave., Ste. A-609
Henderson, NV 89052
Contact: Alison Gray
Ph: (702)507-0093
Fax: (702)507-0093
E-mail: info@solarnv.org
URL: http://www.solarnv.org
Descr: Strives to educate Southern Nevadans about the benefits of renewable energy. Encourages and promotes the use of sustainable energy technology.

Works as a clearinghouse and local resource for renewable energy information.

7922 ■ SUNRISE, Sustainable Resources Group
PO Box 19074
Reno, NV 89511-0837
Contact: Philip Moore, Pres.
E-mail: president@sunrisenevada.org
URL: http://www.sunrisenevada.org
Descr: Represents the interests of members. **Fnd:** 1996.

New Hampshire

7923 ■ New Hampshire Department of Environmental Services
29 Hazen Dr.
PO Box 95
Concord, NH 03302-0095
Contact: Tom Burack, COmmnr.
Ph: (603)271-3503
Free: 800-735-2964
Fax: (603)271-2867
E-mail: pip@des.state.nh.us
URL: http://www.des.state.nh.us/
Descr: Mission is to help sustain a high qualify of life for all citizens by protecting and restoring the environment and public health in New Hampshire.

New Jersey

7924 ■ New Jersey Association of Wildlife Rehabilitators (NJAWR)
24 Mountain Church Rd.
Hopewell, NJ 08525
Contact: Dave Purdy, Treas.
Ph: (609)660-8737
E-mail: membership@njawr.com
URL: http://www.njawr.com

7925 ■ New Jersey Department of Environmental Protection
401 E. State St., 7th Fl., E. Wing
PO Box 402
Trenton, NJ 08625-0402
Contact: Mark N. Mauriello, Commnr.
Ph: (609)292-2885
Free: 877-927-6337
Fax: (609)292-7695
URL: http://www.state.nj.us/dep/

New Mexico

7926 ■ New Mexico Environment Department
PO Box 5469
Santa Fe, NM 87502-5469
Contact: Ron Curry, Sec.
Ph: (505)827-2855
Free: 800-219-6157
Fax: (505)827-2836
E-mail: ron_curry@nmenv.state.nm.us
URL: http://www.nmenv.state.nm.us/
Descr: Mission is to provide the highest quality of life throughout the state by promoting a safe, clean, and productive environment.

7927 ■ New Mexico Solar Energy Association (NMSEA)
1009 Bradbury SE, No. 35
Albuquerque, NM 87106
Contact: Rose M. Kern, Development Dir.
Ph: (505)246-0400
Free: 888-886-6765
Fax: (505)246-2251
E-mail: info@nmsea.org
URL: http://www.nmsea.org
Staff: 2. **Descr:** Aims to further solar and related arts, sciences and technologies with concern for the ecological, social and economic fabric of the region. Serves to inform public institutions and governmental bodies, and seeks to raise the level of public awareness of its purposes. **Fnd:** 1972. **Mem:** 253. **State Groups:** 1. **Pub:** *The Sunpaper* (bimonthly).

New York

7928 ■ Columbia-Greene Board of Realtors (CGBR)
337 Fairview Ave.
Hudson, NY 12534
Contact: Rick Rielly, Pres.
Ph: (518)828-7871
Fax: (518)828-6899
E-mail: columbiagreenerealtors@hotmail.com
URL: http://www.columbiagreenerealtors.com
Staff: 4. **Descr:** Strives to develop real estate business practices. Advocates for the right to own, use and transfer real property. Provides a facility for professional development, research and exchange of information among members and the general public.

7929 ■ Izaak Walton League of America, Central New York Chapter
PO Box 121
Fayetteville, NY 13066
Contact: Conrad Strozik, Pres.
Ph: (315)655-2752
E-mail: centralnewyorkiwla@gmail.com
URL: http://www.iwla.org/centralnewyork
Staff: 30. **Descr:** Works to conserve, maintain, protect, and restore the natural resources. **Fnd:** 1922.

7930 ■ Mental Health Association of Columbia-Greene Counties
713 Union St.
Hudson, NY 12534
Contact: Peter Cameron, Pres.
Ph: (518)828-4619
Fax: (518)828-1196
E-mail: info@mhacg.org
URL: http://www.mhacg.org
Descr: Aims to promote mental health and prevent mental disorders. Educates the public about ways to preserve and strengthen its mental health. Strives for access to effective care and discrimination against people with mental and addictive disorders. Fosters research, practice, services and policy concerning mental health.

7931 ■ New York Solar Energy Industries Association (NYSEIA)
533 Woodford Ave.
Endicott, NY 13760
Contact: Gay Canough, Exec. Dir.
Ph: (518)485-1454
E-mail: info@nyseia.org
URL: http://www.nyseia.org
Descr: Aims to educate the public about the wide range of available solar products and their advantages for consumers and society. Promotes an ethical industry of quality products and services. Encourages public policy and commercial practices that foster greater use of renewable energy. Promotes R&D to gain better understanding of the market for renewable energy and disseminate information about and within the industry.

7932 ■ New York State Department of Environmental Conservation
625 Broadway
Albany, NY 12233-0001
Contact: Pete Grannis, Commnr.
Ph: (518)402-8540
Fax: (518)402-9016
E-mail: dpaeweb@gw.dec.state.ny.us
URL: http://www.dec.ny.gov/

7933 ■ New York State Wildlife Rehabilitation Council (NYSWRC)
PO Box 246
Owego, NY 13827
Contact: Kelly Martin, Pres.
E-mail: kmartink@midtel.net
URL: http://www.nyswrc.org

North Carolina

7934 ■ American Solar Energy Society, Appalachian State University
Box 9096
Boone, NC 28608
Contact: Quint David, Pres.
Ph: (252)717-9730
E-mail: fd63828@appstate.edu
URL: http://www.asuses.appstate.edu
Fnd: 1995.

7935 ■ North Carolina Department of Environment and Natural Resources
1601 Mail Service Ctr.
Raleigh, NC 27699-1601
Contact: Dee Freeman, Sec.
Ph: (919)733-4984
Fax: (919)715-3060
URL: http://www.enr.state.nc.us/

7936 ■ Wildlife Rehabilitators of North Carolina (WRNC)
2542 Weymoth Rd.
Winston-Salem, NC 27103
Contact: Elizabeth Hanrahan, Pres.
Ph: (252)482-7139
E-mail: eh11@earthlink.net
URL: http://www.ncwildliferehab.org

North Dakota

7937 ■ North Dakota Department of Health Environmental Health Section
918 E. Divide Ave.
Bismarck, ND 58501-1947
Contact: Dave Glatt, Chf.
Ph: (701)328-5150
Fax: (701)328-5200
E-mail: dglatt@nd.us
URL: http://www.health.state.nd.us/ehs/
Pub: List of publications online.

Ohio

7938 ■ Arthritis Foundation, Ohio River Valley Chapter
7124 Miami Ave.
Cincinnati, OH 45243
Ph: (513)271-4545
Free: 800-383-6843
E-mail: info.orv@arthritis.org
URL: http://www.arthritis.org/chapters/ohio-river-valley
Descr: Seeks to: discover the cause and improve the methods for the treatment and prevention of arthritis and other rheumatic diseases; increase the number of scientists investigating rheumatic diseases; provide training in rheumatic diseases for more doctors; extend knowledge of arthritis and other rheumatic diseases to the lay public, emphasizing the socioeconomic as well as medical aspects of these diseases.

7939 ■ Izaak Walton League of America, Cincinnati Chapter
6793 Midnight Sun Dr.
Maineville, OH 45039
Contact: Kevin S. Flowers
Ph: (513)697-6100
E-mail: kflowers@fuse.net
URL: http://cinci-iwla.org
Descr: Aims to protect America's rich resources to ensure a high quality of life for all people, now and in the future. **Fnd:** 1944.

7940 ■ Izaak Walton League of America, Delta Chapter
402 Adrian St.
Delta, OH 43515-1124
Contact: Martin Roth
Ph: (419)822-4468
Descr: Works to educate the public to conserve, maintain, protect, and restore the soil, forest, water, and other natural resources of the U.S.; promotes

the enjoyment and wholesome utilization of these resources.

7941 ■ Izaak Walton League of America, Fairfield Chapter
936 Symmes Rd.
Fairfield, OH 45014
Contact: Randy Hughes, Pres.
Ph: (513)868-3430
E-mail: bobkraft@fuse.net
URL: http://home.fuse.net/fairfieldiwla
Staff: 8. **Descr:** Works to educate the public to conserve, maintain, protect and restore the soil forest, water and other natural resources of the U.S. **Fnd:** 1976.

7942 ■ Izaak Walton League of America, Fremont Chapter
43 Westwood Dr.
Fremont, OH 43420-9637
Contact: Melvin Balduf Sr.
Ph: (419)334-3095
Descr: Works to educate the public to conserve, maintain, protect, and restore the soil, forest, water, and other natural resources of the U.S.; promotes the enjoyment and wholesome utilization of these resources.

7943 ■ Izaak Walton League of America, Lawrence County Chapter
2069 Co. Rd., No. 54
Kitts Hill, OH 45645
Contact: Wanda Hardy
Ph: (740)532-3824
Descr: Works to educate the public to conserve, maintain, protect, and restore the soil, forest, water, and other natural resources of the U.S.; promotes the enjoyment and wholesome utilization of these resources.

7944 ■ Izaak Walton League of America, Tiffin-Seneca County Chapter
1325 S Township Rd. 159
Tiffin, OH 44883
Contact: Kenneth Sarka
Ph: (419)447-5060
E-mail: washtub_@wcnet.org
Descr: Works to educate the public to conserve, maintain, protect, and restore the soil, forest, water, and other natural resources of the U.S.; promotes the enjoyment and wholesome utilization of these resources.

7945 ■ Ohio Environmental Protection Agency
PO Box 1049
Columbus, OH 43216-1049
Contact: Chris Korleski, Dir.
Ph: (614)644-3020
E-mail: web.requests@epa.state.oh.us
URL: http://www.epa.state.oh.us/
Descr: Mission is to protect the environment and public health by ensuring compliance with environmental laws and demonstrating leadership in environmental stewardship.

7946 ■ Ohio Water Quality Association (OWQA)
3271 Springcrest Dr.
Hamilton, OH 45011
Contact: Dan Schlosser, Exec. Dir.
Ph: (513)895-0695
Free: 800-537-6585
Fax: (513)895-1739
E-mail: dan310@earthlink.net
URL: http://www.owqa.org
Descr: Represents individuals or firms engaged in the manufacturing and/or assembly and distribution and/or retail selling of water treatment equipment, supplies, and services. Promotes the acceptance and use of industry equipment, products, and services. Provides activities, programs, and services

designed to improve economy and efficiency within the industry.

7947 ■ Ohio Wildlife Rehabilitators Association (OWRA)
5 Maple Leaf Dr.
Milford, OH 45150
Contact: Betty Ross, Pres.
E-mail: membership@owra.org
URL: http://www.owra.org

Oklahoma

7948 ■ Appraisal Institute, Green Country of Oklahoma Chapter
PO Box 700902
Tulsa, OK 74170-0902
Contact: Robert D. Bryant SRA, Pres.
Ph: (918)832-9008
Fax: (918)832-9008
E-mail: robtbryant@aol.com
URL: http://www.gccai.org
Descr: General appraisers who hold the MAI or SRPA designations, and residential members who hold the SRA designation. **Mem:** 50.

7949 ■ Izaak Walton League of America, Sanborn Chapter
1905 E 4th Ave.
Stillwater, OK 74074-3919
Contact: R. W. Altman
Ph: (405)372-2746
Descr: Works to educate the public to conserve, maintain, protect, and restore the soil, forest, water, and other natural resources of the U.S.; promotes the enjoyment and wholesome utilization of these resources.

7950 ■ Mothers Against Drunk Driving, Green Country (MADD)
3416 S Yale Ave.
Tulsa, OK 74135-8016
Ph: (918)743-6233
Free: 800-259-6233
Fax: (918)743-6282
E-mail: greencountry.ok@madd.org
URL: http://madd.org/ok
Staff: 2. **Descr:** Victims of drunk driving crashes; concerned citizens. Encourages citizen participation in working towards reform of the drunk driving problem and the prevention of underage drinking. Acts as the voice of victims of drunk driving crashes by speaking on their behalf to communities, businesses, and educational groups. **Fnd:** 1984. **Mem:** 500. **Reg. Groups:** 2. **State Groups:** 1. **Local Groups:** 1.

7951 ■ Oklahoma Department of Environmental Quality
PO Box 1677
Oklahoma City, OK 73101-1677
Contact: J.D. Strong, Sec.
Ph: (405)702-1000
Free: 800-869-1400
Fax: (405)702-1001
E-mail: oseinfo3@environment.ok.gov
URL: http://www.deq.state.ok.us/
Descr: Vision of the DEQ is to eliminate the effects of unintended consequences of historic development, to prevent new adverse environmental impacts, and to provide significant input into decision making, all the while enhancing both the environment and the economy of Oklahoma.

Oregon

7952 ■ Izaak Walton League of America, Oregon Division
15056 Quall Rd. NE
Silverton, OR 97381
Contact: Dawn A. Olson, Pres.
Ph: (503)873-2681
E-mail: olsondaw@juno.com
URL: http://www.iwla.org
Descr: Works on the legislative level, as well as to

educate the public to conserve, maintain, protect, and restore the soil, forest, water, and other natural resources of the U.S.; promotes the enjoyment and wholesome utilization of these resources. Encourages its members to address the type of environmental work in which they are interested. **Fnd:** 1927. **Mem:** 625. **Pub:** *Oregon Ike* (3/year).

7953 ■ Northwest Bottled Water Association (NWBWA)
PO Box 66622
Portland, OR 97290
Contact: Ross Rosette, Pres.
Ph: (503)661-5075
Fax: (503)665-7702
E-mail: nwbwa@comcast.net
URL: http://www.nwbwa.org
Descr: Promotes increased use of bottled water. Fosters and safeguards the general interests of the bottled water industry. Provides technical assistance to members in preparing the highest quality water to consumers.

7954 ■ Oregon Department of Environmental Quality
811 SW 6th Ave.
Portland, OR 97204-1390
Contact: Stephanie Hallock, Dir.
Ph: (503)229-5696
Free: 800-452-4011
Fax: (503)229-6124
E-mail: deq.info@deq.state.or.us
URL: http://www.deq.state.or.us/
Descr: The DEQ is a regulatory agency whose job is to protect the quality of Oregon's environment. **Telecom. Svcs:** TTY toll free number is (800)735-2900.

7955 ■ Solar Oregon
205 SE Grand Ave., Ste. 205
Portland, OR 97214
Contact: Michael VanDerwater, Exec. Dir.
Ph: (503)231-5662
E-mail: info@solaroregon.org
URL: http://www.solaroregon.org
Descr: Provides education and community outreach to encourage Oregonians to choose solar energy. Offers a statewide solar workshop series, and coordinates Oregon's Green and Solar Home Tours. **Fnd:** 1979.

Pennsylvania

7956 ■ Izaak Walton League of America, John Harris Chapter
3201 Larry Dr.
Harrisburg, PA 17109-5711
Contact: Joseph V. Galati, Pres.
Ph: (717)564-4763
Descr: Works to educate the public to conserve, maintain, protect, and restore the soil, forest, water, and other natural resources of the U.S.; promotes the enjoyment and wholesome utilization of these resources.

7957 ■ Izaak Walton League of America, Lebanon County Chapter
65 Monroe Valley Dr.
Jonestown, PA 17038-8223
Contact: Mr. Tracy Longenecker, Membership Sec.
Ph: (717)273-7304
E-mail: trace@mbcomp.com
URL: http://www.iwla.org
Descr: Conserves, maintains, protects and restores the soil, forest, water and other resources around Lebanon County, PA. **Fnd:** 1939. **Mem:** 62. **Reg. Groups:** 6. **State Groups:** 20. **Local Groups:** 332. **Pub:** *Outdoor America* (quarterly).

7958 ■ Pennsylvania Association of Wildlife Rehabilitators (PAWR)
4991 Shimerville Rd.
Emmaus, PA 18049
Contact: Peggy Hentz, Pres.
Ph: (570)739-4393

E-mail: redcreekwildlife@comcast.net
URL: http://www.pawr.com

7959 ■ Pennsylvania Department of Environmental Protection
16th Fl., Rachel Carson State Office Bldg.
PO Box 2063
Harrisburg, PA 17105-2063
Contact: John Hanger, Sec.
Ph: (717)787-2814
Fax: (717)772-5996
E-mail: RA-epcontactus@state.pa.us
URL: http://www.dep.state.pa.us/

Rhode Island

7960 ■ Rhode Island Department of Environmental Management
235 Promenade St.
Providence, RI 02908-5767
Contact: W. Michael Sullivan PhD, Dir.
Ph: (401)222-6800
E-mail: rayna.santoro@dem.ri.gov
URL: http://www.state.ri.us/dem/

South Carolina

7961 ■ American Society of Heating, Refrigerating and Air-Conditioning Engineers Greenville, South Carolina
H2L Consulting Engineers
122 Edgeworth St.
Greenville, SC 29607
Contact: Will Thomason, Pres.
Ph: (864)233-8844
E-mail: treasurer@ashrae4greenville.com
URL: http://www.ashrae4greenville.com
Descr: Advances the arts and sciences of heating, ventilation, air-conditioning and refrigeration. Provides a source of technical and educational information, standards and guidelines. Conducts seminars for professional growth.

7962 ■ American Solar Energy Society, South Carolina
1201 Main St., Ste. 430
Columbia, SC 29201
Contact: Erika Hartwig
Ph: (803)737-8038
E-mail: ehartwig@energy.sc.gov
Descr: Brings together energy professionals to create a sustainable energy economy. Promotes solar energy education, public outreach, and advocacy. Increases the use of solar energy, energy efficiency and other sustainable technologies in the United States.

7963 ■ Children's Tumor Foundation, South Carolina - Greenville Area
101 Hickory Ln.
Mauldin, SC 29662
Contact: Susan Luttrell
Ph: (864)963-2064
E-mail: flowerchildsuziq@msn.com
URL: http://www.ctf.org/south-carolina/south-carolina-chapter.html
Descr: Seeks to improve the health and well-being of individuals and families affected by neurofibromatosis (NF). Encourages and supports research and the development of treatments and cures for neurofibromatosis types 1 and 2, schwannomatosis and related disorders. Raises public awareness of neurofibromatoses and assists in the development of clinical centers and other patient support mechanisms.

7964 ■ Greater Greenville Association of Realtors
50 Airpark Ct.
Greenville, SC 29607
Contact: Nick Sabatine, Exec. Off.
Ph: (864)672-4427
Fax: (864)672-3207
E-mail: nsabatine@aol.com
URL: http://www.ggaronline.com

Descr: Strives to develop real estate business practices. Advocates the right to own, use and transfer real property. Provides information about the real estate industry.

7965 ■ Greater Greenville Laryngectomee Club
10 Dover Dr.
Taylors, SC 29687
Contact: Sapp Funderburk
Ph: (864)268-9719
E-mail: csfund@bellsouth.net
Descr: Promotes and supports the total rehabilitation of persons who have had laryngectomies. Seeks to improve the relations among persons who, due to the removal of the larynx because of cancer or other reasons, have lost their natural voices. Encourages exchange of ideas and methods for training and teaching of alaryngeal methods of communication.

7966 ■ Greenville Area Small Business Development Center
Renaissance Center
135 S Main St., Ste. 600
Greenville, SC 29601
Ph: (864)370-1545
URL: http://scsbdc.moore.sc.edu/AreaOffices.html#Greenville
Descr: Represents and promotes the small business sector. Provides management assistance to current and prospective small business owners. Helps to improve management skills and expand the products and services of members.

7967 ■ Greenville County Taxpayers Association
2019 Wade Hampton Blvd.
Greenville, SC 29615
Ph: (864)244-6632
Fax: (864)268-6895

7968 ■ Greenwood Area Small Business Development Center
PO Box 246
Greenwood, SC 29648
Ph: (864)992-5743
URL: http://scsbdc.moore.sc.edu/AreaOffices.html#Greenwood
Descr: Represents and promotes the small business sector. Provides management assistance to current and prospective small business owners. Helps to improve management skills and expand the products and services of members.

7969 ■ Greenwood Association of Realtors
231 Hampton Ave.
Greenwood, SC 29646
Contact: Susan Birch, Pres.
Ph: (864)229-6022
Fax: (864)229-6386
E-mail: gar@simpledsl.com
URL: http://www.greenwoodassociationofrealtors.com
Descr: Strives to develop real estate business practices. Advocates the right to own, use and transfer real property. Provides information about the real estate industry.

7970 ■ Home Builders Association of Greenville
5 Creekside Park Ct., Ste. A
Greenville, SC 29615-4835
Contact: Todd Usher, Pres.
Ph: (864)254-0133
Fax: (864)254-0134
E-mail: info@hbaofgreenville.com
URL: http://www.hbaofgreenville.com
Descr: Single and multifamily home builders, commercial builders, and others associated with the building industry. **Fnd:** 1960.

7971 ■ Mental Health America of Greenville (MHAGC)
301 University Ridge, Ste. 5600
Greenville, SC 29601-3675
Contact: Jeffrey P. Dunlaevy Esq., Pres.
Ph: (864)467-3344

Fax: (864)467-3547
URL: http://www.mhagc.org
Staff: 5. **Descr:** Seeks to promote mental health and prevent mental health disorders. Improves mental health of Americans through advocacy, public education, research and service.

7972 ■ Mothers Against Drunk Driving - Greenville County
200 Mills Ave.
Greenville, SC 29605
Ph: (864)457-4099

7973 ■ River Management Society, Southeast Chapter
PO Box 167
Columbia, SC 29202
Contact: Mary Crockett, Pres.
Ph: (803)734-9111
Fax: (803)734-9200
E-mail: crokettm@dnr.sc.gov

7974 ■ South Carolina Chapter of the Environmental Information Association (SCEIA)
PO Box 478
Mauldin, SC 29662
Contact: Thomas W. Behnke, Pres.
Ph: (803)561-9024
Fax: (803)561-7790
E-mail: sceia@sceia.org
URL: http://www.sceia.org
Descr: Represents individuals and corporations concerned about environmental management and control. Collects and disseminates information concerning environmental risks in buildings to interested professionals, building owners, and the public. Serves as a clearinghouse of information on effective environmental management.

7975 ■ South Carolina Department of Natural Resources
1000 Assembly St.
PO Box 167
Columbia, SC 29202
Contact: John E. Frampton, Dir.
Ph: (803)734-4007
Free: 800-922-5431
E-mail: framptonj@dnr.sc.gov
URL: http://www.dnr.sc.gov/

7976 ■ South Carolina Solar Council
1201 Main St., Ste. 430
Columbia, SC 29201
Contact: Erika Hartwig
Ph: (803)737-8038
E-mail: ehartwig@energy.sc.gov
URL: http://www.ases.org
Descr: Promotes a wide utilization of solar energy through the application of science and technology.

South Dakota

7977 ■ Izaak Walton League of America, Beadle County Chapter
1060 Colorado Ave. SW
Huron, SD 57350-3232
Contact: Lanny Thomas
Ph: (605)352-0595
Descr: Works to educate the public to conserve, maintain, protect, and restore the soil, forest, water, and other natural resources of the U.S.; promotes the enjoyment and wholesome utilization of these resources.

7978 ■ Izaak Walton League of America, Bon Homme County Chapter
41327 308th St.
Tyndall, SD 57066-5937
Contact: Randy Milne
Ph: (402)358-5562
Descr: Works to educate the public to conserve, maintain, protect, and restore the soil, forest, water, and other natural resources of the U.S.; promotes

the enjoyment and wholesome utilization of these resources.

7979 ■ Izaak Walton League of America, Kampeska Chapter
1224 Crestview Dr.
Watertown, SD 57201
Contact: Jerry Olson, Pres.
Ph: (605)886-5013
E-mail: kbakervinella@yahoo.com
URL: http://sdikes.org
Descr: Works to educate the public to conserve, maintain, protect, and restore the soil, forest, water, and other natural resources of the U.S. **Fnd:** 1979.

7980 ■ Izaak Walton League of America, Madison No. 16 Chapter
1161 Bay Rd.
Madison, SD 57042
Contact: Gerald Ottoson, Pres.
Ph: (605)256-2714
URL: http://sdikes.org
Descr: Works to educate the public to conserve, maintain, protect, and restore the soil, forest, water, and other natural resources of the U.S.

7981 ■ Izaak Walton League of America, McCook Lake Chapter
320 Lakeshore Dr.
McCook Lake, SD 57049
Contact: Keith Rittscher, Pres.
Ph: (712)255-1525
E-mail: kmerchant@unitedwaysiouxland.com
URL: http://sdikes.org/chapters.htm
Descr: Works to educate the public to conserve, maintain, protect, and restore the soil, forest, water, and other natural resources of the U.S.

7982 ■ Izaak Walton League of America, Rapid City Chapter
PO Box 936
Hill City, SD 57745
Contact: Richard Rasmussen
Ph: (605)574-4707
E-mail: rdeadbroke@aol.com
Descr: Works to educate the public to conserve, maintain, protect, and restore the soil, forest, water, and other natural resources of the U.S.; promotes the enjoyment and wholesome utilization of these resources.

7983 ■ Izaak Walton League of America, South Dakota Division
1008 N Huron Ave.
Pierre, SD 57501-1438
Contact: Jerry Schlekeway, Pres.
Ph: (605)224-7780
E-mail: gschlek@pie.midco.net
URL: http://www.sdikes.org
Descr: Individuals and others considered to be "defenders of woods, waters, soil, air, and wildlife". Works to educate the public to conserve, maintain, protect, and restore the soil, forest, water, and other natural resources of the United States; promotes the enjoyment and wholesome utilization of these resources. **Fnd:** 1926. **Mem:** 1200.

7984 ■ Izaak Walton League of America, Sunshine Chapter
PO Box 896
Pierre, SD 57501-3019
Contact: Sharon Gienger, Membership Sec.
Ph: (605)224-4577
E-mail: sandbgienger@pie.midco.net
URL: http://sdikes.org
Descr: Strives to protect natural resources to ensure a high quality of life for all people. Provides outdoor recreation and conservation activities in South Dakota. **Fnd:** 1932.

7985 ■ South Dakota Counseling Association, West River Chapter
14 Stone Dr.
Wall, SD 57790
Contact: Nancy Shrope, Pres.
Ph: (605)347-2686

E-mail: nancy.shrope@ellsworth.af.mil
URL: http://www.sdcounseling.org

7986 ■ South Dakota Department of Environment and Natural Resources
PMB 2020
Joe Foss Bldg.
523 E. Capitol
Pierre, SD 57501
Contact: Steven M. Pirner PE, Sec.
Ph: (605)773-3151
Fax: (605)773-6035
E-mail: denrinternet@state.sd.us
URL: http://www.state.sd.us/denr/denr.html
Descr: Mission is "to protect public health and the environment by providing environmental monitoring and natural resource assessment, technical and financial assistance for environmental projects, and environmental regulatory services; all done in a manner to protect South Dakota's environment and natural resources for today and tomorrow while treating everyone as our customer and exceeding their expectations."

Tennessee

7987 ■ River Counties Association of Realtors (RCAR)
2070 Candies Ln. NW
Cleveland, TN 37312-2615
Contact: Heidi Chock, Exec. Off.
Ph: (423)476-5912
Fax: (423)478-5964
E-mail: rcar@rivercounties.com
URL: http://www.rivercounties.com
Descr: Represents residential and commercial real estate brokers, salespeople, property managers, appraisers, counselors and others engaged in all aspects of the real estate industry. Seeks to advocate for the right to own, use, and transfer real property. Provides a facility for professional development and exchange of information among its members, to the public, and government.

7988 ■ Tennessee Department of Environment and Conservation
401 Church St.
L & C Annex, 1st Fl.
Nashville, TN 37243-0435
Contact: Jim Fyke, Commnr.
Ph: (615)532-0109
Free: 888-891-8332
E-mail: ask.tdec@state.tn.us
URL: http://www.state.tn.us/environment/

7989 ■ Tennessee Onsite Wastewater Association (TOWA)
PO Box 292983
Nashville, TN 37229-2983
Contact: Tom Petty, Pres.
Ph: (615)373-1567
E-mail: tpetty@quanics.net

Texas

7990 ■ Mid-America Bottled Water Association (MABWA)
14101 Hwy. 290 W, Bldg. 1600-B
Austin, TX 78737
Contact: Susan Gibson, Exec. Dir.
Ph: (512)894-4106
Fax: (512)858-0486
E-mail: jmgibson@austin.rr.com
URL: http://www.mabwa.org
Descr: Promotes increased use of bottled water. Fosters and safeguards the general interests of the bottled water industry. Provides technical assistance to members in preparing the highest quality water to consumers.

7991 ■ Southeastern Bottled Water Association (SEBWA)
14101 Hwy. 290 W, Bldg. 1600B
Austin, TX 78737
Contact: Susan Gibson, Exec. Dir.

Ph: (512)894-4106
Fax: (512)858-0486
E-mail: susangibson@austin.rr.com
URL: http://www.sebwa.org
Descr: Promotes increased use of bottled water. Fosters and safeguards the general interests of the bottled water industry. Provides technical assistance to members in preparing the highest quality water to consumers.

7992 ■ Texas Commission on Environmental Quality
PO Box 13087
Austin, TX 78711-3087
Contact: Mark R. Vickery, Exec. Dir.
Ph: (512)239-1000
Fax: (512)239-3939
E-mail: execdir@tceq.state.tx.us
URL: http://www.tceq.state.tx.us/

7993 ■ Texas On-Site Wastewater Association
3205 N University Dr., Ste. D
PMD 411
Nacogdoches, TX 75965
Contact: Tim N. Taylor, Managing Consultant
Free: 888-398-7188
E-mail: txowa@nowra.org
URL: http://www.txowa.org

7994 ■ Texas Renewable Energy Industries Association (TREIA)
PO Box 16469
Austin, TX 78761-6469
Contact: Russel E. Smith, Exec. Dir.
Ph: (512)345-5446
Fax: (512)345-6831
E-mail: rsmith@treia.org
URL: http://www.treia.org
Staff: 3. **Descr:** Represents companies and individuals involved in solar, wind, biomass, geothermal and hydro resources. **Fnd:** 1984. **Mem:** 500. **Pub:** *TREIA Newsletter* (3/year).

Utah

7995 ■ Utah Department of Environmental Quality
168 N. 1950 W.
PO Box 144810
Salt Lake City, UT 84114-4810
Contact: Amanda Smith, Actg.Exec.Dir.
Ph: (801)536-4402
Free: 800-458-0145
Fax: (801)536-0061
E-mail: deqinfo@utah.gov
URL: http://www.eq.state.ut.us/
Descr: Mission is to safeguard public health and our quality of life by protecting and enhancing the environment.

Vermont

7996 ■ Vermont Agency of Natural Resources
Center Bldg.
103 S. Main St.
Waterbury, VT 05671-0301
Contact: Jonathan L. Wood, Sec.
Ph: (802)241-3600
Fax: (802)244-1102
E-mail: george.crombie@state.vt.us
URL: http://www.anr.state.vt.us/

7997 ■ Wild in Vermont (WIV)
PO Box 163
Underhill Center, VT 05490
Contact: Nancy J. Carey, Pres.
Ph: (802)899-1027
E-mail: ofes@ofes.org

Virginia

7998 ■ Eastern Water Quality Association (EWQA)
PO Box 309
New Market, VA 22844

Contact: Greg Gruett, Pres.
Ph: (540)740-3329
Free: 888-450-2409
Fax: (540)740-4556
E-mail: ewqa@shentel.net
URL: http://www.ewqa.org

Descr: Represents individuals or firms engaged in the manufacturing and/or assembly and distribution and/or retail selling of water treatment equipment, supplies, and services. Promotes the acceptance and use of industry equipment, products, and services. Provides activities, programs, and services designed to improve economy and efficiency within the industry.

7999 ■ Izaak Walton League of America, Alexandria Chapter
2729 Garrisonville Rd.
Stafford, VA 22556-3412
Contact: Pete Williams, Membership Sec.
Ph: (540)752-5331
E-mail: iwlaalex@hughes.net
URL: http://www.iwla.us

Descr: Works to educate the public to conserve, maintain, protect, and restore the soil, forest, water, and other natural resources of the U.S.; promotes the enjoyment and wholesome utilization of these resources. **Fnd:** 1938. **Mem:** 800.

8000 ■ Izaak Walton League of America, Arlington-Fairfax Chapter
PO Box 366
Centreville, VA 20122-0366
Contact: Nancy Keaton, Membership Sec.
Ph: (703)631-4495
E-mail: nankea@earthlink.net
URL: http://arlingtonfairfax-iwla.org

Descr: Works to educate the public to conserve, maintain, protect, and restore the soil, forest, water, and other natural resources of the U.S.; promotes the enjoyment and wholesome utilization of these resources. **Fnd:** 1936. **Mem:** 2200. **Pub:** *The News-letter* (quarterly).

8001 ■ Izaak Walton League of America, Loudoun County Chapter (LCCIWLA)
PO Box 1338
Leesburg, VA 20177
Ph: (703)777-9684
E-mail: membership@loudouniwla.org
URL: http://www.loudouniwla.org

Descr: Promotes the means and opportunities for educating the public to conserve, maintain, protect and restore the soil, forest, water, air, wildlife and other natural resources of the United States, in Virginia and more specifically in Loudoun County. **Fnd:** 1951.

8002 ■ Izaak Walton League of America, Prince William Chapter (PWIWLA)
12946 Dunbarton Rd.
Bristow, VA 20136-2570
Contact: Ms. Jerrie Norris
Ph: (703)368-6562
E-mail: pwiwlapr@yahoo.com
URL: http://www.geocities.com/pwiwla

Descr: Works to educate the public to conserve, maintain, protect, and restore the soil, forest, water, and other natural resources of the U.S.; promotes the enjoyment and wholesome utilization of these resources.

8003 ■ Izaak Walton League of America, Virginia Division (IWLA)
7900 Ashton St.
Alexandria, VA 22309-1341
Contact: Ernest L. Embrey Jr., Pres.
Ph: (703)780-5141
E-mail: leeiwla@aol.com
URL: http://www.va-iwla.org

Descr: Works to educate the public to conserve, maintain, protect, and restore the soil, forest, water, and other natural resources of the U.S.; promotes

the enjoyment and wholesome utilization of these resources. **Fnd:** 1929. **Mem:** 7459.

8004 ■ Izaak Walton League of America, Winchester Chapter
PO Box 2954
Winchester, VA 22604
Contact: Michael A. Doran, Pres.
Ph: (540)678-8834
E-mail: mdoran61@yahoo.com
URL: http://www.user.shentel.net/winiwla

Descr: Works to educate the public to conserve, maintain, protect, and restore the soil, forest, water, and other natural resources of the U.S.; promotes the enjoyment and wholesome utilization of these resources.

8005 ■ National Association of Home Builders of the U.S., New River Valley Home Builders Association (NRVHBA)
Local No. 4837
PO Box 2010
Christiansburg, VA 24068-2010
Contact: Ed Tuchler, Pres.
Ph: (540)381-0180
Fax: (540)381-2986
E-mail: info@nrvhba.org
URL: http://www.nrvhba.com

Descr: Single and multifamily home builders, commercial builders, and others associated with the building industry. **Fnd:** 1976.

8006 ■ New River Valley Small Business Development Center - Radford University
Radford University
Business Assistance Center Business Technology Park
6226 University Park Dr.
Radford, VA 24141
Contact: David Shanks, Dir.
Ph: (540)831-6056
Fax: (540)831-6735
E-mail: dshanks@radford.edu
URL: http://btp.radford.edu/ba

Descr: Represents and promotes the small business sector. Provides management assistance to current and prospective small business owners. Helps to improve management skills and expand the products and services of members.

8007 ■ South Atlantic Bottled Water Association (SABWA)
2140 Mt. Carmel Rd.
Alton, VA 24520
Contact: Kirk Crump, Sec.
Ph: (434)753-2515
Fax: (434)753-1413
E-mail: kirk@waterprofessionals.com
URL: http://www.sabwaonline.org

Descr: Promotes increased use of bottled water. Fosters and safeguards the general interests of the bottled water industry. Provides technical assistance to members in preparing the highest quality water to consumers.

8008 ■ Virginia Department of Environmental Quality
629 E. Main St.
PO Box 1105
Richmond, VA 23219
Contact: David K. Paylor, Dir.
Ph: (804)698-4000
Free: 800-592-5482
E-mail: dkpaylor@deq.virginia.gov
URL: http://www.deq.state.va.us/

8009 ■ Virginia Onsite Wastewater Recycling Association (VOWRA)
PO Box 155
Star Tannery, VA 22654
Contact: Bob Lee, Pres.
Ph: (540)465-9623
Fax: (540)465-9627
E-mail: vowra@shentel.net
URL: http://www.vowra.org

Washington

8010 ■ Izaak Walton League of America, Greater Seattle Chapter
4000 95th Ave. NE
Bellevue, WA 98004
Ph: (425)455-1986
URL: http://sites.google.com/site/greaterseattlechapter/Home

Descr: Works to educate the public to conserve, maintain, protect, and restore the soil, forest, water, and other natural resources of the United States; promotes the enjoyment and wholesome utilization of these resources. **Fnd:** 1965. **Mem:** 50.

8011 ■ Izaak Walton League of America, Washington Division
514 N Shore Blvd.
Fox Island, WA 98333
Contact: Dr. Ernie Karlstrom, Pres.
Ph: (253)549-2155
E-mail: ernmar27@earthlink.net

Descr: Represents the interests of hunters, anglers and other conservation-minded outdoor enthusiasts who work through volunteer, community-based action and education programs to ensure the sustainable use of natural resources. Organizes statewide stream monitoring programs, outdoor ethics campaigns, youth education promotions and wetland protection effort.

8012 ■ Northwest Animal Rights Network
10015 Lake City Way NE, No. 127
Seattle, WA 98125
Ph: (206)250-7301
E-mail: info@narn.org
URL: http://www.narn.org

Staff: 1. **Descr:** Works to end the suffering and exploitation of all animals, with emphasis on farm animals through outreach, education and other legal means. **Fnd:** 1986. **Mem:** 1200.

8013 ■ Solar Washington
5308 Baker Ave. NW
Seattle, WA 98107-2068
Contact: Pamela Burton, Pres.
Ph: (206)222-7113
E-mail: info@solarwashington.org
URL: http://www.solarwashington.org

Descr: Solar energy equipment manufacturers, system integrators, distributors, dealers, designers, consultants, students, and interested people. Promotes the development and effect use of solar and renewable energy and the related arts, sciences, and technologies with concern for the economic, environmental, and social fabric of Washington state through education.

8014 ■ Washington On-Site Sewage Association (WOSSA)
PO Box 9279
Tacoma, WA 98490-0279
Contact: John Thomas, Exec. Dir.
Ph: (253)297-2837
Fax: (253)770-0896
E-mail: wossa1@hotmail.com
URL: http://www.wossa.org

8015 ■ Washington State Department of Natural Resources
PO Box 47000
Olympia, WA 98504-7000
Contact: Peter Goldmark, Commnr.
Ph: (360)902-1000
Fax: (360)902-1775
E-mail: cpl@dnr.wa.gov
URL: http://www.dnr.wa.gov/

Descr: Mission is to provide professional, forward-looking stewardship of Washington state lands, natural resources, and environment; and to provide leadership in creating a sustainable future for the Trusts and all citizens.

8016 ■ Washington Wildlife Rehabilitation Association (WWRA)
13619 Mukilteo Speedway D5
Lynnwood, WA 98087
Contact: Jennifer Convy, Pres.
E-mail: jconvy@paws.org
URL: http://www.wwrawildlife.org

8017 ■ Wilderness Society Pacific Northwest Regional
720 3rd Ave., Ste. 1800
Seattle, WA 98104
Contact: Michelle Ackermann, Dir.
Ph: (206)624-6430
Descr: Works to protect America's wilderness and wildlife and to develop a nationwide network of wild lands through public education, scientific analysis, and advocacy. Ensures that future generations will enjoy the clean air and water, wildlife, beauty, and opportunities for recreation and renewal that pristine forests, rivers, deserts, and mountains provide.

West Virginia

8018 ■ West Virginia Division of Environmental Protection
601 57th St.
Charleston, WV 25304
Contact: Randy C. Huffman, Sec.
Ph: (304)926-0440
Fax: (304)926-0446
E-mail: kcosco@wvdep.org
URL: http://www.wvdep.org/

Wisconsin

8019 ■ Izaak Walton League of America, Labudde Memorial Chapter
5186 County I
Benton, WI 53803
Contact: Sandy Crabtree
Ph: (608)759-4083
E-mail: leadmine@mhtc.net
Descr: Works to educate the public to conserve, maintain, protect, and restore the soil, forest, water, and other natural resources of the U.S.; promotes the enjoyment and wholesome utilization of these resources.

8020 ■ Izaak Walton League of America, Southwestern Chapter
5186 County I
Benton, WI 53803
Contact: Sandy Crabtree
Ph: (608)759-4083
E-mail: leadmine@mhtc.net
Descr: Works to educate the public to conserve, maintain, protect, and restore the soil, forest, water, and other natural resources of the U.S.; promotes the enjoyment and wholesome utilization of these resources.

8021 ■ Izaak Walton League of America, Watertown Chapter
430 Janet Ln.
Watertown, WI 53094-6728
Contact: Herschel Wickert
Ph: (920)261-7224
Descr: Works to educate the public to conserve, maintain, protect, and restore the soil, forest, water, and other natural resources of the U.S.; promotes the enjoyment and wholesome utilization of these resources.

8022 ■ Midwest Renewable Energy Association (MREA)
7558 Deer Rd.
Custer, WI 54423
Contact: Tehri Parker, Exec. Dir.
Ph: (715)592-6595
Fax: (715)592-6596
E-mail: info@the-mrea.org
URL: http://www.the-mrea.org

Staff: 3. **Descr:** Serves as network for sharing ideas, resources, and information with individuals, businesses, and communities to promote a sustainable future through renewable energy and energy efficiency. Works to protect the environment by educating the public about appropriate use of natural resources to meet the energy needs. **Fnd:** 1990. **Mem:** 2100. **State Groups:** 38. **Pub:** *ReNews* (quarterly).

8023 ■ Water Quality Association of Wisconsin (WQAW)
1 S Pinckney St., No. 504
Madison, WI 53703
Contact: Cheryl Lytle
Ph: (608)661-0043
Fax: (608)244-9030
E-mail: info@wqaw.com
URL: http://www.wqaw.com
Descr: Represents individuals or firms engaged in the manufacturing and/or assembly and distribution and/or retail selling of water treatment equipment, supplies, and services. Promotes the acceptance and use of industry equipment, products, and services. Provides activities, programs, and services designed to improve economy and efficiency within the industry.

8024 ■ Wisconsin Department of Natural Resources
101 S. Webster St.
PO Box 7921
Madison, WI 53707-7921
Ph: (608)266-2621
Free: 888-936-7463
Fax: (608)261-4380
URL: http://www.dnr.state.wi.us/
Telecom. Svcs: TTY phone number is (608)267-6897.

8025 ■ Wisconsin Onsite Water Recycling Association (WOWRA)
16 N Carroll St., Ste. 900
Madison, WI 53703
Ph: (608)251-8192
Free: 800-377-6672
URL: http://www.wowra.com
Fnd: 1974.

Wyoming

8026 ■ Wyoming Department of Environmental Quality
122 W. 25th St.
Herschler Bldg.
Cheyenne, WY 82002
Contact: John Corra, Dir.
Ph: (307)777-7937
Fax: (307)777-7682
E-mail: kguill@wyo.gov
URL: http://deq.state.wy.us/
Descr: Contributes to Wyoming's quality of life through a combination of monitoring, permitting, inspection, enforcement, and restoration activities which protect, conserve, and enhance the environment while supporting responsible stewardship of the state's resources.

Publications

8027 ■ *The 6th Day of Creation - A Prose Poem About Vivisection*
Jews for Animal Rights
255 Humphrey St.
Marblehead, MA 01945
Ph: (781)631-7601
E-mail: micah@micahbooks.com
URL: http://www.micahbooks.com/JAR.html
Descr: Delineates a pattern of thought from Descartes to the modern Weltanschauung, which has

created the moral subterranean world of animal experimentation. **Price:** $10/copy.

8028 ■ *365 Ways to Live Green*
Adams Media
4700 E. Galbraith Rd.
Cincinnati, OH 45236
Ph: 800-258-0929
URL: http://www.adamsmedia.com/
Subtitle: Your Everyday Guide to Saving the Environment. **Author:** Diane Gow McDilda. **Pub. Date:** 2008. **Pgs:** 224. **Price:** $7.95.

8029 ■ *Abstracts of Annual Meeting*
American Society for Microbiology
1752 N St. NW
Washington, DC 20036
Ph: (202)737-3600
Fax: (202)942-9333
E-mail: oed@asmusa.org
URL: http://www.asm.org

8030 ■ *Abundant Montana*
Alternative Energy Resources Organization
432 N Last Chance Gulch
Helena, MT 59601-5014
Ph: (406)443-7272
Fax: (406)442-9120
E-mail: aero@aeromt.org
URL: http://www.aeromt.org
Descr: Contains a list of Montana growers for consumers to contact and purchase locally grown food. **Freq:** annual. **Price:** free.

8031 ■ *ACE Archives Directory*
Association for Communication Excellence in Agriculture, Natural Resources, and Life and Human Sciences
PO Box 110811
Gainesville, FL 32611
Ph: (352)392-9588
Fax: (352)392-8583
E-mail: ace@ifas.ufl.edu
URL: http://www.aceweb.org
Descr: Provides a comprehensive documentation of ACE's history.

8032 ■ *ACEEE Series on Energy Conservation and Energy Policy*
American Council for an Energy-Efficient Economy
529 14th St. NW, Ste. 600
Washington, DC 20045
Ph: (202)507-4000
Fax: (202)429-2248
E-mail: info@aceee.org
URL: http://www.aceee.org

8033 ■ *ACEEE Summer Study on Energy Efficiency in Buildings*
American Council for an Energy-Efficient Economy
529 14th St. NW, Ste. 600
Washington, DC 20045
Ph: (202)507-4000
Fax: (202)429-2248
E-mail: info@aceee.org
URL: http://www.aceee.org
Descr: Contains conference proceedings and research papers. **Freq:** biennial.

8034 ■ *ACEEE's Green Book*
American Council for an Energy-Efficient Economy
529 14th St. NW, Ste. 600
Washington, DC 20045
Ph: (202)507-4000
Fax: (202)429-2248
E-mail: info@aceee.org
URL: http://www.aceee.org
Price: $19.95/year online subscription, $8.95 30 days online subscription.

8035 ■ *Acid Rain: Road to a Middleground Solution*
Center for Clean Air Policy
750 First St. NE, Ste. 940
Washington, DC 20002
Ph: (202)408-9260

Fax: (202)408-8896
E-mail: communications@ccap.org
URL: http://www.ccap.org

8036 ■ Action Alert
Rainforest Action Network
221 Pine St., 5th Fl.
San Francisco, CA 94104
Ph: (415)398-4404
Fax: (415)398-2732
E-mail: answers@ran.org
URL: http://www.ran.org
Descr: Reports on issues requiring immediate public action. Includes addresses of influential individuals and organizations for members. **Freq:** bimonthly. **Price:** included in membership dues.

8037 ■ Action Alert
Beauty Without Cruelty U.S.A.
175 W. 12th St., No. 16-G
New York, NY 10011
Ph: (212)989-8073
Fax: (212)989-8073
Freq: 3/year.

8038 ■ Advances in Solar Energy
American Solar Energy Society
2400 Central Ave., Ste. A
Boulder, CO 80301
Ph: (303)443-3130
Fax: (303)443-3212
E-mail: ases@ases.org
URL: http://www.ases.org
Freq: annual.

8039 ■ AERO Sun-Times
Alternative Energy Resources Organization
432 N Last Chance Gulch
Helena, MT 59601-5014
Ph: (406)443-7272
Fax: (406)442-9120
E-mail: aero@aeromt.org
URL: http://www.aeromt.org
Freq: quarterly. **Price:** $15/year. **ISSN:** 1046-0993.

8040 ■ Air Quality and Electricity Restructuring
Center for Clean Air Policy
750 First St. NE, Ste. 940
Washington, DC 20002
Ph: (202)408-9260
Fax: (202)408-8896
E-mail: communications@ccap.org
URL: http://www.ccap.org

8041 ■ Alabama Directory of Environmental Service Providers and Environmental Data Resources
Nationwide Environmental Title Research L.L.C.
2055 E Rio Salado Pky., Ste. 201
Tempe, AZ 85281
Ph: (480)967-6752
E-mail: customerservice@netronline.com
URL: http://datastore.netronline.com
URL(s): http://datastore.netronline.com **Entries include:** Agency, organization, or professional's name, address, phone, fax, e-mail, hyperlink to website. **Price:** Free.

8042 ■ Alaska Directory of Environmental Service Providers and Environmental Data Resources
Nationwide Environmental Title Research L.L.C.
2055 E Rio Salado Pky., Ste. 201
Tempe, AZ 85281
Ph: (480)967-6752
E-mail: customerservice@netronline.com
URL: http://datastore.netronline.com
URL(s): http://datastore.netronline.com **Entries include:** Agency, organization, or professional's name, address, phone, fax, e-mail, hyperlink to website. **Price:** Free.

8043 ■ Alliance Newsletter
Animal Agriculture Alliance
PO Box 9522
Arlington, VA 22219

Ph: (703)562-5160
E-mail: info@animalagalliance.org
URL: http://www.animalagalliance.org
Descr: Contains information on current issues and events related to animal agriculture, animal welfare, food safety, and nutrition as well as animal rights. **Freq:** monthly. **Price:** free to contributors.

8044 ■ Alternatives to Methyl Bromide: Excerpts from the U.N. Methyl Bromide Technical Options Committee Assessment 1995
Pesticide Action Network North America Regional Center
49 Powell St., Ste. 500
San Francisco, CA 94102
Ph: (415)981-1771
Fax: (415)981-1991
E-mail: panna@panna.org
URL: http://www.panna.org
Price: $5.

8045 ■ Amazonia: Voices From the Rainforest
Rainforest Action Network
221 Pine St., 5th Fl.
San Francisco, CA 94104
Ph: (415)398-4404
Fax: (415)398-2732
E-mail: answers@ran.org
URL: http://www.ran.org
Descr: Contains an overview of Amazon rainforest issues. **Price:** $5 plus shipping and handling.

8046 ■ American Photo
North American Nature Photography Association
10200 W 44th Ave., Ste. 304
Wheat Ridge, CO 80033-2840
Ph: (303)422-8527
Fax: (303)422-8894
E-mail: info@nanpa.org
URL: http://www.nanpa.org
Descr: Features masters of photography. **Freq:** bimonthly. **Price:** $11 in U.S., $19 in Canada, $25 international.

8047 ■ The Analyst
Association of Water Technologies
9707 Key West Ave., Ste. 100
Rockville, MD 20850
Ph: (301)740-1421
Fax: (301)990-9771
E-mail: hzimmerman@awt.org
URL: http://www.awt.org
Freq: quarterly. **Price:** included in membership dues, $100 for nonmembers in U.S., $125 for nonmembers in Canada, Mexico, $200 for nonmembers in other countries.

8048 ■ The Angry Samaritan Chronicles
Conservative Majority for Citizen's Rights
302 Briarwood Cir. NW
Fort Walton Beach, FL 32548-3904
Ph: (850)862-6211
E-mail: jharkins@americangospel.org
URL: http://www.americangospel.org
Descr: Consists of three volumes.

8049 ■ Animal Agriculture: Myths and Facts
Animal Agriculture Alliance
PO Box 9522
Arlington, VA 22219
Ph: (703)562-5160
E-mail: info@animalagalliance.org
URL: http://www.animalagalliance.org

8050 ■ Animal Rights Coalition News
Animal Rights Coalition
2615 E Franklin Ave.
Minneapolis, MN 55406
Ph: (612)822-6161
E-mail: animalrightscoalition@msn.com
URL: http://www.animalrightscoalition.com

Freq: semiannual. **Price:** included in membership dues.

8051 ■ Antimicrobial Agents and Chemotherapy
American Society for Microbiology
1752 N St. NW
Washington, DC 20036
Ph: (202)737-3600
Fax: (202)942-9333
E-mail: oed@asmusa.org
URL: http://www.asm.org
Descr: Covers all aspects of antimicrobial, antiparasitic, antiviral, and anticancer agents and chemotherapy. **Freq:** monthly. **Price:** $49/year for members, $263/year for nonmembers. **ISSN:** 0066-4804.

8052 ■ Applied and Environmental Microbiology
American Society for Microbiology
1752 N St. NW
Washington, DC 20036
Ph: (202)737-3600
Fax: (202)942-9333
E-mail: oed@asmusa.org
URL: http://www.asm.org
Descr: Publishes research in the areas of industrial microbiology, biotechnology, food microbiology, and microbial ecology. **Freq:** monthly. **Price:** $50/year for members, $265/year for nonmembers. **ISSN:** 0099-2240.

8053 ■ Arizona Directory of Environmental Service Providers and Environmental Data Resources
Nationwide Environmental Title Research L.L.C.
2055 E Rio Salado Pky., Ste. 201
Tempe, AZ 85281
Ph: (480)967-6752
E-mail: customerservice@netronline.com
URL: http://datastore.netronline.com
URL(s): http://environmental.netronline.com **Entries include:** Agency, organization, or professional's name, address, phone, fax, e-mail, hyperlink to website. **Price:** Free.

8054 ■ Arkansas Directory of Environmental Service Providers and Environmental Data Resources
Nationwide Environmental Title Research L.L.C.
2055 E Rio Salado Pky., Ste. 201
Tempe, AZ 85281
Ph: (480)967-6752
E-mail: customerservice@netronline.com
URL: http://datastore.netronline.com
URL(s): http://environmental.netronline.com **Entries include:** Agency, organization, or professional's name, address, phone, fax, e-mail, hyperlink to website. **Price:** Free.

8055 ■ ASM Directory of Members
American Society for Microbiology
1752 N St. NW
Washington, DC 20036
Ph: (202)737-3600
Fax: (202)942-9333
E-mail: oed@asmusa.org
URL: http://www.asm.org
Price: available to members only.

8056 ■ ASM News
American Society for Microbiology
1752 N St. NW
Washington, DC 20036
Ph: (202)737-3600
Fax: (202)942-9333
E-mail: oed@asmusa.org
URL: http://www.asm.org
Descr: Provides information on a range of scientific and policy issues to the worldwide community of microbiologists. **Freq:** monthly. **Price:** included in

membership dues, $25/year for nonmembers. **ISSN:** 0044-7897.

8057 ■ *Audubon*
National Audubon Society Inc.
225 Varick St., 7th Fl.
New York, NY 10014
Ph: (212)979-3000
Free: 800-274-4201
Fax: (212)979-3188
E-mail: editor@audubon.org
URL: http://www.audubon.org
Key Personnel: David Siedeman, Editor-in-Chief.
URL(s): http://magazine.audubon.org **Descr:** Consumer magazine of the National Audubon Society covering environmental issues and wildlife. **Freq:** Bimonthly. **Price:** Included in membership.

8058 ■ *Autobiography of a Revolutionary: Essays on Animal and Human Rights*
Jews for Animal Rights
255 Humphrey St.
Marblehead, MA 01945
Ph: (781)631-7601
E-mail: micah@micahbooks.com
URL: http://www.micahbooks.com/JAR.html
Price: $12.

8059 ■ *Bear Facts*
North American Bear Center
1926 Hwy. 169
Ely, MN 55731
Ph: (218)365-7879
URL: http://www.bear.org
Freq: quarterly.

8060 ■ *Better Boater Bathrooms: A Sourcebook for River Managers*
River Management Society
PO Box 9048
Missoula, MT 59807-9048
Ph: (406)549-0514
Fax: (406)542-6208
E-mail: rms@river-management.org
URL: http://www.river-management.org

8061 ■ *Big Green Purse*
Avery, a member of Penguin Group
375 Hudson St.
New York, NY 10014
Ph: (212)366-2000
URL: http://www.us.penguingroup.com/
Subtitle: Use Your Spending Power to Create a Cleaner, Greener World. **Author:** Diane MacEachern. **Pub. Date:** 2008. **Pgs:** 432. **Price:** $17.95.

8062 ■ *Big Sky or Big Sprawl Montana at the Crossroads*
Alternative Energy Resources Organization
432 N Last Chance Gulch
Helena, MT 59601-5014
Ph: (406)443-7272
Fax: (406)442-9120
E-mail: aero@aeromt.org
URL: http://www.aeromt.org

8063 ■ *Biodiversity: Its Importance to Human Health*
Center for Health and the Global Environment
Harvard Medical School
401 Park Dr., 2nd Fl. E
Boston, MA 02115
Ph: (617)384-8530
Fax: (617)384-8585
E-mail: chge@hms.harvard.edu
URL: http://chge.med.harvard.edu

8064 ■ *Biological and Physical Signs of Climate Change: Focus on Mosquito-Borne Diseases*
Center for Health and the Global Environment
Harvard Medical School
401 Park Dr., 2nd Fl. E
Boston, MA 02115
Ph: (617)384-8530
Fax: (617)384-8585

E-mail: chge@hms.harvard.edu
URL: http://chge.med.harvard.edu

8065 ■ *Bottled Water and Packaged Ice*
NSF International
789 N Dixboro Rd.
PO Box 130140
Ann Arbor, MI 48113-0140
Ph: (734)769-8010
Fax: (734)769-0109
E-mail: info@nsf.org
URL: http://www.nsf.org
Freq: periodic.

8066 ■ *Bottled Water Reporter*
International Bottled Water Association
1700 Diagonal Rd., Ste. 650
Alexandria, VA 22314
Ph: (703)683-5213
Fax: (703)683-4074
E-mail: ibwainfo@bottledwater.org
URL: http://www.bottledwater.org
Descr: Includes statistics, feature articles, and lists new products and technologies. **Freq:** bimonthly. **Price:** $50 for nonmembers in U.S. and Canada, $100 for nonmembers outside U.S. and Canada, included in membership dues.

8067 ■ *Bubble, Bubble, Toil and Trouble: Reprocessing Nuclear Spent Fuel*
Health and Energy Institute
615 Kennebec Ave.
Takoma Park, MD 20912
Ph: (301)585-5831
Fax: (301)585-9474
E-mail: kitbob@erols.com

8068 ■ *Buildings: Inside and Out*
Sustainable Buildings Industry Council
1112 16th St. NW, Ste. 240
Washington, DC 20036
Ph: (202)628-7400
Fax: (202)393-5043
E-mail: sbic@sbicouncil.org
URL: http://www.sbicouncil.org
Freq: periodic.

8069 ■ *The Bulletin*
Center for Health and the Global Environment
Harvard Medical School
401 Park Dr., 2nd Fl. E
Boston, MA 02115
Ph: (617)384-8530
Fax: (617)384-8585
E-mail: chge@hms.harvard.edu
URL: http://chge.med.harvard.edu
Descr: Provides the latest information on timely topics related to human health and global environmental change.

8070 ■ *Calendar Handbook*
Green Bay Education Association
2256 Main St.
Green Bay, WI 54311
Ph: (920)468-4232
Fax: (920)468-6766
E-mail: gbea@gbea.org
URL: http://www.gbea.org
Freq: annual. **Price:** $3.

8071 ■ *California Directory of Environmental Service Providers and Environmental Data Resources*
Nationwide Environmental Title Research L.L.C.
2055 E Rio Salado Pky., Ste. 201
Tempe, AZ 85281
Ph: (480)967-6752
E-mail: customerservice@netronline.com
URL: http://datastore.netronline.com
URL(s): http://environmental.netronline.com **Entries include:** Agency, organization, or professional's name, address, phone, fax, e-mail, hyperlink to website. **Price:** Free.

8072 ■ *Campus Green Buying Guide*
Green Seal
1001 Connecticut Ave. NW, Ste. 827

Washington, DC 20036-5525
Ph: (202)872-6400
Fax: (202)872-4324
E-mail: greenseal@greenseal.org
URL: http://www.greenseal.org
Descr: Provides focus on implementing and maintaining a green procurement plan and gives an index of products.

8073 ■ *Canada EarthSaver*
EarthSave Canada
SPEC Bldg.
2150 Maple St.
Vancouver, BC, Canada V6J 3T3
Ph: (604)731-5885
Fax: (604)731-5805
URL: http://www.earthsave.ca
Descr: Contains locally-written articles on issues relevant to EarthSave's mission, as well as news on EarthSave events and programs. **Freq:** bimonthly.

8074 ■ *Canadian Environmental Network News*
Canadian Environmental Network
300-945 Wellington St. W
Ottawa, ON, Canada K1Y 2X5
Ph: (613)728-9810
Fax: (613)728-2963
E-mail: info@cen-rce.org
URL: http://www.cen-rce.org
Descr: Contains information on environmental issues in Canada. **Freq:** annual. **ISSN:** 1183-4528.

8075 ■ *Catalyst*
Union of Concerned Scientists
2 Brattle Sq.
Cambridge, MA 02238-9105
Ph: (617)547-5552
Fax: (617)864-9405
URL: http://www.ucsusa.org
Descr: Includes updates on UCS issues, new reports, and new projects/campaigns. **Freq:** semiannual. **Price:** included in membership dues.

8076 ■ *CBE Review*
Midwest Center for Environmental Science and Public Policy
1845 N Farewell Ave., Ste. 100
Milwaukee, WI 53202
Ph: (414)271-7280
Fax: (414)273-7293
E-mail: mcespp@mcespp.org
Freq: semiannual.

8077 ■ *Central Atlantic Environmental Directory*
Harbinger Communications
112 Glenview St.
Santa Cruz, CA 95062
E-mail: info@environmentaldirectory.net
URL: http://www.environmentaldirectory.net
Key Personnel: Bill Leland, Exec. Dir. **URL(s):** http://www.environmentaldirectory.net **Covers:** Over 1,065 nonprofit organizations, government agencies, and other groups in New Jersey, New York, and Pennsylvania concerned with environmental education and action. **Entries include:** Organization name, address, phone, website, name and title of contact, number of employees, geographical area served, financial data, branch office or subsidiary names or addresses, requirements for membership, admission, eligibility, descriptions of product/service. **Freq:** Biennial, even years. **Price:** $50, individuals, plus $2 shipping and handling.

8078 ■ *CGA in Action*
Common Ground Alliance
1421 Prince St., Ste. 410
Alexandria, VA 22314
Ph: (703)836-1709
Fax: (309)407-2244

E-mail: bobk@commongroundalliance.com
URL: http://www.commongroundalliance.com

8079 ■ Chemical Sensitivity: A Report to the New Jersey Department of Health
National Center for Environmental Health Strategies
1100 Rural Ave.
Voorhees, NJ 08043
Ph: (856)429-5358
E-mail: info@ncehs.org
URL: http://www.ncehs.org

8080 ■ Children and Dogs
Animal Rights Coalition
2615 E Franklin Ave.
Minneapolis, MN 55406
Ph: (612)822-6161
E-mail: animalrightscoalition@msn.com
URL: http://www.animalrightscoalition.com

8081 ■ Children's Environmental Health
Children's Environmental Health Network
110 Maryland Ave. NE, Ste. 505
Washington, DC 20002
Ph: (202)543-4033
Fax: (202)543-8797
E-mail: cehn@cehn.org
URL: http://www.cehn.org
Descr: Contains information about training for Pediatric and Practice Residency Faculty.

8082 ■ Choose Green Report
Green Seal
1001 Connecticut Ave. NW, Ste. 827
Washington, DC 20036-5525
Ph: (202)872-6400
Fax: (202)872-4324
E-mail: greenseal@greenseal.org
URL: http://www.greenseal.org
Descr: Contains product reports and their general impact, and recommendations on brand names.
Freq: monthly. **Price:** $169/year, $25/copy.

8083 ■ City Government Environmental Programs Directory
infoUSA Inc.
5711 S 86th Cir.
PO Box 27347
Omaha, NE 68127-0347
Ph: (402)593-4593
Fax: (402)596-7688
E-mail: internet@abii.com
URL: http://www.infousa.com
Entries include: Name, address, phone (including area code), size of advertisement, year first in "Yellow Pages," name of owner or manager, number of employees. Compiled from telephone company "Yellow Pages," nationwide. **Freq:** Annual. **Price:** Please inquire.

8084 ■ Class II Biohazard Cabinetry
NSF International
789 N Dixboro Rd.
PO Box 130140
Ann Arbor, MI 48113-0140
Ph: (734)769-8010
Fax: (734)769-0109
E-mail: info@nsf.org
URL: http://www.nsf.org
Freq: periodic.

8085 ■ Climate Change and U.S. Agriculture: The Impacts of Warming and Extreme Weather Events on Productivity, Plant Diseases, and Pests
Center for Health and the Global Environment
Harvard Medical School
401 Park Dr., 2nd Fl. E
Boston, MA 02115
Ph: (617)384-8530
Fax: (617)384-8585
E-mail: chge@hms.harvard.edu
URL: http://chge.med.harvard.edu

8086 ■ Clinical Microbiology Reviews
American Society for Microbiology
1752 N St. NW

Washington, DC 20036
Ph: (202)737-3600
Fax: (202)942-9333
E-mail: oed@asmusa.org
URL: http://www.asm.org
Descr: Presents reviews of developments in clinical microbiology and immunology. Covers bacteriology, virology, mycology, and parasitology. **Freq:** quarterly.
Price: $20/year for members, $121/year for nonmembers. **ISSN:** 0893-8512.

8087 ■ Co-op America's National Green Pages
Co-op America
1612 K St. NW, Ste. 600
Washington, DC 20006
Ph: (202)872-5307
Free: 800-584-7336
Fax: (202)331-8166
E-mail: info@coopamerica.org
URL: http://www.coopamerica.org
Key Personnel: Russ Gaskin, Ch. Business Off.; Dennis F. Greenia, Division Dir.; Denise Hamler, Publisher. **URL(s):** http://www.coopamerica.org/pubs/greenpages **Covers:** 2,000 businesses and nonprofit organizations in the U.S. that produce environmentally benign products such as non-toxic household products, plant based paints, cruelty free body care products, organic foods, and energy saving devices. Also companies that offer socially responsible financial services. **Entries include:** Company or organization name, address, phone, product/service, e-mail and web addresses. **Freq:** Annual, Fall.

8088 ■ Committee Reports
Energy Bar Association
1990 M St. NW, Ste. 350
Washington, DC 20036
Ph: (202)223-5625
Fax: (202)833-5596
E-mail: admin@eba-net.org
URL: http://www.eba-net.org
Freq: annual. **Price:** $30 in U.S., $36 in Canada, $42 outside U.S. and Canada. **ISSN:** 0270-9163.

8089 ■ Common Ground, Common Voices
Green Bay Education Association
2256 Main St.
Green Bay, WI 54311
Ph: (920)468-4232
Fax: (920)468-6766
E-mail: gbea@gbea.org
URL: http://www.gbea.org

8090 ■ The Compassionate Shopper
Beauty Without Cruelty U.S.A.
175 W. 12th St., No. 16-G
New York, NY 10011
Ph: (212)989-8073
Fax: (212)989-8073
Descr: Provides lists of manufacturers that do not test products on animals and celebrities who disapprove of the use of fur in apparel. **Freq:** 3/year. **Price:** included in membership dues.

8091 ■ Connector
Recycling Council of Alberta
PO Box 23
Bluffton, AB, Canada T0C 0M0
Ph: (403)843-6563
Fax: (403)843-4156
E-mail: info@recycle.ab.ca
URL: http://www.recycle.ab.ca
Freq: quarterly. **Price:** free. **ISSN:** 1201-3218.

8092 ■ Conservation Directory
National Wildlife Federation
11100 Wildlife Center Dr.
Reston, VA 20190-5362
Ph: (703)638-6000
Free: 800-822-9919
Fax: (703)438-6061
E-mail: admin@nwf.org
URL: http://www.nwf.org/
Key Personnel: Bill Street, Contact, street@nwf.org. **URL(s):** http://www.nwf.org/

conservationdirectory/ **Covers:** Over 4,000 organizations, agencies, colleges and universities with conservation programs and more than 18,000 officials concerned with environmental conservation, education, and natural resource use and management. **Entries include:** Agency name, address, branch or subsidiary office name and address, names and titles of key personnel, descriptions of program areas, size of membership (where appropriate), telephone, fax, e-mail and URL addresses.
Freq: Annual, latest edition March 2007.

8093 ■ Conservative Majority Newsletter
Conservative Majority for Citizen's Rights
302 Briarwood Cir. NW
Fort Walton Beach, FL 32548-3904
Ph: (850)862-6211
E-mail: jharkins@americangospel.org
URL: http://www.americangospel.org
Freq: quarterly.

8094 ■ Cooling the Greenhouse Effect: Options and Costs for Reducing CO2 Emissions from the American Electric Power Company
Center for Clean Air Policy
750 First St. NE, Ste. 940
Washington, DC 20002
Ph: (202)408-9260
Fax: (202)408-8896
E-mail: communications@ccap.org
URL: http://www.ccap.org

8095 ■ Cooper's Comprehensive Environmental Desk Reference
John Wiley & Sons Inc.
605 Third Ave.
New York, NY 10158-0012
Ph: (212)850-6000
Free: 800-225-5945
Fax: (212)850-6088
E-mail: info@wiley.com
URL: http://www.wiley.com/legacy/about/share/1998/corpinfo.html
Key Personnel: Peter B. Wiley, Chm.; William J. Pesce, Pres. & CEO; Andre R. Cooper, Editor. **URL(s):** http://www.wiley.com **Descr:** Covers topics in environmental issues, including Superfund sites, environmental engineering, threatened and endangered species, and OSHA standards. **Publication includes:** Agency contact information. **Freq:** latest edition February 2007. **Price:** $250, individuals.

8096 ■ Coordinator's Report
Animal Rights International
PO Box 1292
Middlebury, CT 06762
Ph: (203)598-0554
E-mail: info@ari-online.org
URL: http://www.ari-online.org
Freq: periodic.

8097 ■ Counterpoint
Green Bay Education Association
2256 Main St.
Green Bay, WI 54311
Ph: (920)468-4232
Fax: (920)468-6766
E-mail: gbea@gbea.org
URL: http://www.gbea.org

8098 ■ Creating a Healthy Household
Healthy House Institute
430 N Sewell Rd.
Bloomington, IN 47408
Ph: (812)332-5073
Fax: (812)332-5073
E-mail: healthy@bloomington.in.us
URL: http://www.hhinst.com

8099 ■ CRWI Update
Coalition for Responsible Waste Incineration
1615 L St. NW, Ste. 1350
Washington, DC 20036
Ph: (202)452-1241
Fax: (202)887-8044
E-mail: mel@crwi.org
URL: http://www.crwi.org

Freq: monthly.

8100 ■ *Currents*
North American Nature Photography Association
10200 W 44th Ave., Ste. 304
Wheat Ridge, CO 80033-2840
Ph: (303)422-8527
Fax: (303)422-8894
E-mail: info@nanpa.org
URL: http://www.nanpa.org
Descr: Contains articles about the association and its members. **Freq:** bimonthly. **Price:** included in membership dues.

8101 ■ *Cut Waste, Not Trees*
Rainforest Action Network
221 Pine St., 5th Fl.
San Francisco, CA 94104
Ph: (415)398-4404
Fax: (415)398-2732
E-mail: answers@ran.org
URL: http://www.ran.org
Descr: Contains information about reducing wood and paper consumption; includes resource information. **Price:** $5 plus shipping and handling.

8102 ■ *Cycle and Recycle*
Bicycle Network
PO Box 8194
Philadelphia, PA 19101
Ph: (215)222-1253
Fax: (215)222-1253
E-mail: cyclerecycle@hotmail.com
Descr: Features a reusable wall calendar. **Freq:** annual. **Price:** $11 1-3 copies, $12 1-3 copies in Canada, $10 4-9 copies, $11 4-9 copies in Canada.

8103 ■ *The Dark at the End of the Tunnel: Federal Clean-up Standards for Nuclear Power Plants*
Public Citizen's Critical Mass Energy and Environment Program
215 Pennsylvania Ave. SE
Washington, DC 20003
Ph: (202)546-4996
E-mail: member@citizen.org
URL: http://www.citizen.org/CMEP
Descr: Examines the Nuclear Regulatory Commission's Enhanced Rulemaking on Residual Radioactivity (ERORR). **Price:** $30.

8104 ■ *The Dark Face of Science*
Jews for Animal Rights
255 Humphrey St.
Marblehead, MA 01945
Ph: (781)631-7601
E-mail: micah@micahbooks.com
URL: http://www.micahbooks.com/JAR.html
Price: $12.

8105 ■ *Defense Waste & Fraud Camouflaged as Reinventing Government, 1999 Report*
Project on Government Oversight
666 11th St. NW, Ste. 900
Washington, DC 20001-4542
Ph: (202)347-1122
Fax: (202)347-1116
E-mail: info@pogo.org
URL: http://www.pogo.org

8106 ■ *The Delicate Balance*
National Center for Environmental Health Strategies
1100 Rural Ave.
Voorhees, NJ 08043
Ph: (856)429-5358
E-mail: info@ncehs.org
URL: http://www.ncehs.org
Descr: Covers issues related to indoor contaminants, outdoor toxins, legislative and policy updates, research summaries, information on consumer products. **Freq:** quarterly. **Price:** included in membership dues, $15/year for nonmembers. **ISSN:** 1045-2036.

8107 ■ *Demise of the Dirty Dozen Chart*
Pesticide Action Network North America Regional Center

49 Powell St., Ste. 500
San Francisco, CA 94102
Ph: (415)981-1771
Fax: (415)981-1991
E-mail: panna@panna.org
URL: http://www.panna.org
Descr: Gives registration status of 18 hazardous pesticides in over 75 countries. **Price:** $3.

8108 ■ *Directory of Anti-Nuclear Activists*
Public Citizen's Critical Mass Energy and Environment Program
215 Pennsylvania Ave. SE
Washington, DC 20003
Ph: (202)546-4996
E-mail: member@citizen.org
URL: http://www.citizen.org/CMEP
Freq: semiannual.

8109 ■ *Directory of Environmental Organizations*
Educational Communications Inc.
PO Box 351419
Los Angeles, CA 90035-9119
Ph: (310)559-9160
Fax: (310)559-9160
E-mail: ecnp@aol.com
URL: http://www.ecoprojects.org
Key Personnel: Nancy Sue Pearlman, Editor, ecnp@aol.com. **URL(s):** http://www.ecoprojects.org **Covers:** Over 7,000 environmental and conservation organizations worldwide, with emphasis on southern California; governmental agencies, activist groups, print and broadcast media, and educational institutions interested in environmental issues. **Entries include:** Organization name, address, phone, fax, e-mail, website and area of interest. **Freq:** Annual, 29th edition. **Price:** $30, individuals, plus $3.50 shipping (printed format); $300, individuals, diskette; $200, institutions, mailing labels.

8110 ■ *The Directory of Environmental Websites*
U.S. Environmental Directories Inc.
PO Box 65156
Saint Paul, MN 55165
Ph: (612)331-6050
E-mail: earthdirectory@att.net
URL: http://www.earthdirectory.net
Key Personnel: John C. Brainard, Editor. **URL(s):** http://www.earthdirectory.net **Covers:** Over 3000 Websites for regional, national, and international environmental organizations. Approximately 150 primary Websites include description. Also covers government agencies related to environmental affairs for over 100 countries and the United Nations. **Freq:** latest edition 2008. **Price:** $79, book, includes postage; $89, CD-ROM, includes postage; $109, book and CD-ROM, includes postage.

8111 ■ *Directory of HEAL Members in the Healthcare Professions*
Human Ecology Action League
PO Box 509
Stockbridge, GA 30281
Ph: (770)389-4519
Fax: (770)389-4520
E-mail: healnatnl@aol.com
URL: http://www.healnatl.org
Price: $15 for members, $30 for nonmembers.

8112 ■ *Dirty Dozen Fact Sheets*
Pesticide Action Network North America Regional Center
49 Powell St., Ste. 500
San Francisco, CA 94102
Ph: (415)981-1771
Fax: (415)981-1991
E-mail: panna@panna.org
URL: http://www.panna.org
Descr: Contains updated summaries of the health

and environmental effects of the Dirty Dozen pesticides. **Price:** $5.

8113 ■ *Dissection: Biology or Cruelty?*
Animal Rights Coalition
2615 E Franklin Ave.
Minneapolis, MN 55406
Ph: (612)822-6161
E-mail: animalrightscoalition@msn.com
URL: http://www.animalrightscoalition.com

8114 ■ *E-News*
Greenpeace Canada
33 Cecil St.
Toronto, ON, Canada M5T 1N1
Ph: (416)597-8408
Fax: (416)597-8422
E-mail: greenpeace.toronto@dialb.greenpeace.org
URL: http://p2-raw.greenpeace.org/canada/en/about-greenpeace
Descr: Contains information on individual's contribution committed to environmental protection. **Freq:** monthly.

8115 ■ *Earthwise*
Union of Concerned Scientists
2 Brattle Sq.
Cambridge, MA 02238-9105
Ph: (617)547-5552
Fax: (617)864-9405
URL: http://www.ucsusa.org
Descr: Provides updates on current UCS research and advocacy. **Freq:** quarterly.

8116 ■ *EASI Does It*
Environmental Alliance for Senior Involvement
5615 26th St. N
Arlington, VA 22207-1407
Ph: (703)241-4927
Fax: (703)538-5504
E-mail: easi@easi.org
URL: http://www.easi.org
Freq: bimonthly.

8117 ■ *EBA Update*
Energy Bar Association
1990 M St. NW, Ste. 350
Washington, DC 20036
Ph: (202)223-5625
Fax: (202)833-5596
E-mail: admin@eba-net.org
URL: http://www.eba-net.org
Freq: quarterly.

8118 ■ *EcoDwell Online*
International Institute for Baubiologie and Ecology
PO Box 387
Clearwater, FL 33757
Ph: (727)461-4371
Fax: (727)441-4373
E-mail: baubiologie@earthlink.net
URL: http://www.buildingbiology.net
Price: included in membership dues.

8119 ■ *The Ecofeminist Journal*
Feminists for Animal Rights
PO Box 10017
Berkeley, CA 94709
E-mail: contact@farinc.org
URL: http://www.farinc.org
Descr: Contains information on feminist, animal advocacy, and environmental issues and the connections between them.

8120 ■ *Energy Audit II: A State-by-State Profile of Energy Consumption and Conservation*
Public Citizen's Critical Mass Energy and Environment Program
215 Pennsylvania Ave. SE
Washington, DC 20003
Ph: (202)546-4996
E-mail: member@citizen.org
URL: http://www.citizen.org/CMEP
Descr: Details energy use in all fifty states, ranking each according to its dependence on nonrenewable

resources, use of renewable energy, and consumption. **Price:** $40.

8121 ■ *Energy White Paper*
National Dome Council
1201 15th St. NW
Washington, DC 20005
Ph: (202)266-8200
Fax: (202)266-8400
E-mail: efulton@nahb.com
URL: http://www.nahb.org
Freq: periodic.

8122 ■ *ENfacts*
Safe Energy Communication Council
1717 Massachusetts Ave. NW, Ste. 106
Washington, DC 20036
Fax: (202)234-9194
Descr: Newspaper graphics service. **Freq:** periodic.

8123 ■ *Enviro Business Guide*
Recycling Council of Alberta
PO Box 23
Bluffton, AB, Canada T0C 0M0
Ph: (403)843-6563
Fax: (403)843-4156
E-mail: info@recycle.ab.ca
URL: http://www.recycle.ab.ca

8124 ■ *Environ*
Wary Canary Press
2013 Orchard Pl.
Fort Collins, CO 80522-3212
Ph: (970)224-0083
Descr: Publication focusing on the production of a healthier environment by educating people about ecological lifestyles **Freq:** 2-3/year. **Price:** $18, individuals; $30, industry.

8125 ■ *Environment and Health: Species Loss and Ecosystem Disruption - the Implications for Human Health*
Center for Health and the Global Environment
Harvard Medical School
401 Park Dr., 2nd Fl. E
Boston, MA 02115
Ph: (617)384-8530
Fax: (617)384-8585
E-mail: chge@hms.harvard.edu
URL: http://chge.med.harvard.edu

8126 ■ *Environment (News)*
Global Information Network
146 W 29th St., Ste. No. 7E
New York, NY 10001
Ph: (212)244-3123
Fax: (212)244-3522
E-mail: ipsgin@igc.org
URL: http://www.globalinfo.org/
URL(s): http://www.globalinfo.org/eng/topictoday. asp?TopicId=4 **Descr:** Publication covering environmental issues. **Freq:** Daily. **Price:** Free.

8127 ■ *Environmental Choices and a Technical Journal*
Environmental Information Association
6935 Wisconsin Ave., Ste. 306
Chevy Chase, MD 20815-6112
Ph: (301)961-4999
Fax: (301)961-3094
E-mail: info@eia-usa.org
URL: http://www.eia-usa.org
Freq: quarterly.

8128 ■ *Environmental Forum*
Environmental Law Institute
2000 L St. NW, Ste. 620
Washington, DC 20036
Ph: (202)939-3800
E-mail: law@eli.org
URL: http://www.eli.org

Descr: Contains information regarding environmental policy. **Freq:** bimonthly. **Price:** $95/year.

8129 ■ *The Environmental Guide to Cars and Trucks*
American Council for an Energy-Efficient Economy
529 14th St. NW, Ste. 600
Washington, DC 20045
Ph: (202)507-4000
Fax: (202)429-2248
E-mail: info@aceee.org
URL: http://www.aceee.org

8130 ■ *Environmental Guide to the Internet*
Government Institutes
15200 NBN Way, Bldg. B
Blue Ridge Summit, PA 17214-0191
Ph: (717)794-3800
Free: 800-462-6420
Fax: (717)794-3803
E-mail: custserv@rowman.com
URL: http://www.govinstpress.com
Key Personnel: Carol Briggs-Erickson, Editor; Toni Murphy, Editor. **URL(s):** http://www.govinstpress.com **Covers:** 1,200 resources covering the environment on the Internet, including organizations, products, and resources, including discussion groups, electronic journals, newsgroups, and discussion groups. **Entries include:** Name, online address, description, e-mail address. **Price:** $75, individuals, softcover; $18.75, individuals, discounted price.

8131 ■ *The Environmental Guidebook*
Environmental Frontlines
PO Box 43
Menlo Park, CA 94026
Ph: (650)323-8452
Fax: (650)323-8452
E-mail: info@envirofront.org
Key Personnel: Jeff Staudinger, Dir. of Oper., Publisher. **URL(s):** http://www.envirofront.org/ **Covers:** Environmental and related organizations such as federal government agencies, committees, and regulatory bodies; multinational groups; nongovernmental organizations; political, business, and trade organizations; and groups with opposing viewpoints. **Entries include:** Name, address, phone, fax, key reports and publications, and budget information. **Price:** $19.95, individuals.

8132 ■ *Environmental Key Contacts and Information Sources*
Government Institutes
15200 NBN Way, Bldg. B
Blue Ridge Summit, PA 17214-0191
Ph: (717)794-3800
Free: 800-462-6420
Fax: (717)794-3803
E-mail: custserv@rowman.com
URL: http://www.govinstpress.com
Key Personnel: Charlene Ikonomou, Editor; Diane Pacchione, Editor. **URL(s):** http://www.govinstpress. com **Covers:** Over 2,700 federal, state, and local environmental agencies and organizations involved in environmental protection, hazardous waste materials, clean water and air, environmental assessment and management, pesticides, pollution control, recycling, natural resources, and conservation. **Entries include:** Names of key personnel; names of department, division, and agency heads; address, telephone, fax, e-mail, URL. **Price:** $18.75.

8133 ■ *Environmental Law Reporter*
Environmental Law Institute
2000 L St. NW, Ste. 620
Washington, DC 20036
Ph: (202)939-3800
E-mail: law@eli.org
URL: http://www.eli.org
Price: $1255/year, $520 each.

8134 ■ *Environmental Management Systems Standards and Guidance Documents*
NSF International
789 N Dixboro Rd.
PO Box 130140

Ann Arbor, MI 48113-0140
Ph: (734)769-8010
Fax: (734)769-0109
E-mail: info@nsf.org
URL: http://www.nsf.org

8135 ■ *Environmental Resource Book*
Ontario Environment Network
PO Box 1412, Station Main
North Bay, ON, Canada P1B 8K6
Ph: (705)840-2888
Fax: (705)840-5862
E-mail: oen@oen.ca
URL: http://www.oen.ca/
Key Personnel: Phillip Penna, Office Coord. **URL(s):** http://www.oen.ca/public.html **Covers:** About 700 organizations in Ontario, Canada, concerned with the environment. **Entries include:** Organization name, address, description. List of print and audiovisual resources. **Freq:** Biennial, Latest edition 2006-2007. **Price:** $12.50, individuals, for individuals and nonprofit organizations; $22.50, institutions, for government; $27.50, institutions, for business; $10, for bulk orders (10 or more).

8136 ■ *Environmental Success Index*
Renew the Earth
1900 Oracle Way, Ste. 717
Reston, VA 20190
Ph: (703)689-4670
E-mail: information@renew-the-earth.org
URL: http://www.renew-the-earth.org
Descr: Lists of environmental programs. Includes contact names, addresses, and phone numbers. **Freq:** annual.

8137 ■ *Everyone's Backyard*
Center For Health, Environment and Justice
PO Box 6806
Falls Church, VA 22040-6806
Ph: (703)237-2249
Fax: (703)237-8389
E-mail: chej@chej.org
URL: http://www.chej.org
Descr: Includes science and legal articles and coverage of local grassroots groups. **Freq:** quarterly. **Price:** $35/year, $5/copy. **ISSN:** 0749-3940.

8138 ■ *Eye on Bureaucracy*
The Conservative Caucus Research, Analysis and Education Foundation
450 Maple Ave. E
Vienna, VA 22180
Ph: (703)281-6782
E-mail: corndorf@cais.com
URL: http://www.conservativeusa.org/TCCFMission. htm
Freq: monthly. **Price:** $50.

8139 ■ *Factory Farming: Mechanized Madness*
Animal Rights Coalition
2615 E Franklin Ave.
Minneapolis, MN 55406
Ph: (612)822-6161
E-mail: animalrightscoalition@msn.com
URL: http://www.animalrightscoalition.com

8140 ■ *Feminists for Animal Rights Newsletter*
Feminists for Animal Rights
PO Box 10017
Berkeley, CA 94709
E-mail: contact@farinc.org
URL: http://www.farinc.org
Freq: semiannual. **Price:** free for members, $3.50 for nonmembers.

8141 ■ *Food Irradiation: Who Wants It? (1987)*
Health and Energy Institute
615 Kennebec Ave.
Takoma Park, MD 20912

Ph: (301)585-5831
Fax: (301)585-9474
E-mail: kitbob@erols.com

8142 ■ Footprints
Florida Keys Wild Bird Rehabilitation Center
93600 Overseas Hwy.
Tavernier, FL 33070
Ph: (305)852-4486
Fax: (305)852-3186
E-mail: info@fkwbc.org
URL: http://www.fkwbc.org
Freq: quarterly.

8143 ■ For R Information
Association of Municipal Recycling Coordinators
127 Wyndham St. N, Ste. 100
Guelph, ON, Canada N1H 4E9
Ph: (519)823-1990
Fax: (519)823-0084
E-mail: amrc@amrc.ca
URL: http://www.amrc.ca
Freq: quarterly.

8144 ■ Forest Magazine
Forest Service Employees for Environmental Ethics
PO Box 11615
Eugene, OR 97440-3815
Ph: (541)484-2692
Fax: (541)484-3004
E-mail: fseee@fseee.org
URL: http://www.fseee.org
Descr: Includes articles on the use and abuse of public lands. **Freq:** quarterly. **Price:** $3.50.

8145 ■ GEMI News
Global Environmental Management Initiative
1155 15th St. NW, Ste. 500
Washington, DC 20005
Ph: (202)296-7449
Fax: (202)296-7442
E-mail: info@gemi.org
URL: http://www.gemi.org
Freq: monthly. **Price:** included in membership dues.

8146 ■ Global Pesticide Campaigner
Pesticide Action Network North America Regional Center
49 Powell St., Ste. 500
San Francisco, CA 94102
Ph: (415)981-1771
Fax: (415)981-1991
E-mail: panna@panna.org
URL: http://www.panna.org
Descr: Includes features on the pesticide industry, sustainable agriculture, and other related topics globally. **Freq:** quarterly. **Price:** $35/year. **ISSN:** 1055-548X.

8147 ■ Global Pesticide Campaigner
Pesticide Action Network North America
49 Powell St., Ste. 500
San Francisco, CA 94102
Ph: (415)981-1771
Fax: (415)981-1991
E-mail: panna@panna.org
URL: http://www.panna.org
Freq: 3/year.

8148 ■ Go Green, Go Rich
Broadway Books
1745 Broadway
New York, NY 10019
Ph: (212)940-7381
URL: http://www.ramdomhouse.com/broadway/
Subtitle: 50 Simple Ways to Save the Earth and Get Rich Trying. **Author:** David Bach, Hillary Rosner. **Pub. Date:** 2008. **Pgs:** 192. **Price:** $14.95.

8149 ■ Gone to Seed: Transgenic Contaminants in the Traditional Seed Supply
Union of Concerned Scientists
2 Brattle Sq.
Cambridge, MA 02238-9105
Ph: (617)547-5552

Fax: (617)864-9405
URL: http://www.ucsusa.org
Price: $15 each.

8150 ■ Good Times Made Simple: The Lost Art of Fun
Center for a New American Dream
6930 Carroll Ave., Ste. 900
Takoma Park, MD 20912-4466
Ph: (301)891-3683
Fax: (301)891-3684
E-mail: newdream@newdream.org
URL: http://www.ibuydifferent.org
Price: $4.

8151 ■ Good Times Made Simple & Tips for Parenting in a Commercial Culture
Center for a New American Dream
6930 Carroll Ave., Ste. 900
Takoma Park, MD 20912-4466
Ph: (301)891-3683
Fax: (301)891-3684
E-mail: newdream@newdream.org
URL: http://www.ibuydifferent.org
Price: $6.

8152 ■ Great Lakes Environmental Directory
Harbinger Communications
112 Glenview St.
Santa Cruz, CA 95062
E-mail: info@environmentaldirectory.net
URL: http://www.environmentaldirectory.net
Key Personnel: Bill Leland, Exec. Dir. **URL(s):** http://www.environmentaldirectory.net **Entries include:** Company name, address, phone, name and title of contact, number of employees, geographical area served, financial data, branch office or subsidiary name, requirements for membership, descriptions of product/service.

8153 ■ Green Chic: Saving the Earth in Style
Sourcebooks, Inc.
1935 Brookdale Rd., Ste. 139
Naperville, IL 60563
Ph: (630)961-3900
Fax: (630)961-2168
URL: http://www.sourcebooks.com/
Author: Christie Matheson. **Descr:** Offers ways in which women can go green but not give up great style. Includes how to have a great wardrobe, how to travel in style, and how to create a lavish but environmentally friendly home. **Pub. Date:** 2008. **Pgs:** 240. **Price:** $12.95.

8154 ■ Green Goes With Everything
Atria, a part of Simon & Schuster
URL: http://www.simonandschuster.net/content/destination.cfm?tab=1&pid=427719
Subtitle: Simple Steps to a Healthier Life and a Cleaner Planet. **Author:** Sloan Barnett. **Pub. Date:** 2008. **Pgs:** 320. **Price:** $19.95.

8155 ■ Green Living for Dummies
Wiley
10475 Crosspoint Blvd.
Indianapolis, IN 46256
Ph: 877-762-2974
Fax: 800-597-3299
URL: http://www.wiley.com/
Author: Yvonne Jeffery, Liz Barclay, Michael Grosvenor. **Descr:** Includes tips on how to go green, how to make environmentally friendly home improvements, how to save money, how to reduce waste, and much more. **Pgs:** 384. **Price:** $19.99.

8156 ■ Green Up Your Cleanup
Creative Homeowner
24 Park Way
PO Box 38
Upper Saddle River, NJ 07458
Ph: 800-631-7795
E-mail: info@creativehomeowner.com/
URL: http://www.creativehomeowner.com/
Author: Jill Schoff. **Descr:** Offers information on how to green-clean your kitchen, bathroom, and other

areas of the house. **Pub. Date:** 2008. **Pgs:** 240. **Price:** $16.95.

8157 ■ Green Worker
Alliance for Sustainable Jobs and the Environment
PO Box 1361
Eureka, CA 95502
Ph: (707)498-4481
E-mail: bluegreen@asje.org
URL: http://www.asje.org

8158 ■ Greener Pastures: How Grass-fed Beef and Milk Contribute to Healthy Eating
Union of Concerned Scientists
2 Brattle Sq.
Cambridge, MA 02238-9105
Ph: (617)547-5552
Fax: (617)864-9405
URL: http://www.ucsusa.org
Price: $15 each.

8159 ■ Greening Garbage Trucks: New Technologies for Cleaner Air
INFORM
5 Hanover Sq., Fl. 19
New York, NY 10004
Ph: (212)361-2400
Fax: (212)361-2412
E-mail: ramsey@informinc.org
URL: http://www.informinc.org

8160 ■ Greenopia Green Living Los Angeles
Green Media Group
745 The Alameda
PO Box 11314
Berkeley, CA 94707-1930
Ph: (510)528-8124
Fax: (510)534-3470
URL: http://www.seashellsplus.net
URL(s): http://www.greenopia.com/USA/buy_the_guide.aspx **Covers:** Organic restaurants, grocery stores, dry cleaners, organic pest control services, building suppliers, landscapers, interior designers engaged in the green market in Los Angeles. **Freq:** Latest edition 2nd. **Price:** $17.95, individuals.

8161 ■ Greenopia New York City
Green Media Group
745 The Alameda
PO Box 11314
Berkeley, CA 94707-1930
Ph: (510)528-8124
Fax: (510)534-3470
URL: http://www.seashellsplus.net
URL(s): http://www.greenopia.com/USA/buy_the_guide.aspx **Covers:** Organic restaurants, grocery stores, dry cleaners, organic pest control services, building suppliers, landscapers, interior designers engaged in the green market in New York City. **Price:** $17.95, individuals.

8162 ■ Greenopia San Francisco Bay Area
Green Media Group
745 The Alameda
PO Box 11314
Berkeley, CA 94707-1930
Ph: (510)528-8124
Fax: (510)534-3470
URL: http://www.seashellsplus.net
URL(s): http://www.greenopia.com/USA/buy_the_guide.aspx **Covers:** Organic restaurants, grocery stores, dry cleaners, organic pest control services, building suppliers, landscapers, interior designers engaged in the green market in San Francisco Bay Area. **Freq:** Latest edition 1st. **Price:** $16.95, individuals.

8163 ■ Harbinger File
Harbinger Communications
112 Glenview St.
Santa Cruz, CA 95062
E-mail: info@environmentaldirectory.net
URL: http://www.environmentaldirectory.net
Key Personnel: Bill Leland, Exec. Dir. **URL(s):**

http://www.environmentaldirectory.net **Price:** $50, individuals, plus 2 shipping and handling charges.

8164 ■ Hastings Center Report
Hastings Center
21 Malcolm Gordon Rd.
Garrison, NY 10524-4125
Ph: (845)424-4040
Fax: (845)424-4545
E-mail: mail@thehastingscenter.org
URL: http://www.thehastingscenter.org
Descr: Contains articles, case studies, regular columns and letters explores a wide range of issues and perspectives in bioethics and the environment. **Freq:** bimonthly. **Price:** included in membership dues, $76 for nonmembers in U.S., $125 for institutions and libraries in U.S., $94 for nonmembers outside U.S. **ISSN:** 0093-0334.

8165 ■ HEAL's Service List
Human Ecology Action League
PO Box 509
Stockbridge, GA 30281
Ph: (770)389-4519
Fax: (770)389-4520
E-mail: healnatnl@aol.com
URL: http://www.healnatl.org

8166 ■ The Healthy House
Healthy House Institute
430 N Sewell Rd.
Bloomington, IN 47408
Ph: (812)332-5073
Fax: (812)332-5073
E-mail: healthy@bloomington.in.us
URL: http://www.hhinst.com

8167 ■ The Healthy House Answer Book
Healthy House Institute
430 N Sewell Rd.
Bloomington, IN 47408
Ph: (812)332-5073
Fax: (812)332-5073
E-mail: healthy@bloomington.in.us
URL: http://www.hhinst.com

8168 ■ Healthy House Building for the New Millennium
Healthy House Institute
430 N Sewell Rd.
Bloomington, IN 47408
Ph: (812)332-5073
Fax: (812)332-5073
E-mail: healthy@bloomington.in.us
URL: http://www.hhinst.com

8169 ■ The Healthy House Video Series
Healthy House Institute
430 N Sewell Rd.
Bloomington, IN 47408
Ph: (812)332-5073
Fax: (812)332-5073
E-mail: healthy@bloomington.in.us
URL: http://www.hhinst.com

8170 ■ The Healthy Household
Healthy House Institute
430 N Sewell Rd.
Bloomington, IN 47408
Ph: (812)332-5073
Fax: (812)332-5073
E-mail: healthy@bloomington.in.us
URL: http://www.hhinst.com

8171 ■ Heat, High Water, and Rock Instability at Hanford
Health and Energy Institute
615 Kennebec Ave.
Takoma Park, MD 20912
Ph: (301)585-5831
Fax: (301)585-9474
E-mail: kitbob@erols.com

Descr: Covers technological and geologic problems with siting high-level nuclear waste at Hanford.

8172 ■ Home Hazardous Product Survey
Household Hazardous Waste Project
University of Missouri Extension
Columbia, MO 65211
Ph: (573)882-5011
E-mail: owm@missouri.edu
URL: http://outreach.missouri.edu/owm/hhw.htm
Price: $.75/copy.

8173 ■ The Home Town Advantage: How to Defend Your Main Street Against Chain Stores and Why It Matters
Institute for Local Self-Reliance
927 15th St. NW, 4th Fl.
Washington, DC 20005
Ph: (202)898-1610
E-mail: info@ilsr.org
URL: http://www.ilsr.org

Price: $14 plus shipping and handling.

8174 ■ Household Hazardous Waste: Consumer Information
Household Hazardous Waste Project
University of Missouri Extension
Columbia, MO 65211
Ph: (573)882-5011
E-mail: owm@missouri.edu
URL: http://outreach.missouri.edu/owm/hhw.htm

8175 ■ How to Avoid Dangerous Climate Change
Union of Concerned Scientists
2 Brattle Sq.
Cambridge, MA 02238-9105
Ph: (617)547-5552
Fax: (617)864-9405
URL: http://www.ucsusa.org
Price: $10 each.

8176 ■ How Safe is Mexico's Atomic City
Southwest Research and Information Center
PO Box 4524
Albuquerque, NM 87106
Ph: (505)262-1862
Fax: (505)262-1864
E-mail: info@sric.org
URL: http://www.sric.org

8177 ■ Howard Phillips Issues and Strategy
The Conservative Caucus Research, Analysis and Education Foundation
450 Maple Ave. E
Vienna, VA 22180
Ph: (703)281-6782
E-mail: corndorf@cais.com
URL: http://www.conservativeusa.org/TCCFMission.htm
Freq: semimonthly.

8178 ■ Human Ecologist
Human Ecology Action League
PO Box 509
Stockbridge, GA 30281
Ph: (770)389-4519
Fax: (770)389-4520
E-mail: healnatnl@aol.com
URL: http://www.healnatl.org
Descr: Includes association news, book and video reviews, environmental health tips for children, and pesticide update. **Freq:** quarterly. **Price:** $26/copy for nonmembers, $20/year for low-income individuals, $32 in Canada, $38 foreign.

8179 ■ I Love Animals and Broccoli Activity Book
Vegetarian Resource Group
PO Box 1463
Baltimore, MD 21203
Ph: (410)366-8343

Fax: (410)366-8804
E-mail: vrg@vrg.org
URL: http://www.vrg.org

8180 ■ IBWA Audit Handbook
International Bottled Water Association
1700 Diagonal Rd., Ste. 650
Alexandria, VA 22314
Ph: (703)683-5213
Fax: (703)683-4074
E-mail: ibwainfo@bottledwater.org
URL: http://www.bottledwater.org
Descr: Assists members in preparing for the annual plant inspection. **Price:** $25 for members, $1500 for nonmembers.

8181 ■ IBWA Membership Roster
International Bottled Water Association
1700 Diagonal Rd., Ste. 650
Alexandria, VA 22314
Ph: (703)683-5213
Fax: (703)683-4074
E-mail: ibwainfo@bottledwater.org
URL: http://www.bottledwater.org
Descr: Lists all IBWA members in four sections. **Freq:** annual. **Price:** $25 for members, $1500 for nonmembers.

8182 ■ In Pity and in Anger
Jews for Animal Rights
255 Humphrey St.
Marblehead, MA 01945
Ph: (781)631-7601
E-mail: micah@micahbooks.com
URL: http://www.micahbooks.com/JAR.html
Price: $10.

8183 ■ Infection and Immunity
American Society for Microbiology
1752 N St. NW
Washington, DC 20036
Ph: (202)737-3600
Fax: (202)942-9333
E-mail: oed@asmusa.org
URL: http://www.asm.org
Descr: Directed toward microbiologists, immunologists, epidemiologists, pathologists, and clinicians. Topics covered include ecology and epidemiology. **Freq:** monthly. **Price:** $51/year for members, $368/year for nonmembers. **ISSN:** 0019-9567.

8184 ■ Institute of Scrap Recycling Industries Directory of Members
Institute of Scrap Recycling Industries
1615 L St. NW, Ste. 600
Washington, DC 20036-5610
Ph: (202)662-8500
Fax: (202)626-0900
E-mail: robinwiener@isri.org
URL: http://www.isri.org
Freq: annual.

8185 ■ International Energy Conservation Code
Building Officials and Code Administrators International
Chicago District Office
4051 W Flossmoor Rd.
Country Club Hills, IL 60478
E-mail: webmaster@iccsafe.org
URL: http://www.iccsafe.org
Freq: triennial.

8186 ■ International Forum Addresses Alternatives to Animal Research
International Foundation for Ethical Research
53 W Jackson Blvd., Ste. 1552
Chicago, IL 60604
Ph: (312)427-6025
Fax: (312)427-6524
E-mail: ifer@navs.org
URL: http://www.ifer.org

8187 ■ International Journal of Phytoremediation
Association for the Environmental Health of Soils
150 Fearing St.

Amherst, MA 01002
Ph: (413)549-5170
Fax: (413)549-0579
E-mail: paul@aehs.com
URL: http://www.aehs.com

Freq: periodic. **Price:** $65/year for members.

8188 ■ International Journal of Systematic Bacteriology
American Society for Microbiology
1752 N St. NW
Washington, DC 20036
Ph: (202)737-3600
Fax: (202)942-9333
E-mail: oed@asmusa.org
URL: http://www.asm.org

Descr: Presents papers concerned with the systematics of bacteria, yeasts, and yeast-like organisms, including taxonomy, nomenclature and identification. **Freq:** quarterly. **Price:** $35/year for members, $158/year for nonmembers. **ISSN:** 0020-7713.

8189 ■ International Society for Animal Rights—Report
International Society for Animal Rights
PO Box F
Clarks Summit, PA 18411
Ph: (570)586-2200
Fax: (570)586-9580
E-mail: contact@isaronline.org
URL: http://www.isaronline.org

Descr: Reports on legal cases and other programs undertaken by ISAR on legislative issues affecting animals; includes global news on animal rights. **Freq:** quarterly. **Price:** included in membership dues.

8190 ■ Intervenor
Canadian Environmental Law Association
130 Spadina Ave., Ste. 301
Toronto, ON, Canada M5V 2L4
Ph: (416)960-2284
Fax: (416)960-9392
E-mail: theresa@cela.ca
URL: http://www.cela.ca

Freq: quarterly. **Price:** $20.

8191 ■ Is Global Warming Harmful to Health?
Center for Health and the Global Environment
Harvard Medical School
401 Park Dr., 2nd Fl. E
Boston, MA 02115
Ph: (617)384-8530
Fax: (617)384-8585
E-mail: chge@hms.harvard.edu
URL: http://chge.med.harvard.edu

8192 ■ ISEA's Heliograph
Illinois Solar Energy Association
800 W Evergreen Ave.
Chicago, IL 60622
Ph: (312)401-4859
E-mail: contactisea@illinoissolar.org
URL: http://www.illinoissolar.org

Freq: quarterly. **Price:** included in membership dues.

8193 ■ ISRI Digest
Institute of Scrap Recycling Industries
1615 L St. NW, Ste. 600
Washington, DC 20036-5610
Ph: (202)662-8500
Fax: (202)626-0900
E-mail: robinwiener@isri.org
URL: http://www.isri.org

Freq: bimonthly.

8194 ■ ISRI Focus
Institute of Scrap Recycling Industries
1615 L St. NW, Ste. 600
Washington, DC 20036-5610
Ph: (202)662-8500
Fax: (202)626-0900
E-mail: robinwiener@isri.org
URL: http://www.isri.org

Price: free for members.

8195 ■ JAR Newsletter
Jews for Animal Rights
255 Humphrey St.
Marblehead, MA 01945
Ph: (781)631-7601
E-mail: micah@micahbooks.com
URL: http://www.micahbooks.com/JAR.html

Freq: semiannual. **Price:** free for members.

8196 ■ Journal of Applied Communications
Association for Communication Excellence in Agriculture, Natural Resources, and Life and Human Sciences
PO Box 110811
Gainesville, FL 32611
Ph: (352)392-9588
Fax: (352)392-8583
E-mail: ace@ifas.ufl.edu
URL: http://www.aceweb.org

Descr: Features abstracts of articles and full text of reviews. **Freq:** quarterly. **Price:** $75/year for libraries and nonmembers, $15/back issue for nonmembers, included in membership dues. **ISSN:** 1051-0834.

8197 ■ Journal of Bacteriology
American Society for Microbiology
1752 N St. NW
Washington, DC 20036
Ph: (202)737-3600
Fax: (202)942-9333
E-mail: oed@asmusa.org
URL: http://www.asm.org

Descr: Contains research articles on structure and function, cell surfaces, eucaryotic cells, genetics and molecular biology, and bacteriophages. **Freq:** semimonthly. **Price:** $79/year for members, $378/year for nonmembers. **ISSN:** 0021-9193.

8198 ■ Journal of Clinical Microbiology
American Society for Microbiology
1752 N St. NW
Washington, DC 20036
Ph: (202)737-3600
Fax: (202)942-9333
E-mail: oed@asmusa.org
URL: http://www.asm.org

Descr: Covers current research on the microbiological aspects of human and animal infections and infestations. **Freq:** monthly. **Price:** $49/year for members, $264/year for nonmembers. **ISSN:** 0095-1137.

8199 ■ Journal of the Grassroots Movement
Center For Health, Environment and Justice
PO Box 6806
Falls Church, VA 22040-6806
Ph: (703)237-2249
Fax: (703)237-8389
E-mail: chej@chej.org
URL: http://www.chej.org

8200 ■ Journal of Pesticide Reform
Northwest Coalition for Alternatives to Pesticides
PO Box 1393
Eugene, OR 97440-1393
Ph: (541)344-5044
Fax: (541)344-6923
E-mail: info@pesticide.org
URL: http://www.pesticide.org

URL(s): http://www.pesticide.org/JPR.html **Descr:** Journal covering alternatives to pesticides. **Freq:** Quarterly. **Price:** $5, individuals; $15, individuals.

8201 ■ Journal of Pesticide Safety Education
American Association of Pesticide Safety Educators
Washington State University
PO Box 646382
Pullman, WA 99164-6382
Ph: (509)335-9222
Fax: (509)335-1009

E-mail: ramsay@wsu.edu
URL: http://www.aapse.org

8202 ■ Journal of Soil Contamination
Association for the Environmental Health of Soils
150 Fearing St.
Amherst, MA 01002
Ph: (413)549-5170
Fax: (413)549-0579
E-mail: paul@aehs.com
URL: http://www.aehs.com

Freq: periodic. **Price:** $65/year for members.

8203 ■ Journal of Virology
American Society for Microbiology
1752 N St. NW
Washington, DC 20036
Ph: (202)737-3600
Fax: (202)942-9333
E-mail: oed@asmusa.org
URL: http://www.asm.org

Descr: Contains research reports on viruses, including the areas of biochemistry, biophysics, genetics, immunology, morphology, and physiology. **Freq:** monthly. **Price:** $81/year for members, $380/year for nonmembers. **ISSN:** 0022-538X.

8204 ■ Judaism and Animal Rights: Classical and Contemporary Responses
Jews for Animal Rights
255 Humphrey St.
Marblehead, MA 01945
Ph: (781)631-7601
E-mail: micah@micahbooks.com
URL: http://www.micahbooks.com/JAR.html

Descr: Features an anthology of 41 articles from classical and contemporary sources by rabbis, veterinarians and conservationists. **Price:** $17.95/copy.

8205 ■ The Key to Sustainable Cities
Institute for Sustainable Communities
535 Stone Cutters Way
Montpelier, VT 05602
Ph: (802)229-2900
Fax: (802)229-2919
E-mail: isc@iscvt.org
URL: http://www.iscvt.org

Price: $15 plus $3 for shipping and handling.

8206 ■ Kids: Lets Talk About Animal Rights
Animal Rights Coalition
2615 E Franklin Ave.
Minneapolis, MN 55406
Ph: (612)822-6161
E-mail: animalrightscoalition@msn.com
URL: http://www.animalrightscoalition.com

8207 ■ Krupin's Toll-Free Environmental Directory
Direct Contact Publishing
PO Box 6726
Kennewick, WA 99337
Fax: (509)582-9865

Key Personnel: Paul J. Krupin, Author. **Covers:** over 4,500 environmental organizations, companies, and government agencies that utilize toll-free phone numbers. **Entries include:** Agency name, address, phone. **Price:** $14.95, individuals.

8208 ■ LEAF Briefs
Legal Environmental Assistance Foundation
1114 Thomasville Rd., Ste. E
Tallahassee, FL 32303-6290
Ph: (850)681-2591
Fax: (850)224-1275
E-mail: leaf@leaflaw.org
URL: http://www.leaflaw.org

Freq: quarterly. **Price:** free for members.

8209 ■ Legislative Alerts
Beyond Pesticides - National Coalition Against the Misuse of Pesticides
701 E St. SE, Ste. 200
Washington, DC 20003
Ph: (202)543-5450

Fax: (202)543-4791
E-mail: info@beyondpesticides.org
URL: http://www.beyondpesticides.org
Freq: periodic.

8210 ■ *Lessons in Household Hazardous Waste Management*
Household Hazardous Waste Project
University of Missouri Extension
Columbia, MO 65211
Ph: (573)882-5011
E-mail: owm@missouri.edu
URL: http://outreach.missouri.edu/owm/hhw.htm
Descr: For grades K-3 or 4-8.

8211 ■ *Life Behind Bars*
Farm Sanctuary
PO Box 150
Watkins Glen, NY 14891
Ph: (607)583-2225
Fax: (607)583-2041
E-mail: info@farmsanctuary.org
URL: http://www.farmsanctuary.org
Price: free.

8212 ■ *Living Like Ed*
Clarkson Potter, a division of Random Hosue
1745 Broadway
New York, NY 10019
Ph: (212)782-9000
URL: http://www.randomhouse.com/crown/clarksonpotter.html
Subtitle: A Guide to the Eco-Friendly Life. **Author:** Ed Begley, Jr. **Pub. Date:** 2008. **Pgs:** 240. **Price:** $18.

8213 ■ *Maine Sun*
Maine Solar Energy Association
17 Rockwell Rd. SE
Jonesport, ME 04649
E-mail: sunwatt@juno.com
URL: http://www.mainesolar.org
Freq: quarterly. **Price:** free to members.

8214 ■ *Manna Newsletter*
Alliance for Sustainability
University of Minnesota
1521 University Ave. SE
Minneapolis, MN 55414
Ph: (612)331-1099
Fax: (612)379-1527
E-mail: sean@afors.org
URL: http://www.allianceforsustainability.net
Descr: Covers worldwide agricultural topics. Includes book reviews, calendar of events, conference reports, and information on new members. **Freq:** monthly. **Price:** free for members, $15/year for nonmembers.

8215 ■ *Marine Ecosystems: Emerging Diseases as Indicators of Change*
Center for Health and the Global Environment
Harvard Medical School
401 Park Dr., 2nd Fl. E
Boston, MA 02115
Ph: (617)384-8530
Fax: (617)384-8585
E-mail: chge@hms.harvard.edu
URL: http://chge.med.harvard.edu

8216 ■ *Material Safety Data Sheets: Identifying Product Hazards*
Household Hazardous Waste Project
University of Missouri Extension
Columbia, MO 65211
Ph: (573)882-5011
E-mail: owm@missouri.edu
URL: http://outreach.missouri.edu/owm/hhw.htm
Price: $.50/copy.

8217 ■ *Membership Brochure*
North American Nature Photography Association
10200 W 44th Ave., Ste. 304
Wheat Ridge, CO 80033-2840
Ph: (303)422-8527
Fax: (303)422-8894

E-mail: info@nanpa.org
URL: http://www.nanpa.org

8218 ■ *Messing with Mother Nature Can Be Hazardous to Your Health*
Americans for Indian Opportunity
1001 Marquette Ave. NW
Albuquerque, NM 87102
Ph: (505)842-8677
Fax: (505)842-8658
E-mail: aio@aio.org
URL: http://www.aio.org

8219 ■ *Microbiological Reviews*
American Society for Microbiology
1752 N St. NW
Washington, DC 20036
Ph: (202)737-3600
Fax: (202)942-9333
E-mail: oed@asmusa.org
URL: http://www.asm.org
Descr: Covers aspects of microbiology including bacteriology, virology, mycology, and parasitology. **Freq:** quarterly. **Price:** $25/year for members, $120/year for nonmembers. **ISSN:** 0146-0749.

8220 ■ *Molecular and Cellular Biology*
American Society for Microbiology
1752 N St. NW
Washington, DC 20036
Ph: (202)737-3600
Fax: (202)942-9333
E-mail: oed@asmusa.org
URL: http://www.asm.org
Descr: Contains articles concerning all aspects of the molecular biology of eucaryotic cells, including regulation of gene expression, and transcription. **Freq:** monthly. **Price:** $80/year for members, $379/year for nonmembers. **ISSN:** 0270-7306.

8221 ■ *Montana's Sustainable Agriculture Farming with Foresight*
Alternative Energy Resources Organization
432 N Last Chance Gulch
Helena, MT 59601-5014
Ph: (406)443-7272
Fax: (406)442-9120
E-mail: aero@aeromt.org
URL: http://www.aeromt.org
Descr: Includes research results.

8222 ■ *My Time*
Jews for Animal Rights
255 Humphrey St.
Marblehead, MA 01945
Ph: (781)631-7601
E-mail: micah@micahbooks.com
URL: http://www.micahbooks.com/JAR.html
Price: $4.95.

8223 ■ *MYTHBusters Series*
Safe Energy Communication Council
1717 Massachusetts Ave. NW, Ste. 106
Washington, DC 20036
Fax: (202)234-9194
Freq: periodic.

8224 ■ *National Directory of Safe Energy Organizations*
Public Citizen's Critical Mass Energy and Environment Program
215 Pennsylvania Ave. SE
Washington, DC 20003
Ph: (202)546-4996
E-mail: member@citizen.org
URL: http://www.citizen.org/CMEP
Descr: Contains the names and addresses of more than 1000 citizen groups which work to promote renewable energy as alternatives to nuclear power. **Freq:** annual. **Price:** $30/year.

8225 ■ *The National Environmental Directory*
Harbinger Communications
112 Glenview St.
Santa Cruz, CA 95062
E-mail: info@environmentaldirectory.net
URL: http://www.environmentaldirectory.net

URL(s): http://www.environmentaldirectory.net **Covers:** More than 12,000 organizations concerned with environmental issues. Includes contact information as well as groups' mission statements, publications, activities and more. **Price:** $350, individuals, plus $2 shipping/handling.

8226 ■ *National Environmental Directory Software Program CD*
Harbinger Communications
112 Glenview St.
Santa Cruz, CA 95062
E-mail: orders@environmentaldirectory.net
URL: http://www.environmentaldirectory.net
URL(s): http://www.environmentaldirectory.net **Covers:** Sources for environmental educators and activists. **Entries include:** Organization name and address, URL, e-mail, activities, names and titles of key personnel, number of employees, programs, funding sources, publications, description, budget.

8227 ■ *National Environmental Enforcement Journal*
National Association of Attorneys General
2030 M St. NW, 8th Fl.
Washington, DC 20036-3306
Ph: (202)326-6000
Fax: (202)331-1427
URL: http://www.naag.org
Descr: Covers environmental enforcement issues on the federal, state, and local levels; covers civil proceedings, criminal prosecutions, and others. **Freq:** 11/year. **Price:** $195/year, $95/year for libraries, government and nonprofit organizations.

8228 ■ *National Green Pages*
Co-op America Business Network
1612 K St. NW, Ste. 600
Washington, DC 20006
Free: 800-584-7336
E-mail: cabn@coopamerica.org
URL: http://www.coopamerica.org/
URL(s): http://www.coopamerica.org; http://www.greenpages.org/about.cfm **Covers:** 2,000 small companies that utilize recycling and environmental practices in the U.S. **Entries include:** Company name, address, phone, product/service. **Freq:** Annual, Fall.

8229 ■ *National Landscape Conservation System*
The Wilderness Society
1615 M St. NW
Washington, DC 20036
E-mail: member@tws.org
URL: http://www.wilderness.org
Descr: Features nation's newest system of public lands.

8230 ■ *National Passive Conference Proceedings*
American Solar Energy Society
2400 Central Ave., Ste. A
Boulder, CO 80301
Ph: (303)443-3130
Fax: (303)443-3212
E-mail: ases@ases.org
URL: http://www.ases.org
Freq: annual.

8231 ■ *National Wetlands Newsletter*
Environmental Law Institute
2000 L St. NW, Ste. 620
Washington, DC 20036
Ph: (202)939-3800
E-mail: law@eli.org
URL: http://www.eli.org
Freq: bimonthly. **Price:** $48/year in U.S., $55/year outside U.S.

8232 ■ *National Woodlands Magazine*
American Resources Group
374 Maple Ave. E, Ste. 310
Vienna, VA 22180-4751
Ph: (703)255-2700
Fax: (703)281-9200

E-mail: info@firetower.org
URL: http://www.firetower.org
Descr: Covers current forestry and legislative issues.
Freq: quarterly.

8233 ■ *A Natural Approach: Forestry and Global Climate Changes*
Center for Clean Air Policy
750 First St. NE, Ste. 940
Washington, DC 20002
Ph: (202)408-9260
Fax: (202)408-8896
E-mail: communications@ccap.org
URL: http://www.ccap.org

8234 ■ *Natural Trails and Waters Coalition— Membership List*
Natural Trails and Waters Coalition
c/o Cathrine Walters Adams, Prog. Assoc.
Wildlands CPR
PO Box 7516
Missoula, MT 59807
Ph: (406)543-9551
URL: http://www.naturaltrails.org
URL(s): http://www.naturaltrails.org/our-members
Covers: Member organizations engaged in environment conservation.

8235 ■ *Nature Photographer*
North American Nature Photography Association
10200 W 44th Ave., Ste. 304
Wheat Ridge, CO 80033-2840
Ph: (303)422-8527
Fax: (303)422-8894
E-mail: info@nanpa.org
URL: http://www.nanpa.org
Descr: Contains articles on nature photography.
Freq: quarterly. **Price:** $15 in U.S., $23 in Canada, $27 international.

8236 ■ *Nature's Best*
North American Nature Photography Association
10200 W 44th Ave., Ste. 304
Wheat Ridge, CO 80033-2840
Ph: (303)422-8527
Fax: (303)422-8894
E-mail: info@nanpa.org
URL: http://www.nanpa.org
Descr: Features winning images from the annual Nature's Best Photography Awards. **Freq:** quarterly.
Price: $21 in U.S., $31 in Canada, $56 international.

8237 ■ *Nature's Voice*
Natural Resources Defense Council
40 W 20th St.
New York, NY 10011
Ph: (212)727-2700
Fax: (212)727-1773
E-mail: nrdcinfo@nrdc.org
URL: http://www.nrdc.org
Freq: bimonthly.

8238 ■ *NCRP Commentary*
National Council on Radiation Protection and Measurements
7910 Woodmont Ave., Ste. 400
Bethesda, MD 20814-3076
Ph: (301)657-2652
Fax: (301)907-8768
E-mail: schauer@ncrponline.org
URL: http://www.ncrponline.org
Freq: periodic.

8239 ■ *NCRP Report*
National Council on Radiation Protection and Measurements
7910 Woodmont Ave., Ste. 400
Bethesda, MD 20814-3076
Ph: (301)657-2652
Fax: (301)907-8768
E-mail: schauer@ncrponline.org
URL: http://www.ncrponline.org

Freq: periodic.

8240 ■ *NCRP Statement*
National Council on Radiation Protection and Measurements
7910 Woodmont Ave., Ste. 400
Bethesda, MD 20814-3076
Ph: (301)657-2652
Fax: (301)907-8768
E-mail: schauer@ncrponline.org
URL: http://www.ncrponline.org
Freq: periodic.

8241 ■ *New England Environmental Directory*
Harbinger Communications
112 Glenview St.
Santa Cruz, CA 95062
E-mail: info@environmentaldirectory.net
URL: http://www.environmentaldirectory.net
Key Personnel: Bill Leland, Contact. **URL(s):** http://www.environmentaldirectory.net **Entries include:** Company name, address, phone, name and title of contact, number of employees, geographical area served, financial data, branch office or subsidiary names and addresses, requirements for membership, admission, eligibility, descriptions of product/service. **Price:** $15, individuals.

8242 ■ *New Environment Bulletin*
New Environment Association
821 Euclid Ave.
Syracuse, NY 13210
Ph: (315)446-8009
E-mail: hs38@mailbox.syr.edu
URL: http://www.newenvironment.org
Descr: Contains articles, book reviews, commentaries, reports of recent activities, schedule of upcoming events, letters, etc. **Freq:** monthly. **Price:** $12/year, $22/2 years.

8243 ■ *The New Environment Process*
New Environment Association
821 Euclid Ave.
Syracuse, NY 13210
Ph: (315)446-8009
E-mail: hs38@mailbox.syr.edu
URL: http://www.newenvironment.org
Price: $.75 plus postage.

8244 ■ *New Mexico's Right to Know: The Impacts of the Los Alamos National Laboratory Operations on Public Health and the Environment*
Concerned Citizens for Nuclear Safety
107 Cienega St.
Santa Fe, NM 87501
Ph: (505)986-1973
Fax: (505)986-0997
E-mail: ccns@nuclearactive.org
URL: http://www.nuclearactive.org

8245 ■ *The New Resource Wars: Native and Environmental Struggles Against Multinational Corporations*
Center for Alternative Mining Development Policy
210 Avon St., Ste. 4
La Crosse, WI 54603
Ph: (608)784-4399
Fax: (608)785-8486
E-mail: gedicks.al@uwlax.edu
Price: $18.

8246 ■ *The Newsletter*
Izaak Walton League of America, Arlington-Fairfax Chapter
PO Box 366
Centreville, VA 20122-0366
Ph: (703)631-4495
E-mail: nankea@earthlink.net
URL: http://arlingtonfairfax-iwla.org
Freq: quarterly. **Price:** for members.

8247 ■ *Northeast Sun*
Northeast Sustainable Energy Association
50 Miles St.
Greenfield, MA 01301
Ph: (413)774-6051

Fax: (413)774-6053
E-mail: nesea@nesea.org
URL: http://www.nesea.org
Freq: semiannual. **Price:** included in membership dues.

8248 ■ *Northern California Sun*
Northern California Solar Energy Association
PO Box 3008
Berkeley, CA 94703
Ph: (530)852-0354
Fax: (530)852-0381
E-mail: solarinfo@norcalsolar.org
URL: http://www.norcalsolar.org
Freq: quarterly.

8249 ■ *NRS Sells the Environment Down the River: Radiation Flows Unchecked into the Colorado River*
Project on Government Oversight
666 11th St. NW, Ste. 900
Washington, DC 20001-4542
Ph: (202)347-1122
Fax: (202)347-1116
E-mail: info@pogo.org
URL: http://www.pogo.org

8250 ■ *Nuclear Legacy: An Overview of the Places, Problems and Politics of Radioactive Waste in the United States*
Public Citizen's Critical Mass Energy and Environment Program
215 Pennsylvania Ave. SE
Washington, DC 20003
Ph: (202)546-4996
E-mail: member@citizen.org
URL: http://www.citizen.org/CMEP
Descr: Provides a comprehensive, state-by-state analysis of the amounts, radioactivity levels, and types of radioactive waste from nuclear power plants. **Price:** $40.

8251 ■ *Nuclear Lemons: An Assessment of America's Worst Commercial Nuclear Reactors*
Public Citizen's Critical Mass Energy and Environment Program
215 Pennsylvania Ave. SE
Washington, DC 20003
Ph: (202)546-4996
E-mail: member@citizen.org
URL: http://www.citizen.org/CMEP
Descr: Examines each American nuclear power plant based on eleven key indicators of safety and performance. **Price:** $40.

8252 ■ *Nuclear Power in a Warming World*
Union of Concerned Scientists
2 Brattle Sq.
Cambridge, MA 02238-9105
Ph: (617)547-5552
Fax: (617)864-9405
URL: http://www.ucsusa.org
Price: $15 each.

8253 ■ *Office Green Buying Guide*
Green Seal
1001 Connecticut Ave. NW, Ste. 827
Washington, DC 20036-5525
Ph: (202)872-6400
Fax: (202)872-4324
E-mail: greenseal@greenseal.org
URL: http://www.greenseal.org
Descr: Provides focus on implementing and maintaining green procurement plan, index of product lists.

8254 ■ *Official Recycled Products Guide*
Recycling Data Management Corp.
PO Box 577
Ogdensburg, NY 13669
Ph: 877-825-6555
Free: 800-267-0707
Fax: 877-471-3258
E-mail: info@recyclingmarkets.net
URL: http://www.recyclingdata.com
Key Personnel: Jerrold Boulanger, Subscription

Mgr. **URL(s):** http://www.recyclingmarkets.net; http://www.recyclingdata.com **Covers:** Nearly 650 manufacturers, distributors, and converters of recycled products in North America. **Entries include:** Company name, address, phone, fax, products, name and title of contact; company type; percentages of certified minimum recycled content; brand names. **Freq:** Annual, spring.

8255 ■ *Oil: A Life Cycle Analysis of its Health and Environmental Impacts*
Center for Health and the Global Environment
Harvard Medical School
401 Park Dr., 2nd Fl. E
Boston, MA 02115
Ph: (617)384-8530
Fax: (617)384-8585
E-mail: chge@hms.harvard.edu
URL: http://chge.med.harvard.edu

8256 ■ *OnEarth*
Natural Resources Defense Council
40 W 20th St.
New York, NY 10011
Ph: (212)727-2700
Fax: (212)727-1773
E-mail: nrdcinfo@nrdc.org
URL: http://www.nrdc.org
Freq: quarterly.

8257 ■ *Onsite Journal*
National Onsite Wastewater Recycling Association
3540 Soquel Ave., Ste. A
Santa Cruz, CA 95062
Ph: (831)454-4884
Fax: (831)464-4881
E-mail: info@nowra.org
URL: http://www.nowra.org

8258 ■ *Oregon Ike*
Izaak Walton League of America, Oregon Division
15056 Quall Rd. NE
Silverton, OR 97381
Ph: (503)873-2681
E-mail: olsondaw@juno.com
URL: http://www.iwla.org
Freq: 3/year.

8259 ■ *Orientation of Dog Guide Users to New Environments*
Leader Dogs for the Blind
1039 S Rochester Rd.
Rochester, MI 48307
Ph: (248)651-9011
Fax: (248)651-5812
E-mail: leaderdog@leaderdog.org
URL: http://www.leaderdog.org

8260 ■ *Outdoor America*
Izaak Walton League of America, Fort Dodge/Phil Fox Chapter
2137 Richmill Rd.
Fort Dodge, IA 50501
Ph: (515)955-3258
Freq: quarterly.

8261 ■ *Outdoor America*
Izaak Walton League of America Midwest Office
1619 Dayton Ave., Ste. 202
St. Paul, MN 55104
Ph: (651)649-1446
Fax: (651)649-1494
E-mail: midwestoffice@iwla.org
URL: http://www.iwla.org
Descr: Features conservation issues. **Freq:** quarterly. **Price:** included in membership dues. **ISSN:** 0021-3314.

8262 ■ *Outdoor America*
Izaak Walton League of America, Lebanon County Chapter
65 Monroe Valley Dr.
Jonestown, PA 17038-8223
Ph: (717)273-7304
E-mail: trace@mbcomp.com
URL: http://www.iwla.org

Freq: quarterly.

8263 ■ *Outdoor Photographer*
North American Nature Photography Association
10200 W 44th Ave., Ste. 304
Wheat Ridge, CO 80033-2840
Ph: (303)422-8527
Fax: (303)422-8894
E-mail: info@nanpa.org
URL: http://www.nanpa.org
Descr: Contains information on how to improve one's own photography. **Freq:** monthly. **Price:** $11 in U.S., $21 in Canada, $21 international.

8264 ■ *Pacific Northwest Environmental Directory*
Harbinger Communications
112 Glenview St.
Santa Cruz, CA 95062
E-mail: info@environmentaldirectory.net
URL: http://www.environmentaldirectory.net
Key Personnel: Bill Leland, Exec. Dir. **URL(s):** http://www.environmentaldirectory.net **Price:** $50, individuals, plus $2 shipping and handling.

8265 ■ *PAL Companion*
People-Animals-Love
4900 Massachusetts Ave. NW, Ste. 330
Washington, DC 20016
Ph: (202)966-2171
Fax: (202)966-2172
E-mail: info@peopleanimalslove.org
URL: http://www.peopleanimalslove.org
Freq: quarterly.

8266 ■ *Partners Update*
Pesticide Action Network North America
49 Powell St., Ste. 500
San Francisco, CA 94102
Ph: (415)981-1771
Fax: (415)981-1991
E-mail: panna@panna.org
URL: http://www.panna.org

8267 ■ *Passive Solar Design Strategies: Guidelines for Home Builders*
Sustainable Buildings Industry Council
1112 16th St. NW, Ste. 240
Washington, DC 20036
Ph: (202)628-7400
Fax: (202)393-5043
E-mail: sbic@sbicouncil.org
URL: http://www.sbicouncil.org
Price: $50.

8268 ■ *Payment Due: A Reactor-by-Reactor Assessment of the Nuclear Industry's $25 Billion Decommissioning Bill*
Public Citizen's Critical Mass Energy and Environment Program
215 Pennsylvania Ave. SE
Washington, DC 20003
Ph: (202)546-4996
E-mail: member@citizen.org
URL: http://www.citizen.org/CMEP
Descr: Examines the cost to decommission each of the United States commercial nuclear reactors, the funds already set aside, and the amount still needed. **Price:** $40.

8269 ■ *Pest Control Without Toxic Chemicals*
Beyond Pesticides - National Coalition Against the Misuse of Pesticides
701 E St. SE, Ste. 200
Washington, DC 20003
Ph: (202)543-5450
Fax: (202)543-4791
E-mail: info@beyondpesticides.org
URL: http://www.beyondpesticides.org
Price: $2.

8270 ■ *Pesticides and You*
Beyond Pesticides - National Coalition Against the Misuse of Pesticides
701 E St. SE, Ste. 200
Washington, DC 20003
Ph: (202)543-5450

Fax: (202)543-4791
E-mail: info@beyondpesticides.org
URL: http://www.beyondpesticides.org
Freq: quarterly. **Price:** included in membership dues.

8271 ■ *Pet Shops: Love for Sale*
Animal Rights Coalition
2615 E Franklin Ave.
Minneapolis, MN 55406
Ph: (612)822-6161
E-mail: animalrightscoalition@msn.com
URL: http://www.animalrightscoalition.com

8272 ■ *Poison Poles: Their Toxic Trail and the Safer Alternatives*
Beyond Pesticides - National Coalition Against the Misuse of Pesticides
701 E St. SE, Ste. 200
Washington, DC 20003
Ph: (202)543-5450
Fax: (202)543-4791
E-mail: info@beyondpesticides.org
URL: http://www.beyondpesticides.org
Price: $22.

8273 ■ *Popular Photography*
North American Nature Photography Association
10200 W 44th Ave., Ste. 304
Wheat Ridge, CO 80033-2840
Ph: (303)422-8527
Fax: (303)422-8894
E-mail: info@nanpa.org
URL: http://www.nanpa.org
Descr: Features advice on how to improve one's own photography. **Freq:** monthly. **Price:** $10 in U.S., $18 in Canada, $18 international.

8274 ■ *Position Papers*
American Association of Pesticide Safety Educators
Washington State University
PO Box 646382
Pullman, WA 99164-6382
Ph: (509)335-9222
Fax: (509)335-1009
E-mail: ramsay@wsu.edu
URL: http://www.aapse.org

8275 ■ *ProbeAbilities*
Pollution Probe
625 Church St., Ste. 402
Toronto, ON, Canada M4Y 2G1
Ph: (416)926-1907
Fax: (416)926-1601
E-mail: pprobe@pollutionprobe.org
URL: http://www.pollutionprobe.org
Freq: 3/year. **Price:** available to members only.

8276 ■ *Protecting Environmental and Nuclear Whistleblowers: A Litigation Manual*
Government Accountability Project
1612 K St. NW, Ste. 1100
Washington, DC 20006
Ph: (202)408-0034
E-mail: info@whistleblower.org
URL: http://www.whistleblower.org

8277 ■ *Public Health Mosquito Management Strategy*
Beyond Pesticides - National Coalition Against the Misuse of Pesticides
701 E St. SE, Ste. 200
Washington, DC 20003
Ph: (202)543-5450
Fax: (202)543-4791
E-mail: info@beyondpesticides.org
URL: http://www.beyondpesticides.org

8278 ■ *Public Power*
American Public Power Association
1875 Connecticut Ave. NW, Ste. 1200
Washington, DC 20009
Ph: (202)467-2900
Fax: (202)467-2910
E-mail: mrufe@appanet.org
URL: http://www.appanet.org

Descr: Includes annual directory. **Freq:** bimonthly.

8279 ■ *Public Power Weekly*
American Public Power Association
1875 Connecticut Ave. NW, Ste. 1200
Washington, DC 20009
Ph: (202)467-2900
Fax: (202)467-2910
E-mail: mrufe@appanet.org
URL: http://www.appanet.org
Descr: Covers current events that affect local public power systems. **Freq:** weekly.

8280 ■ *Publications Catalog*
American Council for an Energy-Efficient Economy
529 14th St. NW, Ste. 600
Washington, DC 20045
Ph: (202)507-4000
Fax: (202)429-2248
E-mail: info@aceee.org
URL: http://www.aceee.org

8281 ■ *Radiation Research*
Radiation Research Society
PO Box 7050
Lawrence, KS 66044
Fax: (785)843-1274
E-mail: info@radres.org
URL: http://www.radres.org
Descr: Reports original research in the natural sciences relating to radiation. **Freq:** monthly. **Price:** $68 for members, $720/year for institutions in U.S. and Canada, $820/year for institutions outside U.S. and Canada. **ISSN:** 0033-7587.

8282 ■ *Radio Pesticides*
Association of Farmworker Opportunity Programs
1726 M St. NW, Ste. 800
Washington, DC 20036
Ph: (202)826-6006
Fax: (202)826-6005
E-mail: afop@afop.org
URL: http://www.afop.org
Price: $50.

8283 ■ *Raising Baby Green*
Jossey-Bass, an imprint of Wiley
10475 Crosspoint Blvd.
Indianapolis, IN 46256
Ph: 877-762-2974
Fax: 800-597-3299
E-mail: info@wiley.com/
URL: http://www.josseybass.com/
Subtitle: The Earth-Friendly Guide to Pregnancy, Childbirth, and Baby Care. **Author:** Alan Greene. **Pub. Date:** 2007. **Pgs:** 320. **Price:** $16.95.

8284 ■ *The Real Price of Fashion*
Animal Rights Coalition
2615 E Franklin Ave.
Minneapolis, MN 55406
Ph: (612)822-6161
E-mail: animalrightscoalition@msn.com
URL: http://www.animalrightscoalition.com

8285 ■ *Recycling Economic Development Through Scrap-Based Manufacturing*
Institute for Local Self-Reliance
927 15th St. NW, 4th Fl.
Washington, DC 20005
Ph: (202)898-1610
E-mail: info@ilsr.org
URL: http://www.ilsr.org
Price: $20.

8286 ■ *Renewable Energy: A National Directory of Resources, Contacts, and Companies*
Public Citizen's Critical Mass Energy and Environment Program
215 Pennsylvania Ave. SE
Washington, DC 20003
Ph: (202)546-4996
E-mail: member@citizen.org
URL: http://www.citizen.org/CMEP
Descr: Lists more than 1,650 domestic organiza-

tions working to promote, buy, sell, develop, and research renewable-energy technologies. **Price:** $40.

8287 ■ *Renewable Energy Research and Development: An Alternative Budget for FY'1993 1995*
Public Citizen's Critical Mass Energy and Environment Program
215 Pennsylvania Ave. SE
Washington, DC 20003
Ph: (202)546-4996
E-mail: member@citizen.org
URL: http://www.citizen.org/CMEP
Descr: Outlines proposed expanded levels of federal funding for 1993-95 and redirected programs for the further development of solar and other energies. **Price:** $30.

8288 ■ *ReNews*
Midwest Renewable Energy Association
7558 Deer Rd.
Custer, WI 54423
Ph: (715)592-6595
Fax: (715)592-6596
E-mail: info@the-mrea.org
URL: http://www.the-mrea.org
Descr: Contains articles and calendar of events pertaining to renewable energy issues. **Freq:** quarterly. **Price:** $6.

8289 ■ *Reseau Vert*
Greenpeace Canada
33 Cecil St.
Toronto, ON, Canada M5T 1N1
Ph: (416)597-8408
Fax: (416)597-8422
E-mail: greenpeace.toronto@dialb.greenpeace.org
URL: http://p2-raw.greenpeace.org/canada/en/about-greenpeace
Freq: 3/year.

8290 ■ *RESNET Notes*
Residential Energy Services Network
PO Box 4561
Oceanside, CA 92052-4561
Ph: (760)806-3448
E-mail: info@natresnet.org
URL: http://www.net.us
Freq: monthly. **Price:** included in membership dues.

8291 ■ *Resource Guide to State Environmental Management*
Council of State Governments
2760 Research Park Dr.
PO Box 11910
Lexington, KY 40578-1910
Ph: (859)244-8000
Free: 800-800-1910
Fax: (859)244-8001
URL: http://www.csg.org
Covers: Over 750 state environmental protection officials and other contacts in the state environmental protection agencies. **Entries include:** address, phone, associated organization. **Freq:** Biennial, December of even years. **Price:** $40, individuals.

8292 ■ *Ripples*
North American Nature Photography Association
10200 W 44th Ave., Ste. 304
Wheat Ridge, CO 80033-2840
Ph: (303)422-8527
Fax: (303)422-8894
E-mail: info@nanpa.org
URL: http://www.nanpa.org
Freq: bimonthly.

8293 ■ *River Information Digest*
River Management Society
PO Box 9048
Missoula, MT 59807-9048
Ph: (406)549-0514
Fax: (406)542-6208
E-mail: rms@river-management.org
URL: http://www.river-management.org
Descr: Features one of seven regional chapters on

a rotating schedule. Reports timely river news. **Freq:** quarterly. **Price:** included in membership dues.

8294 ■ *The River Rat*
Ledyard Canoe Club
PO Box 9
Hanover, NH 03755
Ph: (603)643-6709
E-mail: lcc@dartmouth.edu
URL: http://www.dartmouth.edu/~lcc
Freq: semiannual.

8295 ■ *River Research and Applications*
John Wiley & Sons Inc.
111 River St.
Hoboken, NJ 07030-5774
Ph: (201)748-6000
Free: 800-825-7550
Fax: (201)748-6088
E-mail: info@wiley.com
URL: http://www.wiley.com
Key Personnel: Prof. James Gore, Regional Ed.; Prof. G.E. Petts, Editor-in-Chief; Prof. K.F. Walker, Editorial Board. **Descr:** Journal devoted to river management problems and river research. Topics include major dams, canals, and erosion and sedimentation. **Freq:** 10/yr. **Price:** $1,696, other countries, print only; $2,261, institutions, other countries, print only; $1,459, institutions, other countries, print only; $1,154, institutions, print only.

8296 ■ *Rockville Chapter*
Izaak Walton League of America, Rockville Chapter
PO Box 2255
Germantown, MD 20875
Ph: (301)972-1645
E-mail: info@iwla-rockville.com
URL: http://www.iwla-rockville.com
Freq: monthly.

8297 ■ *Rocky Mountain Environmental Directory*
Harbinger Communications
112 Glenview St.
Santa Cruz, CA 95062
E-mail: info@environmentaldirectory.net
URL: http://www.environmentaldirectory.net
Key Personnel: Bill Leland, Author. **URL(s):** http://www.environmentaldirectory.net **Entries include:** Organization name, address, phone, name and title of contact, number of employees, geographical area served, financial data, branch office or subsidiary names and addresses, requirements for membership, admission, eligibility, descriptions of product/service. **Price:** $20, individuals, plus shipping.

8298 ■ *rrNEWS*
Radiation Research Society
PO Box 7050
Lawrence, KS 66044
Fax: (785)843-1274
E-mail: info@radres.org
URL: http://www.radres.org
Freq: quarterly.

8299 ■ *Safe Use, Storage and Disposal of Paint*
Household Hazardous Waste Project
University of Missouri Extension
Columbia, MO 65211
Ph: (573)882-5011
E-mail: owm@missouri.edu
URL: http://outreach.missouri.edu/owm/hhw.htm
Price: $.25/copy.

8300 ■ *Safe Use, Storage and Disposal of Pesticides*
Household Hazardous Waste Project
University of Missouri Extension
Columbia, MO 65211
Ph: (573)882-5011
E-mail: owm@missouri.edu
URL: http://outreach.missouri.edu/owm/hhw.htm

Price: $.25/copy.

8301 ■ SAGE Bulletin
Senior Action in a Gay Environment
305 7th Ave., 16th Fl.
New York, NY 10001
Ph: (212)741-2247
Fax: (212)366-1947
E-mail: info@sageusa.org
URL: http://www.sageusa.org
Freq: monthly. **Price:** free for members.

8302 ■ Satya
Stealth Technologies Inc.
539 First St.
Brooklyn, NY 11215
Ph: (718)832-9557
Fax: (718)832-9558
E-mail: feedback@satyamag.com
URL: http://www.satyamag.com
Key Personnel: Beth Gould, Publisher, bgould@
interport.net; Kymberlie Adams Matthews, Managing
Editor; Martin Rowe, Founding Ed. **URL(s):** http://
www.satyamag.com/ **Descr:** Consumer magazine
covering environmentalism, vegetarianism, and
animal advocacy. **Freq:** Monthly. **Price:** $20, individu-
als; $40, out of country; $35, two years, U.S.

8303 ■ Savings From the Sun
Sustainable Buildings Industry Council
1112 16th St. NW, Ste. 240
Washington, DC 20036
Ph: (202)628-7400
Fax: (202)393-5043
E-mail: sbic@sbicouncil.org
URL: http://www.sbicouncil.org

8304 ■ Scrap Magazine
Institute of Scrap Recycling Industries
1615 L St. NW, Ste. 600
Washington, DC 20036-5610
Ph: (202)662-8500
Fax: (202)626-0900
E-mail: robinwiener@isri.org
URL: http://www.isri.org
Freq: bimonthly. **Price:** free for members.

**8305 ■ Setting Up Collection Sites for Anti-
freeze**
Household Hazardous Waste Project
University of Missouri Extension
Columbia, MO 65211
Ph: (573)882-5011
E-mail: owm@missouri.edu
URL: http://outreach.missouri.edu/owm/hhw.htm
Price: $.50/copy.

**8306 ■ Setting Up Collection Sites for Used
Oil**
Household Hazardous Waste Project
University of Missouri Extension
Columbia, MO 65211
Ph: (573)882-5011
E-mail: owm@missouri.edu
URL: http://outreach.missouri.edu/owm/hhw.htm

8307 ■ Show Animal Care and Handling Guide
Animal Agriculture Alliance
PO Box 9522
Arlington, VA 22219
Ph: (703)562-5160
E-mail: info@animalagalliance.org
URL: http://www.animalagalliance.org

8308 ■ Sierra
Sierra Club
85 Second St., 2nd Fl.
San Francisco, CA 94105-3441
Ph: (415)977-5500
Fax: (415)977-5799
E-mail: sierra.letters@sierraclub.org
URL: http://www.sierraclub.org
Key Personnel: Bob Sipchen, Editor-in-Chief, bob.
sipchen@sierraclub.org; Kristi Rummel, National
Advertising Dir., kristi.rummel@sieraclub.org; Steve
Hawk, Acting Dep. Ed. **URL(s):** http://www.sierraclub.
org/sierra/ **Descr:** Magazine on conservation and

the environment. **Freq:** Bimonthly. **Price:** Included in
membership.

8309 ■ Signals
Association for Communication Excellence in Agricul-
ture, Natural Resources, and Life and Human Sci-
ences
PO Box 110811
Gainesville, FL 32611
Ph: (352)392-9588
Fax: (352)392-8583
E-mail: ace@ifas.ufl.edu
URL: http://www.aceweb.org
Descr: Features news of interest to members.
Includes articles with a professional development
focus. **Freq:** bimonthly.

**8310 ■ Soil and Groundwater Cleanup Maga-
zine**
Association for the Environmental Health of Soils
150 Fearing St.
Amherst, MA 01002
Ph: (413)549-5170
Fax: (413)549-0579
E-mail: paul@aehs.com
URL: http://www.aehs.com
Freq: 9/year.

8311 ■ Solar Energy Resource Guide
Northern California Solar Energy Association
PO Box 3008
Berkeley, CA 94703
Ph: (530)852-0354
Fax: (530)852-0381
E-mail: solarinfo@norcalsolar.org
URL: http://www.norcalsolar.org
Descr: Contains information on local solar resources,
state financial incentives and articles on the uses of
various solar technologies in buildings. **Freq:** annual.

8312 ■ Solar Enews
Northern California Solar Energy Association
PO Box 3008
Berkeley, CA 94703
Ph: (530)852-0354
Fax: (530)852-0381
E-mail: solarinfo@norcalsolar.org
URL: http://www.norcalsolar.org
Descr: Contains solar news, events, policy updates,
incentives, industry news, technology updates, tips
and tricks for solar maintenance. **Freq:** bimonthly.

8313 ■ Solar Flare
Minnesota Renewable Energy Society
2928 5th Ave. S
Minneapolis, MN 55408
Ph: (612)308-4757
E-mail: info@mnrenewables.org
URL: http://www.mres-solar.org
Descr: Contains news and events about the society.
Freq: monthly.

8314 ■ Solar Today
American Solar Energy Society
2400 Central Ave., Ste. A
Boulder, CO 80301
Ph: (303)443-3130
Fax: (303)443-3212
E-mail: ases@ases.org
URL: http://www.ases.org
Descr: Reports on the solar energy industry; includes
information on new technologies and products.
Contains calendar of events and product updates.
Freq: bimonthly. **Price:** included in membership
dues, $29/year for nonmembers.

8315 ■ Solutions
Environmental Defense
257 Park Ave. S
New York, NY 10010
Ph: (212)505-2100
Fax: (212)505-2375
E-mail: members@environmentaldefense.org
URL: http://www.environmentaldefense.org
Descr: Reports on environmental protection
activities. Includes staff and trustee profiles. **Freq:**

bimonthly. **Price:** included in membership dues, free
for nonmembers; single copy only. **ISSN:** 0163-2566.

8316 ■ Southeast Environmental Directory
Harbinger Communications
112 Glenview St.
Santa Cruz, CA 95062
E-mail: info@environmentaldirectory.net
URL: http://www.environmentaldirectory.net
URL(s): http://www.environmentaldirectory.net **Entries include:** Company name, address, phone,
name and title of contact, number of employees,
geographical area served, financial data, branch office or subsidiary names and addresses, requirements for membership, descriptions of product/
service. **Price:** $50, software; Free, online.

8317 ■ Stored Waste Abatement Program
Household Hazardous Waste Project
University of Missouri Extension
Columbia, MO 65211
Ph: (573)882-5011
E-mail: owm@missouri.edu
URL: http://outreach.missouri.edu/owm/hhw.htm
Price: $.75/copy.

**8318 ■ Strengthening Demand Side Manage-
ment In Ohio**
Center for Clean Air Policy
750 First St. NE, Ste. 940
Washington, DC 20002
Ph: (202)408-9260
Fax: (202)408-8896
E-mail: communications@ccap.org
URL: http://www.ccap.org
Descr: Includes information of the progress of Ohio's
investor-owned utilities to implement DSM programs.
Price: $30.

8319 ■ The Sunpaper
New Mexico Solar Energy Association
1009 Bradbury SE, No. 35
Albuquerque, NM 87106
Ph: (505)246-0400
Fax: (505)246-2251
E-mail: info@nmsea.org
URL: http://www.nmsea.org
Freq: bimonthly.

8320 ■ Sustainability Communicator
Izaak Walton League of America Midwest Office
1619 Dayton Ave., Ste. 202
St. Paul, MN 55104
Ph: (651)649-1446
Fax: (651)649-1494
E-mail: midwestoffice@iwla.org
URL: http://www.iwla.org
Descr: Features update on Sustainability Education
Project. **Freq:** bimonthly.

**8321 ■ Sustainable Agriculture Curriculum-
Grades 4-6**
Alternative Energy Resources Organization
432 N Last Chance Gulch
Helena, MT 59601-5014
Ph: (406)443-7272
Fax: (406)442-9120
E-mail: aero@aeromt.org
URL: http://www.aeromt.org
Descr: Includes research results.

8322 ■ Sustainable Communities Review
Environmental Alliance for Senior Involvement
5615 26th St. N
Arlington, VA 22207-1407
Ph: (703)241-4927
Fax: (703)538-5504
E-mail: easi@easi.org
URL: http://www.easi.org
Freq: biennial.

**8323 ■ Sustainable Planet: Solutions for the
21st Century**
Center for a New American Dream
6930 Carroll Ave., Ste. 900
Takoma Park, MD 20912-4466

Ph: (301)891-3683
Fax: (301)891-3684
E-mail: newdream@newdream.org
URL: http://www.ibuydifferent.org
Price: $15.50.

8324 ■ Sustainable Slopes: Annual Report
National Ski Areas Association
133 S Van Gordon St., Ste. 300
Lakewood, CO 80228
Ph: (303)987-1111
Fax: (303)986-2345
E-mail: nsaa@nsaa.org
URL: http://www.nsaa.org

8325 ■ Symposium Proceedings
National Council on Radiation Protection and Measurements
7910 Woodmont Ave., Ste. 400
Bethesda, MD 20814-3076
Ph: (301)657-2652
Fax: (301)907-8768
E-mail: schauer@ncrponline.org
URL: http://www.ncrponline.org
Freq: periodic.

8326 ■ Tackling Toxics in Everyday Products
INFORM Inc.
5 Hanover Sq., Fl. 19
New York, NY 10004-2638
Ph: (212)361-2400
Fax: (212)361-2412
E-mail: info@informinc.org
URL: http://www.informinc.org
Key Personnel: Gina Goldstein, Editor, goldstein@informinc.org. **URL(s):** http://www.informinc.org **Covers:** Over 253 government agencies, public interest groups, academic institutions, and industry and professional associations worldwide that are working to examine, prevent, or alleviate problems caused in whole or in part by the use and disposal of consumer and building products containing toxic chemicals. **Price:** $19.95.

8327 ■ Talking Points
Global Environment Facility
1818 H St. NW, MSN G6-602
Washington, DC 20433
Ph: (202)473-0508
Fax: (202)522-3240
E-mail: secretariat@thegef.org
URL: http://www.gefweb.org

8328 ■ Technical Reference and Training Manual
Association of Water Technologies
9707 Key West Ave., Ste. 100
Rockville, MD 20850
Ph: (301)740-1421
Fax: (301)990-9771
E-mail: hzimmerman@awt.org
URL: http://www.awt.org
Price: $100 for members, $250 for nonmembers.

8329 ■ Technical Report
Beyond Pesticides - National Coalition Against the Misuse of Pesticides
701 E St. SE, Ste. 200
Washington, DC 20003
Ph: (202)543-5450
Fax: (202)543-4791
E-mail: info@beyondpesticides.org
URL: http://www.beyondpesticides.org
Descr: Provides the most current information on pesticide issues. **Freq:** monthly. **Price:** $50.

8330 ■ Technical Supplement
Environmental Information Association
6935 Wisconsin Ave., Ste. 306
Chevy Chase, MD 20815-6112
Ph: (301)961-4999
Fax: (301)961-3094
E-mail: info@eia-usa.org
URL: http://www.eia-usa.org
Descr: Covers laboratory/field analysis and monitor-

ing techniques, and environmental control methodologies. **Freq:** periodic.

8331 ■ TREIA Newsletter
Texas Renewable Energy Industries Association
PO Box 16469
Austin, TX 78761-6469
Ph: (512)345-5446
Fax: (512)345-6831
E-mail: rsmith@treia.org
URL: http://www.treia.org
Descr: Provides updates and archival record on policy issues and industry activities. **Freq:** 3/year. **Price:** free for members.

8332 ■ Turf News
Lawn Institute
2 E Main St.
East Dundee, IL 60118
Ph: (847)649-5555
Fax: (847)649-5678
E-mail: info@thelawninstitue.org
URL: http://www.lawninstitute.com
Descr: Provides the latest information on lawn and sports turf establishment, maintenance, and renovation. **Freq:** annual. **Price:** free.

8333 ■ Understanding Ventilation
Healthy House Institute
430 N Sewell Rd.
Bloomington, IN 47408
Ph: (812)332-5073
Fax: (812)332-5073
E-mail: healthy@bloomington.in.us
URL: http://www.hhinst.com

8334 ■ U.S. Nuclear Plants in the 21st Century: The Risk of a Lifetime
Union of Concerned Scientists
2 Brattle Sq.
Cambridge, MA 02238-9105
Ph: (617)547-5552
Fax: (617)864-9405
URL: http://www.ucsusa.org
Price: $10 each.

8335 ■ Unnecessary Risks
Beyond Pesticides - National Coalition Against the Misuse of Pesticides
701 E St. SE, Ste. 200
Washington, DC 20003
Ph: (202)543-5450
Fax: (202)543-4791
E-mail: info@beyondpesticides.org
URL: http://www.beyondpesticides.org
Price: $10.

8336 ■ The Untold Story: The Silver Lining for West Virginia in Acid Rain Control
Center for Clean Air Policy
750 First St. NE, Ste. 940
Washington, DC 20002
Ph: (202)408-9260
Fax: (202)408-8896
E-mail: communications@ccap.org
URL: http://www.ccap.org

8337 ■ Uranium Mining and Milling: A Primer
Southwest Research and Information Center
PO Box 4524
Albuquerque, NM 87106
Ph: (505)262-1862
Fax: (505)262-1864
E-mail: info@sric.org
URL: http://www.sric.org

8338 ■ Uranium and the Nuclear Cycle
Health and Energy Institute
615 Kennebec Ave.
Takoma Park, MD 20912

Ph: (301)585-5831
Fax: (301)585-9474
E-mail: kitbob@erols.com

8339 ■ Urban Home Composting Rhodent-Resistant Bins and Environmental Health Standards
City Farmer Society
Box 74567
Kitsilano RPO
Vancouver, BC, Canada V6K 4P4
Ph: (604)685-5832
Fax: (604)685-5862
E-mail: cityfarm@interchange.ubc.ca
URL: http://www.cityfarmer.org
Price: $10.

8340 ■ VIEWPOINT
Safe Energy Communication Council
1717 Massachusetts Ave. NW, Ste. 106
Washington, DC 20036
Fax: (202)234-9194
Descr: Newspaper editorial service. **Freq:** periodic.

8341 ■ Walk Softly
Yukon Conservation Society
302 Hawkins St.
Whitehorse, YT, Canada Y1A 1X6
Ph: (867)668-5678
Fax: (867)668-6637
E-mail: ycs@ycs.yk.ca
URL: http://www.yukonconservation.org
Freq: quarterly. **Price:** included in membership dues.

8342 ■ Walking a Nuclear Tightrope: Unlearned Lessons of Year-plus Reactor Outages
Union of Concerned Scientists
2 Brattle Sq.
Cambridge, MA 02238-9105
Ph: (617)547-5552
Fax: (617)864-9405
URL: http://www.ucsusa.org
Price: $10 each.

8343 ■ Waltonian
Izaak Walton League of America, Minnesota Division
161 St. Anthony Ave., Ste. 910
St. Paul, MN 55103
Ph: (651)221-0251
E-mail: ikes@minnesotaikes.org
URL: http://www.minnesotaikes.org
Descr: Includes member activities and conservation issues. **Freq:** quarterly. **Price:** included in membership dues.

8344 ■ Wastewater Treatment Units and Related Products and Components
NSF International
789 N Dixboro Rd.
PO Box 130140
Ann Arbor, MI 48113-0140
Ph: (734)769-8010
Fax: (734)769-0109
E-mail: info@nsf.org
URL: http://www.nsf.org
Freq: periodic.

8345 ■ Water Courses
Izaak Walton League of America Midwest Office
1619 Dayton Ave., Ste. 202
St. Paul, MN 55104
Ph: (651)649-1446
Fax: (651)649-1494
E-mail: midwestoffice@iwla.org
URL: http://www.iwla.org
Descr: Features update on the Save Our Streams Program. **Freq:** semiannual.

8346 ■ Water Treatment Fundamentals
Water Quality Association
4151 Naperville Rd.
Lisle, IL 60532-1088
Ph: (630)505-0160
Fax: (630)505-9637
E-mail: info@wqa.org
URL: http://www.wqa.org

Descr: Covers water quality, chemistry, water problems, treatment technologies, and installation procedure issues. **Price:** $154.

8347 ■ Water Treatment Fundamentals Seminar Audio Cassette Series
Water Quality Association
4151 Naperville Rd.
Lisle, IL 60532-1088
Ph: (630)505-0160
Fax: (630)505-9637
E-mail: info@wqa.org
URL: http://www.wqa.org
Descr: Contains a must-know information - ideal for person wanting to take the Certified Water Specialist exam. **Price:** $200.

8348 ■ What Your Home Haz
Household Hazardous Waste Project
University of Missouri Extension
Columbia, MO 65211
Ph: (573)882-5011
E-mail: owm@missouri.edu
URL: http://outreach.missouri.edu/owm/hhw.htm
Price: $.75/copy.

8349 ■ WildAlert
The Wilderness Society
1615 M St. NW
Washington, DC 20036
E-mail: member@tws.org
URL: http://www.wilderness.org
Freq: weekly.

8350 ■ Wilderness
The Wilderness Society
1615 M St. NW
Washington, DC 20036
E-mail: member@tws.org
URL: http://www.wilderness.org
Freq: annual. **Price:** included in membership dues.

8351 ■ Wilderness
Wilderness Society - California/Nevada Regional Office
655 Montgomery St., Ste. 1000
San Francisco, CA 94111
Ph: (415)398-1111
Fax: (415)398-1632
E-mail: ca@tws.org
URL: http://www.wilderness.org
Freq: annual.

8352 ■ Wilderness Act Handbook-40th Anniversary Edition (2004)
The Wilderness Society
1615 M St. NW
Washington, DC 20036
E-mail: member@tws.org
URL: http://www.wilderness.org
Descr: Serves as reference for those working to protect what is left of wild America. **Freq:** periodic.

8353 ■ Wilderness Magazine
Wilderness Society, Northeast Regional Office
9 Union St., 3rd Fl.
Hallowell, ME 04347
Ph: (207)626-5553
E-mail: jeremy_sheaffer@tws.org
Freq: annual.

8354 ■ Wilderness Report
The Wilderness Society
1615 M St. NW
Washington, DC 20036
E-mail: member@tws.org
URL: http://www.wilderness.org
Freq: biweekly.

8355 ■ The Wilderness Society
Wilderness Society - California/Nevada Regional Office
655 Montgomery St., Ste. 1000
San Francisco, CA 94111
Ph: (415)398-1111
Fax: (415)398-1632

E-mail: ca@tws.org
URL: http://www.wilderness.org
Freq: quarterly.

8356 ■ Wilderness Society Newsletter
Wilderness Society, Northeast Regional Office
9 Union St., 3rd Fl.
Hallowell, ME 04347
Ph: (207)626-5553
E-mail: jeremy_sheaffer@tws.org
Freq: quarterly.

8357 ■ The Wilderness Society's Newsletter
The Wilderness Society
1615 M St. NW
Washington, DC 20036
E-mail: member@tws.org
URL: http://www.wilderness.org
Freq: quarterly.

8358 ■ Wildlife Rehabilitation
National Wildlife Rehabilitators Association
2625 Clearwater Rd., Ste. 110
St. Cloud, MN 56301
Ph: (320)230-9920
Fax: (320)230-3077
E-mail: nwra@nwrawildlife.org
URL: http://www.nwrawildlife.org
Freq: annual.

8359 ■ Wildlife Rehabilitation Bulletin
National Wildlife Rehabilitators Association
2625 Clearwater Rd., Ste. 110
St. Cloud, MN 56301
Ph: (320)230-9920
Fax: (320)230-3077
E-mail: nwra@nwrawildlife.org
URL: http://www.nwrawildlife.org
Freq: semiannual. **Price:** included in membership dues.

8360 ■ The Wildlife Rehabilitator
National Wildlife Rehabilitators Association
2625 Clearwater Rd., Ste. 110
St. Cloud, MN 56301
Ph: (320)230-9920
Fax: (320)230-3077
E-mail: nwra@nwrawildlife.org
URL: http://www.nwrawildlife.org
Descr: Contains information on NWRA accomplishments and activities. **Freq:** semiannual. **Price:** $7.

8361 ■ Wisconsin's Strategy: Cleaning the Air, Protecting the Climate, Sustaining the Economy
Center for Clean Air Policy
750 First St. NE, Ste. 940
Washington, DC 20002
Ph: (202)408-9260
Fax: (202)408-8896
E-mail: communications@ccap.org
URL: http://www.ccap.org

8362 ■ World Directory of Environmental Organizations
California Institute of Public Affairs
PO Box 189040
Sacramento, CA 95818
Ph: (916)442-2472
Fax: (916)442-2478
E-mail: info@cipahq.org
URL: http://www.interenvironment.org/cipa/index.htm
Key Personnel: Thaddeus C. Trzyna, Editor, ted_trzyna@interenvironment.org. **URL(s):** http://www.interenvironment.org/wd/index.htm, http://www.interenvironment.org **Covers:** over 1,500 governmental, intergovernmental, United Nations, and non-governmental environmental protection organizations in over 200 countries. **Entries include:** Organization name, address, phone, fax, website, Geographical area served, description of services and projects.

8363 ■ World Resource Review
Global Warming International Center
PO Box 50303

Palo Alto, CA 94303-0303
Ph: (630)910-1551
Fax: (630)910-1561
E-mail: gw17@globalwarming.net
URL: http://www.globalwarming.net
Freq: quarterly. **Price:** $167. **ISSN:** 1042-8011.

8364 ■ WQA NewsFax
Water Quality Association
4151 Naperville Rd.
Lisle, IL 60532-1088
Ph: (630)505-0160
Fax: (630)505-9637
E-mail: info@wqa.org
URL: http://www.wqa.org
Freq: bimonthly.

Multimedia Resources

8365 ■ Air We Breathe in Industrial Environments
Film Library/Greater Los Angeles Safety Council
600 Wilshire Blvd., No. 1263
Los Angeles, CA 90017
Ph: (213)385-6461
Free: 800-421-9585
Fax: (213)385-8405
URL: http://www.lasafety.org
Format(s): Videocassette. **Descr:** This tape looks at the composition of air in various working environments and how to protect workers through protective equipment and proper ventilation. **Prod. Date:** 198?. **Length:** 16.

8366 ■ Animal Safety Is Fun!
Glencoe Animal Hospital
3712 N. High St
Columbus, OH 43214-3590
Ph: (614)268-0540
Format(s): Videocassette. **Descr:** Veterinarian Michael Cornwall shares safety tips for children and adults when dealing with dogs. Suggestions include avoiding stray dogs and standing still if approached by a dog, plus more. **Prod. Date:** 1992. **Length:** 15. **Price:** $49.95.

8367 ■ Building With Awareness
Gaiam, Inc.
833 W. South Boulder Rd.
PO Box 3095
Boulder, CO 80307-3095
Free: 877-989-6321
URL: http://www.gaiam.com
Format(s): DVD. **Descr:** An in-depth look on how to build solar-powered home for a sustainable living environment, without sacrificing comfort. **Price:** $20.

8368 ■ Don't Panic: Responding to a Hazardous Materials Incident
LearnCom HR Consulting and Training
38 Discovery, Ste. 250
Irvine, CA 92618
Ph: (515)440-0890
Free: 800-698-8263
Fax: (515)221-3149
E-mail: nhartline@learncom.com
URL: http://www.learncomhr.com
Format(s): Videocassette. **Descr:** Step-by-step instruction on containing and cleaning up chemical spills. Includes a leader's guide and 10 workbooks. **Prod. Date:** 1995. **Length:** 13. **Price:** $395.00.

8369 ■ Energy-Efficient Living
Rodale Press, Inc.
33 E. Minor St
Emmaus, PA 18098-0099
Ph: (610)967-5171
Fax: (610)967-8963
E-mail: customer_service@rodale.com
URL: http://www.rodale.com
Format(s): Videocassette. **Descr:** Amory and Hunter Lovins demonstrate their "soft path" approach to energy conservation in the first program on this cassette, "Lovins' on the Soft Path." The second program, "Living Lightly," documents the energy-

efficient lifestyle of a 76-year-old rural mountain woman. **Prod. Date:** 1980. **Length:** 55.

8370 ■ *Environmental Dog*
Pyramid Media
PO Box 1048/WEB
Santa Monica, CA 90406
Ph: (310)828-7577
Free: 800-421-2304
Fax: (310)453-9083
E-mail: info@pyramedia.com
URL: http://www.pyramedia.com
Format(s): Videocassette. **Descr:** A pollution-pocked pup becomes a mutt with a mission in this tale of the environmental effects of effluent affluence. **Prod. Date:** 1990. **Length:** 20. **Price:** $325.00.

8371 ■ *Environmental Health Connections for the Equine*
EquiVid.com
HorseTV Media Group, Inc
26850 Agoura Rd
Calabasas, CA 91301
Ph: (818)598-1000
Free: 800-USA-WHOA
Fax: (818)880-0803
E-mail: info@horsetv.com
URL: http://www.equivid.com/menu/menu.html
Format(s): Videocassette. **Descr:** Examination of the effects of environmental pollution and its continuing build-up in living things. Specifically, it targets the effect pollution may play in the development of EPM (Equine Protozoal Myelitis) in horses. **Prod. Date:** ?. **Length:** ?. **Price:** $49.95.

8372 ■ *Free Energy: The Race to Zero Point*
The Video Collection
PO Box 2284
South Burlington, VT 05407-2284
Format(s): Videocassette. **Descr:** Documentary takes a look at the quest to find safe non-polluting energy sources that are available to everyone. Features segments on Nikola Tesla's method of "broadcasting" free energy, electric cars, zero-point "space" energy and cold fusion. **Prod. Date:** 1998. **Length:** 120. **Price:** $29.95.

8373 ■ *Getting Started with Roses*
AGCOM International
4005 N. Lugano Way
Flagstaff, AZ 86004
E-mail: larryklass@aol.com
Format(s): Videocassette. **Descr:** Provides simple, step-by-step instructions on how to grow roses, discusses which types of roses are best for specific situations and describes the role of roses in mythology and history. Features Keith Mills, Horticultural Supervisor of the world-famous Tyler Rose Garden. **Prod. Date:** 1998. **Length:** 28. **Price:** $19.95.

8374 ■ *Growing Green Babies*
Gaiam, Inc.
833 W. South Boulder Rd.
PO Box 3095
Boulder, CO 80307-3095
URL: http://www.gaiam.com
Format(s): DVD. **Descr:** Tips on how to have an organic pregnancy and raise a "green" baby. **Price:** $19.98.

8375 ■ *Hazardous Material Sampling*
Williams Learning Network
15400 Calhoun Dr
Rockville, MD 20855-2762
Ph: (301)315-6700
Free: 800-848-1717
Fax: (301)315-6880
E-mail: mait@willearn.com
URL: http://www.willearn.com
Format(s): Videocassette. **Descr:** Discusses principles of sampling hazardous materials, which include keeping incompatible substances separate and keeping toxic materials away from the person taking the sample. Depicts sampling techniques using gas bombs, glove bags, and other equipment.

Includes Leader's Guide and 25 Program Guides. **Length:** 12.

8376 ■ *Hazardous Materials Awareness: Maintenance Personnel*
Bergwall Productions, Inc.
1224 Baltimore Pike, Ste. 203
Kennett Square, PA 19317
Ph: (610)361-0334
Free: 800-934-8696
Fax: (610)361-0092
E-mail: bergwall@bergwall.com
URL: http://www.bergwall.com
Format(s): Videocassette. **Descr:** Details the dangers of mishandling hazardous materials, demonstrates responsible attitudes toward hazardous materials, and explains correct handling procedures. **Prod. Date:** 1993. **Length:** 67. **Price:** $599.00.

8377 ■ *Hazardous Materials Awareness: Managerial Resources*
Bergwall Productions, Inc.
1224 Baltimore Pike, Ste. 203
Kennett Square, PA 19317
Ph: (610)361-0334
Free: 800-934-8696
Fax: (610)361-0092
E-mail: bergwall@bergwall.com
URL: http://www.bergwall.com
Format(s): Videocassette. **Descr:** Three programs introduce the dangers of hazardous materials handling by employees. **Prod. Date:** 1993. **Length:** 52. **Price:** $449.00.

8378 ■ *Hazardous Materials: First Responder*
Media Resources, Inc.
9012-B NW Holly Rd
Bremerton, WA 98321
Ph: (360)693-3344
Free: 800-666-0106
Fax: (360)693-1760
Format(s): Videocassette. **Descr:** A training program for people who have to work near hazardous materials. **Prod. Date:** 1988. **Length:** 30. **Price:** $675.00.

8379 ■ *Hazardous Materials—Flammables*
Film Library/Greater Los Angeles Safety Council
600 Wilshire Blvd., No. 1263
Los Angeles, CA 90017
Ph: (213)385-6461
Free: 800-421-9585
Fax: (213)385-8405
URL: http://www.lasafety.org
Format(s): Videocassette. **Descr:** This film stresses individual responsibility for following company procedure and basic safety rules concerning the handling of chemicals and flammables. **Prod. Date:** 198?. **Length:** 14.

8380 ■ *Hazardous Materials—Handle with Care*
Film Library/Greater Los Angeles Safety Council
600 Wilshire Blvd., No. 1263
Los Angeles, CA 90017
Ph: (213)385-6461
Free: 800-421-9585
Fax: (213)385-8405
URL: http://www.lasafety.org
Format(s): Videocassette. **Descr:** This film offers a detailed look at how to properly handle solvents and corrosives in industry. **Prod. Date:** 198?. **Length:** 13.

8381 ■ *The Healthy House Video Series*
Healthy House Institute
430 N. Sewell Rd
Bloomington, IN 47408
Ph: (812)332-5073
Fax: (812)332-5073
E-mail: healthy@bloomington.in.us
URL: http://www.hhinst.com
Format(s): Videocassette. **Descr:** Hosts John and Lynn Bower show the viewer how to build their house to optimize air quality, thereby reducing pollutants in the home and leading to a healthier life. Thirteen

volumes on five videocassettes. **Prod. Date:** 2000. **Length:** 352. **Price:** $99.95.

8382 ■ *Home Energy Conservation Series*
Bullfrog Films, Inc.
PO Box 149
Oley, PA 19547
Ph: (610)779-8226
Free: 800-543-3764
Fax: (610)370-1978
E-mail: video@bullfrogfilms.com
URL: http://bullfrogfilms.com
Format(s): Videocassette. **Descr:** This three-program series shows how to reduce fossil fuel consumption in the home. Programs are available individually. **Prod. Date:** 1981. **Length:** 28.

8383 ■ *If One Green Bottle?*
Film Library/Greater Los Angeles Safety Council
600 Wilshire Blvd., No. 1263
Los Angeles, CA 90017
Ph: (213)385-6461
Free: 800-421-9585
Fax: (213)385-8405
URL: http://www.lasafety.org
Format(s): Videocassette. **Descr:** An employee in a British factory sues his employer when he loses his sight on the job. **Prod. Date:** 198?. **Length:** 22.

8384 ■ *Legacy of an Oil Spill: Ten Years After Exxon Valdez*
The Media Guild
11722 Sorrento Valley Rd., Ste. E
San Diego, CA 92121
Ph: (858)755-9191
Free: 800-886-9191
Fax: (858)755-4931
E-mail: info@mediaguild.com
URL: http://www.mediaguild.com
Format(s): Videocassette. **Descr:** Examines the environmental impact of 1989's Exxon Valdez oil spill in Alaska's Prince William Sound and the struggle of animal species to recover. **Prod. Date:** 2000. **Length:** 28. **Price:** $99.95.

8385 ■ *MARPOL Oil Pollution Regulations Part I*
John Sabella & Associate
805 W. Emerson St
Seattle, WA 98119
Ph: (206)281-8626
Fax: (206)217-0899
E-mail: sales@johnsabella.com
URL: http://www.johnsabella.com
Format(s): Videocassette. **Descr:** This two-part series examines the MARPOL oil pollution regulations as they relate to the shipping industry. Part I examines the regulations as they apply to all ships and the use of the Oil Record Book for machinery space oils. **Length:** 23. **Price:** $125.

8386 ■ *MARPOL Oil Pollution Regulations Part II*
John Sabella & Associate
805 W. Emerson St
Seattle, WA 98119
Ph: (206)281-8626
Fax: (206)217-0899
E-mail: sales@johnsabella.com
URL: http://www.johnsabella.com
Format(s): Videocassette. **Descr:** This two-part series examines the MARPOL oil pollution regulations as they relate to the shipping industry. Part II examines the regulations as they apply to tankers and the use of the Oil Record Book for cargo oils. **Length:** 30. **Price:** $125.

8387 ■ *Pesticide Handlers and the Worker Protection Standard*
Michigan State University
Instructional Media Center
PO Box 710
East Lansing, MI 48826-0710
Ph: (517)353-3960
Fax: (517)432-2650
E-mail: imcclass@msu.edu

URL: http://www.msu.edu/unit/imc
Format(s): Videocassette. **Descr:** Training requirements implemented by the federal Worker Protection Standard for pesticide handlers. **Prod. Date:** ????.
Length: 47. **Price:** $25.00.

8388 ■ The Pesticide Safety Series
American Nurseryman Publishing Co.
Book Dept
223 W. Jackson Blvd., Ste. 500
Chicago, IL 60606
Ph: (312)427-7339
Free: 800-621-5727
Fax: (312)427-7346
E-mail: books@amerinursery.com
URL: http://www.amerinursery.com
Format(s): Videocassette. **Descr:** Two part series dramatizes and offers step-by-step pesticide safety instruction. Covers orchards, golf courses, greenhouses, crops, etc. Advice includes labeling, wearing protective clothing, mixing and loading instruction, and much more. **Prod. Date:** 1993. **Length:** 30.
Price: $94.99.

8389 ■ Pesticide Safety: Worker Protection II
University of Idaho
Agricultural Publications
PO Box 442240
Moscow, ID 83844-2240
Ph: (208)885-7982
Fax: (208)885-4648
E-mail: calspubs@uidaho.edu
URL: http://info.ag.uidaho.edu
Format(s): Videocassette. **Descr:** Explains requirements set by the Environmental Protection Act for training agricultural workers and pesticide handlers under the Worker Protection Standard's regulations.
Prod. Date: 1997. **Length:** 64. **Price:** $35.00.

8390 ■ Pesticides
Emergency Film Group
Detrick Lawrence Corp
PO Box 1928
Edgartown, MA 02539
Ph: (508)627-8844
Free: 800-842-0999
Fax: (508)627-8863
E-mail: info@efilmgroup.com
URL: http://www.efilmgroup.com
Format(s): Videocassette. **Descr:** Offers important lessons about handling pesticide incidents including where they may be encountered, when it's best to let a fire burn, symptoms and first aid for pesticide exposure, decontamination procedures, and more.
Prod. Date: 1994. **Length:** 28. **Price:** $395.00.

8391 ■ Renovation Nation: Recycle, Reuse and Reclaim
Gaiam, Inc.
833 W. South Boulder Rd.
PO Box 3095
Boulder, CO 80307-3095
Free: 877-989-6321
URL: http://www.gaiam.com
Format(s): DVD. **Price:** $20.

8392 ■ Renovation Nation: Save Water, Save Money
Gaiam, Inc.
833 W. South Boulder Rd.
PO Box 3095
Boulder, CO 80307-3095
Free: 877-989-6321
URL: http://www.gaiam.com
Format(s): DVD. **Descr:** Former "This Old House" host Steve Thomas visits with ecology-minded homeowners who have "greened" their houses. **Price:**
$19.98.

8393 ■ Saving Energy & Money Too
Bullfrog Films, Inc.
PO Box 149
Oley, PA 19547
Ph: (610)779-8226
Free: 800-543-3764
Fax: (610)370-1978

E-mail: video@bullfrogfilms.com
URL: http://bullfrogfilms.com
Format(s): Videocassette. **Descr:** Low cost/no cost tips for reducing energy usage in the home are provided in this program. **Prod. Date:** 1982. **Length:** 25.

8394 ■ Seabrook 1977
Turning Tide Productions
PO Box 864
Wendell, MA 01379
Ph: (978)544-8313
Free: 800-557-6414
Fax: (978)544-7989
E-mail: info@turningtide.com
URL: http://www.turningtide.com
Format(s): Videocassette. **Descr:** Chronicles the 1977 environmenal protest where 1414 people were arrested at a nuclear power plant under construction in Seabrook, New Hampshire. Special pricing available to high schools, libraries and community organizations. **Length:** 53. **Price:** $189.

8395 ■ Simple Steps to a Greener Home
Gaiam, Inc.
833 W. South Boulder Rd.
PO Box 3095
Boulder, CO 80307-3095
Free: 877-989-6321
URL: http://www.gaiam.com
Format(s): DVD. **Price:** $14.98.

8396 ■ Spill Control and Containment
Williams Learning Network
15400 Calhoun Dr
Rockville, MD 20855-2762
Ph: (301)315-6700
Free: 800-848-1717
Fax: (301)315-6880
E-mail: mait@willearn.com
URL: http://www.willearn.com
Format(s): Videocassette. **Descr:** Profiles specialized training necessary for hazardous spill control and containment. Provides information on offensive and defensive strategies used in control and containment. Emphasizes specialized training and proper PPE. Includes Leader's Guide and 25 Program Guides. **Length:** 11.

8397 ■ The Thermal Wilderness
Film Library/Greater Los Angeles Safety Council
600 Wilshire Blvd., No. 1263
Los Angeles, CA 90017
Ph: (213)385-6461
Free: 800-421-9585
Fax: (213)385-8405
URL: http://www.lasafety.org
Format(s): Videocassette. **Descr:** A dramatization of how heat, humidity and solar radiation affects a summer back-packing party. **Prod. Date:** 198?. **Length:** 29.

8398 ■ Toxic Waste: Information Is the Best Defense
Bullfrog Films, Inc.
PO Box 149
Oley, PA 19547
Ph: (610)779-8226
Free: 800-543-3764
Fax: (610)370-1978
E-mail: video@bullfrogfilms.com
URL: http://bullfrogfilms.com
Format(s): Videocassette. **Descr:** In two parts this program shows how community groups can organize protests and ordinances to fight toxic dumping. **Prod. Date:** 1986. **Length:** 26.

8399 ■ Trucking Hazardous Materials
Emergency Film Group
Detrick Lawrence Corp
PO Box 1928
Edgartown, MA 02539
Ph: (508)627-8844
Free: 800-842-0999
Fax: (508)627-8863

E-mail: info@efilmgroup.com
URL: http://www.efilmgroup.com
Format(s): Videocassette. **Descr:** Outlines a course of instruction in how to safely and legally transport hazardous materials by truck, including recognizing the nine hazard classes, proper packaging, labelling and placarding, loading and unloading, proper preparation of shipping papers, and action to take in an emergency. **Prod. Date:** 1993. **Length:** ?. **Price:** $325.00.

8400 ■ Using Respirators in Hazardous Environments
Williams Learning Network
15400 Calhoun Dr
Rockville, MD 20855-2762
Ph: (301)315-6700
Free: 800-848-1717
Fax: (301)315-6880
E-mail: mait@willearn.com
URL: http://www.willearn.com
Format(s): Videocassette. **Descr:** Explains the limitations, such as restricting visibility, mobility, and communication, of respirators. Covers approaches for dealing with these limitations, describes precautions when working in hazardous atmospheres and confined spaces, and provides basic techniques for respirator cleaning and inspection after they have been used. Includes Leader's Guide and 25 Program Guides. **Prod. Date:** 19??. **Length:** 11.

8401 ■ Using Solar Energy
Rodale Press, Inc.
33 E. Minor St
Emmaus, PA 18098-0099
Ph: (610)967-5171
Fax: (610)967-8963
E-mail: customer_service@rodale.com
URL: http://www.rodale.com
Format(s): Videocassette. **Descr:** Two programs which describe how to use solar energy to help heat your home and how to build a solar-powered greenhouse are contained on this cassette: "Opening Your Home to Solar Energy" and "The Attached Solar Greenhouse." **Prod. Date:** 1980. **Length:** 55.

8402 ■ Waste Minimization - It's Everyone's Job
Williams Learning Network
15400 Calhoun Dr
Rockville, MD 20855-2762
Ph: (301)315-6700
Free: 800-848-1717
Fax: (301)315-6880
E-mail: mait@willearn.com
URL: http://www.willearn.com
Format(s): Videocassette. **Descr:** Outlines practical waste minimization techniques. Uses examples of workers in real-life settings doing their part to maximize safety and minimize waste. Includes Leader's Guide and 25 Program Guides. **Length:** 12.

8403 ■ What You Don't Know & Health Hazards in the Environment
Aquarius Productions
Olde Medfield Sq
18 N Main St
Sherborn, MA 01770
Ph: (508)650-1616
Free: 888-440-2963
Fax: (508)650-1665
E-mail: tm@aquariusproductions.com
URL: http://www.aquariusproductions.com
Format(s): Videocassette. **Descr:** Discusses health hazards in the environment and their consequences with a focus on air pollution and contaminated water.
Prod. Date: 2001. **Length:** 28. **Price:** $99.00.

8404 ■ What You Don't Know: Learning About Hazardous Materials
LearnCom HR Consulting and Training
38 Discovery, Ste. 250
Irvine, CA 92618
Ph: (515)440-0890
Free: 800-698-8263

Fax: (515)221-3149
E-mail: nhartline@learncom.com
URL: http://www.learncomhr.com
Format(s): Videocassette. **Descr:** Companies, supervisors, and workers learn how to protect their environment from hazardous substances. Includes a leader's guide and 10 workbooks. **Prod. Date:** 19??.
Length: 12. **Price:** $295.00.

8405 ■ *Working with Asbestos*
Williams Learning Network
15400 Calhoun Dr
Rockville, MD 20855-2762
Ph: (301)315-6700
Free: 800-848-1717
Fax: (301)315-6880
E-mail: mait@willearn.com
URL: http://www.willearn.com
Format(s): Videocassette. **Descr:** Summarizes the use of personal protection equipment in the presence of asbestos. Includes Leader's Guide and 25 Program Guides. **Length:** 9.

8406 ■ *Working Safely with Pesticides*
American Nurseryman Publishing Co.
Book Dept
223 W. Jackson Blvd., Ste. 500
Chicago, IL 60606
Ph: (312)427-7339
Free: 800-621-5727
Fax: (312)427-7346
E-mail: books@amerinursery.com
URL: http://www.amerinursery.com
Format(s): Videocassette. **Descr:** Offers safety tips for those working with pesticides. Covers labeling, protective equipment, emergency procedures, storage, and disposal. Fulfills federal and state training requirements. **Prod. Date:** 1989. **Length:** 17. **Price:** $59.99.

8407 ■ *Your House, Your Health: A Non-Toxic Building Guide*
Healthy House Institute
430 N. Sewell Rd
Bloomington, IN 47408
Ph: (812)332-5073
Fax: (812)332-5073
E-mail: healthy@bloomington.in.us
URL: http://www.hhinst.com
Format(s): Videocassette. **Descr:** With the help of a 1568 square foot model house, the viewer is shown how to build a healthy house. Three basic principles are put into practice: eliminate toxic materials from the premises; separate those you must keep from the living space; and finally, have a controlled ventilation system. Overviews important features of a "healthy house," such as energy efficiency (superinsulation), steel framing, a solar hot water heater, and a superior ventilation system. **Prod. Date:** 1992. **Length:** 28. **Price:** $19.95.

Media Contacts

8408 ■ Associated Press
2021 K St. NW, 6th Fl.
Washington, DC 20006-1082
Contact: Josef Hebert, Energy Correspondent
Ph: (202)776-9472
Fax: (202)726-9570
E-mail: jherbert@ap.org
URL: http://www.ap.org

Alabama

8409 ■ *Birmingham News*
Newhouse Newspapers
2201 Fourth Ave. N.
Birmingham, AL 35203
Contact: Katherine Bouma, Environmental Reporter
Ph: (205)325-2457
E-mail: kbouma@bhamnews.com
URL: http://www.bhamnews.com

Arizona

8410 ■ *Arizona Daily Star*
Lee Enterprises, Inc.
PO Box 26807
Tucson, AZ 85726-6807
Contact: Anthony Davis, Environment Reporter
Ph: (520)806-7746
E-mail: tdavis@azstarnet.com
URL: http://www.azstarnet.com

8411 ■ *The Arizona Republic*
Gannet Co., Inc.
PO Box 1950
Phoenix, AZ 85001
Contact: Shaun McKinnon, Environment Issues Reporter
Ph: (602)444-8632
E-mail: shaun.mckinnon@arizonarepublic.com
URL: http://www.azcentral.com

8412 ■ *The Arizona Republic*
Gannet Co., Inc.
PO Box 1950
Phoenix, AZ 85001
Contact: Ginger Richardson, Environment Issues Reporter
Ph: (602)444-4834
URL: http://www.azcentral.com

California

8413 ■ *Contra Costa Times*
Knight Ridder, Inc.
2640 Shadelands Dr.
Walnut Creek, CA 94598-2578
Contact: Mike Taugher, Environment Reporter
Ph: (925)925-2671
E-mail: mtaugher@cctimes.com
URL: http://www.contracostatimes.com

8414 ■ *Contra Costa Times*
Knight Ridder, Inc.
2640 Shadelands Dr.
Walnut Creek, CA 94598-2578
Contact: Janis Mara, Energy Reporter
E-mail: jmara@bayareanewsgroup.com
URL: http://www.contracostatimes.com

8415 ■ *The Fresno Bee*
The McClatchy Company
1626 E St.
Fresno, CA 93786-0001
Contact: Mark Grossi, Environment Reporter
Ph: (559)441-6316
E-mail: mgrossi@fresnobee.com
URL: http://www.fresnobee.com

8416 ■ *Los Angeles Times*
Tribune Company
202 W. First St.
Los Angeles, CA 90012
Contact: Janet Wilson, Environment Writer
Ph: (213)237-7847
E-mail: janet.wilson@latimes.com
URL: http://www.latimes.com

8417 ■ *Los Angeles Times*
Tribune Company
202 W. First St.
Los Angeles, CA 90012
Contact: Ken Weiss, Environment Writer
Ph: (213)237-7847
E-mail: ken.weiss@latimes.com
URL: http://www.latimes.com

8418 ■ *Los Angeles Times*
Tribune Company
202 W. First St.
Los Angeles, CA 90012
Contact: Julie Cart, Environment Writer
Ph: (213)237-7847

E-mail: julie.cart@latimes.com
URL: http://www.latimes.com

8419 ■ *Los Angeles Times*
Tribune Company
202 W. First St.
Los Angeles, CA 90012
Contact: Margot Roosevelt, Environment Writer
Ph: (213)237-7847
E-mail: margot.roosevelt@latimes.com
URL: http://www.latimes.com

8420 ■ *Los Angeles Times*
Tribune Company
202 W. First St.
Los Angeles, CA 90012
Contact: Bettina Boxall, Environment Writer
Ph: (213)237-7847
E-mail: bettina.boxall@latimes.com
URL: http://www.latimes.com

8421 ■ *Orange County Register*
625 N. Grand Ave.
Santa Ana, CA 92701-4347
Contact: Pat Brennan, Environment Editor
Ph: (714)796-7865
E-mail: pbrennan@ocregister.com
URL: http://www.ocregister.com

8422 ■ *The Press-Enterprise*
3450 Fourteenth St.
Riverside, CA 92501
Contact: David Danelski, Environment Reporter
Ph: (951)368-9471
E-mail: ddanelski@pe.com
URL: http://www.pe.com

8423 ■ *San Diego Union-Tribune*
Copley Press, Inc.
PO Box 120191
San Diego, CA 92112-0191
Contact: Cathy Lubenski, Garden Editor
Ph: (619)293-3131
E-mail: cathy.lubenski@uniontrib.com
URL: http://www.uniontrib.com

8424 ■ *San Francisco Chronicle*
Hearst Newspapers
901 Mission St.
San Francisco, CA 94103-2988
Contact: David R. Baker, Energy Reporter
Ph: (415)777-8400
E-mail: dbaker@sfchronicle.com
URL: http://www.sfchronicle.com

8425 ■ *San Francisco Chronicle*
Hearst Newspapers
901 Mission St.
San Francisco, CA 94103-2988
Contact: Simar Khanna, Home and Garden Editor
Ph: (415)777-6247
E-mail: skhanna@sfchronicle.com
URL: http://www.sfchronicle.com

8426 ■ *San Francisco Chronicle*
Hearst Newspapers
901 Mission St.
San Francisco, CA 94103-2988
Contact: Jane Kay, Environment Reporter
Ph: (415)777-8704
E-mail: jkay@sfchronicle.com
URL: http://www.sfchronicle.com

8427 ■ *San Jose Mercury News*
MediaNews Group, Inc.
750 Ridder Pk. Dr.
San Jose, CA 95190
Contact: Tracy Seipel, Green Tech Reporter
Ph: (408)920-5701
E-mail: mnauman@mercurynews.com
URL: http://www.mercurycenter.com

8428 ■ *San Jose Mercury News*
MediaNews Group, Inc.
750 Ridder Pk. Dr.
San Jose, CA 95190
Contact: Paul Rogers, Environmental Reporter
Ph: (408)920-5045

E-mail: progers@mercurynews.com
URL: http://www.mercurycenter.com

Colorado

8429 ■ *Denver Post*
101 W. Colfax Ave.
Denver, CO 80202
Contact: Steven Raabe, Energy Reporter
Ph: (303)954-1948
E-mail: sraabe@denverpost.com
URL: http://www.denverpost.com

8430 ■ *Denver Post*
101 W. Colfax Ave.
Denver, CO 80202
Contact: Mark Jaffe, Environmental Writer
Ph: (303)954-1912
E-mail: mjaffe@denverpost.com
URL: http://www.denverpost.com

District of Columbia

8431 ■ National Public Radio
635 Massachusetts Ave. NW
Washington, DC 20001-3753
Contact: Elizabeth Shogren, Environment Correspondent
Ph: (202)513-2243
Fax: (202)513-3329
E-mail: eshogren@npr.org
URL: http://www.npr.org

Florida

8432 ■ *The Florida Times-Union*
PO Box 1949
Jacksonville, FL 32231
Contact: Steve Patterson, Environment Reporter
Ph: (904)359-4263
E-mail: steve.patterson@jacksonville.com
URL: http://www.jacksonville.com

8433 ■ *The Miami Herald*
The McClatchy Company
One Herald Plaza
Miami, FL 33132-1693
Contact: Curtis Morgan, Environment Reporter
Ph: (305)376-3610
E-mail: cmorgan@miamiherald.com
URL: http://www.herald.com

8434 ■ *Orlando Sentinel*
Tribune Company
633 N. Orange Ave.
Orlando, FL 32801-1349
Contact: Kevin Spear, Environment Reporter
Ph: (407)420-5062
E-mail: kspear@orlandosentinel.com
URL: http://www.orlandosentinel.com

8435 ■ *Sun Sentinel*
Tribune Company
200 E. Las Olas Blvd.
Fort Lauderdale, FL 33301-2293
Contact: Andy Reid, Environmental Reporter
Ph: (954)635-6747
E-mail: abreid@sun-sentinel.com
URL: http://www.sun-sentinel.com

8436 ■ *Tallahassee Democrat*
Gannett Co., Inc.
PO Box 990
Tallahassee, FL 32301
Contact: Bruce Ritchie, Environment/Growth Reporter
Ph: (850)599-2253
E-mail: britchie@tallahassee.com
URL: http://www.tallahassee.com

Georgia

8437 ■ *Atlanta Journal-Constitution*
Cox Newspapers, Inc.
72 Marietta St., NW

Atlanta, GA 30303
Contact: Katie Leslie, Home and Garden Reporter
Ph: (404)526-5969
E-mail: kleslie@ajc.com
URL: http://www.ajc.com

Illinois

8438 ■ *Chicago Tribune*
Tribune Company
435 N. Michigan Ave.
Chicago, IL 60611-4041
Contact: Shaila Wunderlich, Home and Garden Writer
Ph: (312)222-3232
E-mail: swunderlich@tribune.com
URL: http://www.chicagotribune.com

8439 ■ *Chicago Tribune*
Tribune Company
435 N. Michigan Ave.
Chicago, IL 60611-4041
Contact: Michael Hawthorne, Environment Reporter
Ph: (312)222-3315
E-mail: mhawthorne@tribune.com
URL: http://www.chicagotribune.com

Iowa

8440 ■ *Des Moines Register*
Gannett Co., Inc.
PO Box 957
Des Moines, IA 50304
Contact: Dan Piller, Agriculture/Energy Reporter
Ph: (515)284-8161
URL: http://www.DesMoinesRegister.com

8441 ■ *Des Moines Register*
Gannett Co., Inc.
PO Box 957
Des Moines, IA 50304
Contact: Perry Beeman, Environmental Issues Reporter
Ph: (515)284-8538
E-mail: pbeeman@dmreg.com
URL: http://www.DesMoinesRegister.com

8442 ■ *Gardening Today*
WHO-AM
2141 Grand Ave.
Des Moines, IA 50309
Contact: Mohamad Khan, Host
Ph: (515)245-8900
E-mail: news@who-radio.com
URL: http://www.whoradio.com/gardeningtoday/
Descr: Radio program that offers expertise in gardening.

Kentucky

8443 ■ *Courier-Journal*
Gannett Co., Inc.
PO Box 740031
Louisville, KY 40201-7431
Contact: James Bruggers, Environmental Writer
Ph: (502)582-4645
E-mail: jbruggers@courier-journal.com
URL: http://www.courier-journal.com

Louisiana

8444 ■ *New Orleans Times-Picayune*
Newhouse Newspapers
3800 Howard Ave.
New Orleans, LA 70125
Contact: Mark Schleifstein, Environmental Writer
Ph: (504)826-3327
E-mail: mschleifstein@timespicayune.com
URL: http://www.nola.com

Maryland

8445 ■ *The Baltimore Sun*
Tribune Company
501 N. Calvert St.
Baltimore, MD 21278
Contact: Eileen Canzian, Environmental Reporter
Ph: (410)332-6100
URL: http://www.baltimoresun.com

Massachusetts

8446 ■ *Boston Globe*
The New York Times Company
135 Morrissey Blvd.
Boston, MA 02125
Contact: Beth Daley, Environment Reporter
Ph: (617)929-3043
E-mail: b_daley@globe.com
URL: http://www.boston.com

Minnesota

8447 ■ *St. Paul Pioneer Press*
MediaNews Group, Inc.
345 Cedar St.
St. Paul, MN 55101-1057
Contact: Amy Nelson, Home and Garden Reporter
Ph: (651)228-5182
E-mail: asultan@pioneerpress.com
URL: http://www.pioneerpress.com

8448 ■ *Star Tribune*
McClatchy Newspapers, Inc.
425 Portland Ave., S.
Minneapolis, MN 55415
Contact: Kim Palmer, Home and Garden Reporter
Ph: (612)673-4380
E-mail: kpalmer@startribune.com
URL: http://www.startribune.com

8449 ■ *Star Tribune*
McClatchy Newspapers, Inc.
425 Portland Ave., S.
Minneapolis, MN 55415
Contact: Connie Nelson, Home and Garden Editor
Ph: (612)673-7087
E-mail: cnelson@startribune.com
URL: http://www.startribune.com

Missouri

8450 ■ *The Kansas City Star*
Knight Ridder, Inc.
1729 Grand Blvd.
Kansas City, MO 64108
Contact: Karen Dillon, Environmental Reporter
Ph: (816)234-4430
E-mail: kdillon@kcstar.com
URL: http://www.kansascity.com

Nebraska

8451 ■ *Omaha World-Herald*
1314 Douglas St., Ste. 900
Omaha, NE 68102
Contact: Nancy Gaarder, Energy Reporter
Ph: (402)444-1000
E-mail: nancy.gaarder@owh.com
URL: http://www.omaha.com

New Jersey

8452 ■ *Asbury Park Press*
Gannett Co., Inc.
PO Box 1550
Neptune, NJ 07754-1551
Contact: Todd B. Bates, Environmental Reporter

Ph: (732)643-4237
E-mail: tbates@app.com
URL: http://www.app.com

8453 ■ The Star-Ledger
Newhouse Newspapers
One Star-Ledger Plaza
Newark, NJ 07102-1200
Contact: Valerie Sudol, Gardening Writer
Ph: (973)392-5857
E-mail: vsudol@starledger.com
URL: http://www.nj.com

New York

8454 ■ The Journal News
Gannett Co., Inc.
One Gannett Dr.
White Plains, NY 10604
Contact: Gregory Clary, Environmental Writer
Ph: (914)696-8566
E-mail: gclary@lohud.com
URL: http://www.lohud.com

8455 ■ The New York Times
229 W. 43rd St.
New York, NY 10036
Contact: Andrew C. Revkin, Environment Reporter
Ph: (212)556-7326
E-mail: revkin@nytimes.com
URL: http://www.nytimes.com

8456 ■ The New York Times
229 W. 43rd St.
New York, NY 10036
Contact: Jad Mouawad, Energy Reporter
Ph: (212)556-8094
E-mail: jad@nytimes.com
URL: http://www.nytimes.com

North Carolina

8457 ■ The Charlotte Observer
Knight Ridder, Inc.
PO Box 30308
Charlotte, NC 28230-0308
Contact: Bruce Henderson, Environment Reporter
Ph: (704)358-5051
E-mail: bhenderson@charlotteobserver.com
URL: http://www.charlotte.com/observer

Ohio

8458 ■ Akron Beacon Journal
Sound Publishing Holdings, Inc.
PO Box 640
Akron, OH 44309-0640
Contact: Bob Downing, Environment Reporter
Ph: (330)996-3745
Fax: (330)376-9235
E-mail: bdowning@thebeaconjournal.com
URL: http://www.ohio.com

8459 ■ Cleveland Plain Dealer
Newhouse Newspapers
1801 Superior Ave., NE
Cleveland, OH 44114-2198
Contact: Michael Scott, Environmental Reporter
Ph: (216)999-4800
E-mail: mscott@plaind.com
URL: http://www.plaindealer.com

8460 ■ Cleveland Plain Dealer
Newhouse Newspapers
1801 Superior Ave., NE
Cleveland, OH 44114-2198
Contact: John Funk, Energy Reporter
Ph: (216)999-4138
E-mail: jfunk@plaind.com
URL: http://www.plaindealer.com

8461 ■ The Columbus Dispatch
34 S. Third St.
Columbus, OH 43215-4241
Contact: Spencer Hunt, Environment Reporter

Ph: (614)461-6051
E-mail: shunt@dispatch.com
URL: http://www.dispatch.com

Oklahoma

8462 ■ The Oklahoman
Oklahoma Publishing Company
9000 N. Broadway
Oklahoma City, OK 73114
Contact: Jack Money, Energy Reporter
Ph: (405)475-3470
E-mail: jmoney@oklahoman.com
URL: http://www.newsok.com

Pennsylvania

8463 ■ The Philadelphia Inquirer
Philadelphia Media Holdings LLC
400 N. Broad St.
Philadelphia, PA 19103
Contact: Sandy Bauers, Environmental Reporter
Ph: (215)854-5147
E-mail: sbauers@phillynews.com
URL: http://www.philly.com

8464 ■ Pittsburgh Post-Gazette
Block Communications, Inc.
34 Blvd. of the Allies
Pittsburgh, PA 15222
Contact: Elwin Green, Energy Reporter
Ph: (412)263-1969
E-mail: egreen@post-gazette.com
URL: http://www.post-gazette.com

South Carolina

8465 ■ The Post & Courier
134 Columbus St.
Charleston, SC 29403-4800
Contact: Wevoneda Minis, Home and Garden Reporter
Ph: (843)937-5705
E-mail: wminis@postandcourier.com
URL: http://www.charleston.net

8466 ■ The Post & Courier
134 Columbus St.
Charleston, SC 29403-4800
Contact: Bo Peterson, Environment Reporter
Ph: (843)745-5852
URL: http://www.charleston.net

8467 ■ The State
The McClatchy Company
PO Box 1333
Columbia, SC 29202-1333
Contact: Sammy Fretwell, Environmental Issues Reporter
Ph: (803)771-8537
E-mail: sfretwell@thestate.com
URL: http://www.thestate.com

Texas

8468 ■ Fort Worth Star-Telegram
400 W. Seventh St.
Fort Worth, TX 76102
Contact: Jim Fuquay, Energy Writer
Ph: (817)390-7770
Fax: (817)390-7774
E-mail: jfuquay@star-telegram.com
URL: http://www.star-telegram.com

8469 ■ Fort Worth Star-Telegram
PO Box 1870
Fort Worth, TX 76115
Contact: Jessie Milligan, Home and Garden Reporter
Ph: (817)390-7738
E-mail: jlmilligan@star-telegram.com
URL: http://www.star-telegram.com

8470 ■ Houston Chronicle
Hearst Newspapers
801 Texas Ave.

Houston, TX 77002
Contact: Kathy Huber, Garden Editor
Ph: (713)362-7376
E-mail: kathy.huber@chron.com
URL: http://www.houstonchronicle.com

8471 ■ Houston Chronicle
Hearst Newspapers
801 Texas Ave.
Houston, TX 77002
Contact: Brett Clanton, Energy Reporter
Ph: (713)362-7585
E-mail: brett.clanton@chron.com
URL: http://www.houstonchronicle.com

8472 ■ San Antonio Express-News
Hearst Newspapers
PO Box 2171
San Antonio, TX 78297-2171
Contact: Vicki Vaughan, Energy Reporter
Ph: (210)250-3236
E-mail: vvaughan@express-news.net
URL: http://www.mysa.com

8473 ■ San Antonio Express-News
Hearst Newspapers
PO Box 2171
San Antonio, TX 78297-2171
Contact: Tracy Hobson Lehmann, Home and Garden Editor
Ph: (210)250-3425
E-mail: tlehmann@express-news.net
URL: http://www.mysa.com

8474 ■ San Antonio Express-News
Hearst Newspapers
PO Box 2171
San Antonio, TX 78297-2171
Contact: Anton Caputo, Environmental Issues Reporter
Ph: (210)250-3149
E-mail: acaputo@express-news.net
URL: http://www.mysa.com

Utah

8475 ■ The Salt Lake Tribune
90 S. 400 W., Ste. 700
Salt Lake City, UT 84101
Contact: Judy Fahys, Environment Reporter
Ph: (801)257-8792
E-mail: fahys@sltrib.com
URL: http://www.sltrib.com

8476 ■ The Salt Lake Tribune
90 S. 400 W., Ste. 700
Salt Lake City, UT 84101
Contact: Patty Henetz, Environment Reporter
Ph: (801)257-8789
E-mail: phenetz@sltrib.com
URL: http://www.sltrib.com

Vermont

8477 ■ The Burlington Free Press
Gannett Co., Inc.
PO Box 10
Burlington, VT 05402
Contact: Candace Page, Environmental/Land-Use Reporter
Ph: (802)660-1865
Fax: (802)660-1802
E-mail: cpage@afp.burlingtonfreepress.com
URL: http://www.burlingtonfreepress.com

Virginia

8478 ■ Richmond Times-Dispatch
Media General, Inc.
PO Box 85333
Richmond, VA 23293
Contact: Rex Springston, Environment Reporter
Ph: (804)649-6453
Fax: (804)775-8059
URL: http://www.timesdispatch.com

Washington

8479 ■ *Seattle Times*
PO Box 70
Seattle, WA 98111
Contact: Craig Welch, Environment Reporter
Ph: (206)464-2093
E-mail: cwelch@seattletimes.com
URL: http://www.seattletimes.com

Corporate Contacts

8480 ■ Alternative Outfitters Vegan Boutique
408 S. Pasadena Ave., Ste. 1
Pasadena, CA 91105
Ph: (626)396-4972
Free: 866-758-5837
URL: http://www.alternativeoutfitters.com
Descr: Features vegan and cruelty-free products such as non-leather shoes, handbags, cosmetics, and personal care items.

8481 ■ Canusa Hershman Recycling Company
9 Business Park Dr.
Branford, CT 06405

Ph: (203)488-0887
URL: http://www.chrecycling.com/

8482 ■ Creative Recycling
PO Box 19120
Tampa, FL 33686-9120
Free: 800-797-2061
URL: http://www.crsrecycling.com/
Descr: Specializes in recycling electronic products.

8483 ■ Energy Innovations
130 W. Union St.
Pasadena, CA 91103
Ph: (626)585-6900
E-mail: info@energyinnovations.com
URL: http://www.energyinnovations.com/

8484 ■ Mid-America Paper
3865 W. 41st St.
Chicago, IL 60632
Ph: (773)890-5454
E-mail: sales@midamericapaper.com
URL: http://www.midamericapaper.com/

8485 ■ REC Solar
775 Fiero Lane, Ste. 200
San Luis Obispo, CA 93401
Free: 888-OK-SOLAR

E-mail: service@recsolar.com
URL: http://www.recsolar.com/

8486 ■ The Solar Energy Company
6440 Via Real, Ste. 7
Carpinteria, CA 93013
Free: 800-827-5777
E-mail: info@thesolarenergycompany.com
URL: http://www.thesolarenergycompany.com/

8487 ■ SunEdison Solar Electricity
12500 Baltimore Ave.
Beltsville, MD 20705
Free: 866-786-3347
URL: http://www.sunedison.com/

8488 ■ Suntrek
5 Holland, Bldg. 215
Irvine, CA 92618
Ph: (949)348-9276
E-mail: contact@suntreksolar.com
URL: http://www.suntreksolar.com/

8489 ■ SunWize
1155 Flatbush Rd.
Kingston, NY 12401
URL: http://sunwize.com/
Telecom. Svcs: For the East Coast, call (800)817-6527; for West Coast, call (866)476-9493.

Internet Resources

8490 ■ BuySafeDrugs.info
Pharmaceutical Research and Manufacturers of America
1100 Fifteenth St., NW, Ste. 900
Washington, DC 20005
Ph: (202)835-3400
Fax: (202)835-3414
URL: http://www.buysafedrugs.info/

URL(s): www.buysafedrugs.info **Descr:** Provides information about counterfeit prescription drugs and informs consumers of the dangers of buying imported drugs. Strives to promote what it refers to as "safe, legal ways patients can save on prescription drugs." Advocates against legalizing prescription drug importation.

8491 ■ DineSite.com
PO Box 59826
Schaumburg, IL 60159

URL(s): www.dinesite.com/home/ **Descr:** Where to dine tonight? Find restaurants in 12,000 towns around the United States. Users may look up restaurants by cuisine, price bracket, entertainment offerings, and the type of eatery. Each listing may include restaurant name and address, overview, web links, reviews, and messages posted by other users as well as photos and menus when available. Users may submit their own reviews of eateries. Also find information on world cuisines, dining etiquette, cooking at home, and a list of cookbooks. **Type:** Directory; Full-text; Bulletin board. **Updating freq.:** Regularly. **Fees:** Free. **Searching routines or searchable elements:** Fielded searching is available.

8492 ■ Food Storage Information
Food Marketing Institute
2345 Crystal Dr., Ste. 800
Arlington, VA 22202
Ph: (202)452-8444
Fax: (202)429-4519
E-mail: fmi@fmi.org
URL: http://www.fmi.org

URL(s): www.fmi.org/consumer/foodkeeper/ **Descr:** Offers information on the proper storage and handling of shelf-stable foods, food purchased frozen, foods purchased refrigerated, bakery items, and fresh produce. Additional links provide advice on filling your cart at the supermarket, handling foods safely at home, maintaining food temperatures, food product dating, baby foods, and expiration dates.

8493 ■ FoodSafety.gov Consumer Advice
FirstGov.gov
Office of Citizen Services and Communications
1800 F St., NW
Washington, DC 20405
Free: 800-FED-INFO
URL: http://www.firstgov.gov/

Descr: Offers detailed information on food handling, how to report a problem with food, consumer advice for children and seniors, seasonal advice, and product-specific advice. Also provides additional information in Chinese, French, German, Japanese, Korean, Portuguese, Russian, and Spanish.

8494 ■ Rx List - The Internet Drug Index
Healthcentral.com
1655 N. Fort Myer Dr., Ste. 400
Arlington, VA 22209
Contact: Chris Schroeder, CEO
Ph: (703)302-1040
Fax: (703)248-0830
E-mail: schroeder@HTCN.com
URL: http://www.healthcentral.com

URL(s): www.rxlist.com **Descr:** Contains an extensive, easily searchable collection of information on drugs and pharmaceuticals. Includes information such as drug categories, brand names, technical information on clinical pharmacology, results of clinical studies, cautions and warnings, and general information for patients. Provides a section containing approximate costs for therapy on a particular drug. Includes lists of the top 200 prescriptions for the last three years, regular comics and humor, links to other sites, and detailed information on using the various search options. Lets users search by brand name, generic name, or drug category. Offers "fuzzy search" capabilities that will return a cross-referenced list of names that more than likely will have an active link to requested information. Provides simple keyword searching. **Type:** Directory; Full-text. **Fees:** Free.

Federal Government Agencies

8495 ■ 2010 Dietary Guidelines Advisory Committee
Center for Nutrition Policy and Promotion
Department of Agriculture
3101 Park Center Dr., 10th Fl.
Alexandria, VA 22302-1594
Contact: Colette Rihane, Designated Fed.Off.
Ph: (703)305-2403
Fax: (703)305-3300
URL: http://www.cnpp.usda.gov

Staff: Management and support services are provided by the USDA's Center for Nutrition Policy and Promotion and Agricultural Research Service. Technical support is also provided by the Office of Disease Prevention and Health Promotion, Department of Health and Human Services. There are four co-executive secretaries, two from Department of Agriculture and two from Department of Health and Human Services. The Center for Nutrition Policy and Promotion co-executive secretary serves as lead designated federal officer. **Descr:** Committee provides independent, science-based advice and recommendations for the development of the Dietary Guidelines for Americans, 2010, which form the basis

of federal nutrition programs, nutrition standards, and nutrition education for the general public. Committee is established for the single, time-limited task of reviewing the 2005 edition of the Dietary Guidelines for Americans and determining if, on the basis of current scientific and medical knowledge, revision is warranted. **Mem:** Committee is composed of not more than thirteen members, including the chairperson and the vice chairperson. Members are appointed by the Secretaries of Agriculture and Health and Human Services. All members are knowledgeable of current scientific aspects of human nutrition and chronic disease, including cardiovascular disease, cancer, pediatrics, gerontology, epidemiology, general medicine, overweight and obesity, physical activity, public health, nutrition education, and food science. Linda V. VanHorn, PhD, RD, Northwestern University, Chicago, chairs the Committee.

8496 ■ Committee on Military Nutrition Research (CMNR)
Food & Nutrition Board
Institute of Medicine
National Academy of Sciences
500 Fifth St. NW
Washington, DC 20001
Contact: Maria Oria PhD, Prog.Off.
Ph: (202)334-2352
Fax: (202)334-1412
E-mail: iomwww@nas.edu
URL: http://www.iom.edu/CMS/3788/4615.aspx

Descr: Committee was established to advise the Department of the Army, Department of Defense, concerning nutrition and health issues; to identify critical nutritional factors that may influence physical and mental performance of military personnel; to recommend appropriate research strategies and methods for studying the relationship between diet and physical and mental performance; and to review and revise current nutritional guidelines for military programs. **Mem:** Committee comprises nine members who serve three-year terms. Members are knowledgeable in the areas of human nutrition, nutritional biochemistry, performance physiology, food science, and psychology. John W. Erdman Jr., PhD, University of Illinois at Urbana-Champaign, Urbana, IL, serves as chairperson. **Pub:** Mineral Requirements for Military Personnel: Levels Needed for Cognitive and Physical Performance During Garrison Training (March 22, 2006); Nutrient Composition of Rations for Short-Term, High-Intensity Combat Operations (June 6, 2005); Monitoring Metabolic Status: Predicting Decrements in Physiological and Cognitive Performance during Military Operations; Weight Management: State of the Science and Opportunities for Military Programs (August 1, 2003); Fluid Replacement and Heat Stress (third printing); Body Composition and Physical Performance; Nutritional Needs in Hot Environments; Food Components to Enhance Performance; Not Eating Enough; Nutritional Needs in Cold and in High Altitude

Environments. Publications are available from National Academy Press, Washington, D.C.

8497 ■ Emergency Food and Shelter Program National Board
Disaster Assistance Directorate
Federal Emergency Management Agency
500 C St., SW
Washington, DC 20472
Contact: Yvonne Walker, Dir.
Ph: (703)706-9660
Fax: (703)706-9677
URL: http://www.efsp.unitedway.org/efsp/pages/about.htm
Staff: FEMA's primary responsibilities with the program are: to constitute and chair the National Board and provide policy guidance, oversight, federal coordination and staff assistance to the National Board. United Way of America has been designated Secretariat of the program by the National Board. Yvonne Walker, Director, Emergency Food and Shelter Program at United Way of America, serves as executive secretary. **Descr:** National Board governs the Emergency Food and Shelter Program and establishes guidelines, which will be published annually, for carrying out the Program. The guidelines will include methods for identifying localities with the highest need for emergency food and shelter assistance; methods for determining the amount and distribution to such localities; and eligible program costs, including maximum flexibility in meeting needs. **Mem:** Board consists of the designee by the Director of FEMA as chairperson, and six members appointed by the Director. Members are appointed from among persons nominated by the following national nonprofit organizations: the United Way of America, the Salvation Army, the National Council of Churches of Christ in the USA, Catholic Charities USA, United Jewish Communities, and the American Red Cross. Berl D. Jones Jr., Director, Individual Assistance Division, Disaster Assistance Directorate, Federal Emergency Management Agency, is currently serving as chair.

8498 ■ Food Stamp Program
Food & Nutrition Service
Department of Agriculture
3101 Park Center Dr., Rm. 808A
Alexandria, VA 22302
Ph: (703)305-2022
Free: 800-221-5689
Fax: (703)305-2454
URL: http://www.fns.usda.gov/fsp
Descr: Program provides, through state and local welfare agencies, food stamp benefits to needy persons in order to increase the food purchasing power and to improve the diet of those from low-income households. **Pub:** Questions and Answers About Getting and Using Food Stamps; A Small Reason to Find Out if You Qualify for Food Stamps.

8499 ■ Mushroom Council
2880 Zanker Rd., Ste. 203
San Jose, CA 95134
Contact: Bart Minor, Pres.
Ph: (408)432-7210
Fax: (408)432-7213
E-mail: info@mushroomcouncil.org
URL: http://www.mushroomcouncil.org
Descr: Council collects assessments on fresh market mushrooms produced in or imported into the United States, Puerto Rico, and the District of Columbia. **Mem:** Council consists of nine members who are producers.

8500 ■ National Advisory Council on Maternal, Infant and Fetal Nutrition
Supplemental Food Programs Div.
Food & Nutrition Service
U.S. Department of Agriculture
3101 Park Center Dr., Rm. 520
Alexandria, VA 22302
Contact: Robin A. Young, Designated Fed.Off.
Ph: (703)305-2730
Fax: (703)305-2196

E-mail: robin.young@fns.usda.gov
URL: http://www.fns.usda.gov
Staff: Robin A. Young, program analyst, serves as designated federal official. **Descr:** Council was established to make a continuing study of the operation of the Special Supplemental Nutrition Program for Women, Infants and Children (WIC) and related programs such as the Commodity Supplemental Food Program (CSFP) to determine how the programs may be improved. The WIC and CSFP provide special supplemental foods and nutrition education to low-income pregnant, breastfeeding, postpartum women, and infants and young children who are at nutritional risk. **Mem:** Council consists of seventeen members who represent federal and state government, state and local WIC and CSFP programs, the medical field, industry, and WIC and CSFP participants. Donna Seward chairs the Council. **Pub:** Letter Report on the Special Supplemental Nutrition Program for Women, Infants and Children and on the Commodity Supplemental Food Program.

8501 ■ National Peanut Board
2839 Paces Ferry Rd., Ste. 210
Atlanta, GA 30339
Contact: Raffaela Marie Penn, Pres./Managing Dir.
Ph: (678)424-5750
Free: 866-825-7946
Fax: (678)424-5751
E-mail: peanuts@nationalpeanutboard.org
URL: http://www.nationalpeanutboard.org
Descr: Board administers Agricultural Marketing Service programs regarding peanuts. It is a research and promotion board working on behalf of American peanut farmers to support and expand existing markets, develop new markets, and facilitate the economical production of high-quality peanuts for consumers worldwide. It also funds research to reduce production costs, explore nutrition research and investigate potential ways to lessen peanut allergy. **Mem:** Board consists of ten producers from each peanut producing state (Alabama, Florida, Georgia, New Mexico, North Carolina, Oklahoma, South Caroline, Texas, and Virginia). Wes Shannon chairs the Committee. **Pub:** Annual Report; Peanut Quarterly (newsletter). Publications are available upon request by phone or email.

8502 ■ Popcorn Board
401 N. Michigan Ave., Fl. 22
Chicago, IL 60611-4267
Contact: Genny Bertalmio, Admin.
Ph: (312)664-6610
Free: 877-POP-ALOT
Fax: (312)673-4883
URL: http://www.popcorn.org
Descr: Board administers the popcorn marketing order under the Agricultural Research Service supervision. **Mem:** Board consists of nine popcorn processors.

8503 ■ U.S. Department of Health and Human Services (FDA)
Food and Drug Administration
Office of Regulatory Affairs
Atlanta District Office
60 Eighth St. NE
Atlanta, GA 30309
Contact: JoAnn Pittman, Public Affairs Specialist
Ph: (404)253-1272
Fax: (404)253-1202
E-mail: JoAnn.Pittman@fda.hhs.gov

8504 ■ U.S. Department of Health and Human Services (FDA)
Food and Drug Administration
Office of Regulatory Affairs
Baltimore District Office
6000 Metro Dr., Ste. 101
Baltimore, MD 21215
Contact: Stephen King, Public Affairs Specialist
Ph: (410)779-5709

Fax: (410)779-5707
E-mail: Stephen.King@fda.hhs.gov

8505 ■ U.S. Department of Health and Human Services (FDA)
Food and Drug Administration
Office of Regulatory Affairs
Brunswick Resident Post
3820 Center Rd.
Brunswick, OH 44212-0838
Ph: (330)273-1038
Fax: (330)225-7477

8506 ■ U.S. Department of Health and Human Services (FDA)
Food and Drug Administration
Office of Regulatory Affairs
Chicago District Office
550 W. Jackson Blvd., Ste. 1500
Chicago, IL 60661
Ph: (312)596-4205
Fax: (312)596-4206

8507 ■ U.S. Department of Health and Human Services (FDA)
Food and Drug Administration
Office of Regulatory Affairs
Cincinnati District Office
6751 Steger Dr.
Cincinnati, OH 45237-3097
Contact: Brenda Zimmer, Public Affairs Specialist
Ph: (513)679-2700
Fax: (513)679-2771
E-mail: Brenda.Zimmer@fda.hhs.gov

8508 ■ U.S. Department of Health and Human Services (FDA)
Food and Drug Administration
Office of Regulatory Affairs
Dallas District Office
4040 N. Central Expy., Ste. 300
Dallas, TX 75204-3145
Contact: Maria Velasco, Public Affairs Specialist
Ph: (214)253-5205
Fax: (214)253-5318
E-mail: Maria.Velasco@fda.hhs.gov

8509 ■ U.S. Department of Health and Human Services (FDA)
Food and Drug Administration
Office of Regulatory Affairs
Denver District Office
PO Box 25087
Denver, CO 80225-0087
Contact: Devin Koontz, Public Affairs Specialist
Ph: (303)236-3020
Fax: (303)236-3551
E-mail: Devin.Koontz@fda.hhs.gov

8510 ■ U.S. Department of Health and Human Services (FDA)
Food and Drug Administration
Office of Regulatory Affairs
Detroit District Office
300 River Place, Ste. 5900
Detroit, MI 48207
Contact: Evelyn DeNike, Public Affairs Specialist
Ph: (313)393-8109
Fax: (313)393-8139
E-mail: Evelyn.Denike@fda.hhs.gov

8511 ■ U.S. Department of Health and Human Services (FDA)
Food and Drug Administration
Office of Regulatory Affairs
Florida District Office
555 Winderley Pl., Ste. 200
Maitland, FL 32751
Contact: Faye Bronner, Public Affairs Specialist
Ph: (407)475-4715
Fax: (407)475-4768
E-mail: Faye.Bronner@fda.hhs.gov

8512 ■ U.S. Department of Health and Human Services (FDA)
Food and Drug Administration
Office of Regulatory Affairs
Houston Resident Post
1445 N. Loop W., Ste. 420
Houston, TX 77008

Contact: Sheryl Baylor McConnell, Public Affairs Specialist
Ph: (713)802-7534
Fax: (713)802-7503
E-mail: Sheryl.McConnell@fda.hhs.gov

8513 ■ U.S. Department of Health and Human Services (FDA)
Food and Drug Administration
Office of Regulatory Affairs
Indianapolis Resident Post
101 W. Ohio St., Ste. 1300
Indianapolis, IN 46204-1994
Contact: Carol Gallagher, Public Affairs Specialist
Ph: (317)226-6500
Fax: (317)226-6506
E-mail: carol.gallagher@fda.hhs.gov

8514 ■ U.S. Department of Health and Human Services (FDA)
Food and Drug Administration
Office of Regulatory Affairs
Kansas City District Office
11630 W. 80th St.
Lenexa, KS 66214-3338
Contact: Tywanna Paul, Public Affairs Specialist
Ph: (913)752-2141
Fax: (913)752-2111
E-mail: Tywanna.Paul@fda.hhs.gov

8515 ■ U.S. Department of Health and Human Services (FDA)
Food and Drug Administration
Office of Regulatory Affairs
Los Angeles District Office
19701 Fairchild
Irvine, CA 92612-2506
Contact: Rosaria Quintanilla Vior, Public Affairs Specialist
Ph: (818)595-0016
Fax: (949)608-4456
E-mail: rosaria.vior@fda.hhs.gov

8516 ■ U.S. Department of Health and Human Services (FDA)
Food and Drug Administration
Office of Regulatory Affairs
Milwaukee Resident Post
2675 N. Mayfair Rd., Ste. 200
Milwaukee, WI 53226-1305
Contact: Kathy Rozewicz, Public Affairs Specialist
Ph: (414)771-7167
Fax: (414)771-7512
E-mail: Kathleen.Rozewicz@fda.hhs.gov

8517 ■ U.S. Department of Health and Human Services (FDA)
Food and Drug Administration
Office of Regulatory Affairs
Minneapolis District Office
250 Marquette Ave., Ste. 600
Minneapolis, MN 55401
Contact: Susan Seefeld
Ph: (612)758-7130
Fax: (612)334-4134
E-mail: susan.seefeld@fda.hhs.gov

8518 ■ U.S. Department of Health and Human Services (FDA)
Food and Drug Administration
Office of Regulatory Affairs
Nashville Branch
404 BNA Dr., Bldg. 200, Ste. 500
Nashville, TN 37217-2565
Contact: Natalie A. Guidry, Acting Public Affairs Specialist
Ph: (615)366-7807
Fax: (615)366-7805

8519 ■ U.S. Department of Health and Human Services (FDA)
Food and Drug Administration
Office of Regulatory Affairs
New England District Office
One Montvale Ave., 4th Fl.
Stoneham, MA 02180
Contact: Mary B. Yebba, Public Affairs Specialist
Ph: (781)596-7700

Fax: (781)596-7896
E-mail: mary.yebba@fda.hhs.gov

8520 ■ U.S. Department of Health and Human Services (FDA)
Food and Drug Administration
Office of Regulatory Affairs
New Jersey District Office
120 N. Center Dr., Bldg. C
North Brunswick, NJ 08902
Contact: Joan G. Lytle, Public Affairs Specialist
Ph: (732)940-8946
Fax: (732)940-8936
E-mail: Joan.Lytle@fda.hhs.gov

8521 ■ U.S. Department of Health and Human Services (FDA)
Food and Drug Administration
Office of Regulatory Affairs
New York District Office
300 Pearl St., Ste. 100
Olymic Towers
Buffalo, NY 14202
Contact: Diana Monaco, Public Affairs Specialist
Ph: (716)541-0318
Fax: (716)551-3845
E-mail: Diana.Monaco@fda.hhs.gov

8522 ■ U.S. Department of Health and Human Services (FDA)
Food and Drug Administration
Office of Regulatory Affairs
New York District Office
158-15 Liberty Ave.
Jamaica, NY 11433-1034
Contact: Dilcia Granville, Public Affairs Specialist
Ph: (718)340-7000
Fax: (718)662-5665
E-mail: Dilcia.Granville@fda.hhs.gov

8523 ■ U.S. Department of Health and Human Services (FDA)
Food and Drug Administration
Office of Regulatory Affairs
Philadelphia District Office
900 US Customhouse
2nd and Chestnut St.
Philadelphia, PA 19106
Contact: Anitra D. Brown-Reed, Public Affairs Specialist
Ph: (215)597-4390
Fax: (215)597-4660
E-mail: Anitra.Brownreed@fda.hhs.gov

8524 ■ U.S. Department of Health and Human Services (FDA)
Food and Drug Administration
Office of Regulatory Affairs
Phoenix Resident Post
51 W. Third St., Ste. E-265
Tempe, AZ 85281-2831
Contact: Gilbert V. Meza, Public Affairs Specialist
Ph: (480)829-7396
Fax: (480)829-7677
E-mail: Gilbert.Meza@fda.hhs.gov

8525 ■ U.S. Department of Health and Human Services (FDA)
Food and Drug Administration
Office of Regulatory Affairs
Portland Resident Post
9780 SW Nimbus Ave.
Beaverton, OR 97008-7163
Contact: Alan Bennett, Public Affairs Specialist
Ph: (503)671-9332
Fax: (503)671-9445
E-mail: Alan.Bennett@fda.hhs.gov

8526 ■ U.S. Department of Health and Human Services (FDA)
Food and Drug Administration
Office of Regulatory Affairs
Raleigh Resident Post
300 Fayetteville St. Mall, Ste. 422
Raleigh, NC 27601
Contact: Mary C. Lewis, Public Affairs Specialist
Ph: (919)856-4456

Fax: (919)856-4776
E-mail: Mary.Lewis@fda.hhs.gov

8527 ■ U.S. Department of Health and Human Services (FDA)
Food and Drug Administration
Office of Regulatory Affairs
St. Louis Branch
12 Sunnen Dr., Ste. 122
St. Louis, MO 63143
Ph: (314)645-1167
Fax: (314)645-2969
E-mail: Donald.Aird@fda.hhs.gov

8528 ■ U.S. Department of Health and Human Services (FDA)
Food and Drug Administration
Office of Regulatory Affairs
San Francisco District Office
1431 Harbor Bay Pkwy.
Alameda, CA 94502-7070
Contact: Janet McDonald PhD, Public Affairs Specialist
Ph: (510)337-6845
Fax: (510)337-6708
E-mail: Janet.McDonald@fda.hhs.gov

8529 ■ U.S. Department of Health and Human Services (FDA)
Food and Drug Administration
Office of Regulatory Affairs
San Juan District Office
466 Fernandez Juncos Ave.
Puerta de Tierra Station
San Juan, PR 00901-3223
Contact: Nilda Villegas, Public Affairs Specialist
Ph: (787)474-9567
Fax: (787)729-6851
E-mail: Nilda.Villegas@fda.hhs.gov

8530 ■ U.S. Department of Health and Human Services (FDA)
Food and Drug Administration
Office of Regulatory Affairs
Seattle District Office
22201 23rd Dr., SE
Bothell, WA 98021-4421
Contact: Stephanie MaGill, Public Affairs Specialist
Ph: (425)483-4953
Fax: (425)483-4989
E-mail: Stephanie.MaGill@fda.hhs.gov

8531 ■ US Highbush Blueberry Council
2390 E. Bidwell St., Ste 300
Folsom, CA 95630-3873
Contact: Mark Villata, Admin.
Ph: (916)983-0111
Fax: (916)983-9022
E-mail: admin@ushbc.org
URL: http://www.blueberry.org
Descr: Council administers the Agricultural Marketing Service marketing order on blueberries. **Mem:** Council consists of fourteen members: one producer representative from each of the four regions; one producer representative from each of the top six producing states; one importer; one exporter; one handler; and one public member.

Associations and Other Organizations

8532 ■ Adventist Food Service Association (AFSA)
870 Country Haven Loop
Pasco, WA 99301
Contact: Norman Tagalog, Pres.
Free: 888-285-2843
Fax: (509)266-4692
E-mail: adventistfsa@cs.com
URL: http://afsanews.org
Descr: Advances the skills of managing and/or directing food service operations within the Seventh-day Adventist Church. Encourages and assists in the

development of the profession. Promotes educational programs for members.

8533 ■ Agricultural Producers Union (UPA)
555 Roland-Therrien Blvd., Bureau 100
Longueuil, QC, Canada J4H 3Y9
Contact: Christian Lacasse, Pres. Gen.
Ph: (450)679-0530
E-mail: upa@upa.qc.ca
URL: http://www.upa.qc.ca/fra/index_flash.asp
Staff: 800. **Descr:** Promotes and supports the interests of agricultural producers throughout Canada. Provides information on updated developments on the farming industry. Works as a communications network among Quebec farmers. Protects the rights of individuals within the agricultural producing community. **Fnd:** 1972. **Mem:** 45000. **Reg. Groups:** 16. **Pub:** *Terre de Chez Nous* (weekly).

8534 ■ American Agriculture Movement (AAM)
24800 Sage Creek Rd.
Scenic, SD 57780
Contact: Joyce Jobgen, Treas.
Ph: (605)993-6201
Fax: (605)993-6185
E-mail: jjobgen@hotmail.com
URL: http://www.aaminc.org
Staff: 4. **Descr:** Family farmers and ranchers concerned with governmental agricultural policy. Seeks to: establish a mechanism through which farmers can initiate and approve changes in federal agricultural policies; ensure that foreign and domestically produced agricultural products sell for the same price in the U.S. Promotes: political candidates favoring higher prices for agricultural products; borrower's rights as defined in recent farm credit legislation; cooperation among farmers' organizations and between farm and urban interests; worldwide agricultural supply management and higher prices for agricultural products in international markets. Opposes federal subsidies, excise tax increases, and the patenting of genetically-engineered animals. Achievements include: organization of a grassroots lobbying campaign; bringing the views of U.S. farmers to the attention of international agricultural bodies; changes in elevator bankruptcy laws and FmHa foreclosure procedures. Drafts opinions and supplies information to media on federal and international farm policy issues. **Fnd:** 1977. **State Groups:** 35.

8535 ■ American Egg Board (AEB)
1460 Renaissance Dr., Ste. 301
Park Ridge, IL 60068
Contact: Jacques Klempf, Chm.
Ph: (847)296-7043
Fax: (847)296-7007
E-mail: aeb@aeb.org
URL: http://www.aeb.org
Staff: 20. **Descr:** Board of American egg producers appointed by the Secretary of Agriculture. Offers advertising, educational, research, and promotional programs designed to increase consumption of eggs and egg products. Conducts consumer educators and food-service seminars, and food safety education programs. **Fnd:** 1976. **Mem:** 350. **Pub:** Annual Report (annual).

8536 ■ American Farmland Trust (AFT)
1200 18th St. NW, Ste. 800
Washington, DC 20036
Contact: Jon Scholl, Pres.
Ph: (202)331-7300
Free: 800-431-1499
Fax: (202)659-8339
E-mail: info@farmland.org
URL: http://www.farmland.org
Staff: 60. **Descr:** Works to stop the loss of productive farmland and promote farming practices that lead to a healthy environment. Disseminates information on safeguarding farmlands, through conservation easements and other voluntary conservation programs. Encourages and assists policy makers to revise federal, state, and local policies on farmland preservation. Conducts policy development assistance, public education, and land project programs. Aids landowners in private conservancy

transactions. **Fnd:** 1980. **Reg. Groups:** 3. **State Groups:** 5. **Pub:** *American Farmland* (quarterly); Annual Report (annual).

8537 ■ American Frozen Food Institute (AFFI)
2000 Corporate Ridge, Ste. 1000
McLean, VA 22102
Contact: Kraig R. Naasz, Pres./CEO
Ph: (703)821-0770
Fax: (703)821-1350
E-mail: info@affi.com
URL: http://www.affi.com
Staff: 18. **Descr:** Frozen food processors and allied industry companies who work for the advancement of the frozen food industry. Seeks to improve consumer understanding and acceptance of frozen foods and to increase sales of frozen products through promotional and communications programs. Sponsors retail trade study, consumer and industry education on care and handling of frozen foods. Promotes a cooperative relationship between frozen food processors, suppliers and marketing associates. Represents the frozen food industry before federal, state and local governments. Conducts research to improve the quality of frozen food products. **Fnd:** 1942. **Mem:** 500. **Pub:** *AFFI Capital Connection* (weekly); *Frozen Food Pack Statistics*; *Membership Directory and Buyer's Guide* (annual); Reports.

8538 ■ American Meat Institute (AMI)
1150 Connecticut Ave. NW, 12th Fl.
Washington, DC 20036
Contact: J. Patrick Boyle, Pres./CEO
Ph: (202)587-4200
Fax: (202)587-4300
E-mail: memberservices@meatami.com
URL: http://www.meatami.com
Staff: 32. **Descr:** Represents the interests of packers and processors of beef, pork, lamb, veal, and turkey products and their suppliers throughout North America. Provides legislative, regulatory, and public relations services. Conducts scientific research. Offers marketing and technical assistance. Sponsors educational programs. **Fnd:** 1906. **Mem:** 1100. **Pub:** *Meat and Poultry Facts* (annual); *Weekly Trade Alert* (weekly).

8539 ■ American Vegan Society (AVS)
56 Dinshah Ln.
PO Box 369
Malaga, NJ 08328
Contact: Freya Dinshah, Pres.
Ph: (856)694-2887
Fax: (856)694-2288
URL: http://www.americanvegan.org
Descr: Individuals interested in the "compassionate, harmless way of life found in Veganism and Ahimsa." Defines Veganism as reverence for all life, especially avoiding cruelty and exploitation of the animal kingdom, including use of a total vegetarian diet and non-animal clothing; Ahimsa is a Sanskrit word for non-killing, non-harming. Outlines six guides, each beginning with a letter of Ahimsa: Abstinence from animal products; Harmlessness with reverence for life; Integrity of thought, word, and deed; Mastery over oneself; Service to humanity, nature, and creation; Advancement of understanding and truth. Conducts lectures, meetings, and training programs on how to live a better life. Maintains educational center. **Fnd:** 1960. **Pub:** *American Vegan* (quarterly); Books.

8540 ■ Association for Dressings and Sauces (ADS)
1100 Johnson Ferry Rd., Ste. 300
Atlanta, GA 30342
Ph: (404)252-3663
Fax: (404)252-0774
E-mail: ads@kellencompany.com
URL: http://www.dressings-sauces.org
Staff: 8. **Descr:** Manufacturers of mayonnaise, salad dressing, and condiment sauces; associate members are industry suppliers. Administers technical, quality assurance, and regulatory programs. Conducts consumer awareness programs. **Fnd:** 1933. **Mem:**

175. **Pub:** *Make Mine Mayonnaise!*; *Salad Dressing Isn't Just for Salads Anymore.*

8541 ■ Association of Food and Drug Officials (AFDO)
2550 Kingston Rd., Ste. 311
York, PA 17402
Ph: (717)757-2888
Fax: (717)755-8089
E-mail: afdo@afdo.org
URL: http://www.afdo.org
Staff: 4. **Descr:** Officials who enforce federal, state, district, county, and municipal laws and regulations relating to food, drugs, cosmetics, consumer product safety, and similar areas. Prevents fraud in production, manufacturing, distribution, and sale of these items. Promotes uniform laws and administrative procedures; disseminates information concerning law enforcement. **Fnd:** 1896. **Mem:** 700. **Reg. Groups:** 6. **Pub:** *E-News* (quarterly); Directory (semiannual).

8542 ■ Biodynamic Farming and Gardening Association (BDA)
25844 Butler Rd.
Junction City, OR 97448
Contact: Charles Beedy, Exec. Dir.
Ph: (541)998-0105
Free: 888-516-7797
Fax: (541)998-0106
E-mail: info@biodynamics.com
URL: http://www.biodynamics.com
Staff: 4. **Descr:** Farmers, gardeners, consumers, physicians, and scientists interested in improving nutrition and health through the production of high quality food using bio-dynamic farming. (Bio-dynamic farming stresses restoration of organic matter to the soil, use of special preparations to stimulate biological activity of soil and plant growth, crop rotation, proper cultivation to avoid structural damage to soil, and establishment of beneficial environmental conditions such as forests, wind protection, and water regulation). **Fnd:** 1938. **Mem:** 1500. **Reg. Groups:** 31. **Pub:** *BIODYNAMICS* (quarterly).

8543 ■ Calorie Control Council (CCC)
1100 Johnson Ferry Rd., Ste. 300
Atlanta, GA 30342
Contact: Meagan Stangle
Ph: (404)252-3663
E-mail: ccc@kellencompany.com
URL: http://www.caloriecontrol.org
Descr: Represents manufacturers of low-calorie and reduced-fat foods and beverages. Works to maintain and enhance communication among the industry, government and regulatory bodies, scientific and medical professionals, and consumers. Responds to inquiries for information and references. Conducts research; evaluates data. Maintains speakers' bureau. **Fnd:** 1966. **Mem:** 60. **Pub:** *Calorie Control Council--Commentary* (semiannual); *Fat Replacers: Food Ingredients for Healthy Eating*; *Winning By Losing - A Guide to Effective Weight Control*; Brochures.

8544 ■ Campaign to Label Genetically Engineered Foods
PO Box 55699
Seattle, WA 98155
Contact: Alexander Schauss PhD, Pres.
Ph: (425)771-4049
Fax: (425)740-8967
E-mail: label@thecampaign.org
URL: http://www.thecampaign.org
Descr: Represents food manufacturers who are committed to mandatory labeling of genetically engineered foods; promotes letter writing campaign to implement a moratorium on growing genetically engineered corn because the pollen is polluting organic cornfields; provides educational materials. **Fnd:** 1999. **Pub:** *The Campaign Reporter.*

8545 ■ Canadian Federation of Independent Grocers (CFIG)
2235 Sheppard Ave. E, Ste. 902
Willowdale, ON, Canada M2J 5B5
Contact: John F.T. Scott, Pres.

Ph: (416)492-2311
Free: 800-661-2344
Fax: (416)492-2347
E-mail: info@cfig.ca
URL: http://www.cfig.ca
Descr: Independent retail grocers. Promotes growth and development of members' businesses. Represents the commercial and regulatory interests of independent grocers; conducts promotional activities. **Fnd:** 1962.

8546 ■ Canadian Health Food Association (CHFA)
235 Yorkland Blvd., Ste. 302
Toronto, ON, Canada M2J 4Y8
Contact: Penelope Marrett, Pres./CEO
Ph: (416)497-6939
Free: 800-661-4510
Fax: (416)497-3214
E-mail: info@chfa.ca
URL: http://www.chfa.ca
Staff: 12. **Descr:** Represents producers and distributors of health foods. Seeks to advance the health food industries. Facilitates communication and cooperation among members; represents the commercial and regulatory interests of the health food industries; sponsors educational and promotional programs. **Fnd:** 1964. **Mem:** 1300. **Pub:** *The Natural Voice* (5/year).

8547 ■ Cattlemen's Beef Promotion and Research Board (CBB)
9000 E Nichols Ave., Ste. 215
Centennial, CO 80112-3450
Contact: Tom Ramey, CEO
Ph: (303)220-9890
Fax: (303)220-9280
E-mail: beefboard@beefboard.org
URL: http://www.mybeefcheckoff.com
Staff: 11. **Descr:** Beef producers. Coordinates public relations, marketing, and dissemination of information through the Beef Checkoff Program. Conducts promotional, consumer information, and industry information campaigns; fosters communication among beef producers; sponsors research. Produces television and radio advertisements. **Fnd:** 1986. **Mem:** 108. **Pub:** *Update* (periodic); Annual Report (annual).

8548 ■ City Farmer Society (CF)
Box 74567
Kitsilano RPO
Vancouver, BC, Canada V6K 4P4
Contact: Michael Levenston, Exec. Dir.
Ph: (604)685-5832
Fax: (604)685-5862
E-mail: cityfarm@interchange.ubc.ca
URL: http://www.cityfarmer.org
Descr: Promotes urban agriculture. Provides information and assistance to urban dwellers wishing to grow crops on vacant land or in window boxes. Conducts educational programs on the City's "Grow Natural" Program. **Fnd:** 1978. **Pub:** *Food Gardening in Vancouver*; *Gardening with People with Disabilities*; *Urban Gardens*; *Urban Home Composting Rhodent-Resistant Bins and Environmental Health Standards*.

8549 ■ CME Group
20 S Wacker Dr.
Chicago, IL 60606
Contact: Craig S. Donohue, CEO
Ph: (312)930-1000
Free: 800-331-3332
E-mail: info@cmegroup.com
URL: http://www.cmegroup.com
Staff: 880. **Descr:** Commodity futures exchange for live hogs, feeder cattle, live beef cattle, frozen pork bellies (bacon), lumber, gold, foreign currencies, government securities, bank debt, and equity financial instruments; deals with options on equity futures, interest rates, foreign currencies, and livestock. Maintains speakers' bureau; conducts research programs to help develop new contracts and update existing contracts; compiles statistics. **Fnd:** 1898. **Mem:** 2724. **Pub:** *Bibliography and Information*

Source Lists (annual); *Chicago Mercantile Exchange--Annual Report* (annual); *RCR Report* (quarterly).

8550 ■ Compatible Technology International (CTI)
800 Transfer Rd., Ste. 6
St. Paul, MN 55114
Contact: Mr. Roger Salway, Exec. Dir.
Ph: (651)632-3912
Fax: (651)204-9033
E-mail: cti@compatibletechnology.org
URL: http://www.compatibletechnology.org
Staff: 4. **Descr:** Seeks to increase the food production capabilities of small farms in the developing world through the introduction of more effective farming techniques and technologies. Develops, introduces, and trains indigenous people to make use of appropriate technologies and improved productive techniques. Encourages establishment of agricultural microenterprises to increase the economic viability of rural areas in the developing world. **Fnd:** 1981. **Pub:** *Harvest* (annual); *Post Harvest* (bimonthly).

8551 ■ Council for Responsible Nutrition (CRN)
1828 L St. NW, Ste. 510
Washington, DC 20036-5114
Contact: Steven M. Mister Esq., Pres./CEO
Ph: (202)204-7700
Fax: (202)204-7701
E-mail: webmaster@crnusa.org
URL: http://www.crnusa.org
Staff: 11. **Descr:** Manufacturers, distributors, and other companies involved in the production and sale of nutritional supplements, including vitamins, minerals and herbal products. Seeks an improvement in the general health of the U.S. population through responsible nutrition, including the appropriate use of nutritional supplements. Acts as a liaison between vitamin and mineral products manufacturers and government regulatory agencies, such as the Food and Drug Administration, the Federal Trade Commission, and the U.S. Congress. Keeps members informed of relevant legislative developments. Provides a forum to review governmental actions and evaluate current nutrition information. Acts as a clearinghouse to keep members informed of new scientific developments in nutrient safety, health, and nutrition. **Fnd:** 1973. **Mem:** 100. **Pub:** *CRN News* (monthly); Reports.

8552 ■ Dairy Management, Inc. (DMI)
10255 W Higgins Rd., Ste. 900
Rosemont, IL 60018-5616
Contact: Joe Bavido
Ph: (847)627-3252
Free: 800-853-2479
Fax: (847)803-2077
E-mail: marykateg@rosedmi.com
URL: http://www.dairyinfo.com
Staff: 20. **Descr:** Operates under the auspices of the United Dairy Industry Association. Milk producers, milk dealers, and manufacturers of butter, cheese, ice cream, dairy equipment, and supplies. Conducts programs of nutrition research and nutrition education in the use of milk and its products. **Fnd:** 1915. **Mem:** 24. **Local Groups:** 27. **Pub:** *Current Awareness* (bimonthly); *Dairy Council Digest* (bimonthly); *Nutrition News* (quarterly); Catalogs.

8553 ■ Distilled Spirits Council of the United States (DISCUS)
1250 Eye St. NW, Ste. 400
Washington, DC 20005
Contact: Dr. Peter H. Cressy, Pres./CEO
Ph: (202)628-3544
Fax: (202)682-8888
E-mail: fcoleman@discus.org
URL: http://www.discus.org
Staff: 56. **Descr:** Serves as national trade association of producers and marketers of distilled spirits sold in the U.S. Provides statistical and legal data for industry and the public and serves as public information source; conducts educational programs. **Fnd:** 1973. **Mem:** 24. **Pub:** *Summary of State Laws and*

Regulations Relating to Distilled Spirits (biennial); Brochures.

8554 ■ Do It Now Foundation (DINF)
PO Box 27568
Tempe, AZ 85285-7568
Ph: (480)736-0599
Fax: (480)736-0771
E-mail: email@doitnow.org
URL: http://www.doitnow.org
Staff: 5. **Descr:** Works to provide factual information to students and adults about prescription drugs, over-the-counter drugs, street drugs, alcohol, eating disorders, AIDS, and related health issues. Assists organizations engaged in alcohol and drug abuse education. **Fnd:** 1968. **Mem:** 40. **Pub:** *Straight Talk*.

8555 ■ Ecological Farming Association (EFA)
406 Main St., Ste. 313
Watsonville, CA 95076
Contact: Helge Hellberg, Exec. Dir.
Ph: (831)763-2111
Fax: (831)763-2112
E-mail: info@eco-farm.org
URL: http://www.eco-farm.org
Staff: 10. **Descr:** Organic farmers; wholesalers and retailers of natural foods; university level researchers and educators; consumers concerned with food safety, environmental, and land use issues. Seeks to promote agricultural practices that are "ecologically sound, economically viable, and socially just." Works to increase the number of growers using sustainable practices and consumers demanding organically-grown foods. Sponsors harvest fairs, farm tours, and ecological farming conference, and other educational events for sustainable agriculture. **Fnd:** 1981. **Mem:** 2000. **Pub:** *Organic Matters* (annual); *Participant Directory* (annual).

8556 ■ Family Farm Defenders (FFD)
PO Box 1772
Madison, WI 53701
Contact: John E. Peck, Exec. Dir.
Ph: (608)260-0900
Fax: (608)260-0900
E-mail: familyfarmdefenders@yahoo.com
URL: http://www.familyfarmdefenders.org
Staff: 1. **Descr:** Represents individuals and organizations dedicated to principles of sustainable agriculture, family farm livelihood, food safety, animal welfare, consumer right to know, workers' rights, fair trade, rural justice, and democratic sovereignty. **Fnd:** 1994. **Mem:** 1500. **Pub:** *The Defender* (quarterly).

8557 ■ FarmFolk/CityFolk Society
1937 W 2nd Ave.
Vancouver, BC, Canada V6J 1J2
Contact: Heather Pritchard, Exec. Dir.
Ph: (604)730-0450
Free: 888-730-0452
Fax: (604)730-0451
E-mail: info@ffcf.bc.ca
URL: http://www.ffcf.bc.ca
Staff: 4. **Descr:** Promotes food, farming and related issues; promotes policies and solutions that ensure food is grown, processed, and distributed in healthy ways. **Fnd:** 1993. **Mem:** 400. **State Groups:** 3. **Pub:** *Farm Folk/City Folk* (quarterly).

8558 ■ Food Research and Action Center (FRAC)
1875 Connecticut Ave. NW, Ste. 540
Washington, DC 20009-5728
Contact: James D. Weill, Pres.
Ph: (202)986-2200
Fax: (202)986-2525
E-mail: foodresearch@frac.org
URL: http://www.frac.org
Staff: 20. **Descr:** Renders technical assistance, training, research, information, and community organizing assistance to low-income organizations endeavoring to make federal food assistance programs more responsive to the acute needs of millions of hungry Americans. Seeks to enhance public awareness of problems of hunger and poverty. Researches, writes, and publishes analyses of

federal food programs and offers strategies for local and statewide anti-hunger activities. Coordinates nationwide "Campaign to End Childhood Hunger" and "Building Blocks Project." **Fnd:** 1970. **Pub:** *State of the States: A Profile of Food and Nutrition Programs Across the Nation (2005, 9th Edition); State of the States: A Profile of Food and Nutrition Programs Across the Nation (2004, 8th Edition).*

8559 ■ Food and Water (F&W)
PO Box 543
Montpelier, VT 05601
Contact: Michael Colby, Dir.
Ph: (802)229-6222
E-mail: info@broadsides.org
URL: http://www.broadsides.org
Staff: 4. **Descr:** Educates the public about various threats to the nutritional integrity of the food and water supply. Researches and publicizes environmental and health impacts of food irradiation and other food treatments, before and after harvest. Exposes what it considers to be the critical interconnections between health and environmental problems and challenges the need for technologies, processes, or additives which threaten both. Focuses on the issue of food irradiation and the possible dangers which this technology poses. Delves into the radical, underlying philosophies of those movements seeking substantive change. **Fnd:** 1986. **Mem:** 4000. **Pub:** *Food and Water Journal* (quarterly).

8560 ■ Food and Water Watch
1616 P St. NW, Ste. 300
Washington, DC 20036
Contact: Wenonah Hauter, Exec. Dir.
Ph: (202)683-2500
Fax: (202)683-2501
E-mail: foodandwater@fwwatch.org
URL: http://www.foodandwaterwatch.org
Descr: Works to ensure clean water and safe food. Empowers people to take action and be more conscious about what they eat and drink. Provides research and public and policymaker education about food and water. Advocates for policies that guarantee safe, wholesome food produced in a humane and sustainable manner. **Fnd:** 2005. **Pub:** *Agwatch Europe; Current; Defend the Global Commons; Food Alert!.*

8561 ■ Free Store/Food Bank (FS/FB)
1250 Tennessee Ave.
Cincinnati, OH 45229
Contact: John J. Young MEd, Pres./CEO
Ph: (513)482-4500
E-mail: jmorrow@freestorefoodbank.org
URL: http://www.freestorefoodbank.org
Descr: Seeks to help those in need, including poor people and victims of disasters and emergencies. Supplies food, clothing, beds, blankets, stoves, refrigerators, and space heaters to the needy. Attempts to raise levels of fixed income programs for the poor; monitors food stamp legislation; offers advocacy services on behalf of the poor. Works to educate government officials, business people, church members, and others about poverty, its causes, and its real costs to taxpayers. Operates regional food banks in southwestern Ohio, northern Kentucky, and southeastern Indiana. Facilitates legislative advocacy around food and nutrition issues. Compiles statistics. **Fnd:** 1971. **Mem:** 450. **State Groups:** 3. **Pub:** Annual Report.

8562 ■ The Glutamate Association (TGA)
PO Box 14266
Washington, DC 20044-4266
Ph: (202)783-6135
URL: http://www.msgfacts.com
Descr: Represents manufacturers, distributors, and processed food users of glutamic acid and its salts, including monosodium glutamate (MSG). Gathers and disseminates information on glutamates; sponsors research on glutamates and food safety; supports public information programs concerning glutamates; provides technical and scientific assistance to industry and government; represents the industry in governmental affairs. **Fnd:** 1977. **Mem:**

12. **Pub:** *Monosodium Glutamate: A Look at the Facts.*

8563 ■ Humane Farming Association (HFA)
PO Box 3577
San Rafael, CA 94912
Contact: Bradley S. Miller, Natl. Dir.
Ph: (415)771-2253
Fax: (415)485-0106
E-mail: hfa@hfa.org
URL: http://www.hfa.org
Staff: 8. **Descr:** Protects farm animals from cruelty and abuse, the public from the dangerous use of antibiotics, hormones, and other chemicals used in factory farming, and the environment from the devastating impacts of industrialized animal factories. Designs campaigns to expose to the American public the horrors of factory farming and to see to it that farm animal abuse is outlawed. **Fnd:** 1985. **Mem:** 135000. **Local Groups:** 1.

8564 ■ Institute of Food Technologists (IFT)
525 W Van Buren, Ste. 1000
Chicago, IL 60607
Contact: Marianne Gillette, Pres.-Elect
Ph: (312)782-8424
Free: 800-438-3663
Fax: (312)782-8348
E-mail: info@ift.org
URL: http://www.ift.org
Staff: 50. **Descr:** Scientific educational society of technical personnel in food industries, production, product development, research, and product quality. Promotes application of science and engineering to the evaluation, production, processing, packaging, distribution, preparation, and utilization of foods. Aids educational institutions in developing curricula for training in this area. **Fnd:** 1939. **Mem:** 28000. **Reg. Groups:** 55. **Pub:** *Food Technology* (monthly); *IFT Membership Directory* (annual); *IFT Program and Directory* (annual); *Journal of Food Science* (bimonthly); *Journal of Food Science Education*; Newsletter (weekly).

8565 ■ International Aloe Science Council (IASC)
8630 Fenton St., Ste. 918
Silver Spring, MD 20910
Contact: Walt Jones, Chm.
Ph: (301)588-2420
Fax: (301)588-1174
E-mail: info@iasc.org
URL: http://www.iasc.org
Staff: 2. **Descr:** Manufacturers and marketers of foods, drugs, and cosmetics containing gel of the aloe vera plant. Aims to provide scientific research for support of product claims. Educates members on the plant and its products and uses. Acts as a liaison for government agency regulations on aloe vera business. **Fnd:** 1981. **Mem:** 262. **Local Groups:** 1. **Pub:** *Inside Aloe* (monthly).

8566 ■ International Aromatherapy and Herb Association (IAHA)
3541 W Acapulco Ln.
Phoenix, AZ 85053
Contact: Jeffrey Schiller, Pres.
Ph: (602)938-4439
E-mail: aromaherbshow@hotmail.com
URL: http://www.aromaherbshow.com
Staff: 15. **Descr:** Represents people interested in aromatherapy, herbs and natural health. **Fnd:** 1996. **Mem:** 300. **Pub:** *Making Scents* (semiannual).

8567 ■ International Association of Milk Control Agencies (IAMCA)
New York Dept. of Agriculture and Markets
10 B Airline Dr.
Albany, NY 12235
Contact: Charles Huff, Sec.-Treas.
Ph: (518)457-5731
E-mail: charlie.huff@agmkt.state.ny.us
URL: http://www.maine.gov/agriculture/mmc/iamca
Descr: State and provincial agencies administering regulations dealing with milk pricing. Compiles

statistics. **Fnd:** 1935. **Mem:** 26. **Pub:** Proceedings (annual); Membership Directory (annual).

8568 ■ International Food Information Council (IFIC)
1100 Connecticut Ave. NW, Ste. 430
Washington, DC 20036
Contact: Jeff Strei, Dir.
Ph: (202)296-6540
Fax: (202)296-6547
E-mail: foodinfo@ific.org
URL: http://ific.org
Staff: 22. **Descr:** Serves as an information and educational resource on nutrition and food safety. Provides science-based information to journalists, health professionals, educators, government officials and other opinion leaders who communicate with the public. **Fnd:** 1985. **Mem:** 31. **Pub:** *Food Insight* (bimonthly); *Guidelines* (bimonthly); Brochures.

8569 ■ International Society for Behavioral Nutrition and Physical Activity (ISBNPA)
University of Minnesota
308 Harvard St. SE
Minneapolis, MN 55455
Contact: Johannes Brug PhD, Pres.
Ph: (612)625-0606
Fax: (612)626-2359
E-mail: kubik002@umn.edu
URL: http://www.isbnpa.org
Descr: Seeks to address the professional interests of researchers from multiple disciplines engaged in investigating behavioral issues in nutrition and physical activity. Promotes the understanding of the determinants of healthy eating and physical activity behaviors and the development of successful intervention programs. **Fnd:** 2000. **Mem:** 400. **Pub:** *International Journal for Behavioral Nutrition and Physical Activity*; Newsletter.

8570 ■ International Union of Nutritional Sciences (IUNS)
UCLA School of Public Health
Dept. of Community Health Sciences
PO Box 951772
Los Angeles, CA 90095-1772
Contact: Dr. Osman M. Galal, Sec. Gen.
Ph: (310)206-9639
Fax: (310)794-1805
E-mail: info@iuns.org
URL: http://www.iuns.org
Descr: Promotes advancement in nutrition science, research and development through international cooperation at the global level. Encourages communication and collaboration among nutrition scientists as well as to disseminate information in nutritional sciences through modern communication technology. **Fnd:** 1946. **Mem:** 80.

8571 ■ Islamic Food and Nutrition Council of America (IFANCA)
777 Busse Hwy.
Park Ridge, IL 60068
Contact: Dr. Muhammad Munir Chaudry, Pres.
Ph: (847)993-0034
Fax: (847)993-0038
URL: http://www.ifanca.org
Descr: Promotes Halal food and the institution of Halal. Certifies products in all food industries, cosmetics, meat and poultry slaughter, packaging materials and chemicals. Provides consulting on product development, marketing and quality assurance to help consumers choose authentic Halal products. **Pub:** *Halal Digest*.

8572 ■ Joint Committee of the States (JCS)
4401 Ford Ave., Ste. 700
Alexandria, VA 22302-1473
Contact: James M. Sgueo, Pres./CEO
Ph: (703)578-4200
Fax: (703)820-3551
E-mail: info@nabca.org
URL: http://www.nabca.org
Descr: A committee of the National Alcohol Beverage Control Association and the national Conference of State Liquor Administrators. Undertakes studies in

areas of mutual interest and concern to state liquor control agencies. **Pub:** *NABCA Contacts Directory*; *NABCA Survey Book* (annual).

8573 ■ Kamut Association of North America (KANA)
PO Box 6447
Great Falls, MT 59406
Contact: Tara Blyth, Public Relations Dir.
Ph: (406)452-7227
Free: 800-644-6450
Fax: (406)452-7175
URL: http://www.kamut.com
Staff: 2. **Descr:** Growers, manufacturers, and distributors of kamut grain. Educates the public, consumers, retailers, and manufacturers on the nutritional and flavor benefits of kamut grain. Compiles statistics. Sponsors research and educational programs. **Fnd:** 1990. **Mem:** 80. **Reg. Groups:** 1.

8574 ■ Kids with Food Allergies (KFA)
73 Old Dublin Pike, Ste. 10, No. 163
Doylestown, PA 18901
Contact: Lynda Mitchell, Pres.
Ph: (215)230-5394
Fax: (215)340-7674
E-mail: info@kidswithfoodallergies.org
URL: http://www.kidswithfoodallergies.org
Descr: Aims to foster optimal health, nutrition, and well-being of children with food allergies by providing education and a caring support community for their families and caregivers. Provides online support groups, online educational information, and food and cooking resources including a recipe database and other various programs and services for family support. Supports public health, awareness, advocacy, and research initiatives about food allergies and anaphylaxis. **Fnd:** 2005. **Mem:** 16500. **Pub:** *Kids with Food Allergies e-news* (semimonthly); *Kids With Food Allergies Support Net* (semiannual); Brochure.

8575 ■ Latino Nutrition Coalition (LNC)
266 Beacon St., 1st Fl.
Boston, MA 02116
Contact: Kezia Frayjo, Program Mgr.
Ph: (617)421-5500
Fax: (617)421-5511
E-mail: kfrayjo@oldwayspt.org
URL: http://www.latinonutrition.org
Descr: Seeks to inspire Latinos to improve and maintain their health through traditional foods and active lifestyles. Addresses and transforms the current dietary trends of Latinos in the United States. Creates and organizes programs and materials about healthy eating, drinking and lifestyle. Provides the Latino community, and those that serve them, with nutrition, cooking, shopping and health information. **Fnd:** 2005.

8576 ■ Mushroom Council
2880 Zanker Rd., Ste. 203
San Jose, CA 95134
Contact: Robert Crouch, Sec.
Ph: (408)432-7210
Fax: (408)432-7213
E-mail: info@mushroomcouncil.org
URL: http://www.mushroomcouncil.org
Descr: Promotes mushrooms; provides information about mushrooms and recipes. **Pub:** Reports.

8577 ■ National Association of Sports Nutrition (NASN)
7710 Balboa Ave., Ste. 227B
San Diego, CA 92111
Contact: Jeff Kotterman, Dir.
Ph: (858)694-0317
E-mail: nasn@nasnutrition.com
URL: http://www.nasnutrition.com
Descr: Aims to advance the scientific and clinical study of human sports nutrition. Seeks to enhance the proficiency of members in sports nutrition

counseling. Grants licensure or certification to qualified professionals. **Fnd:** 1996.

8578 ■ National Association of State Departments of Agriculture (NASDA)
1156 15th St. NW, Ste. 1020
Washington, DC 20005
Contact: Stephen Haterius, Exec. Dir.
Ph: (202)296-9680
Fax: (202)296-9686
E-mail: nasda@nasda.org
URL: http://www.nasda.org
Staff: 9. **Descr:** Directors of state and territorial departments of agriculture. Coordinates policies, procedures, laws, and activities between the states and federal agencies and Congress. Conducts research. **Fnd:** 1916. **Mem:** 54. **Reg. Groups:** 4. **Pub:** *NASDA Directory* (annual); *NASDA News* (weekly); Annual Report (annual); Brochure.

8579 ■ National Dairy Council (NDC)
10255 W Higgins Rd., Ste. 900
Rosemont, IL 60018
Contact: Gregory D. Miller PhD, Exec. VP for Science and Research
Ph: (312)240-2880
E-mail: ndc@dairyinformation.com
URL: http://www.nationaldairycouncil.org
Descr: Promotes the health benefits of dairy products, including milk, cheese and yogurt. Provides nutrition information to the media, physicians, dietitians, nurses, educators, consumers and others concerned about fostering a healthier society. Sponsors educational programs for school children. **Fnd:** 1915. **Pub:** Brochures; Booklets.

8580 ■ National Family Farm Coalition (NFFC)
110 Maryland Ave. NE, Ste. 307
Washington, DC 20002
Contact: Katherine Ozer, Exec. Dir.
Ph: (202)543-5675
Free: 800-639-3276
Fax: (202)543-0978
E-mail: kozer@nffc.net
URL: http://www.nffc.net
Staff: 3. **Descr:** Small farm and rural organizations including the Federation of Southern Cooperatives and Land Assistance Fund, Groundswell Inc. of Minnesota, North American Farm Alliance, and the RAFI-USA. Seeks to assure U.S. consumers of ample quantities of domestically produced food that is affordably priced and of high quality, and to reestablish a stable rural society by preserving economically viable family-owned and operated farms. Strives to increase the political participation and awareness of rural Americans, and works to develop an alliance with supportive urban Americans. Supports sustainable agriculture, the restoration of federal farm price supports and effective supply management, debt restructuring programs, and emergency aid to farm families in need of food, shelter, and health care. Coalition is distinct from group of same name listed in index as defunct. **Fnd:** 1986. **Mem:** 39. **Pub:** *Family Farm Agenda* (quarterly).

8581 ■ National Frozen Pizza Institute (NFPI)
2000 Corporate Ridge, Ste. 1000
McLean, VA 22102
Contact: Robert L. Garfield, Exec. Dir./Sec.
Ph: (703)821-0770
Fax: (703)821-1350
E-mail: info@affi.com
URL: http://www.affi.com/index.asp?sid=28
Descr: Aims to advance the interests of the frozen pizza industry. Monitors federal regulatory agency activities affecting frozen pizza processors and serves as an information resource for the trade and general public about the nutrition, value and convenience of frozen pizza and pizza products. **Fnd:** 1975. **Mem:** 40. **Pub:** Membership Directory (biennial).

8582 ■ National Pork Producers Council (NPPC)
122 C St. NW, Ste. 875
Washington, DC 20001

Contact: Neil Dierks, CEO
Ph: (202)347-3600
Fax: (202)347-5265
E-mail: intern@nppc.org
URL: http://www.nppc.org
Staff: 10. **Descr:** Federation of state pork producer associations. Promotes the pork industry through research programs, consumer education, and lobbying activities. Compiles statistics; maintains speakers' bureau and hall of fame. **Fnd:** 1954. **State Groups:** 44. **Pub:** *Annual Research Review, Seminar Proceedings*; *Pork Leader* (biweekly); *Pork Report* (bimonthly).

8583 ■ National Turkey Federation (NTF)
1225 New York Ave., Ste. 400
Washington, DC 20005
Contact: Joel Brandenberger, Pres.
Ph: (202)898-0100
Fax: (202)898-0203
E-mail: info@turkeyfed.org
URL: http://www.eatturkey.com
Staff: 9. **Descr:** Serves as the national advocate for all segments of the turkey industry. Provides services and conducts activities that increase demand for its members' products by protecting and enhancing their ability to profitably provide wholesome, high-quality, and nutritious products. **Fnd:** 1939. **State Groups:** 48. **Pub:** *Turkey Today and Tomorrow* (monthly); Brochure (annual).

8584 ■ New York Wine/Grape Foundation (NY-WGF)
800 S Main St., Ste. 200
Canandaigua, NY 14424
Contact: James Trezise, Pres.
Ph: (585)394-3620
Fax: (585)394-3649
E-mail: info@newyorkwines.org
URL: http://www.newyorkwines.org
Staff: 4. **Descr:** Grape growers from New York State; wineries and juice processors, suppliers, financiers, insurance representatives, consultants to growers, restaurateurs, and consumers. Promotes the demand for and sale of grapes and grape products through advertising and promotional work; assist members by performing services relative to the production, harvesting, and marketing of wine grapes, and any related research; provide members with production and marketing information; promote mutual understanding and goodwill between growers and processors of grapes. Seeks to educate consumers on the variety and quality of grapes grown and grape products made in New York State. Sponsors Women for New York State Wines, consisting of women supporting the New York State wine industry; WNYSW promotes wine sales and holds wine tasting to teach people how to read wine labels and distinguish between wines made from various types of wine grapes. **Fnd:** 1985. **Mem:** 335. **Pub:** *Uncork New York*; *Wine Country Calendar* (annual); *Wine Press* (weekly); Reports.

8585 ■ North American Vegetarian Society (NAVS)
PO Box 72
Dolgeville, NY 13329
Contact: Jennie O. Kerwood, Pres.
Ph: (518)568-7970
E-mail: navs@telenet.net
URL: http://www.navs-online.org
Staff: 4. **Descr:** Individual vegetarians and vegetarian organizations. Educates the public and the media about the nutritional, economical, ecological, and ethical benefits of a vegetarian diet. Provides a support network for vegetarians and related groups. Founded World Vegetarian Day (Oct. 1st). Hosts the annual Vegetarian Summerfest Conference. **Fnd:** 1974. **Mem:** 3800. **Local Groups:** 155. **Pub:** *Good Nutrition*; *Vegetarian Voice* (quarterly); Videos; Books.

8586 ■ Northern Nut Growers Association (NNGA)
PO Box 6216
Hamden, CT 06517-0216

Contact: Mr. Alan Van Antwerp, Pres.
E-mail: tuckerh@epix.net
URL: http://www.northernnutgrowers.org
Descr: Consists of nut tree culturists, farmers, amateur and commercial nut tree growers, experiment station workers, horticultural teachers, scientists, nut tree breeders, nursery people, and foresters. Conducts visits to amateur and commercial orchards, experimental and research sites, nurseries and nut processing plants. **Fnd:** 1911. **Mem:** 850. **Pub:** *A Guide to Nut Tree Culture in North America, Vol. 1*; *Bench Grafting Nut Trees*; *The Hazel Book*; *The Nutshell* (quarterly); Membership Directory (annual); Annual Report (annual).

8587 ■ Nutrition for Optimal Health Association (NOHA)
PO Box 262
Western Springs, IL 60558
Ph: (708)246-3663
E-mail: contact@nutrition4health.org
URL: http://www.nutrition4health.org
Descr: Consists of individuals interested in making informed health decisions through better nutrition. Promotes good nutrition as a means of achieving and maintaining optimal health. Advances and disseminates scientifically based information on the practical application of sound nutritional principles to daily living. Offers nutrition education programs and seminars. Maintains tape list. **Fnd:** 1972. **Mem:** 230. **Pub:** *NOHA News* (quarterly).

8588 ■ Peanut Institute
PO Box 70157
Albany, GA 31708-0157
Ph: (229)888-0216
Free: 888-8PE-ANUT
Fax: (229)888-5150
E-mail: info@peanut-institute.org
URL: http://www.peanut-institute.org
Descr: Promotes the peanut as a nutritionally healthy food; provides information on nutrition, diets, and educational materials. Conducts peanut recipe contests.

8589 ■ Pear Bureau Northwest
4382 SE International Way, Ste. A
Milwaukie, OR 97222-4635
Contact: Cristie Mather, Communications Mgr.
Ph: (503)652-9720
Fax: (503)652-9721
E-mail: info@usapears.com
URL: http://www.usapears.com
Descr: Promotes pears grown in the Northwest; provides materials for uses and recipes for pears; provides information to consumers, educators, health professionals and food industry members. **Fnd:** 1931. **Pub:** Newsletter (periodic); Reports.

8590 ■ People Food and Land Foundation (PFLF)
35751 Oak Springs Dr.
Tollhouse, CA 93667-9611
Contact: George Elfie Ballis, Coor.
Ph: (559)855-3710
Free: 888-303-0103
E-mail: sunmt@sunmt.org
URL: http://www.sunmt.org
Staff: 4. **Descr:** Small farmers, consumers, and individuals concerned with low-water use, arid land crops, organic methods for small farmers and gardeners, and low-tech passive solar models for farm, food processing, and home use. Sponsors Sun Mountain Research Center. Activities include: a "Seminar in Reality"; herbal food preparation; floral; medicinal, and culinary uses of native plants; shamanism; self-healing. Operates speakers' bureau. Sponsors intern program. **Fnd:** 1974. **Mem:** 500. **Pub:** Bulletin (monthly).

8591 ■ Southern U.S. Trade Association (SUSTA)
2 Canal St., Ste. 2515
New Orleans, LA 70130
Contact: Sonja Page, Office Mgr.
Ph: (504)568-5986

Fax: (504)568-6010
E-mail: susta@susta.org
URL: http://www.susta.org
Staff: 10. **Descr:** Departments of agriculture of the Southern states; food and agricultural manufacturers and exporters operating in the southern United States. Promotes the export of high-value food and agricultural products of the South. Participates in international trade exhibitions and conducts point of sale promotions in food chains and restaurants worldwide; organizes overseas trade missions and other promotional campaigns; provides information and assistance with transportation and financing of export sales and works closely on an individual basis with its export company membership to develop and expand their share of agricultural export markets. Sponsors economics and marketing research and educational programs. **Fnd:** 1973. **Mem:** 285. **Reg. Groups:** 4. **State Groups:** 16. **Local Groups:** 185. **Pub:** *Insight* (bimonthly).

8592 ■ Spoons Across America
505 Court St., Ste. 2E
Brooklyn, NY 11231
Contact: Jacques Pepin
E-mail: info@spoonsacrossamerica.org
URL: http://www.spoonsacrossamerica.org
Descr: Encourages healthy eating and creates awareness of the benefits of preparing home-cooked meals that ensure long-term health and well-being. Develops and supports food- and nutrition-based educational programs for children. Provides a network for sharing information and resources among culinary professionals, educators and parents. **Fnd:** 2001.

8593 ■ Sweet and Fortified Wine Association (SFWA)
PO Box 193
Applegate, CA 95703
Contact: Peter Prager, Pres.
Ph: (916)258-7115
Fax: (530)323-6762
E-mail: sweetandfortified@sbcglobal.net
URL: http://sweetandfortifiedwine.org
Descr: Aims to expand and develop the market for sweet and fortified wines. Provides a forum for industry partners and the general public to share ideas and information on sweet and fortified wines. Advocates for responsible consumption of alcoholic beverages.

8594 ■ True Food Network
2601 Mission St., Ste. 803
San Francisco, CA 94110
Contact: Andrew Kimbrell, Exec. Dir.
Ph: (415)826-2770
E-mail: office@centerforfoodsafety.org
URL: http://www.truefoodnow.org
Descr: Aims to stop genetic engineering of food and farms. Engages farmers in the struggle against genetically engineered crops. Creates a socially just, democratic and sustainable food system. **Fnd:** 2000. **Mem:** 40000.

8595 ■ United Egg Producers (UEP)
1720 Windward Concourse, Ste. 230
Alpharetta, GA 30005
Contact: Gene Gregory, Pres./CEO
Ph: (770)360-9220
Fax: (770)360-7058
E-mail: gene@unitedegg.com
URL: http://www.unitedegg.org
Staff: 19. **Descr:** Represents regional egg marketing cooperatives whose members are independent egg producers. Aids members in improving efficiency in production, distribution, and marketing of eggs. Maintains legislative office in Washington, DC, which serves as congressional liaison. Compiles statistics; provides specialized education programs. **Fnd:** 1968. **Mem:** 500. **Pub:** *The New Yolk Times* (quarterly); Newsletter (biweekly).

8596 ■ United Fresh Produce Association
1901 Pennsylvania Ave. NW, Ste. 1100
Washington, DC 20006

Contact: James P. Lemke, Chm.
Ph: (202)303-3400
Fax: (202)303-3433
E-mail: united@unitedfresh.org
URL: http://www.unitedfresh.org
Staff: 22. **Descr:** Promotes the growth and success of produce companies and their partners. Represents interests of growers, shippers, processors, brokers, wholesalers and distributors of produce, working together with their customers at retail and food service, suppliers at every step in the distribution chain, and international partners. Provides leadership to shape business, trade and public policies that drive the industry. Works with thousands of industry members, provides fair and balanced forum to promote business solutions; helps build strong partnerships among all segments of the industry, promotes increased produce consumption; provides scientific and technical expertise essential to competing effectively in today's marketplace. **Fnd:** 1904. **Reg. Groups:** 9. **Pub:** *United Fresh* (weekly).

8597 ■ United States Potato Board (USPB)
7555 E Hampden Ave., Ste. 412
Denver, CO 80231-4835
Contact: Tim O'Connor, Pres./CEO
Ph: (303)369-7783
Fax: (303)369-7718
E-mail: toconnor@uspotatoes.com
URL: http://www.healthypotato.com
Staff: 19. **Descr:** Growers of five or more acres of potatoes. Provides a way to organize and finance a national promotion program for potatoes, to increase consumption, expand markets, and make the growing and marketing of potatoes a better business for all; carries out effective and continuous coordinated marketing research, retail marketing, consumer advertising, public relations, and export programs. **Fnd:** 1971. **Mem:** 4000. **Pub:** *Industry Update* (semimonthly); Brochures.

8598 ■ Vegetarian Resource Group (VRG)
PO Box 1463
Baltimore, MD 21203
Contact: Charles Stahler, Co-Dir.
Ph: (410)366-8343
Fax: (410)366-8804
E-mail: vrg@vrg.org
URL: http://www.vrg.org
Staff: 10. **Descr:** Health professionals, activists, and educators working with businesses and individuals to bring about healthy changes in schools, workplaces, and communities. Educates the public about vegetarianism (abstinence from meat, fish, and fowl) and veganism (abstinence from meat, fish, and fowl, and other animal products such as dairy products, eggs, wool and leather). Examines vegetarian issues as they relate to issues of health, nutrition, animal rights, ethics, world hunger, and ecology. Promotes World Vegetarian Day (October 1). Offers internships and children's services. Provides information and referral services. Conducts research. Operates speakers' bureau. Holds cooking demonstrations. **Fnd:** 1982. **Mem:** 20000. **Pub:** *Conveniently Vegan*; *I Love Animals and Broccoli Activity Book*; *Leprechaun Cake and Other Tales*; *The Lowfat Jewish Vegetarian Cookbook*; *Meatless Meals for Working People*; *Simply Vegan*; *Vegan Handbook*; *Vegan in Volume*; *Vegan Meals for 1 or 2*; *Vegetarian Journal* (quarterly); *Vegetarian Journal's Food Service Update* (quarterly).

8599 ■ Vinegar Institute (VI)
1100 Johnson Ferry Rd., Ste. 300
Atlanta, GA 30342
Contact: Pamela A. Chumley, Pres.
Ph: (404)252-3663
Fax: (404)252-0774
E-mail: vi@kellencompany.com
URL: http://www.versatilevinegar.org
Staff: 3. **Descr:** Represents manufacturers and bottlers of vinegar and suppliers to the industry. Seeks to improve the quality of vinegar and increase its ac-

ceptance to the consumer. **Fnd:** 1964. **Mem:** 45. **Pub:** Membership Directory (annual).

8600 ■ Wine Appreciation Guild (WAG)
360 Swift Ave., Unit 30-40
South San Francisco, CA 94080
Contact: Bryan Imelli
Ph: (650)866-3020
Free: 800-231-9463
E-mail: info@wineappreciation.com
URL: http://www.wineappreciation.com
Descr: Represents winery owners and distributors. Disseminates information on wine, with emphasis on American wines. Conducts wine evaluations and research programs on wine and health, cooking with wine, and consumer wine. Offers wine study courses and compiles statistics. Sponsors competitions. **Fnd:** 1973. **Reg. Groups:** 2.

8601 ■ Women, Food and Agriculture Network (WFAN)
PO Box 611
Ames, IA 50010
Contact: Stacey Brown, Chair
Ph: (515)232-4082
E-mail: info@wfan.org
URL: http://www.wfan.org
Descr: Represents farmers, urban gardeners, environmental educators, community activists, academics, and others who care about food and the environment. Provides a forum for women to voice their opinions on issues of food systems, sustainable communities, and environmental integrity. Advocates change by exploring alternative options in handling issues concerning systemic rural, agricultural, and environmental problems and gender relation in these domains. **Fnd:** 1997. **Mem:** 150. **Pub:** Newsletter (quarterly).

State and Local Organizations and Agencies

Alabama

8602 ■ Alabama Cattlemen's Association (ACA)
201 S Bainbridge St.
Montgomery, AL 36102-2499
Contact: Dr. Billy Powell, Exec. VP
Ph: (334)265-1867
Fax: (334)834-5326
E-mail: mdavis@bamabeef.org
URL: http://www.bamabeef.org
Staff: 10. **Descr:** Works to protect, promote, and advance the beef cattle industry. **Fnd:** 1944. **Mem:** 12000. **Local Groups:** 67. **Pub:** *Alabama Cattleman* (monthly).

8603 ■ Alabama Department of Agriculture and Industries
Richard Beard Bldg.
1445 Federal Dr.
Montgomery, AL 36107
Contact: Ron Sparks, Commnr.
Ph: (334)240-7100
Fax: (334)240-7190
E-mail: ron.sparks@agi.alabama.gov
URL: http://www.agi.alabama.gov/
Descr: Mission is to provide timely, fair, and expert regulatory control over product, business entities, movement, and application of goods and services for which applicable state and federal law exists and strive to protect and provide service to Alabama consumers.

Alaska

8604 ■ Alaska Department of Natural Resources
Division of Agriculture
1800 Glenn Hwy., Ste. 12
Palmer, AK 99645-6736
Contact: Franci Havemeister, Dir.

Ph: (907)761-3851
Fax: (907)745-7112
URL: http://dnr.alaska.gov/

Arizona

8605 ■ Arizona Department of Agriculture
1688 W. Adams St.
Phoenix, AZ 85007
Contact: Donald Butler, Dir.
Ph: (602)542-4373
Fax: (602)542-5420
E-mail: dbutler@azda.gov
URL: http://www.azda.gov/

8606 ■ United Dairymen of Arizona (UDA)
PO Box 26877
Tempe, AZ 85285-6877
Contact: Kaye Lunsford, Ed.
Ph: (480)966-7211
Fax: (480)966-8074
E-mail: uda@udaz.org
URL: http://www.uda.coop
Staff: 180. **Descr:** Represents dairy products manufacturing plants. Serves as a milk marketing association. Promotes members' interests; conducts lobbying activities. **Fnd:** 1960. **Mem:** 105. **Pub:** Magazine (monthly).

Arkansas

8607 ■ Arkansas State Plant Board
1 Natural Resource Dr.
Little Rock, AR 72205
Contact: Darryl Little, Dir.
Ph: (501)225-1598
Fax: (501)219-1697
E-mail: info@aspb.ar.gov
URL: http://www.plantboard.org/

California

8608 ■ California Beef Council (CBC)
4640 Northgate Blvd., Ste. 115
Sacramento, CA 95834
Contact: Bill Dale, Exec. Dir.
Ph: (916)925-2333
Fax: (916)925-8155
E-mail: askus@calbeef.org
URL: http://www.calbeef.org
Descr: Aims to increase the opportunity for all segments of the beef industry to earn a fair return on investment through promotion, research, education, and public information programs that build demand for beef products to satisfy both domestic and international consumer needs and wants. **Fnd:** 1954. **Mem:** 42.

8609 ■ California Department of Food and Agriculture
1220 N St.
Sacramento, CA 95814
Contact: A.G. Kawamura, Sec.
Ph: (916)654-0466
Fax: (916)657-4240
E-mail: cdfapublicaffairs@cdfa.ca.gov
URL: http://www.cdfa.ca.gov/
Descr: Mission is to help the governor and Legislature ensure delivery of safe food and fiber through responsible environmental stewardship in a fair marketplace for all Californians. **Telecom. Svcs:** TTY/TDD tol free number is (800)735-2929.

8610 ■ San Francisco Vegetarian Society (SFVS)
PO Box 2510
San Francisco, CA 94126-2510
Contact: Dixie Mahy, Pres.
Ph: (415)273-5481
E-mail: contact@sfvs.org
URL: http://www.sfvs.org
Descr: Promotes the nutritional, economical, ecological, and ethical benefits of a vegetarian diet. **Fnd:** 1967. **Mem:** 254. **Local Groups:** 1.

Colorado

8611 ■ Colorado Department of Agriculture
700 Kipling St., Ste. 4000
Lakewood, CO 80215-8000
Contact: John R. Stulp, Commnr.
Ph: (303)239-4100
Fax: (303)239-4125
URL: http://www.ag.state.co.us/

Connecticut

8612 ■ Connecticut Department of Agriculture
165 Capitol Ave.
Hartford, CT 06106
Contact: F. Philip Prelli, Commnr.
Ph: (860)713-2500
Free: 800-861-9939
Fax: (860)713-2514
E-mail: ctdeptag@ct.gov
URL: http://www.ct.gov/doag/site/default.asp

8613 ■ Connecticut Pork Producers Association
139 Wolf Den Rd.
Brooklyn, CT 06234
Contact: Joyce Meader
Ph: (860)774-9600
Fax: (860)974-9480
E-mail: joyce.meader@uconn.edu
Descr: Promotes the pork industry through research programs, consumer education, and lobbying activities.

Delaware

8614 ■ Delaware Beef Advisory Board (DBAB)
PO Box 0515
Camden, DE 19934
Contact: Wally Gott, Pres.
E-mail: excessacres@verizon.net
URL: http://www.delawarebeef.org
Descr: Comprises of beef producers. Provides safety, wholesome, and delicious beef in Delaware.

8615 ■ Delaware Department of Agriculture
2320 S. DuPont Hwy.
Dover, DE 19901
Contact: Ed Kee, Sec.
Ph: (302)698-4500
Free: 800-282-8685
Fax: (302)697-4463
URL: http://dda.delaware.gov
Descr: Mission is to sustain and promote the viability of food, fiber, and agricultural industries in Delaware through quality services that protect and enhance the environment, health, and welfare of the general public.

8616 ■ Delaware Pork Producers Association
2582 Arthursville Rd.
Hartly, DE 19953-3239
Contact: John Tigner
Ph: (302)492-8794
Descr: Promotes the pork industry through research programs, consumer education, and lobbying activities.

Florida

8617 ■ Florida Beef Council (FBC)
PO Box 421929
Kissimmee, FL 34742-1929
Contact: Jim Handley, CEO
Ph: (407)846-6221
Fax: (407)933-8209
E-mail: fbcfcajimhandley@aol.com
URL: http://www.floridacattlemen.org/flbeefcouncil.htm

Descr: Promotes the importance of the consumption of beef, both for health and industry reasons.

8618 ■ Florida Cattlemen's Association (FCA)
PO Box 421929
Kissimmee, FL 34742-1929
Contact: Jim Handley, Exec. VP
Ph: (407)846-6221
Fax: (407)933-8209
E-mail: fbcfcajimhandley@aol.com
URL: http://www.floridacattlemen.org
Staff: 7. **Descr:** Strives to support cattle ranching families as an integral part of economy in Florida and as leaders in protecting the natural landscape. **Fnd:** 1934. **Pub:** *The Florida Cattleman* (monthly).

8619 ■ Florida Department of Agriculture and Consumer Services
The Capitol
Tallahassee, FL 32399-0800
Contact: Charles Bronson, Commnr.
Ph: (850)488-3022
Fax: (850)922-4936
E-mail: commissioner@doacs.state.fl.us
URL: http://www.doacs.state.fl.us/

Georgia

8620 ■ Georgia Beef Board
PO Box 24570
Macon, GA 31212-4510
Contact: Jim Collins, Exec. VP
Ph: (478)474-1815
Free: 877-444-BEEF
E-mail: jim@gabeef.org
URL: http://www.gabeef.org
Descr: Provides education, promotion, and research for the beef producers of Georgia.

8621 ■ Georgia Department of Agriculture
19 Martin Luther King Jr. Dr., SW
Atlanta, GA 30334
Contact: Tommy Irvin, Commnr.
Ph: (404)656-3645
Free: 800-282-5852
Fax: (404)657-8387
E-mail: tirvin@agr.state.ga.us
URL: http://agr.georgia.gov/
Telecom. Svcs: TTY phone number is (404)657-8387.

8622 ■ Vegetarian Society of Georgia (VSG)
PO Box 56174
Atlanta, GA 30343
Contact: Jill Howard Church, Pres.
Ph: (770)365-7464
E-mail: info@vegsocietyofga.org
URL: http://www.vegsocietyofga.org
Descr: Promotes the nutritional, economical, ecological, and ethical benefits of a vegetarian diet.

Hawaii

8623 ■ Hawaii Beef Industry Council (HBIC)
64-957 Mamalahoa Hwy.
Kamuela, HI 96743
Contact: Alan Winters, Chm.
Ph: (808)885-5599
Fax: (808)887-1607
E-mail: hicattlemens@hawaii.rr.com
URL: http://www.hicattle.org/Industry/Default.aspx
Descr: Seeks to promote beef and beef products in the State of Hawaii, as well as research and education. Provide grant monies to approved bonafide beef promotion or education efforts. Provide recipes, posters and other promotional materials. **Mem:** 110.

8624 ■ Hawaii Department of Agriculture
Office of the Chairperson
1428 S. King St.
Honolulu, HI 96814
Contact: Sandra Lee Kunimoto, Chm.
Ph: (808)973-9560
Fax: (808)973-9613

E-mail: hdoa.info@hawaii.gov
URL: http://www.hawaii.gov/hdoa

8625 ■ Vegetarian Society of Hawaii (VSH)
PO Box 23208
Honolulu, HI 96823
Contact: William Harris MD, Board Member
Ph: (808)944-8344
E-mail: info@vsh.org
URL: http://www.vsh.org
Staff: 1. **Descr:** Educates the public about the benefits of vegetarianism through speakers, outings, and a weekly TV show. **Fnd:** 1990. **Mem:** 1800. **State Groups:** 1. **Pub:** *The Island Vegetarian* (quarterly).

Idaho

8626 ■ Idaho Beef Council
2118 Airport Way
Boise, ID 83705
Contact: Kim Brackett, Chm.
Ph: (208)376-6004
Fax: (208)376-6002
E-mail: beefcouncil@idbeef.org
URL: http://www.idbeef.org
Descr: Strives to maintain and build consumer demand for beef through support of integrated state, national and international programs, thereby enhancing the opportunity for producer profitability and return on checkoff investment. **Fnd:** 1967. **Pub:** Annual Report (annual).

8627 ■ Idaho Department of Agriculture
PO Box 790
Boise, ID 83701-0790
Contact: Celia R. Gould, Dir.
Ph: (208)332-8500
Fax: (208)334-2170
E-mail: info@agri.idaho.gov
URL: http://www.agri.state.id.us/

8628 ■ United Dairymen of Idaho
10221 W Emerald St., Ste. 180
Boise, ID 83704
Contact: Deana Sessions, Admin.
Ph: (208)327-7050
Fax: (208)327-7054
E-mail: dsessions@udidaho.org
URL: http://www.idahodairycouncil.com
Descr: Responsible for increasing demand for U.S. produced dairy products on behalf of Idaho's dairy farm families.

Illinois

8629 ■ Illinois Beef Association (IBA)
2060 W Iles Ave., Ste. B
Springfield, IL 62704
Contact: Maralee Johnson, Exec. VP
Ph: (217)787-4280
Fax: (217)793-3605
E-mail: maralee@illinoisbeef.com
URL: http://www.illinoisbeef.com
Descr: Promotes and markets Illinois beefs. Delivers detailed analysis and presentation on beef industry by giving up-to-date news, important issues and other beef-related information that are essential for beef producers and consumers in the region.

8630 ■ Illinois Department of Agriculture
State Fairgrounds
PO Box 19281
Springfield, IL 62794-9281
Contact: Thomas E. Jennings, Dir.
Ph: (217)782-2172
Fax: (217)785-4505
E-mail: agri.pio@illinois.gov
URL: http://www.agr.state.il.us/
Telecom. Svcs: TTY phone number is (217)524-6858.

Indiana

8631 ■ Indiana Beef Council
5738 W 74th St.
Indianapolis, IN 46278
Contact: Julia Wickard
Ph: (317)293-2333
Fax: (317)295-8421
E-mail: jwickard@indianabeef.org
URL: http://www.indianabeef.org
Descr: Beef producers. Works to increase profit opportunities and build stronger rural communities. **Fnd:** 1965. **Mem:** 1300. **Pub:** *Indiana Beef* (bimonthly).

8632 ■ Indiana State Department of Agriculture
101 W. Ohio St., Ste. 1200
Indianapolis, IN 46204
Contact: Joseph M. Kelsey, Dir.
Ph: (317)232-8770
Fax: (317)232-1362
E-mail: ahazlett@isda.in.gov
URL: http://www.in.gov/isda/

Iowa

8633 ■ Iowa Beef Industry Council
PO Box 451
Ames, IA 50010
Contact: Nancy Degner, Exec. Dir.
Ph: (515)296-2305
Fax: (515)296-4873
E-mail: nancy@iabeef.org
URL: http://www.iabeef.org
Descr: Seeks to promote beef and beef products in the State of Iowa, as well as research and education.

8634 ■ Iowa Department of Agriculture and Land Stewardship
Wallace State Office Bldg.
502 E. 9th St.
Des Moines, IA 50319
Contact: Bill Northey, Sec.
Ph: (515)281-5321
Fax: (515)281-7046
E-mail: agri@idals.state.ia.us
URL: http://www.agriculture.state.ia.us/

Kansas

8635 ■ Kansas Beef Council (KBC)
6031 SW 37th St.
Topeka, KS 66614-5128
Contact: Todd Johnson, Exec. Dir.
Ph: (785)273-5225
Fax: (785)273-3399
E-mail: kbc@kansasbeef.org
URL: http://www.kansasbeef.org
Staff: 5. **Descr:** Promotes beef industry in Kansas state. **Fnd:** 1973. **Pub:** *Review* (monthly).

8636 ■ Kansas Department of Agriculture
109 SW 9th St.
Topeka, KS 66612-1280
Contact: Adrian J. Polansky, Sec.
Ph: (785)296-3556
Fax: (785)296-8389
E-mail: ksag@kda.ks.gov
URL: http://www.ksda.gov/
Descr: Charged by law to ensure: a safe food supply; responsible and judicious use of pesticides and nutrients; the protection of Kansas' natural and cultivated plants; integrity of weighing and measuring devices in commerce; and, that the state's waters are put to beneficial use.

Kentucky

8637 ■ Kentucky Beef Council
176 Pasadena Dr.
Lexington, KY 40503-2900
Contact: Alison Smith, Dir. of Consumer Affairs
Ph: (859)278-0899

Fax: (859)260-2060
URL: http://www.kybeef.com
Descr: Aims to increase the opportunity for all segments of the beef industry to earn a fair return on investment through promotion, research, education, and public information programs that build demand for beef products to satisfy both domestic and international consumer needs and wants. **Fnd:** 1973.

8638 ■ Kentucky Department of Agriculture
32 Fountain Place
Frankfort, KY 40601
Contact: Richie Farmer, Commnr.
Ph: (502)564-4696
Fax: (502)564-2133
E-mail: richie.farmer@ky.gov
URL: http://www.kyagr.com/

Louisiana

8639 ■ Louisiana Department of Agriculture and Forestry
PO Box 631
Baton Rouge, LA 70821
Contact: Mike Strain DVM, Commnr.
Ph: (225)922-1234
Free: 866-927-2476
Fax: (225)922-1253
E-mail: commissioner@ldaf.state.la.us
URL: http://www.ldaf.state.la.us/

8640 ■ Louisiana Pork Producers Association (LPPA)
319 W Claud St.
Lake Charles, LA 70605
Contact: Butch Racca, Pres.
Ph: (337)562-8776
E-mail: laporkproducers@bellsouth.net
URL: http://www.laporkproducers.com
Descr: Promotes the pork industry through research programs, consumer education, and lobbying activities.

Maine

8641 ■ Maine Beef Industry Council (MBIC)
149 Clark Ln.
Whitefield, ME 04353-3223
Contact: Judy Powell, Exec. Dir.
Ph: (207)549-5972
Fax: (207)549-4602
E-mail: mbic@midmaine.com
URL: http://www.mainebeef.org
Descr: Aims to provide information and linkages to enhance and further develop the beef industry in Maine and the nation. **Pub:** Newsletter (monthly).

8642 ■ Maine Department of Agriculture, Food and Rural Resources
Deering Bldg. (AMHI)
28 State House Station
Augusta, ME 04333-0028
Contact: Seth H. Bradstreet III, Commnr.
Ph: (207)287-3419
Fax: (207)287-7548
E-mail: agriculture.commissioner@maine.gov
URL: http://www.maine.gov/agriculture/index.shtml

Maryland

8643 ■ Maryland Department of Agriculture
50 Harry S. Truman Pkwy.
Annapolis, MD 21401
Contact: Earl F. Hance, Sec.
Ph: (410)841-5700
Fax: (410)841-5914
E-mail: hanceef@mda.state.md.us
URL: http://www.mda.state.md.us/

Massachusetts

8644 ■ Boston Vegetarian Society (BVS)
PO Box 38-1071
Cambridge, MA 02238-1071

Contact: Evelyn B. Kimber, Pres.
Ph: (617)424-8846
E-mail: info@bostonveg.org
URL: http://www.bostonveg.org
Descr: Promotes the nutritional, environmental, and ethical benefits of a vegetarian diet. Seeks to make a better world for people, animals, and the Earth through advancing a healthful vegetarian diet and a compassionate ethic. Provides education, encouragement, and community support for vegetarians and for anyone wishing to learn more about a healthy, environmentally friendly, and humane way of life. **Fnd:** 1986. **Pub:** *Email Announcements List* (weekly); *Newsletter of the Boston Vegetarian Society* (periodic); *Postcard Notifications* (periodic).

8645 ■ Massachusetts Department of Agricultural Resources
251 Causeway St., Ste. 500
Boston, MA 02114-2151
Contact: Scott J. Soares, Commnr.
Ph: (617)626-1700
Fax: (617)626-1850
E-mail: doug.petersen@state.ma.us
URL: http://www.mass.gov/agr/
Descr: Mission is to support promote and enhance the long-term viability of Massachusetts agriculture with the aim of helping the state's agricultural businesses become as economically and environmentally sound as possible.

Michigan

8646 ■ Dietitians of West Michigan
6986 Valley View Ct.
Allendale, MI 49401
Contact: Chanel Kerschbaum, Pres.-Elect
Ph: (616)913-1497
E-mail: kerschbc@trinity-health.org
URL: http://www.dietitianswestmichigan.org
Descr: Represents the interests of food and nutrition professionals. Seeks to improve the public's health and nutrition. Advances the profession of dietetics through research, education and advocacy.

8647 ■ Michigan Department of Agriculture
Box 30017
Lansing, MI 48909
Contact: Don Koivisto, Dir.
Ph: (517)373-1052
Free: 800-292-3939
Fax: (517)335-1423
E-mail: mda-info@michigan.gov
URL: http://www.michigan.gov/mda

8648 ■ VegMichigan
PO Box 2161
Royal Oak, MI 48068-2161
Contact: Mr. Harry Pianko, Pres./Treas.
Free: 877-778-3464
E-mail: info@vegmichigan.org
URL: http://www.vegmichigan.org
Staff: 4. **Descr:** Promotes the awareness of the health, ecological and ethical consequences of food choices. Provides support to members while reaching out to educate the public about the many benefits of shifting towards a plant-based lifestyle. **Fnd:** 1999. **Mem:** 83. **Pub:** *News For Life* (monthly).

Minnesota

8649 ■ Minnesota Department of Agriculture
625 Robert St. N.
St. Paul, MN 55155-2538
Contact: Gene Hugoson, Commnr.
Ph: (651)201-6000
Free: 800-967-2474
Fax: (651)297-5522
E-mail: mda.info@state.mn.us
URL: http://www.mda.state.mn.us/default.htm
Telecom. Svcs: TTY toll-free phone is (800)627-3529.

Mississippi

8650 ■ Mississippi Department of Agriculture and Commerce
121 N. Jefferson St.
Jackson, MS 39201
Contact: Lester Spell Jr.DVM, Commnr.
Ph: (601)359-1100
Fax: (601)354-6290
E-mail: webmaster@mdac.state.ms.us
URL: http://www.mdac.state.ms.us/

Missouri

8651 ■ Missouri Department of Agriculture
PO Box 630
1616 Missouri Blvd.
Jefferson City, MO 65102
Contact: John Hagler, Dir.
Ph: (573)751-4211
Fax: (573)751-1784
E-mail: aginfo@mda.mo.gov
URL: http://www.mda.mo.gov/
Telecom. Svcs: TDD toll-free phone is (800)735-2966.

Montana

8652 ■ Montana Department of Agriculture
PO Box 200201
Helena, MT 59620-0201
Contact: Ron de Yong, Dir.
Ph: (406)444-3144
Fax: (406)444-5409
E-mail: agr@mt.gov
URL: http://www.agr.state.mt.us/
Pub: Four publications are available as PDF files at agr.mt.gov/business/mktPubs.asp.

Nebraska

8653 ■ Nebraska Department of Agriculture
PO Box 94947
301 Centennial Mall S.
Lincoln, NE 68509-4947
Contact: Greg Ibach, Dir.
Ph: (402)471-2341
Fax: (402)471-6876
E-mail: agr.webmaster@nebraska.gov
URL: http://www.agr.state.ne.us/

Nevada

8654 ■ Nevada Beef Council
201 S Roop St., Ste. 101
Carson City, NV 89701
Contact: Bob Butler, Exec. Dir.
Ph: (775)841-6224
Fax: (775)883-7398
E-mail: bbutler@nevadabeef.org
URL: http://www.nevadabeef.org
Descr: Optimizes the profit potential for cattle owners within the state of Nevada.

8655 ■ Nevada Department of Agriculture
405 S. 21st St.
Sparks, NV 89431
Contact: Tony Lesperance, Dir.
Ph: (775)353-3600
Free: 888-228-5239
Fax: (775)353-3638
URL: http://agri.state.nv.us/

8656 ■ Nevada Pork Producers Association
38 N Bybee Ln.
Yerington, NV 89447
Contact: Kris Simkins
Ph: (775)463-5504
Fax: (775)255-4612
E-mail: nevadapork@earthlink.net
Descr: Promotes the pork industry through research programs, consumer education, and lobbying activities.

New Hampshire

8657 ■ New Hampshire Department of Agriculture, Markets and Food
PO Box 2042
Concord, NH 03302-2042
Contact: Lorraine S. Merrill, Commnr.
Ph: (603)271-3551
Fax: (603)271-1109
E-mail: lmerrill@agr.state.nh.us
URL: http://www.nh.gov/agric/contactus.htm
Descr: Mission is to promote agriculture in the public interest and to serve farmers and consumers in the marketplace. The Department ensures safe and healthy food supplies, provides accurate information on prices and availability of farm commodities and crops, and develops markets for the state's farmers.

8658 ■ New Hampshire Pork Producers Council (NHPPC)
206 Currier Rd.
Hill, NH 03243
Contact: William Colby, Pres.
E-mail: colbyfarms@comcast.net
URL: http://www.nhpork.org
Descr: Promotes the pork industry through research programs, consumer education, and lobbying activities.

New Jersey

8659 ■ New Jersey Department of Agriculture
PO Box 330
Trenton, NJ 08625
Contact: Douglas H. Fisher, Sec.
Ph: (609)292-3976
Fax: (609)292-3978
URL: http://www.nj.gov/agriculture/

New Mexico

8660 ■ Farmington Small Business Development Center
San Juan College
5101 College Blvd.
Farmington, NM 87402
Contact: Carmen Martinez, Dir.
Ph: (505)566-3528
Fax: (505)566-3698
E-mail: bumbyj@sanjuancollege.edu
URL: http://www.nmsbdc.org/farmington
Descr: Represents and promotes the small business sector. Provides management assistance to current and prospective small business owners. Helps to improve management skills and expand the products and services of members.

8661 ■ New Mexico Department of Agriculture
PO Box 30005, MSC 3189
Las Cruces, NM 88003-8005
Contact: I. Miley Gonzalez PhD, Dir./Sec.
Ph: (505)646-3007
Fax: (505)646-8120
E-mail: nmagsec@nmda.nmsu.edu
URL: http://nmdaweb.nmsu.edu/

8662 ■ Vegetarian Society of New Mexico (VSNM)
PO Box 94495
Albuquerque, NM 87199-4495
Contact: Julie Hughes, Sec.
Ph: (505)237-0347
E-mail: info@vsnm.org
URL: http://www.vsnm.org
Descr: Promotes the nutritional, economical, ecological, and ethical benefits of a vegetarian diet. Pub: New Mexico Vegetarian (quarterly).

New York

8663 ■ Club Veg: Philly
PO Box 625 WVS
Binghamton, NY 13905
Contact: Allison Geiger

Ph: (607)272-1126
E-mail: clubveg@clubveg.org
URL: http://www.clubveg.org
Descr: Educates the public, health care professionals, and health organizations about the benefits of a healthy vegetarian lifestyle. Pub: Newsletter (bimonthly).

8664 ■ Club Vegetarian Triple Cities
PO Box 625
Westview Sta.
Binghamton, NY 13905
Contact: Ms. Amie Hamlin, Pres./Founder
Ph: (607)272-1126
E-mail: triplecities@clubveg.org
URL: http://www.clubveg.org
Descr: Works to educate people about plant-based diet. Fnd: 1995. Mem: 100. Local Groups: 3. Pub: Club Veg (quarterly).

8665 ■ Mid-Hudson Vegetarian Society (MHVS)
47 South St.
Rhinebeck, NY 12572
Contact: Roberta Schiff, VP
Ph: (845)876-2626
E-mail: info@mhvs.org
URL: http://www.all-creatures.org/mhvs
Staff: 15. Descr: Promotes the vegetarian ethic in the Mid-Hudson, NY region. Educates the community and provides aid to anyone in the pursuit of a totally vegetarian (vegan), cruelty-free and healthful lifestyle. Sponsors speakers, dinners, workshops, and conferences. Fnd: 1995. Mem: 150. Pub: The Vegetarian Viewpoints (quarterly).

8666 ■ New York Beef Industry Council (NYBIC)
PO Box 250
Westmoreland, NY 13490-0250
Contact: Carol Gillis, Exec. Dir.
Ph: (315)339-6922
Fax: (315)339-6931
E-mail: cgillis@nybeef.org
URL: http://www.nybeef.org
Staff: 3. Descr: Strives to promote the beef industry in New York and educate consumers through a variety of programs and resources.

8667 ■ New York Department of Agriculture and Markets
10B Airline Dr.
Albany, NY 12235
Contact: Patrick Hooker, Commnr.
Ph: (518)457-8876
Free: 800-554-4501
Fax: (518)457-3087
E-mail: patrick.hooker@agmkt.state.ny.us
URL: http://www.agmkt.state.ny.us/

8668 ■ New York Pork Producers Cooperative
4124 MacDougall Rd.
Waterloo, NY 13165
Contact: Jamie Mesmer
Ph: (315)585-6276
E-mail: amsinc@wildblue.net
URL: http://www.newyorkpork.org
Descr: Promotes the pork industry through research programs, consumer education, and lobbying activities. Fnd: 1950.

8669 ■ Rochester Area Vegetarian Society (RAVS)
PO Box 20185
Rochester, NY 14602-0185
Contact: Ted D. Barnett MD
Ph: (585)234-8750
E-mail: drveggie@aol.com
URL: http://ravs.enviroweb.org
Descr: Vegetarians and others wishing to adopt a vegetarian lifestyle. Disseminates information on vegetarianism; conducts educational programs. Fnd: 1989. Mem: 150. Pub: Cookbook: Vegetarianism--A Diet for Life; Vegetarian Advocate (quarterly).

North Carolina

8670 ■ North Carolina Cattlemen's Beef Council (NCCBC)
2228 N Main St.
Fuquay Varina, NC 27526-8572
Contact: Bryan K. Blinson, Exec. Dir.
Ph: (919)552-9111
Fax: (919)552-9216
E-mail: ncbeef@nccattle.com
URL: http://www.nccattle.com
Staff: 5. Descr: Promotes beef through the administration of the beef check-off.

8671 ■ North Carolina Department of Agriculture and Consumer Services
1001 Mail Service Ctr.
Raleigh, NC 27699-1001
Contact: Steve Troxler, Commnr.
Ph: (919)733-7125
Fax: (919)733-1141
URL: http://www.agr.state.nc.us/

8672 ■ North Carolina Pork Producers Council (NCPC)
2300 Rexwoods Dr., Ste. 340
Raleigh, NC 27607
Contact: Deborah Johnson, CEO
Ph: (919)781-0361
Fax: (919)510-8546
E-mail: deborah@ncpork.org
URL: http://www.ncpork.org
Staff: 7. Descr: Pork producers organized to protect and advance industry and member interests. Maintains political action committee. Conducts seminars and workshops. Sponsors Annual North Carolina Barbecue competition. Conducts charitable activities. Fnd: 1962. Mem: 4000. Pub: NC Pork Report (monthly); Newsletter (periodic).

8673 ■ Triangle Vegetarian Society (TVS)
PO Box 3364
Chapel Hill, NC 27515-3364
Contact: Dilip Barman, Pres.
Ph: (919)489-3340
E-mail: barman@jhu.edu
URL: http://www.trianglevegsociety.org
Descr: Promotes the nutritional, economical, ecological, and ethical benefits of a plant-based diet. Fnd: 1986. Mem: 175.

North Dakota

8674 ■ North Dakota Department of Agriculture
600 E. Blvd. Ave., Dept. 602
Bismarck, ND 58505-0020
Contact: Doug Goehring, Commnr.
Ph: (701)328-2231
Free: 800-242-7535
Fax: (701)328-4567
E-mail: ndda@nd.gov
URL: http://www.agdepartment.com/

8675 ■ North Dakota Turkey Federation
2558 95th Ave. NE
Tolna, ND 58380
Contact: Sharlene Wittenburg, Pres.
Ph: (701)242-8209
E-mail: carl@wisper-wireless.com
URL: http://www.ndturkey.org
Descr: Promotes turkey consumption and supports turkey production and education to turkey growers.

Ohio

8676 ■ Ohio Department of Agriculture
8995 E. Main St.
Reynoldsburg, OH 43068-3399
Contact: Robert J. Boggs, Dir.
Ph: (614)728-6201
Free: 800-282-1955
Fax: (614)728-6310
E-mail: agri@agri.ohio.gov
URL: http://www.agri.ohio.gov/

Telecom. Svcs: TTY Ohio Relay Service toll-free number is (800)750-0750.

8677 ■ Ohio Poultry Association (OPA)
5930 Sharon Woods Blvd.
Columbus, OH 43229
Contact: Terry Wehrkamp, Pres.
Ph: (614)882-6111
E-mail: info@ohiopoultry.org
URL: http://www.ohiopoultry.org
Staff: 3. **Descr:** Serves and promotes Ohio's poultry farms. **Fnd:** 1948. **Mem:** 600. **State Groups:** 4. **Pub:** *Ohio Poultry Association Newsletter* (quarterly).

8678 ■ Vegetarian Society of the Greater Dayton Area (VSGDA)
PO Box 750742
Dayton, OH 45475
E-mail: vsgda@yahoo.com
Descr: Promotes the nutritional, economical, ecological, and ethical benefits of a vegetarian diet. **Pub:** *VSGDA E-News* (monthly).

Oklahoma

8679 ■ Oklahoma Agriculture, Food & Forestry
2800 N. Lincoln Blvd.
Oklahoma City, OK 73105
Contact: Terry L. Peach, Commnr.
Ph: (405)521-3864
Fax: (405)522-3864
E-mail: odaweb@oda.state.ok.us
URL: http://www.oda.state.ok.us/

Oregon

8680 ■ Oregon Department of Agriculture
635 Capitol St., NE
Salem, OR 97301-2532
Contact: Katy Coba, Dir.
Ph: (503)986-4550
Fax: (503)986-4747
E-mail: info@oda.state.or.us
URL: http://www.oregon.gov/ODA/

8681 ■ Oregon Pork Producers Association
7365 Meridian Rd. NE
Silverton, OR 97381
Contact: Glenn Goschie, Pres.
Ph: (503)873-5638
Fax: (503)873-3309
E-mail: glenn@goschiefarms.com
URL: http://oregonporkproducers.com
Descr: Promotes the pork industry through research programs, consumer education, and lobbying activities.

Pennsylvania

8682 ■ Club VEG Philly
PO Box 324
Phoenixville, PA 19460
Contact: Allison Marie Memmo Geiger
Ph: (267)481-0487
E-mail: philly@clubveg.org
URL: http://www.clubveg.org/philly
Descr: Promotes the nutritional, economical, ecological, and ethical benefits of a vegetarian diet. Sponsors educational exhibit tables at various events. **State Groups:** 3. **Pub:** *Club Veg Newsletter* (bimonthly).

8683 ■ Institute for Plant Based Nutrition (IPBN)
333 Bryn Mawr Ave.
Bala Cynwyd, PA 19004-2606
Contact: James Oswald, Founder/Co-Dir.
Ph: (610)667-6876
Fax: (610)667-1501
E-mail: info@plantbased.org
URL: http://www.plantbased.org
Descr: Healthcare workers, nutritionists, dietitians, farmers, food manufacturers, restaurateurs, writers, editors, educators, organic gardeners. Dedicated to plant-based nutrition education. **Pub:** *Plant Based Nutrition* (quarterly); Booklet.

8684 ■ Pennsylvania Department of Agriculture
2301 N. Cameron St.
Harrisburg, PA 17110
Contact: Russell Redding, Actg.Sec.
Ph: (717)787-4737
Fax: (717)705-8402
URL: http://www.agriculture.state.pa.us/

8685 ■ Pennsylvania Food Merchants Association (PFMA)
PO Box 870
Camp Hill, PA 17001-0870
Contact: David McCorkle, Pres./CEO
Ph: (717)731-0600
Free: 800-543-8207
Fax: (717)731-5472
E-mail: pfma@pfma.net
URL: http://www.pfma.org
Staff: 75. **Descr:** Owners and operators of convenience stores and retail grocery stores. Represents industry interests. Conducts lobbying activities; holds coupon clearinghouse and money order company seminars; sponsors Best Bagger Contest. **Fnd:** 1952. **Mem:** 1900. **Pub:** *Food Industry Advisor* (monthly); *Hotline* (monthly); *Scanning Certification Program* (quarterly).

Puerto Rico

8686 ■ Puerto Rico Department of Agriculture
PO Box 10163
Santurce, PR 00908-1163
Contact: Javier Rivera Aquino, Sec.
Ph: (787)722-0871
Fax: (787)723-8512
URL: http://www.nasda.org/cms/7195/8617/8829.aspx

Rhode Island

8687 ■ Rhode Island Division of Agriculture, DEM
235 Promenade St.
Providence, RI 02908-5767
Contact: W.Michael Sullivan PhD, Dir.
Ph: (401)222-2781
Fax: (401)222-6047
E-mail: stephen.volpe@dem.ri.gov
URL: http://www.dem.ri.gov/

South Carolina

8688 ■ South Carolina Beef Board
PO Box 11280
Columbia, SC 29211-1280
Ph: (803)734-9806
Fax: (803)734-9808
E-mail: scbeef@scda.sc.gov
URL: http://www.sccattle.org
Staff: 2. **Descr:** Works to increase the demand for beef and beef products within the state of South Carolina through support of the national and state joint programs in promotion, consumer information/education, research, industry information, producer communications and market development programs.

8689 ■ South Carolina Department of Agriculture
State Capitol Complex
PO Box 11280
Columbia, SC 29211
Contact: Beverly Cleare, Dir. of Admin.
Ph: (803)734-2210
Fax: (803)734-2192
E-mail: bcleare@scda.sc.gov
URL: http://www.scda.state.sc.us/

8690 ■ South Carolina Poultry Federation
1921-A Pickens St.
Columbia, SC 29201
Contact: Connie Smith, Pres.
Ph: (803)779-4700
Fax: (803)779-5002
E-mail: martyg@scpoultry.com
Staff: 4. **Descr:** Represents the interests of poultry industry companies and personnel. Promotes the poultry industry. **Fnd:** 1987. **Mem:** 625. **Pub:** *Palmetto Poultry Life* (quarterly).

South Dakota

8691 ■ South Dakota Beef Industry Council (SDBIC)
PO Box 7051
Pierre, SD 57501
Contact: Barry Jennings, Exec. Dir.
Ph: (605)224-4722
Fax: (605)224-4457
E-mail: sdbic@sdbeef.org
URL: http://www.sdbeef.org
Descr: Promotes the beef industry in South Dakota.

8692 ■ South Dakota Department of Agriculture
523 E. Capitol Ave.
Pierre, SD 57501-3182
Contact: Bill Even, Sec.
Ph: (605)773-5425
Free: 800-228-5254
Fax: (605)773-5926
E-mail: agmail@state.sd.us
URL: http://www.state.sd.us/doa/

8693 ■ South Dakota Farm Bureau Federation
PO Box 1426
Huron, SD 57350
Contact: Michael Held, CEO
Ph: (605)353-8050
Fax: (605)353-8057
E-mail: marsha@sdfbf.org
URL: http://sdfb.fb.org
Descr: Promotes political, social, economic, and personal status of South Dakota farm and ranch families.

8694 ■ South Dakota Poultry Industries Association
2208 St. Charles Cir.
Sioux Falls, SD 57103
Ph: (605)332-1116
Descr: Works to provide services and conduct activities that increase demand for its members' products by protecting and enhancing their ability to profitably provide wholesome, high-quality, nutritious products.

8695 ■ South Dakota Stockgrowers Association (SDSGA)
426 St. Joseph St.
Rapid City, SD 57701
Contact: Margaret Nachtigall, Exec. Dir.
Ph: (605)342-0429
Free: 877-529-2333
Fax: (605)342-0463
E-mail: margaret.sdsga@midconetwork.com
URL: http://www.southdakotastockgrowers.org
Descr: Strives to advance the economic, political and social interests of its members and the South Dakota cattle industry. Services include managing the industry issues, overseeing the brand program, influencing government, influencing public opinion, serving as spokesman for the industry and providing information.

Tennessee

8696 ■ Tennessee Department of Agriculture
Ellington Agricultural Ctr.
PO Box 40627
Nashville, TN 37204
Contact: Ken Givens, Commnr.
Ph: (615)837-5103
Fax: (615)837-5333

E-mail: tn.agriculture@tn.gov
URL: http://www.state.tn.us/agriculture/

8697 ▪ Vegetarian Society of East Tennessee (VSET)
PO Box 1974
Knoxville, TN 37901
Contact: Laura Broderick, Pres.
Ph: (865)681-7691
E-mail: info@vegsociety-east-tn.org
URL: http://www.vegsociety-east-tn.org
Descr: Promotes the nutritional, ecological, and ethical benefits of a vegetarian diet. Promotes animal rights and local veg-friendly businesses; conducts affordable monthly cooking school and potluck, restaurant socials, publishes free quarterly newsletter, attends local events and distributes veggie food and information, and Vegetarian Thanksgiving Potluck. **Fnd:** 1982. **Pub:** *Vegetarian Voice* (quarterly).

8698 ▪ Volunteer Section, Institute of Food Technologists
University of Tennessee
Dept. of Food Science and Technology
2509 River Dr.
Knoxville, TN 37996-4539
Contact: Dr. Prof. P. Michael Davidson, Interim Hd.
Ph: (865)974-8400
Fax: (865)974-2750
E-mail: foodsci@utk.edu
URL: http://foodscience.tennessee.edu
Staff: 6. **Descr:** Management personnel in the food industry in academia and food regulators in the mideastern Tennessee area. Disseminates technical information on food and the food industry. **Fnd:** 1970. **Mem:** 160. **Reg. Groups:** 1. **Pub:** Directory (annual); Newsletter (periodic).

Texas

8699 ▪ San Antonio Vegetarian Society (SAVS)
PO Box 791222
San Antonio, TX 78279-1222
Contact: Kaz Sephton, Pres.
E-mail: savs@satx.rr.com
URL: http://www.geocities.com/SAVSTexas
Staff: 4. **Descr:** Promotes the nutritional, economical, ecological, and ethical benefits of a vegetarian diet. **Fnd:** 1989. **Mem:** 100. **Reg. Groups:** 1.

8700 ▪ Texas Department of Agriculture
1700 N. Congress Ave.
Austin, TX 78711
Contact: Todd Staples, Commnr.
Ph: (512)463-7664
Free: 800-835-5832
Fax: 888-223-8861
E-mail: pub.info@tda.state.tx.us
URL: http://www.agr.state.tx.us/
Telecom. Svcs: TTY toll free number is (800)735-2989.

8701 ▪ Vegetarian Network of Austin (VNA)
PO Box 49833
Austin, TX 78765
Contact: Ken Jaffe, Pres.
E-mail: vna_pres@yahoo.com
URL: http://www.vegnetaustin.org
Descr: Seeks to foster social contact for area vegetarians, to provide mutual support for those choosing or desiring to lead a vegetarian lifestyle, and to be a forum for self-education and information exchange regarding subjects of interest to vegetarians. Offers public education and awareness regarding matters related to vegetarianism, including nutrition, cooking, lifestyle, and ethical matters. **Pub:** *Austin Vegetarian Living* (bimonthly).

8702 ▪ Vegetarian Society of Houston (VSH)
1733 Crestdale Dr.
Houston, TX 77080
Contact: Dan McClure, Dir.
Ph: (832)331-3450
E-mail: vshouston@bigfoot.com

Descr: Unites to promote vegan diet and advocate social change toward a vegetarian lifestyle.

Utah

8703 ▪ State of Utah Department of Agriculture & Food
PO Box 146500
Salt Lake City, UT 84114-6500
Contact: Leonard Blackham, Commnr.
Ph: (801)538-7100
Fax: (801)538-7126
E-mail: udaf-information@utah.gov
URL: http://www.ag.utah.gov/
Telecom. Svcs: TDD/Hearing Impaired phone number is (801)538-7100.

8704 ▪ Utah Pork Producers Association
55 E 300 N
Providence, UT 84332
Contact: Haven Hendricks
Ph: (435)752-1208
Fax: (435)752-1214
E-mail: havenh@ext.usu.edu
Descr: Promotes the pork industry through research programs, consumer education, and lobbying activities.

Vermont

8705 ▪ Vermont Agency of Agriculture, Food and Markets
116 State St.
Montpelier, VT 05620
Contact: Roger Allbee, Sec.
Ph: (802)828-2430
Fax: (802)828-2361
E-mail: roger.allbee@state.vt.us
URL: http://www.vermontagriculture.com/

8706 ▪ Vermont Vegetarian Society (VVS)
562 Pond Rd.
North Ferrisburg, VT 05473
Contact: Judy Miner, Coor.
Ph: (802)453-3945
E-mail: vvs@ivu.org
URL: http://vermontvegetarians.org
Descr: Provides information and support to people who are interested in vegetarianism. Sponsors potlucks, restaurant dinners, picnics, social gatherings and some informational events such as speakers, panels, cooking classes and video nights. Distributes literature on vegetarianism. **Pub:** Newsletter (quarterly).

Virginia

8707 ▪ Vegetarian Society of Richmond (VSR)
PO Box 15451
Richmond, VA 23227
Contact: Lois R. Angeletti, Pres.
Ph: (804)344-4356
E-mail: lois@vegetarianrichmond.org
URL: http://vegetarianrichmond.org
Descr: Promotes the nutritional, economical, ecological, and ethical benefits of a vegetarian diet. Sponsors outreach services and social activities. **Fnd:** 1995. **Mem:** 150. **Pub:** Newsletters (bimonthly).

8708 ▪ Virginia Beef Industry Council (VBIC)
PO Box 9
Daleville, VA 24083-0009
Contact: Bill McKinnon, Exec. Dir.
Ph: (540)992-1992
Fax: (540)992-4632
E-mail: bmckinnon@vacattlemen.org
URL: http://www.vabeef.org
Staff: 3. **Descr:** Promotes and markets Virginia's beef. Delivers detailed analysis and presentation on beef industry by giving up-to-date news, important issues and other beef-related information that are

essential for beef producers and consumers in the region. **Fnd:** 1985.

8709 ▪ Virginia Cattle Industry Board
PO Box 9
Daleville, VA 24083
Contact: Bill McKinnon, Exec. Dir.
Ph: (540)992-1992
Fax: (540)992-4632
URL: http://www.vabeef.org
Descr: Beef producers. Coordinates public relations, marketing, and dissemination of information through the Beef Checkoff Program. Conducts promotional, consumer information, and industry information campaigns; fosters communication among beef producers; sponsors research. Produces television and radio advertisements.

8710 ▪ Virginia Department of Agriculture and Consumer Services
102 Governor St.
Richmond, VA 23219
Contact: Todd P. Haymore, Commnr.
Ph: (804)786-2373
Fax: (804)371-6097
E-mail: webmaster.vdacs@vdacs.virginia.gov
URL: http://www.vdacs.virginia.gov/
Telecom. Svcs: TDD/Hearing Impaired toll-free number is (800)828-1120.

Washington

8711 ▪ Washington Pork Producers
2001 VanTine Rd.
Garfield, WA 99130
Contact: Don VanTine
Ph: (509)397-2694
E-mail: dvantine@colfax.com
Descr: Promotes the pork industry through research programs, consumer education, and lobbying activities.

8712 ▪ Washington State Department of Agriculture
1111 Washington St., SE
PO Box 42560
Olympia, WA 98504-2560
Contact: Dan Newhouse, Dir.
Ph: (360)902-1858
Fax: (360)902-2092
E-mail: dnewhouse@agr.wa.gov
URL: http://agr.wa.gov/
Descr: Mission is to protect and reduce the risk of public health by ensuring the safety of the state's food supply; to ensure safe and legal distribution, use, and disposal of pesticides and fertilizers in Washington state; to protect Washington's natural resources; and to facilitate the movement of Washington agricultural products in domestic and international markets. **Telecom. Svcs:** TDD/Hearing Impaired phone number is (360)902-1996.

West Virginia

8713 ▪ West Virginia Beef Industry Council (WVBIC)
PO Box 668
Buckhannon, WV 26201
Contact: James D. Bostic, Exec. Sec.
Ph: (304)472-4020
E-mail: wvbic@msys.net
URL: http://www.wvbeef.org/wvbic
Descr: Aims to provide information and linkages to enhance and further develop the beef industry in West Virginia and the nation.

8714 ▪ West Virginia Department of Agriculture
1900 Kanawha Blvd., E.
State Capitol, Rm. E-28
Charleston, WV 25305-0170
Contact: Gus R. Douglass, Commnr.
Ph: (304)558-3200
Fax: (304)558-2203

E-mail: douglass@ag.state.wv.us
URL: http://www.wvagriculture.org/index.html

8715 ■ West Virginia Pork Producers Council
HC 32, Box 418
Petersburg, WV 26847-9612
Contact: Jack Yokum
E-mail: wvporkpc@frontiernet.net
Descr: Promotes the pork industry through research programs, consumer education, and lobbying activities.

Wisconsin

8716 ■ Wisconsin Beef Council
632 Grand Canyon Dr.
Madison, WI 53719
Contact: John W. Freitag, Exec. Dir.
Ph: (608)833-7177
Fax: (608)833-4725
URL: http://www.beeftips.com
Descr: Represents the interests of educators, dietitians, home economists, restaurateurs, meat managers, nurses, physician assistants, and various other thought leaders to strengthen beef's position in the marketplace and to maintain and expand domestic and foreign markets.

8717 ■ Wisconsin Department of Agriculture, Trade and Consumer Protection
2811 Agriculture Dr.
PO Box 8911
Madison, WI 53708-8911
Contact: Rod Nilsestuen, Sec.
Ph: (608)224-5012
Fax: (608)224-4939
E-mail: winocall@datcp.state.wi.us
URL: http://www.datcp.state.wi.us/
Telecom. Svcs: TDD phone number is (608)224-5058.

Wyoming

8718 ■ Wyoming Department of Agriculture
2219 Carey Ave.
Cheyenne, WY 82002-0100
Contact: John Etchepare, Dir.
Ph: (307)777-7321
Fax: (307)777-6593
E-mail: jetche@state.wy.us
URL: http://wyagric.state.wy.us/

Publications

8719 ■ *The 150 Healthiest Foods on Earth*
Fair Winds Press, Inc.
100 Cummings Ctr., Ste. 406-L
Beverly, MA 01915
Ph: (978)282-9590
Fax: (978)283-2742
E-mail: e-info@rockpubats.com
URL: http://www.fairwindspress.com/
Subtitle: The Surprising, Unbiased Truth About What You Should Eat and Why. **Author:** Jonny Bowden.
Pgs: 360. **Price:** $24.99.

8720 ■ *About Methadone*
Drug Policy Alliance
925 15th St. NW, 2nd Fl.
Washington, DC 20005
Ph: (202)216-0035
Fax: (202)216-0803
E-mail: dc@drugpolicy.org
URL: http://www.drugpolicy.org
Freq: periodic.

8721 ■ *AFFI Capital Connection*
American Frozen Food Institute
2000 Corporate Ridge, Ste. 1000
McLean, VA 22102
Ph: (703)821-0770
Fax: (703)821-1350
E-mail: info@affi.com
URL: http://www.affi.com

Freq: weekly.

8722 ■ *Agwatch Europe*
Food and Water Watch
1616 P St. NW, Ste. 300
Washington, DC 20036
Ph: (202)683-2500
Fax: (202)683-2501
E-mail: foodandwater@fwwatch.org
URL: http://www.foodandwaterwatch.org
Descr: Contains sustainable agriculture and food safety within the European community.

8723 ■ *Alabama Cattleman*
Alabama Cattlemen's Association
201 S Bainbridge St.
Montgomery, AL 36102-2499
Ph: (334)265-1867
Fax: (334)834-5326
E-mail: mdavis@bamabeef.org
URL: http://www.bamabeef.org
Freq: monthly. **Price:** free for members.

8724 ■ *The Ally*
Drug Policy Alliance
925 15th St. NW, 2nd Fl.
Washington, DC 20005
Ph: (202)216-0035
Fax: (202)216-0803
E-mail: dc@drugpolicy.org
URL: http://www.drugpolicy.org
Freq: semiannual.

8725 ■ *American Drug Index*
Facts & Comparisons
77 Westport Plz., Ste. 450
Saint Louis, MO 63146
Ph: (314)216-2100
Free: 800-223-0554
E-mail: fc-salessupport@wolterskluwer.com
URL: http://www.factsandcomparisons.com
Key Personnel: Scott Schlesner, VP, Sales & Mktg.; Cathy Reilly, VP of Publishing. **URL(s):** http://www.factsandcomparisons.com **Entries include:** Manufacturer, generic name, composition and strength, dosage forms, package size, and use. **Publication includes:** List of prescription and over-the-counter medicines. **Freq:** Annual, Latest edition 2009. **Price:** $87, individuals.

8726 ■ *American Vegan*
American Vegan Society
56 Dinshah Ln.
PO Box 369
Malaga, NJ 08328
Ph: (856)694-2887
Fax: (856)694-2288
URL: http://www.americanvegan.org
Descr: Includes articles on compassionate living, health, nutrition, recipes, reviews, notices, etc. **Freq:** quarterly. **Price:** $20/year, $10 low income, students. **ISSN:** 1536-3767.

8727 ■ *Annual Research Review, Seminar Proceedings*
National Pork Producers Council
122 C St. NW, Ste. 875
Washington, DC 20001
Ph: (202)347-3600
Fax: (202)347-5265
E-mail: intern@nppc.org
URL: http://www.nppc.org

8728 ■ *APUA Newsletter*
Alliance for the Prudent Use of Antibiotics
75 Kneeland St.
Boston, MA 02111-1901
Ph: (617)636-0966
Fax: (617)636-3999
E-mail: apua@tufts.edu
URL: http://www.tufts.edu/med/apua

Descr: Includes pharmacology reviews. **Freq:** quarterly. **Price:** included in membership dues.

8729 ■ *Artificial Nutrition/Hydration and End-Of-Life Decision Making*
Last Acts Partnership
1620 I St. NW, No. 202
Washington, DC 20006
Ph: (202)296-8071
Fax: (202)296-8352
URL: http://www.lastactspartnership.org
Price: $5.95/copy.

8730 ■ *Austin Vegetarian Living*
Vegetarian Network of Austin
PO Box 49833
Austin, TX 78765
E-mail: vna_pres@yahoo.com
URL: http://www.vegnetaustin.org
Freq: bimonthly.

8731 ■ *Bench Grafting Nut Trees*
Northern Nut Growers Association
PO Box 6216
Hamden, CT 06517-0216
E-mail: tuckerh@epix.net
URL: http://www.northernnutgrowers.org

8732 ■ *BIODYNAMICS*
Biodynamic Farming and Gardening Association
25844 Butler Rd.
Junction City, OR 97448
Ph: (541)998-0105
Fax: (541)998-0106
E-mail: info@biodynamics.com
URL: http://www.biodynamics.com
Descr: Includes calendar of events. **Freq:** quarterly.

8733 ■ *Biotechnology and Pharmaceutical Manufacturers*
Firstmark Inc.
25 Vintinner Rd.
PO Box 1270
Campton, NH 03223-4669
Ph: (603)726-4800
Free: 800-729-2600
Fax: (603)726-4840
E-mail: info@firstmark.com
URL: http://www.firstmark.com
URL(s): http://www.firstmark.com **Covers:** 5,860 manufacturers of biotechnology and pharmaceutical products, including prescription and over-the-counter products; 13,760 executive decision-makers. **Entries include:** Company name, address, and contact name. **Price:** $160, individuals, one-time use w/ phone; $350, individuals, multi-use w/ phone; $50, individuals, e-mail, CD/Disk.

8734 ■ *A Boy, A Chicken, and The Lion of Juelah - How Ari Became a Vegetarian*
Jews for Animal Rights
255 Humphrey St.
Marblehead, MA 01945
Ph: (781)631-7601
E-mail: micah@micahbooks.com
URL: http://www.micahbooks.com/JAR.html
Price: $8.

8735 ■ *Calorie Control Council—Commentary*
Calorie Control Council
1100 Johnson Ferry Rd., Ste. 300
Atlanta, GA 30342
Ph: (404)252-3663
E-mail: ccc@kellencompany.com
URL: http://www.caloriecontrol.org
Descr: Summarizes scientific, regulatory, and other developments related to sweeteners, fat substitutes, dietetic foods and beverages, etc. **Freq:** semiannual. **Price:** free. **ISSN:** 1049-1791.

8736 ■ *The Campaign Reporter*
Campaign to Label Genetically Engineered Foods
PO Box 55699
Seattle, WA 98155
Ph: (425)771-4049
Fax: (425)740-8967

E-mail: label@thecampaign.org
URL: http://www.thecampaign.org

8737 ■ CIR Annual Report
Cosmetic Ingredient Review
1101 17th St. NW, Ste. 412
Washington, DC 20036-4702
Ph: (202)331-0651
Fax: (202)331-0088
E-mail: cirinfo@cir-safety.org
URL: http://www.cir-safety.org
Freq: annual. **Price:** free.

8738 ■ Club Veg Newsletter
Club VEG Philly
PO Box 324
Phoenixville, PA 19460
Ph: (267)481-0487
E-mail: philly@clubveg.org
URL: http://www.clubveg.org/philly
Freq: bimonthly.

8739 ■ Common Sense Pest Control
Bio-Integral Resource Center
PO Box 7414
Berkeley, CA 94707
Ph: (510)524-2567
Fax: (510)524-1758
E-mail: birc@igc.org
URL: http://www.birc.org

8740 ■ Common Sense Pest Control Quarterly
Bio-Integral Resource Center
PO Box 7414
Berkeley, CA 94707
Ph: (510)524-2567
Fax: (510)524-1758
E-mail: birc@igc.org
URL: http://www.birc.org
Descr: Features least-toxic solutions to pest problems. **Freq:** quarterly. **Price:** $30/year.

8741 ■ Conveniently Vegan
Vegetarian Resource Group
PO Box 1463
Baltimore, MD 21203
Ph: (410)366-8343
Fax: (410)366-8804
E-mail: vrg@vrg.org
URL: http://www.vrg.org
Price: $15/copy.

8742 ■ Cookbook: Vegetarianism—A Diet for Life
Rochester Area Vegetarian Society
PO Box 20185
Rochester, NY 14602-0185
Ph: (585)234-8750
E-mail: drveggie@aol.com
URL: http://ravs.enviroweb.org
Price: $1.

8743 ■ Council Communications
Foodservice and Packaging Institute
201 Park Washington Ct.
Falls Church, VA 22046
Ph: (703)538-3552
Fax: (703)241-5603
E-mail: fpi@fpi.org
URL: http://www.fpi.org
Freq: semiannual.

8744 ■ CRN News
Council for Responsible Nutrition
1828 L St. NW, Ste. 510
Washington, DC 20036-5114
Ph: (202)204-7700
Fax: (202)204-7701
E-mail: webmaster@crnusa.org
URL: http://www.crnusa.org
Freq: monthly. **Price:** free, for members only.

8745 ■ Current
Food and Water Watch
1616 P St. NW, Ste. 300
Washington, DC 20036
Ph: (202)683-2500

Fax: (202)683-2501
E-mail: foodandwater@fwwatch.org
URL: http://www.foodandwaterwatch.org
Descr: Features community news, legislative updates and action alerts.

8746 ■ Current Awareness
Dairy Management, Inc.
10255 W Higgins Rd., Ste. 900
Rosemont, IL 60018-5616
Ph: (847)627-3252
Fax: (847)803-2077
E-mail: marykateg@rosedmi.com
URL: http://www.dairyinfo.com
Freq: bimonthly.

8747 ■ Dairy Council Digest
Dairy Management, Inc.
10255 W Higgins Rd., Ste. 900
Rosemont, IL 60018-5616
Ph: (847)627-3252
Fax: (847)803-2077
E-mail: marykateg@rosedmi.com
URL: http://www.dairyinfo.com
Descr: Provides current nutrition research to health professionals; includes annual index. **Freq:** bimonthly. **ISSN:** 0011-5568.

8748 ■ Dairyland News
Wisconsin Paralyzed Veterans of America
2311 S 108th St.
West Allis, WI 53227-1901
Ph: (414)328-8910
Fax: (414)328-8948
E-mail: info@wisconsinpva.org
URL: http://www.wisconsinpva.org
Price: $25.

8749 ■ Defend the Global Commons
Food and Water Watch
1616 P St. NW, Ste. 300
Washington, DC 20036
Ph: (202)683-2500
Fax: (202)683-2501
E-mail: foodandwater@fwwatch.org
URL: http://www.foodandwaterwatch.org
Descr: Provides news updates from water struggles from around the world and communities defending the right to water.

8750 ■ The Defender
Family Farm Defenders
PO Box 1772
Madison, WI 53701
Ph: (608)260-0900
Fax: (608)260-0900
E-mail: familyfarmdefenders@yahoo.com
URL: http://www.familyfarmdefenders.org
Freq: quarterly. **Price:** included in membership dues.

8751 ■ Direct-to-Consumer Prescription Drug Advertising
DES Action Canada
5890 Monkland Ave., Ste. 107
Montreal, QC, Canada H4A 1G2
Ph: (514)482-3204
E-mail: desact@web.net
URL: http://www.web.net/~desact

8752 ■ Drinking Water Additives-Health Effects
NSF International
789 N Dixboro Rd.
PO Box 130140
Ann Arbor, MI 48113-0140
Ph: (734)769-8010
Fax: (734)769-0109
E-mail: info@nsf.org
URL: http://www.nsf.org
Freq: periodic.

8753 ■ The Drug War: How Much Longer Will This Scene be Accepted?
Family Council on Drug Awareness
PO Box 1716
El Cerrito, CA 94530
Ph: (510)215-8326

Fax: (510)234-4460
E-mail: chris@fcda.org
URL: http://www.fcda.org

8754 ■ E-News
Association of Food and Drug Officials
2550 Kingston Rd., Ste. 311
York, PA 17402
Ph: (717)757-2888
Fax: (717)755-8089
E-mail: afdo@afdo.org
URL: http://www.afdo.org
Freq: quarterly.

8755 ■ Earthsave Canada—Vegetarian Directory
Earthsave Canada
2150 Maple St.
Vancouver, BC, Canada V6J 3T3
Ph: (604)731-5885
Fax: (604)731-5805
URL: http://www.earthsave.ca
URL(s): http://www.earthsave.ca/vegdirectory **Covers:** 100 restaurants and other business organizations related to vegetarianism. **Entries include:** Name, address, and opening hours. **Freq:** Latest edition 2008.

8756 ■ Executive Briefs
Foodservice and Packaging Institute
201 Park Washington Ct.
Falls Church, VA 22046
Ph: (703)538-3552
Fax: (703)241-5603
E-mail: fpi@fpi.org
URL: http://www.fpi.org
Freq: biweekly.

8757 ■ Family Farm Agenda
National Family Farm Coalition
110 Maryland Ave. NE, Ste. 307
Washington, DC 20002
Ph: (202)543-5675
Fax: (202)543-0978
E-mail: kozer@nffc.net
URL: http://www.nffc.net
Freq: quarterly.

8758 ■ Farm Sanctuary News
Farm Sanctuary
PO Box 150
Watkins Glen, NY 14891
Ph: (607)583-2225
Fax: (607)583-2041
E-mail: info@farmsanctuary.org
URL: http://www.farmsanctuary.org
Descr: Contains legislative and shelter updates. **Freq:** quarterly. **Price:** included in membership dues.

8759 ■ Fat Replacers: Food Ingredients for Healthy Eating
Calorie Control Council
1100 Johnson Ferry Rd., Ste. 300
Atlanta, GA 30342
Ph: (404)252-3663
E-mail: ccc@kellencompany.com
URL: http://www.caloriecontrol.org

8760 ■ Flavors of the Southcoast
Coastline Elderly Services, Inc.
1646 Purchase St.
New Bedford, MA 02740
Ph: (508)999-6400
Fax: (508)993-6510
E-mail: information@coastlineelderly.org
URL: http://www.coastlineelderly.org
Descr: Award-winning cookbook and recipes. **Freq:** annual. **Price:** $14.95 plus shipping and handling.

8761 ■ The Florida Cattleman
Florida Cattlemen's Association
PO Box 421929
Kissimmee, FL 34742-1929
Ph: (407)846-6221
Fax: (407)933-8209
E-mail: fbcfcajimhandley@aol.com
URL: http://www.floridacattlemen.org

Freq: monthly.

8762 ■ Food Additives and Contaminants
Taylor & Francis Group Journals
325 Chestnut St., Ste. 800
Philadelphia, PA 19106
Ph: (215)625-8900
Free: 800-354-1420
Fax: (215)625-2940
E-mail: fac@csl.gov.uk
URL: http://www.tandf.co.uk
Key Personnel: R. Bandyopadhyay, International
Editorial Board; T.H. Begley, International Editorial
Board; J. Hajslova, International Editorial Board.
URL(s): http://www.tandf.co.uk/journals/titles/
0265203x.asp **Descr:** Journal focusing on natural
and man-made additives and contaminants, and their
inclusive processes. **Freq:** Monthly. **Price:** $4,094,
institutions, print and online; $3,889, institutions, on-
line only.

8763 ■ Food Alert!
Food and Water Watch
1616 P St. NW, Ste. 300
Washington, DC 20036
Ph: (202)683-2500
Fax: (202)683-2501
E-mail: foodandwater@fwwatch.org
URL: http://www.foodandwaterwatch.org
Descr: Contains food safety and industrialized
agriculture.

8764 ■ Food Gardening in Vancouver
City Farmer Society
Box 74567
Kitsilano RPO
Vancouver, BC, Canada V6K 4P4
Ph: (604)685-5832
Fax: (604)685-5862
E-mail: cityfarm@interchange.ubc.ca
URL: http://www.cityfarmer.org
Price: $10.

8765 ■ Food Industry Advisor
Pennsylvania Food Merchants Association
PO Box 870
Camp Hill, PA 17001-0870
Ph: (717)731-0600
Fax: (717)731-5472
E-mail: pfma@pfma.net
URL: http://www.pfma.org
Freq: monthly.

8766 ■ Food Insight
International Food Information Council
1100 Connecticut Ave. NW, Ste. 430
Washington, DC 20036
Ph: (202)296-6540
Fax: (202)296-6547
E-mail: foodinfo@ific.org
URL: http://ific.org
Descr: Contains current topics in food safety and
nutrition. **Freq:** bimonthly. **Price:** free.

8767 ■ Food Technology
Institute of Food Technologists
525 W Van Buren, Ste. 1000
Chicago, IL 60607
Ph: (312)782-8424
Fax: (312)782-8348
E-mail: info@ift.org
URL: http://www.ift.org
Descr: Provides information on the development of
new and improved food sources, news, and regula-
tory and legislative developments. **Freq:** monthly.
Price: included in membership dues, $122/year for
nonmembers in U.S., Canada and Mexico, $132/
year for nonmembers outside North America. **ISSN:**
0015-6639.

8768 ■ Food and Water Journal
Food and Water
PO Box 543
Montpelier, VT 05601
Ph: (802)229-6222

E-mail: info@broadsides.org
URL: http://www.broadsides.org
Freq: quarterly. **Price:** $25/year.

8769 ■ Frozen Food Pack Statistics
American Frozen Food Institute
2000 Corporate Ridge, Ste. 1000
McLean, VA 22102
Ph: (703)821-0770
Fax: (703)821-1350
E-mail: info@affi.com
URL: http://www.affi.com

**8770 ■ A Guide to Nut Tree Culture in North
America, Vol. 1**
Northern Nut Growers Association
PO Box 6216
Hamden, CT 06517-0216
E-mail: tuckerh@epix.net
URL: http://www.northernnutgrowers.org
Descr: Contains information on nuts and nut tree
culture.

8771 ■ Guide to Veg Living
Farm Sanctuary
PO Box 150
Watkins Glen, NY 14891
Ph: (607)583-2225
Fax: (607)583-2041
E-mail: info@farmsanctuary.org
URL: http://www.farmsanctuary.org
Price: free.

8772 ■ Guidelines
International Food Information Council
1100 Connecticut Ave. NW, Ste. 430
Washington, DC 20036
Ph: (202)296-6540
Fax: (202)296-6547
E-mail: foodinfo@ific.org
URL: http://ific.org
Descr: Includes tips to scientists, public relations
professionals and journalists. **Freq:** bimonthly.

8773 ■ Halal Digest
Islamic Food and Nutrition Council of America
777 Busse Hwy.
Park Ridge, IL 60068
Ph: (847)993-0034
Fax: (847)993-0038
URL: http://www.ifanca.org
Descr: Contains articles, relevant news, recipes and
other related information about Halal topics. **ISSN:**
1533-3361.

8774 ■ The Hazel Book
Northern Nut Growers Association
PO Box 6216
Hamden, CT 06517-0216
E-mail: tuckerh@epix.net
URL: http://www.northernnutgrowers.org
Descr: Contains information on nuts and nut tree
culture.

**8775 ■ Healthy Water Association—Member-
ship Roster**
Healthy Water Association
c/o Paul Mason
PO Box 1417
Patterson, CA 95363
Ph: (408)897-3023
Fax: (408)897-3028
E-mail: paulmason@mgwater.com
URL: http://www.mgwater.com
URL(s): http://www.mgwater.com/hwa.shtml **Covers:**
Member companies engaged in bottling and water
industry. **Entries include:** Company name, location,
contact information, website and e-mail address.

8776 ■ Herbal Research News
Herb Research Foundation
5589 Arapahoe Ave., Ste. 205
Boulder, CO 80303
Ph: (303)449-2265
Fax: (303)449-7849

E-mail: info@herbs.org
URL: http://www.herbs.org
Freq: quarterly.

8777 ■ HerbalGram
Herb Research Foundation
5589 Arapahoe Ave., Ste. 205
Boulder, CO 80303
Ph: (303)449-2265
Fax: (303)449-7849
E-mail: info@herbs.org
URL: http://www.herbs.org
Descr: Includes current research on botanicals, legal
news, book reviews, and monographs. Published in
conjunction with the American Botanical Council.
Freq: quarterly. **Price:** $35.

8778 ■ HIA Hemp News
Hemp Industries Association
PO Box 575
Summerland, CA 93067
Ph: (707)874-3648
Fax: (707)874-3648
E-mail: info@thehia.org
URL: http://www.testpledge.com
Freq: quarterly. **Price:** included in membership dues.

8779 ■ Hotline
Pennsylvania Food Merchants Association
PO Box 870
Camp Hill, PA 17001-0870
Ph: (717)731-0600
Fax: (717)731-5472
E-mail: pfma@pfma.net
URL: http://www.pfma.org
Freq: monthly.

8780 ■ IFT Membership Directory
Institute of Food Technologists
525 W Van Buren, Ste. 1000
Chicago, IL 60607
Ph: (312)782-8424
Fax: (312)782-8348
E-mail: info@ift.org
URL: http://www.ift.org
Freq: annual. **Price:** included in membership dues.

8781 ■ IFT Program and Directory
Institute of Food Technologists
525 W Van Buren, Ste. 1000
Chicago, IL 60607
Ph: (312)782-8424
Fax: (312)782-8348
E-mail: info@ift.org
URL: http://www.ift.org
Freq: annual.

8782 ■ Indiana Beef
Indiana Beef Council
5738 W 74th St.
Indianapolis, IN 46278
Ph: (317)293-2333
Fax: (317)295-8421
E-mail: jwickard@indianabeef.org
URL: http://www.indianabeef.org
Freq: bimonthly.

**8783 ■ Indoor/Outdoor Activity and Restau-
rant Guide**
Brainerd Lakes Area Chambers of Commerce
124 N 6th St.
PO Box 356
Brainerd, MN 56401-0356
Ph: (218)829-2838
Fax: (218)829-8199
E-mail: info@explorebrainerdlakes.com
URL: http://www.explorebrainerdlakes.com
Descr: Features attractions, shopping, dining, golf
course, and fishing information. **Freq:** annual. **Price:**
free.

8784 ■ Industry Update
United States Potato Board
7555 E Hampden Ave., Ste. 412
Denver, CO 80231-4835
Ph: (303)369-7783

Fax: (303)369-7718
E-mail: toconnor@uspotatoes.com
URL: http://www.healthypotato.com
Descr: Contains industry reports on program activities. **Freq:** semimonthly. **Price:** free.

8785 ■ Infant Feeding and Nutrition
International Formula Council
5775 Peachtree-Dunwoody Rd., Bldg. G, Ste. 500
Atlanta, GA 30342
Ph: (404)252-3663
Fax: (404)252-0774
E-mail: info@infantformula.org
URL: http://www.infantformula.org

8786 ■ Ingredient Report
Cosmetic Ingredient Review
1101 17th St. NW, Ste. 412
Washington, DC 20036-4702
Ph: (202)331-0651
Fax: (202)331-0088
E-mail: cirinfo@cir-safety.org
URL: http://www.cir-safety.org
Descr: Contains information on cosmetic ingredients.

8787 ■ Inside Aloe
International Aloe Science Council
8630 Fenton St., Ste. 918
Silver Spring, MD 20910
Ph: (301)588-2420
Fax: (301)588-1174
E-mail: info@iasc.org
URL: http://www.iasc.org
Freq: monthly. **Price:** included in membership dues.

8788 ■ International Journal for Behavioral Nutrition and Physical Activity
International Society for Behavioral Nutrition and Physical Activity
University of Minnesota
308 Harvard St. SE
Minneapolis, MN 55455
Ph: (612)625-0606
Fax: (612)626-2359
E-mail: kubik002@umn.edu
URL: http://www.isbnpa.org
Price: included in membership dues.

8789 ■ The Island Vegetarian
Vegetarian Society of Hawaii
PO Box 23208
Honolulu, HI 96823
Ph: (808)944-8344
E-mail: info@vsh.org
URL: http://www.vsh.org
Descr: Includes calendar, book and restaurant reviews, recipes, health, environment, and animal rights information. **Freq:** quarterly. **Price:** free for members.

8790 ■ The Jewish Vegetarian Year Cookbook
Jews for Animal Rights
255 Humphrey St.
Marblehead, MA 01945
Ph: (781)631-7601
E-mail: micah@micahbooks.com
URL: http://www.micahbooks.com/JAR.html
Descr: Contains advice about where to find vegetarian pareve products, how to make tofu delicious, useful addresses and bibliography. **Price:** $18.95/copy.

8791 ■ Journal of Food Science
Institute of Food Technologists
525 W Van Buren, Ste. 1000
Chicago, IL 60607
Ph: (312)782-8424
Fax: (312)782-8348
E-mail: info@ift.org
URL: http://www.ift.org
Descr: Contains research articles on all aspects of food science. Includes graphs, charts, tables, and index of authors. **Freq:** bimonthly. **Price:** $70/year for members, $275/year for nonmembers in U.S.,

Canada, and Mexico, $300/year for nonmembers outside North America. **ISSN:** 0022-1947.

8792 ■ Kids with Food Allergies e-news
Kids with Food Allergies
73 Old Dublin Pike, Ste. 10, No. 163
Doylestown, PA 18901
Ph: (215)230-5394
Fax: (215)340-7674
E-mail: info@kidswithfoodallergies.org
URL: http://www.kidswithfoodallergies.org
Descr: Contains announcements, news, recipes, food ideas and other articles relating to food allergies. **Freq:** semimonthly. **Price:** free. **ISSN:** 1939-8166.

8793 ■ Kids With Food Allergies Support Net
Kids with Food Allergies
73 Old Dublin Pike, Ste. 10, No. 163
Doylestown, PA 18901
Ph: (215)230-5394
Fax: (215)340-7674
E-mail: info@kidswithfoodallergies.org
URL: http://www.kidswithfoodallergies.org
Descr: Contains news views and supportive information for families raising children with food allergies. **Freq:** semiannual. **Price:** $2.95 for nonmembers, included in membership dues. **ISSN:** 1940-4115.

8794 ■ The Lowfat Jewish Vegetarian Cookbook
Vegetarian Resource Group
PO Box 1463
Baltimore, MD 21203
Ph: (410)366-8343
Fax: (410)366-8804
E-mail: vrg@vrg.org
URL: http://www.vrg.org

8795 ■ Make Mine Mayonnaise!
Association for Dressings and Sauces
1100 Johnson Ferry Rd., Ste. 300
Atlanta, GA 30342
Ph: (404)252-3663
Fax: (404)252-0774
E-mail: ads@kellencompany.com
URL: http://www.dressings-sauces.org

8796 ■ Making Scents
International Aromatherapy and Herb Association
3541 W Acapulco Ln.
Phoenix, AZ 85053
Ph: (602)938-4439
E-mail: aromaherbshow@hotmail.com
URL: http://www.aromaherbshow.com
Descr: Includes articles of interest, resource lists, and book and product reviews. **Freq:** semiannual. **Price:** included in membership dues.

8797 ■ The Marijuana Conviction
Drug Policy Alliance
925 15th St. NW, 2nd Fl.
Washington, DC 20005
Ph: (202)216-0035
Fax: (202)216-0803
E-mail: dc@drugpolicy.org
URL: http://www.drugpolicy.org

8798 ■ Marijuana Myths, Marijuana Facts
Drug Policy Alliance
925 15th St. NW, 2nd Fl.
Washington, DC 20005
Ph: (202)216-0035
Fax: (202)216-0803
E-mail: dc@drugpolicy.org
URL: http://www.drugpolicy.org
Descr: Provides reliable information about marijuana's effects on people.

8799 ■ Marijuana and The Bible
Family Council on Drug Awareness
PO Box 1716
El Cerrito, CA 94530
Ph: (510)215-8326

Fax: (510)234-4460
E-mail: chris@fcda.org
URL: http://www.fcda.org

8800 ■ Meat and Poultry Facts
American Meat Institute
1150 Connecticut Ave. NW, 12th Fl.
Washington, DC 20036
Ph: (202)587-4200
Fax: (202)587-4300
E-mail: memberservices@meatami.com
URL: http://www.meatami.com
Descr: Contains statistical review. **Freq:** annual.

8801 ■ Membership Directory and Buyer's Guide
American Frozen Food Institute
2000 Corporate Ridge, Ste. 1000
McLean, VA 22102
Ph: (703)821-0770
Fax: (703)821-1350
E-mail: info@affi.com
URL: http://www.affi.com
Freq: annual.

8802 ■ MGA Messenger
Mailorder Gardening Association
5836 Rockburn Woods Way
Elkridge, MD 21075
Ph: (410)540-9830
Fax: (410)540-9827
E-mail: info@mailordergardening.com
URL: http://www.mailordergardening.com

8803 ■ Monosodium Glutamate: A Look at the Facts
The Glutamate Association
PO Box 14266
Washington, DC 20044-4266
Ph: (202)783-6135
URL: http://www.msgfacts.com
Descr: Contains information on MSG and its effect as food ingredient.

8804 ■ NASDA Directory
National Association of State Departments of Agriculture
1156 15th St. NW, Ste. 1020
Washington, DC 20005
Ph: (202)296-9680
Fax: (202)296-9686
E-mail: nasda@nasda.org
URL: http://www.nasda.org
Freq: annual.

8805 ■ NASDA News
National Association of State Departments of Agriculture
1156 15th St. NW, Ste. 1020
Washington, DC 20005
Ph: (202)296-9680
Fax: (202)296-9686
E-mail: nasda@nasda.org
URL: http://www.nasda.org
Freq: weekly.

8806 ■ National Conference of State Liquor Administrators—Official Directory
National Conference of State Liquor Administrators
6183 Beau Douglas Ave.
Gonzales, LA 70737
Ph: (225)473-7209
Fax: (225)257-4498
E-mail: pamsalario@cox.net
URL: http://www.ncsla.org/
Key Personnel: Pamela D. Salario, Exec. Dir., pamsalario@cox.net. **URL(s):** http://www.ncsla.org **Covers:** State alcohol beverage control administrators in 36 jurisdictions in the United States, Puerto Rico, District of Columbia, and Guam. **Entries include:** Name, office address and phone. **Freq:** Annual.

8807 ■ The Natural Voice
Canadian Health Food Association
235 Yorkland Blvd., Ste. 302
Toronto, ON, Canada M2J 4Y8

Ph: (416)497-6939
Fax: (416)497-3214
E-mail: info@chfa.ca
URL: http://www.chfa.ca
Freq: 5/year.

8808 ■ NC Pork Report
North Carolina Pork Producers Council
2300 Rexwoods Dr., Ste. 340
Raleigh, NC 27607
Ph: (919)781-0361
Fax: (919)510-8546
E-mail: deborah@ncpork.org
URL: http://www.ncpork.org
Freq: monthly.

8809 ■ New Mexico Vegetarian
Vegetarian Society of New Mexico
PO Box 94495
Albuquerque, NM 87199-4495
Ph: (505)237-0347
E-mail: info@vsnm.org
URL: http://www.vsnm.org
Freq: quarterly.

8810 ■ The New Yolk Times
United Egg Producers
1720 Windward Concourse, Ste. 230
Alpharetta, GA 30005
Ph: (770)360-9220
Fax: (770)360-7058
E-mail: gene@unitedegg.com
URL: http://www.unitedegg.org
Freq: quarterly.

8811 ■ News For Life
VegMichigan
PO Box 2161
Royal Oak, MI 48068-2161
E-mail: info@vegmichigan.org
URL: http://www.vegmichigan.org
Freq: monthly.

8812 ■ Newsletter of the Boston Vegetarian Society
Boston Vegetarian Society
PO Box 38-1071
Cambridge, MA 02238-1071
Ph: (617)424-8846
E-mail: info@bostonveg.org
URL: http://www.bostonveg.org
Freq: periodic.

8813 ■ NOHA News
Nutrition for Optimal Health Association
PO Box 262
Western Springs, IL 60558
Ph: (708)246-3663
E-mail: contact@nutrition4health.org
URL: http://www.nutrition4health.org
Descr: Includes association news, book reviews and articles by members of NOHA's Professional Advisory Board. **Freq:** quarterly. **Price:** included in membership dues, $8/year for nonmembers.

8814 ■ Nutrition Action HealthLetter
Center for Science in the Public Interest
1875 Connecticut Ave. NW, Ste. 300
Washington, DC 20009
Ph: (202)332-9110
Fax: (202)265-4954
E-mail: cspi@cspinet.org
URL: http://www.cspinet.org
Descr: Promotes public education concerning food and nutrition, the food industry, and relevant government regulations and legislation. **Freq:** 10/year. **Price:** $24/year for individuals. **ISSN:** 0885-7792.

8815 ■ Nutrition News
Dairy Management, Inc.
10255 W Higgins Rd., Ste. 900
Rosemont, IL 60018-5616
Ph: (847)627-3252
Fax: (847)803-2077
E-mail: marykateg@rosedmi.com
URL: http://www.dairyinfo.com

Freq: quarterly.

8816 ■ The Nutshell
Northern Nut Growers Association
PO Box 6216
Hamden, CT 06517-0216
E-mail: tuckerh@epix.net
URL: http://www.northernnutgrowers.org
Descr: Contains articles on nut tree growing, reports and current information of interest to members. **Freq:** quarterly. **Price:** included in membership dues, $5/copy.

8817 ■ Ohio Poultry Association Newsletter
Ohio Poultry Association
5930 Sharon Woods Blvd.
Columbus, OH 43229
Ph: (614)882-6111
E-mail: info@ohiopoultry.org
URL: http://www.ohiopoultry.org
Freq: quarterly. **Price:** included in membership dues.

8818 ■ The Organic Food Guide
Globe Pequot Press
246 Goose Lane
PO Box 480
Guilford, CT 06437
Ph: (203)458-4500
Fax: 800-820-2329
E-mail: info@globepequot.com
URL: http://www.globepequot.com/
Subtitle: How to Shop Smarter and Eat Healthier. **Author:** Steve Meyerowitz. **Pgs:** 96. **Price:** $8.95.

8819 ■ The Organic Food Shopper's Guide
Wiley
10475 Crosspoint Blvd.
Indianapolis, IN 46256
Ph: 877-762-2974
Fax: 800-597-3299
E-mail: info@wiley.com/
URL: http://www.wiley.com/
Author: Jeff Cox. **Descr:** Provides descriptions of more than 100 organic foods, as well as detailed information on preparation and recipes. **Pgs:** 360. **Price:** $14.95.

8820 ■ Organic Matters
Ecological Farming Association
406 Main St., Ste. 313
Watsonville, CA 95076
Ph: (831)763-2111
Fax: (831)763-2112
E-mail: info@eco-farm.org
URL: http://www.eco-farm.org
Freq: annual.

8821 ■ P & G Pharmacy Handbook
CRC Press L.L.C.
6000 Broken Sound Pkwy. NW, Ste. 300
Boca Raton, FL 33487
Ph: (561)994-0555
Free: 800-272-7737
Fax: (561)989-9732
E-mail: orders@crcpress.com
URL: http://www.crcpress.com
Key Personnel: Dennis Worthen, Editor. **URL(s):** http://www.crcpress.com **Descr:** Includes an extensive medical dictionary, medical abbreviations and terms used in prescription writing and tables containing ranges for laboratory tests. **Publication includes:** Contact details for pharmacy associations. **Price:** $119.95, individuals.

8822 ■ Packaging Innovation Insights
Foodservice and Packaging Institute
201 Park Washington Ct.
Falls Church, VA 22046
Ph: (703)538-3552
Fax: (703)241-5603
E-mail: fpi@fpi.org
URL: http://www.fpi.org

Freq: semiannual. **Price:** free.

8823 ■ Palmetto Poultry Life
South Carolina Poultry Federation
1921-A Pickens St.
Columbia, SC 29201
Ph: (803)779-4700
Fax: (803)779-5002
E-mail: martyg@scpoultry.com
Freq: quarterly. **Price:** included in membership dues, $5 for nonmembers.

8824 ■ Participant Directory
Ecological Farming Association
406 Main St., Ste. 313
Watsonville, CA 95076
Ph: (831)763-2111
Fax: (831)763-2112
E-mail: info@eco-farm.org
URL: http://www.eco-farm.org
Freq: annual.

8825 ■ Partnership for a Drug-Free America Newsletter
Partnership for a Drug-Free America
405 Lexington Ave., Ste. 1601
New York, NY 10174
Ph: (212)922-1560
Fax: (212)922-1570
URL: http://www.drugfree.org
Freq: quarterly.

8826 ■ Plant Based Nutrition
Institute for Plant Based Nutrition
333 Bryn Mawr Ave.
Bala Cynwyd, PA 19004-2606
Ph: (610)667-6876
Fax: (610)667-1501
E-mail: info@plantbased.org
URL: http://www.plantbased.org
Freq: quarterly.

8827 ■ Pork Leader
National Pork Producers Council
122 C St. NW, Ste. 875
Washington, DC 20001
Ph: (202)347-3600
Fax: (202)347-5265
E-mail: intern@nppc.org
URL: http://www.nppc.org
Freq: biweekly.

8828 ■ Pork Report
National Pork Producers Council
122 C St. NW, Ste. 875
Washington, DC 20001
Ph: (202)347-3600
Fax: (202)347-5265
E-mail: intern@nppc.org
URL: http://www.nppc.org
Freq: bimonthly.

8829 ■ Prescription Costs: America's Other Drug Crisis
Families U.S.A. Foundation
1201 New York Ave. NW, Ste. 1100
Washington, DC 20005-6100
Ph: (202)628-3030
Fax: (202)347-2417
E-mail: info@familiesusa.org
URL: http://www.familiesusa.org
Descr: Provides an analysis (for years 1985-1991) of the prices of America's 20 top selling drugs and the pharmaceutical companies' profits. **Price:** $5.

8830 ■ PRIDE Quarterly
PRIDE Youth Programs
4 W Oak St.
Fremont, MI 49412
Ph: (231)924-1662
Fax: (231)924-5663
E-mail: info@prideyouthprograms.org
URL: http://www.prideyouthprograms.org
Descr: Discusses the legal, pharmacological, psychological, social, cultural, and physiological effects

of adolescent drug use. Includes overviews. **Freq:** quarterly. **Price:** $25/year.

8831 ■ *Psychedelic Drugs Reconsidered*
Drug Policy Alliance
925 15th St. NW, 2nd Fl.
Washington, DC 20005
Ph: (202)216-0035
Fax: (202)216-0803
E-mail: dc@drugpolicy.org
URL: http://www.drugpolicy.org

8832 ■ *Rabbis and Vegetarianism: An Evolving Tradition*
Jews for Animal Rights
255 Humphrey St.
Marblehead, MA 01945
Ph: (781)631-7601
E-mail: micah@micahbooks.com
URL: http://www.micahbooks.com/JAR.html
Descr: Testifies to a revolution taking place in the traditional Jewish diet. Includes brief biographies. **Price:** $10/copy.

8833 ■ *Red Book*
Advanstar Communications
641 Lexington Ave., 8th Fl.
New York, NY 10022
Ph: (212)951-6600
Free: 800-346-0085
Fax: (212)951-6793
E-mail: info@advanstar.com
URL: http://web.advanstar.com
URL(s): http://www.pdrbookstore.com **Entries include:** Company name, address, trade and generic names, and product characteristics such as NDC numbers, dosage form, strength, package size, therapeutic equivalence, average wholesale prices, federal upper limit prices, etc. **Publication includes:** Product and manufacturer listings for more than 100,000 prescription drugs, over-the-counter medications, and other drug store items. **Freq:** Annual.

8834 ■ *Review*
Kansas Beef Council
6031 SW 37th St.
Topeka, KS 66614-5128
Ph: (785)273-5225
Fax: (785)273-3399
E-mail: kbc@kansasbeef.org
URL: http://www.kansasbeef.org
Freq: monthly.

8835 ■ *The Role of Milk in Your Diet*
American Council on Science and Health
1995 Broadway, 2nd Fl.
New York, NY 10023-5882
Ph: (212)362-7044
Fax: (212)362-4919
E-mail: acsh@acsh.org
URL: http://www.acsh.org
Price: $1.

8836 ■ *Salad Dressing Isn't Just for Salads Anymore*
Association for Dressings and Sauces
1100 Johnson Ferry Rd., Ste. 300
Atlanta, GA 30342
Ph: (404)252-3663
Fax: (404)252-0774
E-mail: ads@kellencompany.com
URL: http://www.dressings-sauces.org

8837 ■ *Scanning Certification Program*
Pennsylvania Food Merchants Association
PO Box 870
Camp Hill, PA 17001-0870
Ph: (717)731-0600
Fax: (717)731-5472
E-mail: pfma@pfma.net
URL: http://www.pfma.org
Freq: quarterly.

8838 ■ *Seed Midden*
Abundant Life Seeds
PO Box 279
Cottage Grove, OR 97424

Ph: (541)767-9606
Fax: (866)514-7333
E-mail: info@abundantlifeseeds.com
URL: http://www.abundantlifeseeds.com
Freq: 3/year.

8839 ■ *Single Service News*
Foodservice and Packaging Institute
201 Park Washington Ct.
Falls Church, VA 22046
Ph: (703)538-3552
Fax: (703)241-5603
E-mail: fpi@fpi.org
URL: http://www.fpi.org
Descr: Covers industry news and association and member activities. Includes information on publications and events of interest. **Freq:** semiannual. **Price:** free for members and related trade associations.

8840 ■ *State of the States: A Profile of Food and Nutrition Programs Across the Nation (2004, 8th Edition)*
Food Research and Action Center
1875 Connecticut Ave. NW, Ste. 540
Washington, DC 20009-5728
Ph: (202)986-2200
Fax: (202)986-2525
E-mail: foodresearch@frac.org
URL: http://www.frac.org
Price: $20.

8841 ■ *State of the States: A Profile of Food and Nutrition Programs Across the Nation (2005, 9th Edition)*
Food Research and Action Center
1875 Connecticut Ave. NW, Ste. 540
Washington, DC 20009-5728
Ph: (202)986-2200
Fax: (202)986-2525
E-mail: foodresearch@frac.org
URL: http://www.frac.org
Price: $20.

8842 ■ *Terre de Chez Nous*
Agricultural Producers Union
555 Roland-Therrien Blvd., Bureau 100
Longueuil, QC, Canada J4H 3Y9
Ph: (450)679-0530
E-mail: upa@upa.qc.ca
URL: http://www.upa.qc.ca/fra/index_flash.asp
Freq: weekly. **Price:** $31.91/year.

8843 ■ *To Buy or Not to Buy Organic*
Da Capo Press
Eleven Cambridge Center
Cambridge, MA 02142
Ph: (617)252-5200
Subtitle: What You Need to Know to Choose the Healthiest, Safest, Most Earth-Friendly Food. **Author:** Cindy Burke. **Pub. Date:** 2007. **Pgs:** 240. **Price:** $14.95.

8844 ■ *Turkey Today and Tomorrow*
National Turkey Federation
1225 New York Ave., Ste. 400
Washington, DC 20005
Ph: (202)898-0100
Fax: (202)898-0203
E-mail: info@turkeyfed.org
URL: http://www.eatturkey.com
Freq: monthly.

8845 ■ *Uncork New York*
New York Wine/Grape Foundation
800 S Main St., Ste. 200
Canandaigua, NY 14424
Ph: (585)394-3620
Fax: (585)394-3649
E-mail: info@newyorkwines.org
URL: http://www.newyorkwines.org

8846 ■ *United Fresh*
United Fresh Produce Association
1901 Pennsylvania Ave. NW, Ste. 1100
Washington, DC 20006
Ph: (202)303-3400
Fax: (202)303-3433

E-mail: united@unitedfresh.org
URL: http://www.unitedfresh.org
Freq: weekly.

8847 ■ *Update*
Cattlemen's Beef Promotion and Research Board
9000 E Nichols Ave., Ste. 215
Centennial, CO 80112-3450
Ph: (303)220-9890
Fax: (303)220-9280
E-mail: beefboard@beefboard.org
URL: http://www.mybeefcheckoff.com
Freq: periodic.

8848 ■ *Vegetarian Advocate*
Rochester Area Vegetarian Society
PO Box 20185
Rochester, NY 14602-0185
Ph: (585)234-8750
E-mail: drveggie@aol.com
URL: http://ravs.enviroweb.org
Descr: Includes updates on activities, recipes, discounts, and articles on nutrition. **Freq:** quarterly. **Price:** included in membership dues, $7/year for nonmembers.

8849 ■ *Vegetarian Journal*
Vegetarian Resource Group
PO Box 1463
Baltimore, MD 21203
Ph: (410)366-8343
Fax: (410)366-8804
E-mail: vrg@vrg.org
URL: http://www.vrg.org
Descr: Contains informative articles, recipes, book reviews, notices about vegetarian events and product evaluations. **Freq:** quarterly. **Price:** $25 for nonmembers, included in membership dues. **ISSN:** 0885-7636.

8850 ■ *Vegetarian Journal's Food Service Update*
Vegetarian Resource Group
PO Box 1463
Baltimore, MD 21203
Ph: (410)366-8343
Fax: (410)366-8804
E-mail: vrg@vrg.org
URL: http://www.vrg.org
Freq: quarterly. **Price:** $10. **ISSN:** 1072-0820.

8851 ■ *Vegetarian Judaism: A Guide for Everyone*
Jews for Animal Rights
255 Humphrey St.
Marblehead, MA 01945
Ph: (781)631-7601
E-mail: micah@micahbooks.com
URL: http://www.micahbooks.com/JAR.html
Descr: Includes practical information about organizations and activism. **Price:** $15.95/copy.

8852 ■ *Vegetarian Sourcebook*
Omnigraphics Inc.
PO Box 31-1640
Detroit, MI 48231
Free: 800-234-1340
E-mail: info@omnigraphics.com
URL: http://www.omnigraphics.com
Key Personnel: Chad T. Kimball, Editor. **URL(s):** http://www.omnigraphics.com **Publication includes:** Resource list for additional help and information on vegetarianism. Principal content of publication is information on vegetarian diets, nutritional concerns, and special concerns for the elderly, the young, and pregnant or nursing women. **Freq:** Published 2002. **Price:** $84, individuals, hardcover.

8853 ■ *The Vegetarian Viewpoints*
Mid-Hudson Vegetarian Society
47 South St.
Rhinebeck, NY 12572
Ph: (845)876-2626
E-mail: info@mhvs.org
URL: http://www.all-creatures.org/mhvs

Freq: quarterly. **Price:** free.

8854 ■ *Vegetarian Voice*
Vegetarian Society of East Tennessee
PO Box 1974
Knoxville, TN 37901
Ph: (865)681-7691
E-mail: info@vegsociety-east-tn.org
URL: http://www.vegsociety-east-tn.org
Freq: quarterly.

8855 ■ *Vegetarian Voice*
North American Vegetarian Society
PO Box 72
Dolgeville, NY 13329
Ph: (518)568-7970
E-mail: navs@telenet.net
URL: http://www.navs-online.org
Descr: Covers health, dietary cooking and lifestyle, plus issues related to environmental and animal protection; healthful recipes in every issue. **Freq:** quarterly. **Price:** included in membership dues. **ISSN:** 0271-1591.

8856 ■ *Vegetarian Voice*
North American Vegetarian Society
PO Box 72
Dolgeville, NY 13329
Ph: (518)568-7970
E-mail: navs@telenet.net
URL: http://www.navs-online.org/
Key Personnel: Maribeth Abrams, Managing Editor; Brian Graff, Exec. Ed. **URL(s):** http://www.navs-online.org/ **Descr:** Consumer magazine covering vegetarianism, health, cooking, environmental and animal protection issues. **Freq:** Quarterly. **Price:** $22, individuals, membership U.S.; $28, U.S., 28; $29, Canada.

8857 ■ *Wholesalers and Distributors of Pharmaceutical and Medicinal Products*
Firstmark Inc.
25 Vintinner Rd.
PO Box 1270
Campton, NH 03223-4669
Ph: (603)726-4800
Free: 800-729-2600
Fax: (603)726-4840
E-mail: info@firstmark.com
URL: http://www.firstmark.com
URL(s): http://www.firstmark.com/fmkcat/twdistribpharm.htm **Covers:** Over 9,700 wholesalers and distributors of over-the-counter pharmaceutical and medicinal products in the U.S. **Entries include:** Company name, address, and contact name. **Price:** $50, individuals, email softcopy; $50, individuals, CD-ROM; $10, individuals, stick-on labels; $5, individuals, Cheshire labels/m plus shipping.

8858 ■ *Wine Country Calendar*
New York Wine/Grape Foundation
800 S Main St., Ste. 200
Canandaigua, NY 14424
Ph: (585)394-3620
Fax: (585)394-3649
E-mail: info@newyorkwines.org
URL: http://www.newyorkwines.org
Freq: annual.

8859 ■ *Wine Press*
New York Wine/Grape Foundation
800 S Main St., Ste. 200
Canandaigua, NY 14424
Ph: (585)394-3620
Fax: (585)394-3649
E-mail: info@newyorkwines.org
URL: http://www.newyorkwines.org
Freq: weekly.

8860 ■ *Winning By Losing - A Guide to Effective Weight Control*
Calorie Control Council
1100 Johnson Ferry Rd., Ste. 300
Atlanta, GA 30342
Ph: (404)252-3663

E-mail: ccc@kellencompany.com
URL: http://www.caloriecontrol.org

8861 ■ *Worried About Your Drinking?*
Moderation Management
22 W 27th St., 5th Fl.
New York, NY 10001
Ph: (212)871-0974
Fax: (212)213-6582
E-mail: mm@moderation.org
URL: http://www.moderation.org
Descr: Features a complete introduction to the programs and precepts of moderation management in a single compact format.

8862 ■ *Worst Pills/Best Pills*
Public Citizen Litigation Group
1600 20th St. NW
Washington, DC 20009
Ph: (202)588-1000
E-mail: litigation@citizen.org
URL: http://www.citizen.org/litigation

8863 ■ *Worst Pills, Best Pills News*
Public Citizen Health Research Group
1600 20th St. NW
Washington, DC 20009
Ph: (202)588-1000
E-mail: hrg1@citizen.org
URL: http://www.citizen.org/hrg
Descr: Contains reports on drug safety issues. **Freq:** monthly. **Price:** $20/year. **ISSN:** 1080-2479.

Multimedia Resources

8864 ■ *Binge Drinking Blowout*
Aquarius Productions
Olde Medfield Sq
18 N Main St
Sherborn, MA 01770
Ph: (508)650-1616
Free: 888-440-2963
Fax: (508)650-1665
E-mail: tm@aquariusproductions.com
URL: http://www.aquariusproductions.com
Format(s): Videocassette. **Descr:** Uses real stories to depict the tragic consequences of binge drinking to young people. **Prod. Date:** 1998. **Length:** 28. **Price:** $149.00.

8865 ■ *Brave New Foods: The Biotech Revolution*
The Learning Seed
330 Telser Rd
Lake Zurich, IL 60047
Free: 800-634-4941
Fax: (847)540-0854
E-mail: info@learningseed.com
URL: http://www.learningseed.com
Format(s): Videocassette. **Descr:** Provides an extensive examination of the potential benefits and risks of bioengineered foods. **Length:** 24. **Price:** $89.

8866 ■ *Consumer's Guide to Meat: Where's the Beef?*
Cambridge Educational
c/o Films Media Group
PO Box 2053
Princeton, NJ 08843-2053
Free: 800-257-5126
Fax: (609)671-0266
E-mail: custserve@filmsmediagroup.com
URL: http://www.cambridgeol.com
Format(s): Videocassette. **Descr:** Explains general butchershop practices such as meat "merchandising tricks" and offers money saving tips that will allow you to buy better cuts and qualities of meats for about half the price. **Prod. Date:** 19??. **Length:** 60. **Price:** $39.95.

8867 ■ *Food Additives*
The Learning Seed
330 Telser Rd
Lake Zurich, IL 60047

Free: 800-634-4941
Fax: (847)540-0854
E-mail: info@learningseed.com
URL: http://www.learningseed.com
Format(s): Videocassette. **Descr:** Provides a non-bias explanation of why food additives are used and if they pose any potential threat to your health. **Length:** 24. **Price:** $89.00.

8868 ■ *Food for Thought*
Aquarius Productions
Olde Medfield Sq
18 N Main St
Sherborn, MA 01770
Ph: (508)650-1616
Free: 888-440-2963
Fax: (508)650-1665
E-mail: tm@aquariusproductions.com
URL: http://www.aquariusproductions.com
Format(s): Videocassette. **Descr:** Explains elements of good nutrition, how eating habits are influenced, and what consumers need to know to make good nutritional decisions for themselves and their families. **Prod. Date:** 2000. **Length:** 28. **Price:** $99.00.

8869 ■ *Herbal Remedies From Your Garden*
Tapeworm Video Distributors
27833 Hopkins Ave., Unit 6
Valencia, CA 91355
Ph: (661)257-4904
Fax: (661)257-4820
E-mail: sales@tapeworm.com
URL: http://www.tapeworm.com
Format(s): Videocassette. **Descr:** Renowned herbalists Amanda McQuade Crawford and James Green present a step-by-step method for using common garden herbs for healing. Includes sections on herbal selection, extraction, preparation and storage methods. **Prod. Date:** 19??. **Length:** 60. **Price:** $24.95.

8870 ■ *Home-Grown Food All Year 'Round*
Rodale Press, Inc.
33 E. Minor St
Emmaus, PA 18098-0099
Ph: (610)967-5171
Fax: (610)967-8963
E-mail: customer_service@rodale.com
URL: http://www.rodale.com
Format(s): Videocassette. **Descr:** "Getting the Most from Your Garden" and "Stocking Up," the two programs comprising this cassette, demonstrate new discoveries in intensive gardening techniques and show the least-expensive, most energy-efficient ways of preserving and storing your home-grown produce. **Prod. Date:** 1980. **Length:** 55.

8871 ■ *How to Read the New Food Label*
Cambridge Educational
c/o Films Media Group
PO Box 2053
Princeton, NJ 08843-2053
Free: 800-257-5126
Fax: (609)671-0266
E-mail: custserve@filmsmediagroup.com
URL: http://www.cambridgeol.com
Format(s): Videocassette. **Descr:** Explains how to read the valuable information provided on food labels in order to avoid the risk of cancer and heart disease. Covers universal labeling, strict definitions, uniform serving sizes, and the daily value. **Prod. Date:** 1991. **Length:** 40. **Price:** $79.95.

8872 ■ *How Safe is Our Food? NewsMatters*
Zenger Media
10200 Jefferson Blvd
Box 802
Culver City, CA 90232
Ph: (310)839-2436
Free: 800-421-4246
Fax: (310)839-2249
E-mail: service@zengermedia.com
URL: http://zengermedia.com
Format(s): Videocassette. **Descr:** Discusses the use of pesticides, antibiotics, careless handling, and

other potential dangers of our nation's food supply. **Prod. Date:** 1999. **Length:** 19. **Price:** $59.95.

8873 ■ *Inside Dope: Marijuana*
Aquarius Productions
Olde Medfield Sq
18 N Main St
Sherborn, MA 01770
Ph: (508)650-1616
Free: 888-440-2963
Fax: (508)650-1665
E-mail: tm@aquariusproductions.com
URL: http://www.aquariusproductions.com
Format(s): Videocassette. **Descr:** Uses true stories to depict the destructive influence of marijuana on teenagers. **Prod. Date:** 1998. **Length:** 16. **Price:** $90.00.

8874 ■ *Keep Off the Grass: Hidden Dangers of Marijuana*
Zenger Media
10200 Jefferson Blvd
Box 802
Culver City, CA 90232
Ph: (310)839-2436
Free: 800-421-4246
Fax: (310)839-2249
E-mail: service@zengermedia.com
URL: http://zengermedia.com
Format(s): Videocassette. **Descr:** Medical professionals, counselors, and users both former and current discuss effects of marijuana and how its use is strangely promoted in the media and socially. **Prod. Date:** 1997. **Length:** 27. **Price:** $141.75.

8875 ■ *Keeping Our Food Safe*
RMI Media
1365 N. Winchester
Olathe, KS 66061
Ph: (913)768-1696
Fax: (913)768-0184
E-mail: actmedia@act.org
URL: http://www.rmimedia.com
Format(s): Videocassette. **Descr:** This tape examines food safety, including contamination, pesticides, and additives. Discusses the people and processes involved in the food supply industry. **Prod. Date:** 1987. **Length:** 28.

8876 ■ *Knives in Food Processing & Food Service Series: Choosing a Knife*
Michigan State University
Instructional Media Center
PO Box 710
East Lansing, MI 48826-0710
Ph: (517)353-3960
Fax: (517)432-2650
E-mail: imcclass@msu.edu
URL: http://www.msu.edu/unit/imc
Format(s): Videocassette. **Descr:** Proper knife selection and knife safety is demonstrated. Making sure that the knife selected is right for the job at hand is also covered. **Prod. Date:** 1988. **Length:** 19.

8877 ■ *Make Way for Baby!*
Leslie T. McClure
PO Box 1223
Pebble Beach, CA 93953
Ph: (831)656-0553
Fax: (831)656-0555
URL: http://www.411videoinfo.com
Format(s): Videocassette. **Descr:** Based on the work of child developmental psychologist Dr. Beatriz Manrique, teaches mothers- and fathers-to-be how to educate and stimulate their pre-natal baby. **Prod. Date:** 1998. **Length:** 55. **Price:** $19.95.

8878 ■ *Menu Planning for Fast Food Addicts*
Cambridge Educational
c/o Films Media Group
PO Box 2053
Princeton, NJ 08843-2053
Free: 800-257-5126
Fax: (609)671-0266

E-mail: custserve@filmsmediagroup.com
URL: http://www.cambridgeol.com
Format(s): Videocassette. **Descr:** Encourages healthy eating and introduces the basic food groups. Also identifies healthy fast food joints to consider when short on time. **Prod. Date:** 1991. **Length:** 15. **Price:** $79.00.

8879 ■ *Minerals You Eat: From Calcium to Zinc*
The Learning Seed
330 Telser Rd
Lake Zurich, IL 60047
Free: 800-634-4941
Fax: (847)540-0854
E-mail: info@learningseed.com
URL: http://www.learningseed.com
Format(s): Videocassette. **Descr:** Examines how minerals influence diet such as calcium, phosphorus, iron, sodium, zinc, selenium, copper and more. **Length:** 22. **Price:** $89.

8880 ■ *Mysteries of the Food Pyramid*
Marshmedia
PO Box 8082
Shawnee Mission, KS 66208
Ph: (816)523-1059
Free: 800-821-3303
Fax: (816)333-7421
E-mail: order@marshmedia.com
URL: http://www.marshmedia.com
Format(s): Videocassette. **Descr:** Talks about the importance of eating a variety of foods each day and drinking plenty of water, six nutrients in building, strengthening, and repairing the body, how many serving to eat from each Food Pyramid group, meal planning, and weight maintenance. **Length:** 16. **Price:** $69.95.

8881 ■ *Natural Cooking with Ease... Macrobiotically*
Tapeworm Video Distributors
27833 Hopkins Ave., Unit 6
Valencia, CA 91355
Ph: (661)257-4904
Fax: (661)257-4820
E-mail: sales@tapeworm.com
URL: http://www.tapeworm.com
Format(s): Videocassette. **Descr:** Explains the Macrobiotic theory of health including: daily balance (yin/yang), seasonal cooking and the five elements & emotions. Also includes dramatic healing stories and a recipe index. **Prod. Date:** 19??. **Length:** 108. **Price:** $22.95.

8882 ■ *Read the Label: Part 1 and Part 2*
Purdue University
Cooperative Extension Service
Media Distribution Center
231 S University St
Lafayette, IN 47907-2094
Ph: (765)494-6795
Free: 888-398-4636
Fax: (765)496-1540
E-mail: media_order@acn.purdue.edu
URL: http://www.ces.purdue.edu
Format(s): Videocassette. **Descr:** Orients amateur gardeners toward useful products and shows which ones to avoid. Demonstrates a typical interaction between a novice gardener, her county extension educator, and a pest control application expert. First part focuses on pesticide selection while second part highlights safety issues. **Prod. Date:** 1990. **Length:** 24. **Price:** $15.

8883 ■ *Safe Galley and Food Handling Procedures*
John Sabella & Associate
805 W. Emerson St
Seattle, WA 98119
Ph: (206)281-8626
Fax: (206)217-0899
E-mail: sales@johnsabella.com
URL: http://www.johnsabella.com
Format(s): Videocassette. **Descr:** Explains proper techniques for the safe preparation, cooking and

storage of food in remote locations. **Prod. Date:** ?. **Length:** 30.

8884 ■ *Secrets of the Food Pyramid*
Marshmedia
PO Box 8082
Shawnee Mission, KS 66208
Ph: (816)523-1059
Free: 800-821-3303
Fax: (816)333-7421
E-mail: order@marshmedia.com
URL: http://www.marshmedia.com
Format(s): Videocassette. **Descr:** Talks about the importance of eating the right amounts and types of food each day, drinking plenty of water, and how to choose nutritious snacks, **Prod. Date:** ????. **Length:** 14. **Price:** $69.95.

8885 ■ *Skills for Food Shopping*
Cambridge Educational
c/o Films Media Group
PO Box 2053
Princeton, NJ 08843-2053
Free: 800-257-5126
Fax: (609)671-0266
E-mail: custserve@filmsmediagroup.com
URL: http://www.cambridgeol.com
Format(s): Videocassette. **Descr:** Encourages healthy eating habits, and overviews important grocery information such as how to read food labels. **Prod. Date:** 1991. **Length:** 15. **Price:** $79.00.

8886 ■ *Snacks: A Consumer's Guide*
The Learning Seed
330 Telser Rd
Lake Zurich, IL 60047
Free: 800-634-4941
Fax: (847)540-0854
E-mail: info@learningseed.com
URL: http://www.learningseed.com
Format(s): Videocassette. **Descr:** Applies basic nutrition to snack foods. Examines fake fats like olestra and polydextrose. Considers if healthful snacks are always healthy, or just well marketed. **Length:** 23. **Price:** $89.

8887 ■ *Stocking Up*
Bullfrog Films, Inc.
PO Box 149
Oley, PA 19547
Ph: (610)779-8226
Free: 800-543-3764
Fax: (610)370-1978
E-mail: video@bullfrogfilms.com
URL: http://bullfrogfilms.com
Format(s): Videocassette. **Descr:** In this film Vic and Betsy Sussman discuss homegrown food and how to preserve it. **Prod. Date:** 1982. **Length:** 28.

8888 ■ *Supermarket Savvy*
Cambridge Educational
c/o Films Media Group
PO Box 2053
Princeton, NJ 08843-2053
Free: 800-257-5126
Fax: (609)671-0266
E-mail: custserve@filmsmediagroup.com
URL: http://www.cambridgeol.com
Format(s): Videocassette. **Descr:** This video is a presentation dealing with what we put into our bodies, before we need to think of exercise or losing weight. Topics include criteria for selecting healthier foods, calculating the percentage of calories from fat, and a look at the basic food groups. Includes a 16-page booklet. **Prod. Date:** 1987. **Length:** 60. **Price:** $49.95.

8889 ■ *Supermarket Shopping*
Zenger Media
10200 Jefferson Blvd
Box 802
Culver City, CA 90232
Ph: (310)839-2436
Free: 800-421-4246
Fax: (310)839-2249

E-mail: service@zengermedia.com
URL: http://zengermedia.com
Format(s): Videocassette. **Descr:** Shares smart shopping secrets and discusses purchasing basics. **Prod. Date:** 1999. **Length:** 16. **Price:** $74.

8890 ■ *Surviving the Checkout: Wise Food Buying*
Cambridge Educational
c/o Films Media Group
PO Box 2053
Princeton, NJ 08843-2053
Free: 800-257-5126
Fax: (609)671-0266
E-mail: custserve@filmsmediagroup.com
URL: http://www.cambridgeol.com
Format(s): Videocassette. **Descr:** Wise shoppers Richard and Larry visit the grocery store and quickly learn about merchandising tricks that induce impulsive buying, how to select fresh foods, read labels, and compare brands and unit prices. Also offers alternatives to supermarket shopping. Complete with manual. **Prod. Date:** 1990. **Length:** 30. **Price:** $79.95.

8891 ■ *Team Up with Team Nutrition!*
Michigan State University
Instructional Media Center
PO Box 710
East Lansing, MI 48826-0710
Ph: (517)353-3960
Fax: (517)432-2650
E-mail: imcclass@msu.edu
URL: http://www.msu.edu/unit/imc
Format(s): Videocassette. **Descr:** Presents ways schools, parents, and the community can educate children know about nutrition. **Prod. Date:** ????. **Length:** 19. **Price:** $25.00.

8892 ■ *The Truth About Sugar*
The Learning Seed
330 Telser Rd
Lake Zurich, IL 60047
Free: 800-634-4941
Fax: (847)540-0854
E-mail: info@learningseed.com
URL: http://www.learningseed.com
Format(s): Videocassette. **Descr:** Investigates common questions about sugar: does it lead to obesity, encourage hyperactive behavior in kids, cause diabetes or cavities? **Length:** 20. **Price:** $89.

8893 ■ *Video Cookbook: Heart Healthy Pan Seared Chicken Breast*
Tapeworm Video Distributors
27833 Hopkins Ave., Unit 6
Valencia, CA 91355
Ph: (661)257-4904
Fax: (661)257-4820
E-mail: sales@tapeworm.com
URL: http://www.tapeworm.com
Format(s): Videocassette. **Descr:** Celebrity chef Jim Coleman teaches you how to prepare and serve pan seared chicken breast on mushroom ragout, asparagus, watercress salad with tomato vinaigrette and lemon ginger Anjou pear with merlot glaze. **Prod. Date:** 1997. **Length:** 60. **Price:** $19.95.

8894 ■ *Video Wine Guide*
Paramount Home Video
5555 Melrose Ave
5555 Melrose Ave
Los Angeles, CA 90038
Ph: (323)956-5000
URL: http://www.paramount.com
Format(s): Videocassette. **Descr:** Dick Cavett introduces the viewer to the world of wine, from the evolution of wine to the pronunciation of those tough labels. Also, learn about wine tasting and enjoy a scenic tour of the wine producing regions of the world. **Prod. Date:** 198?. **Length:** 90. **Price:** $39.95.

8895 ■ *What's Your Beef?*
Brigham Young University
University Hill
Provo, UT 84604

Ph: (801)422-4000
E-mail: it@byu.edu
URL: http://it.byu.edu
Format(s): Videocassette. **Descr:** This tape tells how to avoid problems and confusion in buying beef by detailing the grading process and the various grades used, telling where the tender and less tender cuts come from, and how to select cuts of beef. **Length:** 26.

8896 ■ *Your Nutrition Style: New Dietary Guidelines*
The Learning Seed
330 Telser Rd
Lake Zurich, IL 60047
Free: 800-634-4941
Fax: (847)540-0854
E-mail: info@learningseed.com
URL: http://www.learningseed.com
Format(s): Videocassette. **Descr:** Scientific consensus on diet and health demonstrated by real people making daily diet and activity level changes. **Prod. Date:** 2000. **Length:** 26. **Price:** $89.00.

Media Contacts

8897 ■ Associated Press
2021 K St. NW, 6th Fl.
Washington, DC 20006-1082
Contact: Ricardo Alonso-Zaldivar, Health/FDA Correspondent
Ph: (202)776-9442
Fax: (202)726-9570
E-mail: ralonsozaldivar@ap.org
URL: http://www.ap.org

Arizona

8898 ■ *The Arizona Republic*
Gannet Co., Inc.
PO Box 1950
Phoenix, AZ 85001
Contact: Karen Fernau, Food Reporter
Ph: (602)444-4779
E-mail: karen.fernau@arizonarepublic.com
URL: http://www.azcentral.com

California

8899 ■ *Los Angeles Times*
Tribune Company
202 W. First St.
Los Angeles, CA 90012
Contact: Russ Parsons, In the Kitchen Columnist
Ph: (213)237-4634
E-mail: russ.parsons@latimes.com
URL: http://www.latimes.com

8900 ■ *Los Angeles Times*
Tribune Company
202 W. First St.
Los Angeles, CA 90012
Contact: Jerry Hirsch, Food/Supermarkets Writer
Ph: (213)237-5260
E-mail: jerry.hirsch@latimes.com
URL: http://www.latimes.com

8901 ■ *San Francisco Chronicle*
Hearst Newspapers
901 Mission St.
San Francisco, CA 94103-2988
Contact: Michael Bauer, Exec. Food & Wine Reporter
Ph: (415)777-8463
E-mail: mbauer@sfchronicle.com
URL: http://www.sfchronicle.com

Colorado

8902 ■ *Denver Post*
101 W. Colfax Ave.
Denver, CO 80202
Contact: Kristen Browning-Blas, Food Writer/Columnist
Ph: (303)954-1440

E-mail: kbrowning@denverpost.com
URL: http://www.denverpost.com

8903 ■ *Denver Post*
101 W. Colfax Ave.
Denver, CO 80202
Contact: John Henderson, Food Columnist
Ph: (303)954-1299
E-mail: jhenderson@denverpost.com
URL: http://www.denverpost.com

Florida

8904 ■ *Orlando Sentinel*
Tribune Company
633 N. Orange Ave.
Orlando, FL 32801-1349
Contact: Heather McPherson, Food Editor
Ph: (407)420-5498
E-mail: hmcpherson@orlandosentinel.com
URL: http://www.orlandosentinel.com

8905 ■ *Sun Sentinel*
Tribune Company
200 E. Las Olas Blvd.
Fort Lauderdale, FL 33301-2293
Contact: Deborah S. Hartz, Food Editor
Ph: (954)356-4723
E-mail: dhartz@sun-sentinel.com
URL: http://www.sun-sentinel.com

Illinois

8906 ■ *Chicago Tribune*
Tribune Company
435 N. Michigan Ave.
Chicago, IL 60611-4041
Contact: Robin Mather Jenkins, Good Eating Reporter
Ph: (312)222-3232
E-mail: rjenkins@tribune.com
URL: http://www.chicagotribune.com

8907 ■ *Chicago Tribune*
Tribune Company
435 N. Michigan Ave.
Chicago, IL 60611-4041
Contact: Bill Daley, Food and Wine Columnist
Ph: (312)222-3232
E-mail: wdaley@tribune.com
URL: http://www.chicagotribune.com

Louisiana

8908 ■ *New Orleans Times-Picayune*
Newhouse Newspapers
3800 Howard Ave.
New Orleans, LA 70125
Contact: Judy Walker, Food Editor
Ph: (504)826-3485
URL: http://www.nola.com

Minnesota

8909 ■ *Star Tribune*
McClatchy Newspapers, Inc.
425 Portland Ave., S.
Minneapolis, MN 55415
Contact: Matt McKinney, Food and Agriculture Reporter
Ph: (612)673-7329
E-mail: mckinney@startribune.com
URL: http://www.startribune.com

North Carolina

8910 ■ *The Charlotte Observer*
Knight Ridder, Inc.
PO Box 30308
Charlotte, NC 28230-0308
Contact: Kathleen Purvis, Food Editor
Ph: (704)358-5236
E-mail: kpurvis@charlotteobserver.com
URL: http://www.charlotte.com/observer

Oregon

8911 ■ *The Oregonian*
1320 SW Broadway
Portland, OR 97201
Contact: Leslie Cole, Food Reporter
Ph: (503)294-4069
E-mail: lesliecole@news.oregonian.com
URL: http://www.oregonlive.com

Pennsylvania

8912 ■ *The Philadelphia Inquirer*
Philadelphia Media Holdings LLC
400 N. Broad St.
Philadelphia, PA 19103
Contact: Craig LaBan, Food Critic
Ph: (215)854-2593
E-mail: claban@phillynews.com
URL: http://www.philly.com

Texas

8913 ■ *Fort Worth Star-Telegram*
PO Box 1870
Fort Worth, TX 76115
Contact: Amy Culbertson, Food Editor
Ph: (817)390-7421
E-mail: aculbertson@star-telegram.com
URL: http://www.star-telegram.com

8914 ■ *Forth Worth Star-Telegram*
The McClatchy Company
PO Box 1870
Fort Worth, TX 76101
Contact: Barry Shlachter, Food Industry Writer
Ph: (817)390-7718
Free: 800-776-7827
E-mail: barry@star-telegram.com
URL: http://www.star-telegram.com

Corporate Contacts

8915 ■ 7-Eleven, Inc.
Customer Relations
Loc. 231, PO Box 711
Dallas, TX 75221
Ph: (214)828-7011
Free: 800-255-0711
URL: http://www.7-Eleven.com

8916 ■ AFC Enterprises, Inc.
America's Favorite Chicken Co.
5555 Glenridge Connector NE, Ste. 300
Atlanta, GA 30342
Ph: (404)459-4450
Free: 800-222-5857
Fax: (770)353-3280
URL: http://www.afce.com

8917 ■ Alberto Culver Co.
2525 Armitage Ave.
Melrose Park, IL 60160
Ph: (708)450-3000
Free: 800-333-0005
Fax: (708)450-3435
URL: http://www.alberto.com

8918 ■ Albertson's Inc.
Customer Service
250 E. Parkcenter Blvd.
Boise, ID 83706
Ph: (208)395-6392
Free: 877-932-7948
Fax: (208)395-4382
URL: http://www.albertsons.com

8919 ■ Allied Domecq Quick Service Restaurant
Consumer Care
14 Pacella Park Dr.
Randolph, MA 02368-1756
Ph: (781)961-4020

Free: 800-859-5339
URL: http://www.adqsr.com

8920 ■ Almaden Vinyards
Consumer Relations
12667 Rd. 24
Madera, CA 93637
Free: 800-726-9977
E-mail: crelations@almaden.com
URL: http://www.almaden.com

8921 ■ Anheuser-Busch, Inc.
Customer Call Center
One Busch Pl.
St. Louis, MO 63118
Free: 800-342-5283
URL: http://www.anheuser-busch.com

8922 ■ Arby's Restaurant Group, Inc.
1155 Perimeter Center W.
Atlanta, GA 30338
Ph: (678)514-4100
Fax: (678)514-5347
URL: http://www.arbys.com

8923 ■ Armour Swift Eckrich
Consumer Affairs
PO Box 405020
Cincinnati, OH 45240-5020
Ph: (630)512-1000
Free: 800-722-1127
Fax: (630)512-1124
URL: http://www.armour-eckrich.com
Telecom. Svcs: For Eckrich nutrition, call toll-free (800)325-7424.

8924 ■ Ateeco, Inc.
Consumer Affairs Department
PO Box 606
600 E. Center St.
Shenandoah, PA 17976-0606
Ph: (570)462-2745
Free: 800-233-3170
Fax: (570)462-3299
E-mail: ConsumerContact@pierogies.com
URL: http://www.pierogies.com

8925 ■ Aventis Pharmaceuticals
North American Headquarters
300 Summerset Corporate Blvd.
Bridge Water, NJ 08807
Ph: (908)231-4000
Free: 800-552-3656
URL: http://www.aventis.com

8926 ■ Avon Products, Inc.
Customer Information Center
1251 Ave. of the Americas
New York, NY 10020
Contact: Lynn Baron
Ph: (212)282-7000
Free: 800-367-2866
URL: http://www.avon.com
Telecom. Svcs: Additional toll-free: (800)FOR-AVON; for consumer information center, call (800)445-2866.

8927 ■ Bacardi USA, Inc.
2100 Biscayne Blvd.
Miami, FL 33137-5028
Ph: (305)573-8511
Free: 800-BACARDI
Fax: (305)573-7507
URL: http://www.bacardi.com

8928 ■ Ball Park Brands
Sara Lee Consumer Affairs
PO Box 756
Neenah, WI 54957-0756
Free: 800-925-3326
URL: http://www.ballparkfranks.com

8929 ■ Baskin Robbins
Dunkin Brands Consumer Care
130 Royall St.
Canton, MA 02021
Ph: (781)737-3000

Free: 800-859-5339
E-mail: support@baskinrobbins.com
URL: http://www.baskinrobbins.com

8930 ■ Becton, Dickinson and Co.
1 Becton Dr.
Franklin Lakes, NJ 07417
Ph: (201)847-6800
Free: 888-232-2737
URL: http://www.bd.com

8931 ■ Beech-Nut Nutrition Corp.
Consumer Affairs
100 S. 4th St., Ste. 1010
St. Louis, MO 63102
Ph: (314)436-7667
Free: 800-233-2468
Fax: (314)436-7679
URL: http://www.beechnut.com/index.asp

8932 ■ Beiersdorf, AG
Customer Service
Wilton Corporate Center
187 Danbury Rd.
Wilton, CT 06897
Ph: (203)563-5800
Free: 800-277-4703
URL: http://www.bdfusa.com

8933 ■ Benihana, Inc.
Customer Relations
8685 NW 53rd Terrace
Miami, FL 33166
Ph: (305)593-0770
Free: 800-327-3369
Fax: (305)592-6371
E-mail: customerrelations@benihana.com
URL: http://www.benihana.com

8934 ■ Best Foods
920 Sylvan Ave., 2nd Fl.
Englewood Cliffs, NJ 07632-9976
Ph: (201)894-4000
Free: 800-418-3275
Fax: (201)894-2126
URL: http://www.bestfoods.com
Telecom. Svcs: Medical or product safety emergency: (800)745-9279.

8935 ■ Birds Eye Foods, Inc.
PO Box 20670
Rochester, NY 14602-0670
Ph: (585)383-1850
Free: 800-999-5044
URL: http://www.birdseyefoods.com

8936 ■ Bob Evans Farms, Inc.
Consumer Relations
3776 South High St.
Columbus, OH 43207
Ph: (614)491-2225
Free: 800-272-7675
Fax: (614)497-4330
URL: http://www.bobevans.com
Telecom. Svcs: Direct line to Consumer Relations (800)939-2338.

8937 ■ Bojangles' Restaurants, Inc.
Customer Relations
9432 Southern Pine Blvd.
Charlotte, NC 28273
Ph: (704)527-2675
Free: 800-300-4265
Fax: (704)523-6803
URL: http://www.bojangles.com

8938 ■ Bristol-Myers Squibb Co.
345 Park Ave.
New York, NY 10154
Ph: (212)546-4000
Free: 800-332-2056
URL: http://www.bms.com

Telecom. Svcs: For customer relations, call toll-free (800)332-2056.

8939 ■ Brown-Forman Beverages Worldwide
Consumer Services
PO Box 1080
Louisville, KY 40201
Ph: (502)585-1100
Free: 800-753-4567
E-mail: Brown-Forman@b-f.com
URL: http://www.brown-forman.com

8940 ■ Bush Brothers and Company
Consumer Relations
PO Box 52330
Knoxville, TN 37950-2330
Ph: (865)558-5445
E-mail: letters@bushbros.com
URL: http://www.bushbeans.com

8941 ■ Campbell Soup Co.
Corporate Communications
1 Campbell Pl.
Camden, NJ 08103-1701
Free: 800-257-8443
URL: http://www.campbellsoup.com

8942 ■ Canandaigua Wine Co.
Consumer Response
116 Buffalo St.
Canandaigua, NY 14424
Ph: (716)394-7900
Free: 888-659-7900
Fax: (716)393-6950
URL: http://www.cwine.com

8943 ■ Carvel Corp.
Customer Service Dept.
301 Congress Ave., Ste. 1100
Austin, TX 78701
Ph: (512)236-3829
Free: 800-322-4848
Fax: (512)236-3700
URL: http://www.carvel.com

8944 ■ Celestial Seasonings
4600 Sleepytime Dr.
Boulder, CO 80301-3292
Ph: (303)530-5300
Free: 800-434-4246
URL: http://www.celestialseasonings.com

8945 ■ Chanel, Inc.
Customer Service
9 W. 57th St., 44th Fl.
New York, NY 10019-2790
Ph: (212)688-5055
Free: 800-550-0005
URL: http://www.chanel.com

8946 ■ Chicken of the Sea International
Consumer Affairs
PO Box 85568
San Diego, CA 92186
Ph: (858)597-4242
Free: 800-456-1511
Fax: (858)597-4248
URL: http://www.chickenofthesea.com

8947 ■ The Clorox Co.
Consumer Services
1221 Boadway
Oakland, CA 94612-1888
Ph: (510)271-7000
Free: 800-292-2200
URL: http://www.thecloroxcompany.com
Telecom. Svcs: For laundry products, call toll-free (800)292-2200; for GLAD, call (800)835-4523; for household cleaners, call (800)227-1860; for auto care products, call (800)222-7784.

8948 ■ The Coca-Cola Co.
Industry and Consumer Affairs
PO Box 1734
Atlanta, GA 30301
Ph: (404)676-2121
Free: 800-438-2653
URL: http://www.thecoca-colacompany.com
Telecom. Svcs: TDD toll-free: (800)262-2653.

8949 ■ The Colgate-Palmolive Co.
Consumer Affairs
300 Park Ave.
New York, NY 10022
Contact: Jan Guifarro
Ph: (212)310-2000
Free: 800-468-6502
Fax: (212)310-3243
URL: http://www.colgate.com
Telecom. Svcs: Additional toll-free: (800)763-0246.

8950 ■ Combe, Inc.
Consumer Resources
1101 Westchester Ave.
White Plains, NY 10604-3503
Ph: (914)694-5454
Free: 800-431-2610
Fax: (914)694-6320
URL: http://www.combe.com
Telecom. Svcs: For product questions, call toll-free (800)873-7400.

8951 ■ ConAgra Foods
Consumer Affairs
PO Box 3768
Omaha, NE 68103-0768
Free: 877-266-2472
Fax: (402)595-7880
E-mail: cffcr@conagrafrozen.com
URL: http://www.conagrafoods.com

8952 ■ Constellation Wines U.S.
Centerra Wine Company
235 N. Bloomfield Rd.
Canandaigua, NY 14424
Ph: (585)396-7600
Free: 888-659-7900
URL: http://www.cwinesus.com
Telecom. Svcs: For Pacific Wine Partners, call (831)675-2481; for North Lake Wines, call (866)334-9463.

8953 ■ Coors Brewing Co.
Consumer Information Ctr.
Consumer Relations
311 10th St., NH475
Golden, CO 80401
Ph: (303)279-6565
Free: 800-642-6116
URL: http://www.coors.com

8954 ■ Creative Labs
Customer Service
1523 Cimarron Plaza
Stillwater, OK 74075
Ph: (405)742-6655
Free: 800-998-1000
URL: http://us.creative.com

8955 ■ CVS/pharmacy
Customer Relations Department
One CVS Dr.
Woonsocket, RI 02895
Ph: (401)765-1500
Free: 800-746-7287
Fax: (401)770-6949
E-mail: customercare@cvs.com
URL: http://www.cvs.com
Telecom. Svcs: Customer care specialists: (888)607-4287.

8956 ■ Dairy Queen Corp.
Customer Relations
7505 Metro Blvd.
Minneapolis, MN 55439-0286
Ph: (952)830-0200
URL: http://www.dairyqueen.com

8957 ■ Dannon Co., Inc.
Consumer Response Center
PO Box 90296
Allentown, PA 18109-0296
Free: 877-326-6668
URL: http://www.dannon.com
Telecom. Svcs: Additional toll-free: (877)326-6668.

8958 ■ Del Laboratories, Inc.
Consumer Relations
PO Box 9357
Uniondale, NY 11553
Ph: (516)844-2020
Free: 800-952-5080
Fax: (516)349-0904
URL: http://www.dellabs.com
Telecom. Svcs: Additional toll-free: (800)953-5080.

8959 ■ Del Monte Foods Company
Consumer Affairs
PO Box 80
Pittsburgh, PA 15230-0080
Ph: (415)247-3000
Free: 800-543-3090
URL: http://www.delmonte.com
Telecom. Svcs: TDD toll-free: (800)545-0090.

8960 ■ Denny's, Corp.
203 E. Main St. P-8-6
Spartanburg, SC 29319
Ph: (864)597-8000
Free: 800-733-6697
URL: http://www.dennys.com

8961 ■ The Dial Corp.
15101 N. Scottsdale Rd.
Scottsdale, AZ 85254-1619
Ph: (480)754-3425
Free: 800-258-0849
URL: http://www.dialcorp.com

8962 ■ Diamond of California
Consumer Affairs
1050 S. Diamond St.
Stockton, CA 95201
Ph: (209)467-6260
Fax: (209)467-6205
E-mail: dsamelso@diamondnuts.com
URL: http://www.diamondnuts.com

8963 ■ Dole Food Company, Inc.
Consumer Center
PO Box 5700
Thousand Oaks, CA 91359-5700
Ph: (818)874-4000
Free: 800-356-3111
Fax: (818)874-4997
URL: http://www.dole.com

8964 ■ Domino's Pizza, Inc.
Resource Center
30 Frank Lloyd Wright Dr.
PO Box 997
Ann Arbor, MI 48106
Ph: (734)930-3030
Free: 888—DOMINOS
URL: http://www.dominos.com
Telecom. Svcs: Additional toll-free for Spanish-speaking customers: (888)DOM-INOS.

8965 ■ Dr Pepper Snapple Group
Consumer Relations
PO Box 869077
Plano, TX 75086
Ph: (972)673-7000
Free: 800-696-5891
URL: http://www.drpeppersnapplegroup.com

8966 ■ Dreyer's Grand Ice Cream
Customer Relations
5929 College Ave.
Oakland, CA 94618
Free: 877-437-3937
Fax: (570)301-4538
URL: http://www.dreyers.com/main/index.asp?b=104

8967 ■ DS Waters of America
5660 New Northside Dr., Ste. 500
Atlanta, GA 30328
Free: 800-669-3402

E-mail: customerservice@water.com
URL: http://www.water.com

8968 ■ Dunkin Donuts
Customer Service
130 Royall St.
Canton, MA 02021
Contact: Will Kussell, Pres.
Ph: (781)737-3000
Free: 800-859-5339
URL: http://www.dunkindonuts.com

8969 ■ Eagle Family Foods
Corporate Relations
735 Taylor Rd., Ste. 200
Gahanna, OH 43230
Free: 877-645-6681
Fax: (614)501-4295
URL: http://www.eaglefamilyfoods.com

8970 ■ Eli Lilly & Co.
Consumer Communications
Lilly Corporate Center
Indianapolis, IN 46285
Ph: (317)276-2000
Free: 800-545-5979
URL: http://www.lilly.com

8971 ■ Ernest & Julio Gallo Winery
Consumer Relations
600 Yosemite Blvd.
Modesto, CA 95354
Ph: (209)341-3161
Free: 877-687-9463
Fax: (209)341-6600
E-mail: consumerrelations@ejgallo.com
URL: http://www.gallo.com

8972 ■ The Estee Lauder Companies, Inc.
Consumer Communications
767 Fifth Ave.
New York, NY 10153
Ph: (212)572-4200
Fax: (212)572-3764
URL: http://www.elcompanies.com

8973 ■ Flowers Foods, Inc.
1919 Flowers Cir.
Thomasville, GA 31757
Contact: Marta Turner
Ph: (229)226-9110
URL: http://www.flowersfoods.com

8974 ■ Food Lion, LLC
Customer Relations
PO Box 1330
Salisbury, NC 28145-1330
Free: 800-210-9569
URL: http://www.FoodLion.com

8975 ■ Frito-Lay, Inc.
Consumer Affairs
PO Box 660634
Dallas, TX 75266-0634
Contact: Cathy Dial
Ph: (972)334-7000
Free: 800-352-4477
Fax: (972)334-5071
URL: http://www.fritolay.com

8976 ■ General Mills, Inc.
Consumer Services
PO Box 9452
Minneapolis, MN 55440
Free: 800-248-7310
Fax: (763)764-8330
URL: http://www.generalmills.com

8977 ■ Gerber Products Co.
Consumer Affairs
445 State St.
Fremont, MI 49413-0001
Free: 800-4-GERBER
URL: http://www.gerber.com
Telecom. Svcs: Call toll-free for breastfeeding

advice, (800) 421-4221; for baby formula, (800)828-9119.

8978 ■ Giant Food, Inc.
Consumer Affairs
8301 Professional Place, Suite 115
Landover, MD 20785
Ph: (301)341-4322
Free: 888-469-4426
Fax: (301)618-4968
URL: http://www.giantfood.com
Telecom. Svcs: For TDD, call (301)200-8995.

8979 ■ Glaxo Smith Kline Consumer Healthcare
Consumer Information
PO Box 1467
Pittsburgh, PA 15205
Contact: Laurie Garvey
Ph: (412)928-1000
Free: 800-245-1040
Fax: (412)928-5864
URL: http://www.GSK.com

8980 ■ The Golden Grain Company
PO Box 049003
Chicago, IL 60604-9003
Free: 800-421-2444
URL: http://www.ricearoni.com

8981 ■ Guinness (imported by Diageo Guinness USA)
801 Main Ave.
Norwalk, CT 06851
Ph: (203)229-2100
Free: 800-521-1591
Fax: (203)229-8901
E-mail: guinness@consumer-care.net
URL: http://www.guiness.com

8982 ■ Hain Celestial Group, Inc.
Consumer Relations
4600 Sleepytime Dr.
Boulder, CA 80301
Free: 800-434-4246
URL: http://www.hain-celestial.com

8983 ■ Harry and David
Internet Customer Service
2500 S. Pacific Hwy.
Medford, OR 97501-2675
Free: 877-322-1200
Fax: 800-648-6640
URL: http://www.harryanddavid.com

8984 ■ Hartz Mountain Corporation
Consumer Relations and Info Center
400 Plaza Dr.
Secaucus, NJ 07094
Ph: (201)271-4800
Free: 800-275-1414
URL: http://www.hartz.com

8985 ■ Heinz North America
Consumer Affairs
Consumer Resource Center
Heinz 57 Center
PO Box 57
Pittsburgh, PA 15230
Free: 800-255-5750
Fax: (412)237-5291
URL: http://www.heinz.com

8986 ■ Hershey Food Corp.
Consumer Relations
100 Crystal A Dr.
Hershey, PA 17033
Ph: (717)534-7622
Free: 800-468-1714
URL: http://www.hersheys.com

8987 ■ Highfalls Brewing Company, Inc.
Customer Service Dept.
445 St. Paul St.
Rochester, NY 14605
Ph: (585)263-9446
Free: (80-0)SAY-GENNY

Fax: (716)546-5011
URL: http://www.highfalls.com

8988 ■ Hillshire Farm
Consumer Affairs
PO Box 756
Neenah, WI 54957-0756
Free: 800-328-2426
URL: http://www.gomeat.com

8989 ■ Just Born, Inc.
Customer Relations
1300 Stefko Blvd.
Bethlehem, PA 18017
Ph: (610)867-7568
Free: 800-645-3453
Fax: 800-543-4981
URL: http://www.justborn.com

8990 ■ Kellogg Co.
Consumer Affairs
PO Box CAMB
Battle Creek, MI 49016
Ph: (269)961-2000
Free: 800-962-1413
URL: http://www.kelloggcompany.com
Telecom. Svcs: Additional toll-free: (800)962-1516.

8991 ■ KFC (Kentucky Fried Chicken)
YUM! Brands, Inc.
1441 Gardiner Lane
Louisville, KY 40213
Free: 800-544-5774
URL: http://www.yum.com

8992 ■ Kinetico
10845 Kinsman Rd.
PO Box 193
Newbury, OH 44065
Ph: (440)564-9111
Free: 800-944-9283
Fax: (440)564-9541
E-mail: custserv@kinetico.com
URL: http://www.kinetico.com

8993 ■ Kraft Foods, Inc.
One Kraft Ct.
Glenview, IL 60025
Free: 877-535-5666
Fax: (847)646-7853
URL: http://www.kraftfoods.com

8994 ■ Kroger Co.
1014 Vine St.
Cincinnati, OH 45202-1100
Free: 866-221-4141
URL: http://www.kroger.com

8995 ■ Land O'Lakes, Inc.
Consumer Affairs
PO Box 64101
Mail Station 1070
St. Paul, MN 55164-0101
Ph: (651)481-2135
Free: 800-328-9680
Fax: (651)481-2959
URL: http://www.landolakes.com

8996 ■ Lever Brothers Corp.
Consumer Services
800 Sylvan Ave.
Englewood Cliffs, NJ 07632
Free: 800-598-1223
URL: http://www.unilever.com
Telecom. Svcs: Additional toll-free: (800)598-5005.

8997 ■ Long John Silver's Restaurants, Inc.
1441 Gardiner Ln.
Louisville, KY 40213
Free: 888-806-3474
URL: http://www.ljsilvers.com

8998 ■ M&M/Mars, Inc.
800 High St.
Hackettstown, NJ 07840
Contact: Lesley Verdi
Ph: (908)852-1000

Free: 800-627-7852
URL: http://www.mms.com

8999 ■ Masterfoods USA
800 High St.
Hackettstown, NJ 07840
Ph: (908)852-1000
Free: 800-222-0293
E-mail: askus@masterfoodsusa.com
URL: http://www.masterfoods.com

9000 ■ Maybelline, Inc.
PO Box 1010
Clark, NJ 07066-1010
Free: 800-944-0730
URL: http://www.maybelline.com

9001 ■ McCormick & Co., Inc.
Consumer Affairs
18 Loveton Cir.
Sparks, MD 21152
Ph: (410)771-7301
Free: 800-632-5847
Fax: (410)527-6005
URL: http://www.mccormick.com

9002 ■ McDonald's Corp.
Customer Satisfaction Dept.
2111 McDonald's Dr.
Oak Brook, IL 60523
Free: 800-244-6227
URL: http://www.mcdonalds.com

9003 ■ McKee Foods Corp.
Consumer Affairs
PO Box 750
Collegedale, TN 37315
Free: 800-522-4499
URL: http://www.mckeefoods.com

9004 ■ Medco Health Solutions, Inc.
Public Affairs
100 Parsons Pond Dr.
Franklin Lakes, NJ 07417
Ph: (201)269-3400
Free: 800-251-7690
URL: http://host1.medcohealth.com/consumer/site/home

9005 ■ The Mentholatum Co., Inc.
Consumer Affairs
707 Sterling Dr.
Orchard Park, NY 14127
Ph: (716)677-2500
Free: 800-688-7660
Fax: (716)674-3696
URL: http://www.mentholatum.com

9006 ■ Michelina's
Bellisio Foods Customer Service
PO Box 16630
Duluth, MN 55816
Ph: (218)723-5555
E-mail: michelinas@bellisiofoods.com
URL: http://www.michelinas.com

9007 ■ Miller Brewing Company
3939 W. Highland Blvd.
Milwaukee, WI 53208
Ph: (414)931-2000
URL: http://www.millerbrewing.com

9008 ■ The Milnot Company
Consumer Response
1 Stawberry Ln.
Orrville, OH 44667
Free: 888-656-3245
URL: http://www.milnot.com

9009 ■ Morton International, Inc.
Consumer Affairs
123 N. Wacker Dr.
Chicago, IL 60606-1743
Ph: (312)807-2693
Free: 800-725-8847

Fax: (312)807-2769
URL: http://www.mortonsalt.com

9010 ■ Motts, Inc.
Consumer Services Dept.
900 King St.
Rye Brook, NY 10573
Ph: (914)612-4000
Free: 800-426-4891
URL: http://www.motts.com

9011 ■ Nabisco Foods Group
Consumer Relations Group
1 Kraft Court
Glenview, IL 60025
Ph: (201)503-2000
Free: (80-0)543-5335
URL: http://www.nabiscoworld.com

9012 ■ Near East Food Products
PO Box 049003
Chicago, IL 60604-9003
Ph: (312)222-7111
Free: 800-822-7423
URL: http://www.neareast.com

9013 ■ Nestle USA
Consumer Services Ctr.
800 N. Brand Blvd.
Glendale, CA 91203
Ph: (818)549-6000
Free: 800-225-2270
URL: http://www.nestle.com

9014 ■ Nestle Waters North America Inc.
777 W. Putnam Ave.
Greenwich, CT 06830-5091
Ph: (203)531-4100
URL: http://www.nestle-watersna.com

9015 ■ Neutrogena Corp.
Consumer Affairs
5760 W. 96th St.
Los Angeles, CA 90045
Ph: (310)642-1150
Free: 800-582-4048
E-mail: ntgweb@neuus.jnj.com
URL: http://www.neutrogena.com

9016 ■ Nexxus Products Co.
PO Box 1274
Santa Barbara, CA 93116-9976
Ph: (805)968-6900
Free: 800-444-6399
Fax: (805)968-6540
URL: http://www.nexxusproducts.com

9017 ■ Novartis Pharmaceuticals Corp.
Customer Response Pharmaceuticals
One Health Plaza
East Hanover, NJ 07936-1080
Ph: (862)778-8300
Free: 888-669-6682
Fax: (973)781-8265
URL: http://www.pharma.us.novartis.com
Telecom. Svcs: For over-the-counter-products, call toll-free (800)277-2254.

9018 ■ The NutraSweet Company
Customer Service
1762 Lovers Lane
Augusta, GA 30901
Free: 800-323-5321
URL: http://www.nutrasweet.com

9019 ■ Ocean Spray Cranberries Inc.
Consumer Affairs Dept.
One Ocean Spray Dr.
Lakeville-Middleboro, MA 02349
Ph: (508)946-1000
Free: 800-662-3263
Fax: (508)923-0036
URL: http://www.oceanspray.com

9020 ■ Oreida
PO Box 10
Boise, ID 83707

Free: 800-892-2401
URL: http://www.oreida.com

9021 ■ Orville Redenbacher
PO Box 4800
Fullerton, CA 92834
Ph: (714)680-1431
Free: 800-243-0303
URL: http://www.orville.com

9022 ■ Pepperidge Farm, Inc.
Consumer Affairs
595 Westport Ave.
Norwalk, CT 06851
Free: 888-737-7374
URL: http://www.pepperidgefarm.com

9023 ■ PepsiCo, Inc.
Public Affairs
700 Anderson Hill Rd.
Purchase, NY 10577
Ph: (914)253-2000
Free: 800-433-2652
Fax: (914)767-6177
URL: http://www.pepsico.com

9024 ■ Perdue Farms, Inc.
Consumer Relations
PO Box 1656
Horsham, PA 19044-6656
Free: 800-473-7383
URL: http://www.perdue.com

9025 ■ Pernod Ricard USA
Customer Relations
777 Westchester Ave.
White Plains, NY 10604
Ph: (914)539-4500
URL: http://www.pernod-ricard.com

9026 ■ Perrier Group
777 W. Putnam Ave.
Greenwich, CT 06830
Contact: David Muscato
Ph: (203)531-4100
Fax: (203)863-0256
URL: http://www.perriergroup.com/

9027 ■ Pfizer Inc.
Consumer Affairs
235 E. 42nd St.
New York, NY 10017
Free: 800-879-3477
URL: http://www.pfizer.com
Telecom. Svcs: For non-prescription consumer products, call (800)223-0182.

9028 ■ Pharmacia
PO Box 5110
Chicago, IL 60680
Ph: (847)982-7000
Fax: (847)470-6633
URL: http://www.pharmacia.com

9029 ■ Philip Morris USA
Customer Affairs
Consumer Response Center
PO Box 26603
Richmond, VA 23261
Free: 800-343-0975
URL: http://www.philipmorris.com

9030 ■ Pizza Hut
YUM! Brands, Inc.
14841 Dallas Pkwy.
Dallas, TX 75254
Free: 800-948-8488
URL: http://www.pizzahut.com

9031 ■ Procter & Gamble Co.
Consumer Relations
1 or 2, Procter & Gamble Plaza

Cincinnati, OH 45201
Ph: (513)983-1100
URL: http://www.pg.com

9032 ■ Quaker Oats Co.
Consumer Affairs
PO Box 049003
Chicago, IL 60604-9003
Ph: (312)821-1000
URL: http://www.quakeroats.com

9033 ■ Ralston Purina Co.
Checkerboard Sq.
St. Louis, MO 63164
Free: 800-778-7462
Fax: (314)982-4580
URL: http://www.purina.com

9034 ■ Reckitt Benckiser, Inc.
Consumer Relations
Morris Corporate Center IV
399 Interspace Parkway
PO Box 225
Parsippany, NJ 07054-0225
Ph: (973)404-2600
Free: 800-333-6167
E-mail: consumer.relations@RBNorthAmerica.com
URL: http://www.rb.com/home

9035 ■ Rhone-Poulenc Rorer Pharmaceuticals, Inc.
500 Arcola Dr.
Collegeville, PA 19426
Ph: (908)231-4000
URL: http://www.windhover.com

9036 ■ Rich-Seapak Corporation
Customer Relations
PO Box 20670
McKinnon Airport Rd.
St. Simons Island, GA 31522
Ph: (912)638-5000
Free: 888-732-7251
URL: http://www.seapak.com

9037 ■ Rite Aid Corporation
Customer Service
PO Box 3165
Harrisburg, PA 17105
Ph: (401)825-3900
Free: 800-748-3243
Fax: (401)825-3587
URL: http://www.eckerd.com
Telecom. Svcs: Single check rebate phone number is (888)213-9920.

9038 ■ Safeway, Inc.
Customer Service Center
PO Box 29093
Phoenix, AZ 85038-9093
Ph: (925)467-3000
Free: 877—SAFEWAY
Fax: (623)869-4397
URL: http://www.safeway.com

9039 ■ Sara Lee Foods
Consumer Affairs
PO Box 756
Neenah, WI 54957-0756
Free: 800-328-2426
Fax: 888-514-5970
URL: http://www.saraleefoods.com

9040 ■ Sargento Foods, Inc.
Consumer Affairs
One Persnickety Pl.
Plymouth, WI 53073
Ph: (920)893-8484
Free: 800-243-3737

Fax: (920)893-8399
URL: http://www.sargento.com

9041 ■ Schering-Plough Health Care Products, Inc.
Consumer Relations
3030 Jackson Ave.
Memphis, TN 38151
Ph: (901)320-2010
Free: 800-842-4090
Fax: (901)320-2292
URL: http://www.schering-plough.com

9042 ■ Seneca Foods Corp.
3736 S. Main St.
Marian, NY 14505
Ph: (315)926-8100
Free: 800-872-1100
Fax: (315)926-8300
E-mail: consumer_affairs@senecafoods.com
URL: http://www.senecafoods.com

9043 ■ Shoney's, Inc.
Guest Relations
1727 Elm Hill Pike, Ste. B-1
Nashville, TN 37210
Ph: (615)391-5395
Free: 877-474-6639
Fax: (615)231-2621
URL: http://www.shoneys.com

9044 ■ Slim-Fast Foods Co.
Consumer Services Dept.
PO Box 3625
Englewood, NJ 07631-6065
Ph: (561)833-9920
Free: 877-375-4632
E-mail: support@slimfast.com
URL: http://www.slimfast.com

9045 ■ State Fair Foods, Inc.
Sara Lee Consumer Affairs
PO Box 756
Neenah, WI 54957-0756
Ph: (817)427-7700
Free: 800-261-4754
Fax: (817)427-7777
URL: http://www.statefairbrand.com

9046 ■ Stop & Shop Supermarket Co., Inc.
Consumer Affairs
PO Box 55888
Boston, MA 02205-5888
Free: 800-767-7772
Fax: (617)770-6033
URL: http://www.stopandshop.com

9047 ■ Sweet'N Low
Cumberland Packing Corp.
2 Cumberland St.
Brooklyn, NY 11205
Ph: (718)858-4200
Fax: (718)260-9017
URL: http://www.sweetnlow.com

9048 ■ The Swiss Colony, Inc.
Customer Service
1112 Seventh Ave.
Monroe, WI 53566
Ph: (608)324-4603
Free: 800-544-9036
Fax: (608)242-1001
E-mail: swisscolony@sccompanies.com
URL: http://www.swisscolony.com

9049 ■ Tetley USA, Inc.
Consumer Affairs Dept.
100 Commerce Dr.
PO Box 856

Shelton, CT 06484-0856
Ph: (203)929-9200
Free: 800-728-0084
Fax: (203)929-9263
E-mail: info@tetleyusa.com
URL: http://www.tetleyusa.com
Telecom. Svcs: Additional toll-free: (800)842-8545.

9050 ■ Togo's Eateries
Dunkin Brands
Consumer Service
130 Royall St.
Canton, MA 02021
Free: 800-859-5339
URL: http://www.togos.com

9051 ■ Tone Brothers, Inc.
2301 SE Tone's Dr.
Ankeny, IA 50021
Ph: (515)965-2711
Free: 800-247-5251
E-mail: spiceadvice@achfood.com
URL: http://www.spiceadvice.com

9052 ■ Tyson Foods
Consumer Relations
PO Box 2020
Springdale, AR 72765
Ph: (479)290-4714
Free: 800-233-6332
Fax: (501)290-7930
URL: http://www.tyson.com

9053 ■ UST
Public Relations
100 W. Putnam Ave.
Greenwich, CT 06830
Ph: (203)661-1100
Fax: (203)863-7235
URL: http://www.ustinc.com

9054 ■ Walgreen Co.
Customer Service
200 Wilmot Rd.
Deerfield, IL 60015
Ph: (847)914-2500
Free: 877-250-5823
Fax: (847)914-3105
E-mail: Customerservice@mail2.walgreen's.com
URL: http://www.walgreens.com

9055 ■ Weight Watchers Gourmet Food Co.
Consumer Affairs
11 Madison Ave.
New York, NY 10010
Ph: (212)817-4200
Free: 800-651-6000
E-mail: customerservice@weightwatchers.com
URL: http://www.weightwatchers.com

9056 ■ Wendy's International, Inc.
Consumer Relations
One Dave Thomas Blvd.
Dublin, OH 43017-0256
Ph: (614)764-3100
Free: 800-443-7266
Fax: (614)764-6707
URL: http://www.wendys.com

9057 ■ Wm. Wrigley Jr. Co.
Consumer Affairs
PO Box 3900
Peoria, IL 61614
Ph: (312)644-2121
Free: 800-974-4539
Fax: (312)644-0015
URL: http://www.wrigley.com

Internet Resources

9058 ■ Budget of the United States, Executive Office of the President
U.S. Government Printing Office (GPO)
732 N Capitol St. NW
Washington, DC 20401
Ph: (202)512-0132
Free: 888-293-6498
Fax: (202)512-1355
E-mail: gpoaccess@gpo.gov
URL: http://bookstore.gpo.gov

URL(s): www.access.gpo.gov/usbudget/index.html **Descr:** Contains a summary of the President's budget proposals from Fiscal Year 1997 to 2009, along with the following separately searchable documents: Supplement (Fiscal Year 2008 only); Analytical Perspectives; Historical Tables; Appendix; A Citizen's Guide to the Federal Budget; Principles of Budgeting for Capital Asset Acquisitions (Fiscal Year 2008 only); Includes the *Economic Report of the President, 2007*. **Type:** Full-text. **Fees:** Varies by product.

9059 ■ California Budget Project
1107 9th St., Ste. 310
Sacramento, CA 95814
Contact: Jean Ross, Exec.Dir.
Ph: (916)444-0500
Fax: (916)444-0172
E-mail: cbp@cbp.org

URL(s): www.cbp.org/ **Descr:** California Budget Project contains information on California's fiscal and economic policies, and links to sites of related interest to its membership. Users will find numerous articles on California fiscal issues. Sections on topics such as welfare reform, housing, education, health, and workforce/economic development link to publications that can be read online or downloaded in PDF format. **Type:** Full-text; Directory. **Updating freq.:** Regularly. **Fees:** Free. **Searching routines or searchable elements:** Search by keyword

9060 ■ Code of Federal Regulations
U.S. Government Printing Office (GPO)
732 N Capitol St. NW
Washington, DC 20401
Ph: (202)512-0132
Free: 888-293-6498
Fax: (202)512-1355
E-mail: gpoaccess@gpo.gov
URL: http://bookstore.gpo.gov

URL(s): www.gpoaccess.gov/cfr/index.html **Descr:** Contains the general and permanent rules published in the *Federal Register* by the Executive departments and agencies of the Federal Government. The database is organized into 50 titles which represent broad areas subject to Federal regulation, with each title divided into chapters commonly bearing the name of the issuing agency. Chapters are further subdivided into parts covering specific regulatory areas. **Type:** Full-text.

9061 ■ Concord Coalition
1011 Arlington Blvd., Ste. 300
Arlington, VA 22209
Contact: Robert Bixby, Exec.Dir.
Ph: (703)894-6222
Fax: (703)894-6231
E-mail: concordcoalition@concordcoalition.org
URL(s): www.concordcoalition.org/ **Descr:** The Concord Coalition is a nonpartisan, grassroots organization dedicated to eliminating federal budget deficits while ensuring Social Security, Medicare, and Medicaid are secure for all generations. You will find news on the struggle to reduce the federal budget deficit, congressional voting records, updates on outreach campaigns, links to bulletins describing difficult political situations and actions needed, and a listing of the Coalition's state chapters. The site is clear and easy to navigate, and contains information on its activities and links to sites of related interest to its membership. **Type:** Full-text; Directory. **Updating freq.:** As needed. **Fees:** Free. **Searching routines or searchable elements:** Searching is not available

9062 ■ Congressional Directory
U.S. Government Printing Office (GPO)
732 N Capitol St. NW
Washington, DC 20401
Ph: (202)512-1800
Free: 866-512-1800
Fax: (202)512-2104
E-mail: ContactCenter@gpo.gov
URL: http://bookstore.gpo.gov

URL(s): www.gpoaccess.gov/cdirectory/index.html **Descr:** Official directory of the U.S. Congress containing short bibliographies of each Member of the Senate and the House, listed by States and Districts respectively. Includes committee memberships, terms of service, administrative assistant and/or secretary, room and telephone number. Also lists officials of the courts, the military establishments and other Federal departments and agencies, including the D.C. Government; Governors of States and Territories; foreign diplomats; and members of the press, radio and television galleries. **Type:** Directory; Bibliographic.

9063 ■ Congressional Documents
U.S. Government Printing Office (GPO)
732 N Capitol St. NW
Washington, DC 20401
Ph: (202)512-1800
Free: 866-512-1800
Fax: (202)512-2104
E-mail: ContactCenter@gpo.gov
URL: http://bookstore.gpo.gov

URL(s): www.gpoaccess.gov/serialset/cdocuments/index.html **Descr:** Contains selected Senate, House, and treaty documents from the 104th Congress from 1995-96 to date and from 110th Congress from 2007-08. Includes only documents printed by the U.S. Government Printing Office (GPO). Also includes a list by report number all of the documents currently available. **Type:** Full-text. **Updating freq.:** As needed.

9064 ■ Congressional Record Index
U.S. Government Printing Office (GPO)
732 N Capitol St. NW
Washington, DC 20401
Ph: (202)512-1800
Free: 866-512-1800
Fax: (202)512-2104
E-mail: ContactCenter@gpo.gov
URL: http://bookstore.gpo.gov

URL(s): www.gpoaccess.gov/cri/index.html **Descr:** Indexes the daily issues of the *Congressional Record*. Includes the index, which lists individual, organizations, and topics mentioned in the *Congressional Record*; and History of Bills, which lists legislative actions reported in the *Congressional Record*. **Type:** Full-text; Directory; Bibliographic. **Updating freq.:** Daily.

9065 ■ Congressional Reports
U.S. Government Printing Office (GPO)
732 N Capitol St. NW
Washington, DC 20401
Ph: (202)512-1800
Free: 866-512-1800
Fax: (202)512-2104
E-mail: ContactCenter@gpo.gov
URL: http://bookstore.gpo.gov

URL(s): www.gpoaccess.gov/serialset/creports/index.html **Descr:** Contains Senate, House and executive reports from the 104th Congress (1995-96) to date. Includes a list of all of the current Congressional reports available by report number. **Type:** Full-text. **Updating freq.:** As needed.

9066 ■ Economic Indicators
U.S. Government Printing Office (GPO)
732 N Capitol St. NW
Washington, DC 20401
Ph: (202)512-1800
Free: 866-512-1800
Fax: (202)512-2104
E-mail: ContactCenter@gpo.gov
URL: http://bookstore.gpo.gov

URL(s): www.gpoaccess.gov/indicators/index.html **Descr:** Contains the U.S. economic data as prepared for the Joint Economic Committee by the Council of Economic Advisors. Provides economic information on prices, wages, production, business activity, purchasing power, credit, money and Federal finance. **Type:** Full-text; Numeric; Statistical. **Updating freq.:** Monthly.

9067 ■ Economic Report of the President
U.S. Government Printing Office (GPO)
732 N Capitol St. NW
Washington, DC 20401
Ph: (202)512-1800
Free: 866-512-1800
Fax: (202)512-2104

E-mail: ContactCenter@gpo.gov

URL: http://bookstore.gpo.gov

URL(s): www.gpoaccess.gov/eop/index.html **Descr:** Contains *The Economic Report of the President* which covers current and foreseeable trends and annual numerical goals concerning topics such as production, employment, real income, and Federal budget outlays; employment objectives for significant group of the labor force; annual numeric goals; and a program for carrying out program objectives. **Type:** Full-text.

9068 ■ Government Information Locator Service
U.S. Government Printing Office (GPO)
732 N Capitol St. NW
Washington, DC 20401
Ph: (202)512-1800
Free: 866-512-1800
Fax: (202)512-2104
E-mail: gpoaccess@gpo.gov
URL: http://bookstore.gpo.gov
URL(s): www.gpoaccess.gov/gils/index.html **Descr:** Contains information about publicly available Federal Government information resources, including electronic information resources. Identifies public information resources in the Federal Government; contains descriptive information about these resources; and aids in locating and obtaining the information. **Type:** Full-text.

Federal Government Agencies

9069 ■ Department of Defense Military Family Readiness Council
Under Sec. of Defense for Personnel & Readiness
1000 Defense Pentagon
Washington, DC 20301-1000
Contact: Col. Denise F. Dailey, Designated Fed.Off.
Ph: (703)697-2122
Fax: (703)614-6233
Staff: Support services are provided by the Department of Defense, through the Under Secretary of Defense for Personnel and Readiness. **Descr:** Council reviews and makes recommendations to the Secretary of Defense regarding the policy and plans required under 10 USC 1781b; monitors requirements for the support of military family readiness by the Department of Defense; and evaluates and assesses the effectiveness of the military family readiness programs and activities of the Department of Defense. **Mem:** Council comprises no more than 12 members, as follows: (1) The Under Secretary of Defense for Personnel and Readiness, as chair of the Council; one representative each of the Army, Navy, Marine Corps, and Air Force, appointed by the Secretary of Defense; three members appointed by the Secretary of Defense from among representatives of military family organizations, including military family organizations of families of members of the Active duty components and of families of members of the Reserve components; and the senior enlisted advisors of the Army, Navy, Marine Corps, and Air Force, or the spouse of a senior enlisted member from each of the Army, Navy, Marine Corps, and Air Force.

9070 ■ Director's Council of Public Representatives
Office of Communications & Public Liaison
Office of the Director
National Institutes of Health
One Center Dr., Bldg. 1, Rm. 344, MSC 0188
Bethesda, MD 20892-0188
Contact: Kelli L. Carrington, Exec.Sec.
Ph: (301)594-4575
Fax: (301)496-0017
E-mail: COPR1@palladianpartners.com
URL: http://copr.nih.gov/
Staff: Management and support services are provided by the Office of the Director, National Institutes of Health. Kelli L. Carrington, Officer of Public Liaison, serves as executive secretary. **Descr:** Council advises the Director, National Institutes of Health, on issues important to the development of

the NIH programmatic and research priorities. Council assists the NIH in enhancing the participation of the public in NIH activities, in increasing public understanding of the NIH and its programs, and in bringing important matters of public interest forward for discussion in public settings. **Mem:** Council consists of 21 members appointed by the Director, NIH, who also serves as chair. Members represent the various publics interested in NIH and include patients and family members of patients, health professionals, members of patient advocacy groups, volunteers in the health care field, scientists and students of science, communicators in health, medicine and science; individuals in public service, academia, and professional societies relating to the medical field. Members serve for overlapping terms of up to three years. **Pub:** Community Engagement Framework for Peer Review Guidance (October 2008); Community Engagement Framework for Development of Education/Training for Researchers (October 2008); Definitions of Public Participation and Community Engagement (October 2008); Report and Recommendations on Public Trust in Clinical Research (January 2005); Enhancing Public Input and Transparency in the National Institutes of Health Research Priority-Setting Process (April 2004); COPR Response to IOM Committee Report on the Organizational Structure of NIH (January 2004); annual report.

9071 ■ Farm Credit System
Farm Credit Administration
1501 Farm Credit Dr., Rm. 4243
McLean, VA 22102-5090
Contact: Christine D. Quinn, Staff Contact
Ph: (703)883-4000
Fax: (703)790-3260
E-mail: info-line@fca.gov
URL: http://www.fca.gov/info/index.html
Staff: Christine D. Quinn, Assistant Director, Congressional and Public Affairs, serves as staff contact. **Descr:** Farm Credit System (System) is a network of borrower-owned lending institutions and related service organizations serving all 50 states and the Commonwealth of Puerto Rico. These institutions specialize in providing credit and related services to farmers, ranchers, and producers or harvesters of aquatic products. Loans may also be made to finance the processing and marketing activities of these borrowers. In addition, loans may be made to rural homeowners, certain farm-related businesses, and agricultural, aquatic, and public utility cooperatives. **Mem:** System was composed of the following lending institutions: (1) Four Farm Credit Banks (FCBs) that provide loan funds to 80 Agricultural Credit Association (ACAs) and 11 Federal Land Credit Associations (FLCAs). ACAS make short-, intermediate-, and long-term loans, and FLCAs make long-term loans. (2) One Agricultural Credit Bank (ACB), which has the authority of an FCB and provides loan funds to five ACAs. In addition, the ACB makes loans of all kinds to agricultural, aquatic, and public utility cooperatives and is authorized to finance U.S. agricultural exports and provide international banking services for farmer-owned cooperatives. **Pub:** FCA Annual Reports on the Farm Credit System; Consolidated Reporting System Reports.

9072 ■ Federal Advisory Council (FAC)
Board of Governors
Federal Reserve System
20th St. & Constitution Ave. NW
Washington, DC 20551
Contact: James E. Annable, Sec.
Ph: (202)452-3204
Fax: (202)452-2611
URL: http://www.federalreserve.gov/aboutthefed/fac.htm
Staff: James Annable serves as secretary of the Council. **Descr:** Council advises and confers with the Board of Governors, Federal Reserve System with respect to general business conditions and makes recommendations concerning matters within the Board's jurisdiction. **Mem:** Council consists of twelve representatives of the banking industry, one

from each Federal Reserve district, selected by the Board of Directors of the Reserve Bank of each district. William Downe chairs the council. Members serve three one-year terms.

9073 ■ Federal Asbestos Task Force
National Program Chemicals Div.
Off. of Pollution Prevention & Toxics
Environmental Protection Agency
1200 Pennsylvania Ave. NW
Washington, DC 20460
Staff: Administrative support is provided by the Environmental Protection Agency's Office of Pollution Prevention and Toxics, Chemical Management Division. **Descr:** Task Force was established to coordinate programs administered by the federal government that control potential health hazards to the public from exposure to asbestos and other fibrous materials. It coordinates research, data gathering, and analyses; identifies areas for new research and analyzes the potential health hazards posed by exposure to asbestos and other fibrous materials. In addition, it develops recommendations concerning the identification of areas that should be of priority concern to the agencies represented on the Task Force, the need to consider revisions of existing health standards and regulations, the need to consider new regulatory actions, and the use of nonregulatory actions and educational materials. **Mem:** Task Force is comprised of representatives from federal departments and agencies with authority to regulate and conduct research on the health effects of asbestos and other fibrous materials, or with asbestos management needs. Members include the Environmental Protection Agency, the Occupational Safety and Health Administration, the Mine Safety and Health Administration, the National Cancer Institute, the Consumer Product Safety Commission, the Department of Housing and Urban Development, the Government Services Administration, the National Institute for Occupational Safety and Health, the Defense Logistics Agency, the Department of the Army, the Army Corp of Engineers and others.

9074 ■ Federal Interagency Coordinating Council
Off. of Special Education and Rehabilitative Services
Department of Education
550 12th St. SW, Rm. 5106
Washington, DC 20202
Contact: James Button, Staff Contact
Ph: (202)245-7287
Fax: (202)245-7637
Staff: James Button, Communications and Customer Service Team Director, Office of special Education and Rehabilitative Services, Department of Education, serves as staff contact. **Descr:** Council minimizes duplication across federal, state, and local agencies of programs and activities relating to early intervention services for infants and toddlers (birth to 3 years old) with disabilities and their families and preschool services for children (ages 3 through 5) with disabilities; ensures effective coordination of federal early intervention and preschool program, including federal technical assistance and support activities; and identifies gaps in federal agency programs and services and barriers to federal interagency cooperation. To meet these purposes, the Council seeks to identify areas of conflict, overlap, and omissions in interagency policies related to the provision of services to infants, toddlers, and preschoolers with disabilities; to develop and implement joint policy recommendations on issues related to infants, toddlers, and preschoolers that cut across federal agencies, including modifications of regulations to eliminate barriers to interagency programs and activities; and to coordinate the provision of technical assistance and dissemination of best practice information. **Mem:** Council consists of federal agency representatives from the Departments of Education, Health and Human Services, Agriculture, Defense, and Interior and the Social Security Administration, state and local program representatives and parents of young children with disabilities. Council is chaired by the

Assistant Secretary for Special Education and Rehabilitative Services and cochaired by a parent representative. **Rmks:** Council is also known as the Federal Interagency Coordinating Council for Young Children with Disabilities.

9075 ■ Federal Library and Information Center Committee (FLICC)

Federal Library & Information Network (FEDLINK)
Library of Congress
Adams Bldg.
101 Independence Ave. SE, Rm. 217
Washington, DC 20540-4935
Contact: Susan M. Tarr, Exec.Dir.
Ph: (202)707-4800
Fax: (202)707-4818
E-mail: flicc@loc.gov
URL: http://www.loc.gov/flicc/mmabout.html

Descr: Committee was established to make recommendations on federal library and information programs and procedures to federal agencies and others concerned with libraries and information centers. It coordinates cooperative activities and services among federal libraries and information centers and serves as a forum to consider (1) issues and policies that affect libraries and information centers, (2) needs and priorities in providing information services to the government and to the nation, and (3) efficient and cost-effective use of federal library and information resources and services. Committee fosters excellence in federal library and information services through interagency cooperation and provides guidance and direction for the Federal Library and Information Network (FEDLINK). **Mem:** Committee consists of the following permanent members: the Librarian of Congress, the Director of the National Agricultural Library, the Director of the National Library of Medicine, and one representative each of the Cabinet departments, the Administrative Offices of the U.S. Courts, the Defense Technical Information Center (Department of Defense), the Government Printing Office, the National Aeronautics and Space Administration, the National Archives and Records Service, the National Science Foundation, the National Technical Information Service (Department of Commerce), the Office of Science and Technical Information (Department of Energy), the Smithsonian Institution, the U.S. Supreme Court, and the U.S. Information Agency. Committee also comprises ten representatives of the federal government, appointed for two-year terms by the permanent members, and one representative each of the U.S. Air Force, the U.S. Navy, and the U.S. Army who are nonvoting members appointed for two-year terms by the permanent Department of Defense member. One representative each from the General Accounting Office, the General Services Administration, the U.S. Congress Joint Committee on Printing, the National Commission on Libraries and Information Science, and the Office of Management and Budget observe at Committee meetings. Deanna Marcum, Associate Librarian for Library Services, Library of Congress, chairs the Committee. **Pub:** FEDLINK Technical Notes; Summary of Proceedings: FLICC Forum on Federal Information Policies; Annual Report; Information Alerts; Annual FEDLINK Directory of Services.

9076 ■ Federal Open Market Committee

Federal Reserve System
20th St. & Constitution Ave. NW, Rm. 2000
Washington, DC 20551
Contact: Deborah J. Danker, Dep.Sec.
Ph: (202)452-3253
URL: http://www.federalreserve.gov/FOMC

Staff: Administrative support is provided by staff drawn from the Board of Governors and the Federal Reserve Banks. **Descr:** Committee is responsible for open market operations within the Federal Reserve System. It decides on changes to be made in the Federal Reserve System's portfolio of domestic securities and holdings of foreign currencies, thereby changing the volume of bank reserves and influencing the growth of money and credit and conditions in financial markets. Federal Reserve Banks, in their operations in the open market, are required by law to carry out the decisions of the Federal Open Market

Committee. In practice, all operations, including those involving foreign currencies, are conducted by the Federal Reserve Bank of New York. **Mem:** Committee consists of the 12 members including seven members of the Board of Governors of the Federal Reserve System; the president of the Federal Reserve Bank of New York; and four of the remaining eleven Reserve Bank presidents, who serve one-year terms on a rotating basis. The rotating seats are filled from the following four groups of Banks, one Bank president from each group: Boston, Philadelphia, and Richmond; Cleveland and Chicago; Atlanta, St. Louis, and Dallas; and Minneapolis, Kansas City, and San Francisco. Nonvoting Reserve Bank presidents attend the meetings of the Committee, participate in the discussions, and contribute to the Committee's assessment of the economy and policy options. The Chair of the Board of Governors, Federal Reserve System, Ben S. Bernanke, chairs the Committee; the president and chief executive officer of the Second District Federal Reserve Bank, William C. Dudley, serves as vice chair. **Pub:** Meetings and proceedings of the FOMC are available on the Committee website.

9077 ■ FNS Disaster Team

Food & Nutrition Service
Department of Agriculture
3101 Park Center Dr., Rm. 900
Alexandria, VA 22302
Contact: Brenda Lisi, Staff Contact
Ph: (703)305-2041
Fax: (703)305-2908
URL: http://www.fns.usda.gov/disasters/disasterteam.htm

Staff: Brenda Lisi, Director, Office of Emergency Management and Food Safety, serves as staff contact. **Descr:** Team coordinates overall disaster response activities of the Food Stamp Program and the Food Distribution Program (established in 1936 to make food available, in kind, to eligible recipients, including the elderly and children in the Child Care Food Program, the National School Lunch Program, the School Breakfast Program, the Special Milk Program for Children, and the Summer Food Service Program for Children). Team also expedites approval of disaster requests and policy clarifications, sends representatives to a disaster area as soon as possible after a disaster to assist State and local officials, and maintains liaison with the Federal Emergency Management Agency. **Mem:** Team comprises the following persons from the Food and Nutrition Service: the Administrator, the Associate Administrator, the Disaster Coordinator, the Deputy Administrator for the Food Stamp Program, the Deputy Administrator for Special Nutrition Programs, the Deputy Administrator for Consumer and Governmental Affairs, and the Directors of Public Information, Food Distribution Division and Program Development Division. **Rmks:** Team is also referred to as the FNS Headquarters +Disaster Team.

9078 ■ Homeland Security Information Network Advisory Council (HSINAC)

Office of Operations Coordination
Department of Homeland Security
Washington, DC 20528
Contact: Niklaus P. Welter, Designated Fed.Off.
Ph: (202)282-8336
Fax: (202)282-8806
URL: http://www.dhs.gov/xinfoshare/programs/gc_1156888108137.shtm

Descr: Council provides organizationally independent advice and recommendations to the leadership of the Department of Homeland Security, particularly the Director, Homeland Security Operations Center, on the requirements of end users within state, local, federal and tribal governments and the private sector regarding the Homeland Security Information Network. Council will address operational requirements necessary for effective information sharing and incident management; compatibility and interoperability between the information network and relevant information networks, databases, and resources of other state, local, federal, tribal, and private sector entities; and the security, integrity, and

safety of the information network resources and contents. **Mem:** Council is composed of not more than 20 members appointed by the Secretary for three-year terms. Members are outstanding within their specialty field and maintain the degree of experience and depth within their fields to ensure the Director and DHS leadership is informed of the needs and requirements of the information network users and communities of users. Membership includes representatives from state, tribal and local governments and the private sector, including: two members currently serving Homeland Security Advisors, three members currently serving state, tribal or local law enforcement, one member currently serving federal law enforcement, two members currently serving the fire service, two members currently serving public health, two members currently serving emergency managers, and two members from the private sector. Michael Milstead, representing local law enforcement, chairs the Council.

9079 ■ NASA Advisory Council

Office of External Relations
Mail Code 1
NASA Headquarters
Washington, DC 20546-0001
Contact: Paul Iademarco, Exec.Dir.
Ph: (202)358-1318
Fax: (202)358-3030
URL: http://www.hq.nasa.gov/office/oer/nac/

Staff: Paul Iademarco, Office of External Relations, NASA, serves as executive director and designated federal official. **Descr:** Council was established to consult with and advise the NASA Administrator with respect to plans for, work in progress on, and accomplishments of NASA's aeronautics and space programs. Council reviews and advises on agency and program objectives, policies, and strategies; the degree to which programs achieve their objectives and contribute to overall agency objectives; and the means for the effective coordination of NASA's interests and activities with academic, scientific, and engineering communities and institutions, and with the potential users of NASA's aerospace technologies such as commerce, industry, and state and local government agencies. **Mem:** Council is composed of 34 members, appointed by the NASA Administrator, who are interested or knowledgeable in NASA's aeronautics and space programs, including the chairs of the Council's standing committees. In addition, the Associate NASA Deputy Administrator serves as an ex-officio member. Members serve two-year terms, renewable at the discretion of the Administrator. Dr. Kenneth Ford, chairs the Council.

9080 ■ National Advisory Council on Drug Abuse

Office of Extramural Affairs
National Institute on Drug Abuse, NIH
6101 Executive Blvd., Rm. 211
Bethesda, MD 20892-9547
Contact: Teresa Levitin PhD, Exec.Sec.
Ph: (301)443-2755
Fax: (301)443-0538
URL: http://www.drugabuse.gov/about/organization/nacda/nacdahome.html

Staff: Teresa E. Levitin, PhD, Director, Office of Extramural Affairs, NIDA, National Institutes of Health, serves as designated federal official. **Descr:** Council advises, consults with, and makes recommendations to the Secretary; the Assistant Secretary for Health; the Director, NIH; and, the Director, NIDA, on program and policy matters in the field of drug abuse. Council recommends to the Secretary acceptance of conditional gifts for study, investigation, or research respecting drug abuse, and for the acquisition of grounds, or for the construction, equipping, or maintenance of facilities for the Institute. In addition, the Council makes recommendations to the Director of the Institute regarding research conducted at the Institute; reviews applications for grants and cooperative agreements for research and research training and recommends for approval applications for projects which show promise of making valuable contributions to human knowledge; and, reviews any grant, contract, or cooperative agreement proposed to be made or entered into by the Institute. The Council collects information as to studies which are being carried on in the United States or any other country in the field of drug abuse research and, with the approval of the Director of the Institute, makes available such information through appropriate publications for the benefit of public and private health entities, health professions personnel, and scientists, as well as for the information of the general public. **Mem:** Council consists of 18 members appointed by the Secretary and two nonvoting ex officio members: the Secretary, the Director, NIH, the Director, Department of Veterans Affairs, and the Assistant Secretary of Defense for Health Affairs (or their designees). Members are leading representatives of the health and scientific disciplines (including not less than two individuals who are leaders in the fields of public health and the behavioral or social sciences) relevant to the activities of the Institute. Six members are appointed by the Secretary from the general public and include leaders in the fields of public policy, law, health policy, economics, and management. Members serve for overlapping four-year terms. Nora D. Volkow, MD, Director, National Institute on Drug Abuse, chairs the Council. **Pub:** Annual Report.

9081 ■ National Advisory Council (NAC)
Small Business Admin.
409 3rd St. SW
Washington, DC 20416
Contact: Susan Walthall, Staff Contact
Ph: (202)205-6830
Fax: (202)481-5720
Staff: Administrative support is provided by the Small Business Administration. Susan Walthall, Director, Community Relations, serves as staff contact. **Descr:** Council provides advice, ideas, and diverse opinions on Small Business Administration programs and small business issues, including but not be limited to, the following areas government contracting, access to capital, export promotion, disaster assistance and technical assistance. **Mem:** Council is composed of a Chair; a vice-Chair; 10 regional representatives; 52 state appointments -- one from each state, Puerto Rico/Virgin Islands and the District of Columbia; 50 appointments based on population; 25 appointments of business and trade association representatives; and five appointments at large. John Lewis chairs the Board. **Rmks:** See also Small Business Administration District Advisory Councils.

9082 ■ National Research Advisory Council
Off. of Research & Development
Veterans Health Admin.
Dept. of Veterans Affairs
810 Vermont Ave. NW
Washington, DC 20420
Contact: Dr. Jay Freedman, Designated Fed.Off.
Ph: (202)461-1699
Fax: (202)254-0460
URL: http://www1.va.gov/advisory/page.cfm?pg=20
Staff: Support services are provided by the Office of Research and Development, Department of Veterans Affairs. Dr. Jay Freedman, Special Assistant to the Chief Research and Development Officer, serves as designated federal official. **Descr:** Council advises and makes recommendations to the Chief Research and Development Officer, the Under Secretary for Health, and the Secretary of Veterans Affairs concerning the nature and scope of R&D activities. Council will help to assure that the Office of Research and Development has an appropriate balance of fundamental, applied and outcomes medical research and that it utilizes rigorous scientific merit review processes thus ensuring the allocation of scarce public resources to proposals of the highest quality in areas of the greatest scientific opportunities. **Mem:** Council consists of approximately 12 members with knowledge of R&D issues in the VA, including at least one veteran. Members are knowledgeable in basic biomedical research, rehabilitation research and development, health services research and development, clinical research, geriatric care, primary care, special veterans population health issues, occupational and environ-

mental health research, mental health and behavioral research, and surgery. Richard P. Wenzel, MD, Chairman, Department of Internal Medicine, Virginia Commonwealth University, chairs the Council.

9083 ■ Postal Regulatory Commission (PRC)
901 New York Ave. NW, Ste. 200
Washington, DC 20268-0001
Contact: Ann Fisher, Staff Contact
Ph: (202)789-6800
Fax: (202)789-6891
E-mail: prc-pagr@prc.gov
URL: http://www.prc.gov
Staff: Ann Fisher, Director, Public Affairs and Government Relations, serves as staff contact. **Descr:** Commission promulgates and maintains rules and regulations, establishes procedures for a modern postal ratemaking system, and takes other actions necessary to carry out the Commission's obligations. Commission also has authority to consider formal complaints received from interested persons and act on appeals of the closing or consolidation of post offices. Commission has certain reporting obligations, including an annual compliance report and a report on universal postal service and the postal monopoly. **Mem:** Commission is composed of five commissioners; no more than three of whom represent the same political party. Members are appointed by the President of the United States with approval of the Senate, and serve six-year terms. Dan G. Blair chairs the Commission.

9084 ■ President's Export Council
Department of Commerce, Rm. 4043
1401 Constitution Ave. NW
Washington, DC 20230
Contact: J. Marc Chittum, Exec.Sec.
Ph: (202)482-1124
Fax: (202)482-4452
URL: http://ita.doc.gov/td/pec/
Descr: Council advises the President on matters relating to U.S. trade. It also surveys and evaluates the export expansion activities of the communities represented by the Council's membership; identifies and examines specific problems that business, industrial, and agricultural practices may cause for export trade; and encourages the business, industrial, and agricultural communities to enter into new foreign markets and to expand existing export programs. **Mem:** Council consists of 48 members as follows: not more than twenty-eight private sector members appointed by the President of the United States representing labor, industry, and agriculture; five Senators appointed by the President of the Senate; five Representatives appointed by the Speaker of the House; and ten executive branch agency heads. Members serve at the pleasure of the President and have no set term of office. J.W. Marriott Jr., Chairman/CEO, Marriott International Inc., chairs the Council. **Pub:** The World Is Our Market: Strategies for American Prosperity, The President's Export Council's Final Report to the President (July 2008). The Power to Help: U.S. Business Creating a Better Tomorrow; Export Controls; Trade Promotion Authority, the World Trade Organization and Free Trade Agreements; Services Statistics; U.S. Government Corporate Stewardship Efforts.

9085 ■ Regulatory Negotiation Project
Environmental Protection Agency
Ariel Rios Bldg.
1200 Pennsylvania Ave. NW
Washington, DC 20460

9086 ■ Uniform Formulary Beneficiary Advisory Panel
Tricare Management Activity
Pharmacy Operations
Skyline 5, Suite 810A
5111 Leesburg Pike
Falls Church, VA 22041-3206
Contact: Lt.Col. Thomas A. Bacon, Designated Fed. Off.
Ph: (703)681-2890
Fax: (703)681-1940

E-mail: baprequests@tma.osd.mil
URL: http://www.tricare.mil/pharmacy/bap/
Staff: Lt. Col. Thomas A. Bacon, Director, Department of Defense Pharmacy Utilization Management, serves as designated federal official. **Descr:** Panel reviews and comments on the development of the Uniform Formulary by the Department of Defense Pharmacy and Therapeutics Committee. **Mem:** Panel's membership includes twelve active duty and retired military personnel selected by the Military Coalition, retirees and an active duty family member selected by the National Military and Veteran's Alliance, persons knowledgeable in pharmaceuticals appointed by the Assistant Secretary of Defense (Health Affairs), and a Tricare Management Activity staff member. Robert Washington, Fleet Reserve Association, chairs the Panel.

9087 ■ U.S. Department of Veterans Affairs Veterans Benefits Administration Veterans Affairs Medical and Regional Office Center, Delaware
1601 Kirkwood Hwy.
Wilmington, DE 19805
Free: 800-827-1000
URL: http://www1.va.gov/directory/guide/allstate_flsh.asp?

9088 ■ U.S. Department of Veterans Affairs Veterans Benefits Administration Veterans Affairs Medical and Regional Office Center, Montana
3633 Veterans Dr.
PO Box 188
Fort Harrison, MT 59636
Free: 800-827-1000
URL: http://www1.va.gov/directory/guide/allstate_flsh.asp?

9089 ■ U.S. Department of Veterans Affairs Veterans Benefits Administration Veterans Affairs Medical and Regional Office Center, North Dakota
2101 Elm St.
Fargo, ND 58102-2417
Ph: (701)451-4600
Fax: (701)451-4690
URL: http://www1.va.gov/directory/guide/allstate_flsh.asp?

9090 ■ U.S. Department of Veterans Affairs Veterans Benefits Administration Veterans Affairs Medical and Regional Office Center, South Dakota
2501 W. 22nd St.
Sioux Falls, SD 57117
Contact: David Wherry
Ph: (605)333-6869
Free: 800-827-1000
Fax: (605)333-5316
URL: http://www1.va.gov/directory/guide/allstate_flsh.asp?

9091 ■ U.S. Department of Veterans Affairs Veterans Benefits Administration Veterans Affairs Medical Regional Office Center, Vermont
215 N. Main St.
White River Junction, VT 05009
Free: 800-827-1000
URL: http://www1.va.gov/directory/guide/allstate_flsh.asp?

9092 ■ U.S. Department of Veterans Affairs Veterans Benefits Administration Veterans Affairs Regional Office, Alabama
345 Perry Hill Rd.
Montgomery, AL 36109
Contact: William Rumph
Free: 800-827-1000
Fax: (334)213-3461
URL: http://www1.va.gov/directory/guide/allstate_flsh.asp?

9093 ■ U.S. Department of Veterans Affairs Veterans Benefits Administration Veterans Affairs Regional Office, Arizona
3333 N. Central Ave., Ste. 3026
Phoenix, AZ 85012

Free: 800-827-1000
URL: http://www1.va.gov/directory/guide/allstate_
flsh.asp?

**9094 ■ U.S. Department of Veterans Affairs
Veterans Benefits Administration
Veterans Affairs Regional Office, Arkansas**
2200 Fort Roots Dr., Bldg. 65
North Little Rock, AR 72114-1756
Free: 800-827-1000
URL: http://www1.va.gov/directory/guide/allstate_
flsh.asp?

**9095 ■ U.S. Department of Veterans Affairs
Veterans Benefits Administration
Veterans Affairs Regional Office, California**
8810 Rio San Diego Dr.
San Diego, CA 92108
Free: 800-827-1000
URL: http://www1.va.gov/directory/guide/allstate_
flsh.asp?

**9096 ■ U.S. Department of Veterans Affairs
Veterans Benefits Administration
Veterans Affairs Regional Office, California**
1301 Clay St., 12th Fl.
Oakland, CA 94612
Free: 800-827-1000
Fax: (510)637-6111
URL: http://www1.va.gov/directory/guide/allstate_
flsh.asp?

**9097 ■ U.S. Department of Veterans Affairs
Veterans Benefits Administration
Veterans Affairs Regional Office, California**
Federal Bldg.
11000 Wilshire Blvd.
Los Angeles, CA 90024
Free: 800-827-1000
URL: http://www1.va.gov/directory/guide/allstate_
flsh.asp?

**9098 ■ U.S. Department of Veterans Affairs
Veterans Benefits Administration
Veterans Affairs Regional Office, Colorado**
155 Van Gordon St.
Lakewood, CO 80228
Free: 800-827-1000
URL: http://www1.va.gov/directory/guide/allstate_
flsh.asp?

**9099 ■ U.S. Department of Veterans Affairs
Veterans Benefits Administration
Veterans Affairs Regional Office, Connecticut**
555 Willard Ave., Bldg. 2E
Newington, CT 06111
Contact: Nicholas Oshana, Service Officer
Ph: (860)594-6604
Free: 800-827-1000
URL: http://www1.va.gov/directory/guide/allstate_
flsh.asp?

**9100 ■ U.S. Department of Veterans Affairs
Veterans Benefits Administration
Veterans Affairs Regional Office, District of
Columbia**
1722 I Street, NW
Washington, DC 20421
Free: 800-827-1000
URL: http://www1.va.gov/directory/guide/allstate_
flsh.asp?

**9101 ■ U.S. Department of Veterans Affairs
Veterans Benefits Administration
Veterans Affairs Regional Office, Florida**
PO Box 1437
St. Petersburg, FL 33731
Contact: LeRoy Collins, Exec.Dir.
Ph: (727)319-7400
Free: 800-827-1000
URL: http://www1.va.gov/directory/guide/allstate_
flsh.asp?

**9102 ■ U.S. Department of Veterans Affairs
Veterans Benefits Administration
Veterans Affairs Regional Office, Georgia**
1700 Clairmont Rd.
Decatur, GA 30033

Free: 800-827-1000
URL: http://www1.va.gov/directory/guide/allstate_
flsh.asp?

**9103 ■ U.S. Department of Veterans Affairs
Veterans Benefits Administration
Veterans Affairs Regional Office, Idaho**
805 W. Franklin St.
Boise, ID 83702
URL: http://www1.va.gov/directory/guide/allstate_
flsh.asp?

**9104 ■ U.S. Department of Veterans Affairs
Veterans Benefits Administration
Veterans Affairs Regional Office, Illinois**
2122 W. Taylor St.
Chicago, IL 60612
Free: 800-827-1000
URL: http://www1.va.gov/directory/guide/allstate_
flsh.asp?

**9105 ■ U.S. Department of Veterans Affairs
Veterans Benefits Administration
Veterans Affairs Regional Office, Indiana**
575 N. Pennsylvania St.
Indianapolis, IN 46204
Free: 800-827-1000
URL: http://www1.va.gov/directory/guide/allstate_
flsh.asp?

**9106 ■ U.S. Department of Veterans Affairs
Veterans Benefits Administration
Veterans Affairs Regional Office and Insur-
ance Center, Pennsylvania**
5000 Wissahickon Ave.
Philadelphia, PA 19101
Free: 800-827-1000
URL: http://www1.va.gov/directory/guide/allstate_
flsh.asp?

**9107 ■ U.S. Department of Veterans Affairs
Veterans Benefits Administration
Veterans Affairs Regional Office, Iowa**
210 Walnut St.
Des Moines, IA 50309
Free: 800-827-1000
Fax: (515)323-7407
URL: http://www1.va.gov/directory/guide/allstate_
flsh.asp?

**9108 ■ U.S. Department of Veterans Affairs
Veterans Benefits Administration
Veterans Affairs Regional Office, Kansas**
5500 E. Kellogg
Wichita, KS 67211
Free: 800-827-1000
URL: http://www1.va.gov/directory/guide/allstate_
flsh.asp?

**9109 ■ U.S. Department of Veterans Affairs
Veterans Benefits Administration
Veterans Affairs Regional Office, Kentucky**
321 W. Main St., Ste. 390
Louisville, KY 40202
URL: http://www1.va.gov/directory/guide/allstate_
flsh.asp?

**9110 ■ U.S. Department of Veterans Affairs
Veterans Benefits Administration
Veterans Affairs Regional Office, Louisiana**
1250 Poydras St.
New Orleans, LA 70013
Free: 800-827-1000
URL: http://www1.va.gov/directory/guide/allstate_
flsh.asp?

**9111 ■ U.S. Department of Veterans Affairs
Veterans Benefits Administration
Veterans Affairs Regional Office, Maine**
One VA Center
Augusta, ME 04330-6795
Free: 800-827-1000
URL: http://www1.va.gov/directory/guide/allstate_
flsh.asp?

**9112 ■ U.S. Department of Veterans Affairs
Veterans Benefits Administration
Veterans Affairs Regional Office, Maryland**
31 Hopkins Plaza
Baltimore, MD 21201

Free: 800-827-1000
URL: http://www1.va.gov/directory/guide/allstate_
flsh.asp?

**9113 ■ U.S. Department of Veterans Affairs
Veterans Benefits Administration
Veterans Affairs Regional Office, Massachu-
setts**
JFK Federal Bldg.
Boston, MA 02203
Free: 800-827-1000
URL: http://www1.va.gov/directory/guide/allstate_
flsh.asp?

**9114 ■ U.S. Department of Veterans Affairs
Veterans Benefits Administration
Veterans Affairs Regional Office, Michigan**
Patrick V. McNamara Federal Bldg., 12th Fl.
477 Michigan Ave.
Detroit, MI 48226
Free: 800-827-1000
URL: http://www1.va.gov/directory/guide/allstate_
flsh.asp?

**9115 ■ U.S. Department of Veterans Affairs
Veterans Benefits Administration
Veterans Affairs Regional Office, Minnesota**
One Federal Dr. Bldg., Fort Snelling
St. Paul, MN 55111-4050
Contact: Clark Dyrud
Free: 800-827-1000
Fax: (612)970-5415
URL: http://www1.va.gov/directory/guide/allstate_
flsh.asp?

**9116 ■ U.S. Department of Veterans Affairs
Veterans Benefits Administration
Veterans Affairs Regional Office, Mississippi**
1600 E. Woodrow Wilson Ave.
Jackson, MS 39216
Contact: Betty B. Martin
Ph: (601)364-7000
Free: 800-827-1000
Fax: (601)364-7007
URL: http://www1.va.gov/directory/guide/allstate_
flsh.asp?

**9117 ■ U.S. Department of Veterans Affairs
Veterans Benefits Administration
Veterans Affairs Regional Office, Missouri**
400 S. 18th St.
St. Louis, MO 63103
Contact: Doug Meyer
Ph: (314)552-9885
Free: 800-827-1000
URL: http://www1.va.gov/directory/guide/allstate_
flsh.asp?

**9118 ■ U.S. Department of Veterans Affairs
Veterans Benefits Administration
Veterans Affairs Regional Office, Nebraska**
5631 S. 48th St.
Lincoln, NE 68516
Contact: Garry Morgan
Free: 800-827-1000
URL: http://www1.va.gov/directory/guide/allstate_
flsh.asp?

**9119 ■ U.S. Department of Veterans Affairs
Veterans Benefits Administration
Veterans Affairs Regional Office, Nevada**
5460 Reno Corporate Dr.
Reno, NV 89511
URL: http://www1.va.gov/directory/guide/allstate_
flsh.asp?

**9120 ■ U.S. Department of Veterans Affairs
Veterans Benefits Administration
Veterans Affairs Regional Office, New Hamp-
shire**
Norris Cotton Federal Bldg.
275 Chestnut St.
Manchester, NH 03101

Free: 800-827-1000
URL: http://www1.va.gov/directory/guide/allstate_
flsh.asp?

9121 ▪ U.S. Department of Veterans Affairs
Veterans Benefits Administration
Veterans Affairs Regional Office, New Jersey
20 Washington Pl.
Newark, NJ 07102
Free: 800-827-1000
URL: http://www1.va.gov/directory/guide/allstate_
flsh.asp?

9122 ▪ U.S. Department of Veterans Affairs
Veterans Benefits Administration
Veterans Affairs Regional Office, New Mexico
Dennis Chavez Federal Bldg.
500 Gold Ave., SW
Albuquerque, NM 87102
Free: 800-827-1000
URL: http://www1.va.gov/directory/guide/allstate_
flsh.asp?

9123 ▪ U.S. Department of Veterans Affairs
Veterans Benefits Administration
Veterans Affairs Regional Office, New York
245 W. Houston St.
New York, NY 10014
Free: 800-827-1000
Fax: (212)807-4024
URL: http://www1.va.gov/directory/guide/allstate_
flsh.asp?

9124 ▪ U.S. Department of Veterans Affairs
Veterans Benefits Administration
Veterans Affairs Regional Office, New York
130 S. Elmwood Ave.
Buffalo, NY 14202-2478
Free: 800-827-1000
Fax: (716)857-3396
URL: http://www1.va.gov/directory/guide/allstate_
flsh.asp?

9125 ▪ U.S. Department of Veterans Affairs
Veterans Benefits Administration
Veterans Affairs Regional Office, North Carolina
Federal Bldg.
251 N. Main St.
Winston-Salem, NC 27155
Free: 800-827-1000
URL: http://www1.va.gov/directory/guide/allstate_
flsh.asp?

9126 ▪ U.S. Department of Veterans Affairs
Veterans Benefits Administration
Veterans Affairs Regional Office, Ohio
Anthony J. Celebreeze Federal Bldg.
1240 E. 9th St.
Cleveland, OH 44199
Contact: William Bunkley, Program Coord.
Free: 800-827-1000
Fax: (216)522-8262
URL: http://www1.va.gov/directory/guide/allstate_
flsh.asp?

9127 ▪ U.S. Department of Veterans Affairs
Veterans Benefits Administration
Veterans Affairs Regional Office, Oklahoma
125 S. Main St.
Muskogee, OK 74401-7025
Free: 800-827-1000
Fax: (918)781-7509
URL: http://www1.va.gov/directory/guide/allstate_
flsh.asp?

9128 ▪ U.S. Department of Veterans Affairs
Veterans Benefits Administration
Veterans Affairs Regional Office, Oregon
1220 SW 3rd Ave.
Portland, OR 97204

Free: 800-827-1000
URL: http://www1.va.gov/directory/guide/allstate_
flsh.asp?

9129 ▪ U.S. Department of Veterans Affairs
Veterans Benefits Administration
Veterans Affairs Regional Office, Pennsylvania
1000 Liberty Ave.
Pittsburgh, PA 15222
Free: 800-827-1000
URL: http://www1.va.gov/directory/guide/allstate_
flsh.asp?

9130 ▪ U.S. Department of Veterans Affairs
Veterans Benefits Administration
Veterans Affairs Regional Office, Puerto Rico
150 Carlos Chardon Ave.
Hato Rey, PR 00918
Contact: Luis Ramos
Ph: (787)758-5760
Free: 800-827-1000
Fax: (787)772-7458
URL: http://www1.va.gov/directory/guide/allstate_
flsh.asp?

9131 ▪ U.S. Department of Veterans Affairs
Veterans Benefits Administration
Veterans Affairs Regional Office, Rhode Island
380 Westminster Mall
Providence, RI 02903
Free: 800-827-1000
URL: http://www1.va.gov/directory/guide/allstate_
flsh.asp?

9132 ▪ U.S. Department of Veterans Affairs
Veterans Benefits Administration
Veterans Affairs Regional Office, South Carolina
6437 Garners Ferry Rd.
Columbia, SC 29209
Contact: Phil Butler, Dir.
Ph: (803)255-4255
Free: 800-827-1000
URL: http://www1.va.gov/directory/guide/allstate_
flsh.asp?

9133 ▪ U.S. Department of Veterans Affairs
Veterans Benefits Administration
Veterans Affairs Regional Office, Tennessee
110 Ninth Ave., S.
Nashville, TN 37203
Free: 800-827-1000
URL: http://www1.va.gov/directory/guide/allstate_
flsh.asp?

Telecom. Svcs: TDD phone number is (800)829-4833.

9134 ▪ U.S. Department of Veterans Affairs
Veterans Benefits Administration
Veterans Affairs Regional Office, Texas
One Veterans Plaza
701 Clay Ave.
Waco, TX 76799
URL: http://www1.va.gov/directory/guide/allstate_
flsh.asp?

9135 ▪ U.S. Department of Veterans Affairs
Veterans Benefits Administration
Veterans Affairs Regional Office, Texas
6900 Almeda Rd.
Houston, TX 77030
Free: 800-827-1000
URL: http://www1.va.gov/directory/guide/allstate_
flsh.asp?

9136 ▪ U.S. Department of Veterans Affairs
Veterans Benefits Administration
Veterans Affairs Regional Office, Utah
550 Foothill Dr.
Salt Lake City, UT 84158
Ph: (801)326-2372

Free: 800-827-1000
URL: http://www1.va.gov/directory/guide/allstate_
flsh.asp?

9137 ▪ U.S. Department of Veterans Affairs
Veterans Benefits Administration
Veterans Affairs Regional Office, Virginia
210 Franklin Rd., SW
Roanoke, VA 24011
Contact: Bert Boyd, Dir.
Ph: (540)857-2396
Free: 800-827-1000
URL: http://www1.va.gov/directory/guide/allstate_
flsh.asp?

9138 ▪ U.S. Department of Veterans Affairs
Veterans Benefits Administration
Veterans Affairs Regional Office, Washington
Federal Bldg.
915 Second Ave.
Seattle, WA 98174
Free: 800-827-1000
URL: http://www1.va.gov/directory/guide/allstate_
flsh.asp?

9139 ▪ U.S. Department of Veterans Affairs
Veterans Benefits Administration
Veterans Affairs Regional Office, West Virginia
640 4th Ave.
Huntington, WV 25701
Contact: Mike Craig, Claims Mgr.
Ph: (304)399-9395
Free: 800-827-1000
Fax: (304)399-9355
URL: http://www1.va.gov/directory/guide/allstate_
flsh.asp?

9140 ▪ U.S. Department of Veterans Affairs
Veterans Benefits Administration
Veterans Affairs Regional Office, Wisconsin
5400 W. National Ave.
Milwaukee, WI 53214
Free: 800-827-1000
URL: http://www1.va.gov/directory/guide/allstate_
flsh.asp?

9141 ▪ U.S. Department of Veterans Affairs
Veterans Benefits Administration
Veterans Affairs Regional Office, Wyoming
2360 E. Pershing Blvd.
Cheyenne, WY 82001
Free: 800-827-1000
URL: http://www1.va.gov/directory/guide/allstate_
flsh.asp?

9142 ▪ U.S. Department of Veterans Affairs
Veterans Benefits Administration
Veterans Affairs Spark Matsunaga Medical and Regional Office Center, Hawaii
459 Patterson Rd., E-Wing
Honolulu, HI 96819-1522
Free: 800-827-1000
Fax: (808)433-0478
URL: http://www1.va.gov/directory/guide/allstate_
flsh.asp?

9143 ▪ U.S. Department of Veterans Affairs
Veterans Benefits Administration
Veterans Outpatient Clinic and Regional Office, Alaska
2925 Debarr Rd.
Anchorage, AK 99508-2989
Ph: (907)257-4700
Free: 800-827-1000
Fax: (907)257-6774
URL: http://www1.va.gov/directory/guide/allstate_
flsh.asp?

9144 ▪ U.S. Social Security Administration
Atlanta Region
61 Forsyth St., SW, Ste. 23T29
Atlanta, GA 30303-8907
Contact: Paul D. Barnes, Commnr.
Ph: (404)562-1182
Free: 800-772-1213

Fax: (404)562-1152
URL: http://www.ssa.gov/atlanta/index.htm

9145 ■ U.S. Social Security Administration Boston Region
JFK Federal Bldg., Rm. 1900
Boston, MA 02203
Contact: Manuel J. Vaz, Commnr.
Ph: (617)720-0438
Free: 800-772-1213
Fax: (617)565-2143
URL: http://www.ssa.gov/boston/index.htm

9146 ■ U.S. Social Security Administration Chicago Region
PO Box 8280
Chicago, IL 60680-8280
Contact: James F. Martin, Reg.Commnr.
Ph: (312)886-5252
Free: 800-772-1213
Fax: (312)886-3456
URL: http://www.ssa.gov/chicago/

9147 ■ U.S. Social Security Administration Dallas Southwest Region
1301 Young St., Rm. 630
Dallas, TX 75202-5433
Contact: Ramona Schuenemeyer, Reg.Comm.Dir.
Ph: (214)767-4201
Free: 800-772-1213
Fax: (214)767-8986
E-mail: wes.davis@ssa.gov
URL: http://www.ssa.gov/dallas/index.htm

9148 ■ U.S. Social Security Administration Denver Region
1961 Stout St., Rm. 1052
Federal Office Bldg.
Denver, CO 80294
Contact: Nancy Berryhill, Reg.Commnr.
Ph: (303)844-3674
Free: 800-772-1213
Fax: (303)844-6767
E-mail: Den.RPA@ssa.gov
URL: http://www.ssa.gov/denver/index.htm

9149 ■ U.S. Social Security Administration Kansas City Region
850 Nebraska
Kansas City, MO 66101
Contact: Michael W. Grochowski, Commnr.
Ph: (816)842-6423
Free: 800-772-1213
Fax: (816)842-4250
URL: http://www.ssa.gov/kc/

9150 ■ U.S. Social Security Administration New York Region
26 Federal Plaza, Rm. 40-120
New York, NY 10278
Contact: Beatrice M. Disman, Commnr.
Ph: (212)264-4036
Free: 800-772-1213
Fax: (212)264-1519
E-mail: NY.RPA@ssa.gov
URL: http://www.ssa.gov/ny/index.htm

9151 ■ U.S. Social Security Administration Philadelphia Region
Regional Communications Office, 7th Fl.
PO Box 8788
Philadelphia, PA 19101
Contact: Laurie Watkins, Reg.Commnr.
Ph: (215)597-4100
Free: 800-772-1213
Fax: (215)597-4183
URL: http://www.ssa.gov/phila/index.htm

9152 ■ U.S. Social Security Administration San Francisco Region
PO Box 4201
Richmond, CA 94804
Contact: Peter D. Spencer, Reg.Commnr.
Ph: (415)705-2000
Free: 800-772-1213
Fax: (415)705-2020

E-mail: SF.RPA@ssa.gov
URL: http://www.ssa.gov/sf/

9153 ■ U.S. Social Security Administration Seattle Region
Bank of America Tower, Ste. 2900
701 Fifth St., M/S 904
Seattle, WA 98104-7075
Contact: Don Schoening, Reg.Commnr.
Ph: (206)615-2236
Free: 800-772-1213
Fax: (206)615-2247
URL: http://www.ssa.gov/seattle/index.htm

9154 ■ White House Council on Women and Girls
Executive Office of the President
1600 Pennsylvania Ave. NW
Washington, DC 20500
Contact: Tina Tchen, Exec.Dir.
Staff: The Department of Commerce provides funding and administrative support. Tina Tchen, Director, Public Liaison, serves as Executive Director. **Descr:** Council was established to provide a coordinated federal response to issues that have a distinct impact on the lives of women and girls, including assisting women-owned businesses to compete internationally and working to increase the participation of women in the science, engineering, and technology workforce, and to ensure that federal programs and policies adequately take those impacts into account. Council is responsible for providing recommendations to the President on the effects of pending legislation and executive branch policy proposals; for suggesting changes to federal programs or policies to address issues of special importance to women and girls; for reviewing and recommending changes to policies that have a distinct impact on women in the federal workforce; and for assisting in the development of legislative and policy proposals of special importance to women and girls. In addition, Council will develop and submit to the President a federal interagency plan with recommendations for interagency action consistent with the goals of this order. The plan will include an assessment by each member executive department, agency, or office of the status and scope of its efforts to further the progress and advancement of women and girls. The assessment will include a report on the status of any offices or programs that have been created to develop, implement, or monitor targeted initiatives concerning women or girls. **Mem:** Council consists of the following members: the Senior Advisor and Assistant to the President for Intergovernmental Affairs and Public Liaison, as Chair; the Secretaries of State, the Treasury, Defense, the Interior, Agriculture, Commerce, Labor, Health and Human Services, Housing and Urban Development, Transportation, Energy, Education, Veterans Affairs, and Homeland Security; the Attorney General; the Representative of the United States of America to the United Nations; the United States Trade Representative; the Director of the Office of Management and Budget; the Administrator of the Environmental Protection Agency; the Chair of the Council of Economic Advisers; the Director of the Office of Personnel Management; the Administrator of the Small Business Administration; the Assistant to the President and Director of the Domestic Policy Council; the Assistant to the President for Economic Policy and Director the National Economic Council; and heads of such other executive branch departments, agencies, and offices as the President designates. Valerie Jarrett, Senior Advisor, chairs the Council.

Associations and Other Organizations

9155 ■ 9 to 5, National Association of Working Women
207 E Buffalo St., No. 211
Milwaukee, WI 53202
Contact: Donna Skenadore
Ph: (414)274-0925

Free: 800-522-0925
Fax: (414)272-2870
E-mail: 9to5@9to5.org
URL: http://www.9to5.org
Staff: 14. **Descr:** Represents women office workers. Seeks to build a national network of local office worker chapters that strives to gain better pay, proper use of office automation, opportunities for advancement, elimination of sex and race discrimination, and improved working conditions for women office workers. Works to introduce legislation or regulations at state level to protect video display terminal operators. Produces studies and research in areas such as reproductive hazards of Video Display Terminals (VDTs), automation's effect on clerical employment, family and medical leaves, and stress. Conducts annual summer school for working women. Maintains speakers' bureau. **Fnd:** 1973. **Mem:** 13000. **Local Groups:** 25. **Pub:** The 9 to 5 Guide to Combating Sexual Harassment; 9 to 5 Newsline (5/year); 9 to 5: Working Women's Guide to Office Survival; Videos.

9156 ■ Abstinence Clearinghouse
801 E 41st St.
Sioux Falls, SD 57105
Contact: Leslee J. Unruh, Pres./Founder
Ph: (605)335-3643
Free: 888-577-2966
E-mail: info@abstinence.net
URL: http://www.abstinence.net
Staff: 25. **Descr:** Promotes the practice of sexual abstinence through age-appropriate, factual and medically-accurate materials. **Fnd:** 1997. **Mem:** 1800. **Reg. Groups:** 1. **State Groups:** 1. **Local Groups:** 1. **Pub:** Abstinence Clearinghouse Directory of Abstinence Resources (semiannual); The Abstinence Network (quarterly).

9157 ■ Accuracy in Academia (AIA)
4455 Connecticut Ave. NW, Ste. 330
Washington, DC 20008
Contact: Malcolm A. Kline
Ph: (202)364-3085
Free: 800-787-0429
Fax: (202)364-4098
E-mail: mal.kline@academia.org
URL: http://www.academia.org
Staff: 2. **Descr:** Seeks accurate use of facts and historical information on college and university campuses. Investigates student reports of inaccurate information being communicated by classroom instructors, either through lectures or required reading materials. Publicizes such reports and cases of intolerance on campuses with respect to guest lecturers, students, and professors. Encourages universities to provide students with accurate descriptions of courses in catalogs. **Fnd:** 1985. **Mem:** 1200. **Pub:** Academic License: The War on Academic Freedom; Campus Report (monthly); Cop Killer - How Mumia Abu-Jamal Conned Millions Into Believing He Was Framed; Enemies Within.

9158 ■ American Academy of Wound Management (AAWM)
1155 15th St. NW, Ste. 500
Washington, DC 20005
Contact: Robert J. Snyder DPM, Pres.
Ph: (202)457-8408
Fax: (202)530-0659
E-mail: jmargeson@aawm.org
URL: http://www.aawm.org
Staff: 2. **Descr:** Medical practitioners representing numerous professional specialties with an interest in wound management. Seeks to advance the study and practice of wound treatment. Formulates standards of wound management practice; sponsors examinations and confers certification. Conducts continuing professional education programs. **Fnd:** 1995. **Mem:** 2000. **Pub:** AAWM Quarterly News Briefing (quarterly); National Registry of Board Certi-

fied Wound Specialists (annual); Brochure; Newsletter (quarterly).

9159 ■ American Association of Service Coordinators (AASC)
PO Box 1178
Powell, OH 43065-1178
Contact: Janice C. Monks LSW, Pres.
Ph: (614)848-5958
Fax: (614)848-5954
E-mail: info@servicecoordinator.org
URL: http://www.servicecoordinator.org

Descr: Advances the interests of the service coordinator profession. Increases awareness and understanding of service coordination and service-enriched housing. Provides guidance to members in the creation and maintenance of service-enhanced housing to families, the elderly and persons with disabilities. Strives to enhance the professionalism of its constituents through leadership, education, training, networking, and advocacy. **Fnd:** 1999. **Pub:** *AASC Insight* (quarterly).

9160 ■ American Combat Veterans of War (ACVOW)
3350 La Jolla Village Dr., Rm. 1580
San Diego, CA 92161
Contact: William Rider, Pres./CEO
Ph: (858)552-7501
E-mail: wrider@acvow.org
URL: http://www.acvow.org

Descr: Aims to guide warriors into living a productive and fulfilling life after combat. Provides a forum or safe zone for sharing combat and post combat experiences with other veterans. Helps warriors and their families in their transition from the mental stresses of combat to civilian life. Serves as an advocacy organization which draws attention and awareness to combat veterans suffering from posttraumatic stress. Assists veterans in navigating through government bureaucracies. **Fnd:** 2001.

9161 ■ American Ex-Prisoners of War (AX-POW)
3201 E Pioneer Pkwy., No. 40
Arlington, TX 76010-5396
Contact: Jim Clark
Ph: (817)649-2979
Fax: (817)649-0109
E-mail: hq@axpow.org
URL: http://www.axpow.org

Staff: 7. **Descr:** Former military prisoners of war and civilian internees. Seeks to: acquaint the public with the needs, problems, and handicaps associated with prisoners of war; promote research in the fields connected with injuries, diseases, and syndromes stemming from imprisonment; advocate and foster complete and effective reconditioning programs for ex-prisoners of war; foster patriotism and civic loyalty; encourage fraternal and historical activities. Conducts lobbying activities in Washington, DC to assist ex-POWs. Programs include: Veterans Administration Volunteer Service, a volunteer service in local VA medical centers; National Service Officers, which aids former POWs in filing claims with the VA and assists widows in filing claims; MedSearch, which compiles and distributes medical findings regarding ex-POWs to medical facilities, government agencies, and others. Maintains MedSearch files; local groups maintain museums. **Fnd:** 1942. **Mem:** 27000. **Reg. Groups:** 8. **State Groups:** 40. **Local Groups:** 300. **Pub:** *Ex-POW Bulletin* (11/year); *Medical Research Bulletin* (periodic).

9162 ■ American Fathers Coalition (AFC)
1718 M St. NW, Ste. 187
Washington, DC 20036
Contact: Dr. Linda Nielsen, Pres.
Free: 800-978-3237
Fax: (703)442-5313
E-mail: info@acfc.org
URL: http://www.acfc.org

Descr: Federal lobbying arm of the American Coali-

tion for Fathers and Children; promoting rights of fathers.

9163 ■ American Gulf War Veterans Association (AGWVA)
PO Box 85
Versailles, MO 65084
Contact: Joyce Riley von Kleist RN, Spokesperson
Ph: (573)378-6049
Free: 800-231-7631
Fax: (573)378-5998
E-mail: gmr@msn.com
URL: http://www.gulfwarvets.com/index.html

Descr: Works to assist Gulf War service members and families to obtain treatment for symptoms collectively known as the "Gulf War Illness". **Pub:** Articles.

9164 ■ American National Standards Institute (ANSI)
1819 L St. NW, 6th Fl.
Washington, DC 20036
Contact: Mr. Joe Bhatia, Pres./CEO
Ph: (202)293-8020
Fax: (202)293-9287
E-mail: info@ansi.org
URL: http://www.ansi.org

Staff: 75. **Descr:** Industrial firms, trade associations, technical societies, labor organizations, consumer organizations, and government agencies. Serves as clearinghouse for nationally coordinated voluntary standards for fields ranging from information technology to building construction. Gives status as American National Standards to standards developed by agreement from all groups concerned, in such areas as: definitions, terminology, symbols, and abbreviations; materials, performance characteristics, procedure, and methods of rating; methods of testing and analysis; size, weight, volume, and rating; practice, safety, health, and building construction. Provides information on foreign standards and represents United States interests in international standardization work. **Fnd:** 1918. **Mem:** 1000. **Pub:** *ANSI Reporter* (quarterly); *Catalog of American National Standards* (annual); *Standards Action* (weekly).

9165 ■ American Political Science Association (APSA)
1527 New Hampshire Ave. NW
Washington, DC 20036-1206
Contact: Michael A. Brintnall, Exec. Dir.
Ph: (202)483-2512
Fax: (202)483-2657
E-mail: apsa@apsanet.org
URL: http://www.apsanet.org

Staff: 25. **Descr:** College and university teachers of political science, public officials, research workers, and businessmen. Encourages the impartial study and promotes the development of the art and science of government. Develops research projects of public interest and educational programs for political scientists and journalists; seeks to improve the knowledge of and increase citizen participation in political and governmental affairs. Serves as clearinghouse for teaching and research positions in colleges, universities, and research bureaus in the U.S. and abroad and for positions open to political scientists in government and private business; conducts Congressional Fellowship Program. Conducts Committee on Professional Ethic, and Rights and Freedom. Offers placement service. **Fnd:** 1903. **Mem:** 15000. **Pub:** *American Political Science Review* (quarterly); *Personnel Service* (monthly); *Perspectives on Politics* (quarterly); *PS: Political Science and Politics* (quarterly).

9166 ■ American RehabACTion Network (ARAN)
PO Box 249
Boston, MA 02117
Contact: Jack Duncan
Ph: (617)720-2233
URL: http://www.americanrehabaction.org

Descr: Serves as a network of concerned citizens created to educate Congress and other policymakers and ordinary citizens about the worth, need and

success of the Public Vocational Rehabilitation Program. Focuses exclusively on those programs established and funded under the Rehabilitation Act. Provides assistance to persons with disabilities to become employed and live independently.

9167 ■ American Sons of Liberty (ASL)
1142 S Diamond Bar Blvd., Ste. 305
Diamond Bar, CA 91765
Contact: Gene S. Whitehead, Chm./Founder
E-mail: americansonsofliberty@americansonsofliberty.com
URL: http://www.americansonsofliberty.com

Staff: 5. **Descr:** Represents politically conservative individuals seeking to defend the U.S. Constitution. Concentrates efforts on the right to keep and bear arms; opposes gun control, including restrictions on semiautomatic weapons. Maintains that "mandatory gun registration precedes confiscation, which infringes upon individual freedom". Claims that "less than one percent of registered guns are used for illegal purposes, therefore gun control would constitute harassment of 99

of gun owners". Provides information on the right to bear arms. Compiles statistics; operates speakers' bureau. **Fnd:** 1998. **Mem:** 300. **Pub:** *Liberty Report* (quarterly); Journal (periodic).

9168 ■ Americans for Customary Weight and Measure (ACWM)
PO Box 24A
Wiscasset, ME 04578
Contact: Seaver W. Leslie, Pres.
URL: http://www.bwmaonline.com/ACWM.htm

Descr: Opposes metric conversion by advocating the protection and retention of the "inch-pound-quart" system of measurement. Strongly believes that there should not be U.S. government policy to promote or implement metrics and that conversion would cause widespread confusion, inflation, and an additional burden for U.S. exports. Encourages citizens to write to their representatives in Washington, DC calling for opposition to any metric conversion legislation introduced in Congress. Urges consumers to boycott all American goods produced or packaged in metric sizes. Disseminates information on metric conversion in America. Maintains speakers' bureau. Compiles statistics. **Fnd:** 1978. **Pub:** *Footprint*; *Why America Should Not Go Metric*.

9169 ■ AMVETS - American Veterans
4647 Forbes Blvd.
Lanham, MD 20706-4380
Contact: James B. King, Exec. Dir.
Ph: (301)459-9600
Free: 877-726-8387
Fax: (301)459-7924
E-mail: amvets@amvets.org
URL: http://www.amvets.org

Staff: 27. **Descr:** Works to promote world peace, preserve the American way of life and help veterans to help themselves; membership is open to anyone who is currently serving, or who has honorably served in the Armed Forces of the United States-to include the National Guard and Reserves-at anytime after September 15, 1940. Follows all veterans legislation on Capitol Hill and plays a key role in its enactment. Provides assistance to veterans with claims through a network of service offices through the United States. **Fnd:** 1944. **Mem:** 190000. **Reg. Groups:** 6. **State Groups:** 40. **Local Groups:** 1400. **Pub:** *American Veteran* (quarterly).

9170 ■ Angels 'n Camouflage (AnC)
PO Box 522
McArthur, OH 45651
Contact: Melissa Remy, Founder/CEO
E-mail: info@angelsncamouflage.org
URL: http://www.angelsncamouflage.org

Descr: Promotes the importance of supporting the veterans and deployed service members. Provides aid to all the military, active and retired. Supports veterans and troops through "Mail Call" and emergency assistance for those homeless or injured veterans from combat. **Fnd:** 2002. **Pub:** Newsletter.

9171 ■ Armed Females of America (AFA)
2702 E University Dr., Ste. 103
PMB 213
Mesa, AZ 85213
Contact: Carma Lewis, Exec. Dir.
Ph: (480)924-8202
E-mail: afa@armedfemalesofamerica.com
URL: http://www.armedfemalesofamerica.com
Descr: Defends rights to keep and bear arms guaranteed by U.S. Second Amendment of the Bill of Rights. **Pub:** Newsletter.

9172 ■ Association of Governmental Risk Pools (AGRiP)
PO Box J
Prague, OK 74864-1045
Contact: Harold Pumford, CEO
Ph: (405)567-2611
Fax: (405)567-3307
E-mail: hpumford@agrip.org
URL: http://www.agrip.org
Descr: Works to promote risk pooling as a practical extension of a public entity's obligation to be a good steward of public funds. Aims to act as an advocate for the advancement of intergovernmental pooling as the most appropriate risk financing mechanism for most public entities. Seeks to provide meaningful and significant educational and professional support for the governing bodies and employees of intergovernmental risk pools.

9173 ■ Association of Postal Officials of Canada (APOC)
28 Concourse Gate, Ste. 201
Ottawa, ON, Canada K2E 7T7
Contact: Francois Goulet, Pres.
Ph: (613)727-1310
Fax: (613)727-5354
E-mail: goulet@apoc-aopc.com
URL: http://www.apoc-aopc.com/Default.asp
Staff: 2. **Descr:** Postal officials. Seeks to obtain optimal conditions of employment for members. Represents members before government agencies and the public. **Mem:** 3400. **Reg. Groups:** 9. **Local Groups:** 29.

9174 ■ Better Government Association (BGA)
11 E Adams St., Ste. 608
Chicago, IL 60603
Contact: Mr. Jay E. Stewart, Exec. Dir.
Ph: (312)427-8330
Fax: (312)386-9203
E-mail: info@bettergov.org
URL: http://bettergov.org
Staff: 3. **Descr:** Individuals and corporations concerned with major public policy questions and dedicated to promoting efficient use of tax dollars and high standards of public service. Encourages a responsive and economical government by improving government institutions' performance and maintaining high ethical standards among public officials. Uses official documents, on-the-record interviews, undercover operations, and sophisticated techniques of investigative reporting to uncover corruption. Works closely with national and local media to expose waste, inefficiency, and corruption and to educate the public on the inner workings of the government. Sponsors intern programs for students in law and investigative research. **Fnd:** 1923. **Mem:** 1000. **Pub:** *Consumer's Guide to Long Term Health Care Facilities*; *Watch* (quarterly); Annual Report (annual).

9175 ■ Bold Brave Courageous
48 Bi State Plz.
Old Tappan, NJ 07675-7003
Contact: John N. Clemente Sr., Co-Founder
Ph: (201)512-1680
E-mail: boldbravec@boldbravecourageous.com
URL: http://www.boldbravecourageous.com
Descr: Offers support and services to American troops and their families. Promotes awareness of the needs of the injured servicemen and women in the

armed services. Raises funds for the benefit of the injured and wounded veterans. **Fnd:** 2004.

9176 ■ Bridges to Community
95 Croton Ave.
Ossining, NY 10562
Contact: Rusty Pederson, Interim Exec. Dir.
Ph: (914)923-2200
Fax: (914)923-8396
E-mail: info@bridgestocommunity.org
URL: http://www.bridgestocommunity.org
Descr: Seeks to build a spirit of friendship that transcends politics, economics and religion. Offers educational, service-oriented trips to materially poor areas. Takes volunteers to developing countries to work, learn, and reflect. **Fnd:** 1992. **Pub:** *Bridges* (quarterly).

9177 ■ British American Security Information Council (BASIC)
110 Maryland Ave. NE, Ste. 205
Washington, DC 20002
Contact: Paul Ingram, Exec. Dir.
Ph: (202)546-8055
Fax: (202)546-8056
E-mail: basicus@basicint.org
URL: http://www.basicint.org
Staff: 12. **Descr:** Promotes public awareness of defense, disarmament, military strategy, and nuclear policies of the United States and Britain. Facilitates exchange of information and analysis among military observers in the U.S. and Britain; sponsors research and educational programs. **Fnd:** 1987. **Pub:** Reports; Papers; Newsletter (bimonthly).

9178 ■ Call to Renewal
3333 14th St. NW, Ste. 200
Washington, DC 20010
Contact: Jim Wallis, CEO
Ph: (202)328-8842
Free: 800-714-7474
Fax: (202)328-8757
E-mail: sojourners@sojo.net
URL: http://www.calltorenewal.org
Descr: Aims to overcome poverty, dismantle racism, affirm life, rebuild family and community. Develops and supports connections between Evangelicals, mainline Protestants, Catholics, Historic Black Churches, Historic Peace Churches, Pentecostals and major faith based organizations. Provides a voice to influence national and local direction and public policy, and networks churches and faith-based organizations' leaders to build a movement to overcome poverty. **Pub:** *The Call* (monthly).

9179 ■ Castle Coalition
901 N Glebe Rd., Ste. 900
Arlington, VA 22203
Contact: Christina Walsh
Ph: (703)682-9320
Fax: (703)682-9321
E-mail: info@castlecoalition.org
URL: http://www.castlecoalition.org
Descr: Represents homeowners and citizen activists determined to fight eminent domain abuses.

9180 ■ Center of the American Experiment (CAE)
12 S 6th St., Ste. 1024
Minneapolis, MN 55402-1502
Contact: Ronald J. Schutz, Chm./CEO
Ph: (612)338-3605
Fax: (612)338-3621
E-mail: info@americanexperiment.org
URL: http://www.americanexperiment.org
Staff: 8. **Descr:** Political conservatives. Promotes "conservative common sense" in public policy. Serves as a clearinghouse on conservative approaches to social, economic, and political issues. Produces print and radio commentaries on current affairs; conducts research and educational programs; maintains speakers' bureau. **Fnd:** 1990. **Mem:** 5000.

Pub: *American Experiment Quarterly* (quarterly); Reports; Books.

9181 ■ Center for Policy Alternatives (CPA)
1875 Connecticut Ave. NW, Ste. 710
Washington, DC 20009
Contact: Tim McFeeley, Exec. Dir.
Ph: (202)387-6030
Free: 800-935-0699
Fax: (202)387-8529
E-mail: info@cfpa.org
URL: http://www.cfpa.org
Staff: 12. **Descr:** State and local government officials and community activists interested in restructuring public policies on the state and local level. Acts as national clearinghouse and forum for ideas on progressive public policy. Offers technical assistance to groups and individuals in developing model legislation. Focuses on critical issues of public policy affecting state and local governments such as: tax reform; voter registration; women's economic issues; investment of public employee pension funds; state and local economic development initiatives; housing; toxic and hazardous wastes; government reform; employment policy; and healthcare. **Fnd:** 1975. **Pub:** *Alternatives* (10/year); *Legislative Briefs* (periodic); *Policy Memos* (periodic); *Progressive Victories Report*; *Resources* (periodic); Bibliographies; Books; Manuals; Monographs; Reports; Annual Report (annual).

9182 ■ Center for Responsive Politics (CRP)
1101 14th St. NW, Ste. 1030
Washington, DC 20005-5635
Contact: Sheila Krumholz, Exec. Dir.
Ph: (202)857-0044
Fax: (202)857-7809
E-mail: info@crp.org
URL: http://www.opensecrets.org
Staff: 14. **Descr:** Research group that tracks money in politics, and its effect on elections and public policy. Conducts computer-based research on campaign finance issues for the news media, academics, activists, and the public at large. Aimed at creating a more educated voter, an involved citizenry and a more responsive government. **Fnd:** 1983. **Pub:** *The Big Picture*; *Congressional Preview Package*; *Digital Democracy*; *Do-It-Yourself Congressional Investigation Kit*; *Influence, Inc.*; *Sex, Money and Politics*; *Tracking the Cash*; *Who Paid for This Election?*; *Who's Paying*; *Why Do Donors Give?*.

9183 ■ Center for Science in the Public Interest (CSPI)
1875 Connecticut Ave. NW, Ste. 300
Washington, DC 20009
Contact: Michael F. Jacobson PhD, Sec.
Ph: (202)332-9110
Fax: (202)265-4954
E-mail: cspi@cspinet.org
URL: http://www.cspinet.org
Staff: 60. **Descr:** Scientists, nutrition educators, and lawyers concerned with the effects of science and technology on society. Past work has centered primarily on food safety and nutrition problems at the national level. Monitors current research and federal agencies that oversee food safety, trade, antibiotics, alcoholic beverages, biotechnology, and nutrition. Has initiated legal actions to ban unsafe and poorly tested food additives; has petitioned federal agencies for better food labeling and action against deceptive food advertising, especially advertising directed at children. Produces educational materials and attempts to influence policy decisions with regard to the American health and diet. **Fnd:** 1971. **Mem:** 9000000. **Pub:** *Nutrition Action HealthLetter* (10/year); Videos.

9184 ■ Center for Third World Organizing (CTWO)
1218 E 21st St.
Oakland, CA 94606
Contact: Danielle Mahones, Exec. Dir.
Ph: (510)533-7583
Fax: (510)533-0923
URL: http://www.ctwo.org

Staff: 17. **Descr:** Provides training and resources to sustain direct action organizing in communities of color in the United States. Provides issue analysis research and leads a national campaign for welfare rights. **Fnd:** 1980. **Local Groups:** 200. **Pub:** *CTWO Times* (bimonthly); *Directory of Church Funding Sources* (periodic); *Images of Color: A Guide to Media from and for Asian, Black, Latino, and Native American Communities; Issue Pac* (quarterly); *Surviving America: What You're Entitled to and How to Get it; Third Force* (bimonthly); Manuals.

9185 ■ Center for Women Veterans (CWV)
810 Vermont Ave. NW
Washington, DC 20420
Contact: Irene Trowell-Harris RN, Dir.
Ph: (202)273-6193
Fax: (202)273-7092
E-mail: 00w@va.gov
URL: http://www1.va.gov/womenvet
Descr: Strives to assure that women veterans receive benefits and services on a par with male veterans, that they encounter no discrimination, and are treated with respect and dignity.

9186 ■ Citizen Advocacy Center (CAC)
1400 16th St. NW, Ste. 101
Washington, DC 20036
Contact: David A. Swankin, Pres./CEO
Ph: (202)462-1174
Fax: (202)354-5372
E-mail: cac@cacenter.org
URL: http://www.cacenter.org
Descr: Provides training and support for public members serving on healthcare regulatory agencies, governing boards, and advisory bodies representing consumer interests. **Fnd:** 1987. **Pub:** *Citizen Advocacy News and Views* (quarterly); Reports.

9187 ■ Citizen Soldier (CS)
267 5th Ave., No. 901
New York, NY 10016
Contact: Tod Ensign, Dir.
Ph: (212)679-2250
Fax: (212)679-2252
E-mail: citizensoldier1@aol.com
URL: http://www.citizen-soldier.org
Staff: 2. **Descr:** Individuals concerned with military-civilian relationships within American society. Aims to help Vietnam War veterans who may have been harmed by highly toxic herbicides (including Agent Orange) that were used in Vietnam between 1962 and 1970. Works with veterans who were exposed to low-level radiation at Nevada and South Pacific A-bomb test sites and Persian Gulf War veterans suffering from unexplained chronic ailments. Represents GIs on active duty who are victims of military racism and/or sexism. Assists GIs who have been prosecuted or otherwise punished due to positive results on drug residue urine tests that CS believes to have been inaccurate because of defective laboratory work. Seeks to protect the rights of soldiers testing positive for the AIDS antibody. Advocates for veterans suffering from Persian Gulf Syndrome. Promotes a public service campaign to inform service members of their legal rights regarding the military's HIV testing program. Works with high school and college youths to address concerns on military recruiting practices. Maintains speakers' bureau. Advises GIs who wish alternatives to service in current Iraqi War. **Fnd:** 1969. **Mem:** 7000. **Pub:** *America's Military Today; Metal of Dishonor: Depleted Uranium Weapons.*

9188 ■ Citizen Works
PO Box 18478
Washington, DC 20036
Ph: (202)265-6164
Fax: (202)265-0182
E-mail: information@citizenworks.org
URL: http://www.citizenworks.org
Descr: Aims to advance justice by strengthening citizen participation in power. Provides people with the tools and opportunities to build democracy. Shares information, builds coalitions, and institutes improved mechanisms for banding activists. Recruits,

trains, and activates citizens to support progressive movement. **Fnd:** 2001. **Pub:** *Corporate Reform Weekly* (weekly); Annual Report.

9189 ■ Citizens Against Chemtrails U.S. (CACTUS)
PO Box 4653
Santa Fe, NM 87502
Contact: Clifford E. Carnicom
E-mail: cactusmailbox@yahoo.com
URL: http://www.geocities.com/cactusmailbox/CACTUS.html
Descr: Promotes grassroots group dedicated to halting the aerial spraying of America that is believed to have caused increased epidemics of death due to disease pathogens.

9190 ■ Citizens Against Government Waste (CAGW)
1301 Connecticut Ave. NW, Ste. 400
Washington, DC 20036
Contact: Thomas A. Schatz, Pres.
Ph: (202)467-5300
Fax: (202)467-4253
E-mail: membership@cagw.org
URL: http://www.cagw.org
Staff: 18. **Descr:** Serves as nonpartisan organization that seeks to educate the public, individuals in public administration, and Congress on eliminating waste, mismanagement, and inefficiency in government spending. Promotes the need to reduce the federal deficit and seeks to create public support for programs designed to reduce waste in spending. Seeks to expose cases of mismanagement that may occur at any level of government. Develops national advertising and distributes educational literature. Supports recommendations to improve government spending and operations, such as those proposed by the Grace Commission. **Fnd:** 1984. **Mem:** 600000. **Local Groups:** 436. **Pub:** *Congressional Pig Book Summary* (annual); *Government Wastewatch* (quarterly); *Prime Cuts* (annual).

9191 ■ Citizens for a Better America (CFABA)
PO Box 7647
Van Nuys, CA 91409-7647
Contact: Robert Colaco, Chm./Sr. Treas.
Ph: (818)757-1776
E-mail: hq@cfaba.org
URL: http://www.cfaba.org
Descr: Focuses on electing morality and values-based candidates from the very lowest to the very highest political positions all over the United States of America, who are pro-America first, pro-traditional family, pro-life, pro-Second Amendment, pro-USA sovereignty, pro-constitutional candidates. **Fnd:** 1992. **Pub:** *Commentary and News Release List; The Good News Report (TM)* (periodic); *Have you Been Lied To? (TM).*

9192 ■ Citizens Committee for the Right to Keep and Bear Arms (CCRKBA)
Liberty Park
12500 NE 10th Pl.
Bellevue, WA 98005
Contact: Alan M. Gottlieb, Chm.
Ph: (425)454-4911
Free: 800-486-6963
Fax: (425)451-3959
E-mail: adminforweb@ccrkba.org
URL: http://www.ccrkba.org
Staff: 40. **Descr:** Citizens interested in defending the Second Amendment; more than 150 members of Congress serve on the advisory board. Conducts educational and political activities, in-depth studies on gun legislation and lobbying activities. Sponsors speakers' bureau; compiles statistics. **Fnd:** 1971. **Mem:** 650000. **State Groups:** 50. **Local Groups:** 140. **Pub:** *Gottlieb-Tartaro Report* (monthly); *Gun Rights Fact Book - An Individual Right; Point Blank*

(monthly); *Politically Correct Guns; Politically Correct Hunting; The Rights of Gun Owners.*

9193 ■ Citizens Communications Center Project of the Institute for Public Representation (CCCPIPR)
600 New Jersey Ave. NW
Washington, DC 20001
Contact: Angela J. Campbell, Dir.
Ph: (202)662-9535
Fax: (202)662-9634
E-mail: gulcipr@law.georgetown.edu
URL: http://www.law.georgetown.edu/clinics/ipr/telecom.html
Staff: 3. **Descr:** Project of the Institute for Public Representation of the Georgetown University Law Center. Represents non-profit organizations before the FCC and courts. Seeks to open the regulatory process to participation by citizens. Aids citizens and groups without resources or technical skills in participating in the regulatory and decision-making process relating to communications policy. **Fnd:** 1971.

9194 ■ Citizens for Independent Public Broadcasting (CIPB)
901 Old Hickory Rd.
Pittsburgh, PA 15243
Contact: Jerold M. Starr, Exec. Dir.
Ph: (412)341-1967
Fax: (412)341-6533
E-mail: jmstarr@adelphia.net
URL: http://www.cipbonline.org
Descr: Promotes public broadcasting; supports local initiatives to democratize programming on local public broadcasting stations. Acts as a national clearinghouse. **Pub:** *Air Wars: The Fight to Reclaim Public Broadcasting; How to Make Public Broadcasting Accountable to Your Community: A Manual for Activists.*

9195 ■ Citizens' Research Foundation (CRF)
104 Moses Hall
Institute of Governmental Studies
University of California
Berkeley, CA 94720-2370
Contact: Gerald C. Lubenow, Program Off.
Ph: (510)642-5158
E-mail: jlubenow@uclink4.berkeley.edu
Staff: 3. **Descr:** Scholars, lawyers, and others interested in research on significant aspects of money in politics. Helps increase participation in democracy through better understanding of political finance. Current studies include: financing use of broadcasting facilities for political candidates; public funding of political campaigns; election reform at the federal and state levels; survey of the conditions of successful fundraising. **Fnd:** 1958. **Pub:** *Financing the 1996 Election* (quadrennial).

9196 ■ Citizens for Sensible Safeguards (CSS)
1742 Connecticut Ave. NW
Washington, DC 20009
Contact: Gary Bass, Exec. Dir.
Ph: (202)234-8494
Fax: (202)234-8584
URL: http://www.ombwatch.org/article/articleview/208/1/69
Descr: Coalition of over 300 organizations concerned with environmental, educational, civil rights, disability, health, and social services issues. Works to improve laws and safeguards that protect citizens and believes the federal government plays an important role in protecting the public interest. Opposes actions taken by Congress to dismantle federal laws and safeguards. Operates an information clearing house; coordinates lobbying and media efforts of member organizations. **Fnd:** 1995. **Mem:** 300. **Pub:** Reports.

9197 ■ Citizens for a Sound Economy (CSE)
1775 Pennsylvania Ave. NW, 11th Fl.
Washington, DC 20006-5805
Contact: Matt Kibbe, Pres./CEO
Ph: (202)783-3870
Free: 888-564-6273

Fax: (202)942-7649
E-mail: cse@cse.org
URL: http://cse.org

Staff: 100. **Descr:** Represents corporations and individuals. Strives to advance understanding of the market process in order to restore a sound economy. Seeks to return economic decision-making to citizens by reducing government interference in the economy. Supports tax reduction, federal spending restraints, international free trade, privatization, balanced budget, and deregulation. Distributes studies on economic issues; offers legislative internships; recruits, organizes, and trains citizens in public policy action. **Fnd:** 1984. **Mem:** 250000. **State Groups:** 15. **Pub:** *Capitol Comment* (periodic); *Class Actions: America's New Boom Industry*; *Clinton's Social Security Fix*; *Fiscal Discipline Should Begin at Home*; *Flat Tax Equals Justice Under the Law*; *Giving Parents a Voice: Florida*; *Issue Analysis* (periodic); *Microsoft and Monopoly*; *Tying Regulation to Reality.*

9198 ▪ Citizens United for Alternatives to the Death Penalty (CUADP)
PMB 335
2603 Dr. Martin Luther King Jr. Hwy.
Gainesville, FL 32609
Contact: Abraham J. Bonowitz, Dir./Co-Founder
Free: 800-973-6548
E-mail: cuadp@cuadp.org
URL: http://www.cuadp.org

Staff: 1. **Descr:** Aims to abolish the death penalty in the U.S. through aggressive campaigns of public education and the promotion of tactical grassroots activism. **Fnd:** 1997. **Mem:** 100000000.

9199 ▪ Citizens United Resisting Euthanasia (CURE)
303 Truman St.
Berkeley Springs, WV 25411
Contact:Fr. Paul Marx, Adviser
Ph: (304)258-5433
E-mail: cureltd@verizon.net
URL: http://mysite.verizon.net/cureltd/index.html

Descr: Individuals "bound together in a common cause: uncompromising opposition to euthanasia". Promotes increased awareness of alternatives to voluntary euthanasia. Provides practical help to families besieged by euthanasia practitioners; makes available legal assistance to individuals contemplating voluntary euthanasia; conducts research; lobbies to strengthen statutes criminalizing euthanasia. **Fnd:** 1981. **Pub:** *Life Matters*; Reports; Articles.

9200 ▪ Coalition Against Bigger Trucks (CABT)
901 N Pitt St., Ste. 310
Alexandria, VA 22314
Ph: (703)535-3131
Free: 888-CAB-T123
Fax: (703)535-3322
E-mail: info@cabt.org
URL: http://www.cabt.org

Descr: Individuals and organizations. Opposes use of longer and heavier trucks on public roads. Conducts grass roots campaigns to insure more effective regulation of truck transport; works to improve the safety of public roads and highways; sponsors educational programs; lobbies government agencies on highway safety and trucking regulation issues. **Pub:** Newsletter.

9201 ▪ Coalition on Human Needs (CHN)
1120 Connecticut Ave. NW, Ste. 910
Washington, DC 20036
Contact: Deborah Weinstein, Exec. Dir.
Ph: (202)223-2532
Fax: (202)223-2538
E-mail: info@chn.org
URL: http://www.chn.org

Staff: 3. **Descr:** National advocacy organizations working in areas such as federal budget and tax policy, low wage employment, and welfare policy. Works for adequate federal funding for human needs and income maintenance programs. Promotes public policies which address the needs of low-income and other vulnerable populations. Publishes legislative

update on issues affecting low-income Americans. **Fnd:** 1981. **Mem:** 100. **Pub:** *The Human Needs Report* (biweekly); *Issue Briefs.*

9202 ▪ Coalition to Reduce Nuclear Dangers
110 Maryland Ave. NE, Ste. 505
Washington, DC 20002
Ph: (202)546-0795
Fax: (202)546-7970
E-mail: clw@clw.org
URL: http://www.clw.org/pub/clw/coalition

Descr: Seeks to develop a step-by-step program to reduce the dangers of nuclear weapons and prevent the emergence of new nuclear threats. **Pub:** Reports.

9203 ▪ Committee on Public Doublespeak (CPD)
1111 W Kenyon Rd.
Urbana, IL 61801-1096
Contact: Linda Walters, Admin. Liaison
Ph: (217)328-3870
Free: 800-369-6283
Fax: (217)328-0977
E-mail: public_info@ncte.org

Descr: A committee of the National Council of Teachers of English, comprising NCTE members who are concerned with and interested in the study of public doublespeak and who are willing to speak or write on this subject. Works to study dishonest and inhumane uses of language, especially as transmitted through the mass media. Brings these misuses to public attention. Proposes classroom techniques for the study of public language. **Fnd:** 1972. **Mem:** 10.

9204 ▪ Committee for a Responsible Federal Budget (CRFB)
1630 Connecticut Ave. NW, 7th Fl.
Washington, DC 20009
Contact: Maya MacGuineas, Pres.
Ph: (202)986-6599
Fax: (202)986-3696
E-mail: crfb@newamerica.net
URL: http://www.crfb.org

Staff: 3. **Descr:** Educates the public regarding the budget process and issues that have significant fiscal policy impact. Sponsors analysis and research, conducts educational symposia, and prepares and distributes educational materials to Congress, the Administration, the media, and the public. Consists of former members of Congress, former directors of the Office of Management and Budget and the Congressional Budget Office, and other economic and fiscal policy experts. **Fnd:** 1981. **Mem:** 130.

9205 ▪ Concerned Citizens for Racially Free America (CCfRFA)
PO Box 320497
Birmingham, AL 35232-0497
Contact: Richard A. Peters, Dir.
Ph: (205)856-0481
Fax: (205)856-2244
E-mail: civilrights@bellsouth.net
URL: http://www.concernedcitizensnews.org

Staff: 11. **Descr:** Individuals and organizations. Promotes respect for the rights of the individual and the rule of law; opposes racial discrimination. Provides consulting and legal services to individuals whose rights have been violated. **Fnd:** 1992. **State Groups:** 10. **Local Groups:** 3. **Pub:** *NEWS Magazine* (quarterly).

9206 ▪ Consuming Industries Trade Action Coalition (CITAC)
2000 L St. NW, Ste. 835
Washington, DC 20036
Contact: Steve Alexander, Exec. Dir.
Ph: (202)316-3046
E-mail: info@citac.info
URL: http://www.citac.info

Descr: Represents manufacturers and organizations committed to promoting a trade arena where U.S. consuming industries and their workers have access to global markets for imports that enhance the international competitiveness of American firms. Seeks to increase the involvement and influence of

consuming industries in the trade debate. Provides education and awareness programs for consuming industries and their employees. **Pub:** *Director's Report.*

9207 ▪ Council of Citizens With Low Vision International (CCLVI)
1155 15th St. NW, Ste. 1004
Washington, DC 20005
Contact: John Horst, Pres.
Free: 800-733-2258
E-mail: webmaster@cclvi.org
URL: http://www.cclvi.org

Descr: Partially sighted and low-vision individuals, their families, and professional workers. Provides a vehicle through which partially sighted people may voice their needs, preferences, and interests. Promotes the concept that partially sighted and low-vision individuals are not blind and that they have the right to maximize the use of residual vision through the use of any visual aid, service, or technology. Keeps abreast of all developments benefiting partially sighted persons. Promotes educational, engineering, medical, rehabilitative, scientific, and social research that facilitates the lives of individuals with residual vision. Supports the development of pre-service professional training programs for the establishment and expansion of multidisciplinary low-vision services. Strives to educate the public about the existence, capabilities, and needs of such individuals. Establishes outreach programs to insure access to available services for partially sighted persons. Maintains speakers' bureau. **Fnd:** 1979. **Pub:** *Vision Access* (quarterly).

9208 ▪ Council of Volunteer Americans (CVA)
PO Box 1222
Sterling, VA 20167
Contact: Jack Clayton, VP
Ph: (703)379-9188
E-mail: info@conservativeaction.org
URL: http://conservativeaction.org

Staff: 5. **Descr:** Individuals opposed to the policies of former President Bill Clinton and Senator Hillary Clinton. Seeks to "hold the Clinton White House accountable" for what the group believes are "numerous improprieties and wrongdoings". Advocates the "investigation, impeachment and prosecution of former President Clinton and Senator Hillary Clinton and other administration officials." Operates Clinton Investigative Commission. Conducts petition drives, rallies, and protests against liberal policies in the White House. **Fnd:** 1981. **Mem:** 100000. **Pub:** *Report to Congress* (monthly).

9209 ▪ The Creative Coalition (TCC)
1100 Ave. of the Americas, 3rd Fl.
New York, NY 10036
Contact: Robin Bronk, Exec. Dir.
Ph: (212)512-5876
Fax: (212)512-5023
E-mail: info@thecreativecoalition.org
URL: http://www.thecreativecoalition.org

Descr: Actors, writers, directors and other arts and entertainment professionals. Aims to educate members about social and political issues, particularly in the areas of the First Amendment, arts advocacy and public education. **Fnd:** 1989.

9210 ▪ Demand Response and Smart Grid Coalition (DRSG)
1615 M St. NW
Washington, DC 20036
Contact: Dan Delurey
Ph: (202)296-1686
E-mail: info@drsgcoalition.org
URL: http://www.drsgcoalition.org

Descr: Represents companies that provide products and services in the areas of demand response, energy storage, smart metering and other smart grid technologies and services. Provides customer information and options for managing their electricity use.

9211 ■ Desert Storm Veterans Association
2425 Wilson Blvd.
Arlington, VA 22201
Contact: Arthur R. Hotop, Chm., Scholarship Committee
Ph: (703)604-6565
E-mail: viicorpsdsva@aol.com
URL: http://www.desertstormvets.org
Descr: Assists the families of soldiers who died as a result of participation in Operations Desert Shield/Desert Storm. Preserves and fosters camaraderie among Desert Storm veterans. Provides a means to preserve the history of VII Corps during Operations Desert Shield/Desert Storm. **Pub:** *Desert Dispatch* (quarterly).

9212 ■ Disabled American Veterans (DAV)
PO Box 14301
Cincinnati, OH 45250-0301
Contact: Arthur H. Wilson, CEO
Ph: (859)441-7300
Free: 877-426-2838
Fax: (859)442-2090
E-mail: feedback@davmail.org
URL: http://www.dav.org
Staff: 631. **Descr:** Veterans with service-connected disabilities. Major activity is service to disabled veterans and their families. Employs approximately 260 National Service Officers in Department of Veterans Affairs (VA) offices in 50 states and Puerto Rico to act as free-of-charge attorneys-in-fact, counseling and processing veterans' claims for compensation and benefits. Provides services in areas including disaster relief, employment, legislation, advocacy, and transportation. **Fnd:** 1920. **Mem:** 1200000. **State Groups:** 52. **Local Groups:** 1940. **Pub:** *DAV Magazine* (bimonthly).

9213 ■ Economic Success Clearinghouse
1401 New York Ave. NW, Ste. 800
Washington, DC 20005
Contact: Cheryl D. Hayes, Pres./CEO
Ph: (202)628-4200
Fax: (202)628-1293
E-mail: info@financeproject.org
URL: http://www.financeproject.org/index.cfm?page=24
Descr: Provides information to individuals and organizations on policy choices, practices, program and financial data, funding sources, federal and state legislation and plans, program and management tools, and technical assistance to develop and implement welfare reforms to reduce dependency and promote the well-being of children and families. Offers website with access to more than 9,000 links on more than 400 websites. Maintains a clearinghouse of welfare reform-related information, policy analysis, and technical assistance resources; maintains a database containing information on organizations, experts, publications, state and local initiatives, technical assistance service offerings, and Web sites. **Pub:** *Issue Notes; Resources for Welfare Decisions.*

9214 ■ Empowerment Society of the United States of America (ESUSA)
PO Box 51
Oyster Bay, NY 11771
Contact: Pamela Pfeiffer CEC, Founder/Pres.
Ph: (516)459-4735
E-mail: pam@empowermentsociety.org
URL: http://www.empowermentsociety.org
Descr: Works to assist women of the United States Armed Forces. Provides professional life coaching programs, overseas support and oral histories.

9215 ■ Enterprise Community Partners
10227 Wincopin Cir.
Columbia, MD 21044
Contact: Doris W. Koo, Pres./CEO
Free: 800-624-4298
Fax: (410)964-1918
URL: http://www.enterprisecommunity.org

Descr: Helps rebuild communities. Works with community-based organizations and other partners to provide low-income people with affordable housing, safer streets and access to jobs and child care. **Fnd:** 1982. **Local Groups:** 1900. **Pub:** *Enterprise Annual Report; Enterprise Quarterly* (quarterly).

9216 ■ Equality Federation
2069A Mission St.
San Francisco, CA 94110
Contact: Toni Broaddus, Exec. Dir.
Ph: (415)252-0510
Free: 877-790-2674
Fax: (775)535-8575
E-mail: info@equalityfederation.org
URL: http://www.equalityfederation.org
Descr: Represents state-based lesbian, gay, bisexual and transgender advocacy organizations. Works to achieve equality for LGBT people in every state and territory by building strong and sustainable organizations. **Fnd:** 1997.

9217 ■ Farmer-Veteran Coalition (FVC)
221 G St., Ste. 204
Davis, CA 95616
Contact: Michael O'Gorman, Exec. Dir.
Ph: (530)756-6555
E-mail: info@farmvetco.org
URL: http://www.farmvetco.org
Descr: Seeks to help returning veterans find employment, training and places to heal on America's farms. Aims to mobilize the food and farming community to create healthy and viable futures for America's veterans.

9218 ■ Farmers Market Coalition (FMC)
PO Box 4089
Martinsburg, WV 25402
Contact: Stacy Miller, Pres.
Ph: (304)263-6396
Free: 877-362-0553
E-mail: info@farmersmarketcoalition.org
URL: http://www.farmersmarketcoalition.org
Descr: Aims to strengthen farmers markets across the United States so that they can serve as community assets while providing real income opportunities for farmers. Seeks to serve as an information center for farmers markets. Works to promote farmers markets to the public. Strives to develop and provide educational programming and networking opportunities for farmers market managers and farmers market vendors. **Pub:** *the market beet.*

9219 ■ Federal Superannuates National Association (FSNA)
1052 St. Laurent Blvd.
Ottawa, ON, Canada K1K 3B4
Contact: Stan Hrabarchuk, Pres.
Ph: (613)745-2559
Fax: (613)745-5457
E-mail: info@fsna.com
URL: http://www.fsna.com
Descr: Retired federal government employees. Seeks to insure availability and quality of benefits available to federal retirees. Represents members' interests before government agencies; conducts educational and social programs; facilitates communication and camaraderie among members. **Fnd:** 1963. **Mem:** 155000.

9220 ■ Foundation for American Communications (FACS)
85 S Grand Ave.
Pasadena, CA 91105
Contact: Robert E. Wood, Pres.
Ph: (626)584-0010
Fax: (626)584-0627
URL: http://www.facsnet.org
Staff: 7. **Descr:** Seeks to improve mutual understanding between major American institutions and the news media. Works with individuals, associations, organizations, corporations, and institutions at every point in the communication process. Sponsors short-term professional education programs for the working journalist (from both broadcast and print media) who wants to improve his or her understand-

ing of important issues including economics, business, energy, technology, the environment, ethics, law, corporate and governmental practices, and foreign affairs. Conducts Business/News Media Conferences involving business executives and journalists in an effort to improve the participants' understanding of the news media and its relationship to corporate credibility. Organizes communications programs for individual corporations. Sponsors communications programs for non-profit organizations. **Fnd:** 1976. **Mem:** 19. **Pub:** *Communications Conference Workbook; Human Heart Replacement; Journalism Ethics; Knowledge, Resources and Perspectives; Media Resource Guide; Reporting on Risk: A Journalist's Handbook on Environmental Risk Assessment; Report; Books.*

9221 ■ Freedom of Information Clearinghouse (FOIC)
Public Citizen Litigation Group
1600 20th St. NW
Washington, DC 20009
Ph: (202)588-7783
E-mail: foia@citizen.org
URL: http://www.citizen.org/litigation/free5Finfo
Descr: A program of the Center for the Study of Responsive Law. Provides legal and technical assistance to public interest groups, citizens, and the press in the effective use of laws granting a right of access to government-held information; also litigates cases under the federal Freedom of Information Act and other access laws in an attempt to reduce illegal secrecy and to secure judicial interpretations in areas where these acts are unclear. Testifies before the U.S. Congress and answers individual requests about how to get information from government agencies. **Fnd:** 1972. **Pub:** *The Freedom of Information Act: A User's Guide; Litigation Under the Federal Open Government Laws.*

9222 ■ Friends Committee on National Legislation (FCNL)
245 2nd St. NE
Washington, DC 20002-5761
Contact: Joe Volk, Exec. Sec.
Ph: (202)547-6000
Free: 800-630-1330
Fax: (202)547-6019
E-mail: fcnl@fcnl.org
URL: http://www.fcnl.org
Staff: 21. **Descr:** Quaker lobby in the public interest. Seeks to bring the concerns, experiences, and testimonies of the Religious Society of Friends to bear on policy decisions. Advocates for social and economic justice committees. Compiles statistics. **Fnd:** 1943. **Mem:** 8000. **Pub:** *Action Bulletin* (periodic); *Indian Report* (quarterly); *Perspectives; Washington Newsletter* (monthly); Pamphlets; Papers; Annual Report; Booklets; Brochures.

9223 ■ Friends of the National Parks at Gettysburg (FNPG)
PO Box 4629
Gettysburg, PA 17325
Contact: Barbara J. Finfrock, Chair
Ph: (717)334-0772
Fax: (717)338-1245
E-mail: fnpgmembership@friendsofgettysburg.org
URL: http://www.friendsofgettysburg.org
Staff: 8. **Descr:** Citizens interested in protecting, preserving, and maintaining the two national parks at Gettysburg: Gettysburg National Military Park and the Eisenhower National Historic Site. **Fnd:** 1989. **Mem:** 25000. **Pub:** Newsletter (quarterly).

9224 ■ Global Village Institute (GVI)
PO Box 90
Summertown, TN 38483-0090
Contact: Albert K. Bates, Chm.
Ph: (931)964-4474
Fax: (931)964-2200
E-mail: ecovillage@thefarm.org
URL: http://www.i4at.org
Staff: 5. **Descr:** Engages in scientific research and education relating to small-scale, appropriate tech-

nologies which can provide basic human needs at a minimal economic and environmental cost. Conducts research in food sciences transportation and energy. **Fnd:** 1980.

9225 ■ Government Accountability Project (GAP)
1612 K St. NW, Ste. 1100
Washington, DC 20006
Contact: Mark Cohen, Exec. Dir.
Ph: (202)408-0034
E-mail: info@whistleblower.org
URL: http://www.whistleblower.org
Staff: 19. **Descr:** Provides legal and advocacy assistance to concerned citizens who witness dangerous, illegal or environmentally unsound practices in their own workplaces and communities and choose to "blow the whistle". **Fnd:** 1977. **Mem:** 5000. **Pub:** *Bridging the Gap* (quarterly); *Courage Without Martyrdom: A Survival Guide for Whistleblowers*; *Protecting Environmental and Nuclear Whistleblowers: A Litigation Manual*; *Study of Whistleblower Protections for Federal Employees*; *Whistleblowers Guide to Federal Bureaucracy*; *Whistleblowers Protection - the GAP Between the Law and Reality*.

9226 ■ Guitars For Vets (G4V)
PO Box 617
Milwaukee, WI 53201
Contact: Dan Van Buskirk, Pres.
E-mail: dvb@guitarsforvets.org
URL: http://www.guitarsforvets.org
Descr: Aims to enhance the lives of ailing and injured veterans by providing guitars and music instruction. **Fnd:** 2007.

9227 ■ Help Hospitalized Veterans (HHV)
36585 Penfield Ln.
Winchester, CA 92596
Contact: Mike Lynch, Exec. Dir.
Ph: (951)926-4500
Fax: (951)926-3569
E-mail: hhv@hhv.org
URL: http://www.hhv.org
Staff: 43. **Descr:** Seeks to improve the welfare and morale of hospitalized veterans and aid in their mental and physical rehabilitation. Provides arts and crafts materials in kit form to recreation therapy, occupational therapy, and voluntary service departments and wards of Department of Veterans Affairs Medical Centers, state Veterans Nursing Homes, and military hospitals. **Fnd:** 1970. **Pub:** Newsletter; Annual Report (annual).

9228 ■ Helping Americans Needing Disaster (HANDS)
PO Box 16449
Jackson, MS 39236-6449
Contact: Leisha Pickering
Ph: (601)605-0800
E-mail: questions@hands.ms
URL: http://www.hands.ms
Descr: Seeks to inform, educate, and communicate the needs of the communities. Helps to rebuild, recover, renew and restore the individuals, families and communities devastated by Katrina and other disasters. Partners with churches, charities, foundations and corporations to coordinate a network of volunteers to assist affected individuals and communities. **Fnd:** 2005.

9229 ■ Honest Ballot Association (HBA)
272-30 Grand Central Pkwy.
Floral Park, NY 11005
Free: 800-541-1851
E-mail: info@honestballot.com
URL: http://www.honestballot.com
Descr: Serves as a nonpartisan union of citizens organized to insure clean elections, and to prevent honest votes from being offset by trickery and fraud. Investigates and prevents colonization of voters, fraudulent registrations, repetitious voting, intimidation of voters, and unsuitable polling places. Conducts studies of the adequacy of existing election laws; instructs qualified persons to serve as watchers at polling places. Prints pamphlets summarizing

essential facts of election law and make them available to political parties, schools, colleges, and other groups. Sponsors research, polling, and arbitration. In addition to general public elections, supervises elections involving labor, management, municipalities, school boards, corporations, governments, and other organizations. **Fnd:** 1909.

9230 ■ House of Heroes (HOH)
4713 Milgen Rd.
Columbus, GA 31907-1304
Contact: Wayne Anthony, Pres.
Ph: (706)569-7011
E-mail: coordinator.hoh@knology.net
URL: http://www.houseofheroes.org
Descr: Works to serve the nation's military and public safety veterans. Provides help to improve the living conditions of retired veterans and their families. Gives support to veterans and their spouses who are in need. **Fnd:** 2000.

9231 ■ Independent Progressive Politics Network (IPPN)
PO Box 1041
Bloomfield, NJ 07003
Contact: George Friday, Coor.
Ph: (973)338-5398
E-mail: ippn@igc.org
URL: http://www.ippn.org
Staff: 2. **Descr:** Individuals, organizations, civil rights groups, women's organizations, peace groups, and other progressive political groups. Seeks to bring together grass roots progressive movements into organized framework in order. Represents the political interests of those often disenfranchised and excluded from the existing political and economic system. **Fnd:** 1995. **Mem:** 36. **Pub:** *Independent Politics News* (quarterly).

9232 ■ InfraGard National Members Alliance (INMA)
Eagle Crest Bldg.
225 N Humphreys Blvd., Ste. 3000
Memphis, TN 38120-2107
Contact: Dr. Kathleen Kiernan, Chair
Ph: (901)747-4300
E-mail: dr.k2@comcast.net
URL: http://www.infragardmembers.org
Descr: Aims to provide a trusted forum for the exchange of knowledge, experience and information related to the protection of critical infrastructure from both physical and cyber threats. Collaborates to provide protection to the critical infrastructures and key resources that are vital to national security. Provides information to those responsible for safeguarding these critical infrastructures. **Fnd:** 2003. **Mem:** 26000.

9233 ■ Institute of Public Administration - USA (IPA)
411 Lafayette St., Ste. 303
New York, NY 10003-7032
Contact: David Mammen, Pres.
Ph: (212)992-9898
Fax: (212)995-4876
E-mail: info@theipa.org
Staff: 21. **Descr:** Private research, educational, and consulting agency consisting of research staff, associates, and board of trustees. Conducts domestic and international research and education in public administration, public finance, citizenship and ethics, management, urban development and government organization and policy problems. Makes available consultation and technical services specializing in urban and metropolitan studies, governmental management, charter and code revision and reorganization, personnel and training for governmental service, public enterprise, financing and organization, urban transportation, contracting, ethics, and private-public sector cooperation in the United States and abroad. **Fnd:** 1906. **Pub:** Reports (periodic).

9234 ■ Inter-American Commission of Women (CIM)
17th St. and Constitution Ave. NW
Washington, DC 20006

Contact: Carmen Lomellin, Exec. Sec.
Ph: (202)458-3000
E-mail: oasweb@oas.org
URL: http://portal.oas.org/Default.aspx?tabid=621&language=en-US
Staff: 7. **Descr:** Specialized agency of the Organization of American States, dealing with issues concerning women. Composed of one presidentially-appointed delegate for each member country of OAS: 34 democracies of the Western Hemisphere. Mobilizes, trains, and organizes women "so that they may fully participate in all fields of human endeavor, on a par with men, as two beings of equal value, responsible for the destiny of humanity". Serves as liaison for women's groups throughout the hemisphere and conducts research on laws affecting women. Operates a regional information center in Santiago, Chile; finances development projects in Latin America and the Caribbean. **Fnd:** 1928. **Mem:** 34. **Pub:** *Final Report-Assembly of Delegates* (biennial); *Series: Studies* (periodic); Reports.

9235 ■ International Anticounterfeiting Coalition (IACC)
1730 M St. NW, Ste. 1020
Washington, DC 20036
Contact: Robert C. Barchiesi, Pres.
Ph: (202)223-6667
Fax: (202)223-6668
E-mail: bbarchiesi@iacc.org
URL: http://www.iacc.org
Staff: 3. **Descr:** Works to eliminate counterfeiting of merchandise such as aircraft and auto parts, medical devices, chemicals, apparel, and watches. Maintains that counterfeiting hurts everyone because manufacturers lose money and consumers get low-quality, often dangerous merchandise. Helps secure more strict U.S. customs restrictions on counterfeits and passage of the Trademark Counterfeiting Act of 1984, and the Anti-counterfeiting Consumer Protection Act of 1996 providing strong criminal sanctions against counterfeiters. Promotes the development of innovative anti-counterfeiting technologies to authenticate products. Conducts legislative action programs. Promotes information exchange, provides speakers and compiles statistics. **Fnd:** 1979. **Mem:** 150. **Pub:** *Reality Check* (monthly).

9236 ■ International Coalition for Religious Freedom (ICRF)
7777 Leesburg Pike, Ste. 404 N
Falls Church, VA 22043
Contact: Mr. Dan Fefferman, Pres.
Ph: (703)790-1500
Fax: (703)790-5562
E-mail: icrf@aol.com
URL: http://www.religiousfreedom.com
Staff: 3. **Descr:** Americans of all faiths who are concerned about First Amendment freedoms. Seeks to preserve First Amendment rights protecting the free exercise of religion. Acts as a forum for the religious community of all denominations to effectively deal with the various levels and divisions of government on matters concerning the preservation of religious freedom. Works to educate civic leaders and the public concerning religious freedom; is concerned with matters such as zoning and licensing restrictions on ministries, the application of tax laws to churches and their ministries, curriculum content, and teacher certification in private religious schools. Offers advice to churches. Reports on legislative, judicial, and state and local activities affecting religious institutions. **Fnd:** 1984. **Mem:** 10000. **Pub:** *Assault on Religious Freedom*; *Religious Freedom Alert*; *Religious Freedom Report* (bimonthly).

9237 ■ International Coalition for the Responsibility to Protect (ICRtoP)
Institute for Global Policy
708 3rd Ave., 24th Fl.
New York, NY 10017
Contact: Sapna Chhatpar Considine
Ph: (212)599-1320
Fax: (212)599-1332
E-mail: chhatpar@responsibilitytoprotect.org
URL: http://www.responsibilitytoprotect.org

Descr: Seeks to strengthen normative consensus for Responsibility to Protect (RtoP) at the international, regional, sub-regional and national levels. Strives to further the understanding of RtoP among governments, NGOs and the public. Helps build and fortify a like-minded group of governments in support of RtoP. Mobilizes NGOs to push for action to save lives in RtoP country-specific situations. **Fnd:** 2009.

9238 ■ International Municipal Signal Association (IMSA)
PO Box 539
Newark, NY 14513-0539
Contact: Marilyn Lawrence, Exec. Dir.
Ph: (315)331-2182
Free: 800-723-4672
Fax: (315)331-8205
E-mail: info@imsasafety.org
URL: http://www.imsasafety.org
Staff: 9. **Descr:** Professional organization of government officials responsible for municipal signaling, fire alarms, traffic signals, radio communication, street lighting, signs and marking, and other related services. **Fnd:** 1896. **Mem:** 13500. **Reg. Groups:** 23. **Pub:** *Fire Alarm Manual*; *IMSA Journal* (bimonthly); *Microprocessor Manual for Traffic Signals*; *Preventive Maintenance of Traffic Signals*.

9239 ■ Iraq Action Coalition (IAC)
7309 Haymarket Ln.
Raleigh, NC 27615
Fax: (919)846-7422
E-mail: iac@leb.net
URL: http://iraqaction.org
Descr: Serves as an online media activists' resource center for groups and activists who are working to end the war against the people of Iraq. Maintains listserv. **Pub:** *Iraq Under Siege: The Deadly Impact of Sanctions and War*; *Starving Iraq: One Humanitarian Disaster We Can Stop*.

9240 ■ Korean War Project
PO Box 180190
Dallas, TX 75218-0190
Contact: Hal Barker, Founder
Ph: (214)320-0342
E-mail: hbarker@kwp.org
URL: http://www.koreanwar.org
Descr: Provides support to veterans of the Korean War and their families. **Fnd:** 1979. **Mem:** 4195.

9241 ■ Latin America Trade Coalition
1615 H St. NW
Washington, DC 20062-0001
Contact: Kathleen McInerney
Ph: (202)463-5553
Fax: (202)463-3126
E-mail: kmcinerney@uschamber.com
URL: http://www.latradecoalition.org
Descr: Represents U.S. companies, farmers and business organizations. Aims to secure congressional approval of the U.S.-Colombia Trade Promotion Agreement and the U.S.-Panama Trade Promotion Agreement.

9242 ■ Marine Corps Veterans Association (MCVA)
PO Box 214183
Sacramento, CA 95821-0183
Contact: Dan Robles, Exec. Off.
Ph: (916)486-4050
Fax: (916)486-4050
URL: http://www.marinevets.org
Descr: Offers assistance to marines and navy corpsmen and their families. Provides and conducts programs with the primary purpose of helping marines and their families with their needs. **Fnd:** 2007.

9243 ■ Merchants Payment Coalition
325 7th St. N.W., Ste. 1100
Washington, DC 20004
Contact: Christy Moran
Ph: (202)995-1400
E-mail: info@unfaircreditcardfees.com
URL: http://www.unfaircreditcardfees.com

Descr: Retailers seeking to "fight against unfair credit card fees". Strives to bring about "a more competitive and transparent credit card fee system that better serves American consumers and merchants alike." **Mem:** 50000000.

9244 ■ Mothers of Military Support (MOMS)
1105 D 15th Ave., No. 111
Longview, WA 98632
Contact: Elizabeth Johnston, Pres.
Ph: (360)430-3597
E-mail: lizziee@momsservices.org
URL: http://www.mothersofmilitarysupport.momsservices.org
Descr: Works with the community to contribute, facilitate and promote awareness of the needs of the men and women in the armed service. Offers support information, resources and services to military families. **Fnd:** 2003. **Pub:** Newsletter.

9245 ■ National African American Drug Policy Coalition (NAADPC)
Howard University
Center for Drug Abuse Research
2900 Van Ness St. NW, Ste. 400
Washington, DC 20008
Contact: Arthur L. Burnett Sr., Exec. Dir.
Ph: (202)806-8600
Fax: (202)537-3806
E-mail: info@naadpc.org
URL: http://www.naadpc.org
Descr: Addresses the problem of drug abuse and addiction in the African American community. Develops and promotes policies and practices related to substance abuse in the African American community. Works to evaluate the effectiveness of the drug policies and conduct research projects to determine the impact of drug policies and laws on the African American community. Reviews and monitors federal and state laws and make recommendations for more effective laws and policies. **Fnd:** 2004.

9246 ■ National Alliance Against Racist and Political Repression (NAARPR)
1325 S Wabash Ave., Ste. 105
Chicago, IL 60605
Contact: Clarice Durham, Co-Chair
Ph: (312)939-2750
Fax: (773)929-2613
URL: http://www.naarpr.org/index.html
Descr: Aims to give justice to those who are condemned by the criminal justice system. Campaigns against official and unofficial police crimes, and works to abolish the death penalty. Works to defend and extend affirmative action programs. **Fnd:** 1970. **Mem:** 38. **State Groups:** 5. **Local Groups:** 5. **Pub:** *The Illinois Organizer* (quarterly).

9247 ■ National Alliance for Filipino Concerns (NAFCON)
40-21 69th St.
Woodside, NY 11377
Contact: Pastor Wilson De Ocera
Ph: (718)565-8862
Fax: (718)565-8856
E-mail: info@nafconusa.org
URL: http://nafconusa.org
Descr: Aims to protect and advance the rights and welfare of Filipinos by fighting for social, economic and racial equality. Responds to the basic needs and interests of Filipinos in the U.S. through education, action and national unity. Promotes Filipino heritage as a positive cultural identity and contribution to U.S. society. Gives Filipinos the opportunity to uplift the Philippine homeland and diaspora through social and economic reforms that strive for justice and lasting peace. **Fnd:** 2003.

9248 ■ National Alliance of Highway Beautification Agencies (NAHBA)
PO Box 191
Columbia, SC 29202
Contact: Barbara M. Wessinger, Chair
E-mail: contactnahba@nahba.org
URL: http://www.nahba.org
Descr: Represents employees of federal depart-

ments of transportation, state departments of transportation or highway agencies and political subdivisions or local government associations. Acts as an advocate for developing and promoting innovative ideas and business practices of highway beautification. Addresses critical issues pertaining to policies and regulations affecting highway beautification. **Pub:** *Sign Post* (quarterly); Brochure.

9249 ■ National AMBUCS
PO Box 5127
High Point, NC 27265
Contact: J. Joseph Copeland, Exec. Dir.
Free: 800-838-1845
Fax: (336)852-6830
E-mail: joec@ambucs.org
URL: http://www.ambucs.org
Staff: 6. **Descr:** Dedicated to creating opportunities for independence for people with disabilities. Performs community service; provides physically challenged children with tricycles that can be operated by hand, foot or both: operates the Living Endowment Fund. **Fnd:** 1927. **Mem:** 5600. **Reg. Groups:** 6. **Local Groups:** 125. **Pub:** *The Leader* (11/year); Magazine (quarterly).

9250 ■ National Association of Atomic Veterans (NAAV)
11214 Sageland
Houston, TX 77089
Contact: R.J. Ritter, Natl. Commander
Ph: (281)481-1357
E-mail: cmdr@naav.com
URL: http://www.naav.com
Staff: 7. **Descr:** Veterans of U.S. nuclear weapons testing and Nagasaki/Hiroshima occupation forces who now have cancer or other diseases believed to be radiation-related; their widows and interested persons. Works to assure veterans and widows that such diseases are recognized as service-related illnesses and assist in obtaining proper medical attention, compensation, and other benefits through the Veterans Administration. Participates in related legislative activities. **Fnd:** 1979. **Mem:** 5000. **State Groups:** 40. **Pub:** *Atomic Veterans News* (quarterly).

9251 ■ National Association for Black Veterans (NABVETS)
PO Box 11432
Milwaukee, WI 53211
Contact: Robert A. Cocroft, Chm./Exec. Dir.
Free: 877-622-8387
E-mail: info@nabvets.com
URL: http://www.nabvets.com
Descr: Black and other minority veterans, primarily those who fought in Vietnam. Represents the interests of minority veterans before the Veterans Administration. Operates Metropolitan Veterans Service to obtain honorable discharges for minority and low-income veterans who in the organization's opinion unjustly received a less than honorable discharge. Defends incarcerated veterans through its Readjustment Counseling Program; operates job creation program; offers services to geriatric and homeless veterans. Conducts workshops to acquaint lawyers and clinicians with problems associated with Post Traumatic Stress Disorder. Sponsors geriatric seminar and training program. Operates library of military regulations; compiles statistics; maintains speakers' bureau. **Fnd:** 1970. **Mem:** 25000. **Local Groups:** 13. **Pub:** *Eclipse* (quarterly).

9252 ■ National Association of State Directors of Veterans Affairs (NASDVA)
North Carolina Division of Veterans Affairs
Albemarle Bldg., Ste. 1065
325 N Salisbury St.
Raleigh, NC 27603
Contact: Mr. Charles F. Smith, Pres.
Ph: (919)733-3851
Fax: (919)733-2834
E-mail: president@nasdva.net
URL: http://www.nasdva.net
Descr: Directors of veterans' affairs for state governments. Serves as medium for exchange of ideas among state veterans' officers. Maintains

liaison with all congressionally chartered veterans' organizations. **Fnd:** 1973. **Mem:** 55. **Pub:** *Correspondence Guide* (periodic).

9253 ■ National Association of State Title I Directors (NASTID)
PO Box 5320
Arlington, VA 22205
Contact: Richard Long EdD, Exec. Dir.
Ph: (571)480-9970
E-mail: richlong@titlei.org
URL: http://www.titlei.org
Descr: Aims to improve and implement the Title I program so that more children reach their academic potential. Provides state-based educational leaders with the opportunity to work together to share ideas on effective and innovative programs as well as identifying the needs and finding solutions to problems of Title I families. Provides an opportunity for Title I schools from every state to be publicly recognized for their positive educational achievements.

9254 ■ National Association of State Veterans Homes (NASVH)
5211 Auth Rd.
Suitland, MD 20746
Contact: J.W. Crowley, Pres.
Ph: (301)899-7908
Fax: (301)899-8186
E-mail: info@nasvh.org
URL: http://www.nasvh.org
Descr: Represents state supported veterans' homes. Seeks to maintain high standards of domiciliary, nursing home, and hospital care for veterans and eligible family members. Provides a clearinghouse for techniques and expertise in veteran care and in the management of these institutions. Represents the veterans' needs before Congress and the Veterans Administration. Encourages continued federal financial support for building state facilities and for providing care for veterans currently living in state homes. Works to sustain current veterans' benefits. Assists other states in establishing homes. Compiles statistics. **Fnd:** 1953. **Mem:** 110. **State Groups:** 46. **Pub:** *LINK* (quarterly); Directory (annual).

9255 ■ National Association of State Workforce Agencies (NASWA)
444 N Capitol St. NW, Ste. 142
Washington, DC 20001
Contact: Richard A. Hobbie, Exec. Dir.
Ph: (202)434-8020
Fax: (202)434-8033
E-mail: ceser@naswa.org
URL: http://www.workforceatm.org
Staff: 9. **Descr:** State agencies responsible for administering unemployment insurance, employment and training programs, labor market information and workforce development. Strives to improve the public employment service, unemployment insurance programs, and employment and training programs; to encourage effective state action in training and placing unemployed workers, paying unemployment benefits, stabilizing the labor market and developing labor market information; to engage in public policy research and education in order to secure enactment of sound legislation; to identify the positions of member agencies and act as their collective voice in communicating those positions to federal officials, to national groups and to the public. **Fnd:** 1936. **Mem:** 53. **Pub:** *Workforce Bulletin* (weekly); Brochures; Monographs; Pamphlets.

9256 ■ National Association for Uniformed Services (NAUS)
5535 Hempstead Way
Springfield, VA 22151-4094
Contact: Major Gen. William M. Matz Jr., Pres.
Ph: (703)750-1342
Free: 800-842-3451
Fax: (703)354-4380
E-mail: naus@naus.org
URL: http://www.naus.org
Staff: 10. **Descr:** Members of the uniformed military

services, active, retired or reserve, veteran, enlisted and officers, and their spouses or widows. Develops and supports legislation that upholds the security of the U.S., sustains the morale of the uniformed services, and provides fair and equitable consideration for all service people. Protects and improves compensation, entitlements, and benefits. Provides discount rates on travel, insurance, auto rentals, charge cards, prescription medicine, and legal services. **Fnd:** 1968. **Mem:** 160000. **Pub:** *Uniformed Services Journal* (bimonthly).

9257 ■ National Capital FreeNet (NCF)
Trailhead Bldg., Ste. 302
1960 Scott St.
Ottawa, ON, Canada K1Z 8L8
Contact: John Selwyn, Exec. Dir.
Ph: (613)520-9001
Fax: (613)520-3524
E-mail: office@ncf.ca
URL: http://www.ncf.ca
Staff: 4. **Descr:** Serves as electronic information network available for free use by the public. Also serves as a source for community information, an electronic mailbox for all members, a forum for discussion and exchange of information among members, and a means of access to other public electronic services. Maintains access points at public libraries, throughout the Ottawa area. **Fnd:** 1992. **Mem:** 50000. **Pub:** *FreeNet: An Exciting New Way to Share Information* (periodic).

9258 ■ National Catalog Managers Association (NCMA)
7101 Wisconsin Ave., Ste. 1300
Bethesda, MD 20814-3415
Contact: Mark Richardson, Pres.
Ph: (301)654-6664
Fax: (301)654-3299
E-mail: ncma@aftermarket.org
URL: http://www.ncmacat.org
Descr: Individuals actively engaged in the management, preparation, production, and distribution of automotive product catalogs. Purposes are to: exchange practical and useful ideas in the creation, compilation, production, and distribution of catalogs; raise standards of catalogs in automotive and related industries; create a better understanding of the current developments in the field of graphics; establish a professional and fraternal relationship with colleagues; improve professional recognition of the catalog specialist; promote high standards of ethics in the cataloging industry. Operates placement service. **Fnd:** 1974. **Mem:** 156. **Pub:** Newsletter (semiannual); Membership Directory.

9259 ■ National Caucus and Center on Black Aged (NCBA)
1220 L St. NW, Ste. 800
Washington, DC 20005
Contact: Karyne Jones, Pres./CEO
Ph: (202)637-8400
Fax: (202)347-0895
E-mail: info@ncba-aged.org
URL: http://www.ncba-aged.org
Descr: Seeks to improve living conditions for low-income elderly Americans, particularly blacks. Advocates changes in federal and state laws in improving the economic, health, and social status of low-income senior citizens. Promotes community awareness of problems and issues effecting low-income aging population. Operates an employment program involving 2000 older persons in 14 states. Sponsors, owns, and manages rental housing for the elderly. Conducts training and intern programs in nursing home administration, long-term care, housing management, and commercial property maintenance. **Fnd:** 1970. **Pub:** *The Healing Zone Health Update* (quarterly); *SCSEP Works* (quarterly); *SEE SPAN* (quarterly).

9260 ■ National Center for Charitable Statistics (NCCS)
2100 M St. NW, 5th Fl.
Washington, DC 20037
Contact: Thomas H. Pollak, Program Dir.

Free: 866-518-3874
Fax: (202)833-6231
E-mail: nccs@ui.urban.org
URL: http://nccs.urban.org
Staff: 9. **Descr:** Serves as a data repository for IRS FORM 990 information and statistics on non-profits. **Fnd:** 1982. **Pub:** *Non-Profit Almanac Profiles of Charitable Organizations* (biennial); *Nonprofits and Government: Collaboration and Conflict; Scope and Dimension of the Nonprofit Sector;* Brochure.

9261 ■ National CFIDS Foundation (NCF)
103 Aletha Rd.
Needham, MA 02492
Contact: Gail R. Kansky, Pres.
Ph: (781)449-3535
Fax: (781)449-8606
E-mail: info@ncf-net.org
URL: http://www.ncf-net.org
Descr: Provides education, advocacy and fundraising for research. **Fnd:** 1997. **Mem:** 4000. **Pub:** *The Forum* (quarterly).

9262 ■ National Civic League (NCL)
1640 Logan St.
Denver, CO 80203
Contact: Gloria Rubio-Cortes, Pres.
Ph: (303)571-4343
Fax: (303)571-4404
E-mail: ncl@ncl.org
URL: http://www.ncl.org
Staff: 14. **Descr:** Community leaders, civic leaders, educators, public officials, civic organizations, libraries, nonprofits and businesses interested in community building, transforming democratic institutions and developing techniques of citizen action and participation. Serves as a clearinghouse for information on healthy communities, community renewal, local campaign, finance reform, All-American cities, city and county charters, election systems and techniques of citizen participation. **Fnd:** 1894. **Mem:** 600. **Pub:** *Civic Action* (quarterly); *National Civic Review: Building Successful Communities* (quarterly); Annual Report (annual).

9263 ■ National Committee for the Prevention of Elder Abuse (NCPEA)
1612 K St. NW
Washington, DC 20006
Contact: Randolph W. Thomas, Pres.
Ph: (202)682-4140
Fax: (202)223-2099
E-mail: ncpea@verizon.net
URL: http://www.preventelderabuse.org
Descr: Aims to promote a greater understanding of the problem and the development of services to protect older persons and disabled adults in order to reduce the likelihood of their abuse and neglect. Performs research, advocacy, public awareness, and training services. **Fnd:** 1988. **Mem:** 450. **State Groups:** 3. **Local Groups:** 10. **Pub:** *Journal of Elder Abuse and Neglect* (quarterly); *Nexus* (bimonthly); Membership Directory.

9264 ■ National Community Tax Coalition (NCTC)
Center for Economic Progress
29 E Madison St., Ste. 900
Chicago, IL 60602
Contact: Jackie Lynn Coleman, Co-Coor.
Ph: (312)252-0280
Fax: (312)252-0285
E-mail: info@tax-coalition.org
URL: http://www.tax-coalition.org
Descr: Seeks to improve the economic well being of low- and moderate-income individuals, families and communities. Aims to build a movement to dramatically increase access to tax credits and benefits and asset-building opportunities. Strives to improve the effectiveness and impact of affiliates that provide tax

outreach and assistance and asset-building opportunities.

9265 ■ National Conference of State Liquor Administrators (NCSLA)
6183 Beau Douglas Ave.
Gonzales, LA 70737
Contact: Ms. Pamela D. Salario, Exec. Dir.
Ph: (225)473-7209
Fax: (225)257-4498
E-mail: pamsalario@cox.net
URL: http://www.ncsla.org
Descr: State agencies administering liquor control laws and collecting beverage taxes under a license system rather than a state-controlled monopoly stores system. **Fnd:** 1934. **Mem:** 117. **Reg. Groups:** 4. **Pub:** *NCSLA Official Directory* (annual).

9266 ■ National Conference of State Social Security Administrators (NCSSSA)
Social Security Administration
61 Forsyth St. SW, Ste. 22T64
Atlanta, GA 30303
Contact: Carolyn Fry, Pres.
Ph: (404)562-1324
Fax: (404)562-1583
E-mail: info@ncsssa.org
URL: http://www.ncsssa.org
Staff: 50. **Descr:** State social security administrators and their subordinates. Encourages exchange of ideas on the administration of social security programs for public employees. **Fnd:** 1951. **Mem:** 52. **Reg. Groups:** 5. **Pub:** *History* (periodic); *Manual of Operating Procedure for State Administrators* (periodic); *NCSSSA-Today*; *Roster of Administrators* (annual); Directory (periodic); Proceedings (annual).

9267 ■ National Conference on Weights and Measures (NCWM)
1135 M St., Ste. 110
Lincoln, NE 68508
Contact: Don Onwiler, Exec. Dir.
Ph: (402)434-4880
Fax: (402)434-4878
E-mail: info@ncwm.net
URL: http://www.ncwm.net
Staff: 5. **Descr:** State and local weights and measures officials; representatives of manufacturers of weighing and measuring devices, trade associations, industry (users of devices), and representatives of federal government. Promotes uniformity in weights and measures laws, regulations, specifications and tolerances. Sponsored by National Institute of Standards and Technology. **Fnd:** 1905. **Mem:** 3000. **Pub:** *NIST Handbook 44, Specifications, Tolerances, and Other Technical Requirements for Weighing and Measuring Devices* (annual); *NIST Handbook 130, Uniform Laws and Regulations* (annual); *Printed Reports of National Conference on Weights and Measures* (annual).

9268 ■ National Council of Social Security Management Associations (NCSSMA)
418 C St. NE
Washington, DC 20002
Contact: Greg Heineman, Pres.
Ph: (202)547-8530
Fax: (202)547-8532
E-mail: president@ncssma.org
URL: http://www.ncssma.org
Descr: Managers and supervisors of the 1350 Social Security field offices and teleservice centers in the U.S. and Puerto Rico. Works to represent the interests of members before Congress, the media, and agency heads and to improve the image and professionalism of federal employees. Conducts research on federal employee pay and retirement benefits. Maintains speakers' bureau. **Fnd:** 1970. **Mem:** 3500. **Reg. Groups:** 10. **Pub:** *Frontline* (monthly); Papers; Reports.

9269 ■ National Council of State Human Service Administrators (NCSHSA)
810 1st St. NE, Ste. 500
Washington, DC 20002
Contact: Cari DeSantis, Pres.

Ph: (202)682-0100
Fax: (202)289-6555
URL: http://www.aphsa.org
Descr: Chief executives, managers, and staff aides of state public welfare agencies. Provides a forum for state public welfare administrators to discuss and develop positions on national policy issues affecting state welfare programs and to exchange information on state management practices and experiences. **Fnd:** 1939. **Mem:** 700.

9270 ■ National Drug Strategy Network (NDSN)
8730 Georgia Ave., Ste. 400
Silver Spring, MD 20910
Contact: Eric E. Sterling, Coor.
Ph: (301)589-6020
Fax: (301)589-5056
E-mail: ndsn@ndsn.org
URL: http://www.ndsn.org
Descr: Government officials, business leaders, scholars, religious leaders, attorneys, civil libertarians, health care professionals, criminal justice officials, and community activists sharing information on the "War on Drugs". Sponsors training seminars; maintains speakers' bureau. **Fnd:** 1989. **Pub:** *News Briefs.*

9271 ■ National Even Start Association (NESA)
PO Box 710855
San Diego, CA 92171
Contact: Sue Henry, CEO
Ph: (858)278-1810
Free: 800-977-3731
Fax: (858)278-1568
E-mail: info@evenstart.org
URL: http://www.evenstart.org
Descr: Seeks to generate awareness and support for Even Start Family Literacy programs. Provides professional services that support quality in Even Start Family Literacy programs. Collaborates with other family literacy providers to ensure the quality of Even Start programs. **Pub:** Brochure.

9272 ■ National Families in Action (NFIA)
2957 Clairmont Rd. NE, Ste. 150
Atlanta, GA 30329
Contact: Sue Rusche, Pres./CEO
Ph: (404)248-9676
Fax: (404)248-1312
E-mail: nfia@nationalfamilies.org
URL: http://www.nationalfamilies.org
Descr: Parents and other adults concerned about preventing drug abuse. Seeks to: educate parents, children, and the community about the use of drugs; counteract social pressures that condone and promote drug use; stop drug use. Worked for passage of statewide drug paraphernalia statutes. Collects and disseminates information about the effects of drugs. Maintains Drug Information Center, which contains more than 500,000 documents, studies, books, brochures, and films and videos relating to drug abuse. Operates after-school program for parents and youth. **Fnd:** 1977. **Pub:** *A Step Backward*; *Crack Update*; *False Messengers: How Addictive Drugs Change the Brain*; *Guide to the Legalization Movement and How You Can Stop It*; *12 Reasons Not to Legalize Drugs*; *12 Tips for Helping Your Children Stay Drug-Free*; *You Have the Right to Know Curriculum Series*; Annual Report (annual).

9273 ■ National Family Partnership (NFP)
2490 Coral Way, Ste. 501
Miami, FL 33145
Contact: Peggy B. Sapp, Pres./CEO
Ph: (305)856-4886
Free: 800-705-8997
Fax: (305)856-4815
E-mail: ireyes@informedfamilies.org
URL: http://www.nfp.org
Descr: Provides services, resources, and drug prevention programs for local parent and youth groups across the country. Sponsors Annual Red Ribbon Celebration in October; serves as a clearinghouse for state and federal legislation. **Fnd:** 1980.

Mem: 65. **Reg. Groups:** 32. **State Groups:** 22. **Pub:** *NFP Update* (quarterly); Manuals.

9274 ■ National Fenestration Rating Council (NFRC)
6305 Ivy Ln., Ste. 140
Greenbelt, MD 20770
Contact: James C. Benney, Exec. Dir.
Ph: (301)589-1776
Fax: (301)589-3884
E-mail: info@nfrc.org
URL: http://www.nfrc.org
Staff: 8. **Descr:** Individuals, organizations, and corporations interested in production, regulation, promotion, and development of technology related to fenestration products. Develops national voluntary energy performance rating system for fenestration products; coordinates certification and labeling activities to ensure uniform rating application. Promotes consumer awareness of fenestration ratings in an effort to encourage informed purchase of windows, doors, and skylights. Conducts efficiency testing. Maintains speakers' bureau; conducts educational and research programs. **Fnd:** 1990. **Mem:** 200. **Pub:** *An Introduction to NFRC*; *NFRC 100-1: Procedure for Determining Fenestration Product Thermal Properties*; *NFRC 200-93: Procedure for Determining Fenestration Solar Heat Gain at Normal Incidence*; *NFRC Update* (quarterly); Annual Report (annual).

9275 ■ National Governmental Collectors Association (NGCA)
PO Box 164
Conroe, TX 77305
Contact: Nadine Jerkins, Pres./CEO
Ph: (832)296-4602
E-mail: nadine.jerkins@ngcagov.org
URL: http://www.ngcagov.org
Descr: Seeks to enhance the collection of revenue for governmental entities. Provides opportunities for the development of quality collections professionals committed to the highest standards of excellence. Promotes the continuous implementation of the core values of integrity, diversity, visionary leadership, innovation, and collaboration.

9276 ■ National Institute for Chemical Studies (NICS)
2300 MacCorkle Ave. SE
Charleston, WV 25304
Contact: Deepay Mukerjee, Pres./CEO
Ph: (304)346-6264
Fax: (304)346-6349
E-mail: nicsinfo@nicsinfo.org
URL: http://www.nicsinfo.org
Staff: 4. **Descr:** Participants include representatives of the chemical industry, people living adjacent to chemical plants (plant neighbors), emergency responders, and other interested individuals. Serves as liaison between the chemical industry and the public. Conducts research on environmental and chemical safety issues and shares results with the public and all stakeholders. Provides training on variety of relevant topics; sponsors conferences. Provides services nationally. **Fnd:** 1985.

9277 ■ National Latina Business Women Association (NLBWA)
655 S Main St., Ste. 200-308
Orange, CA 92868
Contact: Cecilia Mota, Pres.
Free: 888-696-5292
E-mail: webmaster@nlbwa.com
URL: http://www.nlbwa.com
Descr: Strives to promote, develop, and support the growth of Latina business owners and professionals. Seeks to create networking and mentoring opportunities for members. **Fnd:** 2003.

9278 ■ National Neighborhood Coalition (NNC)
1221 Connecticut Ave. NW, 2nd Fl.
Washington, DC 20036
Contact: Anne Pasmanick, Exec. Dir.
Ph: (202)429-0790
Fax: (202)429-0795

E-mail: info@neighborhoodcoalition.org
URL: http://www.neighborhoodcoalition.org
Staff: 3. **Descr:** National membership organization that works with inner-city neighborhood groups. Serves as information and educational clearinghouse on national policies and federal programs that affect low and moderate-income neighborhoods. Sponsors regular 2-hour information forums on issues such as housing, community reinvestment banking, and community-based development. **Fnd:** 1979. **Mem:** 125. **Pub:** *Connectivity* (quarterly); *The Voice* (quarterly); Reports; Articles; Videos; Audiotapes.

9279 ■ National Organization for African-American Women (NOAW)
PO Box 29579
Washington, DC 20017
Contact: Cy Hooper
Ph: (202)529-5508
E-mail: cyhooper@noaw.org
URL: http://noaw.gb-design-inc.com
Descr: Seeks to address issues central to the condition of women of color in America. Aims to redefine best practices that will lead to economic, social and political empowerment to all women of color. **Fnd:** 2007.

9280 ■ National Organization for Men (NOM)
30 Besey St.
New York, NY 10007
Contact: Dr. Warren Farrell, Co-Pres.
Ph: (760)753-5000
E-mail: warren@warrenfarrell.com
URL: http://www.orgformen.org
Descr: Men and women united in efforts to promote and advance the equal rights of men in matters such as affirmative action programs, alimony, child custody, men's health, child abuse, battered husbands, divorce, educational benefits, military conscription, and veterans' benefits. Maintains Institute for the Study of Matrimonial Laws, established as a research and education foundation for the study of the nation's divorce, alimony, and custody and visitation laws. Offers support group; lobbies for equal rights for men; compiles statistics. **Fnd:** 1983. **Mem:** 13800. **Reg. Groups:** 26. **Local Groups:** 30. **Pub:** *The Quest* (bimonthly).

9281 ■ National Organization of Social Security Claimants' Representatives (NOSSCR)
560 Sylvan Ave.
Englewood Cliffs, NJ 07632
Contact: Nancy Shor, Exec. Dir.
Ph: (201)567-4228
Free: 800-431-2804
Fax: (201)567-1542
E-mail: nosscr@att.net
URL: http://www.nosscr.org
Staff: 3. **Descr:** Represents attorneys and legal service corporations. Aims to aid members in cases concerning social security disability claims. Collects and disseminates information on social security claim cases; prepares case studies. Operates a referral service to provide legal information and referrals. **Fnd:** 1979. **Mem:** 3900. **Pub:** *The Forum* (monthly).

9282 ■ National People's Action (NPA)
810 N Milwaukee Ave.
Chicago, IL 60622
Contact: Alicia Mendoza
Ph: (312)243-3038
URL: http://www.npa-us.org
Descr: Coalition of neighborhood organizations, unions, senior citizens' groups, and churches concerned with investment in and revitalization of individual neighborhoods. Lobbies for increased involvement on issues concerning: housing; credit and lending policies; community development funds; drugs; utility rates; health care costs. Organizes low- and moderate-income people and was instrumental in passage of legislation, such as the Home Mort-

gage Disclosure Act and the Community Reinvestment Act. **Fnd:** 1972. **Mem:** 302.

9283 ■ National Priorities Project (NPP)
243 King St., Ste. 239
Northampton, MA 01060
Contact: Greg Speeter, Exec. Dir.
Ph: (413)584-9556
Fax: (413)586-9647
E-mail: info@nationalpriorities.org
URL: http://www.nationalpriorities.org
Staff: 7. **Descr:** Offers citizen and community groups' tools and resources to shape federal budget and policy priorities promoting social and economic justice. **Fnd:** 1982. **Pub:** *Factbook*; *Grassroots Factbook*; Annual Reports.

9284 ■ National Stigma Clearinghouse
245 8th Ave., No. 213
New York, NY 10011
Ph: (212)255-4411
E-mail: stigmanet@webtv.net
URL: http://community-2.webtv.net/stigmanet/AbouttheNational
Descr: Works to end exploitation of mental illness, encourage balanced portrayals of people with psychiatric vulnerabilities, promotes accuracy in using medical terms.

9285 ■ National Veterans Services Fund (NVSF)
PO Box 2465
Darien, CT 06820-0465
Contact: Phil Kraft, Pres.
Free: 800-521-0198
E-mail: natvetsvc@nvsf.org
URL: http://www.nvsf.org
Staff: 3. **Descr:** Educates and informs the public about the needs of veterans and their families, primarily concerning the Agent Orange and Gulf War Illness issues; to assess the needs and provide limited assistance, relief and referrals to appropriate agencies using programs that combine family-guided case management (service coordination) and advocacy assistance while building social and community support. Administers a national hotline for veterans and their families. Strives to create partnerships with other agencies that make it possible to secure services and equipment at reduced rates or at no cost for families in need. Gives free educational materials including brochures. **Fnd:** 1978. **State Groups:** 1.

9286 ■ National Vietnam and Gulf War Veterans Coalition (NV&GWVC)
2020 Pennsylvania Ave., No. 961
Washington, DC 20006
Contact: Maj. (Ret.) Ted Streeter, Gen. Sec.
E-mail: veterans-coalition@comcast.net
URL: http://www.veterans-coalition.org
Staff: 7. **Descr:** Coalition of Vietnam & Gulf War veterans' organizations representing 325,000 Vietnam veterans. Fosters public appreciation for the service of Vietnam veterans; supports maximum relief for Agent Orange and Gulf War syndrome victims. Seeks the return of POWs and accountability for MIAs; encourages the appointment of Vietnam veterans to government policymaking positions. Works to secure meaningful job programs for Vietnam & Gulf War veterans and to obtain political support from the national political parties for Vietnam and Gulf War veterans; promotes judicial review of Veterans Administration benefits decisions. **Fnd:** 1983. **Mem:** 90. **Pub:** *Veterans News Journal* (periodic).

9287 ■ Non Commissioned Officers Association (NCOA)
10635 IH 35 N
San Antonio, TX 78233
Contact: Gene Overstreet, Pres.
Ph: (703)549-0311
Free: 800-662-2620
Fax: (703)549-0245
E-mail: execdir@ncoausa.org
URL: http://www.ncoausa.org

Staff: 14. **Descr:** Noncommissioned and petty officers of the United States military serving in grades E1 through E9 from all five branches of the U.S. Armed Forces; includes active duty and retired personnel, members of the Reserve and National Guard components, and personnel who held the rank of NCO/PO at the time of separation from active duty under honorable conditions. Works for patriotic, fraternal, social and benevolent purposes. Offers veterans job assistance, legislative representation, and grants. Conducts charitable program. **Fnd:** 1960. **Mem:** 80000. **State Groups:** 38. **Local Groups:** 120. **Pub:** *Today's NCOA Journal* (bimonthly).

9288 ■ Nonprofit Voter Engagement Network (NVEN)
2314 University Ave. W, Ste. 20
St. Paul, MN 55114
Contact: Rachel Adams
Ph: (651)757-3086
Fax: (651)642-1517
E-mail: info@nonprofitvote.org
URL: http://www.nonprofitvote.org
Descr: Aims to expand the role of America's nonprofits in voting and elections. Provides resources and support to 501(c)(3) nonprofit voter participation initiatives that work year-round to increase the number of nonprofits integrating voter engagement activities into their ongoing work. Seeks to sustain the increasing voter participation in the country. **Pub:** *Nonprofit Voting News*.

9289 ■ OMB Watch (OMBW)
1742 Connecticut Ave. NW
Washington, DC 20009
Contact: Gary D. Bass PhD, Exec. Dir.
Ph: (202)234-8494
Fax: (202)234-8584
E-mail: ombwatch@ombwatch.org
URL: http://www.ombwatch.org
Staff: 20. **Descr:** Collects, researches, and disseminates information on the federal Office of Management and Budget (OMB), particularly information affecting non-profit and community-based organizations. Advocates for more public accountability and increased public knowledge of administrative government actions. Serves as a reaction to events that OMB Watch feels have provided the OMB with unprecedented powers and "allow it to remain unaccountable to Congress and the American people". **Fnd:** 1983. **Mem:** 30000.

9290 ■ Operation Homefront
8930 Fourwinds Dr., Ste. 340
San Antonio, TX 78239
Contact: Mark D. Smith, Pres./CEO
Ph: (210)659-7756
Free: 800-722-6098
Fax: (210)566-7544
E-mail: info@operationhomefront.net
URL: http://www.operationhomefront.net
Descr: Provides emergency assistance and moral support to military, their families and wounded warriors. Conducts social and community outreach to aid military families with the problems of everyday life. Offers computer, furniture and financial assistance programs.

9291 ■ Paralyzed Veterans of America (PVA)
801 18th St. NW
Washington, DC 20006-3517
Contact: Mr. Randy L. Pleva Sr., Pres.
Free: 800-555-9140
E-mail: info@pva.org
URL: http://www.pva.org
Descr: Veterans who have incurred an injury or disease affecting the spinal cord and causing paralysis. Through national service program, assists veterans, dependents, and survivors in obtaining Department of Veterans Affairs benefits due them; works for federal benefits of various kinds. Sponsors wheelchair sporting events. Promotes legislation to create accessibility to establishments and facilities for individuals with a disability. Sponsors research, rehabilitation, and educational programs. Founded the Spinal Cord Research Foundation to fund spinal

cord research projects and fellowships. Also founded the Education and Training Foundation to provide grants to improve the knowledge, abilities, and skills of health professionals, spinal cord impaired patients, and their loved ones. **Fnd:** 1947. **Mem:** 19000. **Reg. Groups:** 32. **Pub:** *Paraplegia News* (monthly); *Sports-n-Spokes* (bimonthly); Booklets.

9292 ■ People for the American Way (PFAW)
2000 M St. NW, Ste. 400
Washington, DC 20036
Contact: Kathryn Kolbert, Pres.
Ph: (202)467-4999
Free: 800-326-7329
Fax: (202)293-2672
E-mail: pfaw@pfaw.org
URL: http://www.pfaw.org
Staff: 90. **Descr:** Nonpartisan constitutional liberties organization. Religious, business, media, and labor figures committed to reaffirming the traditional American values of pluralism, diversity, and freedom of expression and religion. Believes that the individual still matters in the society. Improves the quality of life by strengthening the things that unite citizens. Engages in a mass media campaign to create a positive climate of tolerance and respect for diverse peoples, religions, and values. Maintains speakers' bureau; conducts research programs; compiles statistics. Operates National Resource Center, a collection of printed and visual materials. **Fnd:** 1980. **Mem:** 600000. **State Groups:** 6.

9293 ■ Private Citizen, Inc. (PCI)
PO Box 233
Naperville, IL 60566
Contact: Robert Bulmash, Pres.
Ph: (630)393-2370
Free: 800-CUT-JUNK
E-mail: pci@private-citizen.com
URL: http://www.privatecitizen.com
Staff: 2. **Descr:** Works to allow individuals to preserve their privacy and regulate the intrusion of junk phone calls and junk mail. Subscribers authorize PCI to notify telemarketers not to solicit them; if telemarketers persist in such solicitation, they are levied with a $500 charge for the subscriber's time. Conducts lobbying for the regulation of telemarketing. Operates speakers' bureau and compiles statistics. **Fnd:** 1988. **Mem:** 4000. **State Groups:** 5. **Pub:** *Private Citizen Directory* (semiannual); *The Private Citizen News* (annual); *So...You want to Sue a Telemarketer*.

9294 ■ Private Sector Council (PSC)
1100 New York Ave. NW, Ste. 1090 E
Washington, DC 20005
Contact: Tom Fox
Ph: (202)775-9111
Fax: (202)775-8885
E-mail: bramati@ourpublicservice.org
URL: http://www.ourpublicservice.org/psc
Staff: 5. **Descr:** Serves as a nonpartisan, public service organization dedicated to improving the productivity, efficiency, and management of the federal government through a cooperative sharing of knowledge between the public and private sectors. **Fnd:** 1983. **Mem:** 42. **Pub:** *Communicator* (quarterly).

9295 ■ Project Equality (PE)
PO Box 7085
Kansas City, MO 64113-0085
Contact: Mr. Kirk Perucca, Pres.
Ph: (913)486-7010
E-mail: kirk@kperuccaassociates.com
URL: http://www.projectequality.org
Staff: 4. **Descr:** Provides a nationwide interfaith program enabling religious organizations, institutions, and others to support equal opportunity employers with their purchasing power. Includes services such as: validation of hotels for conventions and meetings of organizations, validations of suppliers to member organizations and institutions, and consultant and educational services to assist employers in affirmative action and equal employment opportunity programs. **Fnd:** 1965. **Mem:** 150. **State Groups:** 1.

Local Groups: 2. **Pub:** *PE Update, Action, EEO News* (quarterly); *Project Equality--Buyer's Guide* (annual).

9296 ■ Project on Government Oversight (POGO)
666 11th St. NW, Ste. 900
Washington, DC 20001-4542
Contact: Danielle Brian, Exec. Dir.
Ph: (202)347-1122
Fax: (202)347-1116
E-mail: info@pogo.org
URL: http://www.pogo.org
Staff: 9. **Descr:** Promotes accountability in government; monitors governmental agencies; exposes abuses of power, and waste and fraud committed by the government and its contractors. **Fnd:** 1981. **Pub:** *A Partial Approach to Clean-Up: EPA Mishandles Superfund Investigations, 2002 Report; The Art of Anonymous Activism: Serving the Public While Surviving Public Service (A Guide for Whistleblowers); At the Federal Election Commission: Things Just Don't Add Up, 2001 Report; Big Dreams Still Need Oversight: Missile Defense Testing & Financial Accountability Are Being Circumvented, 2002 Report; Children's Ears and Antibiotics: Gold Mine for Pharmaceutical Companies, Land Mine for Children; Corporate Welfare for Arms Merchants; Defense Waste & Fraud Camouflaged as Reinventing Government, 1999 Report; Federal Contractor Misconduct: Failures of the Suspension & Debarment System 2002 Report; Fill 'Er Up: Back Door Deal for Boeing Will Leave the Taxpayer on Empty, 2002 Report; The Government's Slick Deal for the Oil Industry; Heavy Lifting for Boeing: Sweetheart Deal Helps Defense Contractor & Hurts Taxpayer, 2001 Report; No Light at the End of this Tunnel: Boston's Central Artery/Third Harbor Tunnel Project* (periodic); *NRS Sells the Environment Down the River: Radiation Flows Unchecked into the Colorado River; Nuclear Power Plant Security: Voices from Inside the Fences, 2002 Report; Pick Pocketing the Taxpayer: The Insidious Effects of Acquisition Reform, 2002 Report; Re-Establishing Institutional Integrity at the FEC: Ten Common Sense Campaign Finance Disclosure Reforms; U.S. Nuclear Weapons Complex: Security at Risk, 2001 Report;* Newsletter (quarterly).

9297 ■ Public Advocate of the U.S. (PAUS)
5613 Leesburg Pike, Ste. 17
Falls Church, VA 22041
Contact: Eugene A. Delgaudio, Pres.
Ph: (703)845-1808
URL: http://www.publicadvocateusa.org
Staff: 4. **Descr:** Grass roots educational organization. Advocates limited federal government. Works to reduce the powers vested in the federal government and reissue control of various programs to state and local levels. **Fnd:** 1981. **Mem:** 300000. **Pub:** *Impact Reports* (periodic); *Register of Opinion* (periodic); *Report to Congress* (semiannual).

9298 ■ Public Affairs Council (PAC)
2033 K St. NW, Ste. 700
Washington, DC 20006
Contact: Douglas G. Pinkham, Pres.
Ph: (202)872-1790
Fax: (202)835-8343
E-mail: pac@pac.org
URL: http://www.pac.org
Staff: 18. **Descr:** Public affairs executives representing member corporations associations. Encourages members of the business community to be active and informed participants in political affairs and to provide thoughtful leadership in the fields of corporate citizenship and social responsibility. Conducts clinics; sponsors Public Affairs Institute each January. Offers counseling services to individual corporations and associations that are initiating or expanding programs in government relations or public affairs. **Fnd:** 1954. **Mem:** 600. **Pub:** *National Directory of Corporate Public Affairs; Public Affairs Council--Impact* (monthly); *Public Affairs News Monitor*

(biweekly); *Public Affairs Review* (annual); Brochures; Book.

9299 ■ Public Citizen (PC)
1600 20th St. NW
Washington, DC 20009
Contact: Joan Claybrook, Pres.
Ph: (202)588-1000
E-mail: member@citizen.org
URL: http://www.citizen.org
Staff: 120. **Descr:** Formed by Ralph Nader to support the work of citizen advocates. Areas of focus include: consumer rights in the marketplace, safe products, a healthful environment and workplace, clean and safe energy sources, corporate and government accountability, and citizen empowerment. Methods for change include lobbying, litigation, monitoring government agencies, research, and public education including special reports, periodicals, expert testimony, and news media coverage. Acquires funding primarily through direct mail and also through payment for publications and court awards. **Fnd:** 1971. **Mem:** 125000. **Reg. Groups:** 2. **Pub:** *Buyers Up News; Health Letter* (monthly); *Public Citizen News* (bimonthly); *Worst Pills/Best Pills;* Books; Monographs; Papers; Reports.

9300 ■ Public Citizen Litigation Group (PCLG)
1600 20th St. NW
Washington, DC 20009
Contact: Brian Wolfman, Dir.
Ph: (202)588-1000
E-mail: litigation@citizen.org
URL: http://www.citizen.org/litigation
Staff: 103. **Descr:** Serves as the litigating arm of Public Citizen and specializes in cases involving health and safety regulation, consumer rights, access to the courts, open government, and the First Amendment, including internet free speech. Litigates cases at all levels of the federal and state judiciaries and has a substantial practice before federal regulatory agencies; efforts are also pursued through programs such as the Alan Morrison Supreme Court Assistance Project and the Freedom of Information Clearinghouse. Aims to promote consumer rights, open government, clean energy, fair trade, environmental protection, and work place safety. **Fnd:** 1972. **Mem:** 105000. **Pub:** *Health Letter* (monthly); *Public Citizen News* (bimonthly); *Worst Pills/Best Pills; Worst Pills Best Pills News* (monthly).

9301 ■ Public Citizen's Congress Watch (PCCW)
1600 20th St. NW
Washington, DC 20009
Contact: David Arkush, Dir.
Ph: (202)588-1000
Fax: (202)547-7392
E-mail: congress@citizen.org
URL: http://www.citizen.org/congress
Staff: 15. **Descr:** Congressional lobby representing consumer interests, specifically citizens' access to government decision-making, campaign finance reform, product safety, product liability health care, and medical malpractice issues and reducing corporate subsidies. **Fnd:** 1971. **Mem:** 150000. **Pub:** *Congressional Voting Index* (annual); *Public Citizen News* (bimonthly).

9302 ■ Public Interest Advocacy Centre (PIAC)
1 Nicholas St., Ste. 1204
Ottawa, ON, Canada K1N 7B7
Contact: Michael Janigan, Exec. Dir./Gen. Counsel
Ph: (613)562-4002
E-mail: piac@piac.ca
URL: http://www.piac.ca
Staff: 8. **Descr:** Individuals. Provides legal representation, research and public advocacy concerning the delivery of important services. Focuses primarily in energy and telecommunications. **Fnd:** 1976. **Mem:** 2500000.

9303 ■ Public Radio Capital (PRC)
Bridges Broadcast Center
7409 S Alton Ct.

Centennial, CO 80112
Contact: Marc Hand, Managing Dir.
Ph: (720)493-4185
Fax: (720)493-4186
E-mail: info@publicradiocapital.org
URL: http://www.pubcap.org
Descr: Works to strengthen and expand noncommercial media. Disseminates information, unbiased news, diverse music and cultural programming. Aims to provide public radio services to the community. **Fnd:** 2001.

9304 ■ Public Service Alliance of Canada (PSAC)
233 Gilmour St.
Ottawa, ON, Canada K2P 0P1
Contact: John Gordon, Pres.
Ph: (613)560-4200
Free: 888-604-7722
Fax: (613)560-4200
E-mail: nat-pres@psac-afpc.com
URL: http://www.psac-afpc.org
Staff: 300. **Descr:** Canadian federal government workers' union founded to protect public service employees' rights and interests. Provides union education programs, collective bargaining, grievance and adjudication representation. Offers assistance on issues of health, safety, human rights, technological change, and others. **Fnd:** 1966. **Mem:** 165000. **Reg. Groups:** 23. **Pub:** *PSAC Union Update* (periodic).

9305 ■ Public Service Research Council (PSRC)
320-D Maple Ave. E
Vienna, VA 22180-4742
Ph: (703)242-3575
Fax: (703)242-3579
E-mail: info@psrconline.org
URL: http://psrconline.org
Staff: 3. **Descr:** Conducts research, education, and public affairs programs in the area of public sector employer-employee relations, including issues such as strikes, growth of unionism, legislation, and political spending. Sponsors Americans Against Union Control of Government. **Fnd:** 1973. **Mem:** 3000.

9306 ■ Responsible Endowments Coalition (REC)
PO Box 2292
Philadelphia, PA 19103-0292
Contact: Morgan Simon, Exec. Dir.
Ph: (215)564-2201
E-mail: info@endowmentethics.org
URL: http://www.endowmentethics.org
Descr: Works to build and unify the college and university-based responsible investment movement, both by educating and empowering a diverse network of individuals to act on their campuses, and by fostering a national network for collective action. Empowers young people to defend human rights and the environment while making both corporations and universities accountable to global stakeholders. Seeks to make social and environmental change by making responsible investment common practice amongst colleges and universities. **Fnd:** 2004.

9307 ■ Save-A-Vet
387 Northgate Rd.
Lindenhurst, IL 60046
Contact: Danny Scheurer, Founder/CEO
Ph: (815)349-9647
E-mail: info@saveavet.org
URL: http://www.save-a-vet.org
Descr: Provides support and care to retired, injured or disabled military and law enforcement K-9s. Advocates for the protection of all working dogs. Seeks to open a facility in every state that provides both military and law enforcement agencies the ability to retire their K-9 partners.

9308 ■ Society of Military Widows (SMW)
2486 N Camino Valle Verde
Tucson, AZ 85715
Contact: Marilyn Savage, Pres.
Free: 800-842-3451

E-mail: mshdgirl@comcast.net
URL: http://www.militarywidows.org
Descr: Widows of deceased career or active duty military personnel; affiliate members are persons who support the society's goals. Seeks to obtain equity for military widows under the Survivor Benefit Plan and to educate the public concerning the problems and needs of military widows. Monitors federal legislation affecting military widows; provides members with fact sheets on changes in survivor benefits. Has introduced bills before Congress and testified before congressional committees. Conducts surveys. Maintains the ROTH (Reach Out To Help) program by local chapter, a support system for the newly widowed, and sponsor social and educational activities. **Fnd:** 1968. **Mem:** 4900. **Local Groups:** 30.

9309 ■ State Department Watch
PO Box 65398
Washington, DC 20035-5398
Contact: Carl Olson, Chm.
E-mail: sdw@statedepartmentwatch.org
URL: http://www.statedepartmentwatch.org
Staff: 1. **Descr:** Nonpartisan, public interest, foreign policy watchdog group concerned with U.S. State Department and other governmental bodies and their actions regarding American foreign policy. Conducts campaigns to stop the U.S. State Department from "giving away" five Alaskan Islands and oil-rich seabeds to the former Soviet Union; to collect World War I and II debts from the former Soviet Union; and to stop the importing of slave-made goods from China and the former Soviet Union. **Fnd:** 1984. **Pub:** Newsletter (monthly).

9310 ■ Step Up 4 Vets
9903 Santa Monica Blvd., No. 700
Beverly Hills, CA 90212-1671
Contact: Patricia Kennedy
E-mail: info@stepup4vets.org
URL: http://www.stepup4vets.org
Descr: Focuses on ameliorating the problems of veterans upon returning home from battle such as homelessness, addiction and Post Traumatic Stress Disorder. Works to assist wounded and recovering veterans. Raises funds for the benefit of those veterans.

9311 ■ Tennessee Regulatory Authority (TRA)
460 James Robertson Pkwy.
Nashville, TN 37243-0505
Contact: Mary W. Freeman, Dir.
Ph: (615)741-2904
Free: 800-342-8359
Fax: (615)741-5015
E-mail: jessica.johnson@state.tn.us
URL: http://www.state.tn.us/tra
Descr: Staff members of state and federal regulatory commissions in the U.S. and Canada. Promotes fair and effective utility regulation in the public interest. Sponsored by National Association of Regulatory Utility Commissioners. **Fnd:** 1996. **Mem:** 150. **Pub:** Proceedings (annual).

9312 ■ U.S. Public Interest Research Group (USPIRG)
218 D St. SE
Washington, DC 20003-1900
Contact: Douglas H. Phelps, Pres./Chm.
Ph: (202)546-9707
Fax: (202)546-2461
E-mail: membershipservices@pirg.org
Staff: 30. **Descr:** Individuals who contribute time, effort, or funds toward public interest research and advocacy. Conducts research, monitors corporate and government actions, and lobbies for reforms on consumer, environmental, energy, and governmental issues. Current efforts include support for: laws to protect consumers from unsafe products and unfair banking practices; laws to reduce the use of toxic chemicals; strengthening clean air laws; efforts to reduce global warming and ozone depletion; energy conservation and use of safe, renewable energy sources. Sponsors internships for college students; provides opportunities for students to receive

academic credit for activities such as legislative research, lobbying, and public education and organizing. Offers summer jobs. **Fnd:** 1983. **Mem:** 1000000. **State Groups:** 30. **Pub:** *Citizen Agenda* (quarterly).

9313 ■ Unwanted Horse Coalition (UHC)
1616 H St. NW, 7th Fl.
Washington, DC 20006
Ph: (202)296-4031
Fax: (202)296-1970
URL: http://www.unwantedhorsecoalition.org
Descr: Represents equine organizations joined together under the American Horse Council. Strives to help horses before they become unwanted by educating existing and potential owners, breeders, sellers and horse organizations about the long-term responsibilities of owning and caring for horses. Seeks to utilize industry resources to put owners of horses in touch with individuals and facilities that will welcome them. **Fnd:** 2005.

9314 ■ Veterans Association of America (VET-SAA)
PO Box 309
New York, NY 10032
Contact: Raphael K. Works PhD, CEO/Chm.
Ph: (646)228-9610
E-mail: rworks@vetsaa.org
URL: http://www.vetsaa.org
Descr: Focuses on the issues that affect the daily living conditions of veterans and their families. Provides assistance to veterans and veterans' families by supporting their rights to receive legal assistance, medical services, business and housing ownership, employment outreach, discharge upgrades and family outreach services. **Fnd:** 2001.

9315 ■ Veteran's Coalition
PO Box 33088
Washington, DC 20033-0088
Contact: Harry Walter, Pres.
Ph: (202)776-5194
Fax: (202)785-3083
URL: http://future4vets.org
Descr: Seeks to improve the lives of service members, veterans, and their families by addressing healthcare and benefits issues across the government and private sectors. **Fnd:** 2006.

9316 ■ Veterans and Families
657 Brickyard Dr.
Sacramento, CA 95831
Contact: John Henry Parker, Founder
Ph: (916)320-4395
E-mail: johnhenry@veteransandfamilies.org
URL: http://www.veteransandfamilies.org
Descr: Aims to help veterans and families "raise happy, healthy children in a safe and stable environment where both parents are supportive and emotionally available." Ensures that veterans get home both mentally and emotionally. Assists homecoming veterans and families in transitioning from military to civilian life. **Fnd:** 2003.

9317 ■ Veterans of Foreign Wars of the United States (VFW)
406 W 34th St.
Kansas City, MO 64111
Contact: Glen Gardner, Commander-in-Chief
Ph: (816)756-3390
Fax: (816)968-1149
E-mail: info@vfw.org
URL: http://www.vfw.org
Staff: 220. **Descr:** Overseas veterans of the Spanish American War, World Wars I and II, the Korean and Vietnam wars, the Persian Gulf War, Grenada, Panama, and Lebanon in which an overseas campaign medal was received. Seeks to: insure the national security through maximum military strength; speed the rehabilitation of the nation's disabled and needy veterans; assist the widows, orphans, and dependents of disabled and needy veterans; promote Americanism through education in patriotism and constructive service to the communities. Sponsors charitable programs; maintains museum. **Fnd:** 1899.

Mem: 200000. **State Groups:** 54. **Local Groups:** 8500. **Pub:** *VFW Magazine* (monthly).

9318 ■ Veterans and Military Families for Progress (VMFP)
PO Box 66353
Washington, DC 20035-6353
Contact: Matthew Cary, Pres.
Ph: (202)841-1687
E-mail: info@vmfp.org
URL: http://www.vmfp.org/index.php
Descr: Ensures the rights and needs of veterans, active-duty service members and their families. Informs the media and the public-at-large of their privileges. Develops strategic plans and programs to reach them and works for their benefits through politics from the grassroots up to the national level. **Fnd:** 2005.

9319 ■ Veterans of the Vietnam War (VVnW)
805 S Township Blvd.
Pittston, PA 18640-3327
Contact: Peter J. Forbes, Natl. Commander
Ph: (570)603-9740
Free: 800-843-8626
Fax: (570)603-9741
E-mail: wnwnatl@epix.net
URL: http://www.vvnw.org
Staff: 3. **Descr:** Veterans and nonveterans united to aid veterans of all eras; POW/MIAs, United Veterans Beacon House Projects (Homeless Program). Maintains collection of literature on such subjects as Agent Orange, post-traumatic stress syndrome, employment, and incarcerated veterans. Maintains speakers' bureau; compiles statistics. **Fnd:** 1978. **Mem:** 15000. **Pub:** *The Veteran Leader* (quarterly).

9320 ■ Veterans2Work (V2W)
734 A St.
San Rafael, CA 94901-3923
Contact: John Reynolds, Founder/Exec. Dir.
Ph: (415)925-1515
E-mail: info@veterans2work.com
URL: http://www.veterans2work.com
Descr: Provides services and support to disabled military veterans. Works to create a full and unfettered access to the opportunities available in society.

9321 ■ Vets4Vets
4192 E Boulder Springs Way
Tucson, AZ 85712
Contact: Abel Moreno, Media Outreach/Marketing Coor.
Ph: (520)319-5500
Fax: (520)325-0772
E-mail: info@vets4vets.us
URL: http://www.vets4vets.us
Descr: Promotes the use of peer support to express emotions, manage challenges and ease reintegration of veterans into society. Provides peer support to help Iraq and Afghanistan-era veterans heal from negative aspects of service and war. Encourages speaking and listening to help veterans share their personal experiences. **Fnd:** 2005.

9322 ■ Vietnam Combat Veterans (VCV)
PO Box 715
White Pine, MI 49971
Contact: John Devitt, Chm./Founder
Ph: (906)885-5599
E-mail: johndv8@aol.com
URL: http://www.themovingwall.org
Descr: Works to make the public aware of American airmen and soldiers who are POW/MIAs in Southeast Asia; seeks the return of live POW/MIAs to the U.S.; sponsors a traveling display of a half-scale model of the Vietnam Veterans Memorial Wall. Conducts research into governmental programs that affect veterans. Sponsors seminars and public announcements on the POW/MIA issue. **Fnd:** 1980. **Mem:** 375.

9323 ■ Vietnam Veterans Against the War (VVAW)
PO Box 408594
Chicago, IL 60640
Contact: Pete Zastrow, Natl. Coor.

Ph: (773)276-4189
E-mail: vvaw@vvaw.org
URL: http://www.vvaw.org
Descr: Works for: improvement of VA conditions and job opportunities; elimination of the possibility of future military conflicts such as Vietnam; no draft or registration; testing and treatment of Agent Orange poisoning. Offers traumatic stress disorder counseling and discharge upgrading; provides Agent Orange self-help information. **Fnd:** 1967. **Mem:** 30000. **Pub:** *Agent Orange*; *The Draft*; *History of the Veterans' Movement*; *Post-Traumatic Stress Disorder*; *Recollections*; *The Veteran* (semiannual).

9324 ■ Vietnam Veterans of America (VVA)
8605 Cameron St., Ste. 400
Silver Spring, MD 20910
Contact: Mr. John Rowan, Pres.
Ph: (301)585-4000
Free: 800-882-1316
Fax: (301)585-0519
E-mail: communications@vva.org
URL: http://www.vva.org
Staff: 30. **Descr:** Acts as congressionally chartered, nationwide veterans service organization formed specifically for Vietnam veterans. Aims to work for the employment, education benefits, improved psychological assistance, and health care of Vietnam veterans. Provides referral services and research and public information programs to help veterans in developing a positive identification with their Vietnam service and with fellow veterans. Offers annual training for veterans' service representatives. **Fnd:** 1978. **Mem:** 50000. **Reg. Groups:** 9. **State Groups:** 46. **Local Groups:** 625. **Pub:** *The VVA Veteran* (bimonthly).

9325 ■ VietNow National (VN)
1835 Broadway
Rockford, IL 61104
Contact: Rich Sanders, Pres.
Ph: (815)227-5100
Free: 800-837-8669
E-mail: vnnatl@inwave.com
URL: http://www.vietnow.com
Staff: 1. **Descr:** Veterans (1957 to present); interested civilians and other veterans are associate members. Aims to provide a forum through which veterans can help other veterans with problems such as drug abuse, delayed stress syndrome, unemployment, and health problems related to Agent Orange exposure. Attempts to educate the public about those missing in action and prisoners of war who have still not been accounted for. Conducts educational and charitable programs; maintains speaker's bureau and 15 standing committees. **Fnd:** 1980. **Mem:** 3000. **Local Groups:** 20. **Pub:** *VietNow Magazine* (quarterly).

9326 ■ Women in Military Service for America Memorial Foundation
Department 560
Washington, DC 20042-0560
Contact: Ann Marie Sharratt, Exec. Dir.
Ph: (703)533-1155
Free: 800-222-2294
Fax: (703)931-4208
E-mail: hq@womensmemorial.org
URL: http://www.womensmemorial.org
Descr: Promotes the nation's first major national memorial dedicated to honoring women who have served in America's armed forces. **Pub:** *In Search Of.*

9327 ■ Women's American ORT
250 Park Ave. S
New York, NY 10003
Ph: (212)505-7700
Free: 800-51-WAORT
E-mail: info@waort.org
URL: http://www.waort.org/
Descr: Committed to strengthening the worldwide Jewish community by empowering people to achieve economic self-sufficiency through technological and vocational education. This is accomplished by providing financial support and leadership within the global

ORT network of schools and programs; advocates on behalf of quality education, democratic values, human rights and the security of Jewish communities globally. **Fnd:** 1927. **Mem:** 50000. **Local Groups:** 500. **Pub:** *The Reporter* (semiannual).

9328 ■ Young Americans for Liberty (YAL)
PO Box 2751
Arlington, VA 22202
Contact: Jeff Frazee, Exec. Dir.
E-mail: contact@yaliberty.org
URL: http://www.yaliberty.org
Descr: Seeks to recruit, train, educate and mobilize students on the ideals of liberty and the Constitution. Aims to empower young people and enhance their capabilities as potential leaders in the future. Provides activism grants to chapters. **Pub:** *Young American Revolution* (quarterly).

State and Local Organizations and Agencies

Alabama

9329 ■ Alabama Department of Veterans' Affairs
RSA Plaza Bldg., Ste. 530
770 Washington Ave.
Montgomery, AL 36130-2755
Contact: W. Clyde Marsh, Commnr.
Ph: (334)242-5077
Fax: (334)242-5102
E-mail: clyde.marsh@va.alabama.gov
URL: http://www.va.state.al.us/
Descr: Mission is to promote awareness, assist eligible veterans, their families, and survivors to receive from the U.S. federal and state governments any and all benefits to which they may be entitled under existing or future laws to be enacted.

9330 ■ Alabama Political Science Association (AlaPSA)
Jacksonville State University
Dept. of Political Science & PA
700 N Pelham Rd.
Jacksonville, AL 36265
Contact: Prof. Tim Barnett, Pres.
Ph: (256)782-5653
E-mail: tbarnett@jsu.edu
URL: http://www.apsanet.org/~alabama
Descr: Represents college and university teachers of political science, public officials, research workers, and businessmen. Encourages the impartial study and promotes the development of the art and science of government. Develops research projects of public interest and educational programs for political scientists and journalists. Seeks to improve the knowledge of and increase citizen participation in political and governmental affairs.

9331 ■ American Ex-Prisoners of War, Department of Alabama
8339 Hwy. 75
Pinson, AL 35126-2121
Contact: Newton J. Duke
Ph: (205)681-3896
Descr: Seeks to: acquaint the public with the needs, problems, and handicaps associated with prisoners of war; promote research in the fields connected with injuries, diseases, and syndromes stemming from imprisonment; advocate and foster complete and effective reconditioning programs for ex-prisoners of war; foster patriotism and civic loyalty; encourage fraternal and historical activities.

9332 ■ International Municipal Signal Association, Southeastern Section
2100 Clinton Ave.
Huntsville, AL 35805
Contact: Jon Hoffman, Dir.
Ph: (256)427-6871
E-mail: jon.hoffman@hsvcity.com
Descr: Serves as a professional organization of government officials responsible for municipal signal-

ing, fire alarms, traffic signals, radio communication, street lighting, signs and marking, and other related services.

9333 ■ National Association For Uniformed Services - Fort Rucker, Alabama Chapter 3
203 Bonnie Dr., No. 500
Ozark, AL 36360-3387
Contact: Charles D. James
Ph: (334)774-3456
Fax: (334)774-2680
E-mail: ursus@knology.net
Descr: Provides assistance and support to active or retired military uniformed service officers. Protects and improves the compensation, entitlements and benefits earned by members of the uniformed services for themselves, their families and survivors and all American citizens with common interests.

9334 ■ National Association For Uniformed Services - North Alabama, Chapter 4
118 Heritage Ln.
Madison, AL 35758
Contact: Boyce W. Allen
Ph: (256)461-9977
Descr: Provides assistance and support to active or retired military uniformed service officers. Protects and improves the compensation, entitlements and benefits earned by members of the uniformed services for themselves, their families and survivors and all American citizens with common interests.

9335 ■ National Funeral Directors and Morticians Association - District 5
102-6th Ave. SW
Birmingham, AL 35211
Contact: Venus N. R. Smith
Ph: (205)243-4671
Fax: (205)856-7804
E-mail: ferragamo8@yahoo.com
Descr: Promotes ethical practices and encourages just and uniform laws pertaining to funeral directing and embalming industry.

9336 ■ Veterans of Foreign Wars of the U.S., Department of Alabama
PO Box 231177
Montgomery, AL 36123-1177
Contact: Travis Whaley, Adjutant
Ph: (334)270-8399
Fax: (334)270-9056
E-mail: vfw@alvfw.org
URL: http://www.alvfw.org
Staff: 3. **Descr:** U.S. armed forces veterans who served overseas in time of war. Represents interests of and provides assistance to veterans and their families. Promotes fraternalism and patriotism. Works to perpetuate memory of veterans who have died. Sponsors educational and historical programs. **Fnd:** 1934. **Mem:** 19388. **Pub:** *VFW News* (quarterly).

9337 ■ Vietnam Veterans of America, Alabama
408 Cedar Trace
Birmingham, AL 35244
Contact: Richard McMillan, Sec.-Treas.
E-mail: mcmill_r@bellsouth.net
URL: http://alabamavva.org

9338 ■ Vietnam Veterans of America, Chapter 373
PO Box 1112
Daleville, AL 36322-1112
Contact: Johnny Smith, Pres.
E-mail: mhroberts@centurytel.net
URL: http://alabamavva.org/chapt373.html

9339 ■ Vietnam Veterans of America, Chapter 416
1610 Pinson Valley Pkwy.
Birmingham, AL 35217-2349
Contact: Scottie Blaikie, Pres.
Ph: (205)951-8929

E-mail: sbla9191@aol.com
URL: http://alabamavva.org/chapt416.html

9340 ■ Vietnam Veterans of America, Chapter 502
PO Box 2326
Anniston, AL 36202
Contact: Ken Rollins, Pres.
E-mail: krroll1234@aol.com
URL: http://alabamavva.org/chapt502.html

9341 ■ Vietnam Veterans of America, Chapter 637
PO Box 217
Gadsden, AL 35902
Contact: Ronald Bates, Pres.
Ph: (256)589-6620
E-mail: ronald1@hopper.net
URL: http://www.alabamavva.org/chapt637.html

9342 ■ Vietnam Veterans of America, Chapter 701
1209 Sarah Dr.
Semmes, AL 36575
Contact: Thomas J. Schwarz, Pres./Membership Chm.
Ph: (251)649-8459
E-mail: watkeison@aol.com
URL: http://www.alabamavva.org/chapt701.html
Fnd: 1997.

9343 ■ Vietnam Veterans of America, Chapter 742
PO Box 195
Sheffield, AL 35660-0195
Contact: Jay Jolly, Pres.
Ph: (256)381-1128
E-mail: parkertwo@roadrunner.com
URL: http://www.alabamavva.org/chapt742.html

9344 ■ Vietnam Veterans of America, Chapter 864
PO Box 1081
Fairhope, AL 36533
Contact: Joe Birindelli, Pres.
Ph: (251)928-3292
E-mail: joeb@gmail.com
URL: http://www.alabamavva.org/chapt864.html

9345 ■ Vietnam Veterans of America, Gary Elmore Chapter 511
PO Box 604
Athens, AL 35612
Ph: (256)230-9511

Alaska

9346 ■ Alaska Department of Military and Veterans Affairs
PO Box 5800 Camp Denali
Ft. Richardson, AK 99505-5800
Contact:Brig. Gen. Thomas H. Katkus, Commnr.
Ph: (907)428-6003
Fax: (907)428-6019
E-mail: dmvawebmaster@ak-prepared.com
URL: http://www.dmva.alaska.gov/

9347 ■ Alaska Society of EAs
PO Box 2163
Kodiak, AK 99615
Contact: H. Joi Soucy EA
Ph: (907)654-6225
E-mail: msbear@att.net

9348 ■ AMVETS, Alaska
855 E 38th Ave.
Anchorage, AK 99503
Contact: Ken Southerland PDC, Exec. Dir.
Ph: (907)561-VETS
E-mail: exec-dir@amvets-alaska.org
URL: http://www.amvetspost2.org

9349 ■ Vietnam Veterans of America, Mat-Su Chapter 891
6701 E Green Glen Dr.
Wasilla, AK 99654
Contact: Noel Gast, Pres.

Ph: (907)373-7186
E-mail: nhgast@mtaonline.net
URL: http://www.vva891.org

Arizona

9350 ■ American Arbitration Association, Arizona
3200 N Central Ave., Ste. 2100
Phoenix, AZ 85012-2441
Contact: Kimberly Banach, VP
Ph: (602)734-9333
Fax: (602)230-2151
E-mail: moorek@adr.org
URL: http://www.adr.org
Descr: Arbitration, mediation, private dispute resolution services, conflict management training and education; various alternative dispute resolution related publications. **Fnd:** 1926.

9351 ■ American Ex-Prisoners of War, POW WOW Chapter
8059 E Michelle Dr.
Scottsdale, AZ 85255
Contact: David Mills
Ph: (480)473-8259
Descr: Seeks to: acquaint the public with the needs, problems, and handicaps associated with prisoners of war; promote research in the fields connected with injuries, diseases, and syndromes stemming from imprisonment; advocate and foster complete and effective reconditioning programs for ex-prisoners of war; foster patriotism and civic loyalty; encourage fraternal and historical activities.

9352 ■ Arizona Department of Veterans' Services (ADVS)
4141 N. Third St.
Phoenix, AZ 85012
Contact: Richard Gregg Maxon, Dir.
Ph: (602)255-3373
Free: 800-406-3373
Fax: (602)255-1038
E-mail: pchorpenning@azdvs.gov
URL: http://www.azvets.com
Descr: Assists veterans, their dependants, and/or survivors in developing and filing claims for federal entitlements in areas of disability, pension, insurance, and burial, through the U.S. Department of Veterans Affairs. Also provides fiduciary services to incapacitated veterans, surviving spouses, or minor children. In addition, operates the Arizona State Veteran Home, a 200-bed skilled nursing facility, to provide long-term care services to veterans and their spouses. The ADVS is designated as the "State Approving Agency," and is responsible for approving and supervising all institutions and establishments in Arizona that offer education and training to veterans. The Department is also responsible for a state veteran ceremony in Sierra Vista.

9353 ■ Arizona Paralyzed Veterans of America (AZPVA)
8126 N 23rd Ave., Ste. J
Phoenix, AZ 85021
Contact: Benjamin Garcia, Pres.
Ph: (602)244-9168
Free: 800-621-9217
Fax: (602)244-0416
E-mail: azpva@azpva.com
URL: http://www.azpva.org
Descr: Improves the quality of life of U.S. Military Veterans and all who have experienced spinal cord injury/dysfunction through advocacy for proper health care, promotion of sports, education, and communication. **Fnd:** 1946. **Pub:** *Desert Oracle* (monthly).

9354 ■ International Municipal Signal Association, Arizona Section
12086 N 91st St.
Scottsdale, AZ 85260
Contact: Norm Akin, Dir.
Ph: (480)391-3306
E-mail: na@imsasafety.org
Descr: Serves as a professional organization of

government officials responsible for municipal signaling, fire alarms, traffic signals, radio communication, street lighting, signs and marking, and other related services.

9355 ■ National Association For Uniformed Services - Tucson, Arizona Chapter 3
100 S Antietam Pl.
Tucson, AZ 85710-4427
Contact: James F. Vaughn
Ph: (602)721-0525
Descr: Provides assistance and support to active or retired military uniformed service officers. Protects and improves the compensation, entitlements and benefits earned by members of the uniformed services for themselves, their families and survivors and all American citizens with common interests.

9356 ■ National Association for Uniformed Services - Phoenix, Arizona Chapter 1/2
5302 E Wonderview Rd.
Phoenix, AZ 85018-1941
Contact: Webb Ellis
Ph: (602)852-0282
E-mail: webb.ellis@cox.net
Descr: Provides assistance and support to active or retired military uniformed service officers. Protects and improves the compensation, entitlements and benefits earned by members of the uniformed services for themselves, their families and survivors and all American citizens with common interests.

9357 ■ National Spa and Pool Institute Region IV
8444 N Oracle Rd.
Tucson, AZ 85704-6502
Ph: (520)575-1300
Fax: (520)297-2644
Descr: Builders, dealers, designers, service companies, retail stores, engineers, manufacturers, distributors, public officials, suppliers, service persons concerned with public and residential swimming pools, spas, and hot tubs. Aims to raise spa and pool industry standards; expand interest and use of swimming pools, spas, and hot tubs; achieve uniformity in federal, state, and local regulations affecting swimming pool, spa, and hot tub operations. Promotes the industry to the consumer; protects interests of the industry through government relations and technical programs. Establishes voluntary standards for the design and construction of swimming pools and spas. Compiles cost of doing business data and other statistics.

9358 ■ National Spa and Pool Institute Southern Arizona Chapter
Patio Pools & Spas
7960 E 22nd St.
Tucson, AZ 85710-8698
Contact: Mark Ragel, Pres.
Ph: (520)886-1211
Free: 800-697-2846
Fax: (520)886-6364
E-mail: philanthropy@patiopoolsaz.com
URL: http://www.patiopoolsaz.com
Descr: Provides stability, reliability and superior quality of Patio Pools and Spas.

9359 ■ Verde Valley Cyclists Coalition
PO Box 172
Cottonwood, AZ 86326-0172
Contact: Daniel Paduchowski, Pres.
Ph: (928)301-1190
E-mail: probike@npgcable.com
URL: http://www.vvcc.us
Descr: Improves the bicycling environment and thereby the quality of life in the region. Promotes bicycle safety, education and facilities, and by encouraging use of the bicycle as an energy-efficient, economical and nonpolluting form of transportation and as a healthful and enjoyable form of recreation.

Serves as the public voice for cyclists. **Fnd:** 2003. **Mem:** 225. **Local Groups:** 1.

9360 ■ Vietnam Veterans of America, Yuma Chapter 835
PO Box 6281
Yuma, AZ 85366-6281
Contact: Bob Lukas, Pres.
Ph: (928)343-1327
E-mail: vvayuma@adelphia.net

Arkansas

9361 ■ Arkansas Department of Veterans' Affairs
1501 W. Maryland Ave.
North Little Rock, AR 72120
Contact: David Fletcher, Dir.
Ph: (501)992-0190
Fax: (501)992-0162
E-mail: dave.fletcher@arkansas.gov
URL: http://www.veterans.arkansas.gov/

9362 ■ Arkansas Political Science Association (ArkPSA)
Henderson State University
Department of Social Sciences
1100 Henderson St.
Arkadelphia, AR 71999
Contact: Haroon Khan, Sec.-Treas.
E-mail: khanh@hsu.edu
URL: http://www.arkpsa.org
Descr: Represents college and university teachers of political science, public officials, research workers, and businessmen. Encourages the impartial study and promotes the development of the art and science of government. Develops research projects of public interest and educational programs for political scientists and journalists. Seeks to improve the knowledge of and increase citizen participation in political and governmental affairs.

California

9363 ■ American Lung Association of California - Redwood Empire Branch
115 Talbot Ave.
Santa Rosa, CA 95404
Contact: Barbara Beedon, Exec. Dir.
Ph: (707)527-5864
Free: 800-LUNG-USA
Fax: (707)542-6111
E-mail: redwood@alac.org
Staff: 4. **Descr:** Works to prevent lung disease and promote lung health. **Fnd:** 1958. **Pub:** *Breath of Life* (3/year); Brochures.

9364 ■ American Lung Association of San Francisco and San Mateo Counties
2171 Junipero Serra Blvd., Ste. 720
Daly City, CA 94014
Contact: Collen Richardson, Exec. Dir.
Ph: (650)994-5864
Free: 800-LUNG-USA
Fax: (650)994-4601
E-mail: lindaj@alasfsm.org
URL: http://www.californialung.org/ALAC/localchapters.html
Staff: 9. **Descr:** Promotes educational programs and research to prevent and control lung disease. Conducts smoking cessation classes; maintains support groups for people with lung diseases. Gathers and disseminates information on occupational health and safety. Conducts programs on self-management techniques in schools for parents, teachers, and children with asthma. **Fnd:** 1908. **Pub:** Newsletter (semiannual).

9365 ■ American Subcontractors Association, Redwood Empire Chapter
PO Box 1132
Windsor, CA 95492
Contact: Janine Feland, Exec. Dir.
Ph: (707)837-9389
Free: 888-310-2722

Fax: (707)837-9389
E-mail: asac@asacalif.com
URL: http://www.asacalif.com
Descr: Union and nonunion subcontractors in Lake, Marin, Mendocino, Napa, and Sonoma counties, CA. Provides educational and business information. Monitors legislative activities through ASA California and ASA National. **Fnd:** 1988. **Mem:** 41. **Pub:** *The Sublet* (monthly).

9366 ■ AMVETS, Redwood City Post 53
1455 Madison Ave.
Redwood City, CA 94064
Ph: (510)490-2237
E-mail: amvetpost53@hotmail.com
URL: http://www.amvets.org/membership/posts_california.html

9367 ■ California Department of Veterans' Affairs
1227 O St.
Sacramento, CA 95814
Contact: Thomas Johnson, Sec.
Ph: (916)653-2158
Free: 800-952-5626
Fax: (916)653-2611
URL: http://www.cdva.ca.gov/
Descr: Mission is to provide California veterans and their families with aid and assistance in presenting their claims for veterans' benefits under the laws of the U.S.; to provide them with beneficial opportunities through direct low-cost loans to acquire farms and homes; and to provide the state's aged or disabled veterans with rehabilitative, residential, and medical care and services in a homelike environment at the California Veterans Homes.

9368 ■ International Municipal Signal Association, Far Western Section
1165 Neva Ct.
Merced, CA 95340
Contact: Clarence Chance, Dir.
Ph: (209)388-9255
E-mail: fwimsa@comcast.com
Descr: Serves as a professional organization of government officials responsible for municipal signaling, fire alarms, traffic signals, radio communication, street lighting, signs and marking, and other related services.

9369 ■ National Association For Uniformed Services - Golden Gate, California Chapter 5
2178 14th Ave.
San Francisco, CA 94116-1839
Contact: Nunzio J. Camarda
Ph: (415)566-8218
E-mail: camtay@comcast.net
Descr: Provides assistance and support to active or retired military uniformed service officers. Protects and improves the compensation, entitlements and benefits earned by members of the uniformed services for themselves, their families and survivors and all American citizens with common interests.

9370 ■ National Association For Uniformed Services - Merced, California Chapter 18
2260 Cascade Dr.
Atwater, CA 95301
Contact: Ed Mentz Sr.
Ph: (209)356-1938
E-mail: ementz.sr@sbcglobal.net
Descr: Provides assistance and support to active or retired military uniformed service officers. Protects and improves the compensation, entitlements and benefits earned by members of the uniformed services for themselves, their families and survivors and all American citizens with common interests.

9371 ■ National Association For Uniformed Services - Monterey Bay, California Chapter 2
1786 Harding St.
Seaside, CA 93955
Contact: Richard Ofenloch
Ph: (831)394-0253
E-mail: richofn@aol.com
Descr: Provides assistance and support to active or

retired military uniformed service officers. Protects and improves the compensation, entitlements and benefits earned by members of the uniformed services for themselves, their families and survivors and all American citizens with common interests.

9372 ■ National Association for Uniformed Services - Pacific Gateway, California Chapter 4
PO Box 1612
Travis AFB, CA 94535-1612
Contact: Carl Hinton
Ph: (707)425-7230
E-mail: jcarlhinton@vtechworld.com
URL: http://www.sonic.net/~cdunn/naus
Descr: Provides assistance and support to active or retired military uniformed service officers. Protects and improves the compensation, entitlements and benefits earned by members of the uniformed services for themselves, their families and survivors and all American citizens with common interests.

9373 ■ National Coalition of Free Men, Northern California Chapter
1875 S Bascom Ave., Ste. 116
PMB 196
Campbell, CA 95008
E-mail: capellanus@cs.com
URL: http://www.ncncfm.8m.com

9374 ■ National Funeral Directors and Morticians Association - District 8
2874-10th St.
Riverside, CA 92507-4947
Contact: Albert Tillman CFSP
Free: 800-300-6433
Fax: (951)682-7863
E-mail: aleaontillman@cox.net
Descr: Promotes ethical practices and encourages just and uniform laws pertaining to funeral directing and embalming industry.

9375 ■ Paralyzed Veterans of America, Bay Area and Western Chapter
3801 Miranda Ave., Bldg. 101
Rm. A1-219, Mail Code 816
Palo Alto, CA 94304
Contact: Ms. Rebecca Sherman, Exec. Dir.
Ph: (650)858-3936
Free: 800-273-6789
Fax: (650)855-9019
E-mail: pvachbaw@mindspring.com
URL: http://www.pva.org
Descr: Veterans who have incurred an injury or disease affecting the spinal cord and causing paralysis. **Mem:** 700. **Pub:** *The Bridge* (bimonthly).

9376 ■ Paralyzed Veterans Association, Cal-Diego Chapter
3350 LaJolla Village Dr., No. 1A-118
San Diego, CA 92161
Contact: Al Kovach, Pres.
Ph: (858)450-1443
Free: 800-423-2778
Fax: (858)450-1852
E-mail: aalvarez@caldiegopva.org
URL: http://www.caldiegopva.org
Descr: Improves the quality of life for veterans of the United States Armed Forces and others who have a spinal cord injury or disease.

9377 ■ Religious Coalition for Reproductive Choice - Southern California Chapter
817 W 34th St.
Los Angeles, CA 90089
Contact: Mary Larson
Ph: (213)748-0200
E-mail: info@rcrcsc.com

9378 ■ Vietnam Veterans of America, California
PO Box 3007
Riverside, CA 92519-3007
Contact: Bob Johnston Sr., Pres.

E-mail: bobj201@yahoo.com
URL: http://www.vvacalsc.com

9379 ■ Vietnam Veterans of America, Chapter 53
PO Box 7000-185
Redondo Beach, CA 90277
Contact: Jerry Yamamoto, Pres.
Ph: (310)540-8820
E-mail: n9140y@ca.rr.com

9380 ■ Vietnam Veterans of America, Chapter 218
PO Box 2241
Santa Barbara, CA 93120
Contact: Keith S. Perkins, Pres.
Ph: (805)682-0550
E-mail: info@vvachapter218.org
URL: http://www.vvachapter218.org

9381 ■ Vietnam Veterans of America, Chapter 355
PO Box 2986
Canyon Country, CA 91386-2986
Contact: Frank LaRosa, Pres.
Ph: (818)508-9626
E-mail: lostpatrol355@msn.com
URL: http://www.vvacalsc.com

9382 ■ Vietnam Veterans of America, Chapter 357
PO Box 4021
Redding, CA 96099
Contact: Eddie McAllister, Pres.
Ph: (530)242-1596
E-mail: coonradt@snowcrest.net
URL: http://www.vvacalsc.com

9383 ■ Vietnam Veterans of America, Chapter 368
PO Box 1566
Mariposa, CA 95338
Contact: Ken Kubichko, Pres.
Ph: (209)966-2292
E-mail: orland123@yahoo.com
URL: http://www.vvacalsc.com

9384 ■ Vietnam Veterans of America, Chapter 391
PO Box 5391
Sonora, CA 95370
Contact: Daniel E. Brown USN, Pres.
E-mail: dabrown@mlode.com
URL: http://www.vietnamveterans391.org

9385 ■ Vietnam Veterans of America, Chapter 400
200 Grand Ave.
Box 208
Oakland, CA 94610
Ph: (510)444-5235
Fax: (510)763-9709
E-mail: fdrdocent@comcast.net
URL: http://www.vvacalsc.com

9386 ■ Vietnam Veterans of America, Chapter 441
782 N Brundage Ave.
Farmersville, CA 93223
Contact: Rod Hughes, Pres.
Ph: (559)594-5710
E-mail: r5926768@yahoo.com
URL: http://www.vvacalsc.com

9387 ■ Vietnam Veterans of America, Chapter 446
1000 E Walnut St., No. 207
Pasadena, CA 91106
Contact: James Maddox, Pres.
Ph: (626)795-8141
Fax: (626)795-8141
E-mail: contact@vva446.org
URL: http://www.vva446.org

9388 ■ Vietnam Veterans of America, Chapter 464
PO Box 747
San Carlos, CA 94070-0747
Contact: Ponce Gonzalez, Pres.

Ph: (650)513-5586
E-mail: vva464@hotmail.com

9389 ■ Vietnam Veterans of America, Chapter 526
PO Box 2222
Culver City, CA 90231
Contact: John Hamilton, Pres.
Ph: (310)260-6910
E-mail: wmctaggart@pmcos.com
URL: http://www.vvacalsc.com

9390 ■ Vietnam Veterans of America, Chapter 535
PO Box 37
Grass Valley, CA 95945
E-mail: haroldgraves@sbcglobal.net
URL: http://www.vvacalsc.com

9391 ■ Vietnam Veterans of America, Chapter 536
1120 Golden State Ave.
Bakersfield, CA 93301
Contact: Don Waak
Ph: (661)868-7313
E-mail: cvafgolden@mindspring.com
URL: http://www.vvacalsc.com

9392 ■ Vietnam Veterans of America, Chapter 547
PO Box 884
Kentfield, CA 94914
Contact: Frank Lurz, Pres.
Ph: (415)388-8939
E-mail: webmaster@vietnamveteransmarin.org
URL: http://www.vietnamveteransmarin.org

9393 ■ Vietnam Veterans of America, Chapter 563
PO Box 751284
Petaluma, CA 94975-1284
Contact: John Cheney, Pres.
Ph: (707)762-9078
E-mail: johnc85393@aol.com
URL: http://www.vvacalsc.com

9394 ■ Vietnam Veterans of America, Chapter 582
PO Box 3070
Paradise, CA 95967
Contact: Stephen Wilson
Ph: (530)893-8435
E-mail: zashiban@sbcglobal.net
URL: http://www.vvacalsc.com

9395 ■ Vietnam Veterans of America, Chapter 643
PO Box 745
Dinuba, CA 93618
Contact: George Madrid, Pres.
Ph: (559)528-2811
E-mail: nafw@sbcglobal.net
URL: http://www.vvacalsc.com

9396 ■ Vietnam Veterans of America, Chapter 691
PO Box 2226
Merced, CA 95344-0226
Contact: Ron Grisby, Pres.
Ph: (209)722-1663
E-mail: rgrisby@sbcglobal.net
URL: http://www.mymerced.com/0704k163.html

9397 ■ Vietnam Veterans of America, Chapter 702
PO Box 355
Yountville, CA 94599
Contact: Ross Hall, Pres.
Ph: (707)252-7537
Fax: (707)944-0955
E-mail: rossisvva@sbcglobal.net
URL: http://www.vvacalsc.com

9398 ■ Vietnam Veterans of America, Chapter 785
2345 Barranca Pkwy.
Irvine, CA 92606
Contact: Jim Huggins, Pres.
Ph: (714)540-8518

E-mail: info@vva785.org
URL: http://www.vva785.org

9399 ■ Vietnam Veterans of America, Chapter 880
PO Box 578726
Modesto, CA 95357
Contact: Bill Motty, Pres.
Ph: (209)632-8701
E-mail: etplumbing21@yahoo.com
URL: http://www.vvacalsc.com

9400 ■ Vietnam Veterans of America, Chapter 933
PO Box 26256
Fresno, CA 93729-6256
Contact: Carl Shepley, Pres.
Ph: (559)855-3565
E-mail: hanniford@comcast.net
URL: http://www.vvacalsc.com

9401 ■ Vietnam Veterans of America, Chapter No. 223
PO Box 1583
Santa Rosa, CA 95402-1583
Contact: John Crooker, Pres.
Ph: (707)526-4218
Fax: (707)526-4218
E-mail: vets@vva223.org
URL: http://www.vva223.org

9402 ■ Vietnam Veterans of America, Lake County - Chapter 951
PO Box 1313
Lakeport, CA 95453
URL: http://www.vva951.org

9403 ■ Vietnam Veterans of America, Sacramento Valley - Chapter 500
PO Box 255484
Sacramento, CA 95865
Contact: Karen Anne Winnett, Pres.
Ph: (916)481-6020
E-mail: vva500@sbcglobal.net
URL: http://www.norcaltrav.com/vva500.htm

Colorado

9404 ■ American Arbitration Association, Colorado
1675 Broadway, Ste. 2550
Denver, CO 80202-4602
Contact: Lance K. Tanaka
Ph: (303)831-0823
E-mail: tanakal@adr.org
Descr: Works to provide exceptional neutrals, proficient case management, dedicated personnel, advanced education and training, and innovative process knowledge to meet the conflict management and dispute resolution needs of the public now and in the future.

9405 ■ American Lung Association of Colorado
5600 Greenwood Plaza Blvd., Ste. 100
Greenwood Village, CO 80111
Contact: Curt Huber, Exec. Dir.
Ph: (303)388-4327
Free: 800-LUNG-USA
Fax: (303)377-1102
E-mail: chuber@lungcolorado.org
URL: http://www.alacolo.org
Descr: Unites to fight lung disease, promote lung health and advocate clean air. **Fnd:** 1908.

9406 ■ American Subcontractors Association of Colorado (ASAC)
2875 W Oxford Ave., No. 3
Englewood, CO 80110
Contact: Richard Forsberg, Pres.
Ph: (303)759-8260
Fax: (303)759-8286
E-mail: info@asacolorado.com
URL: http://www.asacolorado.com
Staff: 12. **Descr:** Works to promote education and ethical business practices. Members include subcontractors and materials suppliers. **Fnd:** 1980. **Mem:**

150. **Pub:** *Construction Risk Management News* (monthly); *The Voice* (weekly); Report (quarterly).

9407 ■ Colorado Division of Veterans' Affairs
7465 East 1st Ave., Unit C
Denver, CO 80230
Contact: E. William Belz, Dir.
Ph: (303)343-1268
Fax: (303)343-7238
E-mail: eugene.belz@state.co.us
URL: http://www.dmva.state.co.us/

9408 ■ International Municipal Signal Association, Rocky Mountain Section
PO Box 580
Fort Collins, CO 80522
Contact: Dan Holland, Dir.
Ph: (970)221-6816
E-mail: dholland@fcgov.com
Descr: Serves as a professional organization of government officials responsible for municipal signaling, fire alarms, traffic signals, radio communication, street lighting, signs and marking, and other related services.

9409 ■ National Association For Uniformed Services - Colorado Springs, Colorado Chapter 2
3001 Springlake Cir. W
Colorado Springs, CO 80906-3731
Contact: Thomas F. Dooley
Ph: (719)576-0019
E-mail: tdooley@ix.netcom.com
Descr: Provides assistance and support to active or retired military uniformed service officers. Protects and improves the compensation, entitlements and benefits earned by members of the uniformed services for themselves, their families and survivors and all American citizens with common interests.

9410 ■ National Association For Uniformed Services - Front Range, Colorado Chapter 3
7676 S Ivanhoe Way
Centennial, CO 80112-6529
Contact: Rio G. Lucas
Ph: (303)741-1945
E-mail: redhorse5@earthlink.net
Descr: Provides assistance and support to active or retired military uniformed service officers. Protects and improves the compensation, entitlements and benefits earned by members of the uniformed services for themselves, their families and survivors and all American citizens with common interests.

9411 ■ National Association For Uniformed Services - Rocky Mountain, Colorado Chapter 1
956 Wheeling St.
Aurora, CO 80011
Contact: Frank Whiteman
Ph: (303)364-1897
E-mail: fwwhiteman@netzero.net
Descr: Provides assistance and support to active or retired military uniformed service officers. Protects and improves the compensation, entitlements and benefits earned by members of the uniformed services for themselves, their families and survivors and all American citizens with common interests.

9412 ■ Paralyzed Veterans of America, Mountain States Chapter
12200 E Iliff Ave., Ste. 107
Denver, CO 80014
Contact: Mr. Mark E. Shepherd Sr., Exec. Dir.
Ph: (303)597-0038
Free: 800-833-9400
Fax: (303)597-0039
E-mail: info@mscpva.org
URL: http://www.mscpva.org
Staff: 2. **Descr:** Veterans who have incurred an injury or disease affecting the spinal cord and caus-

ing paralysis. **Fnd:** 1955. **Mem:** 734. **Pub:** *The SCOOP* (monthly).

9413 ■ Religious Coalition for Reproductive Choice - Colorado Chapter
PO Box 370414
Denver, CO 80237
Contact: Betty Serotta
Ph: (303)756-9996
Free: 800-732-5155
Fax: (303)756-9996
E-mail: bserotta@comcast.net
URL: http://www.corcrc.org

Connecticut

9414 ■ Connecticut Department of Veterans' Affairs
287 West St.
Rocky Hill, CT 06067
Contact: Dr. Linda Schwartz RN, Commnr.
Ph: (860)721-5818
Free: 800-550-0000
Fax: (860)721-5919
E-mail: linda.schwarts@po.state.ct.us
URL: http://www.ct.gov/ctva

9415 ■ Connecticut Society of EAs
554 Boston Rd., Ste. 15
Milford, CT 06460
Contact: Raymond J. Laluna EA
Ph: (203)878-1568
Fax: (203)877-4171
E-mail: ray@lalunatax.com
URL: http://www.naea.org/MemberPortal/StateAffiliates/Listing
Descr: Promotes ethical representation of the financial position of taxpayers before government agencies.

9416 ■ International Municipal Signal Association, New England Section
16 Meadow Dr.
Gales Ferry, CT 06335
Contact: Russ Shaw, Dir.
Ph: (860)464-2500
Fax: (860)445-2554
E-mail: rshaw@pbfd.net
URL: http://www.newengland.imsasafety.org
Descr: Serves as a professional organization of government officials responsible for municipal signaling, fire alarms, traffic signals, radio communication, street lighting, signs and marking, and other related services.

9417 ■ National Association For Uniformed Services - Groton, Connecticut Chapter 1
94 Inchcliffe Dr.
Gales Ferry, CT 06335
Contact: Paul F. Dillon
Ph: (860)464-0234
E-mail: navret2@aol.com
Descr: Provides assistance and support to active or retired military uniformed service officers. Protects and improves the compensation, entitlements and benefits earned by members of the uniformed services for themselves, their families and survivors and all American citizens with common interests.

Delaware

9418 ■ Delaware Commission on Veterans' Affairs
802 Silver Lake Blvd.
Robbins Bldg., Ste. 100
Dover, DE 19904
Contact: Antonio Davila, Dir.
Ph: (302)739-2792
Free: 800-344-9900
Fax: (302)739-2794
E-mail: antonio.davila@state.de.us
URL: http://veteransaffairs.delaware.gov/

Fnd: 1987.

9419 ■ Paralyzed Veterans of America, Colonial Chapter
28 Peddler's Row
Newark, DE 19702
Contact: Phyllis D. Palabrica, Exec. Dir.
Ph: (302)368-4898
Free: 800-786-2039
Fax: (302)368-4293
E-mail: office@colonialpva.org
URL: http://www.colonialpva.org

District of Columbia

9420 ■ American Humanist Association (AHA)
1777 T St. NW
Washington, DC 20009-7125
Contact: Mr. Roy Speckhardt, Exec. Dir.
Ph: (202)238-9088
Free: 800-837-3792
Fax: (202)238-9003
E-mail: rspeckhardt@americanhumanist.org
URL: http://www.americanhumanist.org
Staff: 12. **Descr:** Promotes humanism and raises public awareness and acceptance of humanism. Encourages the continued refinement of the humanist philosophy. Works democratically to establish and protect the rights of humanists in a peaceful, sustainable world of hope, opportunity, and fulfillment for all. **Fnd:** 1941. **Mem:** 7000. **State Groups:** 8. **Local Groups:** 100. **Pub:** *Essays in the Philosophy of Humanism* (annual); *Humanist* (bimonthly).

9421 ■ AMVETS, District of Columbia
PO Box 70261
Washington, DC 20024
Contact: Johnnie Collins Jr., Exec. Dir.
Ph: (703)765-7590
Fax: (703)765-9099
E-mail: dcamvets@aol.com
Descr: Helps veterans and families through community outreach program.

9422 ■ Disabled American Veterans, National Service Office
807 Maine Ave. SW
Washington, DC 20024
Contact: Paul W. Jackson, Natl. Commander
Ph: (202)554-3501
Fax: (202)863-0233
URL: http://www.dav.org
Descr: Represents veterans and their families with claims for benefits from the VA, the armed forces, the Social Security Administration and other government agencies.

9423 ■ District of Columbia Disabled American Veterans
Virginia Regional Office
1722 I St. NW, Rm. 210
Washington, DC 20421-1111
Contact: Lionel O. Smith, Supervisor
Ph: (202)530-9260
Fax: (202)293-2120
URL: http://www.dav.org
Descr: Works to give service to disabled veterans and their families. Provides services in areas including disaster relief, employment, legislation, advocacy and transportation.

9424 ■ District of Columbia Office of Veterans' Affairs
441 4th St., NW, Ste. 570 S.
Washington, DC 20001
Contact: Thomas J. Smith, Dir.
Ph: (202)724-5454
Free: 888-477-2909
Fax: (202)724-7117
E-mail: kerwin.miller@dc.gov
URL: http://www.ova.dc.gov
Descr: Provides veteran benefits, assistance, information, outreach, effective advocacy, and claims processing assistance. Develops, coordinates, and attends veteran commemorative events that recog-

nize military service and sacrifice of veterans. **Fnd:** 2001.

9425 ■ National Association For Uniformed Services - Soldiers Home, District of Columbia Chapter 1
3700 N Capitol St. NW
Washington, DC 20011-8400
Contact: Esker McConnell
Ph: (202)558-5408
E-mail: esker1b@comcast.net
Descr: Provides assistance and support to active or retired military uniformed service officers. Protects and improves the compensation, entitlements and benefits earned by members of the uniformed services for themselves, their families and survivors and all American citizens with common interests.

Florida

9426 ■ American Arbitration Association, Miami
Bank of America Tower, International Pl.
100 SE 2nd Ave., Ste. 2300
Miami, FL 33131
Contact: Mr. Albert J. Orosa, Regional VP
Ph: (305)358-7777
E-mail: orosaa@adr.org
URL: http://www.adr.org/si.asp?id=4623
Descr: Provides business-to-business dispute avoidance, management and resolution services. **Fnd:** 1926. **Reg. Groups:** 35.

9427 ■ American Lung Association of Florida (ALAF)
6852 Belfort Oaks Pl.
Jacksonville, FL 32216
Contact: Martha C. Bogdan, Pres./CEO
Ph: (904)743-2933
Free: 800-940-2933
Fax: (904)743-2916
E-mail: alaf@lungfla.org
URL: http://www.lungfla.org
Staff: 55. **Descr:** Conducts educational programs, advocacy, and research to prevent and control lung disease. **Fnd:** 1920. **Reg. Groups:** 5. **State Groups:** 1.

9428 ■ American Lung Association of Florida - Southeast Area
2701 N Australian Ave., Ste. 100
West Palm Beach, FL 33407-4512
Ph: (561)659-7644
Fax: (561)835-8967
E-mail: alafse@lungfla.org
URL: http://www.lungfla.org
Staff: 12. **Descr:** Provides programs and services in Indian River, Martin, Okeechobee, Palm Beach, St. Lucie and Hendry counties, Florida to prevent lung disease and promote lung health and raise funds for research and advocacy. **Fnd:** 1937. **Pub:** *Literature on Lung Disease and Prevention.*

9429 ■ AMVETS, Crestview Post 35
105 John King Rd.
Crestview, FL 32539
Contact: Craig Sarrasin, Commander
Ph: (850)682-8435
E-mail: amvetspost35@amvetspost35fl.com
URL: http://amvetspost35fl.com

9430 ■ AMVETS, Valparaiso Post 78
910 Valastics Ave.
Valparaiso, FL 32580
Ph: (850)678-3828
E-mail: amvets78@valp.net

9431 ■ Disabled American Veterans, Department of Florida - Al Gray, No. 23
7115 Princess Ln.
Pensacola, FL 32526
Contact: Larry Kyser

Ph: (850)457-2771
URL: http://www.davfla.com

9432 ■ Disabled American Veterans, Department of Florida - Bay Area, No. 112
PO Box 654
Niceville, FL 32588
Contact: Robert Reinhardt
Ph: (850)678-3525
URL: http://www.davfla.com

9433 ■ Disabled American Veterans, Department of Florida - Cpl. PD Lyon Jr., No. 125
5092 E Spencer Field Rd.
Pace, FL 32571-9088
Contact: Raymond Goodwin
Ph: (850)995-0442
URL: http://www.davfla.com

9434 ■ Disabled American Veterans, Department of Florida - Crestview, No. 57
PO Box 63
Crestview, FL 32536
Contact: Harry McDonald
Ph: (850)682-3666
URL: http://www.davfla.com

9435 ■ Disabled American Veterans, Department of Florida - Euchee Valley, No. 98
PO Box 89
Defuniak Springs, FL 32435-0089
Contact: Lea Ann Armstrong
Ph: (850)892-6515
URL: http://www.davfla.com

9436 ■ Disabled American Veterans, Department of Florida - Jackson County, No. 22
2265 Wester Rd.
Grand Ridge, FL 32442
Contact: Lawrence Felton
Ph: (850)209-0024
URL: http://www.davfla.com

9437 ■ Disabled American Veterans, Department of Florida - Lake City, No. 20
202 SW Woodcrest Dr.
Lake City, FL 32024-1118
Contact: Mark Polson
Ph: (386)961-8729
URL: http://www.davfla.com

9438 ■ Disabled American Veterans, Department of Florida - Panama City, No. 17
922 Bob Little Rd.
Panama City, FL 32404
Contact: Ralph Hammond
Ph: (850)785-7707
URL: http://www.davfla.com

9439 ■ Disabled American Veterans, Department of Florida - Playground, No. 72
2A David St.
Fort Walton Beach, FL 32547
Contact: Cathy Magnuson
Ph: (850)862-9215
URL: http://www.davfla.com

9440 ■ Disabled American Veterans, Department of Florida - Suwannee Mem, No. 126
11492 SE 50th Dr.
Jasper, FL 32052
Contact: A.L. Miller
Ph: (386)792-3673
URL: http://www.davfla.com

9441 ■ Disabled American Veterans, Department of Florida - Tallahassee, No. 5 (DAV)
PO Box 12005
Tallahassee, FL 32308
Contact: Morris Shelkofsky
Ph: (850)878-3588
E-mail: info@davfla.com
URL: http://www.davfla.com

9442 ■ Florida Department of Veterans' Affairs
4040 Esplanade Way, Ste. 152
Tallahassee, FL 32399-0950
Contact: LeRoy Collins Jr., Exec.Dir.

Ph: (727)518-3202
Fax: (727)518-3216
E-mail: danielle@fdva.state.fl.us
URL: http://www.floridavets.org/

9443 ■ International Municipal Signal Association, Florida Section
4186 Honey Suckle Cir.
Middleburg, FL 32068
Contact: Don Fullerton, Dir.
Ph: (904)387-8863
Fax: (904)387-8894
E-mail: vms3712@aol.com
Descr: Serves as a professional organization of government officials responsible for municipal signaling, fire alarms, traffic signals, radio communication, street lighting, signs and marking, and other related services.

9444 ■ National Association of Atomic Veterans - North East Florida
8838 Old Plank Rd.
Jacksonville, FL 32220
Contact: James R. Taylor, Area Commander
Ph: (904)783-4416
E-mail: j_taylor40@msn.com

9445 ■ National Association For Uniformed Services - Central Florida, Chapter 4
9453 Westover Club Dr.
Windermere, FL 34786-6203
Contact: Dennis O. Freytes
Ph: (407)297-4080
E-mail: dennisfreytes@hotmail.com
Descr: Provides assistance and support to active or retired military uniformed service officers. Protects and improves the compensation, entitlements and benefits earned by members of the uniformed services for themselves, their families and survivors and all American citizens with common interests.

9446 ■ National Association For Uniformed Services - Panama City, Florida Chapter 10
7115 Maxwell Ct.
Panama City, FL 32404-8458
Contact: Robert C. Thompson
Ph: (850)871-0988
E-mail: robert0931@comcast.net
Descr: Provides assistance and support to active or retired military uniformed service officers. Protects and improves the compensation, entitlements and benefits earned by members of the uniformed services for themselves, their families and survivors and all American citizens with common interests.

9447 ■ Paralyzed Veterans of America, Central Florida Chapter (CFPVA)
2711 S Design Ct.
Sanford, FL 32773
Contact: Gary C. Rudolph, Pres.
Ph: (407)328-7041
Free: 800-940-2378
Fax: (407)328-7139
E-mail: cfpva1977@bellsouth.net
URL: http://www.centralfloridapva.org
Descr: Represents veterans who have incurred an injury or disease affecting the spinal cord and causing paralysis.

9448 ■ Paralyzed Veterans of America, Florida Chapter
3799 N Andrews Ave.
Fort Lauderdale, FL 33309
Contact: Michael Foster, Exec. Dir.
Ph: (954)565-8885
Free: 800-683-2001
Fax: (954)565-8843
E-mail: pvaf@aol.com
URL: http://www.pvaf.org
Descr: Strives to improve the lives of veterans with a spinal cord injury or dysfunction and other persons with disabilities to achieve maximum health, productivity and self-esteem. Services include ensuring quality health care, providing a wide range of wheelchair sports and recreation activities, advocating and educating the public on all issues encompassed in the Americans with Disabilities Act (ADA),

and research and education. **Fnd:** 1956. **Mem:** 1000.
Pub: *PN*; *Sunshine Spokesman.*

9449 ■ Vietnam Veterans of America, Chapter 25
2511 Westgate Ave., Ste. 7
West Palm Beach, FL 33409
Contact: Ronald L. Qualls, Pres.
Ph: (561)252-0902
E-mail: rlqualls@hotmail.com
URL: http://www.vva.org/VVAChapter25.html

9450 ■ Vietnam Veterans of America, Chapter 121
14510 SW 108th St.
Miami, FL 33186
Contact: Alexander Kovac
Ph: (305)387-1125
E-mail: diplomat@netrox.net
URL: http://www.vvafsc.org

9451 ■ Vietnam Veterans of America, Chapter 127
5607 Palmetto Dr.
Fort Pierce, FL 34982
Ph: (772)465-5777
URL: http://www.vvafsc.org

9452 ■ Vietnam Veterans of America, Chapter 195
7138 Ft. King Rd.
Zephyrhills, FL 33541
Ph: (813)788-7228
Fax: (813)788-5538
E-mail: jamerman@tampabay.rr.com
URL: http://www.vvafsc.org

9453 ■ Vietnam Veterans of America, Chapter 562
6214 Cedar Glen Dr.
Wesley Chapel, FL 33544
Ph: (813)973-0640
E-mail: gbeecher@tampabay.rr.com
URL: http://www.vvafsc.org

9454 ■ Vietnam Veterans of America, Chapter 566
PO Box 9313
Port St. Lucie, FL 34985
Ph: (772)785-6161
URL: http://www.vvafsc.org

9455 ■ Vietnam Veterans of America, Chapter 594
1106 SW 15th Ave.
Cape Coral, FL 33991-2644
Ph: (239)772-2745
URL: http://www.vvafsc.org

9456 ■ Vietnam Veterans of America, Chapter 620
PO Box 941406
Miami, FL 33194
Ph: (305)552-1048
URL: http://www.vvafsc.org

9457 ■ Vietnam Veterans of America, Chapter 680
PO Box 30606
Palm Beach Gardens, FL 33420
Ph: (561)236-1664
Fax: (561)841-3391
E-mail: marc3390@bellsouth.net
URL: http://www.vvafsc.org

9458 ■ Vietnam Veterans of America, Chapter 726
Polk Correctional Institution
10800 Evans Rd.
Polk City, FL 33868
Ph: (941)984-2273
URL: http://www.vvafsc.org

9459 ■ Vietnam Veterans of America, Chapter 755
1569 Neptune Rd.
Kissimmee, FL 34744

Ph: (407)847-8855
URL: http://www.vvafsc.org

9460 ■ Vietnam Veterans of America, Chapter 761
5045 Red Bay Dr.
Orlando, FL 32829
Contact: Richard Swoszowski, Pres./Chm.
Ph: (407)282-2291
E-mail: rswoszo611@aol.com
URL: http://vva761.tripod.com

9461 ■ Vietnam Veterans of America, Chapter 787
PO Box 89247
Tampa, FL 33689
Contact: Tom Hall, Pres.
Ph: (813)597-1326
Fax: (813)737-4929
E-mail: vva787@aol.com
URL: http://members.aol.com/vva787

9462 ■ Vietnam Veterans of America, Chapter 826
PO Box 10098
Panama City, FL 32404
Ph: (850)873-7777
URL: http://www.vvafsc.org

9463 ■ Vietnam Veterans of America, Chapter 831
PO Box 560103
Rockledge, FL 32955
Ph: (321)431-1933
E-mail: chapy4313@msn.com
URL: http://www.vvafsc.org

9464 ■ Vietnam Veterans of America, Chapter 916
PO Box 489
Edgewater, FL 32132
Ph: (386)426-0278
Fax: (386)427-1015
URL: http://www.vvafsc.org

9465 ■ Vietnam Veterans of America, Pinellas County - Chapter 522
PO Box 551
Indian Rocks Beach, FL 33785
Contact: Alan Thompson, Pres.
Ph: (727)278-4111
E-mail: president@vva522.org
URL: http://www.vva522.org

Georgia

9466 ■ American Arbitration Association, Georgia
2200 Century Pkwy., Ste. 300
Atlanta, GA 30345-3203
Contact: Chauncey Davis
Ph: (404)325-0101
Free: 800-899-9301
Fax: (404)325-8034
E-mail: davisc@adr.org
URL: http://www.adr.org
Descr: Works to achieve the resolution of disputes through the use of mediation, arbitration, democratic elections, and other voluntary methods. Provides administrative services for arbitrating, mediating, or negotiating disputes and impartial administration of elections. Maintains National Roster of Arbitrators and Mediators for referrals to parties involved in disputes. Conducts skill-building sessions to promote a more complete understanding of conflict resolution processes.

9467 ■ American Ex-Prisoners of War, Mountaineer Chapter
1582 Hwy. 197 N
Clarkesville, GA 30523
Contact: Mr. Ben Purcell, Commander
Ph: (706)754-4134
Descr: Seeks to: acquaint the public with the needs, problems, and handicaps associated with prisoners of war; promote research in the fields connected with injuries, diseases, and syndromes stemming from

imprisonment; advocate and foster complete and effective reconditioning programs for ex-prisoners of war; foster patriotism and civic loyalty; encourage fraternal and historical activities.

9468 ■ American Subcontractors Association, Georgia Chapter
665 Red Oak Rd.
Stockbridge, GA 30281
Contact: Vernon Thomas, Exec. Dir.
Ph: (404)766-1632
Fax: (404)768-7767
URL: http://www.asageorgia.org
Descr: Subcontractors organized to protect and advance industry interests. **Fnd:** 1966. **Mem:** 140.

9469 ■ Georgia Department of Veterans' Service
Floyd Veterans Memorial Bldg., Ste. E-970
Atlanta, GA 30334-4800
Contact: Pete Wheeler, Commnr.
Ph: (404)656-2300
Free: 866-351-0001
Fax: (404)657-9738
E-mail: gavetsvc@vs.state.ga.us
URL: http://www.sdvs.georgia.gov
Descr: Mission is to serve the more than 700,000 veterans residing in Georgia, their dependents, and survivors in all matters pertaining to veterans benefits.

9470 ■ Georgia Political Science Association (GPSA)
Georgia Perimeter College
1000 University Center Ln.
Lawrenceville, GA 30043
Contact: Jim Cox, Treas.
Ph: (678)407-5029
Fax: (678)407-5291
E-mail: jcox@gpc.edu
URL: http://gpsa.mgc.edu/gpsa
Descr: Represents college and university teachers of political science, public officials, research workers, and businessmen. Encourages the impartial study and promotes the development of the art and science of government. Develops research projects of public interest and educational programs for political scientists and journalists. Seeks to improve the knowledge of and increase citizen participation in political and governmental affairs.

9471 ■ Paralyzed Veterans of America, Southeastern Chapter
4010 Deans Bridge Rd.
Hephzibah, GA 30815
Ph: (706)796-6301
Free: 800-292-9335
E-mail: paravet@comcast.net

9472 ■ Religious Coalition for Reproductive Choice - Georgia Chapter
PO Box 8551
Atlanta, GA 31106
Contact: Sarah Meng, Pres.
Ph: (404)532-0022
Fax: (404)532-0025
E-mail: gfchoice@mindspring.com
URL: http://www.georgiansforchoice.org

9473 ■ Vietnam Veterans of America, Chapter 671
PO Box 60358
Savannah, GA 31420
Contact: James R. Crauswell
Ph: (912)631-2320
E-mail: wfhk786@aol.com

9474 ■ Vietnam Veterans of America, Georgia State Council
PO Box 61146
Savannah, GA 31420
Contact: Alan Harvey, Pres.

E-mail: alharv.usmc@juno.com
URL: http://www.vvageorgia.org

9475 ■ Vietnam Veterans of America, Northeast Georgia - Chapter 772
PO Box 775
Gainesville, GA 30503
Contact: Dave Dellinger, Pres.
Ph: (770)718-7676
E-mail: dtdellinger@charter.net
URL: http://www.vva772.org

9476 ■ Vietnam Veterans of Douglas County Chapter, Post 935
3971 Nations Dr.
Douglasville, GA 30135
Contact: Robert Budahazy, Pres.
Ph: (770)947-1866
E-mail: buda2@comcast.net
URL: http://www.gettingaway.com/VVA/VVA.htm

Hawaii

9477 ■ American Lung Association of Hawaii (ALAH)
680 Iwilei Rd., Ste. 575
Honolulu, HI 96817
Contact: Sterling Yee, Pres.
Ph: (808)537-5966
Fax: (808)537-5971
E-mail: lung@ala-hawaii.org
URL: http://www.ala-hawaii.org
Descr: Helps people with lung disease and breathing problems and raises the awareness of individuals on how to prevent or deal with a lung disease on a daily basis. **Fnd:** 1929.

9478 ■ Hawaii Department of Defense Office of Veterans' Services
Tripler Army Medical Ctr.
459 Patterson Rd.
E-Wing, Rm. 1-A103
Honolulu, HI 96819
Contact: Mark S. Moses, Dir.
Ph: (808)433-0420
Fax: (808)433-0385
E-mail: OVS@ovs.hawaii.gov
URL: http://hawaii.gov/dod/ovs/

9479 ■ Hawaii Disabled American Veterans
2333 Amoomoo St.
Pearl City, HI 96782
Contact: Albert Y. Matsumoto, Treas.
Ph: (808)228-7334
URL: http://www.davmembersportal.org/chapters/hi/01

9480 ■ National Association For Uniformed Services - Hawaiian Division, Chapter 1
1563 Molina St.
Honolulu, HI 96818
Contact: Fred Ballard
Free: 808-423-6265
E-mail: fred.ballard@va.gov
Descr: Provides assistance and support to active or retired military uniformed service officers. Protects and improves the compensation, entitlements and benefits earned by members of the uniformed services for themselves, their families and survivors and all American citizens with common interests.

Idaho

9481 ■ Idaho Division of Veterans' Affairs
320 Collins Rd.
Boise, ID 83702
Contact: Richard W. Jones, Division Admin.
Ph: (208)334-3513
Free: 800-827-1000
Fax: (208)334-2627
E-mail: info@veterans.idaho.gov
URL: http://veterans.idaho.gov/
Descr: Mission is to serve Idaho's veterans and their families through advocacy, assistance with benefits and education, long-term care, and interment services in a dignified final resting place.

Illinois

9482 ■ American Camping Association - Illinois Section
67 E Madison St., Ste. 1406
Chicago, IL 60603-3010
Contact: Gordie Kaplan, Section Exec.
Ph: (312)332-0833
Fax: (312)332-4011
E-mail: info@acail.org
URL: http://www.acail.org
Descr: Chartered Section of national organization. Accredits youth camps. Provides information to public free of charge to help them find a camp for their child. Professional development for camp leaders. **Mem:** 250. **Pub:** *CampLine* (3/year).

9483 ■ American Ex-Prisoners of War, Greater Chicago Chapter
12859 Shawnee Rd.
Palos Heights, IL 60463
Contact: Thomas Jundanian, Commander
Ph: (708)448-6862
Descr: Seeks to: acquaint the public with the needs, problems, and handicaps associated with prisoners of war; promote research in the fields connected with injuries, diseases, and syndromes stemming from imprisonment; advocate and foster complete and effective reconditioning programs for ex-prisoners of war; foster patriotism and civic loyalty; encourage fraternal and historical activities.

9484 ■ American Lung Association of Illinois (ALA-NCI)
3000 Kelly Ln.
Springfield, IL 62711
Contact: Harold Wimmer, Pres./CEO
Ph: (217)787-5864
Free: 800-548-8252
Fax: (217)787-5916
E-mail: info@lungil.org
URL: http://www.lungil.org
Descr: Represents voluntary health organizations concerned with controlling, preventing, and curing lung disease through research, education, and advocacy. **Pub:** *Breathing Matters*; Annual Report (annual).

9485 ■ AMVETS, Fisher Post 52
201 Division Ave.
Fisher, IL 61843
Ph: (217)897-6265

9486 ■ AMVETS, Knoxville Post 8
111 N Market St.
Knoxville, IL 61448
Contact: Don Dredge, Commander
Ph: (309)289-4524
E-mail: sixshelties@yahoo.com
URL: http://amvetspost8.homestead.com

9487 ■ AMVETS, Mount Vernon Post 4
1207 Main St.
Mount Vernon, IL 62864
Contact: Clay McDaniel, Commander
Ph: (618)244-1375
E-mail: lghoffman@charter.net
URL: http://geocities.com/ilamvetspost4

9488 ■ AMVETS, Ottawa Post 30
American Legion Post 33
901 Lasalle St.
Ottawa, IL 61350
Ph: (815)434-1029
E-mail: amvets-post30@mchsi.com

9489 ■ Illinois Department of Veterans' Affairs
PO Box 19432
833 S. Spring St.
Springfield, IL 62794-9432
Contact: L. Tammy Duckworth, Dir.
Ph: (217)782-6641
Free: 800-437-9824
Fax: (217)524-0344
E-mail: webmail@dva.state.il.us
URL: http://www.state.il.us/agency/dva/
Descr: Dedicated and committed to assist veterans

and their family members get the services they have rightfully earned.

9490 ■ Lakeview Action Coalition (LAC)
3225 N Sheffield Ave.
Chicago, IL 60657-2210
Contact: Jennifer Ritter-Gonzalez, Exec. Dir.
Ph: (773)549-1947
Fax: (773)549-4639
E-mail: jenrg@lakeviewaction.org
URL: http://www.lakeviewaction.org

Descr: Develops leaders through training, action and reflection. **Fnd:** 1993. **Mem:** 40.

9491 ■ National Funeral Directors and Morticians Association - District 4
7443 S Coles Ave.
Chicago, IL 60649
Contact: Valoria A. Dillon
Ph: (773)375-1509
Fax: (773)785-2523
E-mail: mbalm2@aol.com

Descr: Promotes ethical practices and encourages just and uniform laws pertaining to funeral directing and embalming industry.

9492 ■ Paralyzed Veterans of America, Vaughan Chapter
2235 Enterprise Dr., Ste. 3501
Westchester, IL 60154
Contact: Gary E. McDermott, Pres.
Ph: (708)947-9790
Free: 800-727-2234
Fax: (708)947-9755
E-mail: pvachvaug@mindspring.com
URL: http://www.vaughanpva.org

Staff: 2. **Descr:** Veterans from Illinois, northwestern Indiana, eastern Iowa, southwest Michigan, northern Missouri, and southwest Wisconsin with spinal cord injury or disease. Advocates for rights of veterans, their families, and other disabled individuals. **Fnd:** 1947. **Mem:** 773. **State Groups:** 1. **Pub:** *Getting It Done, A Future Together*; *PN/Paraplegia News* (monthly); *Sports 'N Spokes* (8/year); Newsletter (monthly).

Indiana

9493 ■ AMVETS, Bloomington Post 2000
5227 W Airport Rd.
Bloomington, IN 47403
Contact: Les Compton
Ph: (812)825-4490

9494 ■ AMVETS, Marion Post 5
841 E 38th St.
Marion, IN 46953
Contact: John Lawson, Commander
Ph: (765)674-2400
E-mail: rbpiper@prodigy.net
URL: http://geocities.com/amvetspost5

9495 ■ AMVETS, Muncie Post 12
7621 N State Rd. 3
Muncie, IN 47303
Contact: Gene Farmer, Commander
Ph: (765)287-9054
URL: http://amvetspost12.homestead.com

9496 ■ AMVETS, Rockville Post 61
PO Box 305
Rockville, IN 47872
Contact: Jon Tapia, Commander
Ph: (765)569-3312

9497 ■ AMVETS, West Harrison Post 13
515 S State St.
West Harrison, IN 47060
Contact: Daryl Denham, Commander
Ph: (812)637-2024

E-mail: amvets@amvets13.org
URL: http://www.amvets13.org

9498 ■ Vietnam Veterans of America, Chapter 295
PO Box 269279
Indianapolis, IN 46226-9279
Contact: Eugene Gigli, Pres.
Ph: (317)547-4748
E-mail: genegigli@aol.com
URL: http://www.vva295.org

Iowa

9499 ■ American Ex-Prisoners of War, Iowa Tri-State Chapter
PO Box 125
Lawton, IA 51030-0125
Contact: Adeline Robinson, Commander
Ph: (712)944-5351

Descr: Seeks to: acquaint the public with the needs, problems, and handicaps associated with prisoners of war; promote research in the fields connected with injuries, diseases, and syndromes stemming from imprisonment; advocate and foster complete and effective reconditioning programs for ex-prisoners of war; foster patriotism and civic loyalty; encourage fraternal and historical activities.

9500 ■ American Ex-Prisoners of War, Southwest Iowa Chapter
419 W Willow St.
Clarinda, IA 51632
Contact: Tom Snyder, Commander
Ph: (712)542-3927

Descr: Seeks to: acquaint the public with the needs, problems, and handicaps associated with prisoners of war; promote research in the fields connected with injuries, diseases, and syndromes stemming from imprisonment; advocate and foster complete and effective reconditioning programs for ex-prisoners of war; foster patriotism and civic loyalty; encourage fraternal and historical activities.

9501 ■ AMVETS, Anamosa Post 110
PO Box 442
Anamosa, IA 52205
Contact: Jim Slach, Commander
E-mail: amvets110@yahoo.com
URL: http://geocities.com/amvets110

9502 ■ AMVETS, Cedar Falls Post 49
PO Box 112
Cedar Falls, IA 50613
Contact: John Jasper, Commander
Ph: (319)277-6655
E-mail: jmyers049@mchsi.com
URL: http://amvetspost49.homestead.com

9503 ■ AMVETS, Cedar Rapids Post 6
700 Second St. SW
Cedar Rapids, IA 52404
Contact: Greg Wild, Commander
Ph: (319)363-1316
URL: http://geocities.com/iowaamvets6

9504 ■ Des Moines Citizens for Community Improvement
2005 Forest Ave.
Des Moines, IA 50311
Contact: Sharon Zanders-Ackiss, Dir.
Ph: (515)255-0800
Fax: (515)255-1314
E-mail: sharon@iowacci.org
URL: http://www.iowacci.org

Descr: Aims to empower and unite grassroots people of all ethnic backgrounds to address problems in their community and win social, economic and environmental justice.

9505 ■ International Municipal Signal Association, Midwestern Section
City of Bettendorf
4403 Devils Glen Rd.
Bettendorf, IA 52722
Contact: Bob Webster, Dir.

Ph: (563)344-4081
Fax: (563)344-4101
E-mail: bwebster@bettendorf.org

Descr: Serves as a professional organization of government officials responsible for municipal signaling, fire alarms, traffic signals, radio communication, street lighting, signs and marking, and other related services.

9506 ■ Iowa Citizens for Community Improvement (CCI)
2001 Forest Ave.
Des Moines, IA 50311
Contact: Hugh Espey, Exec. Dir.
Ph: (515)282-0484
Fax: (515)283-0031
E-mail: iowacci@iowacci.org
URL: http://www.iowacci.org

Staff: 15. **Descr:** Organizes programs for constructive change in the community. Sponsors urban and rural chapters that help lower income people organize for constructive change in their communities. **Fnd:** 1974. **Mem:** 1400. **Local Groups:** 5. **Pub:** *Iowa CCI News* (3/year).

9507 ■ Iowa Commission on Veterans' Affairs
Camp Dodge, Bldg. A6A
7105 NW 70th Ave.
Johnston, IA 50131-1824
Contact: Patrick J. Palmersheim, Exec.Dir.
Ph: (515)242-5331
Free: 800-838-4692
Fax: (515)242-5659
E-mail: info@idva.state.ia.us
URL: http://www2.state.ia.us/icva/

9508 ■ Iowa Disabled American Veterans
Federation Bldg.
210 Walnut St.
Des Moines, IA 50309
Contact: Robert E. Peterson, Supervisor
Ph: (515)323-7539
Fax: (515)323-7403
E-mail: info@daviowa.com
URL: http://www.daviowa.org

Descr: Works to give service to disabled veterans and their families. Provides services in areas including disaster relief, employment, legislation, advocacy and transportation.

9509 ■ National Organization of Circumcision Information Resource Centers of Iowa (NOCIRC)
PO Box 184
Ames, IA 50010
E-mail: nocircofames@hotmail.com
URL: http://nocircofiowa.cjb.net

Descr: Seeks to educate professionals and the public about the harm of routine infant male circumcision and the practice of female genital mutilation. **Fnd:** 1997.

9510 ■ Paralyzed Veterans of America, Iowa Chapter
3703 1/2 Douglas Ave.
Des Moines, IA 50310
Ph: (515)277-4782
Free: 888-909-4782
E-mail: iowapva@yahoo.com

9511 ■ Vietnam Veterans of America, Northwest Iowa - Chapter No. 888
6336 Y Ave.
Aurelia, IA 51005-7009
Contact: Dana C. Evans
Ph: (712)282-4360
Fax: (712)225-6708
E-mail: evans@schallertel.net
URL: http://www.geocities.com/dce_69/VVA888.html

Kansas

9512 ■ American Ex-Prisoners of War, Leavenworth POW Chapter
5825 Alhambra Dr.
Fairway, KS 66205

Contact: Benedict Lohman, Commander
Ph: (913)262-6955

Descr: Seeks to: acquaint the public with the needs, problems, and handicaps associated with prisoners of war; promote research in the fields connected with injuries, diseases, and syndromes stemming from imprisonment; advocate and foster complete and effective reconditioning programs for ex-prisoners of war; foster patriotism and civic loyalty; encourage fraternal and historical activities.

9513 ■ American Lung Association in Kansas
2024 N. Woodlawn, Ste. 114
Wichita, KS 67208
Contact: Lynne Crabtree, Sr. Program Dir.
Ph: (316)558-3090
Fax: (316)558-3094
E-mail: dtinker@breathehealthy.org
URL: http://www.lungusa.org/site/c.dvLUK9O0E/b.38003/k.90C5/Local_Lung_Assn.htm
Staff: 8. **Descr:** Promotes educational programs and research to prevent and control lung disease. **Fnd:** 1908. **Pub:** *Better Breathing* (quarterly).

9514 ■ International Municipal Signal Association, Central Section
PO Box 768
Olathe, KS 66051
Contact: David Kumke, Dir.
Ph: (913)971-5165
Fax: (913)971-5173
E-mail: dkumke@olatheks.org

Descr: Serves as a professional organization of government officials responsible for municipal signaling, fire alarms, traffic signals, radio communication, street lighting, signs and marking, and other related services.

9515 ■ Kansas Veterans' Commission
Jayhawk Tower
700 SW Jackson, Ste. 701
Topeka, KS 66603-3743
Contact: Colonel George S. Webb, Exec.Dir.
Ph: (785)296-3976
Fax: (785)296-1462
E-mail: bhayes@kcva.org
URL: http://www.kcva.org/

Kentucky

9516 ■ American Family Association of Kentucky
PO Box 8089
Louisville, KY 40257-8089
Contact: Dr. Frank G. Simon, State Dir.
Ph: (502)893-2444
Fax: (502)897-2426
E-mail: fsimon@afaky.com
Descr: Promotes the flow of God's love to all people. Fosters biblical ethic of decency in American society. **Pub:** *AFAKY Newsletter.*

9517 ■ AMVETS, Vine Grove Post 103
6645 Flaherty Rd.
Vine Grove, KY 40175
Ph: (270)877-2653
E-mail: amvets@bbtel.com

9518 ■ Kentucky Department of Military Affairs
Center for Veterans' Affairs
1111B Louisville Rd.
Frankfort, KY 40601
Contact: Leslie E. Beavers, Commnr.
Ph: (502)564-9203
Free: 800-572-6245
Fax: (502)564-9240
E-mail: melissa.hall@ky.gov
URL: http://www.veterans.ky.gov/
Descr: Mission is to ensure Kentucky's 357,000

veterans and their families receive all the benefits and services they have earned.

9519 ■ Kentucky Political Science Association (KPSA)
IRAPP 110 Combs Bldg.
UPO Box 699
150 University Blvd.
Morehead, KY 40351
Contact: Michael W. Hail PhD
Ph: (859)351-9997
E-mail: info@kpsaweb.org
URL: http://www.kpsaweb.org

Descr: Represents college and university teachers of political science, public officials, research workers, and businessmen. Encourages the impartial study and promotes the development of the art and science of government. Develops research projects of public interest and educational programs for political scientists and journalists. Seeks to improve the knowledge of and increase citizen participation in political and governmental affairs. **Fnd:** 1962. **Mem:** 100.

9520 ■ Kentucky Society of EAs
8333 Alexandria Pike, Ste. 204
Alexandria, KY 41001-1187
Contact: John C. Frazier EA
Ph: (859)694-3000
Fax: (859)448-2762
E-mail: jctaxpro@aol.com
URL: http://www.naea.org/MemberPortal/StateAffiliates/Listing

9521 ■ Religious Coalition for Reproductive Choice - Kentucky Chapter (KRCRC)
PO Box 4065
Louisville, KY 40204-0065
Contact: Anne Maron, Chair
Free: 866-606-0988
E-mail: info@krcrc.org
URL: http://www.krcrc.org

Louisiana

9522 ■ Louisiana Department of Veterans' Affairs
1885 Wooddale Blvd.
PO Box 94095
Baton Rouge, LA 70804-9095
Contact: Lane Carson, Sec.
Ph: (504)922-0500
Fax: (504)922-0511
E-mail: lacarson@vetaffairs.com
URL: http://www.vetaffairs.com/index.asp

Descr: Mission is to assist Louisiana veterans and their dependents in receiving all federal and state benefits, and deliver quality services at War Veterans Homes and Veterans Cemeteries.

9523 ■ Vietnam Veterans of America, Chapter 553
PO Box 2082
Harvey, LA 70059-2082
Contact: Charlene Ellender, Pres.
E-mail: cseangel@bellsouth.net
URL: http://members.tripod.com/vva553

Maine

9524 ■ American Pain Society, Maine
4 Catalpa Ln.
Cumberland Center, ME 04021
Contact: Hilary Doane, Rep.
Ph: (207)232-3097
Free: 800-964-5882
E-mail: hilary.doane@kingpharm.com
Descr: Advances pain-related research, education, treatment and professional practice. Promotes control, management and understanding of pain.

Develops standards for training and ethical management of pain patients.

9525 ■ AMVETS, Liberty Post 150
PO Box 25
Liberty, ME 04949
Ph: (207)589-4218
E-mail: amvetsme150@yahoo.com
URL: http://geocities.com/amvetsme150

Descr: Provides assistance to veterans with claims through a network of service offices through the United States.

9526 ■ Maine Bureau of Veterans' Services
117 State House Station
Augusta, ME 04333-0117
Contact: Peter W. Ogden, Dir.
Ph: (207)626-4464
Fax: (207)626-4471
E-mail: mainebvs@maine.gov
URL: http://www.mainebvs.org/

Descr: Mission is to ensure that Maine veterans and their dependants receive all entitlements due under the law, are relieved to the extent possible of financial hardship, receive every opportunity for self-improvement through higher education, and are afforded proper recognition for their service and sacrifice to the Nation.

9527 ■ Maine Disabled American Veterans
PO Box 3415
Augusta, ME 04330-3415
Contact: Joseph E. Wafford, Supervisor
Ph: (207)623-5725
Fax: (207)623-1528
E-mail: davadmin@gwi.net

Maryland

9528 ■ Associates of Vietnam Veterans of America (AVVA)
PO Box 64732
Baltimore, MD 21264-4732
Contact: Elaine Simmons, Pres.
Ph: (301)585-4000
Free: 800-882-1316
Fax: (301)585-0519
E-mail: pvarnell@avva.org
URL: http://www.avva.org
Descr: Strives to advance the work of the Vietnam Veterans of America through cooperative projects and/or programs. Works to facilitate, enhance and improve communication with members and the general public and to continue legislative efforts to ensure the rights of benefits for all veterans and their families. **Fnd:** 1999. **Mem:** 6000. **Reg. Groups:** 9. **State Groups:** 40. **Pub:** *The Veteran* (quarterly).

9529 ■ Maryland Veterans' Commission
Federal Bldg. Rm. 1231
31 Hopkins Plaza
Baltimore, MD 21201
Contact: James A. Adkins, Sec.
Ph: (410)230-4444
Free: 800-446-4926
Fax: (410)230-4445
E-mail: mdveteransinfo@mdva.state.md.us
URL: http://www.mdva.state.md.us

9530 ■ Vietnam Veterans of America, Chapter 172
17 N Liberty St.
Cumberland, MD 21502
Contact: Roger Krueger, Pres.
Ph: (301)777-7001
Free: 800-482-VETS
URL: http://www.vietnamreflections.com

9531 ■ Vietnam Veterans of America, Chapter 451
6401 Beckley St.
Baltimore, MD 21224
Contact: Ray Kesterson, Pres.

Ph: (410)633-0857
URL: http://www.vva451.org

9532 ■ Vietnam Veterans of America, Chapter 712
PO Box 532
Riva, MD 21140
Contact: Ed Peckman, Pres.
E-mail: info@vva712.org
URL: http://www.vva712.org

9533 ■ Vietnam Veterans of America, Montgomery County - Chapter No. 641
PO Box 1748
Silver Spring, MD 20915
Contact: Dave Gudes, Pres.
E-mail: dgudes@cpsc.gov
URL: http://www.vvachapter641.org
Pub: *Incoming.*

Massachusetts

9534 ■ American Lung Association of Massachusetts
460 Totten Pond Rd., Ste. 400
Waltham, MA 02451-1991
Contact: David Ales, Sr. VP
Ph: (781)890-4262
Fax: (781)890-4280
E-mail: dales@lungma.org
URL: http://www.lungma.org/site/pp.aspx?c=fhJLJTOxFmH&b=1717421
Staff: 39. **Descr:** Dedicated to preventing lung disease and promoting lung health with research, advocacy, community coalition, and education programs. Nationwide priorities are tobacco control, asthma, and environmental health. **Fnd:** 1907. **Local Groups:** 3. **Pub:** *Lung News* (semiannual).

9535 ■ American Pain Society, Massachusetts
Brigham and Women's Hospital
Pain Management Ctr.
850 Boylston St.
Chestnut Hill, MA 02467
Contact: Srdjan S. Nedeljkovic MD, Treas.
Ph: (617)732-9057
Fax: (617)732-9050
E-mail: srdjan@zeus.bwh.harvard.edu
Descr: Advances pain-related research, education, treatment and professional practice. Promotes control, management and understanding of pain. Develops standards for training and ethical management of pain patients.

9536 ■ AMVETS, Cape Cod Post 333
PO Box 332
Dennis Port, MA 02639
Contact: Cleon Turner, State Rep.
Ph: (508)240-7378
E-mail: info@capecodamvetspost333.com
URL: http://capecodamvetspost333.com

9537 ■ Disabled American Veterans, Massachusetts State Department
Rm. 546, Station House
Boston, MA 02133-1042
Contact: Mr. Tom Daley
Ph: (617)727-2974
Fax: (617)742-9843
E-mail: dstack@davma.org
URL: http://www.davma.org
Staff: 9. **Descr:** Provides support and service to disabled veterans and their families. **Fnd:** 1921. **Mem:** 41000. **Pub:** Newsletter (quarterly).

9538 ■ Massachusetts Department of Veterans' Services
600 Washington St., Ste. 1100
Boston, MA 02111
Contact: Thomas G. Kelley, Sec.
Ph: (617)210-5480
Fax: (617)210-5755
E-mail: MDVS@vet.state.ma.us
URL: http://www.mass.gov/veterans
Descr: Establishes policy, proposes legislation, ensures that adequate funding for veterans' pro-

grams is included in the Governor's budget, and represents the interests of veterans in matters coming before the General Court.

9539 ■ Massachusetts Public Interest Research Group (MASSPIRG)
44 Winter St., 4th Fl.
Boston, MA 02108
Contact: Janet S. Domenitz, Exec. Dir.
Ph: (617)292-4800
Fax: (617)292-8057
E-mail: info@masspirg.org
Staff: 9. **Descr:** Promotes clean air, clean water, recycling safe and affordable energy, and consumer rights. **Fnd:** 1973. **Mem:** 55000. **Local Groups:** 1. **Pub:** *MASSPIRG MASSCITIZEN* (quarterly).

9540 ■ National Association For Uniformed Services - Boston, Massachusetts Chapter 1
237 Marion St.
East Boston, MA 02128
Contact: Vincent Manganello
Ph: (617)567-3116
Descr: Provides assistance and support to active or retired military uniformed service officers. Protects and improves the compensation, entitlements and benefits earned by members of the uniformed services for themselves, their families and survivors and all American citizens with common interests.

9541 ■ National Association For Uniformed Services - Southwestern New England, Chapter 3
46 Inward Commons
East Longmeadow, MA 01028
Contact: Lt. Col. Robert Picknally
Ph: (413)525-5254
Descr: Provides assistance and support to active or retired military uniformed service officers. Protects and improves the compensation, entitlements and benefits earned by members of the uniformed services for themselves, their families and survivors and all American citizens with common interests.

9542 ■ New England Chapter Paralyzed Veterans of America (NEPVA)
1600 Providence Hwy., Ste. 101R
Walpole, MA 02081
Contact: Ms. Debra Freed, VP/Sec.
Ph: (508)660-1181
Free: 800-660-1181
Fax: (508)668-9412
E-mail: info@nepva.org
URL: http://www.nepva.org
Staff: 3. **Descr:** Provides unique services on a wide variety of issues involving the special needs of veterans of the armed forces who have experienced spinal cord dysfunction or injury. **Fnd:** 1946. **Mem:** 940. **Pub:** *Cord Word* (monthly).

9543 ■ Religious Coalition for Reproductive Choice - Massachusetts Chapter
PO Box 1129
Brookline, MA 02446
Contact:Rev. Susan Criscione
Ph: (617)522-2964
Fax: (617)426-8389
E-mail: info@rcrcofma.org

9544 ■ Vietnam Veterans of America, Chapter 908
PO Box 8043
Lynn, MA 01904-8043
Contact: Butch Dresser, Pres.
E-mail: info@vva908.org
URL: http://www.vva908.org

9545 ■ Vietnam Veterans of America, Massachusetts State Council
9 K St.
Turners Falls, MA 01376-1408
Contact: Marshall Mudge, Pres.
E-mail: mudgevva72@verizon.net
URL: http://www.baystatevet.com/bsv_004.htm

Michigan

9546 ■ American Arbitration Association, Michigan
27777 Franklin Rd., Ste. 1150, 11th Fl.
Southfield, MI 48034
Contact: Ms. Janice Holdinski, VP
Ph: (248)352-5500
Fax: (248)352-3147
E-mail: holdinskij@adr.org
URL: http://www.adr.org
Descr: Works to the development and use of prompt, effective and economical methods of dispute resolution. Offers a broad range of dispute resolution services to business executives, attorneys, individuals, trade associations, unions, management, consumers, families, communities and all levels of government.

9547 ■ American Association of University Women, Grand Rapids Branch
1740 Malvern Rd.
Jackson, MI 49203
Contact: Marilyn Vankat, Pres.
Ph: (517)784-9523
E-mail: amvankat@comcast.net
URL: http://www.aauwmi.org
Staff: 6. **Descr:** Graduates of accredited four-year colleges and universities. Works to promote equity for all women and girls, lifelong education and positive societal change. Sponsors fundraisers, works on community committees affecting equity, co-sponsors "Science is for Girls" event and organizes study groups. **Fnd:** 1941. **Mem:** 38. **Pub:** *News Brief* (monthly); Directory (annual).

9548 ■ AMVETS, Big Rapids
320 S 4th St.
Big Rapids, MI 49307
Contact: Mike O'Connor, Commander
Ph: (231)796-6998
URL: http://www.amvets1941.com

9549 ■ AMVETS, Cadillac Post 110
127 W Cass St.
Cadillac, MI 49601
Contact: Peggy Cook, Commander
Ph: (231)775-7433

9550 ■ Citizens for Better Care (CBC)
4750 Woodward Ave., Ste. 410
Detroit, MI 48201
Contact: Helen Kozlowski-Hicks, Exec. Dir.
Ph: (313)832-6387
Free: 800-833-9548
Fax: (313)832-7407
E-mail: info@cbcmi.org
URL: http://www.cbcmi.org
Staff: 30. **Descr:** Senior citizens, citizens' groups, and interested professionals. Works to improve the quality of long-term care; disseminates information about nursing homes, homes for the aged, and long-term care programs or services; helps in linking or directing the family with other continuing care resources; provides information about nursing home and adult foster care law and other regulations in long-term care facilities; assists in planning care for frail, elderly, and disabled adults. Sponsors speakers bureau. **Fnd:** 1969. **Mem:** 2500. **Local Groups:** 5. **Pub:** *Directory of Nursing Homes* (periodic); *Rising Standard* (3/year).

9551 ■ International Municipal Signal Association, Michigan Section
3415 Davison Lake Rd.
Ortonville, MI 48462
Contact: Mr. William Moroski, Dir.
Ph: (248)890-1036
E-mail: imsa-misection@charter.net
URL: http://www.imsamichigan.org
Descr: Serves as a professional organization of government officials responsible for municipal signaling, fire alarms, traffic signals, radio communication,

street lighting, signs and marking, and other related services.

9552 ■ Michigan Conference of Political Scientists
Aquinas College
Political Science Department
1607 Robinson Rd. SE
Grand Rapids, MI 49506
Contact: Dr. Roger Durham
Ph: (616)632-2840
E-mail: durharog@aquinas.edu
URL: http://www.apsanet.org/~michigan
Descr: Represents college and university teachers of political science, public officials, research workers, and businessmen. Encourages the impartial study and promotes the development of the art and science of government. Develops research projects of public interest and educational programs for political scientists and journalists. Seeks to improve the knowledge of and increase citizen participation in political and governmental affairs.

9553 ■ Michigan Department of Military and Veterans' Affairs
3411 Martin Luther King Jr. Blvd.
Lansing, MI 48906
Contact: Major General Thomas G. Cutler, Dir./
Adjutant General
Ph: (517)481-8000
Fax: (517)241-0674
E-mail: hessh@michigan.gov
URL: http://www.michigan.gov/dmva/

9554 ■ Paralyzed Veterans of America, Michigan Chapter
40550 Grand River Ave.
Novi, MI 48375
Contact: Michael F. Harris, Exec. Dir.
Ph: (248)476-9000
Free: 800-638-MPVA
Fax: (248)476-9545
E-mail: chapterhq@michiganpva.org
URL: http://www.michiganpva.org
Staff: 7. **Descr:** Veterans who have incurred an injury or disease affecting the spinal cord and causing paralysis. **Fnd:** 1961. **Mem:** 600.

9555 ■ Vietnam Veterans of America, Chapter 154
16945 Twelve Mile Rd.
Roseville, MI 48066-2479
Contact: Pat Daniels, Pres.
Ph: (586)776-9810
E-mail: piofficer@vva154.com
URL: http://www.vva154.com

9556 ■ Vietnam Veterans of America, Chapter 237
PO Box 608
Munising, MI 49862
Contact: Mike Dugas, Pres.
Ph: (906)378-3837
Fax: (906)378-3837
E-mail: namvet@up.net
URL: http://vva_chapter_237.tripod.com

9557 ■ Vietnam Veterans of America, Chapter 267
3001 S Telegraph Rd.
Dearborn, MI 48128
Contact: Raul Roy Flores, Pres.
Ph: (313)562-9090
E-mail: wwrau55lin@aol.com
URL: http://www.vvachapter267.org

9558 ■ Vietnam Veterans of America, Chapter 380
173 US 41 E
Negaunee, MI 49866
Contact: Steve Mahaffey, Pres.
Ph: (906)475-6435
E-mail: vva380@chartermi.net
URL: http://www.vva380.org

Pub: *380 In Review* (bimonthly).

9559 ■ Vietnam Veterans of America, Chapter No. 882
PO Box 2
Hale, MI 48739-0002
Ph: (989)728-8820
E-mail: davenelsey@m33access.com
URL: http://www.halemichigan.net/vva/vva.html

9560 ■ Vietnam Veterans of America, Monroe County - Chapter 142
PO Box 1407
Monroe, MI 48161
Contact: Donald Cannon, Pres.
Ph: (734)242-0526
URL: http://www.vietnamveterans142.org
Descr: Aims to work for the employment, education benefits, improved psychological assistance, and health care of Vietnam veterans.

9561 ■ Vietnam Veterans of America, Washtenaw County - Chapter 310
PO Box 3221
Ann Arbor, MI 48106-3221
Contact: Tim Driscoll, Pres.
Ph: (734)222-4743
E-mail: president@vva310.org
URL: http://www.vva310.org

Minnesota

9562 ■ Minnesota Department of Veterans' Affairs
State Veterans Service Bldg.
20 W. 12th St., Rm. 206C
St. Paul, MN 55155-2006
Contact: Clark Dyrud, Commnr.
Ph: (651)296-2562
Fax: (651)296-3954
E-mail: clark.dyrud@state.mn.us
URL: http://www.mdva.state.mn.us/

9563 ■ Minnesota Paralyzed Veterans of America
1 Veterans Dr., Rm. 4L-131
Minneapolis, MN 55417
Ph: (612)725-2263
Free: 800-663-6782
Fax: (612)726-9472
E-mail: mnpva@qwest.net
URL: http://www.mnpva.org

9564 ■ Minnesota Religious Coalition for Reproductive Choice (MNRCRC)
122 W Franklin Ave., No. 303
Minneapolis, MN 55404
Contact: Kiely Todd Roska, Exec. Dir.
Ph: (612)870-0974
E-mail: info@mnrcrc.org
URL: http://www.mnrcrc.org

9565 ■ Vietnam Veterans of America, Central Minnesota - Chapter 290
PO Box 7004
St. Cloud, MN 56302
E-mail: docsmith1022@charter.net
URL: http://www.vvachapter290mn.org

9566 ■ Waseca County Chapter, American Red Cross
511 S State St.
Waseca, MN 56093-3032
Contact: Robin Roberts, Mgr.
Ph: (507)835-8369
Free: 877-835-8369
Fax: (507)835-8778
E-mail: redcross@platec.net
URL: http://wccarc.4mg.com
Staff: 18. **Descr:** Strives to reduce the suffering of victims of disaster by helping communities to prepare, prevent and respond to disaster. Provides emergency communications to members of the armed forces, veterans and their families. Aids disaster victims and trains people in lifesaving skills and water safety. Provides other activities such as blood services, community services, and service op-

portunities for the youth. **Fnd:** 1917.

Mississippi

9567 ■ American Subcontractors Association of Mississippi (ASAMS)
PO Box 84
Jackson, MS 39205
Contact: Reid Guy, Board Admin.
Ph: (601)352-9273
Free: 888-639-8745
Fax: (601)352-9274
E-mail: reid@msasa.com
URL: http://www.msasa.com
Descr: Works to promote education and ethical business practices. Improves the business environment for the small business entrepreneurs through education, legislation, and networking. **Fnd:** 1977. **Pub:** *Mississippi Subcontractor Publication* (weekly).

9568 ■ National Funeral Directors and Morticians Association - District 6
3580 Robinson Rd.
Jackson, MS 39209
Contact: Gregory Owens
Ph: (601)238-2270
Fax: (601)922-5033
E-mail: intnatmort@aol.com
Descr: Promotes ethical practices and encourages just and uniform laws pertaining to funeral directing and embalming industry.

9569 ■ Paralyzed Veterans of America, Bayou Gulf States Chapter
15489 Dedeaux Rd.
Gulfport, MS 39503-2667
Ph: (228)832-6864
E-mail: bayougulfstates@cableone.net

Missouri

9570 ■ American Arbitration Association, Kansas City, Missouri Regional Office
100 N Broadway, Ste. 1820
St. Louis, MO 63102
Contact: Robert Hughes
Ph: (314)621-7175
E-mail: hughesr@adr.org
URL: http://www.adr.org
Descr: Works to provide exceptional neutrals, proficient case management, dedicated personnel, advanced education and training, and innovative process knowledge to meet the conflict management and dispute resolution needs of the public now and in the future. **Fnd:** 1926.

9571 ■ American Arbitration Association - St. Louis Chapter
100 N Broadway, Ste. 1820
St. Louis, MO 63102
Contact: Robert Hughes, VP
Ph: (314)621-7175
Fax: (314)621-3730
E-mail: hughesr@adr.org

9572 ■ American Ex-Prisoners of War, State Fair Chapter
112 Hill Dr.
Windsor, MO 65360
Contact: Grover C. Mullins
Ph: (660)647-2356
Descr: Seeks to: acquaint the public with the needs, problems, and handicaps associated with prisoners of war; promote research in the fields connected with injuries, diseases, and syndromes stemming from imprisonment; advocate and foster complete and effective reconditioning programs for ex-prisoners of war; foster patriotism and civic loyalty; encourage fraternal and historical activities.

9573 ■ American Lung Association of Missouri (ALAM)
1118 Hampton Ave.
St. Louis, MO 63139
Ph: (314)645-5505
Free: 800-LUNG-USA

Fax: (314)645-7128
E-mail: jdirkers@breathehealthy.org
Staff: 18. **Descr:** Works to prevent lung disease and promotes lung health through research, education and advocacy. **Fnd:** 1907. **Mem:** 80000. **Pub:** *Life and Breath* (semiannual); Annual Report (annual).

9574 ■ Missouri Public Transit Association (MPTA)
606 Dix Rd.
Jefferson City, MO 65109
Contact: Doris Boeckman, Exec. Dir.
Ph: (573)634-4314
Fax: (573)632-6678
E-mail: mpta_org@earthlink.net
URL: http://www.mptaonline.typepad.com
Staff: 3. **Descr:** Represents the interests, policies, requirements and purposes of public transit in Missouri. Exchanges experiences, discussions and comparative studies of industry affairs relating to transportation. Promotes research and investigations toward improving public transit in Missouri. Aids member organizations with special issues and legislation pertaining to public transit. Encourages cooperation among its members, its employees, and the general public. Informs member by the collection, and the compilation of data and information relative to public transit in Missouri. **Fnd:** 1980. **Pub:** *TransitTalk* (quarterly).

9575 ■ Missouri Veterans' Commission
205 Jefferson St.
Jefferson Bldg., 12th Fl.
PO Drawer 147
Jefferson City, MO 65102
Contact: Harold J. Dulle, Exec.Dir.
Ph: (573)751-3779
Free: 866-838-4636
Fax: (573)571-6836
E-mail: Movets.veteran@mvc.dps.mo.gov
URL: http://www.mvc.dps.mo.gov

9576 ■ Paralyzed Veterans of America, Gateway Chapter
9738 Lackland Rd.
St. Louis, MO 63114
Contact: Stanley D. Brown, Pres.
Ph: (314)427-0393
Free: 800-426-4058
Fax: (314)427-4183
E-mail: adjunct@sbcglobal.net
URL: http://www.gatewaypva.org

9577 ■ Religious Coalition for Reproductive Choice - Missouri Chapter
462 N Taylor Ave., Ste. 102
St. Louis, MO 63108
Ph: (314)531-5010
Fax: (314)531-5014
E-mail: execdirector@morcrc.org
URL: http://www.morcrc.org

9578 ■ Vietnam Veterans of America, Chapter 243
PO Box 2164
Lee's Summit, MO 64063
Contact: Charles Stapleton, Pres.
Ph: (816)690-7299
URL: http://www.vva243kc.org
Fnd: 1993.

9579 ■ Vietnam Veterans of America, Chapter 458
75 Lower Dardenne Farms Dr.
St. Charles, MO 63304
Contact: Len Berkel, Pres.
Ph: (636)978-8433
E-mail: lnarmvet70@aol.com
URL: http://missouristatecouncil.bravehost.com

9580 ■ Vietnam Veterans of America, Chapter 611
PO Box 22169
St. Louis, MO 63169
Contact: Rick Luby, Pres.
Ph: (618)337-5610
URL: http://missouristatecouncil.bravehost.com

Descr: Aims to work for the employment, education benefits, improved psychological assistance, and health care of Vietnam veterans.

9581 ■ Vietnam Veterans of America, Chapter 638
PO Box 7042
St. Joseph, MO 64507
Contact: Walter Harper, Pres.
Ph: (816)238-5511
URL: http://missouristatecouncil.bravehost.com
Descr: Aims to work for the employment, education benefits, improved psychological assistance, and health care of Vietnam veterans.

9582 ■ Vietnam Veterans of America, Chapter 794
12775 New Halls Ferry Rd.
Florissant, MO 63033
Contact: Walter Kaiser, Pres.
Ph: (314)921-2132
E-mail: walantel@aol.com
URL: http://missouristatecouncil.bravehost.com

9583 ■ Vietnam Veterans of America, Chapter 859
PO Box 1095
Poplar Bluff, MO 63902
Contact: Larry Thompson, Pres.
Ph: (573)683-8497
Fax: (573)785-0303
URL: http://missouristatecouncil.bravehost.com
Descr: Aims to work for the employment, education benefits, improved psychological assistance, and health care of Vietnam veterans.

9584 ■ Vietnam Veterans of America, Chapter 918
306 S Kirkpatrick St.
El Dorado Springs, MO 64744
Contact: Laddie Tabor, Pres.
Ph: (417)876-3447
E-mail: guesthouse304@yahoo.com
URL: http://missouristatecouncil.bravehost.com

9585 ■ Vietnam Veterans of America, Missouri State Council
5599 Pinehurst Ln.
Columbia, MO 65202
Contact: Alan Gibson, Pres.
Ph: (573)474-2486
Fax: (573)814-0348
E-mail: vvamo1@aol.com
URL: http://missouristatecouncil.bravehost.com

Montana

9586 ■ Montana Department of Military Affairs Veterans' Affairs Division
PO Box 4789
Fort Harrison, MT 59636-4789
Contact: Joseph S. Foster, Admin.
Ph: (406)324-3740
Fax: (406)324-3145
E-mail: lehall@mt.gov
URL: http://discoveringmontana.com/DMA/Veterans/mvad/
Descr: Mission is to establish a statewide network of service for discharged veterans and their families; provide services and assistance for all Montana veterans and surviving spouses and dependents in coordination with associated federal agencies, veterans' services organizations, private organizations, and individuals; continuing education and assistance for the general public, governmental agencies, and elected officials regarding veterans' services, programs, initiatives, and policy; and administer, operate, and maintain Montana's state veterans cemeteries.

9587 ■ National Association of Activity Professionals - Montana
PO Box 471
Broadus, MT 59317
Contact: Susan Richards
Ph: (406)436-2646

Descr: Provides assistance at the state level to promote certification of activity professionals, working toward uniform professional standards for activity practice.

9588 ■ Vietnam Veterans of America, Bitterroot - Chapter No. 938
PO Box 1391
Hamilton, MT 59840
Contact: Dan Mayer, Pres.
E-mail: bugoff95@aol.com

9589 ■ Western Organization of Resource Councils (WORC)
220 S 27th St., Ste. B
Billings, MT 59101
Contact: Patrick Sweeney, Dir.
Ph: (406)252-9672
Fax: (406)252-1092
E-mail: billings@worc.org
URL: http://www.worc.org
Staff: 10. **Descr:** Farmers, ranchers, and other individuals living in rural areas in the western U.S. Seeks to ensure that residents are involved in rural public policy development and decision making. Conducts community organizing. Produces weekly radio news program. **Fnd:** 1979. **Mem:** 9500. **State Groups:** 7. **Local Groups:** 45. **Pub:** *Western Organizing Review* (quarterly).

Nebraska

9590 ■ American Ex-Prisoners of War, Lincoln Chapter
115 Pine St.
Friend, NE 68359
Contact: Robert W. Mead
Ph: (402)947-9217

Descr: Seeks to: acquaint the public with the needs, problems, and handicaps associated with prisoners of war; promote research in the fields connected with injuries, diseases, and syndromes stemming from imprisonment; advocate and foster complete and effective reconditioning programs for ex-prisoners of war; foster patriotism and civic loyalty; encourage fraternal and historical activities.

9591 ■ Disabled Veterans of America Fremont Chapter - Disabled American Veterans No. 18
137 North D
Fremont, NE 68025
Contact: Alfonso G. Martinez, Commander
Ph: (402)727-5959
URL: http://www.davmembersportal.org/chapters/ne/18/default.aspx

Descr: Disabled veterans. Serves veterans and their families. **Fnd:** 1955. **Mem:** 287. **Pub:** *DAV Chapter No. 18 Fremont Nebraska* (monthly).

9592 ■ National Association For Uniformed Services - Omaha, Nebraska Chapter 1
1006 Martin Dr. W
Bellevue, NE 68005
Contact: Richard Brazis
Ph: (402)292-5649
Descr: Provides assistance and support to active or retired military uniformed service officers. Protects and improves the compensation, entitlements and benefits earned by members of the uniformed services for themselves, their families and survivors and all American citizens with common interests.

9593 ■ Nebraska Department of Veterans' Affairs
PO Box 95083
301 Centennial Mall S., 6th Fl.
Lincoln, NE 68509-5083
Contact: John Hilgert, Dir.
Ph: (402)471-2458
Fax: (402)471-2491

E-mail: jhilgert@nebraska.gov
URL: http://www.vets.state.ne.us

9594 ■ Paralyzed Veterans of America, Great Plains Chapter
7612 Maple St.
Omaha, NE 68134
Contact: Mark Linquist, Pres.
Ph: (402)398-1422
Free: 800-454-7782
E-mail: linquist@greatplainspva.org
URL: http://www.greatplainspva.org

Nevada

9595 ■ Nevada Office of Veterans' Services
5460 Reno Corporate Dr.
Reno, NV 89511
Contact: Tim Tetz, Exec.Dir.
Ph: (775)688-1653
Fax: (775)688-1656
URL: http://veterans.nv.gov/

Descr: Mission is to provide a full continuum of quality services to eligible veterans and their families; provide an environment of growth and opportunity to our employees; and to provide our community and partners the opportunity to contribute in this endeavor.

New Hampshire

9596 ■ American Pain Society, New Hampshire
Elliot Hospital, Ste. 200
1 Elliot Way
Manchester, NH 03103
Contact: Eduardo Quesada MD, Rep.
Ph: (603)663-2315
Fax: (603)663-6538
E-mail: ewquesada@netscape.net

Descr: Advances pain-related research, education, treatment and professional practice. Promotes control, management and understanding of pain. Develops standards for training and ethical management of pain patients.

9597 ■ National Association For Uniformed Services - Dover/Southern, New Hampshire Chapter 1
3 Crestview Dr.
Dover, NH 03820-2306
Contact: Eugene Paquette
Ph: (603)742-7031
E-mail: genele56@toast.net

Descr: Provides assistance and support to active or retired military uniformed service officers. Protects and improves the compensation, entitlements and benefits earned by members of the uniformed services for themselves, their families and survivors and all American citizens with common interests.

9598 ■ National Spa and Pool Institute, Region IX
53 Regional Dr., Ste. 1
Concord, NH 03301
Contact: Walter Perry, Exec. Dir.
Ph: (603)228-1231
Fax: (603)228-2118
E-mail: wperry@apsp.org
URL: http://www.apspregion9.org/APSP06/1005/72/index.aspx

Staff: 4. **Descr:** Conducts educational programs for pool and hot tub industry professionals in Maine, New Hampshire, Vermont, Massachusetts, and Rhode Island. **Mem:** 160. **Pub:** Bulletin (bimonthly).

9599 ■ New Hampshire State Veterans' Council
275 Chestnut St., Rm. 517
Manchester, NH 03101-2411
Contact: Mary E. Morin, Dir.
Ph: (603)624-9230
Free: 800-622-9230
Fax: (603)624-9236

E-mail: mary.morin@vba.va.gov
URL: http://www.nh.gov/nhveterans/
Descr: Mission is to assist veterans who are residents of New Hampshire or their dependents in securing all benefits or preferences to which they may be entitled under any state or federal laws or regulations. **Telecom. Svcs:** TDD access using toll-free number (800)735-2964.

New Jersey

9600 ■ American Arbitration Association, New Jersey
220 Davidson Ave., 1st Fl.
Somerset, NJ 08873-4159
Ph: (215)560-9560
Descr: Provides alternative dispute resolution services including arbitration, mediation, and early neutral evaluation.

9601 ■ American Lung Association of New Jersey (ALANJ)
1600 Rt. 22 E
Union, NJ 07083
Ph: (908)687-9340
Free: 800-LUNG-USA
Fax: (908)851-2625
URL: http://www.alanewjersey.org
Staff: 14. **Descr:** Provides lung health education. Advocacy regarding health issues. Researches lung disease. **Fnd:** 1906. **Mem:** 25. **State Groups:** 1. **Pub:** Newsletter (semiannual).

9602 ■ American Subcontractors Association of New Jersey (ASANJ)
40 Brunswick Ave., Ste. 206
Edison, NJ 08817-2589
Contact: Ms. Doreen Siegel, Exec.Dir.
Ph: (732)287-3430
Fax: (732)248-0885
E-mail: info@asa-nj.org
URL: http://www.asa-nj.org
Staff: 2. **Descr:** Works to seek better legislation for the construction industry. Educates subcontractors. It represents the concerns and interests of subcontractors, suppliers, and professional service providers, throughout New Jersey. **Fnd:** 1968. **Mem:** 200. **State Groups:** 50. **Pub:** *Ad Journal* (annual); Newsletter (periodic); Membership Directory (annual).

9603 ■ Center for Civic Responsibility and the Citizens' Campaign
450 Main St., 2nd Fl.
Metuchen, NJ 08840
Contact: Heather Taylor, Communications Dir.
Ph: (732)548-9798
Fax: (732)548-9298
E-mail: info@jointhecampaign.com
URL: http://www.jointhecampaign.com
Descr: Nonpartisan citizens' lobby. Dedicated to fighting for open, honest, and accountable government. **Fnd:** 1997.

9604 ■ International Municipal Signal Association, New Jersey Section
100 Middlesex Blvd., Unit 243
Plainsboro, NJ 08536
Contact: Carmine Guagenti, Sec.-Treas.
Ph: (609)275-6623
E-mail: imsa-nj@worldnet.att.net
URL: http://www.newjersey.imsasafety.org
Descr: Serves as a professional organization of government officials responsible for municipal signaling, fire alarms, traffic signals, radio communication, street lighting, signs and marking, and other related services.

9605 ■ National Association For Uniformed Services - Fort Monmouth, New Jersey Chapter 1
327 Main St.
Port Monmouth, NJ 07758-1040
Contact: Andy Butzko
Ph: (908)495-6176
Descr: Provides assistance and support to active or retired military uniformed service officers. Protects

and improves the compensation, entitlements and benefits earned by members of the uniformed services for themselves, their families and survivors and all American citizens with common interests.

9606 ■ National Association For Uniformed Services - Garden State, Chapter 2
578A Kevin Ct.
Manchester, NJ 08759-7011
Contact: Merle Stouffer
Ph: (732)323-8442
E-mail: msg.stouffer@verizon.net
Descr: Provides assistance and support to active or retired military uniformed service officers. Protects and improves the compensation, entitlements and benefits earned by members of the uniformed services for themselves, their families and survivors and all American citizens with common interests.

9607 ■ New Jersey Department of Military and Veterans' Affairs
PO Box 340
Trenton, NJ 08625-0340
Contact: Col. Stephen Abel, Dep.Commnr.
Ph: (609)530-7045
Free: 800-624-0508
Fax: (609)530-7075
URL: http://www.state.nj.us/military/

9608 ■ New Jersey Disabled American Veterans
20 Washington Pl.
Newark, NJ 07102
Contact: Jenny E. DeRaffele, Supervisor
Free: 800-827-1000
URL: http://www.vba.va.gov/ro/east/newrk
Descr: Works to give service to disabled veterans and their families. Provides services in areas including disaster relief, employment, legislation, advocacy and transportation.

9609 ■ Religious Coalition for Reproductive Choice - New Jersey Chapter
PO Box 13
Mount Freedom, NJ 07970
Contact: Lesley Frost
Ph: (973)656-9494
Fax: (973)451-9898
E-mail: njrcrc@juno.com

9610 ■ Vietnam Veterans of America, Chapter 510
PO Box 448
Cedar Grove, NJ 07009
Contact: Ken O'Brien, Pres.
Ph: (973)239-9733
E-mail: vva510@vva510.org
URL: http://www.vva510.org
Fnd: 1992. **Mem:** 200.

9611 ■ Vietnam Veterans of America, Chapter 825
103 Florida Ave.
Egg Harbor Township, NJ 08234
Contact: Robert E. McNulty Sr., Pres.
Ph: (609)653-0988
E-mail: remcnultysr@yahoo.com
URL: http://vvachapter825.dnswh.com

9612 ■ Vietnam Veterans of America, New Jersey State Council
PO Box 1229
Bayonne, NJ 07002-6229
Contact: Carlton Rhodes, Sec.-Treas.
Ph: (908)553-0133
Fax: (908)925-0134
E-mail: dr-rhodes@worldnet.att.net
URL: http://www.njscvva.org

New Mexico

9613 ■ New Mexico Department of Veterans Services
PO Box 2324
Santa Fe, NM 87504-2324
Contact: John M. Garcia, Cabinet Sec.
Ph: (505)827-6300

Free: 866-433-8387
Fax: (505)827-6372
E-mail: angie.vigil@state.nm.us
URL: http://www.state.nm.us/veterans/

9614 ■ Paralyzed Veterans of America, Zia Chapter
833 Gibson Blvd. SE
Albuquerque, NM 87102
Contact: Christopher Ewer, Pres.
Ph: (505)247-4381
Free: 800-597-5580
Fax: (505)247-9204
E-mail: ziapva@aol.com
URL: http://www.ziapva.org

9615 ■ Religious Coalition for Reproductive Choice - New Mexico Chapter
PO Box 66433
Albuquerque, NM 87193
Ph: (505)890-1010
Free: 866-678-4660
Fax: (505)890-4573
E-mail: info@nmrcrc.org
URL: http://www.nmrcrc.org

9616 ■ Vietnam Veterans of America, Chapter No. 431
PO Box 6836
Las Cruces, NM 88006-6836
Contact: Kenneth W. Daby, Pres.
Ph: (505)522-0455
E-mail: phantom@zianet.com
URL: http://www.zianet.com/phantom/vva

New York

9617 ■ American Ex-Prisoners of War, Central New York Chapter
613 Millbrook Rd.
Rome, NY 13440
Contact: John D. Ringlehan
Ph: (315)336-0478
Descr: Seeks to: acquaint the public with the needs, problems, and handicaps associated with prisoners of war; promote research in the fields connected with injuries, diseases, and syndromes stemming from imprisonment; advocate and foster complete and effective reconditioning programs for ex-prisoners of war; foster patriotism and civic loyalty; encourage fraternal and historical activities.

9618 ■ American Ex-Prisoners of War, Northeast New York Chapter
135 Grandview Ave., Apt. 3B
Catskill, NY 12414
Contact: Coleman C. Duncan
Ph: (518)943-7474
Descr: Seeks to: acquaint the public with the needs, problems, and handicaps associated with prisoners of war; promote research in the fields connected with injuries, diseases, and syndromes stemming from imprisonment; advocate and foster complete and effective reconditioning programs for ex-prisoners of war; foster patriotism and civic loyalty; encourage fraternal and historical activities.

9619 ■ American Farmland Trust, Northeast Region
112 Spring St., Ste. 207
Saratoga Springs, NY 12866
Contact: Kirsten Ferguson, Communication Coor.
Ph: (518)581-0078
Fax: (518)581-0079
E-mail: jcosgrove@farmland.org
URL: http://www.farmland.org
Descr: Promotes farmland conservation in order to stop the loss of productive farmland; promotes farming practices that lead to a healthy environment.

9620 ■ American Lung Association of Mid-New York (ALA-MNY)
587 Main St., Ste. 109
New York Mills, NY 13417
Contact: John Storey, Exec. Dir.
Ph: (315)736-6099

Free: 800-LUNG-USA
Fax: (315)736-5976
E-mail: alamny@aol.com
URL: http://www.lungusa.org/site/pp.
asp?c=9olCLOOxGrF&b=1542043
Staff: 4. **Descr:** Works to prevent, detect, control, and cure lung disease and promote lung health. Sponsors camp for children with asthma. Holds professional education seminars, health education training, and smoking cessation clinic. **Fnd:** 1907. **State Groups:** 1.

9621 ■ AMVETS, Massapequa Post 88
692 Broadway
Massapequa, NY 11758
Contact: Jack Maxwell, Commander
Ph: (516)798-9188
E-mail: ridamart@optonline.net
URL: http://post88amvetsny.us

9622 ■ AMVETS of Schoharie County Post 175
PO Box 264
Warnerville, NY 12187
Contact: Frank Saum, Commander
URL: http://www.amvets175.org
Descr: Provides assistance to veterans with claims through a network of service offices through the United States.

9623 ■ Long Term Care Community Coalition
242 W 30th St., Ste. 306
New York, NY 10001
Contact: Mr. Richard J. Mollot, Exec.Dir.
Ph: (212)385-0355
Fax: (212)239-2801
E-mail: info@ltccc.org
URL: http://www.ltccc.org
Staff: 3. **Descr:** Serves as a public watchdog. Advocates for long term care recipients. **Fnd:** 1982.

9624 ■ National Association For Uniformed Services - Rainbow, New York Chapter
74 Commonwealth Dr.
Glenmont, NY 12077-3216
Contact: Tom Quinlan
Ph: (518)439-3777
E-mail: regionne-naus@yahoo.com
Descr: Provides assistance and support to active or retired military uniformed service officers. Protects and improves the compensation, entitlements and benefits earned by members of the uniformed services for themselves, their families and survivors and all American citizens with common interests.

9625 ■ National Association for Parents of Children with Visual Impairments New York City Chapter (NYC-NAPVI)
New York Institute for Special Education
999 Pelham Pkwy.
Bronx, NY 10469
Contact: Jeannette Christie, Parent Rep./Mgr.
Ph: (718)519-7000
E-mail: jaynycnapvi@aol.com
URL: http://www.nyc-napvi.org
Descr: Represents individuals committed to providing support to the parents of children who have visual impairments. Promotes public understanding of the needs and rights of children who are visually impaired.

9626 ■ New York Disabled American Veterans
200 Atlantic Ave.
Lynbrook, NY 11563
Contact: Robert J. Finnerty, Commander
Ph: (516)887-7100
Fax: (516)887-7175
E-mail: davny@optonline.net
URL: http://www.davny.org
Descr: Works to give service to disabled veterans and their families. Provides services in areas including disaster relief, employment, legislation, advocacy and transportation.

9627 ■ New York Division of Veterans' Affairs
5 Empire State Plaza, Ste. 2836
Albany, NY 12223-1551

Contact: James D. McDonough, Dir.
Ph: (518)474-6114
Free: 888-838-7697
Fax: (518)473-0379
E-mail: jmcdonough@veterans.state.ny.us
URL: http://veterans.state.ny.us/
Descr: Mission is to provide quality service and advocacy to New York State veterans, armed forces members, their dependents, and survivors, ensuring they receive benefits granted by law for their service to New York and the nation.

9628 ■ New York State Political Science Association (NYSPSA)
Empire State College
111 W Ave.
Saratoga Springs, NY 12866-6048
Contact: Frank Vander Valk, Pres.
Ph: (518)587-2100
E-mail: frank.vandervalk@esc.edu
URL: http://www.nyspsa.org
Descr: Represents college and university teachers of political science, public officials, research workers, and businessmen. Encourages the impartial study and promotes the development of the art and science of government. Develops research projects of public interest and educational programs for political scientists and journalists. Seeks to improve the knowledge of and increase citizen participation in political and governmental affairs.

9629 ■ Vietnam Veterans of America, Chapter 49
PO Box 224
Pleasantville, NY 10570
Contact: Al Singerman, Pres.
Ph: (914)682-4949
E-mail: chapter49@aol.com
URL: http://www.hereintown.com/vva/49

9630 ■ Vietnam Veterans of America, Chapter 193
53 W Main St.
Le Roy, NY 14482
Contact: Paul Damrau, Pres.
Ph: (585)768-4410
E-mail: vva193@frontiernet.net
URL: http://www.vva193.org
Mem: 100.

9631 ■ Vietnam Veterans of America, Chapter 333
PO Box 243
New City, NY 10956
Contact: Ed Frank, Pres.
URL: http://www.vva333.org

9632 ■ Vietnam Veterans of America, Chapter 480
PO Box 491
Owego, NY 13827
Contact: Jack T. Hartzel, Pres.
E-mail: president@vva480.org
URL: http://www.vva480.org

9633 ■ Vietnam Veterans of America, New York State Council
8 Queen Diana Ln.
Queensbury, NY 12804
Contact: Ned Foote, Pres.
Ph: (518)338-8147
Fax: (518)793-0952
URL: http://www.nyvietnamvets.org

9634 ■ Vietnam Veterans of America, Thomas P. Coughlin Memorial - Chapter 72
1402 8th Ave.
Brooklyn, NY 11215
Contact: Luigi Masu, Pres.
Ph: (718)499-6372
E-mail: admin@vvachapter72.org

North Carolina

9635 ■ American Arbitration Association, North Carolina (AAA)
200 S College St., Ste. 1800
Charlotte, NC 28202
Contact: Ms. Debi Miller-Moore, VP
Ph: (704)347-0200
Fax: (704)347-2804
E-mail: moored@adr.org
URL: http://www.adr.org
Descr: Works to resolve a wide range of disputes through mediation, arbitration, elections and other out-of-court settlement procedures.

9636 ■ American Ex-Prisoners of War, Greater Greensboro Chapter
3007 Nathaniel Rd.
Greensboro, NC 27408
Contact: Isaiah Huffman
Ph: (336)288-1752
Descr: Represents the interests of former prisoners of war and their families. Aims to aid patriotism and respect for flag and country. **Fnd:** 1978. **Mem:** 60. **State Groups:** 1. **Local Groups:** 1.

9637 ■ American Ex-Prisoners of War, Metrolina Chapter
10815 Wild Azalea Ln.
Charlotte, NC 28277
Contact: Roy G. Hudnall
Ph: (704)841-2174
Descr: Seeks to: acquaint the public with the needs, problems, and handicaps associated with prisoners of war; promote research in the fields connected with injuries, diseases, and syndromes stemming from imprisonment; advocate and foster complete and effective reconditioning programs for ex-prisoners of war; foster patriotism and civic loyalty; encourage fraternal and historical activities.

9638 ■ American Farmland Trust, Southeast Region
PO Box 584
Hillsborough, NC 27278
Ph: (919)732-7885
Descr: Works to stop the loss of productive farmland and promote farming practices that lead to a healthy environment. Disseminates information on safeguarding farmlands, through conservation easements and other voluntary conservation programs. Conducts policy development assistance, public education, and land project programs.

9639 ■ National Association For Uniformed Services - Southeast North Carolina, Chapter 3
610 Shadowood Dr.
Jacksonville, NC 28540
Contact: Richard D. Twiford
Ph: (910)455-9371
Descr: Provides assistance and support to active or retired military uniformed service officers. Protects and improves the compensation, entitlements and benefits earned by members of the uniformed services for themselves, their families and survivors and all American citizens with common interests.

9640 ■ National Funeral Directors and Morticians Association - District 3
512 Lewis St.
Oxford, NC 27565
Contact: William O. Betts CFSP
Ph: (919)693-7185
Fax: (919)693-6585
E-mail: bettsfh@gloryroad.net
Descr: Promotes ethical practices and encourages just and uniform laws pertaining to funeral directing and embalming industry.

9641 ■ North Carolina Division of Veterans' Affairs
1315 Mail Service Ctr.
Raleigh, NC 27699-1315
Contact: Britt Cobb, Sec.
Ph: (919)733-3851
Fax: (919)733-2834

E-mail: ncdva.aso@ncmail.net
URL: http://www.doa.state.nc.us/vets/va.htm

9642 ■ Vietnam Veterans of America, Chapter 272
PO Box 171
Greenville, NC 27835
Contact: Ron Hammeren, Pres.
Ph: (252)757-0817
E-mail: vvachapter272@netzero.net
URL: http://vva272nc.org

9643 ■ Vietnam Veterans of America, Durham - Chapter 530
PO Box 15944
Durham, NC 27702
E-mail: vva-530@verizon.net
URL: http://mysite.verizon.net/bru6/id5.html

North Dakota

9644 ■ American Ex-Prisoners of War, Dakota North Chapter
613 2nd St. SE
Tioga, ND 58852
Contact: Arnold Postovit, Commander
Ph: (701)664-2144
Descr: Seeks to: acquaint the public with the needs, problems, and handicaps associated with prisoners of war; promote research in the fields connected with injuries, diseases, and syndromes stemming from imprisonment; advocate and foster complete and effective reconditioning programs for ex-prisoners of war; foster patriotism and civic loyalty; encourage fraternal and historical activities.

9645 ■ American Lung Association of North Dakota (ALAND)
PO Box 5004
Bismarck, ND 58502-5004
Contact: Judy Mourhess, Office Mgr.
Ph: (701)223-5613
Free: 800-252-6325
Fax: (701)223-5727
E-mail: amerlungnd@gcentral.com
URL: http://lungusa2.org/northdakota
Staff: 4. **Descr:** Promotes educational programs and research to prevent and control lung disease. Sponsors summer camp for asthmatics. Offers smoking cessation classes. Radon and indoor air quality information available. Provides speakers and display booths for conferences, health fairs, etc. **Fnd:** 1909.

9646 ■ North Dakota AMVETS
3253 17th Ave. S, No. 202
Fargo, ND 58103-4530
Contact: James W. Schlenker, Commander
Ph: (701)293-0901
E-mail: ekernem@ideaone.net
URL: http://www.tristateveterans.com/ndamvets

9647 ■ North Dakota Department of Veterans' Affairs
4201 38th St. SW, Ste. 104
PO Box 9003
Fargo, ND 58106-9003
Contact: Lonnie Wangen, Commnr.
Ph: (701)239-7165
Free: 866-634-8387
Fax: (701)239-7166
E-mail: lwangen@nd.gov
URL: http://www.nd.gov/veterans/

Ohio

9648 ■ American Arbitration Association, Ohio
250 E 5th St., Ste. 330
Cincinnati, OH 45202
Contact: James Noll, VP
Ph: (513)241-8434
E-mail: nollj@adr.org
URL: http://www.adr.org
Descr: Works to provide exceptional neutrals, proficient case management, dedicated personnel, advanced education and training, and innovative

process knowledge to meet the conflict management and dispute resolution needs of the public now and in the future.

9649 ■ American Lung Association of Ohio (ALAO)
1950 Arlingate Ln.
Columbus, OH 43228-4102
Contact: Tracy Ross, Pres./CEO
Ph: (614)279-1700
Free: 800-LUNG-USA
Fax: (614)279-4940
URL: http://www.ohiolung.org
Staff: 48. **Descr:** Works to prevent and control lung disease. **Fnd:** 1901. **Mem:** 35. **Reg. Groups:** 8.

9650 ■ AMVETS, Celina Post 91
8263 St., Rte. 703 E
Celina, OH 45822
Contact: Nelson Rupard, Commander
E-mail: amvets91@hotmail.com
URL: http://www.amvets91.freeservers.com

9651 ■ AMVETS, Elyria Post 32
11087 S Middle Ave.
Elyria, OH 44035
Contact: Edward E. Gardiner Sr., Commander
Ph: (440)458-8544
E-mail: post32@ohamvets.org
URL: http://www.ohamvets.org/post32.htm

9652 ■ AMVETS Post 176
3944 Wheatley Rd.
Richfield, OH 44286
Ph: (330)659-3924
E-mail: post176@ohamvets.org
URL: http://www.ohamvets.org/post176.htm

9653 ■ AMVETS, Toledo Post 222
4133 N Summit St.
Toledo, OH 43611
Ph: (419)726-0724

9654 ■ AMVETS, Waverly Post 58
210 N Market St.
Waverly, OH 45690
Contact: Bill Walsh, Adj.
Ph: (740)947-8627
E-mail: commander@amvetspost58.freeservers.com
URL: http://amvetspost58.freeservers.com

9655 ■ Buckeye Chapter Paralyzed Veterans of America
25100 Euclid Ave., Ste. 117
Euclid, OH 44117
Contact: Terry Tyna, Pres./Natl. Dir.
Ph: (216)731-1017
Free: 800-248-2548
Fax: (216)731-6404
E-mail: donorinfo@buckeyepva.org
URL: http://www.buckeyepva.org
Descr: Veterans who have incurred an injury or disease affecting the spinal cord and causing paralysis.

9656 ■ Central Ohio Chapter of National Hemophilia Foundation
834 W 3rd Ave.
Columbus, OH 43212
Contact: Jim Wasserstrom, Pres.
Ph: (614)429-2100
Fax: (614)429-2150
E-mail: coc_nhf@yahoo.com
Descr: Represents individuals dedicated to finding better treatments and cures for bleeding and clotting disorders. Prevents the complications of these disorders through education, advocacy and research. Supports services for people with hemophilia and other hereditary bleeding disorders including complications with HIV/AIDS.

9657 ■ International Municipal Signal Association, Tri-State Section
1114 Wilmore Dr.
Middletown, OH 45042
Contact: Robert Zuehlke, Dir.

Ph: (513)422-1347
E-mail: rz@imsasafety.org
Descr: Serves as a professional organization of government officials responsible for municipal signaling, fire alarms, traffic signals, radio communication, street lighting, signs and marking, and other related services.

9658 ■ Ohio Association of Economists and Political Scientists (OAEPS)
Bowling Green State University
Dept. of Economics
312 Business Administration
Bowling Green, OH 43403-0001
Contact: Michael Carroll, Pres.
Ph: (419)372-6053
E-mail: mcarrol@bgnet.bgsu.edu
URL: http://www.oaeps.org
Descr: Represents college and University teachers of political science, public officials, research workers, and businessmen. Encourages the impartial study and promotes the development of the art and science of government. Develops research projects of public interest and educational programs for political scientists and journalists. Seeks to improve the knowledge of and increase citizen participation in political and governmental affairs.

9659 ■ Ohio Disabled American Veterans
PO Box 15099
Columbus, OH 43215-0099
Contact: Joseph Johnston, Commander
Ph: (614)221-3562
E-mail: commander@ohiodav.org
URL: http://www.ohiodav.org
Descr: Provides services in areas including disaster relief, employment, legislation, advocacy, and transportation.

9660 ■ Ohio Governor's Office on Veterans' Affairs
77 S. High St., 7th Fl.
Columbus, OH 43215
Contact: Bill Hartnett, Dir.
Ph: (614)644-0898
Fax: (614)728-9498
E-mail: ohiovet@dvs.ohio.gov
URL: http://dvs.ohio.gov/

9661 ■ Parents And Children for Equality (PACE)
PO Box 8805
Cincinnati, OH 45208-0805
Contact: Kevin O'Brien, Founder/Exec. Dir.
Ph: (513)624-7223
Fax: (513)624-7223
E-mail: cincinnati@pacegroup.org
URL: http://www.pacegroup.org
Staff: 5. **Descr:** Provides educational and advocacy support to parents and children of divorced and never-married families. **Fnd:** 1995. **Mem:** 1000. **Reg. Groups:** 2. **State Groups:** 5. **Local Groups:** 1. **Pub:** Newsletter (monthly).

9662 ■ Religious Coalition for Reproductive Choice - Ohio Chapter
PO Box 82204
Columbus, OH 43202
Ph: (614)221-3636
Free: 800-587-2330
E-mail: ohiorcrc@sbcglobal.net
URL: http://www.ohiorcrc.org

9663 ■ Veterans of Foreign Wars, Post 870
9 W Blagrove St.
Richwood, OH 43344
Ph: (740)943-3808
Descr: Promotes brotherhood among veterans. Improves the lives of veterans and service personnel through community service programs and special projects.

9664 ■ Veterans of Foreign Wars, Post 7424
1133 N Ottokee St.
Wauseon, OH 43567
Ph: (419)335-1301

Descr: Promotes brotherhood among veterans. Improves the lives of veterans and service personnel through community service programs and special projects.

9665 ■ Vietnam Veterans of America, Buckeye State Council
35 E Chestnut St.
Columbus, OH 43215
Contact: Thomas Burke, Pres.
Ph: (614)228-0188
Fax: (614)228-2711
E-mail: vva_bsc@ameritech.net
Descr: Aims to work for the employment, education benefits, improved psychological assistance, and health care of Vietnam veterans.

9666 ■ Vietnam Veterans of America, Chapter 10
8418 Reading Rd.
Reading, OH 45215
Contact: John W. Erby, Pres.
Ph: (513)761-8007
Fax: (513)761-2858
E-mail: vva10@aol.com
URL: http://www.vva10.com
Descr: Promotes brotherhood among veterans. Improves the lives of veterans and service personnel through community service programs and special projects.

9667 ■ Vietnam Veterans of America, Chapter No. 34
PO Box 30
Cuyahoga Falls, OH 44222
Contact: Mike Arnold, Pres.
Ph: (330)773-6434
Descr: Aims to work for the employment, education benefits, improved psychological assistance, and health care of Vietnam veterans.

9668 ■ Vietnam Veterans of America, Chapter No. 35
2300 Ashland Ave., Rm. 229
Toledo, OH 43620
Contact: Charles M. Kries, Pres.
Ph: (419)242-4293
Fax: (419)242-6773
Descr: Aims to work for the employment, education benefits, improved psychological assistance, and health care of Vietnam veterans.

9669 ■ Vietnam Veterans of America, Chapter No. 40
PO Box 305
Washingtonville, OH 44490-0305
Contact: Thomas S. Schahill, Pres.
Ph: (330)337-3090
Descr: Aims to work for the employment, education benefits, improved psychological assistance, and health care of Vietnam veterans.

9670 ■ Vietnam Veterans of America, Chapter No. 42
334 Shinnick St.
Zanesville, OH 43701
Contact: Jerry B. Combs, Pres.
Ph: (740)455-3895
Descr: Aims to work for the employment, education benefits, improved psychological assistance, and health care of Vietnam veterans.

9671 ■ Vietnam Veterans of America, Chapter No. 55
PO Box 624
Newark, OH 43055
Contact: Mark A. Rehl, Pres.
Ph: (740)927-6272
Descr: Aims to work for the employment, education benefits, improved psychological assistance, and health care of Vietnam veterans.

9672 ■ Vietnam Veterans of America, Chapter No. 89 LZ-Lima
130 W Elm St.
Lima, OH 45801

Contact: Bill Riepenhoff, Pres.
Ph: (419)222-2136
Descr: Aims to work for the employment, education benefits, improved psychological assistance, and health care of Vietnam veterans.

9673 ■ Vietnam Veterans of America, Chapter No. 97 Miami Valley
5657 Rosebury St.
Huber Heights, OH 45424
Contact: Tom Istvan, Pres.
Ph: (937)233-9750
URL: http://www.dayton-vva.org
Descr: Aims to work for the employment, education benefits, improved psychological assistance, and health care of Vietnam veterans.

9674 ■ Vietnam Veterans of America, Chapter No. 135
24 N Brockway Ave.
Youngstown, OH 44509
Contact: Thomas Moschella, Pres.
Ph: (330)799-3319
Descr: Aims to work for the employment, education benefits, improved psychological assistance, and health care of Vietnam veterans.

9675 ■ Vietnam Veterans of America, Chapter No. 199
PO Box 21205
Canton, OH 44701
Contact: Patricia A. Powell, Pres.
Ph: (330)453-7991
Descr: Aims to work for the employment, education benefits, improved psychological assistance, and health care of Vietnam veterans.

9676 ■ Vietnam Veterans of America, Chapter No. 231
PO Box 2947
Ashtabula, OH 44004
Ph: (440)275-9454
URL: http://www.vva231.org
Descr: Aims to work for the employment, education benefits, improved psychological assistance, and health care of Vietnam veterans.

9677 ■ Vietnam Veterans of America, Chapter No. 249
31972 Walker Rd.
Avon Lake, OH 44012-2045
Contact: Ray Donsante, Pres.
Ph: (216)556-0261
E-mail: vvachapter249@hotmail.com
URL: http://www.vvachapter249.com
Descr: Aims to work for the employment, education benefits, improved psychological assistance, and health care of Vietnam veterans.

9678 ■ Vietnam Veterans of America, Chapter No. 255
PO Box 324
Wooster, OH 44691
Contact: Gary Engelhardt, Pres.
Ph: (330)345-7914
Descr: Aims to work for the employment, education benefits, improved psychological assistance, and health care of Vietnam veterans.

9679 ■ Vietnam Veterans of America, Chapter No. 281
PO Box 5500
Chillicothe, OH 45601
Contact: Rudolph Walker
Ph: (740)773-2616
Descr: Aims to work for the employment, education benefits, improved psychological assistance, and health care of Vietnam veterans.

9680 ■ Vietnam Veterans of America, Chapter No. 440
PO Box 101
Fostoria, OH 44830
Contact: David Short, Pres.
Ph: (419)436-0552
Fax: (775)521-0161
Descr: Aims to work for the employment, education

benefits, improved psychological assistance, and health care of Vietnam veterans.

9681 ■ Vietnam Veterans of America, Chapter No. 532 - Roger D. Lewis Memorial
PO Box 129
Newcomerstown, OH 43832-0129
Contact: James Ross, Pres.
Ph: (740)498-8561
Descr: Aims to work for the employment, education benefits, improved psychological assistance, and health care of Vietnam veterans.

9682 ■ Vietnam Veterans of America, Chapter No. 559
2500 S Avon-Belden Rd.
Grafton, OH 44044-9802
Contact: Modesto Garcia, Pres.
Ph: (440)748-1161
Descr: Aims to work for the employment, education benefits, improved psychological assistance, and health care of Vietnam veterans.

9683 ■ Vietnam Veterans of America, Chapter No. 616
1150 N Main St.
Mansfield, OH 44901
Contact: John A. Johnston, Pres.
Ph: (419)525-4455
Fax: (419)524-8023
Descr: Aims to work for the employment, education benefits, improved psychological assistance, and health care of Vietnam veterans.

9684 ■ Vietnam Veterans of America, Chapter No. 634
2572 Smith Bridge Rd.
Jackson, OH 45640
Contact: Ralph Miller, Pres.
Ph: (740)286-3417
Descr: Aims to work for the employment, education benefits, improved psychological assistance, and health care of Vietnam veterans.

9685 ■ Vietnam Veterans of America, Chapter No. 645
16149 SR 104 N
Chillicothe, OH 45601-7010
Contact: Richard Wozniak, Pres.
Ph: (740)774-7050
Descr: Aims to work for the employment, education benefits, improved psychological assistance, and health care of Vietnam veterans.

9686 ■ Vietnam Veterans of America, Chapter No. 646 - Western Stark County
PO Box 251
Massillon, OH 44648
Contact: Bob Jones, Pres.
Ph: (330)833-3100
Descr: Aims to work for the employment, education benefits, improved psychological assistance, and health care of Vietnam veterans.

9687 ■ Vietnam Veterans of America, Chapter No. 649 - Clermont County
PO Box 426
Batavia, OH 45103
Contact: Jack Haigwood, Pres.
URL: http://vva649.org
Descr: Aims to work for the employment, education benefits, improved psychological assistance, and health care of Vietnam veterans.

9688 ■ Vietnam Veterans of America, Chapter No. 670
PO Box 2555
Columbus, OH 43216-2555
Contact: Steve Fulton, Pres.
Ph: (614)751-8820
Fax: (614)751-8903
Descr: Aims to work for the employment, education

benefits, improved psychological assistance, and health care of Vietnam veterans.

9689 ■ Vietnam Veterans of America, Chapter No. 676
PO Box 59
Nelsonville, OH 45764
Contact: Steve Phillips, Pres.
Ph: (740)753-1917
Descr: Aims to work for the employment, education benefits, improved psychological assistance, and health care of Vietnam veterans.

9690 ■ Vietnam Veterans of America, Chapter No. 709
39 Hilda Ext.
Gallipolis, OH 45631
Contact: Larry Marr, Pres.
Ph: (740)446-9629
Descr: Aims to work for the employment, education benefits, improved psychological assistance, and health care of Vietnam veterans.

9691 ■ Vietnam Veterans of America, Chapter No. 717
PO Box 4091
Cuyahoga Falls, OH 44223
Contact: Jay Jenkins, Sec.
Ph: (330)923-2709
E-mail: jjenkins1@neo.rr.com
URL: http://www.vva.org/VVAChapter717.html
Descr: Aims to work for the employment, education benefits, improved psychological assistance, and health care of Vietnam veterans.

9692 ■ Vietnam Veterans of America, Chapter No. 746
PO Box 531
London, OH 43140-0531
Contact: Jerry V. Collier Jr., Pres.
Ph: (740)852-9303
Descr: Aims to work for the employment, education benefits, improved psychological assistance, and health care of Vietnam veterans.

9693 ■ Vietnam Veterans of America, Chapter No. 783
PO Box 683
Celina, OH 45822
Contact: Steve Jones, Pres.
Ph: (419)942-1595
E-mail: sjones35@woh.rr.com
URL: http://www.vva783.com
Descr: Aims to work for the employment, education benefits, improved psychological assistance, and health care of Vietnam veterans.

9694 ■ Vietnam Veterans of America, Chapter No. 822 - Col. Harold F. Lyon Memorial
PO Box 1812
Marion, OH 43301-1812
Contact: Joseph Smith, Pres.
Ph: (740)387-7040
Descr: Aims to work for the employment, education benefits, improved psychological assistance, and health care of Vietnam veterans.

9695 ■ Vietnam Veterans of America, Chapter No. 857 - New Philadelphia
PO Box 170
New Philadelphia, OH 44663
Contact: Patrick L. Walker, Pres.
E-mail: walkman7@verizon.net
URL: http://www.vva.org/vvachapter857.html
Descr: Aims to work for the employment, education benefits, improved psychological assistance, and health care of Vietnam veterans.

9696 ■ Vietnam Veterans of America, Greater Cleveland - Chapter No. 15
1041 Starkweather Ave.
Cleveland, OH 44113
Contact: James Quisenberry, Pres.
Ph: (216)830-8515
Descr: Aims to work for the employment, education

benefits, improved psychological assistance, and health care of Vietnam veterans.

9697 ■ Vietnam Veterans of America, Medina County - Chapter No. 385
PO Box 1267
Medina, OH 44258
Contact: Richard Malone, Pres.
Ph: (440)779-1198
Fax: (973)807-5692
E-mail: vva385@aol.com
URL: http://www.vva.org/VVAChapter385.html
Descr: Aims to work for the employment, education benefits, improved psychological assistance, and health care of Vietnam veterans.

9698 ■ Vietnam Veterans of America, Ross County - Chapter No. 810
81 Amherst Dr.
Chillicothe, OH 45601
Contact: John Daubert, Pres.
Ph: (740)779-0180
Descr: Aims to work for the employment, education benefits, improved psychological assistance, and health care of Vietnam veterans.

Oklahoma

9699 ■ American Lung Association of Oklahoma (ALAO)
1010 E 8th St.
Tulsa, OK 74120
Contact: Brian Lewis, Chm.
Ph: (918)747-3441
E-mail: djenkins@breathehealthy.org
URL: http://www.oklung.org
Staff: 8. **Descr:** Works to prevent and control lung disease. **Reg. Groups:** 1. **Pub:** *Asthma Walk*; *Life and Breath* (quarterly); *Oklahoma Asthma Initiative Insider*.

9700 ■ National Association For Uniformed Services - Northwest Oklahoma, Chapter 4
3406 Whippoorwill Ln.
Enid, OK 73703-1522
Contact: Clyde W. Spence
Ph: (580)233-5619
E-mail: cspence@enid.com
Descr: Provides assistance and support to active or retired military uniformed service officers. Protects and improves the compensation, entitlements and benefits earned by members of the uniformed services for themselves, their families and survivors and all American citizens with common interests.

9701 ■ National Association For Uniformed Services - Wiley Post, Oklahoma Chapter 3
6016 NW 110th St.
Oklahoma City, OK 73162
Contact: William P. Bowden
Ph: (405)722-6279
E-mail: wpbowden@earthlink.net
Descr: Provides assistance and support to active or retired military uniformed service officers. Protects and improves the compensation, entitlements and benefits earned by members of the uniformed services for themselves, their families and survivors and all American citizens with common interests.

9702 ■ National Funeral Directors and Morticians Association - District 7
PO Box 2411
Muskogee, OK 74402
Contact: Keith Biglow
Ph: (918)687-5510
Fax: (918)687-5573
E-mail: biglowfnrl@aol.com
Descr: Promotes ethical practices and encourages just and uniform laws pertaining to funeral directing and embalming industry.

9703 ■ Oklahoma Department of Veterans' Affairs
2311 N. Central
PO Box 53067
Oklahoma City, OK 73105

Contact: Martha Spear, Exec.Dir.
Ph: (405)521-3684
Fax: (405)521-6533
E-mail: sclymer@odva.state.ok.us
URL: http://www.odva.state.ok.us

9704 ■ Oklahoma Political Science Association (OPSA)
PO Box 41
Stillwater, OK 74076
Contact: Saundra Mace
E-mail: maceokla@aol.com
URL: http://www.libarts.ucok.edu/opsa/index.html

Descr: Represents college and university teachers of political science, public officials, research workers, and businessmen. Encourages the impartial study and promotes the development of the art and science of government. Develops research projects of public interest and educational programs for political scientists and journalists. Seeks to improve the knowledge of and increase citizen participation in political and governmental affairs.

9705 ■ Oklahoma Religious Coalition for Reproductive Choice
PO Box 35194
Tulsa, OK 74153
Ph: (918)481-6444
Fax: (918)481-6444
E-mail: contact@okrcrc.org
URL: http://www.okrcrc.org

Staff: 1. **Descr:** Supports legal abortion information and services. Sponsors educational events and public forums. Conducts lobbying activities; holds workshops. Coordinates Clergy for Choice and Clergy Counseling Networks. **Fnd:** 1978. **Mem:** 900. **Pub:** *Religious Voice For Choice* (quarterly).

9706 ■ Religious Coalition for Reproductive Choice - Oklahoma Chapter
PO Box 35194
Tulsa, OK 74153
Ph: (918)481-6444
E-mail: contact@okrcrc.org
URL: http://www.okrcrc.org

Fnd: 1978.

9707 ■ Vietnam Veterans of America, Chapter No. 751
PO Box 2483
Lawton, OK 73502
Contact: Isaac J. Shider, Pres.
Ph: (580)351-1544
Fax: (580)351-1544
URL: http://www.751vva.org

Oregon

9708 ■ American Lung Association of Oregon (ALAO)
7420 SW Bridgeport Rd., Ste. 200
Tigard, OR 97224-7790
Contact: Ms. Sue Fratt, CEO
Ph: (503)924-4094
Free: 800-LUN-GUSA
Fax: (503)924-4120
E-mail: info@lungoregon.org
URL: http://www.lungoregon.org

Staff: 8. **Descr:** Promotes educational programs and research to prevent and control lung disease. **Fnd:** 1915. **Reg. Groups:** 1. **State Groups:** 1. **Pub:** *Breathing in Oregon* (quarterly).

9709 ■ Oregon Department of Veterans' Affairs
700 Summer St., NE
Salem, OR 97301-1285
Contact: Jim Willis, Dir.
Ph: (503)373-2000
Free: 800-828-8801
Fax: (503)373-2362

E-mail: odva@odva.state.or.us
URL: http://www.odva.state.or.us/

9710 ■ Oregon Disabled American Veterans
Virginia Regional Office Federal Bldg.
1220 SW 3rd Ave.
Portland, OR 97204
Contact: Jay E. Woodbury, Supervisor
Ph: (503)412-4750
URL: http://www.dav.org

Descr: Works to give service to disabled veterans and their families. Provides services in areas including disaster relief, employment, legislation, advocacy and transportation.

9711 ■ Oregon Paralyzed Veterans of America (OPVA)
3700 Silverton Rd. NE
Salem, OR 97305-1472
Contact: Anthony Marx, Pres.
Ph: (503)362-7998
Free: 800-333-0782
Fax: (503)362-9837
E-mail: oregonpva@oregonpva.org
URL: http://www.oregonpva.org

Staff: 2. **Descr:** Disabled spinal cord injury/disease veterans and also associates who are not veterans with spinal cord injury or disease. Promotes the interests of members; works for favorable legislation; supports research and sports activities. Awards medical scholarships. **Fnd:** 1976. **Mem:** 332. **Pub:** *Paralog* (bimonthly).

9712 ■ Vietnam Veterans of America, Emerald Valley - Chapter No. 144
3900 N Coburg Rd., Space No. 19
Eugene, OR 97408
Contact: Gary Smith, Pres.
Ph: (541)914-9819
E-mail: runwiththewnd@comcast.net

Pennsylvania

9713 ■ American Ex-Prisoners of War, Brandywine Chapter
206 Whitaker Ave.
Mont Clare, PA 19453
Contact: Louis Liberato
Ph: (610)933-3408

Staff: 3. **Descr:** Former military prisoners of war and civilian internees in Chester County, PA. Works to help those who cannot help themselves. Conducts community services and other charitable activities. Participates in Memorial and Veterans' Day parades. **Fnd:** 1987. **Mem:** 63. **State Groups:** 1. **Pub:** Newsletter (monthly).

9714 ■ American Ex-Prisoners of War, Liberty Bell Chapter
61 New Pond Ln.
Levittown, PA 19054-3811
Contact: Catherine M. Burns, Commander
Ph: (215)945-1014

Descr: Seeks to: acquaint the public with the needs, problems, and handicaps associated with prisoners of war; promote research in the fields connected with injuries, diseases, and syndromes stemming from imprisonment; advocate and foster complete and effective reconditioning programs for ex-prisoners of war; foster patriotism and civic loyalty; encourage fraternal and historical activities.

9715 ■ American Family Association of Pennsylvania
PO Box 1048
Franklin, PA 16323
Contact: Diane Gramley
Ph: (814)271-9078
Fax: (814)437-5432
URL: http://www.afaofpa.org

Descr: Encourages the faith community to break the silence on controversial issues and be a voice for pro-family values. Provides leadership in defending the Biblical ethic of decency. Educates the public on the negative effects of pornography and violence in the media. Defends families. Protects children from

those who would seek to commercialize or propagandize them.

9716 ■ Keystone Paralyzed Veterans of America
1113 Main St.
Pittsburgh, PA 15215
Contact: Fred Tregaskes, Pres.
Ph: (412)781-2474
Free: 800-775-9323
Fax: (412)781-2659
E-mail: keystonepva@comcast.net
URL: http://www.kpva.org

9717 ■ National Funeral Directors and Morticians Association - District 1
1001 N 63rd St.
Philadelphia, PA 19151
Contact: Lisa D. Branch-Tucker
Ph: (215)473-5100
Fax: (215)879-3145
E-mail: lrocke2188@aol.com

Descr: Promotes ethical practices and encourages just and uniform laws pertaining to funeral directing and embalming industry.

9718 ■ Pennsylvania Department of Military Affairs
Bureau of Veterans' Affairs
Fort Indiantown Gap, Bldg. S-0-47
Annville, PA 17003
Contact: Major General Jessica L. Wright, Adjutant General
Ph: (717)861-8500
Free: 800-547-2838
Fax: (717)861-8589
E-mail: ra-dmva_webmaster@state.pa.us
URL: http://www.dmva.state.pa.us

9719 ■ Pennsylvania Disabled American Veterans
1123 E End Blvd., Ste. 10
Wilkes-Barre, PA 18702
Contact: Mr. Aaron Montague, Asst. Supervisor
Ph: (570)821-2520
Fax: (570)821-2524

Descr: Works to give service to disabled veterans and their families. Provides services in areas including disaster relief, employment, legislation, advocacy and transportation.

9720 ■ Pennsylvania Mid-State Lactation Coalition (PA-MILC)
PO Box 821
State College, PA 16804
Contact: Wanda Mertick RN, Ed.
Ph: (814)237-1506
E-mail: wmertick@hotmail.com

Descr: Addresses the needs of lactation professionals in the United States. Increases public and health care worker awareness of lactation and breastfeeding. Fosters continuing education and research in the field.

9721 ■ Pennsylvania Political Science Association (PPSA)
Wilkes University
Political Science Dept.
84 W South St.
Wilkes-Barre, PA 18701
Contact: Thomas J. Baldino, Pres.
Ph: (814)472-7000
Fax: (814)472-3937
E-mail: thomas.baldino@wilkes.edu

Descr: Represents college and university teachers of political science, public officials, research workers, and businessmen. Encourages the impartial study and promotes the development of the art and science of government. Develops research projects of public interest and educational programs for political scientists and journalists. Seeks to improve the knowledge of and increase citizen participation in political and governmental affairs. **Fnd:** 1939. **Pub:** *Pennsylvania Political Scientist.*

9722 ■ Vietnam Veterans of America, Berks County - Chapter 131
PO Box 13735
Reading, PA 19612-3735
Contact: David M. Ciscon, Pres.
Ph: (610)678-5812
E-mail: vva_131@hotmail.com
URL: http://www.vva-pa.org

9723 ■ Vietnam Veterans of America, Bucks County - Chapter 210
PO Box 1095
Doylestown, PA 18901
Contact: Richard Quinn, Pres.
Ph: (215)579-1480
E-mail: boatrider@aol.com
URL: http://www.vva-pa.org

9724 ■ Vietnam Veterans of America, Bucktail - Chapter 720
PO Box 220
St. Marys, PA 15857
Contact: James Swanson, Pres.
Ph: (814)781-7968
E-mail: weeze@ncentral.com
URL: http://www.vva-pa.org

9725 ■ Vietnam Veterans of America, Capital - Chapter 542
8000 Derry St.
Harrisburg, PA 17111-5233
Contact: John M. Travers, Pres.
Ph: (717)731-6028
E-mail: traversjt@netzero.com
URL: http://www.vva-pa.org

9726 ■ Vietnam Veterans of America, Central Pennsylvania - Chapter 791
PO Box 791
Lewistown, PA 17044-0791
Contact: Daniel J. Felmlee, Pres.
Ph: (717)667-2848
URL: http://www.vva-pa.org

9727 ■ Vietnam Veterans of America, Chapter 590
PO Box 63096
Philadelphia, PA 19114-0896
Contact: Thomas Frieze, Pres.
Ph: (215)679-4730
E-mail: caputo_r@msn.com
URL: http://www.vva-pa.org

9728 ■ Vietnam Veterans of America, Chapter 862
260 Brooks Dr.
Beaver Falls, PA 15010
Contact: L. Skip Haswell, Pres.
Ph: (724)843-6930
E-mail: marinenamvet66@yahoo.com
URL: http://www.vva862.org
Mem: 318.

9729 ■ Vietnam Veterans of America, Chapter 948
245 Ford Rd.
St. Marys, PA 15857
Contact: Gary Schreiber, Pres.
Ph: (814)781-7443
E-mail: schrib809@alltel.net
URL: http://www.vva-pa.org

9730 ■ Vietnam Veterans of America, Delaware County - Chapter 67
PO Box 1220
Media, PA 19063
Contact: George E. Brown, Pres.
Ph: (610)626-7598
E-mail: wabarner@aol.com
URL: http://vvachapter67.freeservers.com

Fnd: 1981.

9731 ■ Vietnam Veterans of America, Hainley-English - Chapter 967 Greater Blair County
222 Bedford St.
Hollidaysburg, PA 16648
Contact: John Foy, Pres.
Ph: (814)695-9680
E-mail: susengill@atlanticbb.net
URL: http://www.vva-pa.org

9732 ■ Vietnam Veterans of America, Laurel Highlands - Chapter 364
PO Box 5237
Johnstown, PA 15904-5237
Contact: Thomas W. Haberkorn, Pres.
Ph: (814)269-4427
E-mail: haber2@atlanticbb.net
URL: http://www.johnstownpa.com/vva

9733 ■ Vietnam Veterans of America, Lehigh Valley - Chapter 415
PO Box 1901
Easton, PA 18044
Contact: Barry Willever, Pres.
Ph: (610)252-6171
E-mail: bwillever@enter.net
URL: http://415vva.homestead.com/home.html

9734 ■ Vietnam Veterans of America, Liberty Bell - Chapter 266
1515-17 E Luzerne St.
Philadelphia, PA 19124
Contact: James Chappelle, Pres.
Ph: (215)288-7998
E-mail: jeni-vva266@comcast.net
URL: http://vva266.bravehost.com/index.html

9735 ■ Vietnam Veterans of America, Major James A. Crew - Chapter 359
222 Bedford St.
Hollidaysburg, PA 16648
Contact: William Paige, Pres.
Ph: (814)695-9680
E-mail: susengill@atlanticbb.net
URL: http://www.vva-pa.org

9736 ■ Vietnam Veterans of America, Major Louis Guillerman Chester County Chapter 436
PO Box 189
Phoenixville, PA 19460
Contact: Chris Pitt, Pres.
Ph: (610)436-0392
E-mail: christopher1945@msn.com
URL: http://www.vva-pa.org

9737 ■ Vietnam Veterans of America, North-west Pennsylvania - Chapter 435
4808 E Carver Ave.
Erie, PA 16511
Contact: Kenneth Kensill, Pres.
Ph: (814)899-2858
E-mail: vietken@adelphia.net
URL: http://www.vva-pa.org

9738 ■ Vietnam Veterans of America, Pocono - Chapter 678
PO Box 103
Stroudsburg, PA 18360
Contact: Glen Lippincott, Pres.
Ph: (570)992-6038
E-mail: vva678@hotmail.com
URL: http://www.vva678.net/index.html
Fnd: 1993.

9739 ■ Vietnam Veterans of America, Pottstown Keystone - Chapter 565
PO Box 472
Pottstown, PA 19464
Contact: Frank Strunk, Pres.
Ph: (610)327-1044
URL: http://www.vva-pa.org

9740 ■ Vietnam Veterans of America, Somer-set County - Chapter 587
PO Box 711
Somerset, PA 15501
Contact: John D. Livengood, Pres.

Ph: (814)926-2191
URL: http://www.vva-pa.org

9741 ■ Vietnam Veterans of America, Tri-State - Chapter 623
PO Box 594
Dingmans Ferry, PA 18328
Contact: George N. Savastides, Pres.
Ph: (570)686-4195
E-mail: g.savastides@att.net
URL: http://www.vva-pa.org

9742 ■ Vietnam Veterans of America, Upper Bucks/Lower Lehigh - Chapter 468
PO Box 759
Richlandtown, PA 18955-0759
Contact: Frank Scholes, Pres.
Ph: (215)679-7770
URL: http://www.vva-pa.org

9743 ■ Vietnam Veterans of America, Valley Forge - Chapter 349
650 Sentry Pkwy., Ste. 1
Blue Bell, PA 19422-2318
Contact: Ralph Nealman, Pres.
Ph: (610)941-2160
E-mail: rjbainemarminc@earthlink.net
URL: http://www.vva-pa.org

9744 ■ Vietnam Veterans of America, Veterans of Graterford - Chapter 466
PO Box 244
Graterford, PA 19426-0244
Contact: Commer Glass, Pres.
Ph: (610)489-4151
URL: http://www.vva-pa.org

Puerto Rico

9745 ■ Paralyzed Veterans of America, Puerto Rico Chapter
URB Country Club
812 Moluda St.
San Juan, PR 00924
Ph: (787)757-6465
Free: 888-757-6465
E-mail: puertricochapter@prpva.org

9746 ■ Puerto Rico Public Advocate for Veter-ans' Affairs
PO Box 11737
Fernandez Juncos Station
San Juan, PR 00910-1737
Contact: Luis Ramos Gonzalez, Exec.Dir.
Ph: (787)758-5760
Fax: (787)758-5788
E-mail: luisramos@opv.gobierno.pr
URL: http://www.nasdva.com/puertorico.html

Rhode Island

9747 ■ American Pain Society, Rhode Island
21A Waterview Dr.
Smithfield, RI 02917
Contact: Ashraf Farid MD, Rep.
Ph: (401)524-8242
Fax: (401)767-2515
E-mail: faridashraf@yahoo.com

Descr: Advances pain-related research, education, treatment and professional practice. Promotes control, management and understanding of pain. Develops standards for training and ethical manage-ment of pain patients.

9748 ■ Rhode Island Department of Human Affairs
Division of Veterans' Affairs
480 Metacom Ave.
Bristol, RI 02809
Contact: Daniel J. Evangelista, Assoc.Dir.
Ph: (401)253-8000
Fax: (401)254-2320

E-mail: RBaccus@gw.dhs.state.ri.us
URL: http://www.dhs.state.ri.us/dhs/dvetaff.htm

9749 ■ Vietnam Veterans of America, Rhode Island State Council
PO Box 41364
Providence, RI 02940
Contact: John Weiss, Pres.
Ph: (401)455-1975
E-mail: scpres@rivvasc.com
URL: http://www.rivvasc.org/RIVVAState/VVASC.html

South Carolina

9750 ■ American Association of University Women, South Carolina
745 Tyson's Forest Dr.
Rock Hill, SC 29732
Contact: Beverly James, Pres.
Ph: (803)328-8324
Free: 800-527-7638
Fax: (704)529-1010
E-mail: bevjames1998@yahoo.com
URL: http://www.aauw-sc.org
Staff: 8. **Descr:** Committed to leadership development, mentoring skills and shaping the future for South Carolina women and girls. **Fnd:** 1924. **Mem:** 500. **State Groups:** 1. **Local Groups:** 16. **Pub:** *Palmetto Leaf* (quarterly); Brochure.

9751 ■ American Ex-Prisoners of War, Catawba Chapter of South Carolina
2217 Lynwood Dr.
Lancaster, SC 29720
Contact: Richard A. Walters
Ph: (803)285-0654
Descr: Seeks to: acquaint the public with the needs, problems, and handicaps associated with prisoners of war; promote research in the fields connected with injuries, diseases, and syndromes stemming from imprisonment; advocate and foster complete and effective reconditioning programs for ex-prisoners of war; foster patriotism and civic loyalty; encourage fraternal and historical activities.

9752 ■ South Carolina Division of Veterans' Affairs
1205 Pendleton St., Ste. 369
Columbia, SC 29201
Contact: Phil Butler, Dir.
Ph: (803)734-0200
Fax: (803)734-0197
E-mail: va@oepp.sc.gov
URL: http://www.govoepp.state.sc.us/va/

9753 ■ South Carolina Society of EAs
McDougald-Partain LLC
1309 N Blvd.
Anderson, SC 29621
Contact: Mr. W. Ray Partain
Ph: (864)224-4775
Fax: (864)231-6558
E-mail: ray@mcdougaldpartain.com
URL: http://www.scsea.org

South Dakota

9754 ■ Disabled American Veterans, Department of South Dakota
1519 W 51st St.
Sioux Falls, SD 57105-6648
Contact: Gene A. Murphy, Adjutant/Treas.
Ph: (605)332-6866
Fax: (605)338-5489
E-mail: davsd@midconetwork.com
URL: http://www.davmembersportal.org/sd/default.aspx
Staff: 2. **Descr:** Works to uphold and maintain the Constitution and the laws of the United States; to realize the true American ideals and aims for which those eligible to membership fought; to advance the interests and work for the betterment of all wounded, gassed, injured, and disabled veterans; to cooperate with the United States Department of Veterans Affairs and all other public and private agencies devoted to the cause of improving and advancing the condition, health and interest of all wounded, gassed, injured and disabled veterans; to stimulate a feeling of mutual devotion, helpfulness, and comradeship among all wounded, gassed, injured and disabled veterans; to serve comrades, the communities, and the country; and to encourage in all people that spirit of understanding which will guard against future wars. Provides the following programs and services: DAV National Service Program; DAV Transportation Network; DAV Disaster Relief Fund; DAV Voluntary Service Programs; DAV Employment Program; DAV Outreach programs. **Fnd:** 1938. **Mem:** 4689. **Local Groups:** 12. **Pub:** *Disabled American Veterans Department of South Dakota Bulletin* (quarterly).

9755 ■ South Dakota Division of Veterans' Affairs
Soldiers & Sailors Memorial Bldg.
425 E. Capitol Ave.
Pierre, SD 57501
Contact: Major Gen. Steven Doohen, Sec.
Ph: (605)773-3269
Free: 877-579-0015
Fax: (605)773-5380
E-mail: andy.gerlach@state.sd.us
URL: http://www.state.sd.us/applications/MV91MVAInternetRewrite/default.html

Tennessee

9756 ■ American Ex-Prisoners of War, East Tennessee Chapter
738 Grove Ave.
Erwin, TN 37650
Contact: George Hatcher
Ph: (423)743-6852
Descr: Former prisoners of war. Seeks to: foster patriotism; assist injured and disabled ex-prisoners of war; and care for widows and orphans of ex-prisoners of war. Provides assistance to local charities. Maintains historical records. **Fnd:** 1976. **Mem:** 100. **Reg. Groups:** 3. **State Groups:** 8. **Local Groups:** 1. **Pub:** Newsletter (monthly).

9757 ■ National Association of Activity Professionals - Tennessee
516 Sparrow Dr.
Maryville, TN 37801
Contact: Mary Fran Aptaker
Ph: (865)984-7047
Descr: Provides assistance at the state level to promote certification of activity professionals, working toward uniform professional standards for activity practice.

9758 ■ National Association For Uniformed Services - Chattanooga, Tennessee Chapter 2
4508 Tricia Dr.
Chattanooga, TN 37416-2321
Contact: Ronald W. Howie
Ph: (423)855-0496
E-mail: sgmhowie@comcast.net
Descr: Provides assistance and support to active or retired military uniformed service officers. Protects and improves the compensation, entitlements and benefits earned by members of the uniformed services for themselves, their families and survivors and all American citizens with common interests.

9759 ■ Paralyzed Veterans of America, Mid-South Chapter
1030 Jefferson Ave., Rm. 2D100
Memphis, TN 38104
Ph: (901)527-3018
E-mail: mspva@aol.com

9760 ■ Tennessee Department of Veterans' Affairs
215 Rosa L. Parks Ave.
Nashville, TN 37243-1010
Contact: John A. Keys, Commnr.
Ph: (615)741-2931
Fax: (615)741-4785
E-mail: TN.Veterans@tn.gov
URL: http://www.state.tn.us/veteran/
Descr: Mission is to serve Tennessee's veterans and their families with dignity and compassion; to be the veterans' advocate by ensuring they receive quality care, support, entitlements, and the recognition earned in service to the U.S.; and to enhance our citizens awareness of the sacrifices that veterans have made.

9761 ■ Tennessee Lactation Coalition (TLC)
4110 Granny White Pike
Nashville, TN 37204
Contact: Kate Cropp MSN, Pres.
Ph: (615)936-3434
E-mail: katecroppibclc@hotmail.com
Descr: Addresses the needs of lactation professionals in the United States. Increases public and health care worker awareness of lactation and breastfeeding. Fosters continuing education and research in the field.

9762 ■ Vietnam Veterans of America, Chapter 262
PO Box 1011
Pulaski, TN 38478
Contact: Charles Stanford
E-mail: ssstanford@igiles.net

9763 ■ Vietnam Veterans of America, Chapter 396
PO Box 20346
Clarksville, TN 37042
Contact: Gery P. Ezell, Treas.
E-mail: gpe43@bellsouth.net

9764 ■ Vietnam Veterans of America, Chapter 797 - Lewisburg
PO Box 2451
Lewisburg, TN 37091
Contact: Tom Holt, Pres.
E-mail: tomholtsr@united.net

9765 ■ Vietnam Veterans of America, Chapter 824
508 Garrison Hollow Rd.
Elizabethton, TN 37643
Contact: Jerry Campbell, Pres.
E-mail: jerrydc@xtn.net

9766 ■ Vietnam Veterans of America, Chapter 950
PO Box 375
Charlotte, TN 37036
Contact: Jamie DeLeary, Sec.
E-mail: jimdeleary@bellsouth.net

9767 ■ Vietnam Veterans of America, Columbia - Chapter 128
308 W 7th St.
Columbia, TN 38401
Contact: James Patterson, Pres.
E-mail: jtpatt@edge.net

9768 ■ Vietnam Veterans of America, Edward G. Sharpe - Chapter 596
3011 Cedar Creek Cir.
Cleveland, TN 37312
Contact: Bruce Barnes, VP
E-mail: bdbarnes23@msn.com

9769 ■ Vietnam Veterans of America, Evensville - Chapter 246
5824 Back Valley Rd.
Evensville, TN 37332
Contact: Don E. Mathis, Sec.
Ph: (423)775-7849

9770 ■ Vietnam Veterans of America, West Tennessee - Chapter No. 875
PO Box 36
Oakland, TN 38060
Contact: Mark Lawrence
Ph: (901)527-3665
E-mail: marklawrenceibm@charter.net

Texas

9771 ■ American Association of University Women, Texas Branch
PO Box 27223
Austin, TX 78755
Contact: Linda Conger, Pres.
Ph: (512)458-2289
Free: 800-343-2289
Fax: (512)453-4716
E-mail: lbconger@earthlink.net
URL: http://www.aauwtexas.org
Descr: Women graduates of regionally accredited four-year colleges and universities. Works for the advancement of women through advocacy and emphasis on lifelong learning. **Fnd:** 1923. **Mem:** 300. **Reg. Groups:** 55. **State Groups:** 1. **Local Groups:** 1. **Pub:** *University Women Texas* (quarterly).

9772 ■ American Ex-Prisoners of War, Cen-Tex Chapter No. 1
PO Box 10004
Killeen, TX 76541
Contact: Ruby Williams, Commander
Ph: (254)773-3542
Descr: Seeks to: acquaint the public with the needs, problems, and handicaps associated with prisoners of war; promote research in the fields connected with injuries, diseases, and syndromes stemming from imprisonment; advocate and foster complete and effective reconditioning programs for ex-prisoners of war; foster patriotism and civic loyalty; encourage fraternal and historical activities.

9773 ■ American Ex-Prisoners of War, Highland Lakes Chapter
1400 Ocotilla Dr.
Marble Falls, TX 78654
Contact: John H. Oliver, Commander
Ph: (830)693-8220
Descr: Seeks to: acquaint the public with the needs, problems, and handicaps associated with prisoners of war; promote research in the fields connected with injuries, diseases, and syndromes stemming from imprisonment; advocate and foster complete and effective reconditioning programs for ex-prisoners of war; foster patriotism and civic loyalty; encourage fraternal and historical activities.

9774 ■ American Ex-Prisoners of War, Hub of the Plains Chapter
5212 91st St.
Lubbock, TX 79424
Contact: Homer Jones, Commander
Ph: (806)771-0607
Descr: Seeks to: acquaint the public with the needs, problems, and handicaps associated with prisoners of war; promote research in the fields connected with injuries, diseases, and syndromes stemming from imprisonment; advocate and foster complete and effective reconditioning programs for ex-prisoners of war; foster patriotism and civic loyalty; encourage fraternal and historical activities.

9775 ■ American Lung Association of Texas
5926 Balcones Dr., Ste. 100
Austin, TX 78731
Contact: Susan Dunning
Ph: (512)467-6753
Free: 800-LUNGUSA
E-mail: info@texaslung.org
URL: http://www.texaslung.org
Staff: 5. **Descr:** Fights against lung disease and protects the lung health of individuals in TX. Teaches children how to handle asthma through a summer asthma camp that is medically supervised and offers children how to better manage their asthma while enjoying activities such as horseback riding, swimming, field sports, and arts and crafts. Promotes smoking prevention and cessation. Offers advocacy and support groups for individuals suffering from chronic lung disease. **Fnd:** 1908.

9776 ■ AMVETS, Dallas Post 23
12531 CF Hawn Fwy.
Dallas, TX 75253-5910

Ph: (972)564-3386
E-mail: amvetsdept@sbcglobal.net

9777 ■ Concho Valley Vietnam Veterans
PO Box 2812
San Angelo, TX 76902
Contact: Tom Bright, Pres.
Ph: (325)947-3589
Fax: (325)947-3589
E-mail: smmf501@aol.com
URL: http://vva457.tripod.com
Staff: 8. **Descr:** Association of persons who served in the armed forces in Vietnam from 1961-75. Conducts food drives. Provides specialized services to veterans. **Fnd:** 1988. **Mem:** 53. **Reg. Groups:** 24. **State Groups:** 1. **Local Groups:** 1. **Pub:** Newsletter (periodic).

9778 ■ International Municipal Signal Association, Southwestern Section
PO Box 458
Paris, TX 75461
Contact: Ray Purdy, Sec.-Treas.
Ph: (903)739-9027
Fax: (903)739-9241
E-mail: purdyr@suddenlink.net
Descr: Serves as a professional organization of government officials responsible for municipal signaling, fire alarms, traffic signals, radio communication, street lighting, signs and marking, and other related services.

9779 ■ National Association For Uniformed Services - Alamo, Texas Chapter
7767 Mountain Trail
Boerne, TX 78015
Contact: Art Mace
Ph: (210)698-1634
E-mail: jamlog@earthlink.net
Descr: Provides assistance and support to active or retired military uniformed service officers. Protects and improves the compensation, entitlements and benefits earned by members of the uniformed services for themselves, their families and survivors and all American citizens with common interests.

9780 ■ National Association For Uniformed Services - Coastal Bend, Texas Chapter 27
985 Bella Vista Cir.
Kyle, TX 78640
Contact: Edward Reed
Ph: (512)300-3571
E-mail: edreed@ccbor.org
Descr: Provides assistance and support to active or retired military uniformed service officers. Protects and improves the compensation, entitlements and benefits earned by members of the uniformed services for themselves, their families and survivors and all American citizens with common interests.

9781 ■ National Association for Uniformed Services - Austin, Texas Chapter 10
2502 Barkwood Dr.
Austin, TX 78748-6006
Contact: Bill Millis
Ph: (512)282-2314
E-mail: bjmillis@austin.rr.com
Descr: Provides assistance and support to active or retired military uniformed service officers. Protects and improves the compensation, entitlements and benefits earned by members of the uniformed services for themselves, their families and survivors and all American citizens with common interests.

9782 ■ National Coalition of Free Men, Dallas/Fort Worth Chapter
PO Box 140071
Irving, TX 75014
Ph: (972)445-6253
E-mail: ncfmdfw@yahoo.com
URL: http://ncfmdfw.8m.com

9783 ■ Paralyzed Veterans of America, Lone Star Chapter
3925 Forest Ln.
Garland, TX 75042

Ph: (972)276-5252
Free: 800-583-5252
E-mail: lspva@verizon.net

9784 ■ Paralyzed Veterans of America, Texas Chapter
2807 Old Spanish Trail, Ste. A
Houston, TX 77054
Contact: David Fowler, Pres.
Ph: (713)520-8782
Free: 800-933-4261
Fax: (713)520-8217
E-mail: info@texaspva.org
URL: http://www.texaspva.org

9785 ■ Public Citizen - Texas
1303 San Antonio St.
Austin, TX 78701
Contact: Tom Smith, Exec. Dir.
Ph: (512)477-1155
Fax: (512)479-8302
URL: http://www.citizen.org/texas
Descr: Works to promote cleaner energy, cleaner government, cleaner air, and safe products for all Texans. **Fnd:** 1984.

9786 ■ Religious Coalition for Reproductive Choice - Texas Chapter
PO Box 3934
Austin, TX 78764-3934
Contact: Dr. Fred Campbell
Ph: (210)414-2536
Fax: (512)445-2755
E-mail: contactus@rcrc-texas.org

9787 ■ Texas Veterans' Commission
PO Box 12277
Austin, TX 78711-2277
Contact: James E. Nier, Exec.Dir.
Ph: (512)463-6564
Free: 800-252-8387
Fax: (512)475-2395
E-mail: info@tvc.state.tx.us
URL: http://www.tvc.state.tx.us/

9788 ■ Vietnam Veterans of America, Capital of Texas - Chapter 915
PO Box 14186
Austin, TX 78761-4166
Contact: Roy McCrary, Pres.
Ph: (512)321-4730
E-mail: roymcsr@yahoo.com

9789 ■ Vietnam Veterans of America, Chapter 137
PO Box 224746
Dallas, TX 75222-7268
Contact: Mike McCullough, Sgt. At Arms
E-mail: mikelavonne@attbi.com

9790 ■ Vietnam Veterans of America, Chapter 292
PO Box 1071
Beaumont, TX 77704
Contact: Kerwin B. Stone, Pres.
Ph: (409)898-1924
E-mail: kerwintx@aol.com

9791 ■ Vietnam Veterans of America, Chapter 348
PO Box 353
Orange, TX 77631-0353
Contact: Ed Lampman, Treas.
E-mail: elampman@pnx.com

9792 ■ Vietnam Veterans of America, Chapter 404
1106 Indiana
Borger, TX 79007
Contact: Dennis Thomas Sr., Pres.
E-mail: dthomas@fpc.cc.tx.us

9793 ■ Vietnam Veterans of America, Chapter 685
PO Box 1162
Dickinson, TX 77539
Contact: Jim Rose, Pres.
Ph: (281)991-1467

E-mail: jhr0545@houston.rr.com
URL: http://galvestonvva.us

9794 ■ Vietnam Veterans of America, Chapter 734
PO Box 2493
Conroe, TX 77305
Contact: Lee Derby, Treas.
E-mail: cmdrlee@msn.com

9795 ■ Vietnam Veterans of America, Chapter 910
1642 Sandalwood Dr.
Corpus Christi, TX 78412
Contact: Ram Chavez, Pres.
Ph: (361)992-1434
E-mail: ramchavez@sbcglobal.net

9796 ■ Vietnam Veterans of America, Chapter 923
PO Box 1156
San Marcos, TX 78667-1156
Contact: Rod Metzler, Pres.
E-mail: rampsych@austin.rr.com
Fnd: 1978.

9797 ■ Vietnam Veterans of America, Crossroads - Chapter No. 898
PO Box 1111
Victoria, TX 77902
Contact: Marvin L. Lockhart II, Sec.
E-mail: locntx@hotmail.com

9798 ■ Vietnam Veterans of America, Fort Worth - Chapter 330
PO Box 8092
Fort Worth, TX 76124
Contact: Tommiie Acierno, Pres.
E-mail: proudvietnamvet6@aol.com

9799 ■ Vietnam Veterans of America, Hill Country - Chapter 863
PO Box 291704
Kerrville, TX 78029-1704
Contact: Alan Hill, Pres.
Ph: (830)896-2081
E-mail: alan-dochill04@hotmail.com
Mem: 50.

Utah

9800 ■ International Municipal Signal Association, Great Basin Section
Traffic Operations Center
2060 S 2760 W
Salt Lake City, UT 84104
Contact: David J. Mount, Dir.
Ph: (801)887-3659
Fax: (801)887-3750
E-mail: dmount@dot.ut.us
Descr: Serves as a professional organization of government officials responsible for municipal signaling, fire alarms, traffic signals, radio communication, street lighting, signs and marking, and other related services.

9801 ■ National Association For Uniformed Services - Ogden/Salt Lake City, Utah Chapter
5008 S 1410 E
Ogden, UT 84403
Contact: Tom Cox
Ph: (801)479-5219
E-mail: tomwcox@comcast.net
Descr: Provides assistance and support to active or retired military uniformed service officers. Protects and improves the compensation, entitlements and benefits earned by members of the uniformed services for themselves, their families and survivors and all American citizens with common interests.

9802 ■ Utah Disabled American Veterans
PO Box 581900
Salt Lake City, UT 84158-1900
Contact: Eric D. McGinnis
Ph: (801)326-2375
URL: http://www.dav.org
Descr: Works to give service to disabled veterans

and their families. Provides services in areas including disaster relief, employment, legislation, advocacy and transportation.

9803 ■ Utah Office of Veterans' Affairs
550 Foothill Blvd., Ste. 202
Salt Lake City, UT 84108
Contact: Terry Schow, Dir.
Ph: (801)326-2372
Free: 800-894-9497
Fax: (801)326-2369
E-mail: berni.davis@va.gov
URL: http://veterans.utah.gov/

Vermont

9804 ■ American Lung Association of Vermont
372 Hurricane Ln., Ste. 101
Williston, VT 05495
Contact: Danielle Pinders
Ph: (802)876-6500
Free: 800-LUNG-USA
Fax: (802)876-6505
E-mail: info@vtlung.org
URL: http://www.lungvt.org
Staff: 8. **Descr:** Individuals in Vermont interested in the prevention of lung disease and the promotion of lung health. Offers patient education, advocacy, and research; major areas of focus are asthma, tobacco control and environmental health. Raises funds for programs from individuals, businesses, and grants.

9805 ■ American Pain Society, Vermont
140 Hospital Dr.
Bennington, VT 05201-5003
Contact: Keith Edwards MD, Rep.
Ph: (802)447-7577
Fax: (802)447-2676
E-mail: kedwards@vtneuro.com
Descr: Advances pain-related research, education, treatment and professional practice. Promotes control, management and understanding of pain. Develops standards for training and ethical management of pain patients.

9806 ■ Vermont Disabled American Veterans
PO Box 828
White River Junction, VT 05001-0828
Contact: Marie L. Bushey, Commander
Ph: (802)295-7799
URL: http://www.davmembersportal.org/vt/default.aspx
Descr: Works to give service to disabled veterans and their families. Provides services in areas including disaster relief, employment, legislation, advocacy and transportation.

9807 ■ Vermont State Veterans' Affairs
118 State St.
Montpelier, VT 05620
Contact: Clayton A. Clark, Dir.
Ph: (802)828-3379
Free: 888-666-9844
Fax: (802)828-5932
E-mail: rhonda.boyce@state.vt.us
URL: http://www.va.state.vt.us

9808 ■ Vietnam Veterans of America, Chapter 926
PO Box 386
Bristol, VT 05443
Contact: Brad Bedard, Pres.
Ph: (802)453-5675
E-mail: bbedard@adelphia.net
Fnd: 2003.

9809 ■ Vietnam Veterans of America, Chapter No. 1
15 Wales St.
Rutland, VT 05701
Contact: Andy Megrath, Pres.

E-mail: vthogman@comcast.net
URL: http://www.vvavtsc.com

9810 ■ Vietnam Veterans of America, Chapter No. 601
PO Box 4146
Bennington, VT 05201
Contact: John J. Miner, Pres.
Ph: (802)447-0407
E-mail: malibu1@adelphia.net
URL: http://www.vvavtsc.com

9811 ■ Vietnam Veterans of America, Chapter No. 723
4548 Trebo Rd.
Chester, VT 05143
Contact: Buster Holmberg, Pres.
Ph: (802)886-4357
E-mail: trayberg@hotmail.com
URL: http://www.vvavtsc.com

9812 ■ Vietnam Veterans of America, Chapter No. 753
PO Box 965
St. Albans, VT 05478
Contact: Richard Lancott, Pres.
Ph: (802)868-4492
E-mail: rich_lanc_55@yahoo.com
URL: http://www.vvavtsc.com

9813 ■ Vietnam Veterans of America, Chapter No. 829
PO Box 64
Essex Junction, VT 05453
Contact: Michael Martinez, Pres.
Ph: (802)318-6565
E-mail: vermontveteran@juno.com
URL: http://www.vvavtsc.com

9814 ■ Vietnam Veterans of America, Chapter No. 843
1161 Collins Rd.
Brattleboro, VT 05301
Contact: Lenny Derby, Pres.
Ph: (802)368-7654
E-mail: lenvietvet@yahoo.com
URL: http://www.vvavtsc.com

Virginia

9815 ■ American Lung Association of Virginia, Piedmont Area (ALAV)
9221 Forest Hill Ave.
Richmond, VA 23235
Contact: Melina Davis-Martin, Pres./CEO
Ph: (804)267-1900
Free: 800-586-4872
Fax: (804)267-5634
E-mail: mdavismartin@lungva.org
URL: http://www.lungusa.org/virginia
Staff: 5. **Descr:** Dedicated to the prevention of lung disease and the promotion of lung health. **Fnd:** 1909. **Reg. Groups:** 2. **Pub:** *The Virginia Pulmonary; What's Going On* (quarterly).

9816 ■ American Lung Association of Virginia, Southeast Area
PO Box 8888
Virginia Beach, VA 23450
Contact: Melina Davis-Martin, Pres./CEO
Ph: (757)368-0281
Free: 800-548-8252
E-mail: mdavismartin@lungva.org
URL: http://www.kintera.org/site/c.ivKTL8MWIwG/b.1162245/k.BE12/Home.htm
Staff: 3. **Descr:** Promotes educational programs and research to prevent lung disease and promote lung health. **Fnd:** 1904. **Reg. Groups:** 3. **State Groups:** 1. **Pub:** Newsletter (quarterly).

9817 ■ AMVETS, Virginia
841 Col. Meade Dr.
Suffolk, VA 23434
Contact: Michael Halley, Exec. Dir.
Ph: (757)539-3922

E-mail: mhalley@juno.com
URL: http://www.geocities.com/amvets_va

9818 ■ AMVETS, Virginia Beach Post 69
5668 Indian River Rd.
Virginia Beach, VA 23464
Ph: (757)539-3922
E-mail: amvetsvaexecdir@juno.com

9819 ■ National Association For Uniformed Services - Abraham Lincoln, Virginia Chapter 1
337 Selden Rd.
Newport News, VA 23606-3744
Contact: William J. Davis
Ph: (757)599-3546
E-mail: davisbeno@earthlink.net
Descr: Provides assistance and support to active or retired military uniformed service officers. Protects and improves the compensation, entitlements and benefits earned by members of the uniformed services for themselves, their families and survivors and all American citizens with common interests.

9820 ■ National Association For Uniformed Services - Commonwealth of Virginia, Chapter 5
4007 Longwood Dr.
Fredericksburg, VA 22408
Contact: David A. Ellis, Pres.
Ph: (540)891-7246
E-mail: david_sally@verizon.net
Descr: Provides assistance and support to active or retired military uniformed service officers. Protects and improves the compensation, entitlements and benefits earned by members of the uniformed services for themselves, their families and survivors and all American citizens with common interests.

9821 ■ National Funeral Directors and Morticians Association - District 2
812 Franklin St.
Alexandria, VA 22314
Contact: Billie Watson Hughes
Ph: (703)201-6568
Fax: (703)751-9226
E-mail: msbillie55@hotmail.com
Descr: Promotes ethical practices and encourages just and uniform laws pertaining to funeral directing and embalming industry.

9822 ■ National Spa and Pool Institute Middle Atlantic Chapter
Town & Country Pools, Inc.
7540 Fullerton Ct.
Springfield, VA 22153-4206
Contact: Burton Gray, Pres.
Ph: (703)451-6660
Fax: (703)451-6696
E-mail: townandcountrypools@townandcountrypools.com
URL: http://www.townandcountrypools.com
Descr: Serves individuals in the swimming pool, spa, hot tub and recreational water industries. Works to enhance the business growth and success of its members.

9823 ■ Paralyzed Veterans of America, Virginia Mid-Atlantic Chapter
11620 Busy St.
Richmond, VA 23236
Contact: Michelle L. Shaw-Rich, Exec. Dir.
Ph: (804)378-0017
Free: 800-852-7639
Fax: (804)378-0026
E-mail: vapva@aol.com
URL: http://www.vamapva.com

9824 ■ United Virginia Chapter of the National Hemophilia Foundation (UVC-NHF)
PO Box 188
Midlothian, VA 23113
Contact: Jeff Krecek, Pres.
Ph: (434)295-9515
Free: 800-266-8438
Fax: (804)740-8643

E-mail: vahemophiliaed@verizon.net
URL: http://www.vahemophilia.org
Descr: Represents individuals dedicated to finding better treatments and cures for bleeding and clotting disorders. Prevents the complications of these disorders through education, advocacy and research. Supports services for people with hemophilia and other hereditary bleeding disorders including complications with HIV/AIDS.

9825 ■ Vietnam Veterans of America, Central Virginia - Chapter 78
PO Box 35261
Richmond, VA 23235
Contact: Terry Haskins, Pres.
E-mail: vvachapter78@yahoo.com
URL: http://www.geocities.com/vvachapter78

9826 ■ Vietnam Veterans of America, Chapter 227
PO Box 5653
Arlington, VA 22205
Contact: Bill Dumsick, Pres.
Ph: (703)912-1681
E-mail: vva227@geocities.com
URL: http://www.geocities.com/vva227
Pub: *The Journey.*

9827 ■ Vietnam Veterans of America, Virginia State Council
2258 Bayberry St.
Virginia Beach, VA 23451
Contact: Charlie Montgomery, Pres.
Ph: (757)481-6513
Fax: (757)333-3869
E-mail: gumby173d@cox.net
URL: http://www.vva-vasc.org

9828 ■ Virginia Department of Veterans' Services
900 E. Main St.
Richmond, VA 23219
Contact: Vincent M. Burgess, Commnr.
Ph: (804)786-0286
E-mail: info@dvs.virginia.gov
URL: http://www.dvs.virginia.gov/

Washington

9829 ■ American Arbitration Association, Washington
701 Pike St., Ste. 950
Seattle, WA 98101
Contact: Serena Lee
Ph: (206)622-6435
E-mail: lees@adr.org
Descr: Works to resolve a wide range of disputes through mediation, arbitration, elections and other out-of-court settlement procedures.

9830 ■ American Association of University Women of Washington (AAUW)
PO Box 537
Liberty Lake, WA 99019
Contact: Constance Dunkelberger, Pres.
E-mail: president@aauw-wa.org
URL: http://www.aauw-wa.org
Descr: Graduates of regionally accredited four-year colleges and universities. Works for the advancement of women through advocacy and emphasis on lifelong learning. Sponsors Expanding Your Horizons program. Lobbies for favorable legislation. **Fnd:** 1927. **Mem:** 2400. **State Groups:** 1. **Local Groups:** 44. **Pub:** *Evergreen Leader* (quarterly); *Officers Directory* (annual).

9831 ■ American Farmland Trust, PNW Regional Office
3211 Beacon Ave. S, Ste. No. 26
Seattle, WA 98144
Contact: Don Stuart, Regional Dir.
Ph: (206)860-4222
E-mail: dstuart@farmland.org
Descr: Works to stop the loss of productive farmland

and to promote farming practices that lead to a healthy environment.

9832 ■ Disabled American Veterans, Yakima
911 N 15th Ave.
Yakima, WA 98902-1301
Contact: Jack Rought, Commander
Ph: (509)453-2702
URL: http://www.davmembersportal.org/chapters/wa/08
Descr: Engages in activities for the improvement and advancement of the condition, health and interest of disabled veterans. Provides a network of service available to all veterans and members of their families.

9833 ■ International Municipal Signal Association, Northwest Section
909 SE Everett Mall Way, Ste. A120
Everett, WA 98208-3750
Contact: John Brannan, Sec.-Treas.
Ph: (425)438-1133
E-mail: jbrannan@westernsystemsnetworks.com
URL: http://imsanw.org
Descr: Serves as a professional organization of government officials responsible for municipal signaling, fire alarms, traffic signals, radio communication, street lighting, signs and marking, and other related services.

9834 ■ National Association For Uniformed Services - Seattle, Washington Chapter 2
11905 59th Ave. W
Mukilteo, WA 98275
Contact: Tony Espejo
Ph: (425)512-8204
E-mail: tespejo@comcast.net
Descr: Provides assistance and support to active or retired military uniformed service officers. Protects and improves the compensation, entitlements and benefits earned by members of the uniformed services for themselves, their families and survivors and all American citizens with common interests.

9835 ■ Vietnam Veterans of America, Chapter 102
PO Box 30189
Seattle, WA 98113
Contact: Debra Wood, Pres.
E-mail: info@vva102.org
URL: http://www.vva102.org

9836 ■ Vietnam Veterans of America, Sno-King - Chapter No. 423
PO Box 423
Edmonds, WA 98020
Contact: Rob Hitchings, Pres.
E-mail: rebelranger7@earthlink.net
URL: http://www.wavva.org

9837 ■ Washington Department of Veterans' Affairs
PO Box 41150
Olympia, WA 98504
Contact: John E. Lee, Dir.
Ph: (360)725-2153
Free: 800-562-0132
Fax: (360)725-2216
E-mail: webmaster@dva.wa.gov
URL: http://www.dva.wa.gov
Descr: Mission is to serve as an advocate for veterans; to help heal seen and unseen wounds of war; to help to the homeless; to provide quality care in Veterans Homes; and to honor veterans in their final resting place. **Telecom. Svcs:** TDD phone number is (360)725-2199.

9838 ■ Washington Disabled American Veterans
Virginia Regional Office Federal Bldg.
915 2nd Ave., Rm. 1040
Seattle, WA 98174
Contact: Michele L. Colpaert, Supervisor
Ph: (206)220-6225
Fax: (206)220-4171
URL: http://www.dav.org
Descr: Works to give service to disabled veterans

and their families. Provides services in areas including disaster relief, employment, legislation, advocacy and transportation.

West Virginia

9839 ■ American Lung Association of West Virginia
PO Box 3980
Charleston, WV 25339-3980
Ph: (304)342-6600
Fax: (304)342-6096
E-mail: cfields@lunginfo.org
Descr: Promotes educational programs and research to prevent and control lung disease.

9840 ■ Vietnam Veterans of America, Chapter 306
PO Box 859
Morgantown, WV 26507
Contact: Charles A. Harrington, Pres.
Ph: (304)296-6111
E-mail: presvva306@yahoo.com
URL: http://www.vva306.org

9841 ■ West Virginia Division of Veterans' Affairs
1321 Plaza E., Ste. 101
Charleston, WV 25301-1400
Contact: Larry Linch, Dir.
Ph: (304)558-3661
Free: 888-838-2332
Fax: (304)558-3662
E-mail: wvdva@state.wv.us
URL: http://www.wvs.state.wv.us/va/

9842 ■ West Virginia Political Science Association
PO Box 6317
Morgantown, WV 26506-6317
Contact: Tom Bias, Website Coor.
Ph: (304)293-3811
Fax: (304)293-8644
E-mail: leeann.greathouse@mail.wvu.edu
URL: http://www.polsci.wvu.edu/wvpsa
Descr: Represents college and university teachers of political science, public officials, research workers, and businessmen. Encourages the impartial study and promotes the development of the art and science of government. Develops research projects of public interest and educational programs for political scientists and journalists. Seeks to improve the knowledge of and increase citizen participation in political and governmental affairs.

Wisconsin

9843 ■ American Ex-Prisoners of War, Northeastern Wisconsin Chapter
2401 County Rd. U
Wrightstown, WI 54180
Contact: Milford Roehrborn, Commander
Ph: (920)766-3227
Descr: Seeks to: acquaint the public with the needs, problems, and handicaps associated with prisoners of war; promote research in the fields connected with injuries, diseases, and syndromes stemming from imprisonment; advocate and foster complete and effective reconditioning programs for ex-prisoners of war; foster patriotism and civic loyalty; encourage fraternal and historical activities.

9844 ■ American Ex-Prisoners of War, Southern Wisconsin Chapter
1235 Boynton Ct.
Janesville, WI 53545
Contact: Karl Rannenberg
Ph: (608)752-7027
Descr: Seeks to: acquaint the public with the needs, problems, and handicaps associated with prisoners of war; promote research in the fields connected with injuries, diseases, and syndromes stemming from imprisonment; advocate and foster complete and effective reconditioning programs for ex-prisoners of

war; foster patriotism and civic loyalty; encourage fraternal and historical activities.

9845 ■ American Lung Association of Wisconsin (ALAW)
13100 W Lisbon Rd., Ste. 700
Brookfield, WI 53005-2508
Contact: Susan Gloede Swan, Exec. Dir.
Ph: (262)703-4200
Free: 800-586-4872
Fax: (262)781-5180
E-mail: amlung@lungwisconsin.org
URL: http://www.lungwi.org
Staff: 19. **Descr:** Promotes lung health and works to prevent lung disease through research, public policy, education and community service by focusing on asthma, tobacco and environmental health. **Fnd:** 1908. **Reg. Groups:** 1.

9846 ■ AMVETS, Oak Creek Post 60
Classic Lanes Oak Creek
7501 S Howell Ave.
Oak Creek, WI 53154
Contact: Jim Ruppel
Ph: (414)764-9196
E-mail: jhruppel@yahoo.com
URL: http://www.amvets-wi.org/post60

9847 ■ AMVETS Post 99
4310 Conroe St.
Manitowoc, WI 54220
Ph: (920)684-6577
E-mail: grdgmm@aol.com
URL: http://amvets99.g3z.com

9848 ■ National Association For Uniformed Services - Northern Wisconsin, Chapter 1
1501 Grant St.
Marinette, WI 54143-2321
Contact: Robert D. Saxton
Ph: (715)732-4363
E-mail: bsaxton@cybrzn.com
Descr: Provides assistance and support to active or retired military uniformed service officers. Protects and improves the compensation, entitlements and benefits earned by members of the uniformed services for themselves, their families and survivors and all American citizens with common interests.

9849 ■ National Association For Uniformed Services - Southern Wisconsin, Chapter 2
2468 N 12th St.
Milwaukee, WI 53206-2503
Contact: Floyd S. Jack
Ph: (404)651-1425
E-mail: majorjackwigr@yahoo.com
Descr: Provides assistance and support to active or retired military uniformed service officers. Protects and improves the compensation, entitlements and benefits earned by members of the uniformed services for themselves, their families and survivors and all American citizens with common interests.

9850 ■ Vietnam Veterans of America, Chapter 351
PO Box 1862
Appleton, WI 54912-1862
E-mail: contact@vva351.com
URL: http://www.vva351.com

9851 ■ Wisconsin Department of Veterans' Affairs
30 W. Mifflin St.
PO Box 7843
Madison, WI 53703-7843
Contact: John A. Scocos, Sec.
Ph: (608)266-1311
Free: 800-947-8387
Fax: (608)267-0403
E-mail: wdvaweb@dva.state.wi.us
URL: http://dva.state.wi.us
Fnd: 1945.

9852 ■ Wisconsin Paralyzed Veterans of America (WPVA)
2311 S 108th St.
West Allis, WI 53227-1901

Contact: Phillip E. Rosenberg, Pres.
Ph: (414)328-8910
Fax: (414)328-8948
E-mail: info@wisconsinpva.org
URL: http://www.wisconsinpva.org
Staff: 3. **Descr:** Dedicated solely for the benefit and representation of individuals with spinal cord injury or disease. **Fnd:** 1980. **Pub:** *Dairyland News*; *Paraplegic News* (monthly); *Sports and Spokes* (monthly).

Wyoming

9853 ■ Wyoming Veterans' Commission
5500 Bishop Blvd.
Cheyenne, WY 82009
Contact: Larry Barttelbort, Exec.Dir.
Ph: (307)772-5145
Fax: (307)772-5202
E-mail: lbartt@state.wy.us

Publications

9854 ■ *The 9 to 5 Guide to Combating Sexual Harassment*
9 to 5, National Association of Working Women
207 E Buffalo St., No. 211
Milwaukee, WI 53202
Ph: (414)274-0925
Fax: (414)272-2870
E-mail: 9to5@9to5.org
URL: http://www.9to5.org
Price: $15.

9855 ■ *9 to 5 Newsline*
9 to 5, National Association of Working Women
207 E Buffalo St., No. 211
Milwaukee, WI 53202
Ph: (414)274-0925
Fax: (414)272-2870
E-mail: 9to5@9to5.org
URL: http://www.9to5.org
Freq: 5/year. **Price:** included in membership dues, $25/year for individuals, $40/year for institutions.

9856 ■ *9 to 5: Working Women's Guide to Office Survival*
9 to 5, National Association of Working Women
207 E Buffalo St., No. 211
Milwaukee, WI 53202
Ph: (414)274-0925
Fax: (414)272-2870
E-mail: 9to5@9to5.org
URL: http://www.9to5.org

9857 ■ *12 Tips for Helping Your Children Stay Drug-Free*
National Families in Action
2957 Clairmont Rd. NE, Ste. 150
Atlanta, GA 30329
Ph: (404)248-9676
Fax: (404)248-1312
E-mail: nfia@nationalfamilies.org
URL: http://www.nationalfamilies.org
Price: $15/100 copies.

9858 ■ *100 Questions and Answers about Hypertension*
National Hypertension Association
324 E 30th St.
New York, NY 10016
Ph: (212)889-3557
Fax: (212)447-7032
E-mail: nathypertension@aol.com
URL: http://www.nathypertension.org
Descr: Contains information on hypertension and the importance of controlling high blood pressure.
Price: $14.95.

9859 ■ *380 In Review*
Vietnam Veterans of America, Chapter 380
173 US 41 E
Negaunee, MI 49866
Ph: (906)475-6435

E-mail: vva380@chartermi.net
URL: http://www.vva380.org
Freq: bimonthly.

9860 ■ *A 2004 Policy Guide for Federal, State, and Local Legislators*
American Homeowners Grassroots Alliance
6776 Little Falls Rd.
Arlington, VA 22213-1213
Fax: (703)536-7079
E-mail: ahga@americanhomeowners.org
URL: http://www.americanhomeowners.org

9861 ■ *AALReporter*
American Association for Physical Activity and Recreation
1900 Association Dr.
Reston, VA 20191-1598
Ph: (703)476-3400
Fax: (703)476-9527
E-mail: aapar@aahperd.org
URL: http://www.aahperd.org/aapar
Freq: quarterly.

9862 ■ *AARP Connections North Carolina*
American Association of Retired Persons, North Carolina
225 Hillsborough St., Ste. 440
Raleigh, NC 27603
Ph: (919)508-0290
Fax: (919)755-9684
E-mail: ncaarp@aarp.org
URL: http://www.aarp.org/states/nc
Freq: monthly.

9863 ■ *AASC Insight*
American Association of Service Coordinators
PO Box 1178
Powell, OH 43065-1178
Ph: (614)848-5958
Fax: (614)848-5954
E-mail: info@servicecoordinator.org
URL: http://www.servicecoordinator.org
Freq: quarterly.

9864 ■ *AAWM Quarterly News Briefing*
American Academy of Wound Management
1155 15th St. NW, Ste. 500
Washington, DC 20005
Ph: (202)457-8408
Fax: (202)530-0659
E-mail: jmargeson@aawm.org
URL: http://www.aawm.org
Freq: quarterly.

9865 ■ *About Headaches*
National Headache Foundation
820 N Orleans St., Ste. 217
Chicago, IL 60610-3498
Fax: (312)640-9049
E-mail: info@headaches.org
URL: http://www.headaches.org

9866 ■ *Abstinence Clearinghouse Directory of Abstinence Resources*
Abstinence Clearinghouse
801 E 41st St.
Sioux Falls, SD 57105
Ph: (605)335-3643
E-mail: info@abstinence.net
URL: http://www.abstinence.net
Descr: Contains abstinence-until-marriage resources. **Freq:** semiannual. **Price:** $20.

9867 ■ *The Abstinence Network*
Abstinence Clearinghouse
801 E 41st St.
Sioux Falls, SD 57105
Ph: (605)335-3643
E-mail: info@abstinence.net
URL: http://www.abstinence.net
Descr: Assists those working with young people to

abstain from premarital sexual intercourse. **Freq:** quarterly.

9868 ■ *Academic License: The War on Academic Freedom*
Accuracy in Academia
4455 Connecticut Ave. NW, Ste. 330
Washington, DC 20008
Ph: (202)364-3085
Fax: (202)364-4098
E-mail: mal.kline@academia.org
URL: http://www.academia.org

9869 ■ *ACSH in Action*
American Council on Science and Health
1995 Broadway, 2nd Fl.
New York, NY 10023-5882
Ph: (212)362-7044
Fax: (212)362-4919
E-mail: acsh@acsh.org
URL: http://www.acsh.org
Freq: quarterly.

9870 ■ *Action Alert*
Citizens for Health
2104 Stevens Ave. S
Minneapolis, MN 55404
E-mail: info@citizens.org
URL: http://www.citizens.org
Freq: periodic.

9871 ■ *Action Bulletin*
Friends Committee on National Legislation
245 2nd St. NE
Washington, DC 20002-5761
Ph: (202)547-6000
Fax: (202)547-6019
E-mail: fcnl@fcnl.org
URL: http://www.fcnl.org
Freq: periodic.

9872 ■ *Active Living*
American Amputee Foundation
PO Box 94227
North Little Rock, AR 72190
Ph: (501)835-9290
Fax: (501)835-9292
E-mail: info@americanamputee.org
URL: http://www.americanamputee.org
Freq: quarterly.

9873 ■ *Active Voice*
National Association of People with AIDS
8401 Colesville Rd., Ste. 550
Silver Spring, MD 20910
Ph: (240)247-0880
Fax: (240)247-0574
E-mail: info@napwa.org
URL: http://www.napwa.org
Descr: Provides information about healthcare and advocacy issues. **Freq:** quarterly. **Price:** free.

9874 ■ *ADA News*
American Dental Association
211 E Chicago Ave.
Chicago, IL 60611-2678
Ph: (312)440-2500
Fax: (312)440-2800
E-mail: publicinfo@ada.org
URL: http://www.ada.org
Freq: biweekly. **Price:** $64 for nonmembers. **ISSN:** 0895-2930.

9875 ■ *Adult Day Services: Secrets, Systems, and Strategies for Excellence: Leaders Guide*
National Adult Day Services Association
85 S Washington, Ste. 316
Seattle, WA 98104
Ph: (414)464-3888
Fax: (206)461-3218
E-mail: info@nadsa.org
URL: http://www.nadsa.org
Descr: Contains guidance on goals, the main message and key points, the teasing out of management

skills, handouts, and thought-provoking questions.
Price: $55 for members, $75 for nonmembers.

9876 ■ *AFA Journal*
American Family Association
PO Drawer 2440
Tupelo, MS 38803
Ph: (662)844-5036
Fax: (662)842-7798
E-mail: afa@afa.net
URL: http://www.afa.net
Freq: monthly.

9877 ■ *AFAKY Newsletter*
American Family Association of Kentucky
PO Box 8089
Louisville, KY 40257-8089
Ph: (502)893-2444
Fax: (502)897-2426
E-mail: fsimon@afaky.com

9878 ■ *Agent Orange*
Vietnam Veterans Against the War
PO Box 408594
Chicago, IL 60640
Ph: (773)276-4189
E-mail: vvaw@vvaw.org
URL: http://www.vvaw.org

9879 ■ *AHQA Bulletin*
American Health Quality Association
1155 21st St. NW
Washington, DC 20036
Ph: (202)331-5790
Fax: (202)331-9334
E-mail: info@ahqa.org
URL: http://www.ahqa.org
Descr: Covers medical regulatory and legislative developments. **Freq:** periodic. **Price:** included in membership dues.

9880 ■ *AIBC News Med-Clime Currents*
American Institute of Biomedical Climatology
1050 Eagle Rd.
Newtown, PA 18940-2818
Ph: (215)968-4483
E-mail: info@aibc.cc
Descr: Contains news concerning new publications and research studies. Available via member contributions. **Price:** included in membership dues.

9881 ■ *ALSC Agencies Typical Grade Stamps*
American Lumber Standard Committee
PO Box 210
Germantown, MD 20875-0210
Ph: (301)972-1700
Fax: (301)540-8004
E-mail: alsc@alsc.org
URL: http://www.alsc.org

9882 ■ *Alternatives*
Center for Policy Alternatives
1875 Connecticut Ave. NW, Ste. 710
Washington, DC 20009
Ph: (202)387-6030
Fax: (202)387-8529
E-mail: info@cfpa.org
URL: http://www.cfpa.org
Freq: 10/year. **Price:** $25/copy.

9883 ■ *American Bicyclist*
League of American Bicyclists
1612 K St. NW, Ste. 800
Washington, DC 20006-2850
Ph: (202)822-1333
Fax: (202)822-1334
E-mail: bikeleague@bikeleague.org
URL: http://www.bikeleague.org
Freq: quarterly. **Price:** included in membership dues.

9884 ■ *American CattleWoman*
American National CattleWomen
PO Box 3881
Englewood, CO 80155
Ph: (303)694-0313

Fax: (303)694-2390
E-mail: ancw@beef.org
URL: http://www.ancw.org
Descr: Provides timely information about organizational activities and beef industry issues. **Freq:** quarterly. **Price:** $30. **ISSN:** 1042-5293.

9885 ■ American Experiment Quarterly
Center of the American Experiment
12 S 6th St., Ste. 1024
Minneapolis, MN 55402-1502
Ph: (612)338-3605
Fax: (612)338-3621
E-mail: info@americanexperiment.org
URL: http://www.americanexperiment.org
Freq: quarterly. **Price:** $30/year for nonmembers, included in membership dues. **ISSN:** 1097-1866.

9886 ■ American Farmland
American Farmland Trust
1200 18th St. NW, Ste. 800
Washington, DC 20036
Ph: (202)331-7300
Fax: (202)659-8339
E-mail: info@farmland.org
URL: http://www.farmland.org
Descr: Discusses major challenges confronting farmland today and offers the latest information on tools and techniques being used. **Freq:** quarterly. **Price:** included in membership dues.

9887 ■ American Fitness
Aerobics and Fitness Association of America
15250 Ventura Blvd., Ste. 200
Sherman Oaks, CA 91403
Fax: (818)788-6301
E-mail: contactafaa@afaa.com
URL: http://www.afaa.com
Descr: Features exercise trends, research, interviews, products, health, and nutrition. **Freq:** bimonthly. **Price:** included in membership dues, $27/year for nonmembers. **ISSN:** 0893-5238.

9888 ■ The American Homeopath
North American Society of Homeopaths
PO Box 450039
Sunrise, FL 33345-0039
Ph: (206)720-7000
Fax: (208)248-1942
E-mail: nashinfo@homeopathy.org
URL: http://www.homeopathy.org

9889 ■ American Orthodontic Society Newsletter
American Orthodontic Society
11884 Greenville Ave., Ste. 112
Dallas, TX 75243-3537
E-mail: aos@orthodontics.com
URL: http://www.orthodontics.com
Descr: Provides information on the society's seminars and conventions and news of interest to members. **Freq:** quarterly. **Price:** included in membership dues.

9890 ■ American Orthodontic Society Technique Directory
American Orthodontic Society
11884 Greenville Ave., Ste. 112
Dallas, TX 75243-3537
E-mail: aos@orthodontics.com
URL: http://www.orthodontics.com
Descr: Lists members by city and state; includes the type of orthodontic technique used by listee. **Freq:** biennial. **Price:** $150/year.

9891 ■ American Paddler
American Canoe Association
1340 Central Park Blvd., Ste. 210
Fredericksburg, VA 22401
Ph: (540)907-4460
Fax: 888-229-3792
E-mail: aca@americancanoe.org
URL: http://www.americancanoe.org
Descr: Contains information of upcoming events and

articles about paddlesports. **Freq:** quarterly. **Price:** included in membership dues.

9892 ■ American Political Science Review
American Political Science Association
1527 New Hampshire Ave. NW
Washington, DC 20036-1206
Ph: (202)483-2512
Fax: (202)483-2657
E-mail: apsa@apsanet.org
URL: http://www.apsanet.org
Descr: Covers all aspects of political science. **Freq:** quarterly. **Price:** included in membership dues. **ISSN:** 0003-0554.

9893 ■ American Veteran
AMVETS - American Veterans
4647 Forbes Blvd.
Lanham, MD 20706-4380
Ph: (301)459-9600
Fax: (301)459-7924
E-mail: amvets@amvets.org
URL: http://www.amvets.org
Freq: quarterly. **Price:** included in membership dues, $10/year for nonmembers in U.S., $11/year for nonmembers outside U.S. **ISSN:** 0027-853X.

9894 ■ America's Military Today
Citizen Soldier
267 5th Ave., No. 901
New York, NY 10016
Ph: (212)679-2250
Fax: (212)679-2252
E-mail: citizensoldier1@aol.com
URL: http://www.citizen-soldier.org
Price: $27.95 hard cover.

9895 ■ The Amp
National Amputation Foundation
40 Church St.
Malverne, NY 11565
Ph: (516)887-3600
Fax: (516)887-3667
E-mail: amps76@aol.com
URL: http://www.nationalamputation.org
Freq: bimonthly.

9896 ■ Anishinaabe Niijii (Friends of the Chippewa)
Center for Alternative Mining Development Policy
210 Avon St., Ste. 4
La Crosse, WI 54603
Ph: (608)784-4399
Fax: (608)785-8486
E-mail: gedicks.al@uwlax.edu

9897 ■ Annual Directory of Sheriffs
National Sheriffs' Association
1450 Duke St.
Alexandria, VA 22314-3490
Ph: (703)836-7827
Fax: (703)683-6541
E-mail: nsamail@sheriffs.org
URL: http://www.sheriffs.org
Descr: Includes names, addresses of all 3,096 sheriffs from across the nation. **Freq:** annual. **Price:** $50 for nonmembers, $35 for members.

9898 ■ Annual Directory and Statistical Report
American Public Power Association
1875 Connecticut Ave. NW, Ste. 1200
Washington, DC 20009
Ph: (202)467-2900
Fax: (202)467-2910
E-mail: mrufe@appanet.org
URL: http://www.appanet.org
Freq: annual. **Price:** $50 for APPA/DEED member (first copy free for members), $150 for nonmembers.

9899 ■ Annual Seminar Conferences
National Association of Professional Process Servers
PO Box 4547
Portland, OR 97208-4547
Ph: (503)222-4180
Fax: (503)222-3950

E-mail: administrator@napps.org
URL: http://www.napps.org
Descr: Highlights the annual educational seminars.

9900 ■ Annual Voting Record of U.S. Congress
Consumer Federation of America
1620 I St. NW, Ste. 200
Washington, DC 20006
Ph: (202)387-6121
Fax: (202)265-7989
E-mail: cfa@consumerfed.org
URL: http://www.consumerfed.org

9901 ■ ANSI Reporter
American National Standards Institute
1819 L St. NW, 6th Fl.
Washington, DC 20036
Ph: (202)293-8020
Fax: (202)293-9287
E-mail: info@ansi.org
URL: http://www.ansi.org
Descr: Covers issues that affect the voluntary standards system, including government standards-related proposals and actions. Includes calendar of events. **Freq:** quarterly. **Price:** $100 for nonmembers, included in membership dues. **ISSN:** 0038-9676.

9902 ■ APS Bulletin
American Pain Society
4700 W Lake Ave.
Glenview, IL 60025
Ph: (847)375-4715
Fax: (847)375-6479
E-mail: info@ampainsoc.org
URL: http://www.ampainsoc.org
Freq: bimonthly.

9903 ■ Assault on Religious Freedom
International Coalition for Religious Freedom
7777 Leesburg Pike, Ste. 404 N
Falls Church, VA 22043
Ph: (703)790-1500
Fax: (703)790-5562
E-mail: icrf@aol.com
URL: http://www.religiousfreedom.com

9904 ■ At the Federal Election Commission: Things Just Don't Add Up, 2001 Report
Project on Government Oversight
666 11th St. NW, Ste. 900
Washington, DC 20001-4542
Ph: (202)347-1122
Fax: (202)347-1116
E-mail: info@pogo.org
URL: http://www.pogo.org

9905 ■ At War with Peace: U.S. Covert Operations
National Committee Against Repressive Legislation
3321 12th St. NE
Washington, DC 20017
Ph: (202)529-4225
Fax: (202)526-4611
E-mail: info@ncarl.org
URL: http://ncarl.org

9906 ■ Athlete's View
American Sports Institute
PO Box 1837
Mill Valley, CA 94942
Ph: (415)383-5750
Fax: (415)383-5785
E-mail: info@amersports.org
URL: http://www.amersports.org
Descr: Contains articles, information, and an overview of the programs and services offered by the institute. **Freq:** quarterly.

9907 ■ Atomic Veterans News
National Association of Atomic Veterans
11214 Sageland
Houston, TX 77089
Ph: (281)481-1357
E-mail: cmdr@naav.com
URL: http://www.naav.com

Freq: quarterly.

9908 ■ *Awareness*
National Association for Parents of Children With Visual Impairments
PO Box 317
Watertown, MA 02471
Ph: (617)972-7441
Fax: (617)972-7444
E-mail: napvi@perkins.org
URL: http://www.spedex.com/napvi
Descr: Includes updates, articles, ideas for activities, news and announcements and letters to the editor. **Freq:** quarterly. **Price:** included in membership dues.

9909 ■ *AWUG Public Domain Library Catalog*
AppleWorks Users Group
PO Box 701010
Plymouth, MI 48170
Ph: (734)454-1969
E-mail: membership@awug.org
URL: http://www.awug.org
Descr: Lists hundreds of templates, enhancements and utilities useful in AppleWorks. **Price:** $6 includes postage.

9910 ■ *Badger Tracks*
American Camp Association, Wisconsin
N9659 Hopfensperger Rd.
Appleton, WI 54915
Ph: (920)716-4133
E-mail: acawisconsin@sbcglobal.net
URL: http://www.acawisconsin.org
Descr: Contains news about Wisconsin camping and national camping issues. **Freq:** 5/year. **Price:** free.

9911 ■ *Beep Baseball In A Nutshell*
National Beep Baseball Association
3444 Limerick Ln. NE
Rochester, MN 55906
Ph: (507)208-8383
E-mail: secretary@nbba.org
URL: http://www.nbba.org
Descr: Features a brief description explaining the game and rules. **Freq:** annual. **Price:** free.

9912 ■ *BEEP Newsletter*
National Urban League
120 Wall St., 8th Fl.
New York, NY 10005
Ph: (212)558-5300
Fax: (212)344-5332
E-mail: info@nul.org
URL: http://www.nul.org
Descr: Describes BEEP courses. Includes member news and listing of publications. **Freq:** quarterly.

9913 ■ *Being Well*
Center for the Well Being of Health Professionals
21 W Colony Pl., Ste. 150
Durham, NC 27705-5589
Ph: (919)489-9167
Fax: (919)419-0011
E-mail: cpwb@mindspring.com
URL: http://www.cpwb.org
Freq: quarterly.

9914 ■ *Best of Q & A: A Guide to Regulatory Resources*
Illinois Home Care Council
100 E Washington
Springfield, IL 62701
Ph: (217)753-4422
Fax: (217)528-6545
E-mail: info@ilhomecare.org
URL: http://www.ilhomecare.org

9915 ■ *Bicycling*
League of American Bicyclists
1612 K St. NW, Ste. 800
Washington, DC 20006-2850
Ph: (202)822-1333
Fax: (202)822-1334
E-mail: bikeleague@bikeleague.org
URL: http://www.bikeleague.org

Freq: quarterly.

9916 ■ *The Big Picture*
Center for Responsive Politics
1101 14th St. NW, Ste. 1030
Washington, DC 20005-5635
Ph: (202)857-0044
Fax: (202)857-7809
E-mail: info@crp.org
URL: http://www.opensecrets.org
Price: $10.

9917 ■ *Blowing the Whistle: How to Protect Yourself and Win*
National Whistleblower Center
3238 P St. NW
Washington, DC 20007
Ph: (202)342-1902
Fax: (202)342-1904
E-mail: contact@whistleblowers.org
URL: http://www.whistleblowers.org
Price: $50 attorney/institution, $25 layperson.

9918 ■ *The Book of U.S. Government Jobs*
Bookhaven Press L.L.C.
249 Field Club Cir.
McKees Rocks, PA 15136
Ph: (412)494-6926
Free: 800-782-7424
Fax: (412)494-5749
E-mail: bookhaven@aol.com
URL: http://www.bookhavenpress.com
Key Personnel: Dennis V. Damp, Author. **URL(s):** http://www.bookhavenpress.com **Publication includes:** Lists of Washington, D.C., departments and agencies, Websites, and job centers nationwide. **Freq:** Annual, Latest edition 10th, February 2008. **Price:** $22.95, individuals.

9919 ■ *The Bridge*
Paralyzed Veterans of America, Bay Area and Western Chapter
3801 Miranda Ave., Bldg. 101
Rm. A1-219, Mail Code 816
Palo Alto, CA 94304
Ph: (650)858-3936
Fax: (650)855-9019
E-mail: pvachbaw@mindspring.com
URL: http://www.pva.org
Freq: bimonthly.

9920 ■ *Bridges*
Bridges to Community
95 Croton Ave.
Ossining, NY 10562
Ph: (914)923-2200
Fax: (914)923-8396
E-mail: info@bridgestocommunity.org
URL: http://www.bridgestocommunity.org
Freq: quarterly.

9921 ■ *Bridges on Power: Women's Multicultural Alliances*
National Women's Studies Association
7100 Baltimore Ave., Ste. 502
College Park, MD 20740
Ph: (301)403-0407
Fax: (301)403-4137
E-mail: nwsaoffice@nwsa.org
URL: http://www.nwsa.org
Price: $11.

9922 ■ *Bridging the Gap*
Government Accountability Project
1612 K St. NW, Ste. 1100
Washington, DC 20006
Ph: (202)408-0034
E-mail: info@whistleblower.org
URL: http://www.whistleblower.org
Descr: Contains updates on programs and activities. **Freq:** quarterly. **Price:** included in membership dues.

9923 ■ *Buyers Up News*
Public Citizen
1600 20th St. NW
Washington, DC 20009

Ph: (202)588-1000
E-mail: member@citizen.org
URL: http://www.citizen.org

9924 ■ *The Call*
Call to Renewal
3333 14th St. NW, Ste. 200
Washington, DC 20010
Ph: (202)328-8842
Fax: (202)328-8757
E-mail: sojourners@sojo.net
URL: http://www.calltorenewal.org
Freq: monthly.

9925 ■ *Camping Magazine*
American Camp Association
5000 State Rd., 67 N
Martinsville, IN 46151-7902
Ph: (765)342-8456
Fax: (765)342-2065
E-mail: psmith@acacamps.org
URL: http://www.acacamps.org
Descr: Includes association news, book reviews, legislative news, research reports, new product information, and index of advertisers. **Freq:** bimonthly. **Price:** included in membership dues, $24.95/year for nonmembers.

9926 ■ *CampLine*
American Camping Association - Illinois Section
67 E Madison St., Ste. 1406
Chicago, IL 60603-3010
Ph: (312)332-0833
Fax: (312)332-4011
E-mail: info@acail.org
URL: http://www.acail.org
Descr: Contains legal, risk management, legislative, regulatory and personnel management. **Freq:** 3/year. **Price:** $24 associate, business, $40 for nonmembers.

9927 ■ *Campus Report*
Accuracy in Academia
4455 Connecticut Ave. NW, Ste. 330
Washington, DC 20008
Ph: (202)364-3085
Fax: (202)364-4098
E-mail: mal.kline@academia.org
URL: http://www.academia.org
Freq: monthly. **Price:** $30/year. **ISSN:** 0890-4618.

9928 ■ *CAN Update*
Cult Awareness Network
1680 N Vine St., Ste. 415
Los Angeles, CA 90028
E-mail: can@cultawarenessnetwork.org
URL: http://www.cultawarenessnetwork.org
Freq: quarterly.

9929 ■ *Capitol Comment*
Citizens for a Sound Economy
1775 Pennsylvania Ave. NW, 11th Fl.
Washington, DC 20006-5805
Ph: (202)783-3870
Fax: (202)942-7649
E-mail: cse@cse.org
URL: http://cse.org
Freq: periodic.

9930 ■ *Care Management Standards*
National Institute on Community-Based Long-Term Care
1901 L St. NW, 4th Fl.
Washington, DC 20036
Ph: (202)479-1200
Fax: (202)479-0735
E-mail: info@ncoa.org
URL: http://www.ncoa.org/content.cfm?sectionID=42

9931 ■ *Carnegie East House*
Health Advocates for Older People
593 Park Ave.
New York, NY 10065
Ph: (212)980-1700

Fax: (212)980-1717
E-mail: info@hafop.org
URL: http://www.hafop.org
Descr: Contains information about assisted living.
Freq: annual. **Price:** free.

9932 ■ *Catalog of American National Standards*
American National Standards Institute
1819 L St. NW, 6th Fl.
Washington, DC 20036
Ph: (202)293-8020
Fax: (202)293-9287
E-mail: info@ansi.org
URL: http://www.ansi.org
Descr: Lists 11,500 current ANSI-approved standards by subject and by designation. **Freq:** annual.
Price: included in membership dues, $20/year for nonmembers.

9933 ■ *CenterLines*
National Center for Bicycling and Walking
26 DeHart Rd.
Maplewood, NJ 07040
Ph: (973)378-3137
E-mail: info@bikewalk.org
URL: http://www.bikewalk.org
Freq: biweekly.

9934 ■ *Certification Manual*
B.K.S. Iyengar Yoga National Association of the U.S.
1300 Clay St., Ste. 600
Oakland, CA 94612
URL: http://www.iynaus.org

9935 ■ *CFA News*
Consumer Federation of America
1620 I St. NW, Ste. 200
Washington, DC 20006
Ph: (202)387-6121
Fax: (202)265-7989
E-mail: cfa@consumerfed.org
URL: http://www.consumerfed.org
Descr: Provides information about CFA advocacy, conferences and publications. **Freq:** bimonthly.

9936 ■ *CFM Brochure*
Citizens for Midwifery
PO Box 82227
Athens, GA 30608-2227
E-mail: info@cfmidwifery.org
URL: http://cfmidwifery.org
Price: free for members.

9937 ■ *CGA World*
Catholic Golden Age
PO Box 249
Olyphant, PA 18447
E-mail: cgaemail@aol.com
URL: http://www.catholicgoldenage.org
Descr: Reports on human rights, world peace, and health care and Social Security. **Freq:** bimonthly.

9938 ■ *Cigarettes: What the Warning Label Doesn't Tell You*
American Council on Science and Health
1995 Broadway, 2nd Fl.
New York, NY 10023-5882
Ph: (212)362-7044
Fax: (212)362-4919
E-mail: acsh@acsh.org
URL: http://www.acsh.org

9939 ■ *Citizen Activist Register*
RID - U.S.A.
PO Box 520
Schenectady, NY 12301
Ph: (518)372-0034
Fax: (518)370-4917
E-mail: dwi@rid-usa.org
URL: http://www.rid-usa.org
Descr: Lists association leaders geographically.
Freq: semiannual. **Price:** available to members only.

9940 ■ *Citizen Advocacy News and Views*
Citizen Advocacy Center
1400 16th St. NW, Ste. 101

Washington, DC 20036
Ph: (202)462-1174
Fax: (202)354-5372
E-mail: cac@cacenter.org
URL: http://www.cacenter.org
Freq: quarterly. **Price:** $40/copy, $195/year, $330 for 2 years.

9941 ■ *Citizen Agenda*
U.S. Public Interest Research Group
218 D St. SE
Washington, DC 20003-1900
Ph: (202)546-9707
Fax: (202)546-2461
E-mail: membershipservices@pirg.org
Descr: Covers federal legislation on environmental, consumer, nuclear, and other public interest issues; reports on USPIRG's lobbying efforts. **Freq:** quarterly. **Price:** included in membership dues.

9942 ■ *Citizen Outlook*
Committee for a Constructive Tomorrow
PO Box 65722
Washington, DC 20035
Ph: (202)429-2737
E-mail: info@cfact.org
URL: http://www.cfact.org
Freq: bimonthly.

9943 ■ *Citizens for Midwifery News*
Citizens for Midwifery
PO Box 82227
Athens, GA 30608-2227
E-mail: info@cfmidwifery.org
URL: http://cfmidwifery.org
Freq: quarterly. **Price:** included in membership dues, $20 for nonmembers.

9944 ■ *Civic Action*
National Civic League
1640 Logan St.
Denver, CO 80203
Ph: (303)571-4343
Fax: (303)571-4404
E-mail: ncl@ncl.org
URL: http://www.ncl.org
Freq: quarterly. **Price:** free for members.

9945 ■ *Class Actions: America's New Boom Industry*
Citizens for a Sound Economy
1775 Pennsylvania Ave. NW, 11th Fl.
Washington, DC 20006-5805
Ph: (202)783-3870
Fax: (202)942-7649
E-mail: cse@cse.org
URL: http://cse.org

9946 ■ *The Client Protection Webb*
National Client Protection Organization
Colorado Supreme Court
1560 Broadwat, Ste. 1800
Denver, CO 80202
E-mail: info@ncpo.org
URL: http://www.ncpo.org
Freq: quarterly.

9947 ■ *Clinton's Social Security Fix*
Citizens for a Sound Economy
1775 Pennsylvania Ave. NW, 11th Fl.
Washington, DC 20006-5805
Ph: (202)783-3870
Fax: (202)942-7649
E-mail: cse@cse.org
URL: http://cse.org

9948 ■ *Club Director*
National Club Association
1201 15th St., Ste. 450
Washington, DC 20005
Ph: (202)822-9822
Fax: (202)822-9808
E-mail: info@nationalclub.org
URL: http://www.natlclub.org

Freq: bimonthly.

9949 ■ *Club News Briefs*
National Club Association
1201 15th St., Ste. 450
Washington, DC 20005
Ph: (202)822-9822
Fax: (202)822-9808
E-mail: info@nationalclub.org
URL: http://www.natlclub.org
Descr: Highlights and analyzes current trends affecting the private club industry. **Freq:** weekly.

9950 ■ *Coalitions*
Community Anti-Drug Coalitions of America
625 Slaters Ln., Ste. 300
Alexandria, VA 22314-1176
Ph: (703)706-0560
Fax: (703)706-0565
E-mail: info@cadca.org
URL: http://cadca.org
Freq: quarterly.

9951 ■ *Collaborative Case Management Magazine*
American Case Management Association
11701 W 36th St.
Little Rock, AR 72211
Ph: (501)907-2262
Fax: (501)227-4247
URL: http://www.acmaweb.org
Freq: quarterly. **Price:** included in membership dues.

9952 ■ *Commentary and News Release List*
Citizens for a Better America
PO Box 7647
Van Nuys, CA 91409-7647
Ph: (818)757-1776
E-mail: hq@cfaba.org
URL: http://www.cfaba.org

9953 ■ *Communicate*
American Camp Association of New England
80 Westview St.
Lexington, MA 02421
Ph: (781)541-6080
Fax: (781)541-6084
E-mail: camp@acane-camps.org
URL: http://acane-camps.org
Freq: bimonthly.

9954 ■ *Communications Conference Workbook*
Foundation for American Communications
85 S Grand Ave.
Pasadena, CA 91105
Ph: (626)584-0010
Fax: (626)584-0627
URL: http://www.facsnet.org

9955 ■ *Communicator*
Private Sector Council
1100 New York Ave. NW, Ste. 1090 E
Washington, DC 20005
Ph: (202)775-9111
Fax: (202)775-8885
E-mail: bramati@ourpublicservice.org
URL: http://www.ourpublicservice.org/psc
Freq: quarterly.

9956 ■ *Community Solutions: Meeting the Challenge of STDs in Asian Americans and Pacific Islanders*
National Asian Women's Health Organization
4900 Hopyard Rd., Ste. 100
Pleasanton, CA 94588
Ph: (925)468-4120
Fax: (925)463-4824
E-mail: info@nawho.org
URL: http://www.nawho.org
Descr: Features strategies in bringing reproductive and sexual health education to under-served Asian American and Pacific Islander women.

9957 ■ *Community Surveys and Reports*
National Urban League
120 Wall St., 8th Fl.

New York, NY 10005
Ph: (212)558-5300
Fax: (212)344-5332
E-mail: info@nul.org
URL: http://www.nul.org
Freq: periodic.

9958 ▪ Compendium
National Community Reinvestment Coalition
727 15th St. NW, Ste. 900
Washington, DC 20005
Ph: (202)628-8866
Fax: (202)628-9800
E-mail: jtaylor@ncrc.org
URL: http://www.ncrc.org

9959 ▪ Conference Proceedings
National Association on Drug Abuse Problems
355 Lexington Ave.
New York, NY 10017
Ph: (212)986-1170
Fax: (212)697-2939
E-mail: info@nadap.com
URL: http://www.nadap.org
Freq: biennial.

9960 ▪ Congressional Pig Book Summary
Citizens Against Government Waste
1301 Connecticut Ave. NW, Ste. 400
Washington, DC 20036
Ph: (202)467-5300
Fax: (202)467-4253
E-mail: membership@cagw.org
URL: http://www.cagw.org
Descr: Includes list of pork-barrel spending in congressional appropriations' bills. **Freq:** annual.

9961 ▪ Congressional Preview Package
Center for Responsive Politics
1101 14th St. NW, Ste. 1030
Washington, DC 20005-5635
Ph: (202)857-0044
Fax: (202)857-7809
E-mail: info@crp.org
URL: http://www.opensecrets.org

9962 ▪ Congressional Voting Index
Public Citizen's Congress Watch
1600 20th St. NW
Washington, DC 20009
Ph: (202)588-1000
Fax: (202)547-7392
E-mail: congress@citizen.org
URL: http://www.citizen.org/congress
Descr: Records and ratings of how Representatives and Senators voted on various consumer issues. **Freq:** annual.

9963 ▪ Connections
American International Health Alliance
1250 Eye St. NW, Ste. 350
Washington, DC 20005
Ph: (202)789-1136
Fax: (202)789-1277
E-mail: aiha@aiha.com
URL: http://www.aiha.com
Descr: Updates partners on the latest news and activities. **Freq:** monthly.

9964 ▪ Connectivity
National Neighborhood Coalition
1221 Connecticut Ave. NW, 2nd Fl.
Washington, DC 20036
Ph: (202)429-0790
Fax: (202)429-0795
E-mail: info@neighborhoodcoalition.org
URL: http://www.neighborhoodcoalition.org
Freq: quarterly.

9965 ▪ Cop Killer - How Mumia Abu-Jamal Conned Millions Into Believing He Was Framed
Accuracy in Academia
4455 Connecticut Ave. NW, Ste. 330
Washington, DC 20008
Ph: (202)364-3085
Fax: (202)364-4098

E-mail: mal.kline@academia.org
URL: http://www.academia.org

9966 ▪ Cord Word
New England Chapter Paralyzed Veterans of America
1600 Providence Hwy., Ste. 101R
Walpole, MA 02081
Ph: (508)660-1181
Fax: (508)668-9412
E-mail: info@nepva.org
URL: http://www.nepva.org
Freq: monthly. **Price:** free for members.

9967 ▪ Corporate Welfare for Arms Merchants
Project on Government Oversight
666 11th St. NW, Ste. 900
Washington, DC 20001-4542
Ph: (202)347-1122
Fax: (202)347-1116
E-mail: info@pogo.org
URL: http://www.pogo.org

9968 ▪ Correspondence Guide
National Association of State Directors of Veterans Affairs
North Carolina Division of Veterans Affairs
Albemarle Bldg., Ste. 1065
325 N Salisbury St.
Raleigh, NC 27603
Ph: (919)733-3851
Fax: (919)733-2834
E-mail: president@nasdva.net
URL: http://www.nasdva.net
Freq: periodic.

9969 ▪ Courage Without Martyrdom: A Survival Guide for Whistleblowers
Government Accountability Project
1612 K St. NW, Ste. 1100
Washington, DC 20006
Ph: (202)408-0034
E-mail: info@whistleblower.org
URL: http://www.whistleblower.org

9970 ▪ CPCU Course Guides
American Institute for CPCU
720 Providence Rd., Ste. 100
Malvern, PA 19355-3433
Ph: (610)644-2100
Fax: (610)640-9576
E-mail: customerservice@cpcuiia.org
URL: http://www.aicpcu.org
Descr: Contains study guides for each of the CPCU courses. **Freq:** annual.

9971 ▪ CPCU/IIA Catalogue
American Institute for CPCU
720 Providence Rd., Ste. 100
Malvern, PA 19355-3433
Ph: (610)644-2100
Fax: (610)640-9576
E-mail: customerservice@cpcuiia.org
URL: http://www.aicpcu.org
Freq: annual.

9972 ▪ Crack Update
National Families in Action
2957 Clairmont Rd. NE, Ste. 150
Atlanta, GA 30329
Ph: (404)248-9676
Fax: (404)248-1312
E-mail: nfia@nationalfamilies.org
URL: http://www.nationalfamilies.org
Descr: Describes the effects of this highly addictive form of cocaine. **Price:** $35/100 copies.

9973 ▪ Crisis
National Association for the Advancement of Colored People
4805 Mt. Hope Dr.
Baltimore, MD 21215
Ph: (410)580-5777
URL: http://www.naacp.org

Freq: 10/year.

9974 ▪ CTWO Times
Center for Third World Organizing
1218 E 21st St.
Oakland, CA 94606
Ph: (510)533-7583
Fax: (510)533-0923
URL: http://www.ctwo.org
Freq: bimonthly.

9975 ▪ Cultural Network Newsletter
National Association of Peoplecultural Rehabilitation Concerns
Michigan State University
459 Erickson Hall
East Lansing, MI 48824
E-mail: srbrtsn@siu.edu
URL: http://www.namrc.org
Freq: quarterly.

9976 ▪ Data Reports
National Association of Dental Plans
12700 Park Central Dr., Ste. 400
Dallas, TX 75251
Ph: (972)458-6998
Fax: (972)458-2258
E-mail: info@nadp.org
URL: http://www.nadp.org
Freq: quarterly.

9977 ▪ Dateline: Washington
Society of American Florists
1601 Duke St.
Alexandria, VA 22314-3406
Ph: (703)836-8700
Fax: (703)836-8705
E-mail: info@safnow.org
URL: http://www.safnow.org

9978 ▪ DAV Chapter No. 18 Fremont Nebraska
Disabled Veterans of America Fremont Chapter - Disabled American Veterans No. 18
137 North D
Fremont, NE 68025
Ph: (402)727-5959
URL: http://www.davmembersportal.org/chapters/ne/18/default.aspx
Freq: monthly. **Price:** free.

9979 ▪ DAV Magazine
Disabled American Veterans
PO Box 14301
Cincinnati, OH 45250-0301
Ph: (859)441-7300
Fax: (859)442-2090
E-mail: feedback@davmail.org
URL: http://www.dav.org
Descr: Covers issues affecting disabled veterans and their families; includes association, department, chapter, and member news. **Freq:** bimonthly. **Price:** included in membership dues, $15/year for nonmembers. **ISSN:** 0885-6400.

9980 ▪ The December Wars
Americans for Religious Liberty
PO Box 6656
Silver Spring, MD 20916
Ph: (301)260-2988
Fax: (301)260-2989
E-mail: arlinc@verizon.net
URL: http://www.arlinc.org
Price: $18.95.

9981 ▪ Desert Dispatch
Desert Storm Veterans Association
2425 Wilson Blvd.
Arlington, VA 22201
Ph: (703)604-6565
E-mail: viicorpsdsva@aol.com
URL: http://www.desertstormvets.org

Descr: Contains information on the status of issues pertinent to Gulf War veterans. **Freq:** quarterly.

9982 ■ *Desert Oracle*
Arizona Paralyzed Veterans of America
8126 N 23rd Ave., Ste. J
Phoenix, AZ 85021
Ph: (602)244-9168
Fax: (602)244-0416
E-mail: azpva@azpva.com
URL: http://www.azpva.org
Freq: monthly.

9983 ■ *The Director*
National Funeral Directors Association
13625 Bishop's Dr.
Brookfield, WI 53005-6607
Ph: (262)789-1880
Fax: (262)789-6977
E-mail: nfda@nfda.org
URL: http://www.nfda.org
Descr: Contains articles regarding funeral service. Includes advertisers' index, calendar of events, and book reviews. **Freq:** monthly. **Price:** included in membership dues, $30/year for nonmembers, $36 for nonmembers (foreign). **ISSN:** 0199-3186.

9984 ■ *Director's Report*
Consuming Industries Trade Action Coalition
2000 L St. NW, Ste. 835
Washington, DC 20036
Ph: (202)316-3046
E-mail: info@citac.info
URL: http://www.citac.info

9985 ■ *Directory of Church Funding Sources*
Center for Third World Organizing
1218 E 21st St.
Oakland, CA 94606
Ph: (510)533-7583
Fax: (510)533-0923
URL: http://www.ctwo.org
Freq: periodic.

9986 ■ *Directory of State and Local Officials*
Division of Federal-State Relations
Food and Drug Administration
5600 Fishers Ln.
Rockville, MD 20857-0001
Ph: (301)827-6906
Free: 888-463-6332
Fax: (301)443-2143
URL: http://www.fda.gov
Key Personnel: Lauren Dipaola, Contact, lauren.dipaola@fda.hhs.gov. **URL(s):** http://www.fda.gov/ora/fed_state/directorytable.htm **Entries include:** Agency name; address; units within the agency; name, title, and phone of each unit's chief executive; areas of responsibility for the unit. **Freq:** Annual, Latest edition 2006.

9987 ■ *Disabled American Veterans Department of South Dakota Bulletin*
Disabled American Veterans, Department of South Dakota
1519 W 51st St.
Sioux Falls, SD 57105-6648
Ph: (605)332-6866
Fax: (605)338-5489
E-mail: davsd@midconetwork.com
URL: http://www.davmembersportal.org/sd/default.aspx
Freq: quarterly. **Price:** free for members.

9988 ■ *Discipline*
National Center for the Study of Corporal Punishment and Alternatives
Temple University
253 Ritter Annex
Philadelphia, PA 19122
Ph: (215)204-6091
E-mail: ncscpa@blue.vm.temple.edu
URL: http://www.ruaneproductions.com/NCSCPA/about.html

Descr: Contains research papers. **Freq:** periodic.

9989 ■ *Do-It-Yourself Congressional Investigation Kit*
Center for Responsive Politics
1101 14th St. NW, Ste. 1030
Washington, DC 20005-5635
Ph: (202)857-0044
Fax: (202)857-7809
E-mail: info@crp.org
URL: http://www.opensecrets.org

9990 ■ *The Docket Sheet*
National Association of Professional Process Servers
PO Box 4547
Portland, OR 97208-4547
Ph: (503)222-4180
Fax: (503)222-3950
E-mail: administrator@napps.org
URL: http://www.napps.org
Freq: bimonthly. **Price:** included in membership dues, $35/year for nonmembers.

9991 ■ *The Draft*
Vietnam Veterans Against the War
PO Box 408594
Chicago, IL 60640
Ph: (773)276-4189
E-mail: vvaw@vvaw.org
URL: http://www.vvaw.org

9992 ■ *Drug-Supplement Interaction*
American Council on Science and Health
1995 Broadway, 2nd Fl.
New York, NY 10023-5882
Ph: (212)362-7044
Fax: (212)362-4919
E-mail: acsh@acsh.org
URL: http://www.acsh.org
Price: $1.

9993 ■ *The Dry-Cleaning Chemical Perc*
American Council on Science and Health
1995 Broadway, 2nd Fl.
New York, NY 10023-5882
Ph: (212)362-7044
Fax: (212)362-4919
E-mail: acsh@acsh.org
URL: http://www.acsh.org
Price: $1.

9994 ■ *Eagle News*
Central Minnesota Chapter 115, The Retired Enlisted Association
906 Lookout Pl.
Elk River, MN 55330
Ph: (763)441-2630
E-mail: r.l.donais@izoom.net
URL: http://www.trea115.org
Freq: 3/year.

9995 ■ *Eclipse*
National Association for Black Veterans
PO Box 11432
Milwaukee, WI 53211
E-mail: info@nabvets.com
URL: http://www.nabvets.com
Freq: quarterly.

9996 ■ *Eggs*
American Council on Science and Health
1995 Broadway, 2nd Fl.
New York, NY 10023-5882
Ph: (212)362-7044
Fax: (212)362-4919
E-mail: acsh@acsh.org
URL: http://www.acsh.org
Price: $1.

9997 ■ *Enemies Within*
Accuracy in Academia
4455 Connecticut Ave. NW, Ste. 330
Washington, DC 20008
Ph: (202)364-3085
Fax: (202)364-4098

E-mail: mal.kline@academia.org
URL: http://www.academia.org

9998 ■ *Enterprise Annual Report*
Enterprise Community Partners
10227 Wincopin Cir.
Columbia, MD 21044
Fax: (410)964-1918
URL: http://www.enterprisecommunity.org

9999 ■ *Enterprise Quarterly*
Enterprise Community Partners
10227 Wincopin Cir.
Columbia, MD 21044
Fax: (410)964-1918
URL: http://www.enterprisecommunity.org
Descr: Contains information on housing and community development programs and financing. **Freq:** quarterly. **Price:** free.

10000 ■ *Equality*
Indianapolis Urban League
777 Indiana Ave.
Indianapolis, IN 46202
Ph: (317)693-7603
Fax: (317)693-7613
E-mail: gneal@indplsul.org
URL: http://www.indplsul.org
Descr: Covers programs and services. **Freq:** semiannual.

10001 ■ *Essays in the Philosophy of Humanism*
American Humanist Association
1777 T St. NW
Washington, DC 20009-7125
Ph: (202)238-9088
Fax: (202)238-9003
E-mail: rspeckhardt@americanhumanist.org
URL: http://www.americanhumanist.org
Freq: annual.

10002 ■ *Ex-POW Bulletin*
American Ex-Prisoners of War
3201 E Pioneer Pkwy., No. 40
Arlington, TX 76010-5396
Ph: (817)649-2979
Fax: (817)649-0109
E-mail: hq@axpow.org
URL: http://www.axpow.org
Descr: Provides news of comrades and events. Includes book reviews, chapter news, legislative reports, etc. **Freq:** 11/year. **Price:** included in membership dues, $20/year for nonmembers in U.S., $30/year for nonmembers outside U.S. **ISSN:** 0161-7451.

10003 ■ *Expecting Better: A State-by-State Analysis of Parental Leave Programs*
National Partnership for Women and Families
1875 Connecticut Ave. NW, Ste. 650
Washington, DC 20009
Ph: (202)986-2600
Fax: (202)986-2539
E-mail: info@nationalpartnership.org
URL: http://www.nationalpartnership.org

10004 ■ *Factbook*
National Priorities Project
243 King St., Ste. 239
Northampton, MA 01060
Ph: (413)584-9556
Fax: (413)586-9647
E-mail: info@nationalpriorities.org
URL: http://www.nationalpriorities.org

10005 ■ *FACTFINDER*
Federation of American Consumers and Travelers
PO Box 104
Edwardsville, IL 62025
Fax: (618)656-5369
E-mail: cservice@usafact.org
URL: http://usafact.org
Descr: Covers consumer affairs including information on goods and services, health and safety, insur-

ance, and helpful hints. Contains statistics. **Freq:** quarterly. **Price:** free.

10006 ■ *Factor Nine News*
Coalition for Hemophilia B
825 Third Ave., Ste. 226
New York, NY 10022
Ph: (212)520-8272
E-mail: info@coalitionforhemophiliab.org
URL: http://www.coalitionforhemophiliab.org

10007 ■ *Facts about AIDS*
National Association of People with AIDS
8401 Colesville Rd., Ste. 550
Silver Spring, MD 20910
Ph: (240)247-0880
Fax: (240)247-0574
E-mail: info@napwa.org
URL: http://www.napwa.org
Descr: Provides an introduction of HIV and related issues.

10008 ■ *Faith and Choices*
Religious Coalition for Reproductive Choice
1025 Vermont Ave. NW, Ste. 1130
Washington, DC 20005
Ph: (202)628-7700
Fax: (202)628-7716
E-mail: info@rcrc.org
URL: http://www.rcrc.org
Freq: quarterly.

10009 ■ *Faith & Freedom*
Indiana Religious Coalition for Reproductive Choice
PO Box 723
Lafayette, IN 47902-0723
Fax: (501)644-3168
E-mail: info@ircrc.org
URL: http://www.ircrc.org
Descr: Provides news, commentary, information, and helpful resources. **Freq:** 3/year.

10010 ■ *False Messengers: How Addictive Drugs Change the Brain*
National Families in Action
2957 Clairmont Rd. NE, Ste. 150
Atlanta, GA 30329
Ph: (404)248-9676
Fax: (404)248-1312
E-mail: nfia@nationalfamilies.org
URL: http://www.nationalfamilies.org

10011 ■ *Family Directory*
National Challenged Homeschoolers Associated Network
PO Box 310
Moyie Springs, ID 83845
Ph: (208)267-6246
E-mail: nathanews@aol.com
URL: http://www.nathhan.com
Freq: annual.

10012 ■ *FDA's Regulatory Proceedings Concerning ECT*
Committee for Truth in Psychiatry
PO Box 1214
New York, NY 10003
Ph: (212)473-4786
E-mail: andrel@pie.org
URL: http://www.harborside.com/~equinox/ect.htm
Price: free.

10013 ■ *Federal Contractor Misconduct: Failures of the Suspension & Debarment System 2002 Report*
Project on Government Oversight
666 11th St. NW, Ste. 900
Washington, DC 20001-4542
Ph: (202)347-1122
Fax: (202)347-1116
E-mail: info@pogo.org
URL: http://www.pogo.org

10014 ■ *Fellows News*
American Bar Foundation
750 N Lake Shore Dr.
Chicago, IL 60611-4403

Ph: (312)988-6500
Fax: (312)988-6579
E-mail: anita@abfn.org
URL: http://www.americanbarfoundation.org/index.html

10015 ■ *Final Report-Assembly of Delegates*
Inter-American Commission of Women
17th St. and Constitution Ave. NW
Washington, DC 20006
Ph: (202)458-3000
E-mail: oasweb@oas.org
URL: http://portal.oas.org/Default.aspx?tabid=621&language=en-US
Freq: biennial.

10016 ■ *Financial Aid for Veterans, Military Personnel, and Their Dependents*
Reference Service Press
5000 Windplay Dr., Ste. 4
El Dorado Hills, CA 95762-9600
Ph: (916)939-9620
Fax: (916)939-9626
E-mail: info@rspfunding.com
URL: http://www.rspfunding.com
Key Personnel: Sandy Perez, Contact; Gail A. Schlachter, Author, gailschlachter@rspfunding.com; R. David Weber, Author, editors@rspfunding.com.
URL(s): http://www.rspfunding.com **Covers:** Organizations that offer approximately 1,100 scholarships, fellowships, loans, grants, awards, and internships to veterans, military personnel, and their families. **Entries include:** Organization name, address, phone, financial data, requirements for eligibility, duration, special features and limitations, deadline, number of awards. **Freq:** Biennial, Latest edition 2008-2010. **Price:** $40, individuals, Hardcover.

10017 ■ *Financing the 1996 Election*
Citizens' Research Foundation
104 Moses Hall
Institute of Governmental Studies
University of California
Berkeley, CA 94720-2370
Ph: (510)642-5158
E-mail: jlubenow@uclink4.berkeley.edu
Freq: quadrennial.

10018 ■ *The First Book on Male Liberation and Sex Equality*
Male Liberation Foundation
701 NE 67th St.
Miami, FL 33138
Ph: (305)756-6249
Fax: (305)756-6006
URL: http://malelib.org
Price: included in membership dues, $50/copy.

10019 ■ *First and Second Line Supervisors Program*
National Sheriffs' Association
1450 Duke St.
Alexandria, VA 22314-3490
Ph: (703)836-7827
Fax: (703)683-6541
E-mail: nsamail@sheriffs.org
URL: http://www.sheriffs.org

10020 ■ *Fiscal Discipline Should Begin at Home*
Citizens for a Sound Economy
1775 Pennsylvania Ave. NW, 11th Fl.
Washington, DC 20006-5805
Ph: (202)783-3870
Fax: (202)942-7649
E-mail: cse@cse.org
URL: http://cse.org

10021 ■ *Floral Management*
Society of American Florists
1601 Duke St.
Alexandria, VA 22314-3406
Ph: (703)836-8700
Fax: (703)836-8705
E-mail: info@safnow.org
URL: http://www.safnow.org
Descr: Informs members of developments in the

floral industry; features articles on marketing, government trends, and business practices. **Freq:** monthly. **Price:** included in membership dues, $24/year for nonmembers.

10022 ■ *Focus*
National Association for Women's Health
300 W Adams St., Ste. 328
Chicago, IL 60606-5101
Ph: (312)786-1468
Fax: (312)786-0376
URL: http://nawh.org
Descr: Features women's health issues. **Freq:** quarterly.

10023 ■ *FOI Advocate*
Freedom of Information Center
University of Missouri-Columbia
133 Neff Annex
Columbia, MO 65211
Ph: (573)882-5736
Fax: (573)884-6204
E-mail: edwardsm@missouri.edu
URL: http://foi.missouri.edu
Price: free. **ISSN:** 1535-458X.

10024 ■ *Footprint*
Americans for Customary Weight and Measure
PO Box 24A
Wiscasset, ME 04578
URL: http://www.bwmaonline.com/ACWM.htm

10025 ■ *The Forestry Advantage*
American Resources Group
374 Maple Ave. E, Ste. 310
Vienna, VA 22180-4751
Ph: (703)255-2700
Fax: (703)281-9200
E-mail: info@firetower.org
URL: http://www.firetower.org
Freq: quarterly.

10026 ■ *The Forum*
National Organization of Social Security Claimants' Representatives
560 Sylvan Ave.
Englewood Cliffs, NJ 07632
Ph: (201)567-4228
Fax: (201)567-1542
E-mail: nosscr@att.net
URL: http://www.nosscr.org
Freq: monthly.

10027 ■ *The Forum*
National CFIDS Foundation
103 Aletha Rd.
Needham, MA 02492
Ph: (781)449-3535
Fax: (781)449-8606
E-mail: info@ncf-net.org
URL: http://www.ncf-net.org
Freq: quarterly. **Price:** included in membership dues.

10028 ■ *The Freedom of Information Act: A User's Guide*
Freedom of Information Clearinghouse
Public Citizen Litigation Group
1600 20th St. NW
Washington, DC 20009
Ph: (202)588-7783
E-mail: foia@citizen.org
URL: http://www.citizen.org/litigation/free5Finfo
Price: free.

10029 ■ *FreeNet: An Exciting New Way to Share Information*
National Capital FreeNet
Trailhead Bldg., Ste. 302
1960 Scott St.
Ottawa, ON, Canada K1Z 8L8
Ph: (613)520-9001
Fax: (613)520-3524
E-mail: office@ncf.ca
URL: http://www.ncf.ca

Freq: periodic.

10030 ■ *Friday Facts*
National Association for Children's Behavioral Health
1025 Connecticut Ave. NW, Ste. 1012
Washington, DC 20036-3536
Ph: (202)857-9735
Fax: (202)362-5145
E-mail: nacbh@verizon.net
URL: http://www.nacbh.org
Freq: weekly.

10031 ■ *Frontline*
National Council of Social Security Management Associations
418 C St. NE
Washington, DC 20002
Ph: (202)547-8530
Fax: (202)547-8532
E-mail: president@ncssma.org
URL: http://www.ncssma.org
Freq: monthly. **Price:** included in membership dues.

10032 ■ *Future Trends in State Courts*
National Center for State Courts
300 Newport Ave.
Williamsburg, VA 23185-4147
Ph: (757)259-1816
Fax: (757)564-2067
E-mail: webmaster@ncsc.org
URL: http://www.ncsconline.org
Freq: annual.

10033 ■ *The Game Plan*
National Senior Games Association
PO Box 82059
Baton Rouge, LA 70884-2059
Ph: (225)766-6316
Fax: (225)766-9115
E-mail: nsga@nsga.com
URL: http://www.nsga.com
Freq: semiannual.

10034 ■ *Gay/Lesbian Guide to Great Cities in North America*
National Gay/Lesbian Travel Desk
2790 Wrondel Way
PMB No. 444
Reno, NV 89502
E-mail: nglbtraveldesk@aol.com

10035 ■ *Getting It Done, A Future Together*
Paralyzed Veterans of America, Vaughan Chapter
2235 Enterprise Dr., Ste. 3501
Westchester, IL 60154
Ph: (708)947-9790
Fax: (708)947-9755
E-mail: pvachvaug@mindspring.com
URL: http://www.vaughanpva.org

10036 ■ *Giving Parents a Voice: Florida*
Citizens for a Sound Economy
1775 Pennsylvania Ave. NW, 11th Fl.
Washington, DC 20006-5805
Ph: (202)783-3870
Fax: (202)942-7649
E-mail: cse@cse.org
URL: http://cse.org

10037 ■ *GLAD Briefs*
Gay and Lesbian Advocates and Defenders
30 Winter St., Ste. 800
Boston, MA 02108
Ph: (617)426-1350
Fax: (617)426-3594
E-mail: gladlaw@glad.org
URL: http://www.glad.org
Descr: Includes information on recent cases, legislation affecting civil rights issues, and organization activities. **Freq:** periodic.

10038 ■ *The Good News Report* (TM)
Citizens for a Better America
PO Box 7647
Van Nuys, CA 91409-7647
Ph: (818)757-1776

E-mail: hq@cfaba.org
URL: http://www.cfaba.org
Freq: periodic.

10039 ■ *Gottlieb-Tartaro Report*
Citizens Committee for the Right to Keep and Bear Arms
Liberty Park
12500 NE 10th Pl.
Bellevue, WA 98005
Ph: (425)454-4911
Fax: (425)451-3959
E-mail: adminforweb@ccrkba.org
URL: http://www.ccrkba.org
Descr: Features what's happening in the gun rights movement. **Freq:** monthly. **Price:** $30/year.

10040 ■ *Government Giveaways for Entrepreneurs III*
Information USA Inc.
12081 Nebel St.
Rockville, MD 20852
Free: 800-955-7653
URL: http://www.lesko.com
Key Personnel: Matthew Lesko, Author. **URL(s):** http://www.lesko.com **Covers:** about 300 government programs and 9,000 sources of free help for persons wanting to start or expand a business. **Freq:** Biennial, 5th edition, October 1996.

10041 ■ *Government Information on the Internet*
Bernan Associates
15200 NBN Way
Blue Ridge Summit, PA 17214
Ph: (301)459-7666
Free: 800-865-3457
Fax: (301)459-6988
E-mail: query@bernan.com
URL: http://www.bernan.com
Key Personnel: Greg R. Notess, Editor. **URL(s):** http://www.bernan.com/ **Covers:** over 5,000 internet sites for U.S. Government, state government, international government, intergovernmental organizations, foreign countries, and nongovernmental resources and over 1,400 online publications from government organizations' websites. **Entries include:** Government name, site description, website address. **Freq:** latest edition 6, 2003. **Price:** $39.50, institutions.

10042 ■ *Government Wastewatch*
Citizens Against Government Waste
1301 Connecticut Ave. NW, Ste. 400
Washington, DC 20036
Ph: (202)467-5300
Fax: (202)467-4253
E-mail: membership@cagw.org
URL: http://www.cagw.org
Freq: quarterly. **Price:** free for members.

10043 ■ *The Government's Slick Deal for the Oil Industry*
Project on Government Oversight
666 11th St. NW, Ste. 900
Washington, DC 20001-4542
Ph: (202)347-1122
Fax: (202)347-1116
E-mail: info@pogo.org
URL: http://www.pogo.org

10044 ■ *GPHA Matters*
Georgia Public Health Association
PO Box 80524
Atlanta, GA 30366-0524
Ph: (678)302-1132
Fax: (678)302-1134
E-mail: director@gapha.org
URL: http://www.gapha.org
Descr: Contains information on the association and its members. **Freq:** quarterly.

10045 ■ *Grassroots Factbook*
National Priorities Project
243 King St., Ste. 239
Northampton, MA 01060

Ph: (413)584-9556
Fax: (413)586-9647
E-mail: info@nationalpriorities.org
URL: http://www.nationalpriorities.org
Descr: Provides updates on impact of current spending proposals and debate on nation's states and cities.

10046 ■ *The Great Quotations on Religious Freedom*
Americans for Religious Liberty
PO Box 6656
Silver Spring, MD 20916
Ph: (301)260-2988
Fax: (301)260-2989
E-mail: arlinc@verizon.net
URL: http://www.arlinc.org
Price: $18.

10047 ■ *The Group Circle*
American Group Psychotherapy Association
25 E 21st St., 6th Fl.
New York, NY 10010
Ph: (212)477-2677
Fax: (212)979-6627
E-mail: info@agpa.org
URL: http://www.agpa.org
Freq: quarterly.

10048 ■ *Group Works!*
American Group Psychotherapy Association
25 E 21st St., 6th Fl.
New York, NY 10010
Ph: (212)477-2677
Fax: (212)979-6627
E-mail: info@agpa.org
URL: http://www.agpa.org
Descr: Contains information about group psychotherapy. **Freq:** quarterly. **Price:** included in membership dues.

10049 ■ *Guide to Graduate Work in Women's Studies, 2000 Edition*
National Women's Studies Association
7100 Baltimore Ave., Ste. 502
College Park, MD 20740
Ph: (301)403-0407
Fax: (301)403-4137
E-mail: nwsaoffice@nwsa.org
URL: http://www.nwsa.org
Descr: Includes addresses, phone numbers, and contact people. **Price:** $15 for members, $20 for nonmembers.

10050 ■ *Guidelines for Guardianship Service Programs*
The Center for Social Gerontology
2307 Shelby Ave.
Ann Arbor, MI 48103
Ph: (734)665-1126
Fax: (734)665-2071
E-mail: tcsg@tcsg.org
URL: http://www.tcsg.org
Price: $10.

10051 ■ *Handbook for Single Adoptive Parents*
National Council for Single Adoptive Parents
PO Box 567
Mount Hermon, CA 95041-0567
E-mail: info@ncsap.com
Descr: A how to book. **Freq:** biennial. **Price:** $25.
ISSN: 9634-0452.

10052 ■ *Have you Been Lied To?* (TM)
Citizens for a Better America
PO Box 7647
Van Nuys, CA 91409-7647
Ph: (818)757-1776
E-mail: hq@cfaba.org
URL: http://www.cfaba.org

10053 ■ *The Headache Handbook*
National Headache Foundation
820 N Orleans St., Ste. 217
Chicago, IL 60610-3498
Fax: (312)640-9049

E-mail: info@headaches.org
URL: http://www.headaches.org

10054 ■ *Helper*
American Social Health Association
PO Box 13827
Research Triangle Park, NC 27709
Ph: (919)361-8400
Fax: (919)361-8425
E-mail: info@ashastd.org
URL: http://www.ashastd.org
Descr: Reports on the latest research on the herpes simplex virus; includes information on strategies for coping with the virus and on treatments. **Freq:** quarterly. **Price:** $25/year.

10055 ■ *Highlights from Our Third Annual Menopause Symposium*
American Menopause Foundation
350 5th Ave., Ste. 2822
New York, NY 10118
Ph: (212)714-2398
Fax: (212)714-1252
E-mail: menopause@earthlink.net
URL: http://www.americanmenopause.org

10056 ■ *History*
National Conference of State Social Security Administrators
Social Security Administration
61 Forsyth St. SW, Ste. 22T64
Atlanta, GA 30303
Ph: (404)562-1324
Fax: (404)562-1583
E-mail: info@ncsssa.org
URL: http://www.ncsssa.org
Freq: periodic.

10057 ■ *History of NBBA*
National Beep Baseball Association
3444 Limerick Ln. NE
Rochester, MN 55906
Ph: (507)208-8383
E-mail: secretary@nbba.org
URL: http://www.nbba.org

10058 ■ *History of the Veterans' Movement*
Vietnam Veterans Against the War
PO Box 408594
Chicago, IL 60640
Ph: (773)276-4189
E-mail: vvaw@vvaw.org
URL: http://www.vvaw.org

10059 ■ *HME Answer Book*
American Association for Homecare
625 Slaters Ln., Ste. 200
Alexandria, VA 22314-1171
Ph: (703)836-6263
Fax: (703)836-6730
URL: http://www.aahomecare.org
Descr: Provides information and guidance on Medicare coverage, billing and payment rules for DMEPOS claims processing under DMERCs. **Freq:** quarterly.

10060 ■ *Home Care Advocate*
Associated Home Health Industries of Florida
1331 E Lafayette St., Ste. C
Tallahassee, FL 32301
Ph: (850)222-8967
Fax: (850)222-9251
E-mail: blolley@homecarefla.org
URL: http://www.ahhif.org
Freq: monthly. **Price:** included in membership dues.

10061 ■ *How to Make Public Broadcasting Accountable to Your Community: A Manual for Activists*
Citizens for Independent Public Broadcasting
901 Old Hickory Rd.
Pittsburgh, PA 15243
Ph: (412)341-1967
Fax: (412)341-6533

E-mail: jmstarr@adelphia.net
URL: http://www.cipbonline.org

10062 ■ *How to Pack 'Em In: A Guide to Planning Workshops*
National Association for Parents of Children With Visual Impairments
PO Box 317
Watertown, MA 02471
Ph: (617)972-7441
Fax: (617)972-7444
E-mail: napvi@perkins.org
URL: http://www.spedex.com/napvi

10063 ■ *HPV News*
American Social Health Association
PO Box 13827
Research Triangle Park, NC 27709
Ph: (919)361-8400
Fax: (919)361-8425
E-mail: info@ashastd.org
URL: http://www.ashastd.org
Descr: Includes latest research on HPV/genital warts and information on coping strategies. **Freq:** quarterly. **Price:** $25/year.

10064 ■ *The Human Needs Report*
Coalition on Human Needs
1120 Connecticut Ave. NW, Ste. 910
Washington, DC 20036
Ph: (202)223-2532
Fax: (202)223-2538
E-mail: info@chn.org
URL: http://www.chn.org
Descr: Contains legislative update on human needs issues. **Freq:** biweekly.

10065 ■ *Humanist*
American Humanist Association
1777 T St. NW
Washington, DC 20009-7125
Ph: (202)238-9088
Fax: (202)238-9003
E-mail: rspeckhardt@americanhumanist.org
URL: http://www.americanhumanist.org
Descr: Critical inquiry and social concern. **Freq:** bimonthly. **Price:** $20 intro. **ISSN:** 0018-7399.

10066 ■ *Hypertension and What You Can Do About It*
National Hypertension Association
324 E 30th St.
New York, NY 10016
Ph: (212)889-3557
Fax: (212)447-7032
E-mail: nathypertension@aol.com
URL: http://www.nathypertension.org
Freq: annual. **Price:** $1.

10067 ■ *ICTA Washington Wire*
Industry Council for Tangible Assets
PO Box 1365
Severna Park, MD 21146-8365
Ph: (410)626-7005
Fax: (410)626-7007
E-mail: eloiseullman@comcast.net
URL: http://ictaonline.org
Descr: Covers federal and state legislation affecting the industry. **Freq:** quarterly. **Price:** included in membership dues.

10068 ■ *Illinois Blue Book*
Illinois Secretary of State - Communications Dept.
Michael J. Howlett Bldg.
2nd & Edwards Sts., Rm. 474
Springfield, IL 62756
Ph: (217)782-5763
URL: http://www.sos.state.il.us
Key Personnel: Tad Kicielinski, Contact. **URL(s):** http://www.cyberdriveillinois.com **Covers:** State officials, departments and agencies, legislators, the congressional delegation, and the judiciary; county and municipal governments; news media; state universities. **Entries include:** Each section includes description of the department, board, etc. , and names of executives or members; legislator, state of-

ficial, and some judicial listings include biography. **Freq:** Biennial, Latest edition 2007-2008. **Price:** Free.

10069 ■ *The Illinois Organizer*
National Alliance Against Racist and Political Repression
1325 S Wabash Ave., Ste. 105
Chicago, IL 60605
Ph: (312)939-2750
Fax: (773)929-2613
URL: http://www.naarpr.org/index.html
Freq: quarterly.

10070 ■ *Impact Reports*
Public Advocate of the U.S.
5613 Leesburg Pike, Ste. 17
Falls Church, VA 22041
Ph: (703)845-1808
URL: http://www.publicadvocateusa.org
Freq: periodic.

10071 ■ *Impact of Unfunded Federal Mandates and Cost on U.S. Cities*
United States Conference of City Human Services Officials
1620 Eye St. NW, 4th Fl.
Washington, DC 20006
Ph: (202)293-7330
Fax: (202)293-2352
E-mail: info@usmayors.org
URL: http://www.usmayors.org/humanservices
Descr: Features the preliminary report on cost in 59 cities.

10072 ■ *IMSA Journal*
International Municipal Signal Association
PO Box 539
Newark, NY 14513-0539
Ph: (315)331-2182
Fax: (315)331-8205
E-mail: info@imsasafety.org
URL: http://www.imsasafety.org
Freq: bimonthly. **Price:** $50/year, $5/copy for members, $6/copy for nonmembers.

10073 ■ *Incitement*
American Disabled for Attendant Program Today
201 S Cherokee St.
Denver, CO 80223
Ph: (303)733-9324
E-mail: adapt@adapt.org
URL: http://www.adapt.org
Freq: periodic.

10074 ■ *Incoming*
Vietnam Veterans of America, Montgomery County - Chapter No. 641
PO Box 1748
Silver Spring, MD 20915
E-mail: dgudes@cpsc.gov
URL: http://www.vvachapter641.org

10075 ■ *Independent Politics News*
Independent Progressive Politics Network
PO Box 1041
Bloomfield, NJ 07003
Ph: (973)338-5398
E-mail: ippn@igc.org
URL: http://www.ippn.org
Freq: quarterly. **Price:** $10/year.

10076 ■ *Index of Worker Freedom: A National Report Card*
Alliance for Worker Freedom
722 12th St. NW, 4th Fl.
Washington, DC 20005
Ph: (202)785-0266
Fax: (202)785-0261
E-mail: info@workerfreedom.org
URL: http://www.workerfreedom.org
Freq: annual.

10077 ■ *Influence, Inc.*
Center for Responsive Politics
1101 14th St. NW, Ste. 1030
Washington, DC 20005-5635

Ph: (202)857-0044
Fax: (202)857-7809
E-mail: info@crp.org
URL: http://www.opensecrets.org
Price: $20.

10078 ■ INFORM
American Oil Chemists' Society
PO Box 17190
Urbana, IL 61803-7190
Ph: (217)359-2344
Fax: (217)351-8091
E-mail: general@aocs.org
URL: http://www.aocs.org
Descr: Contains information on new products and
publications, Washington reports, and calendar of
events. **Freq:** monthly. **Price:** $160/year for individu-
als, for nonmembers students and institution. **ISSN:**
0897-8026.

10079 ■ Information Booklet
National Association of Health Unit Coordinators
1947 Madron Rd.
Rockford, IL 61107-1716
Ph: (815)633-4351
Fax: (815)633-4438
E-mail: office@nahuc.org
URL: http://www.nahuc.org
Freq: annual. **Price:** $5.

10080 ■ Inhalants: The Silent Epidemic
National Inhalant Prevention Coalition
322-A Thompson St.
Chattanooga, TN 37405
Ph: (423)265-4662
Fax: (423)265-4889
E-mail: nipc@io.com
URL: http://www.inhalants.org

**10081 ■ Innovations for Children's Services
in the 21st Century**
American Humane Association Children's Services
63 Inverness Dr. E
Englewood, CO 80112-5117
Ph: (303)792-9900
Fax: (303)792-5333
E-mail: info@americanhumane.org
URL: http://www.americanhumane.org

10082 ■ Insight
Southern U.S. Trade Association
2 Canal St., Ste. 2515
New Orleans, LA 70130
Ph: (504)568-5986
Fax: (504)568-6010
E-mail: susta@susta.org
URL: http://www.susta.org
Freq: bimonthly.

10083 ■ The Inspector
American Construction Inspectors Association
530 S Lake Ave., No. 431
Pasadena, CA 91101
Ph: (626)797-2242
Fax: (626)797-2214
URL: http://www.acia.com
Descr: Contains technical information for the con-
struction industry. **Freq:** bimonthly. **Price:** free for
members.

10084 ■ Interaction
Ohio Public Health Association
PO Box 6036
Worthington, OH 43085
Ph: (614)635-0207
E-mail: ohiopha@gmail.com
URL: http://www.ohiopha.org
Descr: Contains information on the organization and
its members. **Freq:** bimonthly.

10085 ■ Interlink
National Board for Certified Clinical Hypnotherapists
1110 Fidler Ln., Ste. 1218
Silver Spring, MD 20910
Ph: (301)608-0123
Fax: (301)588-9535

E-mail: admin@natboard.com
URL: http://www.natboard.com
Freq: periodic.

**10086 ■ International Journal of Group Psy-
chotherapy**
American Group Psychotherapy Association
25 E 21st St., 6th Fl.
New York, NY 10010
Ph: (212)477-2677
Fax: (212)979-6627
E-mail: info@agpa.org
URL: http://www.agpa.org
Freq: quarterly. **Price:** included in membership dues,
$90/year for nonmembers, $375/year for institutions.
ISSN: 0020-7284.

10087 ■ Iowa CCI News
Iowa Citizens for Community Improvement
2001 Forest Ave.
Des Moines, IA 50311
Ph: (515)282-0484
Fax: (515)283-0031
E-mail: iowacci@iowacci.org
URL: http://www.iowacci.org
Freq: 3/year.

**10088 ■ Iraq Under Siege: The Deadly Impact
of Sanctions and War**
Iraq Action Coalition
7309 Haymarket Ln.
Raleigh, NC 27615
Fax: (919)846-7422
E-mail: iac@leb.net
URL: http://iraqaction.org
Price: $16/copy.

10089 ■ Issue Analysis
Citizens for a Sound Economy
1775 Pennsylvania Ave. NW, 11th Fl.
Washington, DC 20006-5805
Ph: (202)783-3870
Fax: (202)942-7649
E-mail: cse@cse.org
URL: http://cse.org
Freq: periodic.

10090 ■ Issue Briefs
Coalition on Human Needs
1120 Connecticut Ave. NW, Ste. 910
Washington, DC 20036
Ph: (202)223-2532
Fax: (202)223-2538
E-mail: info@chn.org
URL: http://www.chn.org

10091 ■ Issue Notes
Economic Success Clearinghouse
1401 New York Ave. NW, Ste. 800
Washington, DC 20005
Ph: (202)628-4200
Fax: (202)628-1293
E-mail: info@financeproject.org
URL: http://www.financeproject.org/index.
cfm?page=24

10092 ■ Issue Pac
Center for Third World Organizing
1218 E 21st St.
Oakland, CA 94606
Ph: (510)533-7583
Fax: (510)533-0923
URL: http://www.ctwo.org
Freq: quarterly.

10093 ■ Issues and Insights
American Society of General Surgeons
PO Box 4834
Englewood, CO 80155
Ph: (303)771-5948
Fax: (303)771-2550
E-mail: stephanie@goddardassociates.com
URL: http://www.theasgs.org

10094 ■ Jail Technician Program
National Sheriffs' Association
1450 Duke St.

Alexandria, VA 22314-3490
Ph: (703)836-7827
Fax: (703)683-6541
E-mail: nsamail@sheriffs.org
URL: http://www.sheriffs.org

**10095 ■ Journal of the American Society of
Questioned Document Examiners**
American Society of Questioned Document Examin-
ers
PO Box 18298
Long Beach, CA 90807
Ph: (562)901-3376
Fax: (562)901-3378
E-mail: webeditor@asqde.org
URL: http://www.asqde.org
Descr: Includes research in forensic document
examination. **Freq:** semiannual. **Price:** $70 indi-
vidual, $110 agency/distribution, $85 individual
international, $125 agency/distribution international.
ISSN: 1524-7287.

10096 ■ The Journal of At-Risk Issues
National Dropout Prevention Center/Network
Clemson University
209 Martin St.
Clemson, SC 29631-1555
Ph: (864)656-2599
Fax: (864)656-0136
E-mail: ndpc@clemson.edu
URL: http://www.dropoutprevention.org
Freq: quarterly.

10097 ■ Journal of Elder Abuse and Neglect
National Committee for the Prevention of Elder
Abuse
1612 K St. NW
Washington, DC 20006
Ph: (202)682-4140
Fax: (202)223-2099
E-mail: ncpea@verizon.net
URL: http://www.preventelderabuse.org
Freq: quarterly. **Price:** included in membership dues.

10098 ■ The Journal of Pain
American Pain Society
4700 W Lake Ave.
Glenview, IL 60025
Ph: (847)375-4715
Fax: (847)375-6479
E-mail: info@ampainsoc.org
URL: http://www.ampainsoc.org
Descr: Contains original articles related to all
aspects of pain, including clinical and basic research,
patient care, education, and health policy. **Freq:**
monthly. **Price:** included in membership dues.

**10099 ■ Journal of Surfactants and Deter-
gents**
American Oil Chemists' Society
PO Box 17190
Urbana, IL 61803-7190
Ph: (217)359-2344
Fax: (217)351-8091
E-mail: general@aocs.org
URL: http://www.aocs.org
Descr: Contains research articles, short communica-
tions, and methods papers related to surfactants and
detergents field. **Freq:** quarterly. **Price:** $145 in-
cludes air mail.

10100 ■ The Journey
Vietnam Veterans of America, Chapter 227
PO Box 5653
Arlington, VA 22205
Ph: (703)912-1681
E-mail: vva227@geocities.com
URL: http://www.geocities.com/vva227

10101 ■ Juvenile and Family Court Journal
National Juvenile Court Services Association
University of Nevada
PO Box 8970
Reno, NV 89507
Ph: (775)784-6895

Fax: (775)784-6628
E-mail: support@njcsacertification.org
URL: http://www.njcsa.org
Descr: Contains articles of interest to the field of juvenile justice and related areas. **Freq:** quarterly. **Price:** included in membership dues.

10102 ■ *Keep Your Wits Not Your Nits*
National Pediculosis Association
PO Box 610189
Newton, MA 02461
Fax: 800-235-1305
E-mail: npa@headlice.org
URL: http://www.headlice.org

10103 ■ *Keepers of the Water*
Center for Alternative Mining Development Policy
210 Avon St., Ste. 4
La Crosse, WI 54603
Ph: (608)784-4399
Fax: (608)785-8486
E-mail: gedicks.al@uwlax.edu

10104 ■ *Key Information*
American Institute for CPCU
720 Providence Rd., Ste. 100
Malvern, PA 19355-3433
Ph: (610)644-2100
Fax: (610)640-9576
E-mail: customerservice@cpcuiia.org
URL: http://www.aicpcu.org
Freq: annual.

10105 ■ *Knowledge, Resources and Perspectives*
Foundation for American Communications
85 S Grand Ave.
Pasadena, CA 91105
Ph: (626)584-0010
Fax: (626)584-0627
URL: http://www.facsnet.org
Price: $10.

10106 ■ *Korean American Voice*
National Association of Korean Americans
3883 Plaza Dr.
Fairfax, VA 22030
Ph: (703)267-2388
Fax: (703)267-2396
E-mail: nakausa@naka.org
URL: http://www.naka.org
Freq: quarterly.

10107 ■ *LAND GRAB: The Corporate Theft of Wisconsin's Mineral Resources*
Center for Alternative Mining Development Policy
210 Avon St., Ste. 4
La Crosse, WI 54603
Ph: (608)784-4399
Fax: (608)785-8486
E-mail: gedicks.al@uwlax.edu

10108 ■ *Latest Greatest Coloring Book About Lice*
National Pediculosis Association
PO Box 610189
Newton, MA 02461
Fax: 800-235-1305
E-mail: npa@headlice.org
URL: http://www.headlice.org
Price: $25/pack.

10109 ■ *The Leader*
National AMBUCS
PO Box 5127
High Point, NC 27265
Fax: (336)852-6830
E-mail: joec@ambucs.org
URL: http://www.ambucs.org
Descr: Contains important reminders and program announcements. **Freq:** 11/year.

10110 ■ *Legislative Briefs*
Center for Policy Alternatives
1875 Connecticut Ave. NW, Ste. 710
Washington, DC 20009
Ph: (202)387-6030

Fax: (202)387-8529
E-mail: info@cfpa.org
URL: http://www.cfpa.org
Freq: periodic.

10111 ■ *Liberty Report*
American Sons of Liberty
1142 S Diamond Bar Blvd., Ste. 305
Diamond Bar, CA 91765
E-mail: americansonsofliberty@americansonsofliberty.com
URL: http://www.americansonsofliberty.com
Freq: quarterly.

10112 ■ *Life Matters*
Citizens United Resisting Euthanasia
303 Truman St.
Berkeley Springs, WV 25411
Ph: (304)258-5433
E-mail: cureltd@verizon.net
URL: http://mysite.verizon.net/cureltd/index.html

10113 ■ *Life Notes*
National Transplant Society
3149 Dundee Rd., Ste. 314
Northbrook, IL 60062
E-mail: info@organdonor.org
URL: http://www.organdonor.org

10114 ■ *LINK*
National Association of State Veterans Homes
5211 Auth Rd.
Suitland, MD 20746
Ph: (301)899-7908
Fax: (301)899-8186
E-mail: info@nasvh.org
URL: http://www.nasvh.org
Freq: quarterly.

10115 ■ *Lipids*
American Oil Chemists' Society
PO Box 17190
Urbana, IL 61803-7190
Ph: (217)359-2344
Fax: (217)351-8091
E-mail: general@aocs.org
URL: http://www.aocs.org
Freq: monthly. **Price:** $145 includes air mail. **ISSN:** 0024-4201.

10116 ■ *Listen*
American Health and Temperance Association
12501 Old Columbia Pike
Silver Spring, MD 20902
Ph: (301)680-6733
Fax: (301)680-6464
E-mail: dewitt.williams@nad.adventist.org
URL: http://www.nadhealthministries.org
Freq: monthly.

10117 ■ *Living with HIV*
National Association of People with AIDS
8401 Colesville Rd., Ste. 550
Silver Spring, MD 20910
Ph: (240)247-0880
Fax: (240)247-0574
E-mail: info@napwa.org
URL: http://www.napwa.org
Descr: Provides information on resources for treatment and offers prevention against further infection.

10118 ■ *Malvern Examiner*
American Institute for CPCU
720 Providence Rd., Ste. 100
Malvern, PA 19355-3433
Ph: (610)644-2100
Fax: (610)640-9576
E-mail: customerservice@cpcuiia.org
URL: http://www.aicpcu.org
Descr: Contains program updates, new study material listings, news items, and more. **Freq:** annual. **Price:** free.

10119 ■ *Managing Anxiety During Menopause*
American Menopause Foundation
350 5th Ave., Ste. 2822

New York, NY 10118
Ph: (212)714-2398
Fax: (212)714-1252
E-mail: menopause@earthlink.net
URL: http://www.americanmenopause.org

10120 ■ *Managing Herpes*
American Social Health Association
PO Box 13827
Research Triangle Park, NC 27709
Ph: (919)361-8400
Fax: (919)361-8425
E-mail: info@ashastd.org
URL: http://www.ashastd.org
Price: $21.95 plus shipping and handling.

10121 ■ *Mande*
Center for Human Services
7200 Wisconsin Ave., Ste. 600
Bethesda, MD 20814
Ph: (301)654-8338
Fax: (301)941-8427
E-mail: webmaster@urc-chs.com
URL: http://www.chs-urc.org
Descr: Contains information about health and monthly celebrations.

10122 ■ *Manual of Operating Procedure for State Administrators*
National Conference of State Social Security Administrators
Social Security Administration
61 Forsyth St. SW, Ste. 22T64
Atlanta, GA 30303
Ph: (404)562-1324
Fax: (404)562-1583
E-mail: info@ncsssa.org
URL: http://www.ncsssa.org
Freq: periodic.

10123 ■ *Mark of Merit*
American Board for Certification in Orthotics and Prosthetics
330 John Carlyle St., Ste. 210
Alexandria, VA 22314
Ph: (703)836-7114
Fax: (703)836-0838
E-mail: info@abcop.org
URL: http://www.abcop.org
Freq: bimonthly.

10124 ■ *MASSPIRG MASSCITIZEN*
Massachusetts Public Interest Research Group
44 Winter St., 4th Fl.
Boston, MA 02108
Ph: (617)292-4800
Fax: (617)292-8057
E-mail: info@masspirg.org
Freq: quarterly. **Price:** free for members.

10125 ■ *Member Facilities*
National Association for Children's Behavioral Health
1025 Connecticut Ave. NW, Ste. 1012
Washington, DC 20036-3536
Ph: (202)857-9735
Fax: (202)362-5145
E-mail: nacbh@verizon.net
URL: http://www.nacbh.org
Freq: annual.

10126 ■ *Membership Directory and Civil Rules Guide*
National Association of Professional Process Servers
PO Box 4547
Portland, OR 97208-4547
Ph: (503)222-4180
Fax: (503)222-3950
E-mail: administrator@napps.org
URL: http://www.napps.org
Freq: semiannual. **Price:** available to members only.

10127 ■ *Membership List*
American Institute of Biomedical Climatology
1050 Eagle Rd.

Newtown, PA 18940-2818
Ph: (215)968-4483
E-mail: info@aibc.cc
Descr: Available to members only.

10128 ■ *Microsoft and Monopoly*
Citizens for a Sound Economy
1775 Pennsylvania Ave. NW, 11th Fl.
Washington, DC 20006-5805
Ph: (202)783-3870
Fax: (202)942-7649
E-mail: cse@cse.org
URL: http://cse.org

10129 ■ *The Mini Scope*
National Funeral Directors and Morticians Association
3951 Snapfinger Pkwy., Ste. 570
Decatur, GA 30035
Fax: (404)286-6573
E-mail: info@nfdma.com
URL: http://www.nfdma.com
Freq: quarterly. **Price:** included in membership dues.

10130 ■ *MMT's*
American Council on Science and Health
1995 Broadway, 2nd Fl.
New York, NY 10023-5882
Ph: (212)362-7044
Fax: (212)362-4919
E-mail: acsh@acsh.org
URL: http://www.acsh.org
Price: $1.

10131 ■ *More Fun, Less Stuff Starter Kit*
Center for a New American Dream
6930 Carroll Ave., Ste. 900
Takoma Park, MD 20912-4466
Ph: (301)891-3683
Fax: (301)891-3684
E-mail: newdream@newdream.org
URL: http://www.ibuydifferent.org
Price: $10.

10132 ■ *More Fun, Less Stuff: The Challenges and Rewards of a New American Dream*
Center for a New American Dream
6930 Carroll Ave., Ste. 900
Takoma Park, MD 20912-4466
Ph: (301)891-3683
Fax: (301)891-3684
E-mail: newdream@newdream.org
URL: http://www.ibuydifferent.org
Price: $10.

10133 ■ *NABCA Contacts Directory*
Joint Committee of the States
4401 Ford Ave., Ste. 700
Alexandria, VA 22302-1473
Ph: (703)578-4200
Fax: (703)820-3551
E-mail: info@nabca.org
URL: http://www.nabca.org
Descr: Compiles names and addresses of every member organization and its top officials. **Price:** included in membership dues, $295 for nonmembers.

10134 ■ *NABCA Survey Book*
Joint Committee of the States
4401 Ford Ave., Ste. 700
Alexandria, VA 22302-1473
Ph: (703)578-4200
Fax: (703)820-3551
E-mail: info@nabca.org
URL: http://www.nabca.org
Descr: Covers operational and regulatory information from the 19 control jurisdictions. **Freq:** annual. **Price:** included in membership dues, $295 for nonmembers.

10135 ■ *NABOB News*
National Association of Black Owned Broadcasters
1155 Connecticut Ave. NW, Ste. 600
Washington, DC 20036
Ph: (202)463-8970
Fax: (202)429-0657

E-mail: nabob@nabob.org
URL: http://www.nabob.org
Freq: monthly.

10136 ■ *NACAA Forum*
National Association of Consumer Agency Administrators
2 Brentwood Commons, Ste. 150
750 Old Hickory Blvd.
Brentwood, TN 37027
Ph: (615)498-1563
Fax: (615)369-6225
E-mail: eowen@nacaa.net
URL: http://www.nacaa.net

10137 ■ *NACAA News*
National Association of Consumer Agency Administrators
2 Brentwood Commons, Ste. 150
750 Old Hickory Blvd.
Brentwood, TN 37027
Ph: (615)498-1563
Fax: (615)369-6225
E-mail: eowen@nacaa.net
URL: http://www.nacaa.net
Descr: Includes reports from members and others about enforcement, administrative, educational, and legislative activities. **Freq:** bimonthly. **Price:** free for members, $75/year for consumer agencies and organizations, $95/year for businesses, media, and others. **ISSN:** 0739-392X.

10138 ■ *NADAP News/Report*
National Association on Drug Abuse Problems
355 Lexington Ave.
New York, NY 10017
Ph: (212)986-1170
Fax: (212)697-2939
E-mail: info@nadap.com
URL: http://www.nadap.org
Descr: Covers current issues in the field of substance abuse. **Freq:** quarterly. **Price:** free.

10139 ■ *NADSA Voice*
National Adult Day Services Association
85 S Washington, Ste. 316
Seattle, WA 98104
Ph: (414)464-3888
Fax: (206)461-3218
E-mail: info@nadsa.org
URL: http://www.nadsa.org
Descr: Reports on adult day care and other aging issues with a focus on public policy. **Freq:** quarterly. **Price:** free for members.

10140 ■ *NAFC News*
National Alliance for Fair Contracting
905 16th St. NW, 4th Fl.
Washington, DC 20006
Fax: (202)942-2228
E-mail: webmaster@faircontracting.org
URL: http://www.faircontracting.org
Price: included in membership dues.

10141 ■ *NAN Bulletin*
National Association of Neighborhoods
1300 Pennsylvania Ave. NW, Ste. 700
Washington, DC 20004
Ph: (202)332-7766
URL: http://www.nanworld.org
Descr: Includes updates on state and federal legislation affecting neighborhoods. **Freq:** quarterly. **Price:** included in membership dues, $25/year for nonmembers.

10142 ■ *NASH News*
North American Society of Homeopaths
PO Box 450039
Sunrise, FL 33345-0039
Ph: (206)720-7000
Fax: (208)248-1942

E-mail: nashinfo@homeopathy.org
URL: http://www.homeopathy.org

10143 ■ *NATHHAN News*
National Challenged Homeschoolers Associated Network
PO Box 310
Moyie Springs, ID 83845
Ph: (208)267-6246
E-mail: nathanews@aol.com
URL: http://www.nathhan.com
Freq: quarterly.

10144 ■ *National Aesthetician and Nail Artist*
World International Nail and Beauty Association
1221 N Lake View Ave.
Anaheim, CA 92807
Ph: (714)779-9892
Fax: (714)779-9971
E-mail: dkellenberger@inmnails.com
Freq: quarterly.

10145 ■ *National Directory*
Women of Color Resource Center
1611 Telegraph Ave., No. 303
Oakland, CA 94612
Ph: (510)444-2700
Fax: (510)444-2711
E-mail: info@coloredgirls.org
URL: http://www.coloredgirls.org
Price: $22.95.

10146 ■ *National Directory of Corporate Public Affairs*
Public Affairs Council
2033 K St. NW, Ste. 700
Washington, DC 20006
Ph: (202)872-1790
Fax: (202)835-8343
E-mail: pac@pac.org
URL: http://www.pac.org
Descr: Contains information on the public functions of 1,700 major U.S. corporations and descriptions of their PACs, foundation and charitable funds. **Price:** $159 for nonmembers.

10147 ■ *National Member News*
Association of Pool and Spa Professionals
2111 Eisenhower Ave., Ste. 500
Alexandria, VA 22314-4679
Ph: (703)838-0083
Fax: (703)549-0493
E-mail: memberservices@theapsp.org
URL: http://www.theapsp.org
Descr: Reports on the pool and spa industry. **Freq:** monthly. **Price:** included in membership dues.

10148 ■ *National Partnership News*
National Partnership for Women and Families
1875 Connecticut Ave. NW, Ste. 650
Washington, DC 20009
Ph: (202)986-2600
Fax: (202)986-2539
E-mail: info@nationalpartnership.org
URL: http://www.nationalpartnership.org
Descr: Reports on women's legal rights in the areas of employment and family law, including Supreme Court decisions and legislative developments. **Freq:** quarterly. **Price:** included in membership dues; first issue is free to the public. **ISSN:** 0736-9433.

10149 ■ *National Report on Shoplifting*
National Association for Shoplifting Prevention
380 N Broadway, Ste. 306
Jericho, NY 11753
Ph: (516)932-0165
Fax: (516)932-9393
E-mail: nasp@shopliftingprevention.org
URL: http://www.shopliftersalternative.org
Descr: Contains information for retailers and the criminal justice system. **Freq:** semiannual. **Price:** $30/2 years.

10150 ■ *National Resource Directory*
American Amputee Foundation
PO Box 94227

North Little Rock, AR 72190
Ph: (501)835-9290
Fax: (501)835-9292
E-mail: info@americanamputee.org
URL: http://www.americanamputee.org
Descr: Features national listings of organizations and agencies of interest to individuals with disabilities. **Freq:** biennial. **Price:** $10.

10151 ■ *The Natural Activist*
Citizens for Health
2104 Stevens Ave. S
Minneapolis, MN 55404
E-mail: info@citizens.org
URL: http://www.citizens.org
Freq: bimonthly. **Price:** included in membership dues.

10152 ■ *The Natural Advocate*
Coalition for Natural Health
1220 L St. NW
PMB 100-408
Washington, DC 20005
Fax: 800-598-4264
E-mail: cnh@naturalhealth.org
URL: http://www.naturalhealth.org
Descr: Includes articles on the various modalities comprised by traditional naturopathy. **Freq:** annual. **Price:** free for members.

10153 ■ *NBBA Newsletter*
National Beep Baseball Association
3444 Limerick Ln. NE
Rochester, MN 55906
Ph: (507)208-8383
E-mail: secretary@nbba.org
URL: http://www.nbba.org
Descr: Includes score statistics, tournament information and rule changes. **Freq:** quarterly. **Price:** included in membership dues.

10154 ■ *NCARL Letter*
National Committee Against Repressive Legislation
3321 12th St. NE
Washington, DC 20017
Ph: (202)529-4225
Fax: (202)526-4611
E-mail: info@ncarl.org
URL: http://ncarl.org
Freq: monthly.

10155 ■ *NCBW Forum*
National Center for Bicycling and Walking
26 DeHart Rd.
Maplewood, NJ 07040
Ph: (973)378-3137
E-mail: info@bikewalk.org
URL: http://www.bikewalk.org
Freq: quarterly.

10156 ■ *NCIL Newsletter*
National Council on Independent Living
1710 Rhode Island Ave. NW, 5th Fl.
Washington, DC 20036
Ph: (202)207-0334
Fax: (202)207-0341
E-mail: ncil@ncil.org
URL: http://www.ncil.org
Freq: quarterly.

10157 ■ *NCOA Networks*
National Institute on Community-Based Long-Term Care
1901 L St. NW, 4th Fl.
Washington, DC 20036
Ph: (202)479-1200
Fax: (202)479-0735
E-mail: info@ncoa.org
URL: http://www.ncoa.org/content.cfm?sectionID=42
Freq: bimonthly.

10158 ■ *NCOA Week*
National Institute of Senior Centers
1901 L St. NW, 4th Fl.
Washington, DC 20036
Ph: (202)479-1200

Fax: (202)479-0735
E-mail: info@ncoa.org
URL: http://www.ncoa.org/content.cfm?sectionID=44
Descr: Reports on senior citizen centers, including legislative updates, program and funding information, and current issues. **Freq:** weekly. **Price:** free for members.

10159 ■ *NCSLA Official Directory*
National Conference of State Liquor Administrators
6183 Beau Douglas Ave.
Gonzales, LA 70737
Ph: (225)473-7209
Fax: (225)257-4498
E-mail: pamsalario@cox.net
URL: http://www.ncsla.org
Descr: Lists state liquor control administrators; arranged geographically. **Freq:** annual. **Price:** included in membership dues.

10160 ■ *NCSSSA-Today*
National Conference of State Social Security Administrators
Social Security Administration
61 Forsyth St. SW, Ste. 22T64
Atlanta, GA 30303
Ph: (404)562-1324
Fax: (404)562-1583
E-mail: info@ncsssa.org
URL: http://www.ncsssa.org

10161 ■ *Need a Lift?*
American Legion National Headquarters
700 N Pennsylvania St.
PO Box 1055
Indianapolis, IN 46206
Ph: (317)630-1200
Fax: (317)630-1223
E-mail: acy@legion.org
URL: http://www.legion.org
Key Personnel: Robert K. Caudell, Editor, rcaudell@legion.org. **URL(s):** http://www.legion.org **Covers:** Sources of career, scholarship, and loan information or assistance. Coverage emphasizes, but is not limited to, programs for children of veterans. **Entries include:** Name and address of source, description of information or assistance offered and any requirements or limitations. **Freq:** Annual, fall. **Price:** $4.95, individuals, payment with order.

10162 ■ *Network*
Death with Dignity National Center
520 SW 6th Ave., Ste. 1030
Portland, OR 97204
Ph: (503)228-4415
Fax: (503)228-7454
E-mail: info@deathwithdignity.org
URL: http://www.deathwithdignity.org
Freq: semiannual. **Price:** free.

10163 ■ *New Research on Diet and Uterine Myomas*
American Menopause Foundation
350 5th Ave., Ste. 2822
New York, NY 10118
Ph: (212)714-2398
Fax: (212)714-1252
E-mail: menopause@earthlink.net
URL: http://www.americanmenopause.org

10164 ■ *The New Resource Wars*
Center for Alternative Mining Development Policy
210 Avon St., Ste. 4
La Crosse, WI 54603
Ph: (608)784-4399
Fax: (608)785-8486
E-mail: gedicks.al@uwlax.edu

10165 ■ *New World*
American Spanish Committee
PO Box 42
Leonia, NJ 07605-0042
Ph: (201)567-7417

Fax: (201)816-9797
E-mail: americanspanishcommittee@yahoo.com

10166 ■ *News Briefs*
National Drug Strategy Network
8730 Georgia Ave., Ste. 400
Silver Spring, MD 20910
Ph: (301)589-6020
Fax: (301)589-5056
E-mail: ndsn@ndsn.org
URL: http://www.ndsn.org
Descr: Provides complete citations to news stories, journal articles, research, legislation and regulations.

10167 ■ *NEWS Magazine*
Concerned Citizens for Racially Free America
PO Box 320497
Birmingham, AL 35232-0497
Ph: (205)856-0481
Fax: (205)856-2244
E-mail: civilrights@bellsouth.net
URL: http://www.concernedcitizensnews.org
Freq: quarterly.

10168 ■ *News Report*
National Hypertension Association
324 E 30th St.
New York, NY 10016
Ph: (212)889-3557
Fax: (212)447-7032
E-mail: nathypertension@aol.com
URL: http://www.nathypertension.org
Freq: annual.

10169 ■ *Newslink*
American Case Management Association
11701 W 36th St.
Little Rock, AR 72211
Ph: (501)907-2262
Fax: (501)227-4247
URL: http://www.acmaweb.org
Freq: quarterly. **Price:** included in membership dues.

10170 ■ *Nexus*
National Committee for the Prevention of Elder Abuse
1612 K St. NW
Washington, DC 20006
Ph: (202)682-4140
Fax: (202)223-2099
E-mail: ncpea@verizon.net
URL: http://www.preventelderabuse.org
Descr: Provides updates on the affiliates' activities. **Freq:** bimonthly. **Price:** included in membership dues.

10171 ■ *NFP Update*
National Family Partnership
2490 Coral Way, Ste. 501
Miami, FL 33145
Ph: (305)856-4886
Fax: (305)856-4815
E-mail: ireyes@informedfamilies.org
URL: http://www.nfp.org
Freq: quarterly. **Price:** $25/year for individuals, $100/year for groups.

10172 ■ *NFPRHA Quarterly*
National Family Planning and Reproductive Health Association
1627 K St. NW, 12th Fl.
Washington, DC 20006
Ph: (202)293-3114
Fax: (202)293-1990
E-mail: info@nfprha.org
URL: http://www.nfprha.org
Freq: quarterly.

10173 ■ *NFPRHA Report*
National Family Planning and Reproductive Health Association
1627 K St. NW, 12th Fl.
Washington, DC 20006
Ph: (202)293-3114
Fax: (202)293-1990

E-mail: info@nfprha.org
URL: http://www.nfprha.org
Descr: Reports on public policy affecting family planning and reproductive health. **Price:** included in membership dues, $200 for nonmembers.

10174 ■ *NFRC 100-1: Procedure for Determining Fenestration Product Thermal Properties*
National Fenestration Rating Council
6305 Ivy Ln., Ste. 140
Greenbelt, MD 20770
Ph: (301)589-1776
Fax: (301)589-3884
E-mail: info@nfrc.org
URL: http://www.nfrc.org
Price: $40 for members, $75 for nonmembers.

10175 ■ *NFRC Update*
National Fenestration Rating Council
6305 Ivy Ln., Ste. 140
Greenbelt, MD 20770
Ph: (301)589-1776
Fax: (301)589-3884
E-mail: info@nfrc.org
URL: http://www.nfrc.org
Freq: quarterly. **Price:** free.

10176 ■ *NHF Head Lines*
National Headache Foundation
820 N Orleans St., Ste. 217
Chicago, IL 60610-3498
Fax: (312)640-9049
E-mail: info@headaches.org
URL: http://www.headaches.org
Descr: Includes information on headache causes and treatments, foundation news, book reviews, research reports, support group updates, and reader Q&A. **Freq:** bimonthly. **Price:** included in membership dues, $20/year for nonmembers.

10177 ■ *NIST Handbook 44, Specifications, Tolerances, and Other Technical Requirements for Weighing and Measuring Devices*
National Conference on Weights and Measures
1135 M St., Ste. 110
Lincoln, NE 68508
Ph: (402)434-4880
Fax: (402)434-4878
E-mail: info@ncwm.net
URL: http://www.ncwm.net
Freq: annual.

10178 ■ *No End in Sight*
Montana People's Action
208 E Main St.
Missoula, MT 59802
Ph: (406)728-5297
Fax: (406)728-4095
E-mail: mpa@mtpaction.org
URL: http://www.mtpaction.org

10179 ■ *No Light at the End of this Tunnel: Boston's Central Artery/Third Harbor Tunnel Project*
Project on Government Oversight
666 11th St. NW, Ste. 900
Washington, DC 20001-4542
Ph: (202)347-1122
Fax: (202)347-1116
E-mail: info@pogo.org
URL: http://www.pogo.org
Freq: periodic.

10180 ■ *Non-Profit Almanac Profiles of Charitable Organizations*
National Center for Charitable Statistics
2100 M St. NW, 5th Fl.
Washington, DC 20037
Fax: (202)833-6231
E-mail: nccs@ui.urban.org
URL: http://nccs.urban.org
Freq: biennial.

10181 ■ *Nonhormonal Management of Menopause for Women: Phytoestrogens*
American Menopause Foundation
350 5th Ave., Ste. 2822

New York, NY 10118
Ph: (212)714-2398
Fax: (212)714-1252
E-mail: menopause@earthlink.net
URL: http://www.americanmenopause.org

10182 ■ *Nonprofits and Government: Collaboration and Conflict*
National Center for Charitable Statistics
2100 M St. NW, 5th Fl.
Washington, DC 20037
Fax: (202)833-6231
E-mail: nccs@ui.urban.org
URL: http://nccs.urban.org
Price: $29.50 paper.

10183 ■ *Nouvelles CSN*
Confederation of National Trade Unions
1601 Ave. de Lorimier
Montreal, QC, Canada H2K 4M5
Ph: (514)598-2121
E-mail: csnexecutif@csn.qc.ca
URL: http://www.csn.qc.ca
Freq: biweekly. **ISSN:** 0712-8789.

10184 ■ *NSAA Journal*
National Ski Areas Association
133 S Van Gordon St., Ste. 300
Lakewood, CO 80228
Ph: (303)987-1111
Fax: (303)986-2345
E-mail: nsaa@nsaa.org
URL: http://www.nsaa.org
Descr: Features current industry trends, technologies and issues impacting the ski industry. **Freq:** bimonthly.

10185 ■ *Nuclear Monitor*
Nuclear Information and Resource Service
6930 Carroll Ave., Ste. 340
Takoma Park, MD 20912
Ph: (301)270-6477
Fax: (301)270-4291
E-mail: nirsnet@nirs.org
URL: http://www.nirs.org
Freq: biweekly. **Price:** $250/year, $150/year for public and university libraries, $35/year for activists. **ISSN:** 0889-3411.

10186 ■ *Nuclear Power Plant Security: Voices from Inside the Fences, 2002 Report*
Project on Government Oversight
666 11th St. NW, Ste. 900
Washington, DC 20001-4542
Ph: (202)347-1122
Fax: (202)347-1116
E-mail: info@pogo.org
URL: http://www.pogo.org

10187 ■ *NVA News*
National Vulvodynia Association
PO Box 4491
Silver Spring, MD 20914-4491
Ph: (301)299-0775
Fax: (301)299-3999
E-mail: chris@nva.org
URL: http://www.nva.org
Freq: 3/year. **Price:** included in membership dues.

10188 ■ *NWSA Directory of Women's Studies Programs, Women's Centers, and Women's Research Centers*
National Women's Studies Association
7100 Baltimore Ave., Ste. 502
College Park, MD 20740
Ph: (301)403-0407
Fax: (301)403-4137
E-mail: nwsaoffice@nwsa.org
URL: http://www.nwsa.org
Price: $5.

10189 ■ *NWSAction*
National Women's Studies Association
7100 Baltimore Ave., Ste. 502
College Park, MD 20740
Ph: (301)403-0407

Fax: (301)403-4137
E-mail: nwsaoffice@nwsa.org
URL: http://www.nwsa.org
Descr: Contains calendar of events, conference reports, fellowship and employment opportunity listings, association news, and resources listings. **Freq:** semiannual. **Price:** included in membership dues.

10190 ■ *O&P Almanac*
American Board for Certification in Orthotics and Prosthetics
330 John Carlyle St., Ste. 210
Alexandria, VA 22314
Ph: (703)836-7114
Fax: (703)836-0838
E-mail: info@abcop.org
URL: http://www.abcop.org
Freq: monthly.

10191 ■ *The Obesity Crisis*
National Hypertension Association
324 E 30th St.
New York, NY 10016
Ph: (212)889-3557
Fax: (212)447-7032
E-mail: nathypertension@aol.com
URL: http://www.nathypertension.org
Descr: Features sedentary lifestyle.

10192 ■ *Online Update!*
Friends of the National Institute of Dental and Craniofacial Research
1901 Pennsylvania Ave. NW, Ste. 607
Washington, DC 20006
Ph: (202)223-0667
Fax: (202)463-1257
E-mail: peter@fnidcr.org
URL: http://www.fnidcr.org
Freq: monthly. **Price:** included in membership dues.

10193 ■ *Opportunity Journal*
National Urban League
120 Wall St., 8th Fl.
New York, NY 10005
Ph: (212)558-5300
Fax: (212)344-5332
E-mail: info@nul.org
URL: http://www.nul.org
Descr: Contains in-depth and scholarly analysis of issues. **Freq:** periodic. **Price:** $4.95 plus shipping and handling.

10194 ■ *An Ounce of Prevention*
National Association of People with AIDS
8401 Colesville Rd., Ste. 550
Silver Spring, MD 20910
Ph: (240)247-0880
Fax: (240)247-0574
E-mail: info@napwa.org
URL: http://www.napwa.org
Descr: Informs family members and caregivers about the prevention of further HIV infection.

10195 ■ *Our Greatest Threats: Live Longer Live Better*
National Hypertension Association
324 E 30th St.
New York, NY 10016
Ph: (212)889-3557
Fax: (212)447-7032
E-mail: nathypertension@aol.com
URL: http://www.nathypertension.org
Descr: Contains information on the importance of a healthy lifestyle.

10196 ■ *Paralog*
Oregon Paralyzed Veterans of America
3700 Silverton Rd. NE
Salem, OR 97305-1472
Ph: (503)362-7998
Fax: (503)362-9837
E-mail: oregonpva@oregonpva.org
URL: http://www.oregonpva.org

Freq: bimonthly. Price: $10/year.

10197 ■ *Paraplegia News*
Paralyzed Veterans of America
801 18th St. NW
Washington, DC 20006-3517
E-mail: info@pva.org
URL: http://www.pva.org
Descr: Reports on organization efforts to ensure better care for persons with spinal cord injuries and diseases. Contains chapter and veteran news. **Freq:** monthly. **Price:** $23/year in U.S., $39/2 years in U.S., $32/year outside U.S., $57/2 years outside U.S. **ISSN:** 0031-1766.

10198 ■ *Paraplegic News*
Wisconsin Paralyzed Veterans of America
2311 S 108th St.
West Allis, WI 53227-1901
Ph: (414)328-8910
Fax: (414)328-8948
E-mail: info@wisconsinpva.org
URL: http://www.wisconsinpva.org
Freq: monthly. **Price:** $25.

10199 ■ *Parents to the Rescue*
National Association for Parents of Children With Visual Impairments
PO Box 317
Watertown, MA 02471
Ph: (617)972-7441
Fax: (617)972-7444
E-mail: napvi@perkins.org
URL: http://www.spedex.com/napvi

10200 ■ *A Partial Approach to Clean-Up: EPA Mishandles Superfund Investigations, 2002 Report*
Project on Government Oversight
666 11th St. NW, Ste. 900
Washington, DC 20001-4542
Ph: (202)347-1122
Fax: (202)347-1116
E-mail: info@pogo.org
URL: http://www.pogo.org

10201 ■ *PASS*
American Sports Institute
PO Box 1837
Mill Valley, CA 94942
Ph: (415)383-5750
Fax: (415)383-5785
E-mail: info@amersports.org
URL: http://www.amersports.org

10202 ■ *PCB's*
American Council on Science and Health
1995 Broadway, 2nd Fl.
New York, NY 10023-5882
Ph: (212)362-7044
Fax: (212)362-4919
E-mail: acsh@acsh.org
URL: http://www.acsh.org
Price: $1.

10203 ■ *PE Update, Action, EEO News*
Project Equality
PO Box 7085
Kansas City, MO 64113-0085
Ph: (913)486-7010
E-mail: kirk@kperuccaassociates.com
URL: http://www.projectequality.org
Descr: Provides information about project advocacy, action focus, and program work with employers and members, equal employment opportunities. **Freq:** quarterly. **Price:** included in membership dues.

10204 ■ *Pennsylvania Political Scientist*
Pennsylvania Political Science Association
Wilkes University
Political Science Dept.
84 W South St.
Wilkes-Barre, PA 18701
Ph: (814)472-7000

Fax: (814)472-3937
E-mail: thomas.baldino@wilkes.edu

10205 ■ *Personnel Service*
American Political Science Association
1527 New Hampshire Ave. NW
Washington, DC 20036-1206
Ph: (202)483-2512
Fax: (202)483-2657
E-mail: apsa@apsanet.org
URL: http://www.apsanet.org
Descr: Contains lists of job openings at colleges and universities. **Freq:** monthly.

10206 ■ *Perspectives*
Friends Committee on National Legislation
245 2nd St. NE
Washington, DC 20002-5761
Ph: (202)547-6000
Fax: (202)547-6019
E-mail: fcnl@fcnl.org
URL: http://www.fcnl.org
Descr: Contains information and analysis missing from most news programs and daily papers.

10207 ■ *Perspectives on Politics*
American Political Science Association
1527 New Hampshire Ave. NW
Washington, DC 20036-1206
Ph: (202)483-2512
Fax: (202)483-2657
E-mail: apsa@apsanet.org
URL: http://www.apsanet.org
Descr: Contains integrative and review essays and book reviews. **Freq:** quarterly. **Price:** included in membership dues.

10208 ■ *Perspectives: The Newsletter on Prejudice, Ethnoviolence and Social Policy*
Prejudice Institute/Center for the Applied Study of Ethnoviolence
2743 Maryland Ave.
Baltimore, MD 21218
Ph: (410)366-9654
E-mail: prejinst@aol.com
URL: http://www.prejudiceinstitute.org
Freq: bimonthly. **Price:** $50 subscription. **ISSN:** 1097-5955.

10209 ■ *Place Your Bets: The Gambling Industry and the 1996 Presidential Elections*
Center for Public Integrity
910 17th St. NW, Ste. 700
Washington, DC 20006
Ph: (202)466-1300
Fax: (202)466-1101
E-mail: cristina@nhli.org
URL: http://www.publicintegrity.org
Price: $10.

10210 ■ *PN*
Paralyzed Veterans of America, Florida Chapter
3799 N Andrews Ave.
Fort Lauderdale, FL 33309
Ph: (954)565-8885
Fax: (954)565-8843
E-mail: pvaf@aol.com
URL: http://www.pvaf.org

10211 ■ *PN/Paraplegia News*
Paralyzed Veterans of America, Vaughan Chapter
2235 Enterprise Dr., Ste. 3501
Westchester, IL 60154
Ph: (708)947-9790
Fax: (708)947-9755
E-mail: pvachvaug@mindspring.com
URL: http://www.vaughanpva.org
Descr: Covers PVA news and all aspects of life related to spinal cord injury or disease. **Freq:** monthly. **Price:** free for members, $23/year for nonmembers, $39 for 24 issues, $32/year, outside U.S.

10212 ■ *Point Blank*
Citizens Committee for the Right to Keep and Bear Arms

Liberty Park
12500 NE 10th Pl.
Bellevue, WA 98005
Ph: (425)454-4911
Fax: (425)451-3959
E-mail: adminforweb@ccrkba.org
URL: http://www.ccrkba.org
Descr: Fosters public awareness on the right of citizens to bear arms. Reports on gun control legislation, pro-gun candidates, and committee activities. **Freq:** monthly. **Price:** included in membership dues, $15/year for nonmembers.

10213 ■ *Policy Memos*
Center for Policy Alternatives
1875 Connecticut Ave. NW, Ste. 710
Washington, DC 20009
Ph: (202)387-6030
Fax: (202)387-8529
E-mail: info@cfpa.org
URL: http://www.cfpa.org
Freq: periodic.

10214 ■ *Policy and Procedural Manual*
National Institute of Senior Centers
1901 L St. NW, 4th Fl.
Washington, DC 20036
Ph: (202)479-1200
Fax: (202)479-0735
E-mail: info@ncoa.org
URL: http://www.ncoa.org/content.cfm?sectionID=44

10215 ■ *Polish-American Guardian Society Annual Newsletter*
Polish-American Guardian Society
8861 Wheeler Dr.
Orland Park, IL 60462
Ph: (708)403-9492
Descr: Describes activities and future plans. **Freq:** annual. **Price:** included in membership dues.

10216 ■ *Politically Correct Guns*
Citizens Committee for the Right to Keep and Bear Arms
Liberty Park
12500 NE 10th Pl.
Bellevue, WA 98005
Ph: (425)454-4911
Fax: (425)451-3959
E-mail: adminforweb@ccrkba.org
URL: http://www.ccrkba.org
Descr: Lists some of America's most "outrageous" gun laws. **Price:** $14.95.

10217 ■ *Politically Correct Hunting*
Citizens Committee for the Right to Keep and Bear Arms
Liberty Park
12500 NE 10th Pl.
Bellevue, WA 98005
Ph: (425)454-4911
Fax: (425)451-3959
E-mail: adminforweb@ccrkba.org
URL: http://www.ccrkba.org
Descr: Contains hunting humor; discusses the moral and ethical aspects of hunting. **Price:** $14.95.

10218 ■ *Positive Voice Update*
National Association of People with AIDS
8401 Colesville Rd., Ste. 550
Silver Spring, MD 20910
Ph: (240)247-0880
Fax: (240)247-0574
E-mail: info@napwa.org
URL: http://www.napwa.org
Freq: periodic.

10219 ■ *Practice Analysis Report On the Scope of Practice in Prosthetics and Orthotics*
American Board for Certification in Orthotics and Prosthetics
330 John Carlyle St., Ste. 210
Alexandria, VA 22314
Ph: (703)836-7114
Fax: (703)836-0838

E-mail: info@abcop.org
URL: http://www.abcop.org

10220 ■ Premature Ovarian Failure is not an Early Menopause
American Menopause Foundation
350 5th Ave., Ste. 2822
New York, NY 10118
Ph: (212)714-2398
Fax: (212)714-1252
E-mail: menopause@earthlink.net
URL: http://www.americanmenopause.org

10221 ■ Presidential Frequent Fliers
Center for Public Integrity
910 17th St. NW, Ste. 700
Washington, DC 20006
Ph: (202)466-1300
Fax: (202)466-1101
E-mail: cristina@nhli.org
URL: http://www.publicintegrity.org
Price: $5.

10222 ■ President's Bulletin
National Council on Independent Living
1710 Rhode Island Ave. NW, 5th Fl.
Washington, DC 20036
Ph: (202)207-0334
Fax: (202)207-0341
E-mail: ncil@ncil.org
URL: http://www.ncil.org
Freq: monthly.

10223 ■ Prime Cuts
Citizens Against Government Waste
1301 Connecticut Ave. NW, Ste. 400
Washington, DC 20036
Ph: (202)467-5300
Fax: (202)467-4253
E-mail: membership@cagw.org
URL: http://www.cagw.org
Descr: Includes list of budget-cutting proposals from public and private sources; catalog of recommended budget cuts from various sources. **Freq:** annual.

10224 ■ Printed Reports of National Conference on Weights and Measures
National Conference on Weights and Measures
1135 M St., Ste. 110
Lincoln, NE 68508
Ph: (402)434-4880
Fax: (402)434-4878
E-mail: info@ncwm.net
URL: http://www.ncwm.net
Descr: Includes conference proceedings. **Freq:** annual.

10225 ■ Private Citizen Directory
Private Citizen, Inc.
PO Box 233
Naperville, IL 60566
Ph: (630)393-2370
E-mail: pci@private-citizen.com
URL: http://www.privatecitizen.com
Descr: Lists subscribers. **Freq:** semiannual. **Price:** free.

10226 ■ The Private Citizen News
Private Citizen, Inc.
PO Box 233
Naperville, IL 60566
Ph: (630)393-2370
E-mail: pci@private-citizen.com
URL: http://www.privatecitizen.com
Freq: annual. **Price:** included in membership dues.

10227 ■ Private Club
National Club Association
1201 15th St., Ste. 450
Washington, DC 20005
Ph: (202)822-9822
Fax: (202)822-9808
E-mail: info@nationalclub.org
URL: http://www.natlclub.org

Descr: Serves as a reference guide for club decision-makers. **Freq:** annual.

10228 ■ Private Parties: Political Party Leadership in Washington's Mercenary Culture
Center for Public Integrity
910 17th St. NW, Ste. 700
Washington, DC 20006
Ph: (202)466-1300
Fax: (202)466-1101
E-mail: cristina@nhli.org
URL: http://www.publicintegrity.org
Price: $10.

10229 ■ Procedure Manual
Excess Line Association of New York
1 Exchange Plz.
55 Broadway, 29th Fl.
New York, NY 10006
Ph: (646)292-5500
E-mail: elany@elany.org
URL: http://www.elany.org

10230 ■ Professional Educator Newsletter
National Association of Professional Educators
900 17th St., Ste. 300
Washington, DC 20006
Ph: (202)848-8969
E-mail: acrocke@tenet.edu
Descr: Keeps educators informed of association activities and current educational issues. Includes list of events and educational opportunities. **Freq:** 7/year. **Price:** included in membership dues.

10231 ■ Progressive Victories Report
Center for Policy Alternatives
1875 Connecticut Ave. NW, Ste. 710
Washington, DC 20009
Ph: (202)387-6030
Fax: (202)387-8529
E-mail: info@cfpa.org
URL: http://www.cfpa.org
Descr: Describes 80 proactive and progressive measures that became law in the first half of 2004.

10232 ■ Project Equality—Buyer's Guide
Project Equality
PO Box 7085
Kansas City, MO 64113-0085
Ph: (913)486-7010
E-mail: kirk@kperuccaassociates.com
URL: http://www.projectequality.org
Descr: Lists employers that have provided current equal employment opportunity data and have been validated by the project. **Freq:** annual. **Price:** included in membership dues, $25/copy for nonmembers.

10233 ■ Protecting Children
American Humane Association Children's Services
63 Inverness Dr. E
Englewood, CO 80112-5117
Ph: (303)792-9900
Fax: (303)792-5333
E-mail: info@americanhumane.org
URL: http://www.americanhumane.org
Descr: Reports on research and programs concerned with child abuse, protection, and related social work. Includes book reviews and federal legislative news. **Freq:** quarterly. **Price:** included in membership dues, $40/year for libraries. **ISSN:** 0893-4231.

10234 ■ PS: Political Science and Politics
American Political Science Association
1527 New Hampshire Ave. NW
Washington, DC 20036-1206
Ph: (202)483-2512
Fax: (202)483-2657
E-mail: apsa@apsanet.org
URL: http://www.apsanet.org

Descr: Covers political ideas and professional news. **Freq:** quarterly. **Price:** included in membership dues.

10235 ■ PSAC Union Update
Public Service Alliance of Canada
233 Gilmour St.
Ottawa, ON, Canada K2P 0P1
Ph: (613)560-4200
Fax: (613)560-4200
E-mail: nat-pres@psac-afpc.com
URL: http://www.psac-afpc.org
Freq: periodic.

10236 ■ The Public i
Center for Public Integrity
910 17th St. NW, Ste. 700
Washington, DC 20006
Ph: (202)466-1300
Fax: (202)466-1101
E-mail: cristina@nhli.org
URL: http://www.publicintegrity.org

10237 ■ Public Affairs Council—Impact
Public Affairs Council
2033 K St. NW, Ste. 700
Washington, DC 20006
Ph: (202)872-1790
Fax: (202)835-8343
E-mail: pac@pac.org
URL: http://www.pac.org
Descr: Includes calendar of events and personnel changes in the field. **Freq:** monthly. **Price:** included in membership dues, $15/year for nonmembers.

10238 ■ Public Affairs News Monitor
Public Affairs Council
2033 K St. NW, Ste. 700
Washington, DC 20006
Ph: (202)872-1790
Fax: (202)835-8343
E-mail: pac@pac.org
URL: http://www.pac.org
Descr: Provides summaries of major national news stories dealing with public affairs issues. **Freq:** biweekly. **Price:** free for members.

10239 ■ Public Affairs Review
Public Affairs Council
2033 K St. NW, Ste. 700
Washington, DC 20006
Ph: (202)872-1790
Fax: (202)835-8343
E-mail: pac@pac.org
URL: http://www.pac.org
Descr: Contains challenging articles and the annual reports of the Public Affairs Council and the Foundation for Public Affairs. **Freq:** annual. **Price:** free, $5 for additional copy.

10240 ■ Public Citizen News
Public Citizen's Congress Watch
1600 20th St. NW
Washington, DC 20009
Ph: (202)588-1000
Fax: (202)547-7392
E-mail: congress@citizen.org
URL: http://www.citizen.org/congress
Freq: bimonthly.

10241 ■ Public Citizen News
Public Citizen
1600 20th St. NW
Washington, DC 20009
Ph: (202)588-1000
E-mail: member@citizen.org
URL: http://www.citizen.org
Descr: Covers consumer issues including nuclear power and nuclear safety, banking, pesticides, pollution and separation of power. **Freq:** bimonthly. **Price:**

included in membership dues, $20/year for nonmembers. **ISSN:** 0738-5927.

10242 ■ Public Land Private Profit
Southwest Research and Information Center
PO Box 4524
Albuquerque, NM 87106
Ph: (505)262-1862
Fax: (505)262-1864
E-mail: info@sric.org
URL: http://www.sric.org

10243 ■ Public Records Online
BRB Publications, Inc.
PO Box 27869
Tempe, AZ 85285
Free: 800-929-3811
Fax: 800-929-4981
E-mail: brb@brbpub.com
URL: http://www.brbpub.com
Key Personnel: Carl R. Ernst, Founder & CEO; Michael L. Sankey, Editor; Peter J. Weber, Editor. **URL(s):** http://www.brbpub.com **Covers:** Over 11,000 online databases of sources for public records in the U.S. Including proprietary online systems and databases, government agencies offering online access, CD-ROMs offering public data, and national and regional public record search firms. **Entries include:** description of information offered, how to access, and restrictions on usage. **Freq:** Latest edition 6th, June 2006. **Price:** $21.95, individuals.

10244 ■ Quality Care
National Association for Continence
PO Box 1019
Charleston, SC 29402-1019
Ph: (843)377-0900
Fax: (843)377-0905
E-mail: memberservices@nafc.org
URL: http://www.nafc.org
Freq: quarterly. **Price:** $25/year for consumers, $100/year for professionals, $250/year for group professionals.

10245 ■ The Quest
National Organization for Men
30 Besey St.
New York, NY 10007
Ph: (760)753-5000
E-mail: warren@warrenfarrell.com
URL: http://www.orgformen.org
Freq: bimonthly. **Price:** included in membership dues.

10246 ■ Questions and Answers about BHP Billiton's Proposed Crandon Mine in Wisconsin
Center for Alternative Mining Development Policy
210 Avon St., Ste. 4
La Crosse, WI 54603
Ph: (608)784-4399
Fax: (608)785-8486
E-mail: gedicks.al@uwlax.edu

10247 ■ Rapport
National Juvenile Court Services Association
University of Nevada
PO Box 8970
Reno, NV 89507
Ph: (775)784-6895
Fax: (775)784-6628
E-mail: support@njcsacertification.org
URL: http://www.njcsa.org
Descr: Contains news and information concerning juvenile justice administration, local and regional activities, member activities. **Freq:** quarterly. **Price:** $10/year for nonmembers, $2/copy for nonmembers, included in membership dues.

10248 ■ RCRC National Report
Religious Coalition for Reproductive Choice
1025 Vermont Ave. NW, Ste. 1130
Washington, DC 20005
Ph: (202)628-7700

Fax: (202)628-7716
E-mail: info@rcrc.org
URL: http://www.rcrc.org
Freq: bimonthly. **Price:** included in membership dues.

10249 ■ Re-membering: NWSA 1977-1987
National Women's Studies Association
7100 Baltimore Ave., Ste. 502
College Park, MD 20740
Ph: (301)403-0407
Fax: (301)403-4137
E-mail: nwsaoffice@nwsa.org
URL: http://www.nwsa.org
Descr: Includes personal essays covering the first ten years of the organization. **Price:** $11.

10250 ■ Reaching Out
Friends: The National Association of Young People Who Stutter
38 S Oyster Bay Rd.
Syosset, NY 11791
E-mail: lcaggiano@aol.com
URL: http://www.friendswhostutter.org
Descr: Contains articles, reflections, stories, and information about the stuttering experience of young people and their families. **Freq:** bimonthly. **Price:** included in membership dues.

10251 ■ Reality Check
International Anticounterfeiting Coalition
1730 M St. NW, Ste. 1020
Washington, DC 20036
Ph: (202)223-6667
Fax: (202)223-6668
E-mail: bbarchiesi@iacc.org
URL: http://www.iacc.org
Descr: Includes complete update of all IACC activities. **Freq:** monthly.

10252 ■ Recollections
Vietnam Veterans Against the War
PO Box 408594
Chicago, IL 60640
Ph: (773)276-4189
E-mail: vvaw@vvaw.org
URL: http://www.vvaw.org

10253 ■ The Record
Maryland Public Health Association
PO Box 716
Bel Air, MD 21014
Ph: (410)955-3660
Fax: (410)614-7642
E-mail: mpha@jhsph.edu
URL: http://www.mdpha.org
Descr: Includes event, news, and update about the activities of the association. **Freq:** quarterly. **Price:** free.

10254 ■ The Red Book
Maryland Department of Planning
301 W Preston St., Ste. 1101
Baltimore, MD 21201-2305
Ph: (410)767-4500
Free: 877-767-6272
Fax: (410)767-4480
URL: http://www.mdp.state.md.us
URL(s): http://www.mdp.state.md.us/clhouse/redbook/redbook.html; http://www.mdredbookonline.com **Covers:** Programs, grants, loans, and regulatory, technical, and advisory services available to state and local agencies and to the general public. **Entries include:** Program title, administrating agency name; name, address, phone, website address, and e-mail address of contact; type of assistance available, eligibility requirements, available funding, program description. **Price:** Free.

10255 ■ Register of Opinion
Public Advocate of the U.S.
5613 Leesburg Pike, Ste. 17
Falls Church, VA 22041

Ph: (703)845-1808
URL: http://www.publicadvocateusa.org
Descr: Promotes the transferring powers of the federal government to more local levels. **Freq:** periodic.

10256 ■ Rehabilitation Newsletter
National Institute for Rehabilitation Engineering
PO Box T
Hewitt, NJ 07421
Ph: (973)853-6585
E-mail: nire@theoffice.net
URL: http://www.angelfire.com/nj/nire2
Descr: Features announcements of upcoming seminars. **Freq:** quarterly. **Price:** included in membership dues.

10257 ■ Reinvest Works
National Community Reinvestment Coalition
727 15th St. NW, Ste. 900
Washington, DC 20005
Ph: (202)628-8866
Fax: (202)628-9800
E-mail: jtaylor@ncrc.org
URL: http://www.ncrc.org
Descr: Includes articles by NCRC members. **Freq:** quarterly.

10258 ■ Religious Freedom Alert
International Coalition for Religious Freedom
7777 Leesburg Pike, Ste. 404 N
Falls Church, VA 22043
Ph: (703)790-1500
Fax: (703)790-5562
E-mail: icrf@aol.com
URL: http://www.religiousfreedom.com
Descr: Provides news and commentary on religious freedom and other church/state issues. **Price:** included in membership dues, $15/year for nonmembers.

10259 ■ Religious Freedom Report
International Coalition for Religious Freedom
7777 Leesburg Pike, Ste. 404 N
Falls Church, VA 22043
Ph: (703)790-1500
Fax: (703)790-5562
E-mail: icrf@aol.com
URL: http://www.religiousfreedom.com
Freq: bimonthly. **Price:** $25/year in U.S., $35/year outside U.S.

10260 ■ Religious Liberty in Crisis
Americans for Religious Liberty
PO Box 6656
Silver Spring, MD 20916
Ph: (301)260-2988
Fax: (301)260-2989
E-mail: arlinc@verizon.net
URL: http://www.arlinc.org

10261 ■ Religious Voice For Choice
Oklahoma Religious Coalition for Reproductive Choice
PO Box 35194
Tulsa, OK 74153
Ph: (918)481-6444
Fax: (918)481-6444
E-mail: contact@okrcrc.org
URL: http://www.okrcrc.org
Freq: quarterly.

10262 ■ Report to Congress
Public Advocate of the U.S.
5613 Leesburg Pike, Ste. 17
Falls Church, VA 22041
Ph: (703)845-1808
URL: http://www.publicadvocateusa.org
Freq: semiannual.

10263 ■ Report to Congress
Council of Volunteer Americans
PO Box 1222
Sterling, VA 20167

Ph: (703)379-9188
E-mail: info@conservativeaction.org
URL: http://conservativeaction.org
Freq: monthly.

10264 ■ *The Reporter*
Women's American ORT
250 Park Ave. S
New York, NY 10003
Ph: (212)505-7700
E-mail: info@waort.org
URL: http://www.waort.org/
Freq: semiannual. **Price:** included in membership dues.

10265 ■ *Resource Rebels: Native Challenges to Mining and Oil Corporations*
Center for Alternative Mining Development Policy
210 Avon St., Ste. 4
La Crosse, WI 54603
Ph: (608)784-4399
Fax: (608)785-8486
E-mail: gedicks.al@uwlax.edu
Price: $18.

10266 ■ *Resources*
Center for Policy Alternatives
1875 Connecticut Ave. NW, Ste. 710
Washington, DC 20009
Ph: (202)387-6030
Fax: (202)387-8529
E-mail: info@cfpa.org
URL: http://www.cfpa.org
Freq: periodic.

10267 ■ *Resources for Welfare Decisions*
Economic Success Clearinghouse
1401 New York Ave. NW, Ste. 800
Washington, DC 20005
Ph: (202)628-4200
Fax: (202)628-1293
E-mail: info@financeproject.org
URL: http://www.financeproject.org/index.cfm?page=24

10268 ■ *Responsible Purchasing Guide for Faith Communities*
Center for a New American Dream
6930 Carroll Ave., Ste. 900
Takoma Park, MD 20912-4466
Ph: (301)891-3683
Fax: (301)891-3684
E-mail: newdream@newdream.org
URL: http://www.ibuydifferent.org
Price: $5.

10269 ■ *A Review of Progesterone*
American Menopause Foundation
350 5th Ave., Ste. 2822
New York, NY 10118
Ph: (212)714-2398
Fax: (212)714-1252
E-mail: menopause@earthlink.net
URL: http://www.americanmenopause.org
Freq: semiannual.

10270 ■ *Rising Standard*
Citizens for Better Care
4750 Woodward Ave., Ste. 410
Detroit, MI 48201
Ph: (313)832-6387
Fax: (313)832-7407
E-mail: info@cbcmi.org
URL: http://www.cbcmi.org
Freq: 3/year. **Price:** free for members and donors.

10271 ■ *Roster of Administrators*
National Conference of State Social Security Administrators
Social Security Administration
61 Forsyth St. SW, Ste. 22T64
Atlanta, GA 30303
Ph: (404)562-1324
Fax: (404)562-1583

E-mail: info@ncsssa.org
URL: http://www.ncsssa.org
Freq: annual.

10272 ■ *Roster of Members*
American Institute of Constructors
PO Box 26334
Alexandria, VA 22314
Ph: (703)683-4999
Fax: (703)683-5480
E-mail: admin@aicnet.org
URL: http://www.aicnet.org
Freq: annual. **Price:** included in membership dues, $100 for nonmembers.

10273 ■ *SABC Business & Technology Directory*
Swiss-American Business Council
PO Box 641724
Chicago, IL 60601
Ph: (312)624-7697
E-mail: info2008@sabcnow.com
URL: http://www.sabcnow.com
Price: included in membership dues.

10274 ■ *Saving for a Rainy Day: How Congress Turns Leftover Campaign Cash Into Golden Parachutes*
Center for Public Integrity
910 17th St. NW, Ste. 700
Washington, DC 20006
Ph: (202)466-1300
Fax: (202)466-1101
E-mail: cristina@nhli.org
URL: http://www.publicintegrity.org
Price: $5.

10275 ■ *Saving for a Rainy Day II: How Congress Spends Leftover Campaign Cash*
Center for Public Integrity
910 17th St. NW, Ste. 700
Washington, DC 20006
Ph: (202)466-1300
Fax: (202)466-1101
E-mail: cristina@nhli.org
URL: http://www.publicintegrity.org
Price: $10.

10276 ■ *The SCOOP*
Paralyzed Veterans of America, Mountain States Chapter
12200 E Iliff Ave., Ste. 107
Denver, CO 80014
Ph: (303)597-0038
Fax: (303)597-0039
E-mail: info@mscpva.org
URL: http://www.mscpva.org
Descr: Contains membership information (various topics from liaison to sports and recreation). **Freq:** monthly.

10277 ■ *Scope and Dimension of the Nonprofit Sector*
National Center for Charitable Statistics
2100 M St. NW, 5th Fl.
Washington, DC 20037
Fax: (202)833-6231
E-mail: nccs@ui.urban.org
URL: http://nccs.urban.org

10278 ■ *SCSEP Works*
National Caucus and Center on Black Aged
1220 L St. NW, Ste. 800
Washington, DC 20005
Ph: (202)637-8400
Fax: (202)347-0895
E-mail: info@ncba-aged.org
URL: http://www.ncba-aged.org
Descr: Reports developments concerning elderly blacks. Includes association news and legislative

update. **Freq:** quarterly. **Price:** included in membership dues.

10279 ■ *SEE SPAN*
National Caucus and Center on Black Aged
1220 L St. NW, Ste. 800
Washington, DC 20005
Ph: (202)637-8400
Fax: (202)347-0895
E-mail: info@ncba-aged.org
URL: http://www.ncba-aged.org
Descr: Provides SEE program enrollees' information about the SEE program, activities, health and wellness, and other useful resources. **Freq:** quarterly.

10280 ■ *Self-Regulatory Guidelines for Children's Advertising*
Children's Advertising Review Unit
70 W 36th St., 12th Fl.
New York, NY 10018
E-mail: caru@caru.bbb.org
URL: http://www.caru.org

10281 ■ *Sensitivity toward European Americans: Diversity within Diversity*
Resisting Defamation
440 El Camino Real
Sunnyvale, CA 94087
E-mail: bosears@resistingdefamation.org
URL: http://www.resistingdefamation.org
Descr: Contains a syllabus for free, one-hour seminars. **Freq:** annual. **Price:** $3.

10282 ■ *SER America*
SER - Jobs for Progress National
122 W John Carpenter Fwy., Ste. 200
Irving, TX 75039
Ph: (469)524-1200
Fax: (469)524-1287
E-mail: info@ser-national.org
URL: http://www.ser-national.org
Freq: quarterly.

10283 ■ *SER—Jobs for Progress—Annual Report*
SER - Jobs for Progress National
122 W John Carpenter Fwy., Ste. 200
Irving, TX 75039
Ph: (469)524-1200
Fax: (469)524-1287
E-mail: info@ser-national.org
URL: http://www.ser-national.org
Descr: Contains financial information, statistics, description of programs offered, and training center locations. **Freq:** annual. **Price:** free.

10284 ■ *SER—Jobs for Progress—Network Directory*
SER - Jobs for Progress National
122 W John Carpenter Fwy., Ste. 200
Irving, TX 75039
Ph: (469)524-1200
Fax: (469)524-1287
E-mail: info@ser-national.org
URL: http://www.ser-national.org
Descr: Includes main offices of local SER corporations, affiliates, and satellites. **Freq:** annual. **Price:** free.

10285 ■ *Series: Studies*
Inter-American Commission of Women
17th St. and Constitution Ave. NW
Washington, DC 20006
Ph: (202)458-3000
E-mail: oasweb@oas.org
URL: http://portal.oas.org/Default.aspx?tabid=621&language=en-US
Freq: periodic.

10286 ■ *Sex, Money and Politics*
Center for Responsive Politics
1101 14th St. NW, Ste. 1030
Washington, DC 20005-5635
Ph: (202)857-0044

Fax: (202)857-7809
E-mail: info@crp.org
URL: http://www.opensecrets.org

10287 ■ Sheriff
National Sheriffs' Association
1450 Duke St.
Alexandria, VA 22314-3490
Ph: (703)836-7827
Fax: (703)683-6541
E-mail: nsamail@sheriffs.org
URL: http://www.sheriffs.org
Descr: Covers association activities and topics of interest to the law enforcement community including legal updates and criminal justice strategies. **Freq:** bimonthly. **Price:** included in membership dues, $25/year for nonmembers. **ISSN:** 1070-8170.

10288 ■ Short-Changed: How Congress and Special Interests Benefit at the Expense of the American People
Center for Public Integrity
910 17th St. NW, Ste. 700
Washington, DC 20006
Ph: (202)466-1300
Fax: (202)466-1101
E-mail: cristina@nhli.org
URL: http://www.publicintegrity.org
Price: $5.

10289 ■ Simplify the Holidays Guide
Center for a New American Dream
6930 Carroll Ave., Ste. 900
Takoma Park, MD 20912-4466
Ph: (301)891-3683
Fax: (301)891-3684
E-mail: newdream@newdream.org
URL: http://www.ibuydifferent.org
Price: $4.

10290 ■ Sleeping With the Industry: The U.S. Forest Service and Timber Interests
Center for Public Integrity
910 17th St. NW, Ste. 700
Washington, DC 20006
Ph: (202)466-1300
Fax: (202)466-1101
E-mail: cristina@nhli.org
URL: http://www.publicintegrity.org
Price: $10.

10291 ■ The Society Pages
American Society of Questioned Document Examiners
PO Box 18298
Long Beach, CA 90807
Ph: (562)901-3376
Fax: (562)901-3378
E-mail: webeditor@asqde.org
URL: http://www.asqde.org
Freq: semiannual.

10292 ■ The Source
Native American Water Association
1662 Hwy. 395, Ste. 212
Minden, NV 89423
Ph: (775)782-6636
Fax: (775)782-1021
E-mail: nawa@msn.com
URL: http://www.nawainc.org
Freq: quarterly. **Price:** included in membership dues.

10293 ■ Source Book
National Ski Areas Association
133 S Van Gordon St., Ste. 300
Lakewood, CO 80228
Ph: (303)987-1111

Fax: (303)986-2345
E-mail: nsaa@nsaa.org
URL: http://www.nsaa.org

10294 ■ The Source on Women's Issues in Congress
Women's Policy, Inc.
409 12th St. SW, Ste. 310
Washington, DC 20024
Ph: (202)554-2323
Fax: (202)554-2346
E-mail: webmaster@womenspolicy.org
URL: http://www.womenspolicy.org
Freq: weekly.

10295 ■ So...You want to Sue a Telemarketer
Private Citizen, Inc.
PO Box 233
Naperville, IL 60566
Ph: (630)393-2370
E-mail: pci@private-citizen.com
URL: http://www.privatecitizen.com
Price: $10 for nonmembers, $5 for members.

10296 ■ Spinal Connection
National Scoliosis Foundation
5 Cabot Pl.
Stoughton, MA 02072-4624
Fax: (781)341-8333
E-mail: nsf@scoliosis.org
URL: http://www.scoliosis.org
Descr: Contains information about the different activities for members. **Freq:** biennial. **Price:** free.

10297 ■ Squeeze Play: The United States, Cuba, and the Helms-Burton Act
Center for Public Integrity
910 17th St. NW, Ste. 700
Washington, DC 20006
Ph: (202)466-1300
Fax: (202)466-1101
E-mail: cristina@nhli.org
URL: http://www.publicintegrity.org
Price: $10.

10298 ■ Stamp Out Hunger
Montana People's Action
208 E Main St.
Missoula, MT 59802
Ph: (406)728-5297
Fax: (406)728-4095
E-mail: mpa@mtpaction.org
URL: http://www.mtpaction.org

10299 ■ Standards Action
American National Standards Institute
1819 L St. NW, 6th Fl.
Washington, DC 20036
Ph: (202)293-8020
Fax: (212)293-9287
E-mail: info@ansi.org
URL: http://www.ansi.org
Descr: Lists all ISO, IEC, EN and ANSI standards in progress or newly published. Enables effective participation in the standards development process. **Freq:** weekly. **Price:** included in membership dues. **ISSN:** 0038-9633.

10300 ■ Standards for Public and Residential Pools and Spas
Association of Pool and Spa Professionals
2111 Eisenhower Ave., Ste. 500
Alexandria, VA 22314-4679
Ph: (703)838-0083
Fax: (703)549-0493
E-mail: memberservices@theapsp.org
URL: http://www.theapsp.org

10301 ■ Starving Iraq: One Humanitarian Disaster We Can Stop
Iraq Action Coalition
7309 Haymarket Ln.
Raleigh, NC 27615

Fax: (919)846-7422
E-mail: iac@leb.net
URL: http://iraqaction.org

10302 ■ The State of Black America
National Urban League
120 Wall St., 8th Fl.
New York, NY 10005
Ph: (212)558-5300
Fax: (212)344-5332
E-mail: info@nul.org
URL: http://www.nul.org
Descr: Addresses the issues central to black America. **Freq:** annual. **Price:** $29.95 plus shipping and handling.

10303 ■ A Step Backward
National Families in Action
2957 Clairmont Rd. NE, Ste. 150
Atlanta, GA 30329
Ph: (404)248-9676
Fax: (404)248-1312
E-mail: nfia@nationalfamilies.org
URL: http://www.nationalfamilies.org

10304 ■ Stop the War on the Poor
Montana People's Action
208 E Main St.
Missoula, MT 59802
Ph: (406)728-5297
Fax: (406)728-4095
E-mail: mpa@mtpaction.org
URL: http://www.mtpaction.org

10305 ■ The Story of Salt and How it can Affect Hypertension
National Hypertension Association
324 E 30th St.
New York, NY 10016
Ph: (212)889-3557
Fax: (212)447-7032
E-mail: nathypertension@aol.com
URL: http://www.nathypertension.org
Descr: Includes information on effect of salt to hypertension.

10306 ■ Straight Talk about Discipline
National Dropout Prevention Center/Network
Clemson University
209 Martin St.
Clemson, SC 29631-1555
Ph: (864)656-2599
Fax: (864)656-0136
E-mail: ndpc@clemson.edu
URL: http://www.dropoutprevention.org

10307 ■ StraightTalk
The Conference Board
845 3rd Ave.
New York, NY 10022
Ph: (212)759-0900
Fax: (212)980-7014
E-mail: nick.sutcliffe@conference-board.org
URL: http://www.conference-board.org
Freq: monthly. **Price:** $395/year, $195/year for associates.

10308 ■ Subject Guide to U.S. Government Reference Sources
Libraries Unlimited Inc.
130 Cremona Dr.
PO Box 1911
Santa Barbara, CA 93116-1911
Free: 800-368-6868
Fax: (805)685-9685
E-mail: orders@abc-clio.com
URL: http://lu.com/
Key Personnel: Gayle J. Hardy-Davis, Author; Judith Schiek Robinson, Author. **URL(s):** http://lu.com/showbook.cfm?isbn=9781563081897 **Covers:** 1,350 print and electronic reference sources produced by the U.S. Government Printing Office. **Entries include:** Source citation; Dewey, LC, SuDocs, and OCLC classification or number; frequency;

availability. **Freq:** Periodic. **Price:** $58, individuals, Hardcover.

10309 ■ *Sunshine Spokesman*
Paralyzed Veterans of America, Florida Chapter
3799 N Andrews Ave.
Fort Lauderdale, FL 33309
Ph: (954)565-8885
Fax: (954)565-8843
E-mail: pvaf@aol.com
URL: http://www.pvaf.org

10310 ■ *Surgfax*
American Society of General Surgeons
PO Box 4834
Englewood, CO 80155
Ph: (303)771-5948
Fax: (303)771-2550
E-mail: stephanie@goddardassociates.com
URL: http://www.theasgs.org
Descr: Features timely updates on current issues.
Freq: monthly.

10311 ■ *Surviving America: What You're Entitled to and How to Get it*
Center for Third World Organizing
1218 E 21st St.
Oakland, CA 94606
Ph: (510)533-7583
Fax: (510)533-0923
URL: http://www.ctwo.org

10312 ■ *Synergism*
American College of Eye Surgeons
334 E Lake Rd., No. 135
Palm Harbor, FL 34685-2427
Ph: (727)366-1487
Fax: (727)836-9783
E-mail: quality@aces-abes.org
URL: http://www.aces-abes.org
Freq: periodic.

10313 ■ *The TAPeR Practitioner Times*
American Society of Tax Problem Solvers
2250 Wehrle Dr., Ste. 3
Williamsville, NY 14221
Ph: (716)630-1650
Fax: (716)630-1651
E-mail: ron@astps.org
URL: http://www.astps.org
Descr: Contains information on tax problem solving.
Freq: quarterly. **Price:** included in membership dues.

10314 ■ *Tapes of Conference Programs*
American Health Quality Association
1155 21st St. NW
Washington, DC 20036
Ph: (202)331-5790
Fax: (202)331-9334
E-mail: info@ahqa.org
URL: http://www.ahqa.org

10315 ■ *Target Chronic Pain Notebook*
American Pain Foundation
201 N Charles St., Ste. 710
Baltimore, MD 21201-4111
Fax: (410)385-1832
E-mail: info@painfoundation.org
URL: http://www.painfoundation.org
Freq: biennial.

10316 ■ *Third Force*
Center for Third World Organizing
1218 E 21st St.
Oakland, CA 94606
Ph: (510)533-7583
Fax: (510)533-0923
URL: http://www.ctwo.org
Freq: bimonthly. **Price:** $22/year for individuals.
ISSN: 1067-3237.

10317 ■ *Tips for Parenting in a Commercial Culture*
Center for a New American Dream
6930 Carroll Ave., Ste. 900

Takoma Park, MD 20912-4466
Ph: (301)891-3683
Fax: (301)891-3684
E-mail: newdream@newdream.org
URL: http://www.ibuydifferent.org
Price: $4.

10318 ■ *Today's NCOA Journal*
Non Commissioned Officers Association
10635 IH 35 N
San Antonio, TX 78233
Ph: (703)549-0311
Fax: (703)549-0245
E-mail: execdir@ncoausa.org
URL: http://www.ncoausa.org
Descr: Provides news concerning active duty and retired military personnel. Also includes membership news and calendar of events. **Freq:** bimonthly. **Price:** included in membership dues.

10319 ■ *Toxic Deception*
Center for Public Integrity
910 17th St. NW, Ste. 700
Washington, DC 20006
Ph: (202)466-1300
Fax: (202)466-1101
E-mail: cristina@nhli.org
URL: http://www.publicintegrity.org
Price: $24.95.

10320 ■ *Toxic Temptation: The Revolving Door, Bureaucratic Inertia and the Disappointment of the EPA Superfund Program*
Center for Public Integrity
910 17th St. NW, Ste. 700
Washington, DC 20006
Ph: (202)466-1300
Fax: (202)466-1101
E-mail: cristina@nhli.org
URL: http://www.publicintegrity.org
Price: $10.

10321 ■ *Tracking the Cash*
Center for Responsive Politics
1101 14th St. NW, Ste. 1030
Washington, DC 20005-5635
Ph: (202)857-0044
Fax: (202)857-7809
E-mail: info@crp.org
URL: http://www.opensecrets.org

10322 ■ *Transitions: Journal of Men's Perspectives*
National Coalition of Free Men
PO Box 582023
Minneapolis, MN 55458-2023
Ph: (516)482-6378
E-mail: ncfm@ncfm.org
URL: http://www.ncfm.org
Descr: Features articles on men's issues, movie and book reviews, and research results. **Freq:** bimonthly. **Price:** included in membership dues. **ISSN:** 0886-826X.

10323 ■ *TransitTalk*
Missouri Public Transit Association
606 Dix Rd.
Jefferson City, MO 65109
Ph: (573)634-4314
Fax: (573)632-6678
E-mail: mpta_org@earthlink.net
URL: http://www.mptaonline.typepad.com
Freq: quarterly.

10324 ■ *Tying Regulation to Reality*
Citizens for a Sound Economy
1775 Pennsylvania Ave. NW, 11th Fl.
Washington, DC 20006-5805
Ph: (202)783-3870

Fax: (202)942-7649
E-mail: cse@cse.org
URL: http://cse.org

10325 ■ *Under the Influence: Presidential Candidates and Their Campaign Advisers*
Center for Public Integrity
910 17th St. NW, Ste. 700
Washington, DC 20006
Ph: (202)466-1300
Fax: (202)466-1101
E-mail: cristina@nhli.org
URL: http://www.publicintegrity.org
Price: $10.

10326 ■ *Uniformed Services Journal*
National Association for Uniformed Services
5535 Hempstead Way
Springfield, VA 22151-4094
Ph: (703)750-1342
Fax: (703)354-4380
E-mail: naus@naus.org
URL: http://www.naus.org
Freq: bimonthly.

10327 ■ *United States Government Manual*
Office of the Federal Register
c/o The National Archives and Records Administration
8601 Adelphi Rd.
College Park, MD 20740-6001
Ph: (301)837-0482
Free: 866-272-6272
Fax: (301)837-0483
URL: http://www.archives.gov/federal-register/index.html
Key Personnel: Stephen J. Frattini, Contact; Alfred W. Jones, Editor. **URL(s):** http://www.gpoaccess.gov/gmanual/index.html **Descr:** Provides information on the agencies of the executive, judicial, and legislative branches of the Federal government. Contains a section on terminated or transferred agencies. **Freq:** Annual, latest edition 2008. **Price:** $29, individuals.

10328 ■ *U.S. Government TDD-TYY Directory*
DIANE Publishing Co.
PO Box 617
Darby, PA 19023-0617
Free: 800-782-3833
URL: http://www.dianepublishing.net
URL(s): http://www.dianepublishingcentral.com/ **Descr:** Directory of federal government TDD/TYY numbers. **Publication includes:** Listings of all major government agencies, including congressional listings for the House and Senate. **Price:** $20, individuals.

10329 ■ *U.S. Nuclear Weapons Complex: Security at Risk, 2001 Report*
Project on Government Oversight
666 11th St. NW, Ste. 900
Washington, DC 20001-4542
Ph: (202)347-1122
Fax: (202)347-1116
E-mail: info@pogo.org
URL: http://www.pogo.org

10330 ■ *Update*
Arkansas Public Health Association
Central Region Health Office
5800 W 10th St., Ste. 907
Little Rock, AR 72204
Ph: (501)280-4950
Fax: (501)280-4999
E-mail: carladder.parham@arkansas.gov
URL: http://www.arkpublichealth.org
Descr: Contains information on the association and its members. **Freq:** periodic.

10331 ■ *Update!*
Friends of the National Institute of Dental and Craniofacial Research
1901 Pennsylvania Ave. NW, Ste. 607
Washington, DC 20006

Ph: (202)223-0667
Fax: (202)463-1257
E-mail: peter@fnidcr.org
URL: http://www.fnidcr.org
Freq: quarterly. **Price:** included in membership dues.

10332 ■ *The Urban League News*
National Urban League
120 Wall St., 8th Fl.
New York, NY 10005
Ph: (212)558-5300
Fax: (212)344-5332
E-mail: info@nul.org
URL: http://www.nul.org
Descr: Features information on league program and activities. **Freq:** quarterly. **Price:** included in membership dues.

10333 ■ *The Veteran*
Associates of Vietnam Veterans of America
PO Box 64732
Baltimore, MD 21264-4732
Ph: (301)585-4000
Fax: (301)585-0519
E-mail: pvarnell@avva.org
URL: http://www.avva.org
Descr: Features veteran and family issues. **Freq:** quarterly. **Price:** $4.

10334 ■ *The Veteran*
Vietnam Veterans Against the War
PO Box 408594
Chicago, IL 60640
Ph: (773)276-4189
E-mail: vvaw@vvaw.org
URL: http://www.vvaw.org
Descr: Covers topics of interest to Vietnam veterans; includes book reviews. **Freq:** semiannual. **Price:** $20/year for individuals, $30/year for institutions.

10335 ■ *The Veteran Leader*
Veterans of the Vietnam War
805 S Township Blvd.
Pittston, PA 18640-3327
Ph: (570)603-9740
Fax: (570)603-9741
E-mail: wnwnatl@epix.net
URL: http://www.vvnw.org
Descr: Includes information on VA benefits. **Freq:** quarterly. **Price:** $50/year.

10336 ■ *Veterans News Journal*
National Vietnam and Gulf War Veterans Coalition
2020 Pennsylvania Ave., No. 961
Washington, DC 20006
E-mail: veterans-coalition@comcast.net
URL: http://www.veterans-coalition.org
Descr: Features matters of interest to Vietnam veterans. **Freq:** periodic. **Price:** $7.99/year.

10337 ■ *VFW Magazine*
Veterans of Foreign Wars of the United States
406 W 34th St.
Kansas City, MO 64111
Ph: (816)756-3390
Fax: (816)968-1149
E-mail: info@vfw.org
URL: http://www.vfw.org
Descr: Includes member news, benefits update, and legislative report. **Freq:** monthly. **Price:** included in membership dues, $15/year for nonmembers in U.S., $20/year for nonmembers outside U.S. **ISSN:** 0161-8598.

10338 ■ *VFW News*
Veterans of Foreign Wars of the U.S., Department of Alabama
PO Box 231177
Montgomery, AL 36123-1177
Ph: (334)270-8399
Fax: (334)270-9056
E-mail: vfw@alvfw.org
URL: http://www.alvfw.org

Freq: quarterly. **Price:** $3/year for nonmembers, free to members.

10339 ■ *Vibrant Life*
American Health and Temperance Association
12501 Old Columbia Pike
Silver Spring, MD 20902
Ph: (301)680-6733
Fax: (301)680-6464
E-mail: dewitt.williams@nad.adventist.org
URL: http://www.nadhealthministries.org
Freq: bimonthly.

10340 ■ *VietNow Magazine*
VietNow National
1835 Broadway
Rockford, IL 61104
Ph: (815)227-5100
E-mail: vnnatl@inwave.com
URL: http://www.vietnow.com
Freq: quarterly.

10341 ■ *Viewpoint*
Illinois Public Health Association
223 S Third St.
Springfield, IL 62701-1144
Ph: (217)522-5687
Fax: (217)522-5689
E-mail: jnelson@ipha.com
URL: http://www.ipha.com
Descr: Contains information about the current and upcoming events of the association and contributed articles of the members.

10342 ■ *ViewPoint*
National Inhalant Prevention Coalition
322-A Thompson St.
Chattanooga, TN 37405
Ph: (423)265-4662
Fax: (423)265-4889
E-mail: nipc@io.com
URL: http://www.inhalants.org
Descr: Contains the latest research findings. **Freq:** quarterly.

10343 ■ *Vintage Times*
Association of Retired Americans
6505 E 82nd St., No. 130
Indianapolis, IN 46250
Fax: (317)915-2510
E-mail: ara@ara-usa.org
URL: http://www.ara-usa.org
Freq: quarterly.

10344 ■ *Vision Access*
Council of Citizens With Low Vision International
1155 15th St. NW, Ste. 1004
Washington, DC 20005
E-mail: webmaster@cclvi.org
URL: http://www.cclvi.org
Descr: Reports on research and resources. Available on audiocassette and in large print. **Freq:** quarterly. **Price:** included in membership dues.

10345 ■ *The Voice*
National Neighborhood Coalition
1221 Connecticut Ave. NW, 2nd Fl.
Washington, DC 20036
Ph: (202)429-0790
Fax: (202)429-0795
E-mail: info@neighborhoodcoalition.org
URL: http://www.neighborhoodcoalition.org
Descr: Contains updates on legislation, appropriations, and issues on inner city neighborhoods. **Freq:** quarterly. **Price:** $50 for organizations, $25 for individuals.

10346 ■ *Voice of Reason*
Americans for Religious Liberty
PO Box 6656
Silver Spring, MD 20916
Ph: (301)260-2988
Fax: (301)260-2989

E-mail: arlinc@verizon.net
URL: http://www.arlinc.org
Freq: quarterly. **Price:** $20/year for nonmembers, included in membership dues.

10347 ■ *Voices of People With Pain*
American Pain Foundation
201 N Charles St., Ste. 710
Baltimore, MD 21201-4111
Fax: (410)385-1832
E-mail: info@painfoundation.org
URL: http://www.painfoundation.org

10348 ■ *The VVA Veteran*
Vietnam Veterans of America
8605 Cameron St., Ste. 400
Silver Spring, MD 20910
Ph: (301)585-4000
Fax: (301)585-0519
E-mail: communications@vva.org
URL: http://www.vva.org
Freq: bimonthly. **Price:** $20. **ISSN:** 1061-0220.

10349 ■ *Washington Newsletter*
Friends Committee on National Legislation
245 2nd St. NE
Washington, DC 20002-5761
Ph: (202)547-6000
Fax: (202)547-6019
E-mail: fcnl@fcnl.org
URL: http://www.fcnl.org
Descr: Contains news and analysis for a selection of domestic and international issues. **Freq:** monthly.

10350 ■ *Washington Report*
National Community Development Association
522 21st St. NW, No. 120
Washington, DC 20006-5059
Ph: (202)293-7587
Fax: (202)887-5546
E-mail: ncda@ncdaonline.org
URL: http://www.ncdaonline.org

10351 ■ *Washington Update*
National Association of Community Health Centers
7200 Wisconsin Ave., Ste. 210
Bethesda, MD 20814
Ph: (301)347-0400
Fax: (301)347-0459
URL: http://www.nachc.com
Freq: weekly.

10352 ■ *Watch*
Better Government Association
11 E Adams St., Ste. 608
Chicago, IL 60603
Ph: (312)427-8330
Fax: (312)386-9203
E-mail: info@bettergov.org
URL: http://bettergov.org
Freq: quarterly.

10353 ■ *Weekly Trade Alert*
American Meat Institute
1150 Connecticut Ave. NW, 12th Fl.
Washington, DC 20036
Ph: (202)587-4200
Fax: (202)587-4300
E-mail: memberservices@meatami.com
URL: http://www.meatami.com
Freq: weekly.

10354 ■ *WeTIP's National Crimefighter*
WeTip
PO Box 1296
Rancho Cucamonga, CA 91729-1296
E-mail: info@wetip.com
URL: http://www.wetip.com
Freq: periodic.

10355 ■ *What is Iyengar Yoga?*
B.K.S. Iyengar Yoga National Association of the U.S.
1300 Clay St., Ste. 600

Oakland, CA 94612
URL: http://www.iynaus.org

10356 ■ *What Kids Really Want That Money Can't Buy*
Center for a New American Dream
6930 Carroll Ave., Ste. 900
Takoma Park, MD 20912-4466
Ph: (301)891-3683
Fax: (301)891-3684
E-mail: newdream@newdream.org
URL: http://www.ibuydifferent.org
Price: $19.

10357 ■ *Whistleblowers Guide to Federal Bureaucracy*
Government Accountability Project
1612 K St. NW, Ste. 1100
Washington, DC 20006
Ph: (202)408-0034
E-mail: info@whistleblower.org
URL: http://www.whistleblower.org

10358 ■ *Who Paid for This Election?*
Center for Responsive Politics
1101 14th St. NW, Ste. 1030
Washington, DC 20005-5635
Ph: (202)857-0044
Fax: (202)857-7809
E-mail: info@crp.org
URL: http://www.opensecrets.org

10359 ■ *Who's Paying*
Center for Responsive Politics
1101 14th St. NW, Ste. 1030
Washington, DC 20005-5635
Ph: (202)857-0044
Fax: (202)857-7809
E-mail: info@crp.org
URL: http://www.opensecrets.org

10360 ■ *Why America Should Not Go Metric*
Americans for Customary Weight and Measure
PO Box 24A
Wiscasset, ME 04578
URL: http://www.bwmaonline.com/ACWM.htm

10361 ■ *Why Do Donors Give?*
Center for Responsive Politics
1101 14th St. NW, Ste. 1030
Washington, DC 20005-5635
Ph: (202)857-0044
Fax: (202)857-7809
E-mail: info@crp.org
URL: http://www.opensecrets.org

10362 ■ *Winner*
American Health and Temperance Association
12501 Old Columbia Pike
Silver Spring, MD 20902
Ph: (301)680-6733
Fax: (301)680-6464
E-mail: dewitt.williams@nad.adventist.org
URL: http://www.nadhealthministries.org
Freq: 9/year.

10363 ■ *Workforce Bulletin*
National Association of State Workforce Agencies
444 N Capitol St. NW, Ste. 142
Washington, DC 20001
Ph: (202)434-8020
Fax: (202)434-8033
E-mail: ceser@naswa.org
URL: http://www.workforceatm.org
Freq: weekly. **Price:** $1500.

10364 ■ *You Have the Right to Know Curriculum Series*
National Families in Action
2957 Clairmont Rd. NE, Ste. 150
Atlanta, GA 30329
Ph: (404)248-9676
Fax: (404)248-1312
E-mail: nfia@nationalfamilies.org
URL: http://www.nationalfamilies.org

Price: $10 each.

10365 ■ *Your Child's Information Journal*
National Association for Parents of Children With Visual Impairments
PO Box 317
Watertown, MA 02471
Ph: (617)972-7441
Fax: (617)972-7444
E-mail: napvi@perkins.org
URL: http://www.spedex.com/napvi

Multimedia Resources

10366 ■ *Challenge of the Edith Superstars*
National Fire Protection Association
1 Batterymarch Park
Quincy, MA 02169-7471
Ph: (617)770-3000
Free: 800-344-3555
Fax: (617)770-0700
E-mail: info@nfpa.org
URL: http://www.nfpa.org
Format(s): Videocassette. **Descr:** Exit drills in the home are crucial in the event of a fire. This program presents young "superstars" vs. the clock in attempts to escape fires in single and double family homes and high rise buildings. Instruction devices are demonstrated. **Prod. Date:** 1989. **Length:** 13. **Price:** $350.00.

10367 ■ *Complying with the OSHA Lab Standard*
American Chemical Society
Education Distribution Center
1155 16th St. NW
Washington, DC 20036
Ph: (202)872-4600
Free: 800-227-5558
Fax: (202)872-6067
E-mail: help@acs.org
URL: http://www.chemistry.org
Format(s): Videocassette. **Descr:** The new "Occupational Exposure to Hazardous Chemicals in Laboratories" federal regulation compels all chemical laboratories public and private to pay strict attention to how carefully they carry out their experiments. Panel discussion on conforming to the new guidelines led by the director of the Occupational Health and Safety Administration's Health Standards Program. Recorded on June 5, 1991. Comes with study guide. **Prod. Date:** 1991. **Length:** 120. **Price:** $795.00.

10368 ■ *History of America's National Parks*
OnDeck Home Entertainment
14546 Hesby St
PO Box 5003
Sherman Oaks, CA 91403
Ph: (818)906-7806
E-mail: sales@ondeckvideo.com
URL: http://www.ondeckvideo.com
Format(s): Videocassette. **Descr:** Chronicles the history of the early preservation movement which culminated in the National Park System. **Prod. Date:** 2000. **Length:** 30. **Price:** $19.95.

10369 ■ *How to Buy a Business*
American Institute of Small Business (AISB)
426 Second Street
Excelsior, MN 55331
Free: 800-328-2906
E-mail: AISBOFMN@AOL.COM
URL: http://www.aisb.biz
Format(s): Videocassette. **Descr:** Explains what to look for when buying a business, including valuation and appraisal methods, due diligence, financing, legal ramifications, tax considerations, and more. **Prod. Date:** ????. **Length:** 50. **Price:** $69.95.

10370 ■ *Huff and Puff*
National Film Board of Canada
1123 Broadway, Ste 307

New York, NY 10010
Ph: (212)629-8890
Free: 800-542-2164
Fax: (866)299-9928
URL: http://www.nfb.ca
Format(s): Videocassette. **Descr:** The dangers of hyperventilation in high altitude situations are explored in this film. **Prod. Date:** 1987. **Length:** 8.

10371 ■ *Learn Not to Burn—Wherever You Are*
National Fire Protection Association
1 Batterymarch Park
Quincy, MA 02169-7471
Ph: (617)770-3000
Free: 800-344-3555
Fax: (617)770-0700
E-mail: info@nfpa.org
URL: http://www.nfpa.org
Format(s): Videocassette. **Descr:** Dick Van Dyke demonstrates how you can prevent and survive fire by practicing simple fire safety lessons. **Prod. Date:** 1982. **Length:** 10.

10372 ■ *Log on to Investing*
American Institute of Small Business (AISB)
426 Second Street
Excelsior, MN 55331
Free: 800-328-2906
E-mail: AISBOFMN@AOL.COM
URL: http://www.aisb.biz
Format(s): Videocassette. **Descr:** Deals with how to make trades on-line, keeping records, researching companies, and accessing investmentoriented web sites. **Length:** 50. **Price:** $69.95.

10373 ■ *Lost*
American Educational Products, LLC
401 W Hickory St
PO Box 2121
Fort Collins, CO 80522
Ph: (970)484-7445
Free: 800-289-9299
Fax: (970)484-1198
E-mail: customerservice@amep.com
URL: http://www.amep.com
Format(s): Videocassette. **Descr:** This program in the "Good Life" series discusses, for the benefit of the developmentally disabled, what to do if you get lost. **Prod. Date:** 1981. **Length:** 20.

10374 ■ *Nobody's Perfect*
National Audiovisual Center
5285 Port Royal Rd
Springfield, VA 22161
Ph: (703)605-4603
Free: 800-553-6847
Fax: (703)321-8547
E-mail: orders@ntis.fedworld.gov
URL: http://www.ntis.gov/products/nac/index.asp
Format(s): Videocassette. **Descr:** A scientist's careless actions in the laboratory jeopardize the work and safety of his colleagues and himself. **Prod. Date:** 1980. **Length:** 24.

10375 ■ *One Step Away*
National Film Board of Canada
1123 Broadway, Ste 307
New York, NY 10010
Ph: (212)629-8890
Free: 800-542-2164
Fax: (866)299-9928
URL: http://www.nfb.ca
Format(s): Videocassette. **Descr:** Workers describe various types of roof work and some of the accidents and near accidents that have occurred on the job in this program. **Prod. Date:** 1987. **Length:** 29.

10376 ■ *Reducing the Risks of PCBs*
National Audiovisual Center
5285 Port Royal Rd
Springfield, VA 22161
Ph: (703)605-4603
Free: 800-553-6847

Fax: (703)321-8547
E-mail: orders@ntis.fedworld.gov
URL: http://www.ntis.gov/products/nac/index.asp
Format(s): Videocassette. **Descr:** This video explains Environmental Protection Agency statutes on PCBs, and is of special interest to those in the utilities industries. **Prod. Date:** 1986. **Length:** 12. **Price:** $95.00.

10377 ■ *SL-1*
Direct Cinema Ltd.
PO Box 10003
Santa Monica, CA 90410-1003
Ph: (310)636-8200
Free: 800-525-0000
Fax: (310)636-8228
E-mail: orders@directcinemalimited.com
URL: http://www.directcinema.com
Format(s): Videocassette. **Descr:** A documentary using recently declassified government data regarding a life-taking nuclear accident that happened in the early '60s, discovered to have possibly been caused by worker misconduct. **Prod. Date:** 1984. **Length:** 60.

10378 ■ *Slips, Trips and Falls*
American Media, Inc.
4621 121st St
Urbandale, IA 50323-2311
Ph: (515)224-0919

Free: 888-776-8268
Fax: (515)327-2555
E-mail: custsvc@ammedia.com
URL: http://www.ammedia.com
Format(s): Videocassette. **Descr:** A look at how and why most slips, trips and falls occur and how much these accidents cost physically and monetarily. **Prod. Date:** 198?. **Length:** 12. **Price:** $395.00.

10379 ■ *Survival*
National Film Board of Canada
1123 Broadway, Ste 307
New York, NY 10010
Ph: (212)629-8890
Free: 800-542-2164
Fax: (866)299-9928
URL: http://www.nfb.ca
Format(s): Videocassette. **Descr:** This video demonstrates safe riding strategies for motorcycle owners and offers basic maintenance tips. **Prod. Date:** 1987. **Length:** 17.

10380 ■ *Woodstove Wisdom*
National Fire Protection Association
1 Batterymarch Park
Quincy, MA 02169-7471
Ph: (617)770-3000
Free: 800-344-3555
Fax: (617)770-0700
E-mail: info@nfpa.org
URL: http://www.nfpa.org

Format(s): Videocassette. **Descr:** This program details the fire hazards associated with solid fuel heating. **Prod. Date:** 1982. **Length:** 20.

Media Contacts

California

10381 ■ *Los Angeles Times*
Tribune Company
202 W. First St.
Los Angeles, CA 90012
Contact: Kimi Yoshino, Government Reporter
Ph: (213)237-7847
E-mail: kimi.yoshino@latimes.com
URL: http://www.latimes.com

New York

10382 ■ *The Journal News*
Gannett Co., Inc.
200 N. Route 303
West Nyack, NY 10994
Contact: Laura Incalcaterra, Government Reporter
Ph: (845)578-2486
E-mail: lincalca@thejournalnews.com
URL: http://www.lohud.com